SYMBOLS MOST FREQUENTLY USED IN THE NATIONAL UNION CATALOG

GEORGIA continued

GAU	Atlanta University, Atlanta.
GAuA	Augusta College, Augusta.
GColuC	Columbus College, Columbus.
GCuA	Andrews College, Cuthbert.
GDC	Columbia Theological Seminary, Decatur.
GDS	Agnes Scott College, Decatur.
GDecA*	Agnes Scott College, Decatur.
GDecCT*	Columbia Theological Seminary, Decatur.
GDoS	South Georgia College, Douglas.
GEU	Emory University, Atlanta.
GHi	Georgia Historical Society, Savannah.
GMM	Mercer University, Macon.
GMW	Wesleyan College, Macon.
GMiW	Woman's College of Georgia, Milledgeville.
GMilvC*	Woman's College of Georgia, Milledgeville.
GOgU	Oglethorpe University, Oglethorpe University.
GSDe*	University of Georgia, DeRenne Library.
GU	University of Georgia, Athens.
GU-De	— DeRenne Georgia Library.
GU-Ex	— Georgia State College of Business Administration Library, Atlanta.

HAWAII

HU	University of Hawaii, Honolulu.
HU-EWC	Center for Cultural and Technical Interchange between East and West, Honolulu.

ILLINOIS

I	Illinois State Library, Springfield.
IC	Chicago Public Library.
ICA	Art Institute of Chicago, Chicago.
ICF	Chicago Natural History Museum, Chicago.
ICF-A	— Edward E. Ayer Ornithological Library.
ICHi	Chicago Historical Society, Chicago.
ICIP	Institute for Psychoanalysis, Chicago.
ICJ	John Crerar Library, Chicago.
ICMILC*	Center for Research Libraries, Chicago.
ICMcC	McCormick Theological Seminary, Chicago.
ICN	Newberry Library, Chicago.
ICRL	Center for Research Libraries, Chicago.
ICU	University of Chicago, Chicago.
ICarbS	Southern Illinois University, Carbondale.
IEG	Garrett Theological Seminary, Evanston.
IEN	Northwestern University, Evanston.
IEdS	Southern Illinois University, Edwardsville.
IGK	Knox College, Galesburg.
IHi	Illinois State Historical Library, Springfield.
ILS	St. Procopius College, Lisle.
IMunS	Saint Mary of the Lake Seminary, Mundelein.
INS	Illinois State University, Normal.
IRA	Augustana College Library, Rock Island.
IRivfR	Rosary College, River Forest.
IU	University of Illinois, Urbana.
IU-M	— Medical Sciences Library, Chicago.
IU-U	— Chicago Undergraduate Division, Chicago.

IOWA

IaAS	Iowa State University of Science and Technology, Ames.
IaDL	Luther College, Decorah.
IaDuC	Loras College, Dubuque.
IaDuU	University of Dubuque, Dubuque.
IaDuU-S	— Theological Seminary Library.
IaDuW	Wartburg Theological Seminary, Dubuque.
IaU	University of Iowa, Iowa City.

IDAHO

IdB	Boise Public Library.
IdPI	Idaho State University, Pocatello.
IdPS*	Idaho State University, Pocatello.
IdU	University of Idaho, Moscow.

INDIANA

In	Indiana State Library, Indianapolis.
InAndC	Anderson College, Anderson.
InCollS*	St. Joseph's College, Rensselaer.
InGo	Goshen College Biblical Seminary Library, Goshen.
InHi	Indiana Historical Society, Indianapolis.
InIB	Butler University, Indianapolis.

INDIANA continued

InLP	Purdue University, Lafayette.
InNd	University of Notre Dame, Notre Dame.
InOlH*	St. Leonard College Library, Dayton, Ohio.
InRE	Earlham College, Richmond.
InRenS	St. Joseph's College, Rensselaer.
InStme	St. Meinrad's College & Seminary, St. Meinrad.
InU	Indiana University, Bloomington.

KANSAS

K	Kansas State Library, Topeka.
KAS	St. Benedict's College, Atchison.
KAStB*	St. Benedict's College, Atchison.
KHi	Kansas State Historical Society, Topeka.
KKcB	Central Baptist Theological Seminary, Kansas City.
KMK	Kansas State University, Manhattan.
KStMC*	St. Louis University, School of Divinity Library, St. Louis, Mo.
KU	University of Kansas, Lawrence.
KU-M	— Medical Center Library, Kansas City.
KWiU	Wichita State University, Wichita.

KENTUCKY

Ky-LE	Library Extension Division, Frankfort.
KyBgW	Western Kentucky State College, Bowling Green
KyHi	Kentucky Historical Society, Frankfort.
KyLo	Louisville Free Public Library.
KyLoS	Southern Baptist Theological Seminary, Louisville.
KyLoU	University of Louisville, Louisville.
KyLx	Lexington Public Library.
KyLxCB	Lexington Theological Seminary, Lexington. (Formerly College of the Bible)
KyLxT	Transylvania College, Lexington.
KyMoreT	Morehead State College, Morehead.
KyU	University of Kentucky, Lexington.
KyWA	Asbury College Library, Wilmore.
KyWAT	Asbury Theological Seminary, Wilmore.

LOUISIANA

L	Louisiana State Library, Baton Rouge.
L-M	Louisiana State Museum Library, New Orleans.
LCA	Not a library symbol.
LCS	Not a library symbol.
LHi	Louisiana History Society, New Orleans.
LNHT	Tulane University Library, New Orleans.
LNT-MA	Tulane University, Latin American Library, New Orleans.
LU	Louisiana State University, Baton Rouge.
LU-M	— Medical Center Library, New Orleans.
LU-NO	— Louisiana State University in New Orleans.

MASSACHUSETTS

M	Massachusetts State Library, Boston.
MA	Amherst College, Amherst.
MB	Boston Public Library.
MBAt	Boston Athenaeum, Boston.
MBBC*	Boston College, Chestnut Hill.
MBCo	Countway Library of Medicine. (Harvard-Boston Medical Libraries)
MBH	Massachusetts Horticultural Society, Boston.
MBHo*	Massachusetts Horticultural Society, Boston.
MBM*	Countway Library of Medicine (Harvard-Boston Medical Libraries).
MBMu	Museum of Fine Arts, Boston.
MBU	Boston University.
MBdAF	U.S. Air Force Cambridge Research Center, Bedford.
MBrZ	Zion Research Library, Brookline.
MBrigStJ*	St. John's Seminary, Brighton.
MBtS	St. John's Seminary Library, Brighton.
MCM	Massachusetts Institute of Technology, Cambridge.
MCR	Radcliffe College, Cambridge.
MCSA	Smithsonian Institution, Astrophysical Observatory, Cambridge.
MChB	Boston College, Chestnut Hill.
MH	Harvard University, Cambridge.
MH-A	— Arnold Arboretum.
MH-AH	— Andover-Harvard Theological Library.
MH-BA	— Graduate School of Business Administration Library.
MH-FA	— Fine Arts Library. (Formerly Fogg Art Museum)
MH-G	— Gray Herbarium Library.
MH-HY	— Harvard-Yenching Institute. (Chinese-Japanese Library)

MASSACHUSETTS continued

MH-L	— Law School Library.
MH-P	— Peabody Museum Library.
MH-PR	— Physics Research Library.
MHi	Massachusetts Historical Society, Boston.
MMeT	Tufts University, Medford.
MNF	Forbes Library, Northampton.
MNS	Smith College, Northampton.
MNoeS	Stonehill College Library, North Easton.
MNtcA	Andover Newton Theological School, Newton Center.
MSaE	Essex Institute, Salem.
MShM	Mount Holyoke College, South Hadley.
MU	University of Massachusetts, Amherst.
MWA	American Antiquarian Society, Worcester.
MWAC	Assumption College, Worcester.
MWC	Clark University, Worcester.
MWH	College of the Holy Cross, Worcester.
MWalB	Brandeis University, Waltham.
MWelC	Wellesley College, Wellesley.
MWhB	Marine Biological Laboratory, Woods Hole.
MWiW	Williams College, Williamstown.
MWiW-C	— Chapin Library.

MARYLAND

MdAN	U.S. Naval Academy, Annapolis.
MdBE	Enoch Pratt Free Library, Baltimore.
MdBG	Goucher College, Baltimore.
MdBJ	Johns Hopkins University, Baltimore.
MdBJ-G	— John Work Garrett Library.
MdBP	Peabody Institute, Baltimore.
MdBWA	Walters Art Gallery, Baltimore.
MdU	University of Maryland, College Park.
MdW	Woodstock College, Woodstock.

MAINE

MeB	Bowdoin College, Brunswick.
MeBa	Bangor Public Library.
MeU	University of Maine, Orono.
MeWC	Colby College, Waterville.
MeWaC*	Colby College, Waterville.

MICHIGAN

Mi	Michigan State Library, Lansing.
MiAC	Alma College, Alma.
MiD	Detroit Public Library.
MiD-B	— Burton Historical Collection.
MiDA	Detroit Institute of Arts, Detroit.
MiDU	University of Detroit, Detroit.
MiDW	Wayne State University, Detroit.
MiEM	Michigan State University, East Lansing.
MiEalC*	Michigan State University, East Lansing.
MiGr	Grand Rapids Public Library.
MiH*	Michigan College of Mining and Technology, Houghton.
MiHM	Michigan College of Mining and Technology, Houghton.
MiU	University of Michigan, Ann Arbor.
MiU-C	— William L. Clements Library.

MINNESOTA

MnCS	St. John's University, Collegeville.
MnH*	Minnesota Historical Society, St. Paul.
MnHi	Minnesota Historical Society, St. Paul.
MnRM	Mayo Clinic and Foundation Library, Rochester.
MnSJ	James Jerome Hill Reference Library, St. Paul.
MnSSC	College of St. Catherine, St. Paul.
MnU	University of Minnesota, Minneapolis.

MISSOURI

MoHi	Missouri State Historical Society, Columbia
MoK	Kansas City Public Library.
MoKL	Linda Hall Library, Kansas City
MoKU	University of Missouri at Kansas City, Kansas City.
MoS	St. Louis Public Library.
MoSB	Missouri Botanical Garden, St. Louis.
MoSC*	Concordia Seminary Library, St. Louis.
MoSCS	Concordia Seminary Library, St. Louis.
MoSM	Mercantile Library Association, St. Louis.
MoSU	St. Louis University, St. Louis.
MoSU-D	— School of Divinity Library, St. Louis.
MoSW	Washington University, St. Louis.
MoU	University of Missouri, Columbia.

The National Union Catalog

Pre-1956 Imprints

The National Union Catalog

Pre-1956 Imprints

A cumulative author list representing Library of Congress printed cards and titles reported by other American libraries. Compiled and edited with the cooperation of the Library of Congress and the National Union Catalog Subcommittee of the Resources Committee of the Resources and Technical Services Division, American Library Association

Volume 338

LOCKYER, I. -
LOISEAU, CHARLES (1825-97)

Mansell 1974

Mansell Information/Publishing Limited
3 Bloomsbury Place, London WC1

The American Library Association
50 East Huron Street, Chicago, Illinois 60611

The paper on which this catalog has been printed is supplied by
P. F. Bingham Limited and has been specially manufactured by the
Guard Bridge Paper Company Limited of Fife, Scotland.
Based on requirements established by the late William J. Barrow
for a permanent/durable book paper it is laboratory certified
to meet or exceed the following values:

Substance 89 gsm
pH cold extract 9·4
Fold endurance (MIT ½kg. tension) 1200
Tear resistance (Elmendorf) 73 (or 67 × 3)
Opacity 90·3%

*Library of Congress Card Number : 67–30001
ISBN: 0 7201 0417 3*

*Printed by Balding & Mansell Limited, London and Wisbech, England
Bound by Bemrose & Sons Limited, Derby, England*

American Library Association

Resources and Technical Services Division

RESOURCES COMMITTEE

SUBCOMMITTEE ON THE NATIONAL UNION CATALOG

Chairman GORDON R. WILLIAMS
Director CENTER FOR RESEARCH LIBRARIES
5721 Cottage Grove Avenue, Chicago, Illinois 60637

Members

DOUGLAS W. BRYANT *University Librarian*
Widener Library, Harvard University
Cambridge, Massachusetts 02138

VERNER W. CLAPP 1901-1972 *formerly*
Consultant Council on Library Resources, Inc.

JOHN W. CRONIN *formerly*
Director Processing Department
Library of Congress
2129 32nd Place, S.E.
Washington, D.C. 20020

CHARLES W. DAVID *formerly*
Director of Library Development
Marine Historical Association
854 Radnor Road
St. Davids, Pennsylvania 19087

WILLIAM S. DIX *University Librarian*
Princeton University
Princeton, New Jersey 08540

RALPH E. ELLSWORTH *formerly*
Director University of Colorado Libraries
Boulder, Colorado 80302

HERMAN H. FUSSLER *Professor*
Graduate Library School
University of Chicago
Chicago, Illinois 60637

WARREN J. HAAS *Vice President*
for Libraries and Information Services
Columbia University
New York City, New York 10027

RUTHERFORD D. ROGERS *University Librarian*
Yale University
New Haven, Connecticut 06520

GEORGE A. SCHWEGMANN, JR. *formerly*
Chief Union Catalog Division
3534 Porter Street, N.W.
Washington, D.C. 20016

FREDERICK H. WAGMAN *Director*
University of Michigan Libraries
Ann Arbor, Michigan 48104

WILLIAM J. WELSH *Director*
Processing Department
Library of Congress
Washington, D.C. 20540

Publisher's Note

Because of the large number of sources from which the information in the National Union Catalog has been collected over a long period of time an understanding of its scope and an acquaintance with its methods is necessary for the best use to be made of it. Users are therefore earnestly advised to make themselves familiar with the introductory matter in Volume 1. This fully defines the scope of the Catalog and sets out the basis on which the material reported to the National Union Catalog has been edited for publication in book form.

National Union Catalog Designation

Each main entry in the Catalog has been ascribed a unique identifying designation. This alphanumeric combination appears uniformly after the last line of the entry itself and consists of:

1 The letter N, signifying National Union Catalog.
2 The initial letter under which the entry is filed.
3 A number representing the position of the entry within the sequence under its initial letter.

This National Union Catalog designator is sufficient both to identify any main entry in the Catalog and to establish its position within the sequence of volumes. It is, however, recommended that when referring to titles by the National Union Catalog designation a checking element, such as the key word or initials of the title, be added.

Reported Locations

Alphabetic symbols which represent libraries in the United States and Canada follow the National Union Catalog designation. These groups of letters signify which libraries have reported holding copies of the work. The first library so represented usually is the one that provided the catalog information.

Printed on the end sheets of each volume is a list of most frequently used symbols, each followed by the full name of the library. *List of Symbols*, containing a comprehensive list of symbols used, is published as a separate volume with the Catalog. The Library of Congress has also issued *Symbols Used in the National Union Catalog of the Library of Congress*. In cases where a symbol is not identified in these lists the National Union Catalog Division of the Library of Congress will, on enquiry, attempt to identify the library concerned.

Other Developments

Under the terms of their agreement with the American Library Association, the publishers have undertaken to apply, as far as is practicable, new developments in library science and techniques which may have the effect of further enhancing the value of the Catalog. To this end, the publishers will be pleased to receive suggestions and enquiries relating to technical and production aspects of the Catalog and will be glad to consider proposals calculated to improve its utility and amenity. Mansell Information/Publishing Limited will be pleased also to advise libraries on possible applications of the methods and techniques developed for this and similar projects to their own requirements.

J.C.
London, *August 1968*

VOLUME 338

58
L81
    Lockyer, I
      The plough. London, Common Ground
[1950]
      48 p. (The development of tools and
apparatus, CGB, 534; ed. by F. Sherwood
Taylor)

NL 0437944   DNAL

Lockyer, *Sir* Joseph Norman, 1836-1920
... "Appendix to the Bakerian lecture, session 1887-88"
By J. Norman Lockyer ... [London, Harrison and sons,
printers, 1889]
[157]-262 p. illus., diagrs. 21½ᶜᵐ.
Caption title.
From the Proceedings of the Royal society, v. 45.
Title of the Bakerian lecture: Suggestions on the classification of the
various species of heavenly bodies.
CONTENTS.—I. On the spectra of meteoric swarms in the solar system.—
II. On some effects produced by the fall of meteorites on the earth.—
III. Suggestions on the origin of binary and multiple systems.
  1. Meteoritic hypothesis. 2. Astrophysics. 3. Spectrum analysis.

Library of Congress   QB981.L72   6-25780

NL 0438001   DLC

Lockyer, Sir Joseph Norman, 1836-1920, ed.

Guillemin, Amédée Victor, 1826-1893.
  The applications of physical forces. By Amédée Guillemin.
Tr. from the French by Mrs. Norman Lockyer, and ed., with
additions and notes, by J. Norman Lockyer. With coloured
plates and illustrations. London, Macmillan and co., 1877.

Lockyer, Sir Joseph Norman, 1836-1920.
  Arc spectrum of scandium and its relation
to celestial spectra
    see under   Baxandall, Frank E

Lockyer, Sir Joseph Norman, 1836-

Gt. Brit. *Solar physics committee.*
  ... Areas of calcium flocculi on spectroheliograms, 1906-
1908. Measured and reduced at the Solar physics observatory, South Kensington. Under the direction of Sir
Norman Lockyer ... London, H. M. Stationery off., Eyre
and Spottiswoode, ltd. [printers] 1914.

Lockyer, *Sir* Joseph Norman, 1836-
Astronomia. Nuova versione libera con note ed aggiunte di Gio-
vanni Celoria. 6a edizione.
— Milano. Hoepli. 1911. xii, 255 pp. Illus. Plates. Diagrams.
[Manuali Hoepli. Serie scientifica. 5.] 15 cm., in 8s.

I. [569] - S.r. - Astronomy. - Celoria, Giovanni, ed. 1842-

NL 0438005   MB

LOCKYER, Sir JOSEPH NORMAN, 1836-1920.
  ...Astronomia. Versione libera di G. Celoria. Settima edizione aumentata e in parte rinnovata da Luigi Volta... Milano: U. Hoepli. 1925. xii, 347 p. incl. diagrs., tables.
charts, plates, ports. 15cm. (Manuali Hoepli.)

729392A. 1. Astronomy—Elementary and popular works, 1925.
I. Celoria, Giovanni, 1842-1920, translator. II. Volta,
Luigi, 1876- , editor.

NL 0438006   NN

Lockyer, *Sir* Joseph Norman, 1836-1920.
Qk8.177 [Astronomical reprints from the Proceedings of
the Royal society]
    1v. 22cm.

NL 0438007   CtY

Lockyer, Sir Joseph Norman
  Astronomie von N. Lockyer. Deutsche
ausgabe besorgt von A. Winnecke. Strassburg,
Trubner, 1877.
    121 p., illus. (Naturwissenschaftliche
elementarbucher.)

NL 0438008   OC1W

Lockyer, Sir Joseph Norman, 1836-1920.
  ...Astronomie, von N. Lockyer... Deutsche Ausgabe
besorgt von A. Winnecke... Strassburg: K. J. Trübner,
xv, 121 p. diagrs., front., illus., pl. 3. ed., rev. 16°.
(Naturwissenschaftliche Elementarbücher.)

153974A. 1. Astronomy—Ele-   mentary and popular works, 1877.
2. Winnecke, August, 1835-1897,   editor. 3. Ser.
N. Y. P. L.   April 8, 1925

NL 0438009   NN

Lockyer, Sir Joseph Norman.
  ... Astronomie... 5 verb. und verm aufl., durchgesehene von E. Becker... Strassburg, K.I.
Trubner, 1893.
    133 p. illus. (Naturwissenschaftliche
elementarbucher.)

NL 0438010   OU

Lockyer, Sir Joseph Norman.
  Astronomie. Praha, Otty, [1898]
  [152p. il.]

NL 0438011   OC1

Lockyer, *Sir* Joseph Norman, 1836-1920.
אבטרונומיה. תרגום ה. זכאי. בעריכת א. ויונסקי. תל-אביב.
[Tel-Aviv, 1929] היצאת "קרפת-הספר." תרפ"ב.
113 p. illus. 16 cm. [דעה. ב]

1. Astronomy.   *Title transliterated:* Astronomiyah
    A 53-5065
New York. Public Lib
for Library of Congress

NL 0438012   NN DLC

Lockyer, J[oseph] Norman.
  Astronomy. London: Macmillan and Co., 1874. 2 p.l.,
(i)x-xv, 120 p., 1 diagr., 1 pl. 16°. (Science primers.)

1. Astronomy.—Elementary works,   1874.
N. Y. P. L.   April 3, 1912.

NL 0438013   NN

Lockyer, *Sir* Joseph Norman, 1836-1920.
  ... Astronomy. By J. Norman Lockyer ... New York, D.
Appleton and company, 1875.
3 p. l., [ix]-xv, 120 p. incl. front., illus., diagrs. pl. 15½ᶜᵐ. (Half-
title: Science primers, ed. by Professors Huxley, Roscoe, and Balfour
Stewart. [VII])
  Series note also at head of t.-p.

1. Astronomy—Juvenile literature.

    S 27-10
Library, Smithsonian   Institution

NL 0438014   DSI AAF NIC NcD OO

LOCKYER, Sir Joseph Norman.
Astronomy. New York, 1876.

24°. Front. plate, wodcts., etc.,
(Huxley, T.H. Science primers, VII).
    Astr 3055.1

NL 0438015   MH

Lockyer, Joseph Norman
  Astronomy.
London, 1877.
  120 p. 4th ed. 18°

NL 0438016   MWA

520
L8a
N7
Lockyer, Sir Joseph Norman, 1836-
  ...Astronomy, by J. Norman Lockyer...New
York, D. Appleton & co., 1877.
  xv, 120 p. front., illus., plates(partly
doubl.)diagrs. 15½ cm. (Science primers,
7)

NL 0438017   MiU CU MWA ViU OC1 MH

Lockyer, Joseph Norman
  Astronomy. New ed. London, 1879.
  16 cct.

NL 0438018   NN

LOCKYER, Joseph Norman, 1836-1920.
  Astronomy. New ed. London, Macmillan and Co.,
1880.

  15 cm. Plate and other illustr.
  "Science primers."

NL 0438019   MH CU

Lockyer, Sir Joseph Norman, 1836-1920.
  Astronomy. New York, D. Appleton and co.,
1882.

  xv, 120 p. (Appletons' students' library)
At head of title: Science primers.

NL 0438019-1   MH OC1

Lockyer, *Sir* Joseph Norman, 1836-
  ... Astronomy, by J. Norman Lockyer ... With illustrations. New York, D. Appleton and company, 1884.
3 p. l., [ix]-xv, 120 p. incl. front., illus. 15½ᶜᵐ. (Half-title: Science
primers)
  Series title also at head of t.-p.

1. Astronomy—Juvenile and popular literature.

    A 15-488
Title from Enoch Pratt   Free Libr. Printed by L. C.

NL 0438020   MdBE OO PU

Lockyer, Sir Joseph Norman
  Astronomy. New York, D. Appleton &
co. 1885.
  120p. (Science primer)

NL 0438021   MiHM NjP

Lockyer, Sir Joseph Norman, 1836-
  Astronomy. N.Y., Appleton, 1888.
  120 p.(Science primers)

NL 0438022   OOxM

Lockyer, *Sir* Joseph Norman.
  Astronomy. xv,120 p. 49 il. 1 pl. S. (Science primers.) New
York: American Book Co., [189-].

NL 0438023   ICJ PPCCH PP NcRS

VOLUME 338

Lockyer, Joseph Norman
  Astronomy.
  London, 1893.

NL 0438024   PPL

Lockyer, Sir Joseph Norman, 1836-1920.
  ... Astronomy by Sir Norman Lockyer...
Lond. MacMilan. 1920.
  xv,176 p. il. S. (Science primers.)

NL 0438025   OO

Qn4.5
pam
  Lockyer, Joseph Norman, 1836-1920.
  ... The atmosphere of the sun: a lecture delivered at the Senate house, Cambridge, on May
24, 1871 ... London,Macmillan and co.,1872.
  23p. 21cm (The Rede lecture, 1871)

    1.Sun.   I.Ser.

NL 0438026   CtY

Lockyer,Sir Joseph Norman & Lockyer, William J(ames)
S(tewart).
  Behaviour of the short period atmospheric
pressure variation over the earth's surface.
    London, 1904.
    2 pl., (14) p. 21cm.

Roy. Soc. Proc., 73, 1904, p. 457-471.

NL 0438027   DN-Ob

Lockyer, Sir Joseph Norman, 1836-1920.

  Die beobachtung der sterne sonst und jetzt.
Von J. Norman Lockyer ... Autorisirte deutsche
ausg. Ubersetzt von G. Siebert. Mit 217 in den
text eingedruckten holzstichen. Braunschweig,
Friedrich Vieweg und sohn, 1880.
  xviii, 552 p. illus., diagrs. 22cm.

    1. Astronomy. 2. Telescope. I. Siebert, G., tr.
II. Title. Translation of Stargazing: past and present.

NL 0438028   ViU

Physics
D535.8
L815
  Lockyer, Sir Joseph Norman, 1836-1920
  Cantor lectures on some new optical instruments, by J. Norman Lockyer. Delivered before the Society of arts, April 28 and May 5,
1884. London, W. Trounce, 1884.
  16 p. illus.

  At head of title: Society for the encouragement of arts, manufactures, and commerce.

NL 0438029   NNC

Lockyer, Sir [Joseph] Norman, 1836-
  Catalogue of four hundred and seventy of the brighter
stars classified according to their chemistry at the Solar
physics observatory, South Kensington. Under the direction of Sir Norman Lockyer ... London, Printed for
H. M. Stationery off., by Wyman and sons, limited, 1902.
  iii, 63 p. II pl., tables. 30½ x 24½ cm. (On cover: Solar physics committee)

    1. Stars—Classification. 2. Stars—Catalogs. I. Gt. Brit. Solar phys-
ics committee.

    Library of Congress   QB881.L8

                            6-41020

NL 0438030   DLC CaBVaU DN-Ob NjP MiU

Lockyer, Joseph Norman
  Chemical origins of the lines in Nova Persei.
    London, 1902.
    (7) p. 22cm.
  Roy. Soc. Proc., 69, 1901-02, p. 354-360.

NL 0438031   DN-Ob

Lockyer, Sir Joseph Norman, 1836-1920.
  The chemistry of the stars. By Sir Norman Lockyer.
  (*In* Smithsonian institution. Annual report. 1898. Washington,
1899. 23½ cm. p. 167-178)
  "Printed in Nature, November 10, 1898, vol. 59, no. 1515."

    1. Stars—Constitution.   I. Title.

                           S 15-086

Smithsonian inst. Library
for Library of Congress   [Q11.S66 1898]

                     [a37b1]   (506)

NL 0438032   DSI WaS MH MiU OCl PP OO OU

Lockyer, Sir Joseph Norman, 1836-1920.
  The chemistry of the sun, by J. Norman Lockyer ... London and New York, Macmillan and co., 1887.
  xix, [1], 457, [1] p. illus., diagrs. 23½ cm.

    1. Sun. 2. Spectrum, Solar.   I. Title.

                          45-41191

Library of Congress   QB528.L75

MCSA
  PBa PBm DN-Ob NNCoCi PU PSC PPGi MWelC WU CoU CU
  MH MiHM NjR MdBP OU OCl ODW CtY-M CaVCaU MtU PP
NL 0438033   DLC MA DN RP MiU NjP OCU ViU MCM ICJ

QB3
.L8
  Lockyer, Sir Joseph Norman, 1836-1920.
  [Collected papers, reprints, etc. in astronomy]
  7 pam.
    [1] Note préliminaire sur les éléments ex-
istant dans le soleil. 12 p. (C.R. Acad. d.
sci. 8 déc. 1873) [2:II] Spectroscopic notes:
No. II. Ou the evidence of variation in molecular structure. (From: Proc. Roy. soc. no.
153, 1874) [2:III] No. III. On the molecular
structure of vapours in connexion with their
deusities. (Ibid.) [3] On the chief line in the
spectrum of the nebulae. (Ibid. v. 48, 1890.

  p. 167-198) S.   [4] On the new star in Auriga.
Preliminary note.   (Ibid. v. 50. 1892.
p. 407-409) S.   [5] Note on the spectrum of
Nova Aurigae. (Ibid. v. 50. p. 431-43) S.
[6] Note on the new star in Auriga. (Ibid.
v. 50. p. 466-469) S.

NL 0438035   DLC

Lockyer, Sir Joseph Norman, 1836-
Baxandall, Frank E.
  I. Comparison of the spectra of Rigelian, Crucian and
Alnitamian stars. II. A discussion of the line spectrum of
α Orionis and its relation to that of Arcturus and the
Fraunhoferic spectrum. III. The spectrum of γ Cassio-
peiæ. By Frank E. Baxandall ... under the direction of
Sir Norman Lockyer ... London, H. M. Stationery off.,
Eyre and Spottiswoode, ltd. [printers] 1914.

Lockyer, Sir Joseph Norman, 1836-
  Contributions to solar physics. I. A popular account
of inquiries into the physical constitution of the sun, with
special reference to recent spectroscopic researches; II.
Communication to the Royal society of London, and the
French Academy of sciences, with notes. By J. Norman
Lockyer, F. R. S. London, Macmillan and co., 1874.
  xvi, [1] p., 1 l., 676 p. col. front., illus. (incl. port.) VI pl. (2 col., 2 fold.)
tables. 23½ cm.

    1. Sun.

                          5-7707

Library of Congress   QB521.L8

  OC1W ICJ OrP PU PHC PPFr WaS MCSA DSI CU NIC
NL 0438037   DLC MdBP MiU OCl NjP TxU CtY ViU PBa NN

QB
20
.L8
1893
  Lockyer, Joseph Norman, Sir, 1836-1920.
  The dawn of astronomy. A study of
the temple-worship and mythology of the
ancient Egyptians, by J. Norman
Lockyer. New York and London,
Macmillan and co., 1893.
  432p. illus. 25cm.

    1. Astronomy, Egyptian. 2. Temples
--Egypt. 3. Sun-worship. I. Title

NL 0438038   OKentU PPL

Lockyer, Sir Joseph Norman, 1836-1920.
  The dawn of astronomy. A study of the temple-
worship and mythology of the ancient Egyptians,
by J. Norman Lockyer ... London, Paris [etc.]
Cassell and company, limited, 1894.
  xvi, 432 p. incl. front., illus., tables,
diagrs. fold. plan. 24 cm.

  Errata slip tipped to p. [1]

    1. Astronomy, Egyptian. 2. Temples – Egypt.
3. Sun-worship. I   Title.

MB
NL 0438039   Vi CU MoU KEmT OrPR NjNbS CtY PPFr OCl

Lockyer, Sir Joseph Norman, 1836-1920.
  The dawn of astronomy. A study of the temple-worship and mythology of the ancient Egyptians, by J. Norman Lockyer ... New York and London, Macmillan and
co., 1894.
  xvi, 432 p. front., illus., fold. plan, tables, diagrs. 24½ cm.

    1. Astronomy, Egyptian. 2. Temples—Egypt. 3. Sun-worship. I. Title.

Library of Congress   QB20.L8

                          6—5706

NN MB DNLM OU NjP NIC
NL 0438040   DLC OrP OrU DN PPT OCl NBB PPA PSC PP PHC

Lockyer, Sir Joseph Norman, 1836-1920.
  The dawn of astronomy. A study of the ancient
temple-worship and mythology of the ancient
Egyptians, ... N.Y. and Lond., Macmillan and
co., 1894.[c1896]

NL 0438041   OO

Lockyer, Joseph Norman.
  The dawn of astronomy. A study of the temple-worship and
mythology of the ancient Egyptians. xvi,432 p. il. 1 pl. 1 map.
O. New York: Macmillan Co., 1897.

WaWW
NL 0438042   ICJ NjP OCU ODW WaU PPSteph IaU OrSaW

Lockyer, Sir Joseph Norman, 1836-1920.
  The early temple and pyramid builders. By J. Norman
Lockyer.
  (*In* Smithsonian institution. Annual report. 1893. Washington,
1894. 23½ cm. p. 95-105)
  "From Nature, May 18, 1893; vol. XLVIII, p. 55-58."

    1. Architecture—Egypt. 2. Pyramids.   I. Title.

                          S 15-812

Library, Smithsonian   Institution
Library of Congress   Q11.S66 1893

NL 0438043   DSI WaS OU MiU OCl OO OClJC PP PPAmP

Lockyer, Sir Joseph Norman, 1836-
  Education and national progress; essays and addresses, 1870-1905, by Sir Norman Lockyer, K. C. B. With an
introduction by the Right Honourable R. B. Haldane ...
London, Macmillan & co., limited, 1906.
  x p., 1 l., 269 p. incl. tables. 23½ cm.

    1. Education—Gt. Brit. 2. Technical education—Addresses, essays, lec-
tures.

                          7-32356

Library of Congress   LC93.G7L7

NL 0438044   DLC CaBVaU CtY MiU OO ICJ PPL

VOLUME 338

Lockyer, Sir Joseph Norman, 1836-1920.
Elementary lessons in astronomy. By J.
Norman Lockyer ... London, Macmillan and co.,
1868.
xiv p., 1 l., 347, [1] p.   16 cm.

NL 0438045   ViU CaBVaU PU PPF ODW MB

LOCKYER, Sir Joseph Norman,1836-
Elementary lessons in astronomy. by J.
Norman Lockyer. ... London, Macmillan and
co, 1870.

pp. xiv. 1 l. 347, [1] p. Front. (fold)
col.). 78 illus. xiv pl.

NL 0438046   MH DCU-H OO PPFr

Lockyer, *Sir Joseph Norman*, 1836–
Elementary lessons in astronomy. By J. Norman Lockyer ... New ed. London, Macmillan and co., 1871.
xiv p., 1 l., 347, [1] p. front. (fold. col.) 78 illus., xiv pl. 15ᶜᵐ.

1. Astronomy.

Title from Illinois Univ.   Printed by L. C.   A 11–116

NL 0438047   IU OC1W MB

Lockyer, Sir Joseph Norman, 1836-1920.
Elementary lessons in astronomy. By J.
Norman Lockyer... Tenth thousand. London,
Macmillan and co., 1873.
xiv p., 1 l., 348. p. front. (fold. col.)
78 illus., XIV pl. 15 cm.

NL 0438048   CtY DNLM NjP

QB45
.L8
1874
Lockyer, Sir Joseph Norman, 1836-1920
Elementary lessons in astronomy. By J. Norman
Lockyer ... 11th thousand. London, Macmillan
and co., 1874.
xiv p., 1 l., 348. p. front. (fold. col.)
78 illus., XV pl. 15 1/2cm.

1. Astronomy.

NL 0438049   MB MH

LOCKYER, Sir Joseph Norman.
Elementary lessons in astronomy. [With
an appendix]. 6th ed. London,1876.

24°. Plates, wdcts. & diagrs.
(Macmillan's school class books)

NL 0438050   MH

Lockyer, Sir Joseph Norman, 1836–
Elementary lessons in astronomy. London,
1877.
New edition.

NL 0438051   NjP

Lockyer, Sir Joseph Norman, 1836-1920.
Elementary lessons in astronomy. By J. Norman
Lockyer ... New ed. London: Macmillan & co.,
1879.
xiv p. 1 l.,348 p. front.(fold.col.) 78 illus.
xv pl. 17cm.

NL 0438052   ViLxW MH

Lockyer, Joseph Norman, 1836-1920.
Elementary lessons in astronomy. [Stereotyped ed.] L,
Macmillan, 1883.

NL 0438053   MH OC1W

LOCKYER,Joseph Norman,1836-1920.
Elementary lessons in astronomy. London,etc.,
Macmillan and Co.,1888.

17 cm. Plates,folded colored chart and other
illustr.
"First edition printed 1868;...new edition,
1888."

NL 0438054   MH NNC

QB
45
.L8
1889
Lockyer, Sir Joseph Norman, 1836-1920.
Elementary lessons in astronomy, by J.
Norman Lockyer. [New ed.] London, New
York, Macmillan, 1889.
xvi, 363 p. fold. col. front., fold.
chart., illus.

1. Astronomy. I. Title.

NL 0438055   INS MH

Lockyer, Sir Joseph Norman, 1836-1920
Elementary lessons in astronomy... Ned ed.
London, Macmillan and co., c1896.
347 p.

NL 0438056   PPSJ

Lockyer, Sir [Joseph] Norman.
Elementary lessons in astronomy. London : Macmillan and
Co., Ltd., 1909. xvi, 400 p., 7 pl. (1 fold.) illus., tables. [2.
ed. rev.] 16°.

NL 0438057   NN CU IU PU PHC

Lockyer, Sir [Joseph] Norman.
Elements of astronomy: accompanied with numerous illustrations, a colored representation of the solar, stellar, and nebular
spectra, and celestial charts of the northern and the southern
hemispheres. New York: Amer. Book Co. [cop. 1870.] 312 p.,
1 fold. chart, 1 fold. col'd pl.   Amer. ed. 12°.

NL 0438058   NN PP

Lockyer, *Sir Joseph Norman*, 1836–
Elements of astronomy: accompanied with numerous
illustrations, a colored representation of the solar, stellar, and nebular spectra, and celestial charts of the
northern and southern hemisphere. By J. Norman Lockyer ... American ed. rev. ... New York, D. Appleton
and company, 1870.
312 p. fold. col. front., illus., fold. map, diagrs. 19ᶜᵐ.

1. Astronomy.   1–13794

Library of Congress   QB45.L81

NL 0438059   DLC OrP NN NIC NjP OC1 MiU ICJ

Lockyer, Sir Joseph Norman, 1836-1920.
Elements of astronomy accompanied with
numerous illustrations, a colored representation of the solar, stellar, and nebular spectra,
and celestial charts of the northern and the
southern hemisphere. American ed., revised and
specially adapted to the schools of the United
States. New York, D.Appleton and co., 1871.

NL 0438060   MH MdBP PPF

Lockyer, Sir Joseph Norman, 1836-1920.
Elements of astronomy, accompanied with
numerous illustrations, a colored representation
of the solar, stellar, and nebular spectra [etc]
American ed., revised and specially adapted to
the schools of the United States. New York,
D.Appleton and co., 1873.

NL 0438061   MH NcD

Lockyer, Sir Joseph Norman, 1836-1920.
Elements of astronomy: accompanied with
numerous illustrations, a colored representation
of the solar, stellar, and nebular spectra, and
celestial charts of the northern and the
southern hemisphere. American ed., revised and
specially adapted to the schools of the United
States. New York, D.Appleton and co., 1874.

NL 0438062   MH PPSJ

Lockyer, *Sir Joseph Norman*, 1836-1920.
Elements of astronomy: accompanied with numerous illustrations, a colored representation of the solar, stellar, and
nebular spectra, and celestial charts of the northern and the
southern hemisphere. By J. Norman Lockyer ... American
ed., rev. and specially adapted to the schools of the United
States. New York, D. Appleton and company, 1875.

312 p. fold. col. front., illus., fold. pl., diagrs. 19ᶜᵐ.

1. Astronomy.   34–7906

Library of Congress   QB45.L8 1875   520

NL 0438063   DLC

Lockyer, Sir Joseph Norman, 1836-1920.
Elements of astronomy: accompanied with
numerous illustrations, a colored representation
of the solar, stellar, and nebular spectra, and
celestial charts of the northern and the southern hemisphere. American ed., revised and
specially adapted to the schools of the United
States. New York, D.Appleton and co., 1876.

NL 0438064   MH PPL OC1W

QB45
L8
1877
Lockyer, Sir Joseph Norman, 1836-1920.
Elements of astronomy: accompanied with
numerous illustrations, a colored representation of the solar, stellar, and nebular
spectra, and celestial charts of the northern
and southern hemisphere. American ed., rev.
and specially adapted to the schools of the
United States. New York, D. Appleton, 1877.
312 p. col. front., illus., fold. pl. 20cm.

1.Astronomy.

NL 0438065   NcRS ViU MH OCU

QB
45
L82
Lockyer, Sir Joseph Norman, 1836-1920.
Elements of astronomy. American ed., rev.
and adapted to the schools of the United
States. New York, D. Appleton, 1878.
312 p. illus. 19cm.

1. Astronomy.

NL 0438066   NIC ViU MH Nh ODW OU MiU OO

LOCKYER,Sir Joseph Norman,1836-1920.
Elements of astronomy. American ed.,revised
and specially adapted to the schools of the
United States. New York,D.Appleton and Co.,
1880.

NL 0438067   MH

VOLUME 338

Lockyer, *Sir* Joseph Norman, *1836–*
  Elements of astronomy: ... American edition, revised and specially
  adapted to the schools of the United States.
= New York. Appleton & Co. 1881. 312 pp. Illus. Colored plate.
  Map. Diagrams. Tables. 18.5 cm., in 8s.

NL   0438068   MB PU ViU

LOCKYER, Sir Joseph Norman, 1836-1920.
  Elements of astronomy... American ed., revised
  and specially adapted to the schools of the
  United States. New York, D. Appleton and Co.,
  1883.

NL   0438069   MH CU

Lockyer, Sir Joseph Norman, 1836-1920.
  Elements of astronomy, accompanied with
  numerous illustrations, a colored representation
  of the solar, stellar and nebular spectra [etc]
  American ed., revised and specially adapted to
  the schools of the United States. New York,
  D. Appleton and co., 1885.

NL   0438070   MH

  Lockyer, Joseph Norman. Elements of astronomy. American ed., revised and specially
  adapted to the schools of the United States. New
  York. 1886. 12°. *Front., wdcts., diagrs., and
  charts.*   VI. 4254
  The English edition has the title, "Elementary lessons in
  astronomy."

NL   0438071   MH

Lockyer, *Sir* Joseph Norman, 1836–1920.
  Elements of astronomy: accompanied with numerous illustration, a colored representation of the solar, stellar, and
  nebular spectra, and celestial charts of the northern and the
  southern hemisphere. By J. Norman Lockyer ... American
  ed., rev. and specially adapted to the schools of the United
  States. New York, D. Appleton and company, 1888.
    312 p. col. front., illus., fold. chart. 19ᶜᵐ.

  1. Astronomy.

  Library of Congress   QB45.L8 1888   1—13795

NL   0438072   DLC

Lockyer, Sir Joseph Norman, 1836-1920.
  Elements of Astronomy: accompanied with
  Numerous Illustrations, a colored representation
  of the Solar, Stellar, and Nebular Spectra, and
  Celestial charts of the Northern and the Southern
  Hemisphere. American edition revised and
  specially adapted to the schools of the
  of New York, 1889.

NL   0438073   CtY

LOCKYER, Sir J[oseph] Norman.
  Elements of astronomy. American ed. New York
D. Appleton and co., 1890.

NL   0438074   MH-Mu

Lockyer, Sir Joseph Norman, 1836-1920.
  Enhanced lines of titanium, iron, and
  chromium...
          see under   Baxandall, Frank E

Lockyer, Sir Joseph Norman, 1836–
Peddie, John Taylor, 1879–
  First principles of production; a study of the first principles
  of production and the relation of science to industry. By
  J. Taylor Peddie ... Together with contributions by S. Roy
  Illingworth ... Sir Norman Lockyer ... William Lorimer ...
  and Prof. Percy Frankland ... London, New York [etc.]
  Longmans, Green and co., 1915.

Lockyer. Sir Joseph ^Norman^ & Lockyer, William J
  S
  Flow of the River Thames in relation to British
pressure and rainfall changes.
          (London, 1905)
            2 pl. (13) p. 25½cm.

Roy. Soc. Proc., A76, 1905, p. 494-506.

NL   0438077   DN-Ob

Lockyer, Sir Joseph Norman, 1836–1920, ed.
                                    FOR OTHER EDITIONS
                                    SEE MAIN ENTRY
Guillemin, Amédée Victor, 1826–1893.
  The forces of nature: a popular introduction to the study
  of physical phenomena, by Amédée Guillemin. Tr. from the
  French by Mrs. Norman Lockyer; and ed., with additions and
  notes, by J. Norman Lockyer, F. R. S. Illustrated by two coloured plates, a photograph, and 456 woodcuts. 3d ed. London, Macmillan and co., 1877.

Lockyer, (Joseph) Norman
  Further observations of Nova Persei. No. 1-4.
          London, 1901.
            4 nos. 22cm.

Roy. Soc. Proc., 68, 1901, p. 142-146, 230-235,
399-404; 69, 1901-02, p. 133-137.

NL   0438079   DN-Ob NjP

Lockyer, Joseph Norman
  Further researches on the temperature classification of stars.
          London, 1904.
            3 pl. (12) p. 21cm.

Roy. Soc. Proc. 73, 1904, p. 227-238.

NL   0438080   DN-Ob

Lockyer, ^Sir^ Joseph Norman
  Further researches on the temperature classification of the stars. - No. 2.
          London, 1905.
            1 pl. 7 p. 26cm.

Roy. Soc. Proc., 76 A, 1905, p. 145-151.

NL   0438081   DN-Ob

Lockyer, Sir Joseph Norman, 1836–1920, ed.
                                    FOR OTHER EDITIONS
                                    SEE MAIN ENTRY
Guillemin, Amédée Victor, 1826–1893.
  The heavens; an illustrated handbook of popular astronomy,
  by Amédée Guillemin. Ed. by J. Norman Lockyer ... 5th ed.
  Rev. by Richard A. Proctor ... London, R. Bentley & son,
  1872.

Lockyer, *Sir* [Joseph] Norman, 1836–
  Individual observations of the lines widened in sun-
  spot spectra made at the Solar physics observatory,
  South Kensington, during the period November 12th,
  1879, to December 31st, 1897. Under the direction of Sir
  Norman Lockyer ... London, Printed for H. M. Stationery off., by Wyman and sons, limited, 1900.
    viii, 141 p. 30½ x 24½ᶜᵐ. (*On cover:* Solar physics committee)
    Cover-title: Spectra of sun-spots 1879-1897. Deduced from observa-
  tions made at the Solar physics observatory, South Kensington.

  1. Sun-spots.   I. [Gt. Brit. Solar physics committee.

                                                    6-41021
  Library of Congress   QB525.L79

NL   0438083   DLC CaBVaU

Lockyer, *Sir* Joseph Norman, 1836–
  The influence of brain power on history, by Sir Norman
  Lockyer ... New England education league, International education conference. Boston [Press of J. J. Ara-
  kelyan] 1904.
    23, [1] p. 23ᶜᵐ.
    Reprint from the Living age.
    "Inaugural address by Sir Norman Lockyer, president of the Associa-
  tion, at the meeting of the British association for the advancement of science, at Southport, Sept. 9, 1903."—p. [3]

    1. Science—Gt. Brit. 2. Education—Gt. Brit. 3. Education, Higher.
  [2, 3. Higher education—Gt. Brit.]

                                                    E 15-1442 Revised
  Library, U. S. Bur. of   Education Q171.L8

NL   0438084   DHEW NN OO OC1W MH

Lockyer, *Sir* Joseph Norman, 1836–1920.
  Inorganic evolution as studied by spectrum analysis. By
  Sir Norman Lockyer ... London, Macmillan and co., limited,
  1900.
    x, 198 p. illus. 23½ᶜᵐ.
    CONTENTS.—The basis of the inquiry.—Application of the inquiry to
  the sun and stars.—The dissociation hypothesis.—Objections to the
  dissociation hypothesis.—Inorganic evolution.

    1. Cosmogony. 2. Evolution. 3. Stars—Constitution. 4. Spectrum
  analysis.   I. Title.
                                                    2—9298
  Library of Congress   QB981.L82
                                [a36b1]   -523.1

     OC1 ICJ OrSaW OrPR WaS CaBVaU PPFr PPD PPAN MB
NL   0438085   DLC NcRS NcD CU NIC MdBJ CtY OOxM MiU NN

LOCKYER, Sir JOSEPH NORMAN, 1836-1920.
  Inorganic evolution as studied by spectrum analysis. London, Macmillan, 1900. x, 198 p. illus. 24cm.

  Microfiche (neg.) 5 sheets. 11 x 15cm. (NYPL FSN 15, 208)

  1, Spectroscopy, 1900. 2. Stars   --Spectra. t.1900.

NL   0438086   NN

Lockyer, Sir Joseph Norman, 1836–
  Manchester science lectures for the people. Eighth series, 1876-7. By Professor Roscoe, F. R. S., Professor
  Williamson, F. R. S., and J. N. Lockyer, F. R. S. With
  illustrations. London, Macmillan and co., 1880.

Lockyer, *Sir* Joseph Norman, 1836–
  ... Mean annual variations of barometric pressure and
  rainfall in certain regions, being a study of the mean annual pressure variations for a large number of areas
  scattered over the earth's surface in relation to the principal types of mean annual rainfall variations in those
  areas, made at the Solar physics observatory, South
  Kensington, under the direction of Sir Norman Lockyer
  ... London, Printed for H. M. Stationery off., by Wyman
  and sons, limited, 1905.
    iii, 16 p. diagrs. on 17 pl. 30½ x 24½ᶜᵐ.
    At head of title: Solar physics committee.
    1. Atmospheric pressure. 2. Rain and rainfall.   I. Gt. Brit. Solar
  physics committee.
                                                    6-40620* Cancel
  Library of Congress   QC891.L78
  ——— Copy 2.   Library of Congress QC925.L8

NL   0438088   DLC CaBVaU DAS NjP

Lockyer, *Sir* Joseph Norman, 1836–1920.
  The meteoritic hypothesis: a statement of the results
  of a spectroscopic inquiry into the origin of cosmical systems, by J. Norman Lockyer ... London and New York,
  Macmillan and co., 1890.
    xvi, 560 p. illus., vII pl. (incl. front.) 23½ᶜᵐ.

    1. Meteoritic hypothesis.

                                                    4—12896
  Library of Congress   QB981.L78

     NN MB DI-GS
     NBC PPA PBm PU-Math PHC PSC PP NjP WaU ICJ MH
     KEmT TxU NcD ODW MiU OCU OC1W OC1 MiHM PSt PPFr
NL   0438089   DLC WaWW OrCS IdU MtU CaBVaU MdBP CU

VOLUME 338

QB51
.L62
1922

Lockyer, Sir Joseph Norman, 1836–1920.

Miscellaneous papers ₍reprinted from Monthly notices of the Royal Astronomical Society. n. p.₎ 1922–1936.
25 pamphlets in 1 v. illus. 24cm.

1. Astronomy—Addresses, essays, lectures.

NL 0438090   ViU

Lockyer, *Sir* Joseph Norman, 1836–
... Monthly mean values of barometric pressure for 73 selected stations over the earth's surface. Being a comparison of barometric variations of short duration at places widely distributed. Compiled at the Solar physics observatory, South Kensington. Under the direction of Sir Norman Lockyer ... London, Printed for H. M. Stationery off., by Wyman & sons, limited, 1908.
iv p., 1 l., 97, vi p. incl. tables. 32 pl. (incl. 2 charts, diagrs.) 30½ x 24½ᶜᵐ.
At head of title: Solar physics committee.
1. Atmospheric pressure. i. Gt. Brit. Solar physics committee.

Library of Congress   QC891.L8   8–33951 Additions

NL 0438091   DLC NjP CaBVaU

Lockyer, Sir Joseph Norman, 1836–1920.
...The movements of the earth, by J. Norman Lockyer... London ₍etc.₎ Macmillan and co., 1887. xvi, 130 p. illus. 19½cm.
At head of title: Outlines of physiography.
Running title: Physiography.

1. Earth—Motion.
N. Y. P. L.   February 15, 1938

NL 0438092   NN PHC OC1 MH MiU PPL PPAN PBL

Q1
.N2

Lockyer, Sir Joseph Norman, 1836–1920, ed.

Nature; a weekly journal of science. v. 1–
Nov. 4, 1869–
London, New York, Macmillan.

Lockyer, (Joseph) Norman
The new star in Perseus. Preliminary note.
London, 1901.
(6) p. 22cm.

Roy. Soc. Proc., 68, 1901, p. 119–124.

NL 0438094   DN-Ob

Lockyer, *Sir* Joseph Norman, 1836–1920.
... Nociones de astronomía, por J. Norman Lockyer ... Nueva York, D. Appleton y compañía, 1879.
viii, ₍9₎–149 p. incl. front., illus. pl., diagr. 15½ᵐ. (Cartillas científicas ... iv)

1. Astronomy.

Library of Congress   QB46.L83   3–20546

NL 0438095   DLC

Lockyer, Sir Joseph Norman. ... Nociones de astronomía ... Nueva York, D. Appleton y compañía, 1901. 149p. front.,illus.,pl., diagrs. 15cm.

NL 0438096   CU

Lockyer, Sir Joseph Norman, 1836–1920.
Nociones de astronomía. Con láminas. Nueva York, D.Appleton y cia. 1904.

"Cartillas científicas.

NL 0438097   MH

Lockyer, *Sir* Joseph Norman, 1836–1920.
... Nociones de astronomía, por J. Norman Lockyer... Con laminas. Nueva ed. puesta al corriente de los mas recientes descubrimientos, por el dr. Felipe Casteno. Paris, Garnier hermanos, 1923.
115 p. illus. (Cartillas científicas.)

NL 0438098   OU

Lockyer, Sir Joseph Norman, 1836–1920.
"Note on the spectrum of μ Centauri"...
see under   Baxandall, Frank E

Lockyer, *Sir* Joseph Norman, 1836–
... "Observations of sun-spot spectra, 1879–1894." By J. Norman Lockyer ... ₍London, Harrison and sons, printers, 1895₎
p. ₍199₎–201. diagrs. 21½ᶜᵐ.
Caption title.
From the Proceedings of the Royal society, v. 57.

1. Sun-spots.

CA 6—2208 Unrev'd
Library of Congress   QB525.L81

NL 0438100   DLC

Lockyer, Sir Joseph Norman, 1836–
Observations of the lines widened in sun-spot spectra. London, 1900.

NL 0438101   NjP

Lockyer, Sir Joseph Norman, 1836–1920, and **W. J. S. Lockyer.**
...On solar changes of temperature and variations in rainfall in the region surrounding the Indian Ocean. By Sir Norman Lockyer...and W. J. S. Lockyer... ₍London, 1900.₎ p. ₍409–₎ 431. 8°.
Title from cover.
Repr.: Proc. of the Royal Soc. of London. v. 67.

1. Rainfall, India. 2. Sun spots. 3. Lockyer, William James Stewart, 1868– , jt. au.
N. Y. L.   August 24, 1922

NL 0438102   NN DN-Ob

Lockyer, *Sir* Joseph Norman, 1836–1920.
On solar changes of temperature and variations in rainfall in the region surrounding the Indian ocean. By Sir Norman Lockyer, and W. J. S. Lockyer ...
(In Smithsonian institution. Annual report. 1900. Washington, 1901. 23½ᵐ. p. 173–184. II pl.)
"Reprinted ... from Nature, November 29 and December 6, 1900."

1. Rain and rainfall—Indian ocean. 2. Sun-spots. i. Lockyer, William James Stewart, 1868–1936, joint author.
Smithsonian inst. Library
for Library of Congress   [Q11.S66 1900]   S 15–1051
(506)

NL 0438103   DSI NjP WaS MiU OO OC1JC OC1 OU PPAmP

Lockyer, *Sir* Joseph Norman, 1836–
... On some of the phenomena of new stars. Under the direction of Sir Norman Lockyer ... London, H. M. Stationery off., Eyre and Spottiswoode, ltd. ₍printers₎ 1914.
2 p. l., 63 a. illus., IV pl. tables. 30½ x 25ᵐ.
At head of title: Solar physics committee.

1. Stars, New. 2. Stars—Spectra. i. Gt. Brit. Solar physics committee.
15–2748
Library of Congress   QB895.L78

NL 0438104   DLC CaBVaU NBuU CU MiU CtY ViU

Lockyer, Joseph Norman & Lockyer, William J S
On some phenomena which suggest a short period of solar and meteorological changes.
London, 1902.
(5) p. 21cm.

Roy. Soc. Proc., 70, 1902, p. 500–504.

NL 0438105   DN-Ob

Lockyer, *Sir* Joseph Norman, 1836–1920.
... On the appearance of the cleveite and other new gas lines in the hottest stars. By J. Norman Lockyer ... ₍London, Harrison and sons, printers, 1897₎
cover-title, ₍52₎–67 p. illus. 21½ᵐ.
From the Proceedings of the Royal society, v. 62.

1. Stars—Spectra.
CA 6—2426 Unrev'd
Library of Congress   QB875.L78

NL 0438106   DLC

Lockyer, *Sir* Joseph Norman, 1836–1920.
... On the causes which produce the phenomena of new stars. By J. Norman Lockyer ... ₍London, 1891₎
397–448 p. illus., diagrs. 30 x 23ᵐ.
Caption title.
From the Philosophical transactions of the Royal society, v. 182, A.

1. Stars, New.
7—8708
Library of Congress   QB841.L81

NL 0438107   DLC NN

Lockyer, *Sir* Joseph Norman, 1836–
... On the chemistry of the hottest stars. By J. Norman Lockyer ... ₍London, Harrison & sons, printers, 1897₎
cover-title, ₍1₎, 147–209 p. illus., 3 fold. pl. 21½ᵐ.
From the Proceedings of the Royal society, v. 61.

1. Stars—Spectra.
CA 7–5259 Unrev'd
Library of Congress   QB875.L8

NL 0438108   DLC

Lockyer, *Sir* Joseph Norman, 1836–
... On the classification of stars of the δ Cephei class. By J. Norman Lockyer ... ₍London, Harrison and sons, printers, 1897₎
cover-title, p. ₍445₎–455. 21½ᵐ.
From the Proceedings of the Royal society, v. 61.

1. Stars—Spectra.
CA 6—2427 Unrev'd
Library of Congress   QB881.L83

NL 0438109   DLC

Lockyer, Joseph Norman & Baxandall, F E
On the enhanced lines in the spectrum of the chromosphere.
London, 1901.
(12) p. 21cm.

Roy. Soc. Proc., 68, 1901, p. 178–188.

NL 0438110   DN-Ob

Lockyer, *Sir* Joseph Norman, 1836–
... On the general spectra of certain type-stars and the spectra of several of the brighter stars in the green region. Under the direction of Sir Norman Lockyer ... London, Printed for H. M. Stationery off., by Wyman and sons, limited, 1908.
2 p. l., 46 p. pl. 30 x 25ᵐ.
At head of title: Solar physics committee.

1. Stars—Spectra. i. Gt. Brit. Solar physics committee.
8–33950
Library of Congress   QB883.L74

NL 0438111   DLC CaBVaU DN-Ob NjP

VOLUME 338

Lockyer, Sir Joseph Norman, 1836-1920.
On the group IV lines of silicium...
   see under   Baxandall, Frank E

Lockyer, *Sir* [Joseph] Norman, 1836-
On the influence of brain-power on history; an address delivered, before the British association for the advancement of science, at Southport on September 9th, 1903, by Sir Norman Lockyer ... London, New York, Macmillan and co., limited, 1903.

74 p., 1 l. 21½ᶜᵐ.

Appendices: 1. The German universities (Nature, March 12, 1908)—2. The universities of the United States (Nature, May 14, 1908)—3. The requirements of the University of Birmingham (Nature, January 1, 1908)—4. The requirements of the Welsh university and colleges (Nature, July 16, 1908)

4-3360

NL 0438113   DLC OU WaS MiU NN

Lockyer, Joseph Norman
On the iron flame spectrum and those of sun-spots and lower-type stars.
(London, 1911.) By Sir Norman Lockyer.
(3) p. 26cm.

Caption title.
Roy. Soc. Proc., 86 A, 1912, p. 78-80.

NL 0438114   DN-Ob

Lockyer, *Sir* Joseph Norman, 1836-
... "On the iron lines present in the hottest stars. Preliminary note." By J. Norman Lockyer ... [London, Harrison and sons, printers, 1897]

[475-476] p. diagr. 21½ᶜᵐ.

Caption title.
From the Proceedings of the Royal society, v. 60.

1. Stars—Spectra.

CA 7-5260 Unrev'd

Library of Congress   QB875.L84

NL 0438115   DLC

Lockyer, Joseph Norman
On the observations of stars made in some British stone circles. Preliminary note.
London, 1905.
4 p. 26cm.

Roy. Soc. Proc., 76 A, 1905, p. 177-180.

NL 0438116   DN-Ob

Lockyer, Joseph Norman:
On the observations of stars made in some British stone circles. Second note.
London, 1906.
8 p. 26cm.

Roy. Soc. Proc., 77A, 1906, p. 465-472.

NL 0438117   DN-Ob NjP

Lockyear, Sir Joseph Norman, 1836-
On the origin of certain lines in the spectrum of E Orionis, Alnitam
   see under   Baxandall, Frank E.

Lockyer, *Sir* Joseph Norman, 1836-
... On the photographic spectra of some of the brighter stars. By J. Norman Lockyer, F. R. S. [London, Harrison and sons, printers, 1893]

cover-title, p. [326]-331. 21½ᶜᵐ.
From the Proceedings of the Royal society, v. 52.

1. Stars—Spectra.

CA 6-2298 Unrev'd

Library of Congress   QB871.L8

NL 0438119   DLC

Lockyer, Joseph Norman, 1836-1920.
On the photographic spectra on some of the brighter stars.   London, The Royal Soc., 1893.

675-726 p. 5 pl.   4°. (Royal Soc. of London. Phil. Trans. v. 184)
n.t.-p.

NL 0438120   NN

Lockyer, *Sir* Joseph Norman, 1836-
... On the photographic spectrum of γ-Cassiopeiæ. By J. Norman Lockyer ... [London, Harrison and sons, printers, 1894]

cover-title, p. [173]-177. 21½ᶜᵐ.
From the Proceedings of the Royal society, v. 57.

1. Stars—Spectra.

CA 7-3166 Unrev'd

Library of Congress   QB883.L76

NL 0438121   DLC

Lockyer, Sir Joseph Norman, 1836-
On the presence of sulphur in some of the hotter stars. n.p. [1907]

NL 0438122   NjP

Lockyer, Sir Joseph Norman, 1836-
On the relation between the spectra of sunspots and stars.
London, 1904.
(2) p. 22cm.

Roy. Soc. Proc., 74, 1904-05, p. 53-54.

NL 0438123   DN-Ob

Lockyer, Sir Joseph Norman
On the sequence of chemical forms in stellar spectra.
1910
1 pl. (7) p. 25½cm.

Caption title.
Roy. Soc. Proc., A 84, 1910, p. 426-432.

NL 0438124   DN-Ob

Lockyer, *Sir* Joseph Norman & Lockyer, William J S
On the similarity of the short-period pressure variation over large areas.
London, 1902.
1 pl. (2) p.

Roy. Soc. Proc., 71, 1902-03, p. 134-135.

NL 0438125   DN-Ob DAS

Lockyer, Sir Joseph Norman, 1836-
On the spark discharge from metallic poles in water.
London, 1902.
1 pl. 7 p. 22cm.

Roy Soc. Proc., 70, 1902, p. 31-37.

NL 0438126   DN-Ob

Lockyer, Sir Joseph Norman, 1836-
... "On the spectra of meteor-swarms (Group III). By J. Norman Lockyer ... [London, Harrison and sons, printers, 1889]

p. [380]-392. diagr. 21½ᶜᵐ.
Caption title.
From the Proceedings of the Royal society, v. 45.

1. Stars—Spectra.

CA 7-3165 Unrev'd

Library of Congress   QB883.L8

NL 0438127   DLC

Lockyer, *Sir* Joseph Norman, 1836-1920.
... On the variable stars of the δ Cephei class. By J. Norman Lockyer ... [London, Harrison and sons, printers, 1896-

cover-title, [101]-106 p. illus. 21½ᶜᵐ.
From the Proceedings of the Royal society, v. 59

1. Stars—Spectra. 2. Stars, Variable.

CA 6-2429 Unrev'd

Library of Congress   QB895.L8

NL 0438128   DLC

Lockyer, Sir Joseph Norman, 1836-1920.
Outlines of physiography
   see his   Movements of the earth.

Lockyer, *Sir* J[oseph] Norman, 1836-
... "Preliminary report on the results obtained with the prismatic camera during the eclipse of 1896" ...
[London, 1896]

QB543
.96L

NL 0438130   DLC OU

Lockyer, Sir Joseph Norman, 1836-1920.
Preliminary report on the results obtained with the prismatic cameras during the total eclipse of the sun, April 16, 1893.   London, The Royal Soc., 1894.
711-717 p., 3 pl.   4°. (Royal Soc. of London, Phil. Trans. v. 185)
n.t.-p.
Title from cover.

NL 0438131   NN

Lockyer, Sir Joseph Norman & Lockyer, William J S
Probable cause of the yearly variation of magnetic stores and aurorae.
London, 1904.
(6) p. 22cm.

Roy. Soc. Proc., 74, 1904-05, p. 90-95.

NL 0438132   DN-Ob

Lockyer, *Sir* Joseph Norman, 1836-1920.
Progress in astronomy during the nineteenth century. By Sir Norman Lockyer.
(*In* Smithsonian institution. Annual report. 1900. Washington, 1901. 23½ᶜᵐ. p. 123-147)
"Reprinted ... from the Sun, New York, January 13, 1901."

1. Astronomy—Hist.

S 15-1048

Smithsonian Inst. Library
for Library of Congress   Q11.S66 1900

NL   0438133   OCIJC DSI PPAmP WaS NjP MiU OO OClMN OCl

Lockyer, *Sir* [Joseph] Norman.
Recent and coming eclipses. Being notes on the total solar eclipses of 1893, 1896, and 1898. xi,166 p. 58 il. 1 pl. O. London: Macmillan & Co., 1897.

NL 0438134   ICJ MdBJ PPFr PPL MB PU NjP PPD

Lockyer, *Sir* Joseph Norman, 1836-1920.
Recent and coming eclipses, by Sir Norman Lockyer ... 2d ed., containing an account of the observations made at Viziadrug, in India, in 1898, and of the conditions of the eclipses visible in 1900, 1901 and 1905. London, Macmillan and co., limited, 1900.

xv, 236 p. front., illus. 23½ᶜᵐ.

1. Eclipses, Solar.   I. Title.

S 27-11

Smithsonian Inst. Library
for Library of Congress   [a38b1]

NL 0438135   DSI WaWW WaS OU ICJ MH

VOLUME 338

Lockyer, Joseph Norman
Recherches sur les spectres des meteorites.

Paris, 1888.
50 p. 25 m.

Bul. Astr., Paris, 5, 1888, p. 408-424, 460-472,
512-520, 556-568.

NL 0438136   DN-Ob

Lockyer, Norman & Lockyer, William James
Stewart
Relation between solar prominences and terrestrial
magnetism.
London, 1903.
2 pl. (7) p. 21cm.

Roy. Soc. Proc., 71, 1902-03, p. 244-250.

NL 0438137   DN-Ob

Lockyer, *Sir* Joseph Norman, 1836-1920.
... Remarks on a new map of the solar spectrum. By J.
Norman Lockyer, F. R. S. [London, 1875]
[152]-154 p. 21½ᵐ.
From the Proceedings of the Royal society, no. 158, 1875.

1. Spectrum, Solar.

Library of Congress   QC455.L79

          CA 6—2558 Unrev'd

NL 0438138   DLC

Lockyer, *Sir* Joseph Norman, 1836-1920.
... Remarks on the recent eclipse of the sun as observed in
the United States. [London, 1870]
[179]-183 p. 21½ᵐ.
Caption title.
From the Proceedings of the Royal society, no. 116, [vol. 18] 1870.

1. Eclipses, Solar—1870.

Library of Congress   QB543.70I.

          CA 6—2263 Unrev'd

NL 0438139   DLC

Lockyer, Sir Joseph Norman, 1836-   FOR OTHER EDITIONS
Gt. Brit. *Solar physics committee.*   SEE MAIN ENTRY
... Report of the solar eclipse expedition to Palma, Majorca, August 30, 1905, being an account of the observations made by the Solar physics observatory eclipse expedition and the officers and men of H. M. S. "Venus" at Palma, Majorca. Prepared under the direction of Sir Norman Lockyer ... London, Printed for H. M. Stationery off., by Wyman & sons, limited, 1907.

Lockyer, Sir Joseph Norman, 1836-
Report on the total solar eclipse of April 6,
1875.
London, 1879.
(16) p. 29cm.

Phil. Trans., 169, 1878, p. 139-154.

NL 0438141   DN-Ob NN

Lockyer, Sir J[oseph] Norman, 1836-1920.
Researches in spectrum-analysis in connexion
with the spectrum of the sun... n.p., 1872.
253-275 p., 3 pl. 4°. (Royal Soc. Philos.
Trans. 1873)
n.t.-p.

NL 0438142   NN

Lockyer, *Sir* Joseph Norman, 1836-1920.

Baxandall, Frank E.
... Researches on the chemical origin of various lines in solar
and stellar spectra. Being the results of investigations made
at the Solar physics observatory, South Kensington, after discussion, by Frank E. Baxandall ... Solar physics observatory.
Under the direction of Sir Norman Lockyer ... London,
Printed for H. M. Stationery off., by Eyre and Spottiswoode,
ltd., 1910.

Lockyer, *Sir* Joseph Norman, 1836-
... The Royal college of science, London, with which is
incorporated the Royal school of mines. Inaugural address at the opening of the session 1898-99. Delivered by
Professor Sir Norman Lockyer ... London, Printed for
H. M. Stationery off. by Wyman and sons, limited, 1898.
26 p. 24½ᵐ.
Lists of Associates and other students of the College, p. 21-26.

1. [London. Royal college of science.

          7-40568

Library of Congress   T173.L914 1898

NL 0438144   DLC

Lockyer, *Sir* Joseph Norman, 1836-1920.
The rules of golf; being the St. Andrews rules for the
game, codified and annotated by J. Norman Lockyer ...
and W. Rutherford ... New York, Macmillan & co.; London, Macmillan & co., ltd., 1896.
114 p. 13½ᵐ.

1. Golf.   I. Rutherford, William, joint author.

Library of Congress   GV971.L81

          5-23413

NL 0438145   DLC OO NN MB

Lockyer, Sir Joseph Norman, 1836-
Simultaneous solar and terrestrial changes.
1903.

NL 0438146   DAS

Lockyer, Joseph Norman & Lockyer, William J
S
Solar prominence and spot circulation, 1872-1901.

London, 1903.
2 pl. (7) p. 22cm.

Roy. Soc. Proc., 71, 1902-03, p. 446-452.

NL 0438147   DN-Ob

Lockyer, Sir Joseph Norman, 1836-1920.
Some stars with peculiar spectra...
see under Baxandall, Frank E

Lockyer, Sir Joseph Norman, 1836-1920.

Lockyer, William James Stewart, 1868-
... Southern hemisphere surface-air circulation: being
a study of the mean monthly pressure amplitudes, the
tracks of the anticyclones and cyclones, and the meteorological records of several Antarctic expeditions. By
William J. S. Lockyer ... chief assistant, Solar physics
observatory ... ' Under the direction of Sir Norman Lockyer ... London, Printed for H. M. Stationery off., by
Eyre and Spottiswoode, ltd., 1910.

Lockyer, *Sir* Joseph Norman, 1836-1920.
... The spectroscope and its applications. By J. Norman
Lockyer ... London and New York, Macmillan and co., 1873.
xii, 117, [1] p. fold. col. front., illus., diagrs. 18½ᵐ. (*Half-title:*
Nature series)

1. Spectrum analysis.   I. Title.

          22-24075

Library of Congress   QC451.L79 1873 a

NL 0438150   DLC PWcS PHC PP DN OCU MiU OO ICJ MB NN

Lockyer, *Sir* Joseph Norman, 1836-
... The spectroscope and its applications. By J. Norman Lockyer ... 2d ed. London, Macmillan and co.,
1873.
xii, [1], 117, [1] p. fold. col. front., illus., diagrs. 18½ᵐ. (*Half-title:* Nature
series)
Series title also at head of t.-p.

1. Spectrum analysis.

          5-5399

Library of Congress   QC451.L79

NL 0438151   DLC DNLM NIC CU OrP OCl OClJC NjP

Lockyer, *Sir* Joseph Norman, 1836-1920.
Spectroscopic comparison of metals present in certain
terrestrial and celestial light-sources (with special reference
to vanadium and titanium). Undertaken at the Solar physics observatory, South Kensington. Under the direction of
Sir Norman Lockyer ... London, Printed for H. M. Stationery off., by Wyman and sons, ltd., 1907.
2 p. l., 37 p. IV pl. 31 x 25 cm.
On cover: Solar physics committee.

1. Spectrum analysis. 2. Vanadium. 3. Titanium. I. Gt. Brit.
Solar physics committee.
Library of Congress   QC454.L82   8—34427

NL 0438152   DLC CaBVaU NjP ViU

LOCKYER, Joseph Norman.
Spectroscopic observations of the sun. No. 6. 6 pp. Pl.
(Royal soc. Proc. Vol. 18, pp. 354-359. Lond. 1870.)

NL 0438153   MB

QC451   Lockyer, Sir Joseph Norman, 1836-1920.
L583   Das Spectroskop und seine Anwendungen.
Eine übersichtliche Darstellung des gesammten
Gebietes der Spectralanalyse. Eingeführt
und bevorwortet durch H. Schellen.
Braunschweig, G. Westermann, 1874.
xiv, 136 p. illus., col. plate.

1. Spectrum analysis.

NL 0438154   CU MCM PPF

Lockyer, Sir Joseph Norman, 1836-1920
Spectrum analysis of the sun

lvi-lxxxviii p. illus.
(In Half hours with modern scientists, 2d ser.,
1873, p. [113]-146)

NL 0438155   MH

Lockyer, *Sir* Joseph Norman, 1836-1920.

Roscoe, *Sir* Henry Enfield, 1833-1915.
... Spectrum analysis: three lectures. By Prof. Roscoe, William Huggins, and Norman Lockyer. New Haven, Conn., C. C. Chatfield & co., 1872.

Lockyer, Joseph Norman
The spectrum of comet Brooks, 1911. By Sir
Norman Lockyer...
(London, 1912.)
1 pl., (5) p. 25½cm.
caption title.
Roy. Soc. Proc., 86A, 1912, p. 258-262.

NL 0438157   DN-Ob

Lockyer, Sir Joseph Norman, 1836-1920.
The spectrum of γ Cygni, by Sir Norman Lockyer
and F.E. Baxandall. London, Pub. for the Royal
Society by Dulau, 1903.
205-222p. fold.illus., tables. 30cm.
(Philosophical transactions of the Royal Society
of London. Ser.A, v.201)

1. Stars. Spectra. I. Baxandall, Frank E.
jt. author.

NL 0438158   IEN NjP DN-Ob

VOLUME 338

Lockyer, *Sir* Joseph Norman, 1836–1920.
Stargazing: past and present. By J. Norman Lockyer ...
Expanded from shorthand notes of a course of Royal institution lectures with the assistance of G. M. Seabroke, F. R. A. S.
London, Macmillan and co., 1878.
xiv, 496 p. front., illus. (incl. port., diagrs.) 23ᶜᵐ.

1. Astronomy. 2. Telescope.   I. Seabroke, George Mitchell, 1848–1918, ed. II. Title.
4—4434
Library of Congress   QB86.L8
-522

ODW ICJ MH PPFr PSC PPL PU
NL 0438159   DLC IU DSI NIC CU OrP CtY MiU OCU OCl

Lockyer, Sir Joseph Norman, 1836–1920.

Gt. Brit. *Solar physics committee.*
Statement made by the Solar physics committee in June 1909, with special reference to the present and future position of the observatory; with an appendix giving a report by the director on the observatory and its work during the period 1889–1909. Presented to both houses of Parliament by command of His Majesty. London, H. M. Stationery off., printed by Eyre and Spottiswoode, ltd., 1911.

Lockyer, *Sir* Joseph Norman, 1836–1920.
Stonehenge and other British stone monuments astronomically considered, by Sir Norman Lockyer ... London, Macmillan and co., limited, 1906.
xii, 340 p. illus., diagrs. 23½ᶜᵐ.

1. Stonehenge. 2. Gt. Brit. — Antiq. 3. Sun-worship. 4. Druids and druidism. 5. Temples.
7—4831
Library of Congress   GN792.G7L8

PSC PPL
NL 0438161   DLC OrP OkU NcD DN-Ob MiU ICJ MB NN

Lockyer, *Sir* Joseph Norman, 1836–1920.
Stonehenge and other British stone monuments astronomically considered. 2d ed. London, Macmillan, 1909.
xv, 499p. illus., maps, diagrs. 23cm.

1. Stonehenge. 2. Gt. Brit.—Antiq. 3. Sun-worship. 4. Druids & druidism. 5. Temples.

NL 0438162   MB ICJ MB WaU CtY IU NIC OCl PU

Lockyer, (Sir) Joseph Norman
Studien zur Spectralanalyse. Autorisirte Ausgabe. Leipzig Brockhaus 1879 10+251p.
il. col.pls. (part fold.) diagrs. D

For English ed., see his Studies in spectrum analysis.

Internationale wissenschaftliche Bibliothek. 35.

NL 0438163   MCM

Lockyer, *Sir* Joseph Norman, 1836–
Studies in spectrum analysis. By J. Norman Lockyer ... London, C. K. Paul & co., 1878.
xii, 258 p. illus., VIII pl. (part col., incl. front.), diagrs. 19ᶜᵐ.
(*Half-title:* The international scientific series. (London ed.) v. 23)

1. Spectrum analysis.
4—30931
Library of Congress   QC451.L81

PPFr PSC NjP
OCU OU NcU MiHM NN MH PPL ViU MdBP ICJ CU CtY OO
NL 0438164   DLC NIC OU MtU OrP NcD MB MiU OClW OCl

Lockyer, Sir Joseph Norman, 1836–1920.
Studies in spectrum analysis. Ed. 4.
London, Kegan Paul, French & Co., 1886.
258 p. pl. graphs. D.

NL 0438165   PPF

QC
L818s
1893
LOCKYER, Sir Joseph Norman, 1836–1920
Studies in spectrum analysis. New York, Appleton, 1893.
xii, 258 p. illus. (International scientific series, v. 23)

NL 0438166   DNLM NN NcD KEmT NjNbS DN-Ob

QC451
894ℓ
Lockyer, *Sir* Joseph Norman, 1836–1920.
Studies in spectrum analysis. 5th ed.
London, Kegan Paul, Trench, Trübner, 1894.
xii, 258p. plates (part fold.) 20cm. (International scientific series, vol. 23)

1. Spectrum analysis. 2. Physical medicine - Phototherapy. I. Series. II. Title.

NL 0438167   CtY-M

QC451
L81
1897
Lockyer, *Sir* Joseph Norman, 1836–1920.
Studies in spectrum analysis. New York, D. Appleton, 1897.
xii, 258 p. illus., VIII pl. (part col.) tables, diagrs, 19cm. (Half title: The international scientific series. [New York ed.] v. 23)

1. Spectrum analysis.

NL 0438168   MB WaS Wa

Lockyer, Sir Joseph Norman, 1836–
Studies in spectrum analysis. Norman Lockyer..
...London, C.K. Paul & co., 1904. 6th ed.
xii, 258 p.

NL 0438169   ODW IdU

LOCKYER, Joseph Norman.
The sun.
(In Half hours with modern scientists. Series 2, pp. 113–146. New Haven, 1872.)

NL 0438170   MB ODW

Lockyer, *Sir* Joseph Norman, 1836–
The sun's place in nature, by Sir Norman Lockyer ... London, Macmillan and co., limited; New York, The Macmillan company, 1897.
xvi, 360 p. incl. illus., tables. 23½ᶜᵐ.

1. Sun. 2. Helium. 3. Meteoritic hypothesis. 4. Stars. 5. Nebulae.
I. Title.
1—13793
Library of Congress   QB918.L8

ICJ NN MB MiHM
NL 0438171   DLC CaBVaU PPL NjP NcD OCU PP PU PPAmP

Lockyer, *Sir* Joseph Norman, 1836–
The sun's spotted area, 1832–1900. A statement of the mean daily area in each synodic rotation of the sun, based upon data collected at the Solar physics observatory, South Kensington. Under the direction of Sir Norman Lockyer ... London, Printed for H. M. Stationery off., by Wyman & sons, limited, 1902.
iii, 35 p. 2 fold. pl., tables. 30½ × 24ᶜᵐ.
On cover: Solar physics committee.

1. Sun-spots.   I. Gt. Brit. Solar physics committee.
5–25739†* Cancel
Library of Congress   QB525.L87

NL 0438172   DLC CaBVaU DN-Ob DAS NjP MB

Lockyer, Sir Joseph Norman, 1836–
Sunspots and rainfall.
24½cm.
(excerpted from North Am. Review, June, 1901 p. 827,–837)

NL 0438173   DAS

Lockyer, *Sir* Joseph Norman, 1836–
Surveying for archæologists, by Sir Norman Lockyer ... London, Macmillan and co., limited, 1909.
x p., 1 l., 120 p. illus., diagrs. 23½ᶜᵐ.

1. Astronomy, Spherical and practical. 2. Archæology.   I. Title.
13–24861
Library of Congress   CC76.L7

NL 0438174   DLC CU MiU ICJ

Lockyer, *Sir* Joseph Norman, 1836–
Tables of wave-lengths of enhanced lines. Compiled from investigations made at the Solar physics observatory, South Kensington. Under the direction of Sir Norman Lockyer ... London, Printed for H. M. Stationery off., by Wyman & sons, limited, 1906.
2 p. l., 29 p. pl. 31 × 24½ᶜᵐ.
On cover: Solar physics committee.

1. Spectrum analysis—Tables, etc.   I. Gt. Brit. Solar physics committee.
8–34428
Library of Congress   QC453.L82

NL 0438175   DLC NN NjP ViU

Wing
Z
3100
.517
Lockyer, Sir Joseph Norman, 1836–1920.
Technical education: portion of speech delivered by Sir Norman Lockyer at the Borough polytechnic... Lond. 1912. O.

Cover-title.
"Composed by the day students and printed in the workshop, Boro' polytechnic."

NL 0438176   ICN

Lockyer, *Sir* Joseph Norman, 1836–1920.
Tennyson as a student and poet of nature, by Sir Norman Lockyer ... and Winifred L. Lockyer, with an introduction and notes. London, Macmillan and co., 1910.
x p., 1 l., 220 p. 20 cm.

1. Tennyson, Alfred Tennyson, 1st baron, 1809–1892. 2. Nature in poetry.   I. Lockyer, Winifred Lucas, joint author.
A 11—177
Wesleyan Univ. Libr.
for Library of Congress   (a48e½)

CaBVaU OrU
MiU NcD NcU CtY INS FMU OrP NIC KMK OrPR WaSpG CaBVa
NL 0438177   CtW CoU GU MsU TU OO OU OCl OCU NjP NN

Lockyer, *Sir* Joseph Norman, 1836–1920.
... The total eclipse of the sun, April 16th, 1893. Report and discussion of the observations relating to solar physics. By J. Norman Lockyer ...
(*In* Royal society of London. Philosophical transactions ... 1896. Series A. London, 1897. 30 × 23ᶜᵐ. v. 187, p. 551–618. illus., plates)
Report on the African station by A. Fowler: p. 557–567.
Report on the Brazilian station by W. Shackleton: p. 567–573.
1. Eclipses, Solar—1893.   I. Fowler, Alfred, 1868–   II. Shackleton, William.
9—654
Library of Congress   Q41.L8 vol. 187
———— Separate.   (A.184)
QB543.93L7

NL 0438178   DLC

Lockyer, *Sir* Joseph Norman, 1836–1920.
... Total eclipse of the sun, January 22, 1898. Preliminary account of the observations made by the eclipse expedition and the officers and men of H. M. S. "Melpomene," at Viziadrug. By Sir Norman Lockyer ... [London, Harrison and sons, printers, 1898]
cover-title, [27]–42 p. illus. 21½ᶜᵐ.
From the Proceedings of the Royal society, v. 64.

1. Eclipses, Solar—1898.
CA 6—2266 Unrev'd
Library of Congress   QB543.98L

NL 0438179   DLC OU

VOLUME 338

Lockyer, Sir Joseph Norman, 1836-
Total eclipse of the sun, May 28, 1900. Account of the observations made by the Solar Physics Observatory Eclipse Expedition and the officers and men of H.M.S. "Theseus" at Santa Pola, Spain. (Abstract).
London, 1901.
(2) p. 21cm.

Roy. Soc. Proc., 68, 1901, p. 404-405.

NL 0438180   DN-Ob

Lockyer, Sir Joseph Norman.
Total eclipse of the sun May 28, 1900. Account of the observations made by the Solar Physics Observatory Eclipse Expedition and the officers and men of H. M. S. "Theseus," at Santa Pola, Spain.
— London, 1902. 375-415 pp. Illus. Plates. Plan. Diagrams. 4°.
Contents. — General arrangements. By Sir Norman Lockyer. — Observations made by the officers and men of H. M. S. "Theseus." By Captain V. A. Tisdall. — Photographs of the corona. By Howard Payn. — The prismatic cameras. By Dr. Lockyer and Mr. Fowler. — Discussion of results. By Sir Norman Lockyer.
Reprinted from Philosophical Transactions of the Royal Society, vol. 198, 1902 [*3210.1.198].

Dec. 26,   1902
E6627 — Sun. Eclipses.

NL 0438181   MB OU

Lockyer, Sir Joseph Norman, 1836-
Total eclipse of the sun, May 28, 1900. Preliminary account of the observations made by the Solar Physics Observatory Eclipse Expedition and the officers and men of H. M. S. "Theseus", at Santa Pola.
London, 1900.
(10) p. 22cm.

Roy. Soc. Proc., 67, 1900, p. 337-346.

NL 0438182   DN-Ob

523   Lockyer, Sir Joseph Norman, 1836-1920.
L81w   Why the earth's chemistry is as it is. Three lectures ... delivered in the Association hall, Manchester, October, 1876.   London, 1877.
cover-title, 59p. illus.   (Manchester science lectures for the people. 8th ser. 1876-7)

NL 0438183   IU NN

Lockyer, Sir Joseph Norman, 1836-1920.
see also Norman Lockyer Observatory, Salcombe Hill, Sidmouth, Eng.

L2781   Lockyer, Lionel, 1600?-1672.
An advertisement concerning those most excellent pills, called, Pillulae Radijs Solis Extractae. Being an universal medicine...
[London, 1664].

16 p. A-B⁴. 4to
Caption title.

NL 0438185   DFo

LOCKYER, Lionel, 1600?-1672.
An advertisement concerning those most excellent pills called Pilular radiis solis extractae; an universal medicine. [London, 1707].

pp.16. Port.

NL 0438186   MH NNNAM

RS   Lockyer, Lionel, 1600?-1672.
201   An advertisement concerning those most ex-
P5   cellent pills, called Pilulae Radiis Solis Ex-
L6   tractae: being an universal medicine... [Lon-
Cage   don, ca. 1740?].

16 p. A-B⁴. 4to
Caption title.
Corners torn, affecting text.
Signed by Tho. Fyge and John Watts, the successors of Lockyer, and dated 1707 but includes testimonials dated 1739 and an advertisement that the pre-   paration has passed to the descendents of Fyge   and Watts.

NL 0438187   DFo RPJCB MH MWA

FILM   Lockyer, Nicholas, 1611-1685.
13464   [Works. London, 1643-71]
BX   3 reels. On film (positive)

Microfilms of titles from the British Museum, Cambridge Univ. Library and Harvard Univ. Library.

Contents. — Reel 1. Divine discovery of sincerity ... 1649. Baulme for bleeding England ... 1643. A little stone out of the mountain ... 1652. - Reel 2. England faithfully watcht with ... 1646. - Reel 3. Christ's communion with his church militant ... 1645. Sermon preached before the ... House of Commons ... 1646. A memorial of God's judgements ... 1671.

NL 0438188   CU

208   Lockyer, Nicholas, 1611-1685.
L815   The workes of the reverend and faithfull minister of the Gospell, Mᵣ. Nicholas Lockyer, master of arts. In three bookes, viz.1. Christs communion with His church militant. 2. A divine discovery of sincerity. 3. Baulme for bleeding England and Ireland ... London, Printed by I. D. for Iohn Rothwell, at the Sun in Pauls churchyard, 1644.
6 p.l., 92+p. 17cm.

Errors in paging: p.53-84 numbered 52-83.

Imperfect: t.-p. mutilated and mended; lacks all after p.92(i.e. after book 1)
Signatures, with date 1644, of Captain Joshua Price, inside front cover.

NL 0438190   IU

Lockyer, Nicholas, 1611-1685.
Balm for England; or, Useful instructions for evil times. By Nicholas Lockyer ... London, Printed for the Religious tract society and sold by J. Nisbet, 1831.

228 p. 14½ᶜᵐ.

"This work, in its original form, is a course of sermons forming a treatise upon the eleventh and twelfth verses of the first chapter of the epistle to the Colossians. They were preached in the latter end of the year 1642 ... In the present edition, some passages have been omitted."

NL 0438191   MiU

252   Lockyer, Nicholas, 1611-1685.
L815b   Baulme for bleeding England and Ireland. Or, Seasonable instructions, for persecuted Christians. Delivered in severall sermons, by Nicholas Lockyer mᵣ of arts ... London, Printed by John Raworth, for John Rothwell, and are to be sold at his shop at the signe of the Sun in Pauls churchyard, 1643.
7 p.l., 272p. 17½cm.
Upper margins closely trimmed.

1. Sermons. I. Title.

NL 0438192   IU CLU-C ICN MB MH NNUT-Mc

Lockyer, Nicholas, 1611-1685.
*EC65   Baulme for bleeding England and Ireland. Or,
L8153   Seasonable instructions, for persecuted
645b   Christians: delivered in severall sermons, by Nicholas Lockyer ...
London, Printed by E.G. for John Rothwell, and are to be sold at his shop at the signe of the Sun in Pauls church-yard, 1643.
8p.l., 413p. 17.5cm.
Pages 37 & 224 misnumbered 73 & 222.
Caption and running title: Usefull instructions for these evill times.
Inlaid engraved   portrait of the author inserted as front-   ispiece.

NL 0438193   MH CLU-C

Lockyer, Nicholas, 1611-1685.
Baulme for bleeding England and Ireland. Or, Seasonable instructions for persecuted Christians ...   London, Printed by J. D. for J. Rothwell, 1644.
264 p. 17ᶜᵐ.
Book-plate of Allan Maxcey Galer.

NL 0438194   CLU-C NNF CtY MH PPiPT

252   Lockyer, Nicholas, 1611-1685.
L815b   Baulme for bleeding England, and Ireland. Or,
1646   Seasonable instructions for persecuted Christians. Delivered in severall sermons by Nicholas Lockyer ... London, Printed by E. G. for John Rothwell, and are to be sold at his shop at the signe of the Sun and Fountaine in Pauls church-yard, 1646.
4 p.l., 128, 177-235, [1]p. 19cm.
With this is bound the author's England faithfully watcht with, in her wounds. London, 1646.

1. Sermons. I.   Title.

NL 0438195   IU MnU CtY

Lockyer, Nicholas, 1611-1685.
Baulme for bleeding England and Ireland. Or, seasonable instructions for persecuted Christiana Delivered in severall sermons, by Nicholas Lockyer ...
London, Printed by E.G. for John Rothwell, and are to be sold at his shop at the signe of the Sunne in Pauls church yard. 1649.
7p.l., 264p. 17.5cm.
Pages 166,167 & 178 misnumbered 167,166 & 18.
Running title: Usefull instructions for these evill times.

The paging called for in the table of contents does not fit this edition.
No.1 in a volume labelled: Lockyer's Baulme &c.

NL 0438197   MH ICN NNG CLU-C DFo NNUT-Mc

FILM   Lockyer, Nicholas, 1611-1685.
S-8   Christs communion with his Church militant.
reel   First preached, and now published, for the good of
1177   Gods Church in generall ... London, Printed by E.Griffins for I.Rothwell, 1640.
Short-title catalogue no.16651 (carton 1177)

1.Spiritual life--Anglican authors.
2.Consolation--Early works to 1800. I.Title.

NL 0438198   MiU ViU

Rare Book Lockyer, Nicholas, 1611-1685.
Room   Christs commvnion with his chvrch militant.
First preached, and now published for the good
Mhc9   of Gods church in generall. The second edition.
L815   By Nicholas Lockyer ... London, Printed by R.H.
C46   for Iohn Rothwell, at the Sunne in S.Pauls church-yard,1641.
11p.l.,156p. 14½cm.
Signatures: A-Gl² (A₁ [blank?] wanting) H6.
Imperfect: p.35-36 and 73-74 slightly mutilated.

NL 0438199   CtY

Lockyer, Nicholas, 1611-1685.
*EC65   Christs commvnion with his church militant.
L8153   First preached, and now published for the good
B645b   of Gods church in generall. By Nicholas Lockyer ...
London, Printed by I.N.for Iohn Rothwell, at the Sun in Pauls church-yard 1644.
6p.l.,92p. 17cm.
Pages 32 & 53-84 misnumbered 3 & 52-83.
No.2 in a volume lettered on spine: Lockyer's Baulme, 1644.

NL 0438200   MH

VOLUME 338

Lockyer, Nicholas, 1611-1685
Christ's communion with his church militant. First preached, and now published for the good of Gods church in generall. By Nicholas Lockyer ... London, Printed by T.F. for John Rothwell, 1646.
6 p.l., 92 p. 17 cm.
Signatures: A-F⁸G⁴.
Wing: L 2788A.
Bound with this are the author's A divine

discovery ... London, 1645; and his Baulme for bleeding England and Ireland ... London, 1644.

NL 0438202   CtY

[Lockyer, Nicholas, 1611-1685] L
[Christ's communion with his church militant, first preached, and now published for the good of Gods church in generall. By Nicholas Lockyer ...]
[London, Printed by T.F. for Iohn Rothwell, at the Sun and Fountain in Pauls church-yard, 1650.]
6p.l.,92p. 17.5cm.
Numerous errors in paging.
The paging called for in the table of contents do not fit this edition.
No.3 in a vol-   ume labelled: Lockyer's Baulme &c.

Imperfect: p.3-4,19-20 & 75-76 mutilated; t.-p. wanting; title transcribed from the McAlpin catalogue.

NL 0438204   MH NNG ICN CLU-C

Lockyer, Nicholas, 1611-1685.
Christs communion with his church militant. First preached, and now published for the good of Gods church in general. The sixth edition ... London, Printed by S. G. for J. Rothwel, 1656.
106 p. 14ᵐ.

NL 0438205   CLU-C

Lockyer, Nicholas, 1611-1685.
A divine discovery of sincerity, according to its proper and peculiar nature: very profitable for all sorts of persons to peruse. First preached, and now published, for the good of Gods church in generall. By Nicholas Lockyer ...
London, Printed by E.G[riffin]. for Iohn Rothwell, at the Sunne in Pauls church-yard. 1640.
8p.l.,229,[1]p. 16cm.

NL 0438206   MH DFo NcU MiU NNC

Lockyer, Nicholas, 1611-1685.
A divine discovery of sincerity [etc]. First preached and now published for the good of Gods church in generall. London, for J. Rothwell, 1643.
6 p.l., 148 p. 16°. [With his Baulme for bleeding England and Ireland London, 1643. 16°]

NL 0438207   DLC CLU-C NNUT-Mc

Lockyer, Nicholas, 1611-1685
A divine discovery of sincerity, according to its proper and peculiar nature: very profitable for all sorts of persons to peruse. First preached, and now published, for the good of Gods church in generall ... London, Printed by E.Griffin for J.Rothwell, 1645.
6p.l.,148p. 18cm. [Bound with his Christ's communion with His church militant ... London, 1646]

NL 0438208   CtY MH CLU-C

Lockyer, Nicholas, 1611-1685.
A divine discovery of sincerity, according to its proper and peculiar nature: very profitable for all sorts of persons to peruse. First preached, and now published for the good of Gods church in generall. By Nicholas Lockyer, master of arts ... London, Printed for John Rothwell, at the Sun in Pauls church-yard, 1649.
7 p.l., 229, [1]p. 16½cm.

1. Christian life. I. Title.

NL 0438209   IU CLU-C ICN NNG CtY MH NNUT-Mc

Lockyer, Nicholas, 1611-1685.
England faithfully watcht with, in her wounds: or, Christ as a father sitting up with his children in their swooning state: which is the summe of severall lectures, painfully preached upon Colossians I. By Nicho. Lockyer ... Published according to order.   London, Printed by M. S. for John Rothwell, at the Sun and Fountain in Pauls church-yard, and Ben. Allen, at the Bible in Popes-Head alley, 1646.
4 p.l., 184, 161-302(i.e.312) 401-552, [12]p. 19cm. [With his Baulme for bleeding England. London, 1646]

NL 0438210   IU MH CLU-C MnU CtY MB ICN NNUT-Mc

Lockyer, Nicholas, 1611-1685.
Englands warning: or, A friendly admonition to the rulers thereof
see under   [Swinton, John] 1621?-1679, supposed author.

Lockyer, Nicholas, 1611-1685.
A litle stone, out of the mountain. Church-order briefly opened, by Nicholas Lockyer ... Printed at Leith by Evan Tyler. Anno Dom. 1652.
12p.l.,138p. 12.5cm.
Page 59 misnumbered 58.

NL 0438212   MH

Lockyer, Nicholas, 1611-1685.
[Lockyer sermons from manuscript Rawlinson E.159, Bodleian Library. London? 1635/36]
71 ℓ. On film (positive)

Microfilm. Original in Bodleian Library, Oxford; supplied by Mr. Willmer Mason.

1. Sermons, English.   I. Oxford, Eng.   University. Bodleian Library. Mss. (Rawlinson E.159)

NL 0438213   CU

Lockyer, Nicholas, 1611-1685.
A memorial of God's judgments, spiritual and temporal. Or Sermons to call to remembrance. First preached and now published for publick benefit. By Nic. Lockier ...
London, Printed for Dorman Newman, and are to be sold at his shop at the Kings Arms and Bible in the Poultry, 1671.
5p.l.,226(i.e.236)p.,1ℓ. 17cm.
Page 225 misnumbered 226; five divisional title-pages are not included in the paging.
Errata: 1ℓ. at   end.

NL 0438214   MH CtY IU CLU-C MWelC NNUT-Mc

Lockyer, Nicholas, 1611-1685.
An olive-leafe: or, A bud of the spring. Viz. Christ's resurrection, and its end, viz. The conversion of sinners, and a Christians compleat reliefe. Opened by Nicholas Lockyer ...
[London] Printed by E.G. for J.Rothwell, and are to be sold at his shop at the signe of the Sun and Fountain in Pauls church-yard neere the little north gate. 1650.
8p.l.,67p.,1ℓ., [8], 71-254p. 17cm.
Pages 76 & 77 misnumbered 78 & 79.
Errata: verso of   8th prelim. leaf.
"Spiritual in-   spection: or, A review of the heart", with   special t.-p.: p.[69] to end.

NL 0438215   MH CLU-C

Lockyer, Nicholas, 1611-1685.
A sermon preached before the honourable House of commons assembled in Parliament: at their late solemn fast, Octob. 28.1646. In Margarets Westminster. By Nicholas Lockyer, M.A. ... London, Printed by Matthew Simmons, for John Rothwell, at the Sun and Fountaine, in Pauls-church-yard, and Han. Allen, at the Crowne in Popes-Head alley, 1646.
4 p.l., 32p. 19cm.
No.21 in v.4 of a set of volumes lettered: Sermons before Parliament.

NL 0438216   NNUT-Mc PPPrHi MnU NNC TxDaM-P CLU-C
IU DFo PPL CU ICU TxU CSmH NjP MWA MoU

[Lockyer, Nicholas] 1611-1685.
Some seasonable and serious queries upon the late act against conventicles. Tending to discover how much it is against the express word of God, the positive law of the nation, the law & light of nature, and principles of prudence & policy. And therefore adjudged by the law of the land to be void and null ... By a friend to truth and peace ... [London] 1670.
16 p. 18¼ᵐ.
Signatures: A-B⁴.
1. Religious liberty—Gt. Brit. 2. Church and state in Great Britain. 3. Gt. Brit.—Hist.—Charles II, 1660-1685—Pamphlets.   I. Title.

Library of Congress   DA432.1670.L6   41-31732

NL 0438217   DLC CtY MH MoU MHi PSC NNUT-Mc

Lockyer, Sir Nicholas Colston. 1855-
Commerce Act. Butter export trade of Australia. Report by N. Lockyer. [Melbourne] J. Kemp [1910]. 14 p. f°.
(Australia. Comptroller-General of Customs, Office of.)

1. Butter—Trade, etc., Australia.
N. Y. P. L.   June 12, 1915.

NL 0438218   NN

Lockyer, Sir Nicholas Colston, 1855-
... Report on financial position of Tasmania as affected by federation, by Sir Nicholas Lockyer ... [Melbourne] Printed and pub. for the government of the commonwealth of Australia by H. J. Green, government printer for the state of Victoria [1926]
26 p. incl. tables. 33¼ᵐ.
At head of title: 1926. The Parliament of the commonwealth of Australia.

1. Finance—Tasmania.   I. Title.
Library of Congress   HJ1743.L6   26-19226

NL 0438219   DLC NN CtY

Lockyer, Mrs. Norman
see   Lockyer, Winifred (James) d. 1879.

Lockyer, Sir Norman
see
Lockyer, Sir Joseph Norman, 1836-1920.

Lockyer, Robert.
What is a Communist? London, Batchworth Press [1954]
38 p. 19 cm. (A Background book)

1. Communist Party of Great Britain.   I. Title.
JN1129.C62L6   55-30275 ‡

NL 0438222   DLC CaBVaU NN

VOLUME 338

Lockyer, Sibyl.
Practical zoological illustrations ... by S. Lockyer and D. R. Crofts. London, Macmillan & co., ltd., 1937–
v. plates (part col.) 37½ᶜᵐ.
Issued in portfolio.
CONTENTS.—pt. 1. Vertebrates.

1. Anatomy, Comparative—Atlases.   I. Crofts, Doris Rhoda, joint author.

Library of Congress   QL806.L8   42–45268
                                          591.4084

NL 0438223   DLC NNC

Lockyer, Thomas Frederick, ed.

Green, Richard, 1828–1907.
The conversion of John Wesley, by Richard Green ... Edited, with an introduction, by Thomas F. Lockyer, B. A. London, The Epworth press (E. C. Barton) ₁1938₎

BX   Lockyer, Thomas Frederick.
8331   The evangelical succession, or the spiritual lineage of the
L6   Christian Church and ministry. London, C. H. Kelly, 1899.
154 p. 22cm. (Fernley lectures, 1899)

1. Methodist Church (England)--Doctrinal and controversial works. 2. Apostolic succession. I. Title. (Series)

NL 0438225   CBPac ICU

Lockyer, Thomas Frederick
Paul: Luther: Wesley. A study in religious experience as illustrative of the ethic of Christianity, by Thos. F. Lockyer ... London, The Epworth press[1922]
359,[1]p. 19½cm.
"First edition, 1922."

NL 0438226   CtY IaDuW OC1W CLSU MBU-T NcD

BV4253 Lockyer, Thomas Frederick.
.L8   Seeking a country, by Thos. F. Lockyer... London, F. Griffiths, 1904.
vi,167,[1] p. 19½ᶜᵐ.

1. Sermons, English.

NL 0438227   ICU

Lockyer, Thomazine Mary (Browne) *lady.*
Life and work of Sir Norman Lockyer, by T. Mary Lockyer and Winifred L. Lockyer, with the assistance of Prof. H. Dingle and contributions by Dr. Charles E. St. John; Prof. Megh Nad Saha ... ₁and others₎ London, Macmillan and co., limited, 1928.
xii, 474 p. illus., xvii pl. (incl. front., ports.) diagrs. 22¼ᶜᵐ.

1. Lockyer, Sir Joseph Norman, 1836–1920.   I. Lockyer, Winifred Lucas, joint author.   II. Dingle, Herbert.

Library of Congress   QB36.L65L6   29–10169

OC1W OC1 MiU MB PPF NjP NN IU
NL 0438228   DLC CaBVaU InU CU TxU NIC ICJ CtY ODW

Lockyer, William James Stewart, 1868–
Barometric variations of long duration over large areas.
London, 1906.
5 pl. (18) p. 26cm.

Roy. Soc. Proc., 78, 1906, p. 43–60.

NL 0438229   DN-Ob NjP

Lockyer, William James Stewart, 1868–
Dark lightning-flashes. 1899.
p. 224–229 illus. plate. f.
P.4407 2/19/1900

NL 0438230   DAS

Lockyer, William James Stewart, 1868–
Gt. Brit. *Solar physics committee.*
... A discussion of Australian meteorology, being a study of the pressure, rainfall and river changes, both seasonal and from year to year, together with a comparison of the air movements over Australia with those over South Africa and South America. By William J. S. Lockyer ... Under the direction of Sir Norman Lockyer ... London, Printed for H. M. Stationery off., by Eyre and Spottiswoode, ltd., 1909.

Lockyer, William James Stewart, 1868–
Handbook to the Norman Lockyer observatory
see under   Norman Lockyer Observatory, Salcombe Hill, Sidmouth, Eng.

Lockyer, William James Stewart
On a probable relationship between the solar prominences and corona.
London, 1903.
(10) 22cm.

Astron. Soc. Month., Not., 63, 1902–03, p. 481–488.

NL 0438233   DN-Ob

Lockyer, William James Stewart, 1868–1936, joint author.
Lockyer, Sir Joseph Norman, 1836–1920.
On solar changes of temperature and variations in rainfall in the region surrounding the Indian ocean. By Sir Norman Lockyer, and W. J. S. Lockyer ...
(*In* Smithsonian institution. Annual report. 1900. Washington, 1901. 23½ᶜᵐ. p. 173–184. II pl.)

Lockyer, William James Stewart
Prominence and coronal structure.
London, 1908.
1 pl. 1 f.+ (6) p. 25½cm.

Roy. Soc. Proc., 80A, 1908, p. 178–183.

NL 0438235   DN-Ob NjP

Lockyer, William James Stewart, 1868–
Gt. Brit. *Solar physics committee.*
... Report of the Solar eclipse expedition to Vavau, Tonga Islands, April 29, 1911 (eastern date) ... By William J. S. Lockyer ... under the direction of Sir Norman Lockyer ... London, Pub. by H. M. Stationery off., printed by Eyre and Spottiswoode, ltd., 1912.

LOCKYER, William James Stewart.
Resultate aus den beobachtungen des veränderlichen sternes Aquilae. Inaug.-diss, Göttingen,   1897.

Plate and charts.

NL 0438237   MH NjP CtY

Lockyer, William James Stewart
Solar activity 1833–1900.
London, 1901.
(16) p. 22cm.

Roy. Soc. Proc., 68, 1901, p. 285–300.

NL 0438238   DN-Ob

Lockyer, William James Stewart, 1868–
Some world's weather problems. 1906

NL 0438239   DAS

Lockyer, William James Stewart, 1868–1936.
... Southern hemisphere surface-air circulation: being a study of the mean monthly pressure amplitudes, the tracks of the anticyclones and cyclones, and the meteorological records of several Antarctic expeditions. By William J. S. Lockyer ... chief assistant, Solar physics observatory ... Under the direction of Sir Norman Lockyer ... London, Printed for H. M. Stationery off., by Eyre and Spottiswoode, ltd., 1910.
3 p. l., iii, 109, ₁1₎ p. illus., xv pl. (charts, diagrs.; incl. col. front.) 30½ x 24ᶜᵐ.
At head of title: Solar physics committee.
1. Winds. 2. Meteorology—Antarctic regions.   I. Gt. Brit. Solar physics committee.   II.   Lockyer, Sir Joseph Norman, 1836–1920.   III. Title.

Library of Congress   QC940.S7L7   10–31689

NL 0438240   DLC CaBVaU NjP CU DAS ICJ

Lockyer, William James Stewart
Spectroheliograph of the Solar Physics Observatory.
London, 1905.
6 pl. 16 p. 22cm.

Astron. Soc. Month. Not., 65, 1905, p. 473–436.

NL 0438241   DN-Ob

Lockyer, William James Stewart, 1868–
... Sunspot variation in latitude, 1861–1902. By William J. S. Lockyer ... ₁London, Harrison and sons, printers, 1904₎
cover-title, ₁142₎–152 p. 2 fold. pl., diagrs. 21½ᶜᵐ.
From the Proceedings of the Royal society, v. 73.

1. Sun-spots.   CA 6–2209 Unrev'd
                        ₁33b1₎
Library of Congress   QB525.L9

NL 0438242   DLC DN-Ob

Lockyer, Winifred James, d. 1879, tr.
Guillemin, Amédée Victor, 1826–1893.
The applications of physical forces. By Amédée Guillemin. Tr. from the French by Mrs. Norman Lockyer, and ed., with additions and notes, by J. Norman Lockyer. With coloured plates and illustrations. London, Macmillan and co., 1877.

Lockyer, Mrs. Winifred (James) d. 1879, tr.
Guillemin, Amédée Victor, 1826–1893.
The forces of nature: a popular introduction to the study of physical phenomena. By Amédée Guillemin. Tr. from the French by Mrs. Norman Lockyer; and ed., with additions and notes, by J. Norman Lockyer, F. R. S. Illustrated by eleven coloured plates and four hundred and forty-five woodcuts. 2d ed. London, Macmillan and co., 1878.

Lockyer, Winifred (James) d. 1879, tr.
Flammarion, Camille *i. e.* **Nicolas Camille,** 1842–
The marvels of the heavens. By Camille Flammarion. From the French, by Mrs. Norman Lockyer. With forty-eight illustrations. London, R. Bentley, 1870.

Lockyer, Mrs. Winifred (James) d. 1879, tr.
Zurcher, Frédéric, 1816–1890.
Volcanoes and earthquakes. By MM. Zurcher and Margollé. From the French by Mrs. Norman Lockyer ... With sixty-two woodcuts by E. Riou. Philadelphia, J. B. Lippincott & co.; London, R. Bentley, 1869.

VOLUME 338

Lockyer,   Winifred (James) d. 1879, tr.
FOR OTHER EDITIONS
SEE MAIN ENTRY
Flammarion, Camille, 1842-1925.
The wonders of the heavens. By Camille Flammarion.
From the French by Mrs. Norman Lockyer. With forty-eight
illustrations. New York, Scribner, Armstrong, & co., 1874.

Lockyer, Winifred Lucas, joint author.

Lockyer, Thomazine Mary (Browne) *lady.*
Life and work of Sir Norman Lockyer, by T. Mary Lockyer
and Winifred L. Lockyer, with the assistance of Prof. H.
Dingle and contributions by Dr. Charles E. St. John; Prof.
Megh Nad Saha ... ₍and others₎ London, Macmillan and co.,
limited. 1928.

LOCKYER AND BREAM vs. PHOENIX INSURANCE
COMPANY.
The trial between the assignees of Lockyer
and Bream,plaintiffs,and Thomas Worsley,secre-
tary of the Phoenix fire-office,defendant , in
the court of common-pleas,at Guildhall,23d July
1794;with a narrative of the transactions,an
account of the former trial,the trial between
Morgan and Crouch,the arguments on a motion for
arrest of judgment,the proceedings on a writ of
error in the court of King's bench,7th June,
1796 [and] observations.From the short-hand
notes of Mr. Gurney. London,1796].
The work consists   mostly of appendic
each with a special title page and separate
paging.

NL 0438249   MH-L CLL

Locle, Camille du
see   Du Common du Locle, Camille, 1832-
1902.

Locle, Le, *Switzerland*
see
Le Locle, *Switzerland.*

Locman
see   Luqmān.

LOCMARIA, Noël Marie Victor Du Parc,comte de, 1794-1881.
Maria Theresia in Ungarn. Aus dem französische
übersetzt durch Mathilde Seewald. Regensburg, F.Pustel,1862.

A work of fiction.

NL 0438253   MH

DB71
D8x   Locmaria, Noël Marie Victor Du Parc, comte de, 1791-1861
Marie Thérèse en Hongrie, par le comte de Locmaria.
Paris, Putois-Crette, 1861.
xi, 360 p.   23 cm.

1. Maria Theresia, Empress of Austria, 1717-1780.
1. Title.

NL 0438254   CaQMM

DC
261
L6   Locmaria, Noël Marie Victor Du Parc, comte de,
1791-1881.
La révolution du 7 août devant la France,
par le Lieutenant-Colonel N***, secrétaire
particulier de S.A.R. Madame, Duchesse de
Berry. Paris, chez G.-A. Dentu, 1831.
61, ₍1₎ p.   22 cm.

1. FRANCE - HIST. - JULY REVOLUTION, 1830. 1. TITLE.

NL 0438255   MiEM

DC280
.5
C38L6   Locmaria, Noël Marie Victor du Parc, comte de, 1791-
1881.
Souvenirs des voyages de Monseigneur le duc de
Bordeaux en Italie, en Allemagne et dans les états de
l'Autriche. Paris, H.-L. Delloye, 1846.
2 v.

1. Chambord, Henri Charles Ferdinand Marie Dieudonné
d'Artois, duc de Bordeaux, comte de, 1820-1883. 2.
Europe - Descr. & trav. - 1800-1918. I. Title.

NL 0438256   CU MH CtY

DC280
.5
C38L6
1872   Locmaria, Noël Marie Victor du Parc, comte de, 1791-
1881.
Souvenirs des voyages du comte de Chambord en Italie,
en Allemagne et dans des états d'Autriche de 1839 à
1843, par le comte de Locmaria. 3.éd. Paris, Pu-
tois-Cretté, 1872.
435 p.

1. Chambord, Henri Charles Ferdinand Marie Dieudonné d'Artois, duc de Bordeaux, comte de, 1820-1883.
2. Europe - Descr. & trav. - 1800-1918. I. Title.

NL 0438257   CU

Locmaria, Noël Marie Victor Du Parc, *comte de,* 1791-1881.
Tableaux raisonnés de l'histoire de France, 1748-1830.
₍Paris₎ 183-?₎
2 v. 23 cm.
CONTENTS.—1. 1748-1814.—2. 1814-1830.

1. France—Hist.—Bourbons, 1589-1789. 2. France—Hist.—1789-
1900. 1. Title.
DC131.L65   56-53570

NL 0438258   DLC

Loco. v. 1–   May 1910–
Schenectady, N. Y., 1910–
v. illus. 24ᶜᵐ. quarterly.
Published by the Locomotive club, Schenectady, N. Y.
Ceased publication with May 1919 issue.

1. Locomotives—Period. 2. Engineering—Period.   I. Locomotive
club, Schenectady, N. Y.
Library of Congress   TJ1.L68   43-48758
                                             ₍2₎   621.1305

NL 0438259   DLC

...El loco. Aquí no vendrá mal el siguiente lema. Et puer et
demens verum persaepius ajunt, Captus mente nequit duplice
mente capi. D. P. 603...   ₍Valencia: I. Mompié, 1817.₎   4 l.
8°.

Caption-title.
At head of title: Monologo.
In verse.

1. Monologues (Spanish).
N.Y.P.L.   October 20, 1921.

NL 0438260   NN NcU

El Loco de Jerusalem.
Bustamante a ti te hablamos [1832]
see under title

El loco en la penitencia, Roberto el diablo.
De un ingenio de la Corte. [Sevilla, Manuel
Nicolás Vázquez, n.d.]
28 p.   22 cm. (Comedias [Teatro antiguo
español])
At head of title: Comedia famosa, núm. 38.

NL 0438262   MiU NcU

... El LOCO en la penitencia, Roberto
el Diablo. De un ingenio desta cort₍ ₎₎
... ₍Madrid? 16-?₎

32 p.   20 cm.

Caption title.
At head of title: Num. 206. Comedia
famosa.
Not the same as Roberto el Diablo, by
Francisco Viceno.
1. Robert le
Diable. I. Un In-   genio desta corte.

NL 0438263   MnU

El Loco entre los Locos. (Caption title) Colophon, Mejico: Oficina de Don Jose Maria
Betancourt, 1820.
7 p.   8vo.
Signed at end: R.A.
Bound with: Elogio Poetico, Mexico, 1820,
(24)

NL 0438264   CSmH MH

Loco-Foco Party
see   Democratic Party.

**The loco foco party - The credit of the
state - The new constitution.** n.p. n.d.

8 (i.e.7 [3] p.

Includes: The canal revenues and the
state debt. n.p.,n.d.

NL 0438266   OClWHi

Loco-revue.
₍Auray, France₎
v. illus. (part col.) maps, plans. 27-30 cm. 11 no. a year.
"La revue des modélistes et amateurs de chemins de fer" (varies
slightly)
Began with Mar. 1987 issue.
Issues for   accompanied by a supplement
entitled: Synopsis of contents.

1. Railroads—Models—Period.
TF197.L58   625.1'9'05   68-6497

NL 0438267   DLC NN

Loco-Revue.
Les Locomotives à vapeur de la S N C F
see under title

Un LOCO tolerado,o los disparates pifias
i despropositos de un escritor. n. p., n. d.

NL 0438269   MH

₍El loco y el niño, pseud.₎ ₍²Al publico ₍San
Salvador, El Siglo, 1832, ₍3₎p. 33cm. Central American pamphlets, 6:23)

NL 0438270   CU-B

Locock, Charles, 1799-1875.
RC683   De cordis palpitatione. Edinburgh, P. Neill,
821ℓ   1821.
4p. ℓ.,42p. 22cm.

1. Heart - Diseases - Diagnosis. 2. Heart -
Palpitation.

NL 0438271   CtY-M DNLM

VOLUME 338

Locock, Charles Dealtry, 1862–
An examination of the Shelley manuscripts in the Bodleian library. Being a collation thereof with the printed texts, resulting in the publication of several long fragments hitherto unknown, and the introduction of many improved readings into Prometheus unbound, and other poems, by C. D. Locock, B. A. Oxford, At the Clarendon press, 1903.

iv, 75, [1] p. front. (facsim.) 23 x 18ᶜᵐ.

1. Shelley, Percy Bysshe, 1792–1822—Manuscripts. I. Oxford university. Bodleian library.

4—11225

Library of Congress   Z8616.85409

OOxM MiU OC1 NcD CSmH PU MH PBm PSC
NL 0438272   DLC FTaSU OrU AAP NIC TU NjP CtY OU OO

Locock, Charles Dealtry, 1862–   tr.

Tegnér, Esaias, 1782–1846.
… Fritiof's saga, by E. Tegnér; translated in the original metres by C. D. Locock … New York, The Macmillan company, 1924.

Locock, Charles Dealtry, 1862–   tr.

Fröding, Gustaf, 1860–1911.
Guitar & concertina; a century of poems by Gustav Fröding; translated in the original metres by C. D. Locock … London, G. Allen & Unwin, ltd. [1925]

Locock, Charles Dealtry, 1862–
Imagination in chess.   95p.   Leeds, Whitehead & Miller [1937]

NL 0438275   OC1

Locock, Charles Dealtry, 1862–
Imagination in chess, by C. D. Locock … Philadelphia, David McKay company [1939]
95 p. illus. 19ᶜᵐ.
"Printed in England."

1. Chess.

39–31661

Library of Congress   GV1451.L7
794.1

NL 0438276   DLC MB CtY

Locock, Charles Dealtry, 1862–   tr.

Strindberg, August, 1849–1912.
… Master Olof and other plays. New York, J. Cape & H. Smith; London, J. Cape [1931]

Locock, Charles Dealtry, 1862–
Modern croquet tactics. With an introduction by Jarvis Kenrick. — [London.] The Holmesdale Press. 1907. 234 pp. Portraits. Diagrams. 8°.

G5690 — Croquet. — Kenrick, Jarvis, pref.

NL 0438278   MB N

Locock, Charles Dealtry, 1862–
Modern croquet tactics, together with laws (1910); with an introduction by Jarvis Kenrick.   London: E. J. Larby [pref. 1910]. 219 p. diagr., port. 2. ed. 12°.

CENTRAL RESERVE.

1. Croquet.
N.Y.P.L.   September 29, 1916.

NL 0438279   NN

796.354   Locock, Charles Dealtry, 1862–
L819a   Modern croquet tactics; together with the laws (1913) 3d ed. London, E. J. Larby, [pref. 1913]
ix, 224 p. col. plates. 19 cm.

1. Croquet. I. Title.

NL 0438280   N

PT9590   Locock, Charles Dealtry, 1862–   tr.
E5L597   Modern Swedish poetry, part II [supplement] London, H. & W. Brown, 1936.
49 p.

"This … volume is intended as a supplement to my larger book 'Modern Swedish poetry' [i.e. A selection from modern Swedish poetry] (Allen & Unwin, 1929)"

1. Swedish poetry (Collections) I. Title.

NL 0438281   CU

Locock, Charles Dealtry, 1862–
More Olympian echoes, by C. H. Locock …   London: H. & W. Brown, 1935.   94 p.   20cm.
Reprinted in part from various sources.
CONTENTS.—Vox populi.—Art and man.—Euclid in his dotage.—To Colonel Bogey.—Ladies' luggage.—When the Kaiser comes.—To the German professors.—A day's work.—"44/13."—An international limerick.—The great sugar war.—Epigrams.—Woa, Emma.—Atta-boy.—A Keats menu.—The therm.—Metrical experiments.—The three captains.—Little Alice.—More Euclid.—Skating.—Wrong envelopes.—The pirate's reply.—What we may expect.—Between the innings.—A great antiquarian discovery.—Album verses.—Sporting intelligence.—Translations.—Dedication.—Appendix: Some serious verse.

818537A.   1. English literature—   Misc. I. Title.
N.Y.P.L.   May 4, 1936

NL 0438282   NN

LOCOCK, CHARLES DEALTRY, 1862–
One hundred chess maxims for beginners and moderate players, by C.D.Locock…   Leeds: Whitehead and Miller, Ltd. [1930]   28 p.   illus.   18cm.

775256A. 1. Chess—Maxims.

NL 0438283   NN OC1 OrP

Locock, Charles Dealtry, 1862–
One hundred chess maxims for beginners and moderate players, by C. D. Locock. 2d ed. rev. and enl. … Philadelphia, David McKay company [1939]
27 p. illus. 18ᶜᵐ.
"Printed in England."

1. Chess.

40–11517

Library of Congress   GV1447.L6 1939
794.1

NL 0438284   DLC OC1 OLak

Locock, Charles Dealtry, 1862–
120 chess problems and puzzles.   Stroud, The chess amateur, 1912.
160 p.

NL 0438285   OC1 PP

Locock, Charles Dealtry, 1862–   ed.

Shelley, Percy Bysshe, 1792–1822.
The poems of Percy Bysshe Shelley, ed. with notes by C. D. Locock; with an introduction by A. Clutton-Brock. London, Methuen and co., ltd. [1911]

Locock, Charles Dealtry, 1862–   , translator.
A selection from modern Swedish poetry; translated in the original metres, by C. D. Locock.   London: G. Allen & Unwin, Ltd.[, 1929.]   161 p.   12°.

444659A.   1. Poetry, Swedish—   Collections.
N.Y.P.L.   November 30, 1929

NL 0438287   NN Or WaS NcU OC1 MH

Locock, Charles Dealtry, 1862–   tr.
A selection from modern Swedish poetry, translated in the original metres by C. D. Locock. New York, The Macmillan company, 1930.
2 p. l. [7]–161, [2] p. 20¹⁄₂ᶜᵐ.
Half-title: Modern Swedish poetry.
"Printed in Great Britain."
CONTENTS.—Introduction.—Verner von Heidenstam.—Oscar Levertin.—E. A. Karlfeldt.—F. Vetterlund.—Bo Bergman.—S. Siwertz.—Anders Österling.—Ture Nerman.—Harriet Löwenhjelm.—Dan Andersson.—Erik Lindorm.—Karl Asplund.—Albert Henning.—Sten Selander.—G. M. Silfverstolpe.—Erik Blomberg.—F. G. Bengtsson.—Karin Boye.—Epilogue (by Dan Andersson).
1. Swedish poetry—Translations into English. 2. English poetry—Translations from Swedish.   I. Title: Modern Swedish poetry.

30–9133

Library of Congress   PT9590.E5L6

NL 0438288   DLC CU WaE OO PP NN OEac OC1 PU PPGi

Locock, Charles Dealtry, 1862–
Side and screw; being notes on the theory and practice of the game of billiards by C. D. Locock. London, New York and Bombay, 1901.
xiv, 182 p. illus. 19¹⁄₄ᶜᵐ.

1. Billiards.   I. Title.

2—21064

Library of Congress   GV893.L81

NL 0438289   DLC ICJ MiU ICRL ICJ

Locock, Charles Dealtry, 1862–
Thirty-two passages from the Iliad. In English rhymed verse
see under   Homerus. Ilias. English. Selections, abridgments, adaptations, paraphrases, etc., 1922.

Locock, Frances.
A biographical guide to the Divina Commedia of Dante Alighieri. London, Provost & Co., 1874.
pp. (3), 77.

Dante–Indexes‖

NL 0438291   MH InStme NIC OCU

Locock, Frances, tr.

Pégot-Ogier, Eugène, 1824–
The Fortunate Isles; or, The archipelago of the Canaries. By E. Pégot-Ogier. Tr. from the French by Frances Locock. London, R. Bentley and son, 1871.

Locock, Frances, tr.
Sketches of modern Paris
see under   [Ebeling, Adolph] 1827–1897.

PR1105   **Locock, Katharine Beatrice.**
.R7
1905c   **Guillaume** *de Deguilleville, 14th cent.*
The pilgrimage of the life of man, Englished by John Lydgate, A. D. 1426, from the French of Guillaume de Deguileville, A. D. 1330, 1355. The text ed. by F. J. Furnivall … With introduction, notes, glossary and indexes by Katharine B. Locock … Printed for the Roxburghe Club. London, Nichols and sons, 1905.

Locock, William.
Theory and practice of perspective; together with the application of the same to drawing from nature. By William Locock … London, Baily brothers, 1852.
40 p. illus., diagr. on xi pl. 22ᶜᵐ.

1. Perspective.

11–20937

Library of Congress   NC750.L7

NL 0438295   DLC

VOLUME 338

The locomobile book
see under   Locomobile Company of
America.

Locomobile Company of America.
The book of the Locomobile, an illustrated description of
the latest standard & custom models. Bridgeport, Conn.,
1916.
34 p.   col. illus.   24 x 32 cm.

1. Locomobile automobile.   I. Title.

TL215.L6L6 1916   63-5446

NL 0438297   DLC NN NNC CSmH

Locomobile Company of America.
The book of the Locomobile; an illustrated description
of the latest Series Two models. Bridgeport, Conn., 1917.
33 p.   col. illus.   25 x 32 cm.

1. Locomobile automobile.   I. Title: The Locomobile.

TL215.L6A3   63-56514

NL 0438298   DLC NNC

Locomobile company of America.
The book of the Locomobile; an illustrated description of the
latest examples of fine coach work built on the Locomobile
chassis.   Bridgeport, Conn.: Locomobile co. of America, 1918.
47 p.   front., illus., plates.   25½cm.

"This book designed and executed by T. M. Cleland."

860788A. 1. Automobiles—Type—
Maitland, 1880-
N. Y. P. L.   Locomobile, 1918. I. Cleland, Thomas
                                           November 17, 1937

NL 0438299   NN

Locomobile Company of America.
The book of the Locomobile, an illustrated description of
the latest examples of fine coach work built on the Locomobile chassis. ₁Bridgeport, Conn., 1920.
30 p.   illus. (part col.) plates.   26 cm.

1. Locomobile automobile.   I. Title.

TL215.L6L6 1920   63-5447

NL 0438300   DLC NN ICN

TL   Locomobile company of America.
215   ₁The car of 1911; being the latest edition of
.L82   the Locomobile book,which illustrates and de-
1910   scribes 1911 Locomobile models and sets forth
           by word and picture the many and varied advan-
           tages of the Locomobile car. Bridgeport,Conn.
           ₁etc.₁ The Advertising department of the Loco-
           mobile company of America ₁°1910₁
           3 p.l.,11-254 p.,1 l.incl.illus.,plates.
           front.   21 cm.
           On cover: The Locomobile book.

NL 0438301   MiU ICRL PHi CLSU FTaSU CU OrP MH

Locomobile Company of America.
The car of 1912, which is the latest edition of the locomobile
book, the fourteenth annual catalogue of locomobile motor cars,
with which is combined information of general interest to motor-
ists.   Bridgeport, Conn.: the company ₁1911₁.   3 p.l., 11-
209(1) p., 1 pl.   illus.   8°.

1. Automobiles, 1912. 2. Automo-
N. Y. P. L.   biles—Dealers' catalogues.
                                       January 11, 1912.

NL 0438302   NN AAP OKentU CU PPF

Locomobile Company of America
₁Catalogue of Locomobile gasolene touring
cars. Bridgeport, Conn. ₁°1905₁
1 v. (unpaged) illus.

NL 0438303   MiD

₁L b63   Locomobile company of America.
L8   The foundation of a fine car. An appreciation
916   of the Locomobile. [New York,Rand McNally &
            co.,c1916]
            3p.l., [9]-107,[1]p. 18½cm.

1.Automobiles.   I.Title.

NL 0438304   CtY

Locomobile Company of America.
Instruction book for locomobile six cylinder cars: the 38 locomobile, Type R; the 48 locomobile, Type M.   Bridgeport, Conn.
₁Joyce Press, 1914.₁   66 p.   illus.   8°.

1. Automobiles. 1914.
N. Y. P. L.   September 8, 1914.

NL 0438305   NN

Locomobile Company of America.
₁Instruction book for locomobile (six-cylinder) cars: the 38
locomobile, series two; the 48 locomobile, series two.   Bridgeport, Conn.: The Locomobile Co. of America₁, cop. 1917₁.   120 p.
incl. diagrs., front., tables.   diagr., illus. (incl. maps.)   8°.

1. Automobiles—Type—Locomobile,
N. Y. P. L.   1917.   July 7, 1926

NL 0438306   NN

TL   Locomobile Company of America.
215   The locomobile book. Bridgeport, Conn.
L6   ₁1897?₁

             v. illus. 21 cm.
           annual.
             Vols. for - have distinctive titles.

             1. Automobiles—Catalogs. I. Title.
           djg

NL 0438307   IEdS CtY

Locomobile company of America.
The locomobile book; a description of the latest models
... Bridgeport, Conn., The Locomobile company of
America, 1915.
31 p. illus. 30ᵐ.

1. Automobiles—Catalogs.   I. Title.

Library of Congress   TL215.L65   15-12899

NL 0438308   DLC CU NN PPF

Locomobile company of America.
Locomobile custom coach work. ₁Bridgeport, Conn.₁ The
Locomobile company of America, 1917. 12 l. (chiefly illus.)
16cm.

"Designed & executed by T. M. Cleland, New York."

58R0212. 1. Automobiles—Type—
                    Locomobile. 1917.

NL 0438309   NN NNC

Locomobile Company of America.
Locomobile 1907 gasolene cars...manufactured by the Locomobile Company of America. Bridgeport, Conn., cop. 1907.
46 p.   illus. f°.

1. Automobiles—Type—Locomobile,
N. Y. P. L.   1907.   June 6, 1928

NL 0438310   NN

TJ   Locomobile-waggon et machine demi-fixe
710   munies de chaudières à foyer amovible.
.L82   (Extrait du Portefeuille des machines,
           de l'outillage et du matériel.) Paris,
           Imprimé par E.Thunot et cie, 1861.
           14 p. illus. 26cm.

           1.Portable engines.

NL 0438311   MiU

De Locomotief.
Aanteekeningen op het Rapport der Staa₁t₁scom-
missie tot Onderzoek naarde Gouv.-Koffiecultuur
see under   Brooshooft, Pieter, 1845-1921.

Wason   De Locomotief.
DS642   Jan Pieterszoon Coen. Bij de herdenking
L81J3   van zijn sterfdag, 1629 - 21 September - 1929.
++   ₁Semarang₁ 1929.
              ₁72₁ p. illus. 44 cm.

              1. Coen, Jan Pieterszoon , 1587-1629.
            2. Indonesia--Hist.--1478-1798. 3. Neder-
            landsche Oost-Indische Compagnie.

NL 0438313   NIC

Wason   De Locomotief.
DS643   Een₁ land bouwt aan zin toekomst. Uitg.
L81L2   ter gelegenheid van de jaarwisseling 1940/
++   41. ₁Semarang, 1941₁
              1 v. (unpaged) 43 cm.

              Partial contents.--R. Sastromoeljono.
            Stil laten ruziën ....--H.H. Kan. For the
            time being and after.--F.H. Visman. De
            staatkundige ontwikkeling.--Ali Sastroami-
            djojo. Onze cultureele opbouw.--R.A.A.
            Soemitro

            Kolopaking Poerbonegoro. Daad en bezinning.--
            T.S.G. Moelia. Is onze gemeenschapszin ver-
            flauwende?--R. Abdoel Kadir Widjojoatmodjo.
            Idealen buiten de muren van den kaboepaten.--
            Ch.O. van der Plas. In der gerechtigheid.--
            Raden Soepomo. Indië's cultureele toekomst.--
            R.M. Noto Soeroto. Op hooger, geestelijk
            plan.--F.R.J. Verhoeven. Indische geschied-

            beoefening en archiefwezen.--B.W. Lapian.
            Koersverandering geboden.--R. Iso Reksohadi-
            prodjo. Welvaartszorg en vakonderwijs.--M.
            Ulfah Santoso. Beraden op redelijkheid.--
            Ki Hadjar Dewantara. Onderwijs en opvoeding
            op nationale basis.

              1. Indonesia--Hist.--1798-1942. I.
            Title.

NL 0438316   NIC

Wason   De Locomotief.
Pamphlet   De₁ wereld in beeld. ₁Semarang₁ 1938.
A   1 v. (unpaged) chiefly illus. 40 cm.
21++

NL 0438317   NIC

La Locomotion automobile; revue des voitures et véhicules mécaniques...
Année 1-

₁Paris: Vuillemot₁ 1894-
     v. illus. (incl. diagrs.)   27cm.

Monthly, Dec., 1894 – March, 1896; semimonthly, April 15 – Nov. 15, 1896; weekly,
Dec. 3, 1896 –
Année 1 complete in one number.
"Publiée sous le haut patronage du Touringclub de France."
Subtitle varies.
Founded by Raoul Vuillemot.

I. Automobiles--Per. and soc.
II. Touring-club de France.   publ. I. Vuillemot, Raoul, ed.
N. Y. P. L.   April 11, 1941

NL 0438318   NN MiU MiD MnU

VOLUME 338

La LOCOMOTION moderne... Paris, Éditions S. N. E. P. - Illustration [1951] 422 p. illus., maps, plates. 38cm.

Plates reproduced from watercolors by A. Brenet.
CONTENTS.—La marine, par Henri Le Masson.—L'aviation, par Camille Rougeron.—Les chemins de fer, par Robert Barjot.—La route, par Jacques Thomas.—L'automobile, le cycle, par Henri Tinard.

I. Transportation. I. Le Masson, Henri.

NL 0438319   NN IEN OC1 MiD CU

Locomotive, *pseud.*
Irish railways and the Board of trade
see under title

AP
30
.L82   Loco**m**otive. Monatsschrift für den deutschen
Michel von Held. Monat. July-Dec.,1843.
Halle,Selbstverlag. 1843.
Editor: Friedrich W.A.Held.
Supersedes Leipziger locomotive?
I. Held,Friedrich Wilhelm Alexander,1813-
1872,ed.

NL 0438321   MiU

Die Locomotive; Neue Fliegende Blätter aus
Amerika Red. A. Rattermann.   Philadelphia,
1853-
v.   v.
Hrsg. A. Strodtman u. A. Ketterlinus.

NL 0438322   PPG PU CtY NN

The **Locomotive.** Published by the Hartford **steam**
boiler inspection and insurance company.

Hartford, Conn., 18

v.   illus., diagrs. 23ᶜᵐ (v. 1–   : 30ᶜᵐ) monthly.

1. Locomotives—Period.   i. Hartford steam boiler inspection and insurance co., pub.

Library of Congress   TJ1.L7

CA 6—311 Unrev'd

NL 0438323   TU OC1 MiU MB NN ICJ Nh NdU WaS
DLC KyU DNLM NBuU AZTes TxLT ICRL ICJ

The **Locomotive.** *Published by the Hartford steam
boiler inspection and insurance company.*
[Hartford steam boiler inspection and insurance company]
... In memoriam, Lyman Bushnell Brainerd, 1856–1916.
Hartford, Conn., 1916.

Locomotive adhesion. Remarks, by a member of the Society of Engineers, upon a paper read before that body,
and entitled, "On the adhesion of locomotive engines,
and certain expedients for increasing or supplementing
that function. Nov. 20, 1865. London: C. Whiting,
[1865] 28 pp. 12°.
In: VDB. p. v. 2.

NL 0438325   NN

...Locomotive and railway data. N. Y., Industrial press, °1910.
39 p. tables, diagrs. (Machinery's data sheets,
no.14)

NL 0438326   MiD CU

The locomotive and the telegraph; or, Steam
and electricity, as applied to railway travelling; with illustrative anecdotes ...   London,
R.Y.Clarke and co., 1848.
2 p.l., 77, 84 p. illus., plates, diagrs.
17 cm.

Title vignette.

NL 0438327   MH-BA

The locomotive and things you should know about
it
see under   Dickerson, Charles L

Locomotive boilers. Boiler attachments. Heat and steam. The loco-
motive. Valves and valve gears. Locomotive management.
Breakdowns.
— Scranton. International Textbook Co. [1906] 7 parts in 1 v.
Illus. Plans. Diagrams. [International library of technology.
Vol. 68.] 8°.

G2429 — Steam boilers. — Locomotive engines.

NL 0438329   MB

The locomotive booster speeds railroad operation
see under   [Franklin railway supply company.

Locomotive club, Schenectady, N. Y.

TJ1
L68   **Loco.** v. 1–   May 1910–
Schenectady, N. Y., 1910–

Locomotive cyclopedia of American practice. 1st–   ed.;
1906–
New York, Simmons-Boardman Pub. Corp. [etc.]
v. illus. 31 cm.
Title varies: 1st–5th, 1906–19, Locomotive dictionary (varies
slightly)
The 1st–5th ed., 1906–19, comp. and ed. for the American Railway
Master Mechanics' Association; 6th–9th ed., 1922–30 for the American Railway Association, Mechanical Division; 10th–   ed., 1938–
for the Association of American Railroads, Mechanical Division.
Merged with Car builders' cyclopedia of American practice to form
Car and locomotive cyclopedia of American practice.
1. Locomotives—Dictionaries.   i. American Railway Master
Mechanics' Association.   II. American Railway Association. Mechanical Division.   III. Association of American Railroads. Mechanical Division.   IV. Title: Locomotive dictionary.

TJ605.L572   625.2ʹ6ʹ03   71–183263

NL 0438332   OC1 ICJ MB PP CU NIC OLak PPF NjP NN CaBVaU WaE KMK
MtU KU WaS IU OU OrP WaSp Or OrCS PU OrP CaBViPA MiU
DLC WaT CaBVa NcD DSI OCU PSt NcD NcRS

Locomotive dictionary
see **Locomotive** cyclopedia of American practice.

The **Locomotive engineer.** Devoted to the special interests of locomotive engineers and firemen

see

Railway and locomotive engineering.

Locomotive engi**near** and fireman.
Fisher, Ira Walter, 1879–
Pocket ed. of locomotive engineering; a new complete
series of questions and answers treating on the first,
second and third years' progressive examination questions; air brake and mechanical locomotive construction
and mechanical appliances ... written expressly for the
Locomotive engineer and fireman, by Ira W. Fisher and
John J. Williams ... [Chicago? °1911]

Locomotive engineering; a practical journal of railway
motive power and rolling stock
see
Railway and locomotive engineering.

Locomotive engineer's and firemen's book of
instructions
see under   Lee, Harry C

Locomotive engineers journal. v. 1–
Jan. 1867–
Cleveland.
v. in   illus., ports. 24–30 cm. monthly.
Official journal of the Brotherhood of Locomotive Engineers.
Title varies: 1867–   The Locomotive engineers' monthly.—
1927, Brotherhood of Locomotive Engineers' journal (varies
slightly)

1. Locomotive engineers—Period.   2. Trade-unions—Period.
i. Brotherhood of Locomotive Engineers.

HD6350.R32B8   49–33331*

NL 0438338   CU MH-IR ICRL OU MH ICN DL MiU
DLC ICJ OC1WHi ICRL IU NNU PP MiD MShM

The **Locomotive** engineers' monthly
see **Locomotive** engineers journal.

Locomotive firebox company, Chicago.

Schmidt, Edward Charles, 1874–
... Tests of a Mikado-type locomotive equipped with Nicholson thermic syphons; a report of an investigation conducted
by the Engineering experiment station, University of Illinois
in coöperation with the Illinois central railroad company and
the Locomotive firebox company. By Edward C. Schmidt ...
Everett G. Young ... and Herman J. Schrader ... Urbana,
University of Illinois [1930]

Locomotive firemen and enginemen, Brotherhood
of

see

Brotherhood of locomotive firemen and enginemen.

Locomotive firemen's magazine
see   Brotherhood of locomotive firemen
and enginemen's magazine.

The **locomotive** headlight; a review of their development
and aid to train movement, with especial reference to a
reduction of the dangers involved. The merits of different lights by those who know. Comp. and issued by
the railroad men of Tennessee. Nashville [Marshall
& Bruce co. print] 1911.
47, [1] p. incl. illus. (ports.) pl. 26ᶜᵐ.

1. Locomotive headlights.

Library of Congress   TJ668.L6

11-9296

NL 0438343   DLC MB

The locomotive in service
see under   Locomotive Publishing Company,
Ltd.

VOLUME 338

HD6350
.R52L6

The **Locomotive** journal.

London, 19

v. illus. 22½ᵐ. monthly.

Official organ of the Associated society of locomotive engineers and firemen.
Publication began in 1888. *cf.* Willing's press guide. 1944.

1. Locomotive engineers. 2. Trade-unions—Period. ɪ. Associated society of locomotive engineers and firemen.

Library of Congress   HD6350.R32L6

45–14035

NL   0438345   DLC

The **Locomotive** magazine
   see The **Locomotive**, railway carriage & wagon review.

Locomotive Maintenance Officers' Association.
   Annual proceedings ₍of the₎ annual meeting.
   ₍North Little Rock?, Ark.₎

'v. illus. 21 cm.

Each called, on spine, v. 2; the issues of the association's Pre-convention report are called v. 1.

1. Locomotives—Maintenance and repair—Societies, etc.

TJ675.L57

61–46400

NL   0438347   DLC IU ICJ

Locomotive Maintenance Officers' Association.
   Pre-convention report.
   ₍North Little Rock?₎, Ark.₎

v. illus. 20 cm. annual.

Each called, on spine, v. 1; the issues of the association's Annual proceedings of the annual meeting are called v. 2.

1. Locomotives—Maintenance and repair—Societies, etc.

TJ675.L59   625.2'6   67–116945

NL   0438348   DLC

Locomotive Maintenance Officers' Association.
   Proceedings.
19
Chicago ₍19   8°.
   v. illus.
   Vols. for   *issued by the association under*
on earlier name: International Railway General Foremen's Association.

1. Railways.—Officials: Per. and   soc. publ. 2. Railways.—Shops.
N.Y.P.L.   April 15, 1920.

NL   0438349   NN CaBVaU ICU

TF376
.W8   Locomotive Maintenance Officers' Association.
     Wright, Roydon Vincent, 1876–   *comp.*
     Railway shop kinks, comp. under the direction of a committee of the International railway general foremen's association. By Roy V. Wright ... Committee: H. D. Kelley ... C. H. Voges ... L. H. Bryan ... New York, Chicago ₍etc.₎ Railway age gazette, 1911.

Locomotive Maintenance Officers' Association
   see also
Master Boiler Makers Association.

LOCOMOTIVE MANUFACTURERS' ASSOCIATION OF
    GREAT BRITAIN.
   LMA handbook [1. ed.]   London, 1949.   464 p.
illus., diagrs. 20cm.

1. Locomotives—Handbooks, manuals, etc. ɪ. 1949.

NL   0438352   NN

The **locomotive** of to-day
    see under   Locomotive Publishing Company, ltd., London.

... The **locomotive**; or, Cherubims. By a Scripture miner ...
London, Wertheim and Macintosh, 1848.

vii, ₍9₎–108, ₍2₎ p. 16½ᵐ.

1. Bible—Prophecies. ɪ. A Scripture miner.

38–33880

NL   0438354   DLC

... **Locomotive** planning
    see ₍under₎ [Sillcox, Lewis Ketcham] 1836–

---

*BROAD-
SIDE   Locomotive Press, New York.
1841
.L838   ₍Cards printed at the Fair of the₎ American
     Institute, Oct. 1841. ₍New York, 1841₎
     broadside. illus. 4½ x 7½cm.

NL   0438356   ViU

TJ
605
.L818   Locomotive Publishing Company, ltd., London.
     British standard locomotives; names, numbers,
     photographs, diagrams and dimensions. ₍London,
     1953₎
     19 p. illus., diagrs. 21 cm.
     Cover title.

1. Locomotives. I. Title.

NL   0438357   MiU

Locomotive Publishing Company, ltd. London.
   Broad gauge locomotives of the Great Western
   railway 1837–1892
    see under   Bird, George Frederick.
London.

Locomotive publishing co.
   ... Lantern slides arranged in sets... ₍a list₎
   Lond., The Author, n. d.
   ₍24₎ p. illus.

NL   0438359   MiD

Locomotive Publishing Company, ltd., *London.*
   Locomotive engineers' pocket book. 40th ed. Westminster ₍London, 1939 ?₎
   307 p. diagrs. 17 cm.

1. Locomotives—Handbooks, manuals, etc. ɪ. Title.

TJ607.L63   621.1302   48–42688*

NL   0438360   DLC MiD

Locomotive Publishing Company, Ltd.
   The locomotive in service. London,
Locomotive Publishing Co. ₍19--?₎
   187 p. charts (part fold.) tables.

Some of the articles have been taken from
"The Locomotive Magazine"; others have previously appeared in "The Locomotive Handbook"
and "Locomotive Running Shed Notes." - fore.

NL   0438361   MH-BA

621.13   Locomotive publishing co., ltd., London.
L81821   The locomotive in service.   London
[1926]
     187p. illus., tables, diagrs.(part
     fold.)

NL   0438362   IU MiD

Locomotive Publishing Company, ltd., London.
   The locomotive of to-day... London, The
   Locomotive publishing co., limited, 1899.
   178, [4] p. 22 cm.

NL   0438363   ViU

Locomotive **Publishing Company, ltd**
   The locomotive of to-day. ... . Second edition. 194. [4] p.
37 il. 18 pl. 14 paged in. O. London: Locomotive Publishing
Co., 1900.
    Reprinted with revisions and additions, from The Locomotive magazine.

NL   0438364   ICJ CtY

Locomotive publishing co., ltd., London.
   The locomotive of to-day. 2d ed. London, 1903

NL   0438365   MH

TJ605   Locomotive Publishing Company, Ltd.
L82   The locomotive of to-day. Reprinted, with
1904   revisions and additions, from "The Locomotive
     magazine". 3d ed. London, 1904.
     180 p. illus., plates (part fold.) 22ᵃ.

1. Locomotives. I. Title.

NL   0438366   CSt

Locomotive Publishing Company, ltd.
   The locomotive of to-day. 7th ed.   London,
The Locomotive Publishing Co., 1920.
   184, 4 p. 24 numb. plates, charts (part
fold.)

Reprinted, with revisions and additions,
from "The Locomotive Magazine."

NL   0438367   MH-BA

R321.13   LOCOMOTIVE Publishing Company, London.
L818L7   The locomotive of to-day. 7th ed.
     London. 1922. 184, 4p. illus.
     (1 fold.) diagrs. (part fold.)

Reprinted, with revisions and additions,
from the Locomotive magazine.

NL   0438368   WaS

Locomotive publishing co., ltd., *London.*
   The locomotive of to-day. 8th ed. London, The Locomotive publishing co., ltd., 1927.
   316 p. front., illus., fold. pl. 22ᵐ.
   Blank pages for "Notes and sketches" interspersed.

1. Locomotives.

Library of Congress   TJ605.L6 1927

28–13501

NL   0438369   DLC ICJ MiU

VOLUME 338

Locomotive publishing co., ltd., London.
Locomotive repairs in the running shed. An illustrated handbook.
London, The Locomotive Publishing Co., ltd., [etc., etc.], 1911.
50 p. incl. front., 24 illus. 1 fold. diagr. in pocket. 19^{cm}.

NL 0438370   ICJ

621.138 Locomotive publishing company,   comp.
L811   Locomotive running shed notes.
London [1921?]
98p. front., illus., diagrs.

NL 0438371   IU

Locomotive publishing co., ltd., *London*.
Locomotive valve gears and valve setting. London,
The Locomotive publishing co., ltd., 1924.
3 p. l., 159, [1] p. front., illus., fold. plates, diagrs. 22^{cm}.
Seal of the company on t.-p.

1. Locomotives—Valve-gears.

Library of Congress   TJ665.L6   25-496

NL 0438372   DLC

Locomotive Publishing Co., Ltd., London.
Locomotives. London [1927?]
1 v. (unpaged) plates.

Cover-title.
Consists primarily of plates.
Includes The British express locomotive
during the Victorian era. Christmas number of
"The Locomotive Magazine".

NL 0438373   MH-BA MiD

621.13 Locomotive publishing co., ltd., London.
L81811   The locomotives of the London, Brighton & South Coast railway, 1839-1903 ...
London, 1903.
245p. front., illus., plates, tables.

"Reprinted from "The locomotive magazine".

NL 0438374   IU MiD

Locomotive publishing company, ltd., *London*.
Modern locomotives and electric traction of the Southern
railway. Westminster [London] The Locomotive publishing
co., ltd. [1943?]
1 p. l., 30, [2] p. plates. 14 x 22^{cm}.

1. Southern railway company (Gt. Brit.) 2. Locomotives.
I. Title.

Library of Congress   TJ605.L62   44-51544
[3]   621.132942

NL 0438375   DLC

625.1 Locomotive publishing co., ltd., London.
L81q   Questions & answers on railway permanent way.   London [192-?]
32p. diagrs.(part fold.)

NL 0438376   IU

Locomotive publishing co., ltd., London.
Railway carriage and wagon builders' pocket
book. London, The Locomotive publishing co.,
ltd. [1925?]
214, [6] p. incl., tables, diagrs., front.
1. Cars and car building. 2. Railroads. Cars.
I. Title.

NL 0438377   IU MiD

Locomotive publishing Co., ltd., London.
The Railway carriage and wagon handbook
see under title

Locomotive publishing co, ltd., London.
Railway signal and permanent way engineer's
pocket book. [2d ed.] London, Locomotive pub.
co., n. d.
326 p. illus., tables, diagrs. (part fold.)

NL 0438379   MiD

TF
615   Locomotive publishing co.,ltd.,London.
.L82   The railway signal and permanent way engi-
1922 neer's pocket book. London, The locomotive
publishing co.,ltd.; New York, Spon &
Chamberlain; [etc.,etc.,] 1922]
326 p. illus. 14 cm.

"Second edition".

1.Railroads--Signaling--Handbooks,manuals,
etc.

NL 0438380   MiU IU

625.25 The locomotive publishing company, ltd, London.
L81v2   The vacuum automatic brake, with a
note on slipping carriages.   London
[1921?]
103p. front., fold. plates (part
col.) diagrs.

NL 0438381   IU MH MiD

Locomotive Publishing Company, Ltd., London.
The Westinghouse air brake; a description of the system and
its working. London: The Locomotive Pub. Co., Ltd. [1922.]
80 p. diagrs., col'd front., illus., plates. 12°.

72573A. 1. Air-brakes.—Type: Westinghouse. 2. Title.
N.Y.P.L.   February 8, 1923.

NL 0438382   NN

The Locomotive, railway carriage & wagon review
[London, Locomotive Pub. Co.]
v. illus. 28 cm. monthly.
Title varies: The Locomotive magazine.
Separately paged supplements accompany some vols.

1. Railroads—Rolling stock—Period. 2. Locomotives—Period.

TF1.L81   52-25216 ‡

NL 0438383   DLC NN MiU NcD ICJ PPF TxDaDF

TF
573   The Locomotive,railway carriage & wagon review.
L82   [British expresses. [London, Locomotive Pub.Co.,
1898-1902.
8 no.in 1 v. illus.,plates (part col.,part
fold.) 27 cm.
Binder's title.
Consists of 5 unnumbered supplements,3 supplements numbered 5-7,Special series,and 2 fold.col.
plates numbered 17-18,Suppl.to the Coronation
number.
1.Railroads--Ex   press-trains. 2.Loco-
motives.

NL 0438384   MiU

Locomotive, railway carriage and wagon review.
Locomotive super-heating and feed water heating
see under Gairns, John Francis, 1876-1930.

HE
3018 Locomotive,railway carriage and wagon review.
.L82 London.
Railway centenary 1825-1925. Supplement to
the Locomotive,railway carriage & wagon review commemorating the opening of the first
public railway & a souvenir of the tenth International railway congress ... London
[1925]
cover-title,124 p. illus. 28^{cm}.
1.Railroads--Gt.Brit.--Hist. I.Title.

NL 0438386   MiU MiD CSt IU CU PSt

Locomotive, railway carriage & wagon review
Train lighting and heating supplement. Lond.,
n. d.
114 p. illus. forms, tables, diagrs.

Cover title.

NL 0438387   MiD

LOCOMOTIVE, RAILWAY CARRIAGE & WAGON REVIEW.
Train lighting and heating... London: The Locomotive,
railway carriage & wagon review[, 1933]. 133 p. incl.
tables. diagr., illus. 27½cm.

Caption-title.
"The Locomotive (Supplement)."

671384A. 1. Cars—Lighting. 2. Cars—heating and ventilation.

NL 0438388   NN

Locomotive repairs executed by the thermit
process of welding
see under [Goldschmidt Thermit Company]

Locomotive repairs in the running shed
see under Locomotive publishing co.,
ltd., London.

Locomotive sketches, with pen and pencil
see under Bromwell, William.

R621.13 LOCOMOTIVE stock book.
L8183   [London] Railway Correspondence
and Travel Society. illus.

NL 0438392   WaS

Locomotive Stoker Co., Pittsburgh.
Description of and Instructions for Operating,
oiling and Maintaining Type Duplex Locomotive Stoker.
Pittsburg, Loc. Stoker Co., 1920.
68 p.

NL 0438393   PPF

Locomotive Stoker Company, Pittsburgh.
Duplex locomotive stoker.
Pitts.—Company, n.d.
14 p.

NL 0438394   PPF

LOCOMOTIVE stoker company, Pittsburgh.
The Elvin mechnical stoker, "Saves
as it serves"; road service hand book.
This book covers road operation only...
Author. 1925. 55p. illus.
diagrs.

NL 0438395   WaS

VOLUME 338

Locomotive success equals capacity and availability plus capital economy
    see under   Sillcox, Lewis Ketcham.

Locomotive Superheater Company
  see
Combustion Engineering, inc.

Locomotive superheating and feed water heating
    see under   Gairns, John Francis, 1876-
1930.

Locomotive valve gears and valve setting
    see under   Locomotive publishing co.,
ltd., London.

The **Locomotive** world.   v. 1–
May 1908–
Lima, O., Locomotive world publishing company ₁etc.₎
1908–
  v.   illus. 26½ᶜᵐ.   monthly.
Editor: May 1908–   H. C. Hammack.

  1. Locomotives—Period.   ₁. Hammack, Henry C., ed.

                             10-22908†

Library of Congress   TJ1.L75

NL 0438400   DLC

Locomotives.
  ₁Minor publications
  n.p.₎

NL 0438401   ICJ

R621.13
L818   Les **LOCOMOTIVES** à vapeur de la S N C F.
     Montchauvet (S. & O.) Éditions
    "Loco-Revue". 1947. 39p. 100 plates.

NL 0438402   WaS

Locomotives and locomotive building...
    see under   Forney, Matthias Nace, 1835-
1908, comp.

Locomotives des chemins de fer français. no. 1–
1947–
Paris, Éditions P. P. C.
  v. 16 x 24 cm.

  1. Locomotives.

TJ605.L65   54-33740 ‡

NL 0438404   DLC NN MiU ICJ

Locomotives of the Atchison, Topeka & Santa
Fe system...
    see under   Wood, Sylvan Rupert, 1895-

---

q621.13 ₁Locomotives of the British Empire, excluding Can
L8183   ada. A collection of articles taken from vari-
    ous engineering journals, 1865-1945₎ ₁n.p.,
    1945?₎
    162 pieces(in portfolio) illus. 41x28cm.

  1. Locomotives.

NL 0438406   IU

Locomotives of the Great southern railways of
Ireland
    see under   Watson, S   J

The locomotives of the Great West Railway
    see under   Railway Correspondence and
Travel Society.

The locomotives of the London, Brighton &
South Coast railway, 1839-1903
    see under   Locomotive publishing co.,
ltd., London.

The locomotives of the Netherlandish railways.
  ₁Utrecht? Holland? 1951?₎
  1 v. (various pagings) tables.

NL 0438410   MH-BA

Locomotives of the Western Pacific
    see under   Western Pacific Railroad Company.

Thesis   Loconti, Joseph Daniel, 1915-
1946   Lipidoxidase activity - specificity - sec-
L823   ondary oxidation of beta-carotene. ₁Ithaca,
N. Y.₎ 1946.
    50 l. 13 plates. 28 cm.

    Thesis (Ph. D.) - Cornell Univ., June 1946.

    1. Carotin. 2. Oxidation. 3. Lipid meta-
bolism. I. Title. H.-

NL 0438412   NIC

Locorum ex iure Romano anteiustiniano ab incerto
scriptore collectorum fragmenta quae dicuntur
vaticana
    see under   Fragmenta vaticana juris ante-
justinianei.

PQ 6500   Los Locos de mayor marca, representado
A1 L6   en los teatros de esta corte. Para
1791   once personas. Madrid, Librería de
    Quiroga, 1791.
    8 p.   23 cm.
    At head of title: Saynete.

NL 0438414   OU NcU MB

... Los locos de mayor marca, representado
en los teatros de la corte, por once personas.
Sevilla, Aragón y compañía, 1816.
    8p. 21cm.   (Comedias ₁Teatro antiguo espa-
ñol₎)

  At head of title: Saynete ...

NL 0438415   NcU

Los locos de mayor marca ₁saynete nuevo₎ Valencia, Imprenta de Estévan, 1817.
  8p.

  Microcard edition.

NL 0438416   ICRL FU

Los locos de Sevilla ...   Madrid, Librería
Quiroga, 1791.
  8p. 22cm.

  In: Teatro antiguo Borrás. v.4, no.23.
  At head of title: Saynete.

NL 0438417   NcU MB

Los Locos de Sevilla.   Saynete. [Alcalá, 1799]
  8 p.   21 cm.

NL 0438418   MWelC

Los locos de Sevilla. Saynete representado
en los teatros de esta corte, para ocho personas
Madrid, Vda. de Quiroga, 1812.
  ₁1₎8 p.   23cm.

  - Válgame Dios lo que muele,
  - el perdon de nuestras faltas.

NL 0438419   NcU NN

Locqueneuille, Scarsez de
    see   Scarsez de Locqueneuille.

Locquenghien, Franz Freiherr von, 1899-
Ueber abortivbehandlung der syphilis in den
letzten fuenf jahren.
  Inaug. diss. Marburg, 1927
  Bibl.

NL 0438421   ICRL CtY

Locques, Nicolas de, 17th cent.
  Elemens philosophiqves des arcanes et dv
dissolvant general, de leurs vertvs, proprietez,
et effets. Livre sixieme.   Paris, 1668.

  With his Les rvdimens de la philosophie
natvrelle ... 1665.

NL 0438422   WU

Rs5   Locques, Nicolas de
146   Les rvdimens de la philosophie natvrelle,
tovchant le systeme dv corps mixte ... Paris,
G.Marcher,1664-68.
    6v.in 1. front.,illus. 18½cm.
    Contents. v.₁1. Traité premier₎ Livre
premier. Cours théorique. 1665. - v.₁2₎ Livre
second. Cours pratique. 1665. - v.₁3₎ Traité
second. De la fermentation. 1665. - v.₁4₎ Les
vertus magnétiques du sang. 1664. - v.₁5₎
Propositions touchant la physique résolutive.
1665. v.₁6₎ Élémens philosophiques des arcanes
et du dissolvant   général. 1668.

NL 0438423   CtY

Locques, Nicolas de, 17th cent.
  Les rvdimens de la philosophie natvrelle
tovchant le systeme dv corps mixte. Covrs
theotiqve ₁-pratiqve₎. Livre premiere ₁-second₎
Paris, 1665.
  2v. in 1.

  Vol. 2 has part 2 with separate pagination and
t.-p.: Les rvdimens...corps mixte. De la fermentation. Avec le traitte du sang & les propositio-
nes de la chymie resolutive. Traite second.

  The Propositions tovchant la physiqve resolvtive
has special t.-p. and pagination, but continuous
page signatures. This is followed by: Les vertvs
magnetiqves dv sang. Paris 1664, with special
t.-p., pagination, and page signatures.

NL 0438425   WU

VOLUME 338

Locques, Nicolas de, 17th cent.
Les vertus magnetiques du sang, de son usage
interne et externe pour la guerison des maladies.
Paris, Le Gentil, 1664.
54 p.

NL 0438426   PPC

Locquet (Joannes). * De arteria hepatica. 11'].
4°. *Lugd. Bat.*, A. *Elzevier*, 1683.
Also, in: HALLER. Disp. anat. [etc.] 4°. *Gottingae*,
1791, vii, 567–582.

NL 0438427   DNLM

Locquette (Charles) [1874–]. * Sur quelques matières colorantes nouvelles dérivées
d'un camphosulfophénol. 33 pp., 1 l. 4°.
Lyon, 1902. No. 20.

NL 0438428   DNLM

Locquette, Christian, 1904–
... Contribution à l'étude des splénomégalies
tuberculeuses primitives... Lyon, 1928.
Thèse – Univ. de Lyon.
"Bibliographie": p. [57]–61.

NL 0438429   CtY

Locquin. Du traitement des tumeurs érectiles
par les fils caustiques. 16 pp. 12°. *Dijon*, R.
Aubry, 1886.

NL 0438430   DNLM

Locquin, Jacques.
Le landlord tenant system, par Jacques Locquin ... Paris,
Librairie générale de droit & de jurisprudence, R. Pichon et
R. Durand-Auzias, administrateurs, 1936.
196 p. 25ᶜᵐ.

"Bibliographie": p. [189]–194.

1. Land tenure–Gt. Brit.   I. Title.
                                               A C 36–2498
Title from N. Y. Pub.   Libr.   Printed by L. C.

NL 0438431   NN

Locquin, Jean, 1879–
Catalogue raisonné de l'œuvre de Jean-Baptiste Oudry,
peintre du roi (1686–1755)

(*In* Archives de l'art français; recueil de documents inédits publiés
par la Société de l'histoire de l'art français. Paris. 1912. 22ᶜᵐ. Nouvelle période, t. VI.   viii, 209 p.)

"Introduction" signed: Jean Locquin.
"Bibliographie": p. 188–198.

1. Oudry, Jean Baptiste, 1686–1755.
                                               A C 37–38
Michigan. Univ. Library   N6841.A67 n. s., vol. 6
  for Library of Congress   [N6841.A9 n. s., vol. 6]
                                                       (704)

NL 0438432   MiU OC1 NNC DAU PPPM

Locquin, Jean
Catalogue raisonné de l'oeuvre de Jean-Baptiste
Oudry, peintre du roi (1686-1755) ... par Jean
Locquin ... Paris, Schemit, 1912.
3 p. l., [ix]-xvi, 211 p. 21 cm.

Thesis, Paris.
Bibliography: p. [138]-198.

1. Oudry, Jean Baptiste, 1686-1755.

NL 0438433   NNC MiDA MH OC1MA

Locquin, Jean.
... Nevers et Moulins; La Charité-sur-Loire — Saint-
Pierre-le-Moûtier—Bourbon-l'Archambault—Souvigny,
par Jean Locquin.   Ouvrage illustré de 128 gravures
Paris, H. Laurens, 1913.

2 p. l., 180 p. illus. 26¼ᶜᵐ.   (Les villes d'art célèbres)   fr. 4
"Bibliographie": p. [170]–173.

1. Art—Nevers, France. 2. Nevers, France (City)—Descr. 3. Art—
Moulins, France. 4. Moulins, France—Descr. 5. Charité-sur-Loire, La,
France. 6. Saint-Pierre-le-Moûtier, France. 7. Bourbon-l'Archambault,
France. 8. Souvigny, France.

Library of Congress   N6851.N4L6
                                               14–518

NL 0438434   DLC WaS IdU NIC CU MWiCA ODW MiU NjP PBm

Locquin, Jean.
La peinture d'histoire en France de 1747 à 1785; étude
sur l'évolution des idées artistiques dans la seconde moi-
tié du XVIIIᵉ siècle, par Jean Locquin ... Paris, H. Laurens, 1912.

xii, 344 p., 1 l. xxxii pl. 27ᶜᵐ.
"Bibliographie": p. [291]–310.

1. Painting—France—Hist.   I. Title.
                                               15–15570
Library of Congress   ND546.L7

               MoSW MdBWA
NL   NcD OO PPPM CtY OU ICU MH CU PBm MiEM MB OC1MA WaU
  0438435   DLC MiEM MB OC1MA WaU NcU MiU TU NjP

ND546
L7   Locquin, Jean.
          La peinture d'histoire en France de 1747
          à 1785; étude sur l'évolution des idées
          artistiques dans la seconde moitié du XVIIIᵉ
          siècle. Paris, H. Laurens, 1912.
             xii, 344 p. 28cm.
             Photocopy.
             Thèse– Paris.
             "Bibliographie" : p.[291]–310.

             1.Painting – France – Hist.

NL 0438436   CSt MH

FILM   Locquin, Jean, 1879–
759.4   La peinture d'histoire en France de 1747 à
L88p   1785; étude sur l'évolution des idées artisti-
           ques dans la seconde moitié du XVIIIᵉ siècle,
           par Jean Locquin ... Paris, H. Laurens, 1912.
              xii, 344p., 1ℓ. 32 plates. 27cm.

              "Bibliographie": p. [291]–310.
              Microfilm Copy. Washington, Library of Con-
           gress Photo-duplication Service, 1965. 1 reel.
           35mm.
              1. Painting–-France–-Hist. I. Title.

NL 0438437   IU

QD305   Locquin, Rene.
.K2L7   Action de l'acide nitreux et de ses derives sur
            les ethers et sur les acides b-cetoniques a-
            substitues.
            Paris, 1904.
            149p.
            These. Paris.

NL 0438438   DLC

          Locquin, René, ed.

QD251
.G85   Grignard, Victor, 1871–1935, ed.
            Traité de chimie organique, publié sous la direction de V.
          Grignard ... Secrétaire général Paul Baud ... Paris, Masson
          et cⁱᵉ, 1935–

Locraft, Thomas Hall, 1903–
A building for the supreme court of a large republic ... by
Thomas Hall Locraft ... Washington, D. C., 1931.

36 p. illus. 2 fold. pl., plans (1 fold.) 23ᶜᵐ.
Thesis (PH. D.)–Catholic university of America. 1931.
Vita.
"The Society of beaux arts architects, New York city, issued as the
program for the 1928 Paris prize, 'A building for the supreme court of a
large republic.' From the five solutions presented, that which is reproduced herewith was selected, and the Paris prize scholarship was
awarded the author."—Foreword.
Bibliography: p. 35.

1. Architecture—Designs and plans. 2. Public buildings.   I. Title:
The supreme court of a large republic, A building for.

                                               31–31352
Library of Congress   NA4470.L6 1931

                                [3]   725.15

NL 0438440   DLC OrU PU NIC OU MiU

Y   AN LÓCRANN.
8285   Racaireact grinn na tuaite. Ar n-a foillsiú
.T 32   do muintir "An Lócrann" san mbl. 1925. Baile
          áta Cliat,O'Brún is Ó Nualláin[1925?]
          195p. 19cm.

             Title-page and text in Irish character.
             Introduction signed: "An Seabac"

             Many of the stories written by Thaddeus
          O'Connor.

NL 0438441   ICN

Locre, Elza de
      see De Locre, Elza.

Locre, Ferry de, 1571-1614.
Bt5.17   Ferreoli Locrii Pavlinatis Chronicon belgicvm.
          Ab anno CCLVIII. ad annum vsque M.D.C. continuô
          perductum. Tomi tres. Atrebati,Ex officinâ G.
          Riverii,1614-16.
             8p.ℓ.,696,[24]p. 25cm.
             T.2-3 have individual t.-p.'s.
             Catalogvs scriptorvm Artesiensivm: p.677-696.
             Contents. - [T.1] [258-962] 1616. - t.2.
          Chronicon belgicvm [863-1180] In qvo Flandrici
          comitatvs exordia et progressvs, maxime qva ad
          occasvm spectat, continentvr. 1614. - t.3.

             Chronicon belgicvm [1180-1600] In qvo Artesien-
          sis comitatvs origo et progressvs explicantvr.
          1614.

             1.Belgium - Hist. 2.Artois, France - Hist.
          x.Locrius, Ferreolus. x.Locre, Perry de.
          x.Locrius, Perriolus.

NL 0438444   CtY NNC NjR MiU

Locre, Ferry de, d. 1614.
Histoire chronographiqve des comtes, pays et ville de S. Pavl,
en Ternois. Par M. Ferry de Locre...   Dovay: Chez Lavrent
Kellam, 1613. 3 p.l., 82 p., 1 l.   4°.

Bookplate of Theodore Gilman.
Original vellum binding.

179291A. 1. Saint-Pol, France.   2. Saint-Pol, Counts of.
N.Y.P.L.   April 28, 1925

NL 0438445   NN MWA ViW

Locré, Jean Guillaume
      see
Locré de Roissy, Jean Guillaume, *baron de,* 1758-1840.

Locré de Roissy, Jean Guillaume, baron, 1758–1840.
Discussions sur la liberté de la presse, la censure, la pro-
priété littéraire, l'imprimerie et la librairie, qui ont eu lieu
dans le Conseil d'État, pendant les années 1808, 1809, 1810 et
1811. Rédigées et publiées par M. le baron Locré ... Paris,
Garnery [etc.] 1819.

3 p. l., 300 p. 21ᶜᵐ.

1. Liberty of the press.
                                               6–42539 Revised
Library of Congress   Z657.L81

NL 0438447   DLC CtY NcD

Locré de Roissy, Jean Guillaume, baron de,
1758-1840.   FOR OTHER EDITIONS
France. *Laws, statutes, etc.*   SEE MAIN ENTRY
   Esprit du Code de commerce puisé dans
les procès-verbaux du Conseil d'État, les exposés de motifs et
discours, les observations des cours d'appel,
tribunaux et Chambre de commerce, etc., etc.; et complément
du Code de commerce, par la conférence analytique et raisonnée avec ses dispositions, des articles du Code Napoléon,
du Code de procédure civile, et generalement des lois, règle-
mens et décrets impériaux antérieurs qui s'y rapportent, ou
auxquels il se réfère ... par J. G. Locré ... Paris, Garnery,
1811-13.

VOLUME 338

Locré de Roissy, Jean Guillaume, baron de, 1758–1840.
France. *Laws, statutes, etc.*
Esprit du Code de procédure civile, ou Conférence du Code de procédure civile avec les discussions du Conseil, les observations du Tribunat, les exposés de motifs, les discours des orateurs du Tribunat, les dispositions des autres codes. etc. etc. ... par le baron Locré ... (Nota. Le texte est conforme à la nouvelle édition du code.) ... Paris, Imprimerie de P. Didot l'aîné, 1816.

Locré de Roissy, Jean Guillaume, baron de, 1758–1840.
France. *Laws, statutes, etc.*
Esprit du Code Napoléon; tiré de la discussion, ou, Conférence historique, analytique et raisonnée du projet de Code civil, des observations des tribunaux, des procès-verbaux du Conseil d'État, des observations du tribunat, des exposés de motifs, des rapports et discours ... par J. G. Locré ...
Paris, Imprimerie impériale, 1805–1814.

Locre de Roissy, Jean Guillaume, baron de, 1758–1840, ed.
France. *Laws, statutes, etc.*
La législation civile, commerciale et criminelle de la France, ou Commentaire et complément des codes français; tirés, savoir: le commentaire, de la conférence avec le texte des codes, et, entre eux, des procès-verbaux en partie inédits du Conseil d'État qui contiennent la discussion du Code civil; des procès-verbaux entièrement inédits de la discussion du Code de commerce, du Code de procédure, du Code d'instruction criminelle et du Code pénal; des observations, également inédites, de la Section de législation du Tribunat sur les projets des trois premiers codes, et de celles des commissions du Corps législatif sur les deux derniers; enfin, des exposés de motifs, rapports et

discours faits ou prononcés, tant dans l'Assemblée générale du Tribunat, que devant le Corps législatif: le complément. des lois antérieures auxquelles les codes se réfèrent; des lois postérieures qui les étendent, les modifient; des discussions dont ces lois sont le résultat; des ordonnances, décrets, avis du Conseil, et autres actes du pouvoir exécutif et réglementaire destinés à en procurer l'exécution. Le tout précédé de prolégomènes, où l'on expose, dans une première partie, le mode de porter la loi qui était en usage lors de la confection des codes, et quels travaux préparatoires il a produits; où, dans une seconde, on

trace l'histoire générale de chaque code. Par m. le baron Locré ... Paris ₍etc.₎ Treuttel et Würtz, 1827–32.

Locré de Roissy, Jean Guillaume, baron de, 1758–1840.
Législation sur les mines et sur les expropriations pour cause d'utilité publique, ou Lois des 21 avril et 8 mars 1810, expliquées par les discussions du Conseil d'État, les exposés de motifs, rapports, discours, et généralement par tous les travaux préparatoires dont elles sont le résultat; et complétées par les actes de l'autorité publique qui les concernent. Par M. le baron Locré ... Paris ₍etc.₎ Treuttel et Würtz, 1828.
vij, 676 p. 20ᵐ.
1. Mining law—France. ₍1. Mines and mining—France₎ 2. Eminent domain—France. I. France. Conseil d'État. II. France. Laws, statutes, etc. III. Title.

29–23685

NL 0438454   DLC

Locré de Roissy, Jean Guillaume, baron de, 1758–1840.
France. *Conseil d'État.*
Procès-verbaux du Conseil d'État, contenant la discussion du projet de Code civil. ans IX–₍XII₎ ... Paris, Impr. de la République ₍1801₎–04.

Locré de Roissy, Jean Guillaume, baron de, 1758–1840.
Spirito del codice di commercio
see under France. Laws, statutes, etc.

Locre-Izard, Roger.
Résultats éloignés des gastrectomies pour ulcères.
Toulouse, 1942
Thèse - Toulouse

NL 0438457   CtY-M

Locrense, Euriso.
Sugli avvenimenti di Pio IX: canto profetico di un vecchio lombardo fra gli arcadi di Roma.
Napoli, L. Banzoli, 1848.
8 p. 8°.
In: BWL p.v. 1, no. 154.

NL 0438458   NN

Locres, Ferri de.
See
Locre, Ferry de, 1571–1614₎

Locrine.
... König Lokrin, ein trauerspiel in fünf aufzügen von William Shakespeare; deutsche übersetzung, mit literarhistorischer einleitung und anmerkungen von Alfred Neubner. Berlin, H. Paetel, 1908.
li, 141, ₍1₎ p. 25½ᶜᵐ. (Neue Shakespeare-bühne ... ɪv)

1. Neubner, Alfred, 1877– ed. and tr.
10–424

NL 0438460   DLC NN

Locrine.
The lamentable Tragedie of Locrine, the eldest sonne of King Brutus, discoursing the warres of the Britaines, and Hunnes, with their discomfiture: The Britaines victorie with their Accidents; and the death of Albanact. No lesse pleasant then profitable. Newly set foorth, ouerseene and corrected, by W. S. [Creede's device] London Printed by Thomas Creede. 1595.
₍78₎ p. 17½ᶜᵐ.
First edition.

NL 0438461   CLU-C DFo MiU

Locrine. The/lamentable tragedie of/Locrine...London, 1595.

NL 0438462   WU OCl CSmH PU

Locrine.
Locrine [by W. S. London. 1595.
(In Three centuries of drama: English, 1512–1641)
Microprint.
I. S. , W. II. Shakespeare, William.
Spurious and doubtful works.

NL 0438463   MoU

Locrine.
The Lamentable Tragedie of Locrine, the eldest sonne of King Brutus, discoursing the warres of the Britaines, and Hunnes, with their discomfiture: The Britaines victorie with their Accidents, and the death of Albanact. No lesse pleasant then profitable. Newly set foorth, ouerseene and corrected, By VV. S. London Printed by Thomas Crede. 1595. ₍Amersham, Eng.₎ Issued for subscribers by John S. Farmer, 1913₎
1 p. l., ₍76₎ p. 23 cm. (On cover: Old English drama. Students' facsimile edition)

Included in the 3d Shakespeare folio, 1664, but generally attributed to Wentworth Smith or Charles Tilney.
Label pasted on front end-paper reads: ... Locrine ... Entered on the Stationers' co. books, 1594. Date of only known early edition, 1595 ₍B. M. press-mark C. 34, b. 28₎ Next issued in the third folio Shakespeare, 1664. Also issued in the folio of 1685. Reproduced in facsimile ₍Tudor facsimile texts₎ 1911.

1. Smith, Wentworth, fl. 1601–1623, supposed author. II. Tilney, Charles, 1561–1586, supposed author. III. Shakespeare, William. Spurious and doubtful works. Locrine.

A 16—177

Minnesota. Univ. Libr.
for Library of Congress   ₍a50b1₎

NL 0438465   MnU IEN OCl RPB

Locrine.
The lamentable tragedie of Locrine...newly set foorth, ouerseene and corrected, by VV. S. London, 1595. (In: Shakespeare, W. Doubtful plays. 1918. The Shakespeare apocrypha. Oxford, 1918. 8°. p. 39–65.)

First printed under the initials W. S., hence ascribed to Shakespeare and included in the third folio 1664. For discussion of authorship see Cambridge history of English literature. v. 5, p. 268.

252225A. 1. Drama, English.   2. Smith, Wentworth, fl. 160f–1623, supposed author. 3. Shake-   speare, William. 4. Title.
N. Y. P. L.   August 16, 1928

NL 0438466   NN

Y
S 85
.88

Locrine.
Locrine. (in Hazlitt, William, ed. The doubtful plays of William Shakspeare. 1887. p.[57]–104)
Half-title.
Included in the 3d Shakespeare folio, 1664, but generally attributed to Wentworth Smith or Charles Tilney.

NL 0438467   ICN

822
L815
1892

Locrine
... Locrine. Edited, with an introduction, by A. F. Hopkinson. London, M. E. Sims & co., 1892.
2 p.l., xv p., 1 l., 79p. (Shakespeare's doubtful plays)

Imprint fictitious. Printed by the editor for private circulation. cf. Jaggard, Shakespeare bibl., p.552.
Included in the third Shakespeare folio, 1664; attributed also to Wentworth Smith and to Charles

Tilney.
Original title: The lamentable tragedie of Locrine, the eldest sonne of King Brutus, discoursing the warres of the Britaines, and Hunnes, with their discomfiture ... Newly set foorth, ouerseene and corrected, by VV.S. London, Printed by Thomas Creede. 1595.

NL 0438469   IU

Locrine ₎
... Locrine, "newly set foorth, overseene, and corrected, by W. S." 1595. ₍Amersham, Eng.₎ Issued for subscribers by the editor of the Tudor facsimile texts, 1911.
3 p. l., facsim.: 1 p. l., ₍76₎ p. 26ᵐ. (The Tudor facsimile texts)

Included in the 3d Shakespeare folio, 1664, attributed also to Wentworth Smith or Charles Tilney.
Original title: The Lamentable Tragedie of Locrine, the eldest sonne of King Brutus, discoursing the warres of the Britaines, and Hunnes ... London, Printed by Thomas Creede, 1595.

1. Smith, Wentworth, fl. 1601–1623, supposed author. II. Shakespeare, William, 1564–1616.
11–12055 Revised

Library of Congress   PR2862.A1 1911

NL 0438470   DLC NIC MiU ViU NjP MB

Locrine.
The tragedy of Locrine, the eldest son of King Brutus. ₍London: J. Tonson,₎ 1709. 3267–3324 p. incl. front. 8°.

Excerpt: The works of...Shakespeare; edited by Nicholas Rowe... 1709. v. 6.
First printed under the initials W. S., hence ascribed to Shakespeare and included in the third folio 1664; attributed also to Wentworth Smith.

1. Drama, English. 2. Smith, Went-   worth, fl. 1601–1623, supposed author.
3. Shakespeare, William. 4. Rowe,   Nicholas, 1674–1718, editor.
5. Title.
N. Y. P. L.   November 21, 1928

NL 0438471   NN MH

Locrine (*Old play*)
The tragedy of Locrine, the eldest son of King Brutus. ₍London₎ 1714.
p. ₍337₎–397. 164ᵐ.
₍Longe, F. Collection of plays. v. 70, no. 1₎
First printed under the initials W. S. hence ascribed to Shakespeare and included in the third folio 1664; attributed also to Wentworth Smith or Charles Tilney.
Probably from the 9-vol. edition of Shakespeare printed by Jacob Tonson, 1714. "This edition was sold also as separate plays, with the anonymous legend at foot of each title 'Printed in the year MDCCXIV.'"—Jaggard.
For discussion of authorship see Cambridge history of English literature. v. 5, p. 268.
1. Smith, Wentworth, fl. 1601–1623, supposed author. II. Shakespeare, William. Spurious   and doubtful works.

25–16621

Library of Congress   PR1241.L6 vol. 70

NL 0438472   DLC

VOLUME 338

Locrine.
The tragedy of Locrine, the eldest son of **King Brutus.**
₍London₎ 1728.
p.₍361₎-426.   17^cm.
First printed under the initials W. S., hence ascribed to Shakespeare and included in the third folio 1664; attributed also to Wentworth Smith or Charles Tilney.
Probably from the 9-vol. edition of Shakespeare printed by Jacob Tonson, 1728

For discussion of authorship see Cambridge history of English literature, v. 5, p. 268.

NL   0438473   MiU

Locrine.
The tragedy of Locrine, the eldest son of King Brutus. By Mr. William Shakespear. London: Printed for J. Tonson, and the rest of the proprietors, 1734.
59, ₍1₎ p.   front.   16½cm.   (Shakespeare, William.   The works ... ₍1735₎ v. 8 ₍no. 7₎)

The initials W. S. on the title-page of the first edition (1595) led to the inclusion of the play in the Shakespeare folio of 1664.

It has been attributed also to Wentworth Smith and Charles Tilney.
Ford, Shakespeare, 1700-1740, no. 155.

MH NjP
NL   0438475   PU-F MB CSmH IU PBm ICN CtY DFo ICU

Y
S 85
.84
Locrine.
The tragedy of Locrine, the eldest son of King Brutus. (in Simms, W.G., ed. A supplement to the plays of William Shakspeare. 1848. p.₍151₎-178)

Caption title.
Included in the 3d Shakespeare folio, 1664, but generally attributed to Wentworth   Smith or Charles Tilney.

———— ———— (in Simms, W.G., ed. A supplement to the plays of William Shakspeare. 1855. p.₍151₎-178)

NL   0438477   ICN

Locrine.
The tragedy of Locrine, 1595 ... ₍Oxford, Printed for the Malone society by H. Hart, M. A., at the Oxford university press₎ 1908.
xii, ₍78₎ p.   2 facsim.   23^cm.   (The Malone society reprints)
Signatures: A-K¹ (1st leaf (blank?) is wanting in the copies collected for this edition)
Reprint of the quarto of 1595, "prepared by Ronald B. McKerrow ..."

With reproduction of original t.-p.: The Lamentable Tragedie of Locrine, the eldest sonne of King Brutus, discoursing the warres of the Britaines, and Hunnes, with their discomfiture: The Britaines victorie with their Accidents, and the death of Albanact. No lesse pleasant than profitable. Newly set foorth, ouerseene and corrected, by VV. S. London, Printed by Thomas Creede, 1595.
The initials W. S. on the t-p. led to the inclusion of the play in the Shakespeare folio of 1664. It has been attributed also to Wentworth Smith and Charles Tilney.
Facsimiles: A2 recto (t.-p. Bodl.), A3 recto.

I. Smith, Wentworth, fl. 1601-1623, supposed author. II. McKerrow, Ronald Brunlees, 1872–
                                                9—10252
Library of Congress   PR2862.A1 1908
                                ₍a35k1₎

OCl ViU MiU PU-F TxU PBm PSC PHC PU NcGU MU MB NcRS
NL   0438479   DLC MB NjP CaBVaU MtU PP TU NcU OU OCU

Locrine.
The tragedy of Locrine, 1895. [This reprint of the tragedy of Locrine has been prepared by R. B. McKerrow...] London, The Malone Soc., 1909.
xii, 39 l., 2 fac. sim. sq. 8°. (Malone Soc. Reprints)

NL   0438480   NN

Locrine. Phrase index.   n.p., n.d.
see under   [Hopkinson, Arthur Frederick]

Locrius, Ferreolus
see
Loore, Ferry de, 1571-1614.

S599
.P6N4
Locsin, Carlos L.
Victorias Milling Company, inc.
Soils of the Victorias milling district; a handbook for the planters of the district, by Carlos L. Locsin, technical director, and Filomeno T. Tabayoyong, soil chemist. Victorias, Philippines, 1953.

Wason
DS686.5
P78+
Locsin, Teodoro M
Answer to William J. Pomery's "Why I have joined the Huks". ₍Manila? 1951₎
5 p.   27cm.

Bound with Pomery, W.J. Why I have joined the Huks. ₍Manila? 1951₎

1. Communism--Philippine Islands.
I. Title.

NL   0438484   NIC

Lo Curto, Dino.
Ipparco re; poema drammatico in 3 atti di Dino Lo Curto. Palermo, Industrie riunite editoriali siciliane, 1924.
7 p. l., 9-222 p., 1 l.   illus., port.   19^cm.

I. Title.
Library of Congress   PQ4827.O33 I 6 1924   25-1580

NL   0438485   DLC

Lo Curto, Leonardo.
Italia nuova; problemi d'oggi e possibilità di risolverli. ₍Milano₎ A. Vallardi ₍1951₎
248 p.   21 cm.

1. Italy—Econ. condit.—1945–   2. Italy—Civilization.
I. Title.
HC305.L63   A 55-8285
New York Univ.   Wash.   Sq. Library
for Library of Congress   ₍a57b1₎†

NL   0438486   NNU-W DLC

Lo Curzio, Guglielmo, 1894–
Amorelli. Palermo, Priulla [1912]
27,p.   28 plates.   24.5cm.

NL   0438487   OOxM

LO CURZIO, GUGLIELMO, 1894–
...Amorelli. Palermo: Priulla [1934]   27 p.   27 pl.   25cm.

847822A. 1. Amorelli, Alfonso, 1898–   . 2. Paintings, Italian.

NL   0438488   NN

842S28
DL81
Lo Curzio, Guglielmo, 1894–
Un ermetico del Cinquecento.   ₍Palermo₎ Palumbo ₍1955₎
16p.   25cm.

Bibliographical footnotes.

1. Scève, Maurice, 16th cent.

NL   0438489   IU NN

Lo Curzio, Guglielmo, 1894–
Ottocento minore; incontri e pretesti. ₍Palermo₎ Palumbo ₍1950₎
135 p.   23 cm.   (Saggi di letteratura italiana, 11)

1. Italian literature—19th cent.—Hist. & crit.   (Series)
Brown Univ. Library   PQ4086.L62   A 52-6728
for Library of Congress   ₍1₎

NL   0438490   RPB NcU OU IU NN

Lo Curzio, Guglielmo, 1894–
La poesia di G.A. Cesareo.   Palermo, G.B. Palumbo [1947]
125 p.   21 cm.   (Saggi di letteratura italiana, 8)
"Bibliografia": p. [121]-122.
1. Cesareo, Giovanni Alfredo, 1861–
I. Series.

NL   0438491   IEN ICU NN IU MB OrU

Lo Curzio, Guglielmo, 1894–
... La poesia di Luigi Pirandello.   Palermo, Casa editrice Ant. Trimarchi ₍1935₎
121 p., 3 l.   24^m.   (Half-title: Saggi e studi critici. n. 7)
Bibliographical foot-notes.

1. Pirandello, Luigi, 1867-1936.
                                                A 40-2612
Brown univ. Library   PQ4835.I 7Z95
for Library of Congress   ₍2₎

NL   0438492   RPB CoU DLC TU MWelC MiU NN IU

Lo Curzio, Guglielmo, 1894–
Quelli di Follurbe; romanzo. ₍1. ed.₎   Palermo. Edizioni Pantea ₍1945₎   220 p.   19cm.   (Narratori italiani e stranieri. 1)

NL   0438493   NN RPB

840.9
L81r
Lo Curzio, Guglielmo, 1894–
Rimbaud e altri pellegrinaggi.   ₍Palermo₎ Palumbo ₍1950₎
125p.   22cm.   (Studi di letteratura straniere, 1)

Bibliographical footnotes.

NL   0438494   IU NN

Lo Curzio, Guglielmo, 1894–
...Terra d'Africa.   Palermo: Trimarchi ₍1936₎   70 p.   22cm.
Poems.

1. Poetry, Italian. I. Title.
N.Y.P.L.   July 13, 1938

NL   0438495   NN

PQ4827
O2
U65
Lo Curzio, Guglielmo, 1894–
L'uomo, questo nemico: racconti. Catania Camene, 1949.
96p.   19cm.   (Narratori. I)

NL   0438496   RPB

VOLUME 338

Locus standi reports
    see under   Gt. Brit. Parliament.
House of Commons. Court of Referees.

The Locust.

Commerce, Tex.
    v. illus. (incl. ports.) plates. 27½-31¼ᵐ.

Part of the illustrative material is colored.
Published by the students of East Texas state teachers college.
Issues for   published under the college's earlier name: East Texas state normal college.

ı. Texas. State teachers college, Commerce.

                       43–19611

Library of Congress   LB1963.C65L6

                       370.73764

NL 0438498   DLC

Locust bean gum, gum arabic, gum karaya,
    gum tragacanth
      see under   [Innis, Speiden & co.]

Locust Dale academy, Locust Dale, Va. Catalog.
    Library has 1875, 1876, 1878, 1881, 1898, 1900, 1901, 1909.   3131

NL 0438500   Vi

Locust Gap Improvement Company.   622.19 L81
    The charter and by-laws of the Locust Gap Improvement Company, with reports on their coal land, together with a synopsis and supplimentary [!] remarks. Philadelphia, McLaughlin Brothers' Book and Job Printing Office, 1854.
    [2], 45 p. 2 fold. maps (incl. front.) 23ᶜᵐ.

NL 0438501   ICJ NN PU PHi

Locust Gap improvement company
    Report on the landed estate & mines & mineral resources, to which is appended the charter & by-laws.
    Phila., Stun., 1866.
    34 p.

NL 0438502   PU

Locust Grove institute, *Locust Grove, Ga.*
    Annual catalogue and announcement.

Rome, Ga. [etc.],
    v. illus., plates. 23ᶜᵐ.

                   CA 10–5612 Unrev'd

Library of Congress   LD7501.L698

NL 0438503   DLC GU

H
289.777419
L81   Locust Grove Mennonite Church, Burr Oak,
    Michigan, 25th anniversary, 1940-1965
    [n.p., n.d.]

    [12]p. illus. 24cm.

    Cover serves as title-page.

    1. Mennonites in Michigan.

NL 0438504   ViHarEM

PZ262
.L875
1850   Locust grove: or, Lessons from familiar occurrences. By the author of "The state prisoner."
    Ed. by D. P. Kidder. New York, Lane & Scott, 1850.
    68 p.

NL 0438505   ICU

Locust Grove school, Shellville, Calif.
    [Catalogue] [n.p.] 1888.
    1 v. 15 cm.

NL 0438506   CU

26.6
    Locust Grove seminary,
      Locust Grove Seminary. A boarding and day school for young ladies, near Pittsburgh, Pa.
    Pittsburgh, 1854.
    12 p. 18 1/2 cm.

NL 0438507   DLC

Locust grove stories. v.   Philadelphia: Amer. Sunday-
School Union   v. front. 16°.
    Contents:

    v. 4. Dick Mason and Harry Slack. Sympathy for others. Johnnie's lesson. Aunt Clyde's visit.

    1. Juvenile literature.—Fiction.   (American).
N. Y. P. L.   February 23, 1921.

NL 0438508   NN DLC

Locust timber.
    (*In* U. S. Patent office. Report, 1845, p. 981-982. 23ᵐ. Washington, 1846)

    1. Locust tree.

                       Agr 14–707

Library, U. S. Dept. of   Agriculture 1Ag84 1845

NL 0438509   DNAL

Locusteanu, P.   1883 –   ed.
    Cincizeci figuri contimporane
    see under   Iser, Iosif, 1881-

Locusteanu, P.,   1883 –   compiler.
    ...Glasul vitejiei; antologie eroica.   Bucureşti: D. C. Ionescu, 1915.   190 p. 16°.

    1. Poetry (Rumanian).—Collections.
N. Y. P. L.   April 2, 1924.

NL 0438511   NN MChB

Hda84
L81   Locusteanu, P   1883-   ed.
    ... Umorul românesc. Incercare critică şi antologie. Bucureşti, Publicaţiile Casei şcoalelor[1915?]
    1p.ℓ.,[v]-lvi,416p. 21cm.
    On cover: Din publicaţiile Casei şcoălelor. - Biblioteca secundară.

    1.Rumanian literature - Selections, extracts, etc. 2.Authors, Rumanian. I.Title.

NL 0438512   CtY

Locutions et prononciations vicieuses, usitées à Nantes et dans plusieurs autres villes occidentales de la France; nouvelle édition considérablement augmentée; Nantes, n.d.
    20 ǂ 4 p.

NL 0438513   ICN

5195
7025   Locutions modernes (Néologie)
    3ᵉ ed. Impr. de Sien-hsien, 1935.
    288 p. 28cm.

NL 0438514   CU-E CU

The locusts: or, Chancery painted to the life, and the laws ot England try'd in forma pauperis. A poem... London, 1704. 28 p. 8°.

442192A. 1. Law—Gt. Br.—Poetry.   2. Poetry, English.
N. Y. P. L.   October 25, 1929

NL 0438515   NN OCU TxHU DFo DLC

Locuty, Pierre.
    ... Contribution à l'étude du système ternaire sulfate d'ammonium.—Acide sulfurique.—Eau ... Nancy, Société d'impressions typographiques, 1934.
    2 p. l., [7]-82 p., 1 l. incl. illus., tables. fold. diagr. 24½ᵐ.

    Thèse—Nancy.
    "Index bibliographique" : p. [79]

    1. Phase rule and equilibrium. ı. Title.

                       42–35378

Library of Congress   QD501.L8136

NL 0438516   DLC CtY

QS
L819a
1911   LOCY, William Albert, 1857-1924
    Anatomical illustration before Vesalius.
    [n. p., 1911?]
    p. 945-988. illus.
    Reprinted from Journal of morphology, v. 22, no. 4, Dec., 1911.
    Author's autograph presentation copy.

NL 0438517   DNLM

Locy, William Albert, 1857-1924.
    Biology and its makers, with portraits and other illustrations, by William A. Locy ... New York, H. Holt and company, 1908.
    xxvi, 469 p. illus. (incl. ports.) 22½ cm.

    "Reading list": p. 449-460.

    CONTENTS.—An outline of the rise of biology and of the epochs in its history.—Vesalius and the overthrow of authority in science.—William Harvey and experimental observation.—The introduction of the microscope and the progress of independent observation.—The progress of minute anatomy.—Linnæus and scientific natural history.—Cuvier and the rise of comparative anatomy.—Bichat and the birth of histology.—The rise of physiology. Harvey. Haller, Johannes Müller.—Von Baer and the rise of embryology.—The cell-theory. Schleiden. Schwann. Schultze.—Protoplasm the physical basis of life.—The work of Pasteur, Koch, and others.—Heredity and germinal continuity. Mendel. Galton. Weismann.—The science of fossil life.—What evolution is; the evidence upon which it rests, etc—Theories of evolution. Lamarck. Darwin.—Theories continued. Weismann. De Vries.—The rise of evolutionary thought.—Retrospect and prospect. Present tendencies in biology.

    1. Biology—Hist. ı. Title.

Library of Congress   QH305.L7

                       8—21045

    OC1 PBm PV PPD PHC OO OC1ND NcD CU MH OC1W PU-Med NN
NL 0438519   DLC KyU KyU-A DNLM NjP ICJ MB OCU MiD

Locy, William Albert, 1857-1924.
    Biology and its makers, with portraits and other illustration, by William A. Locy ...
    New York, H. Holt and company, 1915 [i. e. 1922]
    xxvi, 477 p. illus. (incl. ports.) 21 cm.
    "Reading list": p. 457-468.
    *3d ed., rev. March, 1922.

    NcRS OC1 PU PSC PPC IMunS NN TxU Or
NL 0438520   ViU DNLM OO OCU OC1W ODW IU OrStbM CU

Locy, William Albert, 1857-1924.
    Biology and its makers, with portriats and other illustrations, by William A. Locy ...
    New York, H. Holt and company [1926]
    xxvi, 477 p. illus. (incl. ports.) 21 cm.
    "Reading list": p. 457-468.
    *3d ed., rev. "January, 1926."

NL 0438521   ViU MH PBa

VOLUME 338

Locy, William Albert, 1857–1924.
Biology and its makers; with portraits and other illustrations;
by William A. Locy...   New York: H. Holt and Co., 1928.
xxvi, 477 p.   illus. (incl. ports.)   3. ed., rev.   8°.

Bibliography, p. 457–468.

NL   0438522   NN OrSaW CaBVaU KU-M OC1

LOCY, William A[lbert], 1857–
Biology and its makers. 3d ed., revised. New
York, H. Holt and Co., [1930, cop.1908].

Ports.and other illustr.
"Reading list", pp.457-468.

NL   0438523   NcD UU LU OC1U OC1W
                     MH MeB NjNbS MNS OC1CC OC1JC OOxM MH-D

QH305   Locy, William Albert, 1857–1924.
.L7   Biology and its makers, with portraits and other illustra-
1936   tions, by William A. Locy ... New York, H. Holt and com-
         pany, c1936.
            xxvi,477 p. illus. (incl. ports.)   21ᶜᵐ.
            "Reading list": p. 457–468.
            *3d. ed. rev.

NL   0438524   ViU PPPL PBm PWcS

---

s570   Locy, William Albert, 1857-1924.
L81b   Biology and its makers, with portraits and other
1940   illustrations, by William A. Locy   3d ed., rev.
         New York, H. Holt and company [1940]
            477p. illus., diagrs.

         "January 1940."

         1. Biology--Hist.

NL   0438525   IU

W.C.L. Locy, William Albert, 1857-1924.
570.9   Biology and its makers. 3d ed., rev. New
L819B   York, Henry Holt and Co., c1945, c1935.
            xxvi, 477 p. illus., ports. 21 cm.

         Bibliography: p. 457-468.

         1. Biology. History. I. Title.

NL   0438526   NcD OC1W KEmT

Locy, William Albert, 1857-1924.
   Biology and its makers, with portraits and
other illustrations, by William A. Locy ...
New York, H. Holt and company [1949]
   xxvi, 477 p. illus. (incl. ports.)   22.5 cm.
   "Reading list": p. 457-468.
   3rd ed., rev.

NL   0438527   ViU MiU

Locy, William Albert, 1857–   L590.4 L81
   [Collected papers.]
      Various paging.
      Extracted or reprinted from various scientific serials.

NL   0438528   ICJ

Locy, William Albert, 1857–
   Contribution to the structure and development of the
vertebrate head ... Boston, Ginn & company, 1895.

   1 p. l., p. [497]-594. illus., xxvi-xxx fold. pl. 25½ᶜᵐ.

   Thesis (PH. D.)—University of Chicago.
   "Literature": p. 580-583.
   "Reprinted from Journal of morphology, vol. xi. no. 3," Dec., 1895.

   1. Vertebrates. 2. Anatomy, Comparative.

                                                       4—24892

Library of Congress   QL805.L8

NL   0438529   DLC NjP Nh NIC CU MB ICJ

Locy, William Albert
   Derivation of the pineal eye, preliminary
announcement.
n.t.p. 1893.
180 p.

NL   0438530   PU-Z

Locy, William Albert. The earliest printed illustrations of
natural history. [Utica. 1921.] 8°. Illustr.
   Scientific monthly, 1921, xiii, 238-258.

NL   0438531   MH-A

Locy, William Albert, 1857–   L591.33 R600
.... The embryology of the bird's lungs. based on observa-
tions of the domestic fowl. Part 1.–[II]. [By] William A. Locy
and Olof Larsell. .... [Philadelphia, The Wistar Institute of
Anatomy and Biology], 1916.
   p. 447-504, 1-44. illus. 26½ᶜᵐ.
   Caption title.
   "Reprinted from the American journal of anatomy, vol. 19, no. 3, May, and vol. 20,
no. 1, July, 1916."
   "Bibliography," pt. 2, p. 44.

NL   0438532   ICJ WaTC

597.3
L82a Locy,William Albert,1857–
         A footnote to the ancestral history of
         the vertebrate brain. [William A.Locy]
         [No imprint]
            5 p.   diagrs.   28 x 23 cm.
            Caption title.
            Reprinted from Science,n.s.,vol.22,no.
         554,Aug.1905.

NL   0438533   MiU

Locy, William Albert, 1857-1924.
   The growth of biology; zoölogy from Aristotle to Cuvier,
botany from Theophrastus to Hofmeister, physiology from
Harvey to Claude Bernard, by the late William A. Locy ...
New York, H. Holt and company, 1925.
   xiv, 481 p. illus. (incl. ports.) 22ᶜᵐ.

   1. Natural history—Hist. 2. Biology—Hist. 3. Zoology—Hist. 4. Botany—Hist. 5. Physiology—Hist.   I. Title.

Library of Congress   QH15.L6   25—22141

                   OrU-D ODW PPC PBm PSC PHC PP
         OC1W CU ViU ICJ NN MB OrPR Or CaBVaU CaBVa WaWW OrSaW
NL   0438534   DLC OrP MtU WaS MH DNLM NcD OU MiU OO OC1

Locy, William Albert, 1857-1924.
   The growth of biology; zoölogy from Aristotle
to Cuvier, botany from Theophrastus to Hofmeister, physiology from Harvey to Claude Bernard.
New York, H. Holt, 1925.
   xiv, 495 p. illus.

NL   0438535   NNC NNBG KyLxT

Locy, William Albert, 1857–
   The main currents of zoölogy, by William A. Locy ...
New York, H. Holt and company, 1918.

   vii, 216 p. ports. 19½ᶜᵐ.

   "Reading lists of books and periodical articles on zoölogical subjects":
p. 191-208.

   1. Zoology—Hist.   1. Title.

Library of Congress   QL15.L7   18—13661

         NN MB ICJ MdBJ
         OCU NIC KEmT TxU TU OrSaW Or WaS PPT PHC PU-Z PP
NL   0438536   DLC WU NcRS NcD NjP ViU OC1JC OO OU MiU

Locy, William Albert, 1857–
   Malpighi, Swammerdam and Leeuwenhoek. By Pro-
fessor William A. Locy ... [New York & London, 1901]
   [561]-584 p. illus., ports. 25ᶜᵐ.
   Caption title.
   The popular science monthly, April, 1901, p. [561]-584.

   1. Malpighi, Marcello, 1628-1694. 2. Swammerdam, Jan, 1637-1680.
2. Leeuwenhoek, Anthony van, 1632-1723.

                                          CA 7-2348 Unrev'd

Library of Congress   QH26.L9

NL   0438537   DLC

Locy, William Albert
   Metaneric segmentation in the medullary
folds & embryonic rim.
n.t.p., 1894.
415 p.

NL   0438538   PU-Z

Locy, William Albert.   3880a.77
   A new cranial nerve in selachians. Plates.
(In Mark anniversary volume. Pp. 39-55. New York, 1903.)
Bibliography, p. 54.

F4413 — Nerves, Cranial. — Selachians.

NL   0438539   MB DNLM

597.3
L82n Locy,William Albert,1857–
         A new cranial nerve in selachians.
         William A.Locy. [No imprint]
            cover-title,1 ℓ.,p.41-55.   pl.v-vi.
         30 x 23½ cm.
            Reprinted from the Mark anniversary
         volume article 3,1903.
            This work is now superseded by the au-
         thor's article "On a newly recognized
         nerve connected with the fore-brain of
         selachians,in Anatomical anzeiger,bd.26,
         no.2 & 3,1905.

NL   0438540   MiU

Locy, William Albert, 1857-1924.
   Observations on the development of Agelena
naevia. [Cambridge, Mass., 1885]
   [63]-103 p. illus. 25 cm. (Harvard University. Museum of Comparative Zoology. Bulletin,
v. 12, no.3)

   Bibliography: p. 95-97.

   1. Spiders. I. T.

NL   0438541   NjP MU FTaSU NIC

VOLUME 338

QL
524
.L82
   ... Observations on the pulsating organs in
the legs of certain Hemiptera. By Wm.A.Locy.
[Philadelphia, 1884]
    13-19 p. pl. 24 cm.
    Caption title.
    Extracted from the American naturalist,v.
XVIII,1884.
    With his Anatomy and physiology of the
family Nepidae. 1884.

NL 0438542   MiU

597.3
L82op Locy,William Albert,1857-
    The optic vesicles of elasmobranchs &
their serial relations to other structures
on the cephalic plate by William A.Locy...
Boston, Ginn & co., 1894.
    1 ℓ.,p.[115]-122. diagrs. 28 x 23 cm.
    Reprinted from the Journal of Morphology,
vol.9,no.1,1894.

NL 0438543   MiU

Locy, William Albert
    Service of zoology to intellectual progress.
n.p., 1909
    357 p.

NL 0438544   PU-Z

Locy, William Albert, 1857-1924.
    The story of biology, by the late William A. Locy ... Garden City, N. Y., Garden City publishing company, inc. [1934]
    xiv, 495 p. illus. (incl. ports.) 23½ᶜᵐ.
    First published 1925 under title: The growth of biology ...
    Bibliography: p. 471-484.

    1. Natural history—Hist. 2. Biology—Hist. 3. Zoöl., —Hist. 4. Botany—Hist. 5. Physiology—Hist. I. Title. II. Title: The growth of biology.

    Library of Congress   QH15.L6 | 1934.   34-39906
                                    [2].00

    CtY-M NIC PCM WaSp WaTC OrStbM CaBVaU IdPI OrU
    ViU FTaSU OClCC PPT OO OKentU NcD ICU PPC PP OLak
NL 0438545   DLC LU TxU MiU OC1JC CU KU-M OEac OU RPB

Lóczi Lóczy, Lajos, 1891-
    see
Lóczy, Lajos, 1891-

Loczka, Alajos,
    A művelődés útja Amerikában; az iskolarendszer vizsgálata. Budapest, 1937.
    340 p.
    Bibliography: p. [325]-332.
    1. Education - U.S.

NL 0438547   NNC DLC-P4

Lóczy, Lajos, 1849- 1920.
    A Balaton földrajzi és társadalmi állapotainak leirása.
Balaton tudományos tanulmányozásának eredményei czimü
monografia-gyüjtemény adatai alapján. Irta Lóczy Lajos...
Budapest: V. Hornyánszky, 1920. 194 p. map, plates
(part col'd). 4°.

    1. Balaton, Lake—Hungary.
N. Y. P. L.   April 22, 1927

NL 0438548   NN NNG

Q115
.M18   **Lóczy, Lajos,** 1849-1920.

Magyar Földrajzi Társaság. *Balaton Bisottság.*
    A Balaton tudományos tanulmányozásának eredményei.
Budapest, Kilián F. könyvárus bizománya, 1897-

Lóczy, Lajos, 1849-1920.
    Beschreibung der palaeon. Resultate der
reise...in Ostasien.   Budapest, 1898.

NL 0438550   NjP

Lóczy, Lajos 1849-1920.
    Direktionsbericht. Übertragung aus dem ungarischen
Original. Budapest: A. Fritz, 1912. 1 p.l., (1)10-19 p. 8°.

    Repr.: Jahresbericht der Kgl. Ungarischen geologischen Reichsanstalt. 1910.
In : PTI p. v. 16. no. 11.

1. Geology. Austria-Hungary.
N. Y. P. L.   April 17, 1914.

NL 0438551   NN

Locsy, Lajos.
    A fosszillis emlos-es puhatestu.
    41876

NL 0438552   DI-GS

Lóczy, Lajos, 1849-1920, *ed.*
    ... A geographical, economic and social survey of Hungary,
ed. by Louis Lóczy ... with contributions by several Hungarian scholars ... Budapest, "Pátria" press, 1919.
    121, [1] p. IV maps (1 fold.) 24ᶜᵐ.
    At head of title: Publications of the Hungarian geographical society.
    An extract from "A geographical, sociological, cultural and economic description of the crown lands of St. Stephens', edited by Louis Lóczy and published by the Hungarian geographical society. *cf.* Pref.

    1. Hungary—Econ. condit.—1918.   2. Hungary—Hist. 3. Physical geography—Hungary. I. Magyar földrajzi társaság, Budapest. II. Title.
                                        20—11283

    Library of Congress   DB906.L6

NL 0438553   DLC CU WaS WaU OU OO OC1 NcD CtY NjP

QE266
.G4   Lóczy, Lajos, 1849-1920.

Geologica hungarica; fasciculi ad illustrandam notionem
geologicam et palaeontologicam regni Hungariae. t. 1,
fasc. 1-
    Budapest, Institutum regni Hungariae geologicum, 1914-

Lóczy, Lajos, 1849-1920.
    Geological map of Hungary and the adjacent
regions of the neighbouring countries. Designed
on the basis of original surveys... by Louis
Lóczy... 1890-1910; re-edited and supplemented
by Charles Papp... Budapest, Hungarian geographical society, 1922.
    2 col. sheets. 69 x 54 cm.
    Scale 1:900,000
    [Geological maps of European countries]

NL 0438555   CtY

Lóczy, Lajos, 1849-1920
    Geologische Karte
Széchenyi, Béla, *gróf,* 1837-
    Die wissenschaftlichen ergebnisse der reise des grafen
Béla Széchenyi in Ostasien 1877-1880 ... Nach dem im
jahre 1890-1897, erschienenen ungarischen originale.
Wien, In commission der verlagsbuchhandlung von E.
Hölzel, 1893-99.

Lóczy, Lajos, 1849-1920.
    Die geologischen formationen der Balatongegend und
ihre regionale tektonik, von Ludwig von Lóczy. Mit 15
tafeln und ingesamt 327 textfiguren ... Budapest, Hofbuchdr. V. Hornyansky, 1916.

    2 p. l., [3]-716 p. illus, xv fold. pl. (incl. 3 maps) 29½ᶜᵐ.
    "Separatabdruck aus dem werke 'Resultate der wissenschaftl. erforschung des Balatonsees', I. band, I. teil, I. sektion."
    Bibliographical foot-notes.

    1. Balaton Lake, Hungary. 2. Geology—Hungary—Balaton Lake.
                                    26-11136

    Library of Congress   QE267.B3L6

NL 0438557   DLC GU CU

Lóczy, Lajos, 1849-1920, *ed.*
    ... La Hongrie géographique, économique et sociale, par
Louis Lóczy ... en collaboration avec plusieurs confrères. Publication de la Société hongr. de géographie. Avec 4 planches.
Budapest, Impr. "Pátria", 1919.
    116 p., 1 l. maps (1 fold.) 24ᶜᵐ.
    Issued also in English.
    A résumé of "Description géographique, économique et sociale des pays de la couronne de Saint Étienne", published by the Hungarian geographical society. *cf.* Pref.

    1. Hungary—Econ. condit. 2. Hungary—Hist. 3. Physical geography—Hungary. I. Magyar földrajzi társaság, Budapest. II. Title.

    Library of Congress   DB906.L62   21—14022

NL 0438558   DLC CSt-H ICJ

Lóczy, Lajos, 1849- 1920 .
    A Khinai birodalom természeti viszonyainak és országainak leirása. Gróf Széchenyi Béla keletázsiai utazása
alatt (1877-1880) szerzett tapasztalatai alapján és a meglevő irodalom fölhasználásával, irta Lóczi Lóczy Lajos.
Kétszáz rajzzal és egy térképmelléklettel. Budapest,
K. M. Természettudományi társulat, 1886.
    xiv, 1 l., 884 p. incl. illus., plates. fold. map. 28ᶜᵐ. (Added t-p.: Természettudományi könyvkiadó-vállalat a Magyar tud. akadémia segítkezésével kiadja a K. M. Természettudományi társulat. xxvi)
    1. Széchenyi, Béla, gróf, 1837- 2. China—Descr. & trav. 3. Mongolia—Descr. & trav. 4. Tibet—Descr. & trav. 5. Natural history—China. 6. Natural history—Mongolia. 7. Natural history—Tibet. 8. Csoma (Kőrösi), Sándor, 1789?-1842.

    Library of Congress   DS709.L84   20-13019

NL 0438559   DLC

Lóczy, Lajos, 1849-1920, *ed.*
    A magyar szent korona országainak földrajzi, társadalomtudományi, közművelődési és közgazdasági leirása; a Magyar kir. vallás- és közoktatásügyi minister úr megbízásából,
Magyarország, Horvát-Szlavonországok és Bosznia-Hercegovina legjelesebb szakférfiainak közreműködésével, szerkesztette Lóczi Lóczy Lajos (I-IX táblával) Kiadta a Magyar földrajzi társaság. Budapest, Kilián Frigyes utóda,
1918.
    vi, [2] p., 2 l., 528 p. IX maps (part fold.) 24 cm.
    An extract was published in English with title: A geographical, economic and social survey of Hungary. Budapest, 1919.
    1. Hungary.   I. Magyar földrajzi társaság, Budapest. II. Title.
    DB906.L58   27—10188

NL 0438560   DLC MH

4DS   Lóczy, Lajos, 1849-1920
China   A mennyei birodalom története.
198   Budapest, Lampel R. [pref. 1901]

    283 p.

    (A Magyar Földrajzi Társaság könyvtára,
2. köt.)

NL 0438561   DLC-P4 NNC

Loczy, Lajos, 1849-1920.

Lóczy, Lajos, 1831—
    My geological researches in western Servia. An account
of the expedition to Servia 1917-1918. With a geological
map, tree [1] tables of sections and four figures. By Lewis de
Lóczy ... Budapest, Printed by: "G. Bethlen" typogr. comp.
lt., 1927.

Lóczy, Lajos, 1849-1920.
    Notes on sand and Loess specimens brought by Dr. M. A.
Stein from the region of Khotan. n. t.-p. n. p. [1900?]
588-590 p. f°.

    Excerpt.

    1. Sand. Asia: Khotan. 2. Stein,   Mark Aurel.
N. Y. P. L.   February 26, 1914.

NL 0438563   NN

Lóczy, Lajos, 1849-1920.   *30402.203.1
    Notes on sand and loess specimens brought by Dr. M. A. Stein from
the region of Khotan.
    (In Stein, Max Aurel. Ancient Khotan. . . . Pp. 588-590. Oxford. 1907.)

    G5666 — Khotan. Geol.

NL 0438564   MB

VOLUME 338

Q115
.M2

Lóczy, Lajos, 1849–1920.

Magyar földrajzi társaság. *Balaton-bizottsága.*
Resultate der wissenschaftlichen erforschung des Balatonsees. Mit unterstützung des Ung. Kön. ackerbaukultus- und
unterrichtsministeriums und anderen mäzenen herausgegeben vom Balaton-ausschusse der Ung. geographischen gesellschaft ... Wien, In kommission von E. Hölzel. 1897–19

Lóczy, Lajos, 1849–1920.
Über die geologischen Anstalten Europas. Übertragung aus
dem ungarischen Original. Budapest: A. Fritz, 1912. 243–
260 p. 8°.
Repr.: Jahresberichte der Kgl. Ungarischen geologischen Reichsanstalt für
1910.

1. Geology, Europe.
N. Y. P. L.   August 9, 1913.

NL 0438566   NN

QE267 Lóczy, Lajos, 1891–
.H97LS Beiträge zur geologie und paläontologie des Villányer und
Báner gebirges (Ungarn) ... Budapest, Hofbuchdr. V.
Hornyánszky, 1915.
xxxii, 101 p. illus., vi pl., fold. map., 2 fo'd. diagr. 30ᶜᵐ.
Inaug.-diss.—Zürich.
Lebenslauf.
Each plate preceded by leaf with descriptive letterpress.
"Einschlägige literatur": p. vi; "Verzeichnis der benützten ... literatur":
p. 7–20.

1. Geology—Hungary.   2. Paleontology—Hungary.

NL 0438567   ICU DI-GS ICRL MH

Lóczy, Lajos, 1891–
Beiträge zur geologie Westserbiens. Mit tafel 1. Von dr.
Ludwig v. Lóczy ... Budapest, Druck des Franklin-verein,
1918.
cover-title, ₁115,–131 p. fold. map. 26 cm.
"Separatabdruck aus dem 'Földtani közlöny,' bd. xlviii, 1918."

1. Geology—Serbia.

QE287.L6   23–2637 rev

NL 0438568   DLC

Lóczy, Lajos, 1891–
Monographie der Villányer Callovien-Ammoniten. Buda-
pest, Institutum Regni Hungariae Geologicum, 1915.
₁255,–502 p. illus., 14 plates, tables (1 fold.) 30 cm. (Geologica
Hungarica, t. 1, fasc. 3–4)
Bibliography : p. 261–274.

1. Ammonoidea.   2. Cephalopoda, Fossil.   i. Title: Villányer
Callovien-Ammoniten.   (Series)

G S 29–167 rev*
U. S. Geol. Survey. Libr.
for Library of Congress   ₁r54b⅜₁

NL 0438569   DI-GS TxU

Lóczy, Lajos, 1891–
My geological researches in western Servia. An account
of the expedition to Servia 1917–1918. With a geological
map, tree ₁!₁ tables of sections and four figures. By Lewis
de Lóczy ... Budapest, Printed by: "G. Bethlen" typogr.
comp. lt., 1927.
cover-title, ₁46,–88 p. incl. illus., tables. iv pl. (incl. fold. col. map)
2 fold. diagr. 28 cm.
Copyright by Geological review (Földtani szemle, vol. i, part 1)
In Appendix with the short report of L. de Lóczy, sen.: Recherches
sur la géologie de la Serbie occidentale.
1. Geology—Serbia.   ii. Lóczy, Lajos, 1849–1920.   iii. Title.

G S 27–383 rev
U. S. Geol. Survey. Libr.   203 (596) qL81g
for Library of Congress   ₁r54c⅜₁

NL 0438570   DI-GS

TN876
T9D3 Lóczy, Lajos, 1891 —
Report on the oil-geology of the neo-
geneous basin of İçel-Adana-Hatay and on
the present exploratory activities of the
Maden Tetkik ve Arama Enstitüsü. [Ankara,
1949]
20 l.
Contains Preliminary geological map of the
western part of Adana Basin, by L. DeLoczy,
and a Preliminary geological map of the eastern part of the Adana, Hatay Basin, scale
1:100 000, by Staff of M.T.A.Institute.

NL 0438571   DI

LÓCZY, Louis.

See LÓCZY , Lajos.

Lóczy, Ludwig
See
Lóczy, Lajos.

Lóczi Lóczy, Lajos, 1849–1920
see
Lóczy, Lajos, 1849–1920.

Lod, *Israel*
see
Lydda, *Israel.*

Loda, Paul.
Die uebertragung der ausuebung des niessbrauchs.
(Auszug).
Inaug. diss. Breslau, n.d.

NL 0438576   ICRL DLC

---

017   Loda, Ill.—A. Herr Smith and E. E.
L82f   Smith public library.
Finding list, July, 1899.   Paxton,
Ill., 1899.
22p.

NL 0438577   IU

Lodares, Baltasar de, padre

see

Baltasar de Lodares, padre.

Lodares Girón, R.
R. Lodares Giron La expiacion. Poema.
Madrid, Nueva imprenta y libreria de San Jose,
1885.

NL 0438579   NNH

Lodato Cossentino, Francesco.
Sul riordinamento dei tributi locali; note alla
legge comunale e provinciale 10 febbraio 1889.
Palermo, coi tipi del "Giornale di Sicilia", 1893.
98 p.
"From Crispi's library." Ms. note of H. N.
Gay on cover.

NL 0438580   MH

Lodberg (Jacobus). De coloribus. Specim.
physiol. 54 pp. sm. 4°. Hafnie, J. P. Bochen.
Lodr. ₁1600₁.

NL 0438581   DNLM

Lodberg, Thorvald.
Stænderdeputeret Ole Christian Kirk og nogle slægthistoriske
undersøgelser fra hans fødesogn Stadil, af Thorv. Lodberg.
Lemvig, G. Nielsen, 1950. 61 p. port. 23cm.

1. Kirk, Ole Christian Christensen,   1788–1876.   2. Stadil, Denmark—
Geneal. 3. Kirk family.

NL 0438582   NN

Lodberg, Thorvald.
...Tarben-Slægten fra Klitten; et Uddrag ved Torben Klinting. Nr. Nebel: V. Nielsen, 1932. 29 p. illus. (ports.),
geneal. table. 24cm.
Blank pages "Til Familieoptegnelser" at end.

745303A. 1. Tarben family.   I. Klinting, Torben, 1852–
editor.
N. Y. P. L.   February 18, 1935

NL 0438583   NN

Lodbrok, *pseud.*
see
Pihlstrand, Ragnar, 1850–1914.

Lodbrokar-quida, carmen Gothicum, famam regi
Ragnari Lodbrochi celebrans ...
see under [Krákumál]

Lodbrokar-quida; or, The death-song of Lodbroc ..
see under Krákumál.

Lodde (A.) ₁1866– ₁. *De l'emploi du chlor-
hydrate d'hyoscine chez les aliénés. 90 pp.
4°. Paris, 1891. No. 279.

NL 0438587   DNLM

Lodder (D.) *De methodo Petitiana in hernio-
tomia. 2 p. l., 37 pp. 8°. Lugd. Bat., C. C. van
der Hoek, 1855.

NL 0438588   DNLM PPC

Lodder, Jacomina.
Die anaskosporogenen hefen. Amsterdam,
N. V. Noord-Hollandsche Uitgeversmaatschappij,
1934–
v. illus. 26cm. (Centraalbureau voor
Schimmelcultures, Amsterdam. Hefesammlung, 2)
Profeschrift - Utrecht.
"Autorenregister": v.1, p.[246]–248.

1. Fungi. I. Title. II. Series.

NL 0438589   IEN IaU NcU LU NNC CU MtBC OU DLC CtY

VOLUME 338

Lodder, Jacomina.
    The anascosporogenous yeasts, by J. Lodder.
Tr. by Adolph Kadner. [Berkeley, Calif.] 1936.
    4 p. l., 394 numb. l., 15 l.   27 cm.
    Type-written copy.
    Pagination of original is also indicated.
    Translation supported by Works progress admin-
istration, project no. 431.
    Original German text a peared in Verhande-
lingen der Koninklijke akademie van wetenschappen
te Amsterdam, Afdooling natuurkunde (tweede
sectie) dool XXXII, as v. 2 of "Die hefesammlung
des 'Centraal bureau veer schimmelcultures."

    Beiträge zu einer monographie der hefcarton."
    Includes references.

NL   0438591   CU

Q57
.A533
deel 28,   Baarn, Netherlands.   Centraalbureau voor **Schimmelcul-**
no. 1, etc.   **tures.**
    Die Hefesammlung des Centraalbureau voor Schimmelcul-
tures. Beiträge zu einer Monographie der Hefearten. Amsterdam, Koninklijke Akademie van Wetenschappen, 1931-
42.

Lodder, Jacomina.
    The yeasts; a taxonomic study, by J. Lodder and N. J. W.
Kreger-van Rij. Amsterdam, North-Holland Pub. Co.,
1952.
    xi, 713 p. illus. 25 cm.
    A condensation and revision of three monographs: Die sporogenen
Hefen, von N. M. Stelling-Dekker in 1931; Die anaskosporogenen
Hefen. 1. Hälfte, von J. Lodder in 1934; 2. Hälfte, von H. A. Diddens
und J. Lodder in 1942.
    Includes bibliographies.
    1. Yeast.   i. Kreger-van Rij, N. J. W., joint author.

    QR151.L76   589.91   53—30397

    PPJ OOxM IU DI NNBG OO OCU
    MtBC MtU WaSpG WaTC TU PBL NcD PPT PPF PSt PPLankH
    ICU ViU CLSU OU MtU ICIU DNAL CaBVaU AAP OkU IdU
NL   0438593   DLC OrCS CU TxU IaU ICJ NcRS NNC MB

Lodder, Johannes.
    The anascosporogenous yeasts
        see   Lodder, Jacomina.

Lodder, Johannes.
    Proeven omtrent den invloed van onverhitte **voedings-**
bodems voor den groei en virulentie van bacteriën en voor de
gifvorming door diphtheriebacillen ... door Johannes Lodder
... Utrecht, H. J. Smits, 1927.
    4 p. l., 70 p., 1 l. incl. tables. pl. 24ᶜᵐ.
    Proefschrift—Utrecht.
    "Literatuurlijst": 1 l. at end.
    "Stellingen" (2 p.) laid in.
    1. Bacteriology—Cultures and culture media. 2. Diphtheria—Bacteri-
ology.
    Library of Congress   QR66.L6 1927   36—35811
                               (a44c1)   (616.01) 580.95

NL   0438596   DLC ICU ICRL

Wason   Lodder, Johannes.
BV3355   Tropendokter; schetzen uit een zendings-
L82   ziekenhuis op Java, door N. Vermeer (pseud.)
          Nijkerk, G.F.Callenbach (194-?)
              230 p. 23cm.

              1. Missions--Java. 2. Missions, Medical
          --Java. I. Title.

NL   0438597   NIC OCl

(Lodder, Johannes)
    Tropendoktor, Skizzen aus einem Missionsspital auf Java,
von Dr. N. Vermeer (pseud. Berechtigte Übersetzung aus
dem Holländischen von Herrn Missionar Huber in Basel)
Basel, Basler Missionsbuchhandlung (1941)
    173, (1) p. 19 cm.

    1. Missions—Java. 2. Missions, Medical.   i. Title.

    BV3355.L63   48–42980 rev ‡

NL   0438598   DLC

Lodder (Kommer). * Jets over de zweetsecre-
tie. 1 p. l., 47 pp. 8°. *Leiden, P. Somerwil,*
1861.

NL   0438599   DNLM

Lodder, Victor de.
    Comptabilité notariale (méthode spéciale) par Victor de
Lodder ... Louvain, Imprimerie Polleunis & Ceuterick, 1902.
    283 p. incl. tables. 24ᶜᵐ.

    1. Notaries—France. 2. Notaries—Accounting.
                                            43–31103
    Library of Congress   HF5686.N6L6

NL   0438600   DLC

96.04
L82   Lodder, W
         Handboek voor de bloemist.   Amsterdam,
         "Kosmos",

             1. Floriculture. Handbooks, manuals, etc.
         I. Lodder, G   joint author.

NL   0438601   DNAL

BR
65
.C63   Lodder, Willem, 1884-
L82   De godsdienstige en zedelijke denkbeelden
        van l Clemens ... door Willem Lodder ... (Lei-
        den, N.v.boekdrukkerij v/h,L. van Nifterik Hz.,
        1915)
            viii,242,(2),iv p. 23ᶜᵐ.
            Proefschrift--Groningen.
            Bibliography: p.7-13.
            "Stellingen": p.(1)-iv at end.

            1.Clemens Romanus. Epistola ad Corinthios.I.

NL   0438602   MiU NcD ICRL NjP CtY MH IU PBm PU CtY-D

Lodder, Willem, 1884-
    De historische betrouwbaarheid van het Nieuwe
Testament in het licht der twintigste eeuw. Derde
bijgewerkte druk. Wageningen, H. Veenman &
Zonen, 1941.
    128 p.

NL   0438603   MH-AH

Lodder, Willem, 1884-
    Met Paulus op reis. Baarn, Bosch & Keuning (1951)
    248 p. maps. 20 cm. (Bibliotheek van boeken bij de Bijbel)

    1. Paul, Saint, apostle. 2. Bible. N. T.—History of contemporary
events, etc.   (Series)
    Harvard Univ. Library   A 52–325
    for Library of Congress

NL   0438604   MH

DS
116
J87L6   Lodder, Willem, 1884-
         Die Schätzung des Quirinus bei Flavius Josephus; eine Unter-
         suchung: hat sich Flavius Josephus in der Datierung der bekannten
         Schätzung (Luk. 2, 2) geirrt? Von W. Lodder. Leipzig, Dörff-
         ling & Franke, 1930.
             96 p. 24cm.

             Bibliographical footnotes.

             1. Jesus Christ--Chronology. 2. Rome--Census. 3. Josephus,
         Flavius. Antiquitates judaicae. 4. Quirinus, Publius Sulpicius.
         I. Title.

NL   0438605   CBPac TxFTC NjPT ICU MH-AH OCH NIC NcWsW

Lodder, William B.
    Films on chemical subjects, 1946
        see under   Chemical Society of Washington,
Washington, D. C.

Lodders, Antonius Gerardus Maria.
    Huismoeder en zienster ... Heerlen,
Uitgave R.K. Uitgeverij Joh. Roosenboom,
1952.
    63 p.

NL   0438607   DCU

Lodders, Rudolf.
    Industriebau und Architekt, und ihre gegenseitige Beein-
flussung, ein Vortrag. Hamburg, Phönix-Verlag, 1946.
    40 p. illus. 21 cm. (Schriftenreihe des Bundes Deutscher Archi-
tekten, Heft 1)

    1. Industrial buildings.   i. Title.   (Series: Bund Deutscher
Architekten. Schriftenreihe, Heft 1)

    NA6400.L6   725.4   53–26500

NL   0438608   DLC OrU NjP IU MH

Lodders, Rudolf.
    Von der Persönlichkeit des Architekten; eine Studie zur
Berufsgeschichte. Hamburg, Phönix-Verlag, 1948.

    43 p. illus., ports. (Bundes deutscher Architekten.
Schriftenreihe, 5)

NL   0438609   MH

Lodderstaedt (Henricus Guilelmus). * De
typho Halis anctunino a. 1848 observato. 29 pp.
8°. *Halis Sax. typ. Schmidtianis,* 1848.

NL   0438610   DNLM PPC

Lodderstaedt (Wilhelm) (1851-   ). * Ueber
parasitäre Sycosis. 36 pp. 8°. *Berlin, G. Lange,*
(1876).

NL   0438611   DNLM ICRL

Loddeweyckx (Hubertus). * De clysteribus
et eorum in morbis usu. 1782.
In: Louvain Diss. 8°. Lovanii 1795, ii, 150–152.

NL   0438612   DNLM

Loddfáfnismál
        see
    Edda Sæmundar. *Loddfáfnismál.*

VOLUME 338

B
463521
Loddi, Serafino Maria.
Genealogia di s. Antonino, arcivescovo di Firenze, e della famiglia de' Frilli tratte da'libri, e documenti pubblici, e compilate esattamente dal padre lettore fr. Serafino Maria Loddi ... Firenze, Nella Stamperia di F. Moücke, 1732.
40p. geneal.tables(part fold.)

1. Antonino, Saint, abp. of Florence, 1389-1459. 2. Frilli family.

NL 0438614   IU

Loddiger, Ernst, Baron Campenhausen-.
See
Campenhausen-Loddiger, Ernst, Baron.

Loddiges, Conrad, & sons.
The botanical cabinet, consisting of coloured delineations of plants, from all countries, with a short account of each, directions for management, &c. &c. By Conrad Loddiges & sons. The plates by George Cooke ... London, J. & A. Arch [etc.] 1817-33.
20 v. 2000 col. pl. 21ᶜᵐ.
Engr. title-pages.
Plates colored by hand.

1. Flowers. 2. Plants, Cultivated.   I. Cooke, George, 1781-1834, illus.   II. Title.

CA 12-150b

Library of Congress   SB407.L82

CU InU PU MBH MiU ViU
NL 0438616   DLC OU NIC PPAmP MB MH WaU OrCS FU WU

Loddiges, Conrad, & sons.
Catalogue of plants, which are sold by Conrad Loddiges & sons, nursery & seedsmen, at Hackney, near London. The eleventh edition. London, Printed by W. Wilson, 1818.
51 p. 16½ x 20ᶜᵐ.

Agr 34-555

Library, U. S. Dept. of   Agriculture 452.5L82
[SB113]

NL 0438617   DNAL

Loddiges, Conrad, & sons.
Catalogue of plants, which are sold by Conrad Loddiges and sons, nurserymen, at Hackney, near London. 12th ed. London, 1820.

On verso of t.-p.: The numbers placed after the names refer to the figures in The botanical cabinet.

NL 0438618   MdBP MH-A

Loddiges, Conrad, & sons.
Catalogue of plants in the collection of Conrad Loddiges & sons, nurserymen at Hackney, near London. Ed. 14. 8°. pp. 78. London, 1826. (In their Botanical cabinet, v. 18.)
—— Ed. 16. 16°. pp. 85. London, 183⁶

NL 0438619   MBH DSI

Loddiges, Conrad, & sons.
Orchideæ, in the collection of Conrad Loddiges and sons, Hackney, near London, arranged according to Dr. Lindley's genera and species; with their native countries, years of introduction, and references to figures. London, Printed by Wilson and Ogilvy [1842]
44, [2] p. 16½ᶜᵐ.

1. Orchidaceæ.

Agr 4-475

Library, U. S. Dept. of   Agriculture, no. 452.3L82.

NL 0438620   DNAL MBH

TN210
N59
no.5
pt.2
Lodding, William
New Jersey's potential feldspar resources. II. Mineral technology and economic evaluation. New Brunswick, Rutgers University Press, 1951.
vii [1] 70 p.   illus., diagrs., tables.
21 cm. (Rutgers University, New Brunswick, N. J. Bureau of Mineral Research. Bulletin no. 5, pt. II).

1. Feldspar - New Jersey. 2. Feldspar - Testing. (Series)

NL 0438621   DI

Loddington, William, 1626?-1711, supposed author.
The Christian a Quaker
see under title

Mhm69
1685
L82
Loddington, William, 1626?-1711.
The good order of truth justified; wherein our womens meetings and order of marriage (by some more especially opposed) are proved agreeable to Scripture and sound reason ... [London] A.Sowle,1685.
15p. 19½cm.

NL 0438623   CtY

[Loddington, William] 1626?-1711.
Plantation uuork the work of this generation. Written in true-love to all such as are weightily inclined to transplant themselves and families to any of the English plantations in America ... London, Printed for B. Clark, 1682.
1 p. l., 18 p. 20ᶜᵐ.
Signed: W. L.
"By some attributed to George Fox."—Winsor, Narr. & crit. hist., v. 3, p. 496-497.
"An abstract of some passages out of divers letters from America relating to Pennsylvania ...": p. 17-18.
1. Gt. Brit.—Colonies—North America. 2. Pennsylvania—Descr. & trav.   I. Fox, George, 1624-1691, supposed author.   II. Title.

Library of Congress   F152.L78

8—10572

PHC
NL 0438624   DLC PHi PSC-Hi CtY MiWi-C CSmH RPJCB

Loddington, William, 1626?-1711.
Quakerism no Paganism; or, a friendly reply to W.R. his unfriendly discourse, intituled Quakerism is paganism ... By W.L., a lover of peace more than of parties.   London, 1674.

NL 0438625   PSC-Hi

Zcia
Mhm69
1682
L8
Loddington, William, d.1711.
A salutation to the church of God the spouse of Christ ... London, T.Cooke, 1682.
1p.ℓ., 22p. 13½cm.

NL 0438626   CtY PHC

Loddington, William, 1626?-1711.
The twelve pagan principles or opinions, for which Thomas Hick's hath published The Quaker to be no Christian, seriously considered, and presented to Mr. N.L., citizen of London. By W.L., a lover of every man whose conversation is honest. [Lond?] 1674.

NL 0438627   PHC

Loddington, William, 1626?-1711.
Tythe no gospel maintenance for gospel ministers.   London, 1695.

NL 0438628   PSC-Hi

Loddo-Canepa, Francesco, ed.
Dispacci di Corte, ministeriali e vice-regi concernenti gli affari politici, giuridici ed ecclesiastici del regno di Sardegna, 1720-1721. Roma, 1934.
xxvii, 271 p. (Società nazionale per la storia del Risorgimento italiano. Biblioteca scientifica, 2.ser., Fonti, 1)

NL 0438629   MH NN DLC-P4 CtY NcU

Loddo-Canepa, Francesco.
... Inventario della R. Segreteria di stato e di guerra del regno di Sardegna (1720-1848)
see under   Sardinia (Kingdom) Segreteria di stato e di guerra. Archivio.

Loddo-Canepa, Francesco.
La Sardegna attraverso i secoli. Torino, Società di Monteponi [1952]
185 p. illus., ports., maps, facsims. 33 cm.

1. Sardinia—Hist.   I. Title.

DG975.S31L6   53-39421

NL 0438631   DLC NN IU

Loddon, D   L
Do they remember? London, Mitre Press [1933]
216 p.

NL 0438632   MH

I
3045
.74
v.2
Loddon, Eng. (Hundred)—Directors and acting guardians of the poor.
Some of the rules, orders, and bye-laws, made from time to time, by the Directors and acting guardians of the poor, in the hundreds of Loddon and Clavering, in the county of Norfolk. Norwich[1781]

NL 0438633   ICN

Lode, Alois, 1866—
Hygienische Bildung; Entwurf einer Rektoratsrede. (In: Innsbruck Universität. Bericht über das Studienjahr 1910-11. Innsbruck, 1912. 8°. p. 69-86.)

1. Hygiene.—Study and teaching.
N.Y.P.L.   July 25, 1913.

NL 0438634   NN

Lode, Alois, 1866–
Hygienische methoden der luftuntersuchung. Von Alois Lode ... (In Abderhalden, Emil, ed. Handbuch der biologischen arbeitsmethoden ... Berlin, 1929. 25ᶜᵐ. abt. IV, Angewandte chemische und physikalische methoden. t. II [hft. 2] [1929]. p. [265]-362. illus.)
Bibliographies interspersed.

1. Air—Analysis.   I. Title.   A C 36-2797

Title from Ohio State   Univ.
Library of Congress   [QH324.A3 1920 abt. 4, t. II]
[2]   (574.072)

NL 0438635   OU

Lode (Heinrich) [1814-60]. * De talipede varo et curvatura manus talipomanus dicta. 2 p. l., 32 pp. 1 pl. 4°. Berolini, I. Weckerle [1837].

NL 0438636   DNLM

VOLUME 338

WO
L821L
1843
LODE, Heinrich, 1814-1860
Lehrbuch des chirurgischen Verbandes; zum Gebrauch für Lehrende und Lernende. Berlin, Förstner, 1843.
viii, 308 p. illus.

NL 0438637   DNLM NNC OClW-H

Lode, J. W.
Auditeuren Lss diotamen ad protocollum, rorande riksens råds förhållande sedan sistledne riksdag. Stockholm, 1772.

NL 0438638   NN

Lode, J W
Secreteraren Lodes Memorial, angående en utkommen skrift, kallad, En patriots tankar, om grund-lagarnes nödwändiga förbättring; ingifwit til högloft. Ridderskapet och adelen den 15 augusti 1769. Stockholm, Tryckt hos Wennberg & Nordström, 1769.
₍4₎ p. 20.5 cm. (In Stridskrifter om lagar, bd. 4, n:o 20)

NL 0438639   MH-BA

Lode (Joh. Clemens). Vom Tripper in Ansehung seiner Natur und Geschichte. 218 pp., 1 l. 12°. *Kopenhagen u. Leipzig, Heineck u. Faber,*1774.
Bound with: Hirschel (L. E.) Gedanken, [etc.] 1°° *Milan.* 1774.

NL 0438640   DNLM

S469
.R92P63
Lode, O. V., joint author.

Filippov, Veniamin Dmitrievich.
Совхоз "Победа." Москва, Изд-во Министерства совхозов СССР, 1955.

ID1491
R92S64
Lode, O V
Возрождение колхозов (восстановление сельского хозяйства в освобождённом от немецко-фашистских оккупантов Солнечногорском районе, Московской области) Москва, "Сельхозгиз," 1943.
46, ₍2₎ p. 14 x 11 cm.

1. Collective farms.   · Solnechnogorsk (Region)
i. Title.   *title transliterated:* Vozrozhdenie kolkhozov.

HD1491.R92S64   49-31647

NL 0438642   DLC DNAL

Lode, Rutofle de, *pseud.*
see
Rutledge, James *or* John James, 1742-1794.

Lode, Urban Huttleston Rogers Broughton, *baron Fairhaven of*
see Fairhaven, Urban Huttleston Rogers Broughton, *baron,* 1896–

Lode, Walter.
... Der einfluss der mittleren hauptspannung auf das fliessen der metalle; mitteilung aus dem Institut für angewandte mechanik der Universität Göttingen, von dr. phil. Walter Lode. Mit 12 abbildungen. Berlin, VDI-verlag g. m. b. h., 1928.
1 p. L., 15, ₍1₎ p. illus., tables, diagrs. 29½ᶜᵐ. (Forschungsarbeiten auf dem gebiete des ingenieurwesens ... hft. 303)
Bibliographical foot-notes.

1. Metals—Testing.   i. Title.

Library of Congress   TA460.L6   28-25766

NL 0438645   DLC ICRL MiU NIC

Lodé-Zwercher, Lily.
Allemagne, boutefeu du monde. Saint-Étienne, Éditions Dumas ₍1945₎
127 p. 19 cm.

1. Germany. 2. Pangermanism. 3. National characteristics, German. i. Title.

DD119.L58   50-57440

NL 0438646   DLC

YA
9276
Lode and Placer Prospecting and Mining assn. [Prospectus, objects, etc.]   Denver, Col., 1880.
14p.

NL 0438647   DLC

Lode Baekelmans ter eere, 1945 ... Antwerpen, De Sikkel, 1946.
2 v. illus., ports., fold. map, facsims. 26 cm.
"Van dit boek werden 300 exemplaren gedrukt ... genummerd van 1 tot 300. Dit is nummer 175."
Bibliographical footnotes.

1. Baekelmans, Lode, 1879–

PT6401.B22Z7   920.2   48-21028*

NL 0438648   DLC CtY CLU ICU NNU-W NN OU

LODE al merito [; poetry]. 2a ed. con appendice. Roma, tip. fratelli Monaldi, 1872.

pp. 27.
Half-title:- Al merito esimio dei professori di sapienza che a compenso dei benefici reciviti dal governo pontificio giurarono pel nuovo ordine di cose, etc.

NL 0438649   MH

Case
Y
712
.L 78
LODE della famosissima & nobilissima citta di Firenze & del suo S.Duca & di suoi figliuoli & casata & di molti altri signori & caualieri ₍Fiorenza,1549₎
₍48₎p. 15cm.

Title vignette (coat of arms)
Signatures: A⁴, b-d⁴, E-F⁴.
In verse.

NL 0438650   ICN

LODE e glorie fatte alla persona del q.illustrissimo ed eccellentiss.signor Rommaso Moresini,governator de galioni in armata. Bassano, [16-].

nar. 24°. pp. (12). Vign.

NL 0438651   MH

Lode-star gold mining company.
Lode-star gold mining company; organized April 18, 1865, under the laws of the state of New York. 300,000 shares; par value $10. Works near Central City, Gilpin County, Colorado Territory. Company's office, no. 326 West Thirty-second street, New-York city ... New York, Press of G. C. Rand & Avery, Boston, 1865.
31 p. 23½ᶜᵐ.
Cover-title: Statement of the Lode-star gold mining co. and description of its water-powers and lode-claims in the Clear Creek Valley, Gilpin County, Colorado Territory.

1. Gold mines and mining—Colorado.

22-14475

Library of Congress   TN423.Z6L7

NL 0438652   DLC

PT5854
.L7S4
1848
LODEESEN,J D.
De schipbreukeling,oorspronkelijk romantisch tooneelspel in vijf bedrijven;door J.D.Lodeesen. Gedrukt voor rekening van den auteur. Amsterdam,1848.
[8],109 p. 19½cm.

NL 0438653   ICU

PT5854
.L77 I5
Lodeizen, Hans, 1924-1950.
Het innerlijk behang, en andere gedichten ₍door₎ J. C. Bloem, J. Greshoff en A. Morriën samengesteld₎ Amsterdam, G. A. van Oorschot, 1952.
198 p. port., facsim. 21 cm.

i. Title.

A 52-8792

Harvard Univ. Library
for Library of Congress   ₍3₎

NL 0438654   MH NIC PU NN NNC DLC

Hgk2
L821
In5
1954
Lodeizen, Hans, 1924-1950.
Het innerlijk behang; en andere gedichten. Amsterdam, G.A. Van Oorschot, 1954.
185 p. port. 20 cm.

NL 0438655   CtY

Lodeman, August, 1842-1902.
German conversation-tables, a new method for teaching German conversation in classes. With copious notes. By Augustus Lodeman ... New York, Holt & Williams ₍etc.₎; Boston, S. R. Urbino, 1871.
36 p. 19ᵐ.

1. German language—Conversation and phrase-books.

Library of Congress   PF3121.L7   10-27449

NL 0438656   DLC MH MiU NN NjP PU

Lodeman, August, 1842-1902, ed.

Fischer, Paul David, 1836-1920.
... Germany and the Germans, containing the greater part of P. D. Fischer's Betrachtungen eines in Deutschland reisenden Deutschen, edited, with notes by A. Lodeman ... New York, Boston ₍etc.₎ Silver, Burdett and company ₍1901₎

Lodeman, August, 1842-1902.   6879.21
Grundriss der Geschichte der deutschen Literatur, nebst einer kurzen Einleitung über die Entwicklung der deutschen Sprache. Entworfen von A. Lodeman.
Boston. Schoenhof & Moeller. 1874. iv, (1), 65 pp. 18½ cm.

D3453 — Germany. Lit. Hist.

NL 0438658   MB NIC MWelC MiU PSC CtY

VOLUME 338

Lodeman, August, 1842-1902.

Methods of teaching modern languages: papers on the value and on methods of modern language instruction. By A. Marshall Elliott, Calvin Thomas, E. S. Joynes, W. T. Hewett, F. C. de Sumichrast, A. Lodeman, F. M. Warren, E. H. Babbitt, C. H. Grandgent, O. B. Super, C. F. Kroeh, W. Stuart Macgowan, H. C. G. von Jagemann. Boston, D. C. Heath & co., 1893.

NL 0438660 MH

LODEMAN, August, 1842-1902.
The place and function of the normal school; a paper read before the Michigan School-Master's Club, at Ann Arbor, October 22, 1887. [Ann Arbor? 1887?]

23 cm. pp. 11.
Without title-page. Caption title.

NL 0438660 MH

Lodeman, August, 1842-1902.
Practical and psychological tests of modern language study, by A. Lodeman ... Boston, D. C. Heath & co., 1892.

1 p. l., 19 p. 18cm.
"References": p. 18-19.

1. Languages, Modern—Study.
E 10-1736
Library, U. S. Bur. of   Education

NL 0438661 DHEW

Lodeman, August, 1842-1902.
The student's manual of exercises for translating into German, with full vocabulary, notes, references, and general suggestions. Prepared and arranged to accompany Brandt's German grammar, by A. Lodeman ... New York & London, G. P. Putnam's sons, 1885.

87 p. 19½cm.

1. German language—Composition and exercises. 2. Brandt, Hermann Carl George, 1850-   Grammar of the German language.
10-27995†
Library of Congress   PF3111.L65 1885

NL 0438662 DLC MH CU OCU NcRS PU

Lodeman, August, 1842-1902.
The student's manual of exercises for translating into German, with full vocabulary, notes, references, and general suggestions. Prepared and arranged to accompany Brandt's German grammar by A. Lodeman ... Boston, Allyn and Bacon, 1888.

87 p. 19cm. [With Brandt, Hermann C. G. A first book in German ... [4th ed.] Boston, 1888]

1. German language—Composition and exercises. 2. Brandt, Hermann Carl George, 1850-1920.
10—25040
Library of Congress   PF3111.B72

NL 0438663 DLC OO

LODEMAN, Ernest Gustavus, d. 1896.
Black-knot of plums and cherries and methods of treatment. Ithaca, N.Y. 1894.

pp. (24). Vignette and woodcuts. (CORNELL UNIVERSITY - Agricultural experiment station. Bulletin, 81.)
"Bibliography," p. (4).

NL 0438664 MH MBH MH-A

634.12 Lodeman, Ernest Gustavus.
L82d   Diseases of the potato.   Ithaca, N.Y., 1896.
250-283p. (Cornell university—Agricultural experiment station—Horticultural division. Bulletin 113. February, 1896.

NL 0438665 IU MBH

Lodeman, Ernest Gustavus.
—— Dwarf apples. Ithaca. 1896. 8°. pp. [31]. Illustr. (Cornell university — Agricultural experiment station. Bulletin, 116.)

NL 0438666 MH-A MBH

Lodeman, Ernest Gustavus, joint author.
Forcing-house miscellanies
see under Bailey, Liberty Hyde, 1858-1954.

Lodeman, Ernest Gustavus. The grafting of grapes. Ithaca. 1894. 8°. pp. [22]. Illustr. (Cornell university — Agricultural experiment station. Bulletin, 77.)

NL 0438668 MH-A MH MBH

Lodeman, Ernest Gustavus.
Pruning and training of grapes.
(In U. S. Dept. of agriculture. Yearbook, 1896, p. 499-542. illus 23cm. Washington, 1897)

1. Grape.
Agr 7-768
Library, U. S. Dept. of   Agriculture

NL 0438669 DNAL OU OCl OO MiU PPAmP

Lodeman, Ernest Gustavus, d. 1896.
Pruning and training of grapes. 1896.
p. 499-539. 23 cm.
Caption title.
Reprinted from the yearbook of the Dept. of agriculture for 1896.

NL 0438670 RPB

Lodeman, Ernest Gustavus
—— Some grape troubles of western New York. 8°. pp. [46]. il. [Ithaca, 1894]. (Cornell university. Agricultural experiment station. Bulletin no. 76.)

NL 0438671 MBH MH-A MH

Lodeman, Ernest Gustavus.
—— Spray calendar. Feb. 1895. [Ithaca. 1895]. Broadside. Illustr. (Cornell university — Agricultural experiment station.)
—— The same. Feb. 1896. [Ithaca. 1896.] Broadside. Illustr. (Cornell university — Agricultural experiment station. Bulletin, 114.)
—— The same. Feb. 1896. 2d ed., revised by H. P. Gould, April 1898. [Ithaca. 1898.] Broadside. Illustr. (Cornell university — Agricultural experiment station. Bulletin, 114.)

NL 0438672 MH-A

Lodeman, Ernest Gustavus
—— The spraying of orchards; apples, quinces, plums. 8°. pp. [34]. il. [Ithaca, 1895]. (Cornell university. Agricultural experiment station. Bulletin no. 86.)

NL 0438673 MBH MH MH-A

Lodeman, Ernest Gustavus
—— The spraying of orchards; the profits of spraying apple orchards; test of some fungicides and insecticides upon peach foliage; some novel insecticides and fungicides. 8°. pp. [40]. pl. 2. [Ithaca, 1893]. (Cornell university. Agricultural experiment station. Bulletin no. 60.)

NL 0438674 MBH MH

Lodeman, Ernest Gustavus, d. 1896.
The spraying of plants; a succinct account of the history, principles and practice of the application of liquids and powders to plants, for the purpose of destroying insects and *Fungi*; by E. G. Lodeman ... with a preface by B. T. Galloway ... New York and London, Macmillan and co., 1896.

xvii, 399 p. incl. front. (port.) illus. 18cm. (*Half-title:* The rural science series, ed. by L. H. Bailey)

1. Spraying.
4—14484
Library of Congress   SB953.L6

MiU ICJ NN CaBVaU MH-A PU NIC TU ViU NNBG
NL 0438675 DLC Or IdU-SB MtU NcRS MBH MH OO OCl

Lodeman, Ernest Gustavus, d. 1896.
Spraying of plants. London, 1897.

NL 0438676 Nh

632.94 Lodeman, Ernest Gustavus, d. 1896.
L82s   The spraying of plants; a succinct account of the history, principles and practice of the application of liquids and powders to plants, for the purpose of destroying insects and *Fungi*; by E. G. Lodeman ... with a preface by B. T. Galloway ... New York and London, Macmillan and co., 1902.

xvii, 399 p. incl. front. (port.) illus. 18cm. (*Half-title:* The rural science series, ed. by L. H. Bailey)

NL 0438677 LU FMU NNBG KEmT CLSU CU

Lodeman, Ernest Gustavus, d. 1896-
The spraying of plants, ... N.Y., Macmillan co 1903.

NL 0438678 OClGC

Lodeman, Ernest Gustavus, d. 1896.
Spraying of plants; ... N.Y. 1906. [c96]
399 p. illus. por. S.

NL 0438679 OCU I

Lodeman, Ernest Gustavus, d. 1896.
The spraying of plants; a succinct account of the history ... N.Y. and London, Macmillan and co., 1910.
399 p. (Half-title: The rural science series, ed. by L.H. Bailey)

NL 0438680 OOxM

Lodeman, Ernest Gustavus, d. 1896.
The spraying of plants; a succinct account of the history, principles and practice of the application of liquids and powders to plants, for the purpose of destroying insects and Fungi; by E. G. Lodeman ... with a preface by B. T. Galloway... New York, The Macmillan company, London, Macmillan & co., ltd., 1916.
xvii, 399 pl. incl. front., (port.) illus. 19.5 cm. (Half-title: The rural science series, ed. by L. H. Bailey)
"Reprinted, January, 1916."

"Thesis presented to the Cornell university for the degree of master of science." Verso of t.-p.
1. Spraying. I. Ser.

NL 0438682 ViU OU OLak

Lodeman, Frank Emile.

Pas Saladin.
Le pas Saladin; an old French poem of the third crusade ... by Frank E. Lodeman ... Baltimore, Md., 1897.

VOLUME 338

Lodemann, August.
    see Lodeman, August, 1842-1902.

Lodemann (Carl). "Bericht über die im Kieler academischen Hospital während der Epidemie in den Jahren 1871-2 behandelten Pockenkranken. 29 pp. 4°. Kiel, C. F. Mohr, 1872.
In: Schrift. d. Univ. zu Kiel. xix 1872, vii. med. I.

NL 0438685   DNLM

Lodemann (Carl Theodor Hans) [1890-   ].
*Ein Beitrag zur Pigmentierung der Conjunktiva und Cornea des Auges. 30 pp., 1 pl. 8°. Berlin, E. Ebering, 1917.

NL 0438686   DNLM ICRL CtY

Lodemann, Ernst, ed.
    Kodifiziertes internationales deutsches kriegsrecht in seinem wortlaut und geltungsbereich gegenüber dem ausland, zusammengestellt von Ernst Lodemann ... Berlin, G. Stilke, 1937.
    viii, 292 p. 23½ᵐ.
    French and German in parallel columns.
    Bibliography: p. [vii]-viii.

    1. War (International law) 2. Military law—Germany.   I. Title.

    Library of Congress   JX4507.L6   41-26102

NL 0438687   DLC NNC CtY-L

Lodemann, Georg, joint author.
                                    FOR OTHER EDITIONS
Kronacher, Carl, 1871-   SEE MAIN ENTRY
    Technik der haar- und wolleuntersuchung, von dr. dr. h. c. Carl Kronacher ... und dr. Georg Lodemann ... mit 214 zum teil mehrfarbigen abbildungen im text. Berlin, Wien, Urban & Schwarzenberg, 1930.

Lodemann, Hans, 1906-
    ... Die regionären Verschiedenheiten der menschlichen Haut... Göttingen, 1934.
    Inaug.-Diss. - Göttingen.
    Lebenslauf.
    "Schrifttum": p. [4]

NL 0438689   CtY MiU

Lodemann (Joannes Georgius) [1769-1846].
*Inquiritur in theoriam Weikardianam de hydrope cerebri, nec non in veram ejusdem morbi indolem. 36 pp. sm. 4°. Göttingae, J. G. Rosenbusch. [1792].

NL 0438690   DNLM PPC

Loden, Adolf.
    Der Lustfeuerwerker... Aufl. 2.
    Quedlinburg, Ernst, 1857.
    138 p.

NL 0438691   PPG

Loden, Adolf.
    Mano di Ferro, der kühne piraten-chef, oder: Der Tuneser in Palermo. Romantisches seeräubergemälde vor Adolf Loden ... Nordhausen, E. F. Fürst, 1840.
    2 v. 17ᶜᵐ.
    Vol. 1 wanting in L. C. copy.

    I. Title.

    Library of Congress   PT2424.L58M3 1840   18-7883

NL 0438692   DLC

Loden, Adolf.
    Rolgar, der fischer von Longueroc; die ermordung des Grafen Karl von Flandern zu Brügge. Romantisches gemälde der vorzeit von Adolf Loden.   Nordhausen, bei Ernst Friedrich Fürst, 1841.
    272 p. 15½cm.

NL 0438693   AzU

Loden, Jimmie H
    see
    James, Sonny.

Lodenius, Elias, 1877-1919.
839.7372   Noveller. Helsingfors, H. Schildt [1920]
L821N   154 p. 19 cm.

    "De flesta av föreliggande noveller och skisser ... ha tidigare varit publicerade, främst i Aftonposten."
    Full name: Karl Gustaf Elias Lodenius.

NL 0438695   NcD

Lodenius, Paul.
    Tidsgissel, nidvisor och mer melodiska melodier, av Paul Lodenius... Stockholm: A. Bonniers förlag [1928]. 156 p. 12°.

428285A.   1. Poetry, Swedish.   2. Title.
N. Y. P. L.   September 3, 1929

NL 0438696   NN MH

QW   Lodenkämper, Hans, 1907—
51   Entwickelung und heutiger Stand
L821e   der Lehre von der Pleomorphie und
1939   Zyklogenie der Bakterien auf Grund
        des Literaturstudiums und eigener
        Untersuchungen. [1. Aufl.], Halle,
        Niemeyer, 1939.
           110 p. (Schriften der Königsberger
        Gelehrten Gesellschaft. Naturwissenschaftliche Klasse. 15. Jahr., Heft 3)

NL 0438697   DNLM ICU N NbU MCM NjR NNC

BX 9473 Lodensteyn, Jodocus van, 1620-1677.
.L7   Beschouwinge van Zion; ofte,
(Rare)   Aandagten en opmerkingen over den
         tegenwoordigen toestand van't
         gereformeerde Christen volk... de
         vierde druk, vermeerderd met een
         voor-berigt. T'Amsterdam, J. van
         Hardenberg, 1718.
            250 p.

            1. Nederlandse Hervormde Kerk. I.
         Title.

NL 0438698   ICU

GW16   Lodensteyn, Jodocus van, 1620-1677.
L82   ... Beschouwinge van Zion: ofte, Aandagten
J   en opmerkingen over den tegenwoordigen toestand
         van't Gereformeerde Christen volk. Gestelt in
         eenige t'zamenspraken ... t'Amsterdam en in
         s'Gravenhage, Adrianus en Johannes Douci [etc.]
         1739.
            16p.l., 337,[15]p. 21cm.
            Contents.- [pt.1] Beschouwinge van Zion. -
         [pt.2] Geestelyke gedagten.

NL 0438699   NNUT

Safe   Lodensteyn, Jodocus van, 1620-1677.
BR1650   Beschouwinge van Zion; ofte aandagten en
.A2L82   opmerkingen over den tegenwoordigen toestand
1739   van 't Gereformeerde Christen Volk. Gestelt in
         eenige t' Zamenspraken. De sesden druk,
         vermeerderd mit een voor-berigt. Amsterdam,
         Adrianus, Adrianus en Johannes Douci; Ottho en Pieter van
         Thol, 1739.
            12, 337p., 11, 38p., 1. 21cm.
            Without separate title page, with this is
         bound: Zions wee-klagen, of droevige nagedagten, over het

         leeven en sterven van D. Jodocus van Lodensteyn
         uytgespooken in de gemeinte Jesu Christi tot
         Utrecht, door H. van Ryp. [38p at end]

            1. Nederlandse Hervormde Kerk--Doctrinal and
         controversial works. 2. Pietism--The Netherlands. 3. Reformed church in the Netherlands.
         I. Title. II. Lodensteyn, Jodocus van, 1620-1677. Zions wee-klagen.

NL 0438701   IEG

BX 9473 Lodensteyn, Jodocus van, 1620-1677.
.L7   Geestelyke gedagten; na sijn dood
(Rare)   uyt-gegeven; aangaande het wesen
         van 's menschen geluksaligheyd.
         T'Amsterdam, J. van Hardenberg, 1718.
            253-337 p. (With his Beschouwinge van
         Zion. Amsterdam, 1718)

NL 0438702   ICU

609.2   LODENSTEYN, Jodocus van, 1620-1677.
L821.4ge Geestelyke opwekker, voor het onver-
1732   loochende, doode, en geesteloose Christendom,
         Voorgestelt in X. predicatien,...De derde
         Druk, meer als de helft vermeerdert en
         verbetert uyt Lodensteyns eygene Schriften,
         door Everardus vander Hooght. Amsterdam,
         Adrianus en Johannes Douci, 1732.
            101,332p. 17cm.

NL 0438703   MH-AH NjNbS

609.2   LODENSTEYN, Jodocus van, 1620-1677.
L821.4ge Geestelyke opwekker, voor het onver-
1740   loochende, doode, en geesteloose Christendom.
         Voorgestelt in X. predicatien,....De tweede
         Druk meer als de helft vermeerdert, en ver-
         betert uyt Lodensteyns eygene Schriften,
         door Everardus vander Hooght. De vyfde druk.
         Amsteldam, Johannes Douci, 1740.
            109,332p. 16cm.

NL 0438704   MH-AH MH NN NjR NjNbS

UD8   Lodensteyn, Jodocus van, 1620-1677
L82h
            De Heerlykheyd van een waar Christelyk
         leven . . . Amsterdam: Jacobus van Hardenberg,
         1711.
            422p. 16cm

NL 0438705   NjNbS

Lodensteyn, Jodocus van, 1620-1677.
    Lodenstein. [Baarn, Hollandia Drukkerij, 1943]
    182 p. illus. 18 cm. [Uren met groote mystici. 1. reeks]
    Name of editor, M. J. A. de Vrijer, at head of title.

    1. Mysticism—Netherlands.   I. Vrijer, Marinus Johannes Antonie de, 1881-   ed.
    BV5080.L57   55-51543 ‡

NL 0438706   DLC NNUT TNV TxU

624.97   [LODENSTEYN, Jodocus van] 1620-1677
K77.4re   t' Samen-sprake nopende de sake der
1675   formulieren van gebeden en onderrichtingen, ende de paginge van D. Jacobus
         Coelman ... daer ontrent. Door Christianus Alethinus. Tot Rotterdam,
         gedruckt bij Henricus Goddaeus, boeckdrucker in den Oppert: anno 1675.
            40p. 15.5cm.
            No.4 in bound volume of Koelman's works.

NL 0438707   MH-AH

VOLUME 338

609.2
L821.4uyt
1695
LODENSTEYN, Jodocus van, 1620-1677
...Uyt-spanningen ... stichtelycke
liederen, en andere gedichten ... Met een
aanhangsel. Den vijfden druk verbetert
en vermeerdert. Tot Amsterdam, by de wed.
de Groot, op den nieuwen-dijck. En
t'Utrecht, by de wed. Klerck, op de Neude.
A.1695...
8p.l., 464,[15]p. music. 16.5cm.
At head of title: "J. van Lodensteyns".

Title vignettes.
Parts 2-4 with separate title-pages
(continuous paging.) Imprints: pt.2: 1693;
pt.3: 1694; pt.4: 1694.

NL 0438709 MH-AH MWA

Lodensteyn, Jodocus van, 1620-1677, *ed.*
Uitspanningen, behelzende eenige stichtelyke liederen,
geestige gedichten, en andere praktikale stoffen. 2. deel.
4. druk. t'Rotterdam, by R. van Doesburg, Boekverkooper,
1725.
[xviii], 127, [1] p. illus. 17 cm.
Bound with the editor's Uytspanningen. Amsterdam, 1727.
Includes hymns with tunes indicated by title.
"Bladt-wyser" ([1] p.) at end.

1. Hymns, Dutch. I. Title.

M2135.L6U9 1727   63-50624/M

NL 0438710 DLC

Lodensteyn, Jodocus van, 1620-1677, *ed.*
Uytspanningen, behelsende eenige stichtelyke liederen, en
andere gedichten. Verdeeld in vier deelen, met een aanhangsel. De 9. druk verbetert en vermeerdert. Tot Amsterdam, by F. Visscher, Boekverkooper, 1727.
[xvi], 464, [13]p. illus. 17 cm.
Unacc. or songs and hymns with tunes indicated by title.
"Blad-wyzer van de liederen" ([13] p.) at end.
Bound with the editor's Uitspanningen. t'Rotterdam, 1725.

1. Hymns, Dutch. I. Title.

M2135.L6U9 1727   63-50625/M

NL 0438711 DLC MH-AH ICU

---

xM2135
L6U9
1733
Lodensteyn, Jodocus van, 1620-1677.
J. van Lodensteyns Uytspanningen, behelfende
eenige stichtelyke liederen, en andere gedichten.
Verdeeld in vier deelen. Mit een aanhangsel.
De tiende druk verbetert en vermeerdert.
Amsterdam, E.Visscher, 1733.
4 pts.in 1v.([16],464,[11]p.) 16cm.

Unaccompanied melodies.

1. Hymns, Dutch. 2. Religious poetry, Dutch.
I. Title.

NL 0438712 IaU InU

Lodensteyn, Jodocus van, 1620-1677.
J. van Lodensteyns Uytspanningen, behelzende eenige stichtelyke liederen en andere gedichten. Verdeeld in vier deelen.
Met een aanhangzel. Den 11. druk merkelijk verbeterd en
met meerder voyzen vermeerderd ... Amsterdam, J. Kannewet
[1739?]
12 p. l., 464, [16] p. 16¾ᶜᵐ.
Added t.-p., engraved.
Principally unaccompanied melodies or songs with tunes indicated by
title.

———— 2. deel. 6. druk ... Rotterdam, P. Losel, 1739.
9 p. l., 3-127, [1] p. 16¾ᶜᵐ.
Bound with the main work.
Preface signed : Daniel Bongardt.
Supplementary material, including songs with tunes indicated by title.

1. Hymns, Dutch. I. Bongardt, Daniel, ed. II. Title.

46-34472
Library of Congress   M2135.L6U9

NL 0438714 DLC

SPEC COLL
M
2135
L6U9
1760
Lodensteyn, Jodocus van, 1620-1677;
J.van Lodensteyns Uyspanningen, behelzende eenige stichtelyke liederen
en andere gedichten. Verdeeld in veer
deelen. Met een aanhangzel. Den veer-
tiende druk merkelijk verbeterd, en op
een zoet vloeyende maat-zang gebragt ende
met doyzen vermeerderd. Amsterdam, J.
Kannewet, 1760.
4v. in 1. illus. 17cm.

NL 0438715 CLSU

609.2
L821.4uyt
1769
LODENSTEYN, Jodocus van, 1620-1677
...Uytspanningen, behelzende eenige
stigtelyke liederen en andere gedichten.
Verdeeld in vier deelen. Met een aanhangzel. Den vijftiende druk merkelijk
verbeterd/ en op een zoetbloeyende maat-
zang gebragt ende met voyzen vermeerderd.
Als mede tot gemak der zang-meesteren
hier by gevoegt een onderrigting, tot
gebruyk der geener die de op-gemelde

liederen, op de instrumente willen
speelen. Te Amsterdam, by Joannes
Kannewet, boekverkooper in de nes in de
gekroonde jugte bybel. 1769...
12p.l.(incl. title plate), 464,[21]p.
music. 16cm.
At head of title: J. van Lodensteyns.

Title vignette.
Pts.2-4 with individual half-title
pages.

NL 0438718 MH-AH IEG

Lodensteyn, Jodocus van, 1620-1667.
J. van Lodenstein wederleyt, ofte antwoort op
de korte aenmerckingen
see under title

609.2
L821.4we
1765
LODENSTEYN, Jodocus van, 1620-1677
De weegschaal van de onvolmaaktheden
der heyligen ... Met een voorafgaande
korte levens beschryving van den autheur.
Vierden druk. t'Utrecht by Samuel de
Waal boekverkoper op't oude kerkhop 1765.
40p.l. 284,[17]p. 16cm.

NL 0438720 MH-AH

M65
L82
W4
Lodensteyn, Jodocus van, 1620-1677.
Weeg-schale der onvolmaacktheden; ofte,
Bedenckingen nopende 't gewigte of de regt-
matige agtinge te maacken van de gebreken en
struyckelingen der geheyligden op der Aerden
... t'Utrecht, By Henricus Versteegh, 1664.
12 p. l., 350, [19] p. 14 cm.

NL 0438721 CtY-D

Lodéon, Paul.
... Les récidives et les séquelles dans les
pancréatites chirurgicales... Toulouse, 1927.
23 cm.
Thèse - Univ. de Toulouse.
"Bibliographie": p. [77]

NL 0438722 CtY

Loder, Arthur Beard, 1875-
Peirce, Frederick, & co.
The Peirce thesaurus of security distribution and invest-
ment, by Frederick Peirce & co. Philadelphia, New York,
Frederick Peirce & co., 1928.

341.63
L821
Loder, Bernard Cornelius Johannes, 1849-
La différence entre l'arbitrage inter-
national et la justice internationale.
Harlem, Tjeenk Willink, 1923
31 p.

1. Arbitration, International 2. International law

NL 0438724 NNUN ViU-L

JX1971
.5
.P3
no. 20
Loder, Bernard Cornelius Johannes, 1849-
Discours présidentiel, prononcé à l'occasion de l
l'ouverture solennelle de la Cour permanent de
justice internationale, le mercredi quinze fevrier
1922, au Palais de la paix. La Haye, par m. le
docteur B.C.J. Loder... [n.p., 1922]
21 p. 15.5 x 19.5 cm.
Pamphlets on the World court, no. 20.

NL 0438725 DLC

Loder, Bernard Cornelis Johannes, 1849-
Impressions de Genève. Discours prononcé par M.
B. C. J. Loder le 29 janvier 1921, devant la société La
Hollande à l'étranger. La Haye, Van Langenhuysen
frères, 1921.
25 p. 21ᶜᵐ.

1. League of nations. I. Title.
Title from Carnegie Endow.   Int. Peace JX1979.L8   A 21-879

NL 0438726 NNCE

Loder, Bernard Cornelis Johannes, 1849-
Central organisation for a durable peace, *The Hague.*
... Institutions judiciaires et de conciliation. Rapport pré-
senté par m. le dr. B. C. J. Loder ... La Haye [Secrétariat,
Organisation centrale pour une paix durable] 1917.

320.1
N301
Loder, Bernard Cornelis Johannes, 1849-
De leer der volkssouvereiniteit in hare ontwikkeling, aanbeve-
ling en bestrijding historisch-kritisch beschouwd ... Door Ber-
nard Cornelis Johannes Loder ... Leiden, P. Somerwil, 1873.
[10], 235, [1] p. 23½ᶜᵐ.
Proefschrift—Leyden.
Bibliographical foot-notes.

NL 0438728 ICJ NN

Loder, Bernard Cornelis Johannes, 1849-
Reglement pacifique des conflits internationaux
see under   Central organization for a
durable peace, The Hague.

Loder, Charles A.
...Hilarity songster. New York, n.d.
(circa 1888)
64 p. 17 cm.

NL 0438730 RPB

Pam
71-179
Loder, Christian C
FAMILY RECORD OF MICHEL YODER FROM GERMANY
AND THOSE RELATED TO HIM BY INTERMARRIAGE FROM
THE YEAR 1822 TO 1932. Sugarcreek, Ohio [n.
d.]
[31] p.

YODER FAMILY
TROYER FAMILY
HERSHBERGER FAMILY
title

NL 0438731 WHi

VOLUME 338

Loder, Dietrich, 1900-
Konjunktur; eine revolutionskomödie aus dem
frühjehr 1933 in 3 akten, von Dietrich Loder ...
Berlin-Halensee, Chronos verlag, g. m. b. h., c1933.

3 p. l., ₍5₎-38 p. 19½cm.

Mimeographed.

1. Germany - History - 1933-   - Drama.
I. Title.

NL 0438732   NCH

Loder, Dietrich, 1900-
... Mars und Cäsar, zwei humoresken ... ₍Leipzig, Reclam-
druck, 1943₎
19, ₍1₎ p. 15½ᵐ. (Reclams reihenbändchen, nr. 22)
"Aus 'Das verrückte auto'."

I. Title.
46-15363
Library of Congress   PT2623.03V45

NL 0438733   DLC

Loder, Dietrich, *1900 —*
Das verrückte auto, von Dietrich Loder. Leipzig, P. Reclam jun. ₍1925₎
74, ₍2₎ p. 15½ᵐ. (On cover: Reclams universal bibliothek. nr. 6589)
"Humoresken und grotesken."

I. Title.
27-2139
Library of Congress   PT2623.03V4 1925

NL 0438734   DLC MB NcU OrPR

Loder, Donald John, 1904-
... The reactivity of the methylated sugars. VI. The action
of dilute alkali on 3-methylglucose, by Donald J. Loder with
W. Lee Lewis. ₍Easton, Pa., 1932₎
cover-title, p. ₍1040₎-1054. diagrs. 23½ᵐ.
"Abstracted from a dissertation submitted by Donald J. Loder to the
Graduate school of Northwestern university ... for the degree of doctor
of philosophy ₍1931₎"
"Reprint from the Journal of the American chemical society, 54 ...
₍1932₎"
1. Sugars. 2. Methylglucose.   I. Lewis, Winford Lee, 1878-
joint author.
32-30145
Library of Congress   QD321.L78 1931
Northwestern Univ. Libr.

———— Copy 2.   547.3

NL 0438735   IEN DLC OU

Loder, Dorothy.
The land and people of Spain. Illustrated from photos.
₍1st ed.₎ Philadelphia, Lippincott ₍1955₎
117 p. illus. 22 cm. (Portraits of the nations series)

1. Spain—Hist.   I. Title.
DP68.L63   946   55-10651 ‡

PWcS WaS WaSp
NL 0438736   DLC CaBVaU Or OrP OrU AAP CU PP TU OC1

₍**Loder,** *Sir Edmund Giles, bart.*₎ Conifers at Leonardslee,
₍Horsham, Sussex. Corrected list₎ sm. 4°. pp. 15. ₍Lon-
don, 1919₎.

NL 0438737   MBH MH-A

Loder, Sir Edmund Giles, bart. List of trees and shrubs
grown in the open air at Leonardslee, Horsham, Sussex.
London. 1913. 8°.
"Private circulation."

NL 0438738   MH-A

Loder, Eduard von
RA989   Bemerkungen über ärztliche Verfassung und
14   Unterricht in Italien während des Jahres 1811.
812i   Leipzig, C. Cnobloch, 1812.
xxiv, 532, [2]p. tables. 20cm.
Bibliography: p. 529-532.

1. Hospitals - Italy.   2. Medicine - Study and
teaching - Italy.

NL 0438739   CtY-M

Loder (Eduardus). * Diss. sistens historiam
phthisis pulmonalis per fistulam thoracicam
sanata. 32 pp. 4°. Göttingae, H. Dieterich,
₍1808₎.

NL 0438740   DNLM

---

*
M1
.A13N Loder, Edward James, 1813–1865.
.L64N53 ₍The night dancers. Ah, no! you'll not forget
1846   me₎
         Ah, no! you'll not forget me! From
the grand opera, of Giselle or The night
dancers. New York, Atwill, 201 Broadway
₍ca. 1846₎
         ₍105₎-108 p. 33cm.
         Caption title.
         1. Operas—Excerpts—Vocal scores with piano.
2. Songs with piano. I. Title. II. Title:
Giselle. III. Title: The night dancers.

NL 0438741   ViU

Loder, Edward James, *1813-1865.*   No. 22 in **M.235.7.1
Ah! sure, sweet maid. Quintette [S. A. T. B. B., and chorus]. Sung
in the opera "The night-dancers." [Accomp. for pianoforte.]
London. Jefferys. [1846?] (1), 8pp. F°.

E3565 — T.r. — Part songs.

NL 0438742   MB

Loder, Edward James, 1813-1865
The Andalusian, or The young guard
For libretti see   Soane, George, 1790-
1860.

---

*
M1
.S444 Loder, Edward James, 1813–1865.
v.122
no.4   The brave old oak, a song of the oak
sung by Mr. H. Russell. The poetry by H. F.
Chorley. Music by Edward T. ₍sic₎ Loder.
Price 50. Philadelphia, George Willig,
171 Chesnut ₍sic₎ St. ₍after 1819?₎
         5 p. 33cm. ₍Sheet music collection, v. 122,
no. 4₎
         1. Songs with piano. I. Chorley, Henry
Fothergill, 1808-1872. The brave old oak. II.
Title.   old

NL 0438744   ViU NN

Loder, Edward James.   8053-537
The brave old oak. [Song. Accomp. for pianoforte.]
= Boston. Bradlee. [183-?] 4 pp. F°.

G5608 — T.r. — Songs. With music.

NL 0438745   MB

Loder, Edward James, 1813-1865.
The brave old oak; a song, the poetry by H. F. Chorley.
₍New York, 1840₎
p. 96. 32 cm.
Caption title.
Detached from the New world. ₍Quarto ed.₎ v. 1.

1. Songs (Medium voice) with piano.   I. Title.

M1.A13L   M 54-30

NL 0438746   DLC

[Loder, Edward James] 1813-1865.
"The brave old oak". Words by H. F. Chorley.
Music arranged by H. Russell. [Song with piano
acc.] [New York] [18-   ]
p. 3-6. F°.
n. t. p.

NL 0438747   NN

---

*
M1
.S444 ₍Loder, Edward James₎ 1813-1865.
v.19
no.28   The brave old oak. 3d ed. Respectfully
dedicated to Dr. Kelsey of Rochester, N. Y.
₍Words by H. F. Chorley. Music arr. by
Henry Russell. c1837 by Henry Russell,
Southern District of New York. New York,
Hewitt & Jaques, 239 Broadway ₍not after
1841₎
         6 p. 35cm. ₍Sheet music collection, v.19, no.28₎
         At head of title: A song of the oak.
         1. Songs ₍Medium   voice₎ with piano. I.
Russell, Henry,   1812-1900, arr.
II. Title.

NL 0438748   ViU

Loder, Edward James, 1813-1865.
The brave old oak as sung by Mr. Russell. The
music by E.J. Loder, arranged for the Spanish guitar
by Edward Fehrman. New York, Published by William
Hall & son, 239 Broadway ₍1848-1858₎
₍2₎ p. 35.5cm.
Caption title.
Date approximated from publishers' list in Wolfe,
R.J. Secular music in America 1801-1825.

1. Guitar music. 2. Vocal music. I. t. II. Fehrman,
Edward.

NL 0438749   MiU-C

Loder, Edward James, 1813-1865.
The bright days of the past. New-York, Firth & Hall
₍184-?₎
5 p. 35 cm.
Caption title.
For voice and piano.

1. Songs (Medium voice) with piano.   I. Title.

M1.A13L   M 60-1851 rev

NL 0438750   DLC

Loder, E[dward] J[ames] 1813-1865.
By the waters of Xarama. Song written by
George Linley, composed by E.J. Loder [Piano
acc.] London, Il'Almaine & Co. [18-]
7 p. f°. (Illustrated Songs, Ballads &
Duets No. 5.)

NL 0438751   NN

Loder, Edward James, 1813-1865.
Columbus! An historical song, written by Jas. Bruton, the
music composed by Edward J. Loder...   London: T. E. Pur-
day₍, 185-?₎ 5 p. f°.
English words; music for 1 voice with piano acc.

1. Songs, English. 2. Bruton,   James, 1815-1867. 3. Title.
N. Y. P. L.   July 5, 1928

NL 0438752   NN

Loder, Edward James, 1813-1865.
The church Bell Ballad Poetry by F. F. Smith.
Music by E.J. Loder. Boston. [18-]
5 p. 4°.

NL 0438753   MH

Loder, Edward James, 1813-1865.
Come from Alhambra: Chains on the cities.
Song with piano acc. The poetry by Mrs. Hemans.
The music by Edward J. Loder.   London,
D'Almaine & Co., [18-   ]
5 p. F°.

NL 0438754   NN

VOLUME 338

Loder, Edward James, 1813-1865.
The Covenanters
For libretti, see under   Dibdin, Thomas
John, 1771-1841.

*
M1
.A13N   Loder, Edward James, 1813-1865.
.L64D6
1850   "Down in the deep", the water elfin's
        song. The poetry by Jas. Bruton. Pr. 50
        cts. Philadelphia, Lee & Walker, 722
        Chesnut St. [185-?]
            7 p.   36cm.

            1. Songs with piano. I. Title.

    NL   0438756   ViU

Loder, Edward James.   *A.5289K.1
    Eliza's flight, a scene from Uncle Tom's cabin.
    [Words] written by Miss M. A. Collier. Music by E. J. Loder. [Song with accompaniment for the pianoforte.]
— Boston. Ditson. 1852. 5 pp. Illustrated cover. 33½ cm.

    D1796 — Double main card. — Lode.. Edward James. (M1) — Collier, M. A
    (M2) — T.r. Song. (1) — Songs. With music. (1)

    NL   0438757   MB ICN

Loder, Edward James, 1813-1865.
    The first principles of singing, with directions
    for the formation of the voice, illustrated with
    numerous rules for singing with expression and
    correct intonation, together with solfeggi, in all
    the principal major and minor keys, to which is
    added popular airs, the whole compiled & composed
    by Edward I. Loder.   London, D'Almaine & Co.
    [185-?   ]
        15 p.   24 cm.

    NL   0438758   ICN

Loder, Edward James, 1813-1865.
    Flow, Rio Verde. Written by Mrs Hemans. Composed
    by E. J. Loder. [n. p., 18-]
        6 p. 33 cm.
        Caption title.
        For voice and piano.

        1. Songs (Medium voice) with piano.   I. Title.

        M1.A13L   M 53-1605

    NL   0438759   DLC

Loder, Edward James.   No. 35 in **M.235.7.1
    Here's a health to the forester. [Chorus, A. T. T. B.   From The
    night-dancers. Accomp. for pianoforte.]
    [London, 1846?] 6 pp. F°.

                May 2,   1902
    E3565 — T.r. — Part songs.

    NL   0438760   MB

Loder, Edward James, 1813-1865.

    I heard a brooklet gushing [by] Edward J. Loder...   [London] Oxford univ. press [c1936]   5 p.   30½cm.

    For 1 voice with piano acc.
    "Reprinted from 'An anthology of song' by John Goss."
    "From the German of Müller."

    1. Songs, English.
    N. Y. P. L.   October 6, 1938

    NL   0438761   NN

*
M1
.A13N   Loder, Edward James, 1813-1865.
.L64I4
1840   I'll be gay, while I may; cavatina.
        Boston, Oliver Ditson, 115 Washington St.
        [184-?] Pl. no. 1629.
            6 p.   34cm.
            Caption title. Cover wanting.

            1. Songs with piano. I. Title.

    NL   0438762   ViU MB

Loder, Edward James.   **M.280.3
    The island of Calypso, an operatic masque, written by George Soane.
    Composed by Edward J. Loder. [Accomp. for pianoforte.]
    London. Cramer & Co. [1851.] (1), 120 pp. F°.

                May 2,   1902
    E3565 — Operas. — Soane, George.

    NL   0438763   MB

Loder, Edward James, 1813-1865, composer.
    The island of Calypso
    For libretto see   Soane, George, 1790-
    1860, librettist.

Loder, Edward James, 1813-1865.
    The last links are broken. Ballad written by
    Miss Fanny Steers. Arranged with symphonies
    and accompaniments by E. J. Loder.   London,
    D'Almaine & Co. [18-]
        5 p.   F°.

    NL   0438765   NN

Loder, Edward James, ed.
    ... Macbeth in complete score, with accompaniment for the pianoforte
    see under   Locke, Matthew, 1630?-1677.

PR
5459   Loder, Edward James, 1813-1865.
.54   The night dancers, a new grand romantic opera,
A19   (in three parts,) partly founded on the story
v.3   of Giselle; by George Soane ... The music by Mr.
        Loder. London, C.Jefferys, 1846.
            vii,[1],[3]-30 p.   20½cm.
            Another edition published 1846 with title: The wilis;
            or,The night dancers.
            Without the music.
            No.6 in volume lettered: Soane's plays. 3.

            I.Title. II.Title: The wilis; or,The night dancers.
            III.Title: Giselle.

    NL   0438766   MiU NIC CU ICN

Loder, Edward James, 1813-1865.
    [The night dancers. Libretto. English]

    The night dancers, a new grand romantic opera, (in three
    parts,) partly founded on the story of Giselle; by George
    Soane ... The music by Mr. Loder. 2d ed. London, C. Jefferys, 1846.
        vii, [1], 9-63 p.   20½cm.
        No. 3 in a volume lettered: Operas.
        [1. Operas—Librettos]   I. Soane, George, 1790-1860. The night
        dancers. II. Adam, Adolphe Charles, 1803-1856. Giselle.
                                    45-34576
    Library of Congress   ML48.O648 no.3

    NL   0438767   DLC

LODER, EDWARD JAMES, 1813-1865.
    [THE NIGHT DANCERS. LIBRETTO. ENGLISH]
    The night dancers; a new grand romantic opera in
    three parts, partly founded on the story of Giselle, by
    George Soane. The music by Mr. Loder. 2d ed.
    London, C. Jeffreys, 1846.   vii, 36 p.   21cm.

    Microfiche (neg.) 1 sheet. 11 x 15cm. (NYPL FSN 14,785)
    Based on the ballet, Giselle, by Adolphe Adam.
    I. Soane, George, 1790-1860.   The night dancers. II. Adam,
    Adolphe, 1803-1856. Giselle.   III. Title.

    NL   0438768   NN

782.1
L821nZ   Loder, Edward James, 1813-1865.
1847   [The night-dancers. Libretto]
        The night-dancers; a grand romantic opera...
        The words written by George Soane.   New York,
        Berford, 1847.
            v,39p. 18cm.   (The Operatic library, no. 2)

            Partly founded on the story of Giselle by
        A. C. Adam.

            I. Soane, George, 1790-1860. The night
        dancers. II. Adam Adolphe Charles, 1803-
        1856. Giselle.   III. Title.

    NL   0438769   IEN MB

Loder, Edward James.   **M.263.15
    The night dancers, opera, by Edward Loder. [Accomp. for pianoforte.]
    London. Jefferys. [185-?] (1), 278 pp. F°.

    E3684 — T.r. — Operas.

    NL   0438770   MB

Loder, Edward James.   **M.263.14
    Nourjahad, a romantic grand opera in 3 acts ... Written by S. I.
    Arnold. Composed by E. J. Loder. [Accomp. for pianoforte.]
    London. Hawes. [1834.] (7), 141 pp. F°.

    [This work must be consulted in the Brown Library on the Special Libraries Floor.]

                April 11,   1902.
    E3684 — Operas. — Arnold, Samuel James.

    NL   0438771   MB

*
M1
.A13N   Loder, Edward James, 1813-1865.
.L6404
1837   Oh little daisy growing wild. Ballad in
        the old English style, sung by Mrs. Loder.
        Pr. 50 cts. New York, Hewitt & Jaques,
        239 Broadway [1837?]
            6 p.   34cm.
            G. W. Quidor, engvr.

            1. Songs with piano. I. Title.

    NL   0438772   ViU

Loder, Edward James, 1813-1865.
    Oh! softly falls the foot of love. Song [with
    piano acc.] The poetry by the Hon. Mrs. Norton.
    The music by E.J. Loder.   London, D'Almaine &
    Co. [18-]
        5 p.   F°.

    NL   0438773   NN

Loder, Edward James, 1813-1865.
    Oh! the merry days when we were young. Pr. 50 cts. New
    York Published by E. Riley & Co 29 Chatham St [183-?]
        5 p. 33 cm.
        Caption title.
        For voice and piano.

        1. Songs (Medium voice) with piano.   I. Title.

        M1.A13L   M 56-164

    NL   0438774   DLC

VOLUME 338

LODER, Edward James.   8053.184
The old house at home. A ballad [S. or T.] from the opera of Francis
the First. [Pianoforte accomp.]
= Boston. Bradlee. [183-?] 5 pp. F°.

NL 0438775   MB

---

*
M1
.A13N   Loder, Edward James, 1813–1865.
.L64F65   [Francis I. The old house at home]
1836
    The old house at home. Ballad, sung by
Mr. H. Phillips in the grand opera of Francis
the First, performed at the Theatre Royal,
Drury Lane. Pr. 50 cts. New York, Millet's
Music Saloon, 375 Broadway [1836?]
    5 p. 34cm.
    1. Operas—Excerpts—Vocal scores with piano.
2. Songs with piano. I. Title. II. Title: Francis
the First.

NL 0438776   ViU

Loder, Edward James.   No. 66 in 8050a.232
The old house a home, a ballad, from the opera of Francis
the First . . . [the accomp.] arranged for the guitar by Henry Chadwick.
= Boston. Ditson. [184-?] 2 pp. F°.

G1184 — Chadwick, Henry, ed. — T.r. — Songs. With music.

NL 0438777   MB

---

*
M1
.A13N   Loder, Edward James, 1813–1865.
.L6408
1843   The outlaw; a song, as sung by Mr. Archer
with unbounded applause at all the principal
theatres in the United States. Poetry by
H. Carl Schiller. Philadelphia, W. R.
Bayley, successor to Ld. Meignen & Co., 30
South Fourth St.; 140 Main St., Cincinnati,
Ohio, °1843. Pl. no. 942.
    5 p. 34cm.
    1. Songs with piano. I. Title.

NL 0438778   ViU

---

*
M1
.S444   Loder, Edward James, 1813–1865.
v.93,
no.4   Philip the falconer. Song, written by
W. H. Bellamy. Price [trimmed] Philadelphia, E. Ferrett & Co., 212 Chesnut St.;
New York, 237 Broadway ... [184-?]
    4 p. 35cm. [Sheet music collection, v. 93,
no. 4]
    Illustrated cover.
    1. Songs with piano. I. Title.

NL 0438779   ViU

Loder, Edward James, 1835–1865.   **M.366.30
Raymond & Agnes, a grand opera in 3 acts. The libretto by Edward
Fitzball [pseud. of Edward Ball], the music by Edward J. Loder.
[Accomp. for pianoforte.]
London. Jefferys. [1859.] 266 pp. L.8°.

       April 11,   1902.
E3684 — Ball, Edward. — Operas.

NL 0438780   MB

Loder, Edward James, 1813–1865.
    The rose that all are praising. Written by Thos. Haynes
Bayly. Arr. for the piano forte. Published by John Cole,
Baltimore [18—] Pl. no. 1038.
    [3] p. 36cm.
    Cover title.
    For voice and piano.

    1. Songs (Medium voice) with piano. I. Title.

    M1.A13L   M 60–940

NL 0438781   DLC

---

*
M1
.S444   Loder, Edward James, 1813–1865.
v.73
no.21   Saw ye aught of my love? Sung by Mrs.
Watson. Baltimore, John Cole [not after
1855] Pl. no. 1199.
    [2] p. 35cm. [Sheet music collection, v. 73,
no. 21]
    Caption title.
    W. H. Duffy, lithographer; A. F. Winnemore,
engraver.
    1. Songs with piano. I. Title.

NL 0438782   ViU

---

*
M1
.A13N   Loder, Edward James, 1813–1865.
.L64B7   [The brave old oak]
1840
    A song of the oak. The brave old oak.
Sung by Mr. Henry Russell. The poetry by
H. T. Chorley. 3d ed. Pr. 50 cts. New
York, Atwill, 201 Broadway [184-?]
    5 p. 34cm.

    1. Songs with piano. I. Title. II. Title:
The brave old oak

NL 0438783   ViU

Lilly
PR 4891   LODER, EDWARD JAMES, 1813–1865
.L 4 R5   Songs, chorusses, &c. in a new and ori-
ginal fairy ballad opera, entitled Robin
Goodfellow. The music by Loder. First per-
formed at the Princess's Theatre ... on
Wednesday, December 6th, 1848 ... on
London,
Printed by S. G. Fairbrother [1848]
    15 p. 20.5 cm.

    First edition.

    Without the music.
    Bound in quarter red morocco.

    I. Loder, Edward James, 1813-1865--Robin
Goodfellow

NL 0438785   InU NIC

Music
ML
48   Loder, Edward James, 1813–1865.
N714   [Francis the first. Libretto. English]
v.1
no.9   Songs, duets, trios, choruses, &c. &c. in
the opera of Francis the first, as performed
for the first time at the Theatre Royal, Drury
Lane, on Tuesday, November 6, 1838. The music
composed by E. J. Loder. London, Printed by
J. Mallett [1838?]
    15 p. 24cm.

    Written to incorporate previously composed
songs by Loder. Cf. Grove. Dictionary of music and musicians. 5th ed.
    No. 9 in vol. lettered: Nineteenth century
operas. Librettos. 1.
    1. Operas--Librettos. I. Title: Francis
the first.

NL 0438787   NIC

LODER, Edward James, 1813–1865.
Songs of the poets, the music composed by E.
J. Loder. London, Monro & May, etc.,[pref. 1844]
f°. pp. (4), 39. Plates.

NL 0438788   MH

Loder, Edward James.   8053.652
There's a light in her laughing eye. [Song. Accomp. for piano-
forte.]
= New York. Firth & Hall. [183-?] 9 pp. F°.

G5681 — T.r. — Songs. With music.

NL 0438789   MB

Loder, Edward James, 1813–1865.
    There's a path by the river. Boston Published by E. H.
Wade, 197 Washington S[t] [185-?]
    7 p. 34cm.
    For voice and piano.

    1. Songs (Medium voice) with piano. I. Title.

    M1.A13L   52–52979

NL 0438790   DLC

Loder, Edward James.   No. 9 in *8050a.730.23
    Three ages of love. A popular ballad [with accompaniment for
pianoforte]. Poetry by H. F. Chorley, Es[q]. Music by E. I.
Loder. 3d edition.
= New York. Jollie. [185-?] 9 pp. 36 cm.

L5216 — Double main card. — Loder, Edward James. (M1) — Chorley, Henry
Fothergill. (M2) — T.r. (1) — Songs. With music. (1)

NL 0438791   MB

Loder, Edward James.   No. 21 in **M.235.7.2
To the hills! The vintagers' song [S. A. B.], in the opera of Francis
the First. [Accomp. for pianoforte.]
London. D'Almaine & Co. [184-?] (1), 7 pp. F°.

E3684 — T.r. — Part songs.

NL 0438792   MB

Loder, Edward James, 1813–1865.
    Woman's Love! Song [with piano acc.] ... in
the grand opera of "Francis the First" ... The
music composed by E.J. Loder. London,
D'Almaine & Co. [1838]
    5 p. F°.

NL 0438793   NN

---

*
M1
.S444   Loder, George, 1816 - 1868.
v.120
no.10   Camp glee, composed and dedicated to the
New York City Guards Glee Club, and performed
by the class of the New York Vocal Institute
in presence of the Mayor and Corporation.
N[ew] Y[ork], Pub. by J. L. Hewitt, Broadway,
and to be had at the rooms of the Institute
Lyceum, 592 Broadway [183- or 184-?]
    5 p. 34cm. [Sheet music collection, v.120, no.10]
    Illustrated cover: Thayer & Cos. Lith., Boston.
G. W. Quidor, Engvr.
    For TTBB and piano.
    1. Choruses, Secu   lar (Men's voices, 4 pts.)
with piano. 2. Glees.   catches, rounds, etc.
I. Title.   ViU 58-10556

NL 0438794   ViU MB

Loder, George, 1816-1868.
    The cat's in the larder
       see under Horncastle, James Henry,
1801-1869.

Loder, George, 1816–1868.   No. 5 in *8050a.747
    Cheerly o'er the mountains: a popular Southern refrain. The poetry
written . . . by George P. Morris. Music arranged from the well
known melody of "Going ober de mountain" by George Loder.
[With accompaniment for pianoforte.]
— New York. Atwill. [1844] 7 pp. Decorated cover. 35½ cm.
    The cover decoration is a lithograph representing a hunting scene.

L9775 — Double main card. — Loder, George. (M1) — Morris, George Pope,
1802-1864. (M2) — T.r. (1) — Songs ref. made.

NL 0438796   MB

VOLUME 338

LODER, GEORGE, 1816-1868, ed.
The New York glee book; containing one hundred glees, quartetts, trios, songs in parts, rounds and catches. Composed, selected and harmonized, with an ad lib. accompaniment for the piano forte. New York, J. & H. G. Langley, 1843. score (272 p.) 28cm.

Chiefly for TTBB, or TTB, with piano acc.
1. Choral music, Secular (Men)--Collections. 2. Glees. 3. Rounds, catches and canons. I. Title.

NL 0438797   NN RPB CoU NNUT MdBP MWA ICN MH CtY

Loder, George.
The New York glee book: containing one hundred glees, quartetts, trios, songs in parts, rounds, and catches. Composed, selected, and harmonized with an libitum accompaniment for the piano forte by George Loder ... 1844, [c1843]

NL 0438798   NNUT

Loder, George, 1816 (ca.)-1868, comp.
The New York glee book: containing one hundred glees, quartetts, trios, songs in parts, rounds, and catches. Composed, selected, and harmonized, with an ad libitum accompaniment for the piano forte. Hartford, S. Andrus, 1848.
272 p. 24cm.
1. Choruses, Secular (Men's voices) with piano. 2. Glees, catches, rounds, etc. I. Title.

NL 0438799   ViU NN

LODER, George, compiler.
The New York glee book, containing one hundred glees, quartetts, trios, songs in parts, rounds and catches. With an accompaniment for the piano forte. Hartford, S. Andrus & son, 1850.

NL 0438800   MH DLC

LODER, George.
The New York glee book, containing one hundred glees, quartetts, trios, songs in parts, rounds and catches. Hartford, S. Andrus & son, 1851 [cop. 1843].

NL 0438801   MH RPB OO CtY

Loder, George,   comp.
The New York glee book: containing one hundred glees, quartetts, trios, songs in parts, rounds, and catches. Composed, selected, and harmonized, with an ad libitum accompaniment for the piano forte. By George Loder ... Hartford, S. Andrus & son, 1855.
v1, [7]-272 p. 25cm.
1. Glees. 2. Choral music. 3. Part-songs. I. Title.

NL 0438802   ViU

Loder, George, 1816-1868.
The pets of the parterre
for libretti see under   Coyne, Joseph Stirling, 1803-1868.

784.1 Loder, George.
L82p   Philadelphia and New York glee book: containing one hundred glees, quartetts, trios, songs in parts, rounds and catches. Composed, selected, and harmonized with an ad libitum accompaniment for the piano-forte. Philadelphia, Lee & Walker, etc., 1857.
272p.

NL 0438804   IU MB CoU NcU OC1

LODER, George, compiler.
Philadelphia and New York glee book, containing one hundred glees, quartetts, trios, songs in parts, rounds and catches. With an accompaniment for the piano-forte. Philadelphia, Lee & Walker, etc., 1860.

NL 0438805   MH

Music   Loder, George, comp.
L8213n   Philadelphia and New York glee book; con-
1864   taining one hundred glees, quartetts, trios,
Harris   songs in parts, rounds and catches. Composed,
Collection selected, and harmonized, with an ad libitum
          accompaniment for the piano-forte.
          Philadelphia, Lee & Walker, 1864.
          v1, [7]-272 p. 24 cm.

Contents identical with The New York glee book.

NL 0438806   RPB PU

Loder, George, 1816-1868.
Philadelphia and New York glee book, containing one hundred glees, quartetts, trios, songs in parts, rounds and catches. Composed, selected, and harmonized, with an ad libitum acc. for the piano forte, by George Loder. Philadelphia, Lee & Walker, 1867.
v1, score (272 p.) 26 cm.
For chorus (TTBB)
1. Glees, catches, rounds, etc. 2. Canons, fugues, etc. (Vocal) 1. Title.
M1550.L6P5   77-206028

NL 0438807   DLC

VM   LODER, GEORGE, 1816-1868, arranger.
1   The serious family polka danced nightly at
F 91   Burton's theatre with the figure invented by M.
no.155 Frederick... New York, S.C. Jollie, 1850.
        [5]p. 35cm.

Piano solo.

NL 0438808   ICN

Loder, George.   8051.569
The Serious family polka . . . [for pianoforte]. 3d edition.
New York. Jollie. 1850. (3) pp. F°.

Eg101 — T.r. — Polkas. — Pianoforte. Music.

NL 0438809   MB MH

Loder, George, 1816-1868, ed.   No. 8 in *8050a.730.23
Take your time, Miss Lucy. A comic ballad. [With accompaniment for pianoforte.] The words by A. Allan, Esq'. Adapted
from the original melody by George Loder.
New York. Atwill. 1842. (4) pp. Decorated cover. 33 cm.

L5216 — Double main card. — Loder, George, ed. (M1) — Allan, A. (M2) —
T.r. (1) — Songs. With music. (1)

NL 0438810   MB NN

Loder, George, 1816-1868.
Touch us gently, time! A ballad..., the poetry
by Barry Cornwall. The music composed...by
George P.H. Loder. New York, Davis & Horn,
cop. 1839.
5 p. f°.

NL 0438811   NN

Thesis Loder, George Edward, 1900-
1935   Bread in Ithaca. Ithaca, N. Y., 1935.
1821   110 l. illus., maps. 28 cm.

Thesis (Ph. D.) - Cornell Univ., 1935.

1. Bread. 2. Bakers and bakeries - Ithaca,
N. Y. 1. Title.

NL 0438812   NIC

Loder, George Edward, 1900–
Bread in Ithaca ... by George Edward Loder. Ithaca, N. Y., 1935.
[5] p. 22½ᵐ.
Abstract of thesis (PH. D.)—Cornell university, 1935.

1. Bread.   36-14725

Library of Congress   HD9057.U6 I 85 1935
                                                    338.4

NL 0438813   DLC OU

Loder, George F., ed.
Tactics and drill of Monroe Commandery Drill
Corps, No. 12, K. T., stationed at Rochester, N. Y.
see under   Freemasons. Rochester, N. Y.
Knights Templars. Monroe Commandery, No. 12.

Loder, Gerald Walter Erskine, 1861–   ed.

Ardingly, Eng. (Parish)
The parish registers of Ardingly, Sussex. 1558-1812.
Ed. by Gerald W. E. Loder. [London, Mitchell, Hughes
and Clarke, printers] 1913.

Loder, George P.H.
see Loder, George, 1816-1868.

Loder, J., tr.

Vasili, Paul, comte, pseud.
Berlin society. By Count Paul Vasili. Tr. from the
French by J. Loder. New York, S. W. Green's son, 1884.

FOLIO   Loder, J   D
MT262   General & comprehensive instruction book,
.163   for the violin, containing upwards of an
1836   hundred progressive exercises in the different
MUSIC   major and minor keys, the whole with proper
LIBRARY   bowing and fingering marked, by J. D. Loder.
          A 3d edition (considerably enlarged & improved)
          London, D'Almaine & Co. [1836]
          73p. 38cm.

NL 0438818   NcU

Loder, James Edwin.
A study of aural learning with and without the speaker
present, by James Edwin Loder ... Lincoln, Neb., 1937.
[1], 46-60 p. 25½ᵐ.
Thesis (PH. D.)—University of Nebraska, 1938.
"Reprinted from the September, 1937, issue of the Journal of experimental education."

1. Radio in education. 1. Title: Aural learning with and without
the speaker present.
                                                    38-18041

Library of Congress   LB1044.5.L6 1938
Univ. of Nebraska Libr.   371.333

NL 0438819   NbU DLC MtU PPT

Loder (J[oh.] N[epomuk]) [-1886]. *Ueber
den Cretinismus. 14 pp., 1 l. 8°. München,
F. S. Hübschmann. 1843.

NL 0438820   DNLM

Loder, John de Vere
see
Wakehurst, John de Vere Loder, baron, 1895–

VOLUME 338

611.084
L821a   LODER, Justus Christian von, 1753-1832.
    Anatomische Tafeln zur Beförderung
der Kenntniss des menschlichen Körpers.
Weimar, im Verlag des Landes Industrie
Comtoirs, 1803.
    13 v. (6 v. each of text and atlas,
and one index vol.)

    Also published in Latin under title
Tabulae anatomicae.

NL 0438822   WaU MiDW-M PPPH WU OU CaBVaU

Loder, Justus Christian von, 1753-1832.   611.7
    Anatomisches Handbuch von D. Just Christian Loder ...   F8
Erster Band: Osteologie, Syndesmologie, Myologie.   Mit Kupfern. Jena, Akademische Buchhandlung, 1788.

    ,10, 709, 21, p. II (i.e. 4) fold. pl. 20½ᶜᵐ.

Each plate in duplicate, one being an outline drawing.
No more published.

NL 0438823   ICJ PPC

Loder, Justus Christian ₍von₎ 1753-1832.
    Anfangsgründe der chirurgie ... von D. Just Christian
Loder. Jena, In der Akademischen buchhandlung, 1799.

    304 p. 20½ᵖ.

"Schriften über die chirurgie": p. 10-31.

1. Surgery.

Library of Congress   RD37.L82   7-2224†

NL 0438824   DLC

Loder, Justus Christian von, 1753-1832.   612.04
    Anfangsgründe der medicinischen Anthropologie und der   L822
Stats-Arzneykunde, entworfen von D. Just Christian Loder
... Zweite verbesserte und mit einem literarischen Anhang
versehene Auflage. Weimar, Industrie-Comptoir, 1793.

    xii, ,4, 782 p. 20½ᶜᵐ.

"Literarisches Verzeichniss der vorzüglichsten Schriften": p. ,629,-782.

NL 0438825   ICJ

Loder, Justus Christian ₍von₎ 1753-1832.
    Anfangsgründe der physiologischen anthropologie und
der staats-arzneykunde entworfen von D. Just. Christian
Loder ... 3. verm. und verb. aufl. Weimar, Industrie-
comptoir, 1800.

    1 p. l., xvi, 674 p, 1 l. 22ᶜᵐ.

1. Physiology. 2. Medical jurisprudence.

Library of Congress   QP34.L82   4-29728†

NL 0438826   DLC NNNAM

RD
30
.L6   Loder, Just Christian, 1753-1832.
    Chirurgisch-medicinische Beobachtungen meh-
rentheils in der Herzoglich Sachsen-Weimar-
schen Medicinisch-Chirurgischen Kranken-An-
stalt zu Jena. Weimar, Im Verlage des In-
dustrie-Comptoirs, 1794-
    v. illus. 20 cm.

1. Surgery. 2. Medicine - Practice.

NL 0438827   WU

    Loder, Justus Christian von, 1753-1832
    Commentatio de Alansonii nova
amputationis methodo. Part I [cum vita
candidati Immanuelis Henrici Goller.]
RBS   Jenae, lit. Strankmannianis, [1784].
137677   12p. 4°.
    Programm - Univ. Jena

NL 0438828   NNNAM

S178
3
L821   Loder, Justus Christian von, 1753-1832, praes
    De graminum fabrica et oeconomia ... Halae
[1804]
    Diss. - Halle (Augustus Babel, resp.)

NL 0438829   CtY

    Loder, Justus Christian von, 1753-1832.
    Descriptio calculi vesiculae
    felleae singularis. [Cum vita candidati
RBS   Ern. J. Heur. Haefner].
137930   Jenae, lit Fiedlerianis [1795].
    8p. 4°.
    Programm - Univ. of Jena

NL 0438830   NNNAM

QS
L821e   LODER, Justus Christian von, 1753-1832
1824   Elementa anatomiae humani corporis ...
    Mosquae, Hartmann, 1823-24.
    2 v. illus.

NL 0438831   DNLM

Loder, Justus Christian von, 1753-1832.   611.02
    Grundriss der Anatomie des menschlichen Körpers; zum   G601
Gebrauche bey Vorlesungen und Secir-Übungen entworfen von
Dr. Just Christian Loder ... Erster Theil. Jena, H. W. C. Seid-
ler, 1806.

    vi, ,2, 278 p. 21ᶜᵐ.

No more published.

NL 0438832   ICJ

    Loder, Justus Christian von, 1753-1832, pr.
    Historiae amputationum feliciter
    institutarum.
    Part II [Cum vita candidati Joannis
RBS   Godofredi Müller].
137926   Jenae, typ. Göpferdtii, [1789] 8p. 4°
    Programm - Univ. of Jena

NL 0438833   NNNAM

QS
L821i   LODER, Justus Christian von, 1753-1832
1823   Index praeparatorum aliarumque rerum
    ad anatomen spectantium quae in Museo
    Caesareae Universitatis Mosquensis ser-
    vantur. Mosquae, Typ. Caesareae
    Univ., 1823.
    xiv, viii, 441 p.   QS L821i
    Text in Latin and Russian.
    I. Moscow. Universitet. Anatomi-
    cheskii muzei

NL 0438834   DNLM

QS
L821i   LODER, Justus Christian von,
1826   Index praeparatorum aliarumque rerum
    ad anatomen spectantium quae in Museo
    Caesareae Universitatis Mosquensis
    servantur. Ed. altera emendata et aucta
    cui additae sunt duae orationes in theatro
    anatomico universitatis palam recitatae.
    Mosquae, Typ. Caesareae Univ. Mos-
    quensis, 1826.
    xiii, 208, 39 p. illus.

    Author's autograph presentation copy.
    I. Moscow. Universitet. Anatomi-
    cheskii muzei

NL 0438836   DNLM

    Loder, Justus Christian von, 1753-1832.
Yb   ... Observatio imperforationis vaginae icone
M4   illustrata.
800   Ienae, Typis Prageri et socior.[1800] 11pp.
    plate. 22½ᶜᵐ.
    Programm - Univ. Jena (invitation to the gra-
    duation of Nicolaus Meyer)
    Meyer's autobiography: pp. 6-10.
    Original loose sheets, uncut, as issued.
    Plate wanting.

NL 0438837   CtY

    1795

    Loder, Justus Christian von, 1753-1832.
    Observationis scroti per sphacelum
    destructi et reproductionis ope restituti.
RBS   Part 1. [Cum vita candidati Joannio Augusti
137925   Freiber].
    Jenae. typ. Göpferdtii. [1795] 8p. 4°.
    Programm - Univ. of Jena.

NL 0438838   NNNAM

QS
L821or   LODER, Justus Christian, 1753-1832
1819   Oratio de inaugurationis novi Theatri
    Anatomici X Novembris MDCCCXIX pub-
    lice habita. Mosquae, Typ. Universitatis
    [1819]
    25, 21 p. illus.

    Text in Latin and Russian.
    1. Moscow. Universitet. Anatomi-
    cheskii muzei

NL 0438839   DNLM

QS
L821o   LODER, Justus Christian von, 1753-1832
1826   Orationes quas in theatro anatomico
    Caesareae Universitatis Mosquensis
    publice recitavit. Mosquae, Typis Uni-
    versitatis, 1826.
    39 p. illus.

NL 0438840   DNLM

Loder (Justus Christianus) [1753-1832]. [Pr.]
praemittitur historia amputationum feliciter in-
stitutarum particula 1. [Cum vita candidati
Guarneri Dethardi Motz.] 8 pp. sm. 4°. Jenae,
typ. Gopferdtii. [1789]. [P. v. 59.]

NL 0438841   DNLM PPC

---

von Loder (Justus Christianus) [1753-1832].
° Prime lineae neurologiae corporis humani commentatio 1. 2 p. l., 34 pp. sm. 4°. _Jenae, ex
off. Fickelscherriana._ [1778].

NL 0438842   DNLM

RG791
.L8   LODER, JUSTUS CHRISTIAN VON, 1753-1832.
    Synchondroseos ossivm pvbis sectionem in partv
    difficili institvendam denvo expendit Ivstvs Chri-
    stianvs Loder... Gottingae, litteris I.C.Dieterich,
    1778.
    58,[4]p. diagr. 24x19cm.
    Title vignette.
    Bibliographical foot-notes.

    1.Symphyseotomy.

NL 0438843   ICU PPC ViRA

QM
25
L82++   Loder, Justus Christian von, 1753-1832.
    Tabvlae anatomicae qvas ad illvstrandam
    hvmani corporis fabricam collegit et cvravit
    Ivstvs Christianvs Loder. Vimariae, Svmti-
    bvs Novi Bibliopolii vulgo Landes-Industrie-
    Comptoir dicti, 1803.
    2 v. in 6 (6 pts. and Index) of text, 2 v.
    in 5 (6 pts.) of plates. 43cm.

    Issued in parts, 1794-1803.
    Plates by various authors.
    Text (exposition of each plate) in Latin.
    Vol.1 of text has Latin t.p.; vol.1 of

Continued in next column

VOLUME 338

Continued from preceding column

plates has German t. p. with title: Anatomische Tafeln zur Beförderung der Kenntniss des menschlichen Körpers gesammelt und hrsg. von Iust Christian Loder.

Contents.—v.1. Tab. I–XC. fasc.1. Osteologia. fasc.2. Syndesmologia. fasc.3. Myologia. fasc.4. Splanchnologia.—v.2. Tab. XCI–CLXXXII. fasc.5. Angiologia. fasc.6. Nevrologia. Index.

NL 0438845   NIC CtY-M PPC MnU WU PBa

RC 133 .R8 L6

Loder, Just Christian, 1753-1832.
Ueber die cholera-Krankheit; ein Sendschreiben. Königsberg, J. H. Bon, 1831.
60 p. 18 cm.

Includes Zusätze zu seiner Schrift über die cholera-Krankheit (45 p.)

1. Cholera, Asiatic - Russia.

NL 0438846   WU ICJ DNLM

Loder, Justus Christianus von, 1753-1832.
———. Verba quibus initio secundi cursus lectionum suarum anatomicarum 4 Octobris mdcccxx artis salutaris studiosos hortatus est. 13 pp. 4°. Mosquae, typ. universitatis, 1820.

NL 0438847   DNLM

Loder, Kate Fanny.   No. 23 in **M.234.6
Bow down Thine ear. Sacred song. [Accomp. for pianoforte.]
(In Haycraft. Sacred Harmony. Pp. 73-76. London. [1851.])

E3684 — T.r. — Church music. Anthems, &c.

NL 0438848   MB

Loder, Kate Fanny.   No. 28 in **M.234.6
Praise the Lord. Anthem. [Accomp. for organ.]
(In Haycraft. Sacred Harmony. Pp. 95-108. London. [1851.])

E3684 — T.r. — Church music. Anthems, &c.

NL 0438849   MB

RA082.2 f1821

Loder, L   A   comp.
Miscellaneous newspaper clippings dating from 1850's through 1930's. n.p., n.d.
1v. 35cm.

Includes newspaper clippings of the Lincoln assassination.

1. Clippings (Books, newspapers, etc.) 2. Scrap-books.

NL 0438850   OC

Loder, Ludwig.
Lues congenita an leber, lunge und nieren.
Inaug. diss. Wuersburg, 1897.
Bibl.

NL 0438851   ICRL DNLM

Loder, M   G   A
Historische Nachricht von der Stadt Wolmar in Liefland
        see in Hupel, August Wilhelm, 1737-1819, ed.
Statistisch-topographische Nachrichten von den Herzogthümern Kurland und Semgalln.

Loder, Marion.   **M.443.III
Cinderella in flowerland, or the lost lady's slipper. Operetta for children. [Vocal score.]
= Boston. Oliver Ditson Co. 1896. 32 pp. 26½ cm.

K7131 — T.r. — Children's operas.

NL 0438853   MB RPB

Loder, Marion.
Cinderella in flowerland; or, The lost lady's slipper. Operetta for children, by Marion Loder.   Boston: O. Ditson co. [etc., etc.,] c1896.   Publ. pl. no. 58987.   30 p.   26cm.   (Oliver Ditson company's standard edition.)

Includes dialogue.

1. Children's music—Operettas.
N. Y. P. L.   August 31, 1937

NL 0438854   NN RPB OCl

Loder, Marion.
...Cinderella in flowerland; or, The lost lady's slipper. Ditson, 1909.
32 p.

NL 0438855   MiD

Loder, Marion.
A golden gift
see under Loder, V.A., composer.

Loder, Martha Katherine, 1914–
... The life and novels of Léon Gozlan, a representative of literary cross currents in the generation of Balzac ... [by] Martha Katherine Loder. Philadelphia, 1943.

3 p. l., v–viii, 101 p. front. (port.) 23cm.

Thesis (PH. D.)—University of Pennsylvania, 1943.
Bibliography: p. 84-101.

1. Gozlan, Léon, d. 1866. 2. French literature—19th cent.—Hist. & crit.
                                                    A 43-8200
Pennsylvania. Univ. Libr.
for Library of Congress   PQ2268.Z5L6
                                                    843.79

NL 0438857   PU MtU LU NIC NcD PPD PBm PPT OCl OCH
            PU OU DLC NcU

Loder, Matthäus, 1781-1821.
Zerrbilder menschlicher thorheiten und schwächen
see under title

L916.76 L821e

Loder, Reginald B
East African journals. [n. p., n. d.]
3v. 27cm.

Typed t. p. supplied.
Typewritten.
Contents.— v.1. 1912-13.— v.2. 1924-25.— v.3. 1926-27.

1. Africa, British East. Descr. & trav.

NL 0438859   IEN

Loder, Robert.
The history of Framlingham, in the county of Suffolk
see under Hawes, Robert.

[Loder, Robert] ed.
Orders, constitutions, and directions, to be observed, for and concerning the Free-school, in Woodbridge, in the county of Suffolk, and of the school-master and scholars thereof, agreed upon at the foundation, 1662; with other matters relating to the same. 2d ed., enl. and cor. Woodbridge, Printed and sold by R. Loder; [etc., etc.] 1796.

1 p. l., 14, 3 p. 28cm. [With his The statutes, and ordinances, for the government of the alms-houses, in Woodbridge. Woodbridge, 1792]

1. Woodbridge, Eng. Free school.   I. Title.
                                                    15-22370
Library of Congress   DA690.W87L7

NL 0438861   DLC

Loder, Robert, ed.
The statutes, and ordinances, for the government of the alms-houses, in Woodbridge, in the county of Suffolk, founded by Thomas Seckford, esquire ... in the twenty-ninth year of the reign of Queen Elizabeth, 1587. Together with others subsequent, made by Sir John Fynch, knight, and Henry Seckford, esquire, 1635, Sir Joseph Jekyle, knight, and Sir Peter King, knight, 1718., Sir Thomas Sewell, knight, and Sir John Eardley Wilmot, knight, 1767. (governors for the time being) To which are annexed, a translation of the queen's letters patent for the foundation of the alms-house;—an abstract of Mr. Seckford's will;—a concise account of the founder;—and a genealogical table of his ancient family ... At the end is prefixed, notes relating to Woodbridge priory; together with the ancient monumental inscriptions in the parochial church, and those of late date. Collected and published by Robert Loder. Woodbridge, Printed and sold by the editor; [etc., etc.] 1792.

2 p. l., x, 24, [2], 7, [1] p. front. (port.) 2 col. pl., plan, fold. geneal. tab. 28cm.

1. Seckford, Thomas, 1515?–1588. 2. Woodbridge, Eng. Seckford almshouses. 3. Woodbridge priory. 4. Seckford family. I. Title.
                                                    15-22369
Library of Congress   DA690.W87L7

NL 0438863   DLC PHi

Loder, Robert, 1589-1640.
Robert Loder's farm accounts, 1610-1620, edited for the Royal historical society by G. E. Fussell ... London, Offices of the Society, 1936.

xxxi, 207 p. front. (facsim.) fold. tab. 21½ x 17 cm. ([Royal historical society. Publications; Camden third series, v. 53)

1. Agriculture—Early works to 1800. 2. Agriculture—accounting. I. Fussell, George Edwin, 1889–   ed. II. Title: Farm accounts.
DA20.R91 3d ser., vol. 53   630.94229   37—5475

ViU PSt MsU OrPS GU OrPR OrU CaBVaU WaSpG
NL 0438864   DLC MB PSC PU PBm PHC OC1W OO OCU OU

ar W 54477 no.11

Loder, Rudolf.
Die Rechte des Gesellschafters einer Gesellschaft mit beschränkter Haftung. Berlin, Gedruckt in der Hofbuchdr. von E. S. Mittler & Sohn, 1915.
48 p. 23cm.

Inaug.-Diss.—Erlangen.

NL 0438865   NIC ICRL

Loder, V   A   composer.
A golden gift; an operetta for children ... music by V. A. Loder. Boston, Ditson, c1906.

35 p.

NL 0438866   OC1

Loder, V. A. [composer.]   8056.297
A golden gift. An operetta for children by Marion Loder. Music by V. A. Loder. [Accomp. for piano.]
= New York. Ditson & Co. 1906. 35 pp. 8°.

G3068 — Children's operas. — Loder, Marion. — Operas.

NL 0438867   MB

VOLUME 338

Loder, Vernon, *pseud.*

see

Vahey, John George Haslette, 1881-

Loder (Wilhelmus). Diss. med. de incubo. 32
pp. sm. 4°. *Duisburgi ad Rhenum, J. Sas,*
1744. [P.–v. 2120.]

NL 0438869   DNLM

Case
X   LODERECKEHUS, PETRUS.
205   Dictionarium septem diuersarum linguarum, vide-
.518   licet latine, italice, dalmatice, bohemice, polo-
       nice, germanice, & vngarice, vna cum cuiuslibet
       lingue registro siue repertorio vernaculo ...
       [Pragae, E typographeo Ottmariano, impensis author-
       is, 1605]
          7pt. in 1v. 16cm.

          Imperfect: t.-p. mounted; closely trimmed,
       several leaves at the beginning and at the end
       tipped in.

NL 0438870   ICN

W 4   Loderer, Clara.
qB29   Die intellektuelle Entwicklung im Spiegel
1942   des Rorschach'schen Formdeutversuches.
       Leipzig, Druck der Spamer, 1942.
          p. [512]-521. illus.

          Inaug.-Diss. - Basel.
          Reprinted from "Der Nervenarzt," 1942,
       Heft 12.
          Bibliography: p. 521.

NL 0438871   DNLM

W 4   Loderhose, August, 1908-
251   Über das Auftreten und die Bedeutung
1940   atelektatischer Vorgänge im Verlaufe der
       Lungentuberkulose. Berlin, Linke [1940]
          15 p. illus.

          Inaug.-Diss. - Friedrich Wilhelms Univ.,
       Berlin.
          Bibliography: p. 14-15.

NL 0438872   DNLM

Loderhose, Karl Erich, 1906-
   Die landschaftsgestaltung in Hermann Löns'
prosawerken ... Frankfurt a./M., 1930.
   80 p. 21cm.

   Inaug.-diss.—Frankfurt a./M.
   Lebenslauf.
   "Literaturverzeichnis": p. 76-79.

1. Löns, Hermann, 1866-1914.

NL 0438873   MiU NjP CtY MH IEN

Lodes, Rudolf, 1909-
   Krebsvorkommen in der oberpfälzischen
kleinstadt Auerbach in der zeit von 1894 bis
1934. ... München, 1938.   47 p.
   Inaug. Diss. - Erlangen, 1938.
   Lebenslauf.

NL 0438874   PPJ

Lodesano, Italy
   see Lodi.

Lodestar.
   New Orleans.

NL 0438876   LNHT

... Lodestone Lem...
   see under [Whitson, John Harvey] 1854-

WZ   Lodetti, Giovanni Antonio
250   Dialogo de gl'inganni d'alcuni malvaggi spe-
E733f   ciali ... nel quale si scoprono molte frodi,
1626   che da detti speciali sono commesse, a pre-
       giuditio si della vita de gli ammalati. Come
       dell'honor de gli eccellenti medici. Padova,
       P. P. Tozzi, 1626.
          69, [1] p. 15 cm.
          Bound with Bovio, T. Z. Flagello de'medici
       rationali. Padova, 1626.

Film
51-144 —— Film copy. Negative.
no. 4

NL 0438879   DNLM NIC

Lodeve, Guillaume Emmanuel Joseph
   Guilhem de Clermont- , baron de Sainte-Croix

see

Sainte-Croix, Guillaume Emmanuel Joseph Guilhem
de Clermont-Lodeve, baron de, 1746-1809.

Lodève, France. (Diocese)
   Conférences ecclésiastiques du diocèse de
Lodève. Paris, J. B. Coignar & Boudet [etc.]
1749.
   v. 17 cm.

NL 0438881   PV

5A   LODÈVE, FRANCE (Diocese) Bishop, 1733-1750
6477   (Jean Georges de Souillac)
no. 7   Ordonnance et instruction pastorale de
       Monseigneur l'Évêque de Lodève, portant con-
       damnation d'un livre intitulé: L'esprit de
       Jesus-Christ & de l'Eglise, sur la fréquente
       communion; par le Pere Pichon ...   A Mont-
       pellier, De l'imprimerie de J. Martel,
       1748.
          55p. 26cm.

NL 0438882   ICN

Lodewick, Albert.
   ...Au delà du rexisme. Ergocratie. Liége: Éditions Ergone
[1937]   232 p. 25½cm.

930901A. 1. Fascism—Belgium.   2. Political science, 1918-
I. Title: Ergocratie.
N. Y. P. L.   April 7, 1938

NL 0438883   NN

Lodewick, John Elton, 1896-
   Effect of certain climatic factors on the diameter growth
of longleaf pine in western Florida.
   (*In* U. S. Dept. of agriculture. Journal of agricultural research.
v. 41, no. 5, Sept. 1, 1930, p. 349-363. diagrs. 23½cm. Washington,
1930)
   Contribution from Forest service (F—61)
   Published September 29, 1930.
   "Literature cited": p. 362-363.

1. Longleaf pine.
                                              Agr 30-1125
                                       [S21.A75 vol. 41, no. 5]
Library, U. S. Dept. of   Agriculture 1Ag84J vol. 41, no. 5

NL 0438884   DNAL CaBViP MH-A DAS NcD OCl OU

SD   Lodewick, John Elton, 1896-
387   Farm forestry for Virginians [by] J. Elton
W6   Lodewick and J. W. O'Byrne. Blacksburg,
L83   Virginia Polytechnic Institute, 1931.
          74 p. illus. 23 cm. (Virginia Polytechnic
       Institute, Blacksburg, Va. Bulletin. v. 24,
       no. 12)

          1. Forests and forestry - Virginia.
          2. Wood-lots. I. O'Byrne, Joseph Wilbur,
       1894-   II.   Title.

NL 0438885   NIC NcD OrCS ICJ MH-A

LODEWICK, JOHN ELTON
   How much is a cord of pulpwood? A study of
pulpwood conversion factors in the Pacific Northwest. Pacific pulp & paper industry, 1935.
   10 p.

NL 0438886   Or

HD9757 Lodewick, John Elton, 1896-
.A5   Log, round timber and burl exports from
L6   Oregon and Washington 1920-1933. [Port-
pam   land, Ore.] U.S.D.A. Forest Service, Pacific
       Northwest Forest Experiment Station [1934]
          3 [10] p. tables (fold.) 27cm.

          1. Lumber - Commerce. I. U.S.D.A. Forest
       Service. Pacific Northwest Forest Experi-
       ment Station.   II. Title.

NL 0438887   OrCS

Lodewick, John Elton, 1896-
   ... Marketing woodland products in Virginia, by J. Elton
Lodewick, the Virginia Agricultural experiment station and
the Department of wood technology of the Virginia polytechnic institute cooperating. Blacksburg, Va., 1930.
   69 p. incl. illus., map, tables, diagrs. 23cm. (Virginia. Agricultural
experiment station, Blacksburg. Bulletin 276)

   1. Timber—Virginia. 2. Lumber trade—Virginia. I. Virginia polytechnic institute, Blacksburg. Department of wood technology. II. Title.

Title from Va. Polytech-   nic Inst.   A 32-2196
Library of Congress   [S123.E2 no. 276]

NL 0438888   ViBlbV ViU

L581.9755
                                                          T100
Lodewick, John Elton, 1896-
   ... Notable trees of Virginia, prepared by J. Elton Lodewick ...
and Mrs. Lynwood R. Holmes ... [Blacksburg, Va.,] Virginia
Polytechnic Institute [1931]
   24 p. illus. 29cm.   (Bulletin of the Virginia Polytechnic Institute ...
vol. XXIV, no. 7)

     NcRS NN MH   ViN Vi KMK
NL 0438889   ICJ WaPS MH-A MH OCl OrCS NcD OU CSt

Lodewick, John Elton, 1896-
   ... Seasonal activity of the cambium in some northeastern
trees, by J. Elton Lodewick ... Syracuse, N. Y., New York
state college of forestry [1928]
   87 p. illus., diagrs. 23 cm. (New York state college of forestry
at Syracuse university. Technical publication no. 23)
   New York state college of forestry at Syracuse university. Bulletin, v. 1, no. 2a. May, 1928.
   Thesis (PH. D.)—New York state college of forestry.
   Bibliography : p. 50-52.

   1. Cambium.
   QK725.L6   Agr 28—1331
U. S. Dept. of Agr. Libr.   99.9N486T no. 23
for Library of Congress   [a51e]

     OU MB PU DLC MU
NL 0438890   DNAL OrU MoU MH-A NNBG ViU NcRS NcD MiU

Lodewick, John Elton, 1896-
   Some summer-wood percentage relationships in the southern
pines ...
   (*In* U. S. Dept. of agriculture. Journal of agricultural research.
v. 46, no. 6, Mar. 15, 1933, p. 543-556. diagrs. 23cm. Washington,
1933)
   Contribution from Forest service (F—61)
   Published May 4, 1933.
   "Literature cited": p. 556.

   1. Pine. 2. Wood—[Specific gravity] I. Title: Summer-wood per-
centage relationships in the southern pines.
                                              Agr 33-442
Library, U. S. Dept. of   Agriculture 1Ag84J vol. 46, no. 6
Library of Congress   [S21.A75 vol. 46, no. 6]

NL 0438891   DNAL OU NcD OCl

VOLUME 338

Lodewick, John Elton, 1896–
Oregon. *State planning board.*
A study of lumber shipments from Oregon and Washington into other states and foreign nations during certain years between 1922 and 1932, with an analysis of the relative trade position of Oregon-Washington lumber and southern pine. A report from the Advisory committee on forestry to the Oregon State planning board, March 30, 1936. Submitted by the board to Governor Charles H. Martin and the Legislative assembly of the state of Oregon, April 1, 1936. Salem, Or., State printing department [1936]

Lodewick, John Elton, 1896–
... Volume of cascara bark shipments from the pacific northwest ... [Portland, Ore.] Pacific northwest forest experiment station, 1935.
3, [2] p. tables.
Mimeographed on one side only.

NL 0438893   WaPS

634.9   LODEWICK, J. Elton
L82w   West Coast log values. U.S. Forest service. Pacific Northwest forest and range experiment station, 1941.

no.1 Douglas fir from the Oregon Cascades. 1941.

NL 0438894   WaWW

4HD   Lodewick, John Elton, 1896–
1971   Wood-using industries of Virginia. Blacksburg, Va., Virginia Polytechnic Institute, 1929.
169 p.

(Engineering Extension Division Series, bull. no. 21)
Virginia Polytechnic Institute. Bulletin, v. 23, no. 1.

NL 0438895   DLC-P4 TU NcD OU DSI ICJ ViU MiU Vi

Lodewig, Fritz.
... Luftkrieg, schutzbauten. Zürich, Orell Füssli [1941]
98, [1] p. illus., plans. 21ᶜᵐ.
"Literaturverzeichnis": p. 91–98.

1. Air raid shelters. 2. Projectiles, Aerial. 3. Building, Bombproof.
I. Title.
Library of Congress   TH1097.L6   42–51014
         623.38

NL 0438896   DLC OCl

Lodewijcksz, Willem, 16th cent. Brevis enarratio.
G159
.B5
pt. 4
Rare Bk.
Coll.
Bry, Johann Theodor de, 1561–1623? *ed.*
[India Orientalis. pt. 4. Latin] Pars qvarta Indiæ Orientalis: qva primvm varij generis animalia, fructus, arbores: item, aromata ... similiter & margaritæ ... ac gemmarum species pleræqz, sicut in India tum effodiantur, tum generentur ... describuntur. Per Ioannem Hvgonem Lintschotanum, & nonnullos alios. Descriptioni huic adiectæ ... sunt annotationes Bernhardi Palvdani ... Secvndo: Nouissima Hollandorum in Indiam Orientalem nauigatio, ad veris anni 1598. introitum suscepta ... mense Iulio an. 1599. confecta, exponitur. Omnia ex Germanico Latinitate donata,

studio & opera Bilibaldi Strobæi. Et insuper in æs incisis iconib. illustrata & edita à Io. Theod. & Io. Israele de Bry. Francofurti, Apud M. Becker, 1601.

[Lodewijcksz, Willem] 16th cent.
D'Eerste Boeck. Historie van Jndien, waer inne verhaelt is de avontueren die de Hollandtsche Schepen begehent zijn: Oock een particulier verhael der Conditien, Religien, Manieren ende huijshoudinge der volckeren... Daer by ghevoecht de Opdoeninghen ende streckinghen vande Eylanden ende Zee-custen... Door G.M.A.W.L. Ghedruckt t'Amstelredam, by Cornelis Claesz., 1598. 64 [i. e. 69] f., 2 l. incl. diagrs., map. maps, plates. 19½ x 26½cm. (4°.)

Tiele: Navigateurs néerlandais, 111.
With engraved map on t.-p.
Numerous errors in foliation.
Journal kept on board the Mauritius during the first expedition under Cornelis de Houtman, 1595 to 1597.
With the double plate of the market at Bantam.
Without the map of Java and Sumatra mentioned on f. 35 [i. e. 36]ᵇ (which, according to Tiele, is wanting in all editions).

1. East Indies—Descr. and trav.,   to 1600. I. L., G. M. A. W.
II. Title.
N. Y. P. L.   October 28, 1941

NL 0438900   NN CtY

[Lodewijcksz, Willem] 16th cent.
D'eerste boeck. Historie van Jndien, waer inne verhaelt is de avontuere die de Hollandtsche schepen begejent zijn: oock een particulier verhael der conditien, religien, manierē eñ huyshoudinge der volckeren ... Daer by gevoecht de opdoeningen eñ streckingen vande eylanden eñ zee-custen ... Door G. M. A. W. L. t'Amstelredam: Ghedruckt by C. Claesz., 1609. 66 [i. e. 70] f., 1 l. incl. diagrs., map. maps, plates. 20 x 26cm. (4°.)

Tiele: Navigateurs néerlandais, 114.

With engraved map on t.-p.
Numerous errors in foliation.
Journal kept on board the Mauritius during the first expedition under Cornelis de Houtman, 1595 to 1597; first published 1598.
With the double plate of the market at Bantam.
Without the map of Java and Sumatra mentioned on f. 35 [i. e. 36]ᵇ (which, according to Tiele, is wanting in all editions).
With bookplate of Isaac Meulman.

1. East Indies—Descr. and trav.,   to 1600. I. L., G. M. A. W. II. Title.
                     Card revised
N. Y. P. L.   October 28, 1941

NL 0438902   NN CSmH

[Lodewijcksz, Willem] 16th cent.
'Teerste boeck. Historie van Jndien, waer inne verhaelt is de avontueren die de Hollantse schepen begejent zijn: oock een particulier verhael der conditien, religien, manieren eñ huys-houdinge der volckeren ... voor alle zeevarende ende curieuse liefhebbers, seer gheneuchlijck om lesen. Door G. M. A. W. L. Tot Amstelredam: By M. Colijn, boeckvercooper, 1617. 83 [i. e. 87] f., 1 l. incl. 2 pl. illus. (incl. maps.) 18½ x 26cm. (4°.)

(In: Colijn, Michiel. Oost-Jndische ende Uvest-Jndische voyagien. Amsterdam, 1619. [nr. 2])
JCB, 1919, II, 118. Tiele: Navigateurs néerlandais, 117.
With engraved map on t.-p.
Numerous errors in foliation.
Last leaf blank.

1. East Indies—Descr. and trav.,   to 1600. I. L., G. M. A. W.
II. Title.   *Card revised*
N. Y. P. L.   October 28, 1941

NL 0438904   NN RPJCB MiU-C

Lodewijcksz, Willem, 16th cent.
D'eerste boeck. 1915
see in Rouffaer, Gerret Pieter, 1860–1928.
De eerste schipvaart der Nederlanders naar Oost-Indië, onder Cornelis de Houtman, 1595–1597, journalen, documenten en anderen bescheiden ...

Lodewijcksz, Willem, 16th cent.

Eerste schip-vaert der Hollanders naer Oost-Indien met vier schepen onder 't beleydt van Cornelis Houtman uyt Texel t' zeyl ghegaen, anno 1595 ... t' Amstrdam, Voor Ioost Hartgers, 1648.

Lodewijcksz, Willem, 16th cent.
De eerste schipvaart der Nederlanders naar Oost-Indië, onder Cornelis de Houtman, 1595–1597, door Willem Lodewyccksz. In opdracht van den Raad van Beheer van het Koloniaal Instituut in het kort beschreven door G. B. Hooijer en, overeenkomstig diens ontwerp, door L. J. Vreugde gebeeldhouwd in de vestibule van het museum in het instituut te Amsterdam. Amsterdam: de Bussy [1921?]. 74 p. illus. 4°.

1. East Indies.—Description and   travel, to 1600. 2. Houtman, Cornelis de, d. 1599. 3. Hooijer, G. B.,   editor. 4. Koloniaal Instituut, Amsterdam.
N. Y. P. L.   August 17, 1922

NL 0438907   NN CU CtY

Lodewijcksz, Willem, 16th cent.
... Historie van Indien, waer inne verhaelt is de avonturen die de Hollantse Schepen bejegent zijn
see his 'Teerste boeck.

Lodewijcksz, Willem, 16th cent. Der Holländer
G159   Schifffahrt.
.B6
pt. 3
Rare Bk.
Coll.
Bry, Johann Theodor de, 1561–1623? *ed.*
[India Orientalis. pt. 3. German] Dritter Theil Indiæ Orientalis, darinnen erstlich das ander Theil der Schifffahrten Joann Huygens von Lintschotten ... so er in Orient gethan, begriffen ... II. Der Holländer Schifffahrt in die orientalische Insulen, Iauan vnd Sumatra ... III. Drey Schifffahrten der Holländer nach ... Indien, durch das Mittnächtigsche oder Eissmeer [von Gerardus de Veer] ... Alles von newem auss den niderländischen Exemplarien in Hochteutsch bracht. Sampt vielen schönen Figurn, vnd Landtafeln, in Kupffer gestochen, vnd an Tag geben, durch

Io. Theodor vnd Io. Israel de Bry. Franckfurt am Mayn, Gedruckt durch M. Becker, 1599.

[Lodewijcksz, Willem] 16th cent.
Indianische historia, ...

(In Bry, Theodor de [India orientalis. 2.ed.] Oppenheim, Gedruckt bey H. Gallern, 1616–17. 30 1/2 cm. 3.th, p. 77–155. pl.)

G169
.B8
office

NL 0438911   DLC

Lodewijcksz, Willem, 16th cent. Kurtze Erzehlung.
G159
.B6
pt. 4
Rare Bk.
Coll.
Bry, Johann Theodor de, 1561–1623? *ed.*
[India Orientalis. pt. 4. German] Vierder Theil der Orientalischen Indien, in welchem erstlich gehandelt wirdt, von allerley Thieren, Früchten, Obs vñ Bäumen, item von allerhand Würtz, Specereyen ... auch von Perlen ... so in ... Indien gefunden werden ... Beschrieben durch Johan Hugen von Lintschotten, vnd andere. Auch mit ... Annotationibus gezieret vnd erkläret durch Bernardum Paludanum. Zum andern, die letzte Reise der Holländer in die Ost-Indien, welche aussgefahren im Frühling dess 1598. Iahrs vnd ... wiederumb glücklich anheim gelanget, im Monat

Iulio dess 1599. Iahrs. Auss niederländischer Sprach in die hochteutsche versetzet durch M. G. A. V. D. Alles mit Kupfferstücken gezieret vnd an Tag geben durch Iohan Dieterich, vnd Iohan Israel de Bry. Franckfurt am Mayn, Getruckt bey W. Richter, 1600.

Lodewijcksz, Willem, 16th cent. Navigatio Hollandorum in insulas Orientales.
G159
.B5
pt. 3
Bry, Johann Theodor de, 1561–1623? *ed.*
[India Orientalis. pt. 3. Latin] Tertia pars Indiæ Orientalis: qua continentur I. Secunda pars nauigationum à Ioanne Hvgone Lintschotano in Orientem susceptarum ... II. Nauigatio Hollandorum in insulas Orientales, Iauan & Svmatram ... III. Tres nauigationes Hollandorum in ... Indiam per Septentrionalem ... Oceanum [Gerardo de Veer auctore] ... De Germanico in Latinum translata, & bono ordine disposita à Bilibaldo Strobæo. Adiectæ svnt tabulæ

cum iconibus alijs, in æs incisæ per Ioan. Theodor. & Ioan. Israel. de Bry: quorum sumptibus quoque hoc opus editum est. Francofvrti, Excudebat M. Beckerus, 1601.

VOLUME 338

B
1598
mLo

Lodewijcksz, Willem
Nova tabula insularum Iavae... Nieuwe caerte
op Java... ₍Amsterdam, Cornelius Nicolai,
1598₎

map   16 x 22 1/2 inches

1. East Indies. Maps.

NL   0438916   MnU

Lodewijcksz, Willem, 16th cent.

Stoomvaart-maatschappij "Nederland."
De oude weg naar Indië, om de Kaap. Wandversiering
in de zalen van het stoomschip Jan Pieterszoon Coen van
de Stoomvaart-maatschappij Nederland, naar de oorspronkelijke kaarten van Petrus Plancius en Jan Huy-
gen van Linschoten vervaardigd door C. A. Lion Cachet.
Met historische toelichting door Dr. F. C. Wieder ...
Amsterdam, Gedrukt voor de Stoomvaart-maatschappij
Nederland, 1915.

G
230
L6
1598
Cage

Lodewijcksz, Willem, 16th century.
Premier liure de l'histoire de la nauigation
aux Indes Orientales, par les hollandois... A
Amstelredam, Par Cornille Nicolas, 1598-1601.

2 pts. in 1 v. Fo. illus.
Pt. 2 has separate titlepage, lower half torn
away: Le second liure, iournal ou comptoir, contenant le vray discours et narration historique, du
voiage faict par les huict navires d'Amsterdam, au
mois de Mars l'an 1598... Aussi est icy adiouté un

vocabulaire des mots françois, iavans & malaites.
Appendix dated 1601.
Leader of the expedition was Cornelis de Houtman.

NL   0438919   DFo NNC

₍Lodewijcksz, Willem₎ 16th cent.
Premier Livre De Lhistoire De La Navigation Avx Indes
Orientales. Par Les Hollandois, Et Des Choses A Evx Advenves:
Ensemble Les Conditions, Les Mevrs, Et Manieres De Vivre Des
Nations, par eux abordees... Par G. M. A. VV. L. Imprimé
a Amstelredam par Cornille Nicolas. Anno 1598. 53 f., 1 l.
incl. pl. illus. (incl. maps, plans), double pl. 34½cm. (f°.)

JCB, 1919, I, 364.   Tiele: Navigateurs néerlandais, 113.
With engraved map on t-p.

With the double plate of the market at Bantam.
Without the map of Java and Sumatra mentioned on f. 24ᵇ (which, according to
Tiele, is wanting in all editions), but with the corresponding De-Bry map inserted.
With this is bound: Veer, Gerrit de. Vraye Description De Trois Voyages.
A Amstelredam, Anno 1598.

———— Second copy.   33cm. (f°.)

Without the double plate and the map of Java and Sumatra.

1. East Indies—Descr. and trav.,   to 1600.   I. L., G. M. A. W.
N. Y. P. L.   *Card revised*
                                    January 19, 1940

NL   0438921   NN RPJCB MB CSmH

₍Lodewijcksz, Willem₎ 16th cent.
Premier livre de l'histoire de la navigation avx Indes orientales, par les Hollandois; et des choses a evx advenves: ensemble les conditions, les meurs. & manieres de vivres des nations,
par eux abordees... Par G. M. A. W. L. A Amsterdam:
Imprimé chez C. Nicolas, l'an 1609. 53 f., 1 l. incl. pl. illus.
(incl. maps, plans), double pl. 35cm. (f°.)

Tiele: Navigateurs néerlandais, 115.
With engraved map on t-p.
With the double plate of the market at Bantam.

Without the map of Java and Sumatra mentioned on f. 24ᵇ (which, according to
Tiele, is wanting in all editions).
With several of the engraved illustrations wrongly placed.
With two de Bry maps inserted.

———— Second copy.   34cm. (f°.)

With several of the engraved illustrations wrongly placed.
Imperfect: f. 40 mutilated, double plate wanting (and the corresponding de Bry
plate inserted).

8-* KB (1609)
———— Third copy.   34cm. (f°.)

Imperfect: double pl. wanting, f. 26-27 mutilated.

———— Fourth copy.   34cm. (f°.)

Imperfect: plates wanting, f. 26-28, 33, 36, 49-50, 52 mutilated.
With supra-libros of Henri Ternaux-Compans.

1. East Indies—Descr. and trav.,   to 1600. I. L., G. M. A. W.
                                       Card revised

NL   0438924   NN ICU CSmH CtY MB NjP RPJCB MH

L₍odewijcksz₎, W₍illem₎ *16th cent.*
Prima pars descriptionis itineris navalis in Indiam Orientalem, earvmqve rervm qvæ navibvs battavis occvrre-
rvnt: vna cvm particvlari enarratione conditionum, mo-
rum, œconomiæ populorum, quos adnavigarunt. Præte-
rea de numismatis, aromatibus, speciebus & mercibus ibi-
dem venalibus, eorumque pretio. Insuper de insularum
apparentijs, tractibus, orisque regionum maritimis, vna
cum incolarum ad vivum delineatione; cuncta diversis ta-
bulis illustrata : omnibus mare navigantibus & rerum exte-

rarum studiosis, lectu periucunda. Authore G. M. A. VV.
L. Amstelrodami, ex officina Cornelij Nicolaj, 1598.
51 numb. l., 1 l. incl. illus., maps, plan. 1 fold. pl. 34ᶜᵐ.
Title vignette : engraved map.
49 engravings—including maps—which in the Dutch edition are on separate plates, are in this edition inserted in the text, with the exception of one
folded plate and one illustration.
Translation of the author's "D'eerste boeck. Historie van Indien," Amsterdam, C. Nicolas (i. e. C. Claesz) 1598.
1. East Indies — Disc. & explor.—Dutch. 2. Java—Descr. & trav.
3. Netherlands — Hist.—Wars of independence, 1556-1648. 4. Houtman,
Cornelis de, d. 1599.
                                           5-21604
Library of Congress   DS618.L82

NL   0438926   DLC IEN NjP NIC MnU RPJCB

Lodewijk, *graaf van Nassau*, 1538-1574.
Correspondentie van en betreffende Lodewijk van Nassau
en andere onuitgegeven documenten, verzameld door dr. P. J.
Blok ... Utrecht, Kemink & zoon, 1887.
xiii, ₍1₎, 210 p. 22½ᶜᵐ.   (*Half-title:* Werken uitgegeven door het Historisch genootschap gevestigd te Utrecht. Nieuwe reeks. nᵒ 47)

1. Netherlands—Hist.—Sources.   2. Netherlands—Hist.—Wars of in-
dependence, 1556-1648.   ɪ. Blok, Petrus Johannes, 1855-1929.
                                         33-9015
Library of Congress   DJ8.H68   no. 47
———— Copy 2.   DH185.L6
                    ₍2₎   (949.20082) 923.2492

NL   0438927   DLC CtY IaU MB

Lodewijk van Velthem, fl. 1293-1326.

Maerlant, Jacob van, 1235?-1300.
Jacob van Maerlant's Spiegel historiael, met de fragmenten
der later toegevoegde gedeelten, bewerkt door Philip Uten-
broeke en Lodewijc van Velthem. Van wege de Maatschappij
der Nederlandsche letterkunde te Leiden uitg. dʳ. M. de Vries
en dʳ. E. Verwijs ... Leiden, E. J. Brill, 1863-79.

Lodewijk van Velthem, *fl.* 1293-1326.
Lodewijk van Velthem's voortzetting van den Spiegel historiael (1248-1316) opnieuw uitgegeven door Herman vander
Linden en Willem de Vreese ... Brussel, Hayez, drukker der
K. Academie van België, 1906-38.
3 v. 30½ᶜᵐ. ₍Académie royale des sciences, des lettres et des beaux-
arts de Belgique, Brussels. Commission royale d'histoire. Publications
in quarto. 38₎
Title varies slightly.
"Tweede deel" (Bruxelles, M. Lamertin, 1931) edited by Herman vander Linden, Willem de Vreese and Paul de Keyser ; "Derde deel" (Brussel, Paleis der academiën, 1938) by Herman vander Linden, Paul de Keyser and Adolf van Loey.

A continuation of Jacob van Maerlant's Spiegel historiael.

ɪ. Maerlant, Jacob van, 1235?-1300. ɪɪ. Linden, Herman vander,
1868-   ed. ɪɪɪ. *Vreese, Willem de, 1869-1938, ed. ɪv. Keyser, Paul
de, 1891-   ed. v. *Loey, Adolphe van, 1905-   ed. vɪ. Title: Spiegel
historiael.
                                     41-30697
Library of Congress   DH403.A2   vol. 38

NL   0438930   NcD CSmH ICN MiU RPB OClW NcU IU
                     DLC DSI ICN MH CtY GU MoU NN ICU NNC

PT5568
.A1
1846

Lodewijk van Velthem, fl. 1293-1326, supposed
comp.

Lancelot. *Dutch.*
Roman van Lancelot (xɪɪɪᵉ eeuw) naar het ₍eenigbekende₎
handschrift der Koninklijke bibliotheek, op gezag van het gouvernement uitgegeven door dr. W. J. A. Jonckbloet. 's Gravenhage, W. P. van Stockum, 1846-49.

PT5569
.LSS6
1840

Lodewijk van Velthem, *fl.* 1293-1326.
Specimen e literis neerlandicis, exhibens Ludovici de Velthem chronici, quod inscribitur Speculum historiale, librum
ɪɪɪ, denuo editum secundum codicem ms. unicum, bibliothecae Acad. Lugd. Bat. atque annotatione illustratum, quod
... proponit Guilielmus Josephus Andreas Jonckbloet ...
Hagae Comitis, apud A. D. Schinkel, 1840.
₍5₎, 136 p. 26x21ᶜᵐ.

1. Dutch language—Early to 1500—Texts.

NL   0438932   ICU MnCS OCl MH

Lodewijk van Velthem, fl. 1296-1326.
Spiegel historiaal, of Rym-spiegel; zynde de Nederlandsche
rym-chronyk, van Lodewyk van Velthem, voor ruym 400 jaaren
dichtmaat gebracht. Behelsende een meenigte van aanmerkens-
waardige geschiedenissen... Beginnende met het jaar 1248, toen
Graaf Willem van Hollandt keyser werdt, en eyndigende met het
jaar 1316 van welke de schryver is tydtgenoot geweest. Nooyt
voor desen gedrukt. Getrouwelyk uytgegeven, volgens het
oorspronklyke handtschrift, op perkement geschreeven, en met

noodige verklaaringen opgeheldert, door Issac Le Long.   T⁺
Amsterdam: H. van Eyl, 1717.   8 p.l., 483 p.   33½cm.

1. Poetry, Dutch, Middle.   ɪ. Le Long, Isaac, 1683-1744, ed.
II. Title.   *Revised*
N. Y. P. L.   May 7, 1935

NL   0438934   NN WaU MiU

Lodewijk, Frans Alexander, Ridder von Rappard.

see

Rappard, Frans Alexander Lodewijk, ridder van,
d. 1888

Lodewijk, Harm
see   Lodewyk, Harm.

Lodewijk, Tom.
Opstand in Zuid-Afrika; roman.   Kampen, J. H.
Kok, 1953.   199 p.   22cm.

1. Fiction, Dutch. 2. Africa, South—Hist.—
Fiction.

NL   0438937   NN

Lodewijk de Geer. Eene bijdrage tot de handel-
geschiedenis van Amsterdam, in de zeventiende
eeuw
     see under ₍Geer van Jutphaas, Jan Lodewijk
Willem, baron de₎ 1784-1857.

Lodewijk de Geer van Finspong en Leufsta
(1587-1652)
     see under ₍Geer van Jutphaas, Jan Lodewijk
Willem, baron de₎ 1784-1857.

Lodewijk de Zestiende, koning van Vrankrijk,
treurspel. In twee bedrijven.   Amsterdam,
W. Holtrop, 1793.
vii (1), 40 p.   16°.

NL   0438940   NN

VOLUME 338

Z
590.7
L 823
   LODEWIJKS, JACOBUS MARINUS.
     Natuur thuis- en buiten. Met tekeningen
en foto's van de schrijver, woord vooraf van
A. J. Portielje.   Amsterdam, Uitg.Ploegsma, 1951.
     153p.   illus., plates.   20cm.

      Contents. -De schoonheid van onze liefhebberij. -De natuur in huis. -De taal der
vissen. -Salamanders en mensen. -Herfstzorgen. -Thuis is toch niet alles.

NL   0438941   PU PU-BZ

Lodewijks, Jacobus Marinus.
   Onderzoekingen over mogelijke oorzaken van neotenie.
Lekkerkerk, Drukkerij Gebr. Den Oudsten [1948]
   92 p. illus. (part col.) 24 cm.

   Proefschrift—Leyden.
   "Stellingen": [1] p. inserted.
   "Literatuur": p. [88]–92.

   1. Neoteny. 2. Salamanders.

   QL669.L75   50–54853

NL   0438942   DLC NIC CtY CU

Lodewijks, Johan Anthon.
   Vegetatieve vermenigvuldiging van oenothera's ... Haarlem, Gedrukt ter boek-, kunst- en handelsdrukkerij, firma Ruijgrok & co. [1908]
   4 p. l., 113 p., 1 l. 24½ᶜᵐ.

   Proefschrift—Amsterdam.
   "Litteratuur-overzicht": p. [109]–113.
   "Stellingen": 2 p. laid in

   1. Oenothera.

                                  Agr 28–439
   Library, U. S. Dept. of   Agriculture 463.6L82

NL   0438943   DNAL MiU

Lodewycksz. Willem,

    see

Lodewijcksz, Willem,

Lodewyckx, Augustin, 1876—
   Australië waarheen? Met een woord vooraf door H. van Werveke. Meppel, J. A. Boom [1950]
   240 p. plates, ports., map (on lining paper) 24 cm. (Terra-bibliotheek)
   Bibliography: p. 237–238.

   1. Australia.   I. Title.

   DU95.L6   53–22761

NL   0438945   DLC CtY ICN OU NN CLU NjR

Lodewyckx, Augustin, 1876-
   Australië waarheen? 2.druk. Meppel, Boom [1952]
   240 p. illus. (Terra-bibliotheek, 7)

NL   0438946   MH

DU260
D5
   Lodewyckx, Augustin, ed.

   Dietrich, Amalie (Nelle) 1821–1891.
     Australische briefe, von Amalie Dietrich; with a biographical sketch, exercises and a vocabulary, edited by Augustin Lodewyckx ... Melbourne and London, Melbourne university press in association with Oxford university press, 1943.

Lodewyckx, Augustin, 1876-
   ... Die Deutschen in Australien, von prof. dr. A. Lodewyckx. Mit 45 abbildungen, 3 karten und 1 kartenbeilage. Stuttgart, Ausland und heimat verlagsaktiengesellschaft, 1932.
     272 p. incl. plates, ports., maps (1 fold.) 23½ᶜᵐ. (Schriften des Deutschen ausland-instituts Stuttgart. A. Kultur-historische reihe. bd. 32)
   "Literatur": p. 253.

   1. Germans in Australia.   I. Title.

                                 33–14748
   Library of Congress   DU122.G4L6
                                 325.3430994

NL   0438948   DLC CU NcD PPLT NN

Lodewyckx, Augustin, 1876-
   Das Deutschtum in Australien, von Dr. A. Lodewyckx.
[Berlin: Deutscher Schutzbund Verlag, 1926?]   20 p. incl. map.
12°. (Taschenbuch des Grenz- und Auslanddeutschtums. Heft 40.)

   1. Germans in Australia.
   N. Y. P. L.   February 7, 1928

NL   0438949   NN

4DU-9   Lodewyckx, Augustin, 1876 -
     Das Deutschtum in Victoria, Festschrift zum hundertjaehrigen Jubilaeum des Staates Victoria, 1834-1934. Unter Mitwirkung von L. Beer und A. Kersten, im Auftrage des Deutschen Hundertjahrfeier-Ausschusses in Melbourne. [
     48 p.

NL   0438950   DLC-P4

Lodewyckx, Augustin, *ed.*
   Five German tales. Fünf märchen. With an introduction and a vocabulary. Edited by Augustin Lodewyckx ... Melbourne and London, Melbourne university press in association with Oxford university press, 1941.
   104 p. 18½ᶜᵐ. [The University of Melbourne. German series. No. 1]

   1. Fairy tales. 2. German language—Chrestomathies and readers.
I. Title. II. Title: Fünf märchen.
                                 45–42937
   Library of Congress   PF3127.F3L6
                                 438.6

NL   0438951   DLC CU IU

Lodewyckx, Augustin, 1876 -
   A handbook of Dutch, comprising grammar, reader, exercises and vocabulary, by Augustin Lodewyckx ... Melbourne and London, Melbourne university press, in association with Oxford university press [1944]
   xiv, 351, [1] p. 18ᶜᵐ.

   "First published 1944."
   "Sources of contemporary texts": p. vii. "Books recommended for further study": p. 351.

   1. Dutch language—Grammar—1870-   2. Dutch language—Chrestomathies and readers.
                                 45–17816
   Library of Congress   PF111.L55
                                 439.318242

NL   0438952   DLC OrP OrCS CtY OCU IEN NN

916.75
1821k
   Lodewyckx, Augustin, 1876-
     Katanga en Zuid-Afrika; vier lezingen.
Gent, A. Hoste [1912?]
     135p. illus. 20cm. ("Uitgave van het Willems-Fonds No. 151.")

     Bibliography: p. [134]-135.

     1. Katanga, Belgian Congo. 2. Belgium. Colonies. Africa. 3. Belgians in Africa. I. Title.

NL   0438953   IEN CU

Lodewyckx, Augustin, 1876 –
   Nieuw-Zeeland, een Eden in de Zuidzee. Meppel, J. A. Boom, 1952.
   304 p. illus. 25 cm. (Terra-bibliotheek [12])

   1. New Zealand.

   DU411.L6   55–42319 ‡

NL   0438954   DLC KyU NN

Lodewyckx, Augustin, 1876 —
   Overzicht der Nederlandsche letterkunde.
[Carlton] Melbourne University Press [1946]
   60 p.

   1. Dutch literature - Hist. and crit.

NL   0438955   NNC MH NcU MiU CU CtY

Lodewyk Philippus, Hertog von Orléans
    see   Orléans, Louis Philippe Joseph,
duc d', 1747-1793.

Lodewyk Theodorus, grave van Nassau La Leck
    see   Nassau la Leck, Lodewijk Theodorus
graaf van, 1697?-1781.

Lodewyk, Harm.
   Thúskomst. Snits, Koster, 1946.
   213 p. 23 cm.

   I. Title.
                                  A 48–3540*
   Harvard Univ. Library
   for Library of Congress   [1]

NL   0438958   MH

Lodewyk, Harm.
   Yn oare wei. Snits, Koster [1949]
   232 p. 30 cm.

   I. Title.
                                  A 50–2648
   Harvard Univ. Library
   for Library of Congress

NL   0438959   MH NNC

Lodewyks (P.)
   Zedig onderzoek van 't Zedig onderzoek of 't Verlangen van Europa beschaafd. Ophelderende de vraag, of de Vereenigde Nederlanden in de tegenwoordige tyts-omstandigheden zig konnen houden buiten 't geschil tusschen de koninginne van Hungaryen en Boheemen, en eenige tegen haare majesteyt verbonden vorsten. 's Gravenhage: L. Berkoske, jr., 1742. 1 p.l., 66 pp. 12°.

NL   0438960   NN

Lodge, *Mrs.*
   Under a ban. By Mrs. Lodge. New York, G. Munro [1884]
   270 p. 18½ᶜᵐ. (*On cover:* The seaside library. Pocket ed. no. 174)

                             CA 9–1995 Unrev'd
   Library of Congress   PZ3.L8205U

NL   0438961   DLC

[LODGE, A.]
   Forty years ago, a sketch of Yorkshire life;
and Poems, by A. L. Huddersfield, J. Woodhead, 1869.

NL   0438962   MH

VOLUME 338

Lodge, Adam, tr.

Schiller, Johann Christoph Friedrich von, 1759–1805.
The dramas of Frederick Schiller: Don Carlos—Mary
Stuart—The maid of Orleans—The bride of Messina; tr. by
R. D. Boylan, Joseph Mellish, Anna Swanwick, and A. Lodge.
London, G. Bell and sons, 1901.

Lodge, Adam, tr.   FOR OTHER EDITIONS
                         SEE MAIN ENTRY

Schiller, Johann Christoph Friedrich von, 1759–1805.
... Historical dramas, etc.: Don Carlos.—Mary Stuart.—The Maid of Orleans.—The bride of Messina. **Tr.
from the German.** London, Bell & Daldy, 1870.

Lodge, Adam, tr.

Schiller, Johann Christoph Friedrich von, 1759–1805.
The Maid of Orleans; the bride of Messina: Wilhelm Tell;
Demetrius; by Friedrich Schiller, tr. by Sir Theodore Martin,
Anna Swanwick, and A. Lodge; ed. by Nathan Haskell Dole.
Boston, F. A. Niccolls & company [1902]

Lodge, Adam, tr.

Schiller, Johann Christoph Friedrich von, 1759–1805.
Schiller's complete works. Ed., with careful revisions and
new translations, by Charles J. Hempel ... Philadelphia,
I. Kohler, 1861.

Lilly
PR 4891
.L 5 W6   LODGE, ADAM
           Won: not wooed; a drama in five acts and
           in verse. Adapted for the English stage from
           "Die Schule des Lebens," By Adam Lodge ...
           London, W. A. Stanley, 1874.
           95, [1] p. 20.5 cm.

           First edition.

NL 0438967   InU MH

LODGE, Adam.
Won, not wooed; a drama in five acts, and in
verse. Adapted for the English stage from "Die
schule des lebens". 2d ed. London, Wyman &
sons, 1877.

pp. 67.

NL 0438968   MH

Lodge, Alfred, 1855? —   517.2 Q200
Differential calculus for beginners, by Alfred Lodge, M.A. ...
With an introduction by Sir Oliver J. Lodge. ... London,
G. Bell & Sons; Cambridge, Deighton, Bell, & Co., 1902.
xxv, 278 p. diagrs. 18½ cm.

NL 0438969   ICJ NIC NN MB

Lodge, Alfred.

QA304   Differential calculus for beginners,
L64   with an introd. by Sir Oliver Lodge.
1905   2d ed., rev. London, G. Bell & sons,
        1905.
text books   xxv, 278 p. diagrs. 19cm.
        (Cambridge mathematical series)

NL 0438970   RPB MiU

Lodge, Alfred, 1855?—   Math 3009.08.5
Differential calculus for beginners; with an introduction by Sir
Oliver Lodge. 3d ed., revised. London, G. Bell & Sons, etc. etc.
1908.
pp. xxvii, 299. (Cambridge, [Eng.] mathematical series.)

Calculus-Differential||Series|

NL 0438971   MH

Lodge, Alfred
**Differential calculus for beginners; with an
introd. by Sir Oliver Lodge. 4th ed. rev.
Bell, 1913.**
299 p.

NL 0438972   MiD

Lodge, Alfred.   3938.160
Differential calculus for beginners. With an introduction by Sir
Oliver Lodge. 5th edition, revised.
London. Bell. 1920. xxvii, 299 pp. [Cambridge Mathematical
series.] 18 cm., in 8s.

M168o — S.r. — Calculus. Differential. — Lodge, Sir Oliver Joseph, pref., 1851–

NL 0438973   MB NBuU MH PP

Lodge, Alfred, 1855?–   ed.

Lodge, *Sir* Oliver Joseph, 1851–
Elementary mechanics including hydrostatics and pneumatics. by Oliver J. Lodge ... New ed. Completely rev. by
the author and by Alfred Lodge ... answers rev. by Charles S.
Lodge, B. A. New York, D. Van Nostrand company [1896]

QA308   **Lodge, Alfred**
L822   **Integral calculus for beginners by Alfred**
1905   **Lodge...London: George Bell and Sons, 1905.**
        xiii, 203 p. 18.5 cm.

NL 0438975   DAU MH NjR

510.77 Lodge, Alfred.
L82i   Integral calculus for beginners.
        London, 1911.
        203p. diagrs. (Cambridge math-
        ematical series)

NL 0438976   IU

LODGE, Alfred, 1855?–
Integral calculus for beginners. London.
Bell. 1920.

xiii, 203 pp. Diagrams.
(Cambridge Mathematical Series.) 18 1/2 cm.

NL 0438977   MBC NBuU MiD

Lodge, Alfred, 1855? —   511.8 P501
Mensuration for senior students. xiii,274 p. il. D. London:
Longmans, Green, & Co., 1895.

NL 0438978   ICJ OC1W MB

Lodge, Anthony   ed.
A selection from some new poetry, edited and
introduced by Anthony Lodge. [Brooklyn, N. Y.,
1951.
cover-title, 35 p. 24cm.

1. English poetry - 20th cent. 2. American
poetry - 20th cent.

NL 0438979   NNC

GZ851   Lodge, B   & Co.
+A32   Ward maps of Albany, N.Y. ...
L8   [Albany] c1916.
        8 plates. maps. 26 x 35 cm.

        Cover title.

        1. Albany, N.Y.   - Maps.

NL 0438980   WHi

Lodge, B., & co.
Ward maps of Albany, N. Y., showing block numbers as desig-
nated in the assessors' books ... Maps drawn by Arthur B.
Murphy. cover-title, 19 maps. obl. 4°. [Albany, N. Y.] B.
Lodge & co. c1916.   4936
NOTE.—The following noted on title-page: "The maps in this book can be
revised periodically at a nominal cost."

NL 0438981   DLC

Lodge, Barton, ed.

Palladius, Rutilius Taurus Æmilianus.
Palladius On husbandrie. From the unique ms. of about
1420 A. D. in Colchester castle. Ed. by the Rev. Barton Lodge
... With a ryme index ed. by Sidney J. H. Herrtage ... London, Pub. for the Early English text society, by N. Trübner &
co., 1873 and 1879.

LODGE, BARTON
Roman sepulchral monument found at Colchester.
[Colchester, 1876] 8 p. 22cm.

1. Colchester, Eng. --Archaeology--Roman remains. 2. Monuments,
Sepulchral--Gt. Br.--Eng.--Colchester. i. subs. for L-, B.

NL 0438983   NN

Lodge, Charles S.

Lodge, *Sir* Oliver Joseph, 1851–
Elementary mechanics including hydrostatics and pneumatics. by Oliver J. Lodge ... New ed. Completely rev. by
the author and by Alfred Lodge ... answers rev. by Charles S
Lodge, B. A. New York, D. Van Nostrand company [1896]

Lodge, E   Ballard.
The human teeth and their preservation. [By] E. Ballard Lodge ... [n. p.] c1897.
27 p. illus. 18¼ᶜᵐ.

1. Teeth—Care and hygiene.

Library of Congress   RK61.L82   7–77501

NL 0438985   DLC

Lodge, Edgar Arthur, 1894–
A mortgage analysis; a twenty-eight year record of the mortgages of Home title insurance company, 1906–1934, by Edgar
A. Lodge ... with foreword by Louis H. Pink ... and comments by Philip A. Benson ... and James Lee Loomis ...
[Brooklyn, Home title guaranty company, 1935]
ix, 81, xi–xx p., 1 l. diagrs. 23ᶜᵐ.

"Of this book there were printed ... five thousand copies for private
distribution."

1. Home title insurance company, Brooklyn. 2. Mortgages—U. S.
i. Home title guaranty company, Brooklyn. ii. Title.

Library of Congress   HG5095.L65   35–13249
—— Copy 2.
Copyright A 84784   332.7

NL 0438986   DLC OrP DNAL PU-W OC1FRB

VOLUME 338

Lodge, Edmund, 1756–1839.
Catalogue of the historical, genealogical, and miscellaneous library of the late Edmund Lodge ... With a portion of the heraldic and miscellaneous library of Stephen Martin Leake. [Sold at auction by Sotheby, 11 Mar. & following day, 1839.] [London, 1839]

28p.
Priced, with buyers' names.

NL 0438987　　MH

Lodge, Edmund, 1756–1839.
The genealogy of the existing British peerage, with brief sketches of the family histories of the nobility. By Edmund Lodge, esq. ... With engravings of the arms. London, Saunders and Otley, 1832.

4 p. l., 409, [1] p. 88 pl. on 44 l. 21ᶜᵐ.

Plates at end are printed on both sides and have special t.-p.: "Arms of the peers, peeresses, &c., of the United Kingdom."

1. Gt. Brit.—Peerage.　　I. Title.

18-5908

Library of Congress　　CS420.L8 1832

NL 0438988　　DLC MdBP PP DS ViU

Lodge, Edmund, 1756–1839,
Genealogy of the existing British Peerage. Ed. 3. London, 1834.
502, 88 p.

NL 0438989　　PHi

Lodge, Edmund, 1756–1839
The genealogy of the existing British peerage, with sketches of the family histories of the nobility, by Edmund Lodge, esq... 6th ed. London, Saunders and Otley, 1838.
531, [1] p. illus. (coats of arms)

NL 0438990　　MiD-B NN

Lodge, Edmund, 1756–1839
The genealogy of the existing British peerage, with sketches of the family histories of the nobility. By Edmund Lodge, esq... 7th ed. With the arms of the peers. London, Saunders and Otley, 1840.
4 p. l., 532, [1] p.

Plates at end are printed on both sides and have special t.-p.: "Arms of the peers, peeresses &c., of the United Kingdom."

NL 0438991　　MiD-B CtY

Lodge, Edmund, 1756–1839.
The genealogy of the existing British peerage, with sketches of the family histories of the nobility, by Edmund Lodge, esq. ... 8th ed. London, Saunders and Otley, 1842.

18 p. l., 531, [1] p. illus. (coats of arms) 23ᶜᵐ.

1. Gt. Brit.—Peerage.　　I. Title.

18-10503

Library of Congress　　CS420.L8 1842

NL 0438992　　DLC

Lodge, Edmund, 1756–1839.
The genealogy of the existing British peerage, with sketches of the family histories of the nobility, by Edmund Lodge... With the arms of the peers. London: Saunders and Otley, 1847.
xxxix, xi–xii, 531 p. illus. (coats of arms.) 23½cm.

246675. 1. Peerage—Gt. Br.　　　*Card revised*
N. Y. P. L.　　　　　　　　December 20, 1940

NL 0438993　　NN

Lodge, Edmund, 1756–1839.
The genealogy of the existing British peerage and baronetage, containing the family histories of the nobility ... By Edmund Lodge, esq. ... With the arms of the peers. New and enl. ed. London, Hurst and Blackett, 1859.

xvi, 870 p. illus. (coats of arms) 24½ᶜᵐ.

1. Gt. Brit.—Peerage.　　I. Title.

18-10504

Library of Congress　　CS420.L8 1859

NL 0438994　　DLC NN OU

Lodge, Edmund.
Holbein's portraits of celebrated personages of the court of Henry VIII
see under　Holbein, Hans, the younger, 1497–1543.

Lodge, Edmund, 1756–1839.
[Manning, Anne] 1807–1879.
The household of Sir Thomas More. Libellus a Margareta More [pseud.] quindecim annos nata, Chelseiæ inceptus ... New York, C. Scribner, 1852.

Lodge, Edmund, 1756–1839.
Illustrations of British history, biography, and manners, in the reigns of Henry VIII, Edward VI, Mary, Elizabeth, and James I, exhibited in a series of original papers, selected from the manuscripts of the noble families of Howard, Talbot, and Cecil; containing, among a variety of interesting pieces, a great part of the correspondence of Elizabeth, and her ministers, with George, the sixth earl of Shrewsbury, during the fifteen years in which Mary queen of Scots remained in his custody: with numerous notes and ob-　　servations. By Edmund

Lodge ... London: Sold by G. Nicol ... 1791.
3 v. 15 pl. (incl. fronts., facsims.) 30 x 22½ᶜᵐ.

First edition.
Signatures: v.1. 1 leaf unsigned, a–f⁴, g¹, h², B–Z⁴, Aa–Zz⁴, 3A–3D⁴ (3B4 blank); v.2. 1 leaf unsigned, B–Z⁴, Aa–Zz⁴, 3A–3H⁴, 3I² (3K–3L⁴ 3I2 blank); v.3. 1 leaf unsigned, B–Z⁴, Aa–Zz⁴, 3A–3G⁴, 3H².
Page 162, v.3 in-　correctly numbered 168.
Marginal notes.
Bound in old sprin-　kled calf, v.1 rebacked.

DFo TU NPV OC1W OKentU AAP IEN WaU CSt CU IaU OC
NL 0438998　　CLU-C CtY MB CSmH OC1 MH PPL PPFr DFi

Lodge, Edmund, 1756–1839.
Illustrations of British history, biography, and manners, in the reigns of Henry VIII, Edward VI, Mary, Elizabeth, & James I, exhibited in a series of original papers, selected from the mss. of the noble families of Howard, Talbot, and Cecil; containing ... a great part of the correspondence of Elizabeth and her ministers, with George, sixth earl of Shrewsbury, during the fifteen years in which Mary, queen of Scots, remained in his custody. With numerous notes and observations by Edmund Lodge ... 2d ed. with additions, rev. and cor. ... London, J. Chidley, 1838.
3 v. front. (port.) 22ᶜᵐ.
1. Gt. Brit.—Hist.　　　Tudors, 1485–1603.　2. Gt. Brit.—
Hist.—James I, 1603–1625.

Library of Congress　　DA310.L62　　2-21531

OCU PPiPT
OC1WHi MiU ViU MB NN PHi PU TxHU CSt ScCleU NjP WU
NL 0438999　　DLC OrP NcU TxU NcD CtY MnU MWA MdBP

[Lodge, Edmund] 1756–1839.
Life of Sir Julius Caesar ... with memoirs of his family and descendants. To which is added, Numerus infaustus, an historical work, by Charles Caesar. London, R. Wilkinson, 1810.
vi, 116p. illus., ports. 37cm.

"Numerus infaustus. A short view of the unfortunate reigns of six kings of England": p. [79]–111.

1. Caesar, Sir Julius, 1558–1636. 2. Gt. Brit.—Kings and　　rulers. I. Caesar, Charles, 1636–1707.

NL 0439000　　IU

Lodge, Edmund, 1756–1839.
Life of Sir Julius Cæsar ... with memoirs of his family and descendants, by Edmund Lodge ... To which is added, Numerus infaustus, an historical work, by Charles Cæsar ... [2d ed.] London, J. Hatchard and son [etc.] 1827.
vi, 116 p. 2 pl., 18 port., fold. geneal. tab. 34½ᶜᵐ.

"Numerus infaustus. A short view of the unfortunate reigns of six kings of England": p. [79]–111.

1. Caesar, Sir Julius, 1558–1636. 2. Caesar family. 3. Gt. Brit.—Kings and rulers. I. Caesar, Charles, 1636–1707.

Library of Congress　　DA378.C2L6　　5–5155

NL 0439001　　DLC PPL MWA IEN ViU CtY NcU

Lodge, Edmund, 1756–1837.
The peerage and baronetage of the British empire ... Ed. 28, rev. & enl. London, Hurst, 1859.
78 + 861 p. illus. O.

NL 0439002　　OC1

Lodge, Edmund
The peerage and baronetage of the British Empire as at present existing...with the arms of the peers. 29th ed. rev. and enl. London, 1860.

NL 0439003　　NN MWA

Lodge, Edmund, 1756–1839.
The peerage and baronetage of the British empire as at present existing; arranged and printed from the personal communications of the nobility ... By Edmund Lodge ... with the arms of the peers. 30th ed., rev. and enl. London, Hurst and Blackett, 1861.
lxxx, 839, [1] p. illus. 23½ᶜᵐ.

Dedication signed: Anne, Eliza, and Maria Innes, editors.
"From motives of benevolence Lodge lent his name to an 'Annual peerage and baronetage,' 4 vols. 12 mo, 1827–9, reissued in 1832 as the 'Peerage of the British empire,' &c., which was in reality the compilation of Anne, Eliza, and Maria Innes. The work is still published as 'Lodge's Peerage'."—Dict. nat. biog.

In his preface to the 1st ed. Lodge says that the work "is classed in two volumes, the one [i. e., The peerage of the British empire; comprising the living subjects of the British peerage, including their collateral branches ... and the other [i. e. The genealogy of the British empire, 1832; exhibiting concise historical sketches of their ancestry and families ... Each volume may be considered either as a whole or as a moiety." They are usually regarded as independent volumes, the latter being by Lodge himself and from its nature not calling for a new ed. each year.

1. Gt. Brit.—Peerage.　　I. Innes, Anne, ed.　II. Innes, Eliza, ed.
III. Innes, Maria, ed.　　　　　　　　　　　　1–3625 Revised

Library of Congress　　CS420.L8 1861

NL 0439005　　DLC

CS420
L8
1862

Lodge, Edmund, 1756–1839.
The peerage and baronetage of the British empire as at present existing. Arranged and printed from the personal communications of the nobility. Under the gracious patronage of the Queen's most excellent majesty...with the arms of the peers. 31st ed., rev. and enl. London, Hurst and Blackett, 1862.
858p. illus. 25cm.

1. Gt. Brit. — Peerage.

NL 0439006　　IaU

Lodge, Edmund, 1756–1839.
The peerage and baronetage of the British Empire as at present existing, arr. and printed from the personal communications of the nobility. With the arms of the peers. 32d ed., rev. and enl. London, Hurst and Blackett, 1863.
lx, 808 p. illus., coats of arms. 24 cm.

1. Gt. Brit.—Peerage.

CS420.L8 1863　　　49–41111*

NL 0439007　　DLC

VOLUME 338

929.72 Lodge, Edmund, 1756-1839.
L82p   The peerage and baronetage of the British empire
1867   as at present existing; arranged and printed from
the personal communications of the nobility ...
36th ed., rev. and enl.   London, Hurst and
Blackett, 1867.
    lxii, 835p.   illus.(coats of arms)
    Title vignette.

    1. Great Britain--Peerage. 2. Great Britain--
Baronetage. 3. Knights and knighthood--Great
Britain. 4. Heraldry--Great Britain.

NL   0439008   IU CtY

Lodge, Edmund, 1756-1839.
    The peerage and baronetage of the British
empire as at present existing. Arranged and
printed from the personal communications of
the nobility... 37th ed., rev. and enl.   London,
Hurst and Blackett, 1868.
    2 p.l., [vii]-lxii, 842 p.   illus. (Coats-of
Arms)

NL   0439009   OClWHi

929.72 Lodge, Edmund, 1756-1839.
L82p   The peerage and baronetage of the British empire
1873   as at present existing; arranged and printed from
the personal communications of the nobility ... 42d
ed., rev. and enl.   London, Hurst and Blackett,
1873.
    lxi, 863p.   illus.(coats of arms)
    Title vignette.

    1. Great Britain--Peerage. 2. Great Britain--
Baronetage. 3. Knights and knighthood--Great
Britain. 4. Heraldry--Great Britain.

NL   0439010   IU NjP

LODGE, Edmund. 1756-1839.   *243?
    The peerage and baronetage of the British empire as at present
isting. With the arms of the peers. 43d, 47th, 50-61st edition.
London : Hurst and Blackett. 1874-92. 14 v. L. 8°.

NL   0439011   MB OCl

F   LODGE, EDMUND, 1756-1839.
0845   The peerage and baronetage of the British em-
.52   pire as at present existing. Arranged and printed
from the personal communications of the nobility
1874   43d edition, revised and enlarged.   London, Hurst
and Blackett, 1874.
    lxv, 869p.   24cm.
    "From motives of benevolence Lodge lent his
name to an 'Annual peerage and baronetage', 4
vols. 1827-9, reissued in 1832 as the 'Peerage of
the British empire', &c., which was in reality the
compilation of Anne.   Eliza, and Maria Innes.
The work is still   published as 'Lodge's
Peerage."--Dict. nat. biog.

NL   0439012   ICN MWelC WHi PU

Lodge, Edmund, 1756-1839.
    The peerage and baronetage of the British
empire as at present existing. Arranged and
printed from the personal communications of the no
nobility... By Edmund Lodge...With the arms of
the peers. 45th ed., rev. and el.   London,
Hurst and Blackett, 1876.
    xlvi, 886 p.   coats of arms. 25 cm.

NL   0439013   NcD

929.72 Lodge, Edmund, 1756-1839.
L82p   The peerage and baronetage of the British empire
1877   as at present existing. Arranged and printed from
the personal communications of the nobility. Under the gracious patronage of the Queen's most excellent majesty ... with the arms of the peers.
46th ed., rev. and enl.   London, Hurst and Blackett, 1877.
    lxiv, 892p.   illus.

    1. Great Britain--Peerage. 2. Great Britain--
Baronetage. 3. Knights and knighthood--Great
Britain. 4. Her-   aldry--Great Britain.

NL   0439014   IU

929.72 Lodge, Edmund, 1756-1839.
L82p   The peerage and baronetage of the British empire
1879   as at present existing. Arranged and printed from
the personal communications of the nobility. Under the gracious patronage of the Queen's most excellent majesty ... with the arms of the peers.
48th ed., rev. and enl.   London, Hurst and Blackett, 1879.
    lxiv, 881p.   illus.

    1. Great Britain--Peerage. 2. Great Britain--
Baronetage. 3. Knights and knighthood--Great Britain. 4. Heraldry--Great Britain.

NL   0439015   IU PHi

CS420 Lodge, Edmund, 1756-1839.
.L82   The peerage and baronetage of the
British empire as at present existing,
arranged and printed from the personal
communications of the nobility, under the
gracious patronage of the queen's most
excellent majesty, by Edmund Lodge ...
5th ed., rev. and enl.   London, Hurst
and Blackett, 1881.
    lxiv, 892 p.   illus.(coats of arms)
24cm.

    Title vignette

NL   0439016   MnHi I

Lodge, Edmund. 1756-1839.
    Peerage and baronetage of the British
empire as at present existing. Arranged and
printed from the personal communications of
the nobility. 56 ed. London, 1887. 8°. 2784
    The same. 57 ed. London, 1888. 8°. 2784

NL   0439017   MdBP

Lodge, Edmund, 1756-1839.
    The peerage and baronetage of the British
empire as at present existing. Arranged and
printed from the personal communications of
the nobility...By Edmund Lodge...With the
arms of the peers. 59th ed., rev. and enl.
London, Hurst and Blackett, limited, 1890.
    2 p.l., vii-lxiv 956, [1] p.   illus.   24 cm.

NL   0439018   CU

Lodge, Edmund
    Peerage and baronetage of the British empire...
London, Hurst, 1897.

NL   0439019   PPRCl MdBP

Lodge, Edmund, 1756-1839.
    The peerage and baronetage of the British
Empire as at present existing, arranged and
printed from the personal communications of
the nobility... With the arms of the peers.
68 ed., rev. and enl.   London, Hurst and
Blackett, 1899.   lxvii,1077 p.   illus.
coats of arms.   24cm.

    1. Peerage-- Great Britain.

NL   0439020   NN WaS

Lodge, Edmund, 1756-1839.
    The peerage and baronetage of the British empire as
at present existing. Arranged and printed from the personal communications of the nobility ... By Edmund
Lodge ... With the arms of the peers. 70th ed., rev. and
enl. London, Hurst and Blackett, limited, 1901.
    lxvii, 1107, [1] p. illus. 24ᶜᵐ.
    "From motives of benevolence Lodge lent his name to an 'Annual peer-
age and baronetage,' 4 vols. 12 mo, 1827-9, reissued in 1832 as the 'Peerage
of the British empire,' &c., which was in reality the compilation of Anne,
Eliza, and Maria Innes. The work is still published as 'Lodge's Peerage.'"--Dict. nat. biog.
    1. Gt. Brit.--Peerage.   I. Innes, Anne, ed. II. Innes, Eliza, ed. III. In-
nes, Maria, ed.

                                   1-3626
    Library of Congress   CS420.L8 1901

NL   0439021   DLC MdBJ

Lodge, Edmund
    Peerage, baronetage & knightage of British
Empire...
    Hurst, 1902.

NL   0439022   PPAp NjP

8 5   LODGE, EDMUND, 1756-1839.
5   Lodge's peerage, baronetage, knightage &
companionage of the British empire for 1908.
With which is incorporated Foster's Peerage,
baronetage and knightage. Edited by Sir Arthur E. Vicars... 77th edition, revised and enlarged. London, Kelly's directories ltd.
[pref.1907]
    2266p.

NL   0439023   ICN PU NN

CS420 Lodge, Edmund, 1756-1839.
.L8   Lodge's peerage, baronetage, knightage &
1911   companionage of the British empire for 1912.
81st ed.
    Lond. [1911].
    1 v   4°

NL   0439024   DLC

Lodge, Edmund, 1756-1839.
    The peerage of the British empire, as at present existing, ar-
ranged and printed from the personal communications of the nobility. By Edmund Lodge... To which is added a view of the
baronetage of the three kingdoms...   London: Saunders and
Otley, 1832.   xxv, 490 p.   20cm.

    Dedication signed: Anne, Eliza, and Maria Innes, editors.
    "From motives of benevolence Lodge lent his name to an 'Annual peerage and
baronetage', 4 vols., 12mo. 1827-9, reissued in 1832 as the 'Peerage of the British
empire', &c., which was in reality the compilation of Anne, Eliza, and Maria Innes.
The work is still published as 'Lodge's Peerage'." --Dict. nat. biog.

    The 28th and later editions were entitled: The peerage and baronetage of the
British empire.

    53832. 1. Peerage--Gt. Br. I. Innes,   Anne, ed. II. Innes, Eliza, ed.
III. Innes, Maria, ed.   *Card revised*
N. Y. P. L.   December 27, 1940

NL   0439026   NN MdBP

VOLUME 338

LODGE, Edmund, 1756-1839.
The peerage of the British Empire, as at present existing, arranged and printed from the personal communications of the nobility. To which is added a view of the baronetage of the three kingdoms. 2d ed. London, Saunders and Otley, 1833
21 cm.

NL 0439027 MH OClWHi

CS420
L8
1837
Lodge, Edmund, 1756-1839
The peerage of the British empire as at present existing; arranged and printed from the personal communications of the nobility. To which is added a view of the baronetage of the three kingdoms. 6th ed. ... with the arms of the peers. London, Saunders and Otley, 1837.
xxxi, 596 p. illus. (coats of arms) 23 cm.
Title vignette.
1. Gt. Brit. - Peerage. I. Title.

NL 0439028 MeB

Bb35
80
Lodge, Edmund, 1756-1839.
The peerage of the British empire as at present existing; arranged and printed from the personal communications of the nobility, by Edmund Lodge ... To which is added a view on the baronetage of the three kingdoms. 7th ed. ... London, Saunders and Otley, 1838.
xxix, 606, [1]p. illus. (coats of arms) 23½cm.
Dedication signed: Anne, Eliza, and Maria Innes, proprietors of "The Annual peerage."
"From motives of benevolence Lodge lent his name to an 'Annual peerage and baronetage,' 4 vols. 12 mo, 1827-9, reissued in 1832 as the 'Peerage of the British empire,' &c., which was in reality the compilation of Anne, Eliza, and Maria Innes. The work is still published as 'Lodge's Peerage'." - Dict.nat.biog.

NL 0439030 CtY PP

H
929.72
L823a
Lodge, Edmund, 1756-1839.
The peerage of the British Empire as at present existing arranged and printed from the personal communications of the nobility... to which is added a view of the Baronetage of the three kingdoms. 8th ed.... with the arms of the peers. London, Saunders and Otley, 1839.
xxix, 608 p. illus. (coats of arms) 24 cm.
1. Gt. Brit. Peerage. I. Title.

NL 0439031 N

Lodge, Edmund, 1756–1839.
The peerage of the British empire as at present existing; arranged and printed from the personal communications of the nobility, by Edmund Lodge ... to which is added the baronetage. 12th ed. ... with the arms of the peers. London, Saunders and Otley, 1843.
2 p. l., vii–xxx, 652, [1] p. illus. (coats of arms) 23½cm.
Title vignette.
Bound in red morocco, hand tooled in gold; doublure of gold tooled leather, with centers of blue moire silk; goffered edges.
"From motives of benevolence Lodge lent his name to an 'Annual peerage and baronetage,' 4 vols. 12mo, 1827–9, reissued in 1832 as the 'Peerage of the British empire,' &c., which was in reality the compilation of Anne, Eliza, and Maria Innes. The work is still published as 'Lodge's Peerage'."—Dict. nat. biog.
1. Gt. Brit.—Peerage. I. Innes, Anne, ed. II. Innes, Eliza, ed. III. Innes, Maria, ed.
15–12044 Revised
Library of Congress CS420.L8 1843

NL 0439033 DLC NN

Lodge, Edmund.
Peerage of the British Empire, as at present existing. Added, the Baronetage. 13th ed. London, 1844.
8°

NL 0439034 MnHi

Lodge, Edmund. 1846
The Peerage of the British Empire...

NL 0439035 NjR

929.72
L822p
Lodge, Edmund, 1756-1839.
The peerage of the British empire as at present existing; arranged and printed from the personal communications of the nobility. With the arms of the peers. To which is added the baronetage. 19th ed. London, Saunders and Otley, 1850.
675p.
Dedication signed: Anne Eliza, and Maria Innes, editors.
"From motives of benevolence Lodge lent his name to an 'Annual peerage and baronetage,' 4 vols. 12mo, 1827-9, reissued in 1832 as the 'Peerage of the British empire,' &c., which was in reality the compilation of Anne, Eliza, and Maria Innes. The work is still published as 'Lodge's Peerage.'"--Dict.nat.biog.
In his preface to the 1st ed. Lodge says that the work "is classed in two volumes,--the one [i.e., The peerage of the British empire] comprising the living subjects of the British peerage, including their collateral branches...and the other [i.e., The genealogy of the British empire, 1832] exhibiting concise historical sketches of their ancestry and families...Each volume may be considered either as a whole or as a moiety." They are usually regarded as independent volumes, the latter being by Lodge himself and from its nature not calling for a new ed. each year.
1. Gt. Brit.--Peerage. I. Innes, Anne, ed. II. Innes, Eliza, ed. III. Innes, Maria, ed. IV. Title.

NL 0439037 ICarbS

Lodge, Edmund, 1756–1839.
The peerage of the British empire as at present existing, arranged and printed from the personal communications of the nobility ... By Edmund Lodge ... With the arms of the peers ... To which is added the baronetage. 20th ed. London, Saunders and Otley, 1851.
lxxv, 676 p. illus. 24½cm.
Dedication signed: Anne, Eliza, and Maria Innes, editors.
"From motives of benevolence Lodge lent his name to an 'Annual peerage and baronetage,' 4 vols. 12mo, 1827-9, reissued in 1832 as the 'Peerage of the British empire,' &c., which was in reality the compilation of Anne, Eliza, and Maria Innes. The work is still published as 'Lodge's Peerage.'"—Dict. nat. biog.
In his preface to the 1st ed. Lodge says that the work "is classed in two volumes,—the one [i. e., The peerage of the British empire] comprising the living subjects of the British peerage, including their collateral branches ... and the other [i. e., The genealogy of the British empire, 1832] exhibiting concise historical sketches of their ancestry and families ... Each volume may be considered either as a whole or as a moiety." They are usually regarded as independent volumes, the latter being by Lodge himself and from its nature not calling for a new ed. each year.
1. Gt. Brit.—Peerage. I. Innes, Anne, ed. II. Innes, Eliza, ed. III. Innes, Maria, ed.
1–3622
Library of Congress CS420.L8 1851

NL 0439038 DLC

Lodge, Edmund, 1756–1839.
The peerage of the British empire as at present existing; arranged and printed from the personal communications of the nobility ... By Edmund Lodge ... With the arms of the peers. To which is added the baronetage. 24th ed. London, Saunders and Otley, 1855.
lxxv, [1], 686 p. illus. 24cm.
"From motives of benevolence Lodge lent his name to an 'Annual peerage and baronetage,' 4 vols. 12 mo. 1827–9, reissued in 1832 as the 'Peerage of the British empire,' &c., which was in reality the compilation of Anne, Eliza, and Maria Innes. The work is still published as Lodge's Peerage.'"—Dict. nat. biog.
1. Gt. Brit.—Peerage. I. Innes, Anne, ed. II. Innes, Eliza, ed. III. Innes, Maria, ed.
1–3623
Library of Congress CS420.L8 1855

NL 0439039 DLC

Lodge, Edmund, 1756–1839.
The peerage of the British empire as at present existing; arranged and printed from the personal communications of the nobility ... by Edmund Lodge ... With the arms of the peers: to which is added the baronetage. 27th ed. London, Hurst and Blackett. 1858.
lxxvi, 705, [1] p. illus. 23½cm.
Dedication signed: Anne, Eliza, and Maria Innes, editors.
"From motives of benevolence Lodge lent his name to an 'Annual peerage and baronetage', 4 vols., 12mo, 1827–9, reissued in 1832 as the 'Peerage of the British empire', &c., which was in reality the compilation of Anne, Eliza, and Maria Innes. The work is still published as 'Lodge's Peerage'."—Dict. nat. biog.
The 28th and later editions were entitled: The peerage and baronetage of the British empire.
1. Gt. Brit.—Peerage. I. Innes, Anne, ed. II. Innes, Eliza, ed. III. Innes, Maria, ed.
Library of Congress CS420.L8 1858 1–3624

NL 0439040 DLC

By58
04
6
[Lodge, Edmund] 1756-1839.
Portraits of illustrious personages of Great Britain. [London, Printed by W.Nicol, at the Shakspeare press, n.d.]
1v. ports. 27½cm.
Each portrait is accompanied by a biographical and historical memoir; each memoir is separately paged.
Binding and lettering indicate that this was issued as v.6 of Jerdan, W. National portrait gallery of illustrious and eminent personages of the nineteenth century. London, Fisher, son, & Jackson, 1830-34.

NL 0439041 CtY

Lodge, Edmund, 1756-1839.
Portraits of illustrious personages of Great Britain; engraved from authentic pictures in the galleries of the nobility, and the public collections of the country. With biographical and historical memoirs of their lives and actions, by Edmund Lodge ... London and New York, J. Tallis and company [n.d.]
10 v. plates (ports.) 29cm.
Vol.1 only has t.-p.; five title-pages with contents bound at end of vol.10 with imprint: The London printing and publishing company.
1. Gt. Brit.--Biog. 2. Bt. Brit.--Biog. --Portraits. I. Title.

NL 0439042 ViU NcD

Lodge, Edmund, 1756-1839.
Portraits of illustrious personages of Great Britain. Engraved from authentic pictures, in the galleries of the nobility, and the public collections of the country. With biographical and historical memoirs of their lives and actions, by Edmund Lodge... London: Lackington, Hughes, Harding, Mavor, and Lepard, 1821–1834. 4 v. port. f°.
Bound in crushed levant morocco by Lewis.
v. 1 has added t.-p.
v. 3-4 published by Harding and Lepard.
DRAPER COLLECTION.
1. Biography (British). 2. Portraits (British). 3. Title.
N. Y. P. L. December 30, 1915.

NL 0439043 NN PP OClWHi MH MB InU ICU PU DLC

Typ
805
23.5293F
Lodge, Edmund, 1756-1839.
Portraits of illustrious personages of Great Britain. Engraved from authentic pictures in the galleries of the nobility and the public collections of the country. With biographical and historical memoirs of their lives and actions, by Edmund Lodge ...
London: Printed for Harding, Mavor and Lepard, 1823-34.
12v. 240 ports. 32.5cm.
Large paper quarto edition, with proofs of the ports. on india paper; also published in large octavo.
Second edition, originally published in 80 parts, 1821-34.
Imprint varies slightly.

NL 0439045 MH DLC NN TxHU OrCS LNHT OrU Vi WaSpG KyLoU CU MiDA CLCM

VOLUME 338

942
qZA1
1831
Lodge, Edmund, 1756-1839.
Lodge's portraits. ₁London? 1831?₎
1 v. of ports. 27 cm.
Title from spine.
Consts of all the portraits, except
eight, from the first ten volumes, and some
of the portraits in the last two volumes
of the author's twelve volume work published
in London, 1835 under title: Portraits of
illustrious personages of Great Britain,
engraved from authentic pictures in the

galleries — of the country with biographical
and historical memoirs of their lives and
actions.

1. Gt. Brit. Biog. Portraits.

NL 0439047   N

---

fE
445
.517
LODGE, EDMUND, 1756-1839.
Portraits of illustrious personages of Great
Britain. Engraved from authentic pictures in
the galleries of the nobility and the public collections of the country. With biographical and
historical memoirs of their lives and actions...
₁5th edition₎   London, Harding₁1832-37₎
12v. ports.

Issued in 80 parts, 1832-1837.
On covers of every part: Fifth edition.

With an entirely new set of plates, and sixty
additional subjects, completing the work to the
present period.
"The first edition was commenced in 1814,
and completed in forty parts in folio (collective edition, 4 vols., 1821-34)"—Dict. nat. biog
The plates are arranged chronologically.

NL 0439049   ICN

Lodge, Edmund, 1756-1839.   Br 197.7
Portraits of illustrious personages of Great Britain; engraved
2 v. from authentic pictures in the galleries of the nobility and the
6) public collections of the country. With biographical and historical
memoirs. London, Harding and Lepard, 1835.
12. vol. l. 8°. Ports.

MH-AH PP-W PP CaBVa WaSp
MWelC MH MiU CtY NjP T MiD-B NIC NcU ViU MB IEG
NL 0439050   MH CSmH MB NN IU OOxM OC1 OC1W ViLxW

Lodge, Edmund, 1756-1839.
Portraits of illustrious personages of Great
Britain, engraved from authentic pictures in the
galleries of the nobility, and the public collections
of the country.   London, Harding & Lepard,
1836.
4 v., v. 1-4. f°.

NL 0439051   NN

---

q920.042
L82p
Lodge, Edmund, 1756-1839.
Portraits of illustrious personages
of Great Britain; engraved from authentic pictures in the galleries of
the nobility ... with biographical
and historical memoirs.   London,
1837.
10v. ports.

NL 0439052   IU

920.42
L821
1840
Lodge, Edmund, 1756-1839.
Portraits of illustrious personages of
Great Britain. Engraved from authentic pictures in the galleries of the nobility and
the public collections of the country.
With biographical and historical memoirs of
their lives and actions.   London, W. Smith,
1840.
10v. in 5. illus. 28cm.

On spine: Lodge's Portraits.

1. Gt. Brit.   Biog. 2. Portraits,
British.

NL 0439053   KU

Lodge, Edmund, 1756-1839.
Portraits of illustrious personages of Great Britain. With
biographical and historical memoirs of their lives and actions.
By Edmund Lodge ... London, H. G. Bohn, 1849-50.
8 v. front., ports. 18½ᶜᵐ. (*Half-title:* Bohn's illustrated library)

1. Gt. Brit.—Biog. 2. Gt. Brit.—Biog.—Portraits.   I. Title.
Library of Congress   DA28.L6   13-20077 Revised

OrP WaS ICN
ViU WaU MeB NN NWM I MdBP PP PHC PPGi CaBVaU OrU
NL 0439054   DLC CMenSP PPL NjNbS MWA NjP CtY ODW OC1

Lodge, Edmund, 1756-1839.
Portraits of illustrious personages of Great Britain. Engraved from authentic pictures in the galleries of the nobility, and the public collections of the country. With biographical and historical memoirs of their lives and actions.
London, New York, London Print. and Pub. Co. ₁1854?₎
5 v. in 4. ports. 28 cm.

1. Gt. Brit.—Biog. 2. Gt. Brit.—Biog.—Portraits.   I. Title.
DA28.L6 1854   44-17572 rev*

NL 0439055   DLC

920.042
L822p
1860
Lodge, Edmund, 1756-1839.
Portraits of illustrious personages of
Great Britain, with biographical and
historical memoirs of their lives and
actions.   London, W. Smith₁1860?₎
8v. fronts., ports. 19 cm.
"Cabinet edition".

1. Gt. Brit.—Biog. 2. Portraits.

NL 0439056   ICarbS MH NN OO WRU DN RPJCB OCU

Lodge, Edmund, 1756-1839.
Portraits of illustrious personages of Great Britain. With
biographical and historical memoirs of their lives and actions,
by Edmund Lodge. Boston, D. Estes & co., 1902.
12 v. fronts., ports. 28½ᶜᵐ.
"Edition de grand luxe. Limited to one thousand copies. Number 3."

1. Gt. Brit.—Biography. 2. Portraits.
A 10—2337
Michigan. Univ. Library
for Library of Congress   ₍a40c1₎

NL 0439057   MiU NcD CoU IdU OrCS OrPR

Lodge, Edmund, 1756-1839
Portraits of illustrious personages of Great
Britain.
London, printed for Lackington, Allen, etc.
₁by Davison₎ 1914.
4 v.

NL 0439058   PPT

Lodge, Edmund, 1756-1839.
Chamberlaine, John, 1745-1812.
Portraits of illustrious personages of the court of
Henry VIII. Engraved in imitation of the original draw-
ings of Hans Holbein, in the collection of His Majesty.
With biographical and historical memoirs by Edmund
Lodge ... Pub. by John Chamberlaine ... London,
Printed by W. Bulmer and co., 1828.

[Lodge, Edward]
A funeral poem, humbly offer'd to the
pious memory of the Reverend Mʳ. Samˡ Pomfret, who dy'd January 11th, 172₂, in the
71st year of his age. To which is added,
his late annual hymns. The second edition,
with large additions. [London] J. Marshall
[1722]
25 p. 20ᵐ. [With Reynolds, Thomas.
Some memoirs of the life of the late ... Mr.
Samuel Pomfret. London, 1722]
Dedication sign-   ed: Edward Lodge.

NL 0439060   CLU-C

Lodge, Edwin A., ed.
The American observer medical monthly
see under title

668.5
L822
Lodge, Edwin A.
The art of manufacturing perfumery: a manual,
containing instructions for preparing all the
most admired articles for the toilet ...
Cin., Printed by E. Shepard, 1849.
120p. 1 illus. 16cm.

1. Perfumery. 2. Cosmetics.

NL 0439062   N ODW OHi

Lodge, Edwin A
Cash price list
see under Detroit Homopathic Pharmacy,

Lodge, Edwin A   ed.
The Christian unionist, consisting of practical
essays and discourses
see under title

Lodge, Edwin A.
Domestic guide, for the use of twenty-four most useful
homœopathic remedies. By Edwin A. Lodge ... Detroit,
Mich., Dr. Lodge's homœopathic pharmacy ₁1869₎
65 p. 11ᵐ.

1. Homeopathy—Popular works.

Library of Congress   RX76.L83   7-13819†

NL 0439065   DLC

VOLUME 338

WZ LODGE, Edwin A　　defendant
100 The legality of drug provings recognized
L822L [partial court evidence in the trial of
1862 Edwin A. Lodge in the death of a house-
servant, Mary Washington] [Detroit,
1862]
24 p.
Caption title.

NL 0439066　DNLM PPHa

Lodge, Eleanor Constance, 1869–1936, ed.

[Toke, Nicholas] 1588–1680.
The account book of a Kentish estate, 1616–1704, edited by Eleanor C. Lodge ... London, Pub. for the British academy by H. Milford, Oxford university press, 1927.

Lodge, Eleanor Constance, 1869–1936.
... Edward I and his tenants-in-chief, by Miss E. C. Lodge ...
(*In* Royal historical society, London. Transactions. **London,** 1924.
22ᶜᵐ. 4th ser., v. 7, p. [1]–26)
Bibliographical foot-notes.

1. Feudalism—Gascony. 2. Edward I, king of England, 1239–1307.
3. Gascony—History.

A C 36—1640

Newberry library
for Library of Congress　[DA20.R9 ser. 4, vol. 7]
[a40c1]　　　　(942.0062)

NL 0439068　ICN OCU OU DLC MB

Lodge, Eleanor Constance, 1869–1936.
The end of the middle age, 1273–1453; by Eleanor C. Lodge ... with an introduction by R. Lodge ... With four-teen maps. London, Methuen & co. [1909]
xxii, 286 p., 1 l. incl. 14 maps, tables. 19½ cm. (*Half-title:* Six ages of European history from A. D. 476 to 1878 ... general ed., A. H. Johnson ... vol. III])
Chronological table: p. xv–xx.
Bibliography for teachers: p. xxi–xxii.
Additional lists of books, suitable for students, at end of chapters.

1. Europe—Hist.—476–1492.　I. Lodge, Sir Richard, 1855–
II. Title.

W 10—150

Washington, D.C. Pub.　Library
for Library of Congress　[D103.S6 vol. 3]
[a50b4]

MB OCX OC1
NL 0439069　DWP WaTC IdU WaWW CaBVa TxU PHC PRosC

Lodge, Eleanor Constance, 1869–1936.
The end of the middle age, 1273–1453; by Eleanor C. Lodge ... with an introduction by R. Lodge ... With fourteen maps.
New York, Macmillan Co., 1910.
xxii, 286 p., 1 l. incl. 14 maps, tables. 19½ᶜᵐ. (*Half-title:* Six ages of European history from A. D. 476 to 1878 ... general ed., A. H. Johnson ... vol. III])
Chronological table: p. xv–xx.
Bibliography for teachers: p. xxi–xxii.
Additional lists of books, suitable for students, at end of chapters.

NL 0439070　IU OO MBrZ ICU MU

940.1 Lodge, Eleanor Constance, 1869–
L83e The end of the middle age, 1273-1453, by Eleanor
C. Lodge... with an introduction by R. Lodge...
with fourteen maps.　New York, The Macmillan co.,
1914.
2 p.l., v–xxii, 286 p. maps, geneal. tables. 119 cm.
(Six ages of European history...v.III)

1. Europe--History--476-1492. I. Title.

NL 0439071　LU

Lodge, Eleanor Constance, 1869–
The end of the middle age, 1273–1453, by Eleanor C.
Lodge ... with an introduction by R. Lodge ... with four-teen maps. 5th ed. London, Methuen & co. ltd. [1924]
xxii, 286 p., 1 l. incl. illus. (maps) geneal. tables. 19ᶜᵐ. (*Half-title:* Six ages of European history ... vol. III])
"Bibliography for teachers": p. xxi–xxii.

1. Europe—Hist.—476–1492.　I. Title.

Library of Congress　　　　D103.S6 vol. III　26–6728

NL 0439072　DLC WaE

Lodge, Eleanor Constance, 1869–1936, *ed.*
English constitutional documents, 1307–1485; edited by Eleanor C. Lodge ... and Gladys A. Thornton ... **Cambridge** [Eng.] The University press, 1935.
xxv p., 1 l., 480 p., 1 l. 20½ᶜᵐ.
Includes bibliographies.

1. Gt. Brit.—Constitutional history. 2. Gt. Brit.—Hist.—Medieval period, 1066–1485—Sources.　I. Thornton, Gladys Amy, joint ed.
II. Title.

35—6249

Library of Congress　　JN111.L6
[a41k1]　　　　　342.4209

PBm WaS WaU-L OrU
NcD CtY OrPR ViU-L ODW OU OCU NNC NN ViU OC1W PSC
NL 0439073　DLC ICU MB MsU InRenS DAU PPiPT NcU PU

Lodge, Eleanor Constance, 1869–1936.
The estates of the archbishop and chapter of Saint-André of Bordeaux under English rule, by Eleanor C. Lodge ...
(*In* Oxford studies in social and legal history ... **Oxford, 1912.** 23ᶜᵐ. vol. III [no. V] 206 p.)

1. Land tenure—Gascony. 2. Agriculture—Gascony. 3. Bordeaux (Archdiocese) 4. Bordeaux. St. André (Cathedral)

15—11695

Library of Congress　HC10.O8, vol. 3

ODW PPPT PPT PU RP WaU-L PPPD
NL 0439074　DLC NcD NcG PU-L OC1 IU NN MB ViU-L OU

Lodge, Eleanor Constance, 1869–
Gascony under English rule, by Eleanor C. Lodge ... with four maps. London, Methuen & co. ltd. [1926]
ix, 261, [1] p. illus. (maps, geneal. tables) 23ᶜᵐ.
Map on lining-paper.
Bibliography: p. 241–249.

1. Gascony—Hist. 2. British in France.　I. Title.

27—14714

Library of Congress　　DC611.G25L5

OrPR OrU
DAU OrU PBm PHC PSC NcU OC1 OCU CtY NN NjP CaBVaU
NL 0439075　DLC ViU CoU NIC FMU MoSU ICarbS CU-I

Lodge, Eleanor Constance, 1869–1936, ed.

John of Gaunt, *duke of Lancaster,* 1340–1399.
John of Gaunt's register, 1379–1383. Edited from the origi-nal record by the late Eleanor C. Lodge ... and Robert Somer-ville ... London, Offices of the Society, 1937–

Lodge, Eleanor Constance, 1869–　joint ed.

Chandos, *herald, fl.* 1350–1380.
Life of the Black Prince, by the herald of Sir John Chandos.
Ed. from the manuscript in Worcester college, with linguistic and historical notes, by Mildred K. Pope ... and Eleanor C.
Lodge ... Oxford, Clarendon press, 1910.

Lodge, Eleanor Constance, 1869–1936.
... Social & economic history [of Berkshire]
... Table of population 1801–1901, by George
S. Minchin.　London, Constable & company limited, 1920.
cover-title, p. 167–243. (The Victoria history of the counties of England)

At head of title: A history of Berkshire, edited by P.H. Ditchfield ... & William Page, pt. 12)

NL 0439078　MH-AH

Lodge, Eleanor Constance, 1869–1936.
Sully, Colbert, and Turgot: a chapter in French economic history, by Eleanor C. Lodge ... London, Methuen & co. ltd. [1931]
xvi, 263, [1] p. 19½ᶜᵐ.
"Authorities" at end of each chapter except the last.

1. Finance—France—Hist. 2. France—Econ. condit. 3. Sully, Maxi-milien de Béthune, duc de, 1559–1641. 4. Colbert, Jean Baptiste, 1619–1683. 5. Turgot, Anne Robert Jacques, baron de l'Aulne, 1727–1781.

Library of Congress　　HJ1079.L6　31—22050
[a38e2]　　　　　330.944

NNCoCi NN MB
NL 0439079　DLC MtU OrU WaTC NcD CtY OC1 OCU OU PBm

Lodge, Eleanor Constance, 1869–1936.
Terms and vacations, by Eleanor C. Lodge, edited by Janet Spens. London, New York [etc.] Oxford university press, 1938.
xii p., 4 l., 250 p., 1 l. front., ports. 23ᶜᵐ.
Erratum slip inserted.
Autobiography.

1. Oxford. University. Lady Margaret hall. 2. Education of women.　I. Spens, Janet, 1876–　ed. II. Title.

38—13460

Library of Congress　LA2377.L6A3 1938
923.742

NL 0439080　DLC WaU

[Lodge, Frank Terrell] 1859–
... "Hvarför gråter du!" ... (Öfversättning från engelskan) [Minneapolis, The Wolfe printing co., [1915]
111 p. col. front. (port.) plates. 18½ᶜᵐ.
Translated by Swan Alfred Larson.

I. Larson, Swan Alfred, tr. II. Title.

15—23604

Library of Congress

NL 0439081　DLC MnHi WaU

Lodge, Frank Terrell, 1859–1930.
The officers of the lodge, by Frank T. Lodge
... [Detroit?] ©1928.
64 p. 15ᶜᵐ.

1. Freemasons—Handbooks, manuals, etc. I. Title.

NL 0439082　MiU

[Lodge, Frank Terrell] 1859–
"Why weepest thou!" (John xx–13:) [Detroit? 1913]
80 p. col. front. (port.) 18½ᶜᵐ.
Preface signed: Frank T. Lodge.
Extracts from some of the text-books of the "Great school."

1. Future life.　I. Richardson, John Emmett, 1853–　II. Title.

Library of Congress　　BF1999.L5　19–3414

NL 0439083　DLC MiU OC1

VOLUME 338

Lodge, George Arthur.
Hand sketching for mining students, by G. A. Lodge...and
N. Harwood... [London:] C. Lockwood & Son, 1914. viii.
107 p. illus. ob. 4°.

1. mines and mining.—Surveying.   2. Harwood, N., jt. au.
N. Y. P. L.   April 1, 1915.

NL 0439084   NN ICJ IU

Lodge, George Arthur.   L622.004 S001
Hand sketching for mining students, by G. A. Lodge, ... and
N. Harwood, ... Second edition, enlarged. [London],
C. Lockwood and Son, 1920.
viii, 127 p. incl. illus., 59 pl., tables, diagrs. 22 x 28ᶜᵐ.

NL 0439085   ICJ

Lodge, George Arthur, joint author.

Coppock, John Bridgeford.
... An introduction to mining science; a theoretical and
practical textbook for mining students, by John B. Coppock
... and G. A. Lodge ... New York [etc.] Longmans, Green &
co., 1915.

Lodge, George Cabot, 1873–1909.
Cain; a drama, by George Cabot Lodge. Boston and
New York, Houghton, Mifflin & company, 1904.
6 p. l., 154, [2] p. 19ᶜᵐ.

1. Title.

Library of Congress   4-33107

PU PP
NL 0439087   DLC OU CaBVaU CSt MB TU NcD OO   NN

Lodge, George Cabot, 1873–1909.
The great adventure, by George Cabot Lodge. Boston and
New York, Houghton, Mifflin and company, 1905.
4 p. l., 5–90 p., 1 l. 19½ᶜᵐ.

1. Title.

Library of Congress   PS3523.O27G7 1905   5-34608

CLSU IEN
NL 0439088   DLC NN WaS TU MB NN NjN NcD ICU PU PBm

Lodge, George Cabot, 1873–1909.
Herakles, by George Cabot Lodge. Boston and New York,
Houghton Mifflin company, 1908.
v, [1] p., 1 l., 271, [1] p., 1 l. 19½ᶜᵐ.

1. Title.

Library of Congress   PS3523.O27H4 1908   8-33151

MB PU PHC PPL OU
NL 0439089   DLC NjP MB WU MsU CLSU PP OCl OO MiU NN

Lodge, George Cabot, 1873–1909.
Ilion [poem]
From– Scribner's Magazine, Nov. 1909.
24 cm.   607 p.

NL 0439090   RPB

Lodge, George Cabot, 1873–1909.
The life of George Cabot Lodge
see under [Adams, Henry] 1838–

Lodge, George Cabot, 1873–1909.
... Poems (1899–1902) New York, Cameron, Blake
& company, 1902.
3 p. l., 152 p. 21ᶜᵐ.

2-8048

NL 0439092   DLC InU MB MWA NcD OO MiU MB NN

Lodge, George Cabot, 1873–1909.
Poems and dramas of George Cabot Lodge. Boston
and New York, Houghton Mifflin company, 1911.
2 v. 19½ᶜᵐ. $2.50.

Library of Congress   PS3523.O27 1911   11-27478

OC1 OOxM MB NN PPT MB PSC PP PU PPL
NL 0439093   DLC OrP NcD IEN FMU CoU TU MH OCl MiU

Lodge, George Cabot, 1873–1909, ed.

Stickney, Trumbull, 1874–1904.
The poems of Trumbull Stickney. Boston and New York,
Houghton, Mifflin & co., 1905.

Lodge, George Cabot, 1873–1909.
The song of the wave, and other poems, by George
Cabot Lodge ... New York, C. Scribner's sons, 1898.
1 p. l., ix, 135 p. 19½ᶜᵐ.

1. Title.

                                                99-65 Revised
Library of Congress   PS3523.O27S6 1898

PU
NL 0439095   DLC MB ViU IEN TU NjP CLSU ViU TxU MB

Lodge, George Cabot, 1873–1909.
The soul's inheritance, and other poems [by] George
Cabot Lodge. Boston, New York [etc.] Houghton Mifflin
company, 1909.
4 p. l., 3–92, [2] p. 19½ᶜᵐ. $1.00.

                                                9-30031
Library of Congress

Nahant, Mass.

NL 0439096   DLC MB NcU NcD MiU TxU MB NN PU

Lodge, George Edward.
Memoirs of an artist naturalist, by George E. Lodge... illus-
trated with 24 plates of which 16 are in colour. London [etc.]
Gurney and Jackson, 1946.
vii, 96 p. col. front., illus., plates (part col.) 26ᶜᵐ.
Each plate accompanied by guard sheet with descriptive letterpress.

1. Birds—Gt. Brit. 2. Birds of prey. 3. Animal painting and illustration.   1. Title.

QL690.G7L6   598.2942   47-21331

NL 0439097   DLC GU FTaSU CU ICU CtY

Lodge, George T.   372.8 P701
Coloured handbook to kindergarten geography. Designed as a
guide to junior teachers, in using the author's maps and diagrams.
.... 31 p. il. 19 maps. sq.O. Nottingham: Sisson & Parker,
[1897].

NL 0439098   ICJ

Lodge, George Townsend.
Correlates of criminal behavior, an analysis
of interrelationships among certain personality
traits, case-history data, criminal records,
diagnostic and prognostic estimates of 250
prisoners examined at the Cleveland criminal
court psychiatric clinic during the year 1939.
88 l.
Thesis – Ph. D. degree – Western Reserve
University, May 15, 1940.

NL 0439099   OClW

FILM   Lodge, Giles, 16th cent., comp.
9621   Giles Lodge's lute-book. n. p.] 1591. Mss. (448.16)
M   21 l. On film (Negative)
Music
Library   Microfilm. Original in Folger Shakespeare Library.
          Title supplied by U.C. Library. Title on spine: Ancient music.
          July and Julian.

1. Lute music. I. Lodge, Giles, 16th cent., comp. II. Title.

NL 0439100   CU

Lodge, Giles Henry, 1805–1888, tr.   FOR OTHER EDITIONS
                                      SEE MAIN ENTRY

Ungern-Sternberg, Alexander, freiherr von, 1806–1868.
The Breughel brothers. From the German of the Baron
von Sternberg. By G. Henry Lodge. Illustrated by Billings.
Boston, J. R. Osgood and company, 1873.

Lodge, Giles Henry, 1805–1888, tr.

Lisfranc, Jacques, 1790–1847.
Diseases of the uterus, a series of clinical lectures, delivered
at the hospital La Pitié, by M. Lisfranc, and edited by H.
Pauly, M. D. Translated from the French by G. Henry Lodge
... Boston, W. D. Ticknor and company, 1846.

Lodge, Giles Henry, 1805–1885, tr.   FOR OTHER EDITIONS
                                      SEE MAIN ENTRY

Winckelmann, Johann Joachim, 1717–1768
The history of ancient art, tr. from the German of John
Winckelmann, by G. Henry Lodge ... Boston, J. R. Osgood
and company, 1880.

Lodge, Giles Henry, 1805–1885.
Life of Winckelmann.
104 p. (Winckelmann, J., Hist. of ancient
art, v. 1, 1880, p. 1.)

NL 0439104   MdBP

Lodge, Gonzalez, 1863–1942, ed.

The Classical weekly. Pub. by the Classical association of
the Atlantic states ... v. 1–
Oct. 5, 1907–
New York, 1907–

VOLUME 338

Lodge, Gonzalez, 1863–   ed.

Plato.
... Georgias, ed. on the basis of Deuschle-Cron's edition, by Gonzalez Lodge ... Boston and London, Ginn & company, 1891.

Lodge, Gonzalez, 1863–   joint author.
FOR OTHER EDITIONS
SEE MAIN ENTRY
Gildersleeve, Basil Lanneau, 1831–1924.
Gildersleeve's Latin grammar. School ed. By Basil L. Gildersleeve ... and Gonzalez Lodge ... New York, Boston [etc.], University publishing company [*1898]

Lodge, Gonzalez.
Greek influence upon Latin literature. (Columbia University. Greek literature. New York, 1912. 8°. p. 267-296.)

1. Roman literature.—Greek influ-   ence on.
N. Y. P. L.   July 9, 1912.

NL   0439108   NN

Lodge, Gonzalez, 1863–
... **Helps** for the teaching of Cæsar. New York, Columbia university press, 1902.

Lodge, Gonzalez, 1863–   joint author.
FOR OTHER EDITIONS
SEE MAIN ENTRY
Gildersleeve, Basil Lanneau, 1831–1924.
... Latin composition, by Basil L. Gildersleeve ... and Gonzalez Lodge ... New York, Boston [etc.], University publishing company [1899]

Lodge, Gonzalez, 1863–1942, joint author.
Latin grammar
    see under   Gildersleeve, Basil Lanneau, 1831–1924.

Lodge, Gonzalez, 1863–1942.
Latin Grammar, by Herbert Charles Elmer [a review]   1929.
    90-96 p.   24 cm.
    From: American journal of philology, v. 50, no. 1 (Jan.-Mar. 1929)

NL   0439112   PLF

PA6609 Lodge, Gonzalez, 1863–
.Z8   Lexicon Plavtinvm, conscripsit Gonzalez Lodge...
1901   Lipsiae, in aedibvs B.G. Tevbneri, 1901-
              v. 26½ᶜᵐ.

    1. Plautus, Titus Maccius-Dictionaries, indexes, etc.   2. Latin language-Dictionaries.

NL   0439113   ICU PU MH NjP MdBJ TU

Lodge, Gonzalez, 1863–
Lexicon Plavtinvm conscripsit Gonzalez Lodge ... Lipsiae, in aedibvs B. G. Tevbneri, 1904 [fasc. 1-2, 1925]–
    v. 26ᶜᵐ.
Issued in   fascicles; fascicles 1-2 of the original issue (1901-03) have been cancelled and replaced by the "impressio correcta", 1925.
Bibliography: v. 1, p. [vii]-x.
"Vocabula punica emucleavit Ricardus J. H. Gottheil": v. 1, p. [915]-917.

1. [Plautus, Titus Maccius.   2. Punic language—Glossaries, vocabularies, etc.

                                                        25-16836
Library of Congress   PA6609.Z8L7

        OC1W OO ICN WaU NBC CtY
NL   0439114   DLC CtY NIC NcU CU NcD OCU MiU OU ViU

LODGE, GONZALEZ
    Marcus Tullius Cicero - citizen. American classical league, 1927.
    8 p.   (Service bureau for classical teachers. Latin notes supplement no.28)

NL   0439115   Or

Lodge, Gonzalez. 1863–   2968.105
On the theory of the ideal condition in Latin.
(In Studies in honor of Basil L. Gildersleeve. Pp. 253-261. Baltimore. 1902.)

G6181 — Latin language. Syntax. — Conditional sentences. Latin.

NL   0439116   MB

Lodge, Gonzalez, 1863–
The oral method of teaching Latin.
(In National education association of the United States. Journal of proceedings and addresses, 1910. p. 493-497)

1. Latin language—Teaching.
                                                        E 11-478
Library, U. S. Bur. of   Education

NL   0439117   DHEW

Lodge, Gonzalez, 1863–
A **reasonable** plea for the classics. NY [1920?]
    16 p.   (American Classical League. Publ., 15)
    Reprinted from Teachers College Record, Nov.1920

NL   0439118   MH CU OC1JC

Lodge, Gonzalez, 1863–   ed.

Lodge, William Jacob, 1832–1904.
A record of the descendents [!] of Robert and Elizabeth Lodge (English Quakers) 1682-1903, by William Jacob Lodge, M. D. Geneva, W. F. Humphrey press inc., 1942.

Lodge, Gonzales, 1863–
Studies in honor of Basil L. Gildersleeve
    see under title

Lodge, Gonzalez, 1863–1942.
The vocabulary of high school Latin, being the vocabulary of: Caesar's Gallic war, books I-V; Cicero against Catiline, on Pompey's command, for the poet Archias; Vergil's Æneid, books I-VI; arranged alphabetically and in the order of occurrence, by Gonzalez Lodge ... New York, Teachers college, Columbia university, 1907.
    2 p. l., iii-viii, 217 p.   23½ cm.   (Half-title: Columbia university contributions to education. Teachers college series, no. 9)

1. Latin language—Glossaries, vocabularies, etc.
                                                        7—39986
Library of Congress   PA2380.L7

NL   0439121   DLC OC1W PWcS PV PBa PU MB NN OC1JC

Lodge, Gonzalez, 1863–
The vocabulary of high school Latin; being the vocabulary of: Caesar's Gallic war, books I-V; Cicero Against Cataline, On Pompeys command, For the poet Archias; Vergil's Æneid, books I-VI; arranged alphabetically and in the order of occurrence, by Gonzalez Lodge ... Rev. ed. New York, Teachers college, Columbia university, 1909.
    2 p. l., iii-vi, 217 p.   23½ cm.   (Half-title: Columbia university contributions to education. Teachers college series, no. 9)

1. Latin language—Glossaries, vocabularies, etc.
                                                        9—28539
Library of Congress   PA2380.L75

        PBm PPT PSC CaBVaU
NL   0439122   DLC MtU OrP WaWW OrCS OrU NBuC WaTC

Lodge, Gonzales, 1863–1942.
Vocabulary of high school Latin... Caesar... Cicero... Vergil... rev. ed. New York, 1912.

NL   0439123   NjP

Lodge, Gonzalez, 1863–
The vocabulary of high school Latin; being the vocabulary of: Caesar's Gallic war, books I-V; Cicero's against Cataline. On Pompey's command, for the poet Archais; Vergil's Aeneid, books I-VI; arranged alphabetically and in the order of occurence by ... Rev. ed. New York, Teachers College, Columbia university, 1915.

NL   0439124   OC1W OOxM

Lodge, Gonzales, 1863–
The vocabulary of high school Latin; being the vocabulary of: Caesar's Gallic war, books I-V; Cicero Against Cataline, On Pompey's command, For the poet Archias; Vergil's Æneid, books I-VI; arranged alphabetically and in the order of occurrence, by Gonzalez Lodge ... Rev. ed. New York, Teachers college, Columbia university, 1922.
    2 p. l., iii- [ ] 217 p.   23½ᶜᵐ.   (Half-title: Columbia university contributions to education. Teachers college series, no. 9)

NL   0439125   ViU MiU ODW OC1 OC1JC OCX OCU PP

Lodge, Gonzales, 1863–1942.
The vocabulary of high school Latin; being the vocabulary of: Caesar's Gallic war, books I-V; Cicero Against Cataline, on Pompey's command, for the poet Archias; Vergil's AEneid, books I-VI; arranged alphabetically and in the order of occurrence, by Gonzalez Lodge...Rev. ed. New York, Teachers college, Columbia university, 1928 [c1909]
    2 p.l., iii-vi, 217 p.   23.5 cm.   (Half-title: Columbia university contributions to education. Teachers college series, no. 9)

NL   0439126   PSt

Lodge, *Mrs.* Harriet (Newell) 1848–
A bit of finesse; a story of fifty years ago, by Harriet Newell Lodge. Indianapolis, The Bowen-Merrill company, 1894.
    2 p. l., 104 p.   19½ᶜᵐ.

                                                        7-14798†
Library of Congress   PZ3.L821B

NL   0439127   DLC CU CtY

VOLUME 338

Lodge, *Mrs.* **Harriet (Newell)** 1848–
Consider the lilies. By Harriet N. Lodge. Cliftondale, Mass., Coates bros. ₁1888₎
1 p. L, 4 numb. l. 13 x 11¼ᶜᵐ.
Verse, printed on one side of leaf only.

1. Title.
                                                    28–9344
Library of Congress   PS2249.L35

NL 0439128   DLC

308t   **Lodge, Helen Chanda,** 1919–
L8215   The influence of the study of biography on the moral ideology of the adolescent at the eighth grade level.
vii,149 l.   tables.

Thesis (Ed.D.) – Univ. of California, June 1953.
Bibliography: p.123–129.

NL 0439129   CU

Lodge, Henry Cabot, 1850–
U. S. *Congress. Senate. Committee on foreign relations.*
... Abrogation of certain agreements relating to Panama canal ... Report. ⟨To accompany S. J. Res. 259.⟩ ... ₁Washington, Govt. print. off., 1923₎

Lodge, Henry Cabot, 1850–1924.
Acceptance and unveiling of the statue of Daniel Webster in Washington on January 18, 1900. Addresses by Senator Chandler, the Secretary of the navy, Hon. John D. Long, Senator Lodge. Washington, Govt. print. off., 1900.

Lodge, Henry Cabot, 1850–1924.
... Accomplishments of the Republican administration and Congress, March 4, 1921–February 14, 1922. Address of Hon. Henry Cabot Lodge before the Republican members of the Massachusetts legislature. February 14, 1922 ... Washington, Govt. print. off., 1922.
12 p. 24ᶜᵐ. (₁U. S.₎ 67th Cong. 2d sess. Senate. Doc. 132)
Presented by Mr. Spencer. Ordered printed February 20 (calendar day, February 21), 1922.
1. U. S.—Pol. & govt.—1921.   2. U. S. 67th Cong. 1st sess., 1921. 3. U. S. 67th Cong. 2d sess., 1921—   4. Republican party. 5. Washington, D. C. Conference on the limitation of armament, 1921–1922. I. Spencer, Selden Palmer, 1862–1925. II. Title.
                                                    22–26213
Library of Congress   JK2357.1922.L6

NL 0439132   DLC MiU OO

Lodge, Henry Cabot, 1850–
Address...
Massachusetts.
A record of the dedication of the monument on Dorchester Heights, South Boston, built by the commonwealth as a memorial of the evacuation of Boston, March 17, 1776, by the British troops. March 17, 1902. Boston, Printed by order of the governor and council, Wright & Potter printing company, state printers, 1903.

Lodge, Henry Cabot, 1850–1924.   2355.126
Address. ₁At the laying of the corner stone of the Pilgrim Monument, Provincetown, Mass., 1907.₎
(In Carpenter, E. J. The Pilgrims and their monument. Pp. 100–111. New York. 1911.)
On the principles of the Mayflower Compact.

L4887 — Mayflower Compact.

NL 0439134   MB

Lodge, Henry Cabot, 1850–   2355.126
Address. ₁At the dedication of the Pilgrim Monument, Provincetown, Mass., 1910.₎
(In Carpenter, E. J. The Pilgrims and their monument. Pp. 210–219. New York. 1911.)
On the idealism of the Pilgrims and the idea of democracy as embodied in the Mayflower Compact.

L4884 — Democracy. — Mayflower Compact.

NL 0439135   MB

Lodge, Henry Cabot, 1850–1924.
Address at the three hundredth anniversary of the founding of the City of Gloucester, Mass., Aug. 28, 1923. Boston, Anchor Linotype Print Co. [1923]
11 p.

NL 0439136   MH

Lodge, Henry Cabot, 1850– 1924.
Address by Hon. Henry Cabot Lodge ... under the auspices of the Union league, at the Academy of music, Philadelphia, October 1, 1900. ₁Philadelphia? 1900?₎
26 p. 24½ᶜᵐ.
Defending the annexation of the Philippine Islands.

                                                    5–1585
Library of Congress

NL 0439137   DLC PHi PU PSC-Hi

Lodge, Henry Cabot, 1850–1924.
... An address commemorative of the life and services of George D. Robinson, governor of the commonwealth, 1884–86, by Henry Cabot Lodge. Proceedings at the Hancock church in Lexington on the one hundred and twenty-first anniversary of the battle ... Boston, G. H. Ellis, printer, 1896.
28 p. 24½ cm.
At head of title: 1775—April nineteenth—1896.
"Published by the town."
1. Robinson, George Dexter, 1834–1896. 2. Lexington, Battle of, 1775. I. Lexington, Mass.
                                                    13—23475
Library of Congress   F70.R66

NL 0439138   DLC MeB Nh MB MWA CtY OFH OClWHi

Lodge, Henry Cabot, 1850–1924.
Address delivered before a joint convention of the Senate and House of representatives of the General court of Massachusetts, on Friday, February 12, 1909, by the Hon. Henry Cabot Lodge, on the occasion of the one-hundredth anniversary of the birth of Abraham Lincoln. Boston, Mass. ₁Wright & Potter printing co.₎ 1909.
24 p. front. (port.) 24ᶜᵐ.
1. Lincoln, Abraham, pres. U. S., 1809–1865—Addresses, sermons, etc.
                                                    14–5068
Library of Congress   E457.8.L81

                    MWA
NL 0439139   DLC CSmH MH NIC IEN MiU-C OClWHi TxU

Lodge, Henry Cabot, 1850–1924.
Address delivered before the citizens of Nahant, Memorial day, 1882. By Henry Cabot Lodge. Cambridge ₁Mass.₎ J. Wilson and son, University press, 1882.
27 p. 23ᶜᵐ.

1. Memorial day addresses. I. Title.
                                                    24–12340
Library of Congress   E642.L82

NL 0439140   DLC MB OClWHi

Lodge, Henry Cabot, 1850–1924.
Address delivered before the Senate *and House of representatives* and invited guests, on Thursday, Jan. 19, 1905. By the Hon. Henry Cabot Lodge, in response to an invitation of the General court. Boston, Mass. ₁Wright & Potter printing co.₎ 1905.
38 p. 2 port. (incl. front.) 24ᶜᵐ.
On cover: Memorial address on the life, character and public services of the Honorable George Frisbie Hoar, January 19, 1905.
1. Hoar, George Frisbie, 1826–1904.
                                                    37–15426
Library of Congress   E664.H65L6
                                                    923.273

NL 0439141   DLC N MH NN MB MWeIC

Lodge, Henry Cabot, 1850–
Address of Hon. Henry Cabot Lodge, delivered at Greenfield, June 9, 1903, on the 150th anniversary of the incorporation of the town. ₁Greenfield, Mass., 1904?₎
21 p. 23½ᶜᵐ.
Caption title.
Also published in Francis M. Thompson's History of Greenfield, Greenfield, 1904.
1. Greenfield, Mass.—Hist.
                                                    7–41352
Library of Congress   F74.G85L8

NL 0439142   DLC

Lodge, Henry Cabot, 1850–1924.
Address of Senator Henry Cabot Lodge of Massachusetts, in honor of Theodore Roosevelt ... before the Congress of the United States, Sunday, February 9, 1919. Washington, Govt. print. off., 1919.
57 p. 29ᶜᵐ.
1. Roosevelt, Theodore, pres. U. S., 1858–1919.
                                                    27–8369
Library of Congress   E757.L822

NL 0439143   DLC OrP NjP MH

Lodge, Henry Cabot, 1850–1924.
... Address of Senator Henry Cabot Lodge of Massachusetts in honor of Theodore Roosevelt, ex-president of the United States, before the Congress of the United States, Sunday, February 9, 1919. Washington, Govt. print. off., 1919.
56 p. 26½ᶜᵐ. (₁U. S.₎ 65th Cong. 3d sess. Senate. Doc. 384)
1. Roosevelt, Theodore, pres. U. S., 1858–1919. I. Title.
                                                    19—26253
Library of Congress   E757.L82
———— Copy 2.   ₁a38f1₎

NL 0439144   DLC WaE OCl OClW OEac OO OClWHi NN

VOLUME 338

Lodge, Henry Cabot, 1850–
Address of the Hon. Henry Cabot Lodge ... at the fourth plenary session of the Conference on the limitation of armament. December 10, 1921. Washington, Govt. print. off., 1921.
6 p. 23ᵐᵐ.
On the proposed treaty between the United States, the British Empire, France, and Japan in regard to the islands of the Pacific (includes draft of the treaty: p. 3-4)

1. Islands of the Pacific. 2. U. S.—Foreign relations—Treaties.
A 22-42
Title from Carnegie   Endow. Int. Peace. Printed by L. C.
JX1974.A62L7

NL 0439145   NNCE

LODGE, Henry Cabot.
An address on free art. [Delivered in House of Rep's, May 20, 1890]. Boston, n.d.

1 sheet.

NL 0439146   MH

Lodge, Henry Cabot, 1850–1924.
An address upon Chief Justice Marshall, delivered at the Auditorium in Chicago, on the fourth day of February, 1901, at the request of the bar associations of the state of Illinois and of the city of Chicago. By Henry Cabot Lodge. Washington, Pearson printing office, 1901.
30 p. 23½ᵐ.

1. Marshall, John, 1755–1835.   12—23849

Library of Congress   E302.6.M4L8

NL 0439147   DLC NcD

Lodge, Henry Cabot, 1850–1924.

Roosevelt, Theodore, *pres. U. S.,* 1858–1919.
... Addresses and presidential messages of Theodore Roosevelt, 1902–1904; with an introduction by Henry Cabot Lodge ... New York and London, G. P. Putnam's sons [1922?]

Lodge, Henry Cabot, 1850–

Wickersham, George Woodward, 1858–
... Addresses by Hon. George W. Wickersham, attorney general of the United States, at Syracuse, N. Y., January 19, 1911, Cleveland, Ohio, March 20, 1911, Princeton, N. J., May 1, 1911 ... Washington [Govt. print. off.] 1911.

Lodge, Henry Cabot, 1850–1924.

U. S. *Congress. Senate. Committee on foreign relations.*
... Adjustment of title to Isle of Pines ... Report. ⟨To accompany Executive J, Fifty-eighth Congress, second session.⟩ ... [Washington, U. S. Govt. print. off., 1922]

Lodge, Henry Cabot, 1850–

U. S. *Congress. Senate. Committee on naval affairs.*
... Administration of justice in the navy ... Report. ⟨To accompany S. 3646.⟩ [Washington, Govt. print. off., 1911]

Lodge, Henry Cabot, 1850–

U. S. *Dept. of state.*
... Affairs of Hungary, 1849–1850. Message from the President of the United States transmitting in response to a Senate resolution of December 7, 1909, correspondence with Mr. A. Dudley Mann (1849–1850), relating to affairs in Hungary, also certain additional papers transmitted by secretary of state Robert Lansing to Senator Henry Cabot Lodge, on September 10, 1918, relating to the same subject ... Washington, Govt. print. off., 1918.

Lodge, Henry Cabot, 1850–
Albert Gallatin, by Henry Cabot Lodge. New York, C. Scribner's sons, 1879.
20 p. 16ᵐ.

1. Gallatin, Albert *i. e.* Abraham Albert Alphonse, 1761–1849.
Library of Congress   E302.6.G16L8   10–30638

NL 0439153   DLC NcD

Lodge, Henry Cabot, Jr.
Alexander Hamilton.   New York, Houghton, Mifflin, n.d.
American statesmen series.

NL 0439154   KyBgW

Lodge, Henry Cabot, 1850–1924.
... Alexander Hamilton, by Henry Cabot Lodge. Boston, New York, Houghton, Mifflin and company, 1882.
vi, 306 p. 18ᵐ. (*Half-title:* American statesmen, ed. by J. T. Morse, jr. [v. 7])
Series title also at head of t-p.

1. Hamilton, Alexander, 1757–1804.
Library of Congress   E176.A53 vol. 7   10–11970

OU WHi OCU PHi PHC PU OO OClStM MH MB
NL 0439155   DLC OClW NIC MB ViU MiU MtHi ICN NIC

Lodge, Henry Cabot, 1850–
... Alexander Hamilton, by Henry Cabot Lodge. Boston, New York, Houghton, Mifflin and company, 1883.
vi, 306 p. 18ᵐ. (*Half-title:* American statesmen, ed. by J. T. Morse, jr. [v. 7])
Series title also at head of t-p.
First published 1882.

1. Hamilton, Alexander, 1757–1804.
10–11972
Library of Congress   E176.A53 vol. 7

NL 0439156   DLC MtU MiU MoU OO NN PPA PU

Lodge, H. C.
Alexander Hamilton. 1884.

NL 0439157   DN NjP

E176
.A53
v.7
1885
Lodge, Henry Cabot, 1850–1924.
... Alexander Hamilton, by Henry Cabot Lodge. Boston, New York, Houghton, Mifflin and company, 1885.
vi, 306 p. 18ᵐ. (*Half-title:* American statesmen, ed. by J. T. Morse, jr. [v. 7])
Series title also at head of t-p.
First published 1882.

NL 0439158   ViU KEmT KyHi OCX

–
302.6
H2L8
Lodge, Henry Cabot, 1850–1924.
Alexander Hamilton. Edinburgh, D. Douglas, 1886.
306p. 19cm. (American statesmen)

1. Hamilton, Alexander. 1757–1804.

NL 0439159   MU ViU MB

Lodge, Henry Cabot.
Alexander Hamilton. Ed.15. Bost.,1887.
(American statesmen)/

NL 0439160   Nh OEac

Lodge, Henry Cabot, 1850–1924.
Alexander Hamilton. Boston, etc., Houghton Mifflin & co., 1888.
306 p. 18 cm.
At head of title: American statesmen [7]

NL 0439161   MH OOxM NjN

Lodge, Henry Cabot.
Alexander Hamilton.
Boston,1889.   12°
(Amer. statesmen ser.)

NL 0439162   I PNt

Lodge, Henry Cabot, 1850–1924.
...Alexander Hamilton... Boston and New York, Houghton, Mifflin and company, 1890.
vii, p., 1 l., 317, [1] p. (Half-title: American statesmen, ed. by J.T. Morse, jr.)

NL 0439163   ODW

Lodge, Henry Cabot, 1850–1924
Alexander Hamilton. Boston, Houghton Mifflin, 1891.
306 p. (American statesmen)

NL 0439164   MH

Lodge, Henry Cabot, 1850–1924.
... Alexander Hamilton, by Henry Cabot Lodge. Boston, New York, Houghton, Mifflin and company, 1892.
vi, 306 p. 18ᵐ. (*Half-title:* American statesmen, ed. by J. T. Morse, jr. [v. 7])
Series title also at head of t-p.
First published 1882.

1. Hamilton, Alexander, 1757–1804.
Library of Congress   E302.6.H2L82   10–11981

NL 0439165   DLC OrPR IdU PU

Lodge, Henry Cabot, 1850–1924.
Alexander Hamilton. Boston, Houghton, Mifflin and company [c.1882] 1893.
vi, 306 p. (American statesmen, ed. by J.T.Morse, jr. [v.7])

NL 0439166   MH KU PP PPPL NBuU

VOLUME 338

Lodge, Henry Cabot, 1850–1924.
... Alexander Hamilton, by Henry Cabot Lodge. Boston,
New York, Houghton, Mifflin and company, 1894.
vi, 306 p. 18ᵐ. (*Half-title:* American statesmen, ed. by J. T. Morse, jr. ₍v. 7₎)
Series title also at head of t.-p.
First published 1882.

NL 0439167   ViU NcD

Lodge, Henry Cabot, 1850–1924.
... Alexander Hamilton, ... Boston,
Houghton, Mifflin & co., 1895.
306 p.
American statesmen series.

NL 0439168   OClWHi NCsC PU

Lodge, Henry Cabot, 1850–1924.
...Alexander Hamilton, by ... Boston,
New York, Houghton, Mifflin and company,
1896.

NL 0439169   OCl

Lodge, Henry Cabot, 1850–1924.
Alexander Hamilton. Boston, New York, Houghton,
Mifflin & Co., 1897.
306p. (American Statesmen)

NL 0439170   ICRL MH

Lodge, Henry Cabot, 1850–1924.
... Alexander Hamilton, by Henry Cabot Lodge. Boston, New York, Houghton, Mifflin and company, 1898.
vi, 306 p. 18½ᵐ. (*Half-title:* American statesmen, ed. by J. T. Morse, jr.)
Series title also at head of t.-p.

1. Hamilton, Alexander, 1757–1804.
              4—17864
Library of Congress   ₍a23k2₎

NL 0439171   DLC OKentU CaBVaU MtBC KU OClND DCU-IA

Lodge, Henry Cabot, 1850–1924.
... Alexander Hamilton, by Henry Cabot Lodge. Boston and New York, Houghton Mifflin company ₍1898₎
viii p., 1 l., 317 p. 18½ cm. (*Half-title:* American statesmen, ed. by J. T. Morse, jr. ₍v. 7₎)
Series title also at head of t.-p.

1. Hamilton, Alexander, 1757–1804.

E302.6.H2L85   17—14578

OClW OCX
PBm WaTC IdPI ICJ MB OU OFH OCl MU AU NIC KyU-A OLak
NL 0439172   DLC DNW PIm MiU ViU NN ICJ PPT PV PWcS

Lodge, Henry Cabot, 1850–1924.
... Alexander Hamilton, by Henry Cabot Lodge.
Boston and New York, Houghton, Mifflin and company, 1899.
viii p., 1 l., 317, ₍1₎ p. 18 cm. (Half-title: American statesmen, ed. by J. T. Morse, jr. ₍v. 7₎)
Series title in part also at head of t.-p.

1. Hamilton, Alexander, 1757–1804.

NL 0439173   Vi MtHi NBuU ViU IU NcD MiU OClWHi

Lodge, Henry Cabot, 1850–1924.
... Alexander Hamilton, by Henry Cabot Lodge. Boston and New York, Houghton, Mifflin and company ₍190–?₎
vii p., 1 l., 317, ₍1₎ p. 18ᵐ. (*Half-title:* American statesmen, ed. by J. T. Morse, jr.)
Series title also at head of t.-p.

1. Hamilton, Alexander, 1757–1804.
              4—17349
Library of Congress   ₍a37m1₎   -923.273

NL 0439174   DLC WaE

Lodge, Henry Cabot, 1850–1924.
... Alexander Hamilton, by Henry Cabot Lodge. Boston and New York, Houghton Mifflin company ₍1909?₎
viii p., 1 l., 317 p. 18ᵐ. (*Half-title:* American statesmen, ed. by J. T. Morse, jr. ₍v. 7₎)
Series title also at head of t.-p.
First published 1882.

1. Hamilton, Alexander, 1757–1804.

Library of Congress   E176.A532 vol. 7   10—12009

NL 0439175   DLC IdB WaU-L NcD PPMSJ

Lodge, Henry Cabot.
Alexander Hamilton. Boston : Houghton Mifflin Co. ₍cop.
1882–1910₎   viii(i), 317 p. 12°. (American statesmen.)

1. Hamilton, Alexander.   2. Series.
N. Y. P. L.

NL 0439176   NN MU LU CoU TU ViU

Lodge, Henry Cabot, 1850–1924.
... Alexander Hamilton, by Henry Cabot Lodge. Boston and New York, Houghton Mifflin company ₍1917?₎
3 p. L, ₍v₎–viii p., 2 l., 317 p. pl., 4 port. (incl. front.) 19½ cm. (American statesmen. ₍vol. vii₎)
Added series t.-p., engraved.
"Standard library edition."
First published 1882.

1. Hamilton, Alexander, 1757–1804.   A 23—1134
James Jerome Hill Ref.   Library   E176.A5   vol. 7
for Library of Congress   [E302.6.H2L]

NL 0439177   MnSJ OrLgE OrStbM IU OClCC OCX OO

Lodge, Henry Cabot, 1850–
U. S. *Congress. Senate. Committee on foreign relations.*
... Amending act for reorganization of consular service ... Report. ⟨To accompany S. 4112.⟩ ₍Washington, Govt. print. off., 1908₎

₍**Lodge, Henry Cabot**₎ 1850–
The amendment of the United States Senate.
(*In the* Political quarterly. London, 1914. 24½ᵐ. vol. I, p. ₍41₎–59₎)

1. U. S. Congress. Senate—Elections.   i. Title.
Library of Congress   JA8.P7   vol. 41   16—116

NL 0439179   DLC

₍LODGE, Henry Cabot.₎
American history. ₍Notes on authorities. Extracted from Harvard College Libr. bulletin, no. 6,7.₎ n.p., 1877.

NL 0439180   MH

Lodge, Henry Cabot, 1850–1924, ed.
André, John, 1751–1780.
... André's journal; an authenic record of the movements and engagements of the British army in America from June 1777 to November 1778 as recorded from day to day by Major John André; ed. by Henry Cabot Lodge. Boston, Issued by the Bibliophile society for members only, 1903.

Lodge, Henry Cabot.   5615.15
The Anglo-Saxon land-law.
(In Adams, Henry. Essays in Anglo-Saxon law. Pp. 55–119. Boston, 1876.)

F686 — Land law.

NL 0439182   MB RPB MH

Lodge, Henry Cabot, 1850–1924.   FOR OTHER EDITIONS
The Anglo-Saxon land-law.   SEE MAIN ENTRY
Essays in Anglo-Saxon law. Boston, Little, Brown, and company, 1905.

Lodge, Henry Cabot, ed.
Anna Cabot Mills Lodge. A memoir.
Privately printed, 1918.

NL 0439184   MBAt

Lodge, Henry Cabot, 1850–1924.
U. S. *Treaties, etc., 1909–1913 (Taft)*
... Arbitration with France. Message from the President of the United States transmitting an authenticated copy of a treaty signed ... August 3, 1911, extending the scope and obligation of the policy of arbitration adopted in the present arbitration treaty of February 10, 1908, between the two countries, so as to exclude certain exceptions contained in that treaty and to provide means for the peaceful solution of all questions of difference which it shall be found impossible in future to settle by diplomacy ... Washington ₍Govt. print. off.₎ 1911.

Lodge, Henry Cabot, 1850–
U. S. *Treaties, etc., 1909–1913 (Taft)*
... Arbitration with Great Britain. Message from the President of the United States transmitting an authenticated copy of a treaty signed ... August 3, 1911, extending the scope and obligation of the policy of arbitration adopted in the present arbitration treaty of April 4, 1908, between the two countries, so as to exclude certain exceptions contained in that treaty and to provide means for the peaceful solution of all questions of difference which it shall be found impossible in future to settle by diplomacy ... Washington ₍Govt. print. off.₎ 1911.

Lodge, Henry Cabot, 1850–   2309.361
Armed merchantmen. Speech . . . in the Senate of the United States, February 18, 1916.
= Washington. 1916. 18 pp. 23 cm.

L5049 — European War. 1914– . Shipping.

NL 0439187   MB OClWHi

VOLUME 338

Lodge, Henry Cabot, 1850-1924.
The Army in the Philippines. Speech of Hon.
Henry Cabot Lodge, of Massachusetts, In the
Senate of the United States, May 5, 1902. Wash-
ington, 1902.
8 vo. Stapled.

NL 0439188   CSmH PPAmP

Lodge, Henry Cabot, 1850-1924.

United mine workers of America.
... Attempt by communists to seize the American labor
movement. Prepared by the United mine workers of
America and published in newspapers of the United
States ... Washington, Govt. print. off., 1924.

Lodge, Henry Cabot, 1850-1924.
The authorship of the Federalist. By Henry Cabot Lodge.
(*In American antiquarian society, Worcester, Mass. Proceedings.
Worcester, Mass. 1885. 25ᶜᵐ. n. s., v. 3, p. 409-420)*

1. The Federalist.   A 38-729

Newberry library
for Library of Congress   [E172.A35 n. s., vol. 3]
                                                        (973.082)

NL 0439190   ICN MH DLC

Lodge, Henry Cabot, 1850-   comp.
Ballads and lyrics. Selected and arranged by Henry
Cabot Lodge. Boston, Houghton, Mifflin and company
[1880]
xii, [13]-394 (i. e. 396) p. 18ᶜᵐ.
Extra pages numbered 192a and 192b follow p. 192.
"Intended for boys and girls between the ages of twelve and eighteen."—
Pref.

1. English poetry (Selections)
                                                        8-17047

Library of Congress   PR1175.L53 1880 a

NL 0439191   DLC MH NjP MWA OU PBm OC1 MB PU PPGi

LODGE, Henry Cabot, 1850- , editor.
Ballads and lyrics, selected and arranged by
H.C.Lodge. 5th ed. Boston, Houghton, Mifflin
and company [cop.1880].

NL 0439192   MH PPL

Lodge, Henry Cabot, 1850-1921, comp
Ballads and lyrics. Selected and
arranged by ... Boston, Houghton, Mifflin
and company [c1880] ed. 6.

NL 0439193   OC1

Lodge, Henry Cabot, compiler and editor.
Ballads and lyrics. 9th edition.
Boston. Houghton, Mifflin & Co. [1880.] 394 pp. 16°.
                                                        **4399.25

G7782 — Lyric poetry. — English literature. Poetry. Colls. — Ballads.

NL 0439194   MB

Lodge, Henry Cabot, 1850-1924.
Ballads and lyrics, selected and arranged by
Henry Cabot Lodge. 10th ed. Boston, etc.,
Houghton, Mifflin and co., 1897.

394 p. 18 cm.
Spine: With biographical notes.

NL 0439195   MH MB

808.8
L82b   **Lodge, Henry Cabot**, 1850-1924, *ed.*
The best of the world's classics, restricted to prose. Henry
Cabot Lodge, editor-in-chief, Francis W. Halsey, associate
editor; with an introduction, biographical and explanatory
notes, etc. ... New York and London, Funk & Wagnalls
company [1909]
10 v. fronts. (ports.) 16 cm.
CONTENTS.—I. Greece.—II. Rome.—III-VI. Great Britain and Ireland.—VII-VIII. Continental Europe.—IX-X. America. Index.

1. Literature—Collections.   I. Halsey, Francis Whiting, 1851-
1919, joint ed. II. Title.

PN6013.L5   808.8   9-27293

                       PBa MB OC1W NcRS CoU OU NN ODW OO OC1 OC1JC LU
NL 0439196   DLC OC1ND OFH PPAmP OrCS NcC OrU PP PPC

Lodge, Henry Cabot, 1850-   ed.
The best of the world's classics, restricted to prose.
Editor-in-chief: Henry Cabot Lodge; associate editor:
Francis W. Halsey; with an introduction, biographical
and explanatory notes, etc. Subscription ed. ... New
York and London, Funk & Wagnalls company [1912]
10 v. fronts., plates, ports. 22ᶜᵐ. $25.00
Title within green ornamental border.
CONTENTS.—I. Greece.—II. Rome.—III-VI. Great Britain and Ireland.—
VII-VIII. Continental Europe.—IX-X. America. Index.

1. Literature—Collections.   I. Halsey, Francis Whiting, 1851-
joint ed.
Library of Congress   PN6013.L6   12-15479

NL 0439197   DLC PV NcD

Lodge, Henry Cabot, 1850- 1924
... Boston, by Henry Cabot Lodge ... London and New
York, Longmans, Green, and co., 1891.
xi, 242 p. 2 fold. maps (incl. front.) 19ᶜᵐ. (*Half-title:* Historic towns)
Series title also at head of t.-p.

1. Boston—Hist.   I. Title.   1-12236
Library of Congress   F73.3.L28

                       PHC CaBVaU PWcS MH ICJ PPL NN MdBP MB NjN DN
NL 0439198   DLC OC1 OCU OC1WHi CU GU MB MWA PP DSI

Lodge, Henry Cabot, 1850-1924
Boston. [2d ed.] L, Longmans, Green, 1892

xi, 242 p. maps.

NL 0439199   MH MB

Lodge, Henry Cabot, 1850-1924.
... Boston, by ... London and New York,
Longmans, Green, and co., 1902.
[Ed. 3.]

NL 0439200   OC1W NcD

Lodge, Henry Cabot, 1850-

U. S. Congress. Senate. Committee on the Philippines.
... Catholic church claims in Philippine Islands ... Report. ⟨To accompany H. R. 16143.⟩ [Washington, Govt.
print. off., 1908]

Lodge, Henry Cabot, 1850-
Certain accepted heroes and other essays in literature
and politics, by Henry Cabot Lodge. New York and London, Harper & brothers, 1897.
5 p. l., [3]-269 p. 19¾ᶜᵐ.
"With the exception of the last, these essays have all been published before in different magazines and reviews."—Note.
CONTENTS.—As to certain accepted heroes.—The last Plantagenet.—
Shakespeare's Americanisms.—Chatterton.—Dr. Holmes.—A liberal education.—The home of the Cabots.—English elections.—Our foreign policy.

1. American literature—Addresses, essays, lectures.   I. Title.

Library of Congress   PS2249.L84C4   12-36279

                       TNJ PHC PP PPL OC1W ODW OCU OCX OOxM NN MB
NL 0439202   DLC GU ICN WaS MWA Wa KEmT FU NIC LU

Lodge, Henry Cabot, 1850-1924.

U. S. Congress. Senate. Committee on foreign rela-
tions.
... Cession of Danish islands in the West Indies ...
Report. ⟨To accompany Executive M., Fifty-seventh
Congress, first session.⟩ [Reprinted for 64th Cong., 1st
sess., 1916] [Washington, Govt. print. off., 1916]

Lodge, Henry Cabot, 1850-

U. S. Congress. Senate. Committee on foreign relations.
... Cession of the Danish West Indies ... Report. ⟨To
accompany Executive D, 64—1.⟩ [Washington, Govt.
print. off., 1917]

Lodge, Henry Cabot, 1850-1924.   FOR OTHER EDITIONS
                                            SEE MAIN ENTRY
Adams, Charles Francis, 1835-1915.
Charles Francis Adams, 1835-1915; an autobiography; with
a Memorial address delivered November 17, 1915, by Henry
Cabot Lodge. Boston & New York, Houghton Mifflin com-
pany, 1916.

Lodge, Henry Cabot, 1850-

U. S. Congress. Senate. Committee on the Philippines.
... Civil government in the Philippine Islands ... Report. ⟨To accompany S. 4829.⟩ [Washington, Govt.
print. off., 1912]

LODGE, Henry Cabot.
Civil service reform. Speech, in the house of
representatives, Feb.13,1891. With an appendix
containing a letter from Theodore Roosevelt to
H.S.Lehblach. Washington, 1891.

8°. pp. 16.

NL 0439207   MH CSmH MB

Lodge, Henry Cabot.
Colonialism in the United States
see his   Colonization in the United States.

VOLUME 338

Lodge, Henry Cabot, 1850–
Colonization in the United States, by Henry Cabot Lodge, reprinted from ₍his₎ Studies in history ... Boston and New York, Houghton, Mifflin and company, The Riverside press, Cambridge, 1898.

p. ₍330₎–366. 17½ᶜᵐ.
Running title: Colonialism in the United States.
The subject of the essay is colonialism. The title of the essay as published in his Studies in history is Colonialism in the United States.

1. U. S.—Civilization.
A 16–1334

Title from Vassar College   Printed by L. C.

NL 0439209   NPV NN

Lodge, Henry Cabot, 1850–
... The compulsory initiative and referendum and the recall of judges. An address by Henry Cabot Lodge, delivered at Princeton university March 8, 1912. Washington, Govt. print. off., 1912.

20 p. 23½ᶜᵐ. (₍U. S.₎ 62d Cong. 2d sess. Senate. Doc. 406)

1. Referendum. 2. Recall. 3. Judges—U. S.   ı. Title.

Library of Congress   JF493.U6L67   12–35387

NL 0439210   DLC MiU OO

Lodge, Henry Cabot, 1850–1924.
King, William Henry, 1863–
... Conditions in Russia. Speech of Hon. William H. King, a senator from the state of Utah, delivered in the Senate, January 22 and April 24, 1924 ... Washington, Govt. print. off., 1924.

Lodge, Henry Cabot, 1850–1924.
Hoar, George Frisbie, 1826–1904.
The Connecticut compromise. Roger Sherman, the author of the plan of equal representation of the states in the Senate, and representation of the people in proportion to numbers in the House. By George F. Hoar.
(*In American antiquarian society, Worcester, Mass. Proceedings. Worcester, Mass., 1904. 25ᶜᵐ. n. s., v. 15, p. 233–258*)

Lodge, Henry Cabot, 1850–1924.
... The Constitution and its makers: an address delivered before the Literary and historical association of North Carolina at Raleigh, N. C., November 28, 1911, by Henry Cabot Lodge ... Washington ₍Govt. print. off.₎ 1911.

25 p. 23½ᶜᵐ. (₍U. S.₎ 62d Cong., 2d sess. Senate. Doc. 122)
Presented by Mr. Overman.
Ordered printed December 5, 1911.

1. U. S. Constitution. 2. Recall.   ı. Title.
11—35042

Library of Congress   JK271.L6

OC1JC OC1WHi NcD MWA PPT
NL 0439213   DLC OC1JC IdB NN TKL DNW ODW OO NN MiU

Lodge, Henry Cabot.
The constitution and its makers. Address of Honorable Henry Cabot Lodge, November 28, 1911. (In: North Carolina. North Carolina Historical Commission. Bulletin 11. Raleigh, 1912. p. 64–97.)

1. Constitutions, U. S.
July 2, 1912.

NL 0439214   NN

Lodge, Henry Cabot, 1850–1924.
... The Constitution and its makers: an address delivered before the Literary and historical association of North Carolina at Raleigh, N. C., November 28, 1911, by Henry Cabot Lodge... Washington [Govt. print. off.] 1912.

24 p. 23.5 cm. ([U.S.] 62d Cong., 2d sess. Senate. Doc. 122)
Presented by Mr. Overman.
Ordered printed December 5, 1911.

NL 0439215   GU

LODGE, HENRY CABOT, 1850–1924.
The constitution and its makers.   2717
Edgehill Road, Cleveland, n.p., 1935.
30 p.

NL 0439216   Or

Lodge, Henry Cabot. 1850–1924
The constitution of the United States; speech, in the Senate of the United States, February 6, 1911.   Washington: ₍Gov. Prtg. Off.,₎ 1911. 16 p.   8°.

YA 5000 517

1. U. S.—Senate: Election.
March 18, 1912.

NL 0439217   NN Or DLC

Lodge, Henry Cabot, 1850–
U. S. *58th Cong., 3d sess., 1904–1905. Senate.*
... Constitutional methods of making and ratifying treaties in certain foreign countries, and also list of arbitration treaties and conventions submitted to and acted upon by the Senate. February 14, 1905.—Presented by Mr. Lodge and ordered to be printed. February 20, 1905.—Ordered reprinted with additions. ₍Washington, Gov't print. off., 1905₎

Lodge, Henry Cabot, 1850–1924.
Paris. *Peace conference, 1919. Commission on the league of nations.*
... Covenant. A draft of the composite covenant made by the legal advisers of the Commission on the league ... Washington, Govt. print. off., 1919.

Lodge, Henry Cabot, 1902–
U. S. *Congress. Senate. Committee on territories and insular affairs.*
... Crime and criminal procedure in Alaska ... Report. ⟨To accompany S. 2254⟩ ... ₍Washington, U. S. Govt. print. off., 1937₎

Lodge, Henry Cabot, 1850–1924.
... Daniel Webster, by Henry Cabot Lodge. Boston, New York, Houghton, Mifflin and company, 1883.

vi, 372 p. 18½ᶜᵐ. (*Half-title:* American statesmen, ed. by J. T. Morse, jr. ₍v. 21₎)
Series title also at head of t.-p.

1. Webster, Daniel, 1782–1852.
10—11976

Library of Congress   E176.A53 vol. 21

KyMdC MtU Or DU WaU–L CU S
NNtCA MH–AH NN DNW PPL PU PPC PPA MU NIC KMK WaT
MdBP DN KEmT OU OC1WHi ICRL MH OEac PPFr OOxM NcRS
NL 0439221   DLC MB ViU ODW OLak NjNbS MB MH NjP MiU

Lodge, Henry Cabot.
Daniel Webster, [Life of].
Boston, 1884.
372 p.   8°

NL 0439222   MWA NjP NcU

Lodge, Henry Cabot, 1850–1924.
Daniel Webster. 5th ed. Boston, Houghton, Mifflin, 1885.

v1, 372 p. 19cm. (American statesmen, vol. 21)
Contains an autograph letter of Daniel Webster, and letters from Mellen Chamberlain and Stephen M. Allen to Elizabeth Porter Gould. Also many newspaper clippings and notes concerning Webster.

1. Webster, Daniel, 1782–1852.   I. Series.

NL 0439223   MB PRosC

Lodge, Henry Cabot, 1850–1924.
Daniel Webster, by Henry Cabot Lodge.   Seventh ed. Boston, New York, Houghton, Mifflin co., 1886.
372 p.

NL 0439224   PSC

~~Lodge, Henry Cabot~~
Daniel Webster (American statesmen.)

Newark has Boston, 1888 edition.

NL 0439225   NjN OEac OOxM

Lodge, Henry Cabot, 1850–1924.
Daniel Webster. Boston, New York, Houghton, Mifflin & Co., 1889.
372p. (American Statesmen)

NL 0439226   ICRL PPT PU

Lodge, Henry Cabot, 1850–1924.
Daniel Webster. Boston, Houghton, Mifflin, 1891.

vi, 372 p. (American statesmen)

NL 0439227   MH

Lodge, Henry Cabot, 1850–1924.
... Daniel Webster, by Henry Cabot Lodge. Boston and New York, Houghton, Mifflin and company ₍1892₎

vi, 372 p. 18ᶜᵐ. (*Half-title:* American statesmen, ed. by J. T. Morse, jr.)
Series title also at head of t.-p.

1. Webster, Daniel, 1782–1852.
4—17350

Library of Congress   E176.A53 vol. 21
923   ₍a26k2₎   E

NL 0439228   DLC WaE OCU MiU

Lodge, Henry Cabot, 1850–1924
Daniel Webster.
Boston, Houghton, 1893.
372 p. (American statesmen)

NL 0439229   PP

VOLUME 338

E176
.A53
v.21
1894

Lodge, Henry Cabot, 1850-1924.
Daniel Webster. Boston, Houghton, Mifflin, 1894.
372 p. 18cm. (American statesmen, vol. XXI)
Added t. p., engraved: American statesmen ...

1. Webster, Daniel, 1782-1852.

NL 0439230   ViU

Lodge, Henry Cabot
Daniel Webster.
Boston, Houghton, 1895.
372 p. (American statesmen)

NL 0439231   PPD PU

E
340
.W4L82
1896

Lodge, Henry Cabot, 1850-1924.
Daniel Webster, by Henry Cabot Lodge.
Boston, Houghton, Mifflin, 1896 [c1883]
vi, 372 p. 18 cm. (American states-
men, [v. 21])
Series title also at head of t.-p.

1. Webster, Daniel, 1782-1852. I. Title.

NL 0439232   NBuU PPC PPPL CtY PPULC MB Nh MH

LODGE, Henry Cabot, 1850.
Daniel Webster. Boston, etc., Houghton,
Mifflin and company, 1897.

(American statesmen,

NL 0439233   MH

Lodge, Henry Cabot, 1850-
Daniel Webster. By Henry Cabot Lodge.
Boston: Hough-
ton, Mifflin and Co., 1898. vi, 372 p. 12°. (Amer. statesmen.)

1. Webster, Daniel, 1782-1852. 2.   Series.   September 14, 1915.

NL 0439234   NN DCU-IA

Lodge, Henry Cabot, 1850-1924.
... Daniel Webster, by Henry Cabot Lodge. [Large paper
ed.] Boston and New York, Houghton, Mifflin and company,
1899.
3 p. l., [v]-viii p. 2 l., 378 p., 1 l. pl., 4 port. (incl. front.) fold. facsim. 22½ᵐ. (Half-title: American statesmen, vol. XXI)
Added t.-p., engraved: American statesmen ...
Five hundred copies printed.

1. Webster, Daniel, 1782-1852.   99-633 Revised
Library of Congress
E176.A54 Vol 21

NL 0439235   OO OC1W MB NcD MtHi GU-L IdPI NIC MWA CaBVaU MH
DLC AU MB OU OC1WHi ViU MU OCU MiU OLak

Lodge, Henry Cabot, 1850-1924.
... Daniel Webster, by Henry Cabot Lodge. Boston
and New York, Houghton Mifflin company [1909?]
vi, 372 p. 18ᵐ. (Half-title: American statesmen, ed. by J. T. Morse,
jr. [v. 21])
Series title also at head of t.-p.
First published 1883.

1. Webster, Daniel, 1782-1852.
    10-12018
Library of Congress   E176.A532 vol. 21

NL 0439236   DLC NcD PPMSJ PV

Lodge, Henry Cabot, 1850-1924.
...Daniel Webster, by ...   Boston and New
York, Houghton Mifflin company c1911.
vi, 372 p. (Half-title: American statesmen,
ed. by J.T. Morse. jr. [v. 21]) First published
1883.

NL 0439237   OFH OCU OC1h MB TU MU IaU OU CoU

Lodge, Henry Cabot, 1850-1924.
Daniel Webster, by Henry Cabot Lodge. Boston and New
York, Houghton Mifflin company [1917?]
3 p. l., [v]-viii p., 2 l., 378 p. pl., 4 port. (incl. front.) 19½ cm.
(American statesmen. [vol. XXI])
Added series t.-p., engraved.
"Standard library edition."
First published 1883.

1. Webster, Daniel, 1782-1852.

[E340.W4L   ]   A 23-1147
James Jerome Hill Ref.   Library
for Library of Congress   [r56t1]

NL 0439238   MnSJ OrStbM WaU-L OC1CC

HU 338.56.11.1 Lodge, Henry Cabot. De summa republica oratio;
latine versa ab X. [J. B. Greenough]. N. P. [190-?] 8°
pp. 5.

NL 0439239   MH

Lodge, Henry Cabot, 1850-1924.
Hollander, Jacob Harry, 1871-
... Debt of Santo Domingo ... Report on the debt of Santo
Domingo, submitted to the President of the United States by
Jacob H. Hollander, special commissioner ... [Washington,
Govt. print. off., 1905]

Lodge, Henry Cabot, 1850-1924.
The democracy of Abraham Lincoln; address to the students
of Boston university School of law, by Hon. Henry Cabot Lodge.
March 14, 1913. [Malden, Mass.: The Dunbar-Kerr co.,
printers, 1913] 23 p. 22½cm.

1. Lincoln, Abraham, 16th pres.   U. S. 2. Recall—U. S. 3. United
States—Politics, 1909-1913. I. Title.
    May 27, 1941

NL 0439241   NN IHi MH CSmH RPB

Lodge, Henry Cabot, 1850-1924.
... The democracy of Abraham Lincoln. Address by Henry
Cabot Lodge, before the students of Boston university School
of law, on March 14, 1913 ... Washington [Govt. print. off.]
1913.
18 p. 23½ᵐ. ([U. S.] 63d Cong. 1st sess. Senate. Doc. 18)
Presented by Mr. Root. Ordered printed May 5, 1913.

1. Lincoln, Abraham, pres. U. S., 1809-1865—Addresses, sermons, etc.
2. Recall. 3. U. S.—Pol. & govt.—1909-1913. I. Title.
    13-35375
Library of Congress   E457.8.L815

NL 0439242   DLC MiU OO

Lodge, Henry Cabot, 1850-1924.
The democracy of the Constitution, and other addresses
and essays, by Henry Cabot Lodge. New York, C. Scribner's
sons, 1915.
5 p. l., 297 p. 21 cm.
CONTENTS.—The Public opinion bill.—The Constitution and its makers.—The compulsory initiative and referendum, and the recall of
judges.—The Constitution and the Bill of rights.—The democracy of
Abraham Lincoln.—John C. Calhoun.—Thomas Brackett Reed.—An
American myth.—As to anthologies.—The origin of certain Americanisms.—Diversions of a convalescent.
1. U. S. Constitution. 2. Democracy. 3. Lincoln, Abraham, pres.
U. S., 1809-1865. 4. Calhoun, John Caldwell, 1782-1850. 5. Reed,
Thomas Brackett, 1839-1902. I. Title.

AC8.L67   15-4687
Library of Congress   [59p4]

TU
DS LU NIC OU OC1W ICJ NN ViU MB OrPR NjNbS WaS WaU-L
NL 0439243   DLC FU PPT PPA NcD NcRS DAU UU PP OC1

Lodge, Henry Cabot, 1850-1924.
Butler, Nicholas Murray, 1862-
... The discontent with democracy. Address by Nicho-
las Murray Butler before the midwinter meeting of the
Republican state editorial association at Indianapolis,
Indiana, February 8, 1924 ... Washington, Govt. print.
off., 1924.

Lodge, Henry Cabot, 1850-
Dr. Holmes. [Two great authors. 1)
From North-American review, Dec. 1894.
23 cm. [669]-677 p.

NL 0439245   RPB

Lodge, Henry Cabot, 1850-
U. S. Congress. Senate. Committee on finance.
... Duties on sugar ... Report. <To accompany H. R.
21213.> [Washington, Govt. print. off., 1912]

Lodge, Henry Cabot, 1850-1924
Early memories. London, Constable & co.,
ltd., 1913.

362 p. 24.5 cm.

NL 0439247   MH NcD PPFr

Lodge, Henry Cabot, 1850-1924.
Early memories, by Henry Cabot Lodge ... New York,
C. Scribner's sons, 1913.
6 p. l., 3-362 p. 23½ᵐ. $2.50

I. Title.
Library of Congress   E664.L7L7   13-20784

DN NcGU ViU OrP WaS IdU Wa MtU OrU CaBVaU
OO OC1WHi OC1 PPA PU PHC PP PPL MeB NN KEmT MH NN AU
NL 0439248   DLC WaTC WaT GU TU ICU NjP OEac OU OOx.4

Lodge, Henry Cabot, 1850-1924.
Early memories. New York, C.Scribner's sons,
1925.

NL 0439249   MH OFH

VOLUME 338

Lodge, Henry Cabot, 1850–1924, ed.

Adams, Henry, 1838–1918.   FOR OTHER EDITIONS SEE MAIN ENTRY
The education of Henry Adams; an autobiography. Boston and New York, Houghton Mifflin company, 1918.

---

*D645
.A6
1918   **Lodge, Henry Cabot,** 1850–1924.
The essential terms of peace. Speech in the Senate of the United States, August 23, 1918. Washington [U. S. Govt. Print. Off.] 1918.
7 p. 24cm.

1. European war, 1914–1918—Peace. 2. U. S.—For. rel.—Germany. 3. Germany—For. rel.—U. S. 4. Peace. I. Title

NL 0439251   MB CSt-H MH

Lodge, Henry Cabot, 1850–

U. S. *Immigration commission,* 1907–
... European immigration, 1899–1909 ... Table showing European immigration, by race or people, into the United States from 1899 to 1909. [Washington, Govt. print. off., 1912]

Lodge, Henry Cabot, 1850–

U. S. *Congress. Senate. Committee on naval affairs.*
... Examination for promotion in the navy ... Report. <To accompany S. 3643> [Washington, Govt. print. off., 1911]

Lodge, Henry Cabot, 1850–1924.
Famous old tales. Selected and arranged by Henry Cabot Lodge. Illustrated. Boston, New York [etc.] Houghton Mifflin company [1915]
2 p. l., 5–188 p. illus., pl. 21cm.

CONTENTS.—Jack the giant-killer.—Jack and the bean-stalk.—Little Red Riding-Hood.—Puss in boots.—The sleeping beauty.—Cinderella.—Bluebeard.—Hop-O'-My-Thumb.—Beauty and the beast.—The princess and the nut.—Fortunatus.—Sir R. Whittington and his cat.

I. Title.

New Haven. Free public   Library   A 16—215
for Library of Congress   [a41b1]

NL 0439254   CtNh OrP NN

Lodge, Henry Cabot, 1850–1924, ed.

The Federalist.   FOR OTHER EDITIONS SEE MAIN ENTRY
The Federalist; a commentary on the Constitution of the United States; being a collection of essays written in support of the Constitution agreed upon September 17, 1787, by the Federal convention, reprinted from the original text of Alexander Hamilton, John Jay, and James Madison, edited by Henry Cabot Lodge ... New York & London, G. P. Putnam's sons, 1908.

Lodge, Henry Cabot, 1850–1924.
"Federalist, The." Authorship and bibliography of. By H. C. Lodge. (Hamilton, Alex. Works, 1886, vol. IX. xxiii.–xlii.)

NL 0439256   MH

Lodge, Henry Cabot, 1850–1924.
A fighting frigate, and other essays and addresses, by Henry Cabot Lodge. New York, C. Scribner's sons, 1902.
4 p. l., 316 p. 21cm.

CONTENTS.—A fighting frigate [the Constitution]—John Marshall.—Oliver Ellsworth.—Daniel Webster: his oratory and his influence.—Three governors of Massachusetts: Frederic T. Greenhalge, George D. Robinson, Roger Wolcott.—The treaty-making powers of the Senate.—Some impressions of Russia.—Rochambeau.—Appendix: Letter from Hon. George F. Hoar in regard to Mr. Sherman and Mr. Ellsworth and the share of each in securing the "Connecticut compromise".

1. U. S.—Hist.—Addresses, essays, lectures. 2. Statesmen, American. I. Title.

Library of Congress   E173.L7.   2–24749

   I NN PWcS PU PP
   NIC ViU WaTC WaT NjP Vi DN NcRS OOxM OCl OO OClW
NL 0439257   DLC OrP WaS CaBVaU OrCS MrB InU OrPS

Lodge, Henry Cabot, 1850–1924.
The first Republican year; a review in which the Republican majority leader in the Senate contends the present Congress has accomplished more effective legislation than any other peace time national legislature, by Henry Cabot Lodge ... [n. p., 1922?]
[4] p. 24cm.
Caption title.

1. U. S.—Pol. & govt.—1921–1923. I. Title.

Library of Congress   E785.L82   24–22350

NL 0439258   DLC

Lodge, Henry Cabot, 1850–1924
The four-power treaty; speech in the Senate of the United States, Mar. 8, 1922. Washington, 1922
16 p.

NL 0439259   MH

Lodge, Henry Cabot, 1850–   *2355.12.56
Francis Parkman.
(*In* Massachusetts Historical Society. Proceedings. Vol. 56, pp. 319–335. Boston. 1923.)

M7729 — Parkman, Francis, Jr., 1823–1893.

NL 0439260   MB

Lodge, Henry Cabot, 1850–
Francis Parkman, by Henry Cabot Lodge. Read before the Massachusetts historical society, June 14, 1923. Boston, 1923.
19 p. 24½cm.
Society's seal below title.
"From the Proceedings of the Massachusetts historical society for June, 1923."

1. Parkman, Francis, 1823–1893. I. Massachusetts historical society, Boston.

Library of Congress   E175.5.P22   24–3319

NL 0439261   DLC NN

451
1906j   **Lodge, Henry Cabot,** 1850–1924.
Franklin and his times.
(*In* The Independent. New York, 1906. 25cm. v.60, p.72–79. illus.(incl. ports.))
One of eight articles published in celebration of the Franklin bicentenary.

NL 0439262   CtY

Lodge, Henry Cabot
The free coinage of silver. Speech ... March 24, 1892.
Wash., 1892.

YA5000   (Congressional speeches, by author)
J 17

NL 0439263   DLC

Lodge, Henry Cabot, 1850–

U. S. *Treaties, etc., 1909–1913 (Taft)*
... Fur seals protection. Message from the President of the United States transmitting a convention looking to the protection and preservation of fur seals and sea otters in a certain defined zone of the North Pacific Ocean, signed by the plenipotentiaries of the United States, Great Britain, Japan, and Russia, at Washington on July 7, 1911 ... Washington [Govt. print. off.] 1911.

Lodge, Henry Cabot, 1850–1924.
A frontier town, and other essays, by Henry Cabot Lodge. New York, C. Scribner's sons, 1906.
4 p. l., 274 p. 21cm.

CONTENTS.—A frontier town [Greenfield, Mass.]—Good citizenship.—The Senate of the United States.—History.—Samuel Adams.—Theodore Roosevelt.—Senator Hoar. — American history. — Certain principles of town government.—Franklin.—The United States at Algeciras.

1. U. S.—Hist.—Addresses, essays, lectures. 2. Statesmen, American. I. Title.

Library of Congress   E173.L79L   6—34821

   TU
   OU OCl MiU ViU ICN NcD NcU NN MB PPA PWcS PHC PP PPL
NL 0439265   DLC OrP CoU NjP KU GU NcRS OOxM OO OFH

Lodge, Henry Cabot, 1850–
General arbitration. Lecture delivered by Hon. Henry Cabot Lodge ... at the Naval war college extension, Washington, D. C., February 13, 1913. Washington, Govt. print. off., 1913.
12 p. 23cm.

1. Arbitration, International. 2. U. S.—For. rel.—Treaties. I. Title.

Library of Congress   JX1963.L5   13–35138

NL 0439266   DLC DNW ICJ

Lodge, Henry Cabot, 1850–
... The general arbitration treaties with Great Britain and France. Speech of Hon. Henry Cabot Lodge, in the Senate of the United States, on February 29, 1912. Washington, Govt. print. off., 1912.
34 p. 23½cm. ([U. S.] 62d Cong., 2d sess. Senate. Doc. 353)
"List of arbitration treaties and conventions submitted to and acted upon by the Senate": p. 30–34.

1. Arbitration, International. 2. U. S.—For. rel.—Gt. Brit. 3. Gt. Brit.—For. rel.—U. S. 4. U. S.—For. rel.—France. 5. France—For. rel.—U. S. 6. U. S.—For. rel.—Treaties—Bibl. I. Title.

Library of Congress   JX1987.G7 1912   12–35349

NL 0439267   DLC MH-L OCl MiU PPAmP

Lodge, Henry Cabot.
George Washington. New York, Houghton Mifflin, n. d.
2 v.
American statesmen series.

NL 0439268   KyBgW

VOLUME 338

Lodge, Henry Cabot, 1850–1924.
... George Washington, by Henry Cabot Lodge ... Boston and New York, Houghton, Mifflin and company, 1889.
2 v. 18ᶜᵐ. (*Half-title:* American statesmen, ed. by J. T. Morse, jr. ᵥᵥ. 4–5ᵧ)
Series title also at head of t.-p.

1. Washington, George, pres. U. S., 1732–1799.
4–17040
Library of Congress ————— Copy 2.
Copyright 1889 : 18172.   E176.A53   vol. 4–5
                              18173
                              ₍36o1₎   -923.173

CMenSP NjP NcD KMK TU NBuC OrP MtU
Or WaWW ICJ WaE PHi Ok PPC PSC PHC OrPR WaSp CoU
OEac OC1StM OU MiU Nh ICJ NN MH MdBP ViU CaBVaU
NL 0439269   DLC IdU-SB DN WaT MU Wa NjP MBAt TKL

Lodge, Henry Cabot
George Washington.
Boston, Houghton, 1890.
2 v. (American statesmen)

NL 0439270   PU PPD NjNbS CtY MH LU

Lodge, Henry Cabot, 1850–1924.
... George Washington, by Henry Cabot Lodge ... Boston and New York, Houghton, Mifflin and company, 1891.
2 v. 18ᶜᵐ. (*Half-title:* American statesmen, ed. by J. T. Morse, jr. ᵥᵥ. 4–5ᵧ)
Series title also at head of t.-p.

1. Washington, George, pres. U. S., 1732–1799.
10–11979
Library of Congress   E312.L82
                          ₍a38p1₎

NL 0439271   DLC WaTC PCM NjN

E176 **Lodge, Henry Cabot,** 1850–1924.
.A53 ... George Washington, by Henry Cabot Lodge ...
v.4–5 Boston and New York, Houghton, Mifflin and com-
1893 pany, 1893.
         2 v. 18ᶜᵐ. (Half-title: American statesmen, ed. by J. T. Morse, jr. v.4–5)

1. Washington, George, pres. U. S., 1732–1799.
I. Ser.

NL 0439272   ViU MH OOxM PP

Lodge, Henry Cabot, 1850–1924.
...George Washington,... Boston and New York, Houghton, Mifflin and company, 1894.
2 v. (Half-title: American statesmen, ed. by J.T. Morse, jr.)

NL 0439273   ODW ViU NcRS MH NN PPULC NcD

973.41 **Lodge, Henry Cabot,** 1850–1924.
W277YL   George Washington.   Boston, Houghton,
             Mifflin, 1895 ₍cl889₎
             2 v. (American statesmen series)

1. Washington, George, Pres. U. S., 1732–1799.

NL 0439274   KEmT

Lodge, Henry Cabot.
George Washington.   Houghton. 1896, c89.
2 v.   (American statesmen)
v. 2 lacking for Reference.
Later edition has title; The life of George Washington.

NL 0439275   WaS

E   **Lodge, Henry Cabot,** 1850–1924.
312   George Washington, by Henry Cabot Lodge.
.L83 Boston, Houghton, Mifflin, 1897 [cl889]
1897   2 v. 18 cm. (American statesmen, ₍v. 4–5₎)
         Series title also at head of t.-p.

1. Washinton, George, Pres. U. S., 1782–1790
I. Title.

NL 0439276   NBuU

Lodge, Henry Cabot, 1850–1924.
... George Washington, by Henry Cabot Lodge ... Boston and New York, Houghton, Mifflin and company, 1896.
2 v. fronts, plates, ports., fold. facsim. 22½ᶜᵐ. (*Half-title:* American statesmen, ed. by J. T. Morse, jr. vol. IV–V)
Series title also at head of t.-p.
Added series t.-p., engraved.
Large paper edition. Five hundred copies printed."

1. Washington, George, pres. U. S., 1732–1799.
                                    98–1846 Revised
Library of Congress   E312.L83
                          E176.A54 vol. 4–5

OLak OC1W Vi MH OrP Wa MtHi OrSaW WaSpG
NL 0439277   DLC ViU MU DCU MoU MB AU OC1WHi MiU PV

Lodge, Henry C.
George Washington.
Cambridge, 1899.
2 vols.   12°

(American statesman.)

NL 0439278   MWA CaBVaU RWoU OC1W OC1WHi MiU I

Lodge, Henry Cabot, 1850–1924.
... George Washington, by Henry Cabot Lodge... Boston and New York, Houghton Mifflin company ₍1909?₎
2 v. 18ᶜᵐ. (*Half-title:* American statesmen, ed. by J. T. Morse, jr. ᵥᵥ. 4–5ᵧ)
Series title also at head of t.-p.
First published 1889.

1. Washington, George, pres. U. S., 1732–1799.
                                    10–12008
Library of Congress   E176.A532 vol. 4–5

NL 0439279   DLC NIC ViU OLak OC1 PPMSJ

Lodge, Henry Cabot, 1850–1924.
... George Washington, by Henry Cabot Lodge ... ₍Stand-ard library ed.₎ Boston and New York, Houghton Mifflin company ₍1917?₎
2 v. 2 pl., 8 port. (incl. fronts.) 19½ᶜᵐ. (American statesmen. ₍vol. IV, V₎)
Added series t.-p., engraved.
First published 1889.

1. Washington, George, pres. U. S., 1732–1799.
                                          A 23—1132
James Jerome Hill ref. libr.   E176.A5   vol. 4, 5
for Library of Congress   [E176.A   vol. 4–5]

OO OC1 PPGi PV
NL 0439280   MnSJ OrStbM IdB WaU CoU ViU OC1h OC1U

Lodge, Henry Cabot, 1850–1924.
George Washington, by Henry Cabot Lodge ... Boston and New York, Houghton Mifflin company, 1924.
2 v. fronts. (ports.) 18ᶜᵐ. (*Half-title:* The great presidents series ... vol. I–II)
First published 1889.
"This edition has been carefully revised."—Pref.

1. Washington, George, pres. U. S., 1732–1799.
                                    41–40495
Library of Congress   E312.L834
                                    923.173

NL 0439281   DLC KyLx TU PV

Lodge, Henry Cabot.
George Washington.   Boston: Houghton Mifflin Co., 1932₍, cop. 1889–1917₎. 2 v. in 1.   12°.
Bicentenary edition.

1. Washington, George.
                          April 20, 1932
NL 0439282   NN WaS NcD

AC1 **Lodge, Henry Cabot,** 1850–1924.
.B5   George Washington von Henry Cabot Lodge. Aus
v.1   dem englischen übersetzt ... Berlin, Weidmann, 1912.
         2 v. 19ᶜᵐ. (Added t.-p.: Bibliothek der amerikanischen kulturgeschichte ... 1.bd.)
         Vol.1 translated by Clarence Sherwood; v.2, by Felix Baumann.

1. Washington, George, pres. U.S., 1732–1799.
I. Sherwood, Clarence, 1863–   , tr. II. Baumann, Felix, 1868–   , joint tr. III. Ser.

NL 0439283   ViU WaS ICU MH CtY CSmH ViU MB MiD NN

Lodge, Henry Cabot, 1850–1924.
... George Washington, the man, by Henry Cabot Lodge. Boston, New York ₍etc.₎ Houghton Mifflin company ₍°1917₎
1 p. L., 94 p. front., port. 18 cm. (The Riverside literature series ₍281₎)
Reprint of final chapter of author's biography of our first president. Of use to students in junior and senior high school grades. *cf.* Foreword.

1. Washington, George, pres. U. S., 1732–1799.   I. Title.
                                                  E 32—3₎
U. S. Office of Education.   Library E312.17
for Library of Congress   ₍a57c₎₎

NL 0439284   DHEW Or Wa NcU NN

LODGE, Henry Cabot.
German peace propaganda; speech in the Senate of the United States, Tuesday, September 17, 1918. Washington, 1918.

pp. 16.

NL 0439285   MH

Lodge, Henry Cabot, 1850–

₍Benjamin, Lewis S₎ 1874–
... German propagandist societies. An article by Lewis Melville ₍pseud.₎ (Reprinted from the London quarterly review and the Living age, Boston) ... Washington, Govt. print. off., 1918.

VOLUME 338

LODGE, Henry Cabot, 1850–
Gloucester and New England fisheries...
Papers and statistics...[presented to the Senate, Washington, 1902.]

27 p.incl.tables.24 cm.
(57th cong.2d sess.Senate. Doc.no.14.)
Caption title.

NL 0439287   MH

HE
1843
.S74   Lodge,Henry Cabot,1850–1924.
Government regulation of railway rates.
Speech of Hon.H.C.Lodge,of Massachusetts,
in the Senate of the United States,Thursday,March 22,1906. Washington, 1906.
46 p.   23ᶜᵐ.
No.13 in a volume lettered: Speeches in
U.S.S.on a railroad rate regulation.1906.

NL 0439288   MiU

Pam   Lodge, Henry Cabot, 1850–1924.
71-   GREAT WORK OF THE LEAGUE TO ENFORCE PEACE.
3149   [New York, League to Enforce Peace, 1916?]
8 p.   port. (League to Enforce Peace.
Publications no. 13)
Address delivered at Washington, May 27,1916.

LEAGUE TO ENFORCE PEACE
title
series

NL 0439289   WHi

Lodge, Henry Cabot.
Hawaiian affairs...Speech...January 19 and 22,
1895.
Wash., 1895.

YA5000   (Congressional speeches,by author)
J 17

NL 0439290   DLC

Lodge, Henry Cabot, 1850–1924.
Henry Cabot Lodge
see under title

Lodge, Henry Cabot, 1850–1924
Henry Cabot Lodge, as he is; his greatest speech, not
made, on his fifth re-election after a re-count.
[Boston, Washburn, 1923]

13 p.

NL 0439292   MH

Lodge, Henry Cabot, 1850–1924.
Henry Cabot Lodge. Memorial addresses
delivered in the Senate and House of Representatives
see under   U.S. 68th cong., 2d Sess.,
1924–1925.

Lodge, Henry Cabot, 1850–
Hero tales from American history. By Henry Cabot Lodge and
Theodore Roosevelt.
New York. The Century Co. 1897. xiv, (2), 335 pp. Illus.
Portraits. Plates. 18½ cm., in 8s.   2328.86
Twelve of the tales are by Lodge and fourteen by Roosevelt.

L371 — Double main card.   Lodge, Henry Cabot, 1850–. (M1)
— Roosevelt, Theodore, 25th President of the United States, 1858–. (M2) —
T.r. (1) — United States. Hist. (1, 2)

NL 0439294   MB

Lodge, Henry Cabot, 1850–1924.
Hero tales from American history, by Henry
Cabot Lodge and Theodore Roosevelt... New
York, The Century co., 1898.
335 p.

NL 0439295   PSC

E178
.3
.L82   Lodge, Henry Cabot, 1850–1924.
1902   Hero tales from American history, by Henry
Cabot Lodge and Theodore Roosevelt. New York,
Century Co., 1902.
xiv, 335 p. illus. 20cm.

1. U. S.—Hist. 2. U. S.—Biog.
I. Roosevelt, Theodore, pres. U. S., 1858–1919,
joint author. II. Title.

NL 0439296   MB DN NjP

Lodge, Henry Cabot, 1850–1924.
Hero tales from American history, by Henry Cabot Lodge
and Theodore Roosevelt ... New York, The Century co., 1895.
xiv, (2), 335 p. incl. front., plates, ports. 19¼ᶜᵐ.

1. U. S.—Hist. 2. U. S.—Biog.   I. Roosevelt, Theodore, pres. U. S.,
1858–1919, joint author. II. Title.

2–5492

Library of Congress   E178.3.L82
[28d³²]   ·973

NL 0439297   DLC

Lodge, Henry Cabot, 1850–1924.
Hero tales from American history, by Henry Cabot Lodge
and Theodore Roosevelt ... New York, The Century co., 1900.
xiv, (2), 335 p. incl. front., plates, ports. 19¼ᶜᵐ.

NL 0439298   NcRS

Lodge, Henry Cabot, 1850–1924, joint author.

Roosevelt, Theodore, pres. U. S., 1858–1919.
... Hero tales from American history; or, The story of some
Americans who showed that they knew how to live and how
to die, by Theodore Roosevelt and Henry Cabot Lodge.
Philadelphia, Gebbie and company, 1903.

E   Lodge, Henry Cabot, 1850–1924
178.3   Hero tales from American history, by
L82   Henry Cabot Lodge and Theodore Roosevelt...
1904   New York, The Century co., 1904
335 p.

U.S.—HIST.
U.S.—BIOG.
Roosevelt, Theodore, pres. U.S. 1858–1919
Title

NL 0439300   KMK MWA

Lodge, Henry Cabot, and Theodore Roosevelt.
Hero tales from American history. New York: The Century Co., 1909. xiv p., 1 l., 335 p. illus., port. 12°.

Contents: George Washington, by H. C. Lodge. Daniel Boone and the founding of Kentucky, by Theodore Roosevelt. George Rogers Clark and the conquest of the Northwest, by Theodore Roosevelt. The battle of Trenton, by H. C. Lodge. Bennington, by H. C. Lodge. King's mountain, by Theodore Roosevelt. The storming of Stony Point, by Theodore Roosevelt. Gouverneur Morris, by H. C. Lodge. The burning of the "Philadelphia," by H. C. Lodge. The cruise of the "Wasp," by Theodore Roosevelt. The "General Armstrong," privateer, by Theodore Roosevelt. The battle of New Orleans, by Theodore Roosevelt. John Quincy Adams and the right of petition, by H. C. Lodge. Francis Parkman, by H. C. Lodge. "Remember the Alamo," by Theodore Roosevelt. Hampton Roads, by Theodore Roosevelt.

The flag-bearer, by Theodore Roosevelt. The death of Stonewall Jackson, by Theodore Roosevelt. The charge at Gettysburg, by Theodore Roosevelt. General Grant and the Vicksburg campaign, by Theodore Roosevelt. Robert Gould Shaw, by H. C. Lodge. Charles Russell Lowell, by H. C. Lodge. Sheridan at Cedar Creek, by H. C. Lodge. Lieutenant Cushing and the ram "Albemarle," by Theodore Roosevelt. Farragut at Mobile bay, by Theodore Roosevelt. Abraham Lincoln, by H. C. Lodge.

1. U. S.—Biography. 2. Title.   CENTRAL CIRCULATION.
3. Fifteen subj. anal.   February 1, 1912.

NL 0439302   NN

CB
B724L   Lodge, Henry Cabot, 1850–1924.
Hero tales from American history by Henry
Cabot Lodge and Theodore Roosevelt. New
York, Century co., 1915.
xiv, 335 p. illus., ports. 20cm.
By Theodore Roosevelt: Daniel Boone and
the founding of Kentucky, p.17–28. - The battle of New Orleans, p.137–147. - The charge
at Gettysburg, p.225–236. - Lieutenant Cushing and the ram "Albemarle," p.291–300.-
King's Mountain, p.69–78.

NL 0439303   NcU MB

Lodge, Henry Cabot, 1850–1924.
Hero tales from American history, by Henry Cabot Lodge
and Theodore Roosevelt ... New York, The Century co., 1917.
xiv, (2), 335 p. incl. front., plates, ports. 19½ᶜᵐ.

NL 0439304   ViU

Lodge, Henry Cabot, 1850–1924.
Hero tales from American history. By Henry
Cabot Lodge and Theodore Roosevelt. New York,
The Century co., 1918.

NL 0439305   MH MB

Lodge, Henry Cabot, and Theodore Roosevelt.   920-L
Hero tales from American history. New York: The Century Co., 1919. 335 p. front., illus., port. 12°.

Contents: George Washington, H. C. Lodge. Daniel Boone and the founding of Kentucky; George Rogers Clark and the conquest of the Northwest, Theodore Roosevelt. The battle of Trenton; Bennington, H. C. Lodge. King's mountain; The storming of Stony Point, Theodore Roosevelt. Gouverneur Morris; The burning of the "Philadelphia," H. C. Lodge. The cruise of the "Wasp"; The "General Armstrong" privateer; The battle of New Orleans, Theodore Roosevelt. John Quincy Adams and the right of petition; Francis Parkman, H. C. Lodge. "Remember the Alamo"; Hampton roads; The flag-bearer; The death of Stonewall Jackson; The charge at Gettysburg,

Theodore Roosevelt. General Grant and the Vicksburg campaign; Robert Gould Shaw; Charles Russell Lowell; Sheridan at Cedar Creek, H. C. Lodge. Lieutenant Cushing and the ram "Albemarle"; Farragut at Mobile Bay, Theodore Roosevelt. Abraham Lincoln, H. C. Lodge.

1. United States—Biog. 2. Fourteen   anal. 3. Title.   January 18, 1928.

NL 0439307   NN

VOLUME 338

Lodge, Henry Cabot, and Theodore Roosevelt.   J920-L
Hero tales from American history.   New York: The Century Co. ₍cop. 1895–1922₎   287 p.   front., illus., pls.   12°.
CONTENTS.—George Washington.   Daniel Boone and the founding of Kentucky. George Rogers Clark and the conquest of the Northwest.   The battle of Trenton. Bennington.   King's mountain.   The storming of Stony Point.   Gouverneur Morris. The burning of the Philadelphia.   The cruise of the Wasp.   The General Armstrong, privateer.   The battle of New Orleans.   John Quincy Adams and the right of petition.   Francis Parkman.   Remember the Alamo.   Hampton Roads.   The flag-bearer. The death of Stonewall Jackson.   The charge at Gettysburg.   General Grant and the Vicksburg campaign.   Robert Gould Shaw.   Charles Russell Lowell.   Sheridan at Cedar creek.   Lieutenant Cushing and the ram Albemarle.   Farragut at Mobile bay. Abraham Lincoln.

1. United States—Biog.   2. Title.   3. Roosevelt, Theodore, jt. au.
                                                    April 29, 1938

NL 0439308   NN OO

E178
.3
.L82   **Lodge, Henry Cabot,** 1850–1924.
1926   Hero tales from American history, by Henry
        Cabot Lodge [and] Theodore Roosevelt.   Oliver
        Cromwell.   New York.   By Theodore Roosevelt.
        New York, C. Scribner's Sons, 1926.
            xxiv, 547 p.   21cm.   (The works of Theodore
        Roosevelt.   National ed.   Vol. X)
            Prepared under the auspices of the Roosevelt
        Memorial Association.

        1. U. S.—Hist.   2. U. S.—Biog.   3. Cromwell,
    Oliver, 1599–1658.   4. New York (City)—Hist.
    I. Roosevelt, Theodore, pres. U. S., 1858–1919,
    joint author.   II. Title.

NL 0439310   MB

Lodge, Henry Cabot, 1850–1924.
    An historical address delivered at the celebration of the
fiftieth anniversary of the incorporation of the town of Nahant, July 14, 1903, by Henry Cabot Lodge.   ₍Nahant₎ The
town of Nahant, 1904.
    2 p. l., 22, ₍1₎ p., 2 l.   map.   24ᶜᵐ.
    Half-title: Nahant: an historical address.
    "A limited edition of five hundred and fifty copies of this volume
was printed by D. B. Updike, the Merrymount press, Boston, in June,
1904."

    1. Nahant, Mass.—Hist.

    Library of Congress   F74.N13L8   4—16785

NL 0439311   DLC NN MB NcU ICU MB WHi NSyU

Lodge, Henry Cabot, 1850–1924.
    Historical and political essays, by Henry Cabot Lodge.
Boston and New York, Houghton, Mifflin and company,
1892.
    4 p. l., 213 p.   20 cm.
    CONTENTS.—William H. Seward.—James Madison.—Gouverneur
Morris.—Why patronage in office is un-American.—The distribution of
ability in the United States.—Parliamentary obstruction in the United
States.—Parliamentary minorities.—Party allegiance.

    1. Seward, William Henry, 1801–1872.   2. Madison, James, pres.
U. S., 1751–1836.   3. Morris, Gouverneur, 1752–1816.   4. U. S.—Pol. &
govt.

    L173.L8   4—13855

    WaT PP WaSp KMK WaS MdBP WaSpG NNC MWA
    TxU NjP DNW MdBP NcD NcRS WHi NIC PU WaS PHC OrP PHi
NL 0439312   DLC OrU MB NcGU NN ViU OCIW ODW OCI MiU

Lodge, Henry Cabot, 1850–1924.
    Historical and political essays.   Boston, Houghton,
Mifflin, 1898.
    213 p.

NL 0439313   MH OO OU CaBVaU

Lodge, Henry Cabot, 1850–1924₎ ed.

    The **history** of nations; Henry Cabot Lodge ... editor-in-chief.   Philadelphia, J. D. Morris and company ₍*1906–
'08₎

Lodge, Henry Cabot, 1850–1924, joint author.

    Garner, James Wilford, 1871–
        ... The history of the United States, by James Wilford Garner, PH. D., and Henry Cabot Lodge, PH. D., LL. D.; with a historical review by John Bach McMaster ...   ₍Éd. de luxe₎
    Philadelphia, J. D. Morris and company, 1906.

Lodge, Henry Cabot.   4329.168
    How foreign treaties are made.   Portrait.
    (In Ship of State, The.   Pp. 199–219.   Boston, 1903.)

    F2647 — Treaties. — United States. For. rel. Treaties.

NL 0439316   MB

Wason   **Lodge,** Henry Cabot, 1850–1924.
DS703   Immigration.   Speech of Hon. Henry Cabot
Z153   Lodge, of Massachusetts, in the House of
        Representatives, Thursday, February 19, 1891.
        Washington, 1891.
            13 p.   23cm.

            In vol. lettered: China and the Chinese.
        Pamphlets.   Vol. 53.

            1. U. S.—Emig. & immig.

NL 0439317   NIC PHi

Lodge, Henry Cabot, 1850–

U. S. *Congress.   Senate.   Committee on the Philippines.*
    Increase in membership of Philippine commission.
    Committee on the Philippines, United States Senate ...
    February 21, 1908.   ₍Washington, Gov't print. off., 1908₎

Lodge, Henry Cabot, 1850–1924.
    ... The Insurrection in the Philippines.   From
the speech of Hon. Henry Cabot Lodge, of Massachusetts, in the Senate of the United States,
Wednesday, March 7, 1900.   [Washington, 1900]
    8 vo.   Stapled.
    At head of title: (No. 2)
    Hoes Collection.   Henkels sale, October 26,
1922.

NL 0439319   CSmH

Lodge, Henry Cabot, 1850–1924.
    Intellectual honesty.   Address of Senator
Lodge at the Alumni dinner, June 26, 1912.
    [8] p.
        From Amherst graduates' quarterly, v. 2, no. 1,
Nov. 1912.   p. 10–17.

NL 0439320   OCIW

Lodge, Henry Cabot, 1850–1924.
    ∴ International court of justice at the Hague
        see under   U.S. Dept. of state.

Lodge, Henry Cabot, 1850–1924₎ ed.
    The **International** review.   v. 1–14;   Jan. 1874–June 1883.
New York, A. S. Barnes & co. ₍etc.₎, 1874–83₎

Lodge, Henry Cabot, 1850–
    Intervention in Cuba.   Speech ... in the Senate ...
April 13, 1898.   Washington ₍Govt. print. off.₎ 1898.
    15 p.   8°.

                                                          1–4965

NL 0439323   DLC OCIWHi NN

Lodge, Henry Cabot, 1850–1924.   FOR OTHER EDITIONS
                                             SEE MAIN ENTRY
U. S. *Congress.   Senate.   Select committee on wages and
prices of commodities.*
    ... Investigation relative to wages and prices of commodities ...   Washington, Govt. print. off., 1911.

Lodge, Henry Cabot, 1850–1924.
    ... Joint debate on the Covenant of Paris.   Henry Cabot
Lodge ... A. Lawrence Lowell ...   Symphony hall, Boston,
March 19, 1919 ...
    (*In* League of nations.   Boston, 1919.   20ᶜᵐ.   vol. II, no. 2, Souvenir
no., 1 p. l., p. ₍49–97₎)

    1. League of nations.   I. Lowell, Abbott Lawrence, 1856–
    II. Title.   III. Title: Covenant of Paris, Joint debate on the.
                                                        C D 22–48
    Library of Congress   Card div.   JX1908.U52 vol. 2, no. 2,
                                                    Souvenir no.

NL 0439325   MB PPT WaU–L OrU Or WaTC

Lodge, Henry Cabot, 1850–
    ... A joint debate on the covenant of the League
of Nations
        see his   Lodge vs. Lowell.

Lodge, Henry Cabot, 1850–   *4451.51.3=**G.500.62.5
    The last forty years of town government.   1782–1822.
    (*In* Winsor, J., editor.   The memorial history of Boston.   Vol. 3,
    pp. 189–216.   Illus.   Portraits.   Autograph facsimiles.   Boston,
    1881.)

    L2683 — Boston. Pol. hist.

NL 0439327   MB

LODGE, Henry Cabot.
    Last of the puritans.   The Sewall diary.
n.p.,n.d.
    pp. 22.
    "Reprinted from the Magazine of American
history, November, 1878."

NL 0439328   MH OCIW

LODGE, Henry Cabot.
    The leather industries and free hides; speech
in the senate of the United States, June – 19,
1909.   Washington, 1909.

NL 0439329   MH NN

Lodge, Henry, 1850–1924
    Life and letters of George Cabot.
Boston, 1871.

NL 0439330   PPL

VOLUME 338

Lodge, Henry Cabot, 1850–
   Life and letters of George Cabot. By Henry Cabot
Lodge. Boston, Little, Brown, and company, 1877.
   xi, 615 p. 23ᶜᵐ.

   1. Cabot, George, 1751–1823.

   Library of Congress   E302.6.C11L8   7–14154

      NN WaU PHC PBm
NL   0439331   DLC OrU MWA TU NcD Vi MiU MiU-C OU OC1

973.4
C116Y18   **Lodge, Henry Cabot, 1850–1924.**
         Life and letters of George Cabot. [2d ed
      Boston, Little, Brown, 1878.
         xi,617p. 23cm.

         1. Cabot, George, 1751–1823.

            MeB
NL   0439332   IEN PPT OU OC1W ODW PP PHi MWA PU MB

Lodge, Henry Cabot.   4329.168
   The life of a Senator. Plate.
   (In Ship of State, The. Pp. 21–40. Boston, 1903.)

               Jan. 9,   1904
F2645 — United States. Congress. Works about. Senate.

NL   0439333   MB

Lodge, Henry Cabot, 1850–1924.
   The life of George Washington, by Henry Cabot Lodge;
with a preface written in 1920 and with illustrations ... Boston and New York, Houghton Mifflin company, 1920.
   2 v. fronts, plates, ports., map, facsims. 21½ cm.
   "Illustrated library edition."

   1. Washington, George, pres. U. S., 1732–1799.

   E312.L833   20—17980

NL   0439334   DLC PPT MB WaT Wa WaS IdU CoU

Lodge, Henry Cabot, 1850–
   *U. S. Congress. Senate. Committee on foreign rela-
tions.*
   ... Limiting the production of habit-forming narcotic
drugs and the raw materials from which they are made
... Report. ⟨To accompany H. J. res. 453⟩ ... [Wash-
ington, Govt. print. off., 1923]

JX1975
.L6   Lodge, Henry Cabot, 1850–1924.
1919   The Lodge-Lowell debate on the pro-
         posed league of nations, between Henry
         Cabot Lodge and A. Lawrence Lowell. Held
         in Symphony Hall, Boston, March 19, 1919.
         Boston, Old Colony Trust Co. [1919]
            55 p. 24cm.

            1. League of Nations.   I. Lowell,
         Abbott Lawrence, 1856–   I. Title.
         II. Title: League of Nations, Joint
         debate on.

NL   0439336   MB MH

JX1975
.L6   Lodge, Henry Cabot, 1850–1924.
1920   The Lodge-Lowell debate on the pro-
         posed league of nations, between Henry
         Cabot Lodge and A. Lawrence Lowell.
         Held in Symphony Hall, Boston, March 19,
         1919. Rev. and auth. by Henry Cabot
         Lodge [and] A. Lawrence Lowell. [2d ed.]
         Boston, Old Colony Trust Co. [192–?]
            51 p. 23cm.
            1. League of Nations.   I. Lowell,
         Abbott Lawrence, 1856–   II. Title.
         III. Title: League of Nations,
         Joint debate   on.

NL   0439337   MB

JX1975
.L6   Lodge, Henry Cabot, 1850–1924.
1920a   The Lodge-Lowell debate on the proposed
         league of nations, between Henry Cabot
         Lodge and A. Lawrence Lowell. Held in
         Symphony Hall, Boston, March 19, 1919.
         Rev. and auth. by Henry Cabot Lodge [and]
         A. Lawrence Lowell. [3d ed.] Boston,
         Old Colony Trust Co. [192–?]
            51 p. 23cm.
            1. League of nations.   I. Lowell,
         Abbott Lawrence, 1856–   II. Title.
         III. Title: League of Nations,
         Joint debate   on.

NL   0439338   MB ICU MiU ViW

Lodge, Henry Cabot.
   Lodge-Lowell debate on the proposed league of
nations. Boston, 1920.

NL   0439339   DAL

Lodge, Henry Cabot, 1850–1924.
   Lodge vs. Lowell; a joint debate on the covenant of
the league of nations; in the affirmative A. Lawrence
Lowell ... in the negative Henry Cabot Lodge ... Sym-
phony hall, Boston, March 19, 1919 ... [Boston, 1919]
   16 p. 29ᶜᵐ.
   Cover-title: A joint debate on the covenant of the league of nations:
Lodge vs. Lowell.
   "Reprinted from the Boston evening transcript ... March 20, 1919."

   1. League of nations.   I. Lowell, Abbott Lawrence, 1856–   II. Title.

   Library of Congress   JX1975.L8   19—7652

NL   0439340   DLC MH NN WaPS MB

Lodge, Henry Cabot, 1850–
   ... Maintenance of peace. Address delivered at the
commencement exercises at Union college in Schenectady, N. Y., held on June 9, 1915, by Henry Cabot Lodge,
United States senator from Massachusetts ... Washington, Govt. print. off., 1919.
   6 p. 23ᶜᵐ. ([U. S.] 65th Cong., 3d sess. Senate. Doc. 443)
   Presented by Mr. Hitchcock. Ordered printed March 1 (calendar day,
March 3), 1919.

   1. Peace.   I. Title.

   Library of Congress   JX1963.L55   19–26255

NL   0439341   DLC Or MiU MB OO

Lodge, Henry Cabot, 1850–1924.

André, John, 1751–1780.
   Major André's journal; operations of the British army un-
der Lieutenant Generals Sir William Howe and Sir Henry
Clinton, June, 1777 to November, 1778, recorded by Major
John André, adjutant general; to which is added The ethics
of Major André's mission, by C. De W. Willcox, col. u. s. a.
Tarrytown, N. Y., W. Abbatt, 1930.

LODGE, Henry Cabot.   4459
   Massachusetts.
         [Bost. Robinson. 189–?] (7) pp. 16°.

NL   0439343   MB

Lodge, Henry Cabot, 1850–
   A memoir of Caleb Strong, United States senator and
governor of Massachusetts. 1745–1818. By Henry Cabot Lodge. Cambridge, Press of J. Wilson and son,
1879.
   29 p. 23½ᶜᵐ.
   "This memoir, prepared at the request of the publishing committee,
is reprinted from the early Proceedings of the Massachusetts historical
society, now in course of publication."

   1. Strong, Caleb, 1745–1819.

   Library of Congress   F69.S92   12–11173

NL   0439344   DLC MWA NcD CtY

Lodge, Henry Cabot, 1850–
   U.S. Congress. Senate. Committee on foreign relations.
   Memorandum upon the bill for the reorganization of
the consular service. Introduced in the Senate by Senator Lodge, December 6, 1905, and referred to the Committee on foreign relations. [Washington, Govt. print. off.,
1906]

Lodge, Henry C.
   Memorial address on life, character and public services of Hon. George F. Hoar. Jan. 19, 1905.
Bost., 1905.
   38 p. 8°

NL   0439346   MWA

JX1425   Lodge, Henry Cabot, 1850–1924.
.L8   Monroe doctrine; speech in the
         Senate of the United States,
         December 30, 1895. Washington,
         G. R. Gray & Co., 1896.
            16 p. 24cm.

            Cover title.
                 YA5000

NL   0439347   MnHi DLC NN MiD   MiU-C OC1WHi

Lodge, Henry Cabot, 1850–
   ... National defense. A speech delivered before the
National security league on January 22, 1916, at Washington, D. C., by Hon. Henry Cabot Lodge ... Washington, Govt. print. off., 1916.
   11 p. 23½ᶜᵐ. ([U. S.] 64th Cong., 1st sess. Senate. Doc. 263)
   Presented by Mr. Weeks. Ordered printed January 28, 1916.

   1. U. S.—Defenses.   I. Title.

   Library of Congress   UA23.L65   16–26149

NL   0439348   DLC Or OO

LODGE, HENRY CABOT, 1850–1924.
   National supervision of national elections. Speech of
Hon. Henry Cabot Lodge...in the House of representatives,
Thursday, June 26, 1890. Washington, D.C.: G. R. Gray,
printer, 1890. 24 p. 22½cm.

   1. United States—Elections—Jurisp., 1890.

NL   0439349   NN MB ICN OC1WHi

VOLUME 338

Lodge, Henry Cabot, 1850–

U. S. *Navy dept. General board.*

... Naval policy with present requirements ... Report of George Dewey, president of the General board of the Department of the navy, made to the secretary of the navy, dated July 30, 1915. ₍Washington, Govt. print. off., 1916₎

Lodge, Henry Cabot, 1850–

U. S. *Congress. Senate. Committee on foreign relations.*

... Naval station in the West Indies. March 31, 1898.—Ordered to be printed. Mr. Lodge, from the Committee on foreign relations, submitted the following report. ⟨To accompany S. 4303⟩ ₍Washington, Govt. print. off., 1898₎

Lodge, Henry Cabot, 1850–

U. S. *Dept. of state.*

... Netherlands and Portuguese insular possessions in region of Pacific Ocean. Copy of a letter addressed by Hon. Charles E. Hughes, secretary of state, to Hon. Henry Cabot Lodge, United States senator, with reference to the notes delivered by the United States government to the minister for foreign affairs of the Netherlands and to the Portuguese government relative to respecting their rights in relation to their insular possessions in the region of the Pacific Ocean ... Washington. Govt. print. off., 1922.

Lodge, Henry Cabot, 1850–1924.

Browne, George Waldo, 1851–1930.

The new America and the Far East; a picturesque and historic description of these lands and peoples, by G. Waldo Browne ... with a general introduction by Edward S. Ellis ... with the following special articles: Hawaii, by the Honorable Henry Cabot Lodge; The Philippines, by Major-General Joseph Wheeler; Japan, by His Excellency Kogoro Takahira; China, by the Honorable John D. Long; Cuba, by General Leonard Wood; Porto Rico, by the Honorable Charles H. Allen. Illustrated by about 1,200 photogravures, colored plates, engravings & maps. Boston, Marshall Jones company ₍°1907₎

Lodge, Henry Cabot, 1850–

U. S. *President, 1923–* (Coolidge)

... New call for disarming. Address by the President of the United States at the annual luncheon of the Associated press conference in New York city, April 22, 1924 ... Washington, Govt. print. off., 1924.

Lodge, Henry Cabot, 1850–1924, ed.

AP2
.N7

The North American review. v. 1–
May 1815–
₍Mount Vernon, Iowa, etc.₎

Lodge, Henry Cabot, 1850–
The old and the new Entente.
(In Pennsylvania Society, New York. War addresses, 1917.
Pp. 28–32. New York. 1918.)
On the spirit of France in the European War.

2307.98

L4859 — European War, 1914– . France

NL 0439356   MB

Lodge, Henry Cabot, 1850–

... On the woolen schedule in the tariff debate ... ₍Washington?₎ D. C.₎ 1910.

1 l. 34ᶜᵐ.

No. 2 of a volume of pamphlets lettered: Wool tariff.
Autographed from typewritten copy.

1. Wool trade and industry—U. S. 2. Tariff—U. S.

CA 13–2091 Unrev'd
Library of Congress   HF2651.W803W8

NL 0439357   DLC

Lodge, Henry Cabot, 1850–
One hundred years of peace, by Henry Cabot Lodge ... New York, The Outlook company, 1912.

1 p. l., 21 p. 25¾ᶜᵐ.

1. U. S.—For. rel.—Gt. Brit. 2. Gt. Brit.—For. rel.—U. S.   I. Title.

12–13505
Library of Congress   E183.7.L82

NL 0439358   DLC

Lodge, Henry Cabot, 1850–1924.
One hundred years of peace, by Henry Cabot Lodge ... New York, The Macmillan company, 1913.

vii, 136 p. front. (facsim.) plates, ports. 20½ᶜᵐ.

"This sketch of the relations between the United States and Great Britain during the century which has elapsed since the war of 1812 appeared first in the 'Outlook' ... Two original articles, revised, corrected, and much enlarged."—Prefatory note.

1. U. S.—For. rel.—Gt. Brit. 2. Gt. Brit.—For. rel.—U. S.   I. Title.

13–18699
Library of Congress   E183.8.G7L84

PHC PU
NcRS NcD OCU OO OCl OClW DN MB IIN NjP WaU ViU PPL
NL 0439359   DLC WaS OrP GU IU NIC LHi NBuU NjNbT

Lodge, Henry Cabot, 1850–
... One hundred years of peace, by Senator Henry Cabot Lodge ... Washington, Govt. print. off., 1913.

36 p. 23½ᶜᵐ. (₍U. S.₎ 62d Cong., 3d sess. House. Doc. 1268)

Ordered printed, Jan. 14, 1913.
Printed in the "Outlook."

1. U. S.—For. rel.—Gt. Brit. 2. Gt. Brit.—For. rel.—U. S.   I. Title.

12–30150
Library of Congress   E183.7.L83

NL 0439360   DLC KEmT WHi MiU OClWHi OO NN

Lodge, Henry Cabot, 1850–
... One hundred years of the Monroe doctrine, by Henry Cabot Lodge, senator from Massachusetts, chairman, Committee on foreign relations ... Washington, Govt. print. off., 1923.

1 p. l., 14 p. 23½ᶜᵐ. (₍U. S.₎ 68th Cong., 1st sess. Senate. Doc. 8)

Presented by Mr. Moses. Ordered printed December 15, 1923.
"Reprinted by permission of Charles Scribner's sons, from Scribner's magazine for October, 1923."

1. Monroe doctrine.   I. Title.

23–27485
Library of Congress   JX1425.L75

NL 0439361   DLC MiU OO PPAmP

Lodge, Henry Cabot, 1850–
Oration delivered before the City council and citizens of Boston, on the one hundred and third anniversary of the Declaration of American independence, July 4, 1879. By Henry Cabot Lodge. Boston, Printed by order of the City council, 1879.

44 pp. 24¼ᶜᵐ.

2–6454
Library of Congress, no.   E286.B739.

NL 0439362   DLC NcD N OCl OU MiU OClWHi MB PHi

Lodge, Henry Cabot, 1850–
Anderson, Chandler Parsons, 1866–

... Organization of the world for peace. A plan by which the United States may cooperate with other nations to achieve and preserve the peace of the world, by Chandler P. Anderson. To accompany Senate Joint resolution 122 ... Washington, Govt. print. off., 1924.

Lodge, Henry Cabot, 1850–1924.
... Panama. Speech of Hon. Henry Cabot Lodge of Massachusetts in the United States Senate, January 5, 1904 ... Washington, Govt. print. off., 1921.

48 p. 23ᶜᵐ. (₍U. S.₎ 67th Cong., 1st sess. Senate. Doc. 37)

Presented by Mr. McCumber. Order printed June 9, 1921.

1. U. S.—For. rel.—Panama. 2. U. S.—For. rel.—Colombia. 3. Panama—For. rel.—U. S. 4. Colombia—For. rel.—U. S. 5. Panama canal.   I. McCumber, Porter James, 1856–1933.   II. Title.

21—26588
Library of Congress   F1566.L8

NL 0439364   DLC DNW MB OO MiU

Lodge, Henry Cabot, 1850–
The payment of government bonds ... Speech of Henry Cabot Lodge in the Senate ... January 27, 1898. Washington ₍Gov't print. off.₎ 1898.

8 p. 23ᶜᵐ.

1. Currency question—U. S. 2. Finance—U. S.—Speeches in Congress.

1–4870
Library of Congress   HG529.L85

NL 0439365   DLC

Lodge, Henry Cabot, 1850–1924
The peace note of the President; speech in the Senate of the United States, Jan. 3 and 4, 1917. Washington, 1917

28 p.

NL 0439366   MH

Lodge, Henry Cabot, 1850–

U. S. *Congress. Senate. Committee on foreign relations.*

... Peace with Germany ... Report. ⟨To accompany S. J. Res. 16⟩ ... ₍Washington, Govt. print. off., 1921₎

Lodge, Henry Cabot, 1850–

U. S. *Congress. Senate. Committee on the Philippines.*

... The Philippine Islands ... a brief compilation of the latest information and statistics obtainable on the numbers, area, population, races and tribes, mineral resources, agriculture, exports and imports, forests, and harbors of the Philippine Islands. ₍Washington, Gov't print. off., 1900₎

VOLUME 338

Lodge, Henry Cabot, 1850-

U. S. *Congress. Senate. Committee on the Philippines.*
... Philippine tariff ... Report (with the views of the minority) [Washington, Govt. print. off., 1902]

Lodge, Henry Cabot, 1850-
The Pilgrims of Plymouth. An address at Plymouth Massachusetts on the three hundredth anniversary on their landing December 21, 1920 ... Boston, Mass. Published by the Pilgrim Tercentenary Commission [1920]

46p. 23cm.
This edition has a poem by LeBaron Russell Briggs

NL 0439370   MWA MH OClWHi RPB NN

PW6014
A7
v.15

Lodge, Henry Cabot, 1850-1924.
... The Pilgrims of Plymouth, by Henry Cabot Lodge. Boston, The Atlantic monthly press, inc. [1921?]

47p. 18½cm. (At head of title: Atlantic readings. no. 15)

Cover-title.
A poem by Le Baron Russell Briggs, p. [43]-47.

NL 0439371   NBuG OrU WaS WaWW

F68
.L82
1921

Lodge, Henry Cabot, 1850-1924.
The pilgrims of Plymouth. Boston and New York, Houghton Mifflin Company, 1921.
55 p. 29 cm.
Autographed by the author.
"An address at Plymouth, Massachusetts on the three hundredth anniversary of their landing, December 21, 1920.
"Five hundred and seventy-five copies of this book were printed ... "

     MH MB MiDB NcRS NNU MWA NBu
NL 0439372   TU ICU MB NcD NNC OU NN NcU OClW CSmH

Lodge, Henry Cabot, 1850-1924.
... The Pilgrims of Plymouth. An address at Plymouth, Massachusetts, December 21, 1920, on the three hundredth anniversary of their landing, by Henry Cabot Lodge, senator Briggs, professor in Harvard university ... Washington, Govt. print. off., 1921.

35 p. 26 cm. ([U. S.] 66th Cong., 3d sess. Senate. Doc. 351)
Presented by Mr. Underwood. Ordered printed January 6, 1921.

1. Pilgrim fathers—Addresses, commemorations, etc. I. Briggs, Le Baron Russell, 1855-1934. II. Underwood, Oscar Wilder, 1862-1929. III. Title.
                          21—26160
Library of Congress   F68.L82

PHi
NL 0439373   DLC MU CU MWA MiU OOxM OU OCl OO MB MH

Lodge, Henry Cabot, 1850-1924
Preface to the history of nations,...
Phila., 1904

D20
.H67

NL 0439374   DLC

LODGE, Henry Cabot.
The president's plan for a world peace; speech, in the Senate of U.S. Feb.1,1917. Washington, 1917.

Pamphlet.

NL 0439375   MH OClWHi

Lodge, Henry Cabot, 1850-

... **Prices** of food products ... Comparison of prices of food products in Detroit, Mich., and Windsor, Ontario, taken from the advertisements in the *Evening record*, of Windsor, and the *Detroit news* for February 25, 1910 ... [Washington, Govt. print. off., 1910]

PZ1
.C658
Pr

Lodge, Henry Cabot, 1850-1924, ed.

Collier's.
Prize stories from Collier's, selected by Henry Cabot Lodge [and others]. New York, P. F. Collier, [1916]

Lodge, Henry Cabot, 1850-
The proposed constitution for a league of nations. Speech of Hon. Henry Cabot Lodge of Massachusetts, in the Senate of the United States. Friday, February 28, 1919. Washington [Govt. print. off.] 1919.
24 p. 23ᶜᵐ.

1. League of nations. I. Title.

Library of Congress   JX1975.L83   19–19933

NL 0439378   DLC

Lodge, Henry Cabot, 1850-

Hale, Edward Everett, 1822-1909.
... Prospero's Island, by Edward Everett Hale; with an introduction by Henry Cabot Lodge. New York, Printed for the Dramatic museum of Columbia university in the city of New York, 1919.

HF1752
.T24
v.3

Lodge, Henry Cabot, 1850-1924.
Protection and free trade... Speech of Hon. Henry Cabot Lodge, of Massachusetts, in the Senate of the United States, April 10, 1894. Washington, 1894.
45 p. 23½cm.
[Tariff speeches. v.3, no.14]

     VA 5000

NL 0439380   ICU DLC MH NN MiD

LODGE, HENRY CABOT, 1850-1924.
The protection of American citizens. Speech of Hon. Henry Cabot Lodge, of Massachusetts, in the Senate of the United States, February 25, 1897. [Washington? D.C., 1897] 8 p. 23cm.

1. Americans in foreign countries.

NL 0439381   NN CSmH

LODGE, Henry Cabot.
Protection or free trade - which? [Boston, 1891.]

8°. pp.(18). Port.
Arena, 1891, 4.652-669.

NL 0439382   MH

LODGE, Henry Cabot. 1850.
The public opinion bill; speech before the Central Labor Union of Boston, Sept. 15, 1907. [Boston?. 1907]

pp. 18+.

NL 0439383   MH

Lodge, Henry Cabot, 1850-1924.
... The Public opinion bill. Speech of Hon. H. C. Lodge before the Central labor union of Boston, September 15, 1907 ... Washington, Govt. print. off., 1907.

16 p. 23ᶜᵐ. ([U. S.] 60th Cong., 1st sess. Senate. Doc. 114)
Presented by Mr. Hale; ordered printed December 18, 1907.
"Public opinion bill as reported to the House of representatives of Massachusetts": p. 16.

1. Referendum. I. Hale, Eugene, 1836-1918. II. Title.

Library of Congress   JF493.U6L7   8—35045

NL 0439384   DLC MiU OO ICJ

LODGE, Henry Cabot.
The question of immigration; a lecture delivered before the Massachusetts Society for Promoting Good Citizenship, April 25, 1892. "Boston, 1892".

Without title-page. Caption-title.

NL 0439385   MH

Lodge, Henry Cabot, 1850-
The question of the canal tolls. Speech of Hon. Henry Cabot Lodge, of Massachusetts, in the Senate of the United States, April 9, 1914. Washington [Govt. print. off.] 1914.
23 p. 23¾ᶜᵐ.

1. Panama canal—Rates and tolls. I. Title.
                          14–10022
Library of Congress   HE537.9.T7L6

NL 0439386   DLC Or OU TxU OO OClWHi NN PHi PPAmP

Lodge, Henry Cabot, 1850-1924
...Reciprocity with Canada and affairs in the Philippines...

(In Root, Elihu, The revision of the tariff. Boston, 1903. 23 1/2 cm.)

25.68

NL 0439387   DLC NN MB RP

Lodge, Henry Cabot, 1850-
U. S. *Congress. Senate. Committee on foreign relations.*
... Remission of Chinese indemnity ... Report. ⟨To accompany H. J. Res. 248⟩ ... Washington, Govt. print. off., 1924]

VOLUME 338

Lodge, Henry Cabot, 1850-

U. S. *Congress. Senate. Committee on foreign relations.*

... Reorganization and improvement of the foreign service ... Report. ⟨To accompany H. R. 6357.⟩ ... ₍Washington, Govt. print. off., 1924₎

Lodge, Henry Cabot, 1850-1924.

U. S. *Congress. Senate. Committee on foreign relations.*

... Reorganization of the consular service ... Report. ⟨To accompany S. 1345.⟩ ₍Washington, Govt. print. off., 1906₎

Lodge, Henry Cabot, 1850-1924.

U. S. *Congress. Senate. Committee on foreign relations.*

... Reorganization of the consular service ... Report. ⟨To accompany S. 10171⟩ ₍Washington, Govt. print. off., 1911₎

Lodge, Henry Cabot, 1850-

U. S. *Congress. Senate. Committee on foreign relations.*

... Reorganization of the foreign service of the United States ... Report. ⟨To accompany H. R. 13880.⟩ ... ₍Washington, Govt. print. off., 1923₎

E 179 U11 v.7 no.17 — Lodge, Henry Cabot, 1850-1924.
Repeal of election laws. Speech of Hon. Henry Cabot Lodge, of Massachusetts, in the Senate of the United States, Wednesday, January 24, 1894. Washington, 1894.
40 p. 25cm.

1. Election law--U. S.

NL 0439393   NIC

Lodge, Henry Cabot, 1850-1924.

Tariff commission, *London.*

... Report of British tariff commission. Reciprocity with Canada. Most-favored-nation agreements in relation to the proposed reciprocal trade agreement between Canada and the United States of America ... Washington ₍Govt. print. off.₎ 1911.

FOR OTHER EDITIONS
SEE MAIN ENTRY

Lodge, Henry Cabot, 1850-1924.

U. S. *Congress. Senate. Committee on foreign relations.*

... Report of the Committee on foreign relations, together with the views of the minority, upon the general arbitration treaties with Great Britain and France, signed on August 3, 1911, and the proposed committee amendments. With appendices ... Washington ₍Govt. print. off.₎ 1911-12.

Lodge, Henry Cabot, 1850-

U. S. *Congress. Senate. Select committee on wages and prices of commodities.*

... Report of the Select committee on wages and prices of commodities ... Washington, Govt. print. off., 1910.

Lodge, Henry Cabot, 1850-

... Reservations to the Treaty of peace with Germany. Statements made to the press regarding the bipartisan conference on reservations to the Treaty of peace with Germany, by Senator Henry Cabot Lodge and Senator Gilbert M. Hitchcock ... Washington, Govt. print. off., 1920.
15 p. 23ᶜᵐ. (₍U. S.₎ 66th Cong., 2d sess. Senate. Doc. 193)
Presented by Mr. Lodge. Ordered printed January 31, 1920.
CONTENTS.—Statement of Senator Lodge, January 31, 1920.—Resolving clause.—Reservation no. 4.—Reservation no. 7.—Reservation no. 10.—Reservation no. 1.—Reservation no. 9.—Reservation no. 11.—Reservation no. 14.—Reservation no. 2.—Reservation no. 5.—Statement of Senator Hitchcock. ⟨From the Washington post, Jan. 31, 1920.⟩
1. Versailles, Treaty of, June 28, 1919 (Germany) 2. League of nations. I. Hitchcock, Gilbert Monell, 1859-   II. Title.
20-26175
Library of Congress   D643.A55 1920 a
₍₎

NL 0439397   DLC Or MiU OO

Lodge, Henry Cabot, 1850-

U. S. *62d Cong., 2d sess.,* 1911-1912.

Resolutions in regard to fifth International congress of chambers of commerce introduced in the United States Senate by Senator Henry Cabot Lodge; introduced in the House of representatives by Congressman Andrew J. Peters. ₍Washington, 1912₎

LODGE, HENRY CABOT, 1850-1924.

The restriction of immigration... Speech of Hon. Henry Cabot Lodge, of Massachusetts, in the Senate of the United States, March 16, 1896. [Washington? D.C., 1896] 16 p. 23cm.

1. Emigration and immigration—U.S., 1896.

NL 0439399   NN MB MH

Lodge, Henry Cabot, 1850-

... The retention of the Philippine Islands. Speech of Hon. Henry Cabot Lodge, of Massachusetts, in the Senate of the United States, March 7, 1900. Washington ₍Govt. print. off.₎ 1900.
48 p. 23ᶜᵐ.

1. U. S.—Colonial question—Speeches in Congress. 2. Philippine Islands—Pol. & govt.—1898-
1-4484
Library of Congress   DS681.5.U4L6 1900 a

NL 0439400   DLC MWA MB DCU-H

Lodge, Henry Cabot, 1850-

Home market club, *Boston.*

The revision of the tariff. By Hon. Elihu Root ... Reciprocity with Canada and affairs in the Philippines. By Hon. Henry Cabot Lodge ... Speeches before the Home market club, April 2, 1903. Boston, Home market club, 1903.

Lodge, Henry Cabot
Sea power of the United States.
Speech...March 2, 1895.
Wash., 1895

YA5000   (Congressional speeches.by author)
J 17

NL 0439402   DLC

Lodge, Henry Cabot, 1850-1924, *ed.*
Selected popular tales. Third series. Selected and arranged by Henry Cabot Lodge ... Boston, G. A. Smith and company, 1881.
74 p. front., illus., plates. 20½ᶜᵐ.
CONTENTS.—Puss in boots.—The sleeping beauty.—Beauty and the beast.—The princess and the nuts.—Fortunatus.—The history of Sir R. Whittington and his cat.—Cinderella.

1. Fairy tales.
Library of Congress   PZ8.L8155e
44-35886

NL 0439403   DLC

Lodge, Henry Cabot, 1850-1924.

Roosevelt, Theodore, *pres. U. S., 1858-1919.*
Selections from the correspondence of Theodore Roosevelt and Henry Cabot Lodge, 1884-1918 ... New York ₍etc.₎ C. Scribner's sons, 1925.

Lodge, Henry Cabot, 1850-
The Senate.
10 p. (541-550)   25 cm.
Caption title.

NL 0439405   RPB

Lodge, Henry Cabot, 1850-1924.
The Senate and the League of nations, by Henry Cabot Lodge. New York ₍etc.₎ C. Scribner's sons, 1925.
4 p. l., 424 p. front. (facsims.) 23ᶜᵐ.

1. U. S.—For. rel—1913-1921. 2. League of nations. 3. European war, 1914-1918—U. S. 4. U. S. Congress. Senate. I. Title.
25—22067
JX1975.L84

OrSaW GU-L CaBVaU KEmT WaS Wa OrU WaTC NcD NjN DN ViU-L ViU TxU NIC NBuHi OrP OrPR Or NBuC PHi PP ViU ICJ MB NN DAU OC1W OC1 OOxM OU ODW OC1ND
NL 0439406   DLC OrCS MtU IdPI CaBVa IdU PPT PHC PU

Lodge, Henry Cabot, 1850-
The Senate of the United States, and other essays and addresses historical and literary, by Henry Cabot Lodge. New York, C. Scribner's sons, 1921.
4 p. l., 248 p. 21ᶜᵐ.
CONTENTS.—The Senate of the United States.—New lamps for old.—A great library.—Value of the classics.—Familiar quotations.—Theodore Roosevelt.—Prospero's island.—After the victory.—The Pilgrims of Plymouth.

1. U. S. Congress. Senate. 2. Harvard university. Library. Widener collection. 3. Roosevelt, Theodore, pres. U. S., 1858-1919. 4. Pilgrim fathers. I. Title.
21—9671
Library of Congress   PS2249.L4S4 1921

PHC PPL MiU OU OC1 OC1W MB MH NN ViU
NL 0439407   DLC WaWW MtU OrP WaU-L NBuU GU-L PSC

VOLUME 338

Lodge, Henry Cabot, 1850–1924.
The Senate of the United States, and other essays and addresses historical and literary, by Henry Cabot Lodge. New York, C. Scribner's sons, 1921.
4 p. l., 248 p. 21 cm.

CONTENTS.—The Senate of the United States.—New lamps for old.—A great library.—Value of the classics.—Familiar quotations.—Theodore Roosevelt.—Prospero's island.—After the victory.—The Pilgrims of Plymouth.

PS2249
.L4S4
.1921a

Photocopy. Ann Arbor, Mich., University Microfilms, 1971.

NL 0439408   OrPS

D619
.L65

Lodge, Henry Cabot, 1850–1924.
Severance of relations with Germany. Speech of Hon. Henry Cabot Lodge of Massachusetts in the Senate of the United States. February, 1917... [Washington, Gov't. Print. off., 1917]
2 p. 23 cm.

NL 0439409   DLC

Lodge, Henry Cabot, 1850–
Shakespeare's Americanisms. (In his: Certain accepted heroes and other essays. New York, 1897. 12°. p. [93–] 114.)
Half-title.

1. Shakespeare, William.—Language of. 2. Americanisms (Verbal).
August 23, 1916.

NL 0439410   NN

Lodge, Henry Cabot, 1850–1924.
A short history of the English colonies in America, by Henry Cabot Lodge. New York, Harper & brothers, 1881.
viii, 560 p. double map. 22ᶜᵐ.

1. U. S.—Hist.—Colonial period.
Library of Congress   E188.L82   2—19013/2

Copyright 1881: 3919   [a39b1]   *73.2

OClWHi PPA PPT KyHi PU PHC PHi DNW I MH NcU NN WaTC Or OrU KMK MdBP DN MiU MWA PCC OCl OU ODW OO
NL 0439411   DLC IdU OrU NjP WaSp NjNbT IdB OrP NNC

Lodge, Henry Cabot, 1850–1924.
A short history of the English colonies in America, by Henry Cabot Lodge. New York, Harper & brothers, 1882.
viii, 560 p. double map. 22ᶜᵐ.
First published 1881.

1. U. S.—Hist.—Colonial period.
Library of Congress   E188.L83   7—31309

NL 0439412   DLC NBuU Vi MWA NcU MiU-C PHi PPPL

E188
L82
1881

Lodge, Henry Cabot, 1850–1924.
A short history of the English colonies in America. Rev. ed. New York, Harper [1881]
viii, 560 p. map. 23cm.

1. U.S. – Hist. – Colonial period. I. Title.

NL 0439413   CoU KEmT KyLx ICJ MeB NjN NIC ViU

Lodge, Henry Cabot, 1850–1924.
A short history of the English colonies in America, by ... rev. ed. New York, Harper and brothers, 1886.

NL 0439414   OClW PSC

E188
.L82
1890

Lodge, Henry Cabot, 1850–1924.
A short history of the English colonies in America, by Henry Cabot Lodge ... Rev. ed. New York, Harper & brothers [189–?]
viii, 560 p. double map. 22ᶜᵐ.

1. U. S.—Hist.—Colonial period.

NL 0439415   MB

LODGE,Henry Cabot,1850–1924.
A short history of the English colonies in America. Revised ed. New York and London, Harper & Brothers,1898[cop.1881].

22 cm. Map.

NL 0439416   MH OEac

Lodge, Henry Cabot, 1850–1924.
A short history of the English colonies in America. Rev. ed. New York, Harper, 1900.

viii, 560 p. map.

NL 0439417   MH OCU OrSaW

Lodge, Henry Cabot, 1850–1924.
A short history of the English colonies in America...rev. ed. New York and London, Harper & Brothers, 1903.
560 p.

NL 0439418   MiU

Lodge, Henry Cabot, 1850–1924.
A short history of the English colonies in America, by Henry Cabot Lodge ... Rev. ed. New York and London, Harper & brothers, 1904 [c1881]
viii, 560 p. map. 23 cm.

NL 0439419   OU NcRS OOxM

Lodge, Henry Cabot, 1850–1924.
A short history of the English colonies in America, by Henry Cabot Lodge ... Rev. ed. New York and London, Harper & brothers [1909]
viii, 560 p. map. 22½ᶜᵐ.

1. U. S.—Hist.—Colonial period.
Library of Congress   E188.L833   9—9452

OOxM
NL 0439420   DLC OU OClh OO OLak PBa PPLT OrU Or

Lodge, Henry Cabot, 1850–1924.
A short history of the English colonies in America, by Henry Cabot Lodge... New York, Harper & brothers [c1923]
viii, 560 p. and London   22ᶜᵐ.

NL 0439421   ViU OrCS

Lodge, Henry Cabot, 1850–1924.
Silver and Cloture. Speeches ... In the Senate of the United States, August 15 and September 21, 1893. Washington, 1893.
8vo. Unbound. Upper corners slightly mutilated.
Brock Collection, October, 1922.

NL 0439422   CSmH

PZ
8
L82

Lodge, Henry Cabot, 1850–1924, ed.
Six popular tales. Boston [J. Wilson, University Press] 1879.
68 p. illus. 21cm.

Contents:—Jack the giant-killer.—Jack and the bean-stalk.—Little red riding-hood.—Puss in boots.—The sleeping beauty.—Cinderella.

With this is bound the editor's 2d series. Boston, 1880.

NL 0439423   NIC MB

Lodge, Henry Cabot, ed.
...Six popular tales. Second series. Selected and arranged by Henry Cabot Lodge... Boston: Lee and Shepard [etc.,] 1880. 64 p. plates. 20cm.

At head of title: Authorised for use in the Boston public schools.
CONTENTS.—Bluebeard.—Hop-o'-My-Thumb.—Beauty and the beast.—The princess and the nuts.—Fortunatus.—The history of Sir R. Whittington and his cat.

1. Juvenile literature—Fiction —Collections.
October 3, 1939.

NL 0439424   NN MB NIC

Lodge, Henry Cabot, 1850–

Hughes, Charles Evans, 1862–
... Some aspects of the work of the Department of state. Address of Charles E. Hughes [secretary of state, before the Chamber of commerce of the United States at convention held in Washington, D. C., on Thursday evening, May 18, 1922 ... Washington, Govt. print. off., 1922.

Lodge, Henry Cabot. 1850–   4223.119
Speech at Symphony Hall, Boston, January 3. 1911.
= [Boston. 1911.] 20 pp. 23½ cm.
On the approaching election of a senator of the United States by the legislature of Massachusetts.

NL 0439426   MB

LODGE, Henry Cabot.
Speech at the Republican State Convention in Tremont Temple, Boston,Oct.,5,1912. Boston, issued by the Republican Club of Mass. [1912].

Pamphlet.

NL 0439427   MH

LODGE, Henry Cabot.
Speech before the Republican state convention of Massachusetts,March 27,1896. [Boston,1896]

pp. 16.
Without title-page. Caption title.

NL 0439428   MH MB

VOLUME 338

Lodge, Henry Cabot, 1850–
... Speech by Henry Cabot Lodge on immigration ...
before the Boston City club, Boston, Mass., on March 20,
1908 ... ₁Washington, Gov't print. off., 1908₎
9 p. 23ᶜᵐ. (₁U. S.₎ 60th Cong., 1st sess. Senate. Doc. 423)
Presented by Mr. Flint and ordered printed, April 7, 1908.

1. U. S.—Emig. & immig.   i. U. S. 60th Cong., 1st sess., 1907-1908.
Senate.
8—35336

Library of Congress   JV6416.A5 1908c

NL 0439429   DLC Or MiU OO NN

LODGE, Henry Cabot.
Speech in the House of Representatives,
Tuesday, January 13, 1891. [Washington? 1891.]

pp. 3.
Without title-page. Caption title.

NL 0439430   MH

LODGE, Henry Cabot.
Speech in the Senate of the U.S:, Jan.6,1915.
Washington, Gov't. printing office,1915.

pp. 16.
Cover serves as title-page.

NL 0439431   MH

Lodge, Henry Cabot, 1850–
Speech of Hon. Henry Cabot Lodge at the Republican
state convention, Springfield, October 6, 1917. ₁Boston,
Anchor linotype printing co., 1917₎
1 p. l., ₁6₎ p. 19½ᶜᵐ.

1. European war, 1914–   —Addresses, sermons, etc.

Library of Congress   D570.15.L6   20—4332

NL 0439432   DLC

E560
.L829 Lodge, Henry Cabot, 1850-1924.
1908   Speech of Hon. Henry Cabot Lodge before the
       Republican State Convention of Massachusetts,
       April 10, 1908 ₁Boston, 1908₎
       13 p. 28 cm.

       Corrections in mss.

       I. Republican Party, Massachusetts. Convention,
       1908.

NL 0439433   MB

E
179   Lodge, Henry Cabot, 1850-1924.
U11   Speech of Senator Lodge of Massachusetts
v.14   with remarks by Senators Foraker and Nelson
no.19 in reply to speeches of Senators Carmack and
       Rawlins on the American army in the Philip-
       pines. In the United States Senate, May,
       1902. Washington, 1902.
       15 p. 25cm.

       1. U.S.--Armed forces--Foreign countries.
       2. Philippine Islands--hist.--insurrection,
       1899-1901. I. Fo   raker, Joseph Benson,
       1846-1917. II. Ne   lson, Wolfred, 1846-1913.

NL 0439434   NIC

Lodge, Henry Cabot, 1850-1924.
Speeches by Henry Cabot Lodge. Boston and New York,
Houghton Mifflin and company, 1892.
3 p. l., 89 p. 22 cm.
CONTENTS.—The independent spirit of the Puritans. December
22, 1884.—The uses and responsibilities of leisure. March 23, 1886.—
The blue and the gray. June 17, 1887.—The Puritans. December
22, 1887.—Harvard college in politics. November 22, 1888.—The day
we celebrate. December 21, 1888.—International copyright. May 2,
1890.—The civilization of the public school; a reply. January 13,
1890.—Massachusetts. October 23, 1891.

E660.L77   5-10678

NL 0439435   AU CtY NjP WaS
                   DLC PPL PHi PPD PHC MH MB OC1 ICU OU

Lodge, Henry Cabot, 1850-1924.
Speeches and addresses, 1884-1909, by Henry Cabot Lodge.
₁2d ed.₎ Boston and New York, Houghton Mifflin company,
1909.
x p., 1 l., ₁3₎-462 p., 1 l. 22ᶜᵐ.
"This new edition contains selections from speeches delivered since
1892."—Note to 2d edition.

1. U. S.—Pol. & govt.—1865–
9—31456

Library of Congress   E660.L82

NL 0439436   MB
                   DLC IdU DN NN PHi PP KMK MiU OC1W NN

G972.085
L821s   Lodge, Henry Cabot, 1850-1924.
        The story of Mexico. [New York] National
        Hughes Alliance ₁19—₎
        23p. 22cm.

        1. Mexico - Hist. - 1910-1946. 2. Vera
        Cruz, Mexico (City) - Hist. - American occupa-
        tion, 1914. I. Title.

NL 0439437   TxU

E208
L82   Lodge, Henry Cabot, 1850-1924.
1903   The story of the American Revolution. London,
        Duckworth, 1903.
        xviii, 604 p. illus. 24 cm.

        Half title: The story of the Revolution.

        1. United States - History - Revolution. I.
        Title. II. Title: The story of the Revolution.

NL 0439438   GU MH CaBVaU

Lodge, Henry Cabot, 1850-1924.
The story of the revolution, by Henry Cabot
Lodge...London, Archibald Constable and co., 1898.
2 v. fronts., illus., paltes, ports., facsims.
23.1 cm. .

NL 0439439   MiU-C CtY NcU OFH OC1W OOxM

Lodge, Henry Cabot, 1850-1924.
The story of the revolution, by Henry Cabot Lodge ... New
York, C. Scribner's sons, 1898.
2 v. fronts., illus., plates, ports., facsims. 23ᶜᵐ.

1. U. S.—Hist.—Revolution. i. Title.
98—1847
E208.L82

                   PP PPL PHi PU
                   MB NcRS DN DNW OC1WHi OC1 I DCU-IA Nh MB PPA PSC
NL 0439440   DLC Or NcD CU NSyU CaOTP KMK CLSU NIC

Lodge, Henry Cabot, 1850-1924.
The story of the revolution, by Henry Cabot Lodge ...
New York, C. Scribner's sons, 1903.
1 p. l., xviii, 1 l., 604 p. incl. illus., plates, ports., facsims. front.
23½ᶜᵐ.
First published, 1898, in 2 vols.

1. U. S.—Hist.—Revolution. i. Title.
3—22840

Library of Congress   E208.L83
                           ₁a37o1–₎   -973.3

                   NN NjP MWA PP PU PHi
NL 0439441   DLC WaT WaS OEac OC1h OC1 TKL ViU MB

Lodge, Henry Cabot
The story of the revolution. ₁Library ed.₎
Scribner, 1919.
450 p.

NL 0439442   MiD

Lodge, Henry Cabot.
Story of the revolution: Greene's campaign
in the South.

Extract from Scribner's magazine,   Sept.
1898.

NL 0439443   NcU

Lodge, Henry Cabot, 1850-1924.
Studies in history, by Henry Cabot Lodge ... Boston,
New York ₁etc.₎, Houghton, Mifflin and company, 1884.
4 p. l., 408 p. 20 cm.
CONTENTS.—The Puritans and the restoration.—A Puritan Pepys
₁Samuel Sewall₎.—The early days of Fox.—William Cobbett.—Alexander Hamilton.—Timothy Pickering.—Caleb Strong.—Albert Gallatin.—Daniel Webster.—Colonialism in the United States.—French
opinions of the United States, 1840-1881.

1. U. S.—Biog. 2. U. S.—Hist. 3. U. S.—Soc. life & cust.
4. Puritans. 5. Fox, Charles James, 1749-1806. i. Title.

E173.L82   5—32496

                   ICU NcU NN OC1W OU MiU OO MH PPA PBm PP PHC PPL
NL 0439444   DLC MB WaS OrP NjP NIC NcU MdBP WaU I

F
83   Lodge, Henry Cabot,   1850-1924.
.52   Studies in history...   Boston,1885.

           Contents.-The Puritans and the res-
        toration.-A Puritan Pepys.-The early days
        of Fox.-William Cobbett.-Alexander Hamil-
        ton.-Timothy Pickering.-Caleb Strong.-
        Albert Gallatin.-Daniel Webster.-Colo-
        nialism in the United States.-French
        opinions of the United States, 1840-1881.

NL 0439445   ICN PHi OC1

LODGE, Henry Cabot, 1850–
Studies in history. Boston, etc., Houghton,
Mifflin and company, 1892, [cop. 1884].

NL 0439446   MH

E
173   Lodge, Henry Cabot, 1850-1924
L82   Studies in history, by Henry Cabot Lodge
        ... Boston, New York ₁etc.₎ Houghton,
        Mifflin and company, 1896 ₁1884c₎
        403 p.

        U.S.--BIOG.
        U.S.--HIST.
        U.S.--SOC. LIFE & CUST.
        PURITANS
        FOX, CHARLES JAMES, 1749-1806

NL 0439447   KMK PU

VOLUME 338

Lodge, Henry Cabot.
The sugar schedule; speech in the Senate of the United States, July 27, 1912. Washington: [Gov. Prtg. Off.] 1912. 31 p. 8°.

1. Sugar.—Tariff, U. S, 1912.

February 13, 1913.

NL 0439448   NN MiU

Lodge, Henry Cabot, 1850–
The tariff—cotton schedule. Speech of Hon. Henry Cabot Lodge ... in the Senate of the United States, Tuesday, June 1, 1909. Washington [Govt. print. off.] 1909.
35 p. 23½ᶜᵐ.

1. Tariff—U. S.—Speeches in Congress. 2. Cotton trade—U. S. I. Title.

CA 9—6306 Unrev'd
Library of Congress   HF2651.C8503L7

NL 0439449   DLC

Lodge, Henry Cabot, 1850–1924.
Theodore Roosevelt, by Henry Cabot Lodge. Boston and New York, Houghton Mifflin company, 1919.
2 p. l., [3]–45 p. front. 20ᶜᵐ.
"Five hundred and seventy-five copies of this book were printed ... in March, 1919, of which five hundred, autographed by the author, are for sale."
Originally published as Senate document no. 384, 65th Congress, 3d session, under title: Address of Senator Henry Cabot Lodge ... in honor of Theodore Roosevelt ... before the Congress of the United States ... February 9, 1919.

1. Roosevelt, Theodore, pres. U. S., 1858–1919.

Library of Congress   E757.L825
19—9040
[a242]

MB NN CU-S MeB DAL
NL 0439450   DLC ViU ICN OrPS ICU MiU-C OCl OClWHi

PS2734
.R5Z696 **Lodge, Henry Cabot,** 1850–1924.
1919a
    Theodore Roosevelt; an address delivered before the Congress of the United States February ninth, nineteen hundred and nineteen. Boston, Privately printed [McGrath-Sherrill Press, 1919]
2 p. l., 7–53, [1] p. port. 19cm.

1. Roosevelt, Theodore, Pres. U. S., 1858–1919.

NL 0439451   ViU NN MH IdB

Lodge, Henry Cabot, 1850–1924.

Nova Scotia. *Laws, statutes, etc.*
... Timber legislation—Canada ... Laws enacted in Nova Scotia, Ontario, British Columbia, Quebec, and New Brunswick, Canada, relative to spruce and other pulp wood cut on crown lands ... [Washington, Gov't print. off., 1911]

Lodge, Henry Cabot, 1850?

U. S. *Congress. Senate. Committee on immigration.*
... To amend section one of the Passenger act of 1882 ... Report. <To accompany S. 5083.> [Washington, Gov't print. off., 1908]

Lodge, Henry Cabot, 1850–1924.
... **Trade** agreements abroad. Articles relating to the resolution (S. 220) "requesting the President to ascertain certain information relating to a recent commercial conference held in Paris, France, by certain European nations", together with the remarks of Senator William J. Stone and Senator Henry Cabot Lodge, delivered in the United States Senate thereon and the message of the President in response thereto. Washington, Govt. print. off., 1916.

Lodge, Henry Cabot, 1850.

China. *Treaties, etc., 1922.*
... Treaty between China and Japan for the settlement of outstanding questions relating to Shantung—with an agreement supplementary thereto. Concluded at Washington on February 4, 1922 ... Washington, Govt. print. off., 1922.

Lodge, Henry Cabot, 1850–
Treaty making powers of the senate... reprinted, by permission of Charles Scribner's Sons, from Scribner's magazine for January, 1902. Washington, 1902.
15 p. 25 cm. (U.S. 57th Cong., 1st sess., Senate doc. 104)
Bound with U.S. Cong. House Committee on foreign affairs. Treaty-making power. [1881]

NL 0439456   RPB CSmH

Lodge, Henry Cabot, 1850–

U. S. *Congress. Senate. Committee on foreign relations.*
... Treaty of peace with Germany ... Report. <To accompany S. doc. 51> ... [Washington, Govt. print. off., 1919]

D643
A7L82 **Lodge, Henry Cabot,** 1850–1924.
Treaty of peace with Germany; speech in the Senate of the United States, Tuesday, August 12, 1919. Washington, 1919.
16 p. 25cm.

1. Versailles, Treaty of, June 28, 1919 (Germany) I.   Title.

NL 0439458   CSt-H Or NIC MB

Lodge, Henry C.
Treaty of peace with Spain Speech of, in the Senate. Jan. 24, 1899.
Wash., 1899.
11 p.. 8°

NL 0439459   MWA CSmH

Lodge, Henry Cabot, 1850–
... Treaty relating to the Pacific Islands. Address of the Hon. Henry Cabot Lodge, member of the American delegation at the fourth plenary session of the Conference on the limitation of armament upon submitting the draft of a treaty agreed upon by the United States, Great Britain, France, and Japan ... Washington, Govt. print. off., 1921.
6 p. 23ᶜᵐ. ([U. S.] 67th Cong., 2d sess. Senate. Doc. 101)

Presented by Mr. Kellogg. Ordered printed, December 13, 1921.
Running title: Address of Hon. Henry Cabot Lodge.

1. Islands of the Pacific. 2. U. S.—For. rel.—Treaties. 3. Gt. Brit.—For. rel.—Treaties. 4. France—For. rel.—Treaties. 5. Japan—For. rel.—Treaties. 6. Arbitration, International. I. Conference on the limitation of armament, Washington, D. C., 1921– II. Kellogg, Frank Billings, 1856– III. Title. IV. Title: Address of Hon. Henry Cabot Lodge.

Library of Congress   DU29.L6
21–27513

NL 0439461   DLC MiU OO

LODGE, HENRY CABOT, 1850–1924
Treaty reservations: a compilation of reservations made to treaties and conventions by the Senate of the United States. Govt. 1919.
12 p.   (U. S. - 66th Cong. 1st sess. - Senate Doc. no.148)

NL 0439462   Or

LODGE, Henry Cabot.
True Americanism. Orations delivered before the Phi Beta Kappa society, June 28, 1894.
n.p., [1894].
pp.16.
"Harvard Graduates Magazine, Sept. 1894".

NL 0439463   MH

Lodge, Henry Cabot.
The true naval policy. Speech.. April 16, 1892.
Wash., 1892.

YA5000   (Congressional speeches, by author)
J 17

NL 0439464   DLC

Lodge, Henry Cabot, 1850–1924.

U. S. *Supreme court.*
... Truman H. Newberry et al. Opinion of the Supreme court of the United States in the case of Truman H. Newberry et al. v. the United States together with the opinions of Chief Justice White and Justice Pitney therein ... Washington, Govt. print. off., 1921.

Lodge, Henry Cabot, 1850–1924.
Two commencement addresses, by Henry Cabot Lodge. Cambridge, Harvard university press, 1915.
44 p. 1 l. 18ᶜᵐ.
CONTENTS.—Address at Radcliffe college commencement.—Address at the presentation of the Widener memorial library.

1. Classical education. 2. Books and reading. 3. Harvard university. Library. Widener collection.

Library of Congress   LC1011.L6
15—16448

OClW OClWHi MB IU ICJ PPT
NL 0439466   DLC CaBVaU OrPS KMK NjP TxU NcD OU OO

LODGE, Henry Cabot, 1850–
"Unconditional surrender", our only terms to Germany; speech in the Senate of the United States, Oct.10,1918. Washington, [Government Printing Office], 1918.
pp. 8.

NL 0439467   MH

Lodge, Henry Cabot, 1850–1924, joint author.

FOR OTHER EDITIONS
SEE MAIN ENTRY

Garner, James Wilford, 1871–1938.
... The United States ... by James Wilford Garner ... and Henry Cabot Lodge ... with a historical review by John Bach McMaster ... New York, P. F. Collier & son corporation [*1939]

VOLUME 338

Lodge, Henry Cabot, 1850-

U. S. *President, 1921-* *(Harding)*
... The unknown American soldier. Address of the President of the United States at the ceremonies attending the burial of an unknown American soldier in Arlington cemetery November 11, 1921 ... Washington, Govt. print. off., 1921.

Classics
LC
1011
.L64   Lodge, Henry Cabot, 1850-1924.
Value of the classics. An address delivered by Henry Cabot Lodge at the Conference on classical studies in liberal education, held at Princeton University, June 2, 1917. ₍Princeton, N. J.,₎ 1917₎
28 p.   23 cm.

NL   0439470   ODW NjP

Lodge, Henry Cabot, 1850-

Belgium. *Corps législatif, 1906. Chambre des représentants.*
... Verbatim report of the five days' Congo debate in the Belgian House of representatives, February 20, 27, 28; March 1, 2, 1906. December 13, 1906.—Presented by Mr. Lodge and ordered to be printed. Washington, Govt. print. off., 1906.

Lodge, Henry Cabot, 1850-

U. S. *Dept. of state.*
... Wages and prices abroad; reports from consular officers of the United States ... giving the present retail and wholesale prices of certain commodities and the prices obtaining in 1900; together with salaries paid various classes of government employees ... Washington, Govt. print. off., 1910.

Lodge, Henry Cabot, 1850-1924.
War addresses, 1915-1917, by Henry Cabot Lodge ... Boston and New York, Houghton Mifflin company, 1917.
viii, 303, ₍1₎ p.   22 cm.

CONTENTS.—Mexico.—Force and peace.—France.—Address at the unveiling of the Soldiers' monument, Brookline.—American rights.—National defence.—Armed merchantmen.—Washington's policies of neutrality and national defence.—Address at the opening and dedication of the new buildings of the Massachusetts Institute of technology.—Address at the unveiling of the Lafayette statue, Fall River.—The policies of the present administration.—Speech before the Harvard Republican club.—The peace note of the President.—Address at the celebration of the one hundredth anniversary of St. John's church, Washington.—The President's plan for a world peace.—On the severance of diplomatic relations with Germany.—The failure of the executive to vindicate American rights.—War with Germany.
With author's autograph.
1. U. S.—Pol. & govt.—1913-1921.   2. European war, 1914-1918—Addresses, sermons, etc.   I. Title.
17—14032
Library of Congress   D619.L6

MB PPL OU OCl OCU OClWHi ViU PPA PP PU NjP
NL   0439474   DLC IdU WaS OrP IEN NIC NcRS NcU ICJ NN

LODGE, Henry Cabot.
The war in Cuba. Speech in the senate of the United States. February 20, 1896. n.p.,n.d.

NL   0439475   MH

LODGE, HENRY CABOT, 1850-1924.
War revenue. Speech of Hon. Henry Cabot Lodge of Massachusetts in the Senate of the United States, Wednesday, August 22, 1912. Washington: [Govt. Prtg. Off.] 1917.
19 p.   23½cm.

747537A. 1. European war, 1914-1918—Finance—U.S.

NL   0439476   NN

Lodge, Henry Cabot, 1850-
War with Germany. Speech of Hon. Henry Cabot Lodge ... in the Senate of the United States. April 4, 1917. Washington ₍Govt. print. off.₎ 1917.
8 p. 23 cm.

1. U. S.—For. rel.—Germany.   2. Germany—For. rel—U. S.   I. Title.
Library of Congress   D619.L67   20-500

NL   0439477   DLC

Lodge, Henry Cabot, 1850-1924.
The war with Spain, by Henry Cabot Lodge ... New York and London, Harper & brothers, 1899.
ix, 276 p. front., plates, ports., maps.   20½ cm.

1. U. S.—Hist.—War of 1898.   I. Title.
E715.L82₁   99—3805

MdBP MH-L MoU OCU NNC NjNbS MiU OClW NcD DAU MB ICJ
NL   0439478   DLC MdBP OrU WaTC OrP DN CU PPD NjN PP

Lodge, Henry Cabot, 1850-
The war with Spain, by Henry Cabot Lodge ... New York and London, Harper brothers ₍1899₎
ix, 287, ₍1₎ p. front., plates, ports., maps.   21½ cm.

1. U. S.—Hist.—War of 1898.   I. Title.
Library of Congress   E715.L832   15-19116

PPL MB NN
NL   0439479   DLC WaS OCU CLSU MiU OClW OU PWcS PU

Lodge, Henry Cabot, 1850-1924.
The war with Spain, by Henry Cabot Lodge. Illustrated. New York and London, Harper & brothers, 1900.
viii, ₍1₎, 287, ₍1₎ p. front., plates, ports., maps.   21½ cm.

1. U. S.—Hist.—War of 1898.   I. Title.
E715.L83   973.89   2—1454

NL   0439480   DLC DNW WaE MoSU

Lodge, Henry C.
The war with Spain... New York a nd London, Harper & brothers, 1902.
viii,p., 1 l., 287, (1) p. front., plates, ports. 21½cm.

NL   0439481   DNW OCl OO OClW

Lodge, Henry Cabot, 1850-
... Washington's policies of neutrality and national defense. Address delivered before the Washington association of New Jersey, at Morristown, N. J., on February 22, 1916, by Hon. Henry Cabot Lodge ... Washington, Govt. print. off., 1916.
12 p.   23½ cm.   (₍U. S.₎ 64th Cong., 1st sess. Senate. Doc. 343)
Presented by Mr. Smith of Michigan. Ordered printed February 23, 1916.
1. U. S.—Neutrality.   2. U. S.—Defenses.   3. Washington, George, pres. U. S., 1732-1799.   I. Title.
Library of Congress   E313.L82   16-26191

NL   0439482   DLC Or MiU OO

Lodge, Henry Cabot, 1850-
Washington's principles of neutrality and defense; an address delivered by Henry Cabot Lodge before the Washington Association of New Jersey, with greeting by Alfred Elmer Mills, president, and proceedings in the celebration at Washington's headquarters in Morristown, N. J. on February 22nd, 1916. ₍Washington? 1916.₎   22 p.   8°.
Cover-title.

1. Washington, George, 1st pres. U. S.   2. Neutrality, U. S. 3. Defence, New Jersey. 5. Mills, Alfred
U. S. 4. Washington Association of Elmer, 1858-
N. Y. P. L.   April 2, 1918.

NL   0439483   NN CSmH

LODGE, Henry Cabot.
William Cobbett.
International review, 1880, pp.67-79.

NL   0439484   MH

Lodge, Henry Cabot, 1850-   *2355.12.50
Witchcraft in Howell's "Familiar letters."
(In Massachusetts Historical Society. Proceedings. Vol. 50. pp. 91-94. Boston. 1917.)

L2947 — Witchcraft. — Howell, James, 1594?-1666.

NL   0439485   MB

Lodge, Henry Cabot, 1850-1924, ed.

Hamilton, Alexander, 1757-1804.
The works of Alexander Hamilton, ed. by Henry Cabot Lodge ... ₍Federal ed.₎ New York and London, G. P. Putnam's sons, 1904.

Lodge, Henry Cabot, 1902-
J87   Address of Henry Cabot Lodge
.V9
1954a   Virginia. *General Assembly.*
Journals of the House of Delegates and Senate of Virginia, including a joint Assembly. Sessions held in the reconstructed capitol at Williamsburg, Friday, January 30, 1954. ₍Richmond, 1954₎

Lodge, Henry Cabot, 1902-

U. S. *Congress. Senate. Committee on military affairs.*
... Amending the Helium act approved March 3, 1925, as amended. Report of the Committee on military affairs on S. 1567, a bill to amend the act entitled "An act to amend the act entitled 'An act authorizing the conservation, production, and exploitation of helium gas, a mineral resource pertaining to the national defense and to the development of commercial aeronautics, and for other purposes'," together with views of the minority ... Washington, U. S. Govt. print. off., 1937.

VOLUME 338

Lodge, Henry Cabot, 1902–
The cult of weakness, by Henry Cabot Lodge, jr. Boston and New York, Houghton Mifflin company, 1932.

ix p., 2 l., ₃₎–172 p. 19¼ᶜᵐ.

Informal essays analyzing the peace issue as a symptom of the American attitude toward other great public questions. *cf.* Pref.

1. U. S.—Pol. & govt. 2. U. S.—For. rel. 3. Public opinion—U. S. 4. Peace. 5. Disarmament.   ɪ. Title.

Library of Congress   JX1961.U6L56
                                                            32–29859

Copyright A 55361   172.4

NL   0439489   DLC MB NN Or WaT ICN NcU CU DN

Lodge, Henry Cabot, 1902–
Cutting the cables. Article by Hon. Henry Cabot Lodge, jr., United States Senator from Massachusetts ... 1937.
8 p.   0.

YA 5000
J 17   (Congressional speeches, by author)

NL   0439490   DLC

Lodge, Henry Cabot, 1902–
J74   U. S. *Congress. Senate. Committee on foreign relations.*
.A36   ... Extension of Inter-American coffee agreement of No-
80th,   vember 28, 1940 ... Report. ⟨To accompany Executive B,
1st sess., Eightieth Congress, first session⟩ ₍Washington, U. S. Govt.
no. 1   print. off., 1947₎

Lodge, Henry Cabot, 1902–
TC623   U. S. *Congress. Senate. Committee on Foreign Relations.*
.1   Great Lakes-St. Lawrence seaway project. Report ₍and
.A5   Minority views₎ to accompany S. J. Res. 111. ₍Washington,
1948   U. S. Govt. Print. Off., 1948₎

Lodge, Henry Cabot, 1902–
Labor relations. Extension of remarks of Hon. Henry Cabot Lodge, jr., of Massachusetts, in the Senate of the United States, Monday, May 17 (legislative day of Thursday, May 13), 1937.
4 p.   0.

YA 5000
J 17   (Congressional speeches, by author)

NL   0439493   DLC

Lodge, Henry Cabot, 1902–

Multilateral peace treaty. Address delivered at the Williamstown institute of politics, August 22, 1928, The multilateral pact for the renunciation of war, by Edwin Borchard together with an article from the Forum. January, 1929, entitled "Should the Senate ratify the Kellogg treaty", by Frank H. Simonds, also an article from Harpers magazine, December, 1928, entitled "The meaning of the Kellogg treaty", by Henry Cabot Lodge, 3d ... Washington, U. S. Govt. print. off., 1929.

Lodge, Henry Cabot, 1902–
U. S. *Congress. Senate. Special committee to investigate unemployment and relief.*
... Public works agency ... Report ₍Minority views and the Individual views of Mr. Davis and Individual views₎ ⟨To accompany S. 2202⟩ ... ₍Washington, U. S. Govt. print. off., 1939₎

Lodge, Henry Cabot, 1902–
D769   **Report** on the war; observations by five members of the
.1   United States Senate on a 45,000-mile trip to the war areas;
.R46   from the Senate Committee on naval affairs: Senator Richard
          B. Russell ... from the Senate Committee on military affairs:
          Senator Albert B. Chandler ... ₍and₎ Senator Henry Cabot
          Lodge, jr. ... from the Special Senate Committee to investi-
          gate the national defense program (Truman committee):
          Senator James M. Mead ... ₍and₎ Senator Ralph O. Brewster
          ... ₍Washington, The United States news, 1943?₎

Lodge, Henry Cabot, 1902–
U. S. *Congress. Senate. Committee on military affairs.*
... Selective-service deferment, on occupational grounds, of persons employed by the federal government ... Report. ⟨To accompany S. 886⟩ ₍Washington, U. S. Govt. print. off., 1943₎

Lodge, Henry Cabot, 1902–
The Supreme court. Extension of remarks of Hon. Henry Cabot Lodge, jr., of Massachusetts, in the Senate of the United States. Tuesday June 8 (legislative day of Monday, June 7), 1937.
[2] p.   Q.

YA 5000
J 17   (Congressional speeches, by author)

NL   0439498   DLC

Lodge, Henry Cabot, 1902–
HV85   U. S. *Congress. Senate. Special committee to investigate
.A5   unemployment and relief.*
1938 e   ... Unemployment and relief ... Preliminary report ₍and
          Preliminary minority views₎ ⟨Pursuant to S. Res. 36⟩ ...
          ₍Washington, U. S. Govt. print. off., 1938₎

Lodge, Henry Cabot, 1902–
HV85   U. S. *Congress. Senate. Special committee to investigate
.A5   unemployment and relief.*
1939 b   ... Unemployment and relief ... Report ₍and Minority views₎
          ⟨Pursuant to S. Res. 36, 75th Cong.⟩ ... ₍Washington, U. S.
          Govt. print. off., 1939₎

Lodge, Henry Cabot, 1902–
The United Nations: a place to promote peace. ₍Washington, U. S. Govt. Print. Off., 1953₎

658–661 p.   27 cm. (Department of State publication 5058. International organization and conference series ɪɪɪ, 91)

"Reprinted from the Department of State bulletin of May 4, 1953."

1. United Nations.

JX1977.L6   341.13   53–61403 ‡

NL   0439501   DLC WaU-L MB PP NNC

Lodge, Henry Cabot, 1902–
E744   U. S. *Congress. Senate. Committee on Foreign Relations.*
.5   The United States Information Service in Europe. Re-
.U5   port pursuant to S. Res. 161, a resolution authorizing the
1948   Committee on Foreign Relations to make an investigation
          of the effects of certain State Department activities ₍and
          Appendix₎ Washington, U. S. Govt. Print. Off., 1948.

Lodge, Henry Cabot, 1902–
What the United Nations means to the United States; ₍an address delivered at the commemorative session of the Virginia General Assembly at the reconstructed colonial capitol in Williamsburg, Virginia, on January 30, 1954₎ Williamsburg, Colonial Williamsburg, 1954.

20 p.   23 cm.

1. United Nations—U. S.   ɪ. Title.

JX1977.2.U5L6   341.13   55–4022 ‡

NL   0439503   DLC NcGU NN PLF Or

Lodge, Henry Cabot, 1902–
JX1977   U. S. *Dept. of State. Office of Public Services.*
.U5124   You and the United Nations.
          ₍Washington, U. S. Govt. Print. Off.₎

Lodge, J. Alexander, comp.
Who's who along the north shore of Massachusetts Bay ...
          see under title

Lodge, J   Friend.
Abraham Lincoln, an address delivered by J. Friend Lodge before a community assemblage in the Bustleton Methodist Episcopal church, Bustleton, Philadelphia, Pa., Sunday afternoon, February 14th, 1926. ₍Philadelphia, Press of S. H. Little, 1926?₎

cover-title. ₍26₎ p. port. 24ᶜᵐ.

"One hundred and fifty copies privately printed and the type distributed. This is no. 137."

1. Lincoln, Abraham, pres. U. S.—Addresses, sermons, etc.
                                                            30–30505

Library of Congress   E457.8.L82   923.173

NL   0439506   DLC

Lodge, J   Friend.
Abraham Lincoln; an address delivered before Harry A. Houseman Lodge No. 717, F. and A. M., Somerton, Philadelphia, Pa., Thursday evening, February 13th, 1936. ₍Philadelphia, 1936₎

₍11₎ p. port. 24 cm.

Cover title.
"One hundred copies privately printed and the type distributed. This is no. 5."

1. Lincoln, Abraham, Pres. U. S.—Addresses, sermons, etc.

E457.8.L819   923.173   56–50983

NL   0439507   DLC

VOLUME 338

q973.7L63 Lodge, J Friend.
GL822a Abraham Lincoln and Ann Rutledge. An address delivered in the banquet hall of Harry A. Houseman Lodge no.717, F. & A.M., Somerton, Philadelphia, Pa., Thursday evening, February 9th, 1939. [Philadelphia? 1939.
5l. mounted port. 30cm.
Cover title.
Fifty copies. Cf. Author's letter.
Author's autograph presentation copy, with autograph letter inserted at front.

NL 0439508 IU

Lodge, James
Survey of the Yakama Reserve, by Berry and Lodge, 1861. 23 x 30 1/2 cm. (Wash.Sup.K. 123.1862)
Tracing. Numbered: 773/273
To be used by permission only.

NL 0439509 WaSp

[Lodge, *Mrs.* James] ed.
A week away from time. Boston, Roberts brothers, 1887.
iv, [2], [3]-349 p. 18½cm.
"Written at Quisset, or Quissit Harbor, near Fairhaven, Mass. Poetical prelude, Mrs. Annie T. Fields; preface, filling in, and Story of a voice, Mrs. James Lodge; Lawyer's story, Mrs. E. E. Pratt; Palace of the closed window, Owen Wister; Happiness, Mrs. Henry Whitman; Improvisatore (a real letter) John Field; trans. of Story of a necklace, Arthur Dexter; War time, unknown." *cf.* Cushing, Anonyms, 1889, p. 714.
I. Fields, Annie (Adams) "Mrs. J. T. Fields," 1834– II. Title.
Library of Congress PZ3.L8212W 7—1501

NL 0439510 DLC OClW RPB PHi PPL MH MB

FILM [Lodge, Mrs. James] ed.
4274 A week away from time. Boston, Roberts
PR Brothers, 1887.
v.3 349 p. (Wright American fiction, v.III,
reel 1876-1900, no.3382, Research Publications, Inc.
L24 Microfilm, Reel L-24)

NL 0439511 CU

Lodge, James Arthur.
The old cider mill, by James Arthur Lodge; illustrated by A. H. Reading. Chicago, J. E. Barnes co. [°1906]
[59] p. incl. illus., pl. 23cm.
6-45342

NL 0439512 DLC Wa

Lodge, James Lee. Coffee; history, growth and cultivation, preparation, effect on the system, medical opinions, influence on society. Birmingham, *etc.* [1894.] sm. 8°. pp. 14.

NL 0439513 MH-A

Lodge, James Llewellyn.
"Close communion." A sermon by J. L. Lodge, D. D., at Gay street Baptist church, Washington, D. C., May 11, 1884. Published by request of the church. Washington, R. H. Darby, 1884.
16 p. 23½cm.
1. Lord's supper. I. Washington, D. C. Gay street Baptist church. II. Title.
27-12009
Library of Congress BV820.L6

NL 0439514 DLC

Lodge, James Llewellyn.
Salvation by grace. A sermon ... North New Jersey Baptist association, at Orange, N.J., June 12, 1878. Hackensack, New Jersey Republican printing house, 1878.
16p. 22 cm.

NL 0439515 NRAB

Lodge, John.
Cock, Albert Arthur.
Songs from camp & college, by Albert A. Cock & John Lodge. London, E. Macdonald [1916]

Lodge, John, engraver. No. 20 in *Map 119.3
An accurate map of Rhode Island, part of Connecticut and Massachusetts, showing Admiral Arbuthnot's station in blocking up Admiral Ternay.
= [London. 1780.] Size, 10⅜ × 14½ inches. Scale, none.
Cut from Political Magazine, vol. 1, 1780 [*7299.1.1].
G646—Connecticut. Geog. Maps. — Massachusetts. Geog. Maps.—Rhode Island. Geog. Maps. — United States. Hist. Rev. Maps.

NL 0439517 MB

Lodge, John, engraver.
An accurate map of the island of St. Christophers... London, 1782.

NL 0439518 RPJCB

Lodge, John, engraver. No. 6 in *Map 106.2
The archipelago of the east, being the Sunda, the Molucca, and Philippe. Islands. The chief settlements of the Dutch in India are in the Sunda and Molucca Islands. [Map.]
London. Bew. 1781. Size, 10⅛ × 14¼ inches. Scale (computed), 236.9 miles to 1 inch.
Cut from the Political Magazine, vol. 2, 1781 [*7299.1.2].
All the geographical names are in French.
H4852 — Malay Archipelago. Geog. Maps.

NL 0439519 MB

Lodge, John, engraver. *2323.9.5=**Adams 141.8.5
Benjamin Franklin, LL.D. & F.R.S. [Portrait.] Engraved from an original picture by Jn° Lodge. Printed according to Act of Parliament for J. Almon . . . London, 21st April, 1777.
(In Remembrancer, The; or, inpartial repository of public events, for the year 1777. Frontispiece. London. 1778.)
K7286 — Franklin, Benjamin. Portraits.

NL 0439520 MB

Cm912.01
1781c Lodge, John, engraver.
Cape Fear River, with the counties adjacent, and the towns of Brunswick and Wilmington, against which Lord Cornwallis detached a part of his army, the 17th of January last. London, Publish'd as the Act directs by J. Bew, Mar. 31st, 1781.
24 x 18 cm.
Scale about 6.5 miles to an inch.
"Jno.Lodge sculp."
Extract from The political magazine. March, 1781.

NL 0439521 NcU MB

Lodge, John, engraver. No. 8 in *Map 119.11
Chart and plan of the Harbour of New York & the counʸ. adjacent, from Sandy Hook to Kingsbridge, comprehending the whole of New York and Staten Islands, and part of Long Island & the Jersey shore: and shewing the defences of New York both by land and sea.
London. Bew. 1781. Size, 16½ × 9½ inches. Scale (computed) 2.4 miles to 1 inch.
Cut from the Political Magazine, vol. 2, 1781 [*7299.1.2].
H4388 — New York, City. Descr. Maps. — United States. Hist. Rev. Maps.

NL 0439522 MB

Lodge, John, engraver.
A chart of the Island of Jamaica... London, 1780

NL 0439523 RPJCB

Lodge, John, engraver. No. 26 in *Map 108.2
A correct map of the African islands of Bourbon, and Mauritius or the Isle of France.
London. Bew. 1781. Size, 10¼ × 14¼ inches. Scale (computed), 10.9 geographical miles to 1 inch.
Cut from the Political Magazine, vol. 2 [*7299.1.2]
G8767 — Mascarene Islands.

NL 0439524 MB

Lodge, John, engraver. No. 15 in *Map 85.1
A correct map of the Island of Minorca, with an accurate plan of Fort St. Philip & its environs, and the French approaches and batteries in 1756.
London. Bew. 1781. Size, 10½ × 14⅛ inches. Scale (computed), 2½ miles to 1 inch.
Submap. — [Plan of Fort St. Philip.]
Cut from Political Magazine, vol. 2, 1881 [*7299.1.2].
H5494 — Minorca. Geog. Maps.

NL 0439525 MB

Lodge, John, engraver.
A draught of the harbours of Port Royal and Kingston... London, 1782. 2 copies

NL 0439526 RPJCB

Lodge, John, engraver. No. 51 in *Map 129.1
The Dutch islands of St. Eustatia, Saba and St. Martins; the French island of St. Bartholomew; the English islands of St. Christophers, Nevis, and Anguilla; with the smaller islands and keys surrounding. [Map.]
London. Bew. 1781. Size, 10 × 7⅞ inches. Scale (computed), 2½ miles to 1 inch.
Cut from the Political Magazine, vol. 2, 1781 [*7299.1.2].
G6749 — Caribbee Islands. Geog. Maps

NL 0439527 MB

VOLUME 338

Greenlee
4891   LODGE, JOHN, *engraver*.
L82   The kingdoms of Portugal and Algarve from
1794   Zannoni's map, by J. Ledge, geographer.
London, Laurie & Whittle, 1794.
map.   57x41cm.

Scale: 20 British miles to the inch.
Included as no.22 in T. Kitchin's A new universal atlas.   1798.

NL 0439528   ICN

Lodge, John, engraver.   No. 27 in *Map 108.2
A map and chart of the Cape of Good Hope, with the soundings in
Table Bay, False Bay & Saldanha Bay.
London. Bew. 1781. Size, 14¾ × 10⅜ inches. Scale, Merca-
tor's.
Cut from the Political Magazine, vol. 2 [*7299.1.2].

G8767 — Cape of Good Hope. Geog. Maps.

NL 0439529   MB

Lodge, John, engraver.   No. 7 in *Map 119.11
A map and chart of those parts of the Bay of Chesapeak, York and
James Rivers which are at present the seat of war.
London. Bew. 1781. Size, 9½ × 14 inches. Scale (computed),
4.1 geographical miles to 1 inch.
Cut from the Political Magazine, vol. 2, 1781 [*7299.1.2].
To illustrate the Siege of Yorktown.

H4388 — Yorktown. Virginia. Hist. Siege, 1781. Maps. — Sailing charts.

NL 0439530   MB

Lodge, John, *engraver*.
A map of Mexico...   London, 1782

NL 0439531   RPJCB

Lodge, John, engraver.   No. 10 in *Map 67.7
A map of the Cape de Verd Islands, with the adjacent coast of
Africa, the settlements of Senegal, Gambia and Goree, also a
plan of Port Praya in St. Jago.
London. Bew. 1781. Size, 8⅛ × 16¾ inches. Scale, Merca-
tor's.
Cut from the Political Magazine, vol. 2, 1781 [*7299.1.2].

H2521 — Cape Verde Islands. Geog. Maps.

NL 0439532   MB

Lodge, John, engraver.   No. 10 in *Map 127.1
A map of the Dutch settlements of Surinam, Demerary, Issequibo,
Berbices, and the islands of Curassoa, Aruba, Bonaire, &c., with
the French colony of Cayenne, and the adjacent Spanish coun-
tries ...
London. Bew. 1781. Size, 10⅛ × 14 inches. Scale, none.
Cut from PoliticalMagazine, vol. 2, 1781 [*7299.1.2].

H5340 — Guiana. Geog. Maps. — Venezuela. Geog. Maps.

NL 0439533   MB

Lodge, John, engraver.   No. 29 in *Map 87.1
A map of the English, French, Spanish, Dutch & Danish islands,
in the West Indies, taken from an improved map of the geographer to the king of France; with the tract of the last West India
fleet, through the Windward Passage.
London. Bew. 1781. Size, 10¼ × 13¾ inches. Scale (computed), 77.9 geographical miles to 1 inch.
Cut from the Political Magazine, vol. 2, 1781 [*7299.1.2].

H3062 — West Indies. Geog. Maps.

NL 0439534   MB

Lodge, John, engraver.   No. 28 in *Map 87.1
A map of the islands of St. Lucia and Martinique, with a part of
Dominica and St. Vincents; shewing the two passages between
Martinique and St. Lucia, and Martinique and Dominica, to Fort
Royal Bay and Harbour, the station of the French fleets in the
West Indies; and to illustrate the late engagement between Sir
Saml. Hood and the Count de Grasse.
London. Bew. 1781. Size, 14⅛ × 10⅛ inches. Scale, Merca-
tor's.
Cut from the Political Magazine, vol. 2, 1781 [*7299.1.2].

H3063—Martinique. Geog. Maps.—St. Lucia, Island, West Indies. Geog. Maps.

NL 0439535   MB

Map   Lodge, John, engraver.
G   A map of the Province of Massachusetts
3760   Bay and Colony of Rhode Island, with part of
1782   Connecticut, New Hampshire, and Vermont.
L6   London, J.Bew, 1782.
map 27 x 37 cm.

No scale given.
"Political Mag. April, 1782."

1. Massachusetts—Maps. 2. Rhode
Island—Maps.   3. Connecticut—Maps.

NL 0439536   NIC MiU-C

LODGE, John, engraver.   *7299.1.3
A new and accurate chart of the harbour of Boston, in New England,
in North America. Size, 8 ¹¹/₁₆ × 6 ¹/₂ inches. Scale (computed), 1.8 miles
to 1 inch.
(In the Political magazine. Vol. 3, p. 628. London, 1782.)

NL 0439537   MB

Lodge, John, *engraver*.
A new and exact map of the island of
Antigua...   London, 1782   2 copies

NL 0439538   RPJCB

Lodge, John, engraver.   No. 8 in *Map 67.6
The Roads of Toulon, with the adjacent country. [Map.]
London. Bew. 1781. Size, 7½ × 10¼ inches. Scale (com-
puted), 3000 feet to 1 inch.
Cut from the Political Magazine, vol. 2 [*7299.1.2].

H2499 — Toulon, France. Harbor.

NL 0439539   MB

---

*BC8   Lodge, John, 1757?–1830.
L8215   Introductory sketches, towards a
7931   topographical history, of the county of Hereford.
By the Rev. John Lodge, B.A. ...
Kington: Printed and sold by J.Barrel; sold
also by J.Allen, Hereford; J.Barrow and F.Harris,
Leominster; and J.Robinson, Paternoster-row,
London. M.DCC.XCIII.
8°.   vii,[1],210p.   21.5cm.

NL 0439540   MH NN NjP CtY

Lodge, John, d. 1774.
The Barry family, by Arthur Collins. ⟨Reprinted⟩
Frankford, Penna., Martin and Allardyce, 1911.
cover-title, [1]; p. incl. pl. (coat of arms) 23ᶜᵐ.
Reprinted from his The peerage of Ireland. Dublin, 1789. v. 1, p. 285–
313.
Wrongly attributed by the publisher to Arthur Collins.

1. Barry family.
                                    12-18198

Library of Congress   CS499.B3

NL 0439541   DLC MWA OClWHi NN

Lodge, John, d. 1774, ed.
Desiderata curiosa Hibernica
see under title

Lodge, John, d. 1774.

Vlieger, Abraham de, 1866–1908.
Historical and genealogical record of the Coote family,
by the Rev. A. de Vlieger, M. A. Lausanne, Printed by
G. Bridel & co., 1900.

CS488   Lodge, John, d. 1774.
L6   The peerage of Ireland, or, A genealogical
1754   history of the present nobility of that kingdom.
With their paternal coats of arms, engraven on
copper.   Collected from the publick records;
authentic manuscripts; approved historians; well-
attested pedigrees; and personal information.
By Mr. Lodge ...   London, Printed for William
Johnston, bookseller, in St. Paul's church-yard,
1754.
4 vols.   plates.   21cm.
1. Ireland.—   Peerage. 2. Heraldry.-
Ireland.   I. Title.

NL 0439544   NBuG CU-A MWA TxU MiD-B MH RP CSmH PHi

Lodge, John, d. 1774.
The peerage of Ireland: or, A genealogical
history of the present nobility of that kingdom ...
Collected from publick records ... by John Lodge ...
London, Printed for William Johnston Bookseller in
St. Paul's Church-Yard, 1759.
4 v.   plates (coats of arms)   21 cm.

NL 0439545   IEdS

Lodge, John, d. 1774.
The peerage of Ireland; or, A genealogical history of
the present nobility of that kingdom ... Collected from
public records ... by John Lodge ... Rev., enl., and continued to the present time; by Mervyn Archdall ...
Dublin, J. Moore, 1789.
7 v. plates (coats of arms) 21½ᶜᵐ.

1. Ireland—Peerage. 2. Heraldry—Ireland.   I. Archdall, Mervyn.
1723–1791.

Library of Congress   CS488.L6   9—19121

NL 0439546   DLC NcD DFo IaU KU InU CtY OCl NN

Lodge, John, d. 1774, reporter.
The trial in ejectment between Campbell Craig ...
see under   Craig, Campbell, lessee of
James Annesley, esq., plaintiff.

VOLUME 338

[Lodge, John, d.1774]
*EC75 The usage of holding parliaments and of
L8215 preparing and passing bills of supply, in Ire-
77010 land, stated from record ... Dublin: Printed
by Boulter Grierson, printer to the King's most
Excellent Majesty. M,DCC,LXX. To which is added,
annotations, together with an address to His
Excellency George lord viscount Townshend, lord
lieutenant and general governor of Ire-
land. By C. Lucas ...
Dublin:Re-printed for Thomas Ewing.M,DCC,LXX.
‹Price 1s. 1d.›

8°. 74p. 21.5cm.
A suppressed pamphlet, described in the
advertisement (p.[3]) as "immediately recalled;
upon a sudden order from the castle"; republished, with notes, by Lucas.

NL 0439549   MH

[Lodge, John] d. 1774.
The usage of holding parliaments, and of
passing bills of supply, in Ireland, stated from
record ... Published by authority. Dublin: Printed by B. Grierson.
M,DCC,LXX. To which is added, together with an
address to His Excellency George, lord viscount Townshend,
lord lieutenant general ... of Ireland. By C. Lucas ... Dublin, Printed; London, Reprinted for Robinson and Roberts,
1770.
76 p. 21ᶜᵐ.

1. Ireland. Parliament.   I. Lucas, Charles, 1713–1771, ed.   II. Title.
9–34390 rev.

Library of Congress   JN1467.L6

NL 0439550   DLC CtY MH

Lodge, John, 1801–1873.
see his later name Ellerton, John Lodge, 1801–1873.

Lodge, John Christian, 1862–1950.
I remember Detroit, by John C. Lodge, in collaboration
with M. M. Quaife. Detroit, Wayne University Press, 1949.
208 p. illus., ports. 24 cm.

1. Detroit—Hist.   I. Title.

F574.D4L6   923.273   50–1889

NL 0439552   DLC OClW NcD MiD OkU MiU NN MiD-P

Lodge, John Christian, 1862–1950.
Miscellaneous material.

NL 0439553   MiD-B

Lodge, John Ellerton, 1878–
Agamemnon; the choral odes and lyric scenes
see under   Aeschylus.

Lodge, John Ellerton, 1878–
The Buddha of measureless light and the land
of bronze; a Chinese Buddhist group in bronze.

(In Bulletin of the Museum of fine arts. Vol.
XXIV, no. 141. Boston, Feb., 1926. 27 1/2 cm.
p. 1-10.)

NL 0439555   DSI

Lodge, John Ellerton, 1878 –
Ch'en Jung's picture of nine dragons.

(In Museum of fine arts bulletin. Vol XV,
no. 92. Boston, 1917. 27 1/2 cm. p. [67]-73.)

NL 0439556   DSI

Lodge, John Ellerton, 1878-
Introduction to the collection of Chinese
sculpture.

(In Museum of fine arts bulletin. Vol. XIII,
no. 78. Boston, Aug., 1915. 27 1/2 cm. p.[49]-61.)

NL 0439557   DSI

Lodge, John Ellerton, 1878 –
... Japanese costumes worn in the Nō drama
see under Boston. Museum of fine arts.

Lodge, John Ellerton, 1878 –
... Japanese netsuke
see under   Boston. Museum of fine arts.

[Lodge, John Ellerton], 1878-
Kuan-yin P'u-sa of the twelfth century.

(In Museum of fine arts bulletin. Vol. XVIII
no. 108. Boston, Aug.,1920. 27 1/2 cm. p. 33-37.)

NL 0439560   DSI

Lodge, John Ellerton, 1878-   joint ed.
Stickney, Trumbull, 1874–1904.
The poems of Trumbull Stickney. Boston and New York,
Houghton, Mifflin & co., 1905.

Lodge, John Ian.
The ionization loss of energy of fast
electrons in condensed matter. [n. p.]
1951.
44, [2] l. plate, tables, diagrs. 28cm.
Typewritten.
Thesis—Univ. of Virginia, 1951.
Bibliography: leaf [46]

1. Ionization. 2. Electrons. 3. Quantum
theory. I. Title.

NL 0439562   ViU

Lodge, Joseph Pierce.

Law

Corbin, William Horace, 1851–1912.
Corbin's New Jersey form book. 3d ed. A collection of
forms relating to contracts, conveyancing and extraordinary
proceedings, including notes, explanations, and references to
authorities, by Joseph Pierce Lodge ... New York, N. J.,
Soney & Sage co. [1944]

Lodge, Joseph Pierce.
Evidence in New Jersey practice, text and annotations supplemented by form questions, by Joseph Pierce Lodge ...
Newark, N. J., Soney & Sage co., 1942.
xxiv, 988 p. 23½ᵐ.

1. Evidence (Law)—New Jersey. 2. Witnesses—New Jersey.
3. Cross-examination—New Jersey.
42–8608

NL 0439564   DLC PPT-L

Lodge, Joseph Pierce.

Honeyman, Abraham Van Doren, 1849–1936.
Honeyman's justice; including various matters within the
judicial cognizance of police magistrates, recorders and mayors,
also duties of constables; practice and forms in New Jersey.
8th ed. By A. Van Doren Honeyman ... Newark, N. J., Soney
& Sage co., 1933.

Lodge, Joseph Pierce.

Kocher, Charles Frederick, 1869–
Kocher's decedents' estates in New Jersey. 2d ed. A discussion of the laws pertaining to wills and the administration
of estates in New Jersey; keyed to the revised statutes of New
Jersey of 1937, with forms. By Joseph Pierce Lodge ... Newark, N. J., Soney & Sage co., 1939.

Lodge, Joseph Pierce.
Legal business forms. Newark, N. J., Soney & Sage Co.,
1951.
3 v. forms. 27 cm. (New Jersey practice, v. 14–16)
Kept up to date by pocket parts.

1. Forms (Law)—New Jersey. I. Title.   (Series)
KFN1880.N4 vol. 14–16 1951   67–118513
347.99'749

NL 0439567   DLC NjN NNC NIC

Lodge, Joseph Pierce.
Mechanics' liens in New Jersey; liens on realty, liens on
contract price, municipal liens. A complete set of forms, copious annotations and statutes to date. By Joseph Pierce Lodge
... Newark, N. J., Soney & Sage co., 1940.
xx, 580 p. 23½ᵐ.
"List of cases cited": p. [473]–495.

1. Mechanics' liens—New Jersey. 2. Forms (Law)—New Jersey.
I. New Jersey. Laws, statutes, etc.

Library of Congress   40–32724

NL 0439568   DLC

Lodge, Joseph Pierce.
Public officers in New Jersey; counties and cities of all
classes, towns, townships, boroughs, villages and other mu-
nicipalities; with annotations and essential forms, by Joseph
Pierce Lodge ... Newark, N. J., Soney & Sage co., 1937.
xxv, 741 p. 23½ᵐ.
"List of cases cited": p. 605–636.

1. Local government—New Jersey. 2. Forms (Law)—New Jersey.
I. Title.   37–1001

Library of Congress   JS451.N73L6
——— Copy 2.
Copyright A 101702   [3]   352.0749

NL 0439569   DLC

VOLUME 338

Lodge, Joseph Pierce.
Realty mortgages in New Jersey, with forms and annotations keyed to the revision of New Jersey statutes of 1937, by Joseph Pierce Lodge ... Newark, N. J., Soney & Sage co., 1939.
xxviii, 1104 p. 23½ᶜᵐ.
"List of cases cited": p. ₍915₎–991.

1. Mortgages—New Jersey. 2. Real property—New Jersey. 3. Forms (Law)—New Jersey. I. Title.
39–21273

NL 0439570   DLC PPT-L

Lodge, Lee Davis, 1865–1923, tr.
Undset, Ingwald Martin, 1853–1893.
Scandinavian archæology. By M. Ingwald Unset ... Translated by Prof. L. D. Lodge.
(*In* Smithsonian institution. Annual report. 1889. Washington, 1890. 23½ᶜᵐ. p. 571–589)

Lodge, Lee Davis, 1865– 1923.
A study in Corneille. By Lee Davis Lodge ... Baltimore, J. Murphy & co., 1891.
313 p. front. (port.) 18½ᶜᵐ.

1. Corneille, Pierre, 1606–1684.
11–19918

Library of Congress   PQ1772.L6

NL 0439572   DLC WU TU ICU PPCH OC1JC OOxM MB PU PPD

Lodge, Lee Davis, 1865–1923.
Winnie Davis school of history; address [delivered at the reunion of the United Confederate Veterans of South Carolina in Chester, S. C.] 33 p. 8°.

NL 0439573   ScU

Lodge, Lois.
Love like a shadow, by Lois Lodge. New York, Phoenix press ₍1935₎.
249 p. 19½ᶜᵐ.

I. Title.
Library of Congress   PZ3.L8215Lo   35–3363

NL 0439574   DLC

Lodge, Louise Finley, 1902–
Angelica in El Bernardo and Las lágrimas de Angélica, by Louise Finley Lodge ... Urbana, Ill., 1937.
1 p. l., 5, ₍1₎ p. 23ᶜᵐ.
Abstract of thesis (PH. D.)—University of Illinois, 1937.
Vita.

1. Valbuena, Bernardo de, 1568–1627. El Bernardo. 2. Barahona de Soto, Luis, 1548?–1595. Las lágrimas de Angélica. I. Title.
Library of Congress   PQ6437.V2Z7 1937   37–29697
Univ. of Illinois Libr.
——— Copy 2.   ₍2₎   861.39

NL 0439575   IU DLC OO

Lodge, Louise Finley, 1902– joint ed.
Lamb, Ruth (Stanton) *ed.*
Una moneda de oro, y otros cuentos mexicanos modernos, edited by Ruth Stanton ... ₍and₎ Louise Lodge ... illustrated by Charles W. Stanton. New York, London, Harper & brothers ₍1946₎.

PQ7276
.L3

Lodge, Margaret Beatrice.
A fairy to stay, by Margaret Beatrice Lodge, illustrated by A. H. Watson. New York, Oxford university press ₍1929₎
150 p. col. front., plates. 21½ᶜᵐ.
"Reprinted 1929 in Great Britain."

I. Title.
Library of Congress   PZ8.L82Fa   30–9228

NL 0439577   DLC PP

Lodge, Margaret Beatrice.
Seven plays of fairy days; illustrated by Millicent Sowerby and Grace Lodge. London: Humphrey Milford ₍1924₎. 255 p. illus., col'd pl. 12°.
Snowdrop and the dwarfs. The frog prince. The sleeping beauty. Beauty and the beast. Mother Holle. Prince Hyacinth and the dear little princess. The yellow dwarf.

1. (J.) Dialogues and plays. 2. (A.)   Dramatization. 3. Title.
N. Y. P. L.   June 5, 1925

NL 0439578   NN

Lodge, Margaret Beatrice.   Z.40d135.1
Seven plays of fairy days. Illustrated by Millicent Sowerby and Grace Lodge.
— London. Oxford University Press. [1924.] 255 pp. Plates, one colored. 18½ cm., in 8s.
Contents. — Snowdrop and the dwarfs. — The frog prince. — The sleeping beauty. — Beauty and the beast. — Mother Holle. — Prince Hyacinth and the dear little princess. — The yellow dwarf.

N2810 — T.r. — Fairy tale plays. — ...erby, Millicent, illus. — Lodge, Grace, illus.

NL 0439579   MB

Lodge, Margaret Beatrice.
Sir Richard Lodge; a biography. Edinburgh, W. Blackwood, 1946.
xvi, 264 p. ports. 22 cm.
"List of the principal writings of Sir Richard Lodge": p. ₍255₎–260.

1. Lodge, Sir Richard, 1855–1936.
A 48–5322*
Harvard Univ. Library
for Library of Congress   ₍2₎

NL 0439580   MH ICU ICN

Lodge, Mrs. Mary Greenwood

See

Lodge, Mrs. James.

Lodge, N   Louise, 1864–
The tribe of Jacob (Piatt) by N. Louise Lodge ... 3d ed. ₍Springfield, Mo., Young-Stone printing co., ᶜ1934₎
2 p. l., 170 p., 2 l. 26ᶜᵐ.

1. Piatt family (Jacob Piatt, 1747–1834)
41–38338
Library of Congress   CS71.P577 1934

NL 0439582   DLC PHi

Lodge, Nevile.
Lodge looks at Wellington. Wellington, A. H. & A. W. Reed ₍1952₎
unpaged. illus. 19 x 26 cm.
Cartoons.

1. New Zealand wit and humor, Pictorial. I. Title.
NC1760.L6A48   741.5   53–40138 ‡

NL 0439583   DLC

Lodge, Nucia (Perlmutter) joint author.
Counts, George Sylvester, 1889–
The country of the blind; the Soviet system of mind control, by George S. Counts and Nucia Lodge. Boston, Houghton Mifflin Co., 1949.

DK32
.7
.C6

Lodge, Nucia (Perlmutter) tr.
₍Marshak, Il′ía fʌkovlevich₎ 1895–1953.
Moscow has a plan; a soviet primer, translated from the Russian of M. Ilin ₍pseud.₎ by G. S. Counts & N. P. Lodge, with illustrations drawn by William Kermode. London, J. Cape ₍1931₎

HC335
.M35
1931b

Lodge, Mrs. Nucia (Perlmutter) tr.
Pinkevich, Al′bert Petrovich, 1884–
The new education in the Soviet republic, by Albert P. Pinkevitch ... translated under the auspices of the International institute, Teachers college, Columbia university, by Nucia Perlmutter ... edited by George S. Counts ... New York, The John Day company ₍ᶜ1929₎

Lodge, Mrs. Nucia (Perlmutter) joint tr.
₍Marshak, Íl′ía fʌkovlevich₎ 1895–
New Russia's primer; the story of the five-year plan, by M. Ilin ₍pseud.₎ translated from the Russian by George S. Counts ... and Nucia P. Lodge ... Boston and New York, Houghton Mifflin company, 1931.

Lodge, Olive.
Peasant life in Jugoslavia, by Olive Lodge ... With 61 illustrations & a map. London, Seeley, Service & co. ltd. ₍1942₎
6 p. l., 25–332 p. front., illus, plates. 22ᶜᵐ.
Maps and genealogical table on lining-papers.
"Published with the aid of grants from: The Jugoslav publication fund administered by the University of London School of Slavonic and east European studies and the Eleanor Lodge historical fund of Lady Margaret hall, Oxford."—3d prelim. leaf.

1. Peasantry—Yugoslavia. 2. Yugoslavia—Soc. life & cust. I. Title.
A 42–4129
Harvard univ. Library
for Library of Congress   DR312 L6
₍3,†   944.97

NRU DLC CtY FU IU WaU MH NBB WaU
NL 0439588   MH CaBVaU CLSU WU ViU OC1 OCU OU MoU

VOLUME 338

Q311
.L65
v.18,
no.23

Lodge, Sir Oliver Joseph, 1851-1940.
    Aberration problems. A discussion concerning
the motion of the ether near the earth, and concerning the connexion between ether and gross
matter; with some new experiments. By Oliver J.
Lodge.
    (In Royal Society of London. Philosophical transac-
tions. London, 1893. Vol. 184, A. (1893) 33cm.
p. 727-804, plates.)
    Cover title.
    Original paper wrappers.
    Inscribed by the author.

    1. Optics, Physical.   I. Title.

NL 0439589   ViU

Lodge, *Sir* Oliver Joseph, 1851-1940.
    ... Address, by Sir Oliver J. Lodge ... Continuity.
[London, Printed by Spottiswoode and co., ltd., 1913]
    40 p. 21¼cm.
    Caption title.
    At head of title: British association for the advancement of science.
Birmingham, 1913.

    1. Science—Addresses, essays, lectures. 2. Continuity.
                                                    14-571
    Library of Congress   Q171.L83

NL 0439590   DLC

Lodge, *Sir* Oliver Joseph, 1851-1940.
    Advancing science; being personal reminiscences of the Brit-
ish association in the nineteenth century by Sir Oliver Lodge.
London, E. Benn limited [1931]
    190, [1] p. illus. 19cm.

    1. British association for the advancement of science. 2. Science—
Hist.   I. Title.
                                                    32-652
    Library of Congress   Q41.B85L6

    OkU
NL 0439591   DLC CU DNLM InU TxU NN MB NIC PPD PU

Lodge, *Sir* Oliver Joseph, 1851-1940.
    Advancing science, by Sir Oliver Lodge. New York, Har-
court, Brace & company, 1932.
    190, [1] p. illus. 19cm.
    Printed in Great Britain.
    "Personal reminiscences of the British association for the advance-
ment of science."—Pref.

    1. British association for the advancement of science. 2. Science—
Hist.   I. Title.
                                                    32-26298
    Library of Congress   Q41.B85L6 1932
                                                    506

NL 0439592   DLC NN OrP MB OLak

Lodge, *Sir* Oliver Joseph, 1851-1940.
    Der äther und die wirklichkeit; eine reihe von vorträgen
über die zahlreichen aufgaben, die der raumäther zu erfüllen
hat, von Sir Oliver Lodge. Aus dem englischen übersetzt von
dr. Walther Rump ... Braunschweig, F. Vieweg & sohn
akt.-ges., 1928.
    vi, [2], 89 p. 22cm. (*Added t.-p.*: Die wissenschaft ... bd. 79)

    1. Ether (of space) 2. Relativity (Physics)   I. Rump, Walther,
1878-   tr.
                                                    28-30502
    Library of Congress   QC177.L64

NL 0439593   DLC ICJ PU

Lodge, *Sir* Oliver Joseph, 1851-1940.
    Atoms and rays; an introduction to modern views on atomic
structure & radiation, by Sir Oliver Lodge, F. R. S. London,
E. Benn limited, 1924.
    ix, 11-208 p. pl. diagrs. 24cm.

    1. Atoms. 2. Radiation.
                                                    24-24939
    Library of Congress   QC171.L8

    OCl OClW PPFr PU
NL 0439594   DLC CaBViP MdBJ MH-PR CU CtY NN MB ICJ

Lodge, *Sir* Oliver Joseph, 1851-1940.
    Atoms and rays; an introduction to modern views on atomic
structure & radiation, by Sir Oliver Lodge, F. R. S. New York,
George H. Doran company [1924]
    ix, 11-208 p. pl. diagrs. 22½cm.

    1. Atoms. 2. Radiation.
                                                    25-2695
    Library of Congress   QC171.L8 1924a

    TU MsSM FTaSU Wa WaTC Or²R
    OOxM OO IdU-SB PPAmP PPT CaBVaU PHC PU PBm OrStbM
NL 0439595   DLC NcRS NcD CtY OU ODW OCU ICU ViU

Lodge, *Sir* Oliver Joseph, 1851-1940.
    ... Atoms and rays: an introduction to modern views on
atomic structure and radiation. London. E. Benn ltd. [1931]
    xiv, 15-222 p. diagrs. 17cm. (Benn's Essex library)
    At head of title: ... Sir Oliver Lodge. F. R. S.
    "First edition 1924 ... Fourth edition (Essex library) 1931."

    1. Atoms. 2. Radiation.
                                                    33-11450
    Library of Congress   QC171.L8 1931
                                    [3]   541.2

    CaBVaU
NL 0439596   DLC KU OU OCU PPF ICU O OU IaAS NBuC

Lodge, Sir Oliver Joseph, 1851-1940
    Attitude of scientific men to phychical
investigation in general & to the spirit-
ualistic hypothesis in particular. An
address—at a Conversation, of the London
Spiritualist Alliance, hel in St. James
Hall on March 29,1897.

NL 0439597   OO

Lodge, Sir Oliver Joseph, 1851-1940.
    Beyond physics; or, The idealisation of mechanism, by Sir
Oliver Lodge... Being a survey and attempted extension of
modern physics in a philosophical and psychical direction. London: G. Allen & Unwin, Ltd.[, 1930.] 172 p. 12°.

    496286A. 1. Science—Philosophy.   2. Physics, Theoretical. 3. Mind
and matter. I. Title.
    N. Y. P. L.   November 3, 1930

NL 0439598   NN MH-AH

Lodge, *Sir* Oliver Joseph, 1851-1940.
    Beyond physics; or, The idealisation of mechanism, by Sir
Oliver Lodge ... being a survey and attempted extension of
modern physics in a philosophical and psychical direction.
London, G. Allen & Unwin ltd. [1930]
    2 p. l., [7]-184 p., 1 l. diagr. 20cm.
    "First published in May 1930. Second edition August 1930."

    1. Physics—Philosophy. 2. Science—Philosophy.   I. Title.
                                                    30-31683
    Library of Congress   QC6.L43 1930 a
                                                    530.1

    OO OCl
NL 0439599   DLC OrP TxU ICJ NcD PPLT PSC NcU OClW

Lodge, Sir Oliver Joseph, 1851-1940.
    Beyond physics; or, the idealisation of
mechanism. by ... being a survey and
attempted extension of modern physics in
a philosophical and psychical direction.
New York, Greenberg [1931].
    [7]-184 p.
    Printed in Great Britain.
    "First published in the U.S.A. 1931."

NL 0439600   MiU NN PU MB MH CU WaS

Lodge, *Sir* Oliver Joseph, 1851-1940.
    ...Cantor lectures on secondary batteries &
the electrical storage of energy; delivered
before the Society of arts, May 21st, and 28th,
1883. Lond., William Trounce, 1883.
    13 p.
    Bound with this: Cantor lectures on
distribution of electricity, by George Forbes.
    At head of title: Society for the encourage-
ment of arts, manufactures and commerce.

NL 0439601   MiD MB

Lodge, *Sir* Oliver Joseph, 1851-1940.
    ... A century's progress in physics, by Sir Oliver Lodge,
F. R. S. Being the second of a series of centenary addresses ...
Delivered on Monday, March 14, 1927. London, University of
London press, ltd., 1927.
    36 p. 22cm. [University college centenary celebrations. 2]
    At head of title: University of London, University college.

    1. Physics—Hist.   I. Title.
                                                    28-14933
    Library of Congress   QC7.L6

NL 0439602   DLC OrU MiU CU NN MB

Lodge, Sir Oliver Joseph, 1851-1940.
    ...Changes in the scientific outlook; the oration delivered by
Sir Oliver Lodge, during the thirty-sixth foundation week on
Thursday, March 17, 1932. London: Univ. of London Press,
Ltd.[, 1932.] 31 p. 21½cm.
    At head of title: University of London. University College. Union Society.

    724941A. 1. Science—Philosophy.   I. London University. Univer-
sity College. Union Society.
    N. Y. P. L.   September 21, 1934

NL 0439603   NN

Lodge, Sir Oliver Joseph, 1851-1940.
    Christopher; a study in human personality, by Sir Oliver
Lodge... London: Cassell and Co., Ltd. [1918] vi, 293(1) p.
front. (port.), pl. 12°.
    A biography of Christopher Tennant of the Welsh guards.

    1. Tennant, Christopher, 1897-1917.   2. European war, 1914- —
Personal narratives (Welsh).   3. Title.
    N. Y. P. L.   June 13, 1919

NL 0439604   NN PU

DA
69.3
.T4
L8

Lodge, Sir Oliver Joseph, 1851-1940.
    Christopher; a study in human personality,
by Sir Oliver Lodge ... London, New York
[etc.] Cassell and company, ltd. [1918]
    vi p.,295,[1] p. front.(port.) pl. 20cm.
    "First published 1918."
    Part II (p.75-289): Memoir [by Tennant's mother]
autobiographical fragment, and representative letters.

    1. Tennant, Christopher, 1897-1917. I. Title.

NL 0439605   MiU CaBVaU

VOLUME 338

Lodge, *Sir* Oliver Joseph, 1851–1940.
   Christopher; a study in human personality, by Sir Oliver
J. Lodge ... New York, George H. Doran company ₍1919₎
   ix p., 1 l., 11–299 p. incl. front. (port.) plates, ports. 21½ cm.
   A biography of Christopher Tennant of the Welsh guards.

   1. Tennant, Christopher, 1897–1917.   I. Title.

DA69.3.T4L6   19—4268

       ViU MoU LU
       PPL PP WaE PU OClW OEac DAU NN ICJ MB OCl PPA PHC
NL   0439606   DLC NIC OKentU CaBVa WaS Or Wa WaT OrP

338.0185
L822c   Lodge, Sir Oliver Joseph, 1851–1940.
       Competition v. [i. e. versus] co-operation.
       Liverpool, Liverpool Fabian Society, 1907.
       17p.   17cm.

       1. Competition.   2. Cooperation.   I. Title.

NL   0439607   IEN

Lodge, Sir Oliver Joseph, 1851–1940.
   Competition v. co-operation, by Sir Oliver Lodge... Liverpool: Liverpool Fabian Soc., 1909.   17 p.   16°.

   1. Competition.   2. Cooperation.
N. Y. P. L.   October 25, 1921.

NL   0439608   NN

Lodge, *Sir* Oliver Joseph, 1851–1940.
   Continuity; the presidential address to the British association for 1913, by Sir Oliver Lodge ... supplemented by explanatory notes.   London,
               Dent, 1913.
   iv p., 1 l., 131 p. 19½ᵐ. $1.00

NL   0439609   KEmT

Lodge, *Sir* Oliver Joseph, 1851–1940.
   Continuity; the presidential address to the British association, Birmingham MCMXIII, by Sir Oliver Lodge. Printed in full and supplemented by explanatory notes. London & Toronto, J. M. Dent & sons, ltd., 1913.
   118 p. 19ᵐ.

   1. Science—Addresses, essays, lectures.   2. Continuity.

   Library of Congress   Q171.L84   14–1474

NL   0439610   DLC PU NjP CaBVaU FMU OCl

Lodge, *Sir* Oliver Joseph, 1851–1940.
   Continuity; the presidential address to the British association for 1913, by Sir Oliver Lodge ... supplemented by explanatory notes. New York and London, G. P. Putnam's sons, 1914.
   iv p., 1 l., 131 p. 19½ᵐ. $1.00

   1. Science—Addresses, essays, lectures.   2. Continuity.
   Library of Congress   Q171.L84 1914   14–2430

       MiU MB NN
NL   0439611   DLC OrP WaS OCU PBm PWcS PHC PP CU DNLM

Lodge, Sir Oliver, 1851–1940.
   Conviction of survival; two discourses in memory of F. W. H. Myers.   London, Methuen & Co. ₍1930₎
   69 p.   19 cm.

   "The Frederick W. H. Myers lecture, 1929."
   "List of F. W. H. Myers's signed contributions to the Proceedings and Journal of the Society for Psychical Research": p. 62–₍70₎

   1. Psychical   research.

NL   0439612   TU MH CaBVaU

156.4
F8725
no.1   Lodge, Sir Oliver Joseph, 1851–1940.
       Conviction of survival; two discourses in memory of F. W. H. Myers, by Sir Oliver Lodge. 2d ed. London, Methuen & Co. ₍1930₎
       69, ₍1₎ p. 19cm. (The Frederic W. H. Myers lecture, 1929 ₍no. 1₎)

       Contents.--Conviction of survival.--In memory of F. W. H. Myers.--List of F. W. H. Myers's signed contributions to the Proceedings and Journal of the Society for Psychical Research.

NL   0439613   NNC C NN OCl

Lodge, Sir Oliver Joseph, 1851–1940
   Demonstrated survival: its influence on science, philosophy and religion, by Sir Oliver Lodge...   London: L. S. A. Publ., Ltd., 1930.   37 p.   12°.

535804A.   1. Spiritism.   I. Title.
N. Y. P. L.   June 29, 1931

NL   0439614   NN MH

Lodge, Sir Oliver Joseph, 1851–1940.
   The discharge of a Leyden jar.
   London, Clowes, 1889.
   12 p.

NL   0439615   PPAmP

Lodge, *Sir* Oliver Joseph, 1851–1940.
   Easy mathematics chiefly arithmetic, being a collection of hints to teachers, parents, self-taught students and adults, and containing a summary or indication of most things in elementary mathematics useful to be known; by Sir Oliver Lodge ... London, Macmillan & co., limited; New York, The Macmillan company, 1905.
   xv p., 1 l. 436 p. tab. 19ᵐ.

   1. Mathematics.

   Washington, D. C.   Public Library   W 6–80* Cancel

NL   0439616   DWP MB OCl MiU OClW OOxM ICJ MB PBm

QA37
L56   Lodge, Sir Oliver Joseph, 1851–1940.
       Easy mathematics, chiefly arithmetic. Being a collection of hints to teachers, parents, self-taught students, and adults, and containing a summary or indication of most things in elementary mathematics useful to be known. London, New York, Macmillan, 1906.
       xv, 436 p.   illus.

       1. Mathematics - 1901-

NL   0439617   CU

AC–S
QA39
.L822e   Lodge, Sir Oliver Joseph, 1851–1940.
1910   Easy mathematics; or, Arithmetic and algebra for general readers, being an elementary treatise addressed to teachers, parents, self-taught students, and adults, by Sir Oliver Lodge ... London, Macmillan and co., ltd., 1910.
       xv, 436p., 1 l. diagrs. 19cm.

       "First edition, 1905. Reprinted ... 1910."
       Sir Owen Richardson Collection on the Atom.

NL   0439618   TxU ICU MH OClU

Lodge, Sir Oliver Joseph, 1851–1940.
   Easy mathematics; or, Arithmetic and algebra for general readers, being an elementary treatise addressed to teachers, parents, self-taught students, and adults. Macmillan, 1917.
   436 p. plate, diagrs., table.

NL   0439619   MiD MdBP

Lodge, Sir Oliver Joseph, 1851–1940.
   Electrical precipitation; a lecture delivered before the Institute of Physics, by Sir Oliver Lodge... London: Oxford Univ. Press, 1925.   40 p. incl. table. plates. 8°. (Institute of Physics, London. Physics in industry. v. 3.)
   Bibliography, p. ₍22₎

   1. Electric precipitation.   2. Ser.
N. Y. P. L.   January 25, 1926

NL   0439620   NN OrCS OrP ICJ DAU MB RPB PPF MH CU

Lodge, Oliver Joseph, 1851–1940
   The electrification of the atmosphere, natural and artificial. 1914.

NL   0439621   DAS

Lodge, *Sir* Oliver Joseph, 1851–1940.
   Electrons; or, The nature and properties of negative electricity, by Sir Oliver Lodge ... London, G. Bell and sons, 1906.
   xv p., 1 l., 230 p. 22ᵐ.

   1. Electrons.   2. Matter—Constitution.

   Washington, D. C. Public   library   W 7–78
   for Library of Congress   ₍QC721.L   ₎

       DSI
NL   0439622   DWP FTaSU CU NcRS OCU MB PU PSC PPD NIC

Lodge, *Sir* Oliver Joseph, 1851–1940.
   Electrons, or, The nature and properties of negative electricity, by Sir Oliver Lodge ... London, G. Bell and sons; New York, The Macmillan co., 1907.
   xv, ₍1₎, 230 p. illus., diagrs. 22ᵐ.
   First published January, 1907; 2d edition, revised, March, 1907.

   1. Electrons.   2. Matter—Constitution.   8–26869

   Library of Congress   QC721.L78

       ODW OClW ICJ PBa PWcS
NL   0439623   DLC DSI CaBVaU WaS IdU CU NN CtY OCl OU

Lodge, Sir Oliver Joseph, 1851–1940.
   Electrons or the nature and Properties of negative electricity.
   London, Bell & Sons, 1910.
   230 p.

NL   0439624   PPF PHC OrPR NBuC

VOLUME 338

Lodge, Sir Oliver Joseph, 1851–1940.
 Electrons; or, The nature ... of negative
electricity. [4. ed.] London, 1913.

NL 0439625   NjP CU MiU OClW

Lodge, Sir Oliver Joseph, 1851–1940.
 Electrons, or, The nature and properties of
negative electricity, by Sir Oliver Lodge...
5th ed. London, G. Bell and sons; New York,
The Macmillan co., 1919.
  xvi, [1] 230 p. illus., diagrs.

NL 0439626   MiD MH PSC DN OClh

Lodge, Sir Oliver Joseph, 1851–1940.
 Electrons; or, The nature and properties of
negative electricity; by Sir Oliver Lodge ...
London, G. Bell and sons, 1923.
 xv,[1], 230 p.   22 cm.
 "Third edition, revised, December 1909. Reprinted 1913, 1919, 1923.
 1923: 6th ed. ?
 1. Electrons. 2. Matter-Constitution.

NL 0439627   CU

Lodge, Sir Oliver Joseph, 1851–1940.
 Elektronen; oder, Die Natur und die Eigenschaften der nega-
tiven Elektrizität. Von Sir Oliver Lodge   Aus dem Englischen
übersetzt von Prof. G. Siebert ...   Leipzig: Quandt & Händel,
1907. x, 203 p. incl. diagrs.   22cm.
  Bibliography, p. [ii]; bibliographical footnotes.

5218B. 1. Electrons. 2. Matter.   I. Siebert, G., tr.   January 23, 1940
N.Y.P.L.

NL 0439628   NN OkU

Lodge, Sir Oliver Joseph, 1851–1940.
 Elementary mechanics; including hydrostatics
and pneumatics. New ed. rev. by Alfred Lodge.
N.Y., Van Nostrand, n.d.
 308 p.

NL 0439629   PPSteph

Lodge, Sir Oliver Joseph, 1851–1940.
 ... Elementary mechanics, including hydrostatics
and pneumatics ...   London and Edinburgh, 1879.
 17.5 cm. (Chambers's elementary science
manuals)

NL 0439630   CtY

Lodge, Oliver J[oseph], 1851–1940.
 Elementary mechanics, including hydrostatics
and pneumatics.   London, W. & R. Chambers, 1881.
 204 p.   16°. (Chambers's elementary science
manuals)

NL 0439631   NN

Lodge, Sir Oliver J[oseph], 1851–1940.
 Elementary mechanics including hydrostatics and pneumatics.
Revised ed. London, etc., W. & R. Chambers, 1885.
 pp. 208. Illus. (Chambers's elementary science manuals.)

NL 0439632   MH OClW

LODGE, Sir Oliver Joseph, 1851–1940.
 Elementary mechanics, including hydrostatics
and pneumatics. Revised ed. London and Edinburgh, W. & R. Chambers, 1886.

 17 cm.
 "Chamber's elementary science manuals."

NL 0439633   MH NjR DBS

Lodge, Sir Oliver Joseph, 1851–1940.
 Elementary mechanics including hydrostatics
and pneumatics. Revised edition.
London, Chambers, 1887.
 208 p.

NL 0439634   PPF

Lodge, Oliver Joseph, 1851–1940.
 ...Elementary mechanics...rev. ed. London and
Edinburgh, 1888.

NL 0439635   DSI PU

Lodge, Sir Oliver Joseph, 1851–1940.
 ...Elementary mechanics, including hy-
drostatics and pneumatics; by Oliver J.
Lodge... Rev. ed. London and Edinburgh,
Chambers, 1889.
 208p. diagrs. (Chambers's elementary
science manuals)
 "Miscellaneous exercises":p. 198-208.

NL 0439636   MiHM

LODGE, Sir Oliver Joseph, 1851–1940.
 Elementary mechanics including hydrostatics
and pneumatics. Revised ed. London, etc.,
1890.

 16°.

NL 0439637   MH MiU

Lodge, Sir Oliver Joseph, 1851–1940.
 ... Elementary mechanics, including hydrostatics and
pneumatics; by Oliver J. Lodge ... Rev. ed. New York,
D. Van Nostrand co., 1891.
 208 p. diagr. 17½ᵐ. (Chambers's elementary science manuals)
 "Miscellaneous exercises": p. [198]-208.

 1. Mechanics.

 Library of Congress   QC127.L82   3—5188

NL 0439638   DLC CU NcD

Lodge, Sir Oliver Joseph, 1851–1940.
 Elementary mechanics including hydrostatics
and pneumatics, by Oliver J. Lodge ... rev. ed.
London and Edinburgh, W. & R. Chambers, 1892.
 4-208 p.   diagrs. 17 cm. (Chambers's
elementary science manuals)

NL 0439639   ViLxW IdU

Lodge, Sir Oliver Joseph, 1851–1940.
 ...Elementary mechanics, including
hydrostatics and pneumatics; by ... rev.
ed. New York, D. Van Nostrand co., (1896?)
 612 p.

NL 0439640   OClW OCl

Lodge, Sir Oliver Joseph, 1851–1940.
 Elementary mechanics including hydrostatics and pneumatics, by Oliver J. Lodge ... New ed. Completely rev. by
the author and by Alfred Lodge ... answers rev. by Charles S.
Lodge, B. A. New York, D. Van Nostrand company [1896]
 xvi, 308 p. diagrs. 18ᵐ.

 1. Mechanics.   I. Lodge, Alfred, 1855?–   ed. II. Lodge, Charles S.
                                                   4—14173
 Library of Congress   QC127.L83
                              [a42m1]   -531

NL 0439641   DLC Or CaBVaU OrP CU OU IU

Lodge, Oliver Joseph, 1851–1940.   531 P605
 Elementary mechanics, including hydrostatics and pneumatics.
New edition, completely revised by the author and by Alfred
Lodge. xvi, 308 p. il. D.   London: W. & R. Chambers, 1897.

NL 0439642   ICJ

ar V Lodge, Sir Oliver Joseph, 1851–1940.
 22309 ... Elementary mechanics, including hydrostatics and pneumatics; by Oliver J. Lodge ... Rev. ed. New York, D. Van
Nostrand co., 1897.
 307 p. diagr. 17½ᵐ. (Chambers's elementary science manuals)
 "Miscellaneous exercises": p. [198]-208.

NL 0439643   NIC

Lodge, Sir Oliver Joseph, 1851–1940.
 Elementary mechanics, including hydrostatics &
pneumatics. New ed. rev. by author & by Alfred
Lodge.
N.Y., Van Nostrand, 1898.
 308 p.

NL 0439644   PPD

Lodge, Sir Oliver Joseph, 1851–1940.
 Elementary mechanics ... new ed ... rev ... by
A. Lodge ... C. S. Lodge. Lond. [19–?]

NL 0439645   NjP

QC
127   Lodge, Sir Oliver Joseph, 1851–1940.
L82e   Elementary mechanics including hydrostat-
1900   ics and pneumatics. New ed. Completely rev.
         by the author and by Alfred Lodge, with
         numerous examples. London, W.&R.Chambers,
         1900.
          xvi,308p. illus. 18cm.

          1. Mechanics.   I. Lodge, Alfred, 1855?–

NL 0439646   NRU ViU PHC

Lodge, Sir Oliver Joseph, 1851–1940
 Elementary mechanics including hydrostatics
and pneumatics, by Oliver J. Lodge ...
New ed. Completely rev. by the author and by
Alfred Lodge ... answers rev. by Charles S.
Lodge.   New York, D. Van Nostrand, 1900.
 308p. diagrs.

NL 0439647   OClJC

VOLUME 338

LODGE, Sir Oliver J[oseph], 1851-1940.
Elementary mechanics including hydrostatics and pneumatics. New ed., completely revised by the author and by Alfred Lodge. Answers revised by Charles S. Lodge. London, etc., .& R. Chambers, Ltd., [1919].

NL 0439648   MH

Lodge, Sir Oliver Joseph, 1851-1940.
Elementary treatise on mechanics, including hydrostatics and pneumatics. Rev. edition. N.Y., Van Nostrand, 1895.
208 p.

NL 0439649   PPF PBa

531.6
L822
Lodge, Sir Oliver Joseph, 1851-1940.
Energy. New York, R. McBride [1927]
124p. 18cm.

Bibliography: p. 123-124.

1. Force and energy.

NL 0439650   IEN

Lodge, Sir Oliver Joseph, 1851-1940.
... Energy, by Sir Oliver Lodge, f. r. s. London, E. Benn limited [1929]
79 p. 16¼ᵐᵒ. (Benn's sixpenny library. [no. 65])
Bibliography: p. 78-79.

1. Force and energy.

Library of Congress   QC73 L6   30-22381
       [3]   531.6

NL 0439651   DLC PPF CaBVaU ICJ NcU OC1 NN MH

Lodge, Sir Oliver Joseph, 1851-1940.
... Energy, by Sir Oliver Lodge, f. r. s. New York, J. Cape & H. Smith [1929]
vi p., 2 l., 7-124 p. 18ᶜᵐ. (The new library)
Bibliography: p. 123-124.

1. Force and energy.

Library of Congress   QC73.L6 1929 a   30-26634
       [3]   531.6

NL 0439652   DLC CU OC1 NN ICJ

Lodge, Sir Oliver Joseph, 1851-1940.
... Energy, by Sir Oliver Lodge, f. r. s. New York, [1929] Robert M. McBride
vi p., 2 l., 7-124 p. 18ᶜᵐ. (The new library)
Bibliography: p. 123-124.

NL 0439653   KEmT OU

Lodge, Sir Oliver Joseph, 1851-1940.
Perojo, José del.
Ensayos sobre educación, por J. del Perojo ... Madrid, Impr. de "Nuevo mundo" [pref. 1907]

Lodge, Sir Oliver Joseph, 1851-1940.
Ether & reality: a series of discourses on the many functions of the ether of space, by Sir Oliver Lodge ... London. Hodder and Stoughton limited [1925]
ix, [1] p., 1 l., 13-179 p. 19ᶜᵐ.
"First published May 1925. Reprinted May 1925."

1. Ether (of space) 2. Relativity (Physics)

Library of Congress   25—11308

Library of Congress   QC177.L6

     CtY OU OC1 MiU OO MB NN NcRS
NL 0439655   DLC MtU CaBViP OrP MdBP TU TNJ LU CU

Lodge, Sir Oliver Joseph, 1851-1940.
Ether & reality; a series of discourses on the many functions of the ether of space, by Sir Oliver Lodge ... New York, George H. Doran company [1925]
ix, [1] p., 1 l., 13-179 p. 19½ᶜᵐ.
Printed in Great Britain.

1. Ether (of space) 2. Relativity (Physics)
          25—25754

Library of Congress   QC177.L6 1925 a

     OC1W ViU ICJ PPFr PPLT PHC PP PPT
NL 0439656   DLC OOxM OCU NIC WaTC IdB Or WaE PBL

Sci
QC
177
Z6
1969
Lodge, Sir Oliver Joseph, 1851-1940.
Ether & reality; a series of discourses on the many functions of the ether of space, by Sir Oliver Lodge. New York, George H. Doran Company [1925]; Ann Arbor, Mich., University Microfilms, 1969]
179p.

NL 0439657   FTaSU

Lodge, Sir Oliver Joseph, 1851-1940.
Ether & reality; a series of discourses on the many functions of the ether of space, by Sir Oliver Lodge ... New York, George H. Doran company [1925]
ix, [1] p., 1 l., 13-179 p. 19½ cm.
Printed in Great Britain.

Photocopy. Ann Arbor, Michigan, University Microfilms, 1970.

NL 0439658   NBuC

Lodge, Sir Oliver Joseph, 1851-1940.
Ether & reality; a series of discourses on the many functions of the ether of space. London, Hodder and Stoughton ltd. [1930]
179p. (Hodder and Stoughton's people's library)

8th ed., June 1927; People's library ed., February 1930.

NL 0439659   ICRL CaBVaU PU-E1 PU

QC
177
L82
LODGE, Sir Oliver, 1851-1940
The ether of space. By Sir Oliver Lodge ... Illustrated. London and New York, Harper & Brothers, 1909 [c1909].
xvi, 155, [5] p. front., illus. (incl. diagrs.), 5 plates (1 fold.) 17 cm. (Half-title: Harper's Library of Living Thought.)

NL 0439660   MBCo NcD

Lodge, Sir Oliver Joseph, 1851-1940.
The ether of space, by Sir Oliver Lodge ... New York and London, Harper & brothers, 1909.
xix, [1] p. 1 l., 167, [1] p. front., pl., diagrs. 17½ cm. (Half-title: Harper's library of living thought)
Added t.-p. with ornamental border.

1. Ether (of space)
          9—13944

Library of Congress   QC177.I6

     CU OCU OC1W OU OC1 OC1L OC1W PBa PP PPPD PPL
NL 0439661   DLC NN MB FTaSU ICJ CaBVaU CU-I WaTC OrP

Lodge, Sir Oliver Joseph, 1851-1940.
Evolution and creation, by Sir Oliver Lodge. London: Hodder and Stoughton, Ltd. [1926.]   xi, 15-164 p. 12°.

257731A. 1. Evolution. 2. Evolution   and religion. 3. Creation.
N.Y.P.L.   September 15, 1926.

MU
NL 0439662   NN PSC OC1W CtY CU IU INS CaBVaU MSohG

Lodge, Sir Oliver Joseph, 1851-1940.
Evolution and creation, by Sir Oliver Lodge, f. r. s. New York, George H. Doran company [1926]
viii p., 2 l., 13-160 p. 19½ cm.

1. Evolution. 2. Religion and science—1900-   [Title

     QH367.L6   26—11243

     NcD OC1 ICJ MB OCU OO OOxM PPT DSI
NL 0439663   DLC CoU MoU GU LU NcU NIC PPL PPC PHC

Lodge, Sir Oliver Joseph, 1851-1940.
Evolution & creation.
N.Y., Doran, 1927.
160 p.

NL 0439664   PP

Lodge, Sir Oliver Joseph, 1851-1940.
...L'évolution biologique et spirituelle de l'homme; essai optimiste. Traduit de l'Anglais par Louise Favre et Frédéric Stéphens. Paris: Éditions de la B. p. s., 1925. 167 p. 12°. (Bibliothèque de philosophie spiritualiste moderne et des sciences psychiques.)

512526A. 1. Evolution. 2. Evolu-   tion and religion. 3. Creation.
I. Favre, Louise, translator.   II. Stéphens, Frédéric, jt. translator.
N.Y.P.L.   March 7, 1931

NL 0439665   NN

Lodge, Sir Oliver Joseph, 1851-1940
Mason, Mrs. Frances (Baker) ed.
The great design; order and progress in nature, edited by Frances Mason ... introduction by Sir J. Arthur Thomson ... New York, The Macmillan company, 1934.

FOR OTHER EDITIONS SEE MAIN ENTRY

VOLUME 338

Lodge, *Sir* **Oliver Joseph,** 1851–1940 .
   The immortality of the soul, by Sir Oliver Lodge. Boston, The Ball publishing co., 1908.
   4 p. l., 101 p. 18½ᶜᵐ.

   "The substance of this book was first given to the public on October 27th, 1907, as a Drew lecture in connection with Hackney college ... It was first published in the Hibbert journal for January and April of 1908."—Pref.

   1. Immortality.   I. Title.

   Library of Congress   BT921.L8   8–29637

   PP NRCR
NL 0439667   DLC Wa WaU MH OCU OC1 OC1h ICJ MB NN

Lodge, Sir Oliver Joseph, 1851–1940.
   In memory of F. W. H. Myers.   (from Society for psychical research. Proceedings, v. 17. 1901) por.

NL 0439668   RPB

Lodge, Oliver Joseph, 1851–1940.
   ...Introductory address delivered at the opening of the Liverpool Royal Infirmary School of Medicine, as the medical faculty of University College, Liverpool, on Monday, 3d October, 1881. 14 pp. 8°. *London, Harrison & Sons 1881.*

NL 0439669   DNLM

Lodge, *Sir* Oliver Joseph, 1851–1940 .
   ... The irrationality of war; on science as an element in the developing of international good will and understanding, by Sir Oliver Joseph Lodge ... New York city, American association for international conciliation, 1912.
   14 p. 19½ᶜᵐ. (International conciliation, pub. monthly by the American association for international conciliation ... no. 56)

   War. 2. Science—Addresses, essays, lectures.

   Library of Congress   JX1907.A8 no. 56   13—9539
   —— Copy 2.   (s19d2)

   PPC PPFr PPT WaS OrPR WaU-L CaBVaU
NL 0439670   DLC DAU OU OC1 OO OC1WHi OC1JC MB IU

BD331
.L83
1908

Lodge, Sir Oliver Joseph, 1851–1940.

   Leben und Materie; Haeckel's Welträtsel kritisiert von Oliver Lodge. Berlin, K. Curtius, 1908.
   x, 150 p. 18cm.
   Translation of : Life and matter.

   1. Haeckel, Ernst Heinrich Philipp August, 1834–1919. Die Welträthsel. 2. Monism. 3. Life—Origin. I. Title.

NL 0439671   ViU OO

Lodge, *Sir* Oliver Joseph, 1851– 1940 .
   Letters from Sir Oliver Lodge, psychical, religious, scientific and personal, with a foreword by Sir Oliver; compiled and annotated by J. Arthur Hill ... with four plates. London (etc.) Cassell and company, ltd. (1932)
   xiv, 267 p. front., ports. 22½ᶜᵐ.

   "Selected from a collection of about two thousand which I received from Sir Oliver Lodge during a period of something over twenty years."—Pref.

   I. Hill, John Arthur, 1872–   ed.

   Library of Congress   QC16.L6A4   33–2512
                              (3)   925.3

NL 0439672   DLC WaU FMU Wa CtY CU NN MB

BD
331
L82

Lodge, Sir Oliver Joseph, 1851–1940.
   Life and matter; a criticism of Professor Haeckel's "Riddle of the universe," New York and London, The Knickerbocker Press, 1905.
   ix, 175 p. 20cm.

   1. Haeckel, Ernst Heinrich Philipp August, 1834–1919. Die Welträthsel. 2. Monism. 3. Life—Origin. 4. Philosophy and reli   gion.

NL 0439673   NIC

Lodge, *Sir* Oliver Joseph, 1851–1940.
   Life and matter; a criticism of Professor Haeckel's "Riddle of the universe", by Sir Oliver Lodge. New York and London, G. P. Putnam's sons, 1905.
   ix, 175 p. 19½ᵐ.

   1. Haeckel, Ernst Heinrich Philipp August, 1834—   Die welträthsel. 2. Monism. 3. Life—Origin. 4. Philosophy and religion. I. Title.
                                                        5–38100

   Library of Congress   BD331.L8

   PP MH MiU
   IdB OrCS ICRL FMU ICJ NN OC1 OO OOxM PBm PPD PPPD
NL 0439674   DLC NNUT ICN CaBVaU NBuC OrP WaWW Or

Lodge, Sir Oliver Joseph, 1851–1940 .   3604.153
Life and matter. A criticism of Professor Haeckel's "Riddle of the universe." The expansion of a presidential address to the Birmingham and Midland Institute. 2d edition.
London. Williams & Norgate. 1905. viii, (1), 200 pp. Sm. 8°.
   Contents.— Monism. — "The law of substance." — The development of life. — Memoranda for would-be materialists. — Religion and philosophy. — Mind and matter. — Professor Haeckel's conjectural philosophy. — Hypothesis and analogies concerning life. — Will and guidance.—Further speculation as to the origin and nature of life.
   "Intended to formulate . . . a certain doctrine concerning the nature of man and the interaction beween mind and matter." — *Preface.*
   Haeckel's The riddle of the universe may be found on shelf-no. 3604.147.

   G1628 — Haeckel, Ernst Heinrich.   mingham and Midland Institute. Addresses. — T.r. — Mind and matter.   June 1, 1906

NL 0439675   MH MB

Lodge, Sir Oliver Joseph, 1851–1940.
   Life and matter; a criticism of Professor Haeckel's #Riddle of the universe", by ... The expansion of a presidential address to the Birmingham and Midland institute. 2nd ed. London. Williams & Norgate, 1906.

NL 0439676   OC1W

Lodge, *Sir* **Oliver Joseph,** 1851–1940.
   Life and matter; a criticism of Professor Haeckel's "Riddle of the universe", by Sir Oliver Lodge. The expansion of a presidential address to the Birmingham and Midland institute. Third impression. London, Williams & Norgate, 1906.
   viii p., 1 l., 200 p. 18½ cm.

   1. Haeckel, Ernst Heinrich Philipp August, 1834–1919. Die welträthsel. 2. Monism. 3. Life—Origin. 4. Philosophy and religion. I. Title.
                                                        E 16—55
   U. S. Office of Education.   Library B3261.W44L8
   for Library of Congress   (BD331.L   )

NL 0439677   DHEW ViU PPAN NjP

Lodge, *Sir* **Oliver** (Joseph), 1851– 1940 .
   Life and matter; a criticism of Professor Haeckel's " Riddle of the universe." 4th ed. London, Williams & Norgate, 1907.
   pp. viii, (1), 200.

NL 0439678   MH NNUT MiU

17.475
11133.9
18221i
1907

LODGE, Oliver Joseph, 1851–1940.
   Life and matter; a criticism of professor Haeckel's "Riddle of the universe". New York, G. P. Putnam's Sons, 1907.
   ix, 175p. 19.5cm.

NL 0439679   MH–AH

B3263
.W469L71

Lodge, Sir Oliver Joseph, 1851–1940.
   Life and matter: an exposition of part of the philosophy of science, with special references to the influence of Professor Haeckel. 2.ed., with an appendix of definitions and explanations. London, Williams & Norgate, 1909. xv, 112 p.

   1. Haeckel, Ernst Heinrich Philipp August, 1834–   Die Welt- räthsel. 2. Monism.

NL 0439680   ICU

Lodge, Sir Oliver (Joseph), 1851–1940 .
   Life and matter; a criticism of Professor Haeckel's "Riddle of the universe." New York: G. P. Putnam's Sons, 1909. ix, 175 p. 12°.

NL 0439681   NN MH PBa

B3263
W44L8
1911

Lodge, Sir Oliver Joseph, 1851–1940.
   Life and matter; an exposition of part of the philosophy of science, with special references to the influence of Professor Haeckel. 2d ed., with an appendix of definitions and explanations. 2d impression. London, Williams and Norgate, 1911. xvi,112 p.

NL 0439682   CU

Lodge, Sir Oliver Joseph, 1851–1940
   Life and matter; an exposition of part of the philosophy of science, with special references to the influence of Prof.Haeckel. 2d ed. L, Williams & Norgate, 1912

   200 p.

NL 0439683   MH ODW PSt PPT

BD 431
.L 83
1912

Lodge, Sir Oliver Joseph, 1851–1940.
   Life and matter; an exposition of part of the philosophy of science, with special references to the influence of Professor Haeckel, by Sir Oliver Lodge ... 2d. ed. with an appendix of definitions and explanations 3d. impression. London, Williams & Norgate, 1912.
   viii p., 1 l., 218 p. 18½cm.

NL 0439684   MdBJ IdU CaBVa OrPR

Lodge, Oliver Joseph, 1851–1940.
   Lightning and lightning conductors.
   Excerpted from the Engineering Magazine, Oct. 1894
39837

NL 0439685   DAS

VOLUME 338

Lodge, *Sir* **Oliver Joseph,** 1851-1940 .
  Lightning conductors and lightning guards. A treatise
on the protection of buildings, of telegraph instruments
and submarine cables, and of electric installations generally, from damage by atmospheric discharges. By
Oliver J. Lodge ... London, Whittaker and co.,
1892.
  xii, 544 p. front., illus., xviii (i. e. 19) pl. (1 fold.) 19½ᶜᵐ. (*Half-
title:* The specialists' series)

NL 0439686   DSI

Lodge. *Sir* **Oliver Joseph,** 1851-1940.
  Lightning conductors and lightning guards. A treatise
on the protection of buildings, of telegraph instruments
and submarine cables, and of electric installations generally,
from damage by atmospheric discharges. By Oliver J.
Lodge ... London, Whittaker and co.; New York, Macmillan & co., 1892.
  xii, 544 p. front., illus., xviii (i. e. 19) pl. (1 fold.) 19½ cm.
(*Half-title:* The specialists' series)

  1. Lightning-conductors.

TH9057.L8   1—13220

      DAS ICJ MH CU
      PPAmP NcRS NcU NjP ODW OU OCl OOxM OC1W OCU ViU
NL 0439687   DLC WaS OrP KMK NIC NjR MiHM PPL PBm

Lodge, *Sir* **Oliver Joseph,** 1851-1940 .
  ... The link between matter and matter, by Sir Oliver Lodge
F. R. S. London [1925?]
  cover-title, 14 p. 22½ᶜᵐ. (The British science guild. The Norman
Lockyer lecture, 1925)

  1. Matter. 2. Radiation. 3. Lockyer, Sir Joseph Norman, 1836-1920.
I. Title.
                                         36-6274
      Library of Congress   QC171.L83
                               [2]   530.1

NL 0439688   DLC OCU NN

Lodge, Sir Oliver Joseph, 1851-1940, ed.
  The London, Edinburgh and Dublin philosophical
magazine and journal of science
        see   The Philosophical magazine; a journal ...

Lodge, *Sir* **Oliver Joseph,** 1851-1940.
  Making of man; a study in evolution, by Sir Oliver
Lodge ... London, Hodder and Stoughton [1924]
  ix p., 1 l., 13-185 p. 19 cm.
  "First published April 1924. Reprinted April 1924."

  1. Man. 2. Evolution.

BD431.L6   24—16025

NL 0439690   DLC WaS WaSp NjP IEG

Lodge, *Sir* **Oliver Joseph,** 1851-1940 .
  Making of man; a study in evolution, by Sir Oliver
Lodge, F. R. S. New York, George H. Doran company
[1924]
  viii p., 2 l., 13-170 p. 21ᶜᵐ. $2.00

  1. Evolution.   I. Title.
                                        24-18300
      Library of Congress   B818.L6

      PBm PSC PU
NL 0439691   DLC KEmT Or OU OC1 OOxM MiU NcU NN MB

BL   Lodge, Sir Oliver Joseph, 1851-1940
240   Man and the universe; a study of the in-
L6   fluence of the advance in scientific knowl-
       edge upon our understanding of Christianity.
       London, Methuen [1908]
         356p. 23cm.
         American ed. (New York, 1908) has title:
       Science and immortality.

         1. Religion and science – 1900-   2.
       Christianity 3. Immortality I. Title

NL 0439692   WU

Lodge, Sir Oliver [Joseph] 1851-1940.
  Man and the universe: a study of the influence of
the advance in scientific knowledge upon our
understanding of Christianity.   London Methuen and
Co., [1908]
  viii, 1 l., 356 p. 8°.
  2. ed.

NL 0439693   NN

Lodge, *Sir* **Oliver Joseph,** 1851-1940   215 Q800
  Man and the universe. A study of the influence of the advance
in scientific knowledge upon our understanding of Christianity.
By Oliver Lodge. . . . . Fifth edition. London, Methuen & Co.,
[1908]
  viii, [2], 356 p. 22½ᶜᵐ.

NL 0439694   ICJ OO

Lodge, *Sir* **Oliver Joseph,** 1851-1940 .
  Man and the universe; a study of the in fluence
of the advance in scientific knowledge upon our
understanding of Christianity... 4th ed.
London, Methmen & co., 1909.
  356 p.

NL 0439695   PPT

Lodge, *Sir* **Oliver Joseph,** 1851-1940 .
  Man and the universe; a study of the influence of the
advance in scientific knowledge upon our understanding
of Christianity, by Oliver Lodge ... 5th ed. London,
Methuen & co. [1909]
  viii p., 1 l., 356 p. 23ᶜᵐ.
  "A great part of this book has appeared from time to time in the 'Hibbert journal,' a smaller part in the 'Contemporary review'; and the whole
has been thoroughly revised and extended."—p. [vii]
  Published New York, 1908, under title "Science and immortality," without the "Glossary of technical terms," etc., and index.
  "Glossary of technical terms and summary statement of mechanical
laws": p. 321-331.
                                        9-8010 Additions

NL 0439696   DLC CaBVa CaBVaU OO PPT PSC PU

Lodge, Sir Oliver Joseph, 1851-1940 .
  Man and the universe. A study of the influence of the advance in
scientific knowledge upon our understanding of Christianity. 6th
edition.
  London. Methuen. 1909. viii, (1), 356 p. 22 cm., in 8s.
  Contents. — Science and faith. — Corporate worship and service. — The
immortality of the soul. — Science and Christianity. — Glossary of technical terms and statement of mechanical laws. — Index.
  Also published, New York, 1908. under the title Science and immortality,
without the Glossary and Index [3457.247].

NL 0439697   MB CU MiU NIC

BL   Lodge, *Sir* Oliver Joseph, 1851-1940 .
240   Man and the universe; a study of the
L6   influence of the advance in scientific
1910   knowledge upon our understanding of
       Christianity. 8th ed. London, Methuen, 1910.
         356p. 20cm.

         "A great part of this book has appeared
       from time to time in the 'Hibbert journal,'
       a smaller part in the 'Contemporary review';
       and the whole has been thoroughly revised
       and extended." - p. [vi]
         1. Religion and   science – 1900- 2.
       Christianity. 3.   Immortality. I. Title.

NL 0439698   MU

LODGE, Sir Oliver (Joseph), 1851-1940 .
  Man and the universe, a study of the influence of the advance in scientific knowledge
upon our understanding of Christianity. 9th ed.
London, Methuen & Co., [1911].

NL 0439699   MH NjNbT CtY OCl OC1W

---

201   Lodge, Sir Oliver Joseph, 1851-1940.
L822m   Man and the universe; a study of the influence
1912   of the advance in scientific knowledge upon our
       understanding of Christianity   London, Methu-
       en & co., ltd. [1912]
         284p.

         1. Religion and science. I. Title.

NL 0439700   IU-M CaBVaU

Lodge, Sir Oliver Joseph, 1851-1940 .
  Man and the universe: a study of the influence
of the advance in scientific knowledge upon our
understanding of Christianity, by Oliver Lodge ...
12th ed. London, Methuen & co. [1912]
  viii p., 1 l., 284p. 18cm. (Methuen's shilling library)
  A great part of this book has appeared from time to time in
the 'Hibbert journal,' a smaller part in the 'Contemporary review';
and the whole has been thoroughly revised and extended.
  Published New York, 1908, under title "Science and immortality"
without the "Glossary of technical terms," etc., and index.
  "Glossary of technical terms and summary statement of mechanical
laws": p.247-256.

NL 0439701   CLSU

Lodge, *Sir* **Oliver Joseph,** 1851- 1940.
  Man and the universe; a study of the influence of the advance in scientific knowledge upon our understanding of
Christianity, by Oliver Lodge ... 14th ed. London, Methuen
& co. ltd. [1913]
  284 p. 17ᶜᵐ. (Methuen's shilling library)
  "A great part of this book has appeared from time to time in the 'Hibbert journal,' a smaller part in the 'Contemporary review'; and the
whole has been thoroughly revised and extended."
  Published New York, 1908, under title "Science and immortality"
without the "Glossary of technical terms", etc., and index.
  "Glossary of technical terms and summary statement of mechanical
laws": p. 247-256. "Fourteenth edition, June 1913."
  1. Religion and science—1900-   2. Christianity. 3. Immortality.
I. Title. II. Ser.

NL 0439702   ViU

LODGE, Sir Oliver, (Joseph), 1851-1940.
  Man and the universe; a study of the influence of the advance in scientific knowledge
upon our understanding of Christianity. 18th
ed. London, Methuen & co., ltd., [1917].

NL 0439703   MH

Lodge, Sir Oliver Joseph, 1851-1940.
  Man and the universe; a study of the influence of
the advance in scientific knowledge upon our
understanding of Christianity, by Oliver Lodge ...
19th ed. London, Methuen & co, [1919]
  viii p., 1 l., 284 p. 17.5 cm.
  "A great part of this book has appeared from time
to time in the 'Hibbert journal, a smaller part in the
'Contemporary review'; and the whole has been
thoroughly revised and extended."
  "Glossary of technical terms and summary statement of mechanical laws": p. 241-256.

NL 0439704   CtY MdBP

VOLUME 338

Lodge, *Sir* Oliver Joseph, 1851–1940.
Man and the universe, by Sir Oliver Lodge ... New York, George H. Doran company [*1920]
vi p., 3 l., 294 p. 22½ᵐ.
"This book appeared originally under the title 'Science and Immortality,' but this represents only a portion of its theme and is inadequate. Its true title, by which it is known in England is now restored to it—'Man and the universe'."
Prefatory note to American ed.

1. Religion and science—1900—   2. Christianity—20th cent. 3. Immortality.   I. Title.   20–5129
Library of Congress   BL240.L6 1920
                              [a44l1]   215

NL   0439705   DLC NN OKentU Or OrCS OC1W

Lodge, Sir Oliver Joseph, 1851–1940.
Milton and the education controversy. An address by the chairman, Sir Oliver Lodge, at a Milton tercentenary celebration, under the auspices of the Evangelical Free Churches in Birmingham, on 8th December, 1908. Birmingham: Birmingham Printers, Ltd., 1909.   7 p.   8°.

1. Milton, John, 1608–74. 2. Educa-   tion, Gt. Br., 1908.
N. Y. P. L.   January 18, 1917

NL   0439706   NN

Lodge, *Sir* Oliver Joseph, 1851–1940.
Modern problems, by Sir Oliver Lodge ... London, Methuen & co., ltd. [1912]
vii, 320 p. 19½ᵐ.
CONTENTS.—Free will and determinism.—The nature of time.—Balfour and Bergson.—Huxley on man's place in nature.—The position of woman in the state.—The responsibility of authors.—Universal arbitration, and how far it is possible.—The irrationality of war.—The functions of money.—The pursuit of wealth.—Public wealth and private expenditure.—Some social reforms.—Poor law reform.—Charity organization.—Squandering a surplus.—The production and sale of drink.—The smoke nuisance.—Competition v. co-operation.—Ruskin's political economy.—Huxley's Lay sermons.—The attitude of Tennyson towards science.

1. Social sciences—Addresses, essays, lectures.   I. Title.
                                                      12–25343
Library of Congress   AC8.L7

NL   0439707   DLC OC1 OU WaT DNLM ICJ NN MB

Lodge, *Sir* Oliver Joseph, 1851–1940.
Modern problems; a discussion of debatable subjects, by Sir Oliver Lodge ... New York, George H. Doran company [*1912]
ix, 336 p. 20½ cm.
CONTENTS.—Free will and determinism.—The nature of time.—Balfour and Bergson.—Huxley on man's place in nature.—The position of woman in the state.—The responsibility of authors.—Universal arbitration, and how far it is possible.—The irrationality of war.—The functions of money.—The pursuit of wealth.—Public wealth and private expenditure.—Some social reforms.—The poor law.—Charity organization. — Squandering a surplus. — The production and sale of drink.—The smoke nuisance.—Competition v. co-operation.—Ruskin's political economy.—Huxley's Lay sermons.—The attitude of Tennyson towards science.
1. Social sciences—   Addresses, essays, lectures.
I. Title.
Library of Congress   AC15.L72   12—26887

NL   0439708   DLC IdB WaWW Or CaBVaU PPA PPL

Lodge, *Sir* Oliver Joseph, 1851–1940.
Modern problems; a discussion of debatable subjects, by Sir Oliver Lodge ... New York, Hodder & Stoughton, George H. Doran company [*1912]
ix, 348 p. 20½ᵐ.
CONTENTS.—Free will and determinism. — The nature of time.—Balfour and Bergson.—Huxley on man's place in nature.—The position of woman in the state.—The responsibility of authors.—Universal arbitration, and how far it is possible.—The irrationality of war.—The functions of money.—The pursuit of wealth.—Public wealth and private expenditure.—Some social reforms. — The poor law. — Charity organization.—Squandering a surplus.—The production and sale of drink.—The smoke nuisance.—Competition v. co-operation.—Ruskin's political economy.—The attitude of Tennyson towards science.
1. Social sciences—Ad-   dresses, essays, lectures.   I. Title.
Library of Congress   AC8.L722
                                                      42–9858

    OO MiU
NL   0439709   DLC WaS TU FTaSU NcU GU LU KEmT NjP

Lodge, Sir Oliver Joseph, 1851–1940.
Modern problems: dealing with pre-war questions of permanent interest. London, Methuen [1912]
218 p.

1. Social sciences.
I. Title.

NL   0439710   CaOTP

AC
8
L823
1932
Lodge, Sir Oliver Joseph, 1851–1940.
Modern problems, dealing with questions, old and new, of permanent interest. 4th ed. London, Methuen [1932]
xii, 210 p. 20cm.

1. Social science—Addresses, essays & lectures.

NL   0439711   NIC OO NcD

QC 71
.L 69
1927
Lodge, Sir Oliver Joseph, 1851–1940.
... Modern scientific ideas, especially the idea of discontinuity, by Sir Oliver Lodge, F. R. S. London, E. Benn, limited, 1927.
79 p.   16½cm.   (Benn's sixpenny library. [no. 101])

Bibliography: p. 78–79.

1. Science -   Addresses, essays, lectures.   I. Title.   II. Title: Discontinuity.

NL   0439712   MdBJ CaBVaU MH MiU PU ICU NN

Lodge, *Sir* Oliver Joseph, 1851–1940.
... Modern scientific ideas, especially the idea of discontinuity, by Sir Oliver Lodge, F. R. S. London, E. Benn, limited [1928]
79 p. 16½ᵐ. (Benn's sixpenny library. [no. 101])
"First published February, 1927 ... Seventh impression May, 1928."
Bibliography: p. 78–79.

1. Science—Addresses, essays, lectures.   I. Title: Discontinuity.
                                                      29–3548
Library of Congress   QC71.L8 1928 a

NL   0439713   DLC OC1 ICJ IU

Lodge, Sir Oliver Joseph, 1851–1940.
... Modern scientific ideas, especially the idea of discontinuity, by Sir Oliver Lodge, F. R. S.
London, E. Benn, limited [1930]
79 p.   16.5 cm.   (Benn's sixpenny library. [no. 101])
"First published February, 1927 ... Eighth impression May, 1930."
Bibliography: p. 78–79.

NL   0439714   CU

Lodge, *Sir* Oliver Joseph, 1851–1940.
The modern theory of light. By Prof. Oliver J. Lodge.
(*In* Smithsonian institution. Annual report. 1889. Washington, 1890. 23½ᵐ. p. 441–448)
"University college magazine, Liverpool, July, 1889, vol. IV, pp. 90–99."

1. Electromagnetic theory.
                                                      S 15—708
Smithsonian inst. Library
for Library of Congress   Q11.S66 1889

NL   0439715   DSI WaS OU MiU MB OC1 DLC OC1MN

Lodge, *Sir* Oliver Joseph, 1851–1940.
... Modern views of electricity, by Oliver J. Lodge ... London and New York, Macmillan and co., 1889.
xvi, 422 p. illus. 18½ᵐ. (Nature series)

1. Electricity.   I. Title.   16–17564

Library of Congress   QC521.L7 1889

    MB MiHM PPL PPA OC1W MiU
NL   0439716   DLC NBuU MdBP INS OrU MdBP CU I ICJ MH

Lodge, Sir Oliver Joseph, 1851–1940.
Modern views of electricity. London: Macmillan and Co., 1892. xvi, 480 p. diagr., illus. 12°. (Nature series.)

NL   0439717   NN CtY DN OC1 ICJ PP PPD PPL PHC DNC

Lodge, Sir Oliver Joseph, 1851–1940.
Modern views of electricity. London and New York, Macmillan, 1892.
480p. illus. (Nature Series)

NL   0439718   ICRL IdU ICJ

QC
521
.L7
1892
Lodge, Oliver Joseph, Sir, 1851–1940.
Modern views of electricity, by Oliver J. Lodge. 2nd edition. London and New York, Macmillan and co., 1892.
xvi, 480 p. illus. 19 cm. (Nature series)

1. Electricity.   I. Title

NL   0439719   OKentU PPF OO OC1W CU

Lodge, Oliver Joseph, 1851–1940.
Modern views of electricity. London: Macmillan & co., 1892.
422p. 55 il. D. (Nature series.)

NL   0439720   MiHM

Lodge, Sir Oliver Joseph, 1851–1940.
Modern views of electricity. London, 1899.

NL   0439721   NjP

Lodge, *Sir* Oliver Joseph, 1851–1940.
Modern views of electricity, by Sir Oliver Lodge ... 3d ed., rev. London, Macmillan and co., limited, 1907.
xiv p., 1 l., 518 p. illus., diagrs. 18½ᵐ. (On cover: Macmillan's manuals for students)
First edition printed 1889; 2d, 1892; 3d, 1907.

1. Electricity.   I. Title.
                                                      8—26866
Library of Congress   QC521.L7

    OC1L OU ODW PBa PPAmP PHC
NL   0439722   DLC CaBVaU OrPR ICJ ODW CU NcRS Nc [?] NN

Lodge (*Sir* Oliver J[oseph]) [1851–1940]. Modern views of matter. pp. 493–530. 8°. *New York,* 1900.
Cutting from: Internat. Month., N. Y., 1900, i.

NL   0439723   DNLM

VOLUME 338

Lodge, Oliver Joseph, 1851-1940.
Modern views on matter. Clarendon press, 1903.
27 p. (Romanes lecture, 1903)

NL 0439724   MiD MH NN

Lodge, *Sir* **Oliver Joseph,** 1851-1940.
... Modern views on matter, by Sir Oliver Lodge ... Delivered in the Sheldonian theatre, Oxford, June 12, 1903. 2d ed. Oxford, Clarendon press, 1903.
29, [1] p. 22½ᶜᵐ. (The Romanes lecture. 1903)

1. Matter —Constitution. 2. Electrons. 3. Radioactivity.   I. Title.

                                    4—2779

Library of Congress   QC173.L82

NL 0439725   DLC MB CU PPL

Lodge, *Sir* **Oliver Joseph,** 1851-1940.
Modern views on matter. By Sir Oliver Lodge ...
(*In* Smithsonian institution. Annual report. 1903. Washington, 1904. 23½ᶜᵐ. p. 215–228)
"The Romanes lecture, delivered in the Sheldonian theater, Oxford, June 12, 1903."

1. Matter—Constitution. 2. Electrons.   I. Title.

                         S 15—1186
Smithsonian Inst. Library
for Library of Congress   [Q11.S66 1903]

NL 0439726   DSI WaS PPAmP

Lodge, *Sir* **Oliver** [Joseph] 1851-1940.
... Modern views on matter, by Sir Oliver Lodge ... Delivered in the Sheldonian theatre, Oxford, June 12, 1903. 3d ed. Oxford, Clarendon press, 1904.
32, [1] p. 22½ᶜᵐ. (The Romanes lecture. 1903)

NL 0439727   ICJ NN

B   Lodge, Sir Oliver Joseph,   1851-1940.
473   ...Modern views on matter... Delivered
.52   in the Sheldonian theatre, Oxford, June
12, 1903. New ed. Ox.1907. O.
(The Romanes lecture, 1903)

NL 0439728   ICN PPAmP CtY ICN NjP OClW

Lodge, Sir Oliver [Joseph] 1851-1940.
Modern views on matter... 5th impression,
Oxford,1915.
23cm. (Oxford lectures on natural science,
1903-1923. [no.1.])

NL 0439729   CtY

Lodge, *Sir* **Oliver Joseph,** 1851-1940.
My philosophy, representing my views on the many functions of the ether of space, by Sir Oliver Lodge ... London, E. Benn limited, 1933.
318 p., 1 l. 24ᶜᵐ.

1. Science—Philosophy. 2. Ether (of space) 3. Psychical research. 4. Immortality.   I. Title.

                             33—30331
Library of Congress   Q175.L6   501

     NcD OCl NN MB
NL 0439730   DLC CaBViP WaS AU FMU MB TxU CtY CU

Lodge, Sir Oliver Joseph, 1851-1940, *tr.*
Richet, Charles Robert, 1850–
The natural history of a savant, by Prof. Charles Richet ... translated from the French by Sir Oliver Lodge. London and Toronto, J. M. Dent & sons, limited, 1927.

Lodge, Sir Oliver Joseph, 1851-1940.
Neueste Anschauungen über Elektricität ... Übersetzt von Anna von Helmholtz und Estelle du Bois-Reymond. Hrsg. durch Richard Wachsmuth. Leipzig, 1896.
18.5 cm.

NL 0439732   CtY

LODGE, Sir Oliver Joseph, 1851-1940.
Oliver Heaviside by Sir Oliver Lodge, and Career of Oliver Heaviside by B.A. Behrend; memorial sketches. n.p., [1925].

fº. pp. (7).
Cover serves as title-page.
"Reprinted from the Electrical World, for February 21,1925", pp. 403-407.

NL 0439733   MH

LODGE, Sir Oliver J[oseph] 1851-1940.
On electrolysis. London,Spottiswoode & Co., 1886.

pp. 50+
(British Association for the Advancement of Science.)
"A communication ordered by the General Committee to be printed in extenso among the reports for 1885."
Cover serves as title-page.

NL 0439734   MH

BF1023   Lodge, Sir Oliver Joseph, 1851-1940.
.H6   ... On survival of death by Sir Oliver Lodge ...
vol. 1,   An abstract of the address delivered by Sir Oliver
no. 23   Lodge, as president of the British association for the
Houdini   advancement of science, at its annual meeting, held
Coll.   in the Central hall, Birmingham ... September 10th,
        1913. (Reprinted from the 'The Two worlds,
        ' September 19th, 1913) ... Manchester, "The Two
        worlds" publishing co., ltd., 1913.
          cover-title, 12 p. 18.5 cm.
          Houdini pamphlets: spiritualism, v. 1, no. 23.
          At head of title "The Two worlds" reprint.

NL 0439735   DLC

Lodge, Sir Oliver Joseph, 1851-1940.
... On the seat of the electromotive forces in the voltaic cell; with an appendix on the paths of electric energy in voltaic circuits. By Professor Oliver Lodge... London, Taylor and Francis, 1885.
1 p.l.,96p. illus.,2 fold.pl. 22cm.
"From the Philosophical magazine,vol.19, 1885."

1. Electric batteries. 2. Electromotive force.

NL 0439736   DP

Lodge, *Sir* **Oliver Joseph,** 1851-1940.
Parent and child, a treatise on the moral and religious education of children, by Sir Oliver Lodge ... New York and London, Funk & Wagnalls company, 1910.
73 p. 18½ᶜᵐ. $0.50

1. Domestic education.   I. Title.

Library of Congress   LC268.L6   10—22756

     ICJ NN MB PU PPC
NL 0439737   DLC CaBVaU Or DNLM MiU OCl OO OCU ViU

Lodge, *Sir* **Oliver Joseph,** 1851-1940.
Past years; an autobiography, by Sir Oliver Lodge ... London, Hodder and Stoughton, limited, 1931.
364 p. front., pl., ports. 23ᶜᵐ.

I. Title.

Library of Congress   QC16.L6A3   32-1450

     NcU CU OClW OU OClh
NL 0439738   DLC WaU CaBViP Or CaBVaU TxU ICJ MH PPF

Lodge, *Sir* **Oliver Joseph,** 1851-1940.
Past years; an autobiography, by Sir Oliver Lodge ... New York, C. Scribner's sons, 1932.
3 p. l., 5-364 p. front., pl., ports. 23ᶜᵐ.

I. Title.

                             32—5855
Library of Congress   QC16.L6A3 1932
                            [a41k1]

     OEac PPA PPD PP PPL
     IdU-SB MoU ICU DAU NcRS OCl OU ViU MB NN OO OOxM
NL 0439739   DLC Wa OrPR IdU CaBVa OrP WaS MiU TxU

Lodge, *Sir* **Oliver Joseph,** 1851-1940.
Phantom walls, by Sir Oliver Lodge ... London, Hodder and Stoughton, limited [1929]
xiii, 15-250, [1] p. 19½ᶜᵐ.
"First published, October 1929. Second edition, November 1929."

1. Psychical research. 2. Immortality. 3. Science—Philosophy. I. Title.

Library of Congress   BF1031.L65 1929 a   30-2632

NL 0439740   DLC CU CaBVa CaBVaU

Lodge, **Sir Oliver Joseph,** 1851-1940.
Phantom walls, by Sir Oliver Lodge ... London, Hodder and Stoughton, limited [1930]
xiii, 15-258, [1] p. 19.5 cm.
"First published, October 1929. Second edition, November 1929. Third edition, January 1930."
1. Psychical research. 2. Immortality. 3. Science-Philosophy.

NL 0439741   CtY

Lodge, *Sir* Oliver Joseph, 1851-1940.   7606.150
Phantom walls.
— New York. Putnam. 1930. 255 pp. Portrait. 19½ cm.

N7199 — T.r. — Spiritualism. — Psychical phenomena.

NL 0439742   MB NN

VOLUME 338

Lodge, *Sir* **Oliver Joseph,** 1851–1940.
Phantom walls, by Sir Oliver Lodge ... New York, London, G. P. Putnam's sons, 1930.
xiv, 255 p. front. (port.) 20½ᵐ.
"First American edition."

1. Psychical research. 2. Immortality. 3. Science—Philosophy.
I. Title.
30—8611
Library of Congress BF1031.L65 1930

NL 0439743   DLC OU MoU Or OrP WaS OC1 OEac ViU PU

**Q1
.P5**

Lodge, Sir Oliver Joseph, 1851–1940, ed.

The Philosophical magazine; a journal of theoretical, experimental and applied physics. v. 1–68, June 1798–Dec. 1826; new ser., v. 1–11, Jan. 1827–June 1832; 3d ser., v. 1–37, July 1832–Dec. 1850; 4th ser., v. 1–50, Jan. 1851–Dec. 1875; 5th ser., v. 1–50, Jan. 1876–Dec. 1900; 6th ser., v. 1–50, Jan. 1901–Dec. 1925; 7th ser., v. 1–
Jan. 1926–
London, Taylor & Francis, ltd. ₍etc.₎

Lodge, Sir Oliver Joseph, 1851–1940.   **3488.165**
A physicist's approach.
(In Hand, James Edward, editor. Ideals of science & faith. Pp. 1–48. New York, 1904.)

NL 0439745   MB

**925.2
L821p
Physics
Lib'y**

Lodge, Sir Oliver Joseph, 1851–1940.
Pioneers of science, by Oliver Lodge ... London and New York, Macmillan and co., 1893.
xv, 404p. incl. front., illus., ports., maps, diagrs. 20cm.
"This book takes its origin in a course of lectures on the history and progress of astronomy arranged for me in the year 1887 by three of my colleagues [at University college, Liverpool]"—Pref.
1. Astronomers. 2. Astrology - Hist. 3. Tides. I. Title.

ViU
NjP PPL-R NIC PPPL OC1W MH OO KU-M OEac ICJ PPT-P
NL 0439746   TxU KEmT OrU-M MB ODW OO MiU OC1 NcRS

Lodge, *Sir* **Oliver Joseph,** 1851–1940.
Pioneers of science, by Sir Oliver Lodge ... London, Macmillan and co., limited; New York, The Macmillan company, 1904.
xv, 404 p. incl. front., illus., ports., maps, diagrs. 19ᵐ.
"First edition, 1893. Reprinted with corrections, 1904."
"This book takes its origin in a course of lectures on the history and progress of astronomy arranged for me in the year 1887 by three of my colleagues at University college, Liverpool."—Pref.

1. Astronomers. 2. Astrology—Hist. 3. Tides. I. Title.
5—4504
Library of Congress QB35.L82

OrU CaBVa MtU Or OrP Wa WaS WaT CaBVaU
NL 0439747   DLC WaS WaTC OrPR Or IdU-SB OrSaW Wa

**520.9
L82p
1908**

Lodge, Sir Oliver Joseph, 1851–1940.
Pioneers of science, by Sir Oliver Lodge ... London, Macmillan and co., 1908.
xv, 404p. incl. front., illus., ports., maps, diagrs. 19cm.
"First edition, 1893. Reprinted with corrections, 1908."
"This book takes its origin in a course of lectures on the history and progress of astronomy arranged for me in the year 1887 by three of my colleagues at University college, Liverpool."—Pref.

NL 0439748   IU ViU CU

Lodge, Sir Oliver ₍Joseph₎, 1851–1940.
Pioneers of science.   London: Macmillan and Co., Ltd.,
1910.   xv, 404 p.   illus., port.   12°.

Copernicus and the motion of the earth. Tycho Brahé and the earliest observatory. Kepler and the laws of planetary motion. Galileo and the invention of the telescope. Galileo and the inquisition. Descartes and his theory of vortices. Sir Isaac Newton. Newton and the law of gravitation. Newton's "Principia." Roemer and Bradley and the velocity of light. Lagrange and Laplace; the stability of the solar system, and the nebular hypothesis. Herschel and the motion of the fixed stars. The discovery of the asteroids. Bessel; the distances of the stars, and the discovery of stellar planets. The discovery of Neptune. Comets and meteors. The tides. The tides, and planetary evolution.

NL 0439749   NN OOxM

Lodge, Sir Oliver Joseph, 1851–1940.
Pioneers of science.
London, Macmillan, 1913.
404 p.

NL 0439750   PU-FA

**QB35
L82**

Lodge, Sir Oliver Joseph, 1851–1940.
Pioneers of science, by Sir Oliver Lodge ... London, Macmillan and co., limited; New York, The Macmillan company, 1919.
404 p.

1. Astronomers.   2. Astronomy - Hist.
3. Tides. I. T.

NL 0439751   NBuU MiU

**QB35
.L82
1922**

Lodge, Sir Oliver Joseph, 1851–1940.
Pioneers of science, by Sir Oliver Lodge ... London, Macmillan and co., limited, 1922.
xv, 404 p. incl. front., illus., ports., maps, diagrs. 20 1/2cm.
"Reprinted with corrections ... 1922."
"This book takes its origin in a course of lectures on the history and progress of astronomy arranged for me in the year 1887 by three of my colleagues at University college, Liverpool."—Prof.
1. Astronomers.   2. Astronomy—Hist.
3. Tides. I. Title

NL 0439752   MB PSC

Lodge, Oliver Joseph, Sir, 1851–1940.
Pioneers of science, by Sir Oliver Lodge. London, Macmillan, 1926 [c1893]
xv, 404 p. illus., diagrs., maps, ports. 20cm.
"This book takes its origin in a course of lectures on the history and progress of astronomy arranged for me in the year 1887 ... at University College, Liverpool." – Pref.

NL 0439753   OCU MeB MB IU NcD

**QB35
.L82
1928**

Lodge, Sir Oliver Joseph, 1851–1940.
Pioneers of science, by Sir Oliver Lodge ... London, Macmillan co., limited, 1928.
xv, 404 p. incl. front., illus., ports., maps, diagrs. 19 1/2cm.
"Reprinted with corrections ... 1928."
"This book takes its origin in a course of lectures on the history and progress of astronomy arranged for me in the year 1887 by three of my colleagues at University college, Liverpool."—Pref.
1. Astronomers. 2. Astronomy—Hist. 3. Tides.
I. Title.

NL 0439754   MB

Lodge, Sir Oliver Joseph, 1851–1940.

The position of woman : actual and ideal, with preface by Sir Oliver Lodge. London, J. Nisbet & co., ltd., 1911.

Lodge, Sir Oliver Joseph, 1851–1940.
... Pourquoi je crois à l'immortalité personnelle. Paris, J. Meyer, 1929.
210 p., 1 l. front. (port.) 19ᵐ. (Bibliothèque de philosophie spiritualiste moderne et des sciences psychiques)
At head of title: Sir Oliver Lodge.

1. Psychical research. 2. Immortality.   I. Title. *Translation of* Why I believe in personal immortality.
29—16967
Library of Congress BF1031.L76

NL 0439756   DLC

Lodge, Sir Oliver Joseph, 1851–1940.
... Public service versus private expenditure. By Sir Oliver Lodge ... London, The Fabian society, 1905.
11, ₍1₎ p. 22ᵐ. (Fabian tract no. 121)
"An address to the Ancient order of foresters at their annual gathering in Birmingham town hall ... October 9th, 1904."

1. Cooperation. 2. Wealth. I. Title.
36—2846
Library of Congress HX11.F25 no. 121
₍2₎   (335.106242) 334

NL 0439757   DLC CU-S INS MH NcD MB NN WaS CaBVaU

**HM131
L822**

Lodge, Sir Oliver Joseph, 1851–1940.
Public service versus private expenditure.
London, Fabian Society, 1926.
11 p.   22cm. (Fabian tract no. 121)

1. Cooperation.   2. Wealth.   I. Title.

NL 0439758   CSt-H

Lodge, Sir Oliver Joseph, 1851–1940.   **535.25 R401**
Radioaktivität und Kontinuität. Zwei Vorträge von Sir Oliver Lodge, ... Leipzig, J. A. Barth, 1914.   **12981**
[4], 217 p. 20½ x 16⁴.
Contents.—1. Die Entdeckung der Radioaktivität und deren Einfluss auf die Entwicklung der physikalischen Wissenschaft. Becquerel-Gedächtnisrede, gehalten am 17. Oktober 1912 vor der Chemical Society. Aus den Transactions of the Chemical Society, vol. 101, 1912, übersetzt von E. E. Fournier d'Albe.—2. Kontinuität. Eröffnungsrede, gehalten auf der Versammlung der British Association zu Birmingham, 1913. Ergänzt durch erläuternde Anmerkungen. Nach der Buchausgabe übersetzt von Max Iklé.

NL 0439759   ICJ

Lodge, *Sir* **Oliver Joseph,** 1851–1940.
Raymond; or, Life and death, with examples of the evidence for survival of memory and affection after death, by Sir Oliver J. Lodge. With eighteen illustrations. London, Methuen & co., ltd. ₍1916₎
xi, 403, ₍1₎ p. front., 1 illus., plates, ports. 23 cm.
The book is named after the author's son who was killed in the war. The first part contains extracts from his letters. "The second part gives specimens of what are considered by most people unusual communications ... The third part ₍Life and death₎ is of a more expository character." cf. Pref.
1. Spiritualism. 2. Future life. 3. European war, 1914–1918—Personal narratives, English. I. Lodge, Raymond, 1889–1915.

BF1261.L182   16—24318

NL 0439760   DLC CaBVa OrP MtU NjP OC1

Lodge, *Sir* **Oliver Joseph,** 1851–1940.
Raymond; or, Life and death, with examples of the evidence for survival of memory and affection after death, by Sir Oliver J. Lodge; with eighteen illustrations. 6th ed. London, Methuen & co. ltd. ₍1916₎
xi, 403, ₍1₎ p. front., illus., plates, ports. 23ᵐ.

1. Spiritualism. 2. Future life. 3. European war, 1914–1918—Personal narratives, English. I. Lodge, Raymond, 1889–1915.

CA 17—3231 Unrev'd
Library of Congress BF1261.L82 1916 b

NL 0439761   DLC CaBVaU CtY

VOLUME 338

Lodge, *Sir Oliver Joseph,* 1851–1940.
Raymond; or, Life and death, with examples of the evidence for survival of memory and affection after death, by Sir Oliver J. Lodge. With eighteen illustrations. New York, George H. Doran company [1916]
xi, 404 p. front., 1 illus., plates, ports. 22ᶜᵐ.
The book is named after the author's son who was killed in the war. The first part contains extracts from his letters. "The second part gives specimens of what at present are considered by most people unusual communications ... The third part [Life and death] ... is of a more expository character." *cf.* Pref.
1. Spiritualism. 2. Future life. 3. European war, 1914–1918—Personal narratives, English. I. Lodge, Raymond, 1889–1915.

17—213

Library of Congress   BL1261.L82

DNLM CSmH OU OClJC OOxM MoU ODW KyLxCB OCU OCl OrPS FU FTaSU UU Wa WaE WaT WaS IdB Or OrPR IdPI WaTC MH
NL 0439762   DLC PPA PPC PPT PSC PHC PHi TNJ-R PU NN

Lodge, Sir Oliver Joseph, 1851–1940.   133.9 R603
Raymond; or, Life and death, with examples of the evidence for survival of memory and affection after death. By Sir Oliver J. Lodge. With eighteen illustrations. Seventh edition. London, Methuen & Co., [1917].
xi, 403, [1] p. front., illus., 10 pl. (incl. ports.) 23ᶜᵐ.
The book is named after the author's son who was killed in the war. The first part contains extracts from his letters.

NL 0439763   ICJ

133.9   Lodge, Oliver Joseph, 1851–1940.
L822R14   Raymond; or, Life and death, with examples of the evidence for survival of memory and affection after death. 14th ed. London, Methuen [1929]
403p. illus., plates.

The book is named after the author's son who was killed in the war. The first part contains extracts from his letters. "The second part gives specimens of what are considered by most people unusual communications. The third part [Life and death] is of a more expository character." *cf.* Pref.

NL 0439764   NBC

Lodge, *Sir Oliver Joseph,* 1851–1940.
Raymond revised; a new and abbreviated edition of "Raymond, or Life and death", with an additional chapter, by Sir Oliver J. Lodge. With twelve illustrations. London, Methuen & co., ltd. [1922]
xv, 224 p. front., plates, ports. 19¼ᶜᵐ.

1. Spiritualism. 2. Future life. 3. European war, 1914–1918—Personal narratives, English. I. Lodge, Raymond, 1889–1915.

23–8632

Library of Congress   BF1261.L82 1922

NL 0439765   DLC CaBVa CtY MB PSC

Lodge, Sir Oliver Joseph, 1851–1940
BF1261   Raymond revised; a new and abbreviated edition
L82   of "Raymond or life or death" with an additional
1932   chapter ... 2nd. edition. London, Methuen & Co.
         [1932]
         xv, 224 p. front., plates, ports. 20 cm.

NL 0439766   RPB

Lodge, Sir Oliver Joseph, 1851–1940.
...The reality of a spiritual world, by Sir Oliver Lodge. [London:] E. Benn, Ltd., 1930. 31 p. 12°. (Affirmations [Section 8].)

516439A. 1. Spiritism.
N. Y. P. L.   February 20, 1931

NL 0439767   NN

Lodge, Sir Oliver Joseph, 1851–1940
BF1031   The reality of a spiritual world.
L66   [London] E. Benn [1931]
1931   31 p. 19 cm. (Affirmations; God in the modern world)

1. Spiritualism. 2. Psychical research.

NL 0439768   RPB

Lodge, *Sir* Oliver Joseph, 1851–1940.   3457-34I
The reality of hell.
(*In* What is hell? Pp. 17–30. New York. 1930.)

NL 0439769   MB

Lodge, *Sir* Oliver Joseph, 1851–1940.
Reason and belief, by Sir Oliver Lodge. London, Methuen & co., ltd. [1910]
xiv, 211, [1] p. 19¼ᶜᵐ.
"References to quotations": p. 202–207.
CONTENTS.—pt. I. Incarnation.—pt. II. The Old Testament in education.—pt. III. The scope of science.

1. Incarnation. 2. Religion and science—1900—   I. Title.
                                          10–29102 Revised

Library of Congress   BR85.L8 1910

NL 0439770   DLC TxU ICRL OCU

Lodge, Sir Oliver Joseph, 1851–1940
Reason and belief; 2d ed. Lond.
[1910]

NL 0439771   ODW

BR   Lodge, Oliver Joseph, Sir, 1851–1940.
85   Reason and belief, by Sir Oliver
.L8   Lodge. New York, George H. Doran
1910b   company [1910]
         166 p. 22 cm.

NL 0439772   OKentU MH Or

Lodge, *Sir* Oliver Joseph, 1851–1940.
Reason and belief, by Sir Oliver Lodge. New York, Moffat, Yard and company, 1910.
ix, 166 p. 20ᶜᵐ.

1. Incarnation. 2. Religion and science—1900—   I. Title.
                                          10–29103
Library of Congress
——— Copy 2.   BR85.L8 1910 a

WaSp WaS CaBVaU
PP PPC KEmT CBDP MH-AH NBuU KyU NIC KyLxCB OrP Wa
NL 0439773   DLC ViU OCl OO OEac OOxM MB CU NN PBa

LODGE, Sir Oliver *Joseph,* 1851–1940.
Reason and belief. 3d ed.
[1911] D.

NL 0439774   ICN

Lodge, *Sir* Oliver Joseph, 1851–1940
Reason and belief, by Sir Oliver Lodge. London, Methuen & co., ltd. [1911]
xiv, 211, [1] p., 1 l. 20ᶜᵐ. $1.25
"Fourth edition."

NL 0439775   ICJ

LODGE, Sir Oliver Joseph, 1851–1940.
Reason and belief. 5th ed. London, Methuen & Co., [1911].

NL 0439776   MH

BR   Lodge, Sir Oliver Joseph, 1851–1940.
85   Reason and belief, by Sir Oliver Lodge.
L8   London, Methuen [1914]
1914   211 p. 18 cm.

1. Incarnation. 2. Religion and science –1900–1925. I. Title.

NL 0439777   NBuU NIC MH-AH

Lodge, Sir Oliver Joseph, 1851–1940.
Reason and belief. By Sir Oliver Lodge....8th ed. (London) Methuen & Co. Ltd...(c1916.)
12 + 212 p. 17½cm.

NL 0439778   DN-Ob

Lodge, *Sir* Oliver Joseph, 1851–1940.
Reason and belief, by Sir Oliver Lodge. New York, George H. Doran company [1920]
ix p., 2 l., 3–166 p. 21½ᶜᵐ.

I. Title.

Library of Congress   BR85.L8 1920   20–26578

NL 0439779   DLC MB

Lodge, Sir Oliver Joseph, 1851–1940.
Relativity; a very elementary exposition, by Sir Oliver Lodge ... London: Methuen & Co., Ltd. [, 1925.] 41 p. 16°.

1. Relativity [physics].
N. Y. P. L.   June 8, 1926

NL 0439780   NN MiU ViU

Lodge, *Sir* Oliver Joseph, 1851–1940.
Relativity; a very elementary exposition, by Sir Oliver Lodge, F. R. S. 3d ed. London, Methuen & co. ltd. [1926]
2 p. l., 41 p., 1 l. 16¼ᶜᵐ.

1. Relativity (Physics)

Library of Congress   QC6.L45 1926 b   27–17833

NL 0439781   DLC CaBVaU OCl OU

Lodge, *Sir* Oliver Joseph, 1851–1940.
Relativity; a very elementary exposition, by Sir Oliver Lodge, F. R. S. New York, George H. Doran company [1926]
45 p. 19¼ cm.

1. Relativity (Physics)

QC6.L45   26—27550

OOxM
NL 0439782   DLC OrP OkU CU PBa PSC ICJ MB ViU MiU

VOLUME 338

1851-1940;
LODGE, Sir Oliver [Joseph], editor.
Report of the committee appointed for the
purpose of considering the subject of electrolysis, in its physical and chemical bearings.
etc. London, Spottiswoode & Co., 1887.

pp.(106). Diagrs. and other illustr.
(British Association for the Advancement of
Science.)
"From the British Association's Report.1886."

NL 0439783   MH

Lodge, *Sir* **Oliver** ᴶoseph, 1851- 1940 .

Cummins, Geraldine Dorothy, 1890-
    The road to immortality, being a description of the after-
life purporting to be communicated by the late F. W. H. Myers
through Geraldine Cummins; foreword by Sir Oliver Lodge
... with evidence of the survival of human personality by E. B.
Gibbes. London, I. Nicholson & Watson, ltd., 1933.

Lodge, *Sir* **Oliver Joseph,** 1851- 1940.

    School teaching and school reform; a course of four lec-
tures on school curricula and methods, delivered to secondary teachers and teachers in training at Birmingham
during February 1905, by Sir Oliver Lodge ... London,
Williams & Norgate, 1905.

viii, 171, ₍1₎ p. diagr. 19ᶜᵐ.

CONTENTS.—I. Curricula and methods.—II. Chiefly on teaching in history and science.—III. Secondary school reform in general.—IV. Chiefly on
boarding-school problems.—Appendix.

1. ᴊTeaching.   2. Course of study.

                                                    E 11-58
Library, U. S. Bur. of   Education LB1025.L82

NL 0439785   DHEW CtY OCU OU MiU ICJ NN MB PU PPPL

Lodge, *Sir* **Oliver Joseph,** 1851- 1940·

    School teaching and school reform; a course of four
lectures on school curricula and methods, delivered to
secondary teachers and teachers in training at Birmingham during February 1905, by Sir Oliver Lodge ... New
York, The Knickerbocker press; ₍etc., etc.₎ 1905.

ix, 149 p. 19ᶜᵐ.

CONTENTS.—I. Curricula and methods.—II. Chiefly on teaching in history
and science.—III. Secondary school reform in general.—IV. Chiefly on
boarding-school problems.—Appendix.

                                                    5-13953

NL 0439786   DLC KEmT

Lodge, *Sir* **Oliver Joseph,** 1851- 1940·
    ... Science and human progress, by Sir Oliver Lodge. Lon-
don, G. Allen & Unwin ltd. ₍1927₎

187 p., 1 l.   20ᶜᵐ.   (Halley Stewart lectures, 1926)

1. Philosophy.   2. Religion and science—1900-   3. Progress.
ɪ. Title.

                                                    27—15718
Library of Congress   BD431.L65

NL 0439787   DLC MtU NcU CaBVa MB NN

Lodge, *Sir* **Oliver Joseph,** 1851- 1940 .
    ... Science and human progress, by Sir Oliver Lodge. Lon-
don, G. Allen & Unwin ltd. ₍1927₎

187 p., 1 l.   20ᶜᵐ.   (Halley Stewart lectures, 1926)
"First published April 1927. Reprinted June 1927."

1. Philosophy.   2. Religion and science.   3. Progress.   ɪ. Title.

                                                    27—20367
Library of Congress   BD431.L65 1927 b

NL 0439788   DLC OkU

Lodge, *Sir* **Oliver Joseph,** 1851-1940.
    Science and human progress ... by Sir Oliver Lodge, ꜰ. ʀ. s.
New York, George H. Doran company ₍1927₎

viii p., 1 l., 11-243 p.   21 cm.   (Halley Stewart lectures, 1926)

1. Philosophy.   2. Religion and science—1926-1945.   3. Progress.
ɪ. Title.

                                                    27—18884
                                    OC1 OC1W PSC PU PP
NL 0439789   DLC Or WaS KEmT MiU OLak OOxM ViU ICJ

Lodge, *Sir* **Oliver Joseph,** 1851-1940.
    Science and immortality, by Sir Oliver Lodge, ꜰ. ʀ. s.
New York, Moffat, Yard and company, 1908.

7 p. l., 294 p.   21½ cm.

"This book is based upon articles by the author which have appeared in the Hibbert Journal and in the Contemporary review, and
incorporates the substance of many of those articles."—Prefatory note
to American edition.
The original edition was published under the title "Man and the
universe," London, Methuen & co., 1908, and contains a "Glossary of
technical terms," etc., and an index not found in the present edition.

1. Religion and science—1900-   2. Christianity—20th cent.
3. Immortality.   ɪ. Title.

BL240.L6 1908   215   8—28409

                KyLx OrP OKentU WaT WaWW
        NNUT MB NN CU PBa PP PSt MeB OC1W OCU KyU NIC KU
NL 0439790   DLC NcD OkU OU DNLM ODW OC1 OOxM ViU

M-film
215   Lodge, Oliver Joseph, 1851-1940.
L821s   Science and immortality.   New York, Moffat,
            Yard, 1909.
                294 p.

            Microfilm (negative) Emporia, Kan., William
            Allen White Library, 1970. 1 reel. 35 mm.

                1. Religion and science - 1900-1925. 2. Im-
            mortality. I. Title.

NL 0439791   KEmT

Lodge, *Sir* **Oliver Joseph,** 1851-1940.
    Science and immortality, by Sir Oliver Lodge, ꜰ. ʀ. s.
New York, Moffat, Yard and company, 1910.

7 p. l., 294 p.   21 cm.
"Published October, 1908 ...   Fourth printing, March, 1910."

1. Religion and science—1900-   2. Christianity—20th cent.
3. Immortality.   ɪ. Title.

BL240.L6 1910   48—42016

NL 0439792   DLC WaSp PPFr NN

Lodge, Sir Oliver Joseph, 1851-1940.
    Science and immortality ... New York,
Moffat, Yard and company, 1914.

NL 0439793   OC1W

Lodge, *Sir* **Oliver Joseph,** 1851-1940 .
    ... Science and religion, by seven men of science ... speak-
ers in Browning hall during science week, 1914 ... London, W. A. Hammond ₍1915?₎

Lodge, *Sir* **Oliver Joseph,** 1851- 1940
    ... Science of to-day, by Sir Oliver Lodge, ꜰ. ʀ. s. New
York and London, Harper & brothers, 1927.

79 p.   17½ᶜᵐ.   (Things-to-know series)
Half-title: Modern science.
Bibliography: p. 78-79.

1. Atoms.   ɪ. Title.

                                                    27—15302
Library of Congress   QC173.L83

NL 0439795   DLC Or WaS OC1 OC1U OC1W MB PSC PPF CU

Lodge, *Sir* **Oliver Joseph,** 1851-1940.
    Scienza e progresso umano. Traduzione dall'inglese di
Mariaclara e Nora Goldschmiedt. Verona, Casa editrice
Europa, 1947.

127 p.   21 cm.   (Collana di problemi del pensiero. v. 2)

1. Philosophy.   2. Religion and science—1900-   3. Progress.
ɪ. Title.

BD431.L655   50-28783

NL 0439796   DLC

Lodge, Sir Oliver Joseph, 1851- 1940 .
    Signalling across space without wires. Being
a description of the work of Hertz & his
successors... new and enlarged edition...
London, "The Electrician", n.d.
    72 p.

NL 0439797   PPD

Lodge, *Sir* **Oliver Joseph,** 1851- 1940 .
    Signalling across space without wires. Being a description
of the work of Hertz & his successors. By Prof. Oliver J.
Lodge, ꜰ. ʀ. s. 3d ed., with additional remarks concerning the
application to telegraphy, and later developments. London,
"The Electrician" printing and publishing company, limited
₍1900₎

1 p. l., ii, 133 p.   illus., diagrs.   22ᶜᵐ.

1. Telegraph, Wireless.   2. Electric waves.   ɪ. Title.

                                                    1—18577
Library of Congress   QC661.L82 1900

        ₍a36k1₎   -621.384

            ODW OU OO MiU OC1W DN PP PPD
NL 0439798   DLC OrP CaBVaU MH ODW ICJ CU NcD PHC

QC661   Lodge, Sir Oliver Joseph, 1851- 1940 .
.L82   Signalling across space without wires;
1906   being a description of the work of Hertz
        and his successors. 3d ed. New York,
        Van Nostrand ₍1906₎?
            ii, 133 p. illus. 22 cm.

NL 0439799   TU

Lodge, *Sir* **Oliver Joseph,** 1851- 1940¯.
    Signalling across space without wires. Being a de-
scription of the work of Hertz & his successors. By Prof.
Sir Oliver Lodge, ꜰ. ʀ. s. 4th ed., with additional remarks concerning the application to telegraphy, and
later developments. And a chapter on the Principles of
tuning in wireless telegraphy. London, "The Electrician" printing and publishing company, limited ₍1908₎

1 p. l., ii, 154 p.   illus., diagrs.   22ᶜᵐ.   (Lettered on cover: "The Electri-
an" series)

1. Telegraph, Wireless.   2. Electric waves.   ɪ. Title.

                                                    15—1246
Library of Congress   QC661.L82 1908

NL 0439800   DLC NcD CtY OU DN ICJ

VOLUME 338

Lodge, *Sir* Oliver Joseph, 1851-1940
Signalling across space without wires. Being a description of the work of Hertz & his successors. By Prof. Sir Oliver Lodge, F. R. S. 4th ed., with additional remarks concerning the application to telegraphy, and later developments. And a chapter on the Principles of tuning in wireless telegraphy. London, "The Electrician" printing and publishing company, limited ₁1909?₎
1 p. l., ii, 154 p. illus. diagrs. 22ᶜᵐ. (*Lettered on cover:* 'The Electrician" series)

NL   0439801   CtY

Lodge, Sir Oliver Joseph, 1851-1940.
Signalling across space without wires. Being a description of the work of Hertz & his successors. By Prof. Sir Oliver Lodge. F. R. S. 4th ed., with additional remarks concerning the application to the telegraphy, and later developments. And a chapter on the Principles of tuning in wireless telegraphy. London, "The Electrician" printing and publishing company, limited [1913]
1 p. l., ii, 154 p. illus., diagrs.   22 cm.
(On cover: "The Electrician" series)

NL   0439802   CU

LODGE, Sir OLIVER JOSEPH, 1851-1940.
Signalling through space without wires, being a description of the work of Hertz & his successors. 3. ed. (2. issue), with additional remarks concerning the application to telegraphy, and later developments. New York, D. Van Nostrand [1900?] ii, 133 p. illus. 22cm. ("The electrician" series)

1. Radio—Hist.

NL   0439803   NN OC1JC OC1

Lodge, *Sir* Oliver Joseph, 1851-1940.
Sir Oliver Lodge on the continuity of life; his presidential address to the annual meeting of the British association. Chicago, Ill., The Progressive thinker publishing house ₁19—₎
cover-title, 26 p. 19½ᶜᵐ.

1. Science—Addresses, essays, lectures.   2. Continuity.

Library of Congress   Q171.L85   504
31-7296

NL   0439804   DLC NN

Lodge, Sir Oliver ₁Joseph, 1851-1940.
Socialism and individualism, by Sidney Webb, Bernard Shaw, Sidney Ball, and Sir Oliver Lodge. New York, John Lane company, 1911.

FOR OTHER EDITIONS
SEE MAIN ENTRY

Lodge, *Sir* Oliver Joseph, 1851-1940.
... "Some debatable problems in physics." ₁Aberdeen, The University press, 1928₎
12 p. 24½ᶜᵐ. (*On cover:* The Faraday society ... First Spiers memorial lecture, 9th Nov., 1928)
Caption title.
At head of title: First Spiers memorial lecture, by Sir Oliver Lodge ...

1. Physics—Addresses, essays, lectures.   I. Title.

Library of Congress   QC71.L83
29-18181

NL   0439806   DLC

530.1
S811
Lodge, *Sir* Oliver Joseph, 1851-1940.
... Some debatable problems in physics. [By Sir Oliver Lodge. London, 1928.]
12 p. 1 diagr. 24½ᶜᵐ.   (The Faraday Society. 1st Spiers memorial lecture.)
Caption title.

NL   0439807   ICJ

133.9
L82s
Lodge, Oliver Joseph, 1851-1940.
Spiritualism recognized as a science ₁including₎ The reality of the spiritual world. Lily Dale, N. Y., Dale News [193-?]
80 p. ports. illus. 19 cm.

1. Spiritualism. I. Title: The reality of the spiritual world.

NL   0439808   N

Lodge, Oliver Joseph, 1851-1940.
... States of mind which make and miss discoveries, with some ideas about metals; nineteenth May lecture... London, 1929.
p. [345]-376.   front. (port.) illus., diagrs. 22 cm.
Cover-title.
Reprinted from the "Journal of the Institute of metals", vol. 41, no. 1, 1929.
At head of title: Institute of metals.

NL   0439809   RPB

Lodge, *Sir* Oliver Joseph, 1851-1940 ₎
The substance of faith allied with science.   A catechism for parents and teachers, by Sir Oliver Lodge ... 6th ed. London, Methuen & co. ₁1907₎
xii, 135, ₁1₎ p. 19½ᶜᵐ.

1. Religion and science.   I. Title.

E 16-211

Library, U. S. Bur. of   Education

NL   0439810   DHEW CaBVaU NIC

Lodge, *Sir* Oliver Joseph, 1851-1940.
The substance of faith allied with science; a catechism for parents and teachers, by Sir Oliver Lodge ... New York and London, Harper & brothers, 1907.
viii, 144 p. 19½ cm.

1. Religion and science—1900-   I. Title.

BL240.L65   215   7—9613

MB NN OC1W OO ViU KEmT IEG TU NN MiU NcU OC1 CoU
NL   0439811   DLC PPL PPPD WaS PHC PP Or OrP PBa PPC

BL240
L63
1908
Lodge, Sir Oliver Joseph, 1851-1940.
The substance of faith allied with science; a catechism for parents and teachers.   9th ed.   London, Methuen ₁1908₎.
xii,135 p.

1. Religion and science - 1900-
I. Title.

NL   0439812   CU ICJ PU

LODGE, Sir Oliver Joseph, 1851-1940.
The substance of faith allied with science; a catechism for parents and teachers. London, Methuen & co., [1915].

NL   0439813   MH

215
L821su
1928
Lodge, Sir Oliver Joseph, 1851-1940.
The substance of faith allied with science. A catechism for parents and teachers, by Sir Oliver Lodge ... 15th ed.   London, Methuen & co. ₁1928₎
xii, 135, ₁1₎ p.

1. Religion and science.   I. Title.

NL   0439814   TxFTC

LODGE, Sir Oliver [Joseph], 1851-1940.
Sur les électrons.   Traduite de l'anglais par E.Nugues [et] J.Péridier.   Préface de P.Langevin.   Paris,Gauthier-Villars, 1906.

At head of title: Actualités scientifiques.

NL   0439815   MH

Lodge, *Sir* Oliver Joseph, 1851-1940.
Marchant, *Sir* James, 1867-   ed.
Survival, by Sir Oliver Lodge ... Stanley De Brath ... Lady Grey of Fallodon ... ₁and others₎ edited by Sir James Marchant.   London and New York, G. P. Putnam's sons ₁1924₎

Lodge, Sir Oliver Joseph, 1851-1940.
The survival of man; a study in unrecognized human faculty.   1909.

NL   0439817   ICN

Lodge, *Sir* Oliver Joseph, 1851-1940.
The survival of man; a study in unrecognised human faculty, by Sir Oliver Lodge, F. R. S.   London, Methuen & co. ₁1909₎
xi, 357, ₁1₎ p. diagrs. 22½ᶜᵐ.

1. Psychical research.   9-29961

Library of Congress   ＼ BF1031.L7

NL   0439818   DLC PSt NN PU OC1

Lodge, *Sir* Oliver Joseph, 1851-1940.
The survival of man; a study in unrecognized human faculty, by Sir Oliver Lodge, F. R. S.   New York, Moffat, Yard and company, 1909.
6 p. l., 361 p. 21 cm.

1. Psychical research.

BF1031.L7 1909a   9—30857

OKentU KyLxCB NIC
NN DNLM ViU NcD NjP TxU OCU IEG MtU Or WaS IdU KEmT
NL   0439819   DLC PU PP PWcS PPD PPL MiU OC1W ICJ MB

LODGE, Sir Oliver [Joseph], 1851-1940.
The survival of man; a study in unrecognised human faculty. 3d ed. London, Methuen & co., [1910].

NL   0439820   MH

VOLUME 338

Lodge, Sir Oliver Joseph, 1851-1940
The survival of man; a study in
unrecognized human faculty ... London,
ₑ1911ₑ
xi, 357 p.

NL 0439821   ODW

Lodge, Sir Oliver Joseph, 1851-1940 .
The survival of man; a study in unrecognised
human faculty ... 5th ed. London, Methuen &
co., ltd. [1911]
xi, 357, ₑ1ₑp. diagrs. 22½cm.

1. Physical research. I. Title.

NL 0439822   CtY-M

133.07   Lodge, Sir Oliver Joseph, 1851-1940.
L82s   The survival of man; a study in unrecognised
1915   human faculty. ₑ5th ed.ₑ London, Methuen
         ₑ1915ₑ
         239p. 18cm.

1. Psychical research. I. Title.

NL 0439823   IU

LODGE, Sir Oliver Joseph, 1851-1940.
The survival of man; a study in unrecognised
human faculty. 7th ed. London, Methuen & Co.
[1916].

NL 0439824   MH

Lodge, *Sir* **Oliver Joseph,** 1851-1940 .
The survival of man; a study in unrecognized human **faculty,**
by Sir Oliver Lodge, f. r. s. New and enl. ed. New York,
George H. Doran company ₑ1920ₑ
3 p. l., v-viii p., 3 l., 379 p. 22½ᵐ.

1. Psychical research.
Library of Congress   BF1031.L7 1920   20—5130

OrCS CaBVa
NL 0439825   DLC OEac OC1 OC1W PSC KU WU CaBVaU OrP

Lodge, Sir Oliver Joseph, 1851-1940

BF1031   The survival of man; a study in unrecognised
L667   human faculty. 10th ed. London, Methuen
1926   [1926]
         239p. 18cm.

NL 0439826   RPB PHC

Lodge, Sir Oliver Joseph , 1851-1940 .
The survival of man; a study in unrecognised human faculty.
London: Methuen & Co., Ltd.ₑ 1909-27.ₑ 357 p. diagr., illus.
11. ed.   12°.

Contents: Aims and objects of psychical research. Experimental telepathy or
thought-transference. Spontaneous telepathy and clairvoyance. Automatism and
lucidity.

1. Title. 2. Psychical research.
N.Y.P.L.   September 4, 1931

NL 0439827   NN

LODGE, Sir Oliver Joseph, 1851-1940 .
The survival of man; a study in unrecognized
human faculty. New York, George H. Doran
Company ₑ1929ₑ
viii, 37ₑpp. 22.1cm.

"New and enlarged edition"

NL 0439828   MH-AH

LODGE, Sir Oliver [Joseph], 1851-1940 .
La survivance humaine; étude de facultés non
encore reconnues. Traduit de l'Anglais sur la
3e éd., par H. Bourbon. Préface de J. Maxwell.
Paris, F. Alcan, 1912.

On cover: Bibliothèque de philosophie con-
temporaine.

NL 0439829   MH PP

Lodge, *Sir* **Oliver Joseph,** 1851-1940 .
Talks about radio, with some pioneering history and some
hints and calculations for radio amateurs, by Sir Oliver Lodge,
f. r. s. New York, George H. Doran company ₑ*1925ₑ
xiv p., 1 l., 17-287 p. diagrs. 21ᵐ.

1. Radio.   ɪ. Title.
                                                    25—23732
Library of Congress   TK6550.L53 1925 a

ICJ MB PP PU
NL 0439830   DLC MtU OrP WaS CU MiU OCU OC1 OOxM ViU

Lodge, *Sir* **Oliver Joseph,** 1851-1940 .
Talks about wireless, with some pioneering history and
some hints and calculations for wireless amateurs, by Sir
Oliver Lodge. London, New York ₑetc.ₑ Cassell and company, ltd. ₑ1925ₑ
xiii, 251, ₑ1ₑ p. diagrs. 19½ᵐ.

1. Radio.   ɪ. Title.
                                                    26—5333
Library of Congress   TK6550.L53 1925

NL 0439831   DLC CaBViP NN

Lodge, Sir Oliver Joseph, 1851-1940.
Les théories modernes de l'électricité; essai
d'une théorie nouvelle. Traduit de l'anglais
et annoté, par E. Meylan.   Paris, Gauthier-
Villars, 1891.
xiii, 216 p. illus. 23 cm.

NL 0439832   OkU DLC-P4 PPF

Joseph, 1851-1940.
Lodge, *Sir* **Oliver,** Prónn og sköpun.
Íslenskað hefur Knútur Arngrímsson.
Reykjavík, Þýðandinn (Prentsm. Guten-
berg), 1927. 8°. pp. 94, (2).   IcM1L815

NL 0439833   NIC

Joseph, 1851-1940.
Lodge, *Sir* **Oliver,** Veruleikur óṡýni-
legs heims. Í íslenzkri þýðingu eftir Harald Níelsson. Sérpr. úr Ísafold. [Reyk-
javík], Ísafoldarprentsmiðja, 1915. sm.
8°. pp. 32.   IcH32M311

NL 0439834   NIC

Lodge, *Sir* Oliver Joseph, 1851-1940.
La vie et la matière, par Sir Oliver Lodge, traduit de l'anglais
par J. Maxwell. 4. éd. Paris, F. Alcan, 1930.
2 p. l., 152, ₑ2ₑ p. 19ᵐ. (*On cover:* Bibliothèque de philosophie con-
temporaine)

1. Haeckel, Ernst Heinrich Philipp August, 1834-1919. Die welt-
räthsel. 2. Monism. 3. Life—Origin. 4. Philosophy and religion.   ɪ.
Maxwell, Joseph, 1858-   tr. ɪɪ. Title.
                                                    45—32512
Library of Congress   BD331.L813

NL 0439835   DLC

Lodge, *Sir* **Oliver Joseph,** 1851-1940 .   **940.9236 R501**
The war and after. Short chapters on subjects of serious practical
import for the average citizen in A.D. 1915 onwards, by Sir Oliver
Lodge, ... London, Methuen & Co., [1915].
xiii, 235, [1] p. 17½ᵐ.

NL 0439836   ICJ NN PP PHC MH NjP

Lodge, Sir Oliver ₑJosephₑ, 1851-1940 .
The war and after; short chapters on subjects of serious practical import for the average citizen in A. D. 1915 onwards.   London: Methuen & Co., Ltd. ₑ1915.ₑ xiii, 240 p.   4. ed.   16°.

NL 0439837   NN

Lodge, *Sir* **Oliver Joseph,** 1851-1940.
The war and after; short chapters on subjects of serious
practical import for the average citizen in A. D. 1915 onwards, by Sir Oliver Lodge ... 5th ed. London, Methuen &
co., ltd ₑ1915ₑ
xiii, 240 p. 17 cm.
"First published August 6th, 1915."

1. European war, 1914-1918.   ɪ. Title.
D517.L57   16—762

NL 0439838   DLC WaS

Lodge, *Sir* **Oliver Joseph,** 1851-1940 .
War & after, short chapters on subjects of
serious practical import for the average citizen
in A.D. 1915 onwards. Ed. 7.
London, Methuen, 1916.
240 p.

NL 0439839   PU

Lodge, *Sir* Oliver Joseph, 1851-1940 .   2309a.456
The war and after. Short chapters on subjects of serious practical
import for the average citizen in A.D. 1915 onwards. 8th edition.
— London. Methuen & Co., Ltd. [1916.] 240 pp. 16½ cm., in 8s.

NL 0439840   MB MH

Lodge, *Sir* **Oliver Joseph,** 1851-1940.
The war and after; short chapters on subjects of serious
practical import for the average citizen from a. d. 1915 onwards, by Sir Oliver Lodge ... New York, George H. Doran
company ₑ*1918ₑ
2 p. l., vii-xiv, 252 p. 20½ cm.
First published in 1915.

1. European war, 1914-1918.   ɪ. Title.
D517.L57 1918   18—9435

PPA PPL PP OU OOxM OC1W ViU
NL 0439841   DLC Wa CaBViP OrSaW LU ICRL TNJ NIC MsU

VOLUME 338

Lodge, *Sir* **Oliver Joseph,** 1851–1940.
Der weltäther, von Sir Oliver Lodge. Übersetzt von Hilde Barkhausen ... Braunschweig, F. Vieweg & sohn, 1911.
5 p. l., 107 p. illus., diagrs. 22½ cm. (*Added t.-p.:* Die wissenschaft; sammlung naturwissenschaftlicher und mathematischer monographien. 41. hft.)

1. Ether (of space)   I. Barkhausen, Hilde, tr.   II. Title.
A 13—522

Johns Hopkins Univ.   Library
for Library of Congress   [a66b]

NL 0439842   MdBJ PU ICJ

Lodge, Sir Oliver Joseph, 1851–1940.
Why I believe in personal immortality, by Sir Oliver Lodge. Garden City, N. Y., Doubleday, Doran [c1928]
xii, 151 p. front. (port.) plates.

1. Psychical research. 2. Immortality.
I. Title.

NL 0439843   WaU NIC OClh OClW

BF
1031
L822w   **Lodge, Sir Oliver Joseph,** 1851–1940.
Why I believe in personal immortality.
London, Cassell, [1928]
vii, 151p. ports., plates. 20cm.

NL 0439844   ICMcC

Lodge, *Sir* **Oliver Joseph,** 1851–1940.
Why I believe in personal immortality, by Sir Oliver Lodge. London [etc.] Cassell and company, ltd. [1928]
viii, 151, [1] p. front. (port.) plates. 19½ᵐ.
"First published June, 1928 ... fourth impression, September, 1928."

1. Psychical research. 2. Immortality.   I. Title.

Library of Congress   BF1031.L75
28-24496

OCl
NL 0439845   DLC CaBVa Or MtBC NN PSC ODW MiU LU-NO

Lodge, *Sir* **Oliver Joseph,** 1851–1940.
Why I believe in personal immortality, by Sir Oliver Lodge. Garden City, N. Y., Doubleday, Doran & company, inc., 1929.
viii p., 1 l., 206 p. 19½ᵐ.

1. Psychical research. 2. Immortality.   I. Title.

Library of Congress   BF1031.L75 1929
29-786

00 00xM ICJ MB NN PP PPC
NL 0439846   DLC OrP WaS MH-AH OKentU MiU NcD ViU

Lodge, *Sir* **Oliver Joseph,** 1851–1940.
Why I believe in personal immortality, by Sir Oliver Lodge. London [etc.] Cassell and company, ltd. [1939]
xii, 151 p. front. (port.) plates. 19½ᵐ.
"First published June 1928 ... sixth edition, November 1939."

1. Psychical research. 2. Immortality.   I. Title.
40-85154

Library of Congress   BF1031.L75 1939
[2]   [159.961] 133.072

NL 0439847   DLC RPB

Lodge, *Sir* **Oliver Joseph,** 1851–1940.
The work of Hertz and some of his successors. Being the substance of a lecture delivered at the Royal institution on Friday evening, June 1, 1894, by Prof. Oliver Lodge, F. R. S. With additions and appendices ... London, "The Electrician" printing and publishing company, limited [1894]
1 p. l., 58 p. front. (port.) illus., diagrs. 22ᵐ.
"Reprinted from 'The Electrician,' and revised by Prof. Lodge."

1. Hertz, Heinrich Rudolph, 1857–1894. 2. Physics—Hist.
44-52734

Library of Congress   QC16.H4L6

MH TxU
NL 0439848   DLC IdU NcD-MC PSt OClW NIC CtY ODW OU

Lodge, Sir Oliver Joseph, 1851–1940.
The work of Hertz and his successors. Being a description of the method of signalling across space without wires by electric waves. By Prof. Oliver Lodge ... London: The Electrician Prtg. and Pub. Co., Ltd. [1897] 2 p. l., 73 p. incl. diagrs., front. (port.), illus., table. 2. ed. 8°. (The electrician series.)

1. Telegraphy (Wireless).—History.   2. Series.
N. Y. P. L.   September 15, 1920.

NL 0439849   NN ICJ

Lodge, Sir Oliver Joseph, 1851–1940.
The work of Hertz and his successors; being a description of the method of signalling across space without wires by electric waves. 2d ed. Van Nostrand [1898]
73 p. port. diagrs. ("The electrician" series)

Later ed. has title: Signalling across space without wires.

NL 0439850   MiD

Lodge, Oliver Raymond William Wynlayne, ed.

Law

Snell, Edmund Henry Turner, 1841–1869.
Rivington's epitome of the twenty-third edition of Snell's equity, by Oliver Lodge. London, Sweet & Maxwell, 1948.

Lodge, Oliver William Foster, 1878–
The betrayer, and other poems, including The labyrinth. Gloucester, Printed by J. Bellows, 1950 [°1949]
96 p. 19 cm.

I. Title.

PR6023.O32B4   821.91   50-20983

NL 0439852   DLC

822
L82l   **Lodge,** Oliver William Foster, 1878 –
The labyrinth, a tragedy in one act.
London, D. Nutt, 1911.
12p. 19cm. (Pilgrim players series, 2)

NL 0439853   IU MiU

Lodge, Oliver William Foster, 1878–
Love's wine corked; a poem in twenty-four measures. Gloucester [Eng.] 1948.
37 p. 19 cm.

I. Title.

PR6023.O32L6   821.91   48-26718*

NL 0439854   DLC RPB

Lodge, Oliver William Foster, 1878–
Poems by Oliver W. F. Lodge...   Birmingham: Cornish Bros., 1915. 3 p.l., (1)6–209(1) p.   8°.
One poem reprinted from the Outlook.

1. Poetry (English).
N. Y. L.   December 8, 1915.

NL 0439855   NN MB OClW MiU MB

Lodge, Oliver William Foster, 1878–
Six Englishmen.   Birmingham, Cornish Bros. 1915.
23 p.   22 cm.
Contents. - Marlowe. - Ben Jonson. - Shelley. - Keats. - Swinburne. - To William Morris.
1. Authors, English. I. Title.

NL 0439856   NIC

Lodge, Oliver William Foster, 1876–
Summer stories. Birmingham, Eng., Cornish Brothers, 1911.
viii, 199 p. 24 cm.

'Sixty copies ... have been printed, and the type distributed. Fifty-five are for sale.'

NL 0439857   MoKU

Lodge, Oliver William Foster, 1878–
What art is, by Oliver W. F. Lodge, with an introduction by Sir Oliver Lodge.   London: Hodder and Stoughton [1927].
56 p.   16°.

1. Aesthetics. 2. Lodge, Sir Oliver   Joseph, 1851–
N. Y. L.   July 30, 1928

NL 0439858   NN

Lodge, John Ellerton, 1878–
... Japanese netsuke
see under   Boston. Museum of fine arts.

D767
.99
.G8U48   **Lodge,** Orlan Robert, 1917–
U. S. *Marine Corps.*
The recapture of Guam [by] O. R. Lodge, USMC. [Washington] Historical Branch, G–3 Division, Headquarters, U. S. Marine Corps, 1954.

B615.06
So132   **LODGE,** Percy G
A short history of the Society of apothecaries of London, with an account of the Apothecaries' hall of Ireland. London, J. & A. Churchill, 1901.
61 p. 19cm.
1. Society of apothecaries of London. 2. Apothecaries' hall of Ireland, Dublin.

NL 0439861   MnU

VOLUME 338

Lodge, R   H

Waipahu at war; the war record of a Hawaiian sugar plantation community. [Waipahu, T. H., Oahu Sugar Co., 1945]

72 p. illus. 36 cm.

1. Waipahu, Hawaii. 2. World War, 1939-1945 - Hawaiian Island. I. Oahu Sugar Co., Ltd.

NL 0439862   CaBVaU

Lodge (R. T.) Small-pox; how to annihilate it; or observations on the pernicious consequences of imperfect vaccination, and on the necessity of re-vaccination. 26 pp. 8°. *Liverpool, H. Greenwood,* 1885. [P., v. 1432.]

NL 0439863   DNLM

Lodge, Raymond, 1889-1915. FOR OTHER EDITIONS SEE MAIN ENTRY
Lodge, *Sir* Oliver Joseph, 1851-
Raymond; or, Life and death, with examples of the evidence for survival of memory and affection after death, by Sir Oliver J. Lodge. With eighteen illustrations. New York, George H. Doran company [°1916]

Lodge, Raymond, 1889-1915.

Lodge, *Sir* Oliver Joseph, 1851-
Raymond revised; a new and abbreviated edition of "Raymond, or Life and death", with an additional chapter, by Sir Oliver J. Lodge. With twelve illustrations. London, Methuen & co., ltd. [1922]

Lodge, Reginald B.
Bird-hunting through wild Europe, by R. B. Lodge ... with 124 illustrations, from photographs by the author. London, R. Culley [1908]

333, [1] p. front., plates. 22ᶜᵐ.

1. Birds—Europe. 2. Photography of birds.

Library of Congress   QL690.A1L7   9-25304

NL 0439866   DLC OrP CtY ICJ

Lodge, Reginald B   3908.162
Bird-hunting through wild Europe. — New York. Appleton & Co. 1909. 333, (1) pp. Plates. 22½ cm., in 8s.

H 1311 — T.r. — Europe. Ornith. — Birds.

NL 0439867   MB

---

s598.2   Lodge, Reginald B
L82b   The birds and their story; a book for young folk. London, C. H. Kelly [1905] 288p. illus., col.plates. 21cm.

1. Birds.

NL 0439868   IU

Lodge, Reginald B   598.2
                           Q918
One hundred photographs from life of British birds, with extensive notes on their habits, by R. B. Lodge ... London, New York [etc.] Cassell and Co., Ltd., 1909.

95 p. incl. plates. 18ᶜᵐ.   (*On cover:* Douglas English nature books. no. 2)

NL 0439869   ICJ

Lodge, Reginald B.
One hundred photographs of bird life. London: S. H. Bousfield & Co., 1907. 95 p. illus. 12°.

1. Birds. 2. Title.
N. Y. P. L.   July 5, 1912.

NL 0439870   NN

Lodge, Reginald B   L598.2 Q312
[1903] Pictures of bird life on woodland, meadow, mountain and marsh, by R. B. Lodge. .... With numerous colour and half-tone illustrations from photographs from life by the author. London, S. H. Bousfield & Co., ltd., 1903.
376 p. col. front., illus., 7 col. pl. 25½ᶜᵐ.

NL 0439871   ICJ CtY

QL
690
A1L6
1904
Lodge, Reginald B
Pictures of bird life on woodland, meadow, mountain and marsh. With over 200 half-tone illustrations from photographs from life by the author. 2d ed. London, S.H. Bousfield [1904]
376 p. illus. (part col.) 26 cm.

1. Birds--Europe. 2. Birds--Pictorial works. I. Title.

NL 0439872   LU IU

Lodge, Reginald B.
The story of hedgerow and pond; illustrations from drawings by G. E. Lodge. London: Charles H. Kelly [1911?]. iii-vii, 298 p., 8 col'd pl. illus. 12°.

1. Birds. 2. Outdoor life. 3. Title.
N. Y. P. L.   June 14. 1912.

NL 0439873   NN

Lmd02   Lodge, Sir Richard, 1855-1936.
S=2   Cardinal Beaufort ... Oxford, T. Shrimpton
1875   & son, 1875.
        1 p. l., 77p. 21½cm. ([Stanhope historical essay, 1875])

1. Beaufort, Henry, cardinal, ca. 1377-1447. I. Ser.

NL 0439874   CtY ICN

Lodge, Richard, 1855-1936.
The close of the middle ages, 1273-1494, by R. Lodge ... London, Rivingtons, 1901.
xi, 570 p. 4 fold. maps. 19¼ᶜᵐ. [Periods of European history, general editor, A. Hassall. Period III]
"Bibliographical note": p. x-xi.

1. Europe—Hist. 2. Middle ages—Hist. I. Title.

Library of Congress   D118.L82   1-22761/4
                                        F04

PP PU PWcS OC1W
NL 0439875   DLC NN TxU FMU Or OrCS WaWW PPFr PPPL

Lodge, *Sir* Richard, 1855-1936.
The close of the middle ages, 1273-1494, by R. Lodge ... New York, The Macmillan company, 1901.
xi, 570 p. incl. geneal. tables. fold. maps. 19½ᶜᵐ. (*On verso of half-title:* Periods of European history. Period III)
"Bibliographical note": p. x-xi.

1. Middle ages—Hist.
                                        1—13067
Library of Congress   D202.L72

NL 0439876   DLC WaS CaBVaU KU OOxM

D
118
.L72
1902
Lodge, Sir Richard, 1855-1936.
The close of the middle ages, 1273-1494, by R. Lodge. 2d.ed. London, Rivingtons, 1902. xxx, 570p. 4 fold.maps. 20cm. (Periods of European history. Period III)

"Bibliographical note": p.x-xi.

1. Europe - History. 2. Middle ages - History. I. Title.

NNUT OC1W OU
NL 0439877   NNCU-G ViU NN InU MBtS MiU NcD IdPI DNW

D202
L72
1904
Lodge, Sir Richard, 1855-1936.
The close of the middle ages, 1273-1494. 3d ed. London, Rivingtons, 1904. xxx, 570 p. 4 fold. maps. 20cm. (Periods of European history. Period III)

1. Middle ages - Hist. 2. Europe - History. I. Title.

CLSU DCU
NL 0439878   COU OEac OO NjP PPPL PPL PU ViU MiU KyU

---

ar W
7353
Lodge, Sir Richard, 1855-1936.
The close of the Middle Ages, 1272-1494. 3d ed. London, Rivingtons, 1906. xxx, 570 p. maps. 20cm. (Periods of European history, period 3)

1. Middle ages--Hist.

NL 0439879   NIC WaTC PV OC1ND PPSteph NjP

D
202
L72
1910
Lodge, Sir Richard, 1855-1936.
The close of the middle ages, 1272-1494, by R. Lodge. 4th ed. London, Rivingtons, 1910. 570p. illus. 20cm. (Periods of European history, Period III)

Includes bibliography.

1. Middle ages - Hist. (Series)

NL 0439880   MU MH PHC PPMSJ OU OC1W NNCU-G

Lodge, Richard, 1855-1936.
The close of the middle ages, 1273-1494, by R. Lodge ... 5th impression—4th ed. London, Rivingtons, 1915.
1 p. l., IVI-xxx, 570 p. incl. geneal. tables. 4 fold. maps. 20ᶜᵐ. ([Periods of European history] Period III)
"Bibliographical note": p. x-xi.

1. Middle ages—Hist.

Library of Congress   D202.L72 1915   16—6798

NL 0439881   DLC ViU

VOLUME 338

Lodge, Sir Richard, 1855-1936
The close of the middle ages, 1273-1494
... New York, The Macmillan company, 1901.
London, Rivingtons, [1915].
xxx

NL 0439882   OC1

D202
L72
1920
Lodge, Sir Richard, 1855-1936.
The close of the middle ages, 1272-1494,
by Sir R. Lodge ... 5th ed., 6th impression.
London, Rivingtons, 1920.
1 p. t., [v]-xxx, 570 p. incl. geneal.
tables. 4 fold. maps. 20cm. ([Periods
of European history] Period III)

1. Middle ages - Hist.

NL 0439883   GU

Lodge, *Sir Richard*, 1855-1936.
The close of the middle ages, 1272-1494, by Sir R. Lodge ...
5th ed., 7th impression. London, Rivingtons, 1922.
1 p. l., [v]-xxx, 570 p. incl. geneal. tables. 4 fold. maps. 20cm. ([Periods
of European history] Period III)
"Bibliographical note": p. x-xi.

1. Middle ages—Hist.
                                                        24—3967
Library of Congress   D202.L72 1922

PSC
NL 0439884   DLC FMU TU MH NcU OC1JC OLak ODW PRosC

Lodge, Sir Richard, 1855-1936
The close of the middle ages 1273-1494
... 5th ed., 9th impression. London,
Rivingtons, 1926.
570 p.

(Periods of European history, Period III)

NL 0439885   OC1h

D
202
L72
1928
Lodge, Sir Richard, 1855-1936.
The close of the middle ages, 1273-1494, by
R. Lodge. 5th ed. London, Rivingtons, 1928.
570p. illus. 20cm. (Periods of European
history, Period III)

Includes bibliography.

1. Middle ages - Hist. (Series)

NL 0439886   MU NN MiU

Lodge, Sir Richard, 1855-1936.
The close of the middle ages, 1273-1494, by Sir
R. Lodge ... 9th impression, 5th ed. London,
Rivingtons, 1928.
1 p. l., [v]-xxx, 570 p. incl. geneal. tables.
4 fold. maps. 20 cm. ([Periods of European
history] Period III)
"Bibliographical note": p. x-xi.

NL 0439887   MiU

Lodge, Sir Richard, 1855-1936.
The close of the middle ages, 1273-
1494, by R. Lodge... 10 impression -
5th ed. London, Rivingtons, 1935.

NL 0439888   KAS

LODGE, Sir RICHARD, 1855-1936.
The close of the Middle Ages, 1273-1494. 5th ed.,
11th impression.   London, Rivington, 1949.

1 p. l., [v]-xxx, 570 p. incl. geneal. tables.
4 fold. maps. (Periods of European history. Period
III)

NL 0439889   DDO

Lodge, Richard, 1855 - 1936.
Conclusion.   (In: La femme; sa situation réelle, sa situation
idéale. Paris, 1913. 12°. p. 231-263.)

1. Woman.
N. Y. P. L.   April 23, 1913.

NL 0439890   NN

Lodge, *Sir Richard*, 1855-1936.

Lodge, Eleanor Constance, 1869-
The end of the middle age, 1273-1453; by Eleanor C. Lodge
... with an introduction by R. Lodge ... With fourteen maps.
London, Methuen & co. [1909]

Lodge, *Sir Richard*, 1855-1936.
The English factory at Lisbon; some chapters in its history, by Sir Richard Lodge ...
(In Royal historical society, London. Transactions. London, 1871-
22cm. 4th ser., v. 16 (1933) p. 211-247)

1. Gt. Brit.—Foreign relations—Portugal. 2. Portugal—Foreign rela-
tions—Gt. Brit. 3. British in Lisbon. I. Title.
Title from Newberry   Libr.   A C 36-3041
Library of Congress   [DA20.R9 ser. 4, vol. 16]
                             [2]   (942.0062)

NL 0439892   ICN

Lodge, *Sir Richard*, 1855-1936.
English neutrality in the war of the Polish succession; a
commentary upon Diplomatic instructions, vol. VI, France,
1727-1744. By Sir Richard Lodge ...
(In Royal historical society, London. Transactions. London,
1871-   22 cm. 4th ser., v. 14 (1931) p. 141-173)

1. Polish succession, War of, 1733-1738. 2. Gt. Brit.—Foreign relations—1727-1760. 3. Gt. Brit.—Neutrality. 4. British diplomatic instructions, 1689-1789 ... edited for the Royal historical society.
I. Title.
[DA20.R9 ser. 4, vol. 14]   A C 36—3021

Newberry Library
for Library of Congress

NL 0439893   ICN OU OCU

Lodge, *Sir Richard*, 1855-1936.
An episode in Anglo-Russian relations during the war of
the Austrian succession, by Sir Richard Lodge ...
(In Royal historical society, London. Transactions. London,
1871-   22 cm. 4th ser., v. 9 (1926) p. 63-83)
The 'episode' was occasioned by Lord Handford's private secretary,
Friedrich Lorentz.

1. Gt. Brit.—Foreign relations—Russia. 2. Russia—Foreign relations—Gt. Brit. 3. Lorentz, Friedrich. I. Title.
[DA20.R9 ser. 4, vol. 9]   (942.0062)   A C 36—1655

Newberry Library
for Library of Congress   [a54c½]

NL 0439894   ICN OU

Lodge, Richard, 1855-1936.   2829.37
Germany and Prussia. A historical sketch.
(In German culture . . . Pp. 1-33. New York. 1915.)

K6490 — Germany. Hist. — Prussia. Hist.

NL 0439895   MB

Lodge, *Sir Richard*, 1855-1936.
Great Britain & Prussia in the eighteenth century, being the Ford lectures delivered in the University of Oxford, Lent term, 1922, by Sir Richard Lodge ... Oxford,
Clarendon press, 1923.
x, 221, [1] p. 23½cm.

1. Gt. Brit.—For. rel.—Prussia. 2. Prussia—For. rel.—Gt. Brit.

Library of Congress   DA47.2.L55   23—14810

PPT DAU GU NjP MeB CtY PHC PU OO NN MB PBm
NL 0439896   DLC OU MiU OC1 OC1W CaBVaU WaTC WaWW

DA47.2
L63
Lodge, Sir Richard, 1855-1936
Great Britain & Prussia in the eighteenth
century, being the Ford lectures delivered in
the University of Oxford, Lent term, 1922.
Oxford, Clarendon Press, 1923.
x, 221 p.
Photocopy. Ann Arbor, Mich., University
Microfilms, 1967. x, 221 p. (on double leaves)
23 cm.
1. Gt. Brit. - For. rel. - Prussia. I. Title.

NL 0439897   CtY AAP

Lodge, *Sir Richard*, 1855-1936.
The history of England from the restoration to the death
of William III. (1660-1702) by Richard Lodge ... London,
New York, Bombay, and Calcutta, Longmans, Green, and
co., 1910.
xix, 517 p. 2 fold. maps, 2 geneal. tab. 23 cm. (Half-title: The
Political history of England ... ed. by W. Hunt ... and R. L. Poole ...
VIII)
"Authorities": p. 477-491.

1. Gt. Brit.—Hist.—1660-1714. 2. Gt. Brit.—Pol. & govt.—1660-
1714.
DA30.P76   10—9488

OrP IdU WaSp OrSaW DAU FTaSU CaBVa Wa CaBVaU WaS
PBm NcD OU MB MiU-C NN OC1 OC1W OOxM OCU OU MU WaU
NL 0439898   DLC ViU OCX MnU MiU TxU PPPD PHC PU PPT

Lodge, Sir Richard, 1855-1936
The history of England from the
restoration to the death of William III.
(1660-1702) by ... London, New York,
Bombay, and Calcutta, Longmans, Green
and co., 1910.
3 ed.

NL 0439899   OO

Lodge, *Sir Richard*, 1855-1936.
The history of England from the restoration to the death of
William III. (1660-1702) by Richard Lodge ... *London, New
York, Bombay,   Calcutta, Longmans, Green, and co., 1918.
xix, 517 p. 2 fold. maps, 2 geneal. tab. 23cm. (Half-title: The polit-
ical history of England ... ed. by W. Hunt ... and R. L. Poole ... VIII)
"Authorities": p. 477-491.
*New impression.

NL 0439900   ViU WaSpG MiU-C PSC

Lodge, *Sir Richard*, 1855-1936.
The history of England from the restoration to
the death of William III. (1660-1702) by Richard
Lodge ... New impr. London, New York, Toronto,
[etc., etc.], Longmans, Green, and co., 1923.
3 p. l., ix-xix, 517 p. 2 fold. maps, 2 geneal.
tab. 23cm. (Half-title: The political history of
England ... ed. by W. Hunt ... and R. L. Poole ...
VIII)
"Authorities": p. 477-491.

NL 0439901   ViU WaT OrPR ODW PRosC

VOLUME 338

Lodge, *Sir Richard,* 1855-1936.
A history of Europe, period 1789-1920, by Sir Richard Lodge ... and D. B. Horn ... London, J. Murray ₁1927₎
xxvi, 608 p. 19ᶜᵐ.
Reissue of the latter part (period 1789-1878) of Sir Richard Lodge's Student's modern Europe, with the addition of supplementary chapters by D. B. Horn covering the period 1871-1920. These supplementary chapters are also issued separately.

1. Europe—Hist.—1789-1900. 2. Europe—Hist.—20th cent. I. Horn, D. B.

Library of Congress   D209.L85
                     29-12429

NL 0439902   DLC CtY DNW

Lodge, Sir Richard, 1855-1936.
History of modern Europe from the capture of Constantinople by the Turks to the Treaty of Berlin 1878.
N.Y., Harper, 1893.
772 p.

NL 0439903   PP

Lodge, Sir Richard, 1855-1936.
A history of modern Europe from the capture of Constantinople, 1453, to the Treaty of Berlin, 1878. 4th ed. London, Murray, 1897.

xxviii, 781 p. (The students modern Europe)

NL 0439904   MH

D208
.L6   Lodge, Sir Richard, 1855-1936.
A history of modern Europe from the capture of Constantinople by the Turks to the treaty of Berlin, 1878. New York and London, Harper, 1898.
xxix, 772p. 20cm. (The student's modern Europe)

NL 0439905   NNU-W PU

Lodge, Richard, 1855-1936.
History of modern Europe, from the capture of Constantinople by the Turks to the treaty of Berlin, 1878. N.Y. 1899.

Student's modern Europe.

NL 0439906   ODW OCU

Lodge, Sir Richard, 1855-1936.
A history of modern Europe, from the capture of Constantinople by the Turks to the Treaty of Berlin, 1878. New York, American Book Co. [1903]

xxix, 772 p. (The student's modern Europe)

NL 0439907   MH

Lodge, Sir Richard, 1855-1936.
History of modern Europe from the capture of Constantinople, 1453, to the treaty of Berlin, 1878. ₂2d ed.₎ London, Murray, 1914.
781 p.

NL 0439908   OC1W

AC-L
W357L
L821h   Lodge, Sir Richard, 1855-1936.
A history of modern Europe from the capture of Constantinople, 1453, to the Treaty of Berlin, 1878, by Richard Lodge ... 12th impression. London, J. Murray, 1918.
xxviii, 781,[1]p. geneal. tabs. 19cm.
Publisher's advertisements ([4]p.) bound in at end.
With autograph and ms. note by E.A.St.J. Waugh and autograph of Margaret Waugh, 1958-9.
With ms. notations in chronological table. From the library of Evelyn Waugh.

NL 0439909   TxU

Lodge, Sir Richard, 1855-1936.
A history of modern Europe, from the capture of Constantinople, 1453, to the treaty of Berlin, 1878... London, John Murray₁1925₎ xxviii, 781p. 18½cm.
Binder's title: The student's modern Europe 1453-1878.
Second edition.

NL 0439910   MWelC

Lodge, Richard, 1855-1936.
A history of modern Europe from the capture of Constantinople, 1453, to the Treaty of Berlin, 1878. [2d ed.] London, J. Murray [1947]
xxviii, 781 p. geneal. tables. 20 cm.
(Student's modern Europe)
Second edition, originally published 1887, had title: The student's modern Europe; a history of modern Europe from the capture of Constantinople by the Turks to the treaty of Berlin, 1878.

NL 0439911   PPT

Lodge, Richard, 1855-1936.
History of modern Europe...
see also his The student's modern Europe.

Lodge, Richard, 1855-1936.
How should history be studied? An inaugural lecture delivered at Edinburgh on 17th October 1899, by Richard Lodge ... Edinburgh, J. Thin, 1901.
24 p. 22½ᶜᵐ.
                    2-12155

NL 0439913   DLC NIC MB

Lodge, Richard, 1855-1936.
The life of Cardinal Richelieu, by Richard Lodge ... with explanatory notes by Henry Ketcham ... New York, A. L. Burt company ₁1903₎
viii, 328 p. front. (port.) plates. 19½ᶜᵐ.
"The chief books on the period": p. 325-326.
First published London, 1896.

1. Richelieu, Armand Jean du Plessis, cardinal, duc de, 1585-1642. I. Ketcham, Henry, ed.

Library of Congress   DC123.9.R5L9
              3-14560

NL 0439914   DLC

Lodge, Sir Richard, 1855-1936.
... Machiavelli's Il principe.
(In Royal historical society, London. Transactions. London, 1871-22ᶜᵐ. 4th ser., v. 13 (1930) p. 1-16)
At head of title: Presidential address ... by Sir Richard Lodge.

1. Machiavelli, Niccolò, 1469-1527. Il principe.
           A C 36-3008

Title from Newberry   Libr.
Library of Congress   [DA20.R9 ser. 4, vol. 13]
          ₂2₎   (942.0062)

NL 0439915   ICN

Lodge, *Sir Richard,* 1855-1936.
... The mission of Henry Legge to Berlin, 1748.
(In Royal historical society, London. Transactions. London, 1871-22 cm. 4th ser., v. 14 (1931) p. 1-38)
At head of title: Presidential address ... by Sir Richard Lodge.

1. Legge, Henry Bilson, 1708-1764. 2. Gt. Brit.—Foreign relations—Prussia. 3. Prussia—Foreign relations—Gt. Brit. I. Title.

[DA20.R9 ser. 4, vol. 14]   A C 36—3016

Newberry Library
for Library of Congress   ₁a63c1₎

NL 0439916   ICN OC1 OCU OU

Lodge, *Sir Richard,* 1855-1936.
The Polwarth papers; a commentary upon the Historical manuscripts commissions Report (1911-1931) by Sir Richard Lodge ...
(In Royal historical society, London. Transactions. London, 1871-22ᶜᵐ. 4th ser., v. 15 (1932) p. 243-269)

1. Gt. Brit. Historical manuscripts commission. Report on the manuscripts of Lord Polwarth. I. Title.
           A C 36—3032

Newberry library
for Library of Congress   [DA20.R9 ser. 4, vol. 15]
          ₁a40c1₎   (942.0062)

NL 0439917   ICN OU MB DLC

Lodge, Sir Richard, 1855-1936.
Presidential address delivered 9 February, 1933. The Treaty of Seville, 1729
see his The treaty of Seville ...

Lodge, Sir Richard, 1855-1936.
Presidential address: Sir Benjamin Keene, K. B.
see his Sir Benjamin Keene ...

Lodge, Sir Richard, 1855-1936, ed.

Chesterfield, Philip Dormer Stanhope, *4th earl of,* 1694-1773.
Private correspondence of Chesterfield and Newcastle, 1744-46 ... edited with an introduction and notes by Sir Richard Lodge ... London, Offices of the Royal historical society, 1930.

Lodge, *Sir Richard,* 1855-1936, ed.

Keene, *Sir Benjamin,* 1697-1757.
The private correspondence of Sir Benjamin Keene, K. B.; edited with introduction and notes by Sir Richard Lodge ... Cambridge ₁Eng.₎ The University press, 1933.

Lodge, *Sir Richard,* 1855-1936.
Richelieu, by Richard Lodge ... London, Macmillan and co., ltd.; New York, Macmillan & co., 1896.
x, 235 p. 19½ᶜᵐ. (Half-title: Foreign statesmen)
"The chief books on the period": p. ₂232₎-233.

1. Richelieu, Armand Jean du Plessis, cardinal, duc de, 1585-1642.

Library of Congress   DC123.9.R5L8
           4—620

PWcS PPL PU PPD
MeB NcRS OCU OU OC1 OOxM OLak OC1W PPGi NN NjP PSC
NL 0439922   DLC DN IdU CU MU Wa CaBVaU WaTC MtU TxU

VOLUME 338

LODGE, Sir RICHARD, 1855-1936.
Richelieu. London, New York, Macmillan, 1896.
v. 235 p. 12°. (Foreign statesmen.)

Film reproduction. Negative.
Bibliography, p. 232-233.

1. Richelieu, Armand Jean du Plessis, cardinal, duc de, 1585-1642. I. Series.

NL 0439923   NN

LODGE, SIR RICHARD, 1855-1936.
Richelieu. Grosset [1903?]
301 p. illus.

NL 0439924   Or PP PIm

944.032
R39984
1896rl   Lodge, Sir Richard, 1855-1936.
Richelieu, by Richard Lodge ... London, Macmillan and co., limited, 1908.
x, 235p. 19½cm. (Half-title: Foreign statesmen)

"First edition 1896. Reprinted 1908."
"The chief books on the period": p.[232]-233.

1. Richelieu, Armand Jean du Plessis, cardinal, duc de, 1585-1642.

NL 0439925   TxU KEmT

Lodge, Richard, 1855-1936.
Richelieu, by ... London, Macmillan and co., ltd.; New York, Macmillan & co. c1896, 1914.

NL 0439926   OC1W ODW OrP

Lodge, *Sir* Richard, 1855-1936.
Richelieu, by Richard Lodge ... London, Macmillan and co., limited, 1924.
x, 235 p. 19½ᵐ. (*Half-title:* Foreign statesmen)
"The chief books on the period": p. [232]-233.
"Reprinted ... 1924."

NL 0439927   ViU PBm

DC
123.9   Lodge, Sir Richard, 1855-1936.
.R518   Richelieu. London, Macmillan, 1930 [c1896]
ix, 235 p. illus. (Foreign statesmen)

1. Richelieu, Armand Jean du Plessis, cardinal, duc de, 1585-1642.

NL 0439928   NBuU WaS

Lodge, Sir Richard, 1855 - 1936.
Richelieu, by Richard Lodge... New York.
Grosset & Dunlap [1936]
xv, 301p. front., plates 21cm.
Illustrated end papers.

NL 0439929   KAS

Lodge, *Sir* Richard, 1855-1936.
... Sir Benjamin Keene, K. B.: a study in Anglo-Spanish relations in the earlier part of the eighteenth century.
(*In* Royal historical society, London. Transactions. London, 1871-22ᵐ. 4th ser., v. 15 (1932) p. 1-43)
At head of title: Presidential address ... by Sir Richard Lodge.

1. Gt. Brit.—Commerce—Spain. 2. Spain—Commerce—Gt. Brit. 3. Keene, Sir Benjamin, 1697-1757.

Title from Newberry   Libr.   A C 36-3025
Library of Congress   [DA20.R9   ser. 4, vol. 15]
     [2]   (942.0062)

NL 0439930   ICN MB

LODGE, Richard, 1855-1936.
The student's modern Europe.— A history of modern Europe. From the capture of Constantinople, 1453, to the treaty of Berlin, 1878.
London, 1885.

sm.8°. pp. xxviii, 772.

NL 0439931   MH PPL PPPD NjP

Lodge, Sir Richard, 1855-1936.
The student's Modern Europe, a history of Modern Europe, from the capture of Constantinople by the Turks to the treaty of Berlin, 1878, by Richard Lodge...New York, Harper & brothers, 1885.
xxix, 772 p. 20 cm.

NL 0439932   DNW

Lodge, Richard, 1855-1936.
The student's Modern Europe. A history of modern Europe, from the capture of Constantinople by the Turks to the treaty of Berlin, 1878; by Richard Lodge ... New York, American Book Co. [1886.]
xxix, 772 p. 20ᵐ. (On verso of t.-p.: The student's series)

NL 0439933   MtU NcD

Lodge, *Sir* Richard, 1855-1936.
The student's Modern Europe. A history of modern Europe, from the capture of Constantinople by the Turks to the treaty of Berlin, 1878; by Richard Lodge ... New York, Harper & brothers, 1886.
xxix, 772 p. 20 cm. (*On verso of t.-p.:* The student's series)

1. Europe—Hist. ɪ. Title.

D209.L82   3—1032

OC1 OC1WHi OOxM DNW ViU
NL 0439934   DLC WaSp NcD DN PHC PP NN OU PSt MH OU

Lodge, Sir Richard, 1855-1936.
The student's Modern Europe. A history of modern Europe, from the capture of Constantinople by the Turks to the treaty of Berlin, 1878; by Richard Lodge ... New York, Harper & brothers, 1887.
xxix, 772 p. 20ᵐ. (On verso of t.-p.: The student's series)

NL 0439935   ViU TU MH PSC

Lodge, *Sir* Richard, 1855-1936.
The student's modern Europe; a history of modern Europe from the capture of Constantinople by the Turks to the treaty of Berlin, 1878, by Richard Lodge ... New York, Harper & brothers, 1890.
xxix, 772 p. 20ᵐ. [The student's series]

1. Europe—Hist. ɪ. Title.

Library of Congress   D209.L82 1890   34—31319
     [a41b1]   940.2

NL 0439936   DLC ICN ViU

Lodge, Sir Richard, 1855-1936.
The student's Modern Europe. A history of modern Europe, from the capture of Constantinople by the Turks to the treaty of Berlin, 1878; by ... New York, Harper & brothers, 1892.

NL 0439937   OC1W

Lodge (Richard) 1855-1936.
The student's modern Europe. A history of modern Europe. From the capture of Constantinople, 1453, to the treaty of Berlin, 1878. *London: J. Murray,* 1893. xxviii, 782 pp. 3 ed. 12°.

NL 0439938   NN

D208
L7
1894   Lodge, Richard, 1855-1936.
Educ.-   The student's modern Europe; a history of modern Europe from
Psych.   the capture of Constantinople by the Turks to the treaty of Berlin,
Library   1878. New York, Harper, 1894.
      xxix, 772 p. (The student's series)

1. Europe – Hist.

NL 0439939   CU ViU IdU

Lodge, Sir Richard, 1855-1936.
The student's Modern Europe. A history of modern Europe, from the capture of Constantinople by the Turks to the treaty of Berlin, 1878; by ... N.Y. Harper, 1896.
772 p.

The student's series.

NL 0439940   OU

Lodge, Richard, 1855-1936.
The student's Modern Europe. A history of modern Europe, from the capture of Constantinople by the Turks to the treaty of Berlin, 1878; by ... New York, Harper & brothers, 1897.
772 p.

(On verso of t.-p.: The student's series)

NL 0439941   MiU OCU

Lodge, Sir Richard, 1855-1936. The student's modern Europe.

Horn, D B.
... A history of Europe, 1871-1920, by D. B. Horn ... London, J. Murray [1927]

Lodge, Richard, 1855-1936.
The student's modern Europe
   see also his   History of modern Europe.

VOLUME 338

Lodge, *Sir* **Richard,** 1855–1936.
Studies in eighteenth-century diplomacy, 1740–1748, by Sir Richard Lodge ... London, J. Murray ₁1930₎
xiii, 421 p. 22½ cm.
CONTENTS.—The so-called treaty of Hanau, 1743.—The treaty of Worms, 13 September, 1743.—D'Argenson's relations with Germany and Sardinia.—D'Argenson and the Dutch.—Breda and Lisbon, August, 1746, to January, 1747.—Sandwich and Macanaz at Breda, January to May, 1747.—Between Breda and Aix-la-Chapelle.—The preliminaries of Aix-la-Chapelle.—The treaty of Aix-la-Chapelle.

1. Europe—Politics—18th cent.   I. Title: Eighteenth-century diplomacy.
Library of Congress   D287.L6
                                           30—6645

CaBVaU WaTC LU OrU CaOTP WaSpG CaBVa MtU IdU
NN MH–L NcD MiU OCU OO OU NcU OC1 DFo OU MB CLSU MB
NL 0439944   DLC CtY–L ViU OKentU MiU PPT PSC PBm PU

Lodge, Sir Richard, 1855–1936, tr.
Bluntschli, Johann Kaspar, 1808–1881
FOR OTHER EDITIONS SEE MAIN ENTRY
The theory of the state, by J. K. Bluntschli ... authorized English translation from the 6th German ed. 3d ed. Oxford, The Clarendon press, 1901.

Lodge, *Sir* **Richard,** 1855–1936.
... The treaty of Seville (1729)
(*In* Royal historical society, London. Transactions. London, 1871–22ᵐ. 4th ser., v. 16 (1933) p. 1–43)
At head of title: Presidential address ... by Sir Richard Lodge.

1. Seville, Treaty of, 1729.
                                           A C 36–3033
Title from Newberry   Libr.
Library of Congress   [DA20.R9 ser. 4, vol. 16]
                           ₍2₎   (942.0062)

NL 0439946   ICN MB OU OCU

Lodge, Richard Walley, 1857–   , and A. H. Low.
...Ensayes de oro, plata, plomo, estaño i cobre, por Richard W. Lodge...y Alberto H. Low...traducidos i estractados por F. A. Sundt. .. Santiago de Chile: Sociedad Imprenta y litografia Universo, 1916.   47 p. incl. tables.   2. ed.   4°.

At head of title: Sociedad nacional de mineria.

554708A. 1. Assaying. I. Low,   Alberto Howard, 1855–   , jt. au.
II. Sundt, F. A., translator.   III. Sociedad nacional de mineria.
Santiago de Chile.
N. Y. P. L.   November 13, 1931

NL 0439947   NN

Lodge, Richard Walley, 1857–
Notes on assaying and metallurgical lamoratory experiments. By Richard W. Lodge ... 1st ed. 1st thousand. New York, J. Wiley & sons; ₁etc., etc.₎ 1904.
viii, 287 p. illus., diagrs. 23½ cm.

1. Assaying. 2. Metallurgy—Laboratory manuals.

TN550.L82   4—32769

NL 0439948   DLC MtU OrPR MiU MB ICJ MiHM PHC

Lodge, Richard W₍**alley**₎ 1857–
Notes on assaying and metallurgical laboratory experiments. By Richard W. Lodge ... 1st ed. 1st thousand. New York, J. Wiley & sons; London, Chapman & Hall, **1905.**
viii, 287 p. illus., diagrs. 23½ᶜᵐ.

NL 0439949   NIC OrCS OO

Lodge, Richard Walley, 1857–
Notes on assaying and metallurgical laboratory experiments. By Richard W. Lodge ... 2d ed., rev. 1st thousand. New York, J. Wiley & sons; ₁etc., etc.₎ 1906.
viii, 312 p. illus., diagrs. 23½ᶜᵐ.

1. Assaying. 2. Metallurgy—Laboratory manuals.
Library of Congress   TN550.L822   6—5156

NL 0439950   DLC FMU CU OC1W MiU IdU CaBVaU

Lodge, Richard Walley, 1857–
Notes on assaying ... 2d ed., rev. New York, John Wiley & Sons, 1907.
312p. illus.

NL 0439951   ICRL PBa MH OC1 OC1W

Lodge, Richard Walley, 1857–
Notes on assaying and metallurgical laboratory experiments. by ... 2d ed., rev. 3d thousand. New York, J. Wiley & sons; ₍etc., etc.₎ 1908.
312 p.

NL 0439952   MiU PPSteph

Lodge, Richard Walley, 1857–
Notes on assaying and metallurgical laboratory experiments. By Richard W. Lodge ... 3d ed., rev. and corr. ... New York, J. Wiley & sons; ₍etc., etc.₎ 1910.
xi, 317 p. illus., diagrs. 24 cm.
1. Assaying. 2. Metallurgy - Laboratory manuals.

NL 0439953   CU WaS

Lodge, Richard Walley, 1857–
Notes on assaying and metallurgical laboratory experiments. By Richard W. Lodge ... 3d ed., rev. and cor., total issue, 4 thousand. New York, J. Wiley & sons; ₍etc., etc.₎ 1911.
xi, 317 p. illus., diagrs. 23½ᶜᵐ.

1. Assaying. 2. Metallurgy—Laboratory manuals.

Library of Congress   TN550.L8 1911   11—27473

NL 0439954   DLC MtBuM NjP OU MiU ICJ

TN550
L8
1915
Lodge, Richard Walley, 1857–
Notes on assaying and metallurgical laboratory experiments. 3d ed., rev. and corr. New York, J. Wiley, 1915.
xi, 317 p. illus. 24cm.

1. Assaying. 2. Metallurgy - Laboratory manuals. I. Title.

NL 0439955   GU OC1

Lodge, Richard Walley, 1857–
Third and fourth year notes on assaying and metallurgical laboratory experiments. ₍New York, 19—?₎ 2 v. in 1. diagrs., tables. 4°.

Binder's title.
Facsimile manuscript.

243795A. 1. Metallurgy—Laboratory   manuals. 2. Assaying.
N. Y. P. L.   July 7, 1926

NL 0439956   NN

---

*EC65
L8213
665s
Lodge, Robert, 1636 (ca.)–1690.
A salutation of love, from the opening of the springs of eternall life, unto the flock of God in bonds, or else where scattered upon the earth, but are one in the endless life of God. From a Freind₍!₎ to all the upright hearted people of God, that wait for the building of distressed Syon; known by the name of Robert Lodge.
[London] Printed in the year, 1665.
8p. 18.5cm.

NL 0439957   MH CtY PHC

Lodge, Rupert Clendon, 1886–
Applied philosophy. London, Routledge and Paul ₍1951₎
xi, 243 p. 22 cm.
American ed. (Boston, Beacon Press) has title: Applying philosophy.
Bibliographical footnotes.

1. Philosophy.   I. Title.

BD21.L6 1951   140   51–1915 rev

NL 0439958   DLC CaBVaU OrCS TxU INS MB LU MSohG NNUT

Lodge, Rupert Clendon, 1886–
Applying philosophy. ₍1st Amer. ed.₎ Boston, Beacon Press ₍°1951₎
243 p.

English ed. (London, Routledge & Paul) has title: Applied philosophy.

NL 0439959   MiD

Lodge, Rupert Clendon, 1886–   tr.

Varisco, Bernardino, 1850–
The great problems, by Bernardino Varisco ... tr. by R. C. Lodge, M. A. London, G. Allen & company, ltd., 1914.

Lodge, Rupert Clendon, 1886–
The great thinkers. London, Routledge & K. Paul ₍1949₎
x, 310 p. 23 cm.
CONTENTS.—Plato.—Aristotle.—Plotinus.—Descartes. — Spinoza.—Leibniz.—Locke.—Berkeley.—David Hume.—Immanuel Kant.—Post-Kantian movements.

1. Philosophy—Hist. 2. Philosophers.   I. Title.

B72.L8 1949   109   50–360

MiU NcD ODW ICU TxU
NL 0439961   DLC CaBViP WaS WaT OrU NcU PPT OC1W PU

Lodge, Rupert Clendon, 1886–
The great thinkers. ₍1st American ed.₎ Boston, Beacon Press ₍1951, °1949₎
x, 310 p. 23 cm.
CONTENTS. — Plato.—Aristotle.—Plotinus.—Descartes.—Spinoza.—Leibniz.—Locke.—Berkeley.—David Hume.—Immanuel Kant.—Post-Kantian movements.

1. Philosophy—Hist. 2. Philosophers.   I. Title.

B72.L8 1951   109   51–10161

NL 0439962   DLC Wa Or OrPS

VOLUME 338

Lodge, Rupert Clendon, 1886–
An introduction to modern logic, by Rupert Clendon Lodge ... Minneapolis, The Perine book company ͵1920͵
1 p. l., v–xiv, 361 p. 19ᶜᵐ.
"For further reading" at end of each chapter.

ɪ. Logic.
20—5668

Library of Congress   BC108.L6

NL 0439963   DLC MtU OO CaBVaU NIC NjP ICJ OC1W MiU

Lodge, Rupert Clendon, 1886–   ed.

Manitoba. University.
Manitoba essays, written in commemoration of the sixtieth anniversary of the University of Manitoba by members of the teaching staffs of the university and its affiliated colleges; R. C. Lodge, editor. Toronto, The Macmillan company of Canada, limited, 1937.

Lodge, Rupert Clendon, 1884–
... The meaning and function of simple modes in the philosophy of John Locke, by Rupert Clendon Lodge ... Minneapolis, 1918.
vi, 86 p. 25½ᶜᵐ. (The University of Minnesota. Studies in the social sciences. no. 12)
"Bulletin of the University of Minnesota, August 1918."
Bibliography: p. ͵81͵–82.

1. Locke, John, 1632–1704.   ɪ. Title.
18—22088
Library of Congress   H31.M65 no. 12
——— Copy 2.   B1298.M6L6

NL 0439965   FMU MoU OC1 OC1W OU OCU OO MiU
DLC PU ICJ MB PSC PBm CaBVaU WaTC IdPI

Lodge, Rupert Clendon, 1886–
Philosophy of business, by Rupert C. Lodge. Chicago, Ill., University of Chicago press ͵1945͵
xiii, 482 p. 20ᶜᵐ.
"Notes" (bibliographical) at end of each chapter.

1. Business.
A 45–4287
Chicago. Univ. Library
for Library of Congress*   HF5353.L6
͵15͵†   650.1

NL 0439966   ICJ OC1 OCU DLC OU OC1W PPD PP PBm PPT CU
ICU OrCS IdU MU NIC CoU FU TxU NcGU NcD

Lodge, Rupert Clendon, 1886–
Philosophy of education, by Rupert C. Lodge ... New York, London, Harper & brothers, 1937.
x p., 1 l., 328 p. 21 cm.
"First edition."
"For further reading" at end of each chapter except the last; Bibliography: p. 320–323.

1. Education—Philosophy.
LB875.L6   370.1   37—2931

NL 0439967   KMK TxU PPT PWcS OO OCU OU OC1W OOxM MB PV PPPL
DLC IdPI KyLxT CaBVaU NN OrU KEmT MtU

Lodge, Rupert Clendon, 1886–
Philosophy of education. Rev. ed. New York, Harper ͵1947͵
x, 350 p. 21ᶜᵐ.
Bibliography: p. 342–346.

1. Education—Philosophy.
LB875.L6 1947   370.1   47—4937*

NL 0439968   OrPR OrMonO OrSaW MtU
IEG MiU TxU NcU MBtS Or OrP OrU CaBVaU IdPI OrCS
DLC ViU MH ICU NcD OCH OrPS OrU-M KEmT

---

184   **Lodge, Rupert Clendon,** 1886–
P71   Plato and freedom. ͵n.p., n.d.͵
XLo2   p. 87–101. 25cm.

From Transactions of the Royal Society of Canada, vol. 43, ser. 3, June, 1949, sec. 2. Bibliographical footnotes.

1. Plato. I. Title.

NL 0439969   CLSU

---

184   **Lodge, Rupert Clendon,** 1886–
P71   The Platonic highest good. [New York,
XLo5   Longmans, Green, 1927]
       p. 428–449, 535–551. 23cm.

Caption-title.
"Read as the presidential address at the meeting of the Western Division of the American Philosophical Association, at the University of Minnesota, April 15, 1927."
From The Philosophical Review, v. 36, no. 5–6
Includes Taeusch, C.F. The significance of professional and business ethics. Bibliographical footnotes.

1. Plato. I. Title.

NL 0439970   CLSU

Lodge, Rupert Clendon, 1886–
Plato's theory of art. London, Routledge & Paul ͵1953͵
viii, 316 p. 22 cm. (International library of psychology, philosophy and scientific method)
Bibliographical references included in "Notes." Bibliography: p. 305–307.

1. Plato. 2. Art—Philosophy. ɪ. Title. (Series)

B398.A4L6   53–12709

NL 0439971   OC1SA OCU PRosC OC1W PSt ScU
PSC CU ICU NIC MH NNC PBL PPLas IaU N OU PBm PJB
CaBVa NcRS KEmT MU NcU TxU IU TU ViU NN NcD DCU
DLC WaS OrCS OrLgE NIC CaBVaU MsSM GAT

---

701   **Lodge, Rupert Clendon,** 1886–
L821p Plato's theory of art. New York, Humanities
1953N Press, 1953.
       viii, 316p. 22cm. (International library of psychology, philosophy and scientific method)

Bibliographical references included in "Notes." Bibliography: p. 305–307.

1. Plato. 2. Art – Philosophy. I. Title. II. Series.

NL 0439972   TxU IEN AU OU MiU MtU OrU

Lodge, Rupert Clendon, 1886–
Plato's theory of education. With an appendix on the education of women according to Plato, by Solomon Frank. London, K. Paul, Trench, Trubner ͵1947͵
viii, 322 p. 22 cm. (International library of psychology, philosophy and scientific method)
Bibliography: p. 309–311.

1. Plato. 2. Education, Greek. ɪ. Frank, Solomon. ɪɪ. Title. (Series)

LB85.P7L6   370.1   48—999*

NL 0439973   PU-Penn PBm NcU TxU TU MH NNC ICU
DLC CaBVaU MoSU CU-I OU InStme MsSM

Lodge, Rupert Clendon, 1886–
Plato's theory of education. With an appendix on the education of women according to Plato by Solomon Frank. New York, Harcourt, Brace ͵1947͵
viii, 322 p. 22 cm. (International library of psychology, philosophy and scientific method)
Bibliography: p. 309–311.

1. Plato. 2. Education, Greek. ɪ. Frank, Solomon. ɪɪ. Title. (Series)

LB85.P7L6 1947a   370.1   48—7113*

NL 0439974   DLC OrCS ViU PPEB PSC OU ICU

Lodge, Rupert Clendon, 1886–
Plato's theory of education, by R. C. Lodge...with an appendix on The education of women according to Plato, by Rabbi Solomon Frank... New York, Harcourt, Brace and co. ͵etc., etc., 1948͵
viii, 322 p. 23cm. (International library of psychology, philosophy and scientific method.)
"Bibliography," p. 309–311.

NL 0439975   NN NBC OrPS

LB   **Lodge, Rupert Clendon,** 1886–
85   Plato's thoery of education. With
P7   an appendix on the education of
L6   women according to Plato, by Solomon
Educ. Frank. London, Routledge & Kegan
       Paul ͵1950͵
       322p. 22cm. (International library of psychology, philosophy and scientific method)
"First published 1947."
Includes bibliography.

1. Plato 2. Education, Greek I. Frank, Solomon II. Title. (Series)

NL 0439976   MU CaBVa IU KEmT

Lodge, Rupert Clendon, 1886–
Plato's theory of ethics: the moral criterion and the highest good, by R. C. Lodge ... London, K. Paul, Trench, Trubner & co., ltd.; New York, Harcourt, Brace and company, 1928.
xiv, 558 p. 22½ cm. (Half-title: International library of psychology, philosophy and scientific method)
Bibliography: p. 543–545.

1. Plato. 2. Ethics.
B398.E8L6   28—19528

NL 0439977   CaBVaU CU MtBC NBuC OrLgE CU-I MiU MB MH NN
OU ODW OCU NcD OC1JC TU NN NIC PBm IdU PPT CaBVa PSC
DLC WaTC CaOTU CoU PU ViU NjP OCX OC1 OO

B   **Lodge, Rupert Clendon,** 1886–
398   Plato's theory of ethics: the moral crite-
E8   rion and the highest good, by R. C. Lodge ...
L6   London, Routledge & K. Paul. ltd. ͵1950͵
1950   xiv, 558 p. 22 cm. (Half-title: International library of psychology, philosophy and scientific method)
"First published 1928."
Bibliography: p. 543–545.

1. Plato. 2. Ethics. I. Title.

NL 0439978   Vi FMU OrPR KEmT

Lodge, Rupert Clendon, 1886–
The questioning mind; a survey of philosophical tendencies, by R. C. Lodge. London, J. M. Dent and sons, ltd. ͵1937͵
vii, 311, ͵1͵ p. 22ᶜᵐ.
"In this book I have tried to write a sort of platonic dialogue, letting the realist, the idealist, and the pragmatist speak each for himself."—Epilogue.
"First published 1937."
"For further reading": p. 311.

1. Philosophy. ɪ. Title. ɪɪ. Title: Philosophical tendencies. A survey of.
37–21256
Library of Congress   B1646.L78Q4
͵3͵   192 a

NL 0439979   NcU OC1U
DLC PSC WaWW OrU OrCS KEmT NIC NcD CtY

VOLUME 338

Lodge, Rupert Clendon, *1885–* 3605.753
The questioning mind. A survey of philosophical tendencies. By R. C. Lodge.
— New York. E. P. Dutton & Co., Inc. [1937.] vii, 311, (1) pp. 21.5 cm., in 8s.
For further reading, pp. 311, 312.
Contents. — Preface. — Questionings. — Knowledge. — The good life. — Mind. — Self. — Education. — Finale. — Epilogue. — Index of names.

NL 0439980 MB OrP OU OO OC1W PU

1829-1897.
Lodge, Samuel, Scrivelsby, the home of the champions; with some account of the Marmion and Dymoke families. Horncastle, *etc.* 1893.
I. 8°. *Coat-of-arms, plates, and portrs.*

NL 0439981 MH PHi

Lodge, Samuel, 1829-1897.
Scrivelsby, the home of the champions. With some account of the Marmion and Dymoke families. Illustrated. By the Rev. Samuel Lodge ... London, S. Stock; [etc., etc.] 1893.
xv, [1], 199, [1] p. col. front., 13 pl., 3 port. 25½ x 19½cm.

1. Scrivelsby, Eng. 2. Marmion family. 3. Dymoke family. 4. Coronations—Gt. Brit.

6—22734
Library of Congress DA690.S42L8

NL 0439982 DLC WaS OC1WHi NIC LNHT NcD

Lodge, Samuel, 1829–1897.
Scrivelsby, the home of the champions, with some account of the Marmion and Dymoke families ... By the Rev. Samuel Lodge ... 2d ed. ... London, E. Stock; [etc., etc.] 1894.
xix, [1], 216 p. col. front. (coat of arms) plates, ports., fold. geneal. tab. 25cm.

1. Scrivelsby, Eng. 2. Marmion family. 3. Dymoke family. 4. Coronations—Gt. Brit. I. Title.

35-17121
Library of Congress DA690.S42L8 1894 942.53

NL 0439983 DLC ICN IU

Lodge, Sydney Johnston.
"Skeeter" McCoy; a tale of American boarding school life, by Sydney Johnston Lodge. [Gaffney, S. C., Printed by E. H. De Camp, °1919]
283, [1] p. incl. front. plates. 22½cm.

I. Title.
19-9098
Library of Congress PZ7.L822S

NL 0439984 DLC

Lodge, Thomas.
Recent advances in radiology. 3d ed. London, J. & A. Churchill, 1955.
x, 358 p. illus. 22 cm.
Previous editions by Peter Kerley.
Includes bibliographies.

1. Radiology, Medical. I. Kerley, Peter, 1900– Recent advances in radiology. II. Title.

A 57-1247
Missouri. Univ. Libr. for Library of Congress [2]

NL 0439985 MoU CaBVaU ICJ NcU PPC PPT-M DNLM FU-HC

Lodge, Thomas, 1558?-1625.
The complete works of Thomas Lodge ⟨1580–1623?⟩ now first collected ... [Glasgow] Printed for the Hunterian club, 1883.
4 v. 24½ x 19½ cm. (*On cover:* Hunterian club. [Reprints] no. 25–28, 35–36, 42–44, 47–49, 52–54, 57–60, 62–63)
With reproductions of original title-pages.
210 copies printed.
Issued in 21 parts, 1875–88.
"Memoir of Thomas Lodge," by E. W. Gosse: v. 1, p. 1–46.
"Bibliographical index": v. 1, p. 1–27.
CONTENTS.
v. 1. Memoir of Thomas Lodge, by E. W. Gosse. Bibliographical index. Reply to Gosson's School of abuse ⟨1580?⟩ An alarum against vsurers, 1584. Scillaes metamorphosis, 1589. Rosalynde; Euphues golden legacie, 1590.

v. 2. The famous, true, and historicall life of Robert second duke of Normandy, 1591. Catharos; Diogenes in his singularitie, 1591. Evphves shadow, the battaile of the sences, 1592. The life and death of William Longbeard, 1593. Phillis: honoured with pastorall, sonnets, elegies, and amorous delights, 1593.—v. 3. The wovnds of ciuill war, 1594. A fig for Momus, 1595. The divel conired, 1596. A Margarite of America, 1596. Prosopopeia, containing the teares of the holy, blessed, and sanctified Marie, the mother of God, 1596.—v. 4. Wits miserie, and the worlds madnesse, 1596. A looking glasse, for London and Englande, 1598. A treatise of the plague, 1603. The poore mans talentt ⟨1623?⟩ Miscellaneous pieces. Glossary.
I. Gosse, Sir Edmund William, 1849–1928.

PR2297.A1 1883 A 15—2014
Chicago. Univ. Libr. for Library of Congress [a66r37d½]†

NcU MiU MH PU-F WaU
NL 0440002 ICU DLC OrU ICarbS GU NIC OU OC1 OCU

STC 16653
Lodge, Thomas, 1558?-1625.
An alarum against vsurers. Containing tryed experiences against worldly abuses. Wherein gentlemen may finde good counsells to confirme them, and pleasant histories to delight them: and euery thing so interlaced with varietie: as the curious may be satisfied with rarenesse, and the curteous with pleasure. Heereunto are annexed the delectable historie of Forbonius and Prisceria: with the lamentable complaint of truth ouer England. Written by Thomas Lodge, of Lincolnes-Inne, gentleman ...

Imprinted at London by T.Este, for Sampson Clarke, and are to be sold at his shop by Guyld hall. 1584.
6p.ℓ., 40 numb.ℓ. 18cm.
Errata: recto of 6th prelim. leaf.
Imperfect: leaves 37-40 wanting ("Trvths complaint ouer England").

NL 0440004 MH DFo

Lodge, Thomas, 1558?-1625
An alarum against usurers. Containing tryed experiences against worldly abuses. Heereunto are annexed the Delectable historie of Forbonius and Prisceria: with the lamentable complaint of truth over England. L, Imprinted by T.Este for S.Clarke, 1584
39 numb.l.
Photostat copy, positive, of the copy in the Huntington Library

NL 0440005 MH

FILM
Lodge, Thomas, 1558?-1625.
An alarum against vsurers ... Heerevnto are annexed the delectable histoṛie of Forbonius and Prisceria: with the lamentable complaint of truth ouer England. Written by Thomas Lodge ... Imprinted at London by T.Este, for Sampson Clarke ... 1584.
University microfilms no.15929 (carton 553)
Short-title catalogue no.16653.

I.Title. II.Title: The delectable historie of Forbonius and Prisceria. III.Title: Forbonius and Prisceria.

NL 0440006 MiU

Lodge, Thomas, 1558?-1625.
Alarum against usurers ... [Glasg., 1879]

NL 0440007 NjP CSmH

STC 16654
Lodge, Thomas, 1558?-1625.
Catharos. Diogenes in his singularitie. Wherein is comprehended his merrie baigh-ing fit for all mens benefits: christened by him, A nettle for nice noses ... At London, Printed by William Hoskins & Iohn Danter, for Iohn Busbie, 1591.
A^2, B-I^4. 4to.
Running title reads "A nettle for nice noses."
A. W. Clifford-Harmsworth copy.

NL 0440008 DFo MH CSmH

FILM
Lodge, Thomas, 1558?-1625.
Catharos. Diogenes in his singularitie. Wherein is comprehended his merrie baighting fit for all mens benefits: christened by him, A nettle for nice noses. By T.L. ... At London, Printed by VVilliam Hoskins & Iohn Danter, for Iohn Busbie 1591.
University microfilms no.15930 (carton 553)
Short-title catalogue no.16654.

I.Title. II.Title: Diogenes in his singularitie. III.Title: A nettle ice noses.

NL 0440009 MiU

Lodge, Thomas, 1558?-1625.
Catharos Diogenes ... [Glasg., 1875]

NL 0440010 NjP

Lodge, Thomas. 1556-1625. No. 5 in **4600a.125.2
The complaint of Elstred.
(In his Phillis . . . At London, printed for Iohn Busbie. 1593. 59-84. [Glasgow, 1883.])

NL 0440011 MB

[Lodge, Thomas], 1558?-1625.
[Defence of Plays] n. p. [1580?]
sm. 8 vo.
Bound (3) with: Gosson, Stephen. Playes Confuted ... n. d.

NL 0440012 CSmH

Lodge, Thomas, 1558?-1625. 2558.131.1
Defence of poetry. 1579.
(In Smith, George G. Elizabethan critical essays. Vol. 1, pp. 61-86. Oxford. 1904.)
List of pamphlets for and against the stage, 1577-1587, pp. 61-63.
Reprinted from the Bodleian copy.
Answers Gosson's School of abuse . . . [2575.8].

K8690 — Drama. English. Bibl. — Go... , Stephen. — Great Britain. Theatres. Bibl. — Poetry.

NL 0440013 MB

Lodge, Thomas, 1558?-1625.
A defence of poetry, music, and stage-plays, by Thomas Lodge, of Lincoln's Inn. To which are added, by the same author, An alarum against usurers; and The delectable history of Forbonius and Prisceria. With introduction and notes. London, Printed for the Shakespeare society, 1853.
lxxvii, 129, [1] p. 22cm. [Shakespeare society. Publications. no. 48]
Vol. xv, no. 3, in the L. C. set, where it is substituted for Heywood's Apology for actors (no. 3) Listed as vol. xx by Lowndes, Bibl. manual.

Continued in next column

VOLUME 338

Continued from preceding column

"A reply to Stephen Gosson's 'Schoole of abuse'." Ed. by David Laing.
"Catalogue of Thomas Lodge's works": p. [xvii]-lxxvii.
"Truth's complaint over England": p. [117]-123.

1. Poetry—Early works to 1800. 2. Music and morals. 3. Theater—Moral and religious aspects. 4. Interest and usury. 5. Gosson, Stephen, 1555-1624. The schoole of abuse. I. Laing, David, 1793-1878, ed. II. Title. III. Title: An alarum against usurers. IV. Title: The delectable history of Forbonius and Prisceria. V. Title: Forbonius and Prisceria.

Library of Congress   PR2888.L3 vol. 15

       16-14443 •

PU
NcD WU PPT NcU OCU OO OCI OClW ViU PU-F PSC PP PBm
NL   0440015   DLC MdBP NN MB OrCS CaBVaU OrU ScU NN

Lodge, Thomas, 1558?-1625.
    A defence of poetry, music, and stage-plays, by Thomas Lodge, of Lincoln's Inn. To which are added by the same author, An alarum against usurers; and The delectable history of Forbonius and Prisceria. With introduction and notes.   London, Printed for the Shakespeare society, 1853.
    lxxvii, 129, [1] p.   22 cm.   [Shakespeare society. Publications. No. 48]
    Microcard edition (3 cds.)

NL   0440016   MiU

[Lodge, Thomas] 1558?-1625.
    The divel coniured. London, Printed by Adam Islip for William Mats, 1596.
    [89]p.   18cm.
    Dedication and preface signed: T.L.

NL   0440017   CtY DFo MH CSmH

FILM
Lodge, Thomas, 1558?-1625.
    The divel coniured. London Printed by Adam Islip for William Mats ... 1596.
    Dedication signed: T.L.
    University microfilms no.15931 (carton 553)
    Short-title catalogue no.16655.

NL   0440018   MiU

Lodge, Thomas, 1558-1625.
    Divel coniured. [Glasg. 1875]

NL   0440019   NjP

STC
16670
Lodge, Thomas, 1558?-1625.
    Euphues golden legacie. Found after his death in his cell at Silexedra ... Imprinted at London for Iohn Smethwick, 1612.
    A-O⁴. (A1, t-p, torn and mounted; some top margins trimmed affecting running titles.) 4to.
    Richard Farmer-Isaac Reed-E. V. Utterson-J. O. Halliwell-Phillipps - W. C. Hazlitt - Warwick Castle library copy.

NL   0440020   DFo

FILM
Lodge, Thomas, 1558?-1625.
    Euphues golden legacie. Found after his death in his cell at Silexedra. Becueathed to Philavtvs sonnes, nursed vp with their father in England. Fetcht from the Canaries, by T.L. London, Imprinted for I.Smethwick, 1612.
    The source of Shakespeare's As you like it.
    Earlier editions published under title: Rosalynde. Euphues golden legacie.
    Short-title catalogue no.16670 (carton 844)
    1.Shakespeare, William. As you like it--Sources. I.Title.

NL   0440021   MiU

STC
16672
copy 1
Lodge, Thomas, 1558?-1625.
    Euphues golden legacie. Found after his death in his cell at Silexedra ... Imprinted at London for Iohn Smethery, 1623.
    A-O⁴. 4to.
    Harmsworth copy.

NL   0440022   DFo CSmH

STC
16673
Lodge, Thomas, 1558?-1625.
    Euphues golden legacie. Found after his death in his cell at Silexedra ... Imprinted at London for Iohn Smethwicke, 1634.
    A-O⁴. 4to.
    Pforzheimer, v. 2, pp. 641-642, no. 620.
    J. O. Halliwell-Phillipps - Warwick Castle library copy.

NL   0440023   DFo CSmH MB

FILM
Lodge, Thomas, 1558?-1625.
    Euphues golden legacie. Found after his death in his cell at Silexedra. Bequeathed to Philavtvs sonnes, nursed vp with their fvther in England. Fetcht from the Canaries, by T.L. London, Imprinted for I.Smethwicke, 1634.
    The source of Shakespeare's "As you like it."
    Short-title catalogue no.16673 (carton 810)
    1.Shakespeare, William--Sources. I.Title.

NL   0440024   MiU

[LODGE, Thomas, 1558?-1625.]
    Euphues golden legacie, found after his death in his cell at Silexedra. Bequeathed to Philautus sonnes, nursed up with their father in England. Fetcht from the Canaries by T.L., gent London, printed for Francis Smethwicke, 1642.
    sm.4°. A-O in 4s. Unpaged.
    Signed at end: Tho.Lodge.
    Originally issued with title "Rosalynde".

NL   0440025   MH DFo

[Lodge, Thomas] 1558?-1625.
    Evphves shadow, the battaile of the sences. Wherein youthfull folly is set downe in his right figure, and vaine fancies are prooued to produce many offences. Hereunto is annexed The deafe mans dialogue ... By T.L. gent. London Printed by Abell Ieffes, for Iohn Busbie, and are to be sould at his shop in Paules churchyard, neere to the West doore of Paules, 1592.
    [102]p.   18cm.
    Signatures: A-N⁴(A₁, blank, wanting)
    Dedication and "To the gentlemen readers" by Robert Greene.

NL   0440026   CtY CSmH DFo NjP

FILM
Lodge, Thomas, 1558?-1625.
    Evphves shadow, the battaile of the sences ... Hereunto is annexed the deafe mans dialogue, contayning Philamis Athanatos ... By T.L. ‹i.e. Thomas Lodge. ... London Printed by Abell Ieffes, for Iohn Busbie ... 1592.
    Editor's dedication signed: Rob.Greene.
    University microfilms no.12356 (case 64, carton 379)
    Short-title catalogue no.16656.
    I.Greene, Robert, 1558-1592, ed. II.Title. III.Title: The deafe mans dialogue.

NL   0440027   MiU DFo ViU

Lodge, Thomas, 1558?-1625, *supposed author.*
    Fair Em
    see
Fair Em.

Lodge, Thomas, 1558?-1625, *tr.*

Josephus, Flavius.
    The famovs and memorable works of Josephvs ... Faithfully tr. out of the Latin, and French, by Theo. Lodge ... Whereunto are newly added the references of the Scriptures throughout the history ... London, Printed by J. L. for A. Hebb, 1640.

FILM
Lodge, Thomas, 1558?-1625.
    The famous, true and historicall life of Robert second duke of Normandy, surnamed for his monstrous birth and behauiour, Robin the diuell ... By T.L. ... Imprinted at London ·by T.Crwin· for N.L.·ing· and Iohn Busbie ... 1591.
    University microfilms no.15932 (case 68, carton 406)
    Short-title catalogue no.16657.
    1.Robert II, duke of Normandy, 1054?-1134.

NL   0440030   MiU ViU CSmH DFo

Lodge, Thomas, 1558?-1625.
    Famous true, and historicall life of Robert II duke of Normandy. [Glasg., 1878]

NL   0440031   NjP

[LODGE, Thomas, 1558?-1625.]
    A fig for Momus, containing pleasant varietie, included in satyres, eclogues, and epistles, by T.L. London, printed for Clement Knight, 1595.
    sm.4°. A-H in 4s, I in 3. Unpaged.
    F3 misprinted E3.
    Impeffect: too closely trimmed. Title-page has been mounted; imprint date defaced.
    Bound by Bradstreet.

NL   0440032   MH NjP CSmH OClW MdBP DFo

Ex
3831
.5
.33
.1595
Lodge, Thomas, 1558?-1625.
    A fig for Momus; containing pleasant varietie, included in satyres, ecologues, and epistles, by T. L. of Lincolnes Inne, gent. At London, Printed for C.Knight, 1595 [18--?]
    facsim.: 70 p.   26 cm.
    Printed text preceded by ms. copy of the same text (49 p.) in the handwriting of Thomas Park.
    I. Park, Thomas, 1759-1834. II.Title.

NL   0440033   NjP

Beinecke
Library
In
B657
816F
3
[Lodge, Thomas] 1558?-1625.
    A fig for Momus: containing pleasant varietie, included in satyres, eclogues, and epistles. By T.L. of Lincolnes Inne, gent. ... At London: Printed for Clement Knight, and are to bee solde at his shop, at the little north doore of Paules Church. 1595 [Auchinleck, Reprinted by Alexander Boswell, 1817]
    1 p.ℓ., reprint ([60] p.), 1 ℓ. 23 cm. (Frondes caducae [3])
    Edited by Alexander Boswell and originally issued separately, later the parts were made into a volume with series t.-p.

NL   0440034   CtY MdBP MH MB NjP

VOLUME 338

Lodge, Thomas, 1558?-1625.
Fig for Momus ... [Glasg. 1878]

NL 0440035 NjP

Lodge, Thomas, 1558?-1625.
Glaucus and Silla. With other lyrical and pastoral poems. By Thomas Lodge. Chiswick, From the press of C. Whittingham, 1819.

xvi, 152 p. 18ᵐᵐ. (*On cover:* Select early English poets. no. v)

With reproduction of original t.-p., 1589.
Preface signed: S. W. S. ɪ. ᵉ. Samuel Weller Singer)

ɪ. Singer, Samuel Weller, 1783-1858, ed. ɪɪ. Title.

24-30026

Library of Congress PR2297.A7 1819

MdBP
NL 0440036 DLC ICN NjP PHC PU MeB NN CSt MeB WU

Lodge, Thomas, 1558?-1625, supposed author.

Lady Alimony; or, The alimony lady. An excellent pleasant new comedy duly authorized, daily acted, and frequently followed ... London, Printed for Tho. Vere and William Gilbertson, and are to be sold at the Angel without New-gate, and at the Bible in Gilt-spur-street, 1659.

Lodge, Thomas, 1558?-1625, supposed author.

Lady Alimony.
Lady Alimony; or, The Alimony Lady.
(*In* Dodsley, Robert, ed. A select collection of old English plays. 4th ed. by W. C. Hazlitt. London, 1874-76. 21¼ᵐᵐ. v. 14, p. (273)-(367))

Lodge, Thomas, 1558?-1625. FOR OTHER EDITIONS SEE MAIN ENTRY

Larum for London.
A Larvm for London, or The siedge of Antwerpe. With the ventrous actes and valorous deeds of the lame Soldier. As it hath been playde by the right Honorable the Lord Charberlaine (!) his Seruants. London, Printed for William Ferbrand, and are to b(e) sold at his shop in Popes-head Alley, ouer against the Tauerne doore, neere the Royall-Exchange, 1602.

Lodge, Thomas, 1558?-1625, tr.

(Goulart, Simon) 1543-1628.
A learned svmmary vpon the famovs poeme of VVilliam of Salvst, lord of Bartas. Wherein are discovered all the excellent secrets in metaphysicall, physicall, morall, and historicall knowledge. Fit for the learned to refresh their memories, and for younger students to abreviat and further their studies: wherein nature is discovered, art disclosed, and history laid open. Tr. out of French, by T. L. D. M. P. London, Printed for Andrew Crooke, 1637.

[LODGE, Thomas, 1558?-1625.]
The life and death of William Long Beard, the most famous and witty English traitor, borne in the citty of London. Accompanied with manye other most pleasant and prettie histories. By T.L., gent. Et nugae seria ducunt. London, printed by Rychard Yardley and Peter Short, 1593.

sm.4°. 2 leaves, A-H in 4s, I in 2. Printer'(s) mark.
Dedication signed Tho.Lodge.
Title-page has been mounted.

NL 0440041 MH PU

FILM
S-8
reel
1209
Lodge, Thomas, 1558?-1625.
The life and death of William Long Beard, the most famous and witty English traitor, borne in the Citty of London. Accompanied with manye other most pleasant and prettie histories, by T.L.of Lincolns Inne, gent. London, Printed by R.Yardley and P.Short, 1593.
Short-title catalogue no.16659 (carton 1209)

1.Fitzosbert, William, d.1196. I.Title.

NL 0440042 MiU ViU NjP

PR
1121
.C69
v.2
Lodge, Thomas, 1558?-1625.
The life and death of William Long beard, the most famous and witty English traitor, borne in the citty of London. Accompanied with manye other most pleasant and prettie histories, by T.L.of Lincolns Inne ... London, Printed by Rychard Yardley and Peter Short, 1593. (Reprinted, London, 1866)
ɪɪ p., reprint: 83 p. 21 cm. (In Collier, J.P., ed. Illustrations of old English literature. London, 1866. v.2)
ɪɪ p. (editor's introd.) follow the t.p. which is part of the reprint.
1.Fitzosbert, William, d.1196. I.Collier, John Payne, 1789-   1883, ed.

NL 0440043 MiU OU

Lodge, Thomas, 1558-1625.
Life and death of William Long beard ...
[Glasg. 1880]

NL 0440044 NjP

Lodge, Thomas, 1558?-1625.
A Looking Glasse for London and England ...
London, 1594.

NL 0440045 CSmH

FILM
Lodge, Thomas, 1558?-1625.
A looking glasse for London and England. Made by Thomas Lodge ... and Robert Greene ... London Printed by Thomas Creede, and are to be sold by William Barley ... 1594.
University microfilms no.15940 (case 56, carton 356)
Short-title catalogue no.16679.

I.Greene, Robert, 1558-1592, joint author. II.Title.

NL 0440046 MiU MoU

Lodge, Thomas, 1558?-1625.
... A looking glasse for London and England, made by Thomas Lodge and Robert Greene, 1594. (Amersham, Eng.) Issued for subscribers by the editor of the Tudor facsimile texts, 1914.
3 p. l., facsim.: (70) p. 26½ᶜᵐ. (The Tudor facsimile texts, under the ... editorship of John S. Farmer)
"Date of earliest known original edition ... 1594."
Reproduced from the British museum copy of the 1598 edition (B. M. C. 34. d. 21) as the 1594 edition was not available.
Original title: A Looking Glasse, for London and Englande. Made by Thomas Lodge, Gentleman, and Robert Greene. In Artibus Magister. (Printer's mark) London, Printed by Thomas Creede, and are to be solde by William Barley ... 1598.
Interleaved.
ɪ. Greene, Robert, 1558-   1592, joint author. ɪɪ. Title.
14-12672
Library of Congress PR2659.L6L5 1914

NL 0440047 DLC GU ViU MB MiU

Lodge, Thomas, 1558?-1625.
A looking-glass for London and England, by Thomas Lodge & Robert Greene, 1594 ... (Oxford, Printed for the Malone society at the Oxford university press, 1932)
xxxiii p., 1 l., reprint ((70) p.), 4 l. facsims. 22 cm. (The Malone society reprints, 1932)
"Prepared under the direction of the general editor." Signed: W. W. Greg.
Printed from photographs of the only known copy of the original now in the Huntington library.
With facsimile of original t.-p.: A Looking Glasse for London and England. Made by Thomas Lodge Gentleman, and Robert Greene. *In Artibus Magister.* (Printer's mark) London Printed by Thomas Creede, and are to be sold by William Barley, at his shop in Gratious streete. 1594.
ɪ. Greene, Robert, 1558-   1592, joint author. ɪɪ. Greg, Walter Wilson, 1875-   ɪɪɪ. Title.
PR2659.L6L5   1594a   822.39   33—7943

ICU PSC
NcGU PBm MU TU MB NcRS ViU MsU FTaSU FMU CaBVaU MtU
NL 0440048 DLC OU OCU OC1 OC1W MiU NcU PPT PU PU-F

PR2297 LODGE, THOMAS, 1558?-1625.
.L8 A looking glasse for London and England. Made by
1594b Thomas Lodge Gentleman, and Robert Greene... London,
Rare bk Printed by T.Creede, and are to be sold by W.Barley,
room 1594. [San Marino, Calif.,1933]
facsim.:69 l. 20cm.
Photostat; original in the Henry E.Huntington library.
Signatures:A-I4.

NL 0440049 ICU

PR2297 LODGE, THOMAS, 1558?-1625.
.L8 A Looking Glasse for London and England Tr:Com:
1598 Geo:--By--Smyth Thos.Lodge & Robt.Green. 1598.
Rare bk [67]p. 18½cm.
room Signatures:A-I4.
Black letter.
Imperfect:t.-p.and leaf at end wanting; other leaves mutilated; title written on fly-leaf in eighteenth-century hand.

Unique copy, with stage directions written in margins. For full description see Baskervill, C.R. A prompt copy of A looking glass for London and England. call no.:PR2297 .L88B3 Rare bk room.

NL 0440051 ICU DFo CSmH

FILM
Lodge, Thomas, 1558?-1625.
A looking glasse, for London and Englande. Made by Thomas Lodge ... and Robert Greene ... London Printed by Thomas Creede, and are to be solde by William Barley ... 1598.
University microfilms no.15941 (case 68, carton 406)
Short-title catalogue no.16680.

I.Greene, Robert, 1558-1592, joint author. II.Title.

NL 0440052 MiU ViU ICU

Lodge, Thomas, 1558?-1625.
A Looking Glasse, for London and Englande. Made by Thomas Lodge, Gentleman, and Robert Greene In Artibus Magister. London Printed by Thomas Creede, and are to be solde by William Barley, at his shop in Gratious streete. 1598. (Amersham, Eng., Issued for subscribers by John S. Farmer, 1914)
1 p. l., (68) p. 23ᶜᵐ. (*On cover:* Old English drama. Students' facsimile edition)
From the British museum copy (C. 34, d. 21)
Label pasted on front end-paper reads: ... A looking glass for London, etc. By Lodge and Greene. Staged as "an old play." 1591-2. Date of earliest known edition, 1594 ... Reproduced in facsimile (Tudor facsimile texts) 1914.
ɪ. Greene, Robert, 1558-   1592, joint author. ɪɪ. Title.
A 16-181
Title from Univ. of Minn.   Printed by L. C.

NL 0440053 MnU PU IEN NIC NjP OC1 OU MiU

VOLUME 338

PR2297 Lodge, Thomas, 1558?-1625.
.L8   A Looking Glasse for London and England Tr:
160-   Com: Geo: --By ... Smyth Thos. Lodge & Rob[t]
Rare bk   Green. 1598 ⸢i.e. 160-?⸣
           ⸢67⸣ p. 18½cm.
           Signatures: A-I⁴; A[1] and I4 (blank?) wanting.
           Black letter.
           Imperfect: t.-p. wanting; other leaves mutil-
           ated; title written on fly-leaf in eighteenth
           century hand.
           Apparently unique copy of this edition, which
           is a page for page reprint of the edition of
           1602, though ⸢ ⸣probably not printed by

           Thomas Creede. For description see W. W. Greg,
           A bibliography of the English printed drama to
           the restoration, v.1, p.199-200; and C. R. Bas-
           kervill, A prompt copy of A looking glass for
           London and England, in Modern philology, v.30,
           1932, p.29-51.
           ---- ---- Photostat copy.

NL 0440055   ICU

FILM
       Lodge, Thomas, 1558?-1625.
           A looking glasse, for London and Englande. Made
       by Thomas Lodge and Robert Greene. London,
       Printed by T.Creede,for T.Pauier, 1602.
           Short-title catalogue no.16681 (carton 810)

           I.Greene,Robert,1558-1592,joint author.
           II.Title.

NL 0440056   MiU

PR2297 LODGE,THOMAS,1558?-1625.
.L8 `   A looking glasse,for London and Englande. Made by
1602a   Thomas Lodge Gentleman and Robert Greene... London,
Rare bk   Printed by T.Creede,for T.Pauier,1602. [London,1933]
room   35 l. 21½x29cm.
           Photostat(negative);original in the British museum.
           Two pages on each leaf.

NL 0440057   ICU

       Lodge, Thomas, 1558?-1625.
           A Looking Glasse For London and England. Made By
       Thomas Lodge Gentleman, and Robert Greene. In Arti-
       bus Magister. ⸢Ornament⸣ London, Imprinted by Bar-
       nard Alsop, and are to be sold at his house within Gartar
       place in Barbican. 1617.
           ⸢70⸣ p. 18ᶜᵐ.
           Signatures: A⁴; B-I⁴.
           Book-plate of Percy Fitz Gerald.

           I. Greene, Robert, 1558-1592, joint author. II. Title.
                                                            25-875

           Library of Congress   PR2659.L6L5 1617

NL 0440058   DLC MB CtY DFo IU CSmH

FILM
       Lodge,Thomas,1558?-1625.
           A looking glasse for London and England. Made
       by Thomas Lodge,and Robert Greene. London, Im-
       printed by B.Alsop, 1617.
           Short-title catalogue no.16682 (carton 810)

           I.Greene,Robert,1558-1592,joint author.
           II.Title.

NL 0440059   MiU

PR2297 LODGE,THOMAS,1558?-1625.
.L8   A looking glasse for London and England. Made by
1617a   Thomas Lodge Gentleman and Robert Greene... London,
Rare bk Imprinted by B.Alsop,1617. [London,1933]
room   facsim.:36 l. 19x29cm.
           Photostat(negative);original in the British museum.
           Two pages on each leaf.

NL 0440060   ICU

       Lodge, Thomas, 1558?-1625.
           Looking glasse for London & Englande. [Glasg.,
       1881]
           I. Greene, R.

NL 0440061   NjP

       Lodge, Thomas, ⸢1558?-1625,⸣ attributed author.
           Lvminalia; or, The festivall of light
           see under   Lvminalia.

       Lodge, Thomas, ⸢1558?-1625.⸣
           Margarite of America.   n.p.,
       1596.

NL 0440063   PU RPJCB

PR   Lodge, Thomas, 1558?-1625.
2297   A Margarite of America. ⸢London⸣
M3   Printed for Iohn Busbie, 1596.
1596a   ⸢95⸣ l. 18cm.

           Photocopy (negative) from the Bodleian
       library copy, 1931.

NL 0440064   NIC

FILM
       Lodge,Thomas,1558?-1625.
           A Margarite of America by T.Lodge. ⸢London⸣
       Printed for Iohn Busbie ... 1596.

           University microfilms no.16581 (case 80,carton 475)
           Short-title catalogue no.16660.

NL 0440065   MiU

       Lodge,Thomas,1558?-1625.
           The Margarite of America, by Thomas Lodge. Ed. by
       James O. Halliwell ... London, Printed by T. Rich-
       ards, 1859.
           viii p., reprint: vi, ⸢7⸣-139 p. 23½ x 17½ᶜᵐ.
           Imprint of reprint: ⸢London⸣ Printed for John Busbie, 1596.
           "The impression of this work is strictly limited to twenty-six copies, no
           extra perfect copy being preserved either in the waste or even in proof-sheets."
           Signed: Thomas Richards.
           Armorial book-plate: L. Johannis Whitefoord MacKenzie armigeri.

           I. Halliwell-Phillipps, James Orchard, 1820-1889, ed. II. Title.

NL 0440066   MiU CSmH MB MH DLC RPJCB NNCoCi

Y   LODGE, THOMAS, 1558?-1625.
155   A Margarite of America... [London]Busbie,
.L 828   1596[repr.Glasgow,Hunterian club,1876]
           94p.

           Forms no.36 of the Hunterian club publica-
       tions.

NL 0440067   ICN ICarbS

       Lodge, Thomas, 1558?-1625.
           Margarite of America. [Glasg., 1879]

NL 0440068   NjP

       Lodge, Thomas, 1558?-1625.
       Greene, Robert, 1558-1592.
           Menaphon, by Robert Greene and A Margarite of America,
       by Thomas Lodge, edited by G. B. Harrison ... Oxford, B.
       Blackwell, 1927.

       Lodge, Thomas, 1558?-1625.
           Miscellaneous pieces. [Glasg., 1882]

NL 0440070   NjP

[LODGE, Thomas, 1558?-1625.]
           A most pleasant historie of Glaucus and Scilli
       With many excellent poems and delectable sonn-
       ets. London,1610.

           3m.4°. A1,* in 2, A2-4,B-E in 4s,F in 2.
           Unpaged.
           Title within ornamental border.
           The dedication signed: Thomas Lodge.
           A reissue of his Scillaes Metamorphosis.
           Imperfect: title-page defaced, and three
       leaves at end torn and repaired.

NL 0440071   MH

       Lodge, Thomas, 1558?-1625, tr.

       Seneca, Lucius Annaeus.
           On benefits, tr. by Thomas Lodge. London, J. M. Dent
       and co., 1899.

       Lodge, Thomas, 1558?-1625.
           Phillis ... [Glasg., 1875]

NL 0440073   NjP

PR2659 Lodge, Thomas, 1558?-1625.
.L6P4   ... Phillis, by Thomas Lodge. Licia by Giles Fletcher.
1896   London, K. Paul, Trench, Trübner and co., 1896.
           xii, 158 p. 18½ᶜᵐ. (Half-title: Elizabethan sonnet-cycles)
           Series title also at head of t.-p.

           IEdS ViU DCU NN
NL 0440074   ICU MB ViU OC1W OU OC1 MoSU NjP OrU

       Lodge, Thomas. 1558-1625.   No. 5 in **4600a.125.2
           Phillis: honoured with pastorall sonnets, elegies, and amorous de-
           lights. Where-vnto is annexed, the tragicall complaynt of El-
           stred. At London, printed for Iohn Busbie. 1593.
           [Glasgow. Hunterian Club. 1883.] 84 pp. [Works. Vol. 2.]
           4°.
           The dedication is signed: Tho. Lodge.
           Reproduces the original spelling.

           F5106 — T.r. — Sonnets.

NL 0440075   MB NN DFo NcD CSmH

VOLUME 338

Lodge, Thomas. 1558?-1625.   *4557.66.2
    Phillis honoured with pastorall sonnets, elegies, and amorous de-
lights. Where-vnto is annexed, the tragicall complaynt of Elstred. At London, printed for Iohn Busbie . . . 1593.
    (In English garner, An. [Edited by Thomas Seccombe.] Vol. 2,
pp. 1-22. New York. [1904.])
    The original is signed: Tho. Lodge.
    Contains the sonnets only. The spelling is modernized.

F5062 — T.r. — Sonnets.

NL   0440076   MB CSmH

      Lodge, Thomas, 1558?-1625.
      Poore mans talentt ...   Glasg., 1881.

NL   0440077   NjP

      Lodge, Thomas, 1558?-1625.
      Prosopopeia ...   [Glasg., 1880]

NL   0440078   NjP

Lodge, Thomas, 1558?-1625.
    ‹A reply to Stephen Gosson's Schoole of Abuse
in defence of poetry musick and stage plays.›
‹1579-80.›
    8°. (wants title)

    STC No. 16663.

NL   0440079   CSmH

FILM
P-620 Lodge, Thomas, 1558?-1625.

    A reply to Stephen Gosson's Schoole of Abuse
in defence of poetry musick and state plays.
‹London, 1579-80›
    Microfilm reproduction.
    Title wanting.
    STC 16663.
    1. Poetry—Early works to 1800. 2. Music and morals.
3. Theater—Moral and religious aspects. 4. Gosson,
Stephen, 1554-1624. Schooleof abuse.

NL   0440080   ViU DFo MiU

Lodge, Thomas, 1558?-1625.
    A reply to Stephen Gosson's Schoole of abuse
in defence of poetry musick and stage plays, by
Thomas Lodge. [Glasgow, Printed by Robert
Anderson] 1580? [1879]
    1 p.l., 48 p.   24cm.   (On cover: Hunterian
club. [Reprints] XLVIII. Sixth year)

    "Reprinted from the first edition (1580?)
... for the Hunterian club 1879."

NL   0440081   NcD NjP

Lodge, Thomas, 1558-1625.
    A reply to Stephen Gosson's School of abuse, in defence of poetry,
musick and stage plays. 1580? 48 pp.
    (In his Complete works. Vol. I. Printed for the Hunterian Club.
[Glasgow.] 1883.)   No. 2 in **4600a.125.1

NL   0440082   MB CSmH

Y   Lodge, Thomas,   1558?-1625.
1095.
.78   A reply to Stephen Gosson's Schoole
of abuse in Defence of poetry, musick,
and stage plays.   (in Saintsbury,
G.E.B., ed.   Elizabethan & Jacobean pamphlets.   1892.   p.[1]-42)

    Caption title (p.2)
    Originally written by Lodge in 1580.
It seems to have been refused a license
and was circu‹   ›lated privately. Gosson

in 1582 answered it in his "Plays confuted in five actions" and Lodge briefly rejoined in the preface to his "Alarum against usurers", 1584.—cf. Dict.
nat. biog.

NL   0440084   ICN MB CSmH

Lodge, Thomas, 1558?-1625.
    ... Rosalind. A novel, by Thomas Lodge. New York,
Cassell & company, limited [1887]
    192 p. 14ᵐ.   (Cassell's national library. [v. 2, no. 62])

    I. Title.

    Library of Congress   PZ3.L8233Ro 6   7—3044

NL   0440085   DLC MH PPL

828
L822r   Lodge, Thomas, 1558?-1625.
1893   Rosalind, a novel. London, Cassell, 1893.
    192 p.   (Cassell's national library, 63)

    1.Shakespeare, William. As you like it--
Source.   I.Title.

NL   0440086   MiU MH CtY

Lodge, Thomas, 1558?-1625.
    ... Rosalind. A novel, by Thomas Lodge. New York,
The Cassell publishing co. [1894?]
    192 p. 14ᵐ.   (Cassell's national library. [v. 2, no. 62])
    Cover dated 1887.

    I. Title.

                                         7—14799

    Library of Congress   PZ3.L8233Ro 8

NL   0440087   DLC WaWW

Lodge, Thomas, 1558?-1625.
    Rosalind, a novel.
London, Cassell, 1899.
    192 p.

NL   0440088   PU

STC   Lodge, Thomas, 1558?-1625.
16664   Rosalynde. Euphues golden legacie: found
after his death in his cell at Silexedra ...
London, Imprinted by Thomas Orwin for T. G.
and John Busbie, 1590.

    A-R⁴, S². (R1-4, lacking, supplied in mss. of
1592 edition [STC 16665] and photostat of Pforzheimer 1590 edition [STC 16664]). 4to.
    Pforzheimer, v. 2, pp. 639-641, no. 619.
    Heber-Britwell Court copy.

NL   0440089   DFo

[Lodge, Thomas, 1558?-1625]
    Rosalynde; Euphues golden legacie, found after his
death in his cell at Silexedra. Bequeathed to Philautus
sonnes, noursed up with their father in England. Fetcht
from the Canaries by T.L., gent. London, Imprinted by
T.Orwin for T.G.and J.Busbie, 1590.

    66 p.
    Photostat copy, negative, of copy in Folger Shakespeare
Library.
    Signed at end: T.Lodge.

NL   0440090   MH

**MICROFORMS
CENTER**
Film   Lodge, Thomas, 1558?-1625
3461   Rosalynd; Euphues golden legacie. Found
after his death in his cell at Silexedra.
Bequeathed to Philautus sonnes, noursed vp
with their father in England. Fetcht from
the Canaries, by T. L. Gent. London, Imprinted by T. Orwin for T. G. and J. Busbie,
1590.
    66p.
    R1-4 lacking, supplied in MSS of 1592 ed.
(STC 16665) and photostat of Pforzheimer

    1590 ed. (STC 16664).
    The source of Shakespeare's As you like it.
    Short-title catalogue no. 16664.
    Microfilm (negative) Washington, The Folger
Shakespeare Library, 1957. 1 reel.
    1. Shakespeare, William, 1564-1616 - Sources
I. Title II. Title: Euphues golden legacie

NL   0440092   WU

FILM
    Lodge, Thomas, 1558?-1625.
    Rosalynde. Euphues golden legacie ... Fetcht
from the Canaries by T.L. ... London, Printed
by Abel Ieffes for T.G.Gubbin, and Iohn Busbie.
1592.

    Dedication signed: Thomas Lodge.
    The source of Shakespeare's "As you like it".
    University microfilms no.16384 (case 80, carton 476)
    Short-title catalogue no.16665.

    1.Shakespeare, William—Sources. I.Title. II.Title:
Evphves golden legacie.

NL   0440093   MiU CtY

[Lodge, Thomas] 1558?-1625.
    Rosalynde. Evphves Golden Legacie, found after
his death in his Cell at Silexedra. Beqveathed To
Philavts Sonnes, noursed vp with their Father in
England. Fetcht from the Canaries by T. L. ...
London, Printed for N. Lyng, and T. Gubbins, 1596.
    sm. 4 to.   Maroon cloth wrapper, in a maroon
morocco solander case; by Zucher.
    Issued later under title: Euphues Golden Legacie.

NL   0440094   CSmH

STC   Lodge, Thomas, 1558?-1625.
16667   Rosalynd. Euphues golden legacie, found
after his death in his cell at Silexedra ...
London, Printed for N. Lyng, and T. Gubbins,
1598.
    Colophon.

    A-O⁴. (A1 and O4 remargined.) 4to.
    Frederick Locker-Lampson copy.

NL   0440095   DFo

VOLUME 338

FILM
Lodge, Thomas, 1558?-1625.
Rosalynd. Evphves golden legacie ... Fetcht
from the Canaries by T.L. ... London Printed
for N.Lyng, and T.Gubbins. 1598.
Dedication signed: Thomas Lodge.
The source of Shakespeare's As you like it.
University microfilms no.15956 (case 56, carton 336)
Short-title catalogue no.16667.

1.Shakespeare,William—Sources. I.Title. II.Title:
Evphves golden   legacie.

NL 0440096   MiU CSmH

[Lodge, Thomas] 1558?-1625.
Rosalynd. Evphves Golden Legacie, found after
his death in his Cell at Silexedra. Beqveathed to
Philavtvs Sonnes nursed vp with their Father in
England. Fetcht from the Canaries by T. L. ...
London, by I. R. for N. Lyng, 1604.
sm. 4 to.   Red morocco by Pratt
Britwell sale, March 1921, no. 146.

NL 0440097   CSmH

STC
16669
Lodge, Thomas, 1558?-1625.
Rosalynd: Euphues golden legacie. Found
after his death in his cell at Silexedra ...
London, Printed for Iohn Smethwick, 1609.

A-O⁴.   (O4 lacking.) 4to.

NL 0440098   DFo

FILM
Lodge, Thomas, 1558?-1625.
Rosalynd: Euphues golden legacie. Found after
his death in his cell at Silexedra. Beqveathed to
Philavtvs sonnes, nursed vp with their father in
England. Fetcht from the Canaries, by T.L. Lon-
don, Printed for I.Smethvvick, 1609.
The source of Shakespeare's As you like it.
Short-title catalogue no.16669 (carton 809)

1.Shakespeare,William—Sources. I.Title.
II.Title: Evphves   golden legacie.

NL 0440099   MiU

Lodge, Thomas, 1558?-1625.
Rosalynde, Euphues' golden legacie found after
his death in his cell at Silexedra...
London, Rodd, 1841.
130 p.

NL 0440100   PU MB MdBP

Lodge, Thomas, 1558?-1625.
Rosalynd. Euphues' golden legacie, found after his death in
his cell at Silexedra, &c. Upon which Shakespeare founded his
"As you like it." (In: J. P. Collier, Shakespeare's library. Lon-
don, 1850. 8°. v. 1.   1 p.l., iv, 130 p.)
Reprinted from Rodd's reprint, 1841, of the edition of 1592.

1. Shakespeare, William.—Single   plays: As you like it. 2. Title.
                                                        April 4, 1911.

NL 0440101   NN

Lodge, Thomas. 1558-1625.   **G.4030.2.6
Rosalynde, Euphues golden legacie.
(In Shakespeare, William. Works ... [Edited] by James O.
Halliwell [Phillipps]. Vol. 6, pp. 3-68. London. 1856.)
This is the source of Shakespeare's As you like it.

NL 0440102   MB

Lodge, Thomas, 1558?-1625.
Rosalynde ...   [Glasg., 1878]

NL 0440103   NjP

Lodge, Thomas, 1558-1625.
Rosalynde; with eight photogravures and several line illustrations by Thomas Maybank. London: George Routledge &
Sons, Ltd. [189-?]   150 p., 8 pl.   illus.   8°.   (The photogravure and colour series.)

NL 0440104   NN

Lodge, Thomas, 1558?-1625.
Rosalynde, a novel, by Thomas Lodge. With eight photogravures and...illus. by Thomas Maybank.   London, G. Routledge & sons [etc., etc., 19—?]   150 p.   illus.   21cm.   (The
photogravure and colour series)

NL 0440105   NN MtBC OClW MiU AAP NNCoCi

[Lodge, Thomas] 1558?-1625.
Rosalynde, Euphues golden legacie, found after his death in
his cell at Silexedra. Bequeathed to Philautus sonnes, nursed up
with their father in England. Fetcht from the Canaries by T. L.,
gent: London: G. Newnes ltd., 1902.   187 p.   front., plates.
16cm.   (Half-title: The Caxton series.)

890380A. 1. Fiction, English. I. L.,   Purchased for J. S. Billings Mem. Coll.
T., gent. II. Title.   October 19, 1937.

MH CaBVaU PU
NL 0440106   NN CU-S LU NcD NNF MH MB IU OC1 MiU

Lodge, Thomas, 1558?-1625.
Rosalynde, or Euphues golden legacie, by Thomas Lodge.
Printed from the edition of 1592. [New Rochelle, N. Y., Elston
press, 1902]
2 p. l., 123, [1] p., 1 l. 24½ᵐ.
Colophon: Here ends the story of Rosalynde, or Euphues golden legacie, written by Thomas Lodge. One hundred and sixty copies have
been printed from the edition of 1592, collated with that of 1598. Printed
and sold by Clarke Conwell at the Elston press, Pelham road, New Ro-
chelle, New York. Finished this seventeenth day of July. MDCCCCII.
Running title and headings in red.
Added t.-p. reprinted from the original t.-p.: Rosalynde. Euphues golden legacie, found after his death in his cell at Silexedra, beqveathed to
Philavtvs sonnes, nvrsed vp with their father in England. Fetcht from
the Canaries by T. L. gent.   London, Printed by Abel Ieffes for
T. G. and Iohn Busbie.   1592.
I. Title.
Library of Congress   PZ3.L8233Ro 12   2—24060

PSC
NL 0440107   DLC OKentU FTaSU NIC MoSW MiU MB NN MH

Lodge, Thomas, 1558?-1625.
Lodge's "Rosalynde"; being the original of
Shakespeare's "As you like it". ed. by W. W. Greg.
London, Chatto, 1906.
208 p.

NL 0440108   PP

Lodge, Thomas, 1558?-1625.
Lodge's 'Rosalynde'; being the original of Shakespeare's 'As you like it'; ed by W. W. Greg, M. A. London, Chatto and Windus, 1907.
xxix, [1], 209, [1] p. front. (facsim.) 17½ᵐ. (Half-titles: The Shakespeare library. General editor, I. Gollancz. [pt. II] The Shakespeare clas-
sics. [v. I])
Illustrated half-titles (Shakespeare's coat of arms, and portrait)
With reproductions of original title-pages, 1590 and 1609.
"Shakspere's As you like it and Lodge's Rosalynde compared. By W. G.
Stone": p. 187-209.
1. Shakespeare, William. As you like it—Sources. I. Greg, Walter
Wilson, 1875- ed. II. Boswell-Stone, Walter George, 1845-1904.
                                                        8—13302
Library of Congress   PR2952.G6 vol. I

PSC MiU OEac InU OU OCU OCl OO OClW PBm NcRS
NL 0440109   DLC NN PHC CU-S MB NN CaBVaU OrPR PPL

Lodge, Thomas, 1558?-1625.
Lodge's 'Rosalynde', being the original of Shakespeare's 'As
you like it' ed. by W. W. Greg, M. A. New York, Duffield &
company; London, Chatto & Windus, 1907.
xxix, [1], 209, [1] p. front. (facsim.) port. 17½ x 14½ᶜᵐ. (First half-
title: The Shakespeare library. General editor, I. Gollancz. Second
half-title: [II] The Shakespeare classics. [v. I])
Printed in Great Britain.
A modernized edition based upon the first edition, with original t.-p.,
reproduced in print: Rosalynde. Euphues golden legacie: found after
his death in his cell at Silexedra ... By T. L. gent. London, Imprinted
by Thomas Orwin for T. G. and John Busbie. 1590. The t.-p. of the edition London, Iohn Smethvick, 1609, is reproduced in photogravure.
Appendix: Shakespere's As you like it and Lodge's Rosalynde compared. By W. G. Stone, esq.
I. Greg, Walter Wilson,   1875-   ed. II. Boswell-Stone,
Walter George, 1845-1904.   III. Title.
                                               9—13613
Library of Congress   PR2297.R7G7

ViU PU-F PU
NL 0440110   DLC KEmT MB TU NjP MH OrP IdU NcD OC1JC

Lodge, Thomas, 1558?-1625.
Rosalynde; or, Euphues' golden legacy, by Thomas Lodge,
ed. with introduction and notes, by Edward Chauncey Baldwin ... Boston, New York [etc.] Ginn and company [*1910]
xxvii, 133 p. 17½ cm. (On cover: Standard English classics.)
Bibliography: p. xxi.

I. Baldwin, Edward Chauncey, 1870-1940, ed. II. Title.

PR2297.R7B3   10—27304

NNC Or MU OrU OrCS
OLak OC1 PBL PPSJ PBm CoU PPT MtU PV PU WaTC PHC WaS
NL 0440111   DLC KEmT MsSM NIC ViU NcD MB NN OOxM OO

Lodge, Thomas, 1558?-1625.
Rosalynde; a novel, with eight photogravures
and several line illus. by Thomas Maybank.
London, G. Routledge; New York, E. P. Dutton
[1928]
150 p. illus. 21cm.

NL 0440112   ViU CaBVaU

Lodge, Thomas, 1558?-1625.
Lodge's 'Rosalynde', being the original of Shakespeare's
'As you like it,' edited by W. W. Greg, M. A. London, H.
Milford, Oxford university press, 1931.
xxix, [1], 209 p. 17½ cm. (Half-title: The Shakespeare library.
General editor: I. Gollancz. [The Shakespeare classics. v. I])
Added half-title contains portrait of Shakespeare and legend, "The
Shakespeare classics," within ornamental border.
"First edition 1907; second edition 1931."
A modernized edition based upon the 1st edition, with reproduc-
tion of original t.-p.: Rosalynde. Euphues golden legacie: found after
his death in his cell at Silexedra ... By T. L. gent. London, Im-
printed by Thomas Orwin for T. G. and John Busbie, 1590.

Appendix: Shakespere's As you like it and Lodge's Rosalynde
compared. By W. G. Stone, esq.

1. Shakespeare, William. As you like it—Sources. I. Greg,
Walter Wilson, 1875- ed. II. Boswell-Stone, Walter George, 1845-
1904. III. Title: Rosalynde.

PR2297.R7G7 1931   823.3   32—24698

NL 0440114   DLC NN PU PWcS OC1CC MiU OCU OC1W OC1

PR
2297
R7
G7
1931
Lodge, Thomas, 1558?-1625.
Lodge's 'Rosalynde', being the original
of Shakespeare's 'As you like it', edited
by W. W. Greg. [2d ed.] London, H. Milford,
Oxford University Press, 1931; [Ann Arbor,
Mich., University Microfilms, 1969]
209p. 17cm. (The Shakespeare library. The
Shakespeare classics, v. 1)
Appendix: Shakespeare's As you like it and
Lodges Rosalynde compared, by W. G. Stone.
Reproduced by microfilm-xerography.

1. Shakespeare, William, 1564-1616 - As
you like it - Sources I. Greg, Walter
Wilson, 1875-1959, Ed. II. Boswell-Stone,
Walter George, 1845-1904 III. Title:
Rosalynde

NL 0440116   WU

VOLUME 338

Lodge, Thomas, 1558?-1625.
Rosalynde; or, Euphues' golden legacy, by
... ed. with introduction and notes, by
Edward Chauncey Baldwin ... Boston, New
York ₍etc.₎ Ginn and company ₍194-₎.
133 p.

NL 0440117   MiU

PR2803
.A2W53   Lodge, Thomas, 1558?-1625. Rosalynde.

Shakespeare, William, 1564-1616.
  Wie es euch gefällt. ₍Deutsch von August Wilhelm
Schlegel₎ Hrsg. und eingeleitet von Paul Wiegler. Berlin,
Transmare Verlag ₍1948₎

Lodge, Thomas. 1558-1625.   *4557.62.2
Rosalynd's madrigal.
(In Arber. An English garner. Vol. 2, pp. 115, 116. London,
1879.)

NL 0440119   MB

Lodge, Thomas, 1558-1625.
  Rosalynd's madrigal. [1590]
  (In: An English garner. [v. 11] Shorter
Elizabethan poems. Westminster, 1906. 8°.
p. 316-317)
  n.t.-p

NL 0440120   NN

STC   Lodge, Thomas, 1558?-1625.
16674   Scillaes metamorphosis: enterlaced with the
vnfortunate loue of Glaucus. Whereunto is annexed
the delectable discourse of the discontented
Satyre: with sundrie other ... poems and sonnets
... Imprinted at London by Richard Ihones, 1589.

A⁴ (+ 2 leaves signed ✗ after A1), B-E⁴, F². 4to.
Cf. Pforzheimer, v. 2, pp. 642-643, no. 621.
Thomas Fuller-Marquess of Downshire copy.

NL 0440121   DFo CSmH

Lodge, Thomas, 1558?-1625
  Scillaes metamorphosis: enterlaced with the unfortunate
love of Glaucus. Whereunto is annexed the delectable
discourse of the Discontented satyre; with sundrie other
most absolute poems and sonnets. L, Imprinted by R.
Jhones, 1589

[48] p.
Photostat copy, positive, of the copy in the Huntington
Library

NL 0440122   MH NbU IaU OClW

Lodge, Thomas, 1558?-1625.
  Scillaes metamorphosis ...   [Glasg., 1876]

NL 0440123   NjP

PO 1173   Lodge, Thomas, 1558?-1625.
.P 39   ₍...Songs and sonnets. Robert Greene, Lyrics
no.6   from romances,etc. Samuel Daniel, Selected verse.
Hull, J.R.Tutin, 1906.
                            (The Pembroke
booklets (first series) VI)

  "Prefatory note" signed: H. Kelsey White.

NL 0440124   MdBJ NcD IU CaBVaU OU

STC   Lodge, Thomas, 1558?-1625.
16676   A treatise of the plague: containing the nature,
signes, and accidents of the same, with the certaine and absolute cure of the feuers, botches
and carbuncles that raigne in these times ...
London, Printed for Edward White and N. L., 1603.

A-L⁴. (L4, blank, lacking. Top margins trimmed
affecting running titles and some text.) 4to.
Pforzheimer, v. 2, pp. 643-644, no. 622.

NL 0440125   DFo DNLM MH

FILM   Lodge, Thomas, 1558?-1625.
  A treatise of the plague: Containing the nature,
signes, and accidents of the same, with the certaine
and absolute cure of the feuers, botches and carbuncles that raigne in these times: and aboue all
things most singular experiments and preseruatiues
in the same, gathered by the obseruation of diuers
worthy trauailers, and selected out of the writings
of the best learned phisitians in this age. London, Printed ₍by V.Sims₎ for E.White and N.L.₍ing₎
1603.

  The table at the end of the book belongs to
S.Kellwaye's "A defensative against the plague."
Short-title catalogue no.16676 (carton 810)

  1.Plague.

NL 0440127   MiU NjR ICU

Lodge, Thomas, 1558?-1625.
  Treatise of the plague ...   [Glasg., 1880]

NL 0440128   NjP

Lodge, Thomas, 1558?-1625.   FOR OTHER EDITIONS
                                SEE MAIN ENTRY
King Leir.
  ... The true chronicle history of King Leir. 1605. ₍Lon-
don₎ Issued for subscribers by the editor of the Tudor facsimile texts, 1910.

---

x828   ₍Lodge, Thomas₎ 1558?-1625.
L821w   VVits miserie, and the vvorlds madnesse: dis-
couering the devils incarnat of this age.
London, Printed by A. Islip, and are to be
sold by C. Burby, 1596.
₍6₎, 111p. 18cm.

  Upper margins closely trimmed with loss of
many running titles and page numerals.
  Bound in maroon levant morocco, gold tooled.
  "The epistle dedicatorie" signed: T. L.
  STC 16677.

NL 0440130   IU DFo CtY MH

FILM   Lodge, Thomas, 1558?-1625.
  VVits miserie, and the vvorlds madnesse: dis-
couering the deuils incarnat of this age.
London, Printed by Adam Islip, and are to be
sold by Cutbert Burby ... 1596.
Dedication signed: T.L.₍i.e.Thomas Lodge₎
University microfilms no.15958 (case 68,carton 406)
Short-title catalogue no.16677.

NL 0440131   MiU ViU CSmH DFo MH

Lodge, Thomas, 1558-1625.
  Wits miserie ...   [Glasg., 1879]

NL 0440132   NjP

Lodge, Thomas, 1558?-1625, ed.

Seneca, Lucius Annaeus.
  The workes of Lucius Annaeus Seneca, newly inlarged
and corrected by Thomas Lodge ... London, Printed by
Willi: Stansby. ₍1620₎

Lodge, Thomas, 1558?-1625.
  The wounds of civil war, lively set forth in the true tragedies of
Marius and Scilla. London, printed by I. Danter, 1594.
  sq. 16°. pp. 78.
  This book may be consulted in the room of the Widener Collection.

NL 0440134   MH NRU CSmH CtY DFo

Lodge, Thomas, 1558?-1625.
  Wounds of civil war. London, 1594.
  (In Three centuries of drama: English,
1512-1641)

  Microprint.

  1. Marius, Gaius--Drama. 2. Sulla, Lucius
Cornelius--Drama. I. Title.

NL 0440135   MoU

FILM   Lodge, Thomas, 1558?-1625.
  The vvounds of ciuill vvar. Liuely set forth
in the true tragedies of Marius and Scilla. As
it hath beene publiquely plaide in London, by
... the Lord High Admirall his seruants.
VVritten by Thomas Lodge ... London, Printed
by Iohn Danter ... 1594.
University microfilms no.15939 (case 68,carton 406)
Short-title catalogue no.16678.

NL 0440136   MiU ViU NBuU

₍Lodge, Thomas₎ 1558?-1625.
  The wounds of civil war.
  (In ₍Dodsley, Robert₎ A select collection of old plays. London, 1825-27.
19¼ᶜᵐ. v. 8, p. ₍1₎-88)

  1. Title.

                                    12-3021
  Library of Congress   PR1263.D6 vol.8

NL 0440137   DLC

₍Lodge, Thomas₎ 1558?-1625.
  The wounds of civil war.
  (In Dodsley, Robert, ed. A select collection of old English plays. 4th
ed. by W. C. Hazlitt. London, 1874-76. 21¼ᶜᵐ. v. 7, p. ₍97₎-197)
  Caption title: The most lamentable and true tragedies of Marius and
Sylla.
  Early edition (1594) has title: The VVovnds of Ciuill VVar. Liuely set
forth in the true Tragedies of Marius and Scilla ... VVritten by Thomas
Lodge Gent.

  1. Title.

                                    14-21862
  Library of Congress   PR1263.D7 vol.7

NL 0440138   DLC RPB CSmH NIC

Lodge, Thomas, 1558?-1625.
  Wounds of civill war ...   [Glasg., 1875]

NL 0440139   NjP

VOLUME 338

Lodge, Thomas, 1558†–1625.
The wounds of civil war, by Thomas Lodge. 1594 ...
₍London, Printed for the Malone society by H. Hart, at
the Oxford university press₎ 1910.
xii, ₍78₎ p. 2 facsim. 22 x 18ᶜᵐ. (The Malone society reprints)
With reproduction of original t-p.: The wovnds of ciuill vvar. Liuely
set forth in the true tragedies of Marius and Scilla ... London, Printed by
John Danter ... 1594.
"This reprint ... has been prepared by J. Dover Wilson."

I. Wilson, John Dover, 1881– ed.
11–12474

Library of Congress   PR2659.L6 1910

NN TxU
MB MU NcU TU OU OCU OC1 OC1W ViU PBm PSC PHC PU MiU
NL 0440140   DLC MtU CaBVaU NjP CSmH PU–F AAP OrPS

Lodge, Thomas, 1882–
Dictatorship in Newfoundland, by T. Lodge ... London
₍etc.₎ Cassell and company, ltd. ₍1939₎
3 p. l., 273 p. incl. front. (map) 19¼ᶜᵐ.
"First published 1939."

1. Newfoundland—Pol. & govt. 2. Newfoundland—Economic policy.
3. Newfoundland—Econ. condit. I. Title.

Library of Congress   F1123.L63   40–2544
971.8

NL 0440141   DLC CaBVaU CaBViP CoU CtY MH OU CU

Lodge, Venerable, *pseud.*
see
Shu, Ch'ing-ch'un, 1898–1960.

Lodge, W.C., *joint author.*
Cameron, Edward Parke, 1893–1931.
... The pulping qualities of fire-killed wood, by E. P. Cameron, ʙ. sc., and W. C. Lodge. ₍Ottawa, F. A. Acland, printer,
1924₎

Lodge, W   C
A retrospect. Poem by Hon. W.C. Lodge,
Claymont, Delaware.
(In Vermont—State normal school, Castleton.
Castleton seminary: memorial anniversary ...
June 29th, 1870. Rutland, Tuttle, 1870 22 cm.
p. 32–34)

NL 0440144   RPB

Lodge, William, 1649–1689, *tr.*
ND611
.B312
Barri, Giacomo, *ca.* 1630–*ca.* 1690.
The painters voyage of Italy. In which all the famous
paintings of the most eminent masters are particularised, as
they are preserved in the several cities of Italy ... Written
originally in Italian by Giacomo Barri ... Englished by W. L.
... London, T. Flesher, 1679.

Lodge, William, 1848–
Rules of management, with practical instructions on
machine building, by William Lodge ... New York ₍etc.₎
McGraw-Hill book company, inc., 1913.
xv, 139 p. 20ᶜᵐ. $2.00

1. Factory management. 2. Efficiency, Industrial. 3. Machine-shops.
I. Title.

Library of Congress   TS155.L7   13–18035

OCU OOxM MB ICJ NN PP PU PSC PPT
NL 0440146   DLC KMK MtU CU ICRL NcRS OC1 OU MiU

Lodge, William C.
Feeding beef cattle in the middle states.
(*In* U. S. Dept. of agriculture. Report, 1867, p. 212–217. pl. XVII. 23ᶜᵐ.
Washington, 1868)

1. Cattle, Beef. 2. Cattle—Feeding.

Agr 13–1040
Library, U. S. Dept. of   Agriculture 1Ag84 1867

NL 0440147   DNAL

Lodge, William C.
Fruits and fruit trees of the middle states; their prop-
agation, influence of stocks, diseases, and enemies.
(*In* U. S. Dept. of agriculture. Report, 1865, p. 199–207. 23ᶜᵐ. Washington, 1866)

1. Fruit and fruit trees.

Agr 13–1041
Library, U. S. Dept. of   Agriculture 1Ag84 1865

NL 0440148   DNAL

Lodge, William C.
Wine-making and vine culture in the middle states.
(*In* U. S. Dept. of agriculture. Report, 1866, p. 118–125. 23ᶜᵐ. Wash-
ington, 1867)

1. Grape—Culture. 2. Wine-making.

Agr 13–1042
Library, U. S. Dept. of   Agriculture 1Ag84 1866

NL 0440149   DNAL MH-A

BF451
L58
Lodge, William J   1912–
A study of some factors affecting responses
on personality questionnaires. ₍Berkeley,
Calif. 1949.
152 l. tables.
Thesis (Ph.D.) – Univ. of California,
Sept. 1949.
Bibliography: p.130–152.

1. Personality tests.

NL 0440150   CU

Lodge, William Jacob, 1832–1904.
A record of the descendents ₍!₎ of Robert and Elizabeth
Lodge (English Quakers) 1682–1903, by William Jacob Lodge,
ᴹ. ᴅ. Geneva, W. F. Humphrey press inc., 1942.
2 p. l., 150 p. front., 2 port. on 1 l. 23½ᶜᵐ.
Preface signed: G. L. ₍i. e. Gonzalez Lodge₎

1. Lodge family. I. Lodge, Gonzalez, 1863– ed.
42–18890
Library of Congress   CS71.L818 1942

NL 0440151   DLC WaS OC1WHi PHi

Lodge, William O
Prognosis in relation to diseases of the ear, nose and
throat. Stockholm ₍Almqvist & Wiksell, 1955₎
24 p. illus. 27 cm. (Acta oto-laryngologica. Supplementum 119)

1. Ear—Diseases. 2. Nose—Diseases. 3. Throat—Diseases.
(Series)
A 56–4530
John Crerar Library
for Library of Congress

NL 0440152   ICJ DNLM ViU PSt MoU

Lodge, William Penn
Lingnan University; a letter...
see under ₍Cadbury, Catherine Jones₎

Lodge, William Penn.
Youth prolonged, by William Penn Lodge ... illustrated by
Edwin John Prittie. Philadelphia, Chicago ₍etc.₎ The John
C. Winston company ₍ᶜ1926₎
2 p. l., 7–190 p. front., illus., ports. 18ᶜᵐ.

1. Hygiene. 2. Physical education and training. I. Title.

Library of Congress   RA776.L8   27–2038

NL 0440154   DLC

A lodge cipher to a correct and complete work
see under ₍Daggett, William Wallace₎

32
10061
Lodge music arranged for elk lodges. [anon.]
[New York, 1876]
18 p. 18°.

NL 0440156   DLC

The lodge of George Washington and his masonic
neighbors
see under ₍Freemasons. Alexandria, Va.
Alexandria. Washington lodge, no. 22₎

366.1
L822
The Lodge of Industry and Perseverance, no.
109 E. C., 1761–1954. ₍Mysore, India,
Printed by K. A. Korula, 1954?₎
472 p. plates, ports. 23 cm.

Title from spine; each part has special
t. p.
Running title: The second lodge of Bengal
in the olden times.
Pt. 1 first published in 1911.
Contents: pt. 1. The second lodge of
Bengal in the   olden times, being a
history of the early days of Lodge Industry
and Perseverance no. 109 of England, 1761–1812,
by W. K. Firminger. pt. 2. Lodge Industry and
Perseverance no. 109 from 1812 to 1950, by
G. D. Robinson.
1. Freemasons. India. I. Firminger, Walter
Kelly, 1870–1940. The second lodge of Bengal in
the olden times. II. Robinson, Guy D. Lodge
Industry and Perseverance no. 109. From 1812 to
1950. III. Title: The second lodge of Bengal
in the olden   times.

NL 0440159   NcD KMK

HS
650
.C14
L82
The Lodge of Industry and Perseverance no.109
E. C., 1761–1954. ₍Mysore, Wesley Press and
Pub.House, 1954?₎
2 pts.in 1 v. (272 p.) plates, ports.
Binder's title.
CONTENTS:--pt.1.The Second Lodge of Bengal
in the olden times: being a history of the
early days of Lodge Industry and Perseverance
no.109 of England,1761–1812, by W.K.Firminger.
--pt.2.Lodge Industry and Perseverance no.109
from 1812 to 1950, by G.D.Robinson.
1.Freemasons. Calcutta. Lodge Industry and
Perseverance. I. Firminger, Walter Kelly,1870–
1940. The Second Lodge of Bengal in the olden
times. II.Robinson,Guy D.Lodge Industry and
Perseverance no.   109 from 1812 to 1950.

NL 0440160   MiU

VOLUME 338

Lodge of Saint Andrew (*Freemasons*) *Boston*
see
Freemasons. *Boston. Lodge of Saint Andrew.*

Lodgen, George E
Survey of the Burroughs newsboys foundation based on a report made to a Committee for investigation of the Foundation by George E. Lodgen.
n.p. [1933]

32 numb. 1. 28.5 cm.
Caption title.
Manifold copy.

NL 0440162   MH

△
BR83
.512   The lodging-houses of London. **Extracted from** the "London City Mission Magazine" of August, 1845. London, Seeley, Burnside and Seeley, 1846.
16 p. 20 cm.
On cover: For private circulation.
Extracted from the London city mission magazine of August, 1845.

NL 0440163   MB

Lodging industry. 6th–
1937–
New York, etc.
v.
"Annual report on hotel and motor hotel operations." (varies)
The 1st–5th studies, 1932–36, were published in the following numbers of the Horwath hotel accountant: July 1933, Aug. 1934, June 1935, Apr. 1936 and May 1937.

NL 0440164   PSt

E158
.W88   **Lodging list of the Americas.**
Boston, Women's Rest Tour Association.
v. 16 cm.
Continues: Women's Rest Tour Association, Boston. America lodging list issued by the Women's Rest Tour Association ...

1. Hotels, taverns, etc.—America.   I. Women's Rest Tour Association, Boston.

E158.W88   647'.947   72–626753

NL 0440165   DLC

Lodgman de Auen (Melchior Wenzl). Ursprung des Lebens, das ist: Beachtsame, und wahrhaftige Beschreibung deren mineralischen Wässern, in denen St. Johannis-Bädern, bey dem Riesengebürg des Königreichs Böheim in dem Königgratzer-Creys, von deren uralten Ursprung, Nutzbarkeit und heilsamen Würkungen durch alte, beständige, und wahre Beweisung, und Experienz, wie auch, wie sich in denenselben je demmänniglich halten und verhalten soll. 7 p. l., 150 pp. 12°. [*n. p.*], *J. K. Factortz,* 1749.

NL 0440166   DNLM

Lodgman von Auen (Joh. [Rudolph]). Inventi neo fontis aquas virtute salubris Sanct-Annaeo ager Modletinensis habet. Das ist: Neü erfundenes Wasser Sanct Annae genannt, welches viele Krancke in der Noth schon erkannt, zn Modletyn, in dem Tschaslauer Creyss, dieses Königreichs Böheimb. Von dessen Cräfften, Wirckung und Gewalt wahrhaffter Bericht und kurtzer Inhalt. 34 l. 12°. *Kuttenberg, G. A. Kintzl,* 1738.

NL 0440167   DNLM

Lodgman von Auen, Joh. Rudolph

——. Uhraltes Heyl-Baad S. Joannis, für Genesung und Ueberkommung des Menschen-Gesundheit. Ohnweit Teutsch-Brod in Tschaslauer Creyss liegend. Dessen Mineralien That und Tugenden in der Kürtze an Tag fürgestellet. 35 l. 1 pl. 16°. [*Prag, L. Grim,* 1747.]

NL 0440168   DNLM

JN1637
.L6   Lodgman von Auen, Rudolf, 1877–
Die autonomie und ihre bedeutung für Oesterreich-Ungarn. Vom reichsratsabgeordneten dr. Rudolf ritter Lodgman von Auen. Prag, Selbstverlag des verfassers, 1918.
29p. 19cm.

1. Autonomy–Austro-Hungarian monarchy.
2. Self-determination, National.

NL 0440169   NNU-W DLC-P4

943.7
L821   Lodgman von Auen, Rudolf, 1877–
Deutschböhmen. Hrsg. unter Mitwirkung von Alfons Dopsch [et al.] von Rudolph Lodgman. Berlin, Ullstein, 1919.

289 p. 17 cm. (Männer und Völker)
1. Germans in Bohemia. I. Title.

NL 0440170   MnU MH CSt-H ICU

Lodgman von Auen, Rudolf, 1877–
Le droit de libre détermination pour la Bohême allemande, discours du docteur Rodolphe Lodgman von Auen ... Avec 2 cartes. [Vienna, Staatsdruckerei, 1919]
17 p. maps. 23ᵐ.
Published also in German and English.

1. Germans in Bohemia. 2. European war, 1914–1918 — Territorial questions—Bohemia.

     28–24188

Library of Congress   DB215.L72

NL 0440171   DLC DNW CSt-H

Lodgman von Auen, Rudolf, 1877–
Für die Selbstbestimmung Deutschböhmens; Rede von Dr. Rudolf Lodgman v. Auen ... Wien: A. Hölder, 1919. 16 p. incl. map. 8°. (Flugblätter für Deutschösterreichs Recht. Nr. 7.)

1. European war, 1914–18.—Territorial questions, Czechoslovakia.
2. Germans in Czechoslovakia. 3. Series.
     January 9, 1923.

NL 0440172   NN MH CSt-H

JS4721
.K6   Lodgman von Auen, Rudolf, 1877–   ed.

Kommunales Jahrbuch für die Tschechoslowakische Republik. 1931–
[Teplitz-Schönau]

Lodgman von Auen, Rudolf, 1877–
Reden und Aufsätze. Festgabe zum 77. Geburtstag des Sprechers der Sudetendeutschen Landsmannschaft, hrsg. von Albert Karl Simon. München, St. Jörg Verlag [1955]
170 p. port. 21 cm.

1. Germans in the Czechoslovak Republic—Addresses, essays, lectures. 2. Refugees, German—Addresses, essays, lectures.   I. Title.

DB200.7.L63   65–84203

NL 0440174   DLC MH InU

Lodgman von Auen, Rudolf, 1877–
The right of self-destination for the Germans of Bohemia; a speech delivered by Dr. Rudolph Lodgman von Auen ... [Vienna, Staatsdruckerei, 1919]
14 p. maps. 23ᵐ.
Published also in German and French.

1. Germans in Bohemia. 2. European war, 1914–1918—Territorial questions—Bohemia.   I. Title.

Library of Congress   DB215.L7   30–1855

NL 0440175   DLC DNW NjP CSt-H NN

Lodgman Von Auen, Rudolf, 1877–
Die Sudetendeutschen Selbstverwaltungskörper
see under title

84
1469.8   Lodgman von Auen, Rudolf, 1877–
Die völkerrechtlichen grundlagen des sudetenproblems und die politische entwicklung seit 1945; von dr. Rudolf Lodgman von Auen ... Sinsheim (Elsenz) F. & A. Wiche [1948]
11 p. 21cm.
"Vortrag: gehalten auf der sudetendeutschen tagung zu Heppenheim am 11.6. 1948".

NL 0440177   MH-L

QK635
L6
Biology
Library   Lodhi, Sher Ahmad
Indian slime-moulds (Myxomycetes) being descriptions of the species collected by the late Mrs. Drake. With a foreword by Haraprasad Chaudhury. Lahore, University of the Panjab, 1934.
54 p. port., 17 plates. [Punjab University, Lahore. Dept. of Botany. Publications, 5]

Bibliography: p.26.

1. Myxomycetes. 2. Fungi – India.
I. Drake, Mrs. S   d. 1929.

NL 0440179   CU NNBG TxCM TxU DLC-P4 IaU

Lodholz, Edward.

Tumors of the cerebellum, by Charles K. Mills, M. D., Charles H. Frazier, M. D., George E. De Schweinitz, M. D., T. H. Weisenburg, M. D., Edward Lodholz, M. D. ... New York, A. R. Elliott publishing company, 1905.

QD401
.L82   Lodholz, Karl.
Beitrag zur kenntnis der tribromchinoline und ihrer beziehung zur den tribromanilinen.
Freiburg, 1891.
36p.
Inaug. diss. Freiburg.

NL 0440181   DLC

VOLUME 338

Lodi, Angelo.
L'Aeronautica italiana nella guerra di liberazione (8 settembre 1943–8 maggio 1945) Pref. del gen. di S. A. Mario Ajmone-Cat. Roma, 1950.

339 p. illus., maps. 24 cm.

At head of title: Ministero difesa, Stato maggiore aeronautica militare, Ufficio storico.
Includes bibliographies.

1. World War, 1939–1945—Aerial operations, Italian.   ɪ. Title.

D792.I 8L6   52–21343

NL   0440182   DLC NN

Lodi, Angelo.
Nuovo meccanismo per la direzione della navigazione aerea, progetto di Angelo Lodi da Bologna ... Torino, Tip. fratelli Canfari ₍1851₎

15, ₍1₎ p. fold. col. pl. 22½ cm.

Illustrated t.-p.

1. Air-ships.   ɪ. Title.

TL654.L63A4   629.13324   34—34121

NL   0440183   DLC MH

Lodi (Carlo). Sull' origine dei rumori respiratorii in genere e della broncofonia in ispecie secondo le idee di Laennec e di Skoda. 41 pp. 4°. *Stradella, G. Perca, 1853.*

NL   0440184   DNLM

---

x B   **Lodi, Costanzo, d.1596.**
G5127?   Vita, et miracoli del beato Giovannibvono Mantoano, eremita agostiniano: morto già trecento, & quarantatre anni. Raccolti, et descritti da f. Costanzo Lodi, da S. Gervaso Bresciano. Teologo dell'istesso Ordine dell'Osseruanza di Lombardia. In Mantoa, Per Francesco Osanna, stampator ducale, 1592.

4 p.l., 86, ₍2₎ p. 20½cm.
Title vignette.
Signatures: a⁴, A–L⁴.
1. Giovanni Buono, Saint, d.1249.

NL   0440185   IU

945.21   **Lodi, Defendente, d.1656.**
L82d   Discorsi historici di Defendente Lodi in materie diverse appartenenti alla città di Lodi.   In Lodi, Presso Paolo Bertoetti, 1629.

8 p.l., 548p. 20½cm.

Title vignette.

1. Lodi—Hist.

NL   0440186   IU

398.2   ₍Lodi, Defendente₎ d.1656.
L82m   Il mar Gerondo, ottavo discorso. ₍In Lodi. Presso Paolo Bertoetti, 1629₎

p. ₍385₎-442. 20cm.

Half-title.
Extracted from Lodi, Defendente. Discorsi historici ... in materie diverse appartenenti alla città di Lodi. Lodi, 1629.

1. Legends—Lodi.

NL   0440187   IU

274.521   **Lodi, Emanuelle.**
L821b   Breve istoria di Meda e traslatione dei santi Aimo e Vermondo.   Milano, 1629.

38p.

Imperfect: lacks t.-p. and pages after p.38.

NL   0440188   IU

274.521   **Lodi, Emanuelle.**
L821b   Breve istoria di Meda, e traslatione
1672   de' santi Aimo, e Vermondo della nobilissima famiglia de' Corij milanesi, con la loro vita.   In Milano, nella stampa di Lodouico Monza, 1672.

42p.

NL   0440189   IU

274.521   Lodi, Emanuelle.
L821b   Breve istoria di Meda, e traslazione de'santi
1741   Aimo e Vermondo della nobilissima famiglia de Corii milanesi, con la loro vita scritta dal dottore teologo Emanuele Lodi ... Di nuovo ristampata. Milano, Nella stamperia di P. A. Frigerio, 1741.

40p.

1. Meda (Benedictine monastery) 2. Aimo, saint, fl.776. 3. Vermondi, saint, fl.776.

NL   0440190   IU

945.2   **Lodi, Emanuelle.**
L821b   Breve storia delle cose memorabili di Trevi.   [Milano, 1647].

244p.

Engraved t.-p.

NL   0440191   IU

PQ4827   **Lodi, Enrico,**
027   Poesie. Milano, Gastaldi ₍1950₎
P63   65p. 18 cm. (Poeti d'oggi, 353)

NL   0440192   RPB NN

HD   **Lodi, Entio.**
7091   Giustizia o carità nella sicurezza sociale?
.L82   Alba (Cuneo) Editiones Paulinae, 1954.

66 p. 23 cm.
Part of thesis - Pontificia Università Gregoriana, Rome.
Bibliographical footnotes.

1. Insurance, Social.   I. Title.

NL   0440193   DCU

Lodi, Euvaldo.
A indústria e a economia nacional. Rio de Janeiro, Irmãos Pongetti, 1949.

121 p. 24 cm.

1. Brazil—Econ. condit.—1918—   ɪ. Title.

HC187.L58   50–27852

NL   0440194   DLC TxU

281.163   **Lodi, Euvaldo.**
L82   Interêsses comuns da agricultura e da indústria. Conferência no Centro Ribeirão Preto. Rio de Janeiro, 1950.

14 p.

1. Agriculture. Economic aspects. Brazil.

NL   0440195   DNAL

---

qLC1047   **Lodi, Euvaldo.**
B716   SENAI, the National Service of Industrial Apprenticeship of Brazil ₍by₎ Euvaldo Lodi ₍and₎ Joaquim Faria Góes Filho. Rio de Janeiro ₍Serviço Nacional de Aprendizagem Industrial, Serviço de Relações Públicas₎ 1950.

9 ℓ.

1. Brazil. Serviço Nacional de Aprendizagem Industrial. 2. Vocational education--Brazil. 3. Trade schools--Brazil. I. Góis, Joaquim Faria, joint author. II. Title.

NL   0440197   PPiU

Lodi, Ferruccio.
Élaboration d'installations électrifiées pour l'arrosage selon le principe de la pluie artificielle. Genève, Nations Unies Commission économique pour l'Europe, 1955.

20 p. tables. 28 cm. (Nations Unies. ₍Document; E/ECE/217, E/ECE/EP/166₎
At head of title: Électrification rurale.
Issued also in English.

1. Sprinkler irrigation.   I. Series: United Nations. Document. French ed. E/ECE/217 ₍etc.₎

JX1977.A212   E/ECE/217, etc.   56–2515
S615.L612

NL   0440198   DLC

Lodi, Ferruccio.
Formulation of a system for electrified spraying plant on the artificial rain principle. Geneva, United Nations Economic Commission for Europe, 1955.

18 p. tables. 28 cm. (United Nations. ₍Document; E/ECE/217, E/ECE/EP/166₎
At head of title: Rural electrification.

1. Sprinkler irrigation.   I. Series: United Nations. Document E/ECE/217 ₍etc.₎

JX1977.A2   E/ECE/217, etc.   56–2473
S615 L6

NL   0440199   DLC

Lodi, Ferruccio.
Выработка конструкции электрических установок для полива по принципу искусственного дождевания. Женева, Организация Объединенных Наций, Европейская экономическая комиссия, 1955.

19 p. tables. 28 cm. (Объединенные Нации. ₍Документ; E/ECE/217, E/ECE/EP/166₎
At head of title: Сельская электрификация.
Issued also in English.
1. Sprinkler irrigation.   I. Title. II. Series: United Nations.
Dokument E/ECE/217 ₍etc.₎
Title transliterated: Vyrabotka konstruktsil électricheskikh ustanovok dlía poliva.

JX1977.A2128   E/ECE/217, etc.   57–17120

NL   0440200   DLC

945.28   **Lodi, Filippo.**
L821s   Sommario della storia di Voghera dalle sue origini fino al 1814 con cenni biografici intorno ai vogheresi che si resero chiari nelle scienze, nelle arti nelle lettere ecc. fino ai giorni nostri.   Voghera, 1891.

303p.

NL   0440201   IU

VOLUME 338

Lodi, F[rancesco]
Nino Bixio. Romanzo storico popolare.
Milano, N. Tommasi, 1891.
126 p.   24°.

NL 0440202   NN

Lodi, Francesco.
Sunto storico della citta di Cento da servire
anche per guida al forestiero
see under Atti, Gaetano.

Lodi, Francesco Melzi d'Eril, duca di

See

Melzi d'Eril, Francesco, duca di Lodi, 1753-
1816.

[Lodi, Giacinto]
Amore prigioniero in Delo. Torneo fatto da' signori academici
Torbidi in Bologna li XX. di marzo M. DC. XXVIII . . .
[Bologna, Per gli heredi di Vittorio Benacci, 1628]   4 p.l.,
123(1) p.   double plates.   30cm. (f°.)

Vinet: Bibliographie...des beaux-arts, 793. Ruggieri: Catalogue, 1873, no. 789.
Lipperheide: Katalog der...Kostümbibliothek, 2817.
First leaf blank.
Dedication signed: Giacinto Lodi.
Illustrations: 15 large etchings by G. B. Coriolano, depicting the tournament and
floats.

NL 0440205   NN DFo

LODI, GIOVANNI.
Mantova e la guerre memorabili nella valle del Po;
considerazioni storiche e militari.   Bologna,
N. Zanichelli, 1877.   520 p.   18cm.

1. Mantua, Italy (Province)--Hist.

NL 0440206   NN IU

Lodi, Jorge Lorenzo
see Lorenzo Lodi, Jorge.

D804   Lodi, Luigi, 1856-
L82   ... Alla ricerca della verecondia, con scritti
di G. Chiarini, E. Panzacchi, E. Nencioni. Roma,
Formiggini, 1927.
2 p. l., [ix]-xxii p., 1 l., 76, [2] p.   17°°.
(Polemiche)
1. Literature and morals. 2. Art and morals.
I. Title. II. Polemiche. III. Chiarini, Giuseppe,
1833-1908. IV. Nencioni, Enrico, 1837-1896. V.
Panzacchi, Enrico, 1840-1904.

NL 0440208   NNC WU

Lodi, Luigi.
Codice di Dante detto l' "Estense."
(In Il bibliofilo. Aprile, 1880. An. i, p. 57)

NL 0440209   NIC

Lodi, Luigi.
Di un nuovo codice della commedia di Dante col
commento di Matte Chirimunio.   (In Il bibliofilo,
Agosto-sett. An. i, p. 127)

NL 0440210   NIC

Lodi, Luigi, 1856-
...Giornalisti.   Bari: G. Laterza & figli, 1930.   253 p.
8°.   (Biblioteca di cultura moderna. v. 188.)

Contents: Il Carducci giornalista. Jorik. Luigi Cesana. Gandolin. Fortis,
Moneta, Torelli. Attilio Luzzatto. Edoardo Scarfoglio. Leonida Bissolati. Fer-
ruccio Macola. Matilde Serao. "Carletta." Luigi Albertini. Vincenzo Morello.
Alberto Bergamini. "Vamba." Maggiorino Ferraris. Eugenio Checchi. Sobrero
il "Corrispondente." Da Barzini a...... Luigi Luzzatti. Benito Mussolini. Ugo
Ojetti. Mario Missiroli. Pier Giulio Breschi. Giuseppe Bottai. Curzio Malaparte.

513199A. 1. Journalists—Italy.   I. Ser.
                                                    March 20, 1931

NL 0440211   NN MWelC MH PU CtW

Lodi, Luigi, 1856-

Annunzio, Gabriele d', 1863–
... Juvenilia. Firenze, G. Barbèra, 1925.

PQ   Lodi, Luigi.
4707   Lorenzo Stecchetti; ricordi, prose e
G3Z65   poesie. Bologna, N. Zanichelli, 1881.
151p.   17cm.

1. Guerrini, Olindo, 1845-1916.

NL 0440213   MU

LODI, Luigi.
Perchè l'Italia combatte. Zurigo, Istituto
italiano, 1917.

pp. 43. Ports., plates and map.
(PAGINE italiane illustrate, I,1.)

NL 0440214   MH

Lodi, Luigi, 1856-
...Venticinque anni di vita parlamentare da Pelloux a Mussolini. Firenze: R. Bemporad & figlio [1923].   258 p.   8°.

1. Italy.—Politics, 1898–1923.   2. Statesmen, Italy.
                                                        June 9, 1924

NL 0440215   NN CtY ICU MH

D463   [Lodi, Luigi Ettore]
L823   Promemoria sulla situazione politica balcani-
ca. [Roma, Tip. Fratelli Paliotta, 1921]
cover-title, 14 p.   24°°.

Signed: L.E.L.; Luigi Ettore Lodi supplied in
manuscript.

1.Eastern question (Balkan) 2.Balkan peninsu-
la - Politics.   I.Title.

NL 0440216   CSt-H

Lodi, Marco da
see Cademosto, Marco.

Lodi, Marinella.
... Terra d'approdo; romanzo. Milano, A. Mondadori, 1929.
3 p. l., [9]-272 p., 2 l.   19°°.

I. Title.
Library of Congress   PQ4827.O4T4 1929
                                                      30-21857

NL 0440218   DLC NN OrP OU WaS

PQ4827 Lodi, Marinella.
.Q4T4   Terra d'approdo; romanzo. Milano, A. Monda-
1933   dori, 1929 [i. e. 1933]
272 p.   19cm.

NL 0440219   MB

Lodi, Pio, ed.
Catalogo delle opere musicali. Città di Modena,
Biblioteca estense
see under [Associazione dei musicologi
italiani]

Lodi, Pio, ed.
Catalogo delle opere musicali teoriche e pratiche
di autori vissuti sino ai primi decenni del secolo xix,
esistenti nelle biblioteche e negli archivi pubblici e
privati d'Italia: Città di Modena
see under Associazione dei musicologi
italiani.

LODI, Raimondo da.
Regole sul raddoppiamento delle consonanti
e tabella ortografica. Montepulciano, dalla
Tipogr. di Angiolo Fumi, 1842.

Pamphlet.

NL 0440222   MH

Lodi, Uguccione da
see Uguçon da Laodho, 13th cent.

Lodi (Vincenzo). L'asilo per i bambini lattanti.
26 pp., 5 pl. 12°. *Bologna, Regia tipog.*, 1900.

NL 0440224   DNLM

945.21 Lodi, Defendente.
L82d   Discorsi historici in materie diverse
appartenenti alla città di Lodi.
Lodi, 1629.
548p.

NL 0440225   IU CLU

VOLUME 338

016.055 Lodi. Biblioteca laudense.
L82c   Catalogo delle pubblicazioni periodiche.
        Lodi, 1954.
        55p. 22cm. (Its Pubblicazioni, 6)

        1. Italian periodicals—Bibl. 2. Periodicals—
    Bibl.—Catalogs.

NL 0440226   IU

Lodi. Civico istituto musicale "F. Gaffurio".
    ... Rassegna nazionale di musica, sotto l'alto patronato di
Sua ecc. Benito Mussolini, 22 novembre 1928–21 aprile 1929
(VII) [Lodi, Società tipografica successori Wilmant. 1930]
    48 p. illus. 31 x 21½cm.
    Includes concert programs, biographical notices of composers, etc.

    1. Lodi. Rassegna nazionale di musica, 1928–1929. 2. Musicians,
Italian.

    Library of Congress   ML38.L58R2   32-25620
                                          780.79452

NL 0440227   DLC

Lodi. Comizio agrario
    see Comizio agrario di Lodi.

945.26 Lodi. Congregazione municipale.
L821r   Reclami dal municipio di Lodi presentati a Sua
        Maestà il re ed al Ministero dell'interno per
        dissuadere dallo smembramento della provincia di
        Lodi e Crema. Lodi, C. Wilmanti e figli, 1860.
        38p.

        1. Lodi—Hist. 2. Crema, Italy—Hist.

NL 0440229   IU

Lodi. Consiglio degli ospitali in Lodi.
    —— Norme pel servizio farmaceutico e farma-
copea dell' Ospitale maggiore approvate dal ...
con delibera 5 novembre 1891, N. 2892. 46 pp.
8°. Lodi, tipog. A. Cima. 1892.

NL 0440230   DNLM

Lodi. Consiglio degli ospitali in Lodi. Norme
per l' assistenza medica ed ostetrica dei poveri
curati a domicilio nella città di Lodi. 15 pp.,
2 tab. roy. 8°. Lodi, A. Cima, 1892.

NL 0440231   DNLM

Lodi, Giunta municipale.
    Ragioni per l'autonomia provinciale della citta
di Lodi e suo territorio. Torino, Tip. Arnaldi,
1862.
    86 p. 4°.

NL 0440232   MH

44.9   Lodi. Istituto sperimentale di caseificio.
L82B   Bollettino.
        Lodi,

        1. Cheese. Research.

NL 0440233   DNAL

LODI.   Laws, statutes, etc.
    Ordines novi civitatis Laudae super victuali-
is et damnis agrorum. [Mediolani], 1562.

    f°. pp.(12), ff.42, pp.(4). Coat-of-arms.
Title within decorated border.
Numerous MS. notes.

NL 0440234   MH

---

x349.45 Lodi. Laws, statutes, etc.
L82s   Statuta & ordinamenta ciuitatis Laude facta &
1538   ordinata tempore & sub felici regimine dominatio
        nis illustris principis ac magnifici & excelsi
        domini domini Galeaz vicecomitis domini Mediolan
        &c ... [Mediolani, 1538]
        20 p.l., cxxxvi numb.l. 27½cm.
        Caption title.
        Colophon: Impressum Mediolani in officina
        libraria Gotardi Pontici apud templum diui Satiri.
        Anno Domini M.D.XXXVII. die. xxvii.nouembris.
        Signatures: AA⁸, BB-CC⁶, A-R⁸.

        Dedication (verso of 1st prelim.leaf) has date:
        M.ccccc.xxxviii. die Sabati xviiii.ianuarii in-
        dictione vndecima.
        Figures representing two early bishops of Lodi,
        and coat-of-arms with motto Plvs vltra on 1st
        leaf. Device of printer on last verso below colo-
        phon.
        Initials.
        Bound in vellum.

NL 0440236   IU NNC NN

---

x349.45 Lodi. Laws, statutes, etc.
L82s   Lavdensivm statvta, sev iura mvnicipalia.
1586   Quibus additus est index, quo, quicquid in ipsis
        continetur, nulla mora, nulloque negotio sciri
        potest. Lavde Pompeia, apud Vincentium Taietum,
        1586.
        27 p.l., cc numb.l. 27½cm.
        Colophon: Impressvm Lavdae, in officina Vincen-
        tij Taietti, anno Domini MDLXXXVI. die 21.iulij.
        Signatures: †⁸, a-b⁴, c⁴(last leaf blank) A-Z⁸,
        Aa-Bb⁶(last verso blank)
        Device of printer on t.-p.; initials.
        Title-page of   cop.2 mutilated.

NL 0440237   IU NN MH

LODI,   Laws, statutes, etc.
    Statuti vecchi, ritrovati e pubblicati da Ce-
sare Vignati. Milano, tip. Bortolotti di dal
Bono e c., 1884.

    f°. Manuscript plate.
    "100 esemplari fuori di commercio."

NL 0440238   MH

---

q945.21 Lodi. [Mandamento]
L8211d   Delegazione III e IV lodigiana. Lettere,
        circolari, ed editti dalli 4 gennaio 1760
        [-10 dicembre 1785. Milano, 1760-1785]
        7v. tables. 38cm.

        Binder's title.
        A few manuscripts are included.

NL 0440239   IU

Lodi. Ospitale maggiore
    Movimento degli ammalati e tavole nosologiche
dello Spedale maggiore di Lodi nel biennio 1882-3 per
cura del direttore, Iginio Tansini. Lodi, Cima &
Moroni, 1884.
    56 p. fol.

NL 0440240   DNLM

Lodi. Ospitale maggiore,
    —— Norme attinenti ai diversi rami di ser-
vizio. Approvate dal consiglio degli ospitali in
Lodi colla delibera 1° dicembre 1895, N. 3277;
dalla r. sotto-prefettura di Lodi col decreto 12
dicembre 1895, N. 10455. D°. 2. 216 pp., 2 l.
roy. 8°. Lodi, tipoc.-litog. Overaia 1896.

NL 0440241   DNLM

Lodi. Ospitale maggiore,
    —— Norme pel servizio farmaceutico e farma-
copea dell' Ospitale maggiore, approvate dal
consiglio degli ospitali in Lodi, con delibera, 5
novembre 1891, N. 2892. 46 pp. 8°. Lodi,
tipog. A. Cima, 1892.

NL 0440242   DNLM

Film   LODI. Ospitale maggiore,
1178   Norme pel servizio farmaceutico e
no. 3   farmacopea dell'Ospitale maggiore,
        approvate dal Consiglio degli ospitali
        in Lodi con delibera 5 novembre 1891,
        N. 2892. Lodi, Cima, 1892.
        46 p.   Film 1178
        Film copy.

NL 0440243   DNLM

Lodi. Ospitale maggiore.
    —— Norme pel servizio farmaceutico e farma-
copea. Rese esecutive con delibera 11 aprile
1900, N. 1083. 59 pp. 8°. Lodi, tipog. Quirico &
Camagni, 1900.

NL 0440244   DNLM

Lodi. Ospitale maggiore,   Norme per le
ispettrici. Approvato con delibera consigliare
18 agosto 1883, N. 2638. 14 pp. 8°. Lodi,
Cima & Moroni, 1883.

NL 0440245   DNLM

Lodi. Ospitale maggiore,
    —— Resoconti statistici-clinici del comparto
medico femminile durante gli anni 1890-91;
1891-2; 1893-4. Dai medici primari. 8°. Lodi,
1892-5.
    Report for 1890-91, by Giovanni Pugliesi, 1891-2, by G.
Pugliesi and Ugo Bergamaschi; 1893-4, by Felicia Senna.
    Report for 1890-91 reads: Relazione statistico-clinica.

NL 0440246   DNLM

Lodi. Ospitale maggiore.
    Sezione chirurgica. Breve rendiconto clinico-
statistico del Dr. Angelo Negretto. Lodi, A. Cima,
1892.
    61 p. roy. 8°.

NL 0440247   DNLM

VOLUME 338

Lodi.
↑Ospitale maggiore
——. Statuto organico. 7 l. roy. 8°. *Lodi,*,
A. Cima, 1892.

NL 0440248 DNLM

Lodi. R. Stazione sperimentale di caseificio.   630.945
Annuario della R. Stazione sperimentale di caseificio di Lodi   1
... Lodi, 1900-1920.
Library has 1899-1919. fold. pl., tables. 22ᶜᵐ.

NL 0440249 ICJ

SF271   Lodi., Stazione sperimentale di caseificio.
.L7   Trent' anni di attività della R. Stazione
sperimentale di caseificio di Lodi (1880-1909
incluso)...
Lodi, 1910

NL 0440250 DLC

Lodi. Stazione sperimentale di caseificio
see also   Lodi. Istituto sperimentale di
caseificio.

Lodi. Stazione sperimentale di praticoltura.
Bresaola, Mario.
... Contributo sperimentale alla battaglia per il grano.
Con prefazione de Ottavio Munerati ... Bergamo, Istituto
italiano d'arti grafiche, 1930.

Lodi, Italy. Stazione Sperimentale di
Praticoltura.
Relazione sull'attività della Stazione
Sperimentale di Praticoltura di Lodi
nell'anno.Lodi, G.Biancardi, 19
v.

NL 0440253 InLP CU

S543   Lodi, Stazione sperimentale di praticoltura.
.L75   ... La stazione sperimentale di practicoltura
di Lodi e la sua attivita 19
Bergamo, 192
4°

NL 0440254 DLC

---

x274.521 Lodi. (Diocese), Synod, 1657.
L82s   Synodvs dioecesana lavdensis qvinta celebrata
1657   anno 1657. Iussu illustriss., ac reuerendiss.
d.d. Petri Vidoni ... Lavdae, typis Caroli
Pitti :1659:
1 p.l., 148, 4 p. 19½cm.
Title vignette (coat of arms)
"Decreta generalia, condita. a perill. et rev
d.d. Francisco Bossio" (with special t.-p.):
p. :97:-132.
"Memoriale per gli agonizanti, et erettione
della scuola, ò congregatione del Ben Morire"
(with special t.-   p.): p. 133 -148.

NL 0440255 IU

---

x274.521 Lodi (Diocese). Synod, 1689.
L82s   Synodvs diœcesana ! lavdensis sexta ab ill. ,
1689   et rev. domino d. Bartholomaeo Menatto Dei, et
Sanctæ Sedis gratia episcopo lauden., & comite
&c. ... Habita, & celebrata feria secunda, tertia.
& quarta post dominicam in Passione scilicet
diebus 28.29., & 30.mensis martij anni 1689.
Additis pluribus Constitutionibus apostolicis,
& Sacrarum congregationum declarationibus, quibus Decreta illustrantur, & confirmantur.
Lavdae, typis Caroli Antonij Sevesi impressoris
episcopalis, 1690.

1 p.l., 172(i.e.272)p. 18½cm.

Errors in pagination: p.272 is numbered 172;
other misprints.
The "Discorso fatto ... nella prima sessione
sinodale" and the "Additamenta" have special
title-pages.

I. Menatti, Bartolomeo, bp., d.1702.

NL 0440257 IU

Lodi, Calif.
Annual report of the city clerk
see   Lodi, Calif. City Clerk.
Report ...

**Lodi, Calif. Chamber of commerce of northern San Joa-
quin County.**
The trail of '49 ... ¡Stockton, Calif., Record print,
1916?¡
illus. sheet. 48 x 64ᶜᵐ fold. to 24 x 11ᶜᵐ.
Map on one side.

1. California—Descr. & trav.   i. Title.
20-22560
Library of Congress   F866.L82

NL 0440259 DLC

F869   Lodi, Calif. City Clerk.
L6A2   Report.
[Lodi, Calif.]
v. illus. 23cm.
Report year ends June 30th.

1. Lodi, Calif. - Pol. & govt.

NL 0440260 CU-B CSt

NA9127   Lodi, Calif. City Planning Commission.
L62A3   A master plan for Lodi, California,   [Lodi, 1954]
Environ.   160 p. maps(part fold.col.)tables.
Design
Library   Cover title: A master plan for the future development of Lodi.
Harold F. Wise, Associates, planning consultants.

1. Cities and towns - Planning - Lodi, Calif.   I. Wise (Harold
F.) Associates.

NL 0440261 CU

A339.4   Lodi, Calif. Union high school.
L82s   Syllabus (revised) for the course in consumer
1938   education at Lodi union high school, Lodi, California. By L. Robert Frembling.   .Lodi, 1938
27 numb.l.

1. Consumption (Economics)--Bibl.   2. Buying--
Bibl. I. Frembling, L. Robert.

NL 0440262 IU PPT

Lodi, Wis. Lodi Union Agricultural Society
see   Lodi Union Agricultural Society, Lodi,
Wis.

LODI, Wis. *Ordinances, etc.*
Revised By-Laws and Ordinances.   Lodi,1905.
(2)+53p. 16 mo.

NL 0440264 MH-L

Lodi; monografia storico-artistica ...
see under [Angeli, Felice de] 1834-   ed.

Lodi caratteristiche del celebre cantore signor Luigi Marchesi ... Siena, Nella stamperia di V. Pazzini Carli e figli,
1781.
x p. 20½ᶜᵐ.
Engraved title vignette and head-piece.

1. Marchesi, Luigi, 1755-1829.
32-19108
Library of Congress   ML420.M31S   927.8

NL 0440266 DLC

Le lodi del porco; cantate da varj poeti vivi e
morti ... [n.p., 1793]
41 p. front. 21.5 cm.
Dedication dated 1793.
1. Italian poetry - Collections.

NL 0440267 CtY

Y   LODI di vario stile nella solenne traslatione di
7184   S. Apollinare, primo martire, & arciuescono di
.516   Rauenna, dall'antica chiesa di Classe, alla
nuoua della citta. Sotto la felice legatione
dell'eminentiss...principe Alderano card. Cybo,
legato di Romagna.   Ravenna, Appresso P. de'Pao-
li,1650.
2v. in 1. 16cm.
Added t.-p., engraved, has title: L'incontro
de cigni nell'arriuo in Rauenna del glorioso
corpo di S.Apollinare...   ICN 55-428
The 2d part, containing Latin verse, has title:
Apostolorum prin-   cipis discipulo martyri
gloriosissimo an-   tiquissimæ ciuitatis
Rauennæ proto epis-   copo D. Apollinari ipsius
55-288   dum sacratissimum   transfertur corpus...

NL 0440268 ICN

... The **Lodi** directory.   Lodi, N. J., P. M. Galanti ¡ᶜ1933–
v. 24½ᶜᵐ.

1. Lodi, N. J.—Direct.
Library of Congress   F144.L75A18   CA 33-784 Unrev'd
Copyright

NL 0440269 DLC

VOLUME 338

Lodi, et canzonette spiritvale. Raccolte da diuersi autori: & ordinate secondo le varie maniere de' versi. Aggiunteui à ciascuna maniera le loro arie nuoue di musica à tre voci assai dilettevoli. Per poter non solo leggersi ad honesto diporto dell' anima: ma ancora cantarsi ò priuatamente da ciascuno, ò in publico nelle chiese, oratorij, & dottrine. In Napoli, Per Tarquinio Longo, 1608.

408, [24], 24, 21, [3] p. 14½ x 7½ᶜᵐ.
Part 1 only, with half-title (p. 25) : Delle lodi spiritvali parte prima. Doue sono le canzonette à due, tre, & quattro versi la stanza ...
Running title: Lodi spiritvali. Parte 1.

1. Title : Lodi spiritvali.

31–4473

Library of Congress   M1490.L75   783.9

NL 0440270   DLC IʷH

Lodi Manufacturing Company, Lodi, New Jersey.   7999·113
An act to incorporate the Lodi Manufacturing Company: for purposes of agriculture, passed 6th February, 1840. With accompanying remarks and documents.
New-York. Cassidy. 1840. 35, (1) pp. 8°.
Relates to manures.

F5516 — Manures.—New Jersey. Acts and laws. Lodi Manufacturing Company.

NL 0440271   MB MH–BA N

Lodi Manufacturing Company, Lodi, N. J.
The farmer's almanac for
is published. For gratuitous circulation ...
see under title

631.816 **Lodi** Manufacturing Company, *Lodi, N. J.*
qL823   Instructions to farmers, market gardeners, dairy men, and others, for the use and application of Poudrette on lands generally, as made by the Lodi Manufacturing Company and only applicable to their Poudrette. New York, Printed by J. Snowden, 1844.
4 p. 24 cm.

1. Fertilizers and manures. I. Title: Poudrette.

NL 0440273   N

Lodi Manufacturing Company, Lodi, New Jersey. 7997.28=B.170.14
The new and improved poudrette, of the Lodi Manufacturing Company.
[New York.] 1850. 28 pp. Plate. 8°.
The title is on the cover.
The copy on shelf-number 7997.28 lacks the cover.

F5520 — Manures. — Poudrette.

NL 0440274   MB MdBJ CtY

LODI manufacturing company, *Lodi, N. J.*
Night soil.
N. p. [1850?] 28 pp. Pl. 8°.

NL 0440275   MB

F869   Lodi Matrix. v. 1–
L6L58

Lodi, Calif., Super Mold Corporation.
v.   illus. 29cm.

Title varies: 1938– Summer 1944 Matrix.
Irregular.

1. U. S. – Indus. I. Super Mold Corporation, Lodi, Calif.

NL 0440276   CU–B

Lodi tribute alla memoria di S. E. il viceammiraglio della Spina raccolte dalla pietà filiale
see under   [Carelli, Giuseppe] comp.

Lodi Union Agricultural Society, Lodi, Wis.
Premium List and Regulations.   Lodi, Wis., 1908.
32 p.   illus.

NL 0440278   WHi

Lodiana. American Presbyterian mission
see   Presbyterian church in the U. S. A.
Lodiana Mission.

Lodiana mission, India

see

Presbyterian church in the U. S. A. Lodiana mission

American pharmacist.
Lodibert. Éloge historique de M. Sérullas. pp. 35–56. 8°. [Paris, 1842.] [P., v. 1745.]

NL 0440281   DNLM

Lodibert (A.-Th.-J.) "Essai sur la péritonite aiguë. 1 p. l., 17 pp. 4°. Strasbourg, 1834, v. 66.

NL 0440282   DNLM

Lodibert (Jean-Antoine-Bonaventure) [1772–1849]. "Sur la thymiatechnie médicale. 41 pp. 4°. Paris, 1808, No. 46, v. 70.

NL 0440283   DNLM PPC

Lodiel,   *Désiré*
Nos raisons de croire, étude historique et critique sur les motifs de crédibilité que présente l'église Catholique par le P.D.Lodiel, S.J. Paris, Maison de la Bonne Presse, n.d.
[iii]–ix p 523 p.   19.5cm.

Bibliographical footnotes.

1.Catholic Church. I.Title

NL 0440284   NNF

Lodieu, J.
Maximilien Robespierre ...   Arras, Degeorge, 1850.
143 p.   front. (port.) 17.5 cm.
1. Robespierre, Maximilien Marie Isidore de, 1758–1794.

NL 0440285   NjP

Lodieu (J.) Die Milchkühe und der höchste Milchertrag. Vollständung und neue Darstellung der charecteristischen Merkmale, nach denen man die Milchergiebigkeit einer Kuh leicht und genau beurtheilen kann, nebst Bemerkungen über die Mastung und das Mastvieh, sowie einer Kritik des Guénon'schen (Milchspiegel) Systems und verschiedenen Abhandlungen über die Milch und ihre Bestandtheile, über Flütterung und Paarung, über Rindviehracen, etc. Ein von der landwirthschaftlichen Gesellschaft des Departement Pas-des-Calais gekröntes Buch. Aus dem Französischen. 288 pp. 24°. Stuttgart, J. Scheible, 1857.

NL 0440286   DNLM

Lodieu, J.   *der*
Die Milchkühe und höchste Milchertrag. Vollständige und neue Darstellung der characteristischen Merkmale, nach denen man die Milchergiebigkeit einer Kuh leicht und genau beurtheilen kann. Von J. Lodieu. Aus dem Französischen. Stuttgart: J. Scheible, 1857. 288 p. 13½cm. (Added t.-p.: Deutscher Bücher-Markt. Theil 6.)

1. Cow—Milk production.

February 20, 1940

NL 0440287   NN

636.2 **Lodieu, J.**
L82v   Vaches laitières, étude complète des caractères à l'aide desquels on peut reconnaitre facilement une bonne laitière, augmentée d'une étude sur l'engraissement et les types les plus aptes à produire de la graisse et du suif ... par J. Lodieu (De Plouvain) ...   Paris, Librairie de V. Masson, 1856.
177p. front.

1. Cows.

NL 0440288   IU

Lodigiani,
Collezione Lodigiani
see under   Galleria Scopinich, Milan.

I LODIGIANI illustri. 1–
Bergamo, Industrie grafiche Cattaneo [1958–
no.   ports.   24cm.

"Collana di monografie storiche."
"VIII° centenario di fondazione di Lodi."

1. Lodi, Italy--Biog.

NL 0440290   NN

Z629.13 **Lodiguine, Alexandre de.**
qZ1   Locomotion aérienne; théorie du bateau
v.7   volant electrique inventé par Alexandre de Lodiguine, de Tamboff (Russie) [n.p. 1870]
11 p.   30cm.   [Aeronautical collection. Quarto group. 7]

Caption title.

1. Aeronautics.   Early works to 1900.

NL 0440291   MnU CoCA

Lodin, Arthur, 1849–
Métallurgie du zinc, par A. Lodin ... Paris, Vᵉ C. Dunod, 1905.
2 p. l., 810 p., 1 l. illus., xxv fold. plans. 25½ᶜᵐ.

1. Zinc—Metallurgy.

G S 19–362

Library, U. S. Geological   Survey 429.5 L82

NL 0440292   DI–GS ICJ

VOLUME 338

QH9
.T6
no. 241
Rare bk.

Lodin, Carl Gustaf, 1797-1847, respondent.

Thunberg, Karl Peter, 1743-1828, *praeses.*
... De acido hydro-cyanico dissertatio medica ... Upsaliæ,
excudebant Palmblad et c. [1825]

Lodin, Ericus, respondent.
... Observationes selectae historiam svecanam
illustrantes...
see under Fant, Erik Mikael, 1754-1817,
praeses.

Lodin, Gustaf Erik, respondent.
Historiola Bibliothecæ Regii gymnasii arosiensis
see under Aurivillius, Pehr Fabian, 1756-
1829, praeses.

Lodin, Herman.
The value of tomography in examination of the intrapul-
monary bronchi. [Translated from the Swedish by Marcia
Skogh] Stockholm, 1953.
109 p. illus. 25 cm. (Acta radiologica. Supplementum 101)
At head of title: From the Roentgen Department (Director: Pro-
fessor F. Knutsson), University Hospital, Upsala, Sweden.
Akademisk avhandling—Uppsala.
Without thesis statement.
Bibliography: p. [106]-109.

1. Bronchi—Radiography. I. Title. (Series)
RC778.L63 616.23 A 54-1728
Wisconsin. Univ. Libr.
for Library of Congress †

NL 0440296 WU DNLM PPT-M MoU ViU DLC

LODIN, Jean Baptiste Émile Gilles Anne.
De jure peregrinorum: de la condition civile
des étrangers, en France, dans l'ancien et dans
le nouveau droit. [Rennes], 1847.

Thèse—Rennes.

NL 0440297 MH-L

Lodin (Joh. Gustavus) [-1815] *De tumoribus salivalibus.* 24 pp. 4°. *Upsaliæ, J. Edman,* [1785].

NL 0440298 DNLM

Lodin, Johan Gustaf, respondent.

QH9
.T6
no. 4-19
Rare bk.
Thunberg, Karl Peter, 1743-1828, *praeses.*
Nova genera plantarum ... Upsaliæ, apud J. Edman
[etc., 1781-1801]

Lodin, O M
*De regno Westro Gothorum in Gallia...
see under Bilmark, Johan, 1728-1801.

Lodin, Sven, 1896–
Carl Olof Rosenius i unga år (1816-1842) ... av Sven Lodin
... Stockholm, Evangeliska fosterlands-stiftelsens bokförlag
[1933]
xxviii, 447 p. 23cm.
Akademisk avhandling.—Lund.
"Källor och litteratur": p. [xiii]-xxviii.

1. Rosenius, Carl Olof, 1816-1868.
[Full name: Sven Albert Vilhelm Lodin]
Library of Congress BX8080.R66L6 1933 35-33732
922.4485

NL 0440301 DLC CtY-D MH CtY PPAmSwM

Lodin de Lalaire, Theophile.
L'exil du Dante. Dijon, 1838.
4 p. 12°.
Extracted from his "Les victimes, poësies",
p. 259-262.

NL 0440302 NIC

Adelmann
QP
251
L86+
Lodin de Lépinay, Joannes Baptiste Josephus
Aegidius.
Quaestio physiologica, Fieri ne potest
conceptio sine coïtu?... Monspelii, Apud
Joannem-Franciscum Picot, 1784.
15 p. 26cm.

Diss.—Montpellier.

1. Reproduction.

NL 0440303 NIC

Lodine, Joseph, tr.

Olécha, Youri.
L'envie; roman inédit, par Youri Olécha.
(*In* Les Oeuvres libres. Paris [°1934] 18cm. v. 153, p. [5]-180)

Lodine, Joseph, tr.

Tolstaïa, Sof'ïa Andreevna (Bers) grafinïa, 1844-1919.
Journal 1910; mémoires inédits de la comtesse Sophie Tols-
toi.
(*In* Les Œuvres libres. Paris, 1936. 18cm. v. 186, p. [5]-88)

Lodine, Joseph, ed.

Dostoevskiĭ, Fëdor Mikhaĭlovich, 1821-1881.
Lettre de Dostoïévsky à A. M. Maïkov. Correspondance
inédite de Fédor Dostoïévsky.
(*In* Les Oeuvres libres. Paris [°1933] 18cm. v. 143, p. [95]-114)

Loding, Henry P.
see Loeding, Henry Peder, 1869-1942.

Lodinger, Martin, fl. 1559.
Martin Lodingers ... Trost-Schrifft und
Brieffe, welche er fast vor zweyhundert Jahren
an seine Lands-Leute im Salzburgischen abgehen
lassen. Samt einem Schreiben des seel. Lutheri
an ihn, vom heil. Abendmahl. Aufs neue mit
einer Vorrede Gustav Georg Zeltners, D.,
worinnen die Kyrchen-Historie besagten Ertz-
Biszthums kürtzlich wiederholet, und denen
Ursachen jetziger Veränderung nachgedacht
wird, nebst der ehemaligen Praefation
des seel. D. Eliä Veils zum Druck
übergeben. Nürnberg, Bey Johann Stein, 1733.
47 p.l., 288, [8] p front. (port.) 17cm.
[With Schelhorn, J.G. ... Historische Nachricht vom Ursprunge, Fortgang und Schicksale
der Evangelischen Religion. Leipzig, 1732]
Page 34 incorrectly numbered 43.
1. Salzburg (Archdiocese) - Hist. I.
Luther, Martin, 1483-1546. II. Zeltner,
Gustav Georg, 1672-1738, ed. III.
Veiel, Elias, 1635-1706. IV. Title:
Trost-Schrifft und Brieffe.

NL 0440309 MdBJ

Lodington, Thomas, 1621-1692.
The honour of the clergy vindicated from contempt of the laity,
in a sermon preached at the arch-deacon of Lincoln his visitation,
holden at Grantham, Oct. 15. 1672. By Thomas Lodington...
London: Printed by J. Macock, for J. Clarke, 1674. 4 p.l., 58+ p.
20 x 16cm.
Imperfect: all after p. 58 wanting.

899606A. 1. Clergy. March 8, 1938

NL 0440310 NN CtY CLU-C MnU FU

Lodispoto, Giuseppe Sacchi
see Sacchi Lodispoto, Giuseppe.

Lodispoto, Terenzio Sacchi
see Sacchi Lodispoto, Terenzio.

CT
1123
.E6
v.4
Lodivici, Sergio S
Storici teorici e critici delle arti figura-
tive d'Italia dall 1800 al 1940. Roma,
Tosi, 1946.
412p. illus., facsims.,ports. 28cm.
(Enciclopedia biografica e biblio-
grafica "Italiana") ser. VI [i.e., IV]
Reference On cover: Dizionari biografici e biblio-
grafici Tosi.
"Ristampa della 1. ed. 1940."
1. Art. Historiography. 2. Art criticism.
History. 3. Aesthetics. History.
4. Italy. Bio- bibliography. I. Title.
(Anal.)

NL 0440313 KU

QE367
.L6
Lodochnikov, Vladimir Nikitich, 1887-1943.
Главнейшие породообразующие минералы. Допущен
в качестве учеб. пособия для геолого-разведочных вузов и
университетов. Москва, Гос. научно-техн. изд-во лит-ры
по геологии и охране недр, 1955.
247 p. illus., port. 23 cm.
Errata slip inserted.
[Bibliography: p. 6-10]
—— Microfilm copy (negative)
Made in 1955 by the Library of Congress
Microfilm Slavic 593 AC
Call No.
1. Mineralogy, Determinative. I. Title.
Title transliterated: Glavneĭshie po-
rodoobrazuíùshchie mineraly.
QE367.L6 56-5001
Library of Congress

NL 0440314 DLC

VOLUME 338

Lodoicus Granatensis, O. P.
    see   Luis de Granada, 1504-1588.

Lodoïdamba, Chadravalyn.
    На Алтае. Перевод с монгольского А. Рнччнэ. Редак
тор А. Золотов. Предисл. Г. Михайлова. Москва, Изд-во
иностранной лит-ры, 1955.
    159 p.   illus.   20 cm.

    I. Title.   *Title transliterated:* Na Altae.

    PL419.L6A78   57-24066 ‡

NL 0440316   DLC

Lodoïk, pseud.
    see   Divonne, L. de. (Supplement)

Lodoïk; ou, leçons de morale pour l'instruction
et l'amusement de la jeunesse.
Londres, 1793.
    6 tomes en 3.

NL 0440318   PPL

Lodoiska; an opera, in three acts ...
    see under   [Storace, Stephen] 1763-1796.

Lodoiska; dramma per musica da rappresentarsi
nel Regio-Ducal Teatro alla Scala di Milano, il
carnevale dell'anno 1800.   In Milano, appresso
Gio. Batista Bianchi [n. d.]
    Scenario of an opera by Johann Simon Mayr,
libretto by Francesco Gonella.

NL 0440320   MH

La lodoiska; dramma serio per musica da
rappresentarsi nel Regio Teatro di via della
Pergola, il carnevale del 1800. In Firenze,
nelle stamperia Albizziniana da S. Maria in
Campo per Pietro Fantosini e figlio, 1800.

NL 0440321   MH

La lodoiska; dramma serio per musica in due atti da
rappresentarsi nel Regio Teatro degl'illustrissimi
signori Accademici Avvalorati in Livorno,
l'autunno dell'anno 1798.   [n. p.] appresso
Giuseppe Zecchini e comp [n. d.]

NL 0440322   MH

Lodoïska, ou, Les Tartares, histoire polonais.
Paris, Delarue; [etc., etc., 18--]
    [3], 16-100 p.   col. front.
    A chap-book.

NL 0440323   OC1

Lodoiska und ihre tochter...
    see under   La Motte-Fouqué, Karoline
Auguste.

Lodola, Acquarius, *pseud.*
    see
Folengo, Girolamo, *in religion* Teofilo, 1496-1544.

Lodoli, Bernardo.
    Serenissimo Venetiarum Dominio ill[r]ustrissi[r]mo, et ecc[r]ellen-
tissi[r]mo Arsenatus regimini Bernardi Lodoli...fidele votvm...
[Venetiis, 1703]   12 l. incl. plates.   36cm. (f°.)

    See: Morazzoni: Libro illustrato veneziano del settcc.nto. 239.
    Engraved throughout, except l. 10-12.
    Announcement and endorsements of a forthcoming work, including its printed
index and engraved t.n.: Il cvore veneto legale formato dalla compilazione delle leggi
...et altre cose notabili stabilite nel corso di cinque secoli per la buona a[m]ministra-

tione...dell Arsenale di Venetia...   Opera dal dottor Bernardo Lodoli...   [Venezia]
1703.
    Illustrations: 3 full-page engravings and t-p. by Suor Isabella Piccini, and "Cvore"
t. p. and 4 leaves of text (one illustrated) engraved by Angela Baroni.
    Binding of paper boards.

    1. Arsenals, Naval—Italy—Venice.   2. Engravings, Italian. I. Venice
    (Republic). Statutes. II cuore   veneto legale. II. Title: Il cuore
    veneto legale. III. Baroni, Angela,   engr. IV. Piccini, Isabella, 1644-
    1734, engr.   t. 1703.

NL 0440327   NN

PQ4712   Lodoli, Carlo, count, 1690-1761.
L3A6   Apologhi immaginati, e sol estemporaneamen-
1787   te in voce esposti agli amici suoi dal fu
        Fra Carlo de' conti Lodoli, Min. osservante
        di S. Francesco, facilmente utili all' onesta
        gioventù, ed ora por la prima volta pubblicati
        nell' occasione del solenne ingresso che fa
        alla procuratia di S. Marco, l'eccellentissimo
        signor Andrea Memmo, cavaliere della stola
        d'oro. [Nuova raccolta] Bassano, 1787.
        91 p.   front.   30cm.

        I. Memmo, Andrea.   1729-1793. II. Title.

NL 0440328   GU

Avery
A
7420   Lodoli, Carlo,^ *count,* 1690-1761.
L82   Apologhi immaginati, e sol estemporaneamente in
        voce esposti agli amici suoi. Da Carlo Lodoli.
        Facilmente utili all' onesta gioventu, ed ora
        ristampati e corretti. Parigi, Presso Gio:
        Claudio Molini, 1800.
        xxiv, 215 p.   16cm.

        1. Art - Philosophy.

NL 0440329   NNC CU

4PQ   Lodoli, Renzo.
-It   Domani posso morire; storie di ar-
1907   diti e fanti legionari. Roma,
        Edizioni di "Roma fascista," 1939.
        263 p.

NL 0440330   DLC-P4

Lodolini, Armando, 1888-1966.
    Acilia. Torino, Edizioni Arione, 1940.
    100 p. illus. 23 cm. (Collana "Le Città di Mussolini," 4)

    1. Acilia, Italy—History. 2. Housing—Acilia, Italy.

    DG975.A22L6   945.6   A 51-51
    New York. Public Libr.   rev
    for Library of Congress   [r73b2]†

NL 0440331   NN DLC

Lodolini, Armando, 1888-
    Rome (City) Archivio di stato.
    ... L'Archivio di stato in Roma e l'Archivio del regno
d'Italia : indice generale storico descrittivo ed analitico, con il
concorso dei funzionari, e sotto l'alta direzione del soprin-
tendente dell'archivio, prof. Eugenio Casanova. Per autoriz-
zazione speciale del Ministero dell'interno del regno d'Italia
agli "Annales institutorum". Roma, Annales institutorum
[etc.] 1932.

Lodolini, Armando, 1888-1966.
    ... Bibliografia mazziniana.   Milano, Federazione italiana
biblioteche popolari, 1932.
    93 p. 16½ cm. (Collezione di manuali bibliografici e guide di
lettura, 16-17)

    1. Mazzini, Giuseppe, 1805-1872—Bibliography.   I. Title.
    II. Series.

    Z8560.5.L82   012   34-20111

NL 0440333   DLC NN

Lodolini, Armando, 1888-1966.
    ... Elementi di diplomatica, la scienza ausiliaria della
storia; con cenni sull'araldica, la cronologia e la sfragistica.
Milano, Hoepli, 1926.
    xiv, 230 p. 16 cm. (Manuali Hoepli)

    1. Diplomatics.   I. Title.

    CD67.L6   417   33-19261

NL 0440334   DLC MH PPT OrU

DF214   Lodolini, Armando, 1888-
L824   L'Italia ritorna in Grecia; storia e avven-
        ture dell'Ellade dalle origini a Roma. Bo-
        logna, L. Cappelli [1941]
        181 p. 19ᵐ.

        1.Greece - Hist. 2.Civilization, Greek.
        I.Title.

NL 0440335   CSt-H

Law
Lodolini, Armando, 1888-1966.
    ... Leggi, ordinamenti e codici del regime fascista; esposi-
zione e commento ad uso delle scuole e delle persone colte.
Lanciano, G. Carabba [1930]
    288 p. 19 cm. (Le Vie del duce)

    1. Law—Italy. 2. Fascism—Italy.   I. Title.

                                           35-23679

NL 0440336   DLC

VOLUME 338

Lodolini, Armando, 1888-
Mazzini, maestro italiano. Milano, Dall'Oglio ₍1950₎
266 p. 18 cm. (I Corvi; collana universale moderna, nr. 28)

1. Mazzini, Giuseppe, 1805-1872. 2. Italy—Hist.—1815-1870.
DG552.8.M3L6   A 51-10186
New York. Public Libr.
for Library of Congress   †

NL 0440337   NN DLC

Lodolini, Armando, 1888-
... Papato, impero, repubblica (l'assedio di Firenze, 1529-
1531) Bologna, L. Cappelli, 1930.
viii, 268 p. illus. (incl. map) plates, ports. 19ᵐ. ₍"Arcobaleno,"
collana di varietà storiche, artistiche, letterarie, IX₎
"Nota bibliografica": p. ₍v₎-viii.

1. Florence—Siege, 1529-1530. I. Title.
                                45-25001
Library of Congress   DG738.13.L6

NL 0440338   DLC IaU NcD CU MH ICN

DG571 Lodolini, Armando.
.L8   ... La repubblica italiana (Studi e vicende del mazzinian-
simo contemporaneo) 1922-1924 ... Milano, Alpes, 1925.
158, ₍1₎ p. 20ᵐ.
At head of title: Armando Lodolini.

1. Italy—Pol. & govt.—1914-   2. Partito nazionale fascista.

NL 0440339   ICU CSt-H CtY MH

Lodolini, Armando, 1888-1966.
... La storia della razza italiana da Augusto a Mussolini,
dedicata agli italiani di Mussolini e specialmente ai giovani
e alle scuole. Roma, Unione editoriale d'Italia ₍1940₎
316 p. 22 cm.
"Il libro è ... nato nel 1936 ... Cambio soltanto il titolo che era
'Dall'impero all' impero.' "—p. 7-8.
"Seconda edizione."

1. Italy—History. 2. Rome—History.   I. Title.
DG467.L63 1940   945   40-6724

NL 0440340   DLC NcD CSt-H

Lodolini, Armando, 1888-1966.
... La storia sociale del lavoro. 2. ed. Roma, Unione editoriale d'Italia, XIX ₍1941₎
380 p. 21 cm.
"Note di letture": p. ₍371₎-380.

1. Labor and laboring classes. 2. Labor and laboring classes—
Italy.   I. Title.
HD4901.L56 1941   331   45-33005

NL 0440341   DLC ICU

Lodolini, Armando, 1888-1966.
... Tecnica e lavoro nella formazione di un'aristocrazia
operaia. Firenze, C. Cya, 1940.
167 p. 24 cm. (Problemi sindacali, 3)
"Letture": p. ₍161₎-164.

1. Labor and laboring classes—Education—Italy. 2. Technical
education—Italy.   I. Title.   II. Series.
LC5056.I 8L6   331.85   45-46601

NL 0440342   DLC NN

D945R66
L82   Lodolini, Armando, 1888-
... Le vie di comunicazione nello Stato pontificio (contributo alla storia del diritto
amministrativo italiano) Roma, Angelo Signo-
relli, 1923.
21 p. 26ᶜᵐ.

1. Roads - Rome.
2. Roads - Italy.
3. Rome (City) - History.

NL 0440343   NNC

Lodolini, Armando, 1888-
...La vita di Mazzini narrata ai giovani fascisti.   Firenze:
R. Bemporad & figlio₍ 1929₎.   121 p.   8°.   (Quaderni
fascisti. no. 20.)

478586A. 1. Mazzini, Giuseppe,   1805-1872.
                                       June 11, 1930
NL 0440344   NN

Hd69   Lodolini, Armando, 1888-1966.
L821   La vittoria degli umili; romanzo. Roma,
V5   L.Puglielli,1955.
328p. 17cm. (I romanzi del lavoro, 1)

I. Title (1) X.Ser.

NL 0440345   CtY RPB

JN5450   Lodolini, Elio, 1922-
L824   La illegittimita' del governo Badoglio; sto-
ria costituzionale del "quinquennio rivoluziona-
rio" (25 luglio 1943 - 1 gennaio 1948) Milano,
Gastaldi ₍1953₎
172 p. 20cm.
Bibliographical footnotes.
Contents.- Il colpo di stato e l'armistizio.-
L'Italia divisa in due.- Il ripristino della
sovranita". Conclusione.

1. Italy - Pol. & govt. - 1943-1947. 2.
Italy (Fascist   Republic, 1943-1945)
3. Italy - Con   stitutional law. I.
Title

NL 0440346   CSt-H NIC MH

HC302   Lodolini, Ezio, comp.
.5
.A2B5 **Biografia** finanziaria italiana.
Roma.

Lodomeria
see Galicia.

Lodomez, Vera Rossi
see
Rossi Lodomez, Vera.

Col   [Lodoño, Enrique Angel]
SF   Cartilla de avicultura. 2. ed. [Bogotá]
488   Imprenta nacional, 1944.
.L7   58 p. ilus. planos. diagrs. tablas. 24.5 cm.
1944   At head of title: Publicación del Ministerio de la
economía nacional.
On cover: Agricultura y ganadería.

NL 0440350   DPU

Tr.R.   Lodor, John A
An address commemorative of their fraternal
dead of 1860, delivered before Halo Lodge, No.
5. Cahaba ₍Ala.₎ Printed by C. E. Haynes,
1861.
20 p. 21 cm.

1. Memorial service. I. Confederate imprint.

NL 0440351   NcD

Nrb34   Lodor, John A
862L   The speculative temple, an address delivered
before the Grand Lodge of the State of Alabama,
Dec. 3, 1861. Montgomery, Advertiser Book and
Job Office, 1862.
16p. 25cm.

1. Freemasons - Addresses, essays, lectures.

NL 0440352   CtY NcU NcD

Lodor, Richard.   VWC p.v.3, no.10
Notes on gun-cotton and other explosives.   Fort Monroe.
1877. 20 p. 4 pl. 8°.   (United States. Artillery School.
Fort Monroe.—Department of Artillery.)

1. Guncotton. 2. Explosives.
                                    December 1, 1915.
NL 0440353   NN DNW

Lodosa, Didaco Gomez
see Gomez Lodosa, Didaco.

Lodovichi, Lodovico.
... La ricostituzione dei vigneti fillosserati nella
provincia di Forli.   Forli, La Poligrafica romagnola
[1926]
2 p.l., [7]-127 p. plates (part. fold.) 16 cm.
1. Viticulture - Italy. 2. Phylloxera.

NL 0440355   CU

Lodovici, Cesare Vico, ₍tr.
1890-
PS3509
.L43M84 **Eliot, Thomas Stearns,** 1888-
... Assassinio nella cattedrale; traduzione di C. V. Lodovici.
Roma, Edizioni italiane ₍1943₎

Lodovici, Cesare Vico.
...La donna di nessuno. La buona novella. Con gli occhi
socchiusi. Le fole del bel tempo. ' Firenze: Vallecchi₍, 1926₎.
278 p. 12°.

Each play in three acts.

1. Drama, Italian. 2. Title. 3. Title: La buona novella. 4. Title: Con gli
occhi socchiusi. 5. Title: Le fole del   bel tempo.
                                            September 8, 1927
NL 0440357   NN MnU ICU RPB OCl PU PP

VOLUME 338

Lodovici, Cesare Vico. La donna serpente.

ML50
.C3358D7
1932   **Casella, Alfredo,** 1883–1947.
        ¡La donna serpente. Libretto. Italian¿

        La donna serpente; opera-fiaba un prologo, tre atti e
        sette quadri. ¡Libretto di¿ C. Lodovici. Tratta dalla fiaba
        omonima di Carlo Gozzi. Milano, New York, G. Ricordi,
        1932.

Lodovici, Cesare Vico.
    L'Eroica, a drama in one act, by Cesare Lodovici. Trans-
    lated from the Italian by Petronelle Sombart.
    (In Poet lore. Boston, 1923. 25½ᶜᵐ. vol. XXXIV, no. 2, p. 159–176)

    I. Sombart, Petronelle, tr. II. Title.

    PN2.P7   vol. 34, no. 2   C D 25–33 rev †

NL 0440359   DLC NN MB

PQ4827 LODOVICI, CESARE VICO.
.04F6   Le fole del bel tempo; commedia in tre atti.
        ¡Milano, Mondadori, 1925¿
        969–985 p. illus.

        Detached from Comoedia, anno VII, N. 19,
        1 ott. 1925.

NL 0440360   InU

Lodovici, Cesare Vico. Il giudizio universale.

M1503
.T699G6
1955   **Tosatti, Vieri,** 1920–
        ¡Il giudizio universale. Piano-vocal score. Italian¿

        Il giudizio universale; dramma musicale in tre atti e
        quattro quadri di Cesare Vico Lodovici, dalla commedia
        omonima di Anna Bonacci. Riduzione per canto e piano-
        forte. ¡Milano¿ Ricordi ¡ᶜ1955¿

Lodovici, Cesare Vico.
    The idiot, a play in three acts, by Cesare Lodovici. Trans-
    lated from the Italian by Petronelle Sombart.
    (In Poet lore. Boston, 1919. 25½ᶜᵐ. ¡vol. XXX, no. 3¿ p. 317–355)

    I. Sombart, Petronelle, tr. II. Title.
    PN2.P7   vol. 30, no. 3   C D 20–8 rev †

    Library of Congress   Card div.
                                    ¡r46e2¿†

NL 0440362   DLC CaBVaU

Lodovici, Cesare Vico.
    The idiot, a play in three acts, by Cesare Lodovici. Tr.
    from the Italian by Petronelle Sombart. ¡Boston, R. G. Bad-
    ger, 19–¿
    317–355 p. 25½ᶜᵐ. (Poet lore plays. New ser.)

    I. Sombart, Petronelle, tr. II. Title.

    St. Paul. Public library   A 20–1150 rev
    for Library of Congress   ¡r47e2¿

NL 0440363   MnS NN MB

Lodovici, Cesare *Vico.*
    ...L'idiota; commedia in 3 atti.   Torino: P. Gobetti, 1923.
    47 p.   12°.

    1. Drama (Italian). 2. Title.
                                              October 1, 1924

NL 0440364   NN CSt

                                              3211

LODOVICI, CESARE VICO, 1890–
    L'incrinatura. Ruota. La donna di nessuno. [Roma]
    G. Casini [1955]   xv,190 p. port. 18cm. (Collezione del
    teatro italiano contemporaneo. 6)

    1. Drama, Italian. I. Title. II. Title: Ruota. III. Title: La donna di
    nessuno.   i. subs. for main entry without date

NL 0440365   NN RPB

Lodovici, Cesare *Vico, 1890–*
PQ4827   ... Ruota, L'incrinatura, La donna di nessuno;
03   prefazione di R. Simoni. Roma, Edizioni Teatro
R8   dell'universita ¡1941¿
         2 p.l., ¡vii¿–xvi, 274 p., 2 l.   15cm. (Teatro
         dell'Università di Roma. Collezione di autori
         italiani, 4)

         "Bibliografia": p. ¡271¿–274.
         At head of title: Cesare Vico Lodovici.

NL 0440366   RPB NNC

PQ4231   Lodovici, Cesare Vico.
.Z9L6   "Rusta"; prologo-monologo epilogo di un
          viaggio di fantasia...
          Roma, ᶜ1937
          4–27p.   25 cm.
              cover-title.

NL 0440367   DLC

Lodovici, Cesare Vico.
    The woman of no one, a play in three acts, by Cesare Lodo-
    vici. Tr. from the Italian by Petronelle Sombart.
    (In Poet lore. Boston, 1921. 25½ᶜᵐ. ¡vol. XXXII, no. 2¿ p. 159–200)

    I. Sombart, Petronelle, tr. II. Title.
    PN2.P7   vol. 32, no. 2   C D 22–84 rev †

    Library of Congress   Card div.
                                    ¡r46b2¿†

NL 0440368   DLC NN MB

Lodovici, Cesare *Vico, 1890–*
    Les yeux mi-clos. Trois scènes.   (Revue des deux mondes.
    Paris, 1925.   8°.   (Période 7, tome 27, p. 581–593.)
    Signed: Cesare Lodovici.
    Translated by Mme. Jean Jacques Bernard.

    1. Drama, Italian—Transla-   French. 2. Drama, French—Trans-
    tions from Italian. 3. Bernard,   Mme. Jean Jacques, translator.
    4. Title.
                                              October 9, 1925

NL 0440369   NN

Lodovici, Francesco de, 16th cent.
Typ   Triomphi di Carlo di messer Francesco d'i
525   Lodovici ...
35.530   [Venice, 1535]

         4°. 4p.l., 215 numb.l.   22cm.
         Colophon: ... stampato in Vinegia per Mapheo
         Pasini & Francesco Bindoni cõpagni al segno
         dell'angiolo Raphaello appresso san Moise l'anno
         della nostra saluto MDXXXV. del mese di settem-
         bre ...
         Woodcut illus. on t.-p. shows author presenting
         book to Andrea   Gritti, doge of Venice.

         Errata: leaf 215ʳ
         In verse.
         First issue, with illus. on t.-p.

NL 0440371   MH PU DFO

LODOVICI, Francesco de.
    Triomphi di Carlo. [Vinegia, M. Pasini & F.
Bindoni], 1536.

    4°. ff. (4), 215.
    The title-page has a woodcut border.
    A reprint of the 1535 ed. with a new title-
page. The prefaces differ slightly.
    A romantic poem based on the story of Charle-
magne.

NL 0440372   MH PU

Lodovici, Jean, 1905–
    ... L'évolution de la notion de pouvoir discrétionnaire ... par
Jean Lodovici ... Lille, Imp. Douriez-Bataille, 1937.
    3 p. l., ¡9¿–182 p. 24ᶜᵐ.
    Thèse—Univ. de Lille.
    "Bibliographie": p. ¡175¿–179.

    1. Administrative law—France. 2. Administrative responsibility—
    France.   I. Title: Pouvoir discrétionnaire.

                                              42-35146

NL 0440373   DLC CtY

Lodovici, Sergio Samek
    see   Samek Ludovici, Sergio.

Lodovico Celestino da Monte Corvino, O.F.M.
    La miracolosa vita del B.Iacopo della
Marga. Descritta dal R.P.F.Lodovico Celestino da Monte Corvino Minore Osservan-
te ...   In Napoli, Appresso Camillo
Cauallo, 1650.
    ¡viii¿, 375, ¡l¿ p.

NL 0440375   DHN

BT   Lodovico da Castelplanio, O.F.M.
1006   Maria nel consiglio dell'eterno; ovvero,
.L82   La Vergine predestinata alla missione medesima
1902   con Gesù Cristo. 2. ed. Napoli, Rondinella
         & Loffredo, 1902.

         3 v. 23 cm.

         1. Mary, Blessed Virgin - Theology.
         2. Mary, Blessed Virgin - Co-redemption.
         II. Title.

NL 0440376   DCU

VOLUME 338

C 4620.73
Lodovico da Castelplanio, O.F.M.
Pio IX.e gli errori moderni. Velletri,
Tip.Colonnesi, 1865.

NL 0440377 MH

Lodovico da Città di Castello, O.F.M.
Giardinello ornato di varij floretti,
raccolto da Frà Lodovico da Città di Castello ... Nuovamente dato in luce à consolatione di quelli,che son devoti del
Serafico Padre S.Francesco. Di nuovo ristampato, e correto ... Perugia,S.Zacchini, 1650.
[24] p.

NL 0440378 DHN

Lodovico da Imola
see Ludovicus Imolensis, 15th cent.

Lodovico da Livorno, *Padre Lettore, Cap.* **FR16.L82
S. Francesco d'Assisi e la contea di Montauto .
Prato. Giachetti, figlio & c. 1884. 56, (1) pp. 27.5 cm., in 4s.
Edizione di soli 400 esemplari. N. 389.

E3610 — Barbolani family. — Fran cesco d'Assisi, Saint, 1.82-1226.
Biog. — Montauto, Italy. Hist. Relig.

NL 0440380 MB DHN RPB

Lodovico da Palma, O.F.M.
Vita di S.Lodovico d'Angiò,principe
reale, Frate Minore, e Vescovo di Tolosa,
compilata dal R.Padre Lodovico da Palma
... Napoli, dalla Stamperia Reale,1855
5 p.f.,229 p., 2 f.

NL 0440381 DHN

Lodovico il Moro
see
Lodovico Sforza, Duke of Milan, 1452-1508.

Lodovico Scarampo, cardinal, d.1465.

See

Scarampo, Lodovico, cardinal, d.1465.

Lodovico Sforza, Duke of Milan, 1452-1508.
Manuscrit Sforza. Facsimilé d'après le manuscrit original appartenant à M. le marquis d'Azeglio, ambassadeur de Sardaigne à Londres. Photographié et publié par C. Silvy ... London [Joseph Clayton, printer] 1860.

2 pts. pl. 21 cm. (pt. [2]: 19 cm.)

Facsimile of a rhetorical exercise composed (under the direction of Francesco Filelfo?) by Lodovico Sforza, signed "Ludovicus maria Sfortia Vicecomes annory xv ... manu propria die xxvij Nouembri 1467." The writing (16 p.) is surrounded by borders of miniatures (including portraits) presumably added at a later date.—Prefixed to

Continued in next column

Continued from preceding column

the plates: "Reproduction et restauration des manuscrits anciens par la photographie. Communication faite à l'Académie Impériale des inscriptions et belles lettres ... 21 sept. 1860 ..." signed C. Silvy.— Under separate cover, with half-title "Manuscrit Sforza (1467)" a description of the manuscript by d'Azeglio (46 p., 1 l., 19 cm.) The two parts are similarly bound, with the monogram of Anatole de Montaiglon on front covers, and with his book plate.

I. Azeglio, Vittorio Emanuele Tapparelli, marchese d', 1816-1890.
II. Silvy, C. III. Title.

ND3399.S5L6 1467a 1-23471

NL 0440385 DLC

Lodovico, Mario
... Italienisch für anfänger und fortgeschrittene nach der methode Paustian..., von Mario Lodovico. 6-15 tausend. Hamburg, Paustian, 1941.
111 p.

Der humor als sprachlehrer!

NL 0440386 ICU

DG545
.8
.M9L82
Lodovico Antonio Muratori - studente; narrazione di L. V. Corredata di documenti inediti.
2.ed. riv. Modena, Tip. P. Toschi, 1882.
63 p.

1. Muratori, Lodovico Antonio, 1672-1750.
I. V., L.

NL 0440387 ICU

16th
cent
Lodovicus, Antonius.
De occvltis proprietatibus, Libri quinque.
Opus praeclarissimum. Olyssippone, 1540.
71 numb. leaves. 28cm.

1. Medicine - 15th-18th cent.

NL 0440388 CtY-M DNLM

Lodowick, Charles
see
Lodwick, Charles.

Lodowick, Christian
see
Ludwig, Christian, 1660-1728.

Lodowick; or, Lessons of morality for the amusement and instruction of youth. London, Printed for the author and sold by J. Bell, R. Edwards, Cadell and Davies, C. Law and Mrs. Peacock, 1795.
6 v.in 1. 18cm.

Contemporary calf, with black and red labels on spine.

NL 0440391 CLU

Lodowijks, W.M.A.W.
see Lodewijcksz,Willem, 16th cent.

[Lodowyck, Francis. *fl.1647-1686*
A common writing: whereby two, although not understanding one the others language, yet by the helpe thereof, may communicate their minds one to another. Composed by a well-willer to learning. [London:] Printed for the author, 1647. 3 p.l., 31 p., 1 l. 12°.

HEFFLEY COLLECTION.
300079A. 1. Shorthand—Systems, English, 1647. 2. Title.
September 8, 1927

NL 0440393 NN CSmH DLC

[Lodowyck, Francis] fl. 1647-1686, supposed author.
The ground-work; or, Foundation laid
see under title

HJ
4714
L63
1927
Lodr,Karel.
Tabulky úročitelů,odúročitelů,stŕadatelů,
zásobitelů,umořovatelů. Ukládací papíry statní;
sociální pojištění-zakon ze dne 9.Října 1924;
pojištění a věcné. Upravil a vydal Karel Lodr,
odborný učitel. Růžodol-Liberec, B.Kobr, 1927.
32 p. (Sborník Číslo a prostor)

1.Taxation—Czechoslovak Republic—Rates and tables. 2.Income—Czechoslovak Republic—Handbooks,manuals,etc. 3.Czechoslovak Republic—Statistics—Handbooks—manuals,etc. I.Title.

NL 0440396 NSyU

Lodre, León Sanz
see Sanz Lodre, León.

Lodrini, Emilio.
Intorno a Dante ed al poema sacro. Brescia, 1892.
15 p. 8°. (Commentarii dell' Ateneo di Brescia per l'anno 1892," p. 116-130)

NL 0440398 NIC

Lodrini, Emilio.
Intorno alla data precisa della nascita dell' altissimo poeta. n.p., 1895.
(In Commentarii dell' Ateneo di Brescia per l'anno 1895. p. 163-171)

NL 0440399 NIC

LODRINI, Emilio.
Se l'opuscolo "Quaestio de aqua et terra" sia d'attribuirsi a Dante Alighieri. [Brescia, 1890.]

8°. pp.(23).
Commentari dell' Ateneo di Brescia,1890,pp.
54-76.
"Sostiene che la Quaestio è una impostura de cinquecentista Moncetti." - Bul. soc. dantesca, v.102.

NL 0440400 MH NIC

N5265
L58
Lodron, ――― Gräfin.

Weber, Eduard Friedrich, 1830-1907.
Galerie Weber, zweiter Teil. Sammlung Gräfin Lodron, Gemälde neuerer Meister. Ausstellung: Sonnabend, den 25. Februar 1928 ... Versteigerung: Dienstag, den 28. Februar 1928 ... Berlin, R. Lepke's Kunst-Auctions-Haus [1928]

VOLUME 338

LODRON, RICHARD.
    Kleiner Katechismus für Sänger; 7 Fragen und
Antworten. Wien, Steffel-Verlag [1948] 62 p. port.
15cm.

1. Singing.

NL   0440402   NN

Judaica   Lods, Adolphe, 1867-1948.
Mch50   La croyance à la vie future et le culte
905l   des morts dans l'antiquité israélite. Paris,
    Fischbacher, 1905.
    viii, 266p. 25cm.
    Thèse - Univ. de Paris.

NL   0440403   CtY DDO

BS1177 Lods, Adolphe, 1867-
.L8   La croyance à la vie future et le culte des morts dans
    l'antiquité israélite, par Adolphe Lods ... Paris, Fisch-
    bacher, 1906.
    2 v. in 1. 25cm.
    "Ouvrages consultés": v. 2, p. [129]-145.

    1. Future life. 2. Cultus, Jewish. 3. Funeral rites and ceremonies.

NL   0440404   ICU NjP MB OCH PPPD PU CtY-D

Lods, Adolphe, 1867-
    La culte des ancêtres dan l'antiquité
Hébraïque et ses rapports, avec l'organisation
familiale et sociale des anciens Israélites.
Thèse de doctorat ès lettres ... Paris:
Fischbacher, 1906.
    148 p.

NL   0440405   OCH CtY

Lods, Adolphe, 1867-1948.
    Evangelii secundum Petrum, et Petri
apocalypseos quae supersunt... Parisiis,
1892
        see under Bible. N. T. Apocryphal
books. Gospel of Peter. Greek. 1892.

Lods, Adolphe, 1867-1948.
    L'évangile et l'apocalypse de Pierre...
Paris, 1893
        see under Bible. N. T. Apocryphal
books. Gospel of Peter. Greek. 1893.

Lods, Adolphe, 1867-1948.
    Histoire de la littérature hébraïque et juive, depuis les
origines jusqu'à la ruine de l'état juif (135 après J.-C.)
Préf. d'André Parrot. Paris, Payot, 1950.
    1054 p. 23 cm. (Bibliothèque historique)
    Includes bibliographies. "Compléments bibliographiques, par An-
dré Parrot": p. [1054]-1043.

    1. Jewish literature—Hist. & crit.

            892.409   50-3027

PPDrop PPEB
NcU CtY DDO NNUT ICU NN NjPT IaU OCH PPLT OC1W NcD
NL   0440408   DLC KyLxCB PPiPT MoSCS NPurMC MoSCS IEG

Lods, Adolphe, 1867-
    ... Israël, des origines au milieu du VIIIᵉ siècle; avec 3 cartes,
38 figures dans le texte et 12 planches hors texte. Par Adolphe
Lods ... Paris, Renaissance du livre, 1930.
    xvi p., 1 l., 595, [1] p. illus., XII pl. on 6 l. 20½cm. (L'évolution de
l'humanité, synthèse collective ... [2. section. XXVII])
    "Bibliographie": p. [567]-579.

    1. Jews—Hist.—To B. C. 586. 2. Jews—Religion. 3. Jews—Civiliza-
tion.   I. Title.   31-3626

    Library of Congress   DS121.L5
                                            933

        OU OCH OCU MiU PPPD PPC
NL   0440409   DLC CU CLSU ViRUT TxFTC ICU KyLoS CaBVaU

Lods, Adolphe, 1867-1948.
    Israël, des origines au milieu du VIIIᵉ siècle. Avec 3 cartes,
38 figures dans le texte et 12 planches hors texte. Paris, A.
Michel, 1949, [1930].
    603 p. illus. 20 cm. (L'Évolution de l'humanité, synthèse collec-
tive, 27)

    1. Jews—Hist. 2. Judaism—Hist.—Ancient period.   I. Title.

    BM165.L6 1949   57-17479 ‡

NL   0440410   DLC DDO PPT

Lods, Adolphe, 1867-1948.
    Israel, from its beginnings to the middle of the eighth cen-
tury, by Adolphe Lods ... Translated by S. H. Hooke ...
London, K. Paul, Trench, Trubner & co., ltd., 1932.
    xxiv, 512 p. illus. (incl. maps) xvi pl. 24½ cm. (Half-title: The
History of civilization. [The early empires])
    Bibliography: p. 489-503.

    1. Jews—Hist.—To 586 B. C. 2. Judaism—Hist.—Ancient period.
    I. Hooke, Samuel Henry, 1874-   tr. II. Title.

    BM165.L5713   933   32—19383

                        (b5541)

        WaSpG MH PPWe TU OrPR
    MtU WaT PPLT OrP OrStbM MB IdU IdPI WaWW WaSp NBuU
    PPPD PPC PHC OCH OC1Tem MH-AH OC1W OC1 Or Wa MiU
NL   0440411   DLC OCU MH-P CU NcD ICU NN ICN PSC PBm

Lods, Adolphe, 1867-
    Israel, from its beginnings to the middle
of the eighth century ... Translated by
S. H. Hooke ... New York, Alfred A. Knopf,
1932.

NL   0440412   OO OC1

---

933   LODS, ADOLPHE, 1867-
L8221Th   Israel, from its beginnings to the middle of
1932r   the eighth century, by Adolphe Lods ... Trans-
    lated by S.H. Hooke ... London, Routledge &
    K. Paul, ltd., 1948.
    xxiv, 512p. illus.(incl. maps) XVI pl.
    24½cm. (Half-title: The history of civiliza-
    tion. [The early empires])
    "First published in England 1932. Second
    impression 1948.
    Bibliography: p.489-403.
    Translation of Israël, des origines au milieu
    du VIIIᵉ siècle.
    1. Jews - Hist. - To B.C. 586. 2. Jews -
    Religion. 3.   Jews - Civilization.
    Hooke, Samuel   Henry, tr. II. Title.
    III. Series.

NL   0440413   TxU MH-AH

DS   Lods, Adolphe, 1867-1948.
121   Israel, from its beginnings to the
L8218   middle of the eighth century. Translated
1953   by S. H. Hooke. London, Routledge & K.
    Paul [1953]
    xxiv, 512 p. illus., maps. 24cm.
    (The History of civilization. [The early
    empires])

        1. Jews—Hist.—To 586 B.C. 2. Judaism—
    Hist.—Ancient period. 3. Jews—Civilization.
    I. Title. II.   Series.

NL   0440414   NIC DCU

4BP   Lods, Adolphe, 1867-1948.
452   Jean Astruc et la critique
    Biblique au XVIIIe siècle. Avec une
    notice biographique par Paul
    Alphandéry. Strasbourg, Librairie
    Istra, 1924.
    85 p.

    (Cahiers de la Revue d'histoire et
    de philosophie religieuses, no 11)
    Extrait de la Revue d'histoire et de philosophie religieuse

NL   0440415   DLC-P4 MH-AH NIC NjPT CtY MH

LODS, Adolphe.
    Les Origines de la Figure de Satan.
Ses Fonctions a la Cour Céleste. Reprinted
from Mélanges Syriens Offerts a M. R.
Dussaud, p. [649]-660.

    1. Devil. 2. Bible-Demonology.

NL   0440416   NNJ

Lods, Adolphe, 1867-
Origine et nature de l'église; conférences prononcées à la
Faculté libre de théologie protestante, par mm. A. Lods, M.
Goguel, A. Wautier d'Aygalliers [et autres] ... Paris, Fisch-
bacher, 1939.

Lods, Adolphe, 1867-1948.
    Les prophètes d'Israël et les débuts du judaïsme; avec 5
figures au trait et 8 planches hors-texte. Paris, La Renaissance du livre, 1935.
    xx, 434 p. illus., plates. 20 cm. (Des prophètes à Jésus, 1)
    L'Évolution de l'humanité, synthèse collective. 2. sect., 28.
    Continued by Le monde juif vers le temps de Jésus, by C. A. H.
Guignebert.
    Bibliography: p. [405]-416.
    1. Jews—Hist.—To 70 A. D. 2. Judaism—Hist.—Ancient period.
    3. Prophets.   I. Title. (Series. (Series: L'évolution de l'hu-
manité, synthèse collective. 2. sect., 28)

    BM165.L6 1935   933   35-15120 rev*

        CaBVaU OC1W NIC
NL   0440418   DLC PPC NN CLamB OCH OCU OC1W MU KyLoS

DS121   Lods, Adolphe, 1867-1948.
L63   Les prophètes d'Israël et les débuts du judaïsme. Paris, A.
1950   Michel, 1950 [c1935]
    xx, 440 p. illus., plates. (Des prophètes à Jésus, 1)

    L'Évolution de l'humanité, synthèse collective. 2. sect., 28.
    Continued by Le monde juif vers le temps de Jésus, by C. A. H.
Guignebert.
    Bibliography: p. [405]-416.

    1. Jews - Hist. - 586 B. C. - 70 A. D. 2. Judaism - Hist. -
Ancient period. 3. Prophets.

NL   0440419   CU DDO PPT InU NN PU WU

VOLUME 338

Lods, Adolphe, 1867–1948.
The prophets and the rise of Judaism, by Adolphe Lods ... translated by S. H. Hooke ... London, K. Paul, Trench, Trubner & co., ltd., 1937.
xxiv, 378 p. illus., VIII pl. (incl. front., facsim.) 24½ cm. (Half-title: The history of civilization, ed. by C. K. Ogden. (The early empires and Greece))
Foreword (p. xi–xxiv) by Henri Berr.
Bibliography: p. 357–368.
1. Jews—Hist.—To 70 A. D. 2. Judaism—Hist.—Ancient period. 3. Prophets. I. Hooke, Samuel Henry, 1874– tr. II. Berr, Henri, 1863–1954. III. Title.

DS121.L84   933   37—4814

PPDrop CU
NL   0440420   DLC NcU IdPI MtU PBL NcU NNC OCU OO PHC

DS
121
L84   Lods, Adolphe, 1867–1948.
The prophets and the rise of Judaism, by Adolphe Lods ... translated by S. H. Hooke ... London, Routledge & K. Paul, 1937.
xxiv, 378 p. illus., VIII pl. (incl. front., facsim.) 24 cm.
Foreword (p. xi–xxiv) by Henri Berr.
Bibliography: p. 357–368.
1. Jews—Hist.—586 B. c.–70 A. D. 2. Jews—Religion. 3. Prophets. I. Hooke, Samuel Henry, 1874– tr. II. Berr, Henri, 1863– III. Title.

NL   0440421   NBuC IaU IdU OrPR

Lods, Adolphe, 1867–1948.
The prophets and the rise of Judaism, by Adolphe Lods ... translated by S. H. Hooke ... New York, E. P. Dutton & company, 1937.
xxiv, 378 p. illus., VIII pl. (incl. front., facsim.) 24 cm.
Foreword (p. xi–xxiv) by Henri Berr.
Bibliography: p. 357–368.
1. Jews—Hist.—586 B. c.–70 A. D. 2. Jews—Religion. 3. Prophets. I. Hooke, Samuel Henry, 1874– tr. II. Berr, Henri, 1863– III. Title.

DS121.L84 1937a   933   38—4362

PPWe GS NcU NN NNC MB OrU ViU ScU ICJ
NL   0440422   DLC NNC TU NcD OC1 OC1Tem OCH OC1W PBm

DS
121
L82p   Lods, Adolphe, 1867–
1950   The prophets and the rise of Judaism. Translated by S.H.Hooke. London, Routledge & Paul [1950]
xxiv,378p. illus.,8 plates. 25cm. (The History of civilization)
Foreword (p.xi–xxiv) by Henri Berr.
Bibliography: p.357–368.

NL   0440423   NRU NIC

DS121
.L84   Lods, Adolphe, 1867–
1955   The prophets and the rise of Judaism; translated by S. H. Hooke. London, Routledge & K. Paul [1955]
xxiv, 378 p. illus., plates. 25cm. (The history of civilization. [Early empires])
Foreword (p. xi–xxiv) by Henri Berr.
Bibliography: p. 357–368.
1. Jews—Hist.—B. C. 586—A. D. 70. 2. Jews—Religion. 3. Prophets. I. Hooke, Samuel Henry, 1874– tr. II. Berr, Henri, 1863– III. Title.

NL   0440424   MB MH-AH

Lods, Adolphe, 1867–1948.
... La religion d'Israël, par Adolphe Lods ... [Paris] Hachette [1939]
256 p. 19 cm. (Histoire des religions)
"Bibliographie": p. [246]–252.

1. Judaism—Hist.—Ancient period. I. Title.

BM165.L62   296   39—22300

NL   0440425   DLC CtY-D KyLoS ViRUT ICU NN OCH IaU

Lods, Adolphe, 1867–   , ed.
Reproduction en héliogravure du manuscrit d'Énoch et des écrits attribués à Saint Pierre ... Paris, 1893
see under   Bible. Manuscripts, Greek. O. T. Apocryphal books. 1 Enoch.

Lods, Armand, 1854–1938.
André Gill,   sa vie, bibliographie de ses oeuvres par Armand Lods et Véga [pseud. Un chapitre de l'histoire de la caricature politique en France] Avec portraits par Emile Cohl et caricatures inédites d'André Gill. Paris, Vanier, 1887.

132 p. port., illus.

NL   0440427   MH CLU NNC

Lods, Armand, 1854–   Fr 1346.138
Centenaire de la révolution française, 1789–1889. L'église réformée de Paris pendant la révolution, 1789–1802. Paris, Fischbacher, 1889.
pp. 45 +. Port. of P. H. Marron, plan and plate.

Paris–Church & religious affairs]

NL   0440428   MH

Lods, Armand, 1854–1938.
Un conventionnel en mission. Bernard de Saintes et la réunion de la principauté de Montbéliard à la France d'après des documents originaux et inédits, par Armand Lods. Avec un portrait de Bernard, par Louis David.   Paris: Librairie Fischbacher, 1888.   301 p.   facsim., front. (port.)   25½cm.
"Extraits des Mémoires de la Société d'émulation de Montbéliard."
"Bibliographie," p. [291]–295.

163341B.   1. Bernard de Saintes,   André Antoine Bernard Des Zeu-
zines, called, 1750–1819. 2. Mont-   béliard, France—Hist.
                                June 17, 1942

NL   0440429   NN MiU MH MnU

Lods, Armand, 1854–   Fr 1727.51.7
De la consécration au ministère évangélique. P, 1885
16 p.

NL   0440430   MH

LODS, Armand, 1854–
De la vente à réméré, précédée d'une étude sur la lex commissoria. Paris, 1879.

NL   0440431   MH-L

Lods, Armand,   1854–
Des dons et legs en faveur des conseils presbytéraux de des consistoires. P, [1885?]

22 p.

NL   0440432   MH-L

Lods, Armand, b.1854
Des rapports des fabriques et des conseils presbytéraux avec les communes, d'après la loi du 5 avril 1884. P, 1885

14 p.

NL   0440433   MH

                            Fr 1728.02
LODS,Armand,1854–
Le droit d'association et la liberté religieuse d'après la loi du 1er juillet 1901. Paris,Lib.Fischbacher etc.,1901.

23 cm. pp.53,(2).

NL   0440434   MH

LODS, Armand, 1854–
Du droit électoral dans les églises protestantes; étude suivie des circulaires ministérielles relatives aux élections (1852–1888). Paris, Grassart, [1888].

At head of title: Renouvellement des consistoires et des conseils presbytéraux.

NL   0440435   MH

Lods, Armand, 1854–1938.
... Du droit électoral dans les églises protestantes. Étude suivie des circulaires ministérielles relatives aux élection (1852–1888) ... Paris, Grassart [1889]
122 p.
At head of title: Renouvellement des consistoires et des conseils presbytéraux.
"Circulaires ministérielles relatives aux élections," p. 39–105; "Jurisprudence," p. 107–118.
1. Protestant churches–France. I. France. Ministere des cultes.

NL   0440436   CU-L

Mgy35   Lods, Armand, 1854–
L82   ... L'Édit de Nantes devant le Parlement de Paris ... Paris,Fischbacher,1899.
23p. 22cm.
At head of title: Troisième centenaire de l'Édit de Nantes.
"Tiré à deux cents exemplaires."

NL   0440437   CtY

ar W   Lods, Armand, 1854–1938.
32874   L'église luthérienne de Paris pendant la Révolution et le chapelain Gambs.   Paris, Fischbacher, 1892.
21 p. 24cm.

1. Gambs, Charles Christian, 1759–1822. 2. Lutheran Church in France. 3. France—Hist. —Revolution—Religious history.

NL   0440438   NIC

VOLUME 338

Lods, Armand, 1854-1938.
    ... L'Église réformée de Paris pendant
la révolution (1789-1802) ...   Paris,
Librairie Fischbacher, 1889.
    45 p., port., 29 .

    At head of title: Centenaire de la
Révolution française (1789-1889).

NL 0440439   NjPT MH

LODS, Armand, 1854-
    L'église réformée de Paris de la révocation
à la révolution,1685-178 . Paris,Lib.
Fischbacher,1889.

    1.8°. pp.16.
    At head of title: Centenaire du premier
exercice public du culte protestant à Paris,
7 juin 1789-7 juin 1889.

NL 0440440   MH

Lods, Armand, 1854-1938.
    Les églises protestantes de l'ancienne
principauté de Montbéliard pendant la révolution et
le pasteur Kilg (1789-1802) ... Paris, 1890.
    30 p. incl. port. 28,5 cm.
    "Tiré à 125 exemplaires."

NL 0440441   CtY

DC
137.5   Lods, Armand, 1854-1938.
.R3   Essai sur la vie de Rabaut de Saint-Étienne;
L6   pasteur à Nîmes, membre de l'Assemblée
        constituante et de la Convention nationale,
        1743-1793. Paris, Fischbacher, 1893.
        33p. 25cm.

        Includes bibliographical footnotes.

        1. Rabaut Saint-Étienne, Jean Paul,
        1743-1793. I.   Title.

NL 0440442   NNCU-G NIC CU

                                Fr 1727.51.7
Lods, Armand, b.1854
    Étude critique du décret sur la comptabilité des con-
seils presbytéraux et de la circulaire du ministre des
cultes. P, 1893

    58 p.

NL 0440443   MH

                                Fr 1727.51.7
Lods, Armand, b.1854
    Étude sur l'organisation de l'Église réformée. P,
1886

    7 p.

NL 0440444   MH

Lods, Armand. 1854-1938. ed.
    La législation des cultes protestants. 1787-1887: recueil
complet des lois, ordonnances, décrets, arrêtés ministériels
et avis du Conseil d'État relatifs aux églises protestantes de
novembre 1787 à janvier 1887, annoté par Armand Lods ...
avec une préface par E. de Pressensé ... Paris, Grassart,
1887.
    xvi, 274 p., 1 l. 23 cm.

    "Bibliographie": p. ,261,-264.

    1. Protestant churches—France. 2. Ecclesiastical law—France.
3. Church and state in France.   i. France.   Laws, statutes, etc.

    BX4843.L6 1887   284.0944   35—23135

NL 0440445   DLC CU CtY-D FU DCU MH CU

                                Fr 1728.02
LODS,Armand,1854-
    La loi de séparation des églises et de l'état
devant la Chambre des députés. Paris,Fisch-
bacher etc.,1905.

    23 cm. pp.58,(1).

NL 0440446   MH NNJ CtY

                                Fr 1727.03.20
Lods, Armand, b.1854
    Le mariage des prêtres devant la loi civile. P, 1888

    15 p.

NL 0440447   MH

LODS,Armand,1854-
    Le nouveau projet du gouvernement et la
séparation des églises et de l'état. Paris,Lib.
Fischbacher,etc.,1905.

    23 cm. p. .58,(1).

NL 0440448   MH

Lods, Armand, 1854-1938, ed.
    La nouvelle législation des cultes protestants en France 1905-
1913. Recueil complet des lois, décrets, arrêtés ministériels,
statuts régissant les associations cultuelles protestantes,
par Armand Lods ... Paris, Librairie Fischbacher, 1914.
    xvii p., 1 l., 376 p. 23 .

    1. Protestant churches—France. 2. Ecclesiastical law—France.
3. Church and state in France.   i. France.   Laws, statutes, etc.
                                22—8542 Revised
    Library of Congress   BX4843.L6 1914
                                ,r42b2,

NL 0440449   DLC NjPT MH

DC
146   Lods, Armand, 1854-1938.
R16   Le pasteur Rabaut-Pomier, membre de la
L82   Convention nationale, 1744-1820. Paris,
        Fischbacher, 1893.
        24 p. illus. 24cm.

        1. Rabaut-Pommier, Jacques Antoine, 1744-
        1820.

NL 0440450   NIC

PQ
2370   Lods, Armand, 1854-1938.
.L6   Les Premières éditions d'Alfred de Musset;
        étude d'histoire littéraire. Paris, 1927.
        30 p. 23 cm. (in binder, 25 cm.)

        "Extrait du Mercure de France."
        Bibliographical footnotes.

        1. Musset, Alfred de, 1810-1857. I. Title.

NL 0440451   WU

                                Fr 1727.51.7
Lods, Armand, b.1854
    Les presbytères et l'indemnité de logement due aux
pasteurs. P, 1887

    12 p.

NL 0440452   MH

Lods, Armand, b.1854
    Les propositions de lois sur la séparation des Eglises
et de l'Etat. P, 1903.

    45 p.

NL 0440453   MH NbU

Lods, Armand, 1854-1938, ed.
    Revue de droit et de jurisprudence des églises séparées de
l'état ... 1.–13. année, mars 1884–mars 1897; 14.–22. année
(nouv. sér., t. 1–9) avr. 1897–déc. 1905; 23.–29. année (3. sér.,
t. 1–7) jan. 1906–déc. 1912. Paris, Librairie Fischbacher,
société anonyme ,etc., 1884–1912,

Lods, Armand, 1854-
    Le rôle des idées magiques dans la mentalité israélite. (In:
Society for Old Testament Study. Old Testament essays. London, 1927. 8°. p. 55–76.)

    Caption-title.
    Signed: A. Lods.
    Bibliographical footnotes.

    1. Magic, Jewish.
                                September 29, 1928

NL 0440455   NN

Lods, Armand, b.1854
    La séparation des Eglises et de l'Etat d'après le
contre-projet du gouvernement. P, 1904.

    47 p.

NL 0440456   MH NjPT

BX4843 Lods, Armand, 1854-1938.
1824   Traité de l'administration des cultes Pro-
1896   testants...avec une introduction par Jacques
        Flach. Paris, Grassart, 1896.
Robbins   xx, 579 p.
Coll.

        1. Protestant churches - France. 2. France
        - Protestants. I. Flach, Jacques. II. Title.
        III. Title: L'administration des cultes
        protestantes,   Traité de.

NL 0440457   CU-L WU MH

VOLUME 338

Lods, Édouard.
... Étude historique et critique sur le Quakérisme. Thèse présentée à la Faculté de théologie protestante de Strasbourg ... le jeudi 30 juillet 1857 ... par Édouard Lods ... Strasbourg, G. Silbermann, 1857.
[iv], 80p. 21cm.

At head of title: Université de France. Faculté de Théologie Protestante de Strasbourg.

NL 0440458   PSC-Hi PHC MH

Fr 428.07
Lods, Édouard,
Sermon pour l'ouverture solennelle de la session du synode général de l'Église de la confession d'Augsbourg prononcé le 10 juin 1884 à l'église de Saint-Martin à Montbéliard. P, 1884

23 p.

NL 0440459   MH

Lods, Frédéric,
Discours pour la cloture de l'assemblée des délégués de l'église de la confession d'Augsbourg ... par m. Lods ... Strasbourg, F.C. Heitz, 1848.
21 p. 21½cm.

"Prononcé à Strasbourg, dans l'église de St. Thomas, le 29 septembre 1848."
"Imprimé par décision de l'assemblée."

NL 0440460   MH-L

791.4
L82f
Lods, Jean.
La formación profesional de los técnicos de cine. Paris, Unesco, 1951.
160p. 22cm. (Prensa, cine y radio en el mundo de hoy)

Unesco. Publicación 603.
Bibliography: p.147-160.
1. Moving-pictures as a profession. I. Title. (Series: United Nations Educational, Scientific and Cultural Organization. Press, film and radio in the world today)

NL 0440461   IU DPU

Lods, Jean.
La formation professionnelle des techniciens du film. Paris, Unesco, 1951.
158 p. table. 22 cm. (La presse, le film et la radio dans le monde d'aujourd'hui)

UNESCO publication no. 601.
"Bibliographie": p. 145-158.
1. Moving-pictures as a profession. I. Title. (Series: United Nations Educational, Scientific and Cultural Organization. La presse, le film et la radio dans le monde d'aujourd'hui. Series: United Nations Educational, Scientific and Cultural Organization. UNESCO publication no. 601)

Southern Calif., Univ. of.   Library
for Library of Congress   A 52-3945

NL 0440462   CLSU

Lods, Jean.
Professional training of film technicians. Paris, UNESCO, 1951.
155 p. 22 cm. (Press, film and radio in the world today; series of studies)

Bibliography: p. 141-155.

1. Cinematography—Study and teaching. I. Title. (Series: United Nations Educational, Scientific and Cultural Organization. Press, film and radio in the world today; series of studies)

TR852.L6   778.507   52-8284

PU MH MB DPU NIC
IdU NcGU NcD NNC MiD CSt CLSU ICU ViU IU PPT PU-Penn
NL 0440463   DLC OrU CaBVaU FTaSU TxU PU CaBVaU UU OU

Lods, Jeanne.
Le roman de Perceforest; origines, composition, caractères, valeur et influence. Genève, Librairie Droz, 1951.
310 p. 26 cm. (Société de publications romanes et françaises. [Publications] 32)
"Bibliographie": p. [297]-302.

1. Perceforest. (Series)
              A 52-2555
Harvard Univ. Library
for Library of Congress

PPT NcU PU OU OrU PBm CaBVaU
NL 0440464   MH IU NNC NjP NIC ViU CtY NN IEN IU TxU

PQ1501
.P3
1953
Lods, Jeanne, ed.
Perceforest.
Les pièces lyriques du roman de Perceforest; édition critique [commentée par] Jeanne Lods. Genève, Droz, 1953.

NL 0440466   MH NBuU OCU OrU FU GA

Lods, Jeanne.
Le roman de Perceforest; origines, composition, caractères, valeur et influence. Genève, Droz, 1951.
310 p. 26 cm. (Société de publications romanes et françaises. [Publications] 32)
"Bibliographie": p. [297]-302.

1. Perceforest. (Series: Publications romanes et françaises, 32)
           A 52-2555 rev
Harvard Univ. Library
for Library of Congress   [r64c1]

Lods, L. J. *Stérilité et perméabilité tubaire (comparaison des 2 méthodes d'exploration: insufflation et injection opaque) 54p. 8° Par., 1936.

NL 0440467   DNLM CtY

Łódskie Towarzystwo Naukowe.
Bulletin. v.11-   1960-
[Łódź]

Supersedes and continues the vol. numbering of the bulletins of the various classes of the society.
Text in French or English.

NL 0440468   MiU

Lodter (Jacob). *Phlebitis. 16 pp. 8°. *Wirceburgi, C. G. Becker, 1832.

NL 0440469   DNLM

Lodter, Wilhelm.
Ueber die "Einwirkung von Natrium auf aromatische Nitrile und aromatische Kohlenwasserstoffe und über den Aldehyd der α-Naphtoesäure" ... München, 1887.
Inaug. -Diss. - München.

NL 0440470   CtY

Lodtmann, Carl Gerhard Wilhelm
see Lodtmann, Karl Gerhard Wilhelm, 1720-1755.

[Lodtmann, Justus Friedrich August] ed.   Ger 6915.1.4
Codex constitutionum Osnabrugensium, oder Sammlung von verordnungen, gemeinen bescheiden, rescripten und andern erläuterenden verfügungen welche das hochstift Osnabrück betreffen. Osnabrück, J. W. Kissling. 1783-1819.
2 pt. in 3 vol. sm. 4°.

Osnabrück. [Title°]

NL 0440472   MH

Lodtmann, Justus Friedrich August, 1743-1808, ed.
Delineatio ivris pvblici osnabrvgensis
see under Lodtmann, Karl Gerhard Wilhelm, 1720-1755.

3901
OGL7
Lodtmann, Karl Gerhard Wilhelm, 1720-1755.
Delineatio ivris pvblici osnabrvgensis, e schedis Car. Gerardi Gvil. Lodtmann ... ed. Ivstvs Frider. Avg. Lodtmann. Osnabrvgi, 1767.
vi, [7-70 p. 20cm. With his Monumenta osnabrugensia ex. Holmstadii, 1753.

1. Law - Osnabrück.
I. Lodtmann, Justus Friedrich August, 1743-1808, ed.
1. L

NL 0440474   CU

170
B299p
Lodtmann, Karl Gerhard Wilhelm.
Kurzer Abriss der Geschichte der Weltweisheit nach der Ordnung der Zeiten zum Gebrauch academischer Vorlesungen entworfen. Helmstädt, C.F. Weygand, 1754.
172p. 2 fold. tables. 18cm. [With Basedow, J.B. Practische Philosophie für alle Stände v.1. Copenhagen, 1758]

1. Intellectual life. Hist. 2. Culture. Hist. I. Title.

NL 0440475   IEN

Lodtmann, Karl Gerhard Wilhelm, 1720-1755, ed.
Monvmenta osnabrvgensia ex historia romana francica saxonica ervta notis illustrata, avctore Carolo Gerardo Gvilielmo Lodtmann ... Helmstadii, Schnorr, 1753.
vii, [1], 159, [1] p. 19 cm.
Has bound with it has: Delineatio juris publici Osnabrugensis. 1767.
1. Osnabrück - Hist. I. Title.

NL 0440476   CU

Lo Duca, Giuseppe, 1905–
... L'affiche, par Lo Duca. 90 dessins d'après H. Daumier, Toulouse-Lautrec, Picasso ... etc. Paris, Presses universitaires de France, 1945.
127, [1] p. incl. front., illus. 17½ᵐ. ("Que sais-je?" Le point des connaissances actuelles. [153])

"1re édition."
"Bibliographie": p. [119]-120.

1. Advertising. 2. Posters. I. Title.

HF5823.L735   47-15363

NL 0440477   ICA NbU DLC MB MH

VOLUME 338

HF5843
.L7
Lo Duca, Giuseppe, 1905–
L'affiche.   Paris, Presses Universi-
taires de France, 1951.
127p. illus. 18cm. ("Que sais-je?")

NL   0440478   NNU-W

Lo Duca, Giuseppe, 1905–
... Art romain primitif.   Paris, Les Éditions du Chêne, 1944.
2 p. l., 7–16 p.   46 pl. on 23 l.   23½°.
At head of title: Lo Duca.

1. Art, Roman.   2. Art, Primitive.   3. Italy—Antiq.   I. Title.

N5740.L6   709.37   47-18335

NL   0440479   DLC PPT CtY MH OU NNC FU NcD

Lo Duca, Giuseppe, 1905–
Martini, Arturo, 1889–
... Arturo Martini; 27 tavole.   Milano, U. Hoepli, 1933.

TR140
.B3L55
Lo Duca, Giuseppe, 1905–
Bayard, Hippolyte, 1801–1887.
... Bayard.   Paris, Prisma, 1943.

TR140
.B3L6
Lo Duca, Giuseppe, 1905–
Bayard, Hippolyte, 1801–1887.
... Bayard, der erste lichtbildkünstler.   Paris, Prisma, 1943.

ND553
.B514A43
Hebr
Lo Duca, Giuseppe, 1905–
Benn, Bencjon, 1905–
בען פּין לא דוקא. פֿון פֿראנצייווייש: י. הירש, פֿאריז. פֿארלאַג
בראהאר. Paris; 1948.

Lo Duca, Giuseppe, 1905–
Dessin animé, histoire, esthetique, technique
(Animated design, history, esthetics, techniques.
Paris, Prisma, 1948.
169 p.   illus, some in color, bibliog.

NL   0440484   PPMoI

Lo Duca, Giuseppe, 1905–
Le dessin animé; histoire, esthétique, technique.   Introd.
de Walt Disney.   Paris, Prisma, 1948.
178 p.   illus. (part col.) ports.   22 cm.
"Bibliographie": p. 170–172.

1. Moving-picture cartoons.   I. Title.

NC1765.L7   741.58   49-17216*

NL   0440485   DLC WaU Mn IaU PP MH CLSU CtY

Lo Duca, Giuseppe, 1905–   , ed.
Dijsinti di Giorgio de Chirico
see under   Chirico, Giorgio de, 1888–

Lo Duca, Giuseppe, 1905–   joint author.

PN1998
.A3M4
Bessy, Maurice, 1910–
Georges Méliès, mage [par] Maurice Bessy et Lo Duca; et
"Mes mémoires" par Méliès.   Paris, Prisma, 1945.

Lo Duca, Giuseppe, 1905–
Giorgio de Chirico
see under   Chirico, Giorgio de, 1888–

ND553
.R67L6
folio
Lo Duca, Giuseppe, 1905–
Rousseau, Henri Julien Félix, 1844–1910.
Henri Rousseau, dit le douanier, par Lo Duca.   Paris,
Éditions du Chêne, 1951.

Lo Duca, Giuseppe, 1905–
... Histoire du cinéma, par Lo Duca; 85 illustrations de
Charlie Chaplin, Émile Cohl, Picasso, Walt Disney, Mimma
Indelli et Jan Mara.   Paris, Presses universitaires de France,
1942.
135, [1] p. incl. front., illus.   17½°.   (Que sais-je? Le point des connaissances actuelles. [81])
"1re édition."
"Bibliographie": p. [131]

1. Moving-pictures—Hist.

Library of Congress   PN1993.5.A1L6
                                            791.409
                                        44-23750

NL   0440490   DLC PJB WU

Lo Duca, Giuseppe, 1905–
... Histoire du cinéma, par Lo Duca. 85 illustrations de Ch.
Chaplin, Émile Cohl, Walt Disney, Picasso, Mimma Indelli,
Fernand Léger et Jan Mara.   Paris, Presses universitaires de
France, 1943.
135, [1] p. incl. front., illus.   17½°.   ("Que sais-je? Le point des
connaissances actuelles. [81])
"Treizième mille."
"1re édition, 15 juin 1942. 2e édition, 15 mai 1943."
"Bibliographie": p. [131]

1. Moving-pictures—Hist.

Library of Congress   PN1993.5.A1L6 1943
                                            791.409
                                        45-18571

NL   0440491   DLC CLSU

791.409
L822h
1947
LO DUCA, GIUSEPPE, 1905–
... Histoire du cinéma, par Lo Duca. 83
illustrations de Chaplin, Émile Cohl, Disney,
Picasso, Garretto, Mimma Indelli, Fernand Léger
et Jan Mara.   Paris, Presses universitaries
de France, 1947.
135,[1]p. incl. front.,illus. 18cm. ("Que
sais-je?" Le point des connaissances actuelles.
[81])
"Vingt-cinquième mille."
"3e édition (revue) ... 1947."
"Bibliographie": p.[132]
1. Moving-pictures - Hist.

NL   0440492   TxU MoU MH-FA IEN

Lo Duca, Giuseppe, 1905–
Histoire du cinéma. 83 illus. de Chaplin [et al.]   Nouv.
éd. Paris, Presses universitaires de France, 1951.
135 p. illus. 18 cm. ("Que sais-je?" Le point des connaissances
actuelles, 81)
Bibliography : p. [132]

1. Moving-pictures—Hist.
PN1993.5.A1L6 1951   *792.93 791.409   53-16504

NL   0440493   DLC

Lo Duca, Giuseppe, 1905–
Journal secret de Napoléon Bonaparte, 1769–1869. Paris,
Éditions de L'Archipel [1949]
290 p. port. 20 cm.

1. Napoléon I, Emperor of the French, 1769–1821—Fiction.
I. Title.

                                        A 49-6543*

New York. Public Libr.
for Library of Congress

NL   0440494   NN FTaSU CtY

TR149
.B4
Lo Duca, Giuseppe, 1905–   joint author.
Bessy, Maurice, 1910–
Louis Lumière, inventeur [par] Maurice Bessy et Lo Duca.
Paris, Éditions Prisma, 1948.

HQ9
.M6
Rare Bk
Coll
Lo Duca, Giuseppe, 1905–   ed.
Das Moderne Lexikon der Erotik von A bis Z. Eine reich
illustrierte aktuelle Enzyklopädie in 10 Bden. (Hrsg. unter
Leitung von Lo Duca. Bearb. von Maria Schulte.)
(München) Desch

PN1993
.5
.A1C5
1947
Lo Duca, Giuseppe, 1905–   ed.
Charensol, Georges, 1899–
Panorama du cinéma. Éd. augm., illus. et remisé à jour
par Lo Duca et Maurice Bessy. Paris, J. Melot [1947]

It
L824s
Lo Duca, Giuseppe, 1905–
La sfera di platino; romanzo [di] Lo Duca.
Pref. di F.T. Marinetti. Tavole fuori testo
del pittore Raffaele Collins. Albenga,
Casa editrice "Il ramarro" [193-]
363p. plates. 20cm.

I. Marinetti, Filippo Tommaso, 1876–1944.
II. Title.

NL   0440498   IEN

792.94
L824h3
Lo Duca, Giuseppe, 1905–
Storia del cinema. [Traduzione dal
francese di Augusto Forti. Milano]
Garzanti [1951]
111p. 19cm. (On cover: Saper tutto,
15)

Originally published in June, 1942,
as Histoire du cinéma.

1.Moving pictures - Hist.   LC StL

NL   0440499   CLSU

VOLUME 338

Lo Duca, Giuseppe, 1905–
... Technique du cinéma, par Lo Duca; 63 illustrations, 14 tableaux. Paris, Presses universitaires de France, 1943.
127, ₁1₎ p. incl. front., illus. 17½ᵐ. (Que sais-je? Le point des connaissances actuelles. ₍118₎)
"1ʳᵉ édition."

1. Cinematography. 2. Moving-pictures.
44–34106
Library of Congress   TR850.L63
778.5

NL   0440500   DLC WU CLSU CoDU AAP MH CtY NNC

Lo Duca, Giuseppe, 1905–
Technique du cinéma. ₃3. éd. rev.₎ Paris, Presses universitaires de France, 1953 ₍*1943₎
127 p. illus. 18 cm. ("Que sais-je?" Le point des connaissances actuelles, 118)

1. Cinematography. 2. Moving-pictures.
TR850.L63   1953   54–34498 ‡

NL   0440501   DLC IEN

Lo Duca, Joseph
see Lo Duca, Giuseppe, 1905–

BX   Lo Duca, Víto.
2535   Vita e opere dell'arc. don Costantino Stella,
.S82   parroco di Resuttano; discorso commemorativo
L7   tenuto in Resuttano il 23 maggio 1920.
Resuttano, Cassa rurale artigiana "Don Stella"
₍1957₎
34 p. port. 21 cm.

1. Stella, Costantino, 1873–1919.

NL   0440503   DCU

Loduchowski, Hans Willi.
Die Tötungsdelikte (Mord, Totschlag und Kindestötung) im Landgerichtsbezirk Koblenz in den Jahren 1910 bis 1939. Jena, Frommann, 1941.
107 p. 25 cm. (Untersuchungen zur Kriminalität in Deutschland, Heft 11)
Issued also as thesis, Bonn.
Bibliography: p. 7–11.

1. Murder—Koblenz. 2. Homicide—Koblenz. 3. Crime and criminals—Koblenz.   I. Title.
HV6535.G33K65   1941   A 53–1148

Columbia Univ.   Libraries
for Library of Congress   †

NL   0440504   NNC IU NN NcD MH CoDU CtY MH-L MiD DLC

Lodwick, Charles   jt. au.
Tr. R. Bayard, Nicholas, 1644?–1707.
Journal of the late actions of the French at Canada, by Col. Nicholas Beyard, and Lieut. Col. Charles Lodowick. New York, Reprinted for J. Sabin, 1868.

Lodwick, Charles.
A narrative of an attempt made by the French of Canada upon the Mohaqués country ...
see under   Bayard, Nicholas, 1644?–1707.

Lodwick, Charles.
... New York in 1692. Letter from Charles Lodwick, to Mr. Francis Lodwick and Mr. Hooker, dated May 20, 1692. Read before the Royal society of London. ⟨Copied from the original in the British museum, for John Carter Brown, esq. of Providence, and by him communicated for publication.⟩
(*In* New York historical society. Collections. New York, 1848. 22½ᵐ. 2d ser., v. 2, pt. 1, p. ₍241₎–250)

1. New York (City)—Descr. 2. New York (State)—Descr. & trav.
11–22438 Revised
Library of Congress   F116.N62 2d ser., vol. 2, pt. 1

NL   0440507   DLC MdBP MiU-C NN

DA745   Lodwick, Edith, joint author.
.C28L6
1954   Lodwick, Malcolm.
The story of Carmarthen, by Malcolm and Edith Lodwick. Carmarthen ₍1954₎

Lodwick, Francis
see   Lodowyck, Francis, fl. 1647–1686.

Lodwick, Jasper Malcolm
see
Lodwick, Malcolm.

Lodwick, John, 1916–
Aegean adventure, by John Lodwick. New York, Dodd, Mead & company, 1946.
ix, 214 p. 21ᵐ.

1. World war, 1939–1945—Fiction.   I. Title.
46–2918
Library of Congress   PZ3.L8236Ae

NL   0440511   DLC MB NIC PP

Lodwick, John, 1916–
Brother Death, a novel. New York, Duell, Sloan and Pearce ₍1951₎
268 p. 21 cm.

I. Title.
PZ3.L8236Br   51–9532

NL   0440512   DLC ViU WaE OrP CaBVa

Lodwick, John, 1916–
The butterfly net, a novel. London, Heinemann ₍1954₎
325 p. 19 cm.

I. Title.
PZ3.L8236Bu   54–36032 ‡

NL   0440513   DLC CtY TxU

Lodwick, John, 1916–
The cradle of Neptune; a novel, by John Lodwick. Melbourne ₍etc.₎ W. Heinemann ₍1951₎   285 p.   19cm.

1. Great Britain. Royal naval   college, Dartmouth—Fiction. I. Title.
February 14, 1952

NL   0440514   NN WU RPB ViU NRU MH

Lodwick, John, 1916–
The cradle of Neptune, a novel. New York, Roy Publishers ₍1955₎
285 p. 19 cm.

1. Dartmouth, Eng. Royal Naval College—Fiction.   I. Title.
PZ3.L8236Cr   55–5921 ‡

NL   0440515   DLC

Lodwick, John, 1916–
The Filibusters, the story of the Special Boat Service. London, Methuen ₍1947₎
v, 188 p. illus., maps. 22 cm.

1. Gt. Brit. Special Boat Service. 2. World War, 1939–1945—Personal narratives, English.   I. Title.
D760.S6L6   940.541242   47–6204

NL   0440516   DLC CaBViP CaBVa

Lodwick, John, 1916–
First steps inside the zoo; a novel... London ₍etc.₎ W. Heinemann ₍1950₎   271 p.   19cm.

543459B.   I. Title.
October 1, 1951

NL   0440517   NN PU

Lodwick, John, 1916–
L'île de Paternoster (Just a song at twilight) roman; traduit de l'anglais par G. Belmont. ₍Paris₎ Gallimard ₍1952₎
342 p. 19 cm. (La Méridienne)

I. Title.
PR6023.O324J9   52–32471 ‡

NL   0440518   DLC

Lodwick, John, 1916–
Just a song at twilight; a novel, by John Lodwick. Melbourne ₍etc.₎ W. Heineman ₍1949₎   299 p.   map.   19cm.

546844B.   I. Title.
April 6, 1951

NL   0440519   NN PU

Lodwick, John, 1916–
Love bade me welcome, a novel. London, W. Heinemann ₍1952₎
318 p. 19 cm.

I. Title.
PZ3.L8236Lo   52–25168 ‡

NL   0440520   DLC WU CaBVa TxU

VOLUME 338

Lodwick, John, 1916–
   Love bade me welcome, a novel.   New York, Roy Publishers [1953]
      318 p.   19 cm.

   ɪ. Title.

   [PZ3]   53–9778
   Printed for U. S. Q. B. R.
   by Library of Congress

NL   0440521   OrP WaT OOxM

Lodwick, John, 1916–
   The man Dormant, a novel.   New York, Duell, Sloan and Pearce [1950]
      253 p.   20 cm.
      London ed. (Heinemann) has title: First steps inside the zoo.

   ɪ. Title.

   PZ3.L8236Man   50–8034

NL   0440522   DLC NN WaE Or OC1

PZ   **Lodwick, John,** 1916–
3   Myrmyda; a novel of the Aegean.   London,
L8236   Methuen [1946]
My   164p.   19cm.

NL   0440523   WU

Lodwick, John, 1916–
   Peal of ordnance.   London, Methuen [1947]
      185 p.   19 cm.

   ɪ. Title.

   PZ3.L8236Pe   48–12840*

NL   0440524   DLC WU

Lodwick, John, 1916–
   ... Running to paradise, by John Lodwick.   New York, Dodd, Mead & company, 1943.
      x p., 2 l., 381 p.   illus. (plan)   22ᵐ.
      At head of title: Winner of the $1000 war novel prize.

   1. World war, 1939–   —Fiction.   ɪ. Title.
                                                    43–5438
   Library of Congress   PZ3.L8236Ru

      OO OC1h CaBVa PSt PP
NL   0440525   DLC PU LU NIC OO Wa WaS IdU OC1 OLak

Lodwick, John, 1916–
   Something in the heart, a novel, by John Lodwick.   Melbourne [etc.] W. Heinemann [1948]   266 p.   19cm.

   499100B.   ɪ. Title.
                                            October 3, 1949

NL   0440526   NN OrU

Lodwick, John, 1916–
   Somewhere a voice is calling, a novel.   London, Heinemann [1953]
      445 p.   21 cm.

   ɪ. Title.

   PZ3.L8236So   53–32911 ‡

NL   0440527   DLC CaBVa CtY MH

Lodwick, John, 1916–
   Somewhere a voice is calling; a novel.   New York, Roy Publishers [1953]
      445 p.   21 cm.

   ɪ. Title.

   [PZ3]   53–9777 ‡
   Printed for U. S. Q. B. R.
   by Library of Congress

NL   0440528   IaU OrP PP NN OCU PPL

Lodwick, John, 1916–
   Stamp me mortal, a novel.   London, Heinemann [1950]
      254 p.   19 cm.

   ɪ. Title.

   PZ3.L8236St   50–34024

NL   0440529   DLC WU PU CtY

Lodwick, John, 1916–
   The starless night.   London, Heinemann [1955]
      399 p.   21 cm.

   ɪ. Title.

   PZ3.L8236Su   55–37180 ‡

NL   0440530   DLC CU MH NN PU IaU

Lodwick, John, 1916–
   Twenty east of Greenwich; or, a Barnum among the Robespierres, a novel.   London, W. Heinemann [1947]
      xiv, 188 p.   20 cm.

   1. World War, 1939–1945—Fiction.   ɪ. Title.

   PZ3.L8236Tw   48–23831*

NL   0440531   DLC WU

Lodwick, John B.
   Caniadau moliant.   Detholiad o donau ac emynau hen a newydd, gan John B. Lodwick ...   Youngstown, O., J. B. Lodwick, ᶜ1898.
      128 p.   22½ᵐ.
      With music.

   1. Hymns, Welsh.   2. Sunday-schools—Hymn-books.   ɪ. Title.
   Library of Congress   M2132.W3LS   0–1035 Revised

NL   0440532   DLC

Lodwick, K. B.
QE340   **Australia.** *Bureau of Mineral Resources. Geology and Geophysics.*
.A392   Magnetic results from Heard Island. 1952–54. [Canberra?]

Lodwick, Malcolm.
   The story of Carmarthen, by Malcolm and Edith Lodwick.   Carmarthen [1954]
      164 p.   illus.   26 cm.

   1. Carmarthen, Wales.   ɪ. Lodwick, Edith, joint author.
                    Full name: Jasper Malcolm Lodwick.

   DA745.C28L6 1954   942.98   55–25275 ‡

NL   0440534   DLC NN

Lodwick, William G
   Brazilian agriculture

      see under

   Joint Brazil – United States Economic
   Development Commission.

Lodwidge, J   G
   L'Australie, 1879–1880; rapport par J. G.
Lodwidge, délégué du Syndicat industriel du
Bassin de Charleroi.   Charleroi, L. Delacre, 1880.
   61 p.   23 cm.   (in binder, 25 cm.)
   1. Australia – Comm.   2. Australia – Indus.
   ɪ. Title.

NL   0440536   WU

Lodwigowski, E   S
   Bukiet melodyi polskich; zebrał i ułozył na
fortepjan.   Warszaw, Gebethner i Wolff, n. d.
   [17 p.]

NL   0440537   OC1

         Lodwyck, Charles

            see

   Lodwick, Charles.

Lodygensky, George.
   Soviet Russia; a brief survey of the
application of its economic and political
philosophy to international relations, by
Doctor George Lodygensky... Comment by Matthew Woll... Washington, D.C., American
coalition of patriotic, civic and fraternal
societies (1923)
   15, (1) p. illus. 23 cm.

NL   0440539   DL

Lodygensky, George.
DK265   La terreur rouge.   Genève [Société générale
L824   d'imprimerie] 1922.
            16 p.   24½ᵐ.
            Cover title.

            1. Russia – Hist. – Revolution – 1917-1921.
            ɪ. Title.

NL   0440540   CSt-H NN NcD

VOLUME 338

Lodygensky, Nicholas N   de

see

Lodyzhenskiĭ, Nikolaĭ Nikolaevich.

Lodygin, Dmitriĭ Mikhaĭlovich
see Ladygin, Dmitriĭ Mikhaĭlovich, *b.* 1721?

Łodygo, J.
Przyroda; opracowali J. Łodygo i F. Nadwórniak. ₍Geneva, World's Alliance of the Young Men's Christian Association, ᵉ1943₎
2 v. in 1. illus.

"Authorized by the United Nations Relief and Rehabilitation Administration."
Contents.–v. 1. Zoologia.–v. 2. Botanika.

NL 0440543   MiD

Łodyński, Marjan, 1884–
Bibljoteka Szkoły rycerskiej, 1767–1794; napisał dr. Marjan Łodyński ... Warszawa, Wojskowy instytut naukowo-wydaw-niczy, 1930.

3 p. l., ₍3₎–85 p., 1 l. 21ᶜᵐ. (*Added t.-p.:* Z dziejów polskich bibljotek wojskowych XVIII i XIX wieku)
Wydawnictwa Centralnej bibljoteki wojsk., nr. 20.
Bibliographical foot-notes.
1. Warsaw. Szkoła rycerska. Bibljoteka. I. Wojskowy instytut naukowo-wydawniczy, Warsaw.
₍*Full name:* Marjan Tadeusz Witold Łodyński₎
44–17007
Library of Congress   Z818.W27L6

NL 0440544   DLC CU NNC IU

Łodyński, Marian.
Les bibliothèques militaires modernes ...
Varsovie, Société des sciences militaires, 1926.
492 p. 24 cm.

NL 0440545   DNW

Łodyński, Marjan, 1884–
... Centralna bibljoteka państwowa i Bibliotheca patria. Kraków, Drukarnia W. L. Anczyca i spółki, 1928.
17 p. 23½ᵐ.
"Osobne odbicie z Przeglądu bibljotecznego, rocznik II, 1928, zeszyt 1."
On a project for a national library in Poland.
1. Libraries—Poland. I. Title.
cA 30–21 Unrev'd
Library of Congress   Z817.L82

NL 0440546   DLC

Łodyński, Marjan   1884–
Nowoczesne bibljotekarstwo wojskowe, napisał Marjan Łodyński. Kraków, 1927. 41 p. incl. tables. 26cm. (Związek bibljotekarzy polskich. Krakowskie koło. Prace bibljoteczne. ₍Tom₎ 3.)

1. Libraries, Army. I. Ser.
November 6, 1935

NL 0440547   NN

Łodyński, Marian   1884–
...Oddział bibljograficzny Centralnej bibljoteki wojskowej. Kraków: Druk W. L. Anczyca i spółki, 1928. 6 p. 23½cm.

At head of title: Marjan Łodyński.
"Osobne odbicie z Przeglądu bibljotecznego, rocznik ii, 1928, zeszyt 3."

1. Libraries, Army–Poland.   2. Army, Polish—Bibl. 3. Military art and science—Bibl.
January 29, 1941

NL 0440548   NN

Łodyński, Marjan, 1884–
Podręcznik bibljotekarski dla kierowników bibljotek wojsko-wych, opracował ppłk. dr. Marjan Łodyński ... przy współu-dziale kust. dr. Jana Niezgody ... oraz bibljotekarza Wiktora Kochanowskiego. Warszawa, Wojskowy instytut naukowo-wydawniczy, 1929.
x, 321, xx, ₍2₎ p. illus. 2 fold. plans, fold. forms. 20½ᵐ. (*Added t.-p.:* Wydawnictwa Centralnej bibljoteki wojsk. nr. 19)
Plans and forms in pocket.
1. Military libraries. 2. Library administration. 3. Libraries—Poland. I. Niezgoda, Jan, 1888– joint author. II. Kochanowski, Wiktor, joint author. III. Title.
₍*Full name:* Marjan Tadeusz Witold Łodyński₎
38–21773
Library of Congress   Z675.M5L8
027.652

NL 0440549   DLC IU CSt-H

Łodyński, Marjan, 1884–
Polskie bibljotekarstwo wojskowe jako odrębna gałąź ogólnego bibljotekarstwa. Warszawa, Druk. Ministerstwa Spraw Wojskowych, 1926.
15 p. 30 cm. (Wydawnictwa Centralnej Bibljoteki Wojskowej, nr. 11)
"Całość wykonano w 500 numerowanych egzemplarzach ... Nr. 231."
1. Military libraries. 2. Libraries—Poland. I. Title. (Series: Warsaw. Centralna Bibljoteka Wojskowa. Wydawnictwa, nr. 11)
Full name: Marjan Tadeusz Witold Łodyński.
Z675.M5L83   53–48390

NL 0440550   DLC

Łodyński, Marjan, 1884–
U kolebki polskiej polityki bibljotecznej, 1774–1794. Warszawa, Nakł. Tow. Naukowego Warszawskiego, 1935.
81 p. 23 cm. (Prace Towarzystwa Naukowego Warszawskiego. Wydział ii. Nauk Historycznych, Społecznych i Filozoficznych, nr. 23)
1. Library legislation–Poland. I. Title. (Series: Towarzystwo Naukowe Warszawskie. Wydział ii. Nauk Historycznych, Społecznych i Filozoficznych. Prace, nr. 23)
Full name: Marjan Tadeusz Witold Łodyński.
AS262.W34 nr. 23   52–49149

NL 0440551   DLC NjP

Łodyński, Marjan, 1884–
U kolebki polskiej polityki bibljotecznej, 1774–1794. Warszawa, Nakł. Tow. Naukowego Warszawskiego, 1935.
81 p. 24 cm. (Prace Towarzystwa Naukowego Warszawskiego. Wydział ii. Nauk Historycznych, Społecznych i Filozoficznych, nr. 23)
Bibliographical references included in "Przypisy" (p. ₍41₎–81)
1. Poland. Komisja Edukacji Narodowej. 2. Library legislation—Poland. I. Title. (Series: Towarzystwo Naukowe Warszaw-skie. Wydział ii. Nauk Historycznych, Społecznych i Filozoficznych. Prace, nr. 23)
Full name: Marjan Tadeusz Witold Łodyński.
AS262.W34 no. 23   52–53013
Z677.4.P6L6

NL 0440552   DLC MH ICN NNC NN

Łodyński, Marjan
Uzależnienie Polski od papiestwa a kanoni-zacja św. Stanisława. Warszawa, 1918.
46 p. 25cm. Towarzystwo naukowe Warszaw-skie. Wydział II, nauk historycznych, społecz-nych i filozoficznych. Prace, 16)

Wydane z zapomogi Kasy pomocy dla osób pracu-jących na polu naukowem imienia Dr. Med. Józefa Mianowskiego.

NL 0440553   NNC MH

Łodyński, Marjan,   1884–
...Z dziejów "Bibljoteki Rzeczypospolitej Załuskich zwanej" w latach 1783–1794. Warszawa: Nakładem Bibljoteki naro-dowej, 1935. 122 p. facsim., plans, plates, port. 23½cm.
"Pamięci ks. Onufrego Kopczyńskiego."
889812A. 1. Kopczyński, Onufry,   1735–1817. 2. Libraries—Poland—Warsaw.
June 30, 1937

NL 0440554   NN

Łodyński, Marjan Witold
see Łodyński, Marjan, 1884–

Lodyzhenski, Georgiĭ
see Lodygensky, George.

Lodyzhenskiĭ, Andreĭ Nikolaevich, 1851–

Bluntschli, Johann Kaspar, 1808–1881.
Современное международное право цивилизованныхъ государствъ, изложенное въ видѣ кодекса I. Блюнтчли. Переводъ со втораго нѣмецкаго изданія В. Ульяницкаго и А. Лодыженскаго подъ редакцiею Гр. Л. Камаровскаго. Мо-сква, Тип. Индрихъ, 1876.

Lodyzhenskiĭ, Ivan Nikolaevich, 1848–
Родословная Молоствовыхъ. С.-Петербургъ, 1900.
39 p. plate. 26 cm.

1. Molostvov family.   *Title transliterated:* Rodoslovnaiā Molostvovykh.
CS859.M6 1900   51–49707

NL 0440558   DLC

Lodyzhenskiĭ, Ivan Nikolaevich, ed.

Russia. *Ministerstvo finansov.*
... Russia, its industries and trade. Issued by order of state secretary S. J. de Witte ... minister of finance. Glasgow, Hay, Nisbet & co., limited, 1901.

VOLUME 338

Lodyzhenskiĭ, Konstantin Nikolaevich, 1858–
Исторія русскаго таможеннаго тарифа. Изслѣдованіе Константина Лодыженскаго. С.-Петербургъ, Тип. В. С. Балашева, 1886.
xvi, 312, 82 p. 22½ᶜᵐ.
Photocopy. Ann Arbor, Mich., University Microfilms, 1967. (on double leaves)

1. Tariff—Russia. 2. Russia—Comm. I. Title.
Title romanized: Istoriia russkago tamozhennago tarifa.   20-15982
Library of Congress   HF2153.L7

NL 0440560   MiU DLC

Lodyzhenskiĭ, Nikolaĭ Nikolaevich.

Irvine, Ingram N   W   1850–1921.
A letter on the Anglican church's claims, by the Rev. Ingram N. W. Irvine ... with a preface by the Rev. Fr. Daniel I. Odell ... and appendices by the Rt. Rev. Geo. F. Seymour ... the Rev. Randall C. Hall ... the Rev. Wm. J. Seabury ... and the Hon. Nicholas N. de Lodygensky ... New York, St. Nicholas' cathedral, English department ₁1906₎

Łódź, *Poland.*
... Annuaire statistique de la ville de Łódz.   Année
Lodz, 19
v. tables. 18¼ᶜᵐ.

1. Łódz, Poland—Stat.   I. Title.
31-29740
Library of Congress   HA1458.L6A3   314.38

NL 0440562   DLC

Łódz ₁Poland₎.
...Budżet zarządu m. Łodzi na rok

Łódź,   4°.
Title varies slightly.
–1916/17 also have German title: Haushaltsplan der Stadt Lodz, and additional text in German.

1. Municipal finance—Poland—Lodz.   March 31, 1925

NL 0440563   NN

Łódz (Poland).
Dziennik zarządu m. Łodzi. Rok

Łódź,   4°.

1. Municipal government, Poland: Lodz.
October 23, 1924

NL 0440564   NN

Łódz, Poland.
Obrachunek zarządu m. Łodzi. 19

₁Lodz, 19   42 – 44½cm.
Annual.
Text reproduced from typewritten copy; ms. cover-title.

1. Municipal finance—Poland—Lodz.
December 8, 1933

NL 0440565   NN

Łódź (Poland).
...Zamierzenia skarbowe na rok

₁Łódz,   obl. 8°–4°.
Title varies slightly.

1. Municipal finance—Poland—Lodz.   March 31, 1925

NL 0440566   NN

Łódz, Poland. *Archives des documents anciens*
see
Łódz, Poland. *Archiwum Akt Dawnych.*

DK651
.L6R6
Łódz, Poland. Archiwum Akt Dawnych.
Rocznik łódzki, poświęcony historji Łodzi i okolicy. t. 1–3; 1928–33. ₁W Łodzi, Nakł. miasta Łodzi.

Łódz, Poland. Arkheologicheskiĭ muzeĭ
see
Łódz, Poland. Muzeum Archeologiczne.

Łódz, Poland. Austellung "Der Osten des Warthelandes."
see **Łódz, Poland.** Heimatschau "Der Osten des Warthelandes," 1941.

Łódz, Poland. Biblioteka Uniwersytecka
see **Łódz, Poland.** Uniwersytet. *Biblioteka.*

Lodz, Poland. Heimatschau "Der Osten des Warthelandes," 1941.
Der Osten des Warthelandes, hrsg. anlässlich der Heimatschau in Litzmannstadt. ₁Litzmannstadt, Ausstellungsleitung "Der Osten des Warthelandes, 1941₎ 319 p. illus. 21cm.

Hrsg: Hubert Müller

539157B. 1. Warthe river and valley.   I. Title.
October 10, 1951

NL 0440572   NN MH DLC-P4 IU NcD CtY CU NNC MiU

Łódz, Poland. Institut scientifique du livre
see **Łódz, Poland.** Państwowy Instytut Książki.

Łódz,
^Instytut Celulozowo-Papierniczy.
Biuletyn. v. 1– ; 1951–
Lodz, Wydawn. Czasopism Technicznych NOT ₁etc.₎
v. illus.
Frequency varies.
Ceased 1965.
Bound with Przegląd papierniczy, v. 7–19, 21.

NL 0440574   ICRL

Łódz. Instytut Celulozowo-Papierniczy.
Prace.
Warszawa.
v. illus. irregular.
Began 1952.
Organ of the Ministerstwo Leśnictwa i Przemysłu Drzewnego.
Summaries in English, German, and Russian.

NL 0440575   ICRL

Łódz, Poland. Instytut Techniki Cieplnej.
Prace. r. 1– (zesz. 1–); 1953–
Łódz ₁etc., Państwowe Wydawn. Naukowe, etc.₎
v. in illus. 24–30 cm. irregular.
Summaries in English and Russian.

1. Heat engineering—Periodicals.
TJ260.L62   73-615441

NL 0440576   DLC

TS1300
.L563
Łódz, Poland. Instytut Włókiennictwa.
Zeszyty informacyjne.
Łódz, 19
₁ v. illus. 29 cm.

1. Textile industry and fabrics—Collected works.
TS1300.L563   64-35527

NL 0440577   DLC

Łódz, Poland. Izba Przemysłowo-Handlowa.
Sprawozdanie o sytuacji gospodarczej okręgu.
₁Łódz₎
v. in 24 cm.
Issues for   are part 3 of the chamber's
Sprawozdanie.

1. Łódz, Poland—Econ. condit.
HC338.L6L64   52-37925

NL 0440578   DLC

Łódz, Poland. Kirchengesang-Verein der St. Trinitatis-Gemeinde
see
Kirchengesang-Verein der St. Trinitatis-Gemeinde zu Lodz.

Łódz, Poland. Lodzinskoe nauchnoe obshchestvo
see
Łódzkie Towarzystwo Naukowe.

DK651
.L6K7
Lodz, Poland. Magistrat.
Księga pamiątkowa dziesięciolecia samorządu miasta Łodzi 1919–1929. ₁Komitet redakcyjny: przewodniczący Jan Holcgreber et al. Łódz, Nakładem Magistratu Łódzkiego, 1930.

VOLUME 338

Łódź, Poland. Magistrat.

Księga pamiątkowa Miejskiej bibljoteki publicznej w Łodzi, 1917–1927. ⟨Łódź, Nakładem Magistratu m. Łodzi, 1929⟩

Łódź, Poland. Magistrat.

Rzewski, Aleksy, *ed.*
Przewodnik dla urzędów stanu cywilnego, uzupełniony tekstami obowiązujących na wszystkich ziemiach polskich ustaw, rozporządzeń i okólników oraz wzorami aktów i formularzy. Opracowali Aleksy Rzewski ... Izydor Szwarcman ... Wyd. 2. zmienione i rozszerzone. Łódź, Nakł. Urzędu stanu cywilnego przy Magistracie m. Łodzi, 1923.

HJ9055
.7
.L6B2

Łódź, Poland. Magistrat.
... Zamierzenia skarbowe zarządu m. Łodzi na rok ... 1928/29. Łódź, 1928–
1 v. 39.5 cm.
At head of title, 1928/29: Magistrat m. Łodzi.
(Text of the 1928/29 report mimeographed)

NL 0440584 DLC

Łódź, Poland. Miejska Bibljoteka Publiczna
see
Łódź, Poland. Miejska Biblioteka Publiczna.

Łódź, Poland. Miejska biblioteka publiczna.
Księga pamiątkowa Miejskiej bibljoteki publicznej w Łodzi, 1917–1927
see under title

61.5
L82

Łódź, Miejski Ogrod Botaniczny.
Catalogus seminum quae Hortus Botanicus Lodziensis pro mutua commutatione offert.
Lodz,

1. Seeds. Exchange lists.

NL 0440587 DNAL

Łódź, Poland. Miejskie Muzeum Historii i Sztuki imienia J. K. Bartoszewiczów
see
Łódź, Poland. Muzeum Sztuki.

Łódź, Poland. Miejskie Muzeum Prehistoryczne
see
Łódź, Poland. Muzeum Archeologiczne.

Łódź, Poland. Miejskie Muzeum Sztuki
see
Łódź, Poland. Muzeum Sztuki.

Łódź, Poland. Musée archéologique
see
Łódź, Poland. Muzeum Archeologiczne.

Łódź, Poland. Muzeum Archeologiczne.
Od motyki do traktora; przewodnik po wystawie objazdowej. Łódź, 1954.
28 p. 21 cm. (Biblioteka Muzeum Archeologicznego w Łodzi, nr. 3)

1. Agriculture—Hist. i. Title.

S419.L748   61–32576 ‡

Library of Congress

NL 0440592 DLC

Łódź, Poland. Muzeum Archeologiczne.
Przewodnik. ⟨Autor: Konrad Jażdżewski⟩ Łódź, Wydawn. Ministerstwa Kultury i Sztuki, 1951.
135 p. illus. 21 cm. (Biblioteka Muzeum Archeologicznego w Łodzi ⟨nr. 1⟩)

i. Jażdżewski, Konrad.

GN800.L58   58–25940 ‡

NL 0440593 DLC MiU PU

302.9438
L82

Łódź, Poland. Muzeum archeologiczne.
Biblioteka.
⟨Wydawnictwa⟩
no.
Łódź,
v. 29ᶜᵐ.

Added t. p. in Russian and French.
Summary in Russian and French.

NL 0440594 NNC

Łódź, Poland. Muzeum Archeologiczne. *Dział Numismatyczny.*
Przewodnik. Łódź, Wydawn. Muzeum Archeologicznego, 1954–
v. illus. 21 cm. (Biblioteka Muzeum Archeologicznego w Łodzi, nr. 4)
At head of title: Anatol Gupieniec.
Includes bibliography.

1. Numismatics—Poland. i. Gupieniec, Anatol.

CJ3032.L6   60–42375 ‡

NL 0440595 DLC PU-Mu MH-P CtY

ŁÓDŹ, Poland. Muzeum etnograficzne.
Katalog garncarstwa ludowego woj. rzeszowskiego, opracowany według zbiorów i materiałów archiwalnych Muzeum etnograficznego w Łodzi. Praca zbiorowa pod kierunkiem Janiny Krajewskiej. ⟨Łódź⟩ Wydawn. Muzeum etnograficznego w Łodzi, 1952. 81 p. illus. plates (128 figs.) 25cm.

Summaries in Russian, French, and English.

1. Pottery, Polish--Collections--Poland--Lodz. i. Krajewska, Janina, ed. ii. Krajewska, Janina.

NL 0440597 NN MH

Lodz(Poland). Muzeum Sztuki.
Międzynarodowa kolekcja sztuki nowoczesnej (Collection Internationale d'art nouveau). Katalog No.2. Lodzi, 1932.
pamph. illus.

NL 0440598 PPPM

Łódź, Poland. Ogólnopolski zjazd przeciwrakowy. 3d, 1932
see Ogólnopolski zjazd przeciwrakowy. 3d, Łódź, Poland, 1932.

Łódź. Der osten des Warthelandes. Ausstellungsleitung.
Der osten des Warthelandes
see under Łódź, Poland. Heimatschau "Der Osten des Warthelandes", 1941.

Lodz, Poland. Państwowy Instytut Biologii Doświadczalnej imienia M. Nenckiego
see Państwowy Instytut Biologii Doświadczalnej imienia M. Nenckiego.

Z2521
.B54

Łódź, Poland. Państwowy Instytut Książki.

Bibliografia bibliografii i nauki o książce. Bibliographia Poloniae bibliographica. 1947–
Warszawa.

Łódź, Poland. Państwowy Instytut Książki.
Biuletyn. t. 1–
Łódź, 1947–
v. in forms. 21 cm.
L. C. copy imperfectly bound: v. 2, t. p. bound at end.

1. Bibliography—Societies, etc.

Z1008.L62   62–43237

NL 0440603 DLC InU CtY

Łódź, Poland. Państwowy Instytut Książki.

Z1007
W34

Warsaw. Biblioteka Narodowa. *Instytut Bibliograficzny.*
Biuletyn. ⟨t.⟩ 1– 1947–
Warszawa ⟨etc.⟩

Łódź, Poland. Państwowy Instytut Książki.
Sprawozdanie. wrzes. 1946–
Łódź.
v. 30 cm.

1. Bibliography—Societies.

Z1008.L63   52–16571

NL 0440605 DLC

VOLUME 338

Łódź, Poland. Państwowy instytut książki.
　　Sprawozdanie Państwowego instytutu książki
za okres od września 1946 do września, 1949.
Łódź, Wrzesień 1949.
　　44 p.

　　"Bibliografia PIK": p. 43-44.

　　1. Łódź, Poland. Państwowy instytut
książki.

NL　0440606　　NNC

Łódź, Poland. Państwowy Instytut Książki
see also Warsaw. Biblioteka Narodowa. *Instytut Bibliograficzny.*

Łódź, Poland. Państwowy teatr wojska polskiego.
　Łódź teatralna.　Rok
　　see under title

**Łódź, Poland. Pierwsze Gimnazjum Męskie Towarzystwa
Żydowskich Szkół Średnich**
see
Towarzystwo Żydowskich Szkół Średnich w Łodzi.
Pierwsze Gimnazjum Męskie.

Łódź, Poland. Polish Book Research Institute
see **Łódź, Poland. Państwowy Instytut Książki.**

Łódź, Poland. Politechnika.
　　Bibliografia dorobku piśmienniczego pracowników Politechniki Łódzkiej. .1945/46–1958/59—
Łódź.
　　　v. 27-29 cm. annual (irregular)
　　　Vols. for 1959/60— issued as Prace Biblioteki Głównej Politechniki Łódzkiej (AS262.L55A25)
　　　Compiler: 1945/46–1958/59— J. Przygocka (with M. Grochulska and J. Śniadecka, 1959/00–1960/61, B. Czajkowska and M. Kleińska-Jurek, 1964–
　　1. Engineering—Bibliography.　ɪ. Przygocka, Jadwiga, comp.
ɪɪ. Title.　　　(Series: Łódź, Poland. Politechnika. Biblioteka
Główna. Prace

　　　AS262.L55A23　　　　　　62-58445

NL　0440611　　DLC

Łódź, Poland. Politechnika.
　　Chemia. zesz. 1–
Łódź ₁Państwowe Wydawn. Naukowe₎ 1954–
　　　no. in　v. illus., diagrs, tables. 24 cm. (*Its Zeszyty
naukowe*)
　　Summaries in Russian, English, French, or German.

　　1. Chemistry—Collected works.　　(Series: Łódź, Poland. Politechnika. Zeszyty naukowe)

　　　QD1.L85　　　　　　63-42545

NL　0440612　　DLC

Łódź, Poland. Politechnika.
Chemia spożywcza. zesz. 1–
Łódź, Państwowe Wydawn. Naukowe, 195ᵅ–

Łódź, Poland. Politechnika.
　　Elektryka. 1–
Łódź ₁Państwowe Wydawn. Naukowe; Oddział w Łodzi₎
1955–
　　　no. in　v. diagrs., tables. 24 cm. (*Its Zeszyty naukowe*)
　　Summaries in Russian, and English or German.

　　1. Electric engineering—Collected works.　ɪ. Title.　(Series)

　　　TK4.L63　　　　　　63-59922

NL　0440614　　DLC

Łódź, Poland. Politechnika.
　　Mechanika. zesz. 1–
Łódź ₁Państwowe Wydawn. Naukowe₎ 1954–
　　　no. in　v. illus., diagrs., tables. 24 cm. (*Its Zeszyty naukowe*)
　　Summaries in Russian and English.

　　1. Mechanical engineering—Collected works.　2. Mechanics—Collected works.　ɪ. Title.　(Series)

　　　TJ4.L6　　　　　　63-58169

NL　0440615　　DLC

Łódź, Poland. Politechnika.
　　Włókiennictwo. zesz. 1–
Łódź, Państwowe Wydawn. Naukowe, 1954–
　　　no. in　v. illus., diagrs. 24 cm. (*Its Zeszyty naukowe*)
　　Summaries in Russian and English.

　　1. Textile industry and fabrics—Collected works.　ɪ. Title.
(Series)

　　　TS1300.L57　　　　　　62-43187

NL　0440616　　DLC

Łódź, Poland. Politechnika. **Katedra Cieplnych
Maszyn Przepływowych.**
CMP, Cieplne maszyny przemysłowe.

　　₁Łódź₎

Łódź, Poland. Polski Instytut Służby Społecznej.
　Biblioteka Służby społecznej
　　see under title

Łódź, Poland. Polski Instytut Służby Społecznej.

**Służba społeczna; czasopismo instrukcyjne Polskiego Instytutu Służby Społecznej. r. 1–　　1946–
Łódź.**

Łódź (Poland). Rada miejska.
　Sprawozdanie z działalności Rady m. Łodzi.

Łódź,　　　　　　　　　　　　　　4°.

1. Municipal government—Poland—　　Lodz.　　April 18, 1925

NL　0440620　　NN

Łódź, Poland. St. Trinitatis-Gemeinde.
Kirchengesang-Verein.
　　Festschrift zur Feier des 75-jährigen
Jubiläums, 1859-1934, hrsg. von der
Vereinsleitung.　Lodz, Druck: "Neue
Lodzer Zeitung," 1934.
　　104 p.

NL　0440621　　DLC-P4

Łódź, Poland. Scientific Society
see **Łódzkie Towarzystwo Naukowe.**

Łódź, Poland. Société des sciences et des lettres
see **Łódzkie Towarzystwo Naukowe.**

Łódź, Poland. Society of Science and Letters
see
Łódzkie Towarzystwo Naukowe.

Lodz, Poland. Statistisches Amt.
　　Strassenverzeichnis von Litzmannstadt, hrsg. vom Oberbürgermeister von
Litzmannstadt, Statistisches Amt.
Litzmannstadt, Verlag der Buchhandlung
S. Seipelt, 1941.
　　196 p.

NL　0440625　　DLC-P4

Łódź, Poland. Technical University
see
Łódź, Poland. Politechnika.

Łódź, Poland. Towarzystwo Naukowe
see **Łódzkie Towarzystwo Naukowe.**

Łódź, Poland. Towarzystwo Żydowskich Szkół Średnich
see
Towarzystwo Żydowskich Szkół Średnich w Łodzi.

Łódź, Poland. Uniwersytet.
　Acta anthropologica. 1-　　Łódź, 1949-
　　see　Acta anthropologica lodziensia.

VOLUME 338

069P
LC2M
no. 2
«etc.» Łódź, Poland. Uniwersytet.
Acta archaeologica.
nr. 1
Łódź, 1948-
v. illus., maps (part fold.) 25-26cm.

Some issues in English or French.
Summaries in Russian and French.
Title varies: v. 1- , 1948/49- , Acta
praehistorica.
Issued as sub-series of Łódzkie Towarzystwo
Naukowe. Wydział II. Nauk historycznych i spo-
łecznych. Prace.

no. 1 is Prace, no. 2.

no. 4 " " no. 18.
no. 5 " " no. 19.

no. 7 " " no. 25.
no. 8 " " no. 29.

no. 9 is Prace, no. 35.
no. 10 " " no. 39.

NL 0440633 NNC

Lodz, Poland. Uniwersytet.
Acta geographica Lodziensia
see
Acta geographica Lodziensia.

Łódź, Poland. Uniwersytet.
Acta praehistorica
see its Acta archaeologica.

Łódź. Uniwersytet.
Acta zoologicae et oecologica
see under Title

378.438 Łódz. Uniwersytet.
L824 Prace z historii myśli społecznej i z badań
społecznych. t.1-
1953-
Łódz, Łódzkie Towarzystwo Naukowe, 1953-
v. 25cm.

A subseries of Łódzkie Towarzystwo Naukowe.
Wydział II: Nauk historycznych i społecznych.

NL 0440637 NcU

LF 4207 ŁÓDŹ, POLAND. Uniwersytet.
.C5 L8 Skład osobowy i spis wykładów na rok
akademicki 19 -
Łódź, 19 -
v.

NL 0440638 InU MiU NN

Łódź, Poland. Uniwersytet.
Uniwersytet łódzki w pierwszym dziesięcioleciu, 1945-
1954; materiały bibliograficzne. Opracowała Janina Racięcka z udziałem Władysławy Skibińskiej i Wandy Świę-
cickiej, pod red. Heleny Więckowskiej. ₁Wyd. 1.₎ Wrocław, Zakład im. Ossolińskich, 1955.

xxxiii, 233 p. 25 cm. (Wydawnictwa bibliograficzne Biblioteki
Uniwersyteckiej w Łodzi, 2)

1. Łódź, Poland. Uniwersytet—Bibl. I. Racięcka, Janina. II.
Więckowska, Helena, ed. III. Title. (Series: Łódź, Poland. Uniwersytet. Biblioteka. Wydawnictwa bibliograficzne, 2)

Z5055.P6L59 56-39169

NL 0440639 DLC OU MiU CoU MH NN CtY NNC RPB

Łódź, Poland. Uniwersytet.
Zeszyty naukowe. Seria 1: Nauki humanistyczno-spo-
łeczne. zesz. 1- 1955-
Łódź ₁Państwowe Wydawn. Naukowe₎
v. in illus., ports. 24 cm. irregular.
Tables of contents also in English, French, and other languages:
summaries in English, French, or other languages.

1. Humanities—Societies, etc. 2. Social sciences—Societies, etc.

AS262.L6A18 61-41809

NL 0440640 DLC MiU CLSU IU TxU KMK KU MoU

ŁODZ, Poland. Uniwersytet.
Zeszyty naukowe. Seria II: Nauki matematyczno-
przyrodnicze.
Łodz. v. illus., plates. 25cm.

Summaries in English, French or German.

1. Science—Per. and soc. publ.

NL 0440641 NN CtW

Z6945
.C97 Łódź, Poland. Uniwersytet. Biblioteka.
Czasopisma zagraniczne w bibliotekach naukowych w Łodzi.
t. 1- 1955/56-
Łódź.

Łódź, Poland. Uniwersytet. *Biblioteka.*
Pierwsze dziesięciolecie Biblioteki Uniwersyteckiej w
Łodzi, 1945-1954. Łódź, 1955.
148 p. 29 cm.

I. Title.

Z818.L85 57-28742 ₁

NL 0440643 DLC CU NNC

Z
818
.L82 Łódź, Poland. Uniwersytet. *Biblioteka.*
A2 Sprawozdanie.
Łódź.
v. tables. 20 cm. annual.

Z818.L86 60-46098

NL 0440644 DLC IU MiU NN CU

Łódź, Poland. Uniwersytet. *Biblioteka.*
Wykaz czasopism zagranicznych.
₁Łódź₎
v. 29 cm.

1. Periodicals—Bibl. I. Title.

Z6945.L82 51-27487

NL 0440645 DLC NN NcU

Łódź, Poland. Uniwersytet. *Biblioteka.*
Wykaz nabytków Biblioteki Uniwersyteckiej w Łodzi.
₁Łódź₎
v. 30 cm. monthly.

I. Title.

Z938.L6 51-27486

NL 0440646 DLC

LODZ, Poland. Uniwersytet. Instytut historyczny.
Prace.
Łódź.
No. 1-2, 5 on film * ZAN-*Q323. Positive.

1. History. 2. Poland—Hist.

NL 0440647 NN

PG7001
.P7 Łódź, Poland. Uniwersytet. Wydział
Filologiczny.
Prace polonistyczne.
Wrocław, Zakład im. Ossolińskich.

HC287
.W3W3 Łódź, Poland. Wirtschaftskammer.
Warthegau-Wirtschaft. Jahrg. -4, Nr. 3;
-März 1943.
₁Posen₎

Lodz (Poland). Wydział finansowo-rachunkowy.
...Sprawozdanie Wydziału finansowo-rachunkowego.

Łódź, obl. 8°.
1919/20 have title: Sprawozdanie kasy głównej m. Łodzi.

1. Municipal finance—Poland—Lodz. April 18, 1925

NL 0440650 NN

Łódź, Poland. Wydział statystyczny.
...Alkoholizm w miastach polskich. Łódź: Nakładem
Sekcji do walki z alkoholizmem przy magistracie miasta Łodzi,
1927. 54 p. incl. tables. 8°.
At head of title: Edward Rosset, naczelnik Wydziału statystycznego magistratu
miasta Łodzi.

506315A. 1. Alcoholism—Poland. December 22, 1930

NL 0440651 NN

VOLUME 338

Lodz. Wydział Statystyczny.
Informator m. Lodzi
see under title

Łódź, Poland. Wydział statystyczny.
...Łódź, miasto pracy; opracował Edward Rosset... Łódź,
1929. 99 p. incl. tables. illus. 8°.

At head of title: Wydawnictwo magistratu m. Łodzi.
Bibliography, p. 91–99.

514347A. 1. Lodz, Poland. 2. Eco-   nomic history—Poland—Lodz.
March 25, 1931

NL 0440653   NN

Lodz, Poland. Wydział stetystyczny.
...Miesiecznik statystyczny...Bulletin
mensuel ...année

1 v. tables. 18½ cm.

NL 0440654   DL

Lodz, Poland. Wydział statystyczny.
...Rocznik statystyczny m. Łodzi... Annuaire statistique
de Lodz.
Łódź,   4°.

has title: Statystyka miasta Łodzi.
In Polish and French.
At head of title, 1922: Miesięcznik statystyczny...Bulletin statistique, août–
décembre 1922.

1. Lodz—Statistics.
March 31, 1925

NL 0440655   NN

Lodz, Poland. Wydział statystyczny.
...Samorząd a problem mleczny.   Łódź: Nakładem magistratu m. Łodzi, 1928. 39 p. incl. tables. 8°.

At head of title: Edward Rosset, naczelnik Wydziału statystycznego magistratu
m. Łodzi.
"Odbitka z 'Dzienika zarządu m. Łodzi.'"

526581A. 1. Milk supply, Poland.
May 5, 1931

NL 0440656   NN

Lodz, Poland. Wydział statystyczny.
Statystyka m. Łodzi opracowana przez Wydział statystyczny
magistratu... Redaktor: dr. Edward Grabowski. Tom 1–
Łódź₁: T. E. Kulisza₁, 1922 ₁v. illus. f°.

Title in French on verso of t.-p.: captions in Polish and French.
Contents: Tom 1. Trzylecie 1918–1920.

1. Lodz—Stat.
March 30, 1927

NL 0440657   NN

Lodz, Poland. Wydział statystyczny.
...Zagadnienia gospodarki samorządowej miasta Łodzi.
Kwestja mieszkaniowa — wodociągi i kanalizacja — opieka
nad niemowleciem — gruźlica — alkoholizm — finanse miejskie.
Łódź, 1926. 86 p. incl. tables. illus. (incl. charts, plans.)
4°.

At head of title: Edward Rosset, naczelnik Wydziału statystycznego magistratu
m. Łodzi.

1. Cities—Social problems and condi-   tions—Poland—Lodz. 2. Municipal
government—Poland—Lodz.   June 29, 1927

NL 0440658   NN

Łódź, Poland. Zarząd Miejski.
Urzędowy plan miasta Łodzi; opracowany przez Wydział
Planowania Przestrzennego Zarządu Miejskiego w Łodzi.
₁W Łodzi₁ Wojskowy Instytut Naukowo-Wydawniczy, 1948.
56 p. fold. col. map (in pocket) 25 cm.
Scale of map, 1 : 25,000.

1. Łódź, Poland—Maps.   I. Title.

G6524.L6 1948.L6   Map 58–106

NL 0440659   DLC

HA1458   Łódź, Poland. Zarząd Miejski.
.L6A32   Rocznik statystyczny miasta Łodzi. 1945/47–
Łódź.

HC337   Łódź, Poland (Voivodeship)
.P72L6   Sprawozdanie wojewody łódzkiego
Łódź.
/ v. tables. 29 cm. annual.

1. Łódź, Poland (Voivodeship)—Econ. condit.

HC337.P72L6   60–57131

NL 0440661   DLC

(Voivodeship)
LODZ, Poland₁ Wojewódzki urząd statystyczny.
Rocznik statystyczny województwa łódzkiego.
Łódź.   v.   diagrs.   21cm.

1. Lodz, Poland (Province)—Stat. I. Title.

NL 0440662   NN

Łódź, Poland (Voivodeship) Wojewódzkie Archiwum
Państwowe, Łódź.
Katalog planów miast w zbiorach Wojewódz-
kiego Archiwum Państwowego w Łodzi
see under   Fijałek, Jan, 1864–1936.

Lodzer young men's benevolent society, New York.
...35th anniversary jubilee book, Lodzer young men's benevolent society...New York, N. Y. Edited by Gustave Eisner.
₁New York, 1937₁ 96 p. illus. (incl. ports.) 28½cm.

At head of title: 1902–1937.
"Advertisements," p. 46–95.

929862A. 1. Mutual aid societies   —U. S.—N. Y.—New York.
T; Eisner, Gustave, ed.   March 15, 1938

NL 0440664   NN OCH

Łódź teatralna.
Rok ₁1₁–

Łódź ₁etc.₁ 1947–   v. illus.   25cm.
Bimonthly?
Rok ₁1₁–   also numbered continuously, nr. 1–
Published by Państwowy wojska polskiego (rok ₁1₁–2, nr. 4 with Teatr T U R
erok 2, nr. 1–4 as Teatr pswazechny₁).

1. Stage—Per. and soc. publ.   I. Łódź, Poland. Państwowy teatr
wojska polskiego.   April 3, 1951

NL 0440665   NN

Łódź w walce i pracy
see under   Front Narodowy. Łódzki Komitet.

947.52   ŁODZIA-CZARNIECKI, K
L826   Herbarz polski podług Niesieckiego
treściwie ułożony i wypisami z później-
szych autorów,z akt grodzkich poznańskich
z ksiąg i akt kościelnych, oraz z doku-
mentów familijnych, powiększony i wy-
dany przez K.Łodzia-Czarnieckiego.
Gniezno,Druk.J.B.Langiego,1872–74.
xxxv,222p. coats of arms. 34cm.
Cover title.

NL 0440667   PU

Lodzinskaîa fabrichnaîa zheleznaîa doroga.
Документы, относящіеся къ устройству Лодзинской фа-
бричной желѣзной дороги въ Царствѣ Польскомъ. ₁Вар-
шава, 1865?₁
49 p. 22 cm.

Title transliterated: Dokumenty, otnosîàshchîeîàsîà k ustroĭ-
stvu Lodzinskoĭ fabrichnoĭ zhelêznoĭ dorogi.

56–53357

NL 0440668   DLC

Lodzinskaîa zhelêznaîa doroga
see
Lodzinskaîa fabrichnaîa zheleznaîa doroga.

ŁODZIŃSKI, STEFAN RADWAN.
Gratvlatio panegyrica, Serenissimo Principi Dno
Dno Michaeli Korybvt Dei gratiâ regi Poloniae...
Sub felicibus coronationis Suae auspicijs debitae
summissionis animo, per Stephanvm Radan Lodzinski
praepositum Scekocinensem, oblata anno Dei hominis
1669. Crac., In Officina Stanislai Piotrkowczyk
₁1669₁ 6 l. coat of arms. 27cm.
1. Michael I, king of Poland, 1638–1673.

NL 0440670   NN

VOLUME 338

Lodzinskoe nauchnoe obshchestvo
    see
Łódzkie Towarzystwo Naukowe.

Łódzki Komitet Frontu Narodowego
    see
Front Narodowy. *Łódzki Komitet.*

063.8   Łódzkie Towarzystwo Naukowe.
LO   Bulletin de la société des sciences et des
         lettres de Łódź. v.1-
         1946-
         Łódź.
             v. illus. 24cm.

             English or French translation of some
         sections of the society's Prace.

NL 0440673   IU CtY NN

Łódzkie Towarzystwo Naukowe.
    Liste des publications. Łódź, 1952
    19 p. 21 cm.

    1. Łódzkie Towarzystwo Naukowe—Bibl.   I. Title.

Z5055.P6L6   55-42654 ‡

NL 0440674   DLC

Q
60   Łódzkie Towarzystwo Naukowe.
.L84   Odczyty.
        Łódź, 19
            v. illus. 24 cm.
            Summary in English.

    1. Science—Addresses, essays, lectures.

Q171.L853   59-35552

NL 0440675   DLC NcD NcU NNC NN MiU

D1   Łódzkie Towarzystwo Naukowe.
.P78
        Przegląd nauk historycznych i społecznych. t. 1-
        Łódź, Zakład im. Ossolińskich we Wrocławiu.

Łódzkie Towarzystwo Naukowe.
    Sprawozdania z czynności i posiedzeń. r. 1-
        (nr. 1-   ) 1946-
    Łódź.
        v. in   illus. 21-25 cm.

AS262.L6A2   60-45480

    ICJ MB IU
NL 0440677   DLC NN MBdAF ICJ NcU MiU OU ICU NN NNC

ŁÓDZKIE TOWARZYSTWO NAUKOWE.
    Szlakami nauki.
Łódź.

NL 0440678   NN

Łodzkie Towarzystwo Naukowe. *Classe 1. Linguistique
lettres, philosophie*
    see
    Łódzkie Towarzystwo Naukowe. *Wyzał 1. Języko-
    znawstwa, Nauki o Literaturze i Filozofii.*

Łodzkie Towarzystwo Naukowe. *Classe 1. de linguistique,
de littérature et de philosophie*
    see Łódzkie Towarzystwo Naukowe. *Wydział 1. Języko-
    znawstwa, Nauki o Literaturze i Filozofii.*

Łodzkie Towarzystwo Naukowe. *Classe 111. des sciences
mathématiques et naturelles*
    see
    Łódzkie Towarzystwo Naukowe. *Wydział 111. Nauk
    Matematyczno-Przyrodniczych.*

Łodzkie Towarzystwo Naukowe. *Classe 11. Histoire et sciences sociales*
    see
    Łódzkie Towarzystwo Naukowe. *Wydział 11. Nauk Hi-
    storycznych i Społecznych.*

Łodzkie Towarzystwo Naukowe. *Classe 111. Sciences mathématiques et naturelles*
    see
    Łódzkie Towarzystwo Naukowe. *Wydział 111. Nauk
    Matematyczno-Przyrodniczych.*

Łodzkie Towarzystwo Naukowe. *Classe 1v. Médecine*
    see
    Łódzkie Towarzystwo Naukowe. *Wydział 1v. Nauk Le-
    karskich.*

Łódzkie Towarzystwo Naukowe. *Komisja Językowa.*
    Rozprawy. t. 1-
    Łódź, Zakład Narodowy im. Ossolińskich, 1954-
        v. in   illus., ports., maps. 25 cm. (Wydawnictwa Łódz-
        kiego Towarzystwa Naukowego)

    1. Language and languages—Societies, etc.

P19.L6A3   60-30807

NL 0440685   DLC NSyU CoU KU OU CaBVaU NN InU

ŁÓDZKIE TOWARZYSTWO NAUKOWE.
    (Wyzdał I i językoznawstwa, nauki o literaturze i
    filozofii.
    Bulletin.
Łódz.   v.   25cm.

    Irregular.
    Name of society appears in French: Société des sciences et des lettres
de Łódz. Classe I de   linguistique. de littérature

    filozofii.   Bulletin.

et de philosophie.

                            * QPA
    1. Philology— Per. and soc. publ.   2. Philosophy— Per. and soc.
publ.

NL 0440687   NN

Łodzkie Towarzystwo Naukowe. Wydział I: Językoznawstwa, nauki o literaturze i filozofii.
    Prace. no. 1-
    1947-
    Lodz.
        v.   25 cm.

    1. Literature - Societies. 2. Philosophy -
Societies.

NL 0440688   CaBVaU IU InU NNC

For NUC
From CSt-H
PG6010   Łódzkie Towarzystwo Naukowe. Wydział I:
L824   Językoznawstwa. Nauki o Literaturze i
        Filozofii.
        Prace polonistyczne. seria I. (194 -
        Łódź, Zakład Narodowy im. Ossolińskich we Wroc-
        ławiu.
            v. 21cm. annual.

        1. Polish literature - Hist. & crit. -
        Yearbooks.   I. Title.

NL 0440689   CSt-H NcU RPB CtY MiU

Łódzkie Towarzystwo Naukowe. *Wydział 1. Językoznawstwa, Nauki o Literaturze i Filozofii. Komisja Językowa*
    see
    Łódzkie Towarzystwo Naukowe. *Komisja Językowa.*

ŁODZKIE Towarzystwo Naukowe. Wydział
II, Nauk Historycznych i Społecznych
    Prace.
    nr. 1-   1948-
    Łódź.
        v.   W1 LO1019V
    1. Public health - period. 2. Social
sciences - period.

NL 0440691   DNLM NNC InU CoU CU NcU MiU CU CaBVaU

Łódzkie Towarzystwo Naukowe. *Wydział 111. Nauk Matematyczno-Przyrodniczych.*
    Bulletin.
    Łódź.
        v. in   illus., maps. (part fold., part col.) 25 cm.
        Published 1946-59.
        Superseded by the academy's Bulletin in 1960.
        French or English.

    1. Science—Collected works.

Q60.L562   63-47496

    NNC MiU NcU OU CSt
NL 0440692   DLC IU AzU CtY ICJ NN PPAN RPB CtY CU

VOLUME 338

AS
262
.L8
Sect.3

Łódzkie Towarzystwo Naukowe. Wydzial III. Nauk
Matematyczno-Przyrodniczych.
Prace. nr.1-   1947-
Łódz.
     v. illus.,maps.
     Each vol.has also special t.p.

NL 0440693   MiU IU ICJ NcD CSt AzU NcU NNM NN FU

W 1
LO101

ŁÓDZKIE Towarzystwo Naukowe. **Wydział**
IV, Nauk Lekarskich
    Bulletin.
    Łódz ₍1950?₎-
      v. illus.
    Articles in English or French.
    1. Medicine - Period.

NL 0440694   DNLM MiU IU

Łodzkie towarzystwo naukowe. *Wydział IV. Nauk Lekarskich*
    Prace.
    ₍1₎-   1951-
    Warszawa, Societas Scientiarum Lodziensis, Lodz.
     v. illus. 24 cm. 6 to 7 mos. a year.

    Summaries in English.

    1. Medicine-period.   2. Medicine-period.-
Poland.

NL 0440695   NcU-H ICJ DNLM MBCo MiU CtY-M

Łódzkie województwo
       see
Łódz, *Poland* (*Voivodeship*)

Loe, Adolf, 1855-
   Ueber den glycerinaether.
   Inaug. diss. Goettingen, 1882

NL 0440697   ICRL

Loë, Alfred, baron de, 1858-   joint author.
    ... Belgique ancienne
      see under   Brussels. Musées royaux d'art
et d'histoire.

PQ3857
.2L82

Loë, Alfred, baron de, 1858-
    Découverte d'antiquités franques
à Harmignies; mémoire de m. le baron
Alfred de Loë.   Anvers, J. Plasky,1886.
    8p. 25cm.
    "Extrait du Compte-rendu du Congrès
d'archéologie et d'histoire de 1885."
    Bibliotheca Belgica.

    1. Harmignies,Belgium - Antiquities.

NL 0440699   NNU-W

PQ3857
.2L83

Loë, Alfred, baron de, 1858-
    Fouilles au "Trou-des-Blaireaux" à
Vaucelles (province de Namur) lieu de
sépulture néolithique habitat de l'âge
du renne, par le Bon A. de Loë, E.
Rahir et E. Houzé. Communication faite
à la Société d'anthropologie de Bruxelles
dans la séance du 29 mai 1905.
Bruxelles, Hayez, 1913.
    27p. illus., plates,tables, diagrs.
25cm.
    "Extrait des Memoires de la Société

d'anthropologie de Bruxelles, tome XXIV,
1905."
    Bibliotheca Belgica.

    1. Vaucelles, Belgium - Antiq.
I. Rahir, Edmond, 1864-   II. Houze,
Émile, joint author. III. Bibliotheca
Belgica.

NL 0440701   NNU-W

Loë, Alfred, baron de, 1858-
    ... Notions d'archéologie préhistorique belgo-
romaine et franque à l'usage des touristes, par
le baron de Loë ... Ouvrage orné de 199 figures
intercalées dans le texte. Bruxelles, F. van
Buggenhoudt ₍1919₎
    2 p. l., ₍3₎-281 p. illus. 24 x 12cm.

    At head of title: Touring club de Belgique.

    1.Belgium - Antiquities. I.Touring club de
Belgique.

NL 0440702   NNC NNU-W

Loë, Alfred, baron de, 1858-
    Rapport sur les recherches & les fouilles faites
en 1897
       see under   Brussels. Musées royaux d'art
et d'histoire.

Loë., Anna Gottliebe Luise Wilhelmine *von*
    see   Alvensleben, Frau Anna Gottliebe Luise
Wilhelmine   (von Loë) *von*

Loë (Bernhard). *Ueber Brustwunden. 35 pp
8°. München, C. Wolf, 1839.

NL 0440705   DNLM

Loë, Didi, ed.
Franz, Robert, 1815-1892.
    Robert Franz-brevier, herausgegeben von Didi Loë.
Mit einem geleitwort und einem bildnis ... Leipzig,
Breitkopf & Härtel, 1915.

Loe, Eric Haldorsen, 1856-   ed.

Opdalslaget.
    Opdalslagets ... aarbok 1921/22-   1ste-
₍Everett? Wash., 1922-

Loë, Friedrich Karl Walther Degenhard, *freiherr* **von,**
1828-1908.
    Erinnerungen aus meinem berufsleben 1849 bis 1867,
von freiherrn v. Loë ... Stuttgart und Leipzig, **Deutsche
verlags anstalt,** 1906.

    viii, ₍9₎-140 p. 25ᶜᵐ.

    "Das werk war in den jahrgängen 1901, 1902 u. 1905 der 'Deutschen
revue' zuerst veröffentlicht worden."

    1. France—Hist.—Second empire, 1852-1870. 2. France—Army. 3. Prus-
sia—Hist.—1815-1870. 4. Austro-Prussian war, 1866.

Library of Congress   DD205.L6   8-12579

NL 0440708   DLC MiU CSt NcD NjP

Loë, Friedrich Karl Walther Deyenhard, Freiherr von, 1828-
1908.
    Der Felddienst der Cavallerie;zum Gebrauche
für Offiziere der Waffe. 3ᵉ Aufl. Bonn,
M.Cohen & Sohn (F.Cohen),1880.

    18 cm. Folded map.

NL 0440709   MH

Loë, Friedrich Karl Walther Degenhard, Freiherr von, 1828-1908.
    Der Felddienst der Kavallerie. Zum Gebrauche der Offiziere
der Waffe. Von Freiherr von Loë... Bonn: M. Cohen & Sohn,
1889. 232 p. map. 5. ed., rev. 12°.

    1. Cavalry—Drill and tactics.   September 9, 1926.

NL 0440710   NN

357
L184C

Loë, Friedrich Karl Walther Degenhard, Freiherr
von, 1828-1908.
    Service de la cavalerie en campagne.
Traduit de l'allemand par G. Gendron. Paris,
L. Baudoin, 1883.
    150 p. plans. 22 cm. ₍With Lahure,
Auguste. Cavalerie. Paris, 1884₎

    "Extrait du Journal des sciences militaires,
avril-mai-août-septembre 1883."

    1. Cavalry.   I. Gendron, G., tr. II.
Title.

NL 0440711   NcD

Loe, *Friedrich Karl Walther Degenhard, Freiherr von, 1828-
1908.*
    Service de la cavalerie en cam-
pagne, par M. le général baron von Loe.
Traduit de l'allemande par G. Gendron...
Paris, L. Baudoin et ce, 1888.
    2p. l., 150 (1) p. 1 fold
map   23 cm.

NL 0440712   DNW

Loe, Gladys St. John-
       see
St. John-Loe, Gladys

Loe (H. J. *van*), *Baron.*
    Onderzoek naar de waare oorzaken onzer onlusten, en
naar de middelen om dezelve te doen strekken tot heil
van 't vaderland... *n. p.,* 1789. 48 pp. nar. 8°.

NL 0440714   NN

VOLUME 338

Loë, (H. J. van) *Baron.*
Reden is niet bestand tegen hartstogten. Waarheid
bukt dikwyls voor vooroordeel. *Zutphen : A. van Eldik,*
1790. 2 p.l., 26 pp. 8°.

NL 0440715   NN

Loë, Hermann Th., ed.
Münch, M   C.
Universal-lexicon der erziehungs- und unterrichtslehre
für schulaufseher, geistliche, lehrer, erzieher und gebildete eltern, von M. C. Münch ... 3. umgearb. und verb.
aufl. hrsg. von Hermann Th. Loë ... Mit einem anhang
enthaltend: biographien der um das schulwesen und die
jugenderziehung besonders verdienter männer &c. von dr
I. B. Heindl ... Augsburg, I. A. Schlosser's buch- und
kunsthandlung, 1859–60.

Loe, J   A
Concrete kerbs; causes and prevention of failures. London, H. M. Stationery Off., 1950.
iv, 18 p. illus. 25 cm. (Road research technical paper no. 18)

1. Pavements, Concrete. 2. Roads, Concrete.   I. Title.   (Series:
Harmondsworth, Eng. Road Research Laboratory. Road research
technical paper no. 18)
TE7.H33 no. 18   625.888   50–4835

NL 0440717   DLC CtY OrP

Loé (Joann. Nepom.) * De angina. 44 pp. 8°.
Monachii. 1818.

NL 0440718   DNLM

Löe, Johann Remaclus, respondent.
Dissertatio ... juridica germano-historico-
canonico-publica De diversarum religionum in eodem
territorio tolerantia ac receptione generica & speciali
see under   Banniza, Johann Peter, 1707-
1775, praeses.

Loe, Kelley, joint author.

Neuberger, Richard Lewis, 1912–
... An army of the aged, by Richard L. Neuberger and
Kelley Loe; with an introduction by Bruce Bliven. Caldwell,
Id., The Caxton printers, ltd., 1936.

Loe, Kelley, 1881–
The story of American labor. [Portland] Oregon State
Federation of Labor [1952]
62 p. 18 cm.

1. Trade-unions—U. S.—Hist.   I. Title: American labor.
HD6508.L6   331.880973   52–845 ‡

NL 0440721   DLC OrCS OrHi OrP OrU

Loe, Kelley, 1881–
A tax report to industrial labor of Oregon [n.p.]
[1947]
16 p.

NL 0440722   OrU OrP Or

Loé (Ludwig). * Ueber Rückenmarks - Erwei-
chung. 28 pp. 8°. *München, C. Wolf, 1840.*

NL 0440723   DNLM

Loë, Ludwig Dietrich Joseph Maria Hubert Paschalis,
in religion Paulus von, 1866–
De vita et scriptis B. Alberti Magni.
(In Analecta Bollandiana. T. 19, pp. 257–284. Bruxellis, 1900.)

Jan. 19,   1903
E710? — Albertus Magnus, Bishop of Ratisbon. 1193?–1280.

NL 0440724   MB

Loë, Ludwig Dietrich Joseph Maria Hubert.
Paschalis, in religion Paulus von, 1866–
Alberts des Grossen Homilie zu Luc.11, 27...
see under   Albertus Magnus, Saint, Bp.
of Ratisbon, 1193?–1280.

Loë, Ludwig Dietrich Joseph Maria Hubert
Paschalis, in religion Paulus von, 1866–
BX   Statistisches über die Ordensprovinz
3534   Saxonia. Leipzig, O. Harrassowitz, 1910.
Q3   64 p. 24cm. (Quellen und Forschungen
no.4   zur Geschichte des Dominikanerordens in
Deutschland, 4. Heft)

1. Dominicans. Provinz Sachsen.

NL 0440726   NIC MH NN

Loë, Ludwig Dietrich Joseph Maria Hubert
Paschalis, in religion Paulus von, 1866–
BX   Statistisches über die Ordensprovinz
3534   Teutonia. Leipzig, O. Harrassowitz, 1907.
Q3   55 p. 24cm. (Quellen und Forschungen
no.1   zur Geschichte des Dominikanerordens in
Deutschland, 1. Heft)

1. Dominicans. Provincia Teutonia.

NL 0440727   NIC NN MH

Frau
L833.8 [Loë,   Margarete Didi (Walde)]
L825   baroness, 1866–
Kleine bilder im engen rahmen, von
M. vom Walde. Mit illustrationen von
E. Giebe. Leipzig, G. Wigand [1889]
75 p. illus., plates. 32cm.

Added t.-p., illustrated.

NL 0440728   IEN

Loë, [Otto], freiherr v[on], 1835–1892.   Ger 2400.14
Erinnerungen aus meinem berufsleben, 1849 bis 1867. 2ᵉ aufl.
Stuttgart, etc., Deutsche verlags-anstalt, 1906.
pp. 140.

NL 0440729   MH

Loë, Otto, *freiherr von,* 1835–1892.
Fürst Bismarck. Urkundliche beiträge zum ruhme eines
grossen mannes, von Otto freiherr von Loë ... Basel, M. Bern-
heim [1887]
271 p. 20½ᵐ.

1. *Bismarck, Otto, fürst von, 1815–1898.   41–27705
Library of Congress   DD218.L84

NL 0440730   DLC MH

Loë, Otto, Freiherr von, 1835–1892.
Fürst Bismarck und die Reichsglocke, Appellations-Rechtferti-
gungsschrift des Freiherrn Otto von Loë; hrsg. von Prof. Ludwig
Stainer. [Paris] Im Selbstverlage des Herausgebers, 1877.
120 p. 21cm.

With bookplate of Albert, Graf v. Schlippenbach.

318871B. 1. Bismarck, Otto, Fürst   von, 1815–1898. I. Stainer, Ludwig,
ed.   April 9, 1946

NL 0440731   NN MH

Loë, Paulus Maria von
see Löe, Ludwig Dietrich Joseph Maria
Hubert Paschalis, in Religion Paulus von, 1866–

Loë, Paulus von
see Loë, Ludwig Dietrich Joseph Maria
Hubert Paschalis, in religion Paulus von, 1866–

W 4   LOE, Ping-kian.
B32   Syphilis en zwangerschap. Batavia,
1941   Keng Po, 1941.
xvi, 314 p.
Proefschrift - Geneeskundige
Hoogeschool, Batavia.
Summary in English.
1. Pregnancy - Complications
2. Syphilis

NL 0440734   DNLM NIC NNC

Loë, Raoul, 1902–
... L'examen radiologique de la vésicule
biliaire par la méthode de Graham, Cole et Copher ..
Hénin-Liétard, Carvin, 1927.
23.5 cm.
Thèse - Univ. de Lille.
"Bibliographie": p. [63]–68.

NL 0440735   CtY

M1621   Loe, Richard.
.L   [A trip to ye Jubillee]
Case   Words to a tune of Mr. Richard Loe's
call'd A trip to ye Jubillee. [London,
ca. 170–?]
[1] l.
First line of text: Come bring us wine.
For voice and continuo; part for flute
at end.
I. Title: A trip to ye Jubillee. II. Title:
Come bring us wine.

NL 0440736   DLC

VOLUME 338

STC 16692
Loe, Robert, fl. 1605.
Effigiatio veri sabbathismi. Authore Roberto Loeo, exoniensis ecclesiæ thesaurario ... Londini, excudebat Ioannes Norton, serenissimæ regiæ maiestatis in Latinis, Graecis, & Hebraicis typographus. 1605.

5p.ℓ., 197p. 19cm.
Printer's mark (McK. 348) on t.-p.
(DLC: BV 109 L83)

NL 0440737   MH DLC

Loe, Thomas.
Works by this author printed in America before 1801 are available in this library in the Readex Microprint edition of Early American Imprints published by the American Antiquarian Society.
This collection is arranged according to the numbers in Charles Evans' American Bibliography.

NL 0440738   DLC

Loe, Thomas.
Doctrine of Justification ...   2d. ed.
London, 1701.
86 p.   12°.

NL 0440739   CtY

QD341 Loe, Wilhelm.
.A2L76 Beitrag zur kenntniss der tetrobromphtalsaeure...
Muenchen, 1886

Inaug. diss. Zuerich.

NL 0440740   DLC

STC 16683
Loe, William, d. 1645.
Come and see. The blisse of brightest beautie: shining out of Sion in perfect glorie. Being the summe of foure sermons preached in the cathedrall church of Glocester ... Imprinted at London by Richard Field for Mathew Law, 1614.

A-I⁴. (A1, probably blank, lacking.) 4to.
Harmsworth copy.

NL 0440741   DFo NNUT-Mc

AW
1
R475:
1246
Loe, William, d. 1645.
Come and see. The blisse of brightest beautie: shining out of Sion in perfect glorie. Being the summe of foure sermons preached in the Cathedrall Church of Glocester ... London, Imprinted by R. Field for M.Law, 1614.
Microfilm of original in the Union Theological Seminary Library, McAlpin Collection. Ann Arbor, Mich., University Microfilms, 1971. (Early English books, 1475-1640, reel 1246)
STC no.16683.
Microfilm.
I.Title.

NL 0440742   MiU CaBVaU

STC 16685.2
Bd.w.
23276
Loe, William, d. 1645.
The ioy of Ierusalem: and woe of the worldlings. A sermon preached at Pauls Crosse the 18. of Iune. 1609. By William Loe batcheler of diuinity.
London, Printed by T. Haueland for C. Knight and I. Harrison, 1609.

A-H⁸. 8vo.
Bullen Reymes - E. G. Troyte-Bullock -
Harmsworth copy.

NL 0440743   DFo MiU

Case
C
9911
.517
LOE, WILLIAM, d.1645.
The kings shoe, made, and ordained to trample on, and to treade downe Edomites; to teach in briefe, what is Edoms doome; what the carefull condition of a king; what the loyall submission of a subiect, and what proiects are onely to best purpose. Deliuered in a sermon before the King at Theobalds, October the ninth, 1622...
London, Printed by I.L. for W.Sheffard, 1623.
[7], 45p. 17cm.

NL 0440744   ICN DFo MiU NNUT-Mc

FILM
FP
1145
Loe, William, d.1645.
The merchant reall. Preached by William Loe ... Hamboroughe, Printed by P.Lang, 1620.
Short-title catalogue no.16688 (carton 1145)

NL 0440745   MiU NNC

STC 16689
Loe, William, d. 1645.
The mysterie of mankind, made into a manual, or The protestants portuize, reduced into explication application, inuocation, tending to illumination, sanctification, deuotion, being the summe of seuen sermons, preached at S. Michaels in Cornehill, London ... London, Printed by Bernard Alsop for George Fayerbeard, 1619.

A¹², a¹², b⁶, C-O¹², P⁶. (A1, probably blank, lacking.) 12mo.
Britwell Court-Harmsworth copy.

NL 0440746   DFo

252
Se661
Loe, William, d. 1645.
A sermon preached at Lambeth, April 21. 1645. at the funerall of that learned and polemicall divine, Daniel Featley, doctor in divinity, late preacher there. With a short relation of his life and death. By William Leo, d. in divinity, sometime preacher at Wandesworth in Surrey   London, Printed for Richard Royston, dwelling in Ivie-lane, 1645.
3 p.l., 32p. front.(port.) 18½cm.
[Sermons and religious pamphlets, 1610-46. 1]
Closely trimmed.

NL 0440747   IU NNUT-Mc CLU-C MoU MH CtY

FILM
Loe, William, d.1645.
Songs of Sion. [S]et for the ioy of Gods deere [o]nes, vvho sitt here by the brookes [o]f this vvorlds Babel, & vveepe vvhen they thinke on Hierusalem vvhich is on highe. [Hamburg, 1620]
Caption title.
Imperfect: all bef[or]e sig. †₄ lacking or not filmed.
Short-title catalogue no.16690 (carton 810)
Microfilm.
I.Title.

NL 0440748   MiU

820.8
G911
v.26
no.2
Loe, William, d. 1645.
The songs of Sion. Edited, with memorial-introduction and notes. Printed for private circulation. [Blackburn, 1870.
183p. 23cm. (Grosart, A.B., ed. Miscellanies of the Fuller worthies' library)

"106 copies only."
Issued as v.1, p.447-624 of the Miscellanies, in this set bound as v.26, no.2 of the Fuller worthies' library.

NL 0440749   OrU

Loe, William, d. 1645.
... The songs of Sion of Dr. William Loe (1620): ed. with memorial-introduction and notes ...

(*In* Grosart, A. B., ed. Miscellanies of the Fuller worthies' library. London, 1870-76. 17ᶜᵐ. v. 1, 1 p. l., 447-624 (i. e. 630), [2] p.)
"Printed for private circulation. 156 copies only."
Imperfect? p. 445-446 wanting?

1. Title.
15-767

Library of Congress   PR1125.F8 vol. 1

NL 0440750   DLC NIC PPL DFo MdBP CSmH

LOE, William. Vox | clamantis. | Mark.1.3. | A | Stil Voice, | To The Three | Thrice-honourable Estates | Of | Parliament | And in them, | to all the Soules | of this our Nation, of what state | or condition soeuer they be. | By William Loe, Doctor of Di- | uinitie, and Chaplaine to the Kings | most excellent Maiestie. |
Printed by T.S. for John Teage, and are | to be sold at the Signe of the Golden- | Ball in Pauls Church-yard, 1621. | Engraved border. 18.9x14.8cm. (10), 72p.

NL 0440751   NNUT-Mc MB CSmH ICN

FILM
Loe, William, d.1645.
Vox clamantis. Mark.1.3. A stil voice, to the three thrice-honourable estates of Parliament: and in them, to all the soules of this our nation, of what state or condition soeuer they be. [London?] Printed by T.S. [nodham] for I.Teage, 1621.
Short-title catalogue no.16691 (carton 844)
Microfilm.

I.Title. II.Title: A stil voice.

NL 0440752   MiU MH CtY

Loe Ping Ing.
Beladjar main schaak. Malang, Kwee Sing Tjay [1936]
[4], 106 p.

Malay text

NL 0440753   OC1

Loe Sjuun
see
Chou, Shu-jên, 1881-1936.

Case
Y
682
L 829
LOEAECHIUS, ANDREA.
Decas anagrammatum. Quibus suis ipsorum demtur nominibus. Mathias Patroconius [et al.] [Cracoviae?ca.1606]
[12]p. 18cm.

Signature: A6.

NL 0440755   ICN

Case
Y
682
L 825
LOEAECHIUS, ANDREA.
Musæ extorres Andreæ Loeaechii Scoti, sibi & fortunæ diffisæ: solo in humanis Sigismundo III. Poloniæ et Sueciæ regi confisæ. Eædem demissæ ambientes Wladislai Pol. et Suec.princ. amicum patrocinium. Utrique ultimum importunæ. Cracoviæ, In officina Lazari, 1607.
[8]p. illus. 18cm.

Signature: A⁴.
The word "solo" in title changed in ink to "solj", and imprint   date M.DC.VII changed to M.DC.VIII.

NL 0440756   ICN

VOLUME 338

Löb Aryeh, *ha-Kohen*
   see
   Aryeh Loeb ben Joseph, *ha-Kohen*, 1745-1813.

Löb ben Baruch Bendet, *18th cent.*
שאנת ארי׳ על מסכת מכות. ביאליסטאק, בבית אהרן
.הלוי הורוזין תקס״ה, [Byelostok, 1805]
[2], 60 l. 36 cm.

1. Talmud. Makkot—Commentaries. I. Title.
Title transliterated: Sha'agat Arye

A 49-4224*

New York. Public Libr.
for Library of Congress

NL 0440758   NN DLC

BM506
.M33L6
1897
Hebr

Löb ben Baruch Bendet, *18th cent.*
שאנת אריה על מסכת מכות. נדפס פעם ב. ווארשא. בדפוס
.י. ז. אונטערהענדלער. תרנ״ז, Bapmasa, 1897.
182 p. 24 cm.

1. Talmud. Makkot—Commentaries. I. Title.
Title transliterated: Sha'agat Aryeh.

BM506.M33L6 1897   58-50168

NL 0440759   DLC

Loeb ben Bezalel, of Prague
   see   Judah Loew ben Bezaleel, d. 1609.

Loeb Zieteler
   see
   Horwitz, Aryeh Loeb, *d.* 1750.

Löb, Abraham, 1884-
   Die Rechtsverhältnisse der Juden im
ehemaligen Königreiche und der jetzigen
Provinz Hannover ... von Abraham Löb ...
Frankfurt a. M., J. Kauffmann, 1908.
viii, 140 p. 20½ cm.

Inaug.-Diss. - Göttingen.
"Literatur-Verzeichnis": p.[137]-140.

NL 0440762   MH-L PP DLC-P4 CtY NN MH OCH CtY CU

Loeb (Adam). *Beitrag zur Lehre vom Meningo-
typhus.* [Heidelberg.] 31 pp. 8°. *Naumburg a. S., Lippert & Co.,* 1896.

NL 0440763   DNLM ICRL PPC

Loeb, Al M
   National and international policies affecting the political development of non-
self-governing peoples: a comparative analysis. [Berkeley, 1952]
v,391 l.

Thesis (Ph.D. in Political Science) - Univ.
of California, Jan.1952.
Bibliography: p.367-391.

NL 0440764   CU

Löb, Albert.
   Elektrolytische untersuchungen mit symmetrischem
und unsymmetrischem wechselstrom ... Halle a. S.,
Druck von W. Knapp, 1905.
3 p. l., 69 p. 21ᶜᵐ.

Inaug.-diss.—Technische hochschule "Fridericiana" Karlsruhe.

1. Electrolysis.   Agr 7-373

Library, U. S. Dept. of   Agriculture 386L78

NL 0440765   DNAL ICRL PU

LOEB, Albert, 1884-
   Über die rotationsdispersion farbiger lösungen. Inaug.-diss., Münster. Neuwied,1908.

NL 0440766   MH-C PU

Löb, Alexander, 1910-
   In welchen entfernungen von der okklusionsebene
werden höchste kaudruckwerte entwickelt? ...
Würzburg, 1936.   26 p.
   Inaug. Diss. - Würzburg, 1936.
Lebenslauf.

NL 0440767   CtY

LOEB, Mrs. ALFRED.
   The "best by test" cook book, compiled by Mrs. Alfred Loeb
for the benefit of the Hebrew Infant Asylum.   New York,
1914.   116 p.   19½cm.

596708A. 1. Cooking, Jewish. I. Home for Hebrew Infants of
the City of New York.

NL 0440768   NN

Loeb (Alfred) [1869-]. *Die totale und
partielle Exstirpation des Kehlkopfes.* 35 pp.
[Bonn.] 8°. *Siesburg. W. Reckinser.* 1891.

NL 0440769   DNLM CU

PZ7
.G2718
Li

Loeb, Anton, *illus.*

Geis, Darlene.
   The little train that won a medal; illus. by Anton Loeb.   New
York, Wonder Books; distributed by Random House [1947]

PZ8
.1
.S425
St

Loeb, Anton, *illus.*

Scott, Theresa Ann, 1904-   *ed.*
   Storytime favorites; illus. by Anton Loeb. New York,
Wonder Books; distributed by Random House [1947]

QD341
.A2L77

Loeb, Arthur, 1876-1916.
   Zur kenntnis der aromatischen sulfon- und
sulfinsaeuren...
Koeln, 1898

Inaug. diss. Heidelberg.
Lebenslauf.

NL 0440772   DLC PPC PU

Loeb, Arthur, 1904-
   Öffentliches recht—privatrecht—sozialrecht, die dreiteilung
im rechtssystem ... Bochum-Langendreer, Druck: H. Pöppinghaus o. h.-g., 1930.
iv, 47 p. 20¼ᵐ.

Inaug.-diss.—Frankfurt am Main.
Lebenslauf.
"Quellen und hilfsmittel": p. 42-46.

1. Law—Philosophy.   I. Title.

32-20311

NL 0440773   DLC MiU

HU 92.54.530

Loeb, Arthur Lehman.
   The inner life and the relative world; an essay on the
concepts of Fielding's moral thought

Honors thesis - Harvard, 1954

NL 0440774   MH

Loeb, Arthur Leopold.
   An interionic attraction theory for regions
of solutions near phase boundaries and an analysis of Langmuir's theory of repulsion between
high potential surfaces in a solution.

Thesis - Harvard, 1949.

NL 0440775   MH-C NNC

Loeb, Berek
   see
   Ber, of Bolechow, 1723-1805

Löb (Berthold) [1867-]. *Ueber Abortus
artificialis bei einem kyphotisch-querverengtem
Becken.* 37 pp., 1 tab. 8°. *Heidelberg, J.
Hörning,* 1893.

NL 0440777   DNLM

Loeb, C. M., *joint author.*

Gere, Ward N.
   Efficiency test on power plant of Jenckes spinning com-
pany, Pawtucket, Rhode Island; a graduating thesis
presented by Ward N. Gere, Richard B. Cross, Benj. S.
Munch, C. M. Loeb, students in the class of 1913 at the
Massachusetts institute of technology ... Boston, Mass.,
S. P. Burton & company [1914]

Loeb, C. M., Jr., *joint author.*
   Molybdän
   see under   Archer, Robert Samuel, 1895-

1650-

Loeb (Carl). *Ein in sich zusammengeknicktes
rachitisches Becken.* 14 pp., 1 l., 1 pl. 8°.
Marburg, C. L. Pfeil. [1874]

NL 0440780   DNLM ICRL

VOLUME 338

Loeb, Carl, 1894–
The black art of cooking, by Dr. Carl Loeb, illustrated by Dr. Harlan Tarbell ... ₁1st ed.₁ ₁Chicago₁ Chicago labor printing co. ₍ᶜ1921₎
6 p. l., 130 p. front., illus., port. 18ᶜᵐ.

1. Vegetarianism. 2. Food. I. Title.

Library of Congress   TX392.L6   21–16663

NL 0440781   DLC ICJ

Loeb, Carl, 1894–
A course in specific light therapy, by Dr. Carl Loeb. 6th rev. and renewed ed. ... Chicago, Actino laboratories, inc. ₍ᶜ1939₎
2 p. l., iv, 156, 156a, 157–197, ₃₁ p. illus., 2 diagr. 24½ᵐ.

1. Phototherapy. I. Title: Light therapy.

Library of Congress   RM838.L6 1939   39–7244
Copyright AA 290914   615.831

NL 0440782   DLC CaBVaU ICJ

Loeb, Carl, 1894– **joint author.**

Tarbell, Harlan E.
Fundamental character analysis, by Doctors Harlan E. Tarbell, John B. Rolle, Carl Loeb. Chicago, The Metaphor system of character anaylsis ₍ᶜ1922₎

Loeb, Carl, 1894–
Handbook of harmono chrome therapy for practitioners and students, by Dr. Carl Loeb. Chicago, Ill., Actino laboratories ₍ᶜ1925₎
4 p. l., 5–82 p., 2 l. illus., plates, fold. diagr. 23½ᵐ.
On cover: Handbook of harmono chrome therapy with the Mountain sun.
"Second edition."

1. Phototherapy. I. Title: Harmono chrome therapy, Handbook of.

Library of Congress   RM838.L6 1925   26–14584

NL 0440784   DLC DNLM

Loeb, Carl, 1894–
Handbook of specific light therapy.
Ed. 3. Actino Laboratories. Chicago, 1927.
82 p. illus. 8°.

NL 0440785   OClW-H

RM 838   LOEB, CARL, 1894–
.L 82   Handbook of specific light therapy; an up-to-date treatise of light therapeutics as applied with the Mountain Sun (Loeb) spectroband and harmonochrome therapy. 5. ed. Chicago, Actino Laboratories ₍1930₎
82 p. illus.

Contains also his Pregnancy; prenatal and post-natal care of infants...and his Actino laboratories Service Bulletins, no.102–108.

1. Phototherapy.

NL 0440786   InU

Loeb (Carl M.) Rhoades and Company, *New York.*
Aluminum, an analysis of the industry in the United States; Aluminum Company of America, Reynolds Metals Company, Kaiser Aluminum & Chemical Corporation Aluminum Limited (Canada) ₁New York, *1950.
76 p. illus., maps. 24 cm.

1. Aluminum industry and trade—U. S. 2. Aluminum Company of America. 3. Aluminum Limited. 4. Kaiser Aluminum and Chemical Corporation. 5. Reynolds Metals Company.

HD9539.A6L6   338.476697   51–1009

NL 0440787   DLC CoU OrU NN

Loeb₍ Carl M.₎ Rhoades & company, *New York.*
... The American aviation industry. ₁New York, c1935₎
3 p. ℓ., 106 numb. ℓ. tables.

At head of title: Carl M. Loeb & company ...
Carbon copy of typewritten report.

NL 0440788   MH-BA

Pamphlet   **Loeb (Carl M.), Rhoades and Company,** New York.
HD   Middle-East aspects of American oil
449+   companies; confidential memorandum. New York, 1949.
36 l. illus., map. 28cm.

1. Petroleum industry and trade--Near East. I. Title.

NL 0440789   NIC

D669.79   *Rhoades*
C615   **Loeb₍ Carl M.₎ ∧& company,** New York.
      Memorandum re Climax molybdenum company. ₁New York₁ Carl M. Loeb & co. ₍c1937₎
cover-title, 18 numb. l. diagrs. 27½ᵐ.

Typewritten copy.

1. Climax molybdenum company. 2. Molybdenum.

NL 0440790   NNC

---

307   **Loeb₍ Carl M.₎ Rhoades & company,** New York
L822   Soybean oil, its development and prospects. July 25, 1940. ₁New York₁ 1940.
13 numb. l. 29cm.

Typewritten.

NL 0440791   DNAL

Loeb (Carl M.) Rhoades and Company, *New York.*
Steel, an analysis of the industry and the eight leading companies: U. S. Steel Corporation, Bethlehem Steel Corporation, Republic Steel Corporation, Jones & Laughlin Steel Corporation, National Steel Corporation, the Youngstown Sheet and Tube Company, Armco Steel Corporation ₁and₁ Inland Steel Company. ₁New York₁ 1951.
102 p. illus. 28 cm.

1. Steel industry and trade—U. S.

HD9514.L6   338.476691   51–7810 ‡

NL 0440792   DLC IdPI NN TU

HD9514
L62   **Loeb (Carl M.) Rhoades and Company,** New York.
     The steel industry and the eight leading companies: U.S. Steel Corporation, Bethlehem Steel Corporation, Republic Steel Corporation, Jones & Laughlin Steel Corporation, National Steel Corporation, the Youngstown Sheet and Tube Company, Armco Steel Corporation ₍and₎ Inland Steel Company. ₍New York₎ 1951.
₍2₎, 13 p. tables (part fold.) 28cm.
"Summary and conclusion of a more complete study."

1. Steel indus-   try & trade – U.S.

NL 0440793   DI NN

Loeb (Carl M.) Rhoades and Company, *New York.*
A summary of recent developments in the aluminum industry; Aluminum Company of America, Reynolds Metals Company, Kaiser Aluminum & Chemical Corporation, Aluminium Limited (Canada) New York, 1952.
19 p. illus. 29 cm.

1. Aluminum industry and trade—U. S. I. Title.

HD9539.A6L62   338.476697   52–2876 ‡

NL 0440794   DLC NN

Loeb (Carolus Fridericus). * De oophoritide acuta. [Leipsic.] 20 pp. 4°. *Dresdæ, ex off.* B. G. Teubneri, [1838].

NL 0440795   DNLM

Loeb, Charles Gerson.
Legal requirements and formalities for marriage of Americans in France, by Charles Gerson Loeb ... ₁Paris, 1918?₁
cover-title, 4 p. 21ᶜᵐ.

1. Marriage law—France. I. Title. II. Title: Marriage of Americans in France.

Library of Congress   HQ1019.F8L6   19–14271

NL 0440796   DLC NcD NNC PPB

Loeb, Charles Gerson.
Legal status of American corporations in France; a treatise on the French law of foreign corporations, companies and partnerships, doing business or negotiating stocks or securities in France, describing their rights and obligations and the preliminary formalities required of, and the taxes and duties applicable to them, with full explanation of French domestic corporations, companies and partnerships, their formation and organisation, including translations of full texts of important French laws, decrees and regulations. By Charles Gerson Loeb ... Paris, The Lecram press, 1921.
5 p. l., vii–xxxviii, 534 p. facsim. 24ᵐ.

1. Corporation law—France. 2. Corporations, Foreign—France. 3. Investments, American—France. I. Title.

22–6815

NL 0440798   DLC ICU CtY-L NcD OCl NcU

Loeb, Charles Harold, 1905–
The future is yours; the history of the Future Outlook League, 1935–1946. Cleveland, Future Outlook League ₍1947₎
124 p. plates, ports. 22 cm.

1. Future Outlook League. 2. Negroes—Cleveland. I. Title.
E185.5.L6   325.2609771   47–26371*

OClJC OU
NL 0440799   DLC NcU IU GU MB FU MiU NcD MU PPT PLF

VOLUME 338

WW
L823h
1909
LOEB, Clarence, 1876-
Hereditary blindness and its prevention. ₁St. Louis, 1909?₁
47, 70, 59, 35 p.
Title page lacking; caption title.
Appeared originally in various issues of the Annals of ophthalmology, 1909.

NL 0440800   DNLM

Loeb, Clarence, 1876-   tr.

Franke, Ernst.
Ocular therapeutics; a manual for the student and the practitioner, by Doctor Ernst Franke ... translated by Clarence Loeb ... St. Louis, The C. V. Mosby co., 1925.

Loeb (Davides). *⁴ De talipedibus varis. vi. 1₁ pp. 1 l. 4°. Bonnæ. ex off. Neusseriana. [1830].*

NL 0440802   DNLM PPC

Loeb, Edwin Meyer, *1894-*
The blood sacrifice complex, by E. M. Loeb ... ₁Menasha, Wis., George Banta publishing company₁ 1923.
cover-title, 40 p. fold. maps. 26 cm.
Thesis (PH. D.)—Yale university, 1922.
Published also as Memoirs of the American anthropological association, no. 30, 1923.
Bibliography: p. 29–40.

1. Sacrifice. 2. Circumcision. 3. Cannibalism. I. Title.
GN473.L6   24—11376

NL 0440803   DLC CU Vi MiU

Loeb, Edwin Meyer, *1894-*
... The blood sacrifice complex, by E. M. Loeb. Menasha, Wis., Pub. for the American anthropological association ₁1923₁
cover-title, 40 p. fold. maps. 26ᵐ. (Memoirs of the American anthropological association. no. 30)
Issued also as thesis (PH. D.) Yale university.
Bibliography: p. 29–40.

1. Sacrifice. 2. Circumcision. 3. Cannibalism. I. Title.
24—4020 Revised
Library of Congress   ₍GN2.A22 no. 30

     OC1W ViU ICJ PU-Mu PPDrop CaBVa OrP OrPR OrU MtBC
NL 0440804   DLC DNLM IEN UU NIC ICJ CU NcD OO OC1MN

Loeb, Edwin Meyer, 1894–
The eastern Kuksu cult, by E. M. Loem ... Berkeley, Calif., University of California press, 1933.
cover-title, 2 p. l., p. ₁139₁–231. map, fold. tab., diagr. 27ᵐ. (University of California publications in American archaeology and ethnology. v. 33, no. 2)

1. Indians of North America—California. 2. Indians of North America—Social life and customs. I. Title. II. Title: Kuksu cult.
A 33—575
California. Univ. Libr.   ₍E51.C15 vol. 33, no. 2₁

     FU ViU MsU MiU OC1 OU OC1WHi PU PPAmP CoU DAU
NL 0440805   CU MoU CaBVaU MB OrP OrU CaBViP CaBViPA

Loeb, Edwin Meyer, *1894-*
History and traditions of Niue, by Edwin M. Loeb ... Honolulu, Hawaii, The Museum, 1926.
3 p. l., ₁3₁–226 p. illus., XIII pl. (incl. fold. map in pocket) on 7 l. 25½ᶜᵐ. (Bernice P. Bishop museum. Bulletin 32)
Bibliography: p. 226.

1. Niue (Island)

Library of Congress   GN670.B4 no. 32   27–13066

     CtY OC1 OU NcD ICJ CtY PU-Mu OrU
NL 0440806   DLC ICarbS TxU CU MoU ICJ CaBVaU PBm CU

Loeb, Edwin Meyer, 1894–
Kuanyama Ambo folklore. ₁Berkeley, University of California Press, 1951₁
289–335 p. illus., map. 28 cm. (Anthropological records, v. 13, no. 4)
Bibliographical footnotes.

1. Folk-lore, Kuanyama. 2. Kuanyama language—Texts.
I. Title. (Series)
[E51.A58   vol. 13, no. 4]   A 52–1658

California. Univ. Libr.
for Library of Congress

     NN
NL 0440807   CU NBuU CoU AU CaBVaU IdPI OrPR MB TxU

572.968
L825r
Loeb, Edwin Meyer, 189₄-
Kuanyama Ambo magic. [Berkeley, 1955]
various pagings. 25cm.

Detached from the Journal of American folklore.

1. Magic, Kuanyama. 2. Kuanyama (Bantu people) I. Title.

NL 0440808   IEN

Loeb, Edwin Meyer, 1894–
Mentawei religious cult, by Edwin M. Loeb ... Berkeley, Calif., University of California press, 1929.
cover-title, 1 p. l., p. ₁185₁–247 p. pl. 69–73. 27 cm. (University of California publications in American archaeology and ethnology. v. 25, no. 2)

1. Mentawi islands—Religion. 2. Religion, Primitive. I. Title.
E51.C15   vol. 25   A 29–128
—— Copy 2.   GN671.M6L6
California. Univ. Libr.
for Library of Congress   ₍a55g1₁†

     NcD DLC CoU DAU NBuU OrP FU ViU MoU OrU CaBViPA
NL 0440809   CU PPAmP PU OO OC1 OU OCU OC1WHi MiU

Loeb, Edwin Meyer, 1894–
Pomo folkways, by Edwin M. Loeb ... Berkeley, Calif., University of California press, 1926.
cover-title, 1 p. l., p. ₁149₁–409. illus., 3 pl. (incl. map) 28ᵐ. (University of California publications in American archaeology and ethnology. v. 19, no. 2)
Plate 1 (map) included in paging.
Bibliography: p. 403–404.

1. Pomo Indians. 2. Indians of North America—Social life and customs. I. Title.
A 26–475
California. Univ. Library
for Library of Congress   E51.C15 ₍vol. 19, no. 2₁
—— Copy 2.   E99.P65L57
     ₍a42h1₁

     Wa
     ICJ ViU CoU DAU MoU DLC FU OrP OrU CaBVaU CaBViPA
NL 0440810   CU NcD OC1 OU OCU OC1MN OC1WHi PPAmP

Loeb, Edwin Meyer, 1894-
Sumatra; its history and people, by Edwin M. Loeb. The archaeology and art of Sumatra, by Robert Heine-Geldern. With two maps, 1 chart and 40 plates ... ₁Vienna₁ Institut für völkerkunde der Universität Wien, 1935.
ix, 350 p. 38 pl. on 19 l., 2 maps (1 fold.) diagr. 24 cm. ("Wiener beiträge zur kulturgeschichte und linguistik" des Institutes für völkerkunde der Universität Wien, vol. III)
Bibliography: p. ₁335₁–342.

1. Sumatra. 2. Ethnology—Sumatra. 3. Sumatra—Antiq. 4. Art—Sumatra. I. *Heine-Geldern, Robert, freiherr von, 1885-
GN4.W5   3. jahrg.   919.21   35—19550

     FTaSU
     TxU OrU OrPR NcGU ICU FU MoSU CaBVaU NcU CU NPurMC
NL 0440811   DLC TxHST CU OU MiU OC1 CtY PU NN PPAN

Asia
Micro
film
583
item 2
Loeb, Edwin Meyer.
Sumatra; its history and people, by Edwin M. Loeb. The archaeology and art of Sumatra, by Robert Heine-Geldern. With 2 maps, 1 chart and 40 plates. ₁Vienna₁ Verlag des Institut für Volkerkunde der Universität Wien, 1935.
350 p. 38 plates on 19 l., 2 maps. (Wiener beiträge zur Kulturgeschichte und linguistik des Instituts für Volkerkunde der Universität Wien, v. 3)

Microfilm (positive) from Library of Congress Photoduplication Service.
Bibliography: p. ₁335₁–342.

1. Sumatra. 2. Ethnology – Sumatra. 3. Sumatra – Antiq. 4. Art – Sumatra. I. Heine-Geldern Robert, freiherr von, 1885- II. Title.

NL 0440813   HU

Loeb, Edwin Meyer, 1894–
Tribal initiations and secret societies, by Edwin M. Loeb ... Berkeley, Calif., University of California press, 1929.
cover-title, 1 p. l. p. ₁249₁–288. illus. (map) 28ᵐ. (University of California publications in American archaeology and ethnology. v. 25, no. 3)

1. Secret societies. 2. Society, Primitive. 3. Indians of North America—Secret societies. I. Title.
A 29–129
California. Univ. Libr.
for Library of Congress   E51.C15 ₍vol. 25₁
—— Copy 2.   GN488.L55

     OC1 OCU OU OC1WHi OC1MN PPAmP
NL 0440814   CU MoU OrP OrU CaBViP FU NBuU CoU DAU

Loeb, Edwin Meyer, 1894–
The western Kuksu cult. Berkeley, 1932.
cover-title, vi, 137 p. 28 cm. ₁California. University₁ University of California publications in American archaeology and ethnology. v. 33, no. 1)

1. Indians of North America—Religion and mythology. 2. Indians of North America—Soc. life & cust. 3. Indians of North America—California. I. Title. II. Title: Kuksu cult. (Series)
E51.C15   vol. 33, no. 1   (572.97)   A 32–926 rev*
California. Univ. Libr.
for Library of Congress   ₍r52j1₁†

     TxU DAU OU OC1 OC1WHi MiU PPAmP MB DLC
NL 0440815   CU MoU OrP OrU CaBViP CaBVa PP FU ViU

Z7070
.M48
Semitic
Div.
Loeb, Elieser, 1837–1892.

Michael, Heimann Joseph, 1792–1846.
אור החיים. הוא ספר ערוך לידיעת חכמי ישראל וספריהם, בלל אלף ומאתים ושלשים ערכים, אשר פעל ועשה ... חיים ב״ד יוסף מיכל זצ״ל. יצא לאור ע״י בניו. פראנקפורט א. מ., י. קויפמאנ, תרנ״א.
₁Frankfurt a. M., J. Kauffmann, 1891₁

VOLUME 338

Loeb, Elinor G.
Let's play garden, originated by Nadine L. Rand, assembled and written by Elinor G. Loeb and Adele Gutman Nathan; illustrations by Fanchette. ₍New York₎ Grosset & Dunlap, inc., °1936₎

₍12₎ p. col. illus. 23¼ x 27¾ᵐᵐ.

End lining-paper and t.-p. illustrated in colors; packages of flower seeds mounted on front lining-paper.

1. Gardening—Juvenile literature.   I. Rand, Nadine, L.   II. Nathan, Mrs. Adele (Gutman) joint author.   III. Title.   36–18142

Library of Congress   PZ7.L825Le

NL   0440817   DLC

Loeb, Else, 1911–
Über adenomyosis interna uteri anhand eines besonderen falles mit decidualer reaktion des stromas bei tubargravidität. ... München, 1938.
Inaug. Diss. – München, 1938.
Lebenslauf.
Literaturverzeichnis.

NL   0440818   CtY

Loeb, Emil.
Kultūra ir spauda; lietuvių kalbon išvertė Vaidevutis. Chicago, Spauda Lietuvos, 1912.
₍153 p.₎

NL   0440819   OCl

LOEB, Ernest M.
Address before the Great Lakes waterways conference, Detroit, Michigan, Oct. 28 and 29, 1915. n.p., ₍1915₎.

pp.16.

NL   0440820   MH-BA

LOEB, Ernest M.
Address before the Orange commercial club Orange, Texas. Oct. 21. 1915. n.p., ₍1915₎

pp.7.

NL   0440821   MH OU

Loeb, Ernest M   L380.4 L82
₍Collected papers on waterways, warehouses, etc.₎
110660

NL   0440822   ICJ

Loeb, Ernest M.
Common cause of the Mississippi Valley: address by Ernest M. Loeb, president of Board of commissioners of the port of New Orleans, before the New Orleans association of commerce. New Orleans, La. ₍Dameron-Pierson co., ltd.₎ 1915.

cover-title, 6 p., 1 l. 23ᵐ.

1. New Orleans—Harbor.   2. New Orleans—Comm.   I. Title.
15–28135

Library of Congress   HE554.N4L6

NL   0440823   DLC PU

LOEB, Ernest M.
Concentration, storage and distribution of cotton. New Orleans, L. Graham co., Ltd., ₍1915₎.

pp.8.

NL   0440824   MH-BA DLC

LOEB, Ernest M.
"Logical port" facilities, the relation which they bear to the proper handling of green coffee a paper read at the convention of the National coffee roasters association, New Orleans, La., Nov. 17, 1914. ₍New York, 1914?₎
(DLC: HD 9199.U5 N3)

pp.8.

NL   0440825   MH-BA DLC

LOEB, Ernest M.
Warehouses as affecting the production, financing, and marketing of cotton. Before the National conference of marketing and farm credits, Chicago. Nov. 28–30, 1915.
n. p., ₍1915₎   (DLC: HD 9076.L65)

pp.8.

NL   0440826   MH-BA DLC

Loeb, Ernst.
Die Berliner grossbanken in den jahren 1895 bis 1902 und die krisis der jahre 1900 und 1901. Von dr. Ernst Loeb ...

(*In* Verein für socialpolitik, Berlin. Schriften CX. Die störungen im deutschen wirtschaftsleben während der jahre 1900 ff. Leipzig, 1903. 22ᶜᵐ. 6. bd., 1. abschnitt, p. ₍81₎–319)

1. Banks and banking—Berlin.   2. Panics.   I. Title.
16—8518

Library of Congress   HB5.V4 110
——— Copy 2, de-   tached. HG3060.B52L6
₍a40b1₎

NL   0440827   DLC ICJ OU

Loeb, Ernst, ed.

Model, Paul, 1872–1895.
... Die grossen Berliner effektenbanken. Aus dem nachlasse des verfassers hrsg. und vervollständigt von dr. jur. Ernst Loeb. Mit einer vorrede von professor dr. Ad. Wagner und einem biographischen geleitworte von dr. O. Köbner. Jena, G. Fischer, 1896.

Loeb, Ernst.   387 Q400
₍38867₎ Die grossen deutschen Schiffahrtsgesellschaften. Ihre finanzielle Lage und ihre finanziellen Aussichten. Von Dr. jur. E. Loeb und B. H. Moldmann. Berlin, Finanzverlag, G. m. b. H., 1904.
64 p. 23ᶜᵐ.
"Benutzte Quellen," p. ₍7₎.

NL   0440829   ICJ

LOEB, Ernst.
Kann der schuldner einer offenen handelsgesellschaft gegen seine schuld eine forderung aufrechnen, der sämtliche gesellschafter als solidarschuldner haften? Erlangen, 1897.

50 p.
Inaug.-diss.,—Erlangen.

NL   0440830   MH-L NIC ICRL

Loeb, Ernst.
Wirtschaftliche Vorgänge, Erfahrungen und Lehren im Europäischen Krieg, von Dr. jur. Ernst Loeb, ... Erster-[zweiter und dritter] Teil. Jena, G. Fischer, 1918–1919.
3 vol. in 1. tables. 24½ᶜᵐ.
Contents.—I. Tl., I. Vom Attentat von Sarajewo bis zum Bekanntgabe der österreichischen Note an Serbien. 2. Die Entwicklung der Reichsbank- und der Darlehnskassen bis zur Ausgabe der ersten Kriegsanleihe. 3. Stockung und Wiederbelebung der Industrie. [4], 108 p.—2. und 3. Tl.: 2. Tl., I. Die Zeichnungen auf die zweite Kriegsanleihe. 2. Die grossen Berliner Effektenbanken im Kriege. 3. Kriegslieferanten auf Aktien im Kriege. 4. Durch den Krieg notleidende Aktiengesellschaften. 3. Tl., I. Allgemeines. 2. Die Finanzierung des Kriegs. 3. Die Börse im Kriege. 4. Die Organisation der Industrie im Kriege. 5. Die deutschen Kriegsanleihen, die Möglichkeit ihrer Verzinsung und Tilgung. 6. Die Kriegs-Not-Gesetzgebung. [4], 92 p.

NL   0440831   ICJ CSt-H DLC-P4 ICJ NN DNW NjP MH ICN

Loeb (Ernst) [1883–   ]. *Ueber Exophthalmus pulsans; eine kasuistische Mitteilung. 23 pp. 8°. München, 1911.

NL   0440832   DNLM

Loeb, Ernst Th   1881
Das Recht auf den Notweg nach dem Bürgerlichen Gesetzbuche und seine Unterschiede vom gemeinen Rechte. Die Ausübung vor und nach dem Urteile in vergleichender Darstellung ... von Ernst Th. Loeb ... Berlin, W. Pilz, 1904.

71, ₍1₎ p. 22cm.

Inaug.-Diss. - Heidelberg.
"Lebenslauf": p. ₍72₎
"Literatur-Verzeichnis": p. ₍5₎–8.

NL   0440833   MH-L ICRL

Loeb, Fannie.
Sweet and sour. Drawings by Helen Boyd. San Antonio, Naylor Co. ₍1947₎
ix, 164 p. illus. 22 cm.

I. Title.

CT275.L648A3   920.7   48–16473*

NL   0440834   DLC TxU

Loeb (Felix) [1886–   ]. *Ueber zwei Fälle von Osteomalacie. 42 pp., 1 l. 8°. München, C. Wolf & Sohn, 1909.

NL   0440835   DNLM

Loeb, Fritz, 1875–
Untersuchungen ueber die aetiologie des ren mobilis. Inaug. Diss. Leipzig, 1902.
Bibl.

NL   0440836   ICRL CtY DNLM

Loeb, Georg, 1885–   ₍Die Behandlung der Darmfisteln. Berlin: Ebering ₍1912₎ 38 S. 8° ¶(Im Buchh. ebd.)
Berlin, Med. Diss. v. 11. März 1912, Ref. Hildebrand
[Geb. 26. Juli 85 Hachenburg; Wohnort: Berlin; Staatsangeh.: Preußen; Vorbildung: Gymn. Limburg Reife O. 05; Studium: Marburg 4, München 2, Berlin 5 S.; Coll. 26. Febr. 12; Approb. 9. März 12.]   ₍U 12. 119

NL   0440837   ICRL DNLM CtY NNC

ar W   Loeb, Georg, 1912–
2125   Die Knochenmarkswirkung der Leberteilstoffe Xanthopterin und l-Tyrosin im Typhusanämietest. Dresden, M. Dittert & Co., 1938.
30 p. 21 cm.

Diss.--Göttingen, 1938.

NL   0440838   NIC

VOLUME 338

Loeb, Gerald M
   The battle for investment survival. ₍New and greatly enl. ed.₎ Boston, Barron's Pub. Co. ₍1952₎
   192 p. illus. 22 cm.

   1. Investments. 2. Speculation. ɪ. Title.
HG4521.L785 1952   332.64   52–11383 ‡

NL 0440839   DLC NIC PV MB ViU NN TxU CU OU

Loeb, Gerald M   9332.6A420
   The battle for investment survival. Boston, Barrow's Publishing Co. [1943]
   65 p. 19 1/2cm.

   1. Investments.   I. Title.

NL 0440840   MB WaU NN

HG
4521
L82   Loeb, Gerald M
1954   The battle for investment survival.
   ₍2d ed. ₎ New York, Hurry House ₍1954₎
   200 p. 21cm.

   1. Investments. 2. Speculation. I. Title.

NL 0440841   NIC NN WaS IdU PBL PP TU WaT OrP CaBVa

JIG4521
.L785
1955   Loeb, Gerald M
     The battle for investment survival. ₍2d ed.₎ New York
Hurry House Publishers ₍1955₎
   242 p. illus. 21 cm.

   1. Investments. 2. Speculation. ɪ. Title.
HG4521.L785 1955   332.64   55–1963

NL 0440842   DLC CaBVa IdU OrU

Loeb, Gerald M
   The battle for investment survival. ₍2d ed., 10th print.₎ New York, Hurry House Publishers ₍1955₎
   254 p. illus. 21 cm.

   1. Investments. 2. Speculation. ɪ. Title.
HG4521.L785 1955ᵉ   332.64   55–3932 ‡

NL 0440843   DLC MB PP MiD ViU OrU IU PP PU-W NcRS

Loeb, Gerald M.
   Realistic speculation, by G. M. Loeb. ₍New York: Barron's pub. co., 1937₎ 39 p. 19½cm.

   Cover-title.
   "Reprint of ... articles in successive numbers of Barron's, beginning with the November 30, 1936 issue."

   1. Speculation.
              November 22, 1939

NL 0440844   NN

Loeb, Gerald M.
   Unorthodox investment, by G. M. Loeb. ₍New York: Barron's pub. co., 1936₎ 36 p. incl. form. 20cm.

   Cover-title.
   Reprint of articles in successive numbers of Barron's, beginning with the April 22, 1935 issue.

   1. Investments.
              November 22, 1939

NL 0440845   NN

   1865–1927
Loeb (Hanau Wolf) ₍How a general practitioner may treat chronic atrophic rhinitis. 2 l. 8°.
St. Joseph, Mo., 1891.
   Repr. from : Med. Herald, St. Joseph, 1891, x.

NL 0440846   DNLM

Loeb, Hanau Wolf, 1865–1927
   ... Military surgery of the ear, nose and throat, by Hanau W. Loeb ... Philadelphia and New York, Lea & Febiger, 1918.
   vi, 7–176 p. 15ᶜᵐ. (Medical war manual no. 8)
   "References": p. 146–176.

   1. Ear—Surgery. 2. Nose—Surgery. 3. Throat—Surgery. 4. Surgery, Military. ɪ. Title.
   Library of Congress   RF51.L68   18–19377

   PPJ PPC
NL 0440847   DLC DNLM ViU OU OClCC MiU DNLM ICJ NN

Loeb, Hanau Wolf, 1865–
   Monographs. 1890–1925. [n. p., n. d.]
   2 v. 24 cm.
   Reprints from various journals bound together and cataloged under binder's title.
   1. Medicine - Collected works.

NL 0440848   MoSU

Loeb, Hanau Wolf, 1865–1927.
   The modern practical university. Alumni oration for 1894. Missouri State University ... Columbia Missouri, E. W. Stephens, 1894.
   30 p., 1 port. 8°.

NL 0440849   NN

              C–9744
              Cat.B
Loeb, Hanau Wolf, 1865–
   Operative surgery of the nose, throat and ear. St. Louis, C. V. Mosby, 1914.
   2v. illus.

NL 0440850   ICRL DNLM

Loeb, Hanau Wolf, 1865–
   Operative surgery of the nose, throat, and ear, for laryngologists, rhinologists, otologists, and surgeons, by Hanau W. Loeb ... in collaboration with Joseph C. Beck ... ₍and others₎ St. Louis, C. V. Mosby company, 1914–17.
   2 v. illus. (part col.) col. pl. 25½ᶜᵐ.

   1. Nose—Surgery. 2. Throat—Surgery. 3. Ear—Surgery.
   Library of Congress   RF51.L7   15–7973 Revised

   OClCC ICJ MiU NcD ViU PPJ PPC
NL 0440851   DLC DNLM OrU–M IdPI ICJ CaBVaU NBuU OU

Loeb, Hanau Wolf, 1865–1927.
   A study of the anatomic relations of the optic nerve to the accessory cavities of the nose.
[St. Louis] 1909.
   34 p., 30 pl. 8°.
   Rept. : Annals of Otology, Rhinology & Laryngology, June, 1909.

NL 0440852   NN

Loeb, Hans, 1905–
   ... Ueber den infraclaviculären Herd ... Bonn, 1929.
   Inaug. - Diss. - Bonn.
   Lebenslauf.
   "Literatur-Verzeichnis": p. 24–26.

NL 0440853   CtY

Loeb, Harold, ₍1891₎– ed.
Broom. ₍An international magazine of the arts₎
   ₍Rome, Italy, 19

Loeb, Harold, 1891–
   The chart of plenty ; a study of America's product capacity based on the findings of the National survey of potential product capacity, by Harold Loeb ... and associates: Felix Frazer, Walter Polakov, Graham Montgomery, William Smith ₍and₎ Montgomery Schuyler, with a foreword by Stuart Chase. New York, The Viking press, 1935.
   xv, 180 p. diagrs. (1 fold.) 22 cm.

   1. U. S.—Econ. condit.—1918– 2. Cost and standard of living— U. S. 3. Income—U. S. 4. Consumption (Economics)—U. S. 5. Supply and demand. ɪ. Frazer, Felix, 1891– joint author. ɪɪ. Polakov, Walter Nicholas, 1879– joint author. ɪɪɪ. National survey of potential product capacity. ɪᴠ. Title. ᴠ. Title: America's product capacity.
              Full name: Harold Albert Loeb.
   HC106.3.L58   330.973   35–3250

   OrCS OrMonO
   OKentU IdU WU WaE WaTC OrP OrSaW Or MtU WaSpG WaS OEac NcD NcRS TU NN Ok PU PBm PPT PP TU KEmT CoU
NL 0440855   DLC MB ViU OClW OOxM OClU KyU OCU OCl

Loeb, Harold, 1891–
   Doodab, by Harold A. Loeb. New York, Boni & Liveright, 1925.
   287 p. 19½ᶜᵐ.

   ɪ. Title.
   Library of Congress   PZ3.L8238Do   26–139

NL 0440857   DLC FU WU WaSp IEN

Loeb, Harold, 1891–
   Full production without war, by Harold Loeb. Princeton, Princeton university press, 1946.
   xviii, 284 p. incl. tables, diagrs. 22½ᶜᵐ.
   "Index ɪ: References": p. 279–280.

   1. Economics. 2. U. S.—Economic policy. ɪ. Title.
              ₍Full name: Harold Albert Loeb₎
   Princeton univ. Library   A 46–2894
   for Library of Congress   HB171.L8
               †

   MB
   WaSp Or CU NIC NcC NcD ViU-L MiHM TxU ICJ ViU OCl
NL 0440858   NjP DLC IdU CaBVa CaBViP OrCS OrP WaS

VOLUME 338

Loeb, Harold, 1891–
Life in a technocracy, what it might be like, by Harold Loeb. New York, The Viking press, 1933.
vi p., 2 l., 3–209 p. 49¼ cm.

1. Technocracy.   I. Title.

HB87.L6   330.1   33—2244

   MH AAP GU MoU WaT OrP MiU OU OrCS NcD
NL 0440859   DLC CU OC1 OC1W OCU OO TU NN MB NcU DAU

Loeb, Harold, 1891–
The non-production of wealth, by Harold Loeb.   New York: Continental committee [1933]   15 p.   illus. (charts.)   22cm.

1. Economic planning—U. S.   I. Continental committee on technocracy.
                                                          November 6, 1942

NL 0440860   NN

Loeb, Harold, 1891–
Production for use [by] Harold Loeb. [New York, Basic books, inc., °1936]
3 p. l., 106 p. illus., diagrs. 19½ᶜᵐ.
An analysis of the findings of the National survey of potential product capacity.

1. U. S.—Econ. condit.—1918–   2. National survey of potential product capacity. 3. U. S.—Soc. condit. 4. U. S.—Indus.   I. Title.
                                                  [Full name: Harold Albert Loeb]
Library of Congress   HC106.3.L585   36—10542
                                                          [35j]   330.973

   OC1h OCU MB TU NN WaS IdPI
NL 0440861   DLC PPT OU OKentU OrPR Or OrU NcD OC1

Loeb, Harold ,
The professors like vodka [by] Harold Loeb. New York, Boni & Liveright, 1927.
252 p. 19¼ᶜᵐ.

I. Title.   27—18823
Library of Congress   PZ3.L8238Pr

NL 0440862   DLC OO MiU OCH OrU FU

Loeb, Harold, 1891–
National survey of potential product capacity.
Report of the National survey of potential product capacity, prepared under the sponsorship of the New York city housing authority and Works division of the Emergency relief bureau, city of New York; William Hodson, chairman, Emergency relief bureau; Langdon W. Post, chairman, New York city housing authority. [New York] 1935.

Loeb, Harold, 1891–
1. The stupidity of poverty. 2. Capacity vs rapacity. By Harold Loeb. New York, Continental committee [1935]
27 p. 23ᶜᵐ.
"Revised reprints from 'Common sense'."

1. U. S.—Economic policy. 2. Consumption (Economics)   I. Title.
II. Title: Capacity vs. rapacity.   [Full name: Harold Albert Loeb]
                                                          38—23428
Library of Congress   HC106.3.L587
                                                                      330.973

NL 0440864   DLC NN

Loeb, Harold 1891–
Tumbling mustard [by] Harold Loeb. New York, H. Liveright, 1929.
405 p. 20ᶜᵐ.

I. Title.
Library of Congress   PZ3.L8238Tu   29—12055

NL 0440865   DLC CaBVaU OrU TxU PP NN ViU

Loeb, Harold Albert
see
Loeb, Harold, 1891–

Loëb, Harry Brunswick.
Gullibles' ravels; an exhausting treatise on the art of singing, by Mutchadoo d'Umph. Translated from the get-tahl-yu-kan dialect by Hal Lowell. Restated, inflated, and hugely adulterated by Harry Brunswick Loëb. New York, Arts and letters publications, Rockefeller center, "Radio city" [1939]
x, 11–80 p. illus. (music) 19 x 19ᶜᵐ.
Harry Brunswick Loëb is the sole author; the other names in the title are fictitious. cf. Letter from publisher.
"First edition."
Head-pieces with one tail-piece at end.

1. Music—Anecdotes, facetiae, satire, etc.   I. Title.

                                                          A 40-3094
New York. Public library
for Library of Congress

NL 0440867   NN

Loëb, Harry Brunswick.   **M.419.36**
The opera in New Orleans. An historical sketch from the earliest days through season 1914-15.
Baton Rouge. Ramires-Jones Printing Co. 1917. 15 pp. 23 cm.
Inserted is an autograph letter from the author to Philip Hale.

L3796 — New Orleans, La. F.a. Music.   Opera. Hist. and crit.

NL 0440868   MB

LOEB, Heinrich.
Beitrage zur casuistik der hirngeschwülste, Strassburg, 1888.

NL 0440869   MBCo DNLM

Loeb, Heinrich.
Circumcision und Syphilis-Prophylaxe.
Leipzig: W. Malende, 1904
6 p.

Ti. taken from paper-cover.
Repr.: Monatsschrift für Harnkrankheiten und sexuelle Hygiene. Jhrg. 1, 1904. Heft 6.

NL 0440870   OCH

Loeb, Henri, 1805-1890,
Histoire sainte, ou Histoire des Israélites depuis la création jusqu'à la dernière destruction de Jérusalem, par le Dr. Henri Loeb. Bruxelles, Société Belge de Librairie, 1843.
285 p. 22 cm.
Lacking part of preface.

1. Jews—Religion. I. Title

NL 0440871   OKentU OCH

Loeb, Henri, 1805-1890.
The road to faith for the use of Jewish elementary schools. Translated from the German. Cincinnati, Bloch [18—]
66 p.

1. Religious education — Text-books for children.

NL 0440872   NNAJHi

Loeb, Henri,
The Road to Faith, for the use of Jewish elementary Schools. Translated by Moses N. Nathan. Phila., 1859.
66 p.

NL 0440873   PHi

Loëb, Henri.
The road to faith, for the use of Jewish elementary schools, translated from the German by M. N. Nathan. Augusta, Ga., Steam Power Press, Chronicle & Sentinel, 1864.
61 p. 16

NL 0440874   OCH

Loeb, Henri.
The road to faith, for the use of Jewish elementary schools, translated from the German of Dr. Henri Loëb ... by M. N. Nathan ... Philadelphia, Hebrew Sunday - School, 5624-[1864]
66 p. 16°.

NL 0440875   NN

LOEB, HENRI, 1805-1890.
...The road to faith, for the use of Jewish elementary schools, translated from the German of Dr. Henri Loeb... Cincinnati: American Hebrew Pub. House [etc., etc., 1870?]
66 p. 15½cm.

Title in Hebrew at head of title.

                                        SCHIFF COLLECTION.

752826A. 1. Judaism—Elementary works.
                                                          April 15, 1935

NL 0440876   NN

Loeb, Henri, 1805-1890.
El sendero de la fe para el uso de las escuelas elementales judaicas. Version española de Raquel N. Curiel del "Road to faith" por Moses N. Nathan, original aleman del Dr. Henry Loeb. Curazao, Imprenta Del Comercio, 1911.
47 p. 17 cm.
Translation of Derekh 'Emuna, Der Weg des Glaubens. (Romanized form).

1. Questions and answers—Judaism.
I. Curiel, Raquel R   tr.
II. Title

NL 0440877   OCH

Löb, Henry, 1893–
... Contribution à l'étude de la réduction des hallucinations ... Paris, 1924.
24 cm.
Thèse - Univ. de Paris.

NL 0440878   DNLM CtY

VOLUME 338

Loeb, Herbert, 1901–
Über ein Cancroidrezidiv des äusseren Lidwinkels mit Übergreifen auf den Bulbus ... Würzburg, 1931.
Inaug. -Diss. - Würzburg.
Lebenslauf.
"Literatur": p. 7.

NL 0440879   CtY DNLM

LÖB, Hermann.
Die bedeutung der mathematik für die erkenntnislehre des Nikolaus von Kues. Inaug.-diss., Freiburg. Berlin,1907.

NL 0440880   MH ICRL NN

Loeb, Hermann, 1900–
Ueber einen Fall von Lymphogranulomatose ... Cassel [1925]
22.5 cm.
Inaug. -Diss. - Berlin.
"Aus dem Landkrankenhaus Cassel. Chefarzt: Geheimer Medizinalrat Professor Dr. Rosenblath.
Lebenslauf.
Literatur: p. 14–15.

NL 0440881   CtY DNLM ICRL

Loeb, Hermann, 1881–
Die extragenitale Syphilisinfektion speziell: Der Primäreffekt der Nase.   Wuerzburg, 1906.
90 p.   8°.
Inaug. - diss. - Wuerzburg.
Bibl.

NL 0440882   ICRL DNLM

SK361
A2S7f
no.70
Loeb, Howard A
Sea lamprey spawning: Michigan streams of Lake Superior, by Howard A. Loeb and Albert E. Hall, jr. [Washington, D.C., 1952].
[2], 68 p.   maps, diagr., tables.   27 cm.
(U.S. Fish and Wildlife Service. Special scientific report: Fisheries, no. 70).
"Literature cited": p. 68.

1. Lampreys.   I. Hall, Albert E., jt. auth.
II. Title.   (Serfiss)

NL 0440883   DI

SK361
A2S7f
no.97
Loeb, Howard A
Sea lamprey spawning: Wisconsin and Minnesota streams of Lake Superior. [Washington, D. C., 1953]
[2], 36 p.   maps, tables.   27 cm.
(U.S. Fish and Wildlife Service. Special scientific report: Fisheries, no. 97)
Bibliography: p. 36.

1. Lampreys.   I. Title. (Series)

NL 0440884   DI

Loeb, Irma H.
    see   Cohen, Mrs. Irma Henriette (Loeb) 1901–

BS
580
J8L6.4
Loeb, Isaac Anderson.
The Jewess of the Apocrypha; a paper by Isaac Anderson Loeb.   Chicago, 1901.
14 p.   19 cm.

1. Judith (Jewish heroine)   I. Title

NL 0440886   OCH

Loeb, Isidor, 1868–
Civil government, local, state, and national, by Isidor Loeb ... and the History of Missouri, by Walter Williams ...   Carrollton, Mo., Democrat printing company [1907]
viii, [9]–274 p. 20ᵐ.

1. Missouri—Pol. & govt. 2. Missouri—Hist. I. Williams, Walter, 1864–1935.
Library of Congress   F466.L82   7—22826

NL 0440887   DLC KAS MoS MoU WaU-L Or

US
961MO
LOE
Loeb, Isidor, 1868–
Constitutions and constitutional conventions in Missouri, by Isidor Loeb. Columbia, Mo., The State historical society of Missouri, 1920.
1 p.l., 7–56 p. 22cm.
"Reprinted from Journal Missouri Constitutional convention of 1875."

NL 0440888   MH-L NIC

Loeb, Isidor, 1868–   342.7782 M502
Constitutions and constitutional conventions in Missouri, by Isidor Loeb. [Columbia, Mo., 1922.]
p. 189–238. 24ᵐ.
"This article is primarily concerned with the Constitutional Convention of 1875."
With this: Lehmann, F. W. The constitution of 1820. p. 239–246.
Both articles extracted from the Missouri historical review, vol. 16, no. 2.

NL 0440889   ICJ

JK5425
1875
.A15
Loeb, Isidor, 1868–   ed.
Missouri. Constitutional convention, 1875.
Debates of the Missouri Constitutional convention of 1875, edited by Isidor Loeb ... and Floyd C. Shoemaker ... Columbia, Mo., The State historical society of Missouri, 1930–44.

NL 0440890

Loeb, Isidor, 1868–
Government in Missouri, local, state, and national, by Isidor Loeb ... New York, Cincinnati [etc.] American book company [1912]
2 p. l., 3–237 p. illus. 19½ᵐ. $1.00
Bound with this: A history of Missouri for the grades, by Jonas Viles ... New York, Cincinnati [etc., *1912]

1. Missouri—Pol. & govt.
Library of Congress   JK5425.1912.L7
                                            12–10640

NL 0440891   DLC MoU ICJ NN

Loeb, Isidor, 1868–
Government in Missouri; local, state, and national, by Isidor Loeb ... New York, Cincinnati [etc.] American book company [1922]
2 p. l., 3–238 p. illus. 19ᵐ.
With this is bound A history of Missouri for the grades, by Jonas Viles ... New York, Cincinnati [etc., *1922]

1. Missouri—Pol. & govt.
Library of Congress   JK5425.1922.L7
                                            22–7445

NL 0440892   DLC

Loeb, Isidor, 1868–
Government in Missouri, local, state, and national, by Isidor Loeb ... New York, Cincinnati [etc.] American book company [*1926]
2 p. l., 3–238 p. illus. 19ᵐ.
With this is bound A history of Missouri for the grades, by Jonas Viles ... New York, Cincinnati [etc., *1926]

1. Missouri—Pol. & govt.
Library of Congress   JK5425.1922.L72
                                            26–17157

NL 0440893   DLC

Loeb, Isidor, 1868–   ed.
Missouri. Constitutional convention, 1875.
Journal Missouri Constitutional convention of 1875 ... with an historical introduction on constitutions and constitutional conventions in Missouri by Isidor Loeb ... and a biographical account of the personnel of the convention by Floyd C. Shoemaker, A. M., editors ... [Jefferson City, The Hugh Stephens co., printers, 1920]

Loeb, Isidor, 1868–
The legal property relations of married parties; a study in comparative legislation ... New York, 1900.
200 p. 23½ cm.
Thesis (PH. D.)—Columbia university.
Vita.
"List of statutes and authorities": p. 180–184.
Pub. also as Studies in history, economics and public law, v. 13, no. 1.
1. Marriage. 2. Property.
                                            A 10—2039
Columbia Univ.   Libraries
for Library of Congress   [a66b½]

NL 0440895   NNC DAU NIC

Loeb, Isidor, 1868–
... The legal property relations of married parties; a study in comparative legislation, by Isidor Loeb ... New York, The Columbia university press, 1900.
197 p. 22½ᵐ. (Studies in history, economics and public law, ed. by the Faculty of political science of Columbia university. vol. XIII, no. 1)
Published also as thesis (PH. D.) Columbia university, 1901.
"List of authorities": p. 182–184.
1. Husband and wife.
                                            2–25099 Revised
Library of Congress   H31.C7   vol. 13, no. 1

NcD NN ViU PBm PPAmP PU PPB WaTC OrP OrU OrCS CaBVaU
NL 0440896   DLC CU NcU MoU WU OCU OCl ODW OU OOxM

Loeb, Isidor, 1868–
The required course in citizenship for college students.
(In National education association of the United States. Addresses and proceedings, 1921. p. 456–460)

1. Citizenship.
Library, U. S. Bur. of   Education
                                            E 22–148

NL 0440897   DHEW OU OO

Loeb, Isidor, 1868–
Syllabus of American citizenship, by Isidor Loeb ... Columbia, Mo., The Missouri book company, 1920.
1 p. l., 5–122 p. 18½ᵐ.
Contains "References."

1. Europe—Hist.—Outlines, syllabi, etc. 2. U. S.—Pol. & govt.—Outlines, syllabi, etc.
Library of Congress   D103.L75
                                            20–21329

NL 0440898   DLC

VOLUME 338

336.43 [Loeb, Isidore]
L822g   The German colonial fiscal system.
[New York, 1900]
[40]-72p.

Extract from American economic association. Publications. August, 1900.
3d series, v.1, no.3, p.[428]-60.

NL 0440899   IU NN

Loeb, Isidore, 1839-1892
A la memoire de Zadoc Kahn
see under title

BM   Loeb, Isidore, 1839-1892.
755   Biographie d'Albert Cohn.   Paris, Durlacher,
068   1878.
L6   180 p. port. 18cm.

1. Cohn, Albert, 1814-1877. I. Title.

NL 0440901   NNJ DLC-P4 MH OCH PPDrop NN

Loeb, Isidore, 1839-1892.
Borach Lévi, par Isidore Loeb. Extrait de l'Annuaire de
la Société des études juives, 3. année. Versailles, Imprimerie
Cerf et fils, 1884.
64p. 18ᶜᵐ.
Bibliography: p. [5]-9.

1. Lévi, Joseph Jean François Élie, originally Borach Lévi, b. 1721.
2. Divorce (Jewish law)

Library of Congress   HQ507.L6   23-1373

NL 0440902   DLC MH

Loeb, Isidore, 1830-1892.   *3494-55.1
La chaine de la tradition, dans le premier chapitre des Pirké Abot.
(*In* Bibliothèque de l'École des hautes études. Sciences religieuses.
Vol. 1, pp. 307-322. Paris. 1889.)

D6738 — Mishnah. Nezikin. Pirké Aboth. Crit., interp., etc.

NL 0440903   MB OCH

[Loeb, Isidore] 1839-92.
La controverse religieuse entre les chrétiens et les juifs au
moyen âge en France et en Espagne.   n. t.-p.   [Paris: E.
Leroux, 1888.]   311-337, 133-156 p.   8°.

Excerpt: Revue de l'histoire des religions. Tome 17-18.

1. Judaism and Christianity.—Con-   troversies. 2. Title.
                                             September 29, 1913.

NL 0440904   NN

Loeb, Isidore, 1839-1892.
La controverse sur le Talmud sous Saint Louis, par Isidore
Loeb... Paris: J. Baer et cie., 1881. 62 p. incl. tables. 8°.

Repr.: Revue des études juives. Tomes 1-3.
Bibliographical footnotes.

1. Talmud—Apologetics.   SCHIFF COLLECTION.
                                             July 6, 1929

NL 0440905   NN OCH

Loeb, Isidore, 1829-1892.
La correspondance de Juifs d'Espagne avec
ceux de Constantinople [Avec une lettre addressée en
1550 par les Juifs de Salonique aux Juifs de Provence]
[Paris, A. Durlacher, 1887]
p. 262-276.
Author's copy, with his Ms. Corrections.

NL 0440906   OCH

Loeb, Isidore, 1839-1892.
La correspondance des Juifs d'Espagne avec ceux de
Constantinople; avec une lettre addressée en 1550 par les
Juifs de Salonique aux Juifs de Provence par Isidore
Loeb ... Paris, A. Durlacher, 1888.
18 p. 23ᶜᵐ.
"Extrait de la Revue des études juives, t. xv."

1. Jews in Spain. 2. Jews in Constantinople. 3. Jews in Saloniki. 4. Jews
in Provence. 5. Jews—Persecutions.   I. Title.

                                             22-25853
Library of Congress   DS135.S7L8

NL 0440907   DLC OCH

Loeb, Isidore, 1839-1892.
Hirtzel Lévy, mort martyr à Colmar en
1754. Versailles: Cerf et fils, 1881.
39 p.

Repr.: Société des Études Juives.
Annuaire, année 1.

NL 0440908   OCH

Loeb, Isidore, 1839-1892.
Une inscription Hebraique de 1144 à
Béziers. Paris: J. Baer & cie., 1878.
8 p.

Repr.: Univers Israélite, no. du 15 juillet,
1878.
Bd. with: Soury, J. — Des études hebraiques
et exegetiques au moyen age ... Paris, 1367.

NL 0440909   OCH

Loeb, Isidore, 1839-1892.
Josef Haccohen et les chroniqueurs juifs.
Paris: A. Durlacher, 1888.
103 p.

Repr.: Revue des Études juives.

NL 0440910   OCH MH

DS   Loeb, Isidore, 1839-1892.
112   Le juif de l'histoire et le juif de la
.L82   légende, par Isidore Loeb. Paris, L.Cerf,
1890.
54 p. 18cm.
"Conférence faite à l'Assemblée générale de la Société juives le 25 janvier
1890."

1. Jews—Civilization.

NL 0440911   MiU NNJ MH OCH NN PPDrop

[Loeb, Isidore] 1839-1892.
Juifs; extrait du Dictionnaire universel de géographie de Vivien
de Saint-Martin publié par la librairie Hachette et cie. ... Paris:
Impr. A. Lahure, 1884. 118 p. 15cm.

"Tiré à 100 exemplaires."
"Bibliographie," p. [115]-118.

                                             SCHIFF COLLECTION.
                                             Revised
395087. 1. Jews. I. Title.   August 20, 1936

NL 0440912   NN

BS1189 Loeb, Isidore, 1839-1892.
.P8L8   La littérature des pauvres dans la Bible, par Isidore Loeb.
Préface de Théodore Reinach.   Paris, L. Cerf, 1892.
xv, 280 p. 24½ᵐ.
"Les différents morceaux dont se compose ce recueil ont paru pour la plupart
dans la Revue des études juives."—Pref.
CONTENTS.—Les Psaumes.—Le prophète Isaïe.—Les morceaux poétiques insé-
rés dans les textes de prose de la Bible.

1. Bible. O. T.—Criticism, interpretation, etc. 2. Poor—Palestine.

NL 0440913   ICU PPDrop PU OCH CtY

Loeb, Isidore, 1839-1892.
Le nombre des Juifs de Castille et de Espagne.
Paris, Durlacher, 1887.
22 p.

NL 0440914   PU-L

Judaica Loeb, Isidore, 1839-1892.
Bg19M   Un procès dans la famille des Ibn Tibbon
886Lb   (Marseille, 1255-1256) 2.éd. Paris, Alcan-
Lévy, 1886.
19p. 23cm.
Deals with Samuel ben Moses ibn Tibbon who
was a central figure in a disputed marriage
case in 1255.

1. Samuel ben Moses ibn Tibbon, fl. 1255.
2. Marriage - Jews.

NL 0440915   CtY OCH

Loeb, Isidore. 1839-1892.
Le saintenfant de La Guardia. Paris:
A. Durlacher, 1888.
32 p.

Repr.: Revue des études juives. Tome 15

NL 0440916   OCH

Loeb, Isidore, 1832-1892.
Sermon sur la mission religieuse de la
femme, prononcé au Temple Israélite de
Mulhouse, le samedi 11 juillet 1868 ...
Colmar: C. Decker, 1868.
19 p.

NL 0440917   OCH

[Loeb, Isidore] 1839-1892.
La situation des Israélites en Serbie et en Roumanie.
Paris, Imprimerie centrale des chemins de fer A. Chaix
et cᵉ, 1876.
141 p., 1 l. 21ᶜᵐ.

1. Jewish question. 2. Jews in Servia. 3. Jews in Rumania. 4. Jews
Turkey. 5. Jews—Persecutions.   I. Title.

                                             22-4952
Library of Congress   DS135.B3L6

NL 0440918   DLC MH NN

Loeb, Isidore, 1839-1892.   Ott 2956-4
La situation des Israélites en Turquie, en Serbie, et en Roumanie. Paris, J. Baer et cie. 1877.
pp. (3), v, 471 +.

Jews-Turkey|Do.-Serbia|Do.-Rumania

NL 0440919   MH TxU IaU ICU CU CtY NN OCH MB PPDrop

VOLUME 338

Loeb, Isidore, 1839-1892.
   Statuts des Juifs d'Avignon (1779)
      see under Avignon. *Jews.*

Loeb, Isidore, 1839-1892.
   Le Taxo dell'assomption de Moise.
Paris: Baer et Ce, 1879.
8 p.

Repr.: L'Univers israélite, année 35. no. 2.

NL 0440921   OCH

Loeb, Isidore, 1839-1892.
   Tables du calendrier juif depuis l'ère chré-
tienne jusqu'au XIXe siècle, avec la concordance
des dates juives et des dates chrétiennes et une
méthode nouvelle pour calculer ces tables.
24,(23)p. Paris, A. Durlacher, 1886. (Société
des études juives, Paris. Publications)

NL 0440922   OC1 DN-Ob CtY OCH PPDrop MH

Loeb, Isidore, 1839-1892.
   Über die Schrift Schaare Jeruschalajim
[by M. Reischer; described by I. Loeb]
Mitgetheilt von H. Steinschneider. [Leipzig,
1881]
   p. (207)°210.

Except: Zeitschrift des Deutschen
Palästina-Vereins. v. 4. 1881

NL 0440923   OCH

Loeb, Isidore, 1829-1892.
   La vie des métaphores dans la Bible, par
Isidore Loeb.   Paris, Leopold Cerf, 1891.
27, [1] p.   18.5 cm.
"Tiré à 150 exemplaires".
Reprinted later in his book "La littérature
des pauvres dans la Bible", Paris, 1892.

NL 0440924   CtY OCH

Loeb, Jacob Moritz, 1875-
   The business man and the public service.
(*In* National education association of the United States. Journal of
proceedings and addresses, 1916. p. 351-355)

1. Education—Societies. 2. Public schools—U. S.   I. Title.

                                                E 17-970

Library, U. S. Bur. of   Education

NL 0440925   DHEW OO OU

F
128.9
J5L6.3   Loeb, Jacob Moritz, 1875-
             Thou shalt not kill. An address
          delivered by Jacob M. Loeb of Chicago
          to the Jews of Greater New York.
          Chicago [1922?]
             31 p.   17 cm.

          1. Jews in New York (City) I. Title

NL 0440926   OCH

Loeb, Jacques, *1859-1924.*
   The antagonistic action of salts. (In: Internat. Congress on
Hygiene and Demography, XV. Washington, 1912. Transac.
Washington, 1913. 8°.   v. 2, p. 457-463.)

1. Salts.
                                                May 8, 1914.

NL 0440927   NN

Loeb, Jacques, 1859-*1924.*
   ... Artificial membrane-formation and chemical fertilization in a starfish (*Asterina*), by Jacques Loeb. Berkeley, The University press, 1905.
   cover-title, p. [147]-158. 27ᶜᵐ. (University of California publications.
Physiology. vol. 2, no. 16)
   From the Rudolph Spreckels physiological laboratory of the University
of California.

1. Fertilization (Biology) 2. Starfishes.

                                                A 11-1264

Title from Univ. of Calif.   Library of Congress

NL 0440928   CU CaBVaU OrU OU OO MiU PPAmP DLC

Loeb, Jacques, 1859-1924.
   Artificial parthenogenesis and fertilization, by Jacques
Loeb ... Originally tr. from the German by W. O. Redman-
King ... supplemented and rev. by the author. Chicago,
Ill., The University of Chicago press [1913]
   x, 312 p. illus. 22 cm.

1. Parthenogenesis (Animals)   I. King, W. O. Redman, tr.
II. Title.
Library of Congress   QH487.L72   13—24757

                PHC PU-BZ PPAN PPC OrP MtU IdU OrPR WaWW OrCS OrU-M
                WaTC NcRS NcD OC1 OC1JC OU MiU ICJ NN ViU PBm PSC CU
NL 0440929   DLC KEmT NIC NjP NcU CtY-M MiU ICRL DNLM

Loeb, Jacques, 1859-1924.
   ... Artificial parthenogenesis in molluscs, by Jacques Loeb.
Berkeley, The University press, 1903.
   cover-title, p. [7]-9. 27ᶜᵐ. (University of California publications.
Physiology. vol. 1, no. 3)

1. Mollusks. 2. Parthenogenesis (Animals) 3. Embryology. [Experi-
mental]
                                                A 11-1265
California. Univ. Library
   for Library of Congress   [QL1.C15 vol. 1, no. 3]
                                 [QH487.L725]
                                 [a39e1]   (612.082)

NL 0440930   CU CaBVaU OrU OU MiU OO DLC PPAmP

Loeb, Jacques, 1859-1924.
   Les bases physico-chimiques de la régénération, par
Jacques Loeb ... tr. de l'anglais par H. Mouton. Paris,
Gauthier-Villars et cⁱᵉ, 1926.
   ix, 172 p. illus. 22½ᶜᵐ.

1. Regeneration (Biology) 2. Regeneration (Botany)   I. Mouton, H.,
tr. II. Title.
                                                26-22451
Library of Congress   QH499.L62

NL 0440931   DLC CtY CU

Loeb, Jacques, 1859-   591.17 Q900
Die Bedeutung der Tropismen für die Psychologie. Von Jacques
Loeb, ... Vortrag gehalten auf dem VI. Internationalen Psycho-
logen-Kongress zu Genf 1909. Leipzig, J. A. Barth, 1909.
   51 p. 21½ᶜᵐ.

NL 0440932   DLC NjP MWelC CU

Loeb, Jacques.
   Beitraege zur gehirnphysiologie der würmer.
Bonn, Strauss, 1894.
   269 p.

NL 0440933   PU-BZ

Loeb, Jacques, 1859-
   ... The chemical character of the process of fertilization and its bearing upon the theory of life phenomena,
by Jacques Loeb. [Berkeley, The University press] 1907.
   p. [61]-80. 27ᶜᵐ. (University of California publications. Physiology.
vol. 3, no. 10)
   Address delivered at the 7th International zoological congress, Boston,
August 22, 1907.

1. Fertilization (Biology) 2. Life.

                                                A 11-1266

Title from Univ. of Calif.   Library of Congress

NL 0440934   CU CtY-M OrU CaBVaU PPAmP DLC NN

Loeb, Jacques, 1859-
   Die chemische entwicklungserregung des tierischen
eies. (Künstliche parthenogenese.) Von Jacques Loeb
... Mit 56 textfiguren. Berlin, J. Springer, 1909.
   xxiv, 259, [1] p. illus. 21½ᶜᵐ.

1. Parthenogenesis.   9-21847

Library of Congress   QH487.L7

                PBm PU-BZ PPAN DNLM ICJ NN MiU
NL 0440935   DLC CSt CtY-M NIC CU CtY NcD NjP PLFM

Loeb, Jacques, 1859-   L591.14
[Collected papers.]

                Extracted or reprinted from various scientific serials.

NL 0440936   ICJ

Loeb, Jacques, 1859-1924.
   Collected reprints of Jacques Loeb ... [Bonn,
etc., 1887-1924]
   7 v. illus., diagrs., plates (part fold.) 25 cm.
   Binder's title.
   With each vol. is bound a copy of : Jacques Loeb,
bibliography, comp. by Nina Kobelt, New York, 1926;
listing contents and also reprints not available.
--- --- Supplement, 1890-1913.
   38 nos. in 1 v.   25 cm.
   1. Biology - Collected works.

NL 0440937   CU MH

LOEB, Jacques, 1859-
   A collection of pamphlets. 1890-1911.

NL 0440938   MH-Z

Loeb, Jacques, 1859-1924.
   Comparative physiology of the brain and comparative psychology, by Jacques Loeb ... New York, G. P. Putnam's
sons; [etc., etc.] 1900.
   3 p. l., v-x p., 1 l., 309 p. illus. 21½ᶜᵐ. (Half-title: The science series, ed. by J. M. Cattell ... and F. E. Beddard ... [v. 8])
   Bibliography at end of each chapter.

1. Brain. 2. Psychology, Comparative.
                                                -29206
Library of Congress   QP361.L86ᴸ 1900

                IdU WaTC OrP Wa WaWW OrMonO OrCS
                NN ICJ MB ViU PWcS PU PPWI PBm CaBVaU CU FMU NBuU
NL 0440939   DLC NIC MtU ICRL NjP NcU OU MiU OO ODW

VOLUME 338

Loeb, Jacques, 1859–
Comparative physiology of the brain and comparative psychology, by Jacques Loeb ... Illustrated. London, J. Murray, 1901.

1 p. l., x p., 1 l., 309 p. illus., diagr. 22ᵐᵐ. (*On cover:* The progressive science series)

Half-title: The science series ...
Bibliography at end of each chapter.
Also pub. as v. 8 of The science series, G. P. Putnam's sons, New York, 1900.

1. Brain. 2. Psychology, Comparative.

2–22048

Library of Congress   QP361.L82

NL   0440940   DLC WU-M CaBVaU MiU

Loeb, Jacques, 1859–   **Philos. Lib.**
Comparative physiology of the brain and comparative psychology. New York, G. P. Putnam's Sons, etc. etc. 1902 [cop. 1900] pp. (3), x, (1), 309. Illus. (Science series, 8.)

NL   0440941   MH ICRL OC1W-H NcD OCU PPT PHC PBa

Loeb, Jacques, 1859–1924.
Comparative physiology of the brain & comparative psychology. New York, 1903.

NL   0440942   NjP

Loeb, Jacques, 1859–1924
Comparative physiology of the brain and comparative psychology, by Jacques Loeb ... New York, G. P. Putnam's sons: [etc., etc.] 1907.
3 p. l., v–x p., 1 l., 309 p. illus. 21½ cm.
(Half-title: The science series, ed. by J. M. Cattell ... and G. E. Beddard ... [v.8])

1. Brain. 2. Psychology, Comparative. I. Ser.

NL   0440943   Vi OC1 PU PPC

Loeb, Jacques, 1859–1924.
570.4   La conception mécanique de la vie, par J.
L825c   Loeb ... Traduit de l'anglais par H. Mouton ...
3. éd. Paris, Librairie Félix Alcan, 1914.
3 p. l., ii, 301, [1] p. illus. 18½ cm.
(On cover: Nouvelle collection scientifique)

Biological essays.

NL   0440944   NcD

Loeb, Jacques, 1859–1924.
... Concerning dynamic conditions which contribute toward the determination of the morphological polarity of organisms. ⟨First communication.⟩ By Jacques Loeb ... [tr. from Pflüger's Archiv, vol. 102, p. 152, by J. B. MacCallum. Berkeley, The University press] 1904.

p. [151]–161. illus. 27 cm. (University of California publications. Physiology. v. 1, no. 17)
From the Rudolph Spreckels physiological laboratory of the University of California.
Issued in single cover with v. 1, no. 16, of the series.

1. Regeneration (Biology) 2. Tubularia.   I. MacCallum, John Bruce, 1876–1906, tr.
[QP1.C2 vol. 1,   no. 17]   A 11—1267
California. Univ. Libr.
for Library of Congress   [a58e½]

NL   0440945   CU OO MiU NcD PPAmP OrU

Loeb, Jacques, 1859–1924.
... The control of heliotropic reactions in fresh water crustaceans by chemicals, especially CO₂. ⟨A preliminary communication.⟩ By Jacques Loeb ... [Berkeley, The University press] 1904.

3 p. 27ᵐᵐ. (University of California publications. Physiology. vol. 2, no. 1)
From the Rudolph Spreckels physiological laboratory of the University of California.

1. Heliotropism.

                                         A 11—1268
California. Univ. Libr.
for Library of Congress   [QP1.C2 vol. 2, no. 1]

NL   0440946   CU OO MiU OrU PPAmP DLC

Loeb, Jacques, 1859–1924.
... The dynamics of living matter, by Jacques Loeb ... New York, The Columbia university press, The Macmillan company, agents; [etc., etc.] 1906.

xi, 233 p. illus. 23ᵐᵐ. (Columbia university biological series. VIII)
"This book owes its origin to a series of eight lectures delivered ... at Columbia university in the spring of 1902."—Pref.

1. Physiological chemistry. 2. Reproduction. 3. Regeneration (Biology)
I. Title.

Library of Congress   QP6.L77   –10659

                PHeM OrPR IdU OrU-M OrSaW WaS CaBVaU OrCS OrU WaTC
                OCU OC1W CU ViU NN MB ICJ PBm PU PPL PPC NIC WaWW
NL   0440947   DLC DNLM NIC CtY-M MtU NcU OC1 OU OO

QD   **LOEB, J[acques],** 1859–1924.
La dynamique des phenomenes de la vie; traduit de l'Allemand par H. Daudin, [and] G. Schaeffer. Ed. française. Paris, F. Alcan, 1908.

Illustr.
Half-title: Bibliotheque scientifique internationale, 109.

NL   0440948   MH CU

Loeb, Jacques, 1859–1924.
Einleitung in die vergleichende gehirnphysiologie und vergleichende psychologie. Mit besonderer berücksichtigung der wirbellosen thiere. Von Jacques Loeb ... Mit 39 abbildungen. Leipzig, J. A. Barth, 1899.

4 p. l., 192 p. illus. 14½ᶜᵐ.
Bibliography at end of each chapter.

1. Brain. 2. Psychology. Comparative.

Library of Congress   QP361.L85   18–18379

                PPWI PPC MiU
NL   0440949   DLC NIC PPWe CtY CtY-M ICRL DNLM PU ICJ

QD   **LOEB, Jacques,** 1859–1924.
431   Die Eiweisskörper und die Theorie der
L576p   kolloidalen Erscheinungen. Berlin,
1924a   Springer, 1924.
         viii, 298 p. illus.
         Translation of Proteins and the theory
of colloidal behavior.
         Title

NL   0440950   DNLM NcD CaBVaU

Loeb, Jacques. 1859–1924.   5823.48
Experimental study of the influence of environment on animals.
(In Seward, Albert C., editor. Darwin and modern science. ... Pp. 247–270. Cambridge. 1909.)

H421 — Environment. — Morphology. Experimental.

NL   0440951   MB

1859–1924
Loeb, Jacques. ^. La fecondation chimique ... Ed. francaise ... Paris, Mercvre de France, 1911. 364 p.   YA 1200

NL   0440952   DLC

Loeb, Jacques, 1859–1924.
... La fécondation chimique. (Parthénogenèse artificielle) Traduit de l'allemand, par Anna Drzewina ... Édition française rev. et augm. par l'auteur. 3. éd. Paris, Mercvre de France, 1911.
x, 366 p., 1 l. illus. 22½ᶜᵐ.
"Achevé d'imprimer le vingt août mil neuf cent onze ..."
Bibliographical foot-notes.

1. Parthenogenesis (Animals) I. Drzewina, Anna, tr.
II. Title. Translation of Die chemische entwicklungserregung des tierischen eies.

NL   0440953   ViU

Loeb, Jacques, 1859–1924.
... The fertilization of the egg of the sea-urchin (Strongylocentrotus purpuratus and Strongylocentrotus franciscanus) by the sperm of the starfish (Asterias ochracea) by Jacques Loeb. Berkeley, The University press, 1908.

cover-title, p. [39]–53. 27 cm. (University of California publications. Physiology. v. 1, no. 6)
L.C. copy has   caption title only.
"Address delivered before the Sigma xi scientific society at Stanford university, October 13, 1908."

1. Fertilization (Biology) 2. Embryology—Echinodermata.
3. Strongylocentrotus. 4. Asteriasochracea.
QP1.C2 vol. 1, no. 6   A 11—1269
———— Copy 2   QH485.L813
California. Univ. Libr.
for Library of Congress

NL   0440954   CU DLC OrU CaBVaU

QT   **Loeb, Jacques,** 1859–1924
4   Fisiologia comparata del cervello
L825c   e psicologia comparata. Traduzione
1907   autorizzata dall'autore di Federico
         Raffaele. Milano, Sandron [1907?]
         xix, 396 p. illus., port.

         Translation of: Comparative physiology
of the brain and comparative psychology.
Includes bibliographies.

NL   0440955   DNLM CU

Loeb, Jacques, 1859–1924.
... Forced movements, tropisms, and animal conduct, by Jacques Loeb ... Philadelphia and London, J. B. Lippincott company [1918]

209 p. illus., plates, diagrs. 21ᶜᵐ. (Half-title: Monographs on experimental biology, ed. by J. Loeb ... T. H. Morgan ... W. J. V. Osterhout, vol. I)

Caption title: Tropisms.
"Literature": p. 173–205.

1. Animals, Habits and behavior of.   I. Title.   II. Title: Tropisms.

Library of Congress   QL751.L6   18–19796

                OrU OrAshS OrU-M
                ViU NcD ICJ NN MB PBm PPT PHC PP PU OC1W CaBVaU OrCS
                OrSaW WaS MiU OC1 OOxM OCU OU ODW ICRL DNLM NjP NcRS
NL   0440956   DLC NIC TU OrPS CU PHeM IdU WaTC MtU OrPR

Loeb, Jacques, 1859–1924.
... Further experiments on heterogeneous hybridization in echinoderms ... By Jacques Loeb [tr. from Pflüger's Archiv, 1904, v. 104, p. 325, by John Bruce MacCallum] [Berkeley, The University press] 1904.

p. [5]–30. illus. 27 cm. (University of California publications. Physiology. vol. 2, no. 2)
Issued in single cover with v. 2, no. 3–4, of the series.

1. Echinodermata. 2. Fertilization (Biology) 3. Embryology.
I. MacCallum, John Bruce, 1876–1906, tr.
[QP1.C2 vol. 2, no. 2]   A 11—1270

California. Univ. Libr.
for Library of Congress   [a58g½]

NL   0440957   CU PPAmP MiU OO OU CaBVaU OrU

VOLUME 338

Loeb, Jacques, 1859–1924.
... Further experiments on the fertilization of the egg of the sea-urchin ₁*Strongylocentrotus purpuratus*₁ with sperm of various species of starfish and a holothurian ₁*Cucumaria*₁ By Jacques Loeb. Berkeley, The University press, 1904.

cover-title. p. ₁83₁–85. 27ᶜᵐ. (University of California publications. Physiology. v. 1, no. 11)

1. Fertilization (Biology) 2. Echinodermata. 3. Embryology. 4. Sea-urchins.

California. Univ. Library
for Library of Congress   [QP1.C2   vol. 1, no. 11]   A 11–1271

₁a38f1₁   (612.082)

NL 0440958   CU OrU CaBVaU MiU OU DLC PPAmP

Loeb, Jacques, 1859–
... Further proof of the identity of heliotropism in animals and plants by Jacques Loeb and S. S. Maxwell. Berkeley, The University press, 1910.

cover-title. p. ₁195₁–197. 27ᶜᵐ. (University of California publications. Physiology. vol. 3, no. 17)

1. Heliotropism.   ɪ. Maxwell, Samuel Steen, 1860–   joint author.

A 11–1272

Title from Univ. of Calif.   Library of Congress

NL 0440959   CU CaBVaU OrU OU OO MiU MH PPAmP

Loeb, Jacques, 1859–1924.
Hayatin mihaniki telâkkisi ₁yazan₁ Jacques Loeb ... fransizcadan çeviren: Mehmet Karahasan ... İstanbul, Devlet basimevi, 1935.

2 p. l., 42 p. illus. 20ᶜᵐ.
"Biografya": p. ₁2₁–3.

1. Life (Biology)   ɪ. Karahasan, Mehmet, tr.   ɪɪ. Title.

Library of Congress   QH311.L73   40–24421

NL 0440960   DLC

QH651
.L6   **Loeb, Jacques,** 1859–1924.
Der Heliotropismus der Thiere und seine Uebereinstimmung mit dem Heliotropismus der Pflanzen. Würzburg, G. Hertz, 1890.

118 p. illus. 23 cm.
Bibliographical footnotes.

1. Phototaxis. 2. Phototropism.   ɪ. Title.

QH651.L62   ₁6₁–39900

ICU RPB NRU MiU CU
NL 0440961   DLC DNLM PPAN PBm CtY-M NNBC HU MdBJ MH

LOEB, Jacques, 1859–1924.
The identity of heliotropism in animals and plants, by Jacques Loeb and Hardolph Wasteneys. n.p., [1915].

pp. 3. Diagr.
"Reprinted from Title taken from cover. From Science, N.S. vol. XLI, no.1052, pp. 328–330, Feb. 26, 1915".

NL 0440962   MH

Loeb, Jacques, 1859–1924.
Jacques Loeb memorial supplement
    see under   The Collecting net.

Loeb, Jacques, 1859–1924, ed.
The **Journal** of general physiology. v. 1–
    Sept. 1918–
    New York, The Rockefeller institute for medical research, 1919–

Loeb, Jacques, 1859– 1924.   577.1 R102
Das Leben. Vortrag gehalten auf dem ersten Monisten-Kongresse zu Hamburg am 10. September 1911, von Jacques Loeb. Leipzig, A. Kröner, 1911.

46 p. 24ᶜᵐ.

NjP IU
NL 0440965   ICJ NCH NBuU NjP NNNAM NNC NNU–W NN

Loeb, Jacques, 1859–1924.
... The limitations of biological research, by Jacques Loeb. Berkeley, The University press, 1903.

cover-title. p. ₁33₁–37. 27 cm. (University of California publications. Physiology. v. 1, no. 5)

"Address delivered at the dedication of the Rudolph Spreckels physiological laboratory of the University of California, August 20, 1903."

1. Biological research—Addresses, essays, lectures.   ɪ. Title.

QP1.C2   vol. 1, no. 5   A 11–1273 rev
—— Copy 2.   QH311.L698
California. Univ. Libr.
for Library of Congress   ₁r64b¼₁†

NL 0440966   CU DLC NjP MiU OU OO PPAmP OrU CaBVaU

Loeb, Jacques, 1859–1924.
The mechanistic conception of life; biological essays, by Jacques Loeb ... Chicago, Ill., The University of Chicago press ₁*1912*₁
5 p. l., 3–232 p. illus. 22½ cm.
Reprinted from various sources.
CONTENTS.—The mechanistic conception of life.—The significance of tropisms for psychology.—Some fundamental facts and conceptions concerning the comparative physiology of the central nervous system.—Pattern adaptation of fishes and the mechanism of vision.—On some facts and principles of physiological morphology.—On the nature of the process of fertilization.—On the nature of formative stimulation (artificial parthenogenesis)—The prevention of the death of the egg through the act of fertilization.—The rôle of salts in the preservation of life.—Experimental   study of the influence of environment on animals.
1. Life (Biology) 2.   Biology—Addresses, essays, lectures.
QH311.L7   12—18019

WaWW Ur WaS IdU FMU ICRL MH
OO OCH OCl OOxM ODW TU PU ViU NcD ICJ KEmT MB OrPR
NL 0440967   DLC PPAmP PBm PPC PHC DNLM CU NN MiU

LOEB, Jacques, 1859– 1924.
The mechanistic conception of life; biological essays. [3d impression]. Chicago, Ill, University of Chicago press. [cop. 1912]

Illustr.
Reprinted from various sources.

NL 0440968   MH

Loeb, Jacques, 1894– 1924.
Méthode générale de calcul de la répartition des éclairements dans les installations d'éclairage par lampes à fluorescence et autres sources linéaires. Genève, Lampes Philips ₁1948₁

54 p. diagrs. 30 cm.

1. Electric lighting.

TK4175.L6   621.327   49–15348*

NL 0440969   DLC

Loeb, Jacques, 1859–   ed.
Monographs on experimental biology
    see under title

Loeb, Jacques, 1859–1924.
...A new proof of the permeability of cells for salts or ions ₁a preliminary communication₁ by ... Berkeley, The University press, 1906.

NL 0440971   00

Loeb, Jacques, 1859–1924.
... A new proof of the permeability of cells for salts or ions ⟨a preliminary communication⟩ by Jacques Loeb. Berkeley, The University press, 1908.

cover-title. p. ₁81₁–86. 27ᶜᵐ. (University of California publications. Physiology. v. 3, no. 11)

From the Herzstein research laboratory.

1. Physiological chemistry. 2. Osmosis. 3. Cells.

A 11–1274
California. Univ. Libr.
for Library of Congress   [QD1.C2   vol. 3, no. 11]

NL 0440972   CU CaBVaU OrU OU MiU PPAmP

Loeb, Jacques, 1859–1924.
... On a method by which the eggs of a sea-urchin ⟨*Strongylocentrotus purpuratus*⟩ can be fertilized with the sperm of a starfish ⟨*Asterias ochracea*⟩. By Jacques Loeb. Berkeley, The University press, 1903.

cover-title, 3 p. 27ᶜᵐ. (University of California publications. Physiology. v. 1, no. 1)

1. Fertilization (Biology) 2. Echinodermata. 3. Embryology. ₁Experimental₁ 4. Sea-urchins.   A 11–1275
California. Univ. Library
for Library of Congress   [QL1.C15   vol. 1, no. 1]
₁a39f1₁   (612.082)

NL 0440973   CU CaBVaU OrU OO MiU DLC NN PPAmP

Loeb, Jacques, 1859–1924.
... On an improved method of artificial parthenogenesis, by Jacques Loeb. Berkeley, The University press, 1905.

3 pt. 27 cm. (University of California publications. Physiology. v. 2, no. 9, 11 and 14)
From the Rudolph Spreckles physiological laboratory of the University of California.

1. Parthenogenesis (Animals) 2. Sea-urchins.
[QP1.C2   vol. 2, no. 9, 11, 14]   A 11–1276

California. Univ. Libr.
for Library of Congress   ₁a55c₁

NL 0440974   CU CaBVaU OrU PPAmP MiU OO OU

Loeb, Jacques, 1859–1924.
... On chemical methods by which the eggs of a mollus (*Lottia gigantea*) can be caused to become mature. By Jacques Loeb ... ₁Berkeley, The University press₁ 1905.

8 p. 27ᶜᵐ. (University of California publications. Physiology. v. 3, no. 1)
From the Herzstein research laboratory at New Monterey.

1. Parthenogenesis (animals) 2. Mollusks.
California. Univ. Library   A 11–1277
for Library of Congress   [QL1.C15   vol. 3, no. 1]
                                  [QH487.L75]
₁a39b1₁   (612.082)

NL 0440975   CU CaBVaU OrU OO MiU DLC PPAmP

LOEB, Jacques, 1859– 1924.
On egg-structure and the heredity of instinct Chicago, 1897.

NL 0440976   MH

VOLUME 338

Loeb, Jacques, 1859–*1924.*
   ... On fertilization, artificial parthenogenesis, and cytolysis of the sea urchin egg. By Jacques Loeb ... ₍tr. by John Bruce MacCallum from Pflüger's Archiv, v. 103, p. 257, 1904₎ ₍Berkeley, The University press₎ 1905.
    p. ₍73₎–81. 27ᶜᵐ. (University of California publications. Physiology. v. 2, no. 8)
    From the Rudolph Spreckles physiological laboratory of the University of California.
    Issued in single cover with v. 2, no. 7, of the series.

    1. Fertilization (Biology) 2. Parthenogenesis (Animals) 3. Cytolysis. 4. Sea-urchins. I. MacCallum, John Bruce, 1876–1906, tr.
                              A 11–1278

   Title from Univ. of Calif.   Library of Congress

  NL 0440977   CU CaBVaU OrU OO MiU PPAmP

Loeb, Jacques, 1859–1924.
   On some facts and principles of physiological morphology.
   25 p. illus.
   Biological lectures delivered at the Marine biological laboratory of Wood's Holl in the summer session of 1893. Third lecture.
   Bound 23rd with 44 other pamphlets with binder's title Physiology – Experimental biology – Cytology.

  NL 0440978   OClW

Loeb, Jacques, 1859– *1924.*
   ... On the changes in the nerve and muscle which seem to underlie the electrotonic effects of the galvanic current. By Jacques Loeb ... Berkeley, The University press, 1905.
    cover-title, p. ₍9₎–15. 27ᵐᵐ. (University of California publications. Physiology. v. 3, no. 2)
    From the Rudolph Spreckles physiological laboratory of the University of California.

    1. Electrophysiology. 2. Nerves. 3. Muscle.
                               A 11–1279

   Title from Univ. of Calif.   Library of Congress

  NL 0440979   CU CaBVaU OrU OO MiU PPAmP DLC

Loeb, Jacques, 1859–1924.
   ... On the counteraction of the toxic effect of hypertonic solutions upon the fertilized and unfertilized egg of the sea-urchin by lack of oxygen. By Jacques Loeb ... ₍Berkeley, The University press₎ 1906.
    p. ₍49₎–56. 27ᵐᵐ. (University of California publications. Physiology. v. 3, no. 7)
    From the Herzstein research laboratory at New Monterey.

    1. Sea-urchins. 2. Embryology, Experimental.
                       A 11–1280
   California. Univ. Library
   for Library of Congress   [QP1.C2 vol. 3, no. 7]
                       ₍a38b1₎   (612.082)

  NL 0440980   CU CaBVaU OrU OO OU MiU DLC PPAmP

Loeb, Jacques, 1859–1924.
   ... On the influence of the reaction of the sea-water on the regeneration and growth of tubularians. By Jacques Loeb ... ₍Berkeley, The University press₎ 1904.
    p. ₍139₎–147. 27ᵐᵐ. (University of California publications. Physiology. v. 1, no. 15)
    Translated from Pflüger's Archiv., vol. 1, p. 340, 1904, by John Bruce MacCallum.
    From the Rudolph Spreckles physiological laboratory of the University of California.

    1. Regeneration (Biology) 2. Tubularia. 3. Zoology—Ecology. I. MacCallum, John Bruce, 1876–1906, tr.
                       A 11–1281
   California. Univ. Library
   for Library of Congress   [QP1.C2 vol. 1, no. 15]
                       [QH531.L6]
                     ₍a37e1₎   (612.082)

  NL 0440981   CU CaBVaU OrU OO OU MiU PPAmP

Loeb, Jacques, 1859–1924.
   ... On the necessity of the presence of free oxygen in the hypertonic sea-water for the production of artificial parthenogenesis. By Jacques Loeb ... ₍Berkeley, The University press₎ 1906.
    p. ₍39₎–47. 27ᵐᵐ. (University of California publications. Physiology. v. 3, no. 6)
    From the Herzstein research laboratory at New Monterey.

    1. Parthenogenesis. 2. Sea-urchins.
                       A 11–1282
   California. Univ. Library
   for Library of Congress   [QP1.C2 vol. 3, no. 6]
                       ₍a38b1₎   (612.082)

  NL 0440982   CU CaBVaU OrU OO MiU DLC PPAmP

Loeb, Jacques, 1859–
   ... On the production and suppression of muscular twitchings and hypersensitiveness of the skin by electrolytes, by Jacques Loeb ... Chicago, The University of Chicago press, 1902.
    13 p. 28½ᵐ.
    Printed from First series, v. 10 (p. 3–13) of the Decennial publications of the University of Chicago.

    1. Animals, Irritability and movements in. 2. Ions. 3. Calcium, Physiological effects of.

   Library of Congress   QP401.L82 Copyright   2–19605

  NL 0440983   DLC OrP WaS OCl OO PU NBuG

Loeb, Jacques. 1859–   *3363.4.Ser.1.10
   On the production and suppression of muscular twitchings and hypersensitiveness of the skin by electrolytes.
   (In University of Chicago. Decennial publications. Series 1. Vol. 10, pp. 1–13. Chicago, 1903.)

  F5752 — Muscles. — Biological experimentation. — Skin.

  NL 0440984   MB NN OU MiU

Loeb, Jacques, 1859–1924.
   ... On the production of a fertilization membrane in the egg of the sea-urchin with the blood of certain gephyrean worms. ⟨A preliminary note.⟩ By Jacques Loeb. ₍Berkeley, The University press₎ 1907.
    p. ₍57₎–58. 27ᵐᵐ. (University of California publications. Physiology. v. 3, no. 8)

    1. Fertilization (Biology) 2. Sea-urchins.
                       A 11–1283
   California. Univ. Library
   for Library of Congress   [QP1.C2 vol. 3, no. 8]
                       ₍a37b1₎   (612.082)

  NL 0440985   CU CaBVaU OrU OO OU MiU PPAmP

Loeb, Jacques, 1859–1924.
   ... On the relative toxicity of distilled water, sugar solutions, and solutions of the various constituents of the sea-water for marine animals. By Jacques Loeb. ₍Berkeley, The University press₎ 1903.
    p. ₍55₎–69. 27 cm. (University of California publications. Physiology. v. 1, no. 7)
    "Translated from Pflüger's Archiv, vol. 97, p. 394, 1903, by J. B. MacCallum."—p. ₍55₎
    Issued in single cover with v. 1, no. 8, of the series.

    1. Toxicology. 2. Marine fauna
   L.C. copy has caption title only.
   QP1.C2 vol. 1, no. 7   A 11—1284
                    QP909.L6
   California. Univ. Libr.
   for Library of Congress   ₍a66e1₎†

  NL 0440986   CU DLC OU OO MiU PPAmP OrU

Loeb, Jacques, 1859–1924.
   ... On the segmental character of the respiratory center in the medulla oblongata of mammals, by Jacques Loeb. ₍Berkeley, The University press₎ 1903.
    p. ₍71₎–75. 27 cm. (University of California publications. Physiology. v. 1, no. 8)
    Issued in single cover with v. 1, no. 8, of the series.
    "Translated from Pflüger's Archiv, vol. 96, p. 536 ... by J. B. MacCallum."

    1. Medulla oblongata. 2. Respiration.
       vol. 1, no. 8   QL933.L6
                            A 11–1285 rev
   California. Univ. Libr.
   for Library of Congress   ₍r64b½₎†

  NL 0440987   CU DLC OO OU MiU PPAmP OrU

Loeb, Jacques, 1859– *1924.*
   The organism as a whole, from a physicochemical standpoint, by Jacques Loeb... New York: G. P. Putnam's Sons, 1916. x p., 1 l., 379 p., 2 pl. illus. 8°. (The science series.)

    1. Biology. 2. Heredity. 3. Series.
                         January 29, 1917.

  NL 0440988   NN NjP

Loeb, Jacques, 1859–1924.
   The organism as a whole, from a physicochemical viewpoint, by Jacques Loeb ... with 51 illustrations. New York and London, G. P. Putnam's sons, 1916.
    x p., 1 l., 379 p. illus., plates. 21½ᵐ.

    1. Biology. 2. Mendel's law. I. Title.
                         16—25201
   Library of Congress   QH307.L7

   MtU OrPR WaWW WaS OrCS OrAshS CaBVaU WaTC
   OOxM ViU NcD PPPL PBm PPT PSC PHC PP CU MiU NIC ICRL
   L 0440989   DLC MBCo ICJ NN TU DNLM OCU OU OClCC OO

Loeb, Jacques, 1859–
   ... El organismo vivo en la biología moderna, desde un punto de vista físico-químico; por Jacques Loeb ... Versión española de Mario Gracia Banús ... Madrid [Impr. Clásica española] 1920.
    xv, 382 p. illus., tables, diagrs. 19 cm.
    At head of t.-p.: Junta para ampliación de estudios é investigaciones científicas.
    I. Gracia Banús, Mario, tr. II. Spain. Junta para ampliación de estudios é investigaciones científicas.

  NL 0440990   CU

QH546   Loeb, Jacques, 1859–1924
L6   Die orientirung der Thiere gegen das Licht
Biological   (Thierischer Heliotropismus; ₍und₎) Die Orien-
Sciences   tirung der Thiere gegen die Schwerkraft der
Library   Erde (Thierischer Geotropismus.)

    (In Sitzungs-Berichte des Physikalische-Medicinischen Gesellschaft zu Würzburg. Jahrgang 1888, no. 1, p. 1–10. 26 cm.) Photoprint.

  NL 0440991   RPB

QP6   Loeb, Jacques, 1859–*1924.*
.L79   [Papers on physiology. Boston[etc.]1892–97]
    4 pam. in 1 v.

    Reprinted or extracted from scientific serials.

    1. Physiology—Collected works.

  NL 0440992   ICU

VOLUME 338

Loeb, Jacques, 1859–1924.
... The possible influence of the amphoteric reaction of certain colloids upon the sign of their electrical charge in the presence of acid and alkalis. By Jacques Loeb ... ₍Berkeley, The University press₎ 1904.
₍149₎–150 p. 27 cm. (University of California publications. Physiology. v. 1, no. 16)
From the Rudolph Spreckels physiological laboratory of the University of California.
Issued in single cover with v. 1, no. 16, of the series.
1. Chemistry, Physical and theoretical. 2. Electrolysis. 3. Ions. 4. Physiological chemistry.
QP1.C2 vol. 1, no. 16
QP525.L7
A 11—1286

California. Univ. Libr.
for Library of Congress ₍a66g½₎†

NL 0440993 CU MiU PPAmP OO OrU DLC

541.3452
L82Nf Loeb, Jacques, 1859–1924.
1924 Les protéines. Traduit de l'anglais par H. Mouton. ₍Paris₎ Alcan, 1924.
viii,242p. illus. 19cm. (Nouvelle collection scientifique)

1. Proteins. 2. Colloids.

NL 0440994 KU NjP MH

Loeb, Jacques, 1859–1924.
Proteins and the theory of colloidal behavior, by Jacques Loeb ... 1st ed. New York ₍etc.₎ McGraw-Hill book company, inc., 1922.
xi, 292 p. incl. illus., tables, diagrs. pl. 21 cm. (Half-title: International chemical series)

1. Proteins. 2. Colloids. I. Title.
22—11435
Library of Congress ₍QD431.L7₎

PSt PPSKF IdU CaBVaU
MiU OO DNLM ICJ OC1JC ViU OC1L PBm PHC PSC PPC MB
NL 0440995 DLC KEmT NcD-MC ViU CU ICRL NcRS OC1CC

Loeb, Jacques, 1859–1924.
Proteins and the theory of colloidal behavior, by Jacques Loeb ... 2d ed. New York ₍etc.₎ McGraw-Hill book company, inc., 1924.
xiv, p., 1 l., 380 p. incl. illus., tables, diagrs. pl. 21ᶜᵐ. (Half-title: International chemical series, H. P. Talbot ... consulting editor) $3.50

1. Proteids. 2. Colloids. I. Title.
24—32121
Library of Congress QD431.L7 1924

PU-BZ
OU MiU DNLM ViU NcD ICJ MB PPT-M WaS WaTC CaBVaU
NL 0440996 DLC OKentU OC1JC MH NIC PPD CU OC1W OC1

Loeb, Jacques. 1859–1924
The recent development of biology.
(In Congress of Arts and Science ... St. Louis, 1904. Vol. 5, pp. 13–24. Boston. 1906.)
*7916.102.5

G2906 — Biology.

NL 0440997 MB

Loeb, Jacques, 1859–1924.
Regeneration from a physico-chemical viewpoint, by Jacques Loeb ... 1st ed. New York ₍etc.₎ McGraw-Hill book company, inc., 1924.
ix p., 1 l., 143 p. illus. 23½ᶜᵐ. (Half-title: Agricultural and biological publications; C. V. Piper, consulting editor)

1. Regeneration (Biology) 2. Regeneration (Botany)
24—10928
Library of Congress QH499.L6

OrU-M WaTC CaBVaU DNLM
OC1JC NcD MtU IdU PPAmP OrPR OrCS PPT PHC PU-BZ OrU
NL 0440998 DLC CU ICRL TxU NcRS OU OCU OC1 OO ICJ

LOEB, Jacques, 1859–1924.
Regeneration from a physico-chemical viewpoint. 1st ed. 2d impression. New York, etc., McGraw-Hill Book Co., Inc., 1924.

Illustrs.
Half-title: McGraw-Hill publications in the agricultural and botanical sciences

NL 0440999 MH

Loeb, Jacques, 1859–1924.
Reprints. ₍v. p., 1887–1926₎
6 v. illus. 25 cm.

Binder's title.
English, German or French.
"Jacques Loeb bibliography, compiled by Nina Kobelt": v. 1 ₍no. 1₎
Includes bibliographies.

Contents.—1. 1887–1904.—2. 1905–1911.—3. 1911–1914.—4. 1915–1918.—5. 1919–1921.—6. 1922–1926.

1. Physiology—Collected works.

QP6.L79
61—57172

NL 0441000 DLC

577.4
L82r Loeb, Jacques, 1859–1924.
The rôle of salts in the preservation of life. [New York, 1911?]
13p.

Reprint from Science, n.s., v.34, no.881, p.653–665, November 17, 1911.

NL 0441001 IU

LOEB, Jacques, 1859–1924.
Die selbstörungen nach verletzung der grosshirnrinde. Nach versuchen am hunde. Strassburg, 1884.

NL 0441002 MBCo DNLM

Loeb, Jacques, 1859–1924.
Studies in general physiology, by Jacques Loeb ... Chicago, The University of Chicago press, 1905.

2 v. illus. 22½ cm. (₍Chicago. University₎ The decennial publications. 2d series. vol. xv)

"Only a small number of these papers appeared originally in English ... The other papers were translated from the German by Professor Martin H. Fischer ..."—Preface.
Paged continuously.

1. Physiology—Collected works. 2. Tropisms. 3. Regeneration (Biology)

QP6.L8
5—6953

OrU-M
PPC ViU ICJ NN MB DNLM NcD WaTC MtU IdU OrPR WaWW
NL 0441003 DLC KEmT NjP CU NcU ICRL PBm PSC PU PHC

Loeb, Jacques, 1859–1924.
La théorie des phénomènes colloïdaux... tr. de l'anglais par H. Mouton... ₍Paris₎ Alcan, 1925.
292 p. illus. 19 ᶜᵐ. (Nouvelle collection scientifique)

Bibliographical foot-notes.

1. Colloids. I. Mouton, Henri, tr.

NL 0441004 NjP

Loeb, Jacques, 1859–1924.
... The toxicity of atmospheric oxygen for the eggs of the sea-urchin ₍Strongylocentrotus purpuratus₎ after the process of membrane formation. By Jacques Loeb ... ₍Berkeley, The University press₎ 1906.
p. ₍33₎–37. 27ᶜᵐ. (University of California publications. Physiology. v. 3, no. 5)
From the Herzstein research laboratory at New Monterey.

1. Sea-urchins. 2. Embryology, Experimental.
A 11—1287
California. Univ. Library
for Library of Congress ₍QP1.C2 vol. 3, no. 5₎
₍a38b1₎ (612.082)

NL 0441005 CU CaBVaU DLC PPAmP

Loeb, Jacques, 1859–1924.
574.162
L825U Über das Wesen der formativen Reizung ... Berlin, J. Springer, 1909.
34 p. illus. 22 cm.

"Vortrag gehalten auf dem XVI. Internationalen Medizinischen Kongress in Budapest 1909."

1. Parthenogenesis. I. Title.

NL 0441006 NcD IU ICJ NjP DNLM CU

Loeb, Jacques, 1859–1924.
... Über den chemischen charakter des befruchtungsvorgangs und seine bedeutung für die theorie der lebenserscheinungen. Vortrag gehalten auf dem Internationalen zoologenkongress zu Boston am 22. august 1907, von Jacques Loeb. Leipzig, W. Engelmann, 1908.
2 p. l., 31 p. 23½ᶜᵐ. (Added t.-p.: Vorträge und aufsätze über entwickelungsmechanik der organismen ... hrsg. von prof. Wilhelm Roux. hft. 11)
"Anmerkungen und literaturnachweise": p. ₍26₎–31.

1. Fertilization (Biology)
A C 35—2594
Title from Princeton Univ. Printed by L. C.

NL 0441007 NjP DNLM PU-Z NjNbS CtY-M CU ICJ

Loeb, Jacques, 1859–1924.
Ueber die natur der bastardlarve zwischen dem echinodermenei; strongylocentrotus franciscanus, und molluskensamen; chlorostoma funebrale. Lpz., Engelmann, 1908.
482 p.

NL 0441008 PU

Loeb, Jacques, 1859–1924.
591.162 Q600
*7235 Untersuchungen über künstliche Parthenogenese und das Wesen des Befruchtungsvorgangs, von Jacques Loeb ... . Deutsche Ausgabe unter Mitwirkung des Verfassers herausgegeben von E. Schwalbe ... . Mit 12 Abbildungen. Leipzig, J. A. Barth, 1906.
viii, 532 p. 12 illus. 20ᶜᵐ.
A collection of papers previously published in various scientific serials.
Contents.—1. Experimente über Furchung. — 2. Über die Natur des Befruchtungsprozesses und die künstliche Erzeugung von normalen Larven (Pfotei) aus den unbefruchteten Eiern des Seeigels. — 3. Über die Ionen der Eiweissubstanzen und ihre Rolle in der Mechanik der Lebenserscheinungen. Der giftige Character einer reinen NaCl-Lösung. — 4. Über die verschiedenen Wirkungen der Ionen auf myogene und neurogene rythmische Zusammenziehungen und auf embryonale und Muskelgewebe.—

künstliche Erzeugung von normalen Larven aus den unbefruchteten Eiern des Seeigels (Arbacia). — 6. Über die künstliche Parthenogenese bei Seeigeln. — 7. Weitere Experimente über künstliche Parthenogenese und die Natur des Befruchtungsprozesses. — 8. Experimente über künstliche Parthenogenese bei Anneliden (Chaetopterus) und die Natur des Befruchtungsprozesses. — 9. Über Eireifung, natürlichen Tod und Verlängerung des Lebens beim unbefruchteten Seesternei (Asterias Forbesii) und deren Bedeutung für die Theorie der Befruchtung. — 10. Über Methoden und Fehlerquellen der Versuche über künstliche Parthenogenese. — 11. Weitere Versuche über künstliche Parthenogenese. — 12. Künstliche Parthenogenesis bei Mollusken. — 13. Über Befruchtung, künstliche Parthenogenese und Cytolyse des Seeigels. — 14. Über die Natur der Lösungen, in welchen sich die Seeigeleier zu entwickeln vermögen.—

15–17. Über eine verbesserte Methode künstlicher Parthenogenesis. — 18. Künstliche Membranbildung und chemische Befruchtung bei einem Seestern (Asterina). — 19. Über eine chemische Methode, durch welche Molluskeneier (Lottia gigantea) zur Reife gebracht werden können. — 20. Über die Befruchtung von Seeigeleiern durch Seesternsamen. — 21. Über die Reaktion des Seewassers und die Rolle der Hydroxylionen bei der Befruchtung der Seeigeleier. — 22. Weitere Versuche über heterogene Hybridisation bei Echinodermen. — 23. Die Giftigkeit des atmosphärischen Sauerstoffes für die Eier des Seeigels (Strongylocentrotus purpuratus) nach dem Prozess der Membranbildung. — 24. Von der Notwendigkeit des Vorhandenseins von freiem Sauerstoff für die hypertonischen Seewasser für die Erzeugung künstlicher Parthenogenese. — 25. Über die Hemmung der Giftwirkung der hypertonischen Lösungen auf das befruchtete und unbefruchtete Ei des Seeigels durch Sauerstoffmangel.

NL 0441011 ICJ WU NIC InU CSt PU-Z NIC DNLM

1859–1924
Loeb, Jacques. Untersuchungen zur physiologischen morphologie der thiere. i. Würzburg. 1891 [1890]. 8°. Bilds. and pl ᵉᵉ. MZ.
Contents:—1. Ueber heteromorphose.

NL 0441012 MH MH-Z PBm

Adelmann Loeb, Jacques, 1859–1924.
QL Untersuchungen zur physiologischen
799 Morphologie der Thiere. Würzburg, G.
L82 Hertz, 1891–92.
2 v. in 1. illus. 24cm.

Contents.—1. Ueber Heteromorphose.—
2. Orgarbildung und Wachsthum.

1. Morphology (Animals)

IaU DNLM
NL 0441013 NIC MWelC NjP CtY-M NcD-MC CU NNC MiU

VOLUME 338

Loeb, Jacques, 1859-1924.
 Kunitz, Moses, 1887-
 Valency rule and alleged Hofmeister series in the colloidal behavior of proteins, by Moses Kunitz ... ₍Baltimore, 1924₎

NL 0441015   CtY-M CU

Loeb, Jacques, 1859-1924.
 Vorlesungen über die Dynamik der Lebenserscheinungen. Von Jacques Loeb ...   Leipzig, J.A. Barth, 1906.
 4 p. l., 324 p.   illus.   24 cm.

NL 0441016   CtY-M CU

Loeb, Jacques, 1859-1924.
 Weitere mittheilungen über pankreon...   München, J. F. Lehmann, n. d.
 Cover-title: 8 p.

 Separatabdruck aus der Münchener medicinischen wochenschrift no.31, 1901.

NL 0441016   MiD-B DNLM

Loeb, Jacques,
 Weitere untersuchungen über den heliotropismus der thiere & seine uebereinstimmung mit dem heliotropismus der pflanzen; heliotropische krümmungen bei thieren.
 Bonn, 1890.
 416 p.

NL 0441017   PBm

Loeb, Jacques,
 Weitere versuche ueber die entwicklungserregung des seeigeleies durch das blutserum von saeugethieren.
 Bonn, Hager, 1908.
 51 p.

NL 0441018   PU

Loeb, Jacques, 1859-1924.   505.3 16 v.4
 Zur neueren Entwicklung der Biologie. Vorgetragen auf dem internationalen Kongress für Kunst und Wissenschaft zu St. Louis von Jacques Loeb.
 (*In* Annalen der Naturphilosophie. Leipzig, 1905. 24ᶜᵐ. Vierter Band, p. [188]-203.)

NL 0441019   ICJ CU

QP341   Loeb, Jacques, 1859-1924.
.L8   ...Zur theorie des galvanotropismus. V. mittheilung. Influenzversuche. Von Jacques Loeb ... Bonn, E.Strauss, 1897.
     cover-title, p.[483]-491. illus. 23ᶜᵐ.
     From the Hull physiological laboratory of the University of Chicago.
     "Separat-abdruck aus dem Archiv für die ges. physiologie, bd.67."

NL 0441020   ICU

Loeb, James, 1867-1933, tr.
 Couat, Auguste Henri, 1846-1898.
 ... Alexandrian poetry under the first three Ptolemies, 324-222 B. C., with a supplementary chapter by Emile Cahen; translated by James Loeb ... London, W. Heinemann, ltd.; New York, G. P. Putnam's sons, 1931.

Loeb, James, 1867- tr.
 Croiset, Maurice, 1846-1935.
 Aristophanes and the political parties at Athens by Maurice Croiset; translated by James Loeb, A. B. London, Macmillan and co., limited, 1909.

Loeb, James, 1867-
 Die bronzen der Sammlung Loeb, hrsg. von Johannes Sieveking. München, 1913.
 vi, 86 p. illus. 46 p. 30½ᶜᵐ.

 1. Bronzes. 2. Art—Private collections.   I. Sieveking, Johannes, ed.
                                                            15-55

Library of Congress   NB135.L6

       MB CU NN NNU CSt
NL 0441023   DLC MdBWA CaBVaU OC1W CtY NcD OC1MN MiU

Loeb, James, 1867-
 ... Bronzen, terrakotten, vasen der sammlung Loeb, herausgegeben von Johannes Sieveking, mit einem geleitwort von James Loeb. München, A. Buchholz, 1930.
 6 p. l., 65 p. illus. 53 pl. 29ᶜᵐ.
 Greek motto at head of title.
 Title within architectural border.
 Bibliography : 4th prelim. leaf.

 1. Art objects, Classical. 2. Art objects—Private collections. 3. Bronzes. 4. Terra-cottas. 5. Vases, Greek.   I. Sieveking, Johannes, ed.
                                                            30-13947

Library of Congress   NK665.L6

       MdBWA OC1MA OCU MiU PU PBm NBuU NcD MsU MU
NL 0441024   DLC CU MiDA CLSU TxHST OC1W CtY MH

Loeb, James, 1867-
 Catalogue of the Loeb collection of ancient bronzes...
         see under   Harvard University.
 William Hayes Fogg Art Museum.

Loeb, James, 1867- tr.
 Decharme, Paul, 1839-1905.
 Euripides and the spirit of his dramas, by Paul Decharme ... tr. by James Loeb, A. B. New York, The Macmillan co.; London, Macmillan & co., ltd. ₍1906₎

Loeb, James, 1867-
 Festschrift für James Loeb zum sechzigsten geburtstag gewidmet
         see under title

Loeb, James, 1867-
 A guide to the Loeb collection of Arretine pottery in the Fogg museum of art, by George H. Chase ... Cambridge, Harvard university, 1908.
 30 p. 23ᶜᵐ.
 "Bibliography": p. 26.

 1. Pottery, Roman.   I. Chase, George Henry. II. Harvard university. William Hayes Fogg art museum. III. Title: Arretine pottery.

NL 0441028   MiU PBm IU

Loeb, James, 1867-1933.
 ... The Loeb collection of Arretine pottery, catalogued, with introduction and descriptive notes, by George H. Chase, PH. D. New York, 1908.
 viii, 167, ₍1₎ p. XXIII pl. (part double) 30ᶜᵐ.
 "The collection is in the Fogg museum of art, Harvard university."—Pref.

 1. Pottery, Roman. 2. Pottery—Private collections. 3. Classical antiquities. I. Chase, George Henry, 1874- II. Harvard university. William Hayes Fogg art museum. III. Title : Arretine pottery.
                                                            8—13284

Library of Congress   NK3850.L8

       OC1 OCU MdBWA PHC PU PPDrop MB
NL 0441029   DLC NcD MH MsU WaS TxU CU MB OC1MA

Loeb, James, 1867- tr.
 Legrand, Philippe Ernest, 1866-
 The new Greek comedy, κωμῳδία νέα, by Ph. E. Legrand ... tr. by James Loeb, A. B., with an introduction by John Williams White ... London, W. Heinemann; New York, G. P. Putnam's sons, 1917.

Loeb, James, 1867-
 ... Die terrakotten der sammlung Loeb, hrsg. von Johannes Sieveking, mit einer einleitung von James Loeb ... München, A. Buchholz, 1916.
 2 v. illus. 128 pl. 29½ᶜᵐ.
 Title within architectural border.

 1. Terra-cottas, Greek. 2. Art objects—Private collections.   I. Sieveking, Johannes, ed. II. Title.
                                                            21—10148

Library of Congress   NB155.L4

       MiU NcD CU NN InU MU NcU IU MiDA CLSU TxU NcU
NL 0441031   DLC FTaSU PU OC1W NPV MdBWA CtY OO OC1

Loeb, James, 1867- 1933.
 Classical conference, *Ann Arbor, Mich.*, 1909.
 The value of humanistic, particularly classical, studies as a training for men of affairs; a symposium from the the Proceedings of the Classical conference held at Ann Arbor, Michigan, April 3, 1909 ... ₍Ann Arbor, Mich., 1909₎

Loeb, Jean.
 ... Etude des phénomènes diastiques dans les farines de froment et contribution à l'étude de fermentation panaire ...   [Strasbourg, n. d.]
 Thèse - Univ. de Strasbourg.
 "Documentation": p. 196-197.

NL 0441033   CtY

Loeb, John Jacob, 1910-
 Among the missing. Words by Paul Francis Webster. Music by John Jacob Loeb.   ₍New York₎ Harms inc., c1933.
 First line: When the evening fog descends.
 Chorus: Searching for a girl among the missing.

                              Printed for the Music Division
 I. Webster, Paul Francis.   II. Song index (3).
 N. Y. P. L.   August 20, 1948

NL 0441034   NN

Loeb, John Jacob, 1910-
 The birthday of a kiss. Words by Paul Francis Webster. Music by John Jacob Loeb and Rudy Vallee...   New York, L. Feist, inc. ₍c1931₎
 First line: Here am I so lonely and blue.
 Chorus: While I'm sitting alone.
 Featured by Ben Alley.
 Portrait of Ben Alley on t-p.

                              Printed for the Music Division
 1. Kissing. 2. Loneliness. 3. Alley,   Ben—Port. I. Webster, Paul Francis,
 1907-   II. Vallee, Rudy, 1901-   III. Song index (3).
 N. Y. P. L.   November 20, 1950

NL 0441035   NN

Loeb, John Jacob, 1910-
 Disillusioned. Lyric by Paul Francis Webster. Music by John Jacob Loeb.   New York, De Sylva, Brown and Henderson, inc. ₍c1934₎
 First line: Love found me so free.
 Chorus: I'm disillusioned with love.

                              Printed for the Music Division
 1. No subject. I. Webster, Paul   Francis. II. Song index (3).
 N. Y. P. L.   April 23, 1946

NL 0441036   NN

VOLUME 338

Loeb, John Jacob, 1910–

The first kiss of spring. Lyric by Paul Francis Webster. Music by John Jacob Loeb. New York, L. Feist, inc., c1934.

First line: The chimes on the steeple.
Chorus: Allow me to take you.

1. Spring. 2. Kissing. I. Webster,
N. Y. P. L.   Paul Francis. II. Song index (3),
                                        April 30, 1946

NL 0441037 NN

Loeb, John Jacob, 1910–

Frosted chocolate... Lyric by Billy Rose and Paul Francis Webster. Music by John Jacob Loeb... New York, Harms inc. ₍c1934₎

First line: Saw a limousine a minute ago.
From the revue Casino de Paree.

1. United States—N.Y.—New   Printed for the Music Division
1899–. II. Webster, Paul   York—Harlem. I. Rose, Billy,
index (2).   Francis, 1907– . III. Song
NN

NL 0441038 NN

Loeb, John Jacob, 1910–

Got the jitters. Lyrics by Billy Rose & Paul Francis Webster. Music by John Jacob Loeb. New York, Keit-Engel inc., c1934.

First line: I get up at nine.

1. Nervousness. 2. Slang phrases.   Printed for the Music Division
Paul Francis. III. Song index (2).   I. Rose, Billy. II. Webster,
N. Y. P. L.   April 30, 1946

NL 0441039 NN

Loeb, John Jacob, 1910–

Horses don't bet on people. Words and music by John Jacob Loeb... New York, Advanced music corp. ₍c1945₎

First line: Sitting alone in the shadows.
Featured by Kay Kyser and his orchestra.
Portrait of Kay Kyser on t.-p.

1. Gambling. 2. Horses. 3. Kyser,   Printed for the Music Division
N. Y. P. L.   Kay—Port. I. Song index (2).
                                        December 5, 1947

NL 0441040 NN

Loeb, John Jacob, 1910–

How can I say I love you. By John Jacob Loeb, Lewis Harris and Cy Coben... New York, Mayfair music corp. ₍c1947₎

First line: There are certain things.
Featured by Tex Beneke and the Glenn Miller orchestra.
Portrait of Tex Beneke on t.-p.

1. Love. 2. Beneke, Tex—Port.   I. Harris, Lewis. II. Coben, Cy.
III. Song index (2).
N. Y. P. L.   August 2, 1948

NL 0441041 NN

Loeb, John Jacob, 1910–

I do! Fox-trot song. Lyric by Paul Francis Webster. Music by John Jacob Loeb and Lester Banker. New York, L. Feist, inc. ₍c1933₎

First line: Here comes my future destiny.
Chorus: Now do I take this girl.

1. Weddings. I. Webster, Paul   Printed for the Music Division
III. Song index (3).   Francis. II. Banker, Lester.
N. Y. P. L.   June 6, 1947

NL 0441042 NN

Loeb, John Jacob, 1910–

Masquerade. Lyric by Paul Francis Webster. Music by John Jacob Loeb. New York, L. Feist, inc. ₍c1932₎

First line: Sometime soon to be.
Chorus: Twilight soon will fade.

1. Parties. I. Webster, Paul   Printed for the Music Division
N. Y. P. L.   Francis. II. Song index (3),
                                  December 5, 1947

NL 0441043 NN

Loeb, John Jacob, 1910–
Me minus you
    see under   Baer, Abel, 1893–

LOEB, JOHN JACOB, 1910–

My religion is you. Lyric by Paul Francis Webster. Music by John Jacob Loeb New York, Red star music co., inc. [c1930]

First line: I was sad the whole day long.
Chorus: You've ended all my guessing.
1. Songs, Popular—1890– I. Webster, Paul Francis, 1907–

NL 0441045 NN

Loeb, John Jacob, 1910–

Reflections in the water. Words by Paul Francis Webster. Music by John Jacob Loeb. New York, L. Feist inc., c1933.

First line: The starlight discovers two shadows that float.

1. Reflections. I. Webster, Paul   Printed for the Music Division
N. Y. P. L.   Francis. II. Song index (2).
                                      August 20, 1948

NL 0441046 NN

Loeb, John Jacob, 1910–

Send me a picture of the baby. Words by Lew Brown. Music by John Jacob Loeb. New York, B. Miller, inc. ₍c1944₎

First line: Johnny wrote home to his sweet little wife.

1. Pictures. 2. Babies. 3. World   Printed for the Music Division
II. Song index (2).   war, 1939–1945. I. Brown, Lew.
N. Y. P. L.   May 12, 1947

NL 0441047 NN

Loeb, John Jacob, 1910–

Somebody else's picture. By John Jacob Loeb. New York, Shapiro, Bernstein & co. inc. ₍c1947₎

First line: I gave you my picture.

1. Pictures. I. Song index (2).   Printed for the Music Division
N. Y. P. L.   August 2, 1948

NL 0441048 NN

Loeb, John Jacob, 1910–

You didn't know me from Adam (and I didn't know you from Eve). Words by Robert Burk. Music by John Jacob Loeb. New York, Donaldson, Douglas & Gumble inc., c1934.

First line: You were standing over in a corner.

1. Slang phrases. I. Burk, Robert.   Printed for the Music Division
N. Y. P. L.   II. Song index (2).
                                        April 23, 1946

NL 0441049 NN

Loeb, Joseph.
Circumcision. n. t.-p. ₍Memphis, Tenn., 1893?₎
    21 p.

Title taken from first p.

Repr.: Jewish spectator of Memphis, Tenn.

NL 0441050 OCH

Loeb, Joseph.
Ueber partielle erweichende Myocarditis, malacia cordis. Würzburg, J.M. Richter, 1880.
35p. 22cm.

Inaug.-Diss.(M.D.) --Würzburg.

1.Myocarditis.

NL 0441051 NcD-MC DNLM

Loeb, Josephine R
Abstract bibliography of the chemistry, processing, and utilization of rice bran and rice bran oil, by Josephine R. Loeb and Nelle J. Morris. New Orleans, Southern Regional Research Laboratory ₍1952₎
iii, 95 p. 27 cm. (U. S. Bureau of Agricultural and Industrial Chemistry. AIC-328)

1. Rice bran—Abstracts. 2. Rice oil—Abstracts.   I. Morris,
Nelle Julian, 1898–   joint author.   (Series)
Z7914.C4U52 no. 328   53–60237
            *016.6647 016.6791318

NL 0441052 DLC MB

MT305
.O45
op. 78
.L6

Loeb, Jules, ed.

Offenbach, Jacques, 1819–1880.
₍Études, violoncelle, op. 78₎
12 études pour violoncelle, avec accompᵗ d'un second violoncelle ad-libitum, par Jacq. Offenbach. Op. 78. Nouv. éd., rev. et doigtée par J. Loeb ... 2.ᵐᵉ livre ... Paris, Costallat & cⁱᵉ ₍19—₎

MT305
.O45
op. 77
.L6

Loeb, Jules, ed.

Offenbach, Jacques, 1819–1880.
₍Petites études, violoncelle, op. 77₎
20 petites études pour le violoncelle avec accompag. de basse ad-libitum, par Jacq. Offenbach. Premier livre. Op. 77. Paris, Costallat & cⁱᵉ ₍19—₎

Q175
.C95

Loeb, Julien.

La Cybernétique; théorie du signal et de l'information ₍par₎ Julien Loeb ₍et al.₎ Réunions d'études et de mises au point tenues sous la présidence de Louis de Broglie. Paris, Éditions de la Revue d'optique théorique et instrumentale, 1951.

Loeb (Julius). * Ein Fall von multiplem Cysticercus cellulosæ der Haut. ₍Strasburg.₎ 64 pp., 1 pl. 8°. *Durkheim & Kaiserslautern, J. Eheinbercer,* ₍s. d.₎.

NL 0441056 DNLM MBCo

Loeb, Julius.
... Das hochdeutsche sprachgebiet in Belgien. Die alte deutsche stadt Arel. Arel, "Areler zeitung," 1918.
vi, ₍1₎–71 p. 19ᶜᵐ.

1. German language—Dialects—Arlon. 2. Germans in Belgium.
3. Arlon, Belgium—Hist. I. Title.
                                        44–13048
Library of Congress   PF5464.A7L6

NL 0441057 DLC NN

VOLUME 338

Loeb (Julius). *Ueber die Polypen des Uterus.*
32 pp. 8°. *Würzburg, Bauer, [n. d.]*

NL 0441058   DNLM ICRL

Beinecke
Library
Zg19
L791
860

Loeb, Julius, 1822-
Gedichte von Julius Loeb. Neustadt a.d.H.,
Buchdruckerei von D. Kranzbühler jun., 1860.
2 p. ℓ., 96 p. 16 cm.

NL 0441059   CtY

Loeb, Julius, *b.* 1822.
Puhna, die königstochter Indiens; frei übertragen von
Julius Loeb. 2. aufl. New York, Verlag der "Jewish
Times", 1872.
3 (*i. e.* 39) p. 20ᶜᵐ.
Last page incorrectly numbered 3.
In verse.

1. Title.

Library of Congress   PT2424.L59P8 1872
22-19853

NL 0441060   DLC

Loeb, Julius, *1881-*
; Ueber zwei bemerkenswerte Fälle
von Pfortaderthrombose. Bonn (1909): Trapp. 26 S. 8°
Bonn, Med. Diss. v. 28. Jan. 1909, Ref. Ribbert
[Geb. 10. Juli 81 Hüffelsheim; Wohnort: Elberfeld; Staatsangeh.: Preußen;
Vorbildung: Gymn. Dillenburg Reife M. 02; Studium: Berlin 1, München
9 S.; Coll. 26. Jan. 09; Approb. 14. Jan. 09.]   [U 09. 352

NL 0441061   ICRL MBCo DNLM

Loeb, Julius, 1894-
HE6375 ... The pony express ... [Federalsburg, Md.,
L7   1930]
p. [91]-120. illus. 25.5 cm.
In a complete number of the American philatelist
November 1930, v. 44, no. 2,
Caption title.
1. Express service—The West. 2. Postal ser-
vice—U. S.—Hist. I. Title.

NL 0441062   CSmH

Loeb, Julius, 1894-   *jurist*
Das dingliche wohnungsrecht (§ 1093 B. G. B.) ... Braun-
schweig, Druckerei R. Sievers [1922]
5 p. l., [1], 30 p., 1 l. 21ᶜᵐ.
Inaug.-diss.—Breslau.
Lebenslauf.
"Literaturverzeichnis": 4th prelim. leaf.

1. Landlord and tenant—Germany.   I. Title.
29-22750

NL 0441063   DLC ICRL CtY

Loeb, Kurt, *1891-*
Die Fälle von Blennorrhoea adultorum an der Heidelberger
Universitäts-Augenklinik von 1910-1917. Bad Dürkheim
1917: Hinckel. 27 S. 8°
Heidelberg, Med. Diss. v. 11. Juni 1917, Ref. Wagenmann
[Geb. 8. Juni 91 Bad Dürkheim; Wohnort: Karlsruhe i. B.; Staatsangeh.:
Bayern; Vorbildung: G. Worms Reife 10; Studium: München 3, Rostock 1,
Heidelberg 6 S.; Coll. 20. April 17; Approb. 11. Aug. 17.]   [U 17. 954

NL 0441064   ICRL CtY DNLM

Loeb, Laurence Farmer, 1895-
... Die Kohlensäuretension in den Lungenalveolen
(Ihre Bedeutung für Regulation der Atmung und für
die Bestimmung der Acidose beim Diabetes mellitus)
...   Berlin, 1920.
1 p. l., [16]-39, [1] p.   23 cm.
Inaug.-Diss. - Berlin.
Lebenslauf.

NL 0441065   CtY

Loeb, Leo.
...Power applications to cotton-finishing plants, by Leo Loeb
...   [New York, 1920.]   19 p.   diagrs., illus.   8°.
"To be presented at the annual meeting of the American Society of Mechanical
Engineers...New York, Dec. 7-10, 1920."

1. Cotton manufacture.
N. Y. P. L.
May 17, 1922.

NL 0441066   NN

Loeb (Leo). *Ueber die Secretionsnerven der
Parotis und über Salivation nach Verletzung des
Bodens der vierten Ventrikels.* 28 pp. 4°.
Giessen, F. C. Pietsch, 1889.

NL 0441067   DNLM ICRL PPC

Loeb, Leo, 1869-*1959*
Beiträge zur analyse des gewebewachstums.
I. Über transplantation regenerierenden epithels
und über serientransplantation von epithel ...
Leipzig, Engelmann, 1907.
cover-title, p. [637]-655.

"Sonderabdruck aus dem Archiv für entwicklungs-
mechanik der organismen ... XXIV. band, 4. heft."

1. Skin-grafting. 2. Epithelium.

NL 0441068   NNC

Loeb, Leo, 1869-
The biological basis of individuality, by Leo Loeb ...
Springfield, Ill., Baltimore, Md., C. C. Thomas, 1945.
xiii, 711 p., 1 l.   25½ cm.
"First edition."
Bibliography: p. 659-695.

1. Individuality. 2. Transplantation of organs, tissues, etc.
I. Title.

QH501.L6   612.605   45—18

MiHM OrP WaSpG OrPR OrPS
PSC PBm PPT CU PCM NcD OrU PPEB CaBVaU OrU-M OrCS
NL 0441069   DLC NcD-MC MB MH OCU OU OO OClCC PPAN

Loeb, Leo, 1869-*1959.*
[Collected papers.]   L591.1 6
Continued.
Extracted or reprinted from various scientific serials.

NL 0441070   ICJ

Loeb, Leo, 1869-1959.
... Edema, by Leo Loeb ...   Baltimore, Williams &
Wilkins company, 1923.
4 p. l., 178 p.   24 cm.   (Medicine monographs. vol. III)
"References": p. 155-178.

1. Edema.

RB149.L6   23—17964

NL 0441071   DLC ViU DNLM NcD ICJ PPC

LOEB, Leo, *1869-1959.*
On regeneration in the pigmented skin of
the frog,***. Baltimore, 1904.

NL 0441072   MH-Z

RC261
L82

Loeb, Leo, 1869-
Some recent contributions to the etiology of
cancer ... [1904?]
cover-title, 7 p.

"Read before the Pathological society of
Philadelphia, December, 1903".

1. Cancer - Etiology and pathogenesis.
2. Tumors.

NL 0441073   NNC

WH
L825u
1897

LOEB, Leo, 1869-
Über die Entstehung von Bindegewebe,
Leucocyten und roten Blutkörperchen
aus Epithel; und über eine Methode,
isolierte Gewebsteile zu züchten.
Chicago, Stern, 1897.
56 p.

NL 0441074   DNLM NNC PPWI

Loeb, Leo, 1869-
... Über transplantation von weisser haut auf
einen defekt in schwarzer haut und umgekehrt
am meerschweinchenohr ... Leipzig, Engelmann,
1897.
46 p.   III double plates.

Inaug.-diss., Zürich, 1897.
"Separat-abdruck aus Archiv f. entwickelungs-
mechnik. VI. band. 1. heft."

1. Skin-grafting. 2. Color of animals. 3.
Guinea-pigs.

NL 0441075   NNC DNLM

QP88
L822

Loeb, Leo, 1869-
... Untersuchungen über umwandlungen und
thätigkeiten in den geweben; zweite mitteilung
... Chicago, Stern, 1897.
cover-title, 12 p.

1. Tissues.

NL 0441076   NNC PPWI

Loeb, Leo, 1869-*1959.*
The venom of *Heloderma*, by Leo Loeb, with the collaboration of Carl L. Alsberg, Elizabeth Cooke, Ellen P. Corson-
White, Moyer S. Fleisher, Henry Fox, T. S. Githens, Samuel
Leopold, M. K. Meyers, M. E. Rehfuss, D. Rivas, and Lucius
Tuttle. Washington, D. C., Carnegie institution of Washington, 1913.
vi, 244 p. incl. illus., tables, diagrs. 25½ᶜᵐ. (On verso of t.-p.: Carnegie institution of Washington. Publication no. 177)

1. Venom. 2. Heloderma.

Library of Congress   QP941.L7   13—13102
Copy 2.   [341]

TU DSI
PP OrPR OrU CaBVaU WaWW OrCS Wa CoU UU CLSU WaU
OC1W OOxM OU ICJ MB PPAmP OrP NN ViU IdU PBm PHC
NL 0441077   DLC DI DNLM KEmT UU NcD OCU OC1MN OC1

Loeb, Leonard Benedict, 1891-
Atomic structure, by Leonard B. Loeb ... Ann Arbor,
Mich., Edwards brothers, inc., [1933.]
3 p. l., 2-117 numb. l. illus., diagrs. 27ᶜᵐ.
Lithoprinted, on one side of leaf only.

1. Atoms.
CA 34-855 Unrev'd
Library of Congress   QC173.L84
539

NL 0441078   DLC CU

VOLUME 338

Loeb, Leonard Benedict, 1891–
Atomic structure, by Leonard B. Loeb ... New York,
J. Wiley & sons, inc.; London, Chapman & Hall, limited, 1938.
xvi, 446 p. illus., diagrs. 23½ᵐ.
Bibliography at end of last chapter.

1. Atoms. I. Title.
Library of Congress   QC173.L84 1938   38—25479
——— Copy 2.
Copyright A 120484   [a40k3]   539

    OrU OrCS CaBVaU KEmT NBC CLU FTaSU OkU
    OC1W ICJ ViU IdPI CU PSC OrPR PPT PPF IdU WaWW MtBC
NL   0441079   DLC Or Tu NRU ICU NcRS NcD OC1 OCU OLak

Loeb, Leonard Benedict, 1891–
Basic processes of gaseous electronics. Berkeley, University of California Press, 1955.
1012 p. illus. 25 cm.
Includes bibliography.

1. Electric discharges through gases. 2. Electronics. I. Title.
II. Title: Gaseous electronics.

QC711.L67   537.53   55—5196 ‡

    OU CaBVaU WaS WaWW OrP
    PP PPF PPD PSt MtBC NN ICJ OrP OrCS IdU OC1W OrU PSC
NL   0441080   DLC CtY-KS MU TU MB ViU TU TxU NcD PBL

QC702
.L6   **Loeb, Leonard Benedict,** 1891–
[Collected papers, reprints, etc. on
ionization]
5 pam.
[1] Gas ion mobilities and their independence
of the nature of the ion. (From Philos. magazine,
v. 48, 1924, p. 446–458) [2] Theory of the range
of alpha-particles. [with] Edward Condon.
(Repr. Jour. Franklin inst. Nov. 1925, p. 595–
607) [3] The mobility of gas ions in HCl mixtures
and the nature of the ion. (Repr. Nat. acad. sci.,
Proc. v. 12, 1926, p. 42–4 [4] Gas ion mobilities in ether-hydrogen mixture (Ibid. v. 12, 1926,

p. 617–621) [5] Ionic mobilities in ammonia-
hydrogen mixture and an anomalous effect of
ammonia. (Ibid. v. 12, 1926, p. 677–684)

NL   0441082   DLC

Loeb, Leonard Benedict, 1891–
The development of human ideas concerning
the physical world, by ... Ann Arbor, Mich.,
Edwards brothers, c1929.
2 p.l., ii–xii, 366 numb. l.   tables, diagrs.
Lithographed.

NL   0441083   OO OU CU

Loeb, Leonard Benedict, 1891–
The development of physical thought; a survey course of
modern physics, by Leonard B. Loeb ... and Arthur S. Adams
... New York, J. Wiley & sons, inc.; London, Chapman &
Hall, limited, 1933.
xiv p., 1 l., 648 p. illus., fold. tab., diagrs. 22ᵐ. $3.75
Adams' revision of Loeb's "The development of human ideas concerning the physical world", published as a mimeographed text in 1929.
cf. Pref.

1. Physics—Hist. I. Adams, Arthur Stanton, 1896– II. Title.
III. Title: Physical thought, The development of.
    33–13612
Library of Congress   QC21.L6

    OrCS PHC PPD PSC WaWW WaS OrU OrPR Or IdU-SB MB
    MiU ViU OU KEmT CaBVaU MtBuM MtU OKentU OrSaW
NL   0441084   DLC NIC CU NcRS NcD TxU OC1 OC1W OU OCU

539.2
L82d   **Loeb, Leonard Benedict,** 1891–
The distribution of electron energies in a gas
in an electrical field. An extention[!] to the
material presented to the Electronics Institute
at the University of Michigan in July and August,
1937. Ann Arbor, Mich., Mimeographed by the
Edwards Letter Shop, c1938.
40ℓ. diagrs. 28cm.

Contains references.

1. Electric discharges through gases. I. Title.

NL   0441085   IU CU

[Loeb, Leonard Benedict] 1891–
... Effect of temperature and pressure on the sp arking voltage. National advisory committee for aeronautics. Preprint
from Fifth annual report. Washington, Govt. print. off., 1919.
11 p. diagrs. 29½ᵐ. ([U. S.] Advisory committee for aeronautics. Report, no. 54)
By L. B. Loeb and F. B. Silsbee.
"This report was confidentially circulated during the war as Bureau of standards Aeronautic power plants report, no. 14."—p. 5.
1. Gas and oil engines—Ignition. 2. Aeroplanes—Motors. I. Silsbee, Francis Briggs, 1889– joint author. II. U. S. National bureau of standards. Aeronautic power plants report, no. 14.
    19—27694
Library of Congress   TL521.A33 no. 54
——— Copy 2.   TJ787.L6

NL   0441086   DLC ICJ OU OC1 OO MiU

Loeb, Leonard Benedict, 1891–
Fundamental processes of electrical discharge in gases, by
Leonard B. Loeb ... New York, J. Wiley & sons, inc.; London, Chapman & Hall, limited, 1939.
xviii, 717 p. illus., diagrs. 23½ cm.
Includes bibliographies.

1. Electric discharges through gases.

QC711.L68   537.53   40—868

    OrCS CaBVaU
    PU OC1W OCU ICJ TU DAS ViU NcD NcRS PPT PPD PSC OrU
NL   0441087   DLC MtBC IdU OrPR WaS PLF CU OC1 OU

Loeb, Leonard Benedict, 1891–

Fundamental processes of electrical
discharge in gases. New York, J. Wiley
[1947]
xviii, 717 p. illus. 24cm.
"References" at end of each chapter.

1. Electric discharges through gases.

NL   0441088   ViU

Loeb, Leonard Benedict, 1891–
Fundamentals of electricity and magnetism, by
Leonard B. Loeb ... Ann Arbor, Mich., Edwards
brothers, c1929.
1 p.l., xiii, 284 numb. l. diagrs. 27 cm.
Lithoprinted copy.
1. Electricity- 1901–   2. Magnetism- 1901–

NL   0441089   CU

Loeb, Leonard Benedict, 1891–
Fundamentals of electricity and magnetism, by Leonard B.
Loeb ... New York. J. Wiley & sons, inc.; London. Chapman
& Hall, limited, 1931.
xx, 432 p. illus., diagrs. 24ᵐ.

1. Electricity. 2. Magnetism. 3. Electromagnetism.
    31—16392
Library of Congress   QC521.L72
——— Copy 2.

    OCU MiU MiHM MB MH OrSaW MtBuM PBm PPT PSC PHC PPD
NL   0441090   DLC NIC ViU WaTC WaS CU NcD OO ODW OC1W

537.02
T801   **Loeb, Leonard Benedict,** 1891–
Fundamentals of electricity and magnetism, by Leonard B.
Loeb ... 2d ed. New York, J. Wiley & sons, inc.; London,
Chapman & Hall, limited, 1938.
xxiv, 554 p. illus., diagrs. 24ᵐ.

1. Electricity. 2. Magnetism. 3. Electromagnetism.
    38—23708
Library of Congress   QC521.L72 1938
——— Copy 2.

    OU MiHM OOxM ICJ NcD PPT PPF PP IdB WaS
NL   0441091   DLC LU NBuC ScU OrP CaBVaU CU OC1JC OC1

Loeb, Leonard Benedict, 1891–
Fundamentals of electricity & magnetism. 3d ed. New
York, J. Wiley, 1947.
xix, 609 p. diagrs. 24 cm.

1. Electricity. 2. Magnetism. 3. Electromagnetism.
QC521.L72 1947   537   47—11162*

    ScCleU   PHC CaBVa OrPR OrPS WaS WaSpG
NL   0441092   DLC MB NcU ScU MtU TxU ICU ICJ TU OrCS

Loeb, Leonard Benedict, 1891–   joint author.

[Silsbee, Francis Briggs] 1889–
... Heat energy of various ignition sparks. National advisory committee for aeronautics. Preprint from Fifth annual report. Washington Govt. print. off., 1919.

QC753
L6   Loeb, Leonard Benedict, 1891–
An introduction to ferromagnetism; physics
121. [Berkeley, 19--]
44 l. diagrs.

Cover title.
Issued by Dept. of Physics, University of
California.

1. Magnetism - 1901–   I. Title: Ferromagnetism.

NL   0441094   CU

Loeb, Leonard Benedict, 1891–
Kinetic theory of gases, being a text and reference book
whose purpose is to combine the classical deductions with
recent experimental advances in a convenient form for student
and investigator, by Leonard B. Loeb ... 1st ed. New York
[etc.] McGraw-Hill book company, inc., 1927.
xvi, 555 p. diagrs. 23½ᵐ. $5.50
"References" and "Books recommended" at end of each chapter.

1. Gases, Kinetic theory of.
    27—6186

    ICJ ViU WaU CU MtBuM
    WaS NcRS NcD OCU ODW OU OC1 OO PU PBm PPT PSC PHC MB
NL   0441095   DLC IdU-SB WaWW OrSaW ViU MoSU OrP OrPR

Loeb, Leonard Benedict, 1891–
The kinetic theory of gases; being a text and reference book
whose purpose is to combine the classical deductions with recent experimental advances in a convenient form for student
and investigator, by Leonard B. Loeb ... 2d ed. New York
and London, McGraw-Hill book company, inc., 1934.
xx, 687 p. illus., diagrs. 23½ᵐ.
"References" and "Books recommended" at end of each chapter;
chapter vi contains "References" at end of two of its sections.

1. Gases, Kinetic theory of.
Library of Congress   QC175.L6 1934   34—18819
——— Copy 2.
Copyright A 73243   [39g1]   533.7

    WaS OrSaW OrCS
    OCU OU OC1 OO OC1U ViU ICJ PU PSC PPF PBa PV CaBVa
NL   0441096   DLC ViU KEmT PPAtR PCM PSt CU TxU TU NcD

537
L822fa   Loeb, Leonard Benedict, 1891–
A laboratory manual of electricity and magnetism. Physics 1C ... Berkeley, Calif., University of California press, 1936.
12Ep. diagrs. (On cover: University of California. Syllabus series ... no.261)

Intended for use, with the author's "Fundamentals of electricity and magnetism", by students in the course "Physics 1C" at the University of California. cf. Preface.

——— [Experiment data sheets. Berkeley, Cal.,
University of California press, 1936]
29 l.

Another printing of the forms at the ends of
the 12 experiments in the manual.

1. Electricity. 2. Magnetism.

NL   0441098   IU OU PPCCH

Loeb, Leonard Benedict, 1891–
A laboratory manual of electricity and magnetism,
Physics 1c, by Leonard B. Loeb. Berkeley, Calif.,
University of California press, 1937.
xii, 125 p. illus. 21 cm. (On verso of t.-p.:
University of California syllabus series ... no. 261)
1. Electricity - Laboratory manuals.
2. Magnetism - Laboratory manuals.

NL   0441099   CU

VOLUME 338

Loeb, Leonard Benedict, 1891–
A laboratory manual of electricity and magnetism, by Leonard B. Loeb. Rev. ed. Stanford University, Calif., Stanford university press ₍1941₎

xii, 121 p., 113 l. diagrs. 23ᶜᵐ.
"Experiment data sheets": 113 leaves (112 detachable) at end.

1. Electricity—Laboratory manuals. 2. Magnetism—Laboratory manuals.
Library of Congress   QC534.L6 1941   42–51439
₍7₎   537.072

NL   0441100   DLC NIC OrSaW CU RPB PU NcD OClW PSt MB

Loeb, Leonard Benedict, 1891–
Lecture notes in physics 1 C. Electricity and magnetism, by Leonard B. Loeb ... August, 1927 ... Ann Arbor, Mich., Edwards brothers, °1927.
1 p.l., vi, 177 numb. l. table, diagrs. 27ᶜᵐ.
Mimeographed.

1. Electricity. 2. Magnetism. 3. Physics—Addresses, essays, lectures.

NL   0441101   ViU DBS CU OU

Loeb, Leonard Benedict, 1891–
Lecture notes in Physics 1c, electricity and magnetism, by Leonard B. Loeb ... August 1928 ... Ann Arbor, Mich., Edwards brothers, c1928.
1 p. L., xi, 180 numb. l. diagrs. 27 cm.
Mimeographed.
1. Electricity. 2. Magnetism.

NL   0441102   CU

Loeb, Leonard Benedict, 1891–
Lecture notes on conduction of electricity in gases. Physics 111 B. [By] L. B. Loeb. Berkeley, Calif. ? 193–?]
160 numb. l. diagrs. 28 cm.
Title from label mounted on cover.
Mimeographed.
1. Electric discharges through gases.

NL   0441103   CU

Loeb, Leonard Benedict, 1891–
Lecture notes on intermediate heat ... from rough lecture notes of Prof. L.B. Loeb. [Berkeley] 1936.
2 p. l., 2–126 numb. l. diagrs. 27 cm.
"Privately mimeographed ... by Charles G. Miller [and] Lester M. Makoff."
"Issued by and for the class in Physics 112 in the University of California."
1. Heat – 1901–

NL   0441104   CU

Loeb, Leonard Benedict, 1891–
Lecture notes on intermediate heat, by Leonard B. Loeb ... Organized from the author's lecture notes for Physics 112 by John Scott Campbell. [Berkeley, Calif.] 1938.
3 p. L., 2–176 numb. l. diagrs. 28 cm.
Mimeographed.
1. Heat – 1901–   I. Campbell, John Scott, ed.

NL   0441105   CU

Loeb, Leonard Benedict, 1891–
Lecture notes on radioactivity and nuclear structure. Physics 111 C. [By] L. B. Loeb. [Berkeley, Calif. ? 1937?]
204 numb. l. illus., tables, diagrs. 28 cm.
Title from label mounted on fly-leaf.
Type-written manuscript.
1. Radioactivity. 2. Atoms. I. Title. II. Title: Nuclear structure.

NL   0441106   CU

537.53
L825m   Loeb, Leonard Benedict, 1891–
The mechanism of the electric spark, by Leonard B. Loeb ... and John M. Meek ... Stanford University, Calif., Stanford university press; London, H. Milford, Oxford university press ₍1941₎
xiii, 188 p. incl. illus., tables, diagrs. plates. 23½ᵐ.
"References" at end of each chapter.

1. Electric spark. I. Meek, John M., joint author. II. Title.

Library of Congress   QC703.L6   41–12694

NL   0441107   ICJ OC1L NcD PPD PPF PU OrCS DAS
              DLC MB CoU OrSaW WaS CU ViU OCl OCU OU

---

ar X
6664   Loeb, Leonard Benedict, 1891–
The nature of a gas. Preliminary ed. Ithaca, N. Y., 1930.
iv, 169 l. illus. 27cm.

NL   0441108   NIC CU

OrPR

Loeb, Leonard Benedict, 1891–
The nature of a gas, by Leonard B. Loeb ... New York, J. Wiley & sons, inc.; London, Chapman & Hall, limited, 1931.
x, 153 p. diagrs. 24ᵐ. (*Half-title:* Monograph no. 1. National research council. Committee on electrical insulation) $2.50
Bibliography: p. 134–136.

1. Gases. 2. Ionization or gases. I. Title.

Library of Congress   QC161.L6₍   31–19229
Copyright A 40125   ₍3–4₎

NL   0441109   OrPR IdU–SB CaBVaU
       MiHM MB NcD ICJ OrPS PPT PSC PPD PPF NBuC MtBuM WaS
       DLC DAU NBuU CU NcRS OU OCU OCl OC1W ViU

Loeb, Leonard Benedict.
... On the mobilities of gas ions in high electric fields ... by Leonard Benedict Loeb ... ₍Lancaster, Pa., and Ithaca, N. Y.₎ 1916₎
1 p. l, p. ₍633₎–650. diagrs. 25½ᵐ.
Thesis (PH. D.)—University of Chicago, 1916.
"A private edition distributed by the University of Chicago libraries."
"Reprinted from the Physical review, n. s., vol. VIII, no. 6, December, 1916."
"References": p. 650.

1. Electric discharges through gases. 2. Ions.

                            17–6388
Library of Congress   QC711.L7

NL   0441110   ICU OU MiU WaU NIC DLC

QC711
.L687   Loeb, Leonard Benedict, 1891–
Основные процессы электрических разрядов в газах. Перевод с английского под ред. Н. А. Капцова. ₍Москва, Гос. изд-во техинко-теорет. лит-ры, 1950.
672 p. illus. 27 cm.
Includes bibliographies.

1. Electric discharges through gases. II. Title.
Title transliterated: Osnovnye proGessy élektricheskikh razrfadov.

QC711.L687   52–21129

NL   0441111   DLC

Loeb, Leonard Benedict, 1891–   ed.
Ioffe, Abram Fedorovich, 1880–
The physics of crystals, by Abram F. Joffé ... edited by Leonard B. Loeb ... 1st ed. New York ₍etc.₎ McGraw-Hill book company, inc., 1928.

Loeb, Leonard Benedict, 1891–
Radioactivity and nuclear structure, by Leonard B. Loeb ... [Berkeley] 1940?]
4 p. L., 2–210 (i. e. 208) numb. l. plates, diagrs. 29 cm.
Numbers 28–29 omitted in the paging.
Mimeographed.
1. Radioactivity. 2. Atoms. I. Title.

NL   0441113   CU

QC703
L63   Loeb, Leonard Benedict, 1891–
Physics   Spark breakdown in uniform fields. Washington, Office of
Library   Naval Research, Dept. of the Navy, 1954.
vii, 141 p. illus., diagrs.

"Sponsored by the Physics Branch of the Office of Naval Research."
Bibliography: p. 137–141.

1. Electric discharges through gases. 2. Electric spark. I. U.S. Office of Naval Research.

NL   0441114   CU NcD GAT

Loeb, Leonard Benedict.

Löb, Leopold, 1907–
Die staatsrechtliche stellung des Memelgebietes ... Rostock, C. Hinstorffs hofbuchdruckerei, 1933.
82 p. 20.5 cm.
Inaug.-diss. - Giessen.
Lebenslauf.
"Literaturverzeichnis": p. 5.
1. Memel (Territory) I. Title.

NL   0441116   CSt–H ICRL PU MiU–L InU

Loeb, Les.
On carcinoma in cattle. 1900.
9 p.

NL   0441117   DNAL

Loeb, Lester.
Better photography; a non-technical guide for everyone who wants better pictures, by Lester Loeb. New York, Philosophical library ₍1947₎
xvii, 274 p. incl. front., illus. 22ᵐ.

1. Photography—Handbooks, manuals, etc. I. Title.

TR146.L6   770   47–3474
Library of Congress

NL   0441118   DLC CaBVa CaBViP WaS Or OEac MiU PP

LOEB, Lucian, 1889–
Allgemeine falschbeurkundung (§ 271–273 RStGB) Inaug.-diss., Heidelberg, Berlin, Frensdorf, 1914.
89 p. 8°
"Lebenslauf", at end.
"Literaturverzeichnis", pp. 5–8.

NL   0441119   MH–L ICRL

W 4
B29   LOEB, Lutz.
1953   Über den Nachweis der von Lennhoff bei zahlreichen Affektionen ungeklärter Ätiologie beschriebenen Spirochäten in histologischen Schnitten und die Frage der Wirksamkeit einer entsprechenden spirochätiziden Therapie. Basel, 1953.
p. ₍13₎–27. illus.
Cover title.
Inaug.-Diss. - Basel.

Reprinted from Dermatologica, v. 107, 1953.
Summary in German, English, and French.
1. Skin - Diseases 2. Spirochaeta

NL   0441121   DNLM

Film
909   LÖB, M
no. 5   Fieberkrankheiten, deren Gefahren und Behandlungsweise mit besonderer Berücksichtigung der Kaltwasserbehandlung. Mannheim, Bensheimer, 1876.
22 p.
Film copy.

NL   0441122   DNLM

VOLUME 338

LOEB, MADELEINE,
Better left unwed, by Hazy, princess of Guess, pil-
fered and pictured by Madeleine H. Loeb. New York:
Mohawk Press[, cop. 1931]. xvii, 7–95 p. incl. plates.
front. 21cm.

A parody on Better left unsaid, by Daisy, princess
of Pless.

568766A. 1. Parody, American. I. Pless, Mary Theresa
Olivia (Cornwallis–West), Fuerstin von, 1873– : Better
left unsaid. II. Title.

NL 0441123   NN MB MH

Loeb, Madeleine.
Please stand by, by Madeleine Loeb and David Schenker.
New York, Mohawk press, inc., 1931.
281 p. 19½ᵐ.

I. Schenker, David, joint author. II. Title.

Library of Congress   PZ3.L82384Pl   31–33379

NL 0441124   DLC MB

Loeb, Mani, pseud.
  see Brahinsky, Mani Leib, 1883–

Loeb, Marjorie.
Checkers, by Marjorie Loeb, with illustrations by Walter
Kumme. Los Angeles, Calif., K. Miles, ʻ1946.
[31] p. illus. (part col.) 26 x 21ᵐ.

I. Kumme, Walter, illus. II. Title.

Library of Congress   PZ10.3.L845Ch   46–1789

NL 0441126   DLC

LA210
.W33   Loeb, Martin B., joint author.
1946   FOR OTHER EDITIONS
                                    SEE MAIN ENTRY
Warner, William Lloyd, 1898–
  Who shall be educated? The challenge of unequal opportunities. [By] W. Lloyd Warner ... Robert J. Havighurst ...
[and] Martin B. Loeb ... London, K. Paul, Trench, Trubner
& co., ltd. [1946]

Loeb, Max, comp.

Wisconsin. University.
  General catalogue of the officers and graduates of the
University of Wisconsin, 1849–1907; comp. for the Uni-
versity by Max Loeb, ʻ05. Madison, Wis., 1907.

Loeb, Max.
  Shorthand for the college man. [New York: Gregg Pub.
Co., 190–?] 4 l. nar. 16°.

                            NAT. SHORTHAND REP. ASSOC.
1. Shorthand.
N. Y. P. L.   June 9, 1914.

NL 0441129   NN

Loeb, Michael.
  Beitraege zur bewegung der samenleiter und der samen
blase.
  Inaug. Diss. Giessen, 1866

NL 0441130   ICRL

Loeb, Michel.
  Control information and frame of reference. Ann Arbor,
University Microfilms, 1953.
  ([University Microfilms, Ann Arbor, Mich.] Publication no. 5511)
  Microfilm copy of typescript. Positive.
  Collation of the original : v, 65 l.
  Thesis–Vanderbilt University.
  Abstracted in Dissertation abstracts, v. 13 (1953) no. 5, p. 887–888.
  Bibliography : leaves 63–65.

  1. Learning, Psychology of. 2. Psychology, Physiological. I. Title.

Microfilm AC–1 no. 5511   Mic A 54–1035

Joint University   Libraries, Nashville
for Library of Congress   [1]†

NL 0441131   TNJ DLC

Loeb, Minna, 1908–
  Die ideengehalte der arbeiterdichtung ...
Giessen, 1932.
  4 p.l., 95,[2] p.,1 l. 23ᶜᵐ.
  Inaug.–diss.–Giessen.
  Lebenslauf.
  "Der titel der vorliegenden arbeit lautet zwar: 'Die
ideengehalte der arbeiterdichtung', doch werden darin
nur die dichter Engelke,Lersch,Bröger und Barthel ein-
gehend behandelt".--Vorwort.
  "Literature": p.[97–98].

  1.German poetry--19th cent.--Hist.& crit. 2.Labor
and laboring classes--Poetry.

NL 0441132   MiU ICRL NjP MdBJ CtY InU

HD9940   Loeb,Moritz,1875–
.G33B5   ...Berliner konfektion,von Moritz Loeb. 5.
L8   aufl. Berlin,H.Seemann nachfolger[1906]
          [3]–91,[1] p. 22ᵐ. (Grossstadt-dokumente,
          hrsg.von Hans Ostwald. Bd.15.)

NL 0441133   ICU

Loeb, Moritz. 1875–   2867.35
  Berliner Konfektion. 6. Auflage.
= Berlin. Seemann. [1906.] 91, (1) pp. [Grossstadt-Dokumente.
  Band 15.] 8°.

G6335 — T.r. — S.r — Dressmaking. — Berlin. Germany. Bus. assoc.

NL 0441134   MB

Loeb, Moritz, 1875–
  ...Berliner konfektion... 9. aufl.
Berlin, (1906)
  91 p. 24 cm.

NL 0441135   DL

Loeb, Moritz, 1875–
  Eduards unselige erben: die kriegshetzer, von Moritz
Loeb. Augsburg, Haas & Grabherr, 1915.
  vi p., 1 l., 133 p. ports. (incl. front.) 19½ᵐᵐ.

  1. Europe—Politics—1871–   2. European war, 1914–   I. Title.

Library of Congress   D511.L6   16–17135
Copyright   A—Foreign   13808

NL 0441136   DLC

Loeb, Moritz, 1875–
  Eduards unselige erben; die kriegshetzer, von Moritz Loeb.
2. aufl. Augsburg, Haas & Grabherr, 1915.
  vi p., 1 l., 133 p. ports. (incl. front.) 19½ᵐᵐ.

  1. Europe—Politics—1871–   2. European war, 1914–1918.
I. Title.

Library of Congress   D511.L6 1915   21—2225

NL 0441137   DLC

LOEB, Moritz,1875–
  Eduards unselige erben; die kriegshetzer.
3e aufl. Augsburg, Haas & Grabherr,1915.

  pp. vi,(2).133. Ports.
                            Ger 2397.115.158

NL 0441138   NjP MH

940.91   Loeb, Moritz, 1875–
L82e   ... Eduards unselige erben. Neue folge.
          Augsburg [c1917]
          149p. front., ports.

          At head of title: Schürer des welt-
        brandes.

NL 0441139   IU

Loeb, Moritz, 1875–
  Der papierne feind; die weltpresse als schürer des
Deutschenhasses, von Moritz Loeb. Augsburg, Haas und
Grabherr, 1918.
  vii, 110 p. 20ᵐ.

  1. European war, 1914–   —Public opinion.   I. Title.

Library of Congress   D631.L7   20–10953

NL 0441140   DLC DNW MiU NN

Loeb, Moritz, 1875–
  Schürer des weltbrandes, von Moritz Loeb; Eduards unselige
erben, neue folge. Augsburg, Haas & Grabherr [1917]
  viii, 149, [1] p. front., ports. 20ᵐ.

  1. Europe—Politics—1871–   2. European war, 1914–1918. I. Title.
II. Title: Eduards unselige erben, neue folge.

                                    33–37304
Library of Congress   D511.L6 1917   940.3112

NL 0441141   DLC DLC-P4 CSt-H

Loeb, Moritz Abraham.
  Der Austritt als Prinzip. Berlin:
"Jüdisches Wochenblatt", [1929].
  18 p.

NL 0441142   OCH

Loeb, Moritz Abraham.
  Um die Zukunft der Berliner jüdischen Gemeinde, von Moritz
A. Loeb... Berlin: E. Nickel & Cie [1931?]   32 p. incl. tables.
21cm.

                                    FREIDUS MEMORIAL COLL.
  1. Jews in Germany—Berlin—   Communal organization.
N. Y. P. L.   May 29, 1941

NL 0441143   NN

Loeb, Morris, 1863–1912.
  The charity aspect of immigration. New York,
Liberal Immigration Legue, 1907.
  6 p. 8°.
  Repr.: The Boston Advocate, Nov. 23, 1906.

NL 0441144   NN

Loeb, Morris, 1863–1912.
  Federation or Consolidation of Jewish Charities.
A paper read before the national conference of the
Jewish Charities.
Chicago, 1900.
  18 p.

NL 0441145   PPDrop

VOLUME 338

Loeb, Morris, 1863-1912.
Morris Loeb, 1863-1912. Memorial volvme
see under title

WG
23887
Loeb, Morris, 1863–
Das Phosgen und seine Abkömmlinge
nebst einigen Beiträgen zu deren Kenntniss.
Berlin, 1887.
51 p.

Inaug.-Diss. - Berlin.

NL   0441147   CtY MH ICRL

Loeb, Morris, 1863–1912.
The scientific work of Morris Loeb ... ed. by Theodore
W. Richards ... Cambridge, Harvard university press,
1913.
xxiii, 349, ₁1₎ p. front. (port.) illus., plates, diagrs. 23ᶜᵐ. $2.00
Includes bibliographies.
CONTENTS.—Introduction. The life and character of Morris Loeb.—
pt. I. Lectures, addresses, and reviews.—pt. II. Original experimental investigations.—Appendix: Laboratory manual. Experiments on speed of
reaction. Chronological bibliography.
1. Chemistry—Collected works. 2. Chemistry, Physical and theoretical.
I. Richards, Theodore William, 1868–
                                                            14—479
Library of Congress   QD3.L7

    OO PBm ViU NN MB PU PPAmP TU IdU OrCS OrP WaS OrU
NL 0441148   DLC NjP OKentU PPF CU NIC OU OCU MiU

Loeb, Morris, 1863-1912.
Shall the Jewish Agricultural and Industrial
Aid Society institute a Trial Farm for accustoming
Jewish immigrants to American methods of farming?
Affirmative argument submitted to members of the
Society.
10 p.

NL   0441149   PPDrop

LOEB, Morris, 1863-1912.
Über den molekularzustand des gelösten
jods. n.p., [1888].

NL   0441150   MH

Loeb, Oswald, 1880–
... Die wirkung des alkohols auf das warmblüterherz ...
Leipzig, Druck von J. B. Hirschfeld, 1905.
2 p. l., 22 p., 1 l. diagrs. 22½ᶜᵐ.
Inaug.-diss.—Heidelberg.
Lebenslauf.

1. Alcohol, Physiological effect of. 2. Heart.

Library of Congress   QP915.A3L8   7-38766†

NL   0441151   DLC DNLM

Loeb, Otto.
Die regelung der fremdwährungs- und goldschuldverhält-
nisse; ein kommentar zur goldklausel- und goldschuldener-
leichterungsverordnung nebst den bezüglichen materialien, entscheidungen, regierungskommentaren und verordnungen, insbesondere auch der Devisenverordnung und Transferverord-
nung, von dr. Otto Loeb und dr. Otto ritter von Komorzyński
Oszczyński ... Wien, Manz, 1933-37.

2 v. 18½ᶜᵐ.

Vol. 2 has title: Die regelung der fremdwährungs- und goldschulder-
verhältnisse. II. teil. Kommentar zum Goldklauselgesetz, von dr. Otto
Loeb ...

1. Gold. 2. Foreign exchange. 3. Currency question—Austria. 4.
Debtor and creditor—Austria. I. Komorzyński-Oszczyński, Otto, ritter
von, joint author. II. Austria. Laws, statutes, etc. III. Title.
                                A C 34-4215 Revised
New York. Public library
    for Library of Congress
                    HG959.L65
                    ₍2₎   332.4200436

NL   0441153   NN DLC

Loeb, Otto.
Wiedergutmachung in Arisierungsangelegenheiten
auf Grund des allgemeinen bürgerlichen Gesetzbuches.
Wien, Manz, 1946.
22 p.

NL   0441154   MH-L IEN

Loeb, Paul Wilhelm, 1894–
Über adenocancroide ... München, 1920.
Ining - dis. - Frankfurt am Main.

NL   0441155   MiU

Loeb, Pierre, 1896–
Regards sur la peinture. Paris, La Hune ₍1950₎
42 p. port. (on cover) 20 cm.
"Conférence prononcée à la salle de la Société de géographie le
mardi, 13 décembre 1949, à Paris."

1. Painting—Addresses, essays, lectures.   I. Title.

ND1150.L6   750.4   50–29342

NL   0441156   DLC IEN NhD

Loeb, Pierre, 1896–
... Voyages à travers la peinture. ₍Paris₎ Bordas ₍1946₎
2 p. l., ₍7₎–144 p., 7 l. XLVIII pl. (incl. ports.) on 24 l. 23ᶜᵐ.

1. Painting. 2. Painters.   I. Title.
ND1142.L6   47–20785

NL   0441157   DLC ICU CtY PPPM NN

LOEB, Richard.
Der milzbrand in Elsass-Lothringen.
Strassburg, 1898.

NL   0441158   MBCo ICRL DNLM PPC

Loeb, Oscar Jules Walther, 1896–
Etude historique des objections et préventions
qui ont été opposées à la pratique des autopsies
et des dissections.
Thèse, Strasbourg, 1924.
Bibl.

NL   0441159   ICRL CtY

Loeb, Richard A., 1905 or 6-1936, defendant.

Leopold, Nathan Freudenthal, 1904 or 5– defendant.
The amazing crime and trial of Leopold and Loeb, by Mau-
reen McKernan, with an introduction by Clarence Darrow
and Walter Bachrach. Chicago, The Plymouth court press,
1924.

Loeb, Richard A., 1905 or 6-1936, defendant.
The crime and trial of Leopold and Loeb
see under Leopold, Nathan Freudenthal,
1904 or 5–   defendant.

Loeb, Richard A   1905 or 6–   defendant.
The Loeb-Leopold case, with excerpts from the evidence of the alienists and including the arguments to the
court by counsel for the people and the defense, by Alvin
V. Sellers. Brunswick, Ga., Classic publishing co., 1926.
321 p. incl. front. 20ᶜᵐ.

1. Franks, Robert, 1909 or 10–1924. I. Leopold, Nathan Freudenthal,
1904 or 5– defendant. II. Sellers, Alvin Victor, 1882– ed. III. Title.
                                    26–20073
Library of Congress

NL   0441162   DLC WaU-L NcD NN IU MH

Loeb, Richard A., 1905 or 6-1936, defendant.
"Not Insanity but Mental Illness;" an analysis
of the defense in the Loeb-Leopold trial
see under Leopold, Nathan Freudenthal,
1904 or 5–   defendant.

Law
Loeb, Richard A., 1905 or 6-1936, defendant.

Darrow, Clarence Seward, 1857–1938.
The plea of Clarence Darrow, August 22nd, 23rd & 25th,
MCMXXIIII, in defense of Richard Loeb and Nathan Leopold,
jr., on trial for murder. Authorized and rev. ed., together
with a brief summary of the facts. Chicago, R. F. Seymour
₍1924₎

Loeb, Robert Frederick, 1895–   ed.
                        FOR OTHER EDITIONS
                        SEE MAIN ENTRY
Martini, Paul, 1889–
Martini's principles and practice of physical diagnosis,
edited by Robert F. Loeb ... from the authorized translation by
George J. Farber ... 2d ed. 30 illustrations in the text.
Philadelphia, Montreal ₍etc.₎, J. B. Lippincott company ₍ᶜ1938₎

Serial
J
Loeb, Robert Frederick, 1895–
Medical education at the mid-century. (In
Journal of medical education, v. 26, no. 5,
Sept. 1951, p. 347-349)

₍Address₎ delivered at the Opening exercises, College of Physicians and Surgeons,
Columbia University, Sept. 11, 1950.

NL   0441166   DNLM

RC46
.C4
1955
Loeb, Robert Frederick, 1895–   joint ed.
                        FOR OTHER EDITIONS
                        SEE MAIN ENTRY
Cecil, Russell La Fayette, 1881–   ed.
A textbook of medicine, edited by Russell L. Cecil ₍and₎
Robert F. Loeb; associated editors: Alexander B. Gutman,
Walsh McDermott ₍and₎ Harold G. Wolff. 9th ed. Phila-
delphia, Saunders, 1955.

Loeb, Robert H
Date bait, the younger set's picture cookbook; illustrated
by Jim Newhall. Chicago, Wilcox and Follett Co. ₍1952₎
107 p. illus. 26 cm.

1. Cookery—Juvenile literature.   I. Title.

TX652.5.L6   641.5   52–4550 ‡

NL   0441168   DLC IU

Loeb, Robert H
He-manners; young man's book of etiquette. Illustrated
by Robert Yahn. New York, Association Press ₍1954₎
183 p. illus. 21 cm.

1. Etiquette.   I. Title.

BJ1855.L57   395   54—13275 ‡

    PPGi
    WaSp WaE WaT KyU-A KyWA IU NcRS OOxM OClW PP PPT
NL 0441169   DLC NBuC CaBVa IdPI Or OrAshS OrPS WaS

Loeb, Robert H
Mary Alden's cook book for children; an R. H. Loeb
recipix book. Pictures by Dorothy King. New York,
Wonder Books ₍ᶜ1955₎
64 p. illus. 21 cm. (Wonder playbooks for children, 2518)

1. Cookery—Juvenile literature.   I. Title.

TX652.5.L62   641.5   56–59166 ‡

NL   0441170   DLC

VOLUME 338

Loeb, Robert H
Nip ahoy; the picture bar guide, illustrated by Joel King. Chicago, Wilcox & Follett Co. [1954]
96 p. illus. 20 cm.

1. Liquors. I. Title.

TX951.L62   663.8   55–17408 ‡

NL 0441171   DLC

Loeb, Robert H
She cooks to conquer; illustrated by Laura Jean Allen. New York, W. Funk [1952]
121 p. illus. 26 cm.

1. Cookery—Anecdotes, facetiae, satire, etc. I. Title.

TX652.L53   641.5   52–9786 ‡

NL 0441172   DLC WaS CaBVa WaT NN

Loeb, Robert H
Wolf in chef's clothing; the picture cook and drink book for men. Illustrated by Jim Newhall. Chicago, Wilcox & Follett [1950]
123 p. col. illus. 29 cm.

1. Cookery. I. Newhall, James W., illus. II. Title.

TX652.L55   641.5   50–58300

NL 0441173   DLC KMK LU PPD NN MB

Loeb, Sally, 1887–
[Ein Beitrag zur Lehre vom Farbengedächtnis. Leipzig: J. A. Barth 1912. 46 S. 8° ¶ (Aus: Zeitschrift f. Psychol. u. Physiol. d. Sinnesorgane. Abt. 2. Bd 46, H. 1/2.)
Berlin, Med. Diss. v. 15. Mai 1912, Ref. Ziehen
[Geb. 2. Juni 87 Vallendar; Wohnort: Hamburg; Staatsangeh.: Preußen; Vorbildung: Gymn. Koblenz Reife O. 06; Studium: Freiburg i. B. 1, Marburg 2, Kiel 2, Berlin 1, München 1, Berlin 3 S.; Coll. 19. Dez. 11; Approb. 3. Mai 12.]

NL 0441174   ICRL CtY DNLM CU

[Loeb, S. S., and co.] *publishers.*
Souvenir. Central Kentucky asylum for the insane, Lakeland, Kentucky. September, 1900. [Pittsburg, Pa., S. S. Loeb & co., 1900]
[40] p. illus. (incl. ports.) 15½ x 23 cm.
Advertisements printed on verso of 10 leaves.

1. Kentucky. Asylum for insane, Lakeland. 2. Insane hospitals—Kentucky.

    8–21332

Library of Congress   RC445.K4L3

NL 0441175   DLC

Loeb (Siegfried). *Zur physiologischen Wirkung der Monobromessigsäure auf die quergestreifte Muskulatur. 17 pp. 8°. Würzburg, F. Scheiner. 1890.*

NL 0441176   DNLM ICRL

Loeb, Sophie Irene (Simon) 1876–1929.
Epigrams of Eve, by Sophie Irene Loeb, with sundry decorations by Ruby Lind. New York, George H. Doran company [1913]
96 p. front., plates. 21 cm. $1.00

I. Title.

    13–25117

Library of Congress   PS3523.O3E6   1913

NL 0441177   DLC NN

Loeb, *Mrs.* **Sophie Irene** (Simon) 1876–
Everyman's child, by Sophie Irene Loeb ... New York, The Century co., 1920.
7 p. l., 3–286 p. front., plates. 19 cm. $2.00

1. Children—Charities, protection, etc.   I. Title.

Library of Congress   HV741.L7   20–17501

    PPFr PPC PU PP NN ICJ MB
NL 0441178   DLC OKentU OrP WaS Or OC1ND OC1 MiU DL

LOEB, SOPHIE IRENE (SIMON), 1876–1929.
An interview, by Sophie Irene Loeb (reprinted from "New York Evening World"). The basis of marriage, by Alice Hubbard. East Aurora Erie County, N.Y.: The Roycrofters [cop. 1910] 21 p. ports. 21cm.

776739A. 1. Marriage. I. Hubbard, Alice (Moore), 1861–1915. The basis of marriage.

NL 0441179   NN

Loeb, Sophie Irene, 1876–
Orphan asylums seen as passing, by Sophie Irene Loeb... New York: Child Welfare Committee of America, Inc. [, 1925.]
7 p. 8°. (Child Welfare Committee of America. Publ. no. 24.)

"Reprint of an article from the New York Evening World, June 6, 1925."

1. Orphans—Asylums—U. S.   2. Child   placing—U. S.
N. Y. P. L.   October 9, 1925

NL 0441180   NN OU

Loeb, Sophie Irene (Simon) 1876–1929.
Palestine awake; the rebirth of a nation, by Sophie Irene Loeb. New York & London, The Century co. [*1926]
ix p., 2 l., 3–249 p. front., plates. 19½ cm.

1. Palestine. 2. Jews in Palestine. 3. Zionism.

Library of Congress   DS107.3.L75   26–19861

    TxU NcU
    PP PPDrop NN MB MtU WaSp WaTC OrP Or WaS WaSp
NL 0441181   DLC CSt-H OC1 OCH OOxM NjN GS ViU Mi PPD

Loeb, *Mrs.* **Sophie Irene** (Simon) 1876–1929.
New York (*State*) *Commission on relief for widowed mothers.*
... Report of the New York state commission on relief for widowed mothers. Transmitted to the Legislature March 27, 1914. Albany, J. B. Lyon company, printers, 1914.

PS
3523
.O3W5x   Loeb, Sophie Irene (Simon) Mrs., 1876–
         1929.
         What Eve said. With seven
         decorations by Ruby Lind. London, Gay
         and Hancock [1915?]
         79 p. illus. 23 cm.
         Author's presentation copy.

NL 0441183   OKentU

Löb, Stor.
Tales from Turkistan; a Scythian's stories, by Stor Löb. Edinburgh and London, W. Blackwood and sons, 1924.
vi p., 3 l., [3]–307, [1] p. plates. 19 cm.
Map on lining-paper.

I. Title. II. Title: Turkistan.

    26–5662
Library of Congress   PR6023.O13T3   1924

NL 0441184   DLC DNW MiU NN

Loeb, Victor.
... Mit dem missionskreuz in den urwald Boliviens. Missions- und reisefahrten herausgegeben von P. August Willmé ... Braine-le-Comte (Belgique) Zech et fils [1929]
121 p. plates, maps. 21 cm.

NL 0441185   CtY-D

Loeb, Virgil.
Unusual cases in oral surgery.
n.p., 1911.
14 p.

NL 0441186   PU-D

Loeb, Walter, 1895–   joint author.

Geyer, Curt, 1891–
Gollancz in German wonderland, by Curt Geyer and Walter Loeb; foreword by James Walker ... Translated from the German by Ed. Fitzgerald. London, New York [etc.], Hutchinson & co., ltd. [1942]

Löb, Walther, 1872–1916.
... Einführung in die biochemie in elementarer darstellung von prof. dr. Walther Löb; mit 12 figuren im text. Leipzig, B. G. Teubner, 1911.
2 p. l., 82, [2] p. illus. 18½ cm. (Aus natur und geisteswelt; sammlung wissenschaftlich-gemeinverständlicher darstellungen. 352. bdchen.)

1. Biological chemistry.   11–27666 Revised

Library of Congress   QH345.L7

NL 0441188   DLC

Löb, Walther, 1872–1916.
... Einführung in die biochemie in elementarer darstellung, von prof. dr. Walther Löb. 2., durchgesehene und verm. aufl. von prof. dr. Hans Friedenthal ... Mit 12 figuren im text. Leipzig und Berlin, B. G. Teubner, 1918.
81, [1] p. illus. diagrs. 18½ cm. (Aus natur und geisteswelt; sammlung wissenschaftlich-gemeinverständlicher darstellungen. 352. bdchen.)

1. Biological chemistry.   I. Friedenthal, Hans Wilhelm Karl, 1870–ed.

    43–44154
Library of Congress   QH345.L7   1918

NL 0441189   DLC MH RPB

Löb, Walther, 1872–1916.
... Einführung in die chemische wissenschaft, gemeinverständlich dargestellt von prof. dr. Walther Löb; mit 16 figuren im text. Leipzig, B. G. Teubner, 1909.
2 p. l., 103, [1] p. illus. 18½ cm. (Aus natur und geisteswelt. 264. bdchen.)

1. Chemistry, Physical and theoretical.

Library of Congress   QD453.L7   9–25447

NL 0441190   DLC MiU

Löb, Walther, 1872–
Die elektrochemie der organischen verbindungen, von dr. Walther Löb ... 3. erweiterte und umgearb. aufl. von: Unsere kenntnisse in der elektrolyse und elektrosynthese organischer verbindungen. Halle a. S., W. Knapp, 1905.
vii, 320 p. illus. 22 cm.

1. Electrochemistry. 2. Chemistry, Organic.

    6–21222
Library of Congress   QD263.L8

NL 0441191   DLC MiU OCU CU ICJ MH PPF

VOLUME 338

Löb, Walther, 1872-1916.
Electrochemistry of organic compounds; authorized translation from the author's enlarged and revised third edition of Electrolysis and electrosynthesis of organic compounds, by H. W. F. Lorenz. New York: John Wiley & Sons, 1906. 308 p. illus. 8°.

CENTRAL CIRCULATION.
1. Electrochemistry. 2. Lorenz,		Henry William Frederick, translator.
N. Y. P. L.		September 26, 1916.

NL 0441192		NN NjP PSC OO

Löb, Walther, 1872-1916.
Electrochemistry of organic compounds, by Dr. Walther Löb ... Authorized translation from the author's enl. and rev. 3d ed. of Electrolysis and electrosynthesis of organic compounds, by H. W. F. Lorenz ... with ten illustrations. 1st ed. 1st thousand. New York, J. Wiley & sons; [etc., etc.] 1906.
x, 308 p. illus. 23½ᵐᵐ.

1. Electrochemistry. 2. Chemistry, Organic.		I. Lorenz, Henry William Frederick, 1871-		tr. II. Title.

Library of Congress		QD263.L84
6—1291

NL 0441193		DLC NIC WaWW ICJ CU OU OC1W PPF PU MB

A—12047
Cat.C

Löb, Walther, 1872-1916.
Electrolysis and electrosynthesis of organic compounds. Authorized translation from the author's enl. and rev. ed. by H. W. F. Lorenz. 1st ed. New York, J. Wiley & Sons, 1898. 103p.

NL 0441194		ICRL NN CU ICJ MB

Löb, Walther, 1872-1916.
Electrolysis and electrosynthesis of organic compounds. By Dr. Walther Löb ... Authorized translation from the author's enlarged and revised edition, by H. W. F. Lorenz ... 1st ed. 1st thousand. New York, J. Wiley & sons; London, Chapman & Hall, limited, 1898.
xiii, 103 p. 19ᵐᵐ.

1. Electrochemistry. 2. Chemistry, Organic.		I. Lorenz, Henry William Frederick, 1871-		tr. II. Title.

Library of Congress		QD273.L82 1898
99—510 Revised

ViU PPD PHC PU-S PPAp
NL 0441195		DLC MeB MB ICJ DN WaS OO MiU OC1W OCU

Löb, Walther, 1872-
Grundzüge der Elektrochemie, von Prof. Dr. Walther Löb. Zweite, vermehrte und verbesserte Auflage, mit 42 in den Text gedruckten Abbildungen. Leipzig: J. J. Weber, 1910. viii, 174 p. incl. diagrs. illus. 17cm.

534766A. 1. Electrochemistry, 1910.
N. Y. P. L.		May 29, 1934

NL 0441196		NN ICRL CU OC1W ICJ MiU

Löb, Walther, 1872-1916.		537.85 P900
¹¹¹⁴ Leitfaden der praktischen Elektrochemie. viii,244 p. 112 il. O. Leipzig: Veit & Co., 1899.

NL 0441197		ICJ GU CU MiU OU PU-S PBm PU OC1W

QD341	**Loeb,** Walther, 1872-
.A5L78	Ueber die einwirkung von amidoacetal auf o- und p-nitrobenzoylchlorid.
	Berlin, [1894]
	38p.
	Inaug. diss. Berlin.

NL 0441198		DLC DNLM CtY

Löb, Walther, 1872-
Unsere kenntnisse in der elektrolyse und elektrosynthese organischer verbindungen. Von dr. Walther Löb. Halle a. S., W. Knapp, 1896. 3 p. l., 42 p. 21 cm. (Half-title: Encyclopädie der electrochemie. VIII bd.)
Bibliographical foot-notes.

NL 0441199		CU NN

QD553 **Löb,** Walther, 1872-
.L8	Unsere kenntnisse in der elektrolyse und elektrosynthese organischer verbindungen. Von dr. Walther Löb ... 2. erweiterte und umgearb. aufl. Halle a. S., W. Knapp, 1899.
[5], 89 p. 21ᵐᵐ. (Half-title: Encyklopädie der electrochemie. VIII. bd.)
Bibliographical foot-notes.

1. Electrochemistry.

NL 0441200		ICU NNC

Löb, Walther, 1872-1916.
Zur kenntnis der assimilation der kohlensäure. 1 pl.
Landw. jahrb. bd. 35, p. 541-578.		Berlin, 1906.

1. Carbon dioxid in plants. 2. Plant nutrition.

Library, U. S. Dept. of		Agriculture		Agr 7-24

NL 0441201		DNAL

1890-
Loeb, Wilhelm. Der Versuch im Reichsstrafgesetzbuch und im Vorentwurf. Breslau: Schletter 1913. IX, 60 S. 8°
¶ Auch als: Strafrechtl. Abhandlungen. H. 176.
Würzburg, Rechts- u. staatswiss. Diss. v. 11. Nov. 1913, Ref. Oetker
[Geb. 6. Sept. 90 Frankenthal Pf.; Wohnort: Würzburg; Staatsangeh.: Bayern; Vorbildung: G. Ludwigshafen a. Rh. Reife 09; Studium: München 1, Genf 1, München 2, Berlin 1, Würzburg 3 S.; Rig. 26. Juli 13.]		[U 13. 1389

NL 0441202		ICRL MH-L

Loeb, Wilhelm, 1890-
Der versuch im Reichsstrafgesetzbuch und im Vorentwurf. Von dr. jur. et rer. pol. Wilhelm Loeb. Breslau, Schletter, 1913.
ix, 60 p. 23½ᶜᵐ. (Added t.-p.: Strafrechtliche abhandlungen ... hft. 176)
Also issued as inaugural dissertation, Würzburg.
"Literatur": [vii]-ix.

1. Criminal attempt. 2. Criminal law—Germany.		I. Title.
36-34279

NL 0441203		DLC NN

Loeb, Wilhelm, 1908-
Der junge Herr Wetterlind; ein heiterer Roman [von] Hannes Peter Stolp [pseud. Leipzig, Rekord-Verlag, ᶜ1937]
262 p. 18 cm.
L. C. copy imperfect: t. p. wanting; title from cover.

I. Title.

PT2623.O313J8		49-57274 rev 2*

NL 0441204		DLC

PT2603 **Löb,** Wilhelm, 1908-		joint author.
.R237K6
Brandt, Erich, *playwright.*
Köpfchen muss man haben, Schwank in einem Vorspiel und drei Akten, von Erich Brandt u. Hannes Peter Stolp [pseud.] Berlin, Drei Masken Verlag, ᶜ1941.

Loeb, Wilhelm, 1908-
Die Sache mit dem Koffer, ein lustiger Schwankroman [von] Hannes Peter Stolp [pseud.] Hamburg-Poppenbüttel, Mardicke [ᶜ1951] 231p.

NL 0441206		CaBVa

Loeb, Willem, 1891-		*comp.*
Hollands Helicon; een keur uit de nederlandsche en vlaamsche dichters vanaf 1900, verzameld en ingeleid door dr. Willem Loeb; met een naschrift: Oor voordragkuns, door Balthazar Verhagen. Pretoria, J. L. van Schaik, bepk., 1940.
166 p., 1 l. 20½ᵐᵐ.

1. Dutch poetry—20th cent. 2. Flemish poetry.		I. Verhagen, Balthazar, 1881-		II. Title.
44-48056

Library of Congress		PT5478.L6
[2]		839.3115082

NL 0441207		DLC OC1

LOEB, William Jr.
The effect of the revolution in Mexico on American-Mexican mining interests. [1916].

NL 0441208		MH

Loeb, Wouter.
De Rauter-troep. Radio-voordrachten. Rijswijk (Z.-H.) V. A. Kramers [194-]
48 p. (p. 48, advertisement) illus. 19 cm. (His Mijn archief, 1. deeltje)
Cover title.

1. World War, 1939-1945—Humor, caricatures, etc.		I. Title.
D745.7.D8L6		A F 48-3021*

California. Univ. Libr
for Library of Congress		[1]†

NL 0441209		CU NN DLC

Loeb-Caldenhof, Richard, 1901-
Die realgemeinden in der provinz Hannover ... von Richard Loeb-Caldenhof ... Göttingen, Göttinger handelsdruckerei, 1934.
viii, 187, [2] p., 1 l. incl. tables. 20.5 cm.
Thesis, Göttingen.
"Literaturverzeichnis": p. [185]-187.
1. Land tenure - Hanover. 2. Mark.

NL 0441210		NNC CtY ICRL MiU

Loeb Classical Library.
152 volumes.

NL 0441211		DFo

The Loeb classical library [Latin authors] founded by James Loeb ... [Cambridge, Mass., Harvard university press; London, W. Heinemann, 1912-38] 112 v.

NL 0441212		OCU DFo

The Loeb classical library [Greek authors] founded by James Loeb ... [Cambridge, Mass., Harvard university press; London, W. Heinemann, 1912-37] 192 v.

NL 0441213		OCU

VOLUME 338

BV
104
.C35
no.69
7091
Loebach, Arnold Francis, 1918–
... The age of reason, puberty, and majority;
a historical synopsis ... Washington, The
Catholic University of America, 1950.
iv, 69 numb. 1. 28cm. (The Catholic
University of America. Canon law studies
[J.C.L. theses, no. 69])
Thesis (J.C.L.)--C.U.A.
Biographical note.
Bibliography: leaves 64–68.

1. Age (Canon law) I. Title.

NL 0441214   DCU

Löbbe, Henrique.
... Adubação verde. 1. ed.   Rio [de Janeiro]
A. Coelho Branco Filho, 1936.
121 p., 1 l., incl. illus., plates.   19 cm.
1. Green manuring.

NL 0441215   CtY

60.3
L78
Ed.2
Löbbe, Henrique.
...Cultura da soja no Brasil, por Henrique
Löbbe. 2ª. edição...   Rio de Janeiro, Di-
rectoria de estatistica da produção, Secção de
publicidade, 1935.
32 p.   illus.   23cm.

At head of title: Ministerio da agricultura.
Departamento nacional da produção vegetal.
Serviço de fomento da produção vegetal.

NL 0441216   DNAL

60.3
L78
Ed.3
Löbbe, Henrique.
Cultura da soja no Brasil.   3. ed.
Rio de Janeiro, Diretoria de Estatistica da
Produção, Secção de Publicidade, 1938.
32 p.

NL 0441217   DNAL

60.3
L78
Ed.4
Löbbe, Henrique.
...Cultura da soja no Brasil, por Henrique
Löbbe.   4ª. edição...   Rio de Janeiro,
Serviço de publicidade agrícola [1939]
33 p.   illus.   23cm.

At head of title: Ministério da agricultura.
Departamento nacional da produção vegetal.
Divisão de fomento da produção vegetal.

1. Soy-bean. I. Brazil. Serviço de fomento
da produção vegetal.

NL 0441218   DNAL

60.3
L78
Ed.5
Löbbe, Henrique.
Cultura da soja no Brasil.   5. ed.
Rio de Janeiro, Serviço de Informação Agricola,
Ministério da Agricultura, 1941 [i.e. 1942]
35 p.

1. Soy-bean. Brazil. I. Brazil. Divisão de
Fomento da Produção Vegetal.

NL 0441219   DNAL NNBG OCl

SB205
.B3B8
1935
Löbbe, Henrique.   FOR OTHER EDITIONS
                        SEE MAIN ENTRY
Brazil. *Serviço de fomento da produção vegetal.*
... Os feijões mulatinho e preto, por H. Löbbe, assistente.
Publicação da 4.ª secção technica. Rio de Janeiro, Directoria
de estatistica da produção, Secção de publicidade, 1935.

Löbbe, Henrique.
... Formação do pomar.   3. ed. ampliada.
Rio [de Janeiro] 1936.
1. Fruit-culture - Brazil.

NL 0441221   CtY

59.22
L78
Löbbe, Henrique.
... O milho, pelo engenheiro agronomo
Henrique Löbbe. O milho devido a sua produc-
ção, facilidade de cultivo, pelas suas
variedades e maior adaptação a differentes
condições de clima e sólo, será no futuro,
ainda mais do que [?]no presente, a planta de
maior valor na America.   São Paulo, Chacaras
e quintaes, 1939.
166 p.   illus.   24cm. (Bibliotheca
agricola popular brasileira)

1. Maize. ser.

NL 0441222   DNAL CtY DPU

Löbbecke, Arnold.
Die Vogelwelt des Kreises Wolfenbüttel. [Göttingen,
Muster-Schmidt, 1950]
32 p.   21 cm.
Bibliography: p. 32.

1. Birds—Germany—Wolfenbüttel (Kreis)

QL690.G3L6   598.2943   51-16455

NL 0441223   DLC

Löbbecke, Arthur.
... Auctions-Catalog einer bedeutenden
Specialsammlung griechischer Münzen von Hispania..
see under   Hirsch, Jacob, firm, Munich.

Löbbecke, Arthur.
Catalogue des collections de m. Arthur Löbbecke...
de feu m. L.M. Beels van Heemstede... Medailles
et plaquettes artistiques des XV-XVIIme siecles.
Vente... 17 juin 1929...
Amsterdam, J. Schulman.
49 p.

NL 0441225   PPPM

F757
L82k
Löbbecke, Arthur.
Kunstmedaillen und Plaketten des XV. bis
XVII. Jahrhunderts. Die öffentliche Verstei-
gerung findet statt: Donnerstag, den 26.
November 1908 und ff. Tage im Locale und
unter Leitung des Experten Jacob Hirsch.
München, J. Hirsch, 1908.
115p.   47 plates. 36cm.

1. Medals. Catalogs. 2. Plaques, plaquettes. Catalogs. I. Title.

NL 0441226   KU CtY MH

Löbbecke, Arthur.
Sammlung Arthur Löbbecke, Kunstmedaillen und Plaketten
des XV.-XVII.Jahrhunderts. Die Versteigerung findet statt:
den 5.Februar 1925... Halle (Saale) Riechmann, 1925
35 p., 27 plates (A.Riechmann & Co.Auktions - Katalog,
32)

NL 0441227   MH-FA

Löbbecke, Arthur.
Werke antiker kunst. Sammlung A.
Loebbecke-Braunschweig, sammlung dr.
Witte-Rostock; beiträge aus verschiedenem
privatbesitz. Berlin, Lepke [1930]
50 p. plates. 30 cm.
Sale, November 12, 1930.

NL 0441228   NjP

Löbbeck, Egbert von.
Die Lebensverhältnisse der ausländischen land-
wirtschaftlichen Wanderarbeiter in Schlesien und
die Auswirkungen der Kontingentierung auf die
schlesische Landwirtschaft unter besonderer
Berücksichtigung des Grossgrundbesitzes ...
München, 1931.
Inaug.-Diss. - München.

NL 0441229   CtY

Löbbecke, Egon von, 1885–   Die Pflichten und Rechte
des Bankiers beim kommissionsweisen Einkauf von Wert-
papieren. Hildesheim 1911: Gerstenberg. IV, 81 S. 8°
Heidelberg, Jur. Diss. v. 16. Jan. 1911, Ref. Heinsheimer
[Geb. 1. Aug. 85 Düsseldorf; Wohnort: Hannover; Staatsangeh.: Preußen;
Vorbildung: Kaiser-Wilhelm-Gymn. Hannover Reife O. 05; Studium: Lausanne 1, Göttingen 1, Berlin 1, Marburg 3 S.; Rig. 8. Dez. 10.]   [U 11. 2061

NL 0441230   ICRL CtY MH-L

Loebbecke, Friedrich.
Inwieweit kann der kaufpreis ausser in geld auch
in anderen sachen bestehen?
Inaug. diss. Leipzig, 1902.
Bibl.

NL 0441231   ICRL

Löbbecke, Karl, 1901–
Über die physikalischen und chemischen eigenschaf-
ten der legierungen auf der Grundlage Kobalt-Chrom-
Wolfram.
Inaug. diss. Braunschweig, Tech. hoch., 1927.

NL 0441232   ICRL

4GV 18
Löbbeck, Otto.
Die grossen Wettspiele.   Potsdam, L.
Voggenreiter [c1929]
144 p. (Deutsches Spielhandbuch, 5. T.)

NL 0441233   DLC-P4

4GV-83
Löbbecke, Otto.
Die grossen Wettspiele. 2. Aufl. Potsdam,
L. Voggenreiter [c1930]
144 p. (Deutsches Spielhandbuch, 5. Teil)

NL 0441234   DLC-P4

LÖBBECKE, Otto Emil Rudolf.
See LÖBBECKE, Rudolf, 1884–

Löbbecke, Rudolf, 1884–
Ueber das Verhaeltnis von Brāhmanas und
Śrautasūtren. Leipzig, 1908.
60 p.   8°.
Inaug. diss. - Leipzig.

NL 0441236   ICRL CtY MH ICU PU

VOLUME 338

Löbbecke, Theodor, 1821-1901.   L594 v.10   J700 pt.1A

Die Gattung *Crassatella* Lam., bearbeitet von Theod. Löbbecke ... und W. Kobelt ... Nürnberg, Bauer & Raspe, 1886.

〔6, 39, 2〕 p. 9 col. pl. 28½. (*Added t.-p.*: Systematisches Conchylien-Cabinet von Martini und Chemnitz ... 10. Bd., 1. Abt. a)

A second t.-p. omits Löbbecke's name.

NL 0441237   ICJ

Löbbecke, Theodor, 1821-1901.   L594 v.4   J700 pt.4

Das Genus *Cancellaria*, von Th. Löbbecke; nebst Anhang *Admete* von Dr. W. Kobelt. Nürnberg, Bauer & Raspe, 1887.

〔4, 108, 2〕 p. 24 col. pl. 28½cm. (*Added t.-p.*: Systematisches Conchylien-Cabinet von Martini und Chemnitz ... 4. Bd., 4. Abt.)

NL 0441238   ICJ

Loebbecke, Werner von, 1892-

Ein beitrag zur konstitutionsfrage des runden magen-und duodenal-geschwuers. Inaug. diss. Halle, 1920.

Bibl.

NL 0441239   ICRL DNLM CtY

Löbbecke, Wolf von, 1911-

Die aufrechnung im öffentlichen recht. ... Emsdetten, 1935. 99 p.

Inaug. Diss. - Göttingen, 1935.

Lebenslauf.

Literatur.

NL 0441240   ICRL

Löbbel, Hermann.   BX 25 .K5 v.5 pt.1

Der Stifter des Carthäuser-Ordens, der heilige Bruno aus Köln. Eine Monographie. Münster i. W., H. Schöningh, 1899.

x, 246 p. 23cm. (Kirchengeschichtliche Studien, Bd. 5, Hft. 1)

1. Bruno, Saint, 1030 (ca.)-1101. 2. Bruno, Saint, 1030 (ca.)-1101--Bibl. 3. Carthusians. I. Title. II. Series.

NL 0441241   DCU NIC CtY NNUT NjPT MH PU ICRL DDO

Loebe, Arthur Johannes, 1901-

Milzexstirpation bei splenomegale. Inaug. diss. Leipzig, 1928.

Bibl.

NL 0441242   CtY

Loebe, August Julius

see Loebe, Julius, 1805-1900.

Loebe, Carl   W.C.L. M780.88 C697PK no.12

America; a collection of national airs varied for the piano forte, by Carl Löbe. Op. 171. Philad〔elphi〕a, E. Ferrett & Co., c1847.

〔17〕 p. 34 cm.

Contents.-Hail Columbia.-Yankee Doodle.-Star spangled banner.-Red white & blue.

〔No. 12, in a vol. of piano music, collected by Anne R. Ehlen.〕

1. National songs, American. I. Title: Hail Columbia. II. Title: Yankee Doodle. III. Title: Star spangled banner. IV. Title: Red white & blue.

NL 0441244   NcD

LÖBE, CARL   Lilly Library

America. A collection of national airs varied for the piano forte, by Carl Löbe ... Philadelphia, Lee & Walker 〔etc., etc.〕 ca. 1857.

4 p. 4to

No plate number. Carries copyright date of 1847. This instrumental version of The star spangled banner may be earlier than the vocal score listed in Muller: 33.

NL 0441245   InU

Löbe, Carl.   * M1 .S444 v.18 no.20

Homage à Jenny Lind; valse brillante composée pour le piano et dediée à la Cantatrice du Nord. Op. 181, no. 207. ©1848 by E. Ferrett & Co., Eastern District of Pennsylvania. Philada., E. Ferrett & Co., 40 South 8th St. 〔184- or 185-〕

7 p. 35cm. 〔Sheet music collection, v.18, no.20〕

1. Waltzes (Piano). I. Title.

NL 0441246   ViU

Loebe, Claus-Victor, 1907-

... Ueber Erfahrungen mit 106 Bluttransfusionen nach der Athrombit-Methode von Neubauer und Lampert ... Greifswald, 1934.

Inaug.-Diss. - Greifswald.

Lebenslauf.

"Literaturverzeichnis": p. 27-28.

NL 0441247   CtY MiU

Löbe, Ernst, 1836-1916.

Das deutsche zollstrafrecht. Die zollstrafrechtlichen vorschriften des Deutschen reichs, unter besonderer berücksichtigung ihrer beziehungen zum Strafgesetzbuche und zur Strafprozessordnung, sowie der rechtsprechung des Reichsgerichts, erläutert von dr. Ernst Löbe ... 2. vollständig neu bearbeitete aufl. Leipzig, E. L. Hirschfeld, 1890.

iv, 〔2〕 p., 1 l., 284 p. 21½cm.

1. Tariff—Germany—Law. 2. Criminal law—Germany. 3. Criminal procedure—Germany. I. Germany. Laws, statutes, etc. II. Title.

37-24742

NL 0441248   DLC

Löbe, Ernst, 1836-1916.

Das deutsche zollstrafrecht. Die zollstrafrechtlichen vorschriften des Deutschen reichs, unter besonderer berücksichtigung ihrer beziehungen zum Strafgesetzbuche und zur Strafprozessordnung sowie der rechtsprechung des Reichsgerichts, erläutert von dr. Ernst Löbe ... 4., vollständig neu bearb. aufl. Tübingen, J. C. B. Mohr (P. Siebeck) 1912.

vi, 〔2〕, 351 p. 24½cm.

1. Tariff—Germany—Law. 2. Criminal law—Germany. 3. Criminal procedure—Germany. I. Germany. Laws, statutes, etc. II. Title.

12-15498

NL 0441249   DLC

Löbe, Ernst, 1836-1916   336.43 L825

Handbuch des königlich sächsischen etat-, kassen- und rechnungswesens mit einschluss der staatshaushaltskontrolle, von dr. Ernst Löbe ... Leipzig, 〔V〕eit & comp., 1884.

ix, 〔1〕, 802p. incl.tables. 22cm.

1. Finance. Saxony

NL 0441250   IEN

Löbe, Ernst, 1836-1916.   HG 111 L6 1904

Handbuch des Königlich Sächsischen Etat-, Kassen- und Rechnungswesens mit Einschluss der rechnungsmässigen Staatshaushaltskontrolle. 2., vollständig neu bearbeitete Auflage. Leipzig, Veit, 1904.

xv, 823 p.

NL 0441251   WaU

Löbe, Ernst, 1836-

Die königlich sächsische verwaltung der indirekten abgaben in ihrer einrichtung und geschäftlichen wirksamkeit, ihrem verhältnisse zum Reiche und zum staatshaushalte und in ihrem beamtenwesen. Hrsg. von dr. Ernst Löbe ... 7., vollständig neubearb. und erweiterte aufl. Leipzig, J. B. Hirschfeld, 1910.

iv, 208 p. 15½cm.

11-16473

NL 0441252   DLC

Löbe, Ernst, 1836-   336.431 L782s

Der staatshaushalt des königreichs Sachsen in seinen verfassungsrechtlichen beziehungen und finanziellen leistungen. Leipzig, 1889.

272p. tables, fold.diagr.

NL 0441253   IU

Löbe, Ernst, 1836-

Der Staatshaushalt des Königreichs Sachsen in seinen verfassungsrechtlichen Beziehungen nach dem Stande der heutigen Gesetzgebung und unter Berücksichtigung der geschichtlichen Entwicklung. Von Dr. Ernst Löbe, ... Zweite neubearbeitete Auflage. Leipzig, Veit & Co., 1906.

vi, 220 p. 23cm.

NL 0441254   ICJ

Loebe, Ernst, 1836-

Der Staatshaushalt des Königreichs Sachsen in seinen verfassungs- und etatrechtlichen Beziehungen nach dem Stande der heutigen Gesetzgebung und unter Berücksichtigung der geschichtlichen Entwicklung. Von Dr. Ernst Löbe... Leipzig: Veit & Comp., 1912. viii, 226 p. 3. ed. 8°.

1. Finance, Germany: Saxony.

N. Y. P. L.   September 10, 1915.

NL 0441255   NN

Löbe, Ernst Conon, 1835-191-?   Z2244 .S28L8

Altenburgica; uebersicht der literatur zur *geschichte des* herzogthums Sachsen-Altenburg, von Ernst Conon Löbe ... Altenburg, Schnuphase, 1878.

71, 〔4〕 p. 20cm.

1. Saxe-Altenburg—Bibl.

NL 0441256   ICU

Löbe, G Paul

see Löbe, Paul, 1875-

Loebe, Hans

Castrum Altenburg, eine verlassene Reichsstadt. Altenburg im Th., Wermann, 1938

125 p. illus.

NL 0441258   MH

VOLUME 338

Löbe, Hans.
Liubusua. Die Polen in Altenburg. Altenburg, Thür.,
Kommissionsverlag der Buchhandlung T. Körner, 1941.
56 p. illus. 21 cm.

1. Altenburg, Ger.—Hist.   I. Title.

DD901.A35L55   54–52915 ‡

NL 0441259   DLC IU MH

Löbe, Hans.
Wie Altenburg entstand. Die wieder aufgefundene An-
fangsgeschichte einer deutschen Stadt mit Kaiserpfalz.
Altenburg, Thür., 1945 ₍i. e. 1946₎
39 p. map. 21 cm.
"Quellenangabe und Abkürzungen": p. ₍4₎

1. Altenburg, Ger.—Hist.   I. Title.
DD901.A35L6   943.24   A F 48–179*
Illinois. Univ. Library
for Library of Congress   ₍1₎†

NL 0441260   IU DLC MH

Film
GR
10
L5
reel
245

Löbe, Julius, 1805-1900.
Aberglaube und Volksmittel aus dem
Altenburgischen. Altenburg, Pierer, 1874.
441-457p.   (Mittheilungen der Geschichts-
und Alterthumsforschenden Gesellschaft des
Osterlandes, 7.Bd.)
Microfilm (positive. Literature of
folklore, reel 245)

1. Superstition. 2. Folk-lore--Germany.
3. Altenburg, Germany--Soc. life and customs.
I. Title.

NL 0441261   UU

PK 1102
.8
.M4 L6
1839

Löbe, Julius, 1805-1900.
Beiträge zur textberichtigung und erklärung
der Skeireins, von dr. Julius Loebe.   Altenburg,
H. A. Pierer, 1839.
viii, 60 p.   22½cm.

A commentary on Ulphilas Gothic translation
of the Gospel of St. John, by H. F. Massmann.

NL 0441262   MdBJ CU PU ICU

Loebe, Julius, 1805-1900.
Glossarium der gothischen sprache. 1843
see under   Gabelentz, H₍ans₎ C₍onon₎ von der,
1807-1874.

Löbe, Julius, 1805-
Gräfin Bertha von Groitzsch oder von Morungen.
Leipzig, 1890.
8°. (Mittheilungen der Deutschen Gesellschaft
in Leipzig, Bd. 8, Heft 3, p. 29-37)

NL 0441264   CtY

Loebe, Julius, 1805-1900.
Grammatik der gothischen sprache. 1846
see under   Gabelentz, H₍ans₎ C₍onon₎ von der,
1807-1874.

Loebe, Julius. 1805—. Noch einmal zur geschichte von *dwis*. 2 pp. (Deutsch. morg. gesells. Zeits.
v. 37, 1883, p. 621.)

NL 0441266   MdBP

Loebe, Julius, 1805-1900.
... Ulfilae, Gothorum episopi, Opera omnia,
sive Veteris et Novi Testamenti verisonis gothicae
fragmenta qua supersunt
see under   Wulfila, bp. of the Goths,
d. 381?

Loebe, Julius, 1805-1900, joint ed.
Ulfilas... Lipsiae, 1836-46.
see under   Bible. Gothic. 1836-46.

(also with dates 1843, 1843-46)

A32b
235
15

Löbe, Karl, 1911-
Bremens Holzwirtschaft. Bremen, A. Geist,
1943.
127p. illus. 24cm. (Bremer wissenschaftliche Gesellschaft. Abhandlungen und Vorträge.
Bd. 15, Heft 4)
Bibliography: p. 124-125.

1. Lumber trade - Bremen.   cdu. No shelf.

NL 0441269   CtY MH ICU CU

AC
831

Löbe, Karl, 1911-
-Der grundsatz der gewaltenteilung in deutschen
verfassungsleben. ... Kiel, 1936.   97 p.
Inaug. Diss. - Kiel, 1936.
Lebenslauf.
Verzeichnis der benutzten literatur.

NL 0441270   ICRL CtY

LÖBE, KARL, 1911-
Holz als Seehafengut. Bremen, Internationale
Verlagsgesellschaft, 1952. 93 p. illus. 21cm.
(Schriftenreihe "Bremische Wirtschaft." Bd. 3)

1. Wood--Trade and stat. 2. Wood industries. 3. Harbors.
t. 1952

NL 0441271   NN

PN
6273
.L6

Löbe, Max, comp.
Altdeutsche Sinnsprüche in Reimen.
Halle, M. Niemeyer, 1883.
164 p.

#Aphorisms and apothegms.
#Proverbs, German.
(A)Altdeutsche Sinnsprüche in Reimen.

NL 0441272   MoU OCl ICN

Loebe, Max.   2864.34
Das herzogliche Residenz-Schloss zu Altenburg.
=   Altenburg. Lippold. 1875. (5), 72 pp. 8°.

July 2,   1900
*D6043 — Herzogliches Residenz-Schloss, Altenburg.

NL 0441273   MB

Y
0595
.52

LÖBE, MAX.
Wahlsprüche, devisen und sinnsprüche der
kurfürsten und herzöge von Sachsen, Ernestinischer
linie. Ein beitrag zur spruchpoesie des 16. und
17. jahrhunderts...   Leipzig, Duncker & Humblot,
1878.
96p.

Cover dated 1877.

NL 0441274   ICN InU NcU ICU OCl

Löbe, Max.
Wahlsprüche, devisen und sinnsprüche deutscher für-
stengeschlechter des xvi. und xvii. jahrhunderts, von dr.
Max Löbe ... Leipzig, J. A. Barth, 1883.
xvi, 267, ₍1₎ p. 24½ᶜᵐ.

1. Mottoes. 2. Germany—Nobility.   I. Title.
20-6597

Library of Congress   CR75.G3L6

NL 0441275   DLC ICU MH OCl NN MiU MB

Löbe, Paul, 1875- 1967·
Erinnerungen eines Reichstagspräsidenten.   ₍1. Aufl.₎
Berlin-Grunewald, Arani ₍1949₎
173 p. ports. 19 cm.
"Entstanden aus einer Reihe von Artikeln in der Berliner Zeit-
schrift 'Das Sozialistische Jahrhundert.' "

1. Germany—Pol. & govt.—20th cent.   I. Title.
A 51-618
Harvard Univ. Library
for Library of Congress   ₍2₎

NL 0441276   MH CaBVaU FU DAU ICarbS PU CSt-H NN NIC

Löbe, Paul, 1875-1967.
Festschrift Paul Löbe ...   [1950]
see under   Oschilewski, Walther Georg,
1904-

Löbe, Paul, 1875-1967.
Lebendige Tradition; Paul Löbe zum
achtzigsten Geburtstag ...
see under   Scholz, Arno, 1904-   ed.

Löbe, Paul, 1875-
... Die österreichisch-deutsche anschluss-
bewegung, von Paul Löbe... und dr. ing.
Neubacher ...   Wurzen (Bezirk Leipzig)
Unikum verlag [1926]
18 p.   16 cm.   (Unikum-sonderdruck
nr. 21)

NL 0441279   CSt-H

₍Loebe, Paul,₎ 1875-   , editor.
Sous le joug de la domination étrangère; les souffrances de
la population rhénane./ Leipzig: F. Koehler, 1923. 96 p.   8°.

1. Rhine valley—Hist.
N. Y. P. L.   October 31, 1925

NL 0441280   NN

Löbe, Paul, 1875-
...Sozialismus! Ja oder nein?   ₍Berlin: J. H. W. Dietz
Nachf., G.m.b.H., 1932.₎ 15 p. 22cm.
Cover-title.

689004A. 1. Socialism.
N. Y. P. L.   March 6, 1934

NL 0441281   NN

Löbe, Paul, 1875- 1967·
Der Weg war lang; Lebenserinnerungen von Paul Löbe,
chemals Präsident des Deutschen Reichstages. ₍2. veränderte und erweiterte Aufl.₎ Berlin-Grunewald, Arani ₍1954₎
302 p. illus. 19 cm.
First ed. published in 1949 under title: Erinnerungen eines Reichstagspräsidenten.

1. Germany—Pol. & govt.—20th cent.   I. Title.

DD247.L62A3 1954   56–47916 ‡

NL 0441282   PU NN NIC CSt-H CaBVaU
               DLC NNC CU CtY CU-S FTaSU NSyU OrPS UU

VOLUME 338

Loebe, R.
Die Beseitigung städtischer Abwässer, mit besonderer Berücksichtigung der Berliner Abwässerfrage von R. Loebe ... Berlin, Maass & Plank, 1909.
63 (1) p. illus. 8°.
Bibliography, p. [64]

NL 0441283   NN

Loebe, Richard, 1888-
Beitrag zur kenntnis der zink- und cadmiumcyanide. Inaug. diss. Berlin, 1902. (Jena)

NL 0441284   ICRL PU NN

LÖBE, Rudolf Ludwig Waldemar

    See LÖBE, Waldemar, 1877-

Loebe, Victor Julius.

... Commentationis de elocutione Callimachi Cyrenensis poetae pars altera. Putbus, August Knaak, 1874.

20 p.

NL 0441286   ViU

Loebe, Victor Julius.

... Commentationis de elocutione Callimachi Cyrenensis poetae pars prior. Putbus, August Knaak, 1867.

22 p.

NL 0441287   ViU

Loebe, Victor Julius
De elocutione Arati Solensis poetae.
Inaug. Diss. Halle, 1864.

NL 0441288   ICRL PU DLC

LÖBE, Waldemar, 1877-
De negationum binembrium usu apud poetas tragicos graecos. Diss.-philol. Berolini, 1907.

NL 0441289   MH ICRL NjP CtY PU

Loebe, Walther Winfried, 1891-
Uber die Intensitätsverteilung von Röntgenstrahlen, die von einer Graphitantikathode ausgehen. Greifswald, Abel, 1914.
38 S. 23 cm.
Greifswald, Phil. Diss. v. 7. März 1914, Ref. Mie
[Geb. 30. Mai 91 Putbus; Wohnort: Greifswald; Staatsangeh.: Preu en; Vorbildung: Pd Putbus Reife 09; Studium: Dresden TeH. I, Leipzig I, Greifswald 8 S.; Rig. 19. Febr. 14]

NL 0441290   CtY

Löbe, Werner, 1911-
... Das Vorkommen von ausgesprochener Wehenschwäche beim partiell infantilen Becken ... Berlin, 1937.
Inaug.-Diss. - Berlin.
Lebenslauf.
"Literaturverzeichnis": p. 23.

NL 0441291   CtY

MANN
S 465 L821
Löbe, William, 1815-1891.
Abriss der Geschichte der deutschen Landwirthschaft von den ältesten Zeiten bis auf die Gegenwart. Berlin, Wiegandt & Hempel, 1873.
xii, 232 p. 19 cm. (Thaer-Bibliothek, Bd. 4)

    1. Agriculture - Germany - Hist.
[I. Title] [II. Title: Geschichte der deutschen Landwirthschaft von den ältesten Zeiten bis auf die Gegenwart.]

NL 0441292   NIC CU ICJ KMK

MANN
SB 107 L82
Löbe, William, 1815-1891.
Anleitung zum rationellen Anbau der Handelsgewächse: der Fabrik-, Farbe-, Gewürz-, Gespinnst-, Oel-, Arznei- und Spezereipflanzen behufs Erzielung einer höhern Bodenrente. Stuttgart, Cohen und Risch, 1868-70.
7 v. in 1. illus., tables. 23 cm.

    Contents.--1. Gewürzpflanzen.--2. Fabrikpflanzen.--3. Gespinnstpflanzen.--4. Oelpflanzen.--5. Farbepflanzen.--6. Arznei- und Spezereipflanzen.--7. Gemüsepflanzen.

    1. Botany, Ec[o]nomic. [I. Title.]

NL 0441293   NIC CU

Löbe, William, 1815-1891.
Anleitung zum rationellen betriebe der ernte, von dr. William Löbe ... Mit 46 abbildungen ... Leipzig, Veit & comp., 1861.
x, 180 p. illus. 24ᶜᵐ.

    1. Agricultural machinery.

                    12-15013

Library of Congress   S695.L82

NL 0441294   DLC

Löbe, William, 1815-1891.
Dr. William Löbes Anleitung zum rationellen betriebe der ernte und zur aufbewahrung der ernteerzeugnisse. 3., verm., verb., nach den erfordernissen der neuzeit gänzlich umgearb. aufl. Mit 92 abbildungen; von dr. Lothar Meyer. Neudamm, I. Neumann, 1909.
viii, 211 p. illus. 21½ᶜᵐ.

    1. Agricultural machinery.   I. Meyer, Lothar Martin Bernhard, 1865- ed.

                    29-16056

Library of Congress   S695.L82 1909

NL 0441295   DLC

Löbe, William, 1815-1891.
Encyclopädie der gesammten Landwirthschaft, der Staats-, Haus- und Forstwirthschaft und der in die Landwirthschaft einschlagenden technischen Gewerbe und Hülfswissenschaften. Herausgegeben unter Mitwirkung einer Gesellschaft ausgezeichneter Landwirthe von William Löbe, ... Erster-[sechster] Band. [Mit 1000 in den Text eingedruckten Abbildungen.] Leipzig, O. Wigand, 1850-1852.
6 vol. illus., 1 fold. pl., 1 fold. table, diagrs. 24ᶜᵐ.
Vol. 5, p. 481-619, wanting.

NL 0441296   ICJ ICU

S 633 L82
Löbe, William, 1815-1891.
Die Fortschritte in der Düngerlehre während der letzten zwölf Jahre. Breslau, E. Trewendt, 1875.
218 p. 23 cm.

    Bibliographical footnotes.

    1. Fertilizers and manures. I. Title.

NL 0441297   NIC PPG

S 411 L82
Loebe, William, 1815-1891.
Fremdwörterbuch für Landwirthe, Gärtner und Forstleute... Berlin, Wiegandt, Hempel & Parey, 1880.
328 p. 19 cm.

    1. Agriculture - Dictionaries - German.
    2. Horticulture - Dictionaries - German.
    3. Forests and forestry - Dictionaries - German. I. Title.

NL 0441298   NIC DP

Löbe, William, 1815-1891.
Geschichte der landwirthschaft im altenburgischen Osterlande. Nach den besten quellen bearb. ... Leipzig, F.A.Brockhaus, 1845.
ii, 220 p.incl.tables. 21.5 cm.

    Bibliographical foot-notes.

NL 0441299   MH-BA MH

Löbe, William, 1815-1891.
Die getreidearten und hülsenfruechte. Aus Deutschlands landwirthschaftlicher flora von dr. William Loebe. Mit dreissig illuminirten kupfertafeln. Leipzig, W. Baensch, 1863.
1 p. 1., [4] p. 54 p.

NL 0441300   OU

Loebe, William, 1815-1891.
Handbuch der rationellen landwirtschaft fuer praktische landwirthe und vekonomieverwalter. Ed. 2. enl.
Lpz, Wigand, 1856.
672 p.

NL 0441301   PU

Loebe, William, 1815-1891.
Handbuch der rationellen Landwirtschaft für praktische Landwirte, Oekonomie-Verwalter und Schüler landwirtschaftlicher Lehranstalten. Weimar, B.F. Voigt, 1887.
viii, 703 p., 2 port. illus. 8°.
7. ed.

NL 0441302   NN

Loebe, William, 1815-1891, ed.
Die handelspflanzen, wurzel-, knollen-, küchengewächse und essbaren schwämme. Aus der Landwirthschaftlichen flora, hrsg. von dr. William Löbe ... 2. aufl. Leipzig, W. Baensch [1868]
1 p. l., 70 (i. e. 72), [6] p. XVIII col. pl. 29½ᶜᵐ.
Paging irregular: no. 67-68 repeated.
Issued in four parts.

    1. Botany, Economic. 2. Germany. Botany. 3. Mushrooms. 4. Vegetables.

                    Agr 9-675

Library, U. S. Dept. of   Agriculture   459L78H

NL 0441303   DNAL

Löbe, William, 1815-1891.
Der höchste Ernte-Ertrag.
see under title

Loebe, William, 1815-1891, editor.
Illustrirtes Lexikon der gesammten Wirtschaftskunde. Für alle Stände... Bearbeitet von Fachmännern und Gelehrten. Hrsg. von William Löbe. Leipzig: O. Wigand, 1853-55. 5 v. illus. 8°.
Universalregister in v. 5, 1855.

1. Encyclopaedias (German).   2. Title.
N. Y. P. L.   January 16, 1923.

NL 0441305   NN

VOLUME 338

Löbe, William, 1815–1891, ed.
Jahres-bericht über die fortschritte der
gesammten land- und hauswirthschaft
see under title

54
L78 Löbe, William, 1815–1891.
Ed.3 Katechismus der Drainierung und der Ent-
wässerung des Bodens überhaupt. 3.,
gänzlich umgearb. Aufl. Leipzig, Weber, 1881.
154 p. (Webers illustrierte Katechismen)

1. Drainage. I. Webers illustrierte Katechismen no.7.

NL 0441307 DNAL CtY

Löbe, William, 1815–1891.
Die Krankheiten der Kartoffeln, ihre Kennzeichen und Ursachen und
ihre Verhütung und Folgen. Herausgegeben von William Löbe.
Leipzig, Gebrüder Reichenbach, 1842.
vi, [2], 130 p. 20cm.

NL 0441308 ICJ

B
631.54 Die krankheiten der kultur-pflanzen auf
L82k aeckern, in obstanlagen, wein-, gemüse- und
blumengarten. Anleitung zur erkenntniss, ber-
hütung und heilung aller innerlichen und äusserlichen krankheiten des getreides, der hülsenfrüchte, futterpflanzen, knollen- und rübenge-
wächse, handelspflanzen, obst- und maulbeer-
bäume, des Weinstocks, der küchengarten- und
zierpflanzen, von Dr. William Löbe... Hamburg,
R. Kittler, 1864.
viii, 243p. 21 cm.

NL 0441309 LU

Loebe, William, 1815–1891.
Die kuenstlichen düngemittel. Hamburg 1864.

NL 0441310 NjR

Löbe, William, 1815–1891.
Kurzgefasstes lexikon der gesammten haus-und
land-wirthschaft. 1861.

NL 0441311 DNAL

Löbe, William, 1815–1891.
Die landwirthschaft und ihr einfluss auf das sociale und
materielle wohl der staaten und völker ... von dr. William
Löbe... Leipzig, O. Wigand, 1854.
2 p. l., (v)–viii, 404 p. illus. 21cm. (Added t.-p.: Bildungs-halle im
sinne und geiste unserer zeit ... 10. bd.)

1. Agriculture—Germany. (1. Germany—Agriculture)

Agr 28–438

Library, U. S. Dept. of Agriculture 33.27L78

NL 0441312 DNAL TU

Löbe, William 1815–1891, ed.

Landwirthschaftliche dorfzeitung ...

Leipzig, F. A. Brockhaus, 18

Loebe, William, 1815–1891.
Landwirthschaftliche flora Deutschlands, oder Abbildung und beschreibung aller für land- und hauswirthe
wichtigen pflanzen, von Dr. William Loebe. 3. verm. und
verb. aufl. ... Leipzig, W. Baensch (1868)
4 p. l., 439, (1) p. 150 pl. (145 col.) 28cm.

1. Botany, Agricultural. 2. Germany. Botany. 3. Grasses and forage
plants.

Agr 8–323

Library, U. S. Dept. of Agriculture 459L78

NL 0441314 DNAL

Löbe, William, 1815–1891.
Landwirthschaftlicher futterbau, von dr.
William Loebe... 2. neu bearb. aufl. ...
Berlin, Wiegandt, Hempel and Parey, 1877.
135,[1] p. illus. (Thaer-bibliothek.)

NL 0441315 OU

SF
91 Die Mastung der hauptsächlichsten land-
L82 wirthschaftlichen Nutzthiere, unter Berück-
1892 sichtigung der neuesten Erfahrungen für den
praktischen Landwirth. 2. Aufl. Bautzen
(Ger.) E. Hübner (E. Kühl's Verlag) 1896.
140 p. 24 cm.

1. Stock and stock-breeding. I. Title.

NL 0441316 NIC

Löbe, William, 1815–1891.
Die milchwirthschaft, von dr. William Löbe...
Berlin, Verlag von Wiegandt, Hempel and Paren,
1879.
154 p. illus. (Thaer-bibliothek.)

NL 0441317 OU

Löbe, William, 1815–1891.
Milchwirtschaft und Käsebereitung. Von Dr. William Löbe.
Zweite, umgearbeitete Auflage. Mit 43 in den Text gedruckten
Abbildungen. Berlin, P. Parey, 1889.
viii, 156 p. incl. illus., diagrs. 19cm. (On cover: Thaer-Bibliothek, Band 52.)
Bibliographical foot-notes.

NL 0441318 ICJ

Loebe, William, 1815–91.
Das Musterdörfchen; eine lehrreiche Geschichte für
den Bürger und Landmann. Dresden, Arnoldische Buchhandlung, 1846–47
2v. in 1 illus.

1. Thalheim, Ger.

NL 0441319 MH

Loebe, William, 1815–1891.
Die neueren und neuesten culturpflanzen für den landwirth und gärtner. Nach arten, abarten und anbau systematisch beschrieben, von dr. William Löbe ... Frankfurt
a. M., J. D. Sauerländer, 1863.
xxxi, 496 p. 22cm.

1. Plants, Cultivated.

Agr 9–676

Library, U. S. Dept. of Agriculture 452L784

NL 0441320 DNAL MBH

Löbe, William, 1815–1891.
Die rationelle Zucht, Haltung und Mastung der
Schweine. Nebst Anleitung zur Vorbeugung und
Heilung der am häufigsten vorkommenden
Krankheiten derselben ... Wien [etc.] 1876.
23 cm.

NL 0441321 CtY

Löbe, William, 1815–1891.
Samen und Saat; Anleitung zur rationellen Besamung des
Ackerlandes, der Wiesen und Weiden, von Dr. William Löbe ...
Berlin, P. Parey, 1890.
vi, 140 p. incl. illus., tables. 19cm. (On cover: Thaer-Bibliothek. Bd. 72)

NL 0441322 ICJ

SB199 Löbe, William, 1815–1891.
.L8 Die wiesen und weiden, ihre bewirthschaftung und
cultur. Gründliche anleitung den werth und ertrag
der wiesen und weiden durch ein rationelles cul-
turverfahren zu erhöhen. Von dr. William Löbe...
Berlin, C. Schotte u. comp., 1863–
v. 19½cm.
Label mounted over imprint v.1:Leipzig und
Stuttgart, H. Johannssen, 1864.
Vol.1 has also special t.-p.
Contents.–1.th. Die wiesen.

NL 0441323 ICU

Løbeck, Engebret Engebretsen, 1864–1922.
Billeder fra dödens dal; fortälling af E. E. Löbeck. Eau
Claire, Wis., "Reforms" trykkeri, 1899.
144 p. front. (port.) 19½cm.

I. Title.

99–3159 Revised

Library of Congress PT9150.L6B5

NL 0441324 DLC

Løbeck, Engebret Engebretsen, 1864–1922.
Billeder fra dödens dal; fortälling.
2. opl. Alexandria, Minn., 1907.

152 p. port. 20cm.

NL 0441325 MnHi

Løbeck, Engebret Engebretsen, 1864–1922.
Forglemmigei; nogle sange. Eau Claire,
Wis., "Reform"s trykkeri, 1894.

26 p. port. 18cm.

NL 0441326 MnU

Loebeck, Maude Elva, 1916–
Studies on the terrestrial fruiting Myxobacteria. Ann
Arbor, University Microfilms (1955)
(University Microfilms, Ann Arbor, Mich.) Publication no. 10,771)
Microfilm copy of typescript. Positive.
Collation of the original: ix, 138 l. illus. (part mounted)
Thesis—University of Washington.
Abstracted in Dissertation abstracts, v. 15 (1955) no. 2, p. 191.
Vita.
Bibliography : leaves 131–138.

1. Myxobacteriales. I. Title : Terrestrial fruiting Myxobacteria.

Microfilm AC–1 no. 10,771 Mic A 55–257

Washington. Univ. Seattle. Library
for Library of Congress (1)†

NL 0441327 WaU IdPI DLC

Loebel, Alexander.
Versuch einer lösung des trinitätsproblems, von Alexander
Loebel. Berlin-Schöneberg, Selbstverlag des verfassers, 1931.
24 p. 23½cm.

1. Trinity. I. Title.

Library of Congress BT113.L6 31–24503
Copyright A—Foreign 13052
(2) 231

NL 0441328 DLC

Loebel, Alfred Hugo Christoph
see Loebl, Alfred Hugo Christoph, 1875–

VOLUME 338

Loebel, Arthur
—— . Die balneologischen Kurmethoden bei
Behandlung der chronischen Para- und Peri-
metritis. 65 pp. 8°. *Halle a. S., C. Marhold,*
1896.
Forms 6. and 7. Hft. of: Arch. d. Balneoth. u. Hydroth.,
Halle a. S., 1896.

NL 0441330   DNLM

Loebel, Arthur
Dorner Dokumente aus dem Franzisko-Josephinischen
Zeitalter. Wien, Hölder, 1909

108 p. illus.

NL 0441331   MH

WBI   LOEBEL, Arthur
L825e   Entwicklung, technische Einrichtung und
1906   therapeutische Bedeutung des Bades
      Dorna. Wien, Hölder, 1906.
      169 p. illus.

NL 0441332   DNLM

Loebel, Arthur
Ein kapitel moderner balneotechnik im lichte
der neueren mineralquellen- und bäderforschung
... Leipzig, Benno Konegen verlag, 1906.
1 p. l., 65 p. illus., plans.

"Literatur": p. 65.

1. Baths.

NL 0441333   NNC DNLM

Loebel, Arthur
—— . Klimatologische und klimatotherapeu-
tische Kurortefragen mit Benützung der
Dorner Beobachtungen. 24 pp. 8°. *Wien*
& Leipzig, R. Coen, 1906.

NL 0441334   DNLM

WR   LOEBEL, Arthur
L825k   Kosmetische Winke für die Pflege der
1894   Haut, der Haare und des Mundes.
      Leipzig, Breitenstein [1894]
      135 p.

NL 0441335   DNLM

Loebei (Arthur). Der Kurgebrauch mit Mine-
ralwässern während der Gravidität. 8°. *Ber-*
lin, L. Heuser, 1888.
Repr. from : Frauenarzt. Berl. 1888. III.

NL 0441336   DNLM

Loebel (Arthur). Leitfaden der hydriatischen
Verordnungen bei chronischen Erkrankungen
mit curdiätischen Regeln. 2 p. l., 82 pp. 12°.
Leipzig & Wien, M. Breitenstein [u. d.]

NL 0441337   DNLM

Loebel, Arthur
—— . Die neueren Behandlungsmethoden der
Metritis chronica bei gleichzeitigem Gebrauche
von Brunnen- und Badecuren. 38 pp., 1 l. 8°.
Leipzig, B. Konegen, 1892.

NL 0441338   DNLM

WBI   LOEBEL, Arthur
L825r   Die Reconstructionsepoche des
1899   Eisenbades Dorna; Reminiscenzen mit
      Benützung amtlicher Quellen. Leipzig,
      Deuticke, 1899.
      163 p. ports.

NL 0441339   DNLM

Loebel, Arthur
—— . Studien und Vorträge über die Wirkungen der Kohlensäure- und Moorbäder. 59 pp.
8°. *Leipzig, B. Konegen, 1906.*

NL 0441340   DNLM

Loebel, Arthur
—— . Ein vortragender Rat als Balneolog.
Denkschrift für Ministerialrat Friedrich von
Walzl 33 pp. 12°. *Leipzig, B. Konegen,*
1906.

NL 0441341   DNLM

Loebel, Arthur
—— . Zur Purpurabehandlung mit Trink- und
Badekuren. 36 pp. 8°. *Halle a. S., 1900.*
Forms 7. Hft., v. 2, of: Arch. d. Balneoth. u. Hydroth.,
Halle a. S., 1900.

NL 0441342   DNLM

Loebel, Avram.
Ueber die einwirkung von organomagnesiumver-
bindungen auf o-aldehydophenoxyessigsaeure und die
ueberfuehrung der entstehenden produkte in derivate
des cumarons.
Inaug. diss. Berlin, tech. hoch. 1910.

NL 0441343   ICRL PU

LÖBEL, Curt.
Naturalleistungen für die bewaffnete
macht in frienden. Borna-Beipzig, 1907.

(8)+75+(1) p.
Inaug.-diss., ——Leipzig.

NL 0441344   MH-L ICRL

Löbel, D   Theophil, 1859–
Deutsch-türkisches wörterbuch ... von D. Theophil Löbel ...
2. verm. und verb. aufl. Constantinopel, O. Keil; [etc., etc.]
1894.
4 p. l., 334 p., 1 l. 14ᶜᵐ.

1. German language—Dictionaries—Turkish.

                                 34–31667

Library of Congress   PL193.G5L6 1894   494.3533

NL 0441345   DLC CLU

Löbel, D   Theophil, 1859–
Hochzeitsbräuche in der Türkei. Nach eigenen beobachtungen und forschungen und nach den verlässlich-
sten quellen, von D. Theophil Löbel ... Mit einer einleitung von Herrn professor H. Vambéry: "Ethnographi-
sche forschungen in der Türkei." Amsterdam, J. H. de
Bussy, 1897.
xv p., 1 l., 298 p. 19¼ᶜᵐ.

                               5–3967

NL 0441346   DLC CtY CU CLU OCl MH MB ICJ

Löbel, David
Etude clinique et hématologique du cancer
myéloïde du crâne á foyers multiples chez
l'enfant (myélocytome, myélosarcome, chlorome).
Paris, A. Legrand, 1924.
59

Thèse.

NL 0441347   DNLM CtY NNC

Loebel, David, 1885–
Ueber den Einfluß des Quecksilbers bei der
Nitrierung aromatischer Verbindungen.
(Berlin, Ebering 1914)
44 S.   23 cm.
Berlin, Phil. Diss. v. 5. Aug. 1914, Ref.
Beckmann, Gabriel.
[Geb. 16. Juni 85 Galatzi; Wohnort; Berlin;
Staatsangeh.: Rumänien; Vorbildung: Staats-G.
Matei-Basarab Bukarest Reife 05; Studium:
Berlin TeH. 6, U. 8 S.; Rig. 16. Juli 14]

NL 0441348   CtY

Loebel, Eduard Leopold Loebenstein-
see   Loebenstein-Loebel, Eduard Leopold,
1779–1819.

Loebel, Fritz: Die Umwandlungen des Knorpelschädels des Kaninchens
vor und nach der Geburt. [Maschinenschrift.] 46 S. 4°. —
Auszug: Breslau (1924): Hochschulverl. 2 Bl. 8°
Breslau, Phil. Diss. v. 31. Juli 1924 [1925]   [U 25. 1111

NL 0441350   ICRL

Löbel, Georg, 1909–
Der ideelle Geschäftswerk vom betriebswirt-
schaftlichen, handelsrechtlichen und
steuerrechtlichen Standpunkt ... Kallmünz, 1933.
Inaug.-Diss. - Frankfurt am Main.

NL 0441351   CtY

---

ar W   Loebel, Hans-Joachim, 1912–
24   Über 6-Arylsulfoester der Monoaceton-
      glucose. Berlin, V D I - Verlag G.m.b.H
      1939.
      29 p. 21cm.

      Inaug.-Diss.—Berlin.

      1. Chemistry, Organic—Experiments.

NL 0441352   NIC

Loebel, Heinrich, 1879–
Ueber halogenverbindungen des urans ...
[Berlin, 1907]
45 [3] p. illus., tables.   22 cm.
Film copy, made in 1942, of the original
in the Philosophical society of Washington.
Negative.
Inaug.-diss. - Berlin
Lebenslauf.

NL 0441353   RPB PU ICRL

Loebel, Hirschel
see   Lewin, Hirschel, 1721–1800.

Löbel, Jean Heinrich, 1911–
... Akkordeon-lexikon. Accordion dictionary. Dictionaire
accordéonistique. Berlin, Schulenburg & co., 1937.
115, [1] p. 21ᶜᵐ. (Schriftenreihe zur akkordeonistischen musikwis-
senschaft, hrsg. von J. H. Löbel, bd. 3)
At head of title: J. H. Löbel.
Text in German.
Pages 81–115, advertising matter.

1. Accordion. 2. Music—Dictionaries.   I. Title.   41–17399

Library of Congress   ML102.A2L6
                            [2]   788.9

NL 0441355   DLC

VOLUME 338

Löbel, Jean Heinrich, 1911–
Führer durch die Akkordeon-Literatur. International guide to accordion music. Berlin, A. Koschke, 1939.
136 p. (p. 109–136 advertisements) 21 cm. (Schriftenreihe zur akkordeonistischen Musikwissenschaft, Bd. 4)

1. Accordion music—Bibl.   I. Title.   II. Title: International guide to accordion music.   (Series)

ML128.A35L6   57-54910

NL   0441356   DLC

Löbel, Johann Gottlob Friedrich.
Der Halley'sche Comet in seiner vierundzwanzigsten Wiederkunft seit dem Jahr sechzehn nach Chr. Geb. im Jahr 1835, von Johann Gottlob Friedrich Löbel, ... Nürnberg, J. P. Raw'sche Buchhandlung, 1835.
vi, [2], 64 p. 20ᶜᵐ.

NL   0441357   ICJ

WB
130
L825m
1935
LÖBEL, Josef, 1882–
Ayons confiance dans la médecine; le passé et l'avenir, adapté de l'allemand par Étienne Frey. Paris, Plon [c1935]
261 p.
Translation of Medizin oder dem Manne kann geholfen werden.
1. Medicine

NL   0441358   DNLM

Löbel, Josef, 1882–
...Danke — gut! Fünfzig neue Kapitel optimistischer Medizin. Leipzig [etc.] Grethlein & Co., 1930.   229 p.   19cm.

289866B. 1. Medicine—Essays and   misc. I. Title.
N. Y. P. L.   February 14, 1945

NL   0441359   NN DNLM OCl

Löbel, Josef, 1882–
Don't be afraid, by Josef Löbel, M. D.; translated by George F. Dunay. New York, London, G. P. Putnam's sons, 1929.
vi, 233 p. 21ᶜᵐ.

1. Medicine.   I. Dunay, George F., tr.   II. Title.
Library of Congress   R710.L67 1929   29-5108

NL   0441360   DLC Or ICRL PU CtY-M OCl MB ICJ

Löbel, Josef, 1882–
... From marriage to love. New York, i. Washburn, 1930.
vi p., 1 l., 9–177 p. 21ᶜᵐ.
At head of title: Josef Loebel, M. D.

1. Marriage. 2. Love.   I. Title.
Library of Congress   HQ739.L68   30-15639
———— Copy 2.
Copyright A 24395   [3]   392.5

NL   0441361   DLC OrU PU CU

Löbel, Josef, 1882–
... Haben sie keine angst! Vierzig kapitel optimistischer medizin. Leipzig, Zürich, Grethlein & co., 1928.
240, [1] p. 19½ᶜᵐ.
At head of title: Josef Löbel-Franzensbad.

1. Medicine.   I. Title.
                                                 28-25437
Library of Congress   R710.L65

NL   0441362   DLC TxU MiD NN OCl

R
512
.K7
Löbel, Josef, 1882–
Historia de un médico afortunado,
Roberto Koch. Versión castellana por el
Dr. Hugo Grünbaum, portada de Rodolfo A.
Brichês. Buenos Aires, Orientación
Integral Humana [c1949]
236 p.
"Título del original en alemán:
Robert Koch, geschichte eines Glücklichen."

1. Koch, Robert, 1843–1910. I. Title.

NL   0441363   DPAHO

WZ
40
L825f
1950
LÖBEL, Josef, 1882–
Historia sucinta de la medicina mundial.
Versión del alemán y notas por Justo
Garate. Buenos Aires, Espasa-Calpe
[1950]
252 p. (Historia y filosofía de la ciencia)

Translation of 5550 Jahre Heilkunde;
eine Weltgeschichte der Medizin.
1. History of medicine I. Garate, Justo,
ed.

NL   0441364   DNLM

W
13
L825k
1930
LÖBEL, Josef, 1882–
Knaurs Gesundheits-Lexikon; ein
Handbuch der Medizin, Hygiene, Körper-
kultur und Schönheitspflege. Berlin,
Knaur [1930]
535 p.

1. Medicine - Dict. - German
Title

NL   0441365   DNLM OCl NN

Löbel, Josef, 1882–
... Lebensretter; detektivromane aus der geschichte der medizin. Bibliothek zeitgenössischer werke [1935]
328, [1] p., 1 l. 19ᶜᵐ.
CONTENTS.—Zucker.—Die pallida.—Als schlachtenbummler im bakterienkrieg.

I. Title.
                                                 37-6580
Library of Congress   PT2623.O314L4 1935
                           [2]   833.91

NL   0441366   DLC NN

Löbel, Josef, 1882–
... Mai paura! Quaranta spunti di medicina ottimistica. 3. ed. Traduzione di D. Secco Suardo, prefazione di E. Bertarelli. Milano, U. Hoepli, 1941.
2 p. l., vii–xii, 294 p. 19½ᶜᵐ.
At head of title: Dottor G. Loebel.

1. Medicine.   I. Secco-Suardo, Dulo, 1889–   tr. II. Title.
Translation of Haben sie keine angst!
                                                 45-40544
Library of Congress   R710.L654 1941
                           [2]   610.4

NL   0441367   DLC

WB
9
L825h
1945
LÖBEL, Josef, 1882–
Mai paura! Quaranta spunti di
medicina ottimistica. 4. ed. Traduzione
di D. Secco Suardo. Milano, Hoepli, 1945.
x, 291 p.
Translation of Haben Sie keine Angst.
1. Medicine - Addresses   Title

NL   0441368   DNLM

Löbel, Josef, 1882–
Medicine; a voyage of discovery, by Josef Löbel, M. D. New York, Farrar & Rinehart [*1934]
vii p., 2 l., 3–334 p. 22ᶜᵐ.
"Translated from the German by L. Marie Sieveking and Ian F. D. Morrow."
London edition (Sidgwick & Jackson, ltd.) has title: Whither medicine?

1. Medicine.   I. Sieveking, Louise Marie, tr.   II. Morrow, Ian Fitzherbert Despard, 1896–   joint tr.
                                                 34-11235 Revised
Library of Congress   R130.L6
———— Copy 2.
Copyright A 72127   [r38n2]   610

OC1ND OCl OCU OEac NN MB PPGi PWcS PP
NL   0441369   DLC OrAshS OrU-M WaS Or WaSp GU ViU ICU

Löbel, Josef, 1882–
Medizin; oder, Dem Manne kann geholfen werden. Berlin: Rowohlt[, cop. 1933]. 307 p. 8°.

1. Medicine.
N. Y. P. L.   May 5, 1933

NL   0441370   NN DLC-P4 NNC OCl DNLM

Löbel, Josef, 1882–
Robert Koch; geschichte eines glücklichen, von d'. Josef Löbel ... Zürich, Bibliothek zeitgenössischer werke [1935]
318, [2] p. 18½ᶜᵐ.

1. Koch, Robert, 1843–1910.
                                                 36-7244
Library of Congress   QR31.K6L6
Copyright A—Foreign   30029
                           [2]   926.1

NL   0441371   DLC NcU

Loebel, Josef, 1882–
Salvadores de vidas; dos novelas de la historia de la medicina. [Traducción del alemán por el Dr. Hugo Grünbaum] Buenos Aires, Espasa-Calpe Argentina [1950]
158 p. 18 cm. (Colección austral, no. 997)

NL   0441372   OU

Löbel, Josef, 1882–
Salvatori di vite.

NL   0441373   OCl OrP

WT
120
L825s
1938
LÖBEL, Josef, 1882–
La segunda juventud femenina; joven
a los 50 años; el secreto de las hormonas.
Buenos Aires, 1938.
202 p.
Title

NL   0441374   DNLM

Loebel, Josef, 1882–

Steinach, Eugen, 1861–
Sex and life; forty years of biological and medical experiments, by Eugen Steinach ... The scientific values adapted to the lay reader by Josef Loebel ... New York, The Viking press, 1940.

Löbel, Josef, 1882–
Spasitelji sivota; detektivski roman iz povijesti medicine... preveo Dr. Josip Bogner. [1935]
Croatian.

NL   0441376   OCl

VOLUME 338

Löbel, Josef, 1882–
... Von der ehe bis zur liebe. Leipzig: Zürich, Grethlein & co., 1929.
212, [1] p. 20ᶜᵐ.
At head of title: Josef Löbel-Franzensbad.

1. Marriage. 2. Love. I. Title.
Library of Congress   HQ739.L67
                                                    30–8484

NL 0441377   DLC OC1 NN

Löbel, Josef, 1882–
Whither medicine? by Josef Loebel ... London, Sidgwick & Jackson, ltd., 1934.
xi, 296 p. 22ᶜᵐ.
American edition (New York, Farrar & Rinehart) has title: Medicine; a voyage of discovery.
"Translated from the original German ('Medizin, oder Dem manne kann geholfen werden') by L. Marie Sieveking and Ian Morrow."

1. Medicine. I. Sieveking, Louise Marie, tr. II. Morrow, Ian Fitzherbert Despard, 1896– joint tr. III. Title.

Library of Congress   R130.L6 1934 a
                                    .3.   35–678
                                                                610

NL 0441378   DLC ICU

Löbel, Leopold.

see

Lobel, Leopold.

Loebel (Levi). *De rheumatismi sthenici et asthenici natura et curatione. 21 pp. 4°. *Jenæ, ex off. Goepferdtii,* [1802].

NL 0441380   DNLM

Loebel, Moritz
Louvois; Schauspiel in fünf Akten. Wien, Wallishausser, 1879.
170 p.

NL 0441381   MiD NN

Loebel, Otto, 1862–
Anatomie der laubblätter, vorzüglich der blattgrün führenden gewebe ... Königsberg, Ostpreussische zeitungs- und verlags-druckerei, 1888.
2 p. l., 52 p. 22ᶜᵐ.
Inaug.-dis.—Königsberg.
Vita.
"Verzeichnis der ... benutzten werke": p. 1-2.

1. Leaves. 2. Botany—Anatomy.

Library of Congress   QK689.L69
                                                    5–16318

NL 0441382   DLC DNLM

3A
2536   **LOEBEL, PAUL.**
Gedichte von Paul Loebel.   Chicago, L.W. H.Neebe, 1879.
32p. 16cm.

NL 0441383   ICN OCU

Loebel, Renatus Gotthelf, 1767-1799.
In Aristotelis notionem tragoediae commentatio. I. Lipsiae, 1786.
26 p.

NL 0441384   PU

PT 2424   **LÖBEL, RENATUS GOTTHELF, 1767-1799**
.L594 M66   Miniaturgemälde. Leipzig, G. D. Meyer,
1795   1795.
312 p. front.

NL 0441385   InU

Löbel, Richard Rudolf, 1911–
... Ein Beitrag zur Frage der Ostitis deformans Paget und der Ostitis fibrosa von Recklinghausen ... Leipzig, 1935.
Inaug.-Diss. - Leipzig.
Lebenslauf.
"Literatur-Verzeichnis": p. [35]

NL 0441386   CtY

Loebel, Rose, 1906–
... Contribution à l'étude de l'interférométrie en gynécologie ... Paris, 1934.
Thèse - Univ. de Paris.
"Bibliographie": p. [67]-71.

NL 0441387   CtY

Löbel, Sali.
Glamour and how to achieve it; the art of living for every-woman and everyman, a chapter for every age, by Sali Löbel. New York, N. Y., Fortuny's [1939]
147, [1] p. illus., plates. 21½ᶜᵐ.
"First edition."

1. Beauty, Personal. 2. Callisthenics. I. Title.
Library of Congress   RA778.L84
                                                    39–33394
———— Copy 2.
Copyright A 135540   [3]   613

NL 0441388   DLC

Loebel (Sigmund). *Plattfuss und Skoliose. [Zürich.] 14 pp. 8°. *Stuttgart,* 1902.

NL 0441389   DNLM

Löbel, Theophil, 1859–

SEE

Löbel, D. Theophil, 1859–

Loebel, Zanvil Charles, 1900–
The behavior of deaminized gelatin ... by Zanvil Charles Loebel ... New York city, 1926.
29 p. diagrs. 23ᶜᵐ.
Thesis (PH. D.)—Columbia university, 1927.
Vita.
Bibliography: p. 28.

1. Gelatine. I. Title: Deaminized gelatin.

Library of Congress   QD431.L75 1927
Columbia Univ. Libr.   [2]   27–10736

NL 0441391   NNC OrU OU NIC CU DLC

Loebell,   *ed.*
Das preussische Enteignungsgesetz vom 11. juni 1874. Erläutert von Loebell ... Leipzig, Veit & comp., 1884.
iv, 233 p. 22½ᶜᵐ.

1. Eminent domain—Prussia. I. Prussia. Laws, statutes, etc. II. Title.

                                                    42–44731

NL 0441392   DLC MH-L

Loebell (Adalbert) [1855–   ]. *Ein Fall von centralem Scotom mit ophthalmoscopisch nachweisbarer Veränderung der Macula lutea. 45 pp. 8°. *Greifswald, C. Sell,* 1882

NL 0441393   DNLM MiU

LOEBELL, Alfred, 1879–
Über congenitalen radiusdefekt. Inaug. diss., Giessen, 1906.
34 pp.

NL 0441394   MBCo DNLM

Loebell, Arthur Robert von, 1848–1928.
Aus Deutschlands ruinen; betrachtungen nach dem zusammenbruch, von Artur von Loebell ... Berlin, Verlags-haus für volksliteratur und kunst, 1919.
31, [1] p. 20 cm.

NL 0441395   CSt-H

Loebell, Arthur Robert von, 1848–1928.
Der Weltkrieg 1914[-17] Gesammelte Berichte von Generalmajor v. Loebell. Leipzig, P. Reclam jun. [1915-17]
4 v. 15 cm. (Reclams Universal-Bibliothek, 5737, 5818, 5852, 5946)
L. C. copy incomplete: v. 2-4 wanting.
No more pub.
CONTENTS.—1. Bd. Bis zu den Kämpfen um Lodz.—2. Bd. Von der Einnahme von Lodz bis zur Befreiung von Lemberg.—3. Bd. Von der Wiedereinnahme von Lemberg bis zum Jahresschluss 1915.—4. Bd. Von Beginn 1916 bis zum Ausbruch des rumänischen Krieges Ende August 1916.

1. European War, 1914-1918.

D521.L57   48–43003*

NL 0441396   DLC

J
27   **LOEBELL, ARTHUR** Robert von, 1848-1928
335.0943   Wie ist der Sozialdemokratie im Heere
Q 600   entgegenzuwirken? Ein Wort an meine Kameraden.   Berlin, H.Walther, 1906.
63p. 23cm.

NL 0441397   ICN ICJ

Löbell (Eduard). *Ein Fall von Sarcom der Uteruswand. 60 pp. 8°. *Freiburg i. B., F. Thiergarten,* 1888

NL 0441398   DNLM

Löbell, Eduard Sigismund, 1791–1869.
Observationes ad Paulli R. S. lib. III., tit. VI. §§ 3. B. et 7. Scripsit Ed. Sigism. Löbell ... Halae, typis Orphanotrophei, 1812.
32 p. 20½ᶜᵐ.
Inaug.-diss.—Halle.

1. Paulus, Julius. Libri quinque sententiarum. 2. Inheritance and succession (Roman law) I. Title.

                                                    34–7935

NL 0441399   DLC

Loebell, Egon von, 1879–   *ed.*
Das 3. Garde-regiment zu fuss im weltkrieg. Bearbeitet von mitkämpfern. Hrsg. von major v. Loebell ... 2. teil. Oldenburg i.O./Berlin, G. Stalling, 1923.
1 v. fold. maps. 22 cm. (Added t.-p.: Erinnerungsblätter deutscher regimenter ... Ehemals preussische truppenteile ... 85. hft.)
Maps under strap on inside of back cover.
Contents.-

II. t. Das 3. Garde-regiment zu fuss im verbande der 5. Garde-inf.-division, von hauptmann d. r. Naumann und leutnant d. r. Michaelis.

NL 0441401   CSt-H

VOLUME 338

Loebell, Egon von, 1879–
Gefechte unter besonderen Verhältnissen. Beispiele und Lehren auf Grund der Kriegserfahrungen. Berlin, E. S. Mittler, 1931.
viii, 83 p.   20 cm.
"Benutzte Quellen": p. ₍vii₎–viii.

1. Tactics.   I. Title.

U167.L68   49–55236*

NL 0441402   DLC DNW

Loebell, Egon von, 1879–
Der nahkampf; beispiele und lehren auf grund der erfahrungen des weltkrieges, von Egon von Loebell ... Berlin, E. S. Mittler & sohn, 1929.
viii, 79 p.   20ᵐ.
"Benutzte quellen": p. ₍vii₎

1. Tactics.   2. European war, 1914–1918.   3. Fighting, Hand-to-hand.
I. Title.
Library of Congress   U167.L7
                                           43–43711

NL 0441403   DLC NN

DD402
.L58A3
Loebell, Egon von, 1879–   ed.
Loebell, Ernst Friedrich Christian von, 1764–
Unter dem preussischen Adler, Erlebnisse eines Kurländers im friderizianischen Heere und während der Befreiungskriege. Hrsg. von Egon v. Loebell. Potsdam, L. Voggenreiter ₍ᶜ1936₎

Loebell, ₍Ernst Friedrich₎ von.
Ein ehrendenkmal für die verteidiger von Danzig, 1807; nach den tagebüchern des generalleutnant von Loebell bearbeitet von oberst A. von Loebell. Berlin, R. Schröder, 1901.
pp. (3), 141 +.   2 maps.

France–Hist. 1805–07₍Danzig₎₍Loebell

NL 0441405   MH

Löbell, Frank, ed.
Nichteuklidische Geometrie

see under

Baldus, Richard, 1885–

Löbell, Frank 1893–
Die überall regulären unbegrenzten flächen fester krümmung ... Tübingen, E. Göbel, 1927.
Thesis – Tübingen
Lebenslauf
Includes bibliography.

NL 0441407   RPB

Loebell, Friedrich Wilhelm von, 1855–1931, ed.
Hindenburg, was er uns Deutschen ist; eine **Festgabe zum 80. Geburtstag.** Mit einem Bildnis Hindenburgs von Max Liebermann und Textzeichnungen von Georg Fritz. Berlin, R. Hobbing, 1927.
287 p.   illus., port.   24 cm.
CONTENTS: Der Soldat und Feldherr, von Generalleutnant a. D. Groener.—Ostpreussens Retter, von Oberpräsident a. D. v. Batocki.—Der Hort in der Zeit des Zusammenbruchs, von Oberpräsident z. D. Winnig.—In Hannover, von F. Hartmann.—Die Wahl zum Reichspräsidenten. Das Amt und der Mann, von Dr. Spahn.—Hindenburg im Urteil des Auslandes und das Auslandsdeutschtum, von Dr.

Schnee.—Hindenburg als Mensch und Christ, von Geh. Konsistorialrat Zierach.—Hindenburg und das Rheinland, von Dr. Jarres.—Hindenburg und die Notgemeinschaft der Deutschen Wissenschaft, von Dr. Schmidt-Ott.—Hindenburg und die Landwirtschaft, von Graf Kalckreuth.—Hindenburg und das Unternehmertum, von E. v. Borsig.—Hindenburg und die Arbeitnehmerschaft, von W. Lambach.—Hindenburg und die sportliche Ertüchtigung der deutschen Jugend, von Dr. Lewald.—Hindenburg und der Frontsoldat, von F. Schauwecker.—Hindenburg auf der Jagd, von Dr. Phil. Hausendorff.—Hindenburg und das deutsche Volk, von F. W. Loebell.

1. Hindenburg, Paul von, Pres. Germany, 1847–1934.

DD231.H5L6   52–56404

NL 0441409   DLC IaU MH CSt

4DD
2358
Loebell, Friedrich Wilhelm von, 1855–1931, ed.
Hindenburg; was er uns Deutschen ist; eine Festgabe zum 80. Geburtstag hrsg. von v. Loebell. Mit Textzeichnungen von Georg Fritz. Berlin, R. Hobbing ₍1927₎₎
305 p.

NL 0441410   DLC-P4

Loebell, ₍Friedrich Wilhelm von₎ 1855–1931.
Rückblick und Ausblick. (Deutschland unter Kaiser Wilhelm II. Berlin, 1914.   4°.   Bd. 3, p. 1697–1701.)

1. Germany.—History, 1888–1913.   2. Title.   MANDEL COLLECTION.
N. Y. P. L.   June 3, 1914.

NL 0441411   NN

LOEBELL, Georg Eduard Alfred

See LOEBELL, Alfred, 1874–

Löbell (Georg H.) *Das Verhalten der Nachgeburt bei 500 Geburten.* 12 pp., 7 pl. 8°.
Würzburg, Köhl & Hacker, 1896.

NL 0441413   DNLM

Loebell, Georg von
Zur Geschichte der evangelischen Kirchengemeinden Berlins während der Jahre 1875–1908. Berlin, Verlag der Landeskirchlichen Vereinigung der Freunde der Positiven Union, 1909

NL 0441414   MH

Loebell, Georgius
De jure filiifamilias.
Inaug. Diss.   Marburg, 1853

NL 0441415   ICRL

Loebell, Hans: Zur Behandlung der Syndaktylie. Sorau N.-L. 1925: Kühn. 14 S. 8° ¶Auch in Maschinenschrift.
Berlin, Med. Diss. v. 7. Okt. 1919 [1925]   [U 25. 90

NL 0441416   ICRL CtY DNLM

Löbell, Heinrich von, 1816–1901, ed.
Jahrbücher für die deutsche armee und marine ... 1.– bd.; oct. 1871–
Berlin, F. Schneider & co., 1871–

Löbell, Heinrich von, 1816–1901, ed.
v. Löbell's jahresberichte über das heer- und kriegswesen ... 1.–   jahrg.; 1874–
Berlin, E. S. Mittler und sohn, 1875–19

Löbell, Heinrich von, 1816–1901.
Was die militair-journale über die expedition nach Mexico erzählen. Vortrag, gehalten in der versammlung der Militairischen gesellschaft zu Berlin, am 10. april 1863 von von Löbell ... Mit einer uebersichtskarte. (Als manuskript gedruckt.) ₍Berlin, Gedruckt bei J. Sittenfeld, 1863₎
52 p.   fold. map.   22½ᶜᵐ.

1. Mexico–Hist.—European intervention, 1861–1867.

Library of Congress   F1233.L79
                                           18–2854

NL 0441419   DLC NN

Loebell, Helmut: Hernia diaphragmatica spuria nach Schußverletzung. [Maschinenschrift.] 33 S. m. Abb. 4°. — Auszug: (Kiel 1921: Schmidt & Klaunig). 2 Bl. 8°
Kiel, Med. Diss. v. 16. März 1922   [U 22. 8431

NL 0441420   ICRL

4PN
843
Loebell, Helmut, 1894–
Die Befehlsprache: Gesundheit, Zweckmässigkeit ₍und₎ Kraft, von H. Loebell und F. K. Roedemeyer. Hrsg. von der Zentralstelle für Sprechpflege und Sprechkunde an der Deutschen Akademie in München. Leipzig, C. Kabitzsch, 1936.
30 p.

NL 0441421   DLC-P4 IaU MH NNC MoU CtY NN

WV
530
L825f
1931
LOEBELL, Helmut, 1894–
Fehlerquellen bei experimentell-phonetischen Untersuchungen, von H. Loebell und F. Wethlo. Leipzig, Kabitzsch, 1931.
66 p.   illus.
"Sonderdruck aus dem Bericht über die 3. Versammlung der Deutschen Gesellschaft für Sprach- und Stimmheilkunde."
1. Speech   2. Voice culture
I. Wethlo. F

NL 0441422   DNLM

WV
100
L825h
1930
LOEBELL, Helmut, 1894–
Die Hals-, Nasen-, Ohrenheilkunde, mit Auswahl und besonderer Berücksichtigung der Grenzgebiete für Studierende der Zahnheilkunde und Zahnärzte. Leipzig, Kabitzsch, 1930.
viii, 89 p.   illus.
1. Otorhinolaryngology

NL 0441423   DNLM PU-D

Loebell, Helmut, 1894–
Die hals-, nasen-, ohrenheilkunde mit auswahl und besonderer berücksichtigung der beziehungen zur zahnheilkunde für studierende, zahnärzte und ärzte. 2. völlig neubearb. aufl. Leipzig, Barth, 1947.
vii, 100 p.   illus.

1. Ear - Diseases.   2. Nose - Diseases.
3. Throat - Diseases.

NL 0441424   DNLM

Loebell, Helmut, 1894–
Die Hals-, Nasen-, Ohrenheilkunde mit Auswahl und besonderer Berücksichtigung der Beziehungen zur Zahnheilkunde für Studierende, Zahnärzte und Ärzte. 3. neubearb. Aufl. Leipzig, J.A. Barth, 1950.
vi, 86 p.   illus.

NL 0441425   ICJ DNLM

WV
100
L825h
1954
LOEBELL, Helmut, 1894–
Die Hals-, Nasen-, Ohrenheilkunde für Studierende der Zahnheilkunde und Zahnärzte. 4., neubearb. Aufl. Leipzig, Barth, 1954.
90 p.   illus.
Subtitle of earlier eds. varies slightly.
1. Otorhinolaryngology

NL 0441426   DNLM

Löbell, J   S
Berlin und Hamburg; oder, Briefe aus dem leben von J.S.Loebell. Erster theil. Breslau, Friedländer, 1836.
162 p.   19½ ᶜᵐ.

No more published.

NL 0441427   NjP

VOLUME 338

Loebell, Johann Wilhelm, 1786-1863
Commentatio de origine marchiae Branden-
burgicae. Wratislaviae, Impensis Josephi
Maxii, 1820.
47p.

NL 0441428   OCl

DC65   Loebell, Johann Wilhelm, 1786-1863.
L58   Disputatio de causis regni Francorum a
Merovingis ad Carolingos translati.   Bonnae,
Litteris Georgianis, 1844.
23 p.

At head of title: Sacram memoriam ...
Friderici Guilelmi III. augustissimi huius
universitatis conditoris natali eius III.
nonas augustas hora XI. ab Litterarum
universitate Fridericia Guilelmia Rhenana
pie celebrandam indicit Ioannes Guilelmus
Loebell.

NL 0441429   CU

PT311   Loebell, Johann Wilhelm, 1786-1863.
L6   Die Entwickelung der deutschen Poesie von Klopstocks erstem
Auftreten bis zu Goethe's Tode. Vorlesungen, gehalten zu Bonn
im Winter 1854 ...   Braunschweig, Schwetschke, 1856-65.
3 v.

Vol. 2-3 have also special title page.

Contents. - 1.bd. [Klopstock]- 2.Bd. C. M. Wieland. - 3.Bd.
G.E. Lessing.

1. German literature - 18th cent. - Hist. & crit. 2. German
literature - 19th cent. - Hist. & crit.

NcD ICU IU GU InU CaBVaU
NL 0441430   CU OCU MWelC NIC OkU NNU-W MB ICU RPB

Loebell, Johann Wilhelm, 1786-1863.
Fragmente zur charakteristik Wilhelms von
Schlegel. Von J.W. Loebell.
(In Vom Rhein. Leben, kunst und dichtung ...
Essen, 1847. 21 cm. jahrgang 1847, p. 217-234)

NL 0441431   CU

Loebell, Johann Wilhelm, 1786-1863.
G. E. Lessing. Aus Bonner vorlesungen. Mit angehängten
annalen der litterarischen thätigkeit Lessings. Herausgegeben
von A. Koberstein. Braunschweig, C. A. Schwetschke und sohn,
1865.
pp. xi, 311. (His Die entwickelung der deutschen poesie von
Klopstocks erstem auftreten bis zu Goethe's tode, 3.)

Lessing.'

NL 0441432   MH MWelC

DC68   Loebell, Johann Wilhelm, 1786-1863.
.L818   Gregor von Tours und seine zeit vornehmlich
aus seinen werken geschildert. Ein beitrag
zur geschichte der entstehung und ersten entwickelung romanisch-germanischer verhältnisse,
von Johann Wilhelm Loebell... Leipzig, F. A.
Brockhaus, 1839.
x, 567, [1] p. fold. geneal. tab. 21cm.
Bibliographical foot-notes.

1. France--Hist.--Carlovingian and early period
987. 2. Gregorius, Saint, bp. of Tours, 544-595.

NL 0441433   ICU OU RPB CtY NNC DLC CU

Loebell, Johann Wilhelm, 1786-1863.
Gregor von Tours und seine zeit vornehmlich aus seinen
werken geschildert. Ein beitrag zur geschichte der entstehung und ersten entwickelung romanisch-germanischer verhältnisse, von Johann Wilhelm Loebell. 2. verm. aufl. Mit
einem vorwort von Heinrich von Sybel. Leipzig, F. A. Brockhaus, 1869.
xii, 459, [1] p. fold. geneal. tab. 23ᶜᵐ.
Edited by Theodor Bernhardt.
With this is bound: Ficker, Julius von. Zur geschichte des Lom-
bardenbundes. Wien, 1869.
1. Gregorius, Saint, bp. of Tours, 538-594. 2. Franks--Hist.--To 768.
3. France--Hist.--Carlovingian and early period to 987. I. Bernhardt,
Theodor, ed. II. *Sybel, Heinrich von, 1817-1895. III. Title.
35-25474
Library of Congress   DC69.8.G7L7 1869   944.01

ViU MdBP ICU MH NNC
NL 0441434   DLC NRCR CLSU MdBP CtY PPLT PU PPC OU

LOEBELL, Johann Wilhelm, 1786-1863.
Grundzüge einer methodik des geschichtlichen
unterrichts auf Gymnasien. Sendschreiben
an den Consistorial-Director Seebeck in Hil
dburghausen. Leipzig, F.U.Brockhaus,1847.

pp.38.

NL 0441435   MH RPB

[Loebell, Johann Wilhelm, 1786-1863.]
Historische briefe über die seit dem ende des sechzehnten jahrhunderts fortgehenden verluste und gefahren des protestantismus.
Frankfurt a. M., etc., Heyder & Zimmer, 1861.
pp. xii, 544.

Protestantism||Title|

NL 0441436   MH

Loebell, Johann Wilhelm, 1786-1863.
Becker, Karl Friedrich, 1777-1806.
Karl Friedrich Becker's Weltgeschichte. 7., verb. und
verm. ausg. (3. abdruck) Hrsg. von Johann Wilhelm
Loebell. Mit den fortsetzungen von J. G. Woltmann und
K. A. Menzel ... Berlin, Duncker und Humblot, 1841.

Loebell, Johann Wilhelm, 1786-1863.
Niebuhr, Barthold Georg, 1776-1831.   FOR OTHER EDITIONS
The life and letters of Barthold George Niebuhr. With   SEE MAIN ENTRY
essays on his character and influence by the Chevalier Bunsen,
and Professors Brandis and Loebell ... London, Chapman
and Hall, 1852.

Loebell, Johann Wilhelm, 1786-1863. On the
character of Niebuhr as an historian. 9 pp. (Niebuhr,
B. G., Life and letters, v. 2, p. 414.)

NL 0441439   MdBP

DB47   [Loebell, Johann Wilhelm] 1786-1863.
.157   Die Politik des Hauses Oesterreich Deutschland und dem Protestantismus gegenüber; nach
der Geschichte betrachtet von einem Protestan-
ten. Göttingen, Vandenhoeck und Ruprecht,
1852.
216 p.
Attributed also to August Schröder. Cf.
Deutsches Anonymen-Lexikon, Bd. 5, p. 232.
1. Church and   state in Austria.

NL 0441440   ICU

DH433 Loebell, Johann Wilhelm, 1786-1863.
L64   Reisebriefe aus Belgien; mit einigen
Studien zur Politik, Geschichte und Kunst.
Berlin, Duncker & Humblot, 1837.
x, 396 p. 19 cm.

1. Belgium - Descr.   trav. - To 1900.
I. Title (1)

NL 0441441   CtY

937.07 Löbell, Johann Wilhelm, 1786-1863.
Au4lo   Ueber das principat des Augustus.
n.p. [1834?]
[213]-280p.

Reprint.

NL 0441442   IU

LOEBELL, Johann Wilhelm, 1786-1863.
Ueber die epochen der geschichschreibung
und ihre verhältniss zur poesie. Ein skizze.
[Bonn? 1840],

Pamphlet.

NL 0441443   MH

Loebell, Johann Wilhelm, 1786-1863.   6
Weltgeschichte in umrissen und ausführungen. Iᵉʳ bd. Leipzig
F. A. Brockhaus, 1846.
pp. xvi, 604 +.

NL 0441444   MH CtY

Loebell, Johann Wilhelm, 1786-1863.
Zur beurtheilung des C. Sallustius Crispus.
Von Johann Wilhelm Loebell... Breslau, W. A.
Holaeufer, 1818.
[3]-58 p., [1]l. 17 cm.

1. Sallustius Crispus, C. I. Title.

NL 0441445   ViU PU

Loebell, Johann Wilhelm, 1786-1863.
Zur würdigung Johann Wilhelm Löbells
see under   Bernhardt, Theodor.

Loebell, Paul: Das Eucupin m. bes. Berücks. seiner Verwendung
bei Affektionen der Mundschleimhaut. [Maschinenschrift.] 34 S.
4°. — Auszug: Greifswald 1923: Adler. 1 Bl. 8°
Greifswald, Med. Diss. v. 13. März 1923   [U 23.4698

NL 0441447   ICRL

Loebell, Paul Georg Rudolf
see
Loebell, Rudolf, 1899-

Loebell, Richard.
Der anti-Necker J. H. Mercks und der minister
Fr. K. v. Moser.
Inaug. diss. Darmstadt tech. hoch., 1896.

NL 0441449   ICRL CU

Loebell, Richard, 1852-
Quaestiones de perfecti homerici forma et usu.
Inaug. Diss.   Leipzig, 1876.

NL 0441450   ICRL NjP CtY

Loebell, Richard, 1852-
Quaestiones de perfecti Homerici forma et usu. Lipsiae, typis
Leopold & Baer, 1877.
pp. 73.

Homerus-Lang.|'

NL 0441451   MH PU

LOEBELL, Richard, 1852-
Über litauische volkspiesie. Oppenheim,
[1884]

pp.(2). 2.
"Beilage zum progr. d. grossherzoglichen
realschule. 1884., nr. 58.

NL 0441452   MH OCl

VOLUME 338

Loebell, Rolf.
Luftpyknometer. Hamburg, Verlag Wasser und Boden, 1955.

59 p. illus., diagrs. 21 cm. (Schriftenreihe des Kuratoriums für Kulturbauwesen, Heft 4)
Based on the author's thesis, Bonn, issued under title: Grundlagen und Entwicklung des Luftpyknometers.
Bibliography: p. 56-58.

1. Soils—Analysis. 2. Pycnometer. I. Title. (Series: Kuratorium für Kulturbauwesen. Schriftenreihe, Heft 4)

S593.L84 61-23247

NL 0441453 DLC CU

Loebell, Rudolf, 1899–
Die verwendung landwirtschaftlicher maschinen und geräte im aushebungsbezirk Ribnitz ... Ribnitz, Buchdruckerei G. Haack, 1926.

72 p. illus. (map) 8 fold. tab. 21½cm.
Inaug.-diss.—Rostock.
Lebenslauf.

1. Agricultural machinery. [1. Agriculture—Implements and machinery] 2. Agriculture—Germany—Ribnitz. [2. Ribnitz, Ger.—Agriculture]
[Full name: Paul Georg Rudolf Loebell]

Library, U. S. Dept. of Agriculture 58LS2 Agr 28-1670

NL 0441454 DNAL CtY

LOEBELL, Wilhelm.
Krieg und staatsverwaltung. Wien,1917.

6-51 p.

NL 0441455 MH-L

Loebell, Wilhelm.
Österreich über alles. Wien, 1946.

44 p. 21 cm. (Schriften des Österreich-Instituts zur Erforschung der öffentlichen Meinung)

1. Austria—Economic policy. 2. Austria—Pol. & govt.—1945-
I. Title. (Series: Österreich-Institut, Vienna. Schriften zur Erforschung der öffentlichen Meinung)

HC265.L6 A 53-746
Harvard Univ. Library
for Library of Congress [1]†

NL 0441456 MH DLC

Loebell, Wilhelm, joint ed.

Arbesser, Wilhelm.
Das Verwaltungsstrafgesetz in der fassung der Verwaltungsstrafgesetznovelle 1932 ... nach dem stande vom 1. oktober 1932 hrsg. von dr. Wilhelm Arbesser ... und dr. Wilhelm Loebell ... Wien, Manz, 1933.

Loebell, Willy
I. Ueber die oxydationsprodukte reiner palmitinsaeure durch salpetersaeure.
Tuebingen, 1896
Dissert.

QD305
.A2-

NL 0441458 DLC NN

Löbell's jahresberichte über das heer- und kriegswesen
see von Löbell's jahresberichte über das heer- und kriegswesen.

Loeben, Charlotte von Zastrow-
see Zastrow, Frau Charlotte (von Loeben) von, 1877-

Loeben, Ferdinand August Otto Heinrich, graf von
see Loeben, Otto Heinrich, graf von, 1786-1825.

Loeben, Max Georg von.
[?] Der Absatz der Plauener Spitzen nach den Vereinigten Staaten von Nordamerika. Eine Studie über Handel von Max Georg von Loeben ... . Dresden, O. V. Böhmert, 1905.
viii, 139 p. 25cm.

NL 0441462 ICJ

[Loeben, Otto Heinrich Graf von] 1786-1825.
Deutsche Worte über die Ansichten der Frau v. Staël von unserer poetischen Litteratur in ihrem Werk über Deutschland ... Heidelberg, Mohr und Zimmer, 1814. 250 p. 17cm.

Signed: Isidorus [pseud.]
With bookplate of Friedrich Lessing.

320077B. 1. Staël-Holstein, Anne de, 1766-1817. De l'Allemagne. 18th-19th cent. I. Title. N. Y. P. L. Louise Germaine (Necker), baronne 2. Poetry, German—Hist. and crit.
January 18, 1946

NL 0441463 NN CU MH NcU CtY

3469 Loeben, Otto Heinrich, graf von, 1786-1825.
.86 Erzählungen.. Dresden, Hilscher,
.332 1822-24.
2 v. in 1. 17cm.

NL 0441464 NjP

---

838 Loeben, Otto Heinrich, Graf von, 1786-1825.
L82 Erzählungen. Wien, C.F.Schade, 1827.
1827 2 v. 13 cm. (Classische Cabinets-Bibliothek; oder, Sammlung auserlesener Werke der deutschen und Fremd-Literatur,143.-144.Bd.)
CONTENTS.--1.Th. Die Todtenmahnung. Lessko und Pariska. Der Turneser und der Pisaner.--2.Th. Der Brillantenschmuck. Die Sühnung. Loreley, eine Sage vom Rhein. Zugabe einiger Gedichte und kleinerer Aufsätze.
Full name: Ferdinand August Otto Heinrich Graf von Loeben.

NL 0441465 MiU OCU PSt

833L82 Loeben, Otto Heinrich, Graf von, 1786-1825.
K1810 Gedichte. Berlin, J. D. Sander, 1810.
xvi, 445p. 17cm.

NL 0441466 IU

Loeben, Otto Heinrich, *graf* von, 1786-1825.
... Gedichte von Otto Heinrich grafen von Loeben, ausgewählt und herausgegeben von Raimund Pissin. Berlin, B. Behr, 1905.

xvii, 171, [1] p. 19cm. (Deutsche literaturdenkmale des 18. und 19. jahrhunderts, no. 135, 3. folge, no. 15)

I. Pissin, Raimund, 1878- ed.
[Full name: Ferdinand August Otto Heinrich graf von Loeben]
6-4423 Revised
Library of Congress PT1136.S4 no. 135

NL 0441467 DLC PSt NcD NjP OCU OU OC1W PBm MB PU

833L82 Loeben, Otto Heinrich, Graf von, 1786-1825.
01 Die Irrsale Klotars und der Gräfin Sigismunda. Eine romantische Geschichte. Altenburg, C. Hahn, 1821.
352p. 21cm.

NL 0441468 IU

[Loeben, Otto, Graf von Heinrich] 1786-1825
Zg19 Lotosblätter. Fragmente von Isidorus
L821 [pseud.] ... Bamberg und Leipzig,C.F.Kunz,
817l 1817.
2v. 15cm.
Essays.

NL 0441469 CtY OC1W

[Loeben, Otto Heinrich, Graf von, 1786-1825]
Romantische Darstellungen, von Isidorus [pseud.]
Mannheim, In der Schwans und Götzischen Buchhandlung,
1817

360 p.

NL 0441470 MH

PT Loeben, Otto Heinrich, Graf von, 1786-1825
2424 Rosengarten; Dichtungen. Altenburg, F. A.
L6 Brockhaus, 1817.
R6 2v. in 1. 17cm.

NL 0441471 WU NNC MH-F

[Loeben, Otto Heinrich, Graf von, 1786-1825]
Der Schwan; Poesieen aus dichtrischer Jugend, mitgetheilt von Isidorus [pseud.] Leipzig, Göschen, 1816

182 p.

NL 0441472 MH

QD305 Loeben, W. von, 1869-
.L82 Ueber δ-methylharnsaure.
Leipzig, 1896.
26p.
Inaug. diss. Leipzig.

NL 0441473 DLC

944.04 Löben Sels, Ernst van
L785b Bijdragen tot de krijgsgeschiedenis van Napoleon Bonaparte. 's Gravenhage, De Erven Doorman, 1839-1842.
4 v. fold. maps, tables.

Contents.- v.1. Veldtogten van 1796-1797, en 1800 in Italië, en 1805 in Duitschland.- v.2. Veldtogten van 1806-1807 in Duitschland en Polen, en van 1809 in Duitschland.- v.3. Veldtogten van 1812 in Rusland, en van 1813 in Duitschland.- v.4. Veldtogten van

1814 in Frankrijk, en van 1815 in de Nederlanden.

1. Napoléon I, emperor of the French, 1769-1821. 2. France - History - Consulate and empire, 1799-1815. 3. Europe - History - 1789-1815. I. Title.

NL 0441475 WaU NIC

DC Löben Sels, Ernst van
242 Précis de la campagne de 1815, dans les
L82 Pays-Bas, par le Major d'artillerie E. Van
1849 Löben Sels. Traduit du hollandais. La Haye, Doorman, 1849.
iv, 379 p. maps. 23cm.

1. Waterloo, Battle of, 1815. I. Title.

NL 0441476 NIC CtY MH DNW

Loeben Sels, Mrs. Helen Adelaide (Ellsworth) van, 1882-
see
Ellsworth, Helen, 1882-

VOLUME 338

LÖBEN SELS, Mauritz Jacob van.
... De probationibus ex principiis juris roman
et hodierni... Lugduni Batavorum, 1818.

(6) 83 (1) p.
Inaug.-diss.,--Leyden.
Law Sch.

NL 0441478   MH-L

Löben Sels, Pieter Justus van.
Beschouwingen over den Noord-Amerikaanschen Staten-
Oorlog van 1861-1864. Zutphen, A. E. C. van Someren,
1878.
xvi, 158 p. 22 cm.
Proefschrift—Utrecht.
Bibliographical footnotes.

1. U. S.—Hist.—Civil War. 2. U. S.—Pol. & govt.—Civil War.
E459.L82   1-15497*

NL 0441479   DLC NN

Löben Sels, Tjaard Maurits Adam van, 1905–
... Het ontstaan van de republiek Indonesia. Arnhem,
S. Gouda Quint, D. Brouwer en zoon, 1946.
51 p. plates. 21 cm.
At head of title: T. M. A. van Löben Sels.

1. Dutch East Indies—Hist. I. Title. II. Title : Republiek Indonesia.
DS644.L6   A F 47-5438
Chicago. Univ. Library
for Library of Congress   (2)†

NL 0441480   ICU CtY NN DLC

Löbenberg, Victoria.
Das deutsche sparkochbuch für kriegs- und
friedenszeit, mit gesundheits- und häuslichem
ratgeber. Hrsg. von frau V. Löbenberg. Verm.
und verb. neu-auflage ... 6. - 16. tausend.
München, Im selbstverlag erschienen, 1916.
192 p. 18 cm.
Advertising matter included in paging.

NL 0441481   CSt-H ICJ

Loebenberg, Frau **Victoria.**
Das deutsche Sparkochbuch für Kriegs- und Friedenszeit
mit Gesundheits- und häuslichem Ratgeber. Hrsg. von Frau v.
Löbenberg. Mit Pilzmerkblatt und farbiger Pilztafel. Mün-
chen: Im Selbstverlag, 1918. 223 p. col'd plate. rev. ed.
12°.
Pilzmerkblatt in pocket at end.
Advertising matter throughout.

3985A. 1. Cookery (German).
N. Y. P. L.   March 17, 1921.

NL 0441482   NN

Löbenberg, Victoria.
Gute gutti; Weihnachts-leckerle und
festtagsgebäck; alkoholfreie Weihnachtsbowlen...
Buchschmuck von Paul Gedon in München... 44 p.
illus. München, Löbenberg, 1919.

NL 0441483   OC1

Das **loebenliche** buche von Floren und von Blant-
scheflur
see under   Floire and Blancheflor. German.

[Löbenstein, Alois]
Glaubensfreiheit.
*GB8   [Wien] Zu haben in der Wollzeile Nr.782.[1848]
V6755R
3.18.48   folder([3]p.) 21x13cm.
Caption title; imprint on p.[3].
Signed & dated at end: Löbenstein Alois,
Candidat des ev. Predigeramtes. Wien, 18. März
1848.

NL 0441485   MH

AC   Loebenstein, Annie, 1914–
875   Eine methode zum austausch des leichten
wasserstoffs gegen deuterium in schwerlöslichen
substanzen. Die dissoziationskonstanten der
hornsäure. ... Basel, 1940.
Inaug. Diss. - Basel, 1940.
Vitae.

(Helvetica Chimica Acta, Vol. XXIII, Fasciculus
Secundus, 1940.)

NL 0441486   DLC CtY MH

QD65   Loebenstein, Annie, 1914–   joint author.
.D4
Dessauer, Friedrich, July 19, 1881–
Neue Karte der Atome, von F. Dessauer und A. Loeben-
stein. Zürich, Rascher (1946)

Loebenstein, Edwin, ed.

Austria. *Laws, statutes, etc.*
Kommentar zum Amtshaftungsgesetz, mit den Materialien und einem ausführlichen Quellen- und Sachverzeichnis, von Edwin Loebenstein und Gustav Kaniak. Wien,
Manz, 1951.

Law   Loebenstein, Edwin, ed.

Austria. *Laws, statutes, etc.*
Das Nationalsozialistengesetz, das Verbotsgesetz 1947, die
damit zusammenhängenden Spezialgesetze, kommentiert
und hrsg. von Ludwig Viktor Heller, Edwin Loebenstein
(und) Leopold Werner. Wien, Manz, 1948.

Law   Loebenstein, Edwin, ed.

Austria. *Laws, statutes, etc.*
Das österreichische Recht, hrsg. von Alfred Heinl, Edwin
Loebenstein (und) Stephan Verosta. (Wien) Österreichischer
Gewerbeverlag (1948–

Loebenstein, Frieda.
Der erste klavierunterricht; ein lehrgang zur erschliessung
des musikalischen im anfangsklavierunterricht, von Frieda
Loebenstein ... Ausg. A für lehrer. Berlin-Lichterfelde,
C. F. Vieweg g. m. b. h., 1927.
viii, 127, (1) p. illus. (music) 22½cm.
"Klavierliteratur": last page.

1. Pianoforte—Instruction and study. I. Title.   29-10645
Library of Congress   MT745.L7

NL 0441491   DLC NN

MT   **Loebenstein, Frieda.**
745   Der erste klavierunterricht; ein lehrgang zur erschliessung
.L7   des musikalischen im anfangsklavierunterricht, von Frieda
1928   Loebenstein ... Ausg. A für lehrer. Berlin-Lichterfelde,
C. F. Vieweg g. m. b. h., 1928.
viii, 127, (1) p. illus. (music) 22½cm.
"Klavierliteratur": last page.
2. Aufl.

NL 0441492   MiEM

Loebenstein, Frieda.
...Klavierpädagogik, von Frieda Loebenstein...   Leipzig: Quelle & Meyer, 1932.   xii, 132 p.   illus. (music.)
22½cm. (Musikpaedagogische Bibliothek. Heft 13.)
Bibliography, p. 131-132.

590859A. 1. Piano playing. I. Title.   II. Ser.
N. Y. P. L.   August 31, 1932

NL 0441493   NN IaU

AC   Loebenstein, Fritz, 1888–
831   Formunterscheidung im ersten lebensjahr. ...
Borna-Leipzig, n.d.   51 p.
Inaug. Diss. - Leipzig, [1927?]
Lebenslauf.

NL 0441494   ICRL CtY

Loebenstein (Fritz Naphtalie) [1888–].
*Untersuchungen über die Angewöhnung im
Tiefenschätzungsvermögen der Einaugigen.
[Heidelberg.] 45 pp. 8°. Frankfurt a. M.,
Gbr. Heilbrunn. 1914.

NL 0441495   DNLM MH ICRL

SB611   **Loebenstein, Gad,** joint author.
.L2
Hebr   **Lachover, David.**
נסויים בהדברה כימית של צמחית חהר. מאת ד. לחובר. ש.
הורביץ וג. ליבנשטין. תל־אביב, ספרית השדה, תשי״ג (1953)

Loebenstein (Jacobus Josephus). *De ulceri-
bus. vi, 34 pp. 8°. Vindobonæ, J. P. Soldinger,
[1841].

NL 0441497   DNLM

Löbenstein, Julius: Über die Resultate der konservativen
Behandlungsmethoden bei Placenta praevia (nach einer
Zusammenstellung der Fälle aus der Heidelberger Klinik
von November 1902 bis Januar 1909). Berlin [1910]:
Loewenthal. 43 S. 8°
Heidelberg, Med. Diss. v. 8. Juli 1910, Ref. Menge
[Geb. 14. Dez. 85 Düsseldorf; Wohnort: Cöln; Staatsangeh.: Preußen; Vor-
bildung: Kgl. Gymn. Düsseldorf Reife O. 04; Studium: Marburg 1, Berlin 7,
Heidelberg 2 S.; Coll. 24. Juli 09; Approb. 27. Juni 10.]   [U 10. 2076]

NL 0441498   ICRL DNLM MH

516.54   **Löbenstein, Klara,** 1885–
L78u   Ueber den satz, dass eine ebene, algebraische kurve 6. ordnung mit 11 sich ein
ander ausschliessenden ovalen nicht exis-
tiert ...   Göttingen, 1910.
cover-title, 37p. diagrs.
Inaug.-diss.--Göttingen.
"Lebenslauf".
Bibliographical foot-notes: p.[5]

NL 0441499   IU MH NN NjP ViU CtY MiU

Löbenstein, Mathias Emanuel.
Der dritte Stand und der Reichstag
see under title

Löbenstein, Philipp, tr.
Siemieński, Lucjan (Hipolit) 1809-1878.
Erzählungen von Lucjan Siemienski. Aus dem pol-
nischen übertragen von Philipp Löbenstein. Leipzig.
P. Reclam, jun. (1895)

VOLUME 338

Loebenstein, Siegmund.
Die Fusion der Aktiengesellschaften, nach geltendem deutschen Rechte. Cassel: Druck von Gebr. Landsiedel, 1909.
4 p.l., 49 p. 8°.

Dissertation, Strassburg. One page of bibliography.

1. Corporations.—Jurisprudence. Germany.
N. Y. P. L. December 11, 1911.

NL 0441502 NN ICRL MH

Loebenstein, William Vaille, 1914–
The nature of the surface of catalytic nickel, by William V. Loebenstein … [Easton, Pa., 1940]
cover-title, p. 2573–2580. diagrs. 26½ x 20ᶜᵐ.
Based on portion of thesis (PH. D.)—Brown university, 1940.
"By W. Walker Russell and William V. Loebenstein."
"Reprinted from the Journal of the American chemical society, 62 … (1940)."

1. Catalysis. 2. Nickel. I. Russell, William Walker, 1896–
joint author. II. Title.

Library of Congress QD501.L8138 1940
[2] 541.39

NL 0441503 DLC RPB

WBC LOEBENSTEIN-LOEBEL, Eduard Leopold,
L821a 1779–1819
1816 Die Anwendung und Wirkung der Weine in lebensgefährlichen Krankheiten, und deren Verfälschungen; nach eignen Ansichten und Erfahrungen. Leipzig, Brockhaus, 1816.
viii, 180 p.

NL 0441504 DNLM ICJ

WS LOEBENSTEIN-LOEBEL, Eduard Leopold,
100 1779–1819
L825e Die Erkenntniss und Heilung der
1813 Gehirnentzündung, des innern Wasserkopfes und der Krampfkrankheiten im kindlichen Alter. Leipzig, Hinrichs, 1813.
xiv. 270 p.

NL 0441505 DNLM MiU

Loebenstein-Loebel (Eduard
Leopold) [1779-1819]. Erkenntniss und Heilung der häutigen Bräune, des Millarschen Asthma und der Keuchhustens. viii, 182 pp., 1 l. 8°. _Leipzig. F. C. W. Vogel_, 1811.

NL 0441506 DNLM

WW LOEBENSTEIN-LOEBEL, Eduard Leopold,
L824g 1779–1819
1817 Grundriss der Semiologie des Auges für Aerzte. Jena, Cröker, 1817.
xliv, 180 p.

NL 0441507 DNLM MB

WBC LOEBENSTEIN-LOEBEL, Eduard Leopold,
L821a 1779–1819
1817 Traité sur l'usage et les effets des vins dans les maladies dangereuses et mortelles, et sur la falsification de cette boisson. Tr. de l'allemand, par J. Fr. Daniel Lobstein. Strasbourg, Levrault, 1817.
xii, 192 p.
Translation of Die Anwendung und Wirkung der Weine in lebensgefährlichen Krankheiten.

NL 0441508 DNLM PU

WLA LOEBENSTEIN-LOEBEL, Eduard Leopold,
L825w 1779–1819
1818 Wesen und Heilung der Epilepsie. Leipzig, Liebeskind, 1818.
xii, 364 p.

NL 0441509 DNLM

LOEBENSTERN, Jacob David.
De senatuconsulto macedoniano. Marburgi, n. d.
8+48 p.
Diss.—— Marburg, 1828.

NL 0441510 MH-L

Löbenthal, T.L.
Ueber die stiftung des eisernen kreuzes. Landsberg, 1840.

NL 0441511 NjP

AC Loeber, Alfred
851 Die bandenmässigkeit bei vermögensdelikten. … Berlin, 1936. 47 p.
Inaug. Diss. - Erlangen, 1936.
Literaturverzeichnis.

NL 0441512 ICRL

HF1317 LOEBER, ANTON WILLEM.
.A3L7 Lastgeving en vertegenwoordiging in Engeland, vergelijking tusschen Engelsch en Nederlandsch recht… Amsterdam, 1930.
[9],143,[1]p. 24cm.
Proefschrift--Leiden.
Bibliography:p.143.

1.Agency(Law) 2.Commercial law--Gt.Brit. 3. Commercial law--Netherlands.

NL 0441513 ICU

Loeber, August
Tirdzniecības tiesību pārskats. Rīgā, Valtera un Rapas, 1926.
483 p.
Includes bibliographies.

NL 0441514 NNC DLC-P4

Loeber, August.
Vekseļtiesību parskats. Rīgā, Valtera un Rapas akciju sabiedrības izdevums, 1927.
94 p. 22 cm.
At head of title: Augusts Loebers.
"Izvilkums no tā paša autora darba 'Tirdzniecības tiesību parskats.'"
Bibliography : p. 12–13.

1. Bills of exchange. I. Title.
65–58681

NL 0441515 DLC

Loeber, August, *jurist*
Ueber strafbare nichterfüllung von lieferungsverträgen nach deutschem und ausländischem strafrecht … von August Loeber … Göttingen, Druck der Univ.-buchdr. von W. F. Kästner, 1889.
3 p. l., 61 p. 21½ᶜᵐ.
Inaug.-diss.—Göttingen.
"Quellen- und litteraturverzeichnis" : p. [1]–2.

1. Public contracts—Germany. 2. Germany. Army—Supplies and stores. 3. Criminal law—Germany. 4. Criminal law. I. Title.
35–33805

NL 0441516 DLC CU MH-L

V Löber, Cäcilia, 1916–
4 Über den Nachweis von Kieselalgen (Diatomeen)
D85 in den Lungen Ertrunkener und seine Bedeutung
1940 für die Feststellung des Ertrinkungstodes im Rhein. Düsseldorf, Nolte, 1940.
14, [6] p. illus.

Diss. -
Bibliography: p. [19]

NL 0441517 DNLM

Loeber, Carl Friedrich
De modo, quo veteres Graeci Romanique versus suos ipsi recitaverint…
Hersfeldiae, 1833.
48 p.

NL 0441518 PU

Loeber (Carolus Christianus). *De curcuma officinarum ejusque genuinis virtutibus.* 28 pp. 4°. _Halæ Magdeb., typ. J. C. Hendelii_, [1748].

NL 0441519 DNLM PPC

Loeber, Charles, 1878–
Jennings family, Garrard County, Kentucky. Address delivered by Charles Loeber, consulting engineer for the Jennings family record … at a meeting held in Garrard County court house, Lancaster, Kentucky, Monday, December 23rd, 1929 … Lancaster, Ky., Printed by Central record [1929]
[12] p. 23ᶜᵐ.
Relates to the establishment of a claim to an estate of the Jennings family in England.

1. Jennings family.
30-9193

Library of Congress CS71.J545 1929

NL 0441520 DLC OC1WHi

Loeber, Charles, 1878–
The Sheffer family, Staunton, Virginia … Staunton, Wright printing co., 1942.
geneal. tables. 43 x 24ᶜᵐ.

1. Sheffer family (Jacob Scaheffer)
44-22703

Library of Congress CS71.S5414 1942

NL 0441521 DLC

[Loeber, Charles] 1878–
The Sheffer family of Shenandoah County, Virginia. December 30, 1728–December 30, 1944. [n. p.], 1944.
16 p. 21 cm.
"Proof printed November 30, 1944."

1. Sheffer family (Jacob Scaheffer, 1728–1815)
CS71.S5414 1944
47-29916*

NL 0441522 DLC

Loeber, Charles G.
Gravity as a motive force. A treatise, showing the adaptability of gravity for general mechanical use. By Charles G. Loeber. Chicago, A. M. & E. Wood, book printers, 1866.
8 p. 22½ᶜᵐ.

1. Gravity.
6-34149†

Library of Congress TJ153.L82

NL 0441523 DLC

VOLUME 338

[Loeber, Charles G]
Prospectus for proving and introducing the Loeber air car.
office, 825 Union street, Brooklyn, N. Y. [Brooklyn, T. J.
Dyson & son, printers, 1892]
[6] p. 27 x 20½ᶜᵐ.
Illustration on p. [2] of cover.
Signed: Charles G. Loeber.

1. Air-ships. I. Title
36–33397
Library of Congress　　　TL654.L65A4
[2]　　　629.13324

NL 0441524　　DLC

Loeber, Charles G
Will it pay to invest in the stock of the Gray
Eagle's Silver Mining Company? Letters... pub.
in the newspapers of... Springfield, Ill. Springfield, Rokker's Print. House, 1876.
16 p.　22 cm.

Cover title.

1. Gray Eagle's Silver Mining Company. I. T.

NL 0441525　　NjP

Loeber, Christian, 1683-1747, praeses.
A30　　　Consideratio dictorum quibus Augustana
A3　　　Confessio de sua et Ecclesiae Romanae con-
1730L　　sensione asseverat. Ronneburgi, 1730.
28 p.
Diss. - Ronneburg (Ch.Neudecker, respondent)

I. Neudecker, Christian　　　respondent.

NL 0441526　　CtY

Loeber, Christian, 1683-1747, praeses.
A30　　　... De fundamento legum naturalium
J4　　　secundum disciplinam Socratis. Ienae,
1706L　　1706.

Diss. - Jena (J.G.Scheller, respondent)

1. Socrates. I. Scheller, Johann Georg
respondent.

NL 0441527　　CtY

686　　LOEBER, Christian, 1683-1747.
Luth　　Evangelisch-lutherische Dogmatik. Mit
L825ev　einem Vorwort von C.F.W. Walther. Nach
1872　　der Original-Ausgabe von 1711 unveraendert
abgedruckt. St. Louis, Mo. & Leipzig, Fr.
Dette, 1872.
viii,664p. 20.5cm.

NL 0441528　　MH-AH PPLT

Löber, Christian, 1683-1747.
Kurtze doch zulängliche Nachricht
Welchergestalt Von denen emigrirenden
Saltzburgern Eine grosse Anzahl In der Stadt
Altenburg Den 10. und 11. Jun. 1732. Glücklich
angekommen, wohl empfangen, freudig
aufgenommen, und mit Thränen wieder dimittiret
worden.　Dresden, Zu finden bey P.G.
Mohrenthalen. [1732]
4 to.　4 unnumbered leaves.
Text begins on verso of title-page.
Bound as the third pamphlet with: Zuverlässige

Relation, von Ankunfft und Aufnahme der
Saltzburgischen Emigranten ... [Part I.
No place] 1732, and others.
Note: This is a digest of Löber's Nachricht
which is bound immediately
before it.
Reference: Dannappel, Die
die Salzburger Emigration, 1886.

NL 0441530　　GU-De

686　　LOEBER, Christian, 1683-1747.
Luth.5　Die Lehre der Warheit zur Gottseligkeit,
L825ie　d. i. Theologia positiva Teutsch, welche
1711　　die Grund-Lehren der heiligen Gottes-
Gelahrtheit, in ihrer so historischen als
natuerlichen Zusammenhangung unter Betrachtung derer unterschiedenen Buendnisse
und Testamenten Gottes deutlich vortraeget
... Altenburg, bey Joh. Ludwig Richtern,
1711.

8p.t.,1096,[13]p. 16.5cm.

With this is bound his Unterricht
von der Creatur-Liebe ... 1712.

NL 0441532　　MH-AH

Löber, Christian, 1683-1747.
Umständliche Nachricht Von denen Saltzburgischen Emigranten, Welche Vom 10 bisz 13 Jun.
1732. Durch Die Fürstl. Sächsz. Residentz-
und Creysz-Stadt Altenburg gezogen, Daselbst
mit aller Liebe angenommen, an Seel und Leib
erqvicket und verpfleget, auch mit gleicher Liebe
wieder fortgelassen worden. Verfasset von D.
Christian Löber, F.S. Consistorial-Rath und
General-Superintend. Altenburg, Gedruckt und
zu finden bey Joh. Ludw. Richtern, F.S.
Hof-Buchdruckern. [1732]

32 p.　4 to.　Signatures: A.-D, each 4 leaves.
Bound as the second pamphlet with: zuverlässige
Relation, von Ankunfft und Aufnahme der
Saltzburgischen Emigranten ... [Part I. No place]
1732, and others.
Reference: Dannapel, Die Literatur
Salzburger Emigration, 1886.

NL 0441534　　GU-De

Loeber (Christianus Fridericus). * De hæmor-
rhagia. 20 pp. 4°. *Erfordia, lit. Groschiana,*
[1729].

NL 0441535　　DNLM

Loeber, Christianus Fridericus, respondent.
... De masticatione ...
see under　Lischowitz, Johannes
Christophorus, 1693-1743, praeses.

Loeber, Christianus Joseph, 1743-94.
—— Anfangsgründe der Wundarzeneikunst,
nebst einer Vorrede von den Vortheilen des
Aderlassens bey Kindern. 6 l., 332 pp., 4 l. 8°.
Langensalza, J. C. Martini, 1770.

NL 0441537　　DNLM

Loeber (Christianus Joseph.) [1743-94]. * De
cordis fabrica et functione atque de sanguinis
per cor et vasa sanguinea circulatione. 2 p. l.,
74 pp. 4°. *Erfordia, lit. H. R. Nonnii,* [1767].

NL 0441538　　DNLM

Loeber, Christianus Joseph, 1743-94.
—— Sendschreiben von dem Wiederkommen
der Pocken nach geschehener Einimpfung. 40
pp. 4°. *Erfurt. Hohmeier,* 1767.
Bound with the following:

NL 0441539　　DNLM

919.47　LOEBER, Christoph Heinrich, 1634-1705.
O 71z　Historia ecclesiastica quae ephoriam
L825h　Orlamundanam in Ducatu Altenburgensi
1702a　describit, potentissimorum ac serenissimorum
Saxoniae Electorum ac Ducum studium propag-
andae veritatis divinae à temporibus refor-
mationis refert, ipsam Reformationem per B.
Lutherum factam, & quae tum temporis in his
terris acta sunt, recenset, multa insuper
notatu dignissima, de Carolstadio praesertim,
& Flacio, qui Orlamundae docuerunt aliquando,
aut innotuerunt　　　de Libris symbolicis

libro interim &c. annectit, Memoriam tandem
omnium ministrorum, qui post pulsas papales
tenebras in hujus ephoriae ecclesiis verbum
Dei docuerunt & adhuc docent, conservat;...
Iene, apud Iohannem Bielckium, 1702.
646p. 17cm.
Title on two leaves.
No. 1 in a volume of works on German
history and　　　government.

NL 0441541　　MH-AH

Löber, Christoph Heinrich, 1634-1705.
... Historische Erzehlung und Bedencken von
etlichen Offenbarungen, so vor Göttlich haben
wollen gehalten werden, darinnen zugleich das
unlängst von dieser materie emanirte Sentschrei-
ben meistlich beantwortet wird ... von Christophoro
Heinrico Lobern ... Rudolstadt, gedruckt mit
Joh. Rudolph Löwens Schrifftten, 1692.
30 p. 21 cm.
At head of title: I. J. N. A.

Bound with: Arnold, Gottfried, 1666-1714.
Die Abwege der Irrungen ... frommer
Menschen ... 1708.
No. 13 of a volume of pamphlets

NL 0441543　　NNUT

C　　LÖBER, CHRISTOPH HEINRICH, 1634-1705.
653　　Schrifftsmässige Entdeckung des Quaker-
.601　Greuels, so verwichenes 1680. Jahr in einem
Quaker-Buche, Helleleuchtender Hertzens-Spiegel
genannt, ausgebreitet worden. Jena, J.Bielcke,
1682.
[16],271p. 17cm.　(with [Müller, Johann]
Quäcker-Grewel. 1661)

NL 0441544　　ICN PHi

LOEBER, Christoph Heinrich, 1634-1705
... Schrifftmässige Vorstellung Des
Quaker=Irrlichtes ... JENA/ Druckts Joh.
David Werther. 1685.
10p.l., 388, [2]p. 17cm.
At head of title: I.N.J.C.A.
No.5 in bound volume of pamphlets.

NL 0441545　　MH-AH PHi

Loeber, Christoph Wilhelm　　　praeses.
A30　　　... De mutatione formarum in vestibus
J4　　　i.e. Von Veraenderung der Kleider-Moden. /
1722L　Ienae,1722.
28 p.
Diss. - Jena (Ch.L.Matthesius, author
and respondent)

I. Matthesius, Christoph Lorenz
author and respondent.

NL 0441546　　CtY

Löber, Christoph Wilhelm, praeses.
... De sepvltvra in templis, qvan ...
svbmittit ... Anthonivs Christianvs
Valentin ... [Jenae?] literis Nisianis
[1710]
1 p.l., [18] p. 19cm.
Diss. - Jena? (Anton Christian
Valentin, respondent)

NL 0441547　　MH-L

VOLUME 338

Loeber, Dietrich André.
Das Eherecht der Sowjetunion und seine Anwendung im internationalen Privatrecht Deutschlands, von Dietrich Loeber. Marburg, 1950.
viii, 258 l. 31 cm.
Inaug.-Diss.—Marburg.
Includes legislation.
Bibliography : leaves 183-225.

1. Marriage law—Russia. 2. Conflict of laws—Marriage—Russia. 3. Conflict of laws—Marriage—Germany. i. Russia (1923- U. S. S. R. Laws, statutes, etc. ii. Title.

52-23047 rev

NL 0441548   DLC

Loeber, E. G.
TS1080
.L3   **Labarre, E   J**
1952   Dictionary and encyclopædia of paper and paper-making, with equivalents of the technical terms in French, German, Dutch, Italian, Spanish & Swedish. 2d ed., rev. and enl. Amsterdam, Swets & Zeitlinger, 1952.

LÖBER, Emanuel Christian, 1696-1763.
.Auszug der sichern und nützlichen Nachrichten von dem Englischen America besonders von Carolina und der fruchtbaren Landschaft Georgia. Jena, [17-?]

NL 0441550   MH PHi

Loeber, Emanuel Christian ., 1696-1763.
——. De sanguinis missione ejusque utilitate in morbis infantum acutis. 26 pp. 4°. Jena, are Wertheriano, [s. d.]

NL 0441551   DNLM

Loeber, Emanuel Christian , 1696-1763.
—— & Geissenhainer (Michael Frider.)
Disp. exhibens historiam morborum ex acido. 1 p. l., 36 pp. 4°. Jena, lit. Wertherianis, [1724.]

NL 0441552   DNLM

Loeber, Emanuel Christian, 1696-1763.
—— & Loeber (Christianus Fridericus).
Disp. sistens plethora naturam ortum atque effectus. 24 pp. 4°. [Jena], C. D. Werther, [1728.]

NL 0441553   DNLM PPC

Loeber, Emanuel Christian ., 1696-1763.
——. Historia contusionum ; respondente Joh. Philip. Wolf. 24 pp. sm. 4°. Jena, lit. Marggrafiani, [1726.]

NL 0441554   DNLM

Loeber (Emanuel Christian)[1696-1763]. * Historia inflammationis ex principiis anatomicis et mechanicis deducta. 41 pp., 2 l. sm. 4°. Hala Magdeb., typ. J. Gruneri, [1722.]

NL 0441555   DNLM

Loeber, Ernst.
Zur Geschichte der Lampenglasbläserei auf dem Thüringer Walde, von Ernst Löber.   Weimar: R. Wagner Sohn, 1926.
22 p.   8°.

1. Glass—Hist.—Germany—Thuringia.
N. Y. P. L.   April 21, 1927

NL 0441556   NN NCorniC

Loëber, F. M.
33347 Traité pratique d'électricité appliquée à l'industrie. Principes, construction, emploi des machines dynamo et accumulateurs. 152 p. 97 il. O. Lyon: A. Rey & cie, 1902.

NL 0441557   ICJ

Loeber, Ferdinand
Ueber die befoerderer des griechischen sprachstudiums im Abendlande...
Schwerin, Hofbuchdruckerei, 1834.
44 p.

NL 0441558   PU

W 4
M96   LOEBER, Frank, 1919-
1944   Über einen Fall von isolierter Pulmonalsklerose, verbunden mit einer Fehlbildung des rechten Hauptastes der Arteria pulmonalis bei einem 3 Monate alten Kind. [München] 1944.
26 l.
Inaug.-Diss.-Munich.
1. Pulmonary artery - Diseases

NL 0441559   DNLM

Loeber (Fridericus Erhardus). * De præstantia martis in morbis chronicis. 21 pp., 1 l. sm. 4°. Jena, lit. Marggrafiani, [1751].

NL 0441560   DNLM

Loeber (Friederich). * De exanthemate miliari et pemphigo. 31 pp. sm. 4°. Erfordia, I. C. Goerling, [1791].

NL 0441561   DNLM PPC

386.2 Löber, Friedrich, 1910-
L78   ...Untersuchungen über die wasserstoffionenkonzentration im vaginalsekret gesunder und geschlechtskranker küho... Giessen, 1938.
33 p.   23½cm.

Diss. - Giessen.
Lebenslauf.
"Schrifttumverzeichnis": p.32-33.

[Full name: Johannes Friedrich Löber.

NL 0441562   DNAL CtY

Gu4   Loeber, G   A
2   ... Die Heiligkeit des Olbaums in Attika ...
3   Stade, A. Pockwitz[1857]
54p. 19cm. [Binder's title: Greek religion, III]
Programm - Gymnasium, Stade.

NL 0441563   CtY MH-A

Loeber, Georg, 1865-
Christentum und Krieg? Von Pfarrer Georg Löber... Zweite, verbesserte und vermehrte Auflage.   Leipzig: A. Strauch, 1916.   38 p.   8°.

1. European war, 1914- —Religious   aspects.
N. Y. P. L.   December 5, 1919.

NL 0441564   NN

Löber, Georg. 1865-
D. Dr. Richard Löber ...; ein Lebens- und Charakterbild ...   Leipzig, Dörffling & Franke, 1908.
58 p., il. port., Q.

NL 0441565   PPLT

Löber, Gertrud, 1906-
Der Geburtenrückgang in Deutschland und die Vorschläge zu seiner Bekämpfung...von Gertrud Löber...   Düren-Rl.: Dissertations-Druckerei, 1934.   118 p. incl. tables.   21½cm.
Inaugural-Dissertation — Frankfurt a.M., 1932.
Lebenslauf.
"Literaturverzeichnis," 6 l. at end.

822496A. 1. Birth rate—Germany.
N. Y. P. I.   May 29, 1936

NL 0441566   NN

Loeber, Gotthilf Fridemann, 1722-1799.
De burggraviis Orlamundanis commentatio. Documentis genuinis et nunquam antehac editis variisque observationibus comitum maxime Orlamundanorum historiam illuminantibus illustrata. Ienae, sumtu Marggrafiano, 1741.
sm. 4°. ff. (4), cvi. Geneal. tables and vign.

Another copy.   4°.   Large paper.   Type on title-page differs.

Orlamünde, Counts of

NL 0441567   MH CtY

Loeber, Gotthilf Friedemann, 1722-1799, praeses.
A30   De titulo Comitis Palatini Saxoniae in litteris Friderici Admorsi. Jenae, 1743.
J4   ... l.
1743L   Diss. - Jena (G.Schüz, respondent)

I. Schüz, Gottfried   respondent.

NL 0441568   CtY

---

687   LOEBER, Gotthilf Friedemann, 1722-1799.
1825pr   Pruefung der Untersuchung Herrn D.
1789   Anton Fr. Buesching, wenn und durch wen der freyen evangelisch-lutherischen Kirche die symbolischen Buecher zuerst aufgelegt worden, nebst der Anfuge einer Ordinationsrede ueber die Sittlichkeit des Religionseides. Altenburg, Richter, 1789.
2p.l.,84p. 18.5cm.

NL 0441569   MH-AH

B610.24
G71H153f Loeber, Gotthold Ernest, respondent.
... De praeparatione olei animalis Christiani Democriti ejusque usu febribus intermittentibus medendi ... Pro ... doctoris rite.   Gottingae, Litteris Hagerianis, 1747.
23 p.   20 cm.

Inaug. Diss. - Göttingen (Albrecht von Haller, praeses)

I. Haller Albrecht von, 1708-1777, praeses.   II. Title.

NL 0441570   MnU-B DNLM

LÖBER, Gustav.
. Ein glücklich geheilter fall von extrauterin schwanger schaft. Jena, 1886.

NL 0441571   MBCo MH DNLM

AC   Löber, Hans, 1903-
831   Zur kenntnis der lössvorkommen in Mittelfranken ... Nürnberg, 1932.   63 p.
Inaug. Diss. Erlangen, 1932.
Lebenslauf.

NL 0441572   ICRL CtY

VOLUME 338

Löber, Hans Helmut, 1907-
... Über Sarcome der Gallenblase ...
Hamburg, 1933.
Inaug.-Diss. - Hamburg.
Lebenslauf.
"Schrifttum": p. 19-20.

NL 0441573   CtY

Löber, Hans J.A., 1910-
... Ausheilung malacischer Prozesse,
sogenannter aseptischer Nekrosen (Nachunter-
suchungen) ...   Marburg-Lahn, 1935.
Inaug.-Diss. - Marburg.
Lebenslauf.
"Literaturverzeichnis": p. [65]-69.

NL 0441574   CtY

LÖBER, Hermann.
Die anwendbarkeit des §183 der konkursordnung
auf den konkurs der handelsgesellschaften.
Borna-Leipzig,1906.

10 - 35 p.
Inaug.-diss.,--Rostock.

NL 0441575   MH-L ICRL

4DD-
1190
Loeber, Irmgard.
Bismarcks Pressepolitik in den Jahren des
Verfassungskonfliktes, 1862-1866.
München, Auslieferung: Zeitungswissen-
schaftlichen Vereinigung, 1935.
100 p.   (Zeitung und Leben, Bd. 24)

NL 0441576   DLC-P4 MnU ICU

Loeber, Irmgard.
... Das niederländische kolonialreich ...   Leipzig, Wilhelm
Goldmann verlag [*1939]
141. [8] p. incl. illus. (maps) tables. 19½ᶜᵐ. ("Weltgeschehen" [hrsg.
von dr. Gerhard Herrmann])
Map on front lining-paper.

1. Netherlands—Colonies.
A C 39-2164
New York. Public library
for Library of Congress   [2]

NL 0441577   NN ICU CtY CU MiU MH MtU

[113
M9
1936
Löber, Irmgard, 1911-
Eigene Erfahrungen auf dem Gebiete der auto-
matischen Regulierungsmethode nach Herbst ...
[Berlin,1936]
Inaug.-Diss. - Münster, i.W.
Lebenslauf.
"Sonder-Abdruck aus der Zeitschrift für zahn-
ärztliche Orthopädie 1936."

NL 0441578   CtY

Löber, Johann Conrad, respondent.
... De testamento mystico sive arcano ...

see under   Henne, Rudolph Christoph,
praeses.

Loeber, Johannes Aarnout, 1869-
Z269
L82
Ein ausflug nach London, von J. A. Loeber, jr.
... Stuttgart, 1892.
15 p. 22cm. Red cloth.
Separatabdruck aus dem Allgem. anzeiger für
buchbindereien.

1. Bookbinding. I. Title.

NL 0441580   CSmH CU

Wason
NK9779
L82
Loeber, Johannes Aarnout, 1869-
Bamboe-ornament der Kajan-Dajaks. Met
21 afbeeldingen naar voorwerpen uit de col-
lectie A. W. Nieuwenhuis in het R. E.
Museum te Leiden.   Den Haag, Vereeniging
Oost en West, 1903.
20 p. illus. 11 plates. 24cm.

1. Decoration and ornament, Kayan.
2. Art, Primitive. I. Nieuwenhuis, A. W.
II. Title.

NL 0441581   NIC

Loeber, Johannes Aarnout, 1869-
...Bamboe-ornament van Nederlandsch Nieuw-Guinea.
Amsterdam, 1920. 42 p. illus. 4°.

1. Art, New Guinea (Dutch).
N. Y. P. L.
2. Bamboo work.
July 5, 1921.

NL 0441582   NN CaBVaU

Loeber, Johannes Aarnout, 1869-
Bamboe-snijwerk en weefsels op Timor.
(In Bijdragen tot de taal-, land- en volkenkunde van Neder-
landsch-Indië. Deel 61, pp. 339-349.) 's Gravenhage. 1908.)

H866 — Timor, Island. Manners. — Bamboo.

NL 0441583   MB

Loeber, Johannes Aarnout, 1869-
... Das batiken, eine blüte indonesischen kunstlebens.
Oldenburg i. O., G. Stalling [*1926]
110 p., 1 l. col. front., illus., plates (part col.) 26½ᶜᵐ.
At head of title: J. A. Loeber jun.

1. Batik.
Library of Congress   NK9503.L6
27-1714

NL 0441584   DLC OC1MA OC1

Loeber, Johannes Aarnout, 1869-
... Been-, hoorn- en schildpadbewerking en het vlecht-
werk in Nederlandsch-Indië, door J. A. Loebèr, jr. ...
Amsterdam, Het Instituut, 1916.
71 p. front., xx (i. e. 21) pl, (part fold.) 22½ᶜᵐ. (Geïllustreerde be-
schrijvingen van Indische kunstnijverheid, no. VII)
At head of title: Koloniaal instituut, Amsterdam.
"Aanteekeningen": p. [70]-71.

1. Art industries and trade—Dutch East Indies.   I. Amsterdam.
Koloniaal instituut.
17-19600
Library of Congress   NK1059.L5

NL 0441585   DLC ICJ NN PU-Mu ICRL

Asia
NK1056
.L64
Loeber, Johannes Aarnout,1869-
Het bladwerk en zijn versiering in
Nederlandsch-Indië. Amsterdam, Het
Instituut, 1914.
47 p. illus. (Geïllustreerde
beschrijvingen van Indische kunst-
nijverheid, no. 4)

At head of title: Koloniaal Instituut,
Amsterdam.

1. Textile   industry and fabrics —
Dutch East   Indies.

NL 0441586   HU InU CtY CaBVaU PU-Mu MH MdBP

Wason
NK1059
L82
Loeber, Johannes Aarnout, 1869-
Geïllustreerde beschrijvingen van
Indische kunstnijverheid, No. 1-8.
Amsterdam, J. H. de Bussy, 1903-1916.
8 nos. in 2 v. illus., plates. 23cm.

Added t.-p.: Techniek en sierkunst in
den Indischen Archipel. 1916.
At head of added t.-p.: Koloniaal
Instituut, Amsterdam.
On spine: Indische kunstnijverheid.

Contents:--1. Het weven in Nederlandsch-
Indië [Bulletin 29 van het Koloniaal
Museum]--2. Bamboe in Nederlandsch-Indië
[Bulletin 43]--3. Het schelpen- en kralenwerk in Nederlandsch-Indië [Bulletin 51]--
4. Het bladwerk en zijn versiering in Nederlandsch-Indië.--5. Textiele versieringen

in Nederlandsch-Indië.--6. Leder- en
perkamentwerk, schorsbereiding en aardewerk in Nederlandsch-Indië.--7. Been-,
hoorn- en schildpadbewerking en het vlechtwerk in Nederlandsch-Indië.--8. Hout-
nijwerk en metaalbewerking in Nederlandsch-
Indië.

NL 0441589   NIC MiU

NK
4780
L642
1916
Loeber, Johannes Aarnout, 1869-
Houtsnijwerk en metaalbewerking in Ned-
erlandsch-Indië, door J.A. Loebèr Jr.
[Amsterdam] Uitgave van het Instituut,
1916.
108 p. 43 numbered plates. 23 cm.
(Geïllustreerde beschrijvingen van Indi-
sche kunstnijverheid, No. 8)
At head of title: Koloniaal Instituut,
Amsterdam.
Bibliog-   raphy: p. [97]-108.
1. Wood-   carving, Indonesian.
2. Metal-   work - Indonesia. I.
Title. II.   Series.

NL 0441590   CaBVaU CtY DLC-P4 InU

Wason
GN431
L82 I3
Loeber, Johannes Aarnout, 1869-
Het Indische vlechtwerk voor export.
Den Haag, Vereeniging "Oost en West,"
1903.
xi, 23 p. illus. 24 cm.

1. Basket making. 2. Art, Indonesian.
I. Title.

NL 0441591   NIC

Loeber, Johannes Aarnout, 1869-
... Leder- en perkamentwerk, schorsbereiding en aardewerk
in Nederlandsch-Indië, door J. A. Loebèr, jr. ... Amsterdam,
Het Instituut, 1915.
84 p. illus., xxiv pl. (incl. front.) 22½ᶜᵐ. (Geïllustreerde beschrijvingen van Indische kunstnijverheid, no. VI)
At head of title: Koloniaal Instituut, Amsterdam.

1. Art industries and trade—Dutch East Indies. 2. Leather work.
3. Parchment. 4. Tapa. 5. Pottery—Dutch East Indies.   I. Amsterdam. Koloniaal instituut.
16-13429 Revised
Library of Congress   NK1059.L6

NL 0441592   DLC KU ICRL PU-Mu ICJ

Asia
NK8643
.L64
Loebèr, Johannes Aarnout,1869-
Het schelpen- en kralenwerk in
Nederlandsch-Indië. Amsterdam, J. H.
de Bussy, 1913.
52 p. illus. (Geïllustreerde
beschrijvingen van Indische Kunst-
nijverheid, no. III)

At head of   title: Bulletin van het

Koloniaal Museum te Haarlem, no. 51.
Bibliographical notes included in
"Aanteekeningen": p. 41-52.

1. Bead-   work. 2. Shellcraft.
I. Haarlem.   Koloniaal Museum.

NL 0441594   HU CaBVaU CtY

VOLUME 338

Loebèr, Johannes Aarnout, 1869-
Het „spinneweb"-motief op Timor. Plates.
(In Bijdragen tot de taal-, land- en volkenkunde van Neder-
landsch-Indië. Deel 60, pp. 93-96. 's Gravenhage. 1907.)

G6987 — "Spiderweb" pattern. In decoration. — Timor, Island. Fine arts.

NL 0441595   MB

Loebèr, Johannes Aarnout, 1869-
...Techniek en sierkunst in de Indischen archipel; geillu-
streerde beschrijvingen van indische kunstnijverheid, door J. A.
Loebèr, jr.   Amsterdam: Het instituut [1903-16]. 8 v. in 1.
diagrs., fronts., illus., plates. 8°.
At head of title: Koloniaal Instituut, Amsterdam.
(v.) 1-3 issued as Bull. 29, 43, 51 of Koloniaal Museum, Haarlem.
Contents.- (v.) 1. Het weven. (v.) 2. Bamboe. (v.) 3. Het schelpen- en kralen-
werk. (v.) 4. Het bladwerk en zijn versiering. (v.) 5. Textiele versieringen. (v.) 6.
Leder- en perkamentwerk, schorsbereiding en aardewerk. (v.) 7. Been-, hoorn- en
schildpadbewerking en het vlechtwerk. (v.) 8. Houtsnijwerk en metaalbewerking.
Register en bibliografie der literatuur over Indische kunstnijverheid.

1. Art industries and trade, East   Indies (Dutch). 2. Koloniaal
Instituut, Amsterdam.
N. Y. P. L.   May 14, 1924.

NL 0441596   NN

Loebèr, Johannes Aarnout, 1869-
... Textiele versieringen in Nederlandsch-Indië, door
J. A. Loebèr jr. ... Amsterdam, Het Instituut, 1914.
79 p. illus. xxii pl. (incl. front.) 22½ᵐ. (Geïllustreerde beschrijvingen
van Indische kunstnijverheid, no. v)
At head of title: Kolonial instituut, Amsterdam.

1. Textile industry and fabrics—Dutch East Indies. 2. Textile design.
1. Vereeniging "Koloniaal instituut" te Amsterdam.
                                                              15-801
Library of Congress   NK8880.L6

NL 0441597   DLC CtY MH-A PU-Mu

Loebèr, Johannes Aarnout, 1869-
Timoreesch snijwerk en ornament; bijdrage tot de Indonesische
kunstgeschiedenis. Uitgegeven door het K. Instituut voor de
taal-, land- en volkenkunde van Nederlandsch-Indië. 'S-Gravenhage, M. Nijhoff, 1903.
1. 8°. pp. 81 +. 22 plates and other illus.

Timor, Island]

NL 0441598   MH NN NNC CtY

Loebèr, Johannes Aarnout, 1869-
UTS1490   Het vlechtwerk in den Indischen Archipel.
L64   Uitg. bij gelegenheid der tentoonstelling van
de Vereeniging "Oost en West", te 's-Gravenhage, Augustus 1902. Haarlem, H. Kleinmann
[1902]
iv, 84 p. 8 plates. 21 cm.

1. Weaving - Indonesia. 2. Basketwork.
Cdu SA

NL 0441599   CtY NIC MH

NK
9085
L65   Loebèr, Johannes Aarnout, 1869-
...Het weven in Nederlandsch-Indië, door J.A.
Loebèr jr.   Amsterdam, J.H. de Bussy, 1903.

68 1 p. front., xxi pl. 22 cm. (Bulletin van het Koloniaal museum te Haarlem. no.29.)

Bibliography at the end.

NL 0441600   PPPM DLC

Loeber, Julius; Zur Physiologie der Blutplättchen. Altenburg
& Frankfurt 1911. 12 S. 8° ¶ (Aus: Pflügers Archiv f. d.
ges. Physiol. d. Menschen u. d. Tiere. Bd 140, H. 5—7.)
Freiburg i. B., Med. Diss. v. 1911, Ref. v. Kries
[Geb. 10. Febr. 87 Buttstädt; Wohnort: Frankfurt a. M.; Staatsangeh.:
S.-Weimar; Vorbildung: Gymn. Jena Reife O. 05; Studium: Kiel 1, Jena 4, Mün-
chen 2, Freiburg i. B. 3 S.; Coll. 3. März 11; Approb. 22. Juni 11.] [U 11. 1092

NL 0441601   ICRL DNLM CtY

Löber, Karl.
Beiträge zur Flora des Dillkreises.
(In Jahrbücher des Nassauischen Vereins für
LJ   Naturkunde. Wiesbaden. 24 cm. Bd.88(1950)
.A348   p.49-69)
Bd.88   Caption title.
Bibliography: p. 52.

1. Botany - Germany - Dillkreis. i.t. ii.s:
Jahrbücher des Nassauischen Vereins für Naturkunde, Bd.88.

NL 0441602   NNBG

Löber, Karl.
BX8023   Haiger und sein Raum; Festschrift zur Feier
H29L6   des 900. Jahrestages der Haigerer Kirchenweihe.
Haiger, Ev.Kirchengemeinde und Stadtgemeinde,
1948.
60 p. illus. maps. 21㎝.
Bibliography: p.58-60.

1.Evangelische Kirche zu Haiger. 2.Haiger -
Church history. I.Title.

NL 0441603   CSt

Löber, Karl, [Trigeminusaffektionen bei Tabes dorsalis. [Maschi-
nenschrift.] 20 S. 4°. — Auszug: (Kiel 1923: Rößler). 1 Bl. 8°
Kiel, Med. Diss. v. 12. Mai [1923]   [U 23. 6629

NL 0441604   ICRL

Löber, Karl Joseph Siegfried
see   Löber, Siegfried, 1893.

Loeber, Kurt; Beiträge zur Lösung und Geschichte des
Malfattischen Problems und seiner Erweiterungen. Halle
a. S. 1914: (Blanke, Berlin). VIII, 62 S., 3 Taf. 8°
Halle, Phil. Diss. v. 3. März 1914, Ref. Wangerin
[Geb. 22. Sept. 88 Berlin; Wohnort: Berlin; Staatsangeh.: Preußen; Vorbildung: Kaiser-Wilhelms-RG. Berlin Reife 06; Studium: Berlin TeH. 2, U.
8 S.; Rig. 24. Nov. 13.]   [U 14. 3789

NL 0441606   ICRL CtY MiU RPB MH

Loeber, Paul Otto Ernst Julius, 1887-
see Loeber, Julius, 1887-

BT40   Löber, Richard, 1828-1907.
L6   Alte Wahrheit in neuer Gestalt. Gotha,
G. Schloessmann, 1874-81.
2 v. in 1.

Contents.- 1.Bd. Allgemeiner Theil. Die
neue Schöpfung.- 2.Bd. Sein und Werden.

1. Theology, Doctrinal. 2. Metaphysics.

NL 0441608   CU CtY

BXZ   Löber, Richard, 1828-1907.
8066   Die beste aller Welten; ein Wort gegen
.L82   phantastistische Glückseligkeit und Unzu-
B5   friedenheit. Gotha, G. Schloessmann, 1886.
x, 130 p. 22 cm.

NL 0441609   DCU

Loeber, Richard, 1828-1907.
Durch Kampf zum Frieden.
Gotha, Schloessmann, 1874.
2 v.

NL 0441610   PPG

Löber, Richard, 1828-1907.
Die gesicherten Ergebnisse der Bibel-
kritik und das von uns verkündete Gottes-
wort... Gotha, G. Schloessmann, 1889.
28 p. 22ᵃ.

NL 0441611   NjPT

YAR   Löber, Richard, 1828-1907.
257   Das innere leben. Gotha, 1867.
394 p.

1. Spiritual life. Theology, Doctrinal.

NL 0441612   DLC ODW

BT165   LÖBER, RICHARD, 1828-1907.
.L82   Das innere leben; oder, Der verkehr des Christen mitt
Gott und menschen. Gemeinverständlich dargestellt, von
d. Richard Löber ... 3., gänzlich umgearb.aufl. Gotha,
G.Schloessmann, 1900.
[5],360 p. 22½cm.

1.Spiritual life. 2.Theology, Doctrinal.

NL 0441613   ICU

Loeber, Richard, 1828-1907.
Die lehre vom gebet aus der immanente.n und ökonomischen
Trinität, abgeleitet von dr. ph. Richard Löber ... 2., umgearb.
und erweiterte aufl. Erlangen, A. Deichert, 1860.
viii p., 1 l., 144 p. 20ᵐ.

1. Prayer.   i. Title.
                                                37-10547
Library of Congress   BV210.L63 1860
                            [2]   248

NL 0441614   DLC CtY

Löber, Siegfried, Arzt: Über die Extensionsbehandlung der
Clavikularfrakturen. Aus d. Krankenh. Bergmannstrost in
Halle a. S. Langensalza 1920: Wendt & Klauwell. 18 S. 8°
Halle, Med. Diss. v. 18. Okt. 1919 [192c], Ref. Schieck, Oberst
[Geb. 16. Jan. 93 Vacha; Wohnort: Halle a. S.; Staatsangeh.: Preußen; Vor-
bildung: G. Jena Reife 11; Studium: Kiel 1, Freiburg 1, Jena 3, München 1,
Freiburg 4, Tübingen 2 S.; Coll. 6. Aug. 19; Approb. 20. Juni 19.] [U 20. 2243

NL 0441615   ICRL CtY MiU DNLM

QM   Löber, Valentin.
345   Anchora sanitatis, dialogice fabricata. Cui
.P52   annexa est Mantissa de venenis, et eorvm anti-
1681   dotis ... Authore Valentino Löbero ... Francofurti & Hamburgi, Impensis J.Naumanni & G.Wolffii,
1671.
239 p. 16½ cm.
With Peyer, J.C. Exercitatio anatomico-medica.
1681.

1.Hygiene -Early works to 1800. 2.Medicine--
15th-18th cent.   3.Poisons. I.Title.

NL 0441616   MiU DNLM

Löber, Valentin, tr.
Teutschredender Owenus
see under   Owen, John, 1560?-1622.

4BV   Löber, Volkmar
577   Im Bunde mit Gott. [Weimar,
Verlag Deutsche Christen, 19]
86 p.

NL 0441618   DLC-P4

VOLUME 338

Löberg, Gunnar, 1893–1950.
Gunnar Löberg, det förbisedda geniet. En introduktion av Bengt V. Wall. Stockholm, H. Geber ₍1952₎
45 p. 55 plates (8 col.) 34 cm.

ı. Wall, Bengt V.
ND793.L6W3   [759.85] 927.5   A 53–3888
Harvard Univ. Library
for Library of Congress   ₍1₎†

NL 0441619   MH MnU DLC

Löberg, Johan Gunnar
see **Löberg, Gunnar,** 1893–1950.

Løberg, Ole Nicolai, 1804–1868.
Norges fiskerier, af O. N. Løberg. Udg. af "Det Kongelige selskab for Norges vel" ... Kristiania, B. M. Bentzens bogtrykkeri, 1864.
2 p. l., ₍iii₎–xi, ₍1₎, 323, ₍1₎ p. 18½ᵐ.
Added t.-p.

1. Fisheries—Norway.
      12–19303
Library of Congress   SH279.L79

NL 0441621   DLC

Løberg, Ole Nicolai, 1804–1868, comp.
Skriftemaal og altergang. En samling af udvalgte kommunionbetragtninger. Efter det tydske av O. N. Løberg ... Kristiania, B. M. Bentzens bogtrykkeri, 1864.
2 p. l., xl, ₍1₎, 119 p. 19ᵐ.
"Ogsaa med omtrykte titelblade: Udvalgte kommunionbetragtninger. Tildels efter Benjamin Schmolck's 'Das kommunionbuch'."—Norsk bokfortegnelse 1848–65. 1870, p. 221.

1. Lord's supper—Prayer-books and devotions—Norwegian.
ı. Schmolck, Benjamin, 1672–1737. ıı. Title.

BX8073.L6   47–35736

NL 0441622   DLC

Löberg (Timandus Jonas) [1819–82]. Cholera i Bergen. 42 pp. 8°. [s. p., 1849.]
Repr. from: Norsk Mag. f. Lægevidensk., Christiania, 1849, III.

NL 0441623   DNLM

LÖBERING, Max.
Zur konstitution des chimonaphtalons und beiträge zur frage der konstitution des pyrophtalons. Inaug.-diss., München 1907.

NL 0441624   MH–C ICRL

Löbern (E. C.) Gründliche Anweisung zu einer glücklichen Blatter-Cur, nebst einem Anhang derer Schriften, die von dieser Seuche und deren Inoculation gehandelt, nach denen mechanischen Lehr-Sätzen verfertiget. 5 p. l., 52 pp. 12°. Jena, Crökerischen Buchhandlung, 1750.

NL 0441625   DNLM

Loebers, Augusts
see
Loeber, August.

AC
831
Loebich, Ernst, 1906–
Beiträge zur standorts-charakterisierung, dargestellt an fichtenbeständen des Schwarzwaldes. ... Quakenbrück, 1934.   62 p.
Inaug. Diss. – Freiburg i. Br., 1934.
Lebenslauf.

NL 0441627   ICRL CtY

Loebich, *Julius Adolf.*
Die Innere Mission in Wuerttemberg im Jahr 1945. ₍Stuttgart, Quell-Verlag der Evang. Gesellschaft, 1946₎

NL 0441628   CtY DCU

Loebich, Otto.
Wissenswertes über zahntechnische Edelmetall-Legierungen in Frage und Antwort. 2. überarb. Aufl. ₍Frankfurt a. M.₎ 1955.
50 p. 22 cm.

1. Dentistry—Metallurgy.   ı. Title.

RK653.L6 1955   56–29441 ‡

NL 0441629   DLC

LOEBICH, Otto, 1902–
Über die ferrisalze substituierter essigsäuren sowie der malonsäure und ihre konstitution. Inaug.-diss., Würzburg, C. J. Becker, 1926.

pp. 29†.
"Lebenslauf" after p. 29.

NL 0441630   MH–C ICRL CtY

Löbig, Horst.
Elektrotechnik für Facharbeiter im Fernmeldebetrieb und Fernmeldebau. Leipzig, Fachbuchverlag, 1954.
249 p. illus. 24 cm. (Fachschriftenreihe der Deutschen Post. Fachrichtung Fernmeldewesen)

1. Electric engineering. 2. Telecommunication. ı. Title.
TK146.L63   A 56–1048
Mass. Inst. of Tech.   Library
for Library of Congress   ₍5₎†

NL 0441631   MCM DLC

Loebinger (Arthur). *Ueber Endocarditis scarlatinosa. 33 pp. 8°. Freiburg i. B., H. Epstein, 1891.

NL 0441632   DNLM

Loebinger, Guenter: Der Irrtum beim Prozessvergleich. [Maschinenschrift.] v, 86 S. 4°. — Auszug: Breslau 1925: Friedrichdruck. 2 Bl. 8°
Breslau, R.- u. staatswiss. Diss. v. 25. Juli 1925   [U 25.745]

NL 0441633   ICRL

Loebinger (Hugo Julius). *Eine Methode der Zungen-Exstirpation. [Erlangen.] 32 pp., 1 pl. 8°. Beuthen, J. Kirsch, 1887.

NL 0441634   DNLM

Loebinger, Rudolf
Die Aufwertungsgesetzgebung
see under
Abraham, Hans Fritz.

Loebinger, Rudolf
Durchführungs-bestimmungen zu den aufwertungsgesetzen
see under
Abraham, Hans Fritz.

Loebinger, Rudolf: Der strafrechtliche Schutz des Versicherers. [Maschinenschrift.] 98 S. 4°. — Auszug: Berlin [1923]: Hermann. 2 Bl. 8°
Breslau, R.- u. staatswiss. Diss. v. 5. Mai 1923   [U 23.1101]

NL 0441637   ICRL

Loebinger, Sofia M., ed.
The American suffragette ... v. 1, v. 2, no. 1–4; June 1909–Dec. 1910. New York city, 1909–10.

Loebis, H   Adnan
see
Lubis, H   Adnan.

Loebis, Madong
see
Lubis, Madong, 1891–

Loebis, Mochtar
see
Lubis, Mochtar, 1919–

Loebis, Tinggi
see
Lubis, Tinggi.

Loebisch (E. J.) *De somno. 28 pp. 8°. Vindobonæ, A. Pichler, 1826.

NL 0441643   DNLM

WS
100
L8253a
1832
**LÖBISCH, J   E   L
1795–1853**
Allgemeine Anleitung zum Kinder-Krankenexamen. Wien, Gerold, 1832.
viii, 82 p.
Later ed. published under title:
Studien der Kinderheilkunde.

NL 0441644   DNLM PPHa

Löbisch, J   E   L 1795–1853.
Entwickelungsgeschichte der seele des kindes. Von J. E. Löbisch ... Wien, C. Haas, 1851.
134 p. 18ᵐ.

1. Child study.
      E 10–2256 Revised
U. S. Off. of educ. Library   LB1115.L82
for Library of Congress   ₍r38b2₎

NL 0441645   DHEW DNLM ViU

WS
L826e
1854
**LÖBISCH, J   E   L
1795–1853**
Die Seele des Kindes in ihrer Entwicklung. 2. Aufl. Wien, Braumüller, 1854.
134 p.
1st ed. has title: Entwicklungsgeschichte der Seele des Kindes.

NL 0441646   DNLM CtY CoP

VOLUME 338

Löbisch, J Ǝ L, 1795-1853.
　　Studien der Kinderheilkunde. Wien, C.Haas, 1848.
　　307 p.
　　Running-title: Vorschule zur Diagnose der
　　Kinderkrankheiten.

NL 0441647　　ICJ

WS
100
L8253a
1852
　　LÖBISCH, J E L
　　1795-1853
　　　　Studien der Kinderheilkunde. 2. Aufl.
　　Wien, Hass, 1852.
　　viii, 307 p.
　　　　Earlier ed. published under title:
　　Allgemeine Anleitung zum Kinder-Kranken-
　　examen.

NL 0441648　　DNLM

Loebisch (Wilhelm Franz) [1839-]. Anlei-
tung zur Harn-Analyse für praktische Aerzte,
Apotheker und Studirende. 238, iv pp. 8°.
Wien, Urban u. Schwarzenberg, 1878.

NL 0441649　　DNLM PPC

Loebisch, Wilhelm Franz, 1839–
　　Anleitung zur Harn-Analyse für praktische Aerzte, Studirende
und Chemiker. Mit besonderer Berücksichtigung der klinischen
Medizin. Von Prof. Dr. W. F. Loebisch, ... Zweite durchaus
umgearbeitete Auflage. Mit 48 Holzschnitten und 1 Farbentafel.
Wien und Leipzig, Urban & Schwarzenberg, 1881.
　　xii, 449. [1] p. illus., 1 col. pl. 25ᶜᵐ.
Bibliographical foot-notes.

NL 0441650　　ICJ DNLM CtY MiU

RS187　**Loebisch, Wilhelm Franz,** 1839–
.L8　　Die neueren arzneimittel in ihrer anwendung und wirkung,
　　dargestellt von dr. W. F. Loebisch ... 2. gänzlich umgearb.
　　und wesentlich verm. aufl. Wien und Leipzig, Urban &
　　Schwarzenberg, 1883.
　　　viii, 268 p. 24ᶜᵐ.
　　"Literatur" at end of most chapters.

　　1. Pharmacology.

NL 0441651　　ICU CtY DNLM

QV
L825n
1888
　　LOEBISCH, Wilhelm Franz, 1839–
　　　Die neueren Arzneimittel, in ihrer
　　Anwendung und Wirkung. 3., gänzlich
　　umgearb. und wesentlich verm. Aufl.
　　Wien, Urban & Schwarzenburg, 1888.
　　viii, 440 p.

NL 0441652　　DNLM

615.1　Loebisch, Wilhelm Franz, 1839–
L825n4　Die neueren Arzneimittel in ihrer Anwendung
　　und Wirkung. 4.gänzlich neu bearb.Aufl.
　　Wien, Urban & Schwarzenberg, 1895.
　　416p. 23cm.

　　Includes bibliographies.

　　1. Materia medica.

NL 0441653　　IU PPC DNLM ICRL

Film
929
no. 3
　　LOEBISCH, Wilhelm Franz, 1839–
　　　Die neueren Arzneimittel in ihrer
　　Anwendung und Wirkung. 4., gänzlich
　　neu bearb. Aufl. Wien, Urban &
　　Schwarzenberg, 1895.
　　viii, 416 p.
　　Film copy.

NL 0441654　　DNLM

Loebker, Carl
　　see Loebker, Karl, 1854-

Löbker, Clemens, 1889-
　　Betrieb und Steuergutschein ... Münster,
　　1934.
　　Inaug.-Diss. - Münster.

NL 0441656　　CtY

Löbker, Ferdinand, 1906-
Münster　... Ueber die entstehung von nierensteinen
diss.　bei bettlägerigen kranken ... Rheine i.W.,
1932　1932.

NL 0441657　　MiU

Loebker, Gerhard
　　Charakter und bestimmung der gymnastik in
Athen. Von herrn gymnasiallehrer Löbker.
Münster, Druck der Coppenrathschen buchdruckerei,
1864.
　　8 p.

NL 0441658　　PU NjP

DF97
.L78
(C1)
　　LÖBKER, GERHARD.
　　　Die gymnastik der Hellenen. Ein versuch von Ger-
　　hard Loebker. Münster, J.H.Deiters, 1835.
　　[8], 104 p. 22cm.

　　1. Physical education and training--Greece.

NL 0441659　　ICU CU MH PU

Loebker (Karl) [1854-]. Bericht über
die in der gynäkologischen Klinik zu Greifswald
ausgeführten Laparotomien: achtzehn Ovario-
tomien, zwei Castrationen, eine Exstirpation
einer Hydronephrose, eine Totalexstirpation des
Uterus. 34 pp. 8°. [*Berlin*, 1879.]
Repr. from: Arch. f. Gynaek., Berl., 1879, xiv.

NL 0441660　　DNLM

Loebker, Karl, 1854-
――. Chirurgische Operationslehre. Ein Leit-
faden für die Operationsübungen an der Leiche.
Mit Berücksichtigung der chirurgischen Anato-
mie. 1. Hälfte. 160 pp. 8°. *Wien u. Leipzig,*
Urban u. Schwarzenberg, 1884.

NL 0441661　　DNLM

WO
100
L825c
1885
　　LÖBKER, Karl, 1854-
　　　Chirurgische Operationslehre; ein
　　Leitfaden für die Operationsübungen an
　　der Leiche, mit Berücksichtigung der
　　chirurgischen Anatomie für Studirende
　　und Ärzte. Wien, Urban & Schwarzen-
　　berg, 1885.
　　viii, 488 p. illus.

NL 0441662　　DNLM MoSU PPC ViU

Löbker, Karl, 1854-
――. Chirurgische Operationslehre. Ein Leitfaden für die Operationsübungen an der Leiche. Mit Berücksichtigung der chirurgischen
Anatomie für Studirende und Ärzte bearbeitet von Dr. Karl Löbker, ... Mit 271 Holzschnitten. Zweite, verbesserte und
theilweise neu bearbeitete Auflage. Wien und Leipzig, Urban &
Schwarzenberg, 1889.
　　viii, 520 p. 271 illus. 24ᶜᵐ.

NL 0441663　　ICJ ICRL PPC

WO
100
L825c
1893
　　LÖBKER, Karl, 1854-
　　　Chirurgische Operationslehre; ein
　　Leitfaden für die Operationsübungen an
　　der Leiche, mit Berücksichtigung der
　　chirurgischen Anatomie für Studirende
　　und Ärzte. 3., verb. und theilweise neu
　　bearb. Aufl. Wien, Urban & Schwarzen-
　　berg, 1893.
　　viii, 559 p. illus.

NL 0441664　　DNLM IU-M

Löbker, Karl, 1854-　　ed.
　　Gesammelte Beiträge aus dem Gebiete der
Chirurgie und Medizin des praktischen Lebens.
Festschrift ...
　　see under title

WO
100
L825c
1890
　　LÖBKER, Karl, 1854-
　　　Traité de médecine opératoire,
　　opérations générales et spéciales, à
　　l'usage des étudiants et des praticiens.
　　Tr. de l'allemand d'après la 2. éd.
　　par Herman Hanquet. Paris, Carré,
　　1890.
　　xii, 534 p. illus.
　　Translation of Chirurgische
　　Operationslehre.

NL 0441666　　DNLM

WO
100
L825c
1893a
　　LÖBKER, Karl, 1854-
　　　Traité de médecine opératoire,
　　opérations générales & spéciales, à
　　l'usage des étudiants & des praticiens.
　　Tr. du dr. Herman Hanquet. 2. éd.
　　française d'après la 3. éd. allemande
　　considérablement augm. Paris, Doin,
　　1893.
　　ix, 576 p. illus.
　　Translation of Chirurgische Operations-
　　lehre.
　　Imprint from label mounted on title
　　page.

NL 0441667　　DNLM

Löbker, Karl, 1854–
　　Über das wesen und die verbreitung der wurmkrankheit
(ankylostomiasis) mit besonderer berücksichtigung ihres auf-
tretens in deutschen bergwerken. Unter mitwirkung von dr.
Löbker ... und dr. Hayo Bruns ... bearbeitet im Kaiserlichen
gesundheitsamt ... Berlin, J. Springer, 1906.
　　vi, 102 p. 27ᶜᵐ.
"Sonderabdruck aus 'Arbeiten aus dem Kaiserlichen gesundheitsamte,'
band XXIII, heft 2."

　　1. Hookworm disease.　　I. Bruns, Hayo. II. Germany. Reichsge-
sundheitsamt.

Library of Congress　　　RC248.L6　　　　7-19822

NL 0441668　　DLC

Löbker (Karl) [1854-]. * Ueber die mechanischen Verletzungen des Augapfels. 37 pp. 8°.
Greifswald. C. Sell, 1877.

NL 0441669　　DNLM

Loebl, Alfred Hugo Christoph, 1875-
　　Eine ausserordentliche Reichshilfe und ihre Ergebnisse in reich-
tagsloser Zeit. (2), 128 pp.
　　(In Kaiserliche Akademie der Wissenschaften. Vienna. Philosophisch-historische Classe. Sitzungsberichte. Band 153, Abh.
2. Wien. 1906.)
Refers to the Turkish invasions of 1592-1593 and the assistance the members of the German Empire rendered the emperor, Rudolf II., at Vienna.

H3891 — Turks in Europe. — Germany. Hist. Rudolf II., 1576-1612.

NL 0441670　　MB MU RPB

VOLUME 338

Loebl, Alfred Hugo Christoph, 1875–
Der Sieg des Fürstenrechtes auch auf dem Gebiete der Finanzen—vor dem dreissigjährigen Kriege. München, Duncker & Humblot, 1916.

vii, 134 p. 23 cm. (Staats- und sozialwissenschaftliche Forschungen, Heft 187)

1. Holy Roman Empire—Constitutional history. 2. Finance—Holy Roman Empire—Hist. (Series)
HB41.S7 Heft 187   17–5978 rev*

NL 0441671   DLC CU ICJ MB PU

Loebl, Alfred Hugo Christoph, 1875–
Zur Geschichte des Türkenkrieges von 1593–1606. Prag, Rohlíček und Sievers, 1899–1904.

2 v. 22 cm. (Prager Studien aus dem Gebiete der Geschichtswissenschaft, Heft 6, 10)
L. C. copy incomplete : v. 2 wanting.
Bibliographical footnotes.
CONTENTS.—1. Vorgeschichte.—2. Oesterreichs innere Zustände. Das zweite Kriegsjahr. Die Hilfsaktion.

1. Turkey—Hist.—1453–1683. (Series)
DR521.L6   49–44661*

NL 0441672   DLC CaBVaU ICU MH

Löbl, Desider, ed.
Budapest pusztulása
see under title

D810
.D6M8

Löbl, Desider.
The Mutilated Budapest. [Budapest] Officina press [1946]

Löbl, Eduard, tr.

Szentesy, Béla.
Die geistige ueberanstrengung des kindes (von einer noch nicht besprochenen seite dargestellt) ... Von Béla Szentesy. Uebers. von dr. med. Eduard Löbl, dr. med. Heinrich Ehrenhaft. Budapest, Pester buchdruckerei aktien-gesellschaft, 1898.

Löbl, Elmar, 1927–
Der Grundverkehr in der Reichsstadt Regensburg und sein Recht. Regensburg, 1952.

vii, 92 l. 30 cm.
Typescript (carbon)
Inaug.-Diss.—Munich.
Vita.
Bibliography : leaves iv–vii.

1. Real property—Ratisbon. 2. Land titles—Registration and transfer—Ratisbon.
    55–17332

NL 0441676   DLC

Löbl, Emil, 1863–1942.
Kultur und presse. Von dr. Emil Löbl. Leipzig, Duncker & Humblot, 1903.
1 p. l., [v]–viii, 291 p. 21 cm.

CONTENTS.—Die zeitung.—Die journalistik.—Presse und gesellschaft.—Presse und staatsgewalt.

1. Journalism. I. Title.

NL 0441677   ViU DLC-P4 PPG NN MH

Löbl, Emil, 1863–
Kultura i prasa. Spolszczone staraniem Kółka Dziennikarskiego we Lwowie. Pod red. i z przedm. Stefana Gorskiego. Warszawa, Gebethner i Wolff, 1905.

155 p. 18 cm. (Biblioteka Tygodnika Illustrowanego, nr. 20)

1. Journalism. 2. Press. I. Title.

PN4731.L5817   52–52249

NL 0441678   DLC IEdS OC1 MB

Löbl, Emil, 1863–
... Kultura ir spauda, lietuvių kalbon išvertė Vaidevutis ... Chicago, Ill., Spauda "Lietuvos," 1912.

152, [1] p. 19 cm.
At head of title: Dr. Emil Loeb [!]

1. Journalism. I. Vaidevutis, ———, tr.   42–26858
Library of Congress   PN4731.L58
    070.1

NL 0441679   DLC

G
569
.517

LÖBL, EMIL, 1863–1942.
Verlorenes paradies, erinnerungen eines alten Wieners. Illustriert von Theo. Zasche und Emil Hübl. Wien, Rikola verlag, 1924.
212p. 19cm. (Die gute, alte zeit)

NL 0441680   ICN WaSp NN OC1

Loebl, Ernst Moshe, 1923–
A cellular method applied to carbon compounds. New York, 1952.
78 l. diagrs., tables. 29cm.

Thesis, Columbia university.
Typescript.
Bibliographical footnotes.

NL 0441681   NNC

Loebl, Ernest Moshe, 1923–
A cellular method applied to carbon compounds. Ann Arbor, University Microfilms [1954]
([University Microfilms, Ann Arbor, Mich.] Publication no. 8720)

Microfilm of typescript.
Collation of the original: 78 l. diagrs., tables.
Thesis—Columbia University.
Abstracted in Dissertation abstracts, v. 14 (1954) no. 9, p. 1310.
Vita.
Bibliographical footnotes.

1. Carbon compounds. I. Title.
Microfilm AC–1 no. 8720   Mic A 55–3367 rev

Columbia Univ.   Libraries
for Library of Congress   [r68b2]†

NL 0441682   NNC DLC

Loebl (Gustav). *De aneurysmate cordis sic dicto partiali. 2 p. l., 9–29 pp., 1 l., 3 pl. 4°.
Vindobonæ V. A. Strauss [1840]

NL 0441683   DNLM

Löbl, Moriz
Edna; trauerspiel in fünf aufzügen. Wien, Genossenschafts-buchdruckerei, 1875. 94 p.

NL 0441684   OC1W

Löbl, Ödön Landy–
see Landy-Löbl, Ödön.

Löbl, Oskar.
Erdung, Nullung und Schutzschaltung, nebst Erläuterungen zu den Erdungsleitsätzen, von Dr.-Ing. Oskar Löbl. Mit 78 Textabbildungen. Berlin: J. Springer, 1933. vii, 111 p. incl. diagrs., tables. illus. 23½cm.

664023A. 1. Electricity—Currents—Grounding. 2. Electricity—Safety appliances.
N. Y. P. L.   August 31, 1933

NL 0441686   NN MdBJ PPF DNAL

Löbl, Oskar, and N. Hammerl.
Spannungsregelung mit Gleittransformatoren, von Dr.-Ing. O. Löbl ... und N. Hammerl ... mit 40 Textabbildungen. Berlin: J. Springer, 1933. 20 p. incl. diagrs. illus. (incl. charts.) 21cm.

842967A. 1. Electricity—Regulators, 1933. 2. Electricity—Transformer, 1933. I. Hammerl, N., jt. au.
N. Y. P. L.   September 15, 1936

NL 0441687   NN

Löbl, Paul, 1905–
... Carcinom-Metastasen der Iris ... Würzburg, 1928.
Inaug.-Diss. - Würzburg.
Lebenslauf.
"Literatur": p. 7.

NL 0441688   CtY

Löbl, Robert.
Dolomiten; ein Bildwerk. Mit einer Einführung von Heinrich Klier; Text-Illustrationen von Hans Lang. Innsbruck, Verlag der Tiroler Graphik [1955?]

24 p. 84 plates (part col.) col. map (on lining paper) 28 cm.
Label mounted on t. p. has imprint: New York, W. S. Heinman.
Part of the introduction also given in English, French and Italian.

1. Dolomite Alps—Descr. & trav.—Views. I. Klier, Heinrich, 1926– ed.
DB465.L64   914.53   55–14725

NL 0441689   DLC PP NN MB

Löbl, Robert.
Karwendel, schönstes Naturschutzgebiet der Kalkalpen; ein Bildwerk, mit einer Einführung von Heinrich Klier. [Gekürzte Übersetzung ins Englische von Karl Heller-Merricks] Innsbruck, Verlag der Tiroler Graphik [1953]

22 p. illus. 28 cm.

1. Karwendelgebirge—Descr. & trav.—Views. I. Title.
DD801.B457L58   56–28665 †

NL 0441690   DLC NN

LÖBL, ROBERT.
Mittenwald; ein Bildband. Text: L. Koegel. Mittenwald-Karwendel, A. Nemayer [1955] 8,[32]p. of illus. 25cm.

1. Karwendel mountains --Views. I. Koegel, Ludwig, 1886–

NL 0441691   NN

LÖBL, ROBERT.
Salzkammergut; ein Bildwerk. Mit einer Einführung von Heinrich Klier. Text-Illus. von H. Zum Tobel. Innsbruck, Verlag der Tiroler Graphik [195–] xxv p., 80 p. of illus. col. plates. map (on lining papers) 27cm.

Summaries in English, French, and Italian; captions in German, English, French and Italian.

1. Salzkammergut, Austria—Views. I. Klier, Heinrich.

NL 0441692   NN

VOLUME 338

Löbl, Robert.
Tirol; ein Bildwerk, mit einer Einführung von Heinrich Klier. Text-Illustrationen von Hans Lang. Innsbruck, Verlag der Tiroler Graphik [1954]

25 p. illus. 84 plates (part col.) maps (on lining paper) 28 cm.

Introduction (abridged) also in English, French and Italian.
Bibliography : p. 17.

1. Tyrol—Descr. & trav.—Views.   I. Klier, Heinrich Emil.

DB769.L6   56–33747

NL 0441693   DLC N NN KyU MiDW

LÖBL, ROBERT.
Winterland Tirol; ein Bildwerk. Mit einer Einführung von Heinrich Klier. Text-Illus. von Viktor Herzner. Innsbruck. Verlag der Tiroler Graphik [1955?] xxii p., 80 plates.   illus., map (on lining papers) 27cm.

Text and picture captions in German, English, French and Italian.
1. Tyrol—Views. 2. Ski-running—Alps.

NL 0441694   NN

Loebl (Wolfgangius). *De compressione et transmissione qua hæmostaticis. 23 pp., 1 l. 8°. *Vindobonæ*, J. de Hirschfeld, 1841.

NL 0441695   DNLM

Loeblein, Fritz, 1901–
Zur Kenntnis der keramischen Eigenschaften von Kalk-Tonerde-Silikaten und anderen feuerfesten und hochfeuerfesten Materialien.
Inaug. diss., Darmstadt, Techn. Hoch., 1929.
Bibl.

NL 0441696   ICRL

1881–
Löblein, Theodor, Medizinalprakt. a Staffelstein: Die Erfolge der vaginalen Totalexstirpation bei Prolaps des Uterus und der Scheide. Nürnberg 1910: Hilz. 30 S. 8°
Erlangen, Med. Diss. v. 26. März 1910, Ref. Jung
[Geb. 13. Nov. 81 Großdechsendorf; Wohnort: Burgwindheim; Staatsangeh.: Bayern; Vorbildung: Gymn. Münnerstadt Reife Juli 02; Studium: München 2, Erlangen 8 S.; Coll. 27. Jan. 10; Approb. 8. Jan. 10.]   [U 10.811]

NL 0441697   ICRL DNLM NIC

Loeblenz, William.
It's the garden the rose and you. Words & music by Gus Proppe [and] Wm. Loeblenz. New York, T. G. Heberlein & co. [c1913]

First line: It was one night in June.
Chorus: When the rose was there.

1. Gardens. 2. Roses. I. Proppe, Gus. II. Song index (3).
N.Y.P.L.   May 26, 1949
Printed for the Music Division

NL 0441698   NN

Loebler, Peter, 1912–
Versuche zur Darstellung von Nitro-hydrazino-säuren, ein Beitrag zur Kenntnis der Nitro-fettsäuren ... Köln, 1938.
Inaug.-Diss. – Köln.
Lebenslauf.
Text reproduced from typewritten copy.

NL 0441699   CtY

Loeblich, Alfred.
Ueber gesammt-(correal-) hypotheken.
Inaug. diss. Leipzig, 1901.
Bibl.

NL 0441700   ICRL

Loeblich, Alfred Richard, 1914–
Bryozoa from the Ordovician Bromide formation, Oklahoma. Chicago, 1941.

53 l. mounted illus. 31 cm.

Typescript (carbon copy)
Thesis—University of Chicago.
Bibliography : leaves 52–53.

1. Polyzoa, Fossil. 2. Paleontology—Ordovician. 3. Paleontology—Oklahoma. I. Title: Bromide formation, Oklahoma.

QE798.L6 1941   62–56211

NL 0441701   DLC

Loeblich, Alfred Richard, 1914–
... *Bryozoa* from the Ordovician Bromide formation, Oklahoma ... by Alfred R. Loeblich, jr. ... [n. p., 1942]

1 p. l., 413–436 p. pl. 61–64 on 2 l. 24ᶜᵐ.

Thesis (PH. D.)—University of Chicago, 1941.
"Reprinted from Journal of paleontology, vol. 16, July, 1942."
"References" : p. 435–436.

1. Polyzoa, Fossil. 2. Paleontology—Ordovician. 3. Paleontology—Oklahoma. I. Title: Bromide formation, Oklahoma.   A 42–5376

Chicago. Univ. Library
for Library of Chicago   QE798.L6
                                                   [2]†

NL 0441702   ICU DLC

Loeblich, Alfred Richard, 1914–
The foraminiferal genus *Halyphysema* and two new tropical Pacific species.
(*In* U. S. National Museum. Proceedings. Washington. 24 cm.
v. 107 (1959) p. 123–126. plate)

1. Halyphysema.

Q11.U55   vol. 107   60–4585

NL 0441703   DLC

Loeblich, Alfred Richard, 1914–
The foraminiferal genus *Triplasia* Reuss, 1854, by Alfred R. Loeblich, Jr. and Helen Tappan. Washington, Smithsonian Institution, 1952.
61 p. illus. 25 cm. (Smithsonian miscellaneous collections, v. 117, no. 15)
Publication 4094.
At head of title: Charles D. and Mary Vaux Walcott Research Fund.
"References" : p. 49–52.
1. Triplasia.   I. Tappan, Helen, 1917–   joint author. (Series : Smithsonian Institution. Smithsonian miscellaneous collections, v. 117, no. 15)
Q11.S7   vol. 117, no. 15   563.12   52–61795
——— Copy 2.   QE772.L58

NL 0441704   DLC MtBuM WaWW NBuU FU TxU NN ViU OCU NNC

Loeblich, Alfred Richard, 1914–
A revision of some glanduline Nodosariidae (Foraminifera) by Alfred R. Loeblich, Jr., and Helen Tappan. Washington, Smithsonian Institution, 1955.
9 p. plate. 25 cm. (Smithsonian miscellaneous collections, v. 126, no. 3)
Publication 4189.
At head of title: Charles D. and Mary Vaux Walcott Research Fund.
Bibliography : p. 8–9.
1. Nodosariidae.   I. Tappan, Helen, 1917–   joint author. II. Title. (Series : Smithsonian Institution. Smithsonian miscellaneous collections, v. 126, no. 3)
Q11.S7   vol. 126, no. 3   55–60380
——— Copy 2.   QE772.L59

NL 0441705   DLC NBuU FU OO OCU TxU ViU

Loeblich, Alfred Richard, 1914–
Revision of some recent foraminiferal genera, by Alfred R. Loeblich, Jr., and Helen Tappan. Washington, Smithsonian Institute, 1955.
37 p. illus. 25 cm. (Smithsonian miscellaneous collections, v. 128, no. 5)
Smithsonian Institution. Publication 4214.
At head of title: Charles D. and Mary Vaux Walcott Research Fund.
Bibliography : p. 29–32.
1. Foraminifera.   I. Tappan, Helen, 1917–   joint author. (Series : Smithsonian Institution. Smithsonian miscellaneous collections, v. 128, no. 5)
Q11.S7   vol. 128, no. 5   55–61719
——— Copy 2.   QL368.F6L62

NL 0441706   DLC WaWW NBuU FU OO OCU TxU ViU PU-BZ

Loeblich, Alfred Richard, 1914–
... Some palmate *Lagenidæ* from the lower Cretaceous Washita group, by Alfred R. Loeblich and Helen Tappan ... Ithaca, N. Y., Paleontological research institution, 1941.

30 p. 3 pl. 25½ cm. (Bulletins of American paleontology, vol. XXVI, no. 99)

Descriptive letterpress on versos facing the plates.

1. Foraminifera, Fossil. 2. Paleontology—Cretaceous. I. Loeblich, Helen (Tappan) joint author. II. Title : Palmate Lagenidæ from the lower Cretaceous Washita group.

                                                   G S 41—101

U. S. Geol. Survey. Libr.
for Library of Congress   [..65e‡]

NL 0441707   DI-GS MoU MU FMU CU OU OO

Loeblich, Alfred Richard, 1914–
Studies of Arctic foraminifera, by Alfred R. Loeblich, Jr. and Helen Tappan. Washington, Smithsonian Institution, 1953.
iv, 150 p. illus. 25 cm. (Smithsonian miscellaneous collections, v. 121, no. 7)
Publication 4105.
At head of title: Charles D. and Mary Vaux Walcott Research Fund.
Bibliography : p. 122–126.
1. Foraminifera—Arctic regions.   I. Tappan, Helen, 1917–   joint author. (Series : Smithsonian Institution. Smithsonian miscellaneous collections, v. 121, no. 7)
Q11.S7   vol. 121, no. 7   593.12   53–60622
——— Copy 2.   QL368.F6L64

                MU NBuU
NL 0441708   DLC CaBVa WaWW OCU OO NNC PP TxU MoU FU

Löblich, Kurt, 1906–
... Über Vestibularisschädigung durch chronische Lärmeinwirkung ... [Berlin, 1932]
Inaug.-Diss. – Berlin.
Lebenslauf.
"Literatur" : p. [18].

NL 0441709   CtY

Löblich, Rudolf
... Rechtschreibung im graphischen gewerbe, stufen 1a und 1b (12 übungsabende) von Rudolf Löblich ... Berlin-Zehlendorf
                                                   40
(Lehrgemeinschaft)

NL 0441710   NN NcU CtY WU MH CU IEN NNC ICU

Pamph.
v. 596
LOEBLICHE Bruederschafft der Sterbenden und Abgestorbenen, unter dem Titul: der Todes-Angst Jesu Christi am Creutze, sammt dero Regeln, Ablass und Andachten in der koeniglichen Capelle der koeniglichen und churfuerstlichen Residentz--Stadt Dressden aufgerichtet, und mit Vemehrung andaechtiger Übungen um ein glueckseliges Sterbe-Stuendelein besser eingerichtet. Gedruckt zu Prag, in der Clementinischer Buchdruckerey [1729?] [32]p. 16cm.

NL 0441711   MH-AH

Eyn löbliche hystory von der demütigen und gehorsamen fraw Griselde die frawen zu gedult und gehorsamkait gegen iren egemahelnziehende
   see under   Griselda.

Löblin, Georg, respondent.
... De nobilitate speciatim franconica ...
   see under   Kirchmaier, Theodor, fl. 1659–1677, praeses.

Loeblin (Ignatius). *De hydrocele. 44 pp. 12°. *Vindobonæ*, A. de Haykul, 1829. [P., v. 2240.]

NL 0441714   DNLM

VOLUME 338

Löblovits, Bernát.

דיבובי חן. ביאורים ופירושים על פסוקי חמשה חומשי תורה
ודרשות הכו"ל. ונמפחו עליהם נצרים מחדושי הלכות. קונםם־
"מיקלאש. בדפום יצחק יהודה שווארץ. תרצ"ג.

Kunszentmiklós, 1933
vii, 855 p. 26 cm.

1. Sermons, Jewish. 2. Sermons, Hebrew. 3. Talmud—Commentaries.   i. Title.   *Title transliterated:* Dibuve ben.

A 52-10581

New York. Public Libr.

NL 0441715   NN

Loeblowitz-Lennard, Henry.
,..The Jew as symbol, by Henry Loeblowitz-Lennard
(New York). [Albany, N.Y.] 1947. p. 34-38.
23cm.

Caption-title.
At head of title: ⟨Reprinted from The Psychoanalytic
quarterly, vol. xvi, no. 1, January, 1947⟩
"References," p. 37-38.
1. Jews—Anti-Semitism. 2. Anti-Semitism.

NL 0441716   NN

Löbmann, Hugo, 1864–
Die "Gesangbildungslehre" nach Pestalozzischen
grundsätzen von Michael Traugott Pfeiffer und Hans
Georg Nägeli in ihrem zusammenhange mit der aesthetik,
der geschichte der pädagogik und der musik. Ein beitrag zur geschichte der musik-pädagogik. Mit einem bildnis Nägelis ... Leipzig ,etc., Druck der Germania, 1908.
94 p., 1 l. incl. front. (port.) 22ᶜᵐ.
Inaug.-diss.—Leipzig.
Lebenslauf.
"Verzeichnis der quellen": p. 93-94.
1. Singing and voice culture. 2. Pestalozzi, Johann Heinrich, 1746-1827.
3. Nägeli, Hans Georg, 1773-1836. Gesangbildungslehre. 4. Pfeiffer, Michael Traugott, 1771-1849.

10-12467
Library of Congress   MT920.L72

NL 0441717   DLC CtY NN PU

Löbmann, Hugo, 1864–
Das glocken-ideal; gedanken und ratschläge, von dr. Hugo
Löbmann. Berlin, Verlag der Germania a.-g., 1928.
4 p. l., 118, ,3, p. 20½ᶜᵐ.

1. Bells.   i. Title.
Library of Congress   ML1040.L6

29-13560

NL 0441718   DLC

Löbmann, Hugo, 1864–   *ed.*
Liederbuch für katholische schulen, von Hugo Löbmann ...
Leipzig, X. Pflugmacher ,1896–
v. 20½ᶜᵐ.

For two children's voices, unaccompanied.
CONTENTS.—I. Unterstufe.

1. School song-books.   i. Title.
Library of Congress   M1994.L822L5

44-14721

NL 0441719   DLC

Löbmann, Hugo, 1864 –
Pflegt das deutsche kirchenlied! Mit einem anhang Vom
schönen singen. Von dr. Hugo Löbmann. Wien, Verlagsanstalt Tyrolia a. g., abteilung Seelsorger-verlag ,1937,
78 p., 1 l. 23ᶜᵐ.

1. Church music—Catholic church. 2. Choral. 3. Singing and voice
culture.   i. Title.

39-34040
Library of Congress   ML3129.L68P5
,2,   [784.93]   783.282

NL 0441720   DLC

Löbmann, Hugo, 1864–
Der schulgesang; eine gesanglehre für schulen aller art
unter berücksichtigung einfacherer schulverhältnisse,
von dr. Hugo Löbmann ... 2. verm. und verb. aufl. Leipzig, Dürr, 1923.
245 p. illus. (music) 23½ᶜᵐ. (*Half-title:* Lebensvoller unterricht; eine
sammlung von handbüchern für den unterricht ... bd. 3)

1. Singing and voice culture. 2. Music—Instruction and study.   i. Title.

24-29730
Library of Congress   MT935.L65

NL 0441721   DLC

Löbmann, Hugo, 1864–
Über glockentöne, zugleich ratschläge für den glocken-
kauf, von dr. Hugo Löbmann ... Leipzig, Breitkopf &
Härtel, 1915.
59 p. 23½ᶜᵐ.

1. Bells.
Library of Congress   TS585.L7

15-24720

NL 0441722   DLC

Löbmann, Hugo, 1864–
Volkslied und musikalische volkserziehung; ein um-
und ausblick, von dr. Hugo Löbmann. Leipzig, R.
Voigtländer ,1916,
3 p. l., 149 p. 20ᶜᵐ.
Cover imprint: Leipzig, Dürr.

1. Folk-songs, German—Hist. & crit. 2. Music—Instruction and study—
Germany.   i. Title.

21-20024
Library of Congress   ML3645.L62

NL 0441723   DLC IU

Löbmann, Hugo, 1864–
Zur geschichte des taktierens und dirigierens, von dr.
Hugo Löbmann. Düsseldorf, L. Schwann, 1913.
2 p. l., 104 p. 17½ᶜᵐ.

1. Conducting (Music)

14-11221
Library of Congress   ML457.L8

NL 0441724   DLC CtY MH MiU

Loebmann, Joseph.
Omnia ad majorem Dei gloriam. [Messe, T. T. B. avec accomp.
d'orgue.]
Paris. Schott. 1868. (1), 26 pp. [Concours international de
musique religieuse. Août 1868. 2e prix.] F°.

April 11,   1902.
E3686 — T.r. — S.r. — Masses.

NL 0441725   MB

Loebmann, Salo, 1904–
Die mechanische koagulation des goethitsols.
Inaug. diss. Berlin, 1929 (Dresden).
Bibl.

NL 0441726   ICRL OU CtY

M/0420   **Löbner, Alfred.**
L825h
         Horizontale und vertikale Staubverteilung in
         einer Grossstadt. Leipzig. 1935.
         p.53-99. 10 pls. 24cm.

(Veröffentlichungen des Geophysikalischen Inst.
der Univ. Leipzig. Zweite Serie, Spezialarbeiten
Bd.7, H.2.)

NL 0441727   DAS CtY ICRL

M/0420   **Löbner, Alfred.**
L825
         Vergleichende Untersuchungen über den Staubge-
halt der Grossstadtluft im Winter und Sommer.
Berlin. 1937.
         p.181-200. plate, maps, tabs. 23½cm.

(From Kleine Mitteilungen. 13. Jahrgang. Nr.6/8.
Juni/August 1937.)

NL 0441728   DAS

Loebner (Antonius) [1890–]. *De prosopal-
gia.* 31 pp. 8°. *Berolini, G. Schade,* [1846].

NL 0441729   DNLM

WAA   **LÖBNER, Arthur**
L825g   Die Gesetzgebung des alten und des
1878   neuen Deutschen Reichs wider Verfäl-
         schung der Nahrungsmittel. Mit einem
         Anhange, enthaltend die wichtigeren
         ausländischen Gesetze. Berlin,
         Heymann, 1878.
         119 p.

NL 0441730   DNLM

Löbner, Arthur.
***** Königlich sächsisches Gesetz über die Landes-Brandversicherungs-
anstalt vom 9. Juli 1910. Einführung in das Gesetz unter Berücksichtigung der Ausführungsverordnung dazu und der Dienst-
anweisung. Von Landtagsabgeordinetem Hofrat Dr. jur. Arthur
Löbner, ... Leipzig, J. Wörner, 1911.
vii, 185 p. 23½ᶜᵐ.

NL 0441731   ICJ

TS1547   **Löbner, C   Heinrich**
I   Studien und Forschungen über Wolle und andere Gespinnst-
         fasern ... mit einem Atlas von 30 Kunstdrucktafeln ... direkt
         nach Mikroskop. Grünberg, Löbner [1898]
         304 columns. illus. , 30 plates. 27x37cm.

1. Wool.

NL 0441732   CU

Loebner, Charlotte (Wreschner) 1870– : Aus d. med. Univer-
sitätspolikl. zu Tübingen. Untersuchungen über das Blut-
serum bei Carcinom. Leipzig: Vogel 1918. 37 S. 8°
¶ Aus: Deutsches Archiv f. klin. Med. Bd 127.
Tübingen, Med. Diss. v. 21. Aug. 1918, Ref. Naegeli
[Geb. 30. April 90 Berlin; Wohnort: Tübingen; Staatsangeh.: Preußen; Vor-
bildung: Luisenstädt. RG. Berlin Reife 10; Studium: Tübingen 3. Bonn 2,
Berlin 2, Jena 2, Breslau 2, Tübingen 5 S.; Coll. 19.Okt.17; Approb. 15.Aug.17]
[Ü 18. 1262]

NL 0441733   ICRL DNLM CtY

Loebner (Fridericus Arminius). *Nonnulla de
nervi oculomotorii paralysi.* 25 pp. 8°. *Lipsiae, typ. E. Pahrii,* 1859.

NL 0441734   DNLM PPC

1885–
Loebner, Georg, Referendar: Der Schrankfachvertrag der
deutschen Banken nach seiner zivilrechtlichen Seite.
Liegnitz 1910: Seyffarth. x, 96 S. 8°
Leipzig, Jur. Diss. v. 13. April 1910
[Geb. 11. März 85 Saarau; Wohnort: Berlin; Staatsangeh.: Preußen; Vor-
bildung: Ritterakad. Liegnitz Reife O. 03; Studium: Tübingen 1, Breslau 1,
Kiel 1, Breslau 3 S.; Rig. 19. Juli 06.]   [Ü 10. 2787]

NL 0441735   ICRL

Löbner, Georg Julius Willy
   see **Löbner, Willy,** 1862–

VOLUME 338

Löbner, Heinrich.
Die Hochzeit: deutsches Gedicht des 12. Jahrh.
Brandenburg a. H., 1887.
2 l., 44 p., 2 l.
Inaug.-Diss. - Berlin
I. Die Hochzeit (Middle High German poem)

NL 0441737   MWelC CU ICRL CtY

4PT   Löbner, Heinrich.
Ger.-   Wintersonnenwende; Erzählung aus den
1854.   Kämpfen der Sachsen um Heimat und Glauben.
Mit Illustrationen von Hans Looschen.
Schutzumschlag und Einband von Max Wulff.
Berlin, Meidinger's Jugendschriften Verlag.
207 p.

NL 0441738   DLC-P4

HS   Löbner, Heinrich.
390   Ein Wort zur Erklärung über die
G37L82   Geschichte, die Entwicklung, die Ziele und
1913   Zwecke des Vereins deutscher Freimaurer.
₍Königsberg?₎ Herausgegeben vom Verein
deutscher Freimaurer, 1913.
16 p. 20cm.
"Ansprache auf der 2. ostpreussischen
Bezirksversammlung des Vereins
deutscher Freimaurer in Königsberg am
30. März 1913."
"Sondera   bdruck aus dem
Wochenbla   tt für Freimaurer "Der
Herold."

NL 0441739   NIC

1892-
Loebner, Hermann, Arzt: Ist das Rosenbach-Semon'sche
Gesetz durch die in der Literatur vorhandenen Fälle be-
wiesen. Aus d. Universitätskl. f. Ohren-, Nasen-, Hals-
krankh. zu Breslau. [In Maschinenschrift.] 33 S., 4 Bl.
Tab. 4⁰(2⁰). — Auszug: Breslau 1921: Breslauer Genossensch.-
Buchdr. 2 Bl. 8⁰
Breslau, Med. Diss. v. 8. Juli 1921, Ref. Hinsberg
[Geb. 24. Juli 92 Bunzlau; Wohnort: Bunzlau; Staatsangeh.: Preußen; Vor-
bildung: Haupt-Kadettenanst. Groß-Lichterfelde Reife 12; Studium: Breslau 2,
Heidelberg 1, Breslau 3, Tübingen 1, Breslau 3 S.; Coll. 30. April 20; Approb.
30. Mai 21.]   [U 21. 3003

NL 0441740   ICRL

Loebner, M. H.
Unyamwesi und Tabora, Deutsch-Ostafrika; Land, Volk und
Missionsarbeit, von M. H. Löbner... Herrnhut: Missionsbuch-
handlung, 1914. 24 p. illus. 8⁰.

1. Unyamwezi, Africa. 2. Tabora,   Africa. 3. Missions (Foreign).
Africa (East), German: Unyamwezi.
N. Y. P. L.   September 28, 19—

NL 0441741   NN

Löbner, Max.
Lehrbuch des Gartenbaues unter besonderer Berücksichtigung
schweizerischer Verhältnisse von Max Löbner, ... Mit 43 Abbildungen. Zürich, C. Schmidt, 1905.
viii, 174 p. 43 illus. 23½cm.

NL 0441742   ICJ

Löbner, Max.
Leitfaden für gärtnerische pflanzenzüchtung. Von
Max Löbner ... Jena, G. Fischer, 1909.
vii, 160 p. illus. (partly col.) 21½cm.

1. Plant breeding.
Agr 11-131

Library, U. S. Dept. of   Agriculture 90L82

NL 0441743   DNAL MBH OU ICJ

Loebner, Max
Der zwerg-obstbaum und seine pflege. Eine
anleitung für gartenfreunde und obstzüchter.
Berlin, Schmidt, 1899.
128 p.

NL 0441744   CU-A

Löbner, Max.
Der zwerg-obstbaum.   Berlin, 1916.

NL 0441745   NjR

Löbner, Otto
Die Karbonisation der Wolle, Gewebe, Lumpen
etc. und die Kunstwoll-Fabrikation. Grünberg i
Schl., F. Weiss Nachf., 1891.
509p. illus.

NL 0441746   ICRL

QD411   Loebner, Paul.
.L82   Ueber das tertiaere phosphin, arsin und
stibin des mesitylens und einige derivate
derselben.
Rostock, 1893.
40p.
Inaug. diss. Rostock.

NL 0441747   DLC

1886 –
Löbner, Ulrich, Arzt: Beobachtungen und Erfahrungen bei
einer vom Ausland eingeschleppten Kruse-Ruhrbazillen-
Epidemie. Aus d. Med. Universitätskl. zu Halle. Herzberg
(Elster) (1918): Schirrmeister. 39 S. 8⁰
Halle, Med. Diss. v. 25. Jan. 1919 [1920], Ref. Schmidt
[Geb. 5. April 86 Herzberg a. d. Elster; Wohnort: Halle a. S.; Staatsangeh.:
Preußen; Vorbildung: G. Eisleben Reife 08; Studium: Erlangen 5, Berlin 1,
Halle 4 S.; Coll. 7. März 18; Approb. 7. Aug. 14.]   U 20. 2244

NL 0441748   ICRL CtY DNLM MiU

Löbner, Walther, 1902-
Ausbilder- und prüferfibel, ein leitfaden für die ausbilder in
den betrieben und für die prüfer bei den industriefacharbeiter-
und gehilfenprüfungen von prof. dr. Walther Löbner. Berlin
₍etc.₎, O. Elsner verlagsgesellschaft, 1943.
98 p. 21ᶜᵐ.

1. Employees, Training of.   i. Title.
46-19120
Library of Congress   T58.L56
₍2₎   658.386

NL 0441749 °   DLC CtY InLP NN

Loebner, Walther, 1902-
Die finanziellen Auswirkungen der Reichswasserstrassenpo-
litik von 1918–1930, von Dr. Walther Löbner. Leipzig: Akademische Verlagsgesellschaft m.b.H., 1931.   140 p. incl. diagrs.,
tables. 4⁰.   (Beiträge zur Finanzkunde. Bd. 6.)
Bibliography, p. 138-140.

1. Waterways—Finance—Germany.   I. Ser.
N. Y. P. L.   January 12, 1932

NL 0441750   NN DLC-P4 ICRL CtY NNC PU

HF1007   Löbner, Walther, 1902-   ed.
.F5   **Findeisen, C   F**
1950   ... Grundriss der Betriebswirtschaft, als Grundriss der
Handelswissenschaft 1875 von C. F. Findeisen begründet
und fortgeführt seit der 11. Aufl. von H. Grossmann. Neu
bearb. von Walther Löbner. 28. neubearb. Aufl. Bad Homburg vor der Höhe, M. Gehlen, 1950.

HF1007   Löbner, Walther, 1902-
.F5   **Findeisen, C   F**
1943   ... Grundriss der handelswissenschaft, begründet von prof.
E. ₍,₎ F. Findeisen 1875, fortgeführt seit der 11. aufl. 1914 und
als wirtschaftslehre des kaufmännischen unternehmens bearbeitet von prof. der betriebswirtschaftslehre dr. Hermann
Grossmann ... und prof. der wirtschaftspädagogik dipl.-hdl.
dr. Walther Löbner ... 26., durchgesehene aufl. Leipzig, Berlin, M. Gehlen. 1943.

HF1007   Löbner, Walther, 1902-   ed.
.F5   **Findeisen, C   F**
1944   ... Leitfaden der handelswissenschaft, die lehre von der
kaufmännischen unternehmung, begründet von professor dr.
C. F. Findeisen 1876, bearbeitet von dipl.-hdl. dr. Hermann
Grossmann ... und dipl.-hdl. dr. Walther Löbner ... 36. unveränderte aufl. Leipzig/Berlin, M. Gehlen, 1944.

4T-   Löbner, Walther, 1902-
6   Wirtschaft und Erziehung.   Langensalza, J.
Beltz, 1935.
135 p.

NL 0441754   DLC-P4

Löbner, Willy, 1862-
... Über Hautableitung bei Erkrankungen der
Hirnhäute ...   Kiel, 1889.
Inaug.-Diss. - Kiel.
Lebenslauf.
"Nachweis über die benutzte Litteratur":
p. [29]
[Full name: Georg Julius Willy Löbner]

NL 0441755   CtY MH DNLM

Löbners Fach-Adressbücher: Textil- und Bekleidungsin-
dustrie, Westdeutschland und Berlin.

M. Gladbach.
v. 31 cm. irregular.

1. Textile industry and fabrics—Germany—Direct. 2. Clothing
trade—Germany—Direct.
TS1312.L64   54-35453 ‡

NL 0441756   DLC

Löbsack, Georg.
... Einsam kämpft das Wolgaland; ein bericht aus 7 jahren
krieg und revolution. Mit 6 bildern und 3 karten. Leipzig,
R. Voigtländer ₍1936₎.
403, ₍1₎ p. front. illus. (incl. maps) 19½ᶜᵐ.

1. Germans in Russia. 2. European war, 1914–1918—Russia. 3. Russia—Hist.—Revolution, 1917-   i. Title.
37-15625
Library of Congress   DK43.L57
Copyright A—Foreign   35541
₍2₎   325.24309473

NL 0441757   DLC IU IaU MH ICU WaU CtY NN ICRL

551.51   Löbsack, Theo, 1923-
L825axR   Earth's envelope; translated from the
German by E. L. & D. Rewald.   London,
Collins, 1859.
256p. illus., plates, maps, tables, diagrs.
22cm.

Originally published as Der Atem der Erde.
Includes bibliography.

1. Atmosphere. 2. Meteorology.

NL 0441758   NcU

VOLUME 338

Löbsack, Theo, 1923–
Zwei auf Unterwasserjagd; zwischen Tangwäldern und Muschelbänken. Reutlingen, Ensslin & Laiblin [1953]
79 p. illus. 19 cm. (Kleine Ensslin-Bücher, 30)

1. Spear fishing. i. Title.

SH458.L6   54–15245 ‡

NL 0441759   DLC

Löbsack, Wilhelm.
Albert Forster, Gauleiter und Reichsstatthalter im Reichsgau Danzig-Westpreussen. Danzig, Danziger Verlagsgesellschaft (P. Rosenberg) [1940]
72 p. illus. 19 cm.

1. Forster, Albert, 1902–

DD247.F6L62   54–53804 ‡

NL 0441760   DLC ICRL CaBVaU MH TU

Löbsack, Wilhelm.
... Albert Forster, gauleiter von Danzig; mit 36 bildern, vielen dokumenten und aufrufen. Hamburg, Hanseatische verlagsanstalt [°1934]
140 p. front., plates, ports., facsims., geneal. tab. 21½ᶜᵐ.

1. Forster, Albert, 1902–   2. Nationalsozialistische deutsche
                              arbeiter-partei.
Library of Congress   DD247.F6L6   35–5204
Copyright A—Foreign   26111
                             [2]   923.243

NL 0441761   DLC MiU IaU NN ICU CtY NcD MH

DK651
.R5D4

Löbsack, Wilhelm.
Das Deutsche Riga; Dokumente, mit 89 Abbildungen. Leipzig, S. Hirzel, 1942.

Löbsack, Wilhelm.
Gauleiter Albert Forster, der deutsche Angestelltenführer. Mit 36 Bildern, vielen Dokumenten und Aufrufen. Hamburg, Hanseatische Verlagsanstalt [°1934]
140 p. illus., ports., geneal. tab. 22 cm.
Cover title: Danzigs Gauleiter, Albert Forster.
"Sonderausgabe für die Deutsche Angestelltenschaft Berlin."

1. Forster, Albert, 1902–   2. Nationalsozialistische Deutsche Arbeiter-Partei.
DD247.F6L6 1934a   923.243   A F 48–2330*

Harvard Univ. Library
for Library of Congress   [1]†

NcD DLC
NL 0441763   MH CaBVaU FMU NN MoU WaU ICRL NNC MiU

Film
DD-1
reel 40,   Löbsack, Wilhelm, ed.
no. 1   FOR OTHER EDITIONS
            SEE MAIN ENTRY
Forster, Albert, 1902–
Das nationalsozialistische gewissen in Danzig; aus sechs jahren kampf für Hitler. Mit 64 abbildungen. Nach reden und niederschriften des gauleiters von Danzig Albert Forster bearbeitet und herausgegeben von Wilhelm Löbsack. Danzig, Verlag A. W. Kafemann [1936]

4HX
650

Löbsack, Wilhelm.
Schulungs-Unterlage Weltbolschewismus.
[31] Herausgeber, Der Reichsorganisationsleiter der NSDAP, Hauptschulungsamt [19   ]
16 p.

NL 0441765   DLC-P4

Löbsack, Wilhelm.
Von den Pflichten und Aufgaben des politischen Führers. [2. geänderte Aufl.]
[Danzig, Gedruckt bei A.W. Kafemann, 1940]
24 p. (Schriften der Adolf Hitler-Schule. Heft 4 a)

NL 0441766   DLC NNC CU

Löbsche,   von der.
Die Schwierigkeiten gangbarer Fehler und die Richtigkeit des Ausdrucks in der Deutschen Sprache. Praktischer Ratgeber in allen zweifelhaften Fällen mit besonderer Rücksicht auf den richtigen Gebrauch des Dativs und Akkusativs. Nebst Heranziehung u. Erklärung der gebräuchlichsten Fremdwörter, von Dr. von der Löbsche. Zweite, gänzlich umgearbeitete, verbesserte und vermehrte Auflage. Mülheim-Ruhr, J. Bagel, [1906].
[4]. 496 p. 20ᶜᵐ.

NL 0441767   ICJ

WZ
240
L825k
1575

[LÖBSCHÜTZ, Benjamin, d. 1582]
Kurtzer Bericht von der Hungerischen Kranckhait, unnd Kindts Blattern, auch Rot Ruer, dem gemainen Mann zu Nutz in Druck auszgangen, durch die wirdige medicam facultatem der hochlöblichen Universitet zu Wienn ... Wienn, Steffan Kreutzer, 1575.
[31] p. 20 cm.
"Der eigentliche Autor derselben war Professor praktikus Dr. Benjamin Löbschütz."—Tiberius von Györy, Morbus Hungaricus. Jena 1901 p. 111.
I. Vienna. Universität. Medizinische Fakultät II. Title

NL 0441768   DNLM

Löbschütz, Benjamin d. 1582. Oratio habita Viennæ publice in æde Divi Stephano quum Diomedi Cornario medicinæ licentiato insignia doctoralia in medicina conferret, die vigesima tertia, mensis Martii anno Domini, 1568. pp. 37–77. sm. 4°. [Lipsiæ, M. Lantzenberger], 1589. [P., v. 1629.]

NL 0441769   DNLM

Loebstein-Loebel, Eduard Ludwig
see Loebenstein-Loebel, Eduard Leopold, 1779–1819.

Loebus, Karl, 1891–
Ueber hemiplegie intra partum.
Inaug. diss. Leipzig, 1905
Bibl.

NL 0441771   ICRL DNLM CtY

Loèche-les-Bains, Valais, Switzerland.
Souvenir de Loèche-les-bains. Hôtels des Alpes et de Bellevue
see under title

Löchel, Gerhard
Die bedeutung geistiger funktionen in der wirtschaft ... von Gerhard Löchel ... Berlin, 1932.
59 p. 21ᶜᵐ.

Thesis, Würzburg.
Bibliography: p. 5–7.

1. Economics. 2. Sociology.

NL 0441773   NNC ICRL CtY PU

Die entwicklung des arbeitsvermittlungswesens in Mecklenburg-Schwerin bis zum inkrafttreten des gesetzes über arbeitsvermittlung und arbeitslosenversicherung am 1.Oktober 1927.
Inaug.-diss.Rostock. Berlin-Schmargendorf, W.Christian,1928.

Diagr.
"Literaturverzeichnis," pp.115–118.
"Lebenslauf," at end.

NL 0441774   MH ICRL CtY MH PU

AC
831

Loechel, Ilselotte, 1908–
Die regelung des internationalen strafrechts im polnischen strafgesetzbuch. ... Würzburg, 1934.
Inaug. Diss. – Jena, 1934.
Lebenslauf.
Literaturverzeichnis.

NL 0441775   ICRL

1885–

Loechel, Karl: Aus d. Psychiatr. u. Nervenkl. d. Univ. Kiel. Eingebildete Gravidität. Kiel 1914: Fiencke. 39 S. 8°
Kiel, Med. Diss. v. 3. Okt. 1914, Ref. Siemerling
[Geb. 23. Juli 85 Danzig; Wohnort: Kiel; Staatsangeh.: Preußen; Vorbildung OR. Graudenz Reife 07; Studium: Würzburg 6, Kiel 4 S.; Coll. 10. Jan. 13; Approb. 20. Juli 14.]   [U 14. 2742]

NL 0441776   ICRL MH CtY DNLM

Løchen, Antonie.
... Smaahistorier om dyr. Kristiania, H. Aschehoug & co. (W. Nygaard) 1909.
2 p. l., 108 p. 18½ᶜᵐ.

11–2113

Library of Congress

NL 0441777   DLC

Løchen, Arne, 1850–   ed.

Wessel, Johan Herman, 1742–1785.
... Digte i udvalg ved dr. Arne Løchen ... Kristiania, H. Aschehoug & co., 1898.

839.822
I122Loec

Løchen, Arne, 1850–1930.
Digtning og videnskap. Kristiania, H. Aschehoug, 1913.
181p. 20cm.

1. Ibsen, Henrik, 1828–1906. 2. Kierkegaard, Søren Aabye, 1813–1855. 3. Goethe, Johann Wolfgang von, Philosophy. I. Title.

NL 0441779   IEN MH

Løchen, Arne, 1850–1930.
... J. S. Welhaven; liv og skrifter. Kristiania, H. Aschehoug & co., 1900.
4 p. l., 562, xxv p. front. (port.) 18½ᶜᵐ.
The first seven chapters published 1898. cf. Prefatory note.

1. Welhaven, Johan Sebastian Cammermeyer, 1807–1873.

Library of Congress   PT8963.Z5L6   3–20156

NL 0441780   DLC MH CU NIC CtY NcU IU

Løchen, Arne, 1850–   ed.

Holberg, Ludwig, baron, 1684–1754.
Holbergs komedier i udvalg ved dr. Arne Løchen ... Kristiania, H. Aschehoug & co., 1897.

VOLUME 338

Løchen, Arne, 1850- ed.

Wergeland, Henrik Arnold, 1808–1845.
... Mindre digte i udvalg ved dr. Arne Løchen ... Kristiania, H. Aschehoug & co., 1897.

Løchen, Arne, 1850- ed.

Norske klassikere i udvalg ved Arne Løchen ... og Moltke Moe ... Kristiania, H. Aschehoug & co., 1896–99.

LØCHEN, Arne, 1850-
Om J. Stuart Mills Logik; en kritisk studie. Kristiania, 1885.

NL 0441784   MH

Løchen, Arne, 1850- ed.

Wergeland, Henrik Arnold, 1808–1845.
... Større digte i udvalg ved dr. Arne Løchen ... Kristiania, H. Aschehoug & co., 1898.

Løchen, Arne, 1850- ed.

Welhaven, Johan Sebastian Cammermeyer, 1807–1873.
Udvalgte digte af J. S. Welhaven ved dr. Arne Løchen ... Kristiania, H. Aschehoug & co.. 1896.

Løchen, Edvard, 1889-
Under vandring. Illustrert av Ulf Aas. Oslo, Gyldendal norsk forlag, 1951.
186 p. illus. 22 cm.

1. Norway—Descr. & trav.—1945-   2. Natural history—Norway.   I. Title.
DL418.L6   53–17524 ‡

NL 0441787   DLC MnU

LØCHEN, EINAR, 1918-
...Europabevegelsen og Europarådet. Utgitt av Chr. Michelsens institutt for videnskap og åndsfrihet.   Bergen, J. Grieg [1950] 31 p.
19cm.   (Tidens ekko; småskrifter om storpolitikk. 1950, nr. 3)

1. European federation, 1939-   I. Ser.

NL 0441788   NN

Løchen, Einar, 1918-
Europas menneskerettighetskonvensjon. Med forord av Herman Smitt Ingebretsen. Bergen, J. Grieg, 1952.
56 p. 22 cm.

"Konvensjon om beskyttelse av menneskerettighetene og de grunnleggende friheter": p. 32–53. "Protokoll til Konvensjonen": p. 54–56.

1. Civil rights—Europe. 2. Liberty.   I. Council of Europe. Convention for the protection of human rights and fundamental freedoms.   II. Title.
                                    54–24868

NL 0441789   DLC

JX3   Løchen, Einar, 1918-
L824n   Norway's views on sovereignty; a report pre-
1955   pared for Unesco, by Einar Løchen, assisted by Rolf N. Torgersen.   Bergen, A. S. John Griegs boktrykkeri, 1955.
102 p. 23ᶜᵐ.   (Chr. Michelsens Institutt for videnskap og åndsfrihet. Beretninger 17,5)
Bibliography: p. [101]-102.

1. Constitutional law - Norway. 2. Sovereignty. 3. United Nations - Norway. I. Title.   Series.

NL 0441790   MiU-L IaU CU NNC WaU MH-L CtY-L

Løchen, Jan Fredrik, 1922-
Vi viste verden vinterveien. Oslo, Aschehoug, 1952.
148 p. illus. 22 cm.

1. Olympic games (winter) 2. Sports—Norway.   I. Title.

GV841.5.L6   *796.48   52–65299 ‡

NL 0441791   DLC IU

KD2854   Løchen, Rolf, 1895-
.Ø2382   Saerregler i den gjensidige skadeforsikring.
1950   Foredrag holdt i Norsk Forsikringsjuridisk Forening den 21. april 1950. [Oslo, 1950]
27 p. (Norsk Forsikringsjuridisk Forenings publikasjoner, nr. 30)

1. Insurance, Accident—Norway. I. Title. Se-

NL 0441792   ICU MH-L

Løchen, Rolf, 1895-   ed.
Utvalg av lover for jord- og skogbruk, ved Rolf Løchen ... Oslo, Grøndahl & søn, 1932.
206, [2] p. 22½ᶜᵐ.

"Lovene er inntatt slikt de lyder pr. 1 januar 1932."—Forord.
"Tillegg til 'Utvalg af lover for jord- og skogbruk' foranlediget ved lover i 1932": 2 p. at end.

1. Agricultural laws and legislation—Norway. 2. Forestry law and legislation—Norway.   I. Norway. Laws, statutes, etc. II. Title.

                                    36–4220
Library of Congress   [2]   333.09481

NL 0441793   DLC CU

Løchen, Rolf, 1895-
... Vardøger, skuespil i tre akter. Oslo, H. Aschehoug & co. (W. Nygaard) 1926.
3 p. l., 127 p. 20ᶜᵐ.

I. Title.

Library of Congress   PT8950.L67V3 1926

                                    27–2287

NL 0441794   DLC

Løchen, Torvald, 1861-

Norway. Statistiske centralbureau.
Statistisk årbok for kongeriket Norge. 1.–   årg., 1880-   Utgit av det Statistiske centralbyraa. Annuaire statistique de la Norvège ... Kristiania, 1881–19

Løcherer, Joseph
Das kleine Himmelblaue Scapulier zu Ehren der Unbefleckten Empfängniss der seligsten Jungfrau Maria. Nach einem zu Rom gedruckten und von der hl. Congregation der Ablässe unterm 12 Sept. 1860 approbirten Büchlein bearbeitet, und mit diese Andacht bezüglichen Gebeten vermehrt. 4. Aufl. Einsiedeln, New York, etc. Karl und Nikolaus Benziger, 1869.

iv, 6–71 p. front., 15 cm.

1. Scapular of the, Immaculate Conception.
2. Mary, Blessed Virgin - Prayerbooks and devotions. I. Title.

NL 0441796   PLatS

Loeches, Juan de.
Tyrocinivm pharmacevticvm theorico-practicvm Galeno-chymicvm, examinandis iuventvs pharmacopolis per vtile ... Avthore d. Ioanne de Loeches, in curia matritensi pharmacopeo. Matriti, apud F. M. Abad, 1719.

8 p. l., 602 p. 19½ᶜᵐ.

1. Pharmacy—Early works to 1800. I. Title.

NL 0441797   MiU DNLM

LOECHES, Juan de.
Tyrocinium pharmaceuticum, theorico-practicum Galeno-chymicum, auctum et reformatum. Joannes de Loeches in curia Matritensi pharmacopeo authores. Gerundae, N. Oliva, etc., etc., 1755,

NL 0441798   MBCo

Loechius, Andreas
see Loeaechius, Andrea.

Löchner, Frank.
... Lehrbuch der rundfunktechnik ... nach dem lehrbuch der Fachgruppe Rundfunk, Berufsförderungslehrgang I. Neubearbeitet und erweitert von ober-ing. Frank Löchner. 3. aufl. Zugelassen zur rundfunktechnischen schulung für zwecke der kriegsmarine. Leipzig, J. Bohn & Berger, 1943-
v. illus., pl., diagrs. 21ᶜᵐ. (Fachbücher des deutschen rundfunk-einzelhandels)
"Das erste manuskript verfasste ober-ing. Rudolf Dreibholz."

1. Radio.   I. Dreibholz, Rudolf. Lehrbuch der rundfunktechnik.

                                    46–6869
Library of Congress   TK6550.L54

                        [2]   621.384

NL 0441800   DLC NNE MiU

Löchner, Frank.
Lehrbuch der Rundfunktechnik. 4., vollständig durchges. Aufl. Leipzig, J. Bohn & Berger [1949]-
v.   diagrs., ports.   22 cm.
1. Radio.

NL 0441801   RPB

Loechner (J.) Ein Zeugniss für das homöopathische Heilverfahren. xi, 80 pp. 12°. Dürkheim, G. Lange, 1877.

NL 0441802   DNLM PPHa

Loechner (Joh.) *De inversione uteri. 28 pp. 8°. Monachii, typ. F. S. Huebschmanni, 1833.

NL 0441803   DNLM

AC   Löchner, Kurt
831   Untersuchungen über die gerbereitechnologischen eigenschaften einiger synthetischer gerbstoffe. ... Darmstadt, 1934.   31 p.
Inaug. Diss. - Techn. Hochsch. Dresden, 1934.

NL 0441804   ICRL

Loechner (Rud.) *Ueber Lithotripsie. 20 pp. 8°. Erlangen, Junge u. Sohn, 1863.   C.

NL 0441805   DNLM

VOLUME 338

Loechner, Walter, 1902–
Grundsaetzliches zum Rationalisierungsproblem... von Diplomvolkswirt Walter Löchner... Nürtingen: I. G. Senner, 1930. 75 p. 8°.

Dissertation, Tübingen.
"Lebenslauf," p. 75.
Bibliography, p. 72–74.

1. Works management—Germany.
N. Y. P. L. July 11, 1931

NL 0441806 NN

Löchstör (Henricus). * De medicamentis Norwegiæ sufficientibus una cum methodo medendi. 20 pp. sm. 4°. Hafniæ, typ. N. J. Möller. [1740].

NL 0441807 DNLM

Löchstøer, Jens, 1889– ed.
Den norske leidangen [av G. P. Harbitz, S. Oppegård og R. Scheen] Oslo, Sjøforsvarets overkommando, 1951.
308 p. illus. 25 cm.

1. Norway—Armed forces. 2. Norway—Defenses. I. Harbitz, Georg Prahl, 1871– II. Title.

UA750.L6 53–28889 ‡

NL 0441808 DLC InU MnU

PF3989 Loeck, Georg Karl Ludwig Heinrich, 1862–
.L8 Die homiliensammlung des Paulus Diakonus, die unmittelbare vorlage des Otfridischen Evangelienbuchs ... Kiel, Druck von C. Schaidt, 1890.
47, [3] p. 22ᵐ.

Inaug.-diss.—Kiel.
Lebenslauf.

1. Otfrid von Weissenburg, 9th cent. Evangeliorum liber. 2. Paulus Diaconus, d. 797? Homiliarium.

NL 0441809 ICU NjP ICRL InU CU CtY MH MB

Loeck, Karl, joint author.
D531
.S8 **Succow, Wilhelm.**
Der Weltkrieg; Urkunden, zeitgenössische Berichte, Geschichte des Krieges und seiner Auswirkungen, bearb. von Wilhelm Succow und Karl Loeck. Langensalza, J. Beltz, 1928.

Loeck (Leo Eugenius Fridericus) [1825–]. * De trismo et tetano rheumatico. 29 pp., 1 l. 8°. Berolini, B. Schlesinger. [1851].

NL 0441811 DNLM

Loeck, Martin, 1864–
Der Bewusstseinszustand im epileptischen Anfall und die Wandlungen in der wissenschaftlichen Auffassung darüber ... Kiel, 1900.
Inaug.-Diss. - Kiel.
Vita.
"Litteratur": p. [33]–34.

NL 0441812 CtY DNLM MH ICRL

Loeck, Paul.
Das deutsche reichsgesetz betreffend die wechselstempelsteuer ...
see under Germany. Laws, statutes, etc.

Loeck, Paul, ed.
Prussia. Laws, statutes, etc., 1888– (William II)
... Preussisches stempelsteuergesetz vom 31. juli 1906 / 26. juni 1909 in der fassung der bekanntmachung vom 30. juni 1909. Mit den gesamten ausführungsbestimmungen. Unter besonderer berücksichtigung der entscheidungen der verwaltungsbehörden und der gerichte hrsg. von ... P. Loeck ... 7. aufl. Berlin, J. Guttentag, g. m. b. h., 1911.

Loeck, Paul.
... Das Reichsgesetz, betreffend die Wechselstempelsteuer, nebst den Ausführungsbestimmungen des Bundesrats und den Entscheidungen der höchsten Gerichte und Verwaltungsbehörden
see under Germany. Laws, statutes, etc.

Loeck, Paul, ed.
... Reichsstempelgesetz (börsensteuergesetz) vom 27. April, 1894 mit den ausführungsvorschriften einem auszug aus den gesetzesmaterialien und den entscheidungen der verwaltungsbehörden und des Reichsgerichts. Text-ausgabe mit anmerkungen, tabellen u. registern. 7. aufl. Von P. Loeck ... Berlin J. Guttentag, 1897.

NL 0441816 CtY

Loeck, Paul, ed.
... Reichsstempelgesetz (börsensteuergesetz) vom 14. juni 1900 mit den ausführungs-bestimmungen, einem auszug aus den gesetzes-materialien und den entscheidungen der verwaltungsbehörden und des Reichsgerichts. Text-ausgabe mit anmerkungen, tabellen u. registern. 8. aufl. Von P. Loeck ... Berlin, J. Guttentag, 1901.
1 p. l., [v]–xi, 470 p. 13½ᶜᵐ. (Guttentag'sche sammlung deutscher reichsgesetze ... nr. 18)
First to 5th editions, 1881–92, edited by Berthold Gaupp.

1. Stamp-duties—Germany. I. Germany. Laws, statutes, etc. II. Gaupp, Berthold.

6–9683 Revised
Library of Congress

NL 0441817 DLC

Loeck, Paul.
Reichsstempelgesetz (Börsensteuergesetz) vom 3. Juni 1906, mit den Ausführungsbestimmungen, unter besonderer Berücksichtigung der Entscheidungen der Verwaltungsbehörden und des Reichsgerichts. Mit einem Anhang: Das Gesetz, betreffend die Wetten bei öffentlich veranstalteten Pferderennen (Totalisatorgesetz) vom 4. Juli 1905 nebst Ausführungsbestimmungen. Berlin: J. Guttentag, G. m. b. H., 1906. vii, 340 p. 9. ed. 12°. (Guttentag'sche Sammlung deutscher Reichsgesetze. Nr. 18.)

1. Securities.—Taxation, Germany. 2. Stock exchange.—Transactions: Taxation, Germany.
N. Y. P. L. November 25, 1913.

NL 0441818 NN

Loeck, Paul.
... Reichsstempelgesetz vom 3. juli 1913. (Gesellschaftsverträge, kuxe, ausländische aktien, renten- und schuldverschreibungen, talon-, börsen-, lotterie- ⟨spiel und wette⟩, frachturkunden-, fahrkarten-, kraftfahrzeug-, tantieme-, scheck-, grundstücksübertragungs- und versicherungsstempel.) Mit den gesamten ausführungsbestimmungen unter besonderer berücksichtigung der entscheidungen der verwaltungsbehörden und des Reichsgerichts. 12. umgearb. und verm. aufl. vom geheimen regierungsrat P. Loeck ... Berlin, J. Guttentag, 1914.
x, 658 p. 19ᶜᵐ. (Guttentag'sche sammlung deutscher reichsgesetze. nr. 18)

I. Germany. Laws, stat- utes, etc., 1888– (William II)

15–22389

NL 0441819 DLC

Loeck, Paul.
... Wechselstempelgesetz vom 15. juli 1909 nebst den ausführungsbestimmungen des Bundesrats, den gesetzesmaterialien und den entscheidungen der höchsten gerichte und verwaltungsbehörden. Textausg. mit anmerkungen, einem chronologischen und einem sachregister. Von geh. regierungsrat P. Loeck ... 11. erweiterte aufl. Berlin, J. Guttentag, 1913.
113 p. 16ᵐᵐ. (Guttentag'sche sammlung deutscher reichsgesetze. nr. 5a)
With Stranz, J. Wechselordnung. Berlin, 1913.
"Abkürzungen": p. 7–8.
I. Germany. Laws, statutes, etc., 1888– (William II) II. Title.

16–4626

NL 0441820 DLC

1939 **Loeck, Robert Earl.**
L822 A study of the catalytic oxidation of olefins ... [Urbana, Ill., 1939]
14 numb. l.

Thesis (B.S.)--University of Illinois, 1939.
Typewritten.
Bibliography: leaf 14.

1. Catalyses. 2. Oxidation. 3. Olefines.

NL 0441821 IU

Löckel, Heinrich.
"Mein geliebtes Deutsch"; Wege zu innerer Sprachbildung. Hannover, H. Schroedel [1952]
viii, 272 p. illus. 21 cm.

Bibliography: p. 266–267.

1. German language. I. Title.

A 53–8671
Wisconsin. Univ. Libr. [1]
for Library of Congress

NL 0441822 WU NRU

Löckel, Heinrich, joint ed.
PF3115
.D42H4 **Herzog, Karl,** ed.
Ratgeber für den Leseunterricht. Bearb. von Karl Herzog und Heinrich Löckel. Langensalza, J. Beltz, 1937–

Loeckener (Bernardus). * De tritu pericardiali absque pericardite. 23 pp. 8°. Gryphiswaldiæ, F. G. Kunike, 1867.

NL 0441824 DNLM

290 **Löcker, Frau Elisabeth (Euler)** 1906–
L79p Philosophische deutung von sündenfall- und Prometheus-mythos. Heidelberg, 1933.
94p.

Inaug.--diss.--Heidelberg.
Lebenslauf.

NL 0441825 IU PBm

Löcker, Erasmus, respondent.
Disputatio juridica de jure ventorum
see under Lincke, Heinrich, praeses.

622.5 **Löcker, Hermann.**
L79w Die Wassereinbrüche in die Dux-Ossegger Kohlengruben, ihre Einwirkung auf die Teplitzer Thermalquellen und ihre Verdämmung. Teplitz, A. Becker, 1899.
122p. illus.(fold. in pocket) fold.col.map (in pocket) 23cm.

Cover title.
Place and name of publisher stamped on cover.

1. Mine water. I. Title.

NL 0441827 IU DLC-P4

Löcker (Julius). Die jod- und bromhaltige Schwefelquelle zu Goisern im Salzkammergut. Ihre Entdeckung, Lage, chemische Zusammensetzung und therapeutische Verwendung. iv (1 l.), 24 pp., 1 pl., 1 map. 8°. Wien, W. Braumüller, 1884.

NL 0441828 DNLM

VOLUME 338

Löcker, Max
Die Befreiung von Gefangenen nach dem geltenden Recht und dem Entwurf zu einem deutschen Strafgesetzbuch von 1927 ... von Max Löcker ... Kallmünz, Michael Lassleben, 1931.

x p., 1 l., 70 p. 21cm.

Inaug.-Diss. - Erlangen.
"Literatur-Verzeichnis": p. [vii]-x.

NL 0441829   MH-L PU CtY ICRL

Loeckle, Werner Ernst, 1916–
Über die Wirkung von Schwingungen auf das vegetative Nervensystem und die Sehnenreflexe. Würzburg, 1941.

306–316 p. illus. 25 cm.

Inaug.-Diss.—Berlin.
"Sonderdruck aus 'Luftfahrtmedizin,' 5. Band, 1. Heft, 1941."
Vita.
"Literatur": p. 316.

1. Nervous system, Autonomic. 2. Vibration—Physiological effect.

QP368.L6   50–47788

NL 0441830   DLC DNLM NIC

Löcklin, Karl
Heiss Flagge. Sprüche zur Flaggenehrung und für Betriebs-Appelle. Öhringen, Verlag der Hohenlohe'schen Buchhandlung, F. Rau, 1939.

32p. 16cm.

NL 0441831   CtY CU

Löcse, Hungary
see Levoča, Czechoslovak Republic.

---

943   A LŐCSEI evangelikus egyházközség
Luth.357   története. A Reformatio négyszáz
L819ev   éves fordulója alkalmából. Kiadja:
1917   Az Egyházközség. Lőcse, Reiss,
1917.
191p. illus., front. 24.5cm.

NL 0441833   MH-AH

Lőcsey, Mária.
... Báthori Zsófia, 1628–1680. Életrajzi vázlat. Irta Lőcsey Mária. Budapest: I. Neuwald utódai könyvnyomda, 1914.
47 p. 8°. (Történeti értekezések. Szám 8.)

1. Báthory, Zsófia, 1628–1680. 2. Ser.
N. Y. P. L.   September 25, 1928

NL 0441834   NN

56.24
L82   Løddesøl, Aasulv, 1896–
Kjemiske undersøkelser av en del norske jord-profiler. Oslo [Brøgger] 1939.
[305]–373 p.

1. Norway. Soils. 2. Soil. Analysis. 3. Soil profiles. I. Braadlie, O   joint author.

NL 0441835   DNAL

Løddesøl, Aasulv, 1896–
Myrene i næringslivets tjeneste. Oslo, Grøndahl, 1948.
330 p. illus., map. 24 cm.

Bibliography: p. [312]–325.

1. Moors and heaths—Norway. 2. Peat-bogs. i. Title.

S598.L55   78–222378

NL 0441836   DLC NN NIC DNAL TU

Løddesøl, Aasulv, 1896–
Myrtyper og myrplanter, av Aasulv Løddesøl og Johannes Lid. Oslo, Grøndahl & søn, 1950. 95 p. illus. 21cm. (Grøndahl & søns landbruksskrifter. nr. 39)

"Litteratur," p. 94–95.

1. Marshes—Norway. 2. Botany   —Norway. I. Lid, Johannes, 1886– , jt. au. II. Ser.

NL 0441837   NN

Loede, Frederick William, jr., joint author.

Hanmer, Lee Franklin, 1871–
Public recreation; a study of parks, playgrounds and other outdoor recreation facilities ... by Lee F. Hanmer ... in collaboration with Thomas Adams, Frederick W. Loede, jr., Charles J. Storey, Frank B. Williams. New York, Regional plan of New York and its environs, 1928.

Löde, Helmut
Die organisation der reichsanstalt fuer arbeitslosenversicherung.
Inaug. Diss. Leipzig, 1930.
Bibl.

NL 0441839   ICRL

Loedel, Enrique, 1901–
Enseñanza de la física. Buenos Aires, Kapelusz [1949]
xxxi, 518 p. illus. 22 cm. (Biblioteca de ciencias de la educación, 4)

1. Physics.   (Series)

QC23.L77   530   50–30377

NL 0441840   DLC

Loedel, Enrique, 1901–
Física relativista. Buenos Aires, Kapelusz [1955]
467 p. illus. 24 cm.

1. Relativity (Physics)   i. Title.
Full name: Enrique Loedel Palumbo.

QC6.L46   56–26542 ‡

NL 0441841   DLC TxU

Loedel   , Enrique, 1901–
Versos de un físico; física y razón vital. La Plata, Talleres gráficos Olivieri y Domínguez, 1934.

NL 0441842   MH

Loedel, Heinrich, 1798–1861.
Dance of death.
Hans Holbein's initial-buchstaben mit dem todtentanz. Nach Hans Lutzelburger's original-holzschnitten im Dresdner kabinet zum ersten mal treu copirt von Heinrich Loedel. Mit erläuternden denkversen und einer geschichtlichen abhandlung über die todtentänze von dr. Adolf Ellissen ... Göttingen, Dieterich, 1849.

Loedel, Heinrich, 1798–1861.
Kleine beiträge zur kunstgeschichte: Über die copie eines kupferstichs des Meisters E. S. von 1466. Berichtigungen über die arbeiten des architekten Daniel Specklin als kupferstecher und Über den namen Hans Memling. Erläutert durch vier treue nachbildungen in kupferstich von H. Loedel. Köln, I. M. Heberle (H. Lempertz) 1857.
7 p. iv pl. (1 col.) 29½ cm.
"Auflage zu 205 numerirten exemplaren, nebst einigen nicht für den handel bestimmten exemplar—auf fein papier." On cover: No. 23.
1. Master E S, 15th cent. 2. Specklin, Daniel, 1536–1589. 3. Memling, Hans, 1430?–1494.   i. Title.

13–3486
Library of Congress   NE805.M3L6

NL 0441844   DLC PU PP

Loedel, Heinrich, 1798–1861.

Weigel, Rudolph, 1804–1867.
Des Strassburger malers und formschneiders Johann Wechtlin, genannt Pilgrim, holzschnitte in clairobscur. in holz nachgeschnitten von Heinrich Loedel ... nebst bemerkungen über die erfindung des clairobscur und die ältere technik des formschnittes von demselben und einem briefe des herrn geh. oberfinanzraths Sotzmann. Mit 5 in den text eingedruckten holzschnitten. (Als fünftes supplement oder blatt 65 bis 77 zu Rudolph Weigel's holzschnittwerk.) Leipzig, R. Weigel, 1863.

Loedel Palumbo, Enrique
see
Loedel, Enrique, 1901–

---

ar W   **Löden, Paul**, 1906–
51959   Zur Vorgeschichte und Geschichte der
no.6   preussischen Grundrechte. Ein Beitrag
zur preussischen Verfassungsgeschichte.
Hamburg [Druck: M. Wilrodt-Schröder Nachf.]
1929.
110 p. 24cm.

Inaug.-Diss.—Hamburg.

NL 0441847   NIC CtY MiU

Löder, Johann Heinrich, d. 1728, *praeses.*
De Germanorum veterum gloria, e Cornelii Taciti Germania. Lipsiæ, Literis C. Guntheri [1689]
[44], 21 p. 21 cm.
Diss.—Leipzig (Gottfried Heinricus, respondent)
No. 4 in a vol. lettered: Variæ de origine & habitv vetervm Germanorvm.

1. Tacitus, Cornelius. Germania. 2. Germanic tribes.   i. Heinricus, Gottfried, respondent.

DD3.V35 no. 4   50–44937

NL 0441848   DLC

Löder, Johann Heinrich, d. 1728, ed.
Protestatio Bohemorum   ...
see under title

Loederer, Richard A   1894–
Immortal men of music. A gallery of the world's twelve great composers, by Richard A. Loederer. New York, The Master prints publishing co. [1941]
2 p. l., 12 port. 37¼ x 28¼ᶜᵐ.
"Complete edition. 1st printing August 1940. 2nd printing March 1941."
Portraits of Bach, Mozart, Beethoven, Schubert, Chopin, Liszt, Wagner, Verdi, Johann Strauss the younger, Brahms, Tschaikovsky and Sibelius.

1. Musicians—Portraits.   i. Title.
42–5059
Library of Congress   ML87.L62
[2]   927.8

NL 0441850   DLC WaS MB NN

Loederer, Richard A   1894–
... Voodoo fire in Haiti, translated by Desmond Ivo Vesey, with illustrations by the author. Garden City, N. Y., Doubleday, Doran & company, inc., 1935.
4 p. l., v–viii p., 1 l., 274 p. incl. front., illus., plates. 24ᶜᵐ.
Maps on lining-papers.
"First edition."
Bibliographical "Acknowledgments": 4th prelim. leaf.

1. Haiti—Descr. & trav. 2. Voodooism. 3. Negroes in Haiti. i. Vesey, Desmond Ivo, tr. ii. Title.
35—20085
Library of Congress   F1925.L582
[44u2]

MoU NcRS OrCS OrU WaSp WaE IdB MtBuM ViHaI
OCl OEac OCU OLak ViU NcD PSC PPL WaTC NjR KMK DAU
NL 0441851   DLC NN OOxM MH MB PP IU WaU NcRS OU CU

VOLUME 338

G917.294
L822wTv
LOEDERER, RICHARD A　　1894-
　　Voodoo fire in Haiti, by Richard A. Loederer;
translated from the German by Desmond I. Vesey.
With fifty-one illustrations in black and white
by the author.　London, Jarrolds, limited,
1935.
　　4p.ℓ.,11-283p. incl. front.,illus.,plates.
24cm.
　　Maps on lining-papers.
　　Translation of Wudu-feuer auf Haiti.
　　1. Haiti - Descr. & trav.　2. Voodooism.
3. Negroes in Haiti. I. Vesey, Desmond Ivo,
tr. II. Title.

NL　0441852　　TxU MH

F
1926
L582
1935
　　Loederer, Richard A　　1894-
　　Voodoo fire in Haiti, translated
by Desmond Ivo Vesey, with
illustrations by the author. New
York,The Literary Guild[1935]
274p. incl. front.,illus.,plates.
24cm.
　　Maps on lining-papers.
　　Includes bibliography.

　　1. Haiti - Description and travel
2. Voodooism 3. Negroes in Haiti I.
Vesey, Desmond Ivo, tr. II. Title.

NL　0441853　　MU OrU CoU NBuU MU ICU NSyU IEN

　　Loederer, Richard A　　1894-
　　... Wudu-feuer auf Haiti; eine abenteuerliche künstlerfahrt
in die tropische wunderwelt zentralamerikas; mit einundfünf-
zig bildern vom verfasser. Wien-Leipzig, A. Wolf [1932]
　　216 p. incl. front., illus., plates. 24½cm.
　　Maps on lining-papers.

　　1. Voodooism. 2. Negroes in Haiti.　I. Title.

Library of Congress　　　F1926.L58　　　　　35-23911
———— Copy 2.
Copyright A—Foreign　　29449
　　　　　　　　　　　　[2]　　　　　　　917.294

NL　0441854　　DLC IaU TxU OCl OClW NN

*
M1
.S444
v.33
no.7
　　Löderman, Aug

(Bröllops) Schwedischer Hochzeits-Marsch.
Bauern-Tanz. [Arrang. v. Benno Schereck]
Berlin, Carl Simon; New York, Edward
Schuberth & Co., 23 Union Square [not after
1892]
5 p.　34cm. [Sheet music collection, v.33,no.7]

　　1. Wedding music. 2. Marches (Piano) I.
Schereck, Benno　　, arr. II. Title.
III. Title: Schwed　　ischer Hochzeits-Marsch.

NL　0441855　　ViU

　　Löderus, Henricus
　　see Löder, Johann Heinrich, d. 1728.

4PH
Hung
208
　　Lödi, Ferenc.
　　Igy akarom.
　　Franklin, 1950.
　　　　63 p.

NL　0441857　　DLC-P4

QL653
.A2H3
　　Löding, Henry Peder, 1869-

Haltom, William L
　　... Alabama reptiles, by William L. Haltom. University,
Ala.,1931.

　　Löding, Henry Peder, 1869-1942.
　　... Catalogue of the beetles of Alabama, by Henry Peter
Löding. University, Ala.,1945.
　　172 p. 23½ cm. (Alabama. State geologist. Monograph 11)
　　At head of title: Geological survey of Alabama ...
　　Biographical introduction by Walter B. Jones.

　　1. Beetles—Alabama.　I. Jones, Walter Bryan, 1895-
　　　　　　　　　　　　　　　　　　　　　　　G S 46—5
U. S. Geol. Survey.　Libr
for Library of Congress　　　　QL584.A2L6
　　　　　　　　　　　　　　[a49e1]†　　(557.61) 595.76

DLC
NL　0441859　　DI-GS WaS IU AAP MsU PP PBm NIC PLF MsSM

　　Löding, Henry Peder, 1869-
　　... A preliminary catalogue of Alabama amphibians and reptiles, by H. P. Löding.　University, Ala.,1922.
　　59 p. 23ᵐ. (Alabama.　Museum of natural history.　Museum paper
no. 5)
　　At head of title: Geological survey of Alabama ...
　　"Important literature": p. 52-53.

　　1. Batrachia—Alabama.　2. Reptiles—Alabama.
　　　　QL653.A2L6　　　　　　　　　　　22-27206

NL　0441860　　DLC MtBuM NcD FTaSU AAP MsU OU OCU OC1MN

　　Loeding, Walter Ludwig Wilhelm Heinrich, 1904-
　　Die deutsch-englischen Bündnisverhandlungen 1898 bis 1901;
ihr Verlauf auf Grund der deutschen und der englischen Akten...
von Walter Löding...　Hamburg, 1929.　111 p.　8°.
　　Dissertation, Hamburg, 1929.
　　Lebenslauf, last page.
　　Bibliography, p. 5-7.

501308A. 1. Germany—For. rel.—　　　Gt. Br., 1898-1901. 2. Great
Britain—For. rel.—Germany, 1876-　　1901.
N. Y. P. L.　　　　　　　　　　　　　　November 5, 1930

NL　0441861　　NN MiU CtY NIC NjP PHC MiU

TP670
.B385
　　Lödl, Anton, 1888-

Becher, Carl, 1900-
　　Neuzeitliche Wachswaren und ihre Herstellung.　Augsburg, Verlag für Chemische Industrie [1954]

　　Lødøen, O. I. K.　Billeder fra Vikingti-
dens gudetro.　Kristiania og Kjøbenhavn, J. W. Cappelen, (1923).　8°. pp. 16,
illustr.　　　　　　　　　IcD1L815
　　"Fagbiblioteket Fri læsning.　Nr. 20."

NL　0441863　　NIC

D810
E5N6L8
　　Lødrup, Hans, 1876-
　　Laereraksjonens sanne bakgrunn; noen vitne-
prov.　Kristiansund, Eget Forlag, 1948.
105 p.　22ᵐ.
Hoover
Library
　　Includes Stenografisk referat fra Akers
Herredsret.

　　1. World War, 1939-1945 - Education and the
war. 2. Teachers　- Norway. 3.World War,
1939-1945 - Nor　way. I.Title.

NL　0441864　　CSt-H NN IEN

　　Lödrup, Hans, 1911-
　　Die Schulzahnpflege in Deutschland und in
Norwegen ...　Bonn, 1935.
　　Inaug.-Diss. - Bonn.
　　Lebenslauf.
　　"Literaturverzeichnis": p. 37-42.

NL　0441865　　CtY

　　Lødrup, Hans Peter Elisa, 1885-
　　A/s Akers mek. verksted, 1841-1951.　Oslo, Akers mek.
verksted, 1951.
　　210 p. illus. 28cm.

　　1. Akers mek. verksted, A/s, Oslo.

　　VM301.L6　　　　　　　　　　54-39192 ‡

NL　0441866　　DLC IEN

DL
528
L6
　　Lødrup, Hans Peter Elisa, 1885-
　　Efter krigen; politik ute og hjemme [af] Hans
P. Lødrup.　Kristiania, J. W. Cappelen [c1924]
191p.　20cm.

　　1. Norway - Pol. & govt. - 1905-　2. Europe -
Politics - 1918-1945 I. Title

NL　0441867　　WU NN

AC-L
qW357L
L823g
　　Lødrup, Hans Peter Elisa, 1885-
　　Gustav Vigeland.　[Oslo] Nasjonalforlaget
[1944]
　　262,[2]p. illus. 29cm.

　　Bookplate of Evelyn Waugh.

　　1. Vigeland, Gustav, 1869-1943.

NL　0441868　　TxU PPiU CaBVaU KU

q735
V681ℓ
1945
　　Lødrup, Hans Peter Elisa, 1885-
　　Gustav Vigeland.　[2.oppl.　Oslo]
Nasjonalforlaget [1945]
262p. illus. 30cm.

　　1. Vigeland, Gustav, 1869-1943.

NL　0441869　　IU PU CU CSt

　　Lødrup, Hans Peter Elisa, 1885-
　　...Gustav Vigeland. [Oslo] Nasjonalforlaget [1946]　262 p.
illus. 29cm.

　　2. oppl.

360948B. 1. Vigeland, Gustav　　　1869-1943.　　　June 25, 1947
N. Y. P. L.

NL　0441870　　NN NjR MnU

　　[Lødrup, Hans Peter Elisa] 1885-
　　De Mekaniske verksteders landsforening, M. V. L., 1889-1949.
[Oslo, 1949]　386 p. illus. 26cm.
　　Written by H. P. E. Lødrup at the request of the association.
　　"Hovedtrekkene i lønnsutviklingen, av professor Erling Petersen," p. 289-344.

517335B. 1. Metals—Trade and　　　stat.—Assoc. and org.—Norway.
I. Petersen, Erling, 1906-　. II. De　Mekaniske verksteders lands-
forening.　　　　　　　　　　　　　　foreining.
N. Y. P. L.　　　　　　　　　　　　　June 26, 1950

NL　0441871　　NN

　　Lødrup, Hans Peter Elisa, 1885-
　　... Sosialisering gjennom statskup?
Oslo, Dreyer, 1952.
　　30 p., 1 ℓ. 19cm.

NL　0441872　　MH-L

D741
L825
　　Lødrup, Hans Peter Elisa, 1885-
　　Det store oppgjør.　Oslo, Dreyer, 1945.
iii, 407 p.　23cm.
　　Bibliography included in "Forord" (p.ii-iii)
Hoover
Library

　　1. World War, 1939-1945 - Causes.　2. National
socialism.　3. World War, 1939-1945 - Norway.
4. Reconstruction (1939-1951) 5. World War,
1939-1945 - Peace.　I. Title.

NL　0441873　　CSt-H IU MnU NjR

VOLUME 338

Lødrup, Hans Peter Elisa, 1885–
... Vinjesvingen, et lite blad av krigens historie i Norge. 25. tusen. Oslo, H. Aschehoug & co. (W. Nygaard) 1945.
3 p. l., 152 p. 2 front. illus. (maps) plates, ports. 19ᵐ.
At head of title: Hans P. Lødrup.
"Forord og rettelser til 2. opplag" ([4] p.) inserted.

1. World war, 1939–1945—Regimental histories—Norway—3. infanteri-regimente. 2. Norway. Hæren. 3. infanteriregimente. 3. World war, 1939–1945—Norway—Vinje (Telemark) I. Title.
46–16991
Library of Congress   D763.N61L6 1945

NL 0441874   DLC WaT WaS WaU MnU

389.7
L822
Löer, Ferdinand.
Die sachgemässe Fütterung der Klein-Haustiere.   Neubearb. von Georg Wilsdorf. Leipzig, Hachmeister & Thal [1949?]
95 p.

NL 0441875   DNAL

Löer, Ferdinand.
Vergleichend physiologische untersuchungen über die normale rektaltemperatur, atem- und pulsfrequenz der vögel, unter besonderer berücksichtigung unseres hausgeflügels ... Berlin, R. Schoetz, 1909.
26 p., 1 l. diagrs. 22ᶜᵐ.
Inaug.-diss.—Bern.
"Literaturverzeichnis": p. 26.

1. Ornithology, Physiological and structural. 2. Poultry. Anatomy and physiology.
Agr 10–246
Library, U. S. Dept. of   Agriculture 413L82

NL 0441876   DNAL DNLM

Löer, Franz
-Der herausgabeanspruch des sicherungseigentümers im konkurs des sicherungsgebers. ... Berlin, 1936. 40 p.
Inaug. Diss. - Erlangen, 1936.
Literaturverzeichnis.

NL 0441877   ICRL

Löer, Klemens, 1910–
Abhängigkeit der mathematischen reserven von sterblichkeit und zins ... von Klemens Löer ... Göttingen, 1936.
cover-title, 39 p., 1 l.   22½ cm.
Inaug.-diss.—Göttingen.
Lebenslauf.
"Sonderdruck aus 'Das versicherungsarchiv', bd. 6, hft. 7/8, 1935/36."

1. Insurance, Life—Mathematics. I. Title.

NL 0441878   ViU

DF895.652
L824
Löer, Wilhelm Ferdinand, 1915–
Das problem der japanischen schrift; grundlagen zu einer neuen darstellung der japanischen sprache und schrift für praktische zwecke. [Bonn] 1947.
65 l.
Microfilm of copy at Bonn University.
Inaug.-diss.--Bonn.
Typescript.
"Quellenverzeichnis": l. 64–65.

NL 0441879   NNC-EA

---

ar W
54559
no.10
Löer, Willy.
Die Unabdingbarkeit des Tarifvertrages und die Versuche, sich ihr zu entziehen.   Coburg, Druckerei des Coburger Tageblatt, 1928.
x, 50 p. 22cm.

Inaug.-Diss.--Erlangen.

NL 0441880   NIC DLC

A30
D8
1731L
Löers, Johann Christian, 1675–1743, praeses.
... De mirabili angeli Jehovae cum Manoacho in oblatione holocausti commercio, ejusque mysterio. Ad Judic. XIII. 19.20. Duisburgi ad Rhenum, 1731.
46 p.
Diss. - Duisburg (J.L.Rocholl, respondent)

I. Rocholl, Johann Leonhard   respondent.

NL 0441881   CtY

A30
D8
1731L
Löers, Johann Christian, 1675–1743, praeses.
Dissertationem theologicam, qua ex facultate intelligendi, hominem ad Dei gloriam conditum esse, probatur ... praeside Joh. Christianus Löers ... et respondens Wilhelmus de Forell ... subjicient. Duisburgi ad Rhenum, 1731.
48 p.
Diss. - Duisburg (W.v.Forell, respondent)

I. Forell, Wilhelm von   respondent.

NL 0441882   CtY

Löf, pseud.
see
Löwendorf, Heinz.

Löf, Axel Em.
Kristinehamns historia...av Axel Em. Löf. Utgiven på uppdrag av Kristinehamns Stadsfullmäktige vid stadens 300 årsjubileum år 1942. [Del] 1- . [Karlstad, 1942-   v. illus. 26cm.
Bibliographies included.
CONTENTS.—Del. 1. Bygden, förhistorien.—Del. 2. Jorden, staden, styrelsen.

1. Kristinehamn, Sweden.   I. Kristinehamn, Sweden. Stadsfullmäktige.

NL 0441884   NN

TD430
U43
no.4
Löf, George Oscar Gage, 1913–
Demineralization of saline water with solar energy. [Washington] 1954.
[1], iii, 80 p. diagrs., tables. 27 cm. (U.S. Dept. of the Interior. Saline water research and development progress report no. 4)
For Saline Water Conversion Program.
Bibliography: p. 77–80.

1. Saline water - Demineralization. 2. Solar radiation. I. Title. (Series)

NL 0441885   DI DNAL

TD430
U43
no. 5
Löf, George Oscar Gage, 1913-
Solar distillation of sea water in the Virgin Islands. [Washington] 1955.
[1], i, 39 p. illus., diagrs., tables. 27 cm. (U.S. Dept. of the Interior. Saline water research and development progress report no. 5)
For Saline Water Conversion Program.
Bibliography: p. 39.

1. Sea-water, Distillation of. I. Title. (Series)

NL 0441886   DI DNAL

Loef, Johannes Jacobus van.
Gamma rays from inelastic neutron scattering. Utrecht, 1955.
83 p. illus., diagrs., tables. 24 cm.
Proefschrift—Utrecht.
Bibliography: p. 81–83.

1. Gamma rays. 2. Neutrons—Scattering.   I. Title.
QC490.L6   56–26606

NL 0441887   DLC MiU CtY NN

Löfberg, David.
Det nationalekonomiska motivet i svensk pedagogik under 1700-talet. Uppsala, 1949.
410 p. 25 cm.
Akademisk avhandling—Uppsala.
"Källor och litteratur": p. [387]–405.

1. Education—Sweden—Hist.   I. Title.
LA901.5.L6   51–36319

NL 0441888   DLC ICU CtY PU-Penn MH

Löfberg, Elisabeth Högström
see Högström-Löfberg, Elisabeth, 1894–

Loefberg, Johan Samuel, respondent.
Arvid Adrian Stjernecrantz...
see under Lenstroem, Carl Julius, 1811–1893, praeses.

Löfberg (JOHAN SAMUEL)
* Adolphus Johannes, comes palatinus ejusque de reductione querelæ. *Upsalia,* 1845. 16 pp. 4°.
In: GFD p. v. 9.

NL 0441891   NN

Löfbladh, Hildegard Kristina, 1880–
Herr Olofs hustru; roman.   Uppsala, J. A. Lindblad [1948]
205 p. 22 cm.

I. Title.
A 49–5409*
Minnesota. Univ. Libr.   [1]
for Library of Congress

NL 0441892   MnU

Loefdahl (C. J.) * De fetu monstroso, judicio medici submisso. 16 pp., 1 pl. 8°. *Lundæ,* C. F. Berling, 1837.

NL 0441893   DNLM

Loefen, Maximilian von.
Anciennetäts-Liste der sämmtlichen Offiziere des Beurlaubtenstandes des Deutschen Reichs-Heeres. Mit Angabe des Datums der Ernennung zu den früheren Chargen, nach den verschiedenen Waffengattungen zusammengestellt von Von Loefen. Erfurt, H.Neumann [1894-95]

2 v.
Contents: 1. Nach dem Stande von 15.August 1894. - 2. Nach dem Stande von 15.Juni 1895.

NL 0441894   MH

VOLUME 338

LOEFEN, W. von.
Handelsstatistik oder zollstatistik: Vorschläge zu vereinfachung und verbesserrung der statistik unseres auswartigen handels. Berlin, Phönix , verlag, [1912].

pp.69.

NL 0441895　　MH

Loefen, W　v[on]
Zur Reform der deutschen Handels-statistik. Vorschläge ...　Berlin, E. Haase, 1905.
52 p.　8°.

NL 0441896　　NN

Löfenberg, Mattias T
Studies on middle English local surnames...
Lund, Gleerup; Lond., Williams & Norgate ᴄ1942ᴐ
255 p.　(Lund studies in English. XI)

NL 0441897　　PBm

Cuinecks Library
№65
K283
P5X
L82

[Loefenius, Michael]
Antiphilippica, oder Rettung vnd ferrnere Beweisung//der Anno 1606. beschehener wolmeynenden Warnung an evangelische und römische catholische friedliebende Freunde/ wider des Regenspurgischen jesuitischen theologi Jacobi Sylvani, alias Jacob Kellers/ aussgangene Philippicam. [n.p.] Gedruckt 1608.
1 p.ℓ., 106 p. illus.　19 cm.
Signatures: A-O⁴(O₃₋₄ [blank?] wanting).
Imperfect: some leaves browned.

1. Keller, Jakob, 1568-1631. Philippica in anonymum praedicantem calvinistam. 2. Jesuits. Province of Germany - Stamp. I. Title.

NL 0441899　　CtY

Div.S.
271.5
L825W

[Löfenius, Michael]
Wolmeinende Warnung an alle christliche Potentaten und Obrigkeiten, wider dess Bapsts unnd seiner Jesuiten hochgefehrliche Lehr und Prackticken; auss bäpstlichen und jesuitischen Büchern gezogen. [n. p., 1606]
58 p.　18 cm.

1. Jesuits. Controversial literature. 2. Regicides. I. Title.

NL 0441900　　NcD

Loefer, John Benjamin.
Comparative studies on growth characteristics of certain *Phytomastigoda* ... ₍by₎ John B. Loefer ... ₍New York₎ 1935₎
cover-title, 6, ₍1₎, ₍456₎-471, ₍1₎, ₍74₎-86 p.　diagrs.　23ᶜᵐ.
Thesis (ᴘʜ. ᴅ.)—New York university.
The first article is reprinted from Biological bulletin, vol. ᴌxvɪ, no. 1, Feb., 1934; the second and third articles are reprints from Archiv für protistenkunde, 84. bd., hft. 3, and 85. bd., hft. 1, 1935.
"Literature cited" at end of each article.
Contents.—The trophic nature of *Chlorogonium* and *Chilomonas*.—Effect of certain carbohydrates and organic acids on growth of *Chlorogonium* and *Chilomonas*.—Effect of certain nitrogen compounds on the growth of *Chlorogonium* and *Chilomonas*.
1. Chlorogonium. 2. Chilomonas. 3. Growth.　ɪ. Title: *Phytomastigoda*, Comparative　studies on.
36-1396
Library of Congress　QL368.F5L6 1933
New York Univ. Libr.　₍3₎　593.16

NL 0441901　　NNU-W DLC OU

Loeff, A　Rutgers van der
see　Rutgers van der Loeff A.

Loeff, An Rutgers van der
see
Rutgers van der Loeff-Basenau, An, 1910-

Loeff, Friedel (Heise) 1906-
... Geliebter Jan; briefe gehen nach dem osten.　Berlin, M. Warneck ₍1944₎
78 p.　15½ᵐ.
At head of title: Friedel Loeff.

ɪ. Title.
46-19017
Library of Congress　PT2623.O315G4
₍2₎　836.91

NL 0441904　　DLC CtY OKentU NbU IU NN CU MB

Loeff, Friedel (Heise) 1906-
Der teufel von Schanghai; abenteuerroman von F. Loeff. Leipzig, F. Rothbarth ₍ᶜ1938₎
237, ₍1₎ p. 19ᶜᵐ.

ɪ. Title.
39-9747 Revised
Library of Congress　PT2623.O315T4　1938

NL 0441905　　DLC

H
B
B734

Loeff, Gerrit Michiel Cornelis
De nederlandsche kerkgeschiedschrijver Geeraardt Brandt... Utrecht, Kemink, 1864.

X [2] 142p. 23cm.

Thesis (doctoral) - University of Utrecht.
Bibliographical footnotes.

NL 0441906　　ViHarEM MH-AH

Loeff, H　J　Schim van der
see　Schim van der Loeff, H　J

Loeff, H. P. Schim van der
see
Schim van der Loeff, H　P.

CD1707
.A7A5
1950

Loeff, J., ed.

Netherlands (*Kingdom, 1815-*　) *Rijksarchief in Gelderland, Arnhem.*
Het archief der Commanderij van St. Jan te Arnhem, door J. Loeff. 's-Gravenhage, Ministerie van Onderwijs, Kunsten en Wetenschappen, 1950.

Loeff, J　*journalist.*
Alle zeilen bij; zeilsport in beeld.　Baarn, De Boekerij ₍1955₎
95 p.　illus.　31 cm.

1. Sailing—Pictorial works.　ɪ. Title.
A 57-402
Ohio State Univ.　Libr.　GV811
for Library of Congress　₍3₎

NL 0441910　　OU

Loeff, Jan Jozef, 1903-
Verhouding staat en rechtsgemeenschap, mede in verband met de traditionele Katholieke staatsleer. Leiden, H. E. Stenfert Kroese, 1955.
27 p. 24 cm.
Rede—Roomsch Katholieke Handelshoogeschool, Tilburg (aanvaarding van het ambt van buitengewoon hoogleraar in de wijsbegeerte van staat en gemeenschap, almede in de inleiding tot de wijsbegeerte en de ethica) 1955.

1. State, The.　ɪ. Title.
JC260.L6　58-19936 †

NL 0441911　　DLC DCU

Loeff, Joannes Aloysius, 1858-1921.
Herziening van het wetboek van str afrecht. 's-Gravenhage, 1900-04.
2 v.

NL 0441912　　PU-L

Loeff, Joannes Aloysius, 1858-1921, ed
Het katholiek Nederland, 1813-1913 ...
see under title

Loeff, Joannes Aloysius, 1858-1921.
Publiekrecht tegenover privaatrecht. Proeve van theoretisch-kritisch onderzoek naar het karakter van het publieke recht ... door Joannes Aloysius Loeff ... Leiden, S. C. van Doesburgh, 1887.
viii p., 1 l., 216 p. 22½ᶜᵐ.
Proefschrift—Leyden.
"Stellingen": p. ₍201₎-207.
"Stellingen ter verkrijging van den graad van doctor in de staatswetenschap aan de Rijks-universiteit te Leiden ... door Joannes Aloysius Loeff ... Leiden, S. C. van Doesburgh, 1887": p. ₍209₎-216.
1. Administrative law. 2. Netherlands—Constitutional law. 3. Law—Philosophy.　ɪ. Title.
36-33346
NL 0441914　　DLC MH-L PU-L

Loeff (Joh.) * De sede fungi sic dicti duræ meningis cerebri. 3 p. l., 43 pp., 1 pl. 8°. Traj. ad Rhenum, P. W. van de Weyer, 1856.

NL 0441915　　DNLM

Loeff, Johannes Jacobus, 1850-
Iets over staatsschulden ... door Johannes Jacobus Loeff ... Utrecht, Gebr. van der Post, 1885.
2 p. l., 51 p. 22½ᵐ.
Proefschrift—Utrecht.
"Stellingen": p. ₍45₎-51.

1. Debts, Public—Netherlands.
40-18491
Library of Congress　HJ8705.L6 1885
₍2₎　336.309492

NL 0441916　　DLC CtY ICRL

Loeff, Manta Meindert Schim van der
see　Schim van der Loeff, Manta Meindert, 1865-

Loeff, Paul
Entwurfe zum bau von kalk-, cement -, gyps- und ziegelbrennereien,...2.aufl. Leipzig, 1873.

NL 0441918　　NN

Loeff, Paul.
Praktisches handbuch für brennerei-anlagen nebst dazu gehörigen entwürfen unter berücksichtigung der neuesten verbesserungen im betriebe. Zum gebrauche für baumeister, bauhandwerker, fabrikanten und landwirthe... Nach eigenen praktischen erfahrungen herausgegeben von Paul Loeff... Leipzig, E. A. Seemann, 1870.
viii,55 p.　illus.,13 pl.,diagrs.　33 1/2cm.

1. Breweries.

NL 0441919　　DP DSI

Loeff, Paul Adriaan van der
... De infanticidio, et quidem eius parte practica ... offert Paulus Adrianus van der Loeff ... Groningae, I. Oomkens ₍1835₎
xvi, 122, ₍6₎ p. 19cm.

Diss.- Groningen.
Bibliographical footnotes.

NL 0441920　　MH-L

VOLUME 338

Loeff, Wolfgang, 1895-
Bismarck; das Leben eines Staatsmannes. Mit Zeichnungen von E.R. Döbrich. Leipzig, Teubner, 1936

88 p. illus. (Deutsches Ahnenerbe; Lesestoffe für den Deutsch- und Geschichtsunterricht)

NL 0441921 MH DLC-P4 NN CtY

Loeff, Wolfgang, 1895-
Derfflinger, ein kurbrandenburgisches Reiterleben. Mit 6 Zeichnungen von Erich R. Döbrich und 3 Kartenskizzen. Leipzig, B.G. Teubner, 1936.
54 p. (Deutsches Ahnenerbe, Lesestoffe für den Deutsch- und Geschichtsunterricht)

NL 0441922 DLC CtY

Loeff, Wolfgang, 1895–
Deutschlands seegeltung vom germanischen einbaum und wikingerschiff zum deutschen schlachtschiff und schnelldampfer, von Wolfgang Loeff. Bildteil von professor Alexander Kircher ... Berlin, Verlag für volkstum, wehr und wirtschaft, H. Kurzeja [1939]

188 p., 1 l. incl. illus. (map) tables (1 fold.) col. plates. 30cm.

"Nachweis der quellen": p. 185–186.

1. Germany—History, Naval. 2. Merchant marine—Germany—Hist. I. Kircher, Alexander, 1867– illus. II. Title.

A 46–2056

New York. Public library for Library of Congress DD106.L6

[2]† 943

NL 0441923 NN DLC MH

Loeff, Wolfgang, 1895-
Drei deutsche Soldaten: Zeppelin, Schlieffen [und] Tirpitz. Eine Roman-Trilogie. Leipzig, Goten-Verlag [c1940] 528 p. ports. 20cm.

Previously published in 3 separate volumes with titles: Der geniale Narr, Der Feldherr ohne Krieg and Der Grossadmiral.

1. Zeppelin, Ferdinand Adolf August Heinrich, Graf von, 1838-1917—Fiction. 2. Schlieffen, Alfred, Graf von, 1833-1913—Fiction. 3. Tirpitz, Alfred Peter Friedrich von, 1849-1930—Fiction. I. Title. II. Loeff, Wolfgang, 1895- Der geniale Narr. III. Loeff, Wolfgang, 1895- Der Feldherr ohne Krieg. IV. Loeff, Wolfgang, 1895- Der Grossadmiral.

NL 0441925 NN CU ICRL MH OCU NNC

Loeff, Wolfgang, 1895–
... England ohne maske; tatsachen britischer kolonialpolitik. Leipzig, Goten-verlag, Herbert Eisentraut [1939]

252 p. incl. illus. (map) tables. plates, ports. 22½cm.

"Nachweis der hauptsächlichen quellen": p. 247–252.

1. Gt. Brit.—Colonies. I. Title.

A C 39–3119

New York. Public library for Library of Congress [2]

NL 0441926 NN OU CtY NcD MH IaU MiU

LOEFF, WOLFGANG, 1895-
Der Feldherr ohne Krieg, ein Schlieffen-Roman. Leipzig, H. Eisentraut [c1936] 240 p. front., (port.) 21cm.

1. Schlieffen, Alfred, Graf von, 1833-1913--Fiction. I. Title.

NL 0441927 NN NNC MH IEN RPB CU CtY DLC-P4

Loeff, Wolfgang, 1895-
PT2623 .O33F4 Der Feldherr ohne Krieg; ein Schlieffen-Roman. Berlin, Deutsche Kulturbuchreihe, 1939.
254 p. 19cm.

NL 0441928 CSt CaBVaU

Loeff, Wolfgang, 1895– *ed.*
Flieger und luftschiffer im weltkrieg, eigenberichte deutscher luftkämpfer, herausgegeben von Wolfgang Loeff. Köln, H. Schaffstein [1936]

79, [1] p. illus. 17cm. [Schaffsteins blaue bändchen. 224]

"1.–5. tausend. Federzeichnungen von Max Bürger."
"Quellenangabe": p. [80]

1. European war, 1914–1918—Aerial operations. 2. European war, 1914–1918—Personal narratives, German. I. Title.

40–17098

Library of Congress D604.L63

[2] 940.44943

NL 0441929 DLC NN NcD CtY

Loeff, Wolfgang, 1895–
... Der geniale "narr"; ein Zeppelin roman. Leipzig, Goten-verlag, H. Eisentraut [c1935]

285, [1] p. 20½cm.

1. Zeppelin, Ferdinand Adolf August Heinrich, graf von, 1838–1917—Fiction. I. Title.

37–24718

Library of Congress PT2623.O316G4 1935

[2] 833.91

NL 0441930 DLC MH CU CtY OCl NN PHC PPG

Loeff, Wolfgang, 1895–
Genie und Fleiss führen deutsche Männer zum Erfolg, von Wolfgang Loeff. Berlin: Dr. H. Riegler Verlag für vaterländische Literatur [1939] 288 p. illus. 19½cm.

CONTENTS.—Georg Reichsfreiherr von Derfflinger.—August Graf Neidhardt von Gneisenau.—Johann Gottlieb Fichte.—Friedrich Ludwig Jahn.—Joseph von Fraunhofer.—Nikolaus von Dreyse.—Friedrich List.—Justus Freiherr von Liebig.—August Borsig.—Robert Bunsen.—Alfred Krupp.—Werner von Siemens.—Heinrich Schliemann.—Heinrich von Stephan.—Philipp Reis.—Adolf Lüderitz.—Ferdinand Graf von Zeppelin.—Robert Koch.—Carl Benz.—Wilhelm Konrad Röntgen.—Carl Peters.—Rudolf Diesel.—Alfred von Tirpitz.—Adolf Hitler.

70280B. 1. Germany—Biog. I. Title.
N. Y. P. L. August 15, 1940

NL 0441931 NN MnU CSt-H DLC-P4

Loeff, Wolfgang, 1895-
Gneisenau; ein Soldatenleben. Mit Zeichnungen von W. Rosch. Leipzig. Teubner, 1935

55 p. illus. (Deutsches Ahnenerbe; Lesestoffe für den Deutsch- und Geschichtsunterricht)

NL 0441932 MH DLC-P4 NN

Loeff, Wolfgang, 1895–
Der grossadmiral, der kampf eines grossen Deutschen; ein Tirpitz-roman, von Wolfgang Loeff. Berlin, Henius & co., verlagsgesellschaft m. b. h. [c1934]

2 p. l., 7–248 p. 20½cm.

1. Tirpitz, Alfred Peter Friedrich von, 1849–1930—Fiction. I. Title.

A C 35–1601

Title from N. Y. Pub. Libr. Printed by L. C.

NL 0441933 NN CtY

Loeff, Wolfgang, 1895–
... Das Kind der Madonna, eine spanische novelle. Berlin, E. Wernitz & co. [1943]

1 p. l., [5]–59 p. 16½ cm. (Die Bunten novellen, bd. 6)

I. Title.

PT2623.O316K5 47–40507

NL 0441934 DLC CtY

Loeff, Wolfgang, 1895–
... Männer deutscher geschichte: Bismarck, Moltke, Krupp, Scheer, Hindenburg. Stuttgart, K. Thienemanns verlag [1938]

239, [1] p. front., illus. (maps) ports., diagrs. 22cm.

1. *Bismarck, Otto, fürst von, 1815–1898. 2. Moltke, Helmuth Karl Bernhard, graf von, 1800–1891. 3. Krupp, Alfred, 1812–1887. 4. Scheer, Reinhard, 1863–1928. 5. *Hindenburg, Paul von, pres. Germany, 1847–1934. I. Title.

A C 39–692

New York. Public library for Library of Congress [3]

NL 0441935 NN ICU DLC NcD

Loeff, Wolfgang, 1895–
... Männer deutscher geschichte: Bismarck, Moltke, Krupp, Scheer, Hindenburg. Stuttgart, K. Thienemann [1944]

254, [1] p. front., illus. (incl. maps) ports., diagrs. 22cm.

"9.–21. tausend."

1. *Bismarck, Otto, fürst von, 1815–1898. 2. Moltke, Helmuth Karl Bernhard, graf von, 1800–1891. 3. Krupp, Alfred, 1812–1887. 4. Scheer, Reinhard, 1863–1928. 5. *Hindenburg, Paul von, pres. Germany, 1847–1934. I. Title.

45–21314

Library of Congress DD217.5.L6 1944

[3] 923.243

NL 0441936 DLC FMU TxU IaU ICRL OCU TxU CU CtY MH

Loeff, Wolfgang, 1895– *ed.*
Panzer, minen und torpedos; selbsterlebnisse von offizieren und mannschaften unserer marine im weltkriege; herausgegeben von Wolfgang Loeff. Köln. Hermann Schaffstein verlag [c1934]

79, [1] p. illus. 20½cm.

Cover illustrated in colors.
"Quellenangabe": p. 78–79.

1. European war, 1914–1918—Naval operations. 2. European war, 1914–1918—Personal narratives, German. I. Title.

A C 35–3161

Title from N. Y. Pub. Libr. Printed by L. C.

NL 0441937 NN CtY ICU NNC MH

Loeff, Wolfgang, 1895– *ed.*
Propeller überm feind; kriegserlebnisse deutscher luftkämpfer, herausgegeben von Wolfgang Loeff. Köln, H. Schaffstein [c1934]

78, [2] p. illus. 20½cm.

"Erstes bis fünftes tausend."
"Quellenangabe": p. [80]

1. European war, 1914–1918—Aerial operations. I. Title.

35–12158

Library of Congress D604.L65

[2] 940.44943

NL 0441938 DLC WU CU NNC NcD NN

Loeff, Wolfgang, 1895- ed.
Propeller überm Feind; Kriegserlebnisse deutscher Luftkämpfer. Köln, H.Schaffstein [c.1936]

NL 0441939 MH

Loeff, Wolfgang, 1895-
Die Reiter von Deutsch-Südwest; gegen Hereros und Engländer. Mit Zeichnungen von H.Zethmeyer. Leipzig, Teubner, 1936

47 p. illus. (Deutsches Ahnenerbe; Lesestoffe für den Deutsch- und Geschichtsunterricht)

NL 0441940 MH CtY NN MH DLC-P4

Loeff, Wolfgang, 1895-
Skagerrak, die grösste Seeschlacht. Leipzig und Berlin, B. G. Teubner, 1936.
48 p.

(Deutsches Ahnenerbe. Lesestoffe für den Deutsch- und Geschichtsunterricht)

NL 0441941 NN MH CtY

Loeff, Wolfgang, 1895–
Skagerrak, die grösste Seeschlacht. 2. Aufl. Mit 6 Zeichnungen von H. Hartmann und 4 Gefechtsskizzen. Leipzig, B. G. Teubner, 1938.

48 p. illus. 19 cm. (Erbe und Verpflichtung, Lesestoffe für den Deutsch- und Geschichtsunterricht)

1. Jutland, Battle of, 1916. (Series)

D582.J8L6 1938 51–52263

NL 0441942 DLC

VOLUME 338

Loeff, Wolfgang, 1895–
Spionage; aus den Papieren eines Abwehr-Offiziers. Stuttgart, H. Riegler, 1950.
326 p. 21 cm.

1. Espionage, German.

HV7961.L6   51–32929

NL 0441943   DLC OC1 ViU NN CSt-H

4PT
Ger.-
2430
Loeff, Wolfgang, 1895–
Ulanen auf Patrouille. Berlin, G. Weise [c1939]
62 p.

NL 0441944   DLC-P4

Loeff-Basenau, An Rutgers van der
see
Rutgers van der Loeff-Basenau, An, 1910–

Löffel, Gerhard, 1911–
... Blutgruppenuntersuchungen bei Haut- und Geschlechtskrankheiten ... Leipzig, 1937.
Inaug.-Diss. - Leipzig.
Lebenslauf.

NL 0441946   CtY

Löffel, Hans.
Die Entstehung, Entwicklung und Funktion der Verbände landwirtschaftlicher Bezugs- und Absatzgenossenschaften in der Schweiz, unter besonderer Berücksichtigung des Verbandes ostschweizerischer landwirtschaftlicher Genossenschaften ... von Hans Löffel... Zürich: Diss.-Druckerei A.G. Gebr. Leemann & Co., 1939. 158 p. tables. 22½cm.

Inaugural-Dissertation — Bern, 1934.
"Literaturverzeichnis," p. 7r-8.

1. Co-operation, Agricultural—   Switzerland.
N. Y. P. L.   June 16, 1941

NL 0441947   NN DLC CtY NNC

442
L826b
Löffel, Kurt, 1908–
Beiträge zur Geschichte von montjoie, mit einem Anhang über die Sitte des Steinwerfens und der Bildung von Steinhaufen. Tübingen, E. Göbel, 1934.
68 p. illus.

Bibliography: p.62-67.
Inaug.-Diss. - Tübingen.

1. French language - Etymology. 2. French language - Words ·   History. 3. Latin language - Words ·   History. I. Title.

NL 0441948   WaU ICRL PU CtY IU

Loeffel, Walter.
Ewiges Licht. Dramatisches Spiel . . . von Walter Loeffel. Vitznau, F. Bucher [194–?] 48 p. 21cm.

1. Drama, Swiss-German.   2. Nero, emperor of Rome, 37–68—
Drama.
N.Y.P.L.   January 29, 1952

NL 0441949   NN CtY

Löffel, Wilhelm.
"Kraut ond rüaba," gedichte, humoresken und anekdoten in schwäbischer und hochdeutscher mundart, von Wilhelm Löffel (Wengerter-Knöpfle) Stuttgart, K. Felger [1929]
88 p. 15½ᵐ.

1. Title.

                                        46–34359
Library of Congress   PF5288.L6

NL 0441950   DLC

PF5288
L6S2
Löffel, Wilhelm
Schwoba-humor, neue schwäbische Witze, Anekdoten, Schnurren, Spitznamen und Heiteres, in schwäbischer Mundart. Stuttgart, P. Mähler [192–?]
39 p.

1. German language - Dialects - Swabia - Texts. I. Title.

NL 0441951   CU CtY

Loeffel, Wilh[elm].
Witz und Humor, sowie Allerhand aus der Stadt und vom Land! Gedichte, Erzählungen, Humoresken und Theaterstücke. Stuttgart, P. Mähler [190–?]
3 p.l., 3–188 p. 16°.

NL 0441952   NN

Loeffel-Jany, Walter
Freiheit durch Treue (Charlotte von Wildermeth) Historisch dramatisches Spiel in drei Akten. [Elgg, Switzerland] Volksverlag Elgg [n.d.]
63 p. 20 cm.

NL 0441953   CtY

Löffelbein, Kurt, 1913–
Zum Umbau der deutschen Wirtschaft, Betriebsprobleme des Unternehmers. München, Leibniz, 1949.
156 p. 21 cm.

1. Germany—Economic policy—1945–

HC286.5.L6   338.943   50–20661

NL 0441954   DLC ICU MH NN

Löffelhardt, Heinz.
Gedanken und Bilder zur Ausstellung wie Wohnen
see under title

LÖFFELHARDT, HEINZ, ed.
Hausrat aus Keramik, Glas, Metall, Holz; bearb. im Referat Formgestaltung des Landesgewerbeamtes Stuttgart, Van Heinz Löffelhardt. Stuttgart, von G. Hatje [1951] illus. 147 p. 24cm.
(Wie wohnen Bd. 1)

"Schriften zur Gewerbeförderung, hrsg. vom Landesgewerbeamt. Stuttgart. [Bd.] 5."

1. House furnishings.   2. Art industries and trade—Germany.
I. Württemberg-Baden. Landesgewerbeamt.

NL 0441956   NN CU

Löffelhardt, Heinz.
Katalog [der Gral-Glas-Werkstätten]
see under   Gral-Glas-Werkstätten, Göppingen.

Löffelholz, Georg Burchard, respondent and author.
...De fatalibus personarum nominibus. [Altdorfi,1682]
Diss. - Altdorf (D.W. Moller, praeses)

I. Moller, Daniel Wilhelm, 1642-1712, praeses.

NL 0441958   CtY

HG1605
.T48
Theisinger, Karl, 1901–   ed.
Die Bank; Lehrbuch und Nachschlagewerk des Bank- und Sparkassenwesens. Herausgeber: Karl Theisinger und Josef Löffelholz. Wiesbaden, T. Gabler [1952]

Löffelholz, Josef, joint ed.

Löffelholz, Josef.
Geschichte der betriebswirtschaft und der betriebswirtschaftlehre, von dr. Josef Löffelholz. Altertum—mittelalter—neuzeit bis zu beginn des 19. jahrhunderts. Stuttgart, C. E. Poeschel verlag, 1935.
xix, 376 p. 24ᵐ. (Added t.-p.: Betriebswirtschaftliche abhandlungen, hrsg. von prof. dr. W. le Coutre, prof. dr. F. Findeisen [u. a.] bd. XXIII.)
Bibliographical foot-notes.

1. Industry—History. 2. Industry—Organization, control, etc. 3. Efficiency, Industrial. 4. Business—History. I. Title.

                                        A 37–719
Illinois. Univ. Library
for Library of Congress   [3]

NL 0441960   IU NNC

Löffelholz, Josef
... Volkswirtschaftslehre (grundlagen der deutschen Volkswirtschaft) von dr. Josef Löffelholz, Berlin, und dr. Wilhelm Schotte, Berlin. Potsdam und Leipzig, Bonness & Hachfeld, 1943.
32p.

(Selbstunterrichtsbriefe Methode Rustin. hrsg. vom Rustinschen Lehrinstitut.)
Cover title

NL 0441961   IU NNC

Löffelholz von Colberg, Friedrich, *freiherr* **von,** 1807–1874.
Die bedeutung und wichtigkeit des waldes, ursache und folgen der entwaldung, die wiederbewaldung, mit rücksicht auf pflanzenphysiologie, klimatologie, meteorologie, forststatistik, forstgeographie und die forstlichen verhältnisse aller länder, für forst- und landwirthe, nationalökonomen und alle freunde des waldes aus der einschlagenden literatur systematisch und kritisch nachgewiesen und bearbeitet von Friedrich freiherrn v. Löffelholz-Colberg ... Leipzig, H. Schmidt, 1872.
vi p., 1 l., 292 p. 21ᵐ.
1. Forests and forestry—Bibl.   I. Title.
[Full name: Sigmund Friedrich Eberhard Wilhelm, freiherr von Löffelholz von Colberg]
Library of Congress   Z5991.L81
                                        3-24741 Revised

NL 0441962   DLC DAS NcD ICU PSt MiU

Loeffelholz von Colberg, Friedrich, freiherr von, 1807–1874.
Beitrag zu einer kritischen nachweisung über die schüttekrankheit der föhre oder kiefer mit angabe der verschiedenen ansichten über entstehung und wesen dieser krankheit überhaupt. Berlin. 1865. 8°. pp. 48.

NL 0441963   MH-A

Löffelholz von Colberg, Friedrich, *freiherr* **von,** 1807–1874.
Forstliche chrestomathie. Beitrag zu einer systematisch-kritischen nachweisung und beleuchtung der literatur der forstbetriebslehre und der dahin einschlagenden grund- und hülfswissenschaften. Mit rücksicht auf die forstlichen verhältnisse und zustände aller länder bearbeitet und zusammengestellt von Friedrich freiherrn von Löffelholz-Colberg ... Berlin, J. Springer, 1866–74.
5 v. in 4. 23ᵐ.
Each volume has both general and special t.-p.
No more published.

CONTENTS.—I. Einleitung in die forstwissenschaft. Forstgeschichte. Forststatistik und forstliteratur. 1866.—II. Forstjournalistik. Forst- und landwirthschaftliche vereine und versammlungen. Forstlicher unterricht überhaupt. Forst- und landwirthschaftliche lehranstalten und akademieen. Wissenschaftliche fortbildungsmittel. Nachträge. 1867.—III. 1. abth. Grundwissenschaften der forstwissenschaft, in specie die literatur der mathematik überhaupt, der geschichte derselben, sowie der arithmetik und algebra. 1871.—III. 2. abth. Die literatur der geometrie, stereometrie, trigonometrie und höheren mathematik überhaupt. 1873.—IV. Angewandte mathematik und in specie forsttaxation. Anhang: masse, gewichte und münzen. Nachträge, ergänzungen und verbesserungen. 1868.—V. 1. abth. Die forstproduktionslehre enthaltend. 1874.
1. Forests and forestry—Bibl.   I. Title.
[Full name: Sigmund Friedrich Eberhard Wilhelm, freiherr von Löffelholz von Colberg]
Library of Congress   Z5991.L82
                                        3-27010 Revised

NL 0441965   DLC DAS NIC MH-A PSt MiU

VOLUME 338

Löffelholz von Colberg, Friedrich, freiherr von, 1807-1874.
———— Praktische anweisung zum holzanbau durch pflanzung; nebst einem anhang die älteren und neueren verordnungen über die waldkultur etc. enthaltend. Ein versuch. Nürnberg. 1832. 8°. pp. 205. Plate.

NL 0441966   MH-A

———

D
534.5 Loeffelholz von Colberg, Georg, Freiherr von, ed.
.L82   Das K.B.3.Feldartillerie-Regiment Prinz Leopold. Nach den Kriegstagebüchern und persönlichen Aufzeichnungen bearb. München, 1929.
         184 p. illus.(incl.2. fold.in pocket) (Erinner ungsblätter deutscher Regimenter. Bayerische Armee, Bd.63)

         1.Germany. Heer. Bayerisches 3.Feldartillerie-Regiment Prinz Leopold. 2.European War,1914-1918--Regimental histories--Germany--Bayerisches 3.Feldartillerie-Regiment Prinz Leopold.

NL 0441967   MiU

———

LÖFFELHOLZ VON COLBERG, Karl, freiherr,1841-
   Die drehung der erdkruste in geologischen zeiträumen. Eine neu geologisch-a tronomische hypothese[With "Berichtigungen und nachträge] München,   1886.
   sm.8°. pp.52.

NL 0441968   MH-Z CU

———

Löffelholz von Colberg, Karl, *freiherr*, 1841-
   Die drehungen der erdkruste in geologischen zeiträumen. Ein neuer geologisch-astronomischer lehrsatz, von Carl freiherr Loeffelholz von Colberg ... 2. gänzlich umgearb. und verm. aufl. München, In commission bei J. A. Finsterlin nachf., 1895.

   xii, 247, [1] p. 23½ᶜᵐ.

                                                G S 15-701
   Library, U. S. Geological   Survey 210 L83d1

NL 0441969   DI-GS CU MB DLC

———

                    von Colberg,
325.343 Löffelholz ‸ Karl, freiherr von, 1841-
L82u   Ueber auswanderungen und colonisationen besonders in bezug auf Deutschland zu östlichen ländern. Als entwurf mitgeheilt ...   Nürnberg, 1843.
          176p.

NL 0441970   IU

———

Löffelholz von Colberg, Sigmund Friedrich Eberhard Wilhelm, *freiherr von*
           see
Löffelholz von Colberg, Friedrich, *freiherr von*, 1807-1874.

———

CJ 2863 LÖFFELHOLZ VON KOLBERG, WILHELM, Baron
.03 L8   Oettingana; neuer Beitrag zur öttingischen Geschichte, insbesondere zur Geschichte des öttingischen Münzwesens. Nördlingen,1883.
          278 + [69] p. 5 plates, geneal. tables.

          Der öttingische Stammbaum; Register über die öttingischen Münzen und Medaillen ... [69] p.

          1. Numismatics-Öttingen (Grafschaft). 2. Öttingen-Wallerste in, House of. I. Title.

NL 0441972   InU

———

Löffelloth, Johann Matthäus
      see
Leffloth, Johann Matthias, 1705-1731.

LÖFFELMANN, Franz.
   Das disciplinar-strafrecht im k. k. heere. Teschen , K.Prochaska, 1876.

NL 0441974   MH

———

                      1884-
Löffelmann, Heinrich. Über Befunde bei Morbus Hodgkin mittelst der Antiforminmethode. Würzburg: Kabitzsch 1912. 21 S. 8° ¶ (Aus: Beiträge z. Klinik d. Tuberkulose. Bd 24.)
Straßburg, Med. Diss. v. 11. Okt. 1912, Ref. Chiari
[Geb. 27. April 84 Paderborn; Wohnort: Paderborn; Staatsangeh.: Preußen; Vorbildung: Gymn. Paderborn Reife O. 06; Studium: Heidelberg 1, Straßburg 1, Münster 2, Berlin 1, München 1, Bonn 4 S.; Coll. 24. Mai 12.]
                                          [U 12. 6733

NL 0441975   ICRL MH

———

                      1884-
Löffelmann, Wilhelm. Ist das gerichtliche Geständnis ein Rechtsgeschäft? Paderborn 1912: Schöningh. 71 S. 8°
Würzburg, Rechts- u. staatsw. Diss. v. 4. Okt. 1912, Ref. Mendelssohn-Bartholdy
[Geb. 28. April 84 Paderborn; Wohnort: Paderborn; Staatsangeh.: Preußen; Vorbildung: Gymn. Paderborn Reife O. 04; Studium: Freiburg i. B. 3, München 1, Münster 1, Berlin 5 S.; Rig. 12. Juni 12.]   [U 12. 6890

NL 0441976   ICRL MH

———

3A
6058 LOEFFIUS, MICHIEL, d.1715.
      Geloofs belydenis van de Gereformeerde en ongereformeerde Roomse Kerke tegen een gestelt, door Michael Loeffius ... Derden druk, verbetert en vermeerdert door den autheur ... Tot Utrecht, Gedrukt by Anthony Schouten, 1699.
      [31]l.,641p. 17cm.
      Half-title, illustrated and engraved, precedes t.-p.

NL 0441977   ICN

———

ar W   Loeffke, Bruno.
53551   Rechtswirksamkeit der aus § 845 der Civilprozessordnung für das Deutsche Reich vom Gläubiger ergehenden Benachrichtigung von bevorstehender Pfändung einer seinem Schuldner gegen einen Dritten zustehenden Geldforderung gegenüber ihrer nach der Benachrichtigung von einem zweiten Gläubiger im Wege der Zwangsvollstreckung in das unbewegliche Vermögen des Schuldners bewirkten Beschlagnahme. Schöneberg, Buchdr. Brüning & Hörhold, 1902.
no.11
          31 p. 22cm.
          Inaug.-Diss.   --Erlangen.

NL 0441978   NIC MH-L ICRL

———

W 4   Loeffke, Christa, 1911-
M96   Lungengangrän. München, Waizmann,
1940   1940.
          30 p.

          Inaug.-Diss. - Munich.
          Bibliography: p. 29.

NL 0441979   DNLM

———

Löffl, V   Karl, 1884-
   ... Die chemische industrie Frankreichs. Eine industriewirtschaftliche studie über den stand der chemischen wissenschaft und industrie in Frankreich. Bearb. von dr. phil. V. Karl Löffl ... Mit 15 kurven. Stuttgart, F. Enke, 1917.
   cover-title, 311, [1] p. diagrs. 25½ᶜᵐ. (Sammlung chemischer und chemisch-technischer vorträge ... xxiv. bd, 1./7. hft.)
   "Literaturverzeichnis": p. 45-47.

   1. Chemicals—Manufacture and industry—France.

                                              21-7998
   Library of Congress   QD1.S2 xxiv. bd.

NL 0441980   DLC MiU NcD ICJ PU

Löffl, V   Karl, 1884-
   ... Technologie der fette und öle. Mit 283 abbildungen. Braunschweig, F. Vieweg & söhn akt.-ges., 1926.
   vii, 510 p. illus., diagrs. 25ᶜᵐ.
   At head of title: Karl Löffl.

   1. Oils and fats. [1. Fats and oils]
                                          Agr 28-1150 Revised
   U. S. Dept. of agr. Library   307L82
   for Library of Congress   TP670.L73
                                        [r42½2]†

NL 0441981   DNAL ICRL NN DLC

———

Loeffl, V. Karl, 1884-
   Technologie der Seifenfabrikation, von Dr. Karl Löffl... Stuttgart: F. Enke, 1928. x, 426 p. incl. diagrs., tables. illus. 8°. (Enke's Bibliothek für Chemie und Technik. Bd. 15.)

   501333A.   1. Soap—Manufacture.   I. Ser.
   N. Y. P. L.   December 10, 1930

NL 0441982   NN CtY ICJ

———

Löffl, V   Karl, 1884-
   Ueber reduktionen in der reihe der cyclischen oxime und nitrosochloride ... Basel, R. G. Zbinden, 1915.
   59, [1] p., 1 l. tables, diagrs. 22½ᶜᵐ.
   Inaug.-diss.—Basel.
   Vita.

   1. Nitroso-compounds.

NL 0441983   MiU MH CtY ICRL PU

———

Löfflath, Bernhard, 1893-
   Fünfzig Jahre Ortsverein Donauwörth im Verbande
      see under   Deutscher Buchdrucker-Verein.
   Ortsverein Donauwörth.

———

TG
445
L6   Loeffler
      Die Fundirung der Eisenbahnbrücke über den Pregel in Königsberg. Berlin, Ernst & Korn, 1867.
      8 p. illus. 45 cm.

      1. Bridges. 2. Pregel Bridge In Königsberg.

NL 0441985   DSI CtY DP

———

Löffler, A   ed.
   Mit modellierholz, schere und kreide, hrsg. von A. Löffler, F. Lindemann, H. Schimpf, mit 80 textabbildungen und 42 tafeln, davon 16 farbig ... Leipzig, A. Hahn [1910]
   83 p. illus., plates (partly col.) 24½†. M. 3.80
   "Literatur": p. 82.

   1. Manual training. I. Lindemann, F., joint author. II. Schimpf, H., joint ed.
                                                    10-16665
   Library of Congress   LB1541.L7

NL 0441986   DLC ICJ

———

372.5 Löffler, A   , ed.
L82m4   Mit modellierholz schere und kreide hrsg. von A. Löffler und F. Lindemann. 4., erweiterte aufl. ...   Leipzig, 1928.
         130p. illus., XVI col.plates, diagrs.

NL 0441987   IU

VOLUME 338

LOEFFLER, A. *photographer.*
International yacht race contenders and others marine photographs, 1893–1899. Photographed by A.Loeffler. Tompkinsville, N.Y. [1893–99] 13 mounted photos. 38x51½cm.

Photographed from plates lent by P. L. Sperr, mounted and bound by The New York Public Library, 1935.

784273A. 1. Yachting—Pictures, illustrations, etc.

NL 0441988　NN

Löffler, A　　J.
Der unterricht in der naturlehre an allgemeinen volksschulen. Eine sammlung von durchgeführten themenwinken und andeutungen. Von prof. A. J. Löffler .. Wien, A. Pichler's witwe & sohn, 1889.

vi, 216 p. 20½ᵐ.

1. Physics—Teaching.

E 11-369 Revised

Library, U. S. Bur. of　　Education QC30.L82

NL 0441989　DHEW

Loeffler, Adolf,
Eine vergleichsweise darstellung des deutschen und schweizerischen scheckrechts.
Inaug. diss. Erlangen, 1928.
Bibl.

NL 0441990　DLC CtY PU

Löffler, Adolf, 1903–
... Ein ganzer kerl. Feldpostausgabe. Berlin, Junge generation verlag [1942]
151, [1] p., 2 l. incl. illus., pl. 15ᵐ.
"4. bis 7. auflage."

1. Pferdekaemper, Fritz, 1876–1915—Fiction.　ɪ. Title.

PJ2623.O318G3　　　833.91　　　A F 47-1186

Yale univ. Library
for Library of Congress　　[4]†

NL 0441991　CtY DLC

Löffler, Adolf, 1903–
... In der weltarena, der kampf Ludwig Haymanns. Berlin, H. Reichel [1941]
315 p. plates, ports. 20½ᵐ.

1. Haymann, Ludwig.　ɪ. Title.

46-43006

Library of Congress　　GV165.H3L6

[2]　　　927.9683

NL 0441992　DLC

Löffler, Adolf, 1903–
... In der weltarena, der kampf Ludwig Haymanns. Berlin, H. Reichel [1943]
313, [1] p. plates, ports. 20½ᵐ.
Second edition.

1. Haymann, Ludwig.　ɪ. Title.

GV165.H3L6 1943　　　　　A F 47-1454

Yale univ. Library
for Library of Congress　　[3]†

NL 0441993　CtY IU DLC

Löffler, Adolf, 1903–
Sport ohne Schminke; um interessante Persönlichkeiten des Sports. Feldpostausgabe. Berlin, Junge Generation Verlag [c.1939]

"2.bis 5.Aufl."

NL 0441994　MH PPT NcD ICU NjP CtY

LÖFFLER, ADOLF, 1903–
Sport ohne Schminke; um interessante Persönlichkeiten des Sports. Feldpostausg. Berlin, Junge Generation Verlag [c1939] 170 p. 16cm.

Film reproduction. Negative.

1. Athletics—Biog.

NL 0441995　NN

R117　Löffler, Adolph Friedrich, 1758–
.L78　　Beyträge zur Arzneywissenschaft und Wundarzneykunst. [2. Aufl.] Leipzig, J. H. Kaven, 1791.
2 pts. in 1 v.
First ed. published in 1788 under title: Beyträge zur Wundarzneykunst.

1. Medicine—Addresses, essays, lectures.

NL 0441996　ICU DNLM

Loeffler (Adolphus Fridericus) [1758–　]. *De nonnullis ad chirurgiam pertinentibus.* 1 p. l., 24 pp. 4°. *Traj. ad Viadr., e typ. Winteriano,* [1795].

NL 0441997　DNLM PPC

WB　LÖFFLER, Adolph Friedrich, b. 1758
100　　Die neuesten und nützlichsten
L825n　praktischen Wahrheiten und Erfahrungen
1803　für Aerzte und Wundärzte. Erfurt, Keyser, 1803-09.
3 v.
Added title page: Handbuch der wissenswürdigsten und zur Beförderung einer glücklichen medicinischen und chirurgischen Praxis vorzüglich geeigneten neuesten Bemerkungen und Entdeckungen.

NL 0441998　DNLM PPL

WB　LÖFFLER, Adolph Friedrich, b. 1758
L825v　Vermischte Aufsätze und
1801　Beobachtungen aus der Arzneykunst, Wundarzneykunst, Geburtshülfe und gerichtlichen Arzneykunde, hrsg. mit einer Vorrede, Zusätzen und Bemerkungen von Samuel Gottlieb Vogel. Stendal, Franzen und Grosse, 1801.
xviii, 428 p. illus.

I. Vogel, Samuel Gottlieb, b. 1750

NL 0441999　DNLM ICU PPHa

Loeffler, Adolphe, 1890–
Sur les séries de Fourier à deux variables et le phénomène de Gibbs...par Adolphe Loeffler... Paris: Gauthier-Villars et Cⁱᵉ, 1920. 70 p. diagrs. 8°.

Dissertation, École polytechnique fédérale de Zurich.
Vita.

1. Series (Fourier's).
N. Y. P. L.　　　　　September 20, 1921

NL 0442001　NN ICRL DLC-P4 CtY RPB IU

Loeffler (Æmilius) [1833–　]. *De morbis febrem intermittentem excipientibus.* 32 pp. 8°. *Berolini, J. Sittenfeld,* 1854.

NL 0442002　DNLM PPC

FILM　Loeffler, Albert L.　　　Jr.
4466
Mechanism of hindered settling and fluidization. [Iowa City, Iowa] 1953.
Microfilm copy (negative) of typescript.
Collation of the original: x, 119 l., tables.
Thesis (Ph.D.)—Iowa State University.
Bibliography: leaves 80–32.

1. Fluidization. I. Title.

NL 0442003　ViU

LÖFFLER, Alexander, 1866–1929.
Die abgrenzung von vorsatz und fahrlässigkeit mit berücksichtigung des deutschen und des österreichischen vorentwürfes. Wien, n. d.

"Sonderabdruck aus der OESTERREICHISCHEN zeitung für strafrecht", 2. p.132–174.

NL 0442004　MH-L

LOEFFLER, Alexander, 1866–1929.
Der begriff der verantwortlichkeit. Berlin , n. d.

p. 387–98.
"Mitteilungen der INTERNATIONALEN kriminalistischen vereinigung, VI. Sonderabdruck".

NL 0442005　MH-L

Löffler, Alexander, 1866–
Die entschädigung unschuldig verhafteter. Vortrag gehalten am 13. dezember 1905 in der Juristischen gesellschaft in Wien, als einleitung zur diskussion über das gleiche thema, von professor dr. Alexander Löffler ... Wien, Manz, 1906.
24 p. 25ᵐ.
"Separatabdruck aus der Allgem. österreich. gerichts-zeitung, 56. jahrg. 1905, nr. 52."

1. False imprisonment—Austria. 2. Compensation for judicial error—Austria. ɪ. Title.

8-29850

NL 0442006　DLC CtY-L NcD

LÖFFLER, Alexander, 1866–
Der entwurf eines gesetzes betreffend die auswanderung; eine kritik. Wien,1913.

19 p.
"Sonderabdruck aus der OESTERREICHISCHEN zeitschrift für strafrecht", 4.
Autograph dedication.

NL 0442007　MH-L

Löffler, Alexander, 1866–
Die körperverletzung ... von professor dr. Alexander Löffler... [Berlin, Otto Liebmann, 1907?]
179 p. 26.5 cm.
Caption title.
"Literatur": p. 1–4.
"Sonderabdruck aus der 'Vergleichenden darstellung des deutschen und ausländischen strafrechts."

NL 0442008　CtY

LÖFFLER, Alexander, 1866–
Die kurpfuscherei im österreichischen strafrechte mit besonderer berücksichtigung der zahnärztlichen praxis. Wien,1904.

13 p.
"Separat-abdruck aus der Oesterreichischen zeitschrift für stomatologie", 4.

NL 0442009　MH-L

LÖFFLER, Alexander, 1866–
Miszellen; die österreichische kriminalistik für 1909. Wien,1913.

NL 0442010　MH-L

VOLUME 338

Löffler, Alexander, 1866–
Das rechtsmittel gegen die entscheidung über anrechnung der untersuchungshaft. Wien, 1912.
8 p.

NL 0442011   MH-L

LOFFLER, Alexander, 1866–
Die reform des österreichischen strafgesetzes
Wien, 1910

2 pt.
"Sonderabdruck aus der OSTERREICHISCHEN zeitschrift für strafrecht", 1, pt. 2, 5. 6.
Autograph dedication.

NL 0442012   MH-L

LÖFFLER, Alexander, 1866–
Die schuldformen des strafrechts in vergleichend-historischer und dogmatischer darstellung. Leipzig, 1895.

v. 1 (pt. 1).

NL 0442013   MH-L CtY

Löffler, Alexander, 1866–1929.
Der Schutz der Gläubigerrechte in den schweizerischen Vorentwürfen. Von Professor Alexander Löffler ... [Bern, Stämpfli & Cie., 1916]

73-94 p. 23cm.

Caption title.
On cover: Schweizerische Zeitschrift für Strafrecht. Revue pénale suisse ... 29.
Jhrg. 1. und 2. Hft.
Bibliographical   footnotes.

NL 0442014   MH-L

LÖFFLER, Alexander, 1866–
Strafe und fürsorgeerziehung; eine studie zum entwurfe eines fürsorgeerziehungsgesetzes.
Wien, 1909.

12 p.
"Sonderabdruck aus der Allgemeinen öster. Gerichts-zeitung", 60.

NL 0442015   MH-L

Löffler, Alexander, 1866– ed.
Das Strafgesetz vom 27. Mai 1852, Nr. 117
RGBl.
          see under   Austria. Laws, statutes, etc.

Law
Löffler, Alexander, 1866–1929, ed.

Austria. *Laws, statutes, etc.*
Die Strafprozess-ordnung vom 23. mai 1873, nr. 119 Rg. b., samt allen ergänzenden und erläuternden gesetzen und verordnungen unter anführung einschlägiger entscheidungen und beschlüsse des Obersten gerichts- als kassationshofes. 13., neu rev. und umgearb. aufl., bearb. von dr. Alexander Löffler ... und Wilhelm Hermann v. Herrnritt ... Wien, Manz, 1914.

Löffler, Alexander, 1866–1929, ed.

Austria. *Laws, statutes, etc.*
Das strafrecht ... herausgegeben von dr. Alexander Löffler ... Leipzig, C. L. Hirschfeld, 1904–05.

Löffler, Alexander, 1866–
Die strafrechtliche behandlung jugendlicher. Eine studie zur österreichischen regierungsvorlage. Von professor Alexander Löffler. Wien, Manz, 1908.
77 p. 28½ᵐ.
"Sonderabdruck aus der Allgemeinen österr. gerichts-zeitung, 59. jahrgang, nr. 21, 22, 23 und 24."

1. Juvenile delinquency—Austria. 2. Juvenile courts—Austria.
i. Title.
                                              38-36933

NL 0442019   DLC MH

Löffler, Alexander, 1866–1929.
Strafrechtliche Bestimmungen. Von Alexander Löffler. [Wien, F. Tempsky, 1917]
1 p.l., [419]-577 p. 24cm.

Caption title.
"Bartsch-Pollak, Konkursordnung II."
"Literaturverzeichnis": p. [491]-420.

NL 0442020   MH-L CtY

Löffler, Alexander, 1866–1929, ed.
Die tierseuchengesetze in der neuen fassung der gesetze vom 6. august 1909 samt den durchführungsverordnungen mit erläuternden anmerkungen und den entscheidungen des K. K. Obersten gerichts- und kassationshofes, herausgegeben von dr. Alexander Löffler ... Wien, Manz, 1910.
viii, [2], 250 p. fold. form. 16°.
"Nachtrag" ([2] p.) inserted after p. viii.
1. Contagion and contagious diseases in animals. 2. Veterinary jurisprudence—Austria. 3. Veterinary medicine—Austria. i. Austria. Laws, statutes, etc. ii. Title.
                                              42-47876
Library of Congress   SF780.A8L6

NL 0442021   DLC MH-L

Löffler, Alexander, 1866–1929.
... Tötung und Körperverletzung. Von. Prof. A. Löffler ... [Leipzig, G. Freytag, 1921]
142-157 p. 23½cm.

Caption title.
"Gleispach, Der Deutsche Strafgesetz-Entwurf."
Bibliographical footnotes.

NL 0442022   MH-L

LÖFFLER, Alexander. 1866–
Ueber unheilbare nichtigkeit im österreichischen strafverfahren. Wien, 1904.

72 p.
"Separat-abdruck aus der... ZEITSCHRIFT' für das privat-und öffentliche recht der gegenwart," 31.

NL 0442023   MH-L NcD

Löffler, Alexander, 1866–1929.
Unrecht und Notwehr. Prolegomena zu einer Revision der Lehre von der Notwehr. Von ... Dr. Alexander Löffler ... [Berlin? 1901?]
46 p. 22cm.

Caption title.
On cover: Sonderabdruck aus Zeitschrift für die gesamte Strafrechtswissenschaft.
Einundzwanzigster Band. 1901.
Bibliographical footnotes.

NL 0442024   MH-L

Löffler, Alexander, 1866–1929.
Zur Lehre vom dolus indirectus. Von
Dr. Alexander Löffler ... [Wien, 1896]

cover-title, 15 p. 23½cm.

"Separat-Abdruck aus Geller's Centralblatt für die juristische Praxis, Wien, August 1896."
Bibliographical footnotes.

NL 0442025   MH-L

LÖFFLER, Alexander. 1866– 1929.
Zur psychologischen tatbestands-diagnostik. [Heidelberg], n. d.

"Sonderabdruck aus der MONATSSCHRIFT für kriminalpsychologie und strafrechtsreform" 3, p. 449-66.

Autograph dedication.

NL 0442026   MH-L

Löffler, Alfred, joint author.

Mebus, Gustav.
... Sensationen; komödie in 3 akten aus dem journalisten-leben, von Gustav Mebus und Alfred Löffler. Berlin, [1911].

W 4   LÖFFLER, Andreas
B29   Spättodesfälle nach traumatischen
1954   Einwirkungen auf die Halsgegend;
         Beitrag zur Frage des Carotissinus-
         Syndromes. Basel, 1954.
         24 p.
         Inaug.-Diss. - Basel.
         1. Carotid sinus 2. Neck - Injuries

NL 0442028   DNLM MiU

Loeffler (Anton). *Ein Beitrag zur Aetiologie der Kindslage. 32 pp. 8°. Würzburg, A. Boegler, 1868.

NL 0442029   DNLM

Löffler, Anton.
Benesch, Stalin & Co. Der Weg eines Auch-Staates. Berlin, Brunnen-Verlag [193-?]
47 p. illus., ports. 21 cm.

1. Czechoslovak Republic—Pol. & govt.

DB215.L74   943.7   50-45204

NL 0442030   DLC NN WU CtY CU

Löffler, August, 1822–1866.
L'Orient pittoresque
          see under   Busch, Moritz, 1821-1899.

LÖFFLER, Bernhard.
Wann und auf welche weise beeinflussen suspendierte Teilchen , etc., Inaug.-diss., Marburg, 1906.

NL 0442032   MH ICRL PU

VOLUME 338

NK1533 Löffler, Bertold, 1874–
.F5   Die fläche; dekorative entwürfe, neue folge..
v.2   Vienna, A. Schroll & co., n.d.
pt.2

     cover title.
     At head of t.p.: Band 2; 12 hefte, je 16 seiten,
     stark sind ein band. 2. heft.

NL 0442033   InU

Loeffler, Bruno.
   Entwicklungsgeschichtliche und vergleichend anatomische
Untersuchung des Stammes und der Uhrfederranken von Bau-
hinia (Phanera) spec. Ein Beitrag zur Kenntnis der rankenden
Lianen von Bruno Löffler. (Ausgeführt mit Benützung der von
Prof. Dr. Heinricher von seiner Studienreise nach Java mitge-
brachten Materialien.) (Kaiserliche Akad. der Wissenschaften.
Denkschriften. Mathematische-naturwissenschaftliche Klasse.
Wien, 1915. f°. Bd. 91, p. 1–17, plates.)

     Aus dem botanischen Institut der K. K. Universität in Innsbruck.

1. Bauhinia. 2. Botany (Physio-   logical and structural). 3. Heinricher, Emil, 1856–
N. Y. P. L.   May 26, 1922

NL 0442034   NN NIC

Löffler, C.
   Bei Mutter Grün. Komische Gerichts-Szene in einem Akt von
Dr. C. Löffler... Berlin: E. Bloch [1921] 15 p. 18½ cm.
(Ludwig Bloch's Herren-Bühne. Nr. 72.)

1. Drama, German. I. Title.
N. Y. P. L.   May 24, 1937

NL 0442035   NN

     Löffler, Carl, 1821–1874
         see   Löffler, Karl Valentin Immanuel,
     1821–1874.

GA
L18
   Löffler, Carl, 1872–
     Ein Verzeichnis von Büchern aus dem Bestande
der Berliner Städtischen Volksbüchereien,
gestaltet von Carl Löffler, Annemarie Mälzer,
Helene Schulte, unter Mitarbeit von Gertrud
Penner, Ortrud Rücker, Joachim Schultz. Berlin,
Hrsg. im Auftrage des Magistrats von Gross-
Berlin [1949]
     67 p. illus. (Goethe-Literatur der Berliner
Volksbüchereien)

NL 0442037   NNC

Loeffler (Carl) [1872–]. * Zur Prognose der
Knochensarkome. 42 pp., 1 l. 8°. *Halle a. S.,
Wischan & Wettengel, 1896.*

NL 0442038   DNLM NNC MBCo

     Löffler, Carl, 1875–1935
         see   Löffler, Karl, 1875–1935.

     Loeffler, Carl, 1901–
     Die staatliche krankenversicherung in den eur-
opäischen kulturlaendern in vergleich zur deutschen sozialgesetzgebung.
     Inaug. diss. – Freiburg, 1927.
     Bibl.

NL 0442040   ICRL CtY MiU PBm

Loeffler, Carl A.

   U. S. *67th Cong., 2d sess., 1921–1922. Senate.*
     ... Fordney-McCumber tariff bill of 1922. Yea-and-nay
votes in the United States Senate Sixty-seventh Congress,
second session, on the bill and all amendments thereto,
H. R. 7456 to provide revenue, to regulate commerce with
foreign countries, to encourage the industries of the
United States, and for other purposes. With index.
Comp. by C. A. Loeffler. Washington, Govt. print. off.,
1922.

NL 0442043   IU

Loeffler, Carl A., comp.

   U. S. *71st Cong., 2d sess., 1929–1930. Senate.*
     ... Hawley-Smoot tariff bill of 1930. Yea-and-nay votes in
the United States Senate, Seventy-first Congress, on the bill
and all amendments thereto, H. R. 2667 to provide revenue,
to regulate commerce with foreign countries, to encourage the
industries of the United States, to protect American labor
and for other purposes; and on Senate resolution 52, by Mr.
McMaster, Senate resolution 91, by Mr. Borah, Senate resolution 108, by Mr. Simmons, and Senate resolution 270, by Mr.
Smoot. With Index. Compiled by C. A. Loeffler. Washington, U. S. Govt. print. off., 1930.

342.731 Loeffler, Carl A
L82p   Proposed amendments to the Constitution of the
United States introduced in Congress from the
69th Congress, 2d session, through the 79th Con-
gress, December 6, 1926, to January 3, 1947. Re-
vised by the Senate Library under direction of
Carl G. Loeffler. Washington, U.S. Govt.
Print. Off., 1947.
     iii, 114p. 23cm.

     1. U.S.--Constitution--Amendments. I. U.S.--
Senate--Library.

NL 0442043   IU

     Löffler, Carl Valentin Immanuel
         see   Loeffler, Karl Valentin Immanuel,
     1821–1874.

Loeffler, Charles Martin Tornov, 1861–1935.
   [A une femme]

     A une femme. Poésie de Paul Verlaine. [19—]
     7 p. 35 cm.
     Copyist's ms.
     For medium voice, violin, and piano.

     1. Songs (Medium voice) with instr. ensemble. I. Title.

     M1621.3.L   M 59-871

NL 0442045   DLC

[**Loeffler, Charles Martin Tornov**] 1861–1935.
   [A une femme]

     A une femme. Poésie de Paul Verlaine. [19—
     [4] p. 33 cm.
     Holograph, in ink.
     In caption of p. [1]: À Mme Richard Aldrich.
     Version for medium voice and piano, without the violin obbligato

     1. Songs (Medium voice) with piano. I. Title.

     ML96.L61   M 59-862

NL 0442046   DLC

Loeffler, Charles Martin Tornov, 1861–1935.
   [Airs tziganes, violin & piano]

     Airs tziganes; pour violon avec piano. [n. d.]
     score ([7] + 35 cm.
     Holograph, in ink (incomplete)
     Composer's copy of score ([2] p.) 35 cm. and part. 28 x 34 cm.
(both incomplete) laid in.

     1. Violin and piano music. I. Title.

     ML96.L61   M 59-1125

NL 0442047   DLC

Loeffler, Charles Martin Tornov, 1861–1935.
   [L'archet. Voice score. French]

     L'archet. [n. p., 19—]
     12 p. 35 cm.
     Caption title.
     Chorus score (SSAA) of the work for soprano solo, chorus (SSAA)
viola d'amore, and piano or orchestra.
     Text partly in Latin.

     1. Choruses, Secular (Women's voices, 4 pts.) with orchestra—
Vocal scores. I. Title.

     M1544.L75A7   M 59-754

NL 0442048   DLC

ML96
.L61
(Case)   **Loeffler, Charles Martin Tornov,** 1861–1935.
     [L'archet. Piano-vocal score. English & French]

     L'archet; légende pour soprano solo, chœur de femmes
avec viole d'amour. The bow; legend for soprano solo,
chorus of women, with viola d'amore and piano or orchestra.
Text adapted from the French. Op. 26. [19—]
     34 p. 33 cm.
     Copyist's ms., with pencil corrections and English text in com-
poser's hand. Text partly in Latin (not translated)

                                         M 59-743

NL 0442049   DLC

Loeffler, Charles Martin Tornov, 1861–1935.
   [Ave Maris Stella]

     Ave Maris Stella; for boys' voices, solo soprano, strings,
piano, and organ, after an old chant by Orazio Vecchi, 1595
(Convito musicale, Venetia, 1595) [n. d.]
     score ([5] p.) and parts. 34 cm.
     Holograph, in ink.
     Organ-vocal score ([2] p.) laid in.
     1. Choruses, Sacred (Unison) with string orchestra—Scores. 2.
Choruses, Sacred (Unison) with string orchestra—Vocal scores with
organ. 3. Ave Maris Stella (Music) I. Vecchi, Orazio, 1550–1605.
Convito musicale.

     ML96.L61   M 59-1205

NL 0442050   DLC

Loeffler, Charles Martin Tornov, 1861–1935.
   [Ballade carnavalesque]

     Ballade carnavalesque. [190–?]
     score (81 p.) 36 cm.
     Copyist's ms., in ink, with composer's corrections, in pencil.
     For flute, oboe, saxophone in E♭, bassoon, and piano.

     1. Quintets (Piano, bassoon, flute, oboe, saxophone) I. Title.

     ML96.L61   M 59-1230

NL 0442051   DLC

VOLUME 338

Loeffler, Charles Martin Tornov, 1861–1935.

Barcarolle, d'après des mélodies arabes. ₁n. d.₁

score (₁9₁ p.) 23 x 30 cm.

Holograph, in ink.
For violin and piano.
Another setting of part of the work (₁5₁ p.) laid in.

1. Violin and piano music. I. Title.

ML96.L61   M 59–1123

NL 0442052   DLC

Loeffler, Charles Martin Tornov, 1861–1935.
₁Beat! Beat! Drums! Arr.₁

Beat! Beat! Drums! For men's voices in unison. Words
from Drum taps, by Walt Whitman. Boston, C. C. Birchard
₁*1932₁

13 p. 28 cm.

With piano acc.; acc. originally for orchestra.

1. Choruses, Secular (Unison) with orchestra—Vocal scores with
piano. I. Title.

M1609.L   M 56–994

NL 0442053   DLC NN MB RPB FTaSU

Loeffler, Charles Martin Tornov, 1861–1935.
₁Berceuse₁

Berceuse. ₁188–?₁

score (₁4₁ p.) 35 cm.

Holograph, in ink.
For violin and piano.
Published (with slight revisions) Paris, J. Hamelle ₁188–?₁

1. Violin and piano music. I. Title.

ML96.L61   M 59–742

NL 0442054   DLC

Loeffler, Charles Martin Tornov, 1861–1935.
₁Berceuse₁

Berceuse, pour violon avec accompagnement de piano,
par M. Loeffler-Tornow. Paris, J. Hamelle ₁188–?₁ Pl. no.
J. 2185. H.

score (5 p.) and part. 34 cm.

1. Violin and piano music. I. Title.

M221.L   M 59–728

NL 0442055   DLC

Loeffler, Charles Martin Tornov, 1861–1935.
₁Bolero triste₁

Bolero triste. ₁A une femme. 19—₁

₁12₁ p. 34 cm.

Holograph, in ink, with pencil corrections.
For medium voice, violin, and piano.
Words of the 1st song by Gustave Kahn; the 2d, by Paul Verlaine

1. Songs (Medium voice) with instr. ensemble. I. Loeffler,
Charles Martin Tornov, 1861–1935. A une femme. II. Title. III.
Title: A une femme.

ML96.L61   M 59–941

NL 0442056   DLC

₁Loeffler, Charles Martin Tornov₁ 1861–1935.
₁Poem, orchestra₁

La bonne chanson. ₁190–?₁

score (44 p.) 34 cm.

Holograph, in ink, with composer's ms. corrections (partly in
pencil, partly pasted in)
At end: 3 years ago I practically reorchestrated this score. 1918.
Published: New York, G. Schirmer, *1923.

1. Symphonic poems—Scores. I. Title.

ML96.L61   63–32412/M

NL 0442057   DLC

Loeffler, Charles Martin, 1861–
[La bonne chanson.] Poem composed for orchestra by Ch. M.
Lœffler. Score.
— New York. G. Schirmer, Inc. [1923.] (4), 60 pp. 32 cm.
This composition is a musical paraphrase of the fifth poem in Paul Ver-
laine's La bonne chanson. Composed in 1901, it was originally entitled
Poem for orchestra . . . Later revised by the composer, it was given the
title La bonne chanson.

N7887 — 1. r. — Symphonic poems.

NL 0442058   MB

Loeffler, Charles Martin Tornov, 1861–1935.
The bow
see his
L'archet.

₁Loeffler, Charles Martin Tornov₁ 1861–r₁
Busslied, aus dem 16ᵗᵉⁿ Jahrhundert. ₁n. d.₁

₁10₁ p. 33 cm.

Holograph, in ink, with corrections, in pencil.
For voice and piano. First line of text: Gott, wie sind meine
Sünden so schwer.

1. Sacred songs (Medium voice) with piano. I. Title.

ML96.L61   M 59–1222

NL 0442060   DLC

₁Loeffler, Charles Martin Tornov₁ 1861–1935.

By-an'-by. ₁19—₁

₁4₁ p. 35 cm.

Holograph, in pencil (incomplete)
For voice and piano.
Composer's copy, in pencil, of the song, and incomplete score of
arrangement for voice and orchestration (₁4₁ p.) laid in.

1. Songs (Medium voice) with piano. I. Title.

ML96.L61   M 59–1124

NL 0442061   DLC

ML96
.L61
Case

Loeffler, Charles Martin Tornov, 1861–1935.
₁Brahms, Johannes, 1833–1897.
₁Concerto, violin, op. 77, D major. Cadenza (Loeffler)₁

Cadence pour le Concerto de Brahms. ₁19—₁

Loeffler, Charles Martin Tornov, 1861–1935.
Cadence pour le 1. concerto de C. St. Saëns. ₁19—?₁

₁2₁ p. 35 cm.

Holograph, in ink, with pencil additions and corrections.

1. Concertos (Violin)—Cadenzas. I. Saint-Saëns, Camille, 1835–
1921. Concerto, violin, no. 1, op. 20, A major.

ML96.L61   M 59–1140
[M1012.5]

NL 0442063   DLC

ML96
.L61
Case

Loeffle, Charles Martin Tornov, 1861–1935.
Paganini, Nicolò, 1782–1840.
₁Concerto, violin, no. 1, op. 6, E♭ major. Cadenza (Loeffler)₁

Cadence pour le premier concerto de Paganini par C. M.
Loeffler. ₁n. d.₁

Loeffler, Charles Martin Tornov, 1861–1935.
₁Canticum fratris solis. Italian₁

The canticle of the sun (words by St. Francis of Assisi)
for voice and chamber-orchestra. ₁1925₁

score (₁64₁ p.) 37 cm. holograph.

In ink, the voice line partly in pencil.
Title on cover: Canticum fratris solis.
On t. p.: To Mrs. Elizabeth Sprague Coolidge in profound admira-
tion. Ch.-M. Loeffler.
Modern Italian version of the words by Gino Perera.
Commissioned and published (1925) by the Elizabeth Sprague
Coolidge Foundation in the Library of Congress. First performed at
the 1st Festival of Chamber Music, Library of Congress, Oct. 28, 1925.

Gift of Mrs. Coolidge, Nov. 2, 1925.

1. Songs (High voice) with chamber orchestra—Scores. I. Francesco d'Assisi, Saint, 1182–1226. Cantico de lo frate sole. II. Loeffler,
Charles Martin Tornov, 1861–1935. MSS. III. U. S. Library of Congress. Elizabeth Sprague Coolidge Foundation. IV. Title. V. Title:
Canticum fratris solis.

ML29c.L82   M 55–1850

NL 0442066   DLC

₁Loeffler, Charles Martin Tornov₁ 1861–1935.
₁Canticum fratris solis; arr.₁

Canticum fratris solis. ₁192–₁

score (32 p.) 32 cm.

Holograph, in ink.
Title from Baker's biog. dict. of musicians, 5th ed.
For chorus (SSA); originally for soprano and chamber orchestra.
Words by St. Francis of Assisi, in a modern Italian version by Gino
Perera.
Commissioned by the Elizabeth Sprague Coolidge Foundation in
the Library of Congress.

1. Choruses, Sacred (Women's voices, 3 pts.) Unaccompanied. 2.
Francesco d'Assisi, Saint, 1182–1226—Musical settings. I. Francesco d'Assisi, Saint, 1182–1226. Cantico de lo frate sole. II. U. S.
Library of Congress.   Elizabeth Sprague Coolidge Foundation. III. Title.

ML29C.L82   63–43180/M

NL 0442067   DLC

Loeffler, Charles Martin Tornov, 1861–1935.
₁Canticum fratris solis. Italian₁

Canticum fratris solis. ₁1925₁

parts. 35 cm.

Copyist's ms., in ink, of a work for soprano and chamber orchestra.
Orchestral acc. only.
Commissioned by the Elizabeth Sprague Coolidge Foundation in
the Library of Congress.

1. Sacred songs (High voice) with chamber orchestra—Parts (instrumental)   I. U. S. Library of Congress. Elizabeth Sprague
Coolidge Foundation. II. Title.

ML29d.L82   63–42659/M

NL 0442068   DLC

Loeffler, Charles Martin Tornov, 1861–1935.
₁Canticum fratris solis. Italian₁

Canticum fratris solis. ₁1925₁

score (₁64₁ p.) 36 cm.

Photocopy (positive) of holograph, with composer's ms. correc-
tions, in ink, pasted in on p. 21–24.
For soprano and chamber orchestra.
Words by St. Francis of Assisi, in a modern Italian version by
Gino Perera.
Commissioned by the Elizabeth Sprague Coolidge Foundation in
the Library of Congress.
1. Sacred songs (High voice) with chamber orchestra—Scores. 2.
Francesco d'Assisi, Saint, 1182–1226—Musical settings. I. Fran-
cesco d'Assisi, Saint, 1182–1226. Cantico de lo frate sole. II. U. S.
Library of Congress.   Elizabeth Sprague Coolidge Founda-
tion. III. Title.

ML29c.L82   63–42660/M

NL 0442069   DLC

₁Loeffler, Charles Martin Tornov₁ 1861–1935.
₁Canticum fratris solis. Italian₁

Canticum fratris solis. ₁1925₁
score (46 p.) 35 cm.
Holograph (unfinished) in ink and pencil.
Title from Baker's biog. dict. of musicians, 5th ed.
For soprano and chamber orchestra.
Words by St. Francis of Assisi, in a modern Italian version by
Gino Perera.
Commissioned by the Elizabeth Sprague Coolidge Foundation in
the Library of Congress.
1. Sacred songs (High voice) with chamber orchestra—Scores. 2.
Francesco d'Assisi, Saint, 1182–1226—Musical settings. I. Fran-
cesco d'Assisi, Saint, 1182–1226. Cantico de lo frate sole. II. U. S.
Library of Congress.   Elizabeth Sprague Coolidge Founda-
tion. III. Title.

ML29c.L82   63–42662/M

NL 0442070   DLC

VOLUME 338

₍Loeffler, Charles Martin Tornov₎ 1861–1935.
₍Canticum fratris solis₎

Canticum fratris solis. ₍1925₎

score (1 v., various pagings) 28–37 cm.

Holograph sketches, in pencil and ink.
Title from Baker's biog. dict. of musicians, 5th ed.
For soprano and chamber orchestra.
Commissioned by the Elizabeth Sprague Coolidge Foundation in the Library of Congress.

ɪ. U. S. Library of Congress. Elizabeth Sprague Coolidge Foundation. ɪɪ. Title.

ML29c.L82   63–42666/M

NL 0442071   DLC

ML29d
.L82
case

Loeffler, Charles Martin Tornov, 1861–1935.
₍Canticum fratris solis. Piano-vocal score. Italian₎

Canticum fratris solis. Canticle of the sun. St. Francis of Assisi; modern Italian version by Gino Perera. Vocal score. ₍1925₎

24 p. 35 cm. MS.

Copyist's MS., in ink, with corrections and annotations by the composer and others. Piano reduction, for rehearsal purposes, of the original for voice and chamber orchestra.
Commissioned and published (1929) by the Elizabeth Sprague Coolidge Foundation in the Library of Congress. First performed at the 1st Festival of Chamber Music, Library of Congress, Oct. 28, 1925.

1. Songs (High voice) with chamber orchestra—Vocal scores with piano. ɪ. Francesco d'Assisi, Saint, 1182–1226. Cantico de lo frate sole. ɪɪ. Loeffler, Charles Martin Tornov, 1861–1935. MSS. ɪɪɪ. Library of Congress. Elizabeth Sprague Coolidge Foundation. ɪᴠ. Title. ᴠ. Title: Canticle of the sun.

ML29d.L82   M 55–1827

NL 0442073   DLC

Loeffler, Charles Martin Tornov, 1861–1935.
₍Canticum fratris solis. Italian₎

Canticum fratris solis. Canticle of the sun. St. Francis of Assisi; modern Italian version by Gino Perera. ₍1925₎

score (64 p.) 43 cm. and 14 parts. 35 cm. MS.

Copyist's MS., in ink, with pencil corrections and annotations by the composer and others.
For voice and chamber orchestra.
Commissioned and published (1929) by the Elizabeth Sprague Coolidge Foundation in the Library of Congress. First performed at the 1st Festival of Chamber Music, Library of Congress, Oct. 28, 1925.
Duration : 17 min.

Photocopy (positive) of the 1st and 2d violin parts laid in container.

1. Songs (High voice) with chamber orchestra—Scores and parts (instrumental) ɪ. Francesco d'Assisi, Saint, 1182–1226. Cantico de lo frate sole. ɪɪ. Loeffler, Charles Martin Tornov, 1861–1935. MSS. ɪɪɪ. U. S. Library of Congress. Elizabeth Sprague Coolidge Foundation. ɪᴠ. Title.

ML29d.L82   M 55–1840

NL 0442075   DLC

Loeffler, Charles Martin Tornov, 1861–1935.
₍Canticum fratris solis. Piano-vocal score. Italian₎

Canticum fratris solis. Hymn to our brother the sun, by St. Francis of Assisi. Set to music for voice and chamber orchestra by Ch.-M. Loeffler. Piano reduction to be used for rehearsal only. 1925.

23 p. 37 cm. holograph.

In ink.
Pages 21–22 wanting : p. 23 blank.
Modern Italian version of the words by Gino Perera.

Commissioned and published (1929) by the Elizabeth Sprague Coolidge Foundation in the Library of Congress. First performed at the 1st Festival of Chamber Music, Library of Congress, Oct. 28, 1925. Gift of Mrs. Loeffler, Oct. 8, 1935.

1. Songs (High voice) with chamber orchestra—Vocal scores with piano. ɪ. Francesco d'Assisi, Saint, 1182–1226. Cantico de lo frate sole. ɪɪ. Loeffler, Charles Martin Tornov, 1861–1935. MSS. ɪɪɪ. U. S. Library of Congress. Elizabeth Sprague Coolidge Foundation. ɪᴠ. Title. ᴠ. Title: Hymn to our brother the sun.

ML29c.L82   M 55–1709

NL 0442077   DLC

Loeffler, Charles Martin Tornov, 1861–1935.
₍Canticum fratris solis. Organ-vocal score. Italian₎

Canticum fratris solis. Organ score. ₍1925₎

24 p. 35 cm. MS.

Copyist's MS., in ink, the t. p. in the composer's hand, in pencil. May be used as an orchestral part in the original acc. for chamber orchestra.
Commissioned and published (1929) by the Elizabeth Sprague Coolidge Foundation in the Library of Congress. First performed at the 1st Festival of Chamber Music, Library of Congress, Oct. 28, 1925. Gift of Mrs. Coolidge, Jan. 22, 1931.

1. Songs (High voice) with chamber orchestra—Vocal scores with organ. ɪ. Francesco d'Assisi, Saint, 1182–1226. Cantico de lo frate sole. ɪɪ. Loeffler, Charles Martin Tornov, 1861–1935. MSS. ɪɪɪ. U. S. Library of Congress. Elizabeth Sprague Coolidge Foundation. ɪᴠ. Title.

ML29d.L82   M 55–1729

NL 0442078   DLC

Loeffler, Charles Martin Tornov, 1861–1935.
₍Canticum fratris solis; arr.₎

Canticum fratris solis. Canticle of the sun; arr. for women's voices by the composer. ᶜ1929.

score (29 p.) 34 cm.

Copyist's ms., in ink.
With piano acc. intended for rehearsal only; originally for soprano and chamber orchestra.
Words by St. Francis of Assisi, in a modern Italian version by Gino Perera.

Commissioned by the Elizabeth Sprague Coolidge Foundation in the Library of Congress.

1. Choruses, Sacred (Women's voices, 3 pts.), Unaccompanied. 2. Francesco d'Assisi, Saint, 1182–1226 — Musical settings. ɪ. Francesco d'Assisi, Saint, 1182–1226. Cantico de lo frate sole. ɪɪ. U. S. Library of Congress. Elizabeth Sprague Coolidge Foundation. ɪɪɪ. Title. ɪᴠ. Title : Canticle of the sun.

ML29d.L82   63–43173/M

NL 0442080   DLC ICU IU MoU

Loeffler, Charles Martin Tornov, 1861–1935.
₍Canticum fratris solis. Piano-vocal score. Italian₎

Canticum fratris solis, set for voice and chamber orchestra to the hymn by St. Francis of Assisi, in a modern Italian version by Gino Perera. Vocal score. Washington, Library of Congress, Elizabeth Sprague Coolidge Foundation ₍1929₎

24 p. 31 cm.

Includes English and French translations of the words printed as text.

1. Songs (High voice) with chamber orchestra—Vocal scores with piano. ɪ. Francesco d'Assisi, Saint, 1182–1226. Cantico de lo frate sole. ɪɪ. U. S. Library of Congress. Elizabeth Sprague Coolidge Foundation. ɪɪɪ. Title.

M1614.L79C2   M 54–238

NL 0442081   DLC IU

Loeffler, Charles Martin Tornov, 1861–1935.
₍Canticum fratris solis. Italian₎

Canticum fratris solis, set for voice and chamber orchestra to the hymn by St. Francis of Assisi, in a modern Italian version by Gino Perera. Washington, Library of Congress, Elizabeth Sprague Coolidge Foundation ₍1929₎

score (95 p.) 35 cm. and parts. 31 cm.

"Limited to 200 copies."
"Played as the first work of chamber music on the first program of the first festival of chamber music held at the Library of Congress, October 28–30, 1925."

Includes translations of the canticle, in English by T. O'Conor Sloane, and in French by T. de Wyzewa, as published in their respective translations of "Den hellige Frans af Assisi" by J. Jorgensen.

1. Songs (High voice) with chamber orchestra—Scores and parts (instrumental) ɪ. Francesco d'Assisi, Saint, 1182–1226. Cantico de lo frate sole. ɪɪ. U. S. Library of Congress. Elizabeth Sprague Coolidge Foundation. ɪɪɪ. Title.

M1613.3.L7C3   29–23901 rev*

NL 0442083   DLC OrP MB OC1 PP

Loeffler, Charles Martin Tornov, 1861–1935.

Capriccio russe, pour violon et piano, par M. L. ₍n. d.₎

score (₍10₎ p.) 36 cm.

Holograph, in ink.
In caption : Dedié à mon ami Leop. Lichtenberg.

1. Violin and piano music. ɪ. Title.

ML96.L61   M 59–1142

NL 0442084   DLC

Loeffler, Charles Martin Tornov, 1861–1935, arr.
... Caprice espagnol ...
see under Ketten, Henri, 1848–1883.

₍Loeffler, Charles Martin Tornov₎ 1861–1935.

La chanson des ingénues. Poésie de Paul Verlaine. ₍n. d.₎

score (₍4₎ + p.) 35 cm.

Holograph (incomplete) in ink, with pencil additions, preceded by the conclusion (5 measures) of another song.
In caption : Canon à l'octave.
For medium voice, viola d'amore, and piano.

1. Songs (Medium voice) with instr. ensemble. ɪ. Title.

ML96.L61   M 59–1159

NL 0442086   DLC

Loeffler, Charles Martin Tornov, 1861–1935.
₍Poèmes, op. 5. La cloche fêlée; arr.₎

La cloche fêlée. Poésie de Ch. Baudelaire. ₍Sérénade. Poésie de Paul Verlaine. 19—₎

score (36 p.) 36 cm.

Holograph, in ink, of the songs, originally for alto, viola, and piano, with orchestra acc.

1. Songs (Low voice) with orchestra—Scores. ɪ. Loeffler, Charles Martin Tornov, 1861–1935. Poèmes, op. 5. Sérénade. ɪɪ. Title. ɪɪɪ. Title : Sérénade.

ML96.L61   M 59–886

NL 0442087   DLC

Loeffler, Charles Martin Tornov, 1861–
...La cloche fêlée; poème pour voix, alto ₍viola₎ et piano. Op.5,no.1. ₍Words by Ch.Baudelaire₎ N.Y., C.Schirmer ₍c1904₎

2v. 36cm.

v.1,piano and voice; v.2,viola.

NL 0442088   OrU

Loeffler, Charles Martin Tornov, 1861–1935.
...La cloche fêlée ... New York, G. Schirmer, inc. ₍c1932₎

2 pts.
Cover-title.
At head of title: Quatre poèmes pour voix, alto et piano. Ch. M. Loeffler, op. 5
Set to a poem by Charles Baudelaire.
"Translated by Henry G. Chapman."
Publisher's plate no.: 17192.
Pt. 1. Score for medium voice, piano and viola. Pt. 2. Viola part (in pocket of pt.1)

NL 0442089   OC1

ML96
L61
Case

Loeffler, Charles Martin Tornov, 1861–1935, arr.

Paganini, Nicolò, 1782–1840.
₍Concerto, violin, no. 2, op. 7, B minor. Rondeau à la clochette; arr.₎

La clochette. ₍n. d.₎

₍Loeffler, Charles Martin Tornov₎ 1861–1935.
₍Clowns₎

Clowns. ₍n. d.₎

score (₍6₎ p.) 41 cm.

Holograph pages from a complete score, in ink.
For jazz orchestra.

ɪ. Title.

ML96.L61   63–31307/M

NL 0442091   DLC

VOLUME 338

Loeffler, Charles Martin Tornov, 1861–1935.
¡Clowns¡

Clowns. ¡1928¡

score (56 p.) 46 cm.

Holograph, in ink with pencil additions, of the work for jazz orchestra with incidental vocal solo. Unfinished score, p. 44–56 blank. Another score of p. 45–50, also unfinished, laid in.
Composed for Leo Reisman's orchestra; first performed at Symphony Hall, Boston, Feb. 19, 1928.
Gift of Leo Reisman, June 30, 1937.

1. Dance-orchestra music—Scores. I. Title.

ML96.L61   M 59–756

NL 0442092   DLC

Loeffler, Charles Martin Tornov, 1861–1935.

Danse bizarre, pour viola seul. ¡1881¡

¡2¡ p. 23 x 31 cm.
Holograph, in ink.
At end: New-York, août .81.

1. Viola music. I. Title.

ML96.L61   M 59–1157

NL 0442093   DLC

¡Loeffler, Charles Martin Tornov¡ 1861–1935.
¡Rapsodies, oboe, viola & piano¡

Deux rapsodies, pour hautbois, alto et piano. 1901.

score (¡14¡, 13 p.) and   parts. 36 cm.

Holograph, in ink, with additions and corrections in pencil.
At end of 2d piece: 27ième Septembre 1901.
Title from published version (New York, G. Schirmer, ¤1905)
CONTENTS.—L'étang.—La cornemuse.

1. Trios (Piano, oboe, viola)   I. Title: Rapsodies.

ML96.L61   62–39434/M

NL 0442094   DLC

sVM   LOEFFLER, CHARLES MARTIN TORNOV, 1861–
322   ...Deux rapsodies pour hautbois, alto et
L 82d   piano... New York, Schirmer¡c1905¡
            42p. ¡& 2 pts.¡

Parts laid in.
Inspired by two poems by Maurice Rollinat.
Plate no.: 17506 (1905)
Contents.—L'étang.—La cornemuse.

NL 0442095   ICN IEN CtY-Mus IU MiU CSt MiEM

ML96
L61
(Case)

Loeffler, Charles Martin Tornov, 1861–1935.

Divagations sur des airs tzigane, Fly to her, my swallow.
¡n. d.¡

score (¡5¡ p.) 33 cm.
Holograph, in ink (unfinished)
For violin and piano.

1. Violin and piano music. I. Title. II. Title: Fly to her, my swallow.

ML96.L61   M 59–1156

NL 0442096   DLC

ML96
.L61
(Case)

Loeffler, Charles Martin Tornov, 1861–1935.
¡Divertimento, violin & orchestra, op. 1, A minor¡

Divertimento (in three movements) for violin and orchestra. ¡189–¡

score (30, 25, 48 p.) 37 cm. and   parts. 34 cm.

Copyist's ms., in ink; additions and corrections in composer's hand in score.

1. Suites (Violin with orchestra)—Scores and parts.

ML96.L61   63–34064/M

Library of Congress

NL 0442097   DLC

Loeffler, Charles Martin Tornov, 1861–1935.
¡Divertimento, violin & orchestra, op. 1, A minor¡

Divertissement pour violon et grand orchestre. ¡189–¡

score (36, 24, 64 p.) 37 cm.

Copyist's ms., in ink, with t. p. and additions and corrections in composer's hand.

1. Suites (Violin with orchestra)—Scores.

ML96.L61   63–34061/M

NL 0442098   DLC

ML96
.L61
(Case)

Loeffler, Charles Martin Tornov, 1861–1935.
¡Divertimento, violin & orchestra, op. 1, A minor; arr.¡

Divertissement pour violon et grand orchestre, op. 1.
¡189–¡

score (40 p.) 36 cm.

Copyist's ms., in ink, of arrangement for violin and piano, with t. p. and additions and corrections in the composer's hand.

1. Suites (Violin with orchestra)—Solo with piano.

ML96.L61   63–34060/M

NL 0442099   DLC

ML96
.L61
(Case)

¡Loeffler, Charles Martin Tornov¡ 1861–1935.
¡Marienlieder. Angelus Domini¡

3 ¡i. e. Drei¡ Marienlieder für gemischten Chor: 1. Angelus Domini. ¡n. d.¡

score (¡8¡ p.) 40 cm.
Holograph, in ink.
For chorus (SSAATTBB) Latin words.

1. Choruses, Sacred (Mixed voices, 8 pts.), Unaccompanied.
I. Title: Marienlieder. II. Title: Angelus Domini.

ML96.L61   62–66595/M

Library of Congress   ¡1¡

NL 0442100   DLC

Loeffler, Charles Martin Tornov, 1861–1935.
¡Beat! Beat! Drums!¡

"Drum taps" ¡by¡ Ch. M. Loeffler. ¡n. p., n. d.¡

pts. 27½ᵐ.

Reproduced from manuscript copy.
Parts: voice.
Words from Whitman's Drum-taps.

1. Choruses, Secular (Unison) with orchestra—Parts (Vocal)
I. Whitman, Walt, 1819–1892. Drum-taps.

45–28049

Library of Congress   M1609.L

NL 0442101   DLC

Loeffler, Charles Martin Tornov, 1861–1935.
¡Beat! Beat! Drums!¡

Drum taps; a soldiers' march and song. ¡191–¡

condensed score (¡8¡ p.) 40 cm.

Holograph, in ink.
For unison men's voices and orchestra.
Words by Walt Whitman.
Holograph sketches for earlier drafts, in ink and pencil (5 items.
35–41 cm.) laid in.

1. Choruses, Secular (Unison) with orchestra—Scores (reduced)
2. Whitman, Walt, 1819–1892—Musical settings. I. Whitman, Walt, 1819–1892. II. Title.

ML96.L61   63–33690/M

NL 0442102   DLC

¡Loeffler, Charles Martin Tornov¡ 1861–1935.

L'étang. ¡La cornemuse. La villanelle du diable¡ Poésie de Maurice Rollinat. ¡n. d.¡

score (48 p.) 28 x 36 cm.
Holograph, in ink, with additions and corrections in pencil.
For voice, clarinet, viola, and piano.
The 1st two works later rescored by the composer for oboe, viola, and piano, and published (New York, G. Schirmer, ¤1905) as Deux rapsodies. The last work later rescored and published as a symphonic poem (New York, G. Schirmer, ¤1905.
1. Songs (Low voice) with instr. ensemble. I. Loeffler, Charles Martin Tornov, 1861–1935. La cornemuse. II. Loeffler, Charles Martin Tornov, 1861–1935. La villanelle du diable. III. Rollinat, Maurice, 1846–1903. IV. Title. V. Title: La cornemuse. VI. Title: La villanelle du diable.

ML96.L61   62–39440/M

NL 0442103   DLC

¡Loeffler, Charles Martin Tornov¡ 1861–1935.
¡Evocation¡

Evocation. ¡1932?¡

score (1 v., various pagings) 35–46 cm.

Holograph sketches, in pencil and ink.
Title from Baker's biog. dict. of musicians, 5th ed.
Published version for women's voices and orchestra (Boston, C. C. Birchard, ¤1932)

I. Title.

ML96.L61   62–66597/M

NL 0442104   DLC NcU NN OC1 CSt ICN OOxM MiU IEN

¡Loeffler, Charles Martin Tornov¡ 1861–1935.
¡Evocation¡

Evocation. ¡1932¡

score (81+ p.) 43 cm.

Holograph, in pencil (incomplete)
For women's voices and orchestra; English words.
Published: Boston, C. C. Birchard, ¤1932.

1. Choruses, Secular (Women's voices, 4 pts.) with orchestra—Scores. I. Title.

ML96.L61   62–66598/M

NL 0442105   DLC

¡Loeffler, Charles Martin Tornov¡ 1861–1935.
¡Evocation¡

Evocation. ¡1932¡

score (46 ¡i. e. 47¡ p.) 43 cm. and   parts. 35 cm.

Holograph (score) in ink and pencil, and copyist's ms. of parts for women's voices, alto flute, bass drum, xylophone, and tam-tam.
For women's voices and orchestra.
Published: Boston, C. C. Birchard, ¤1932.
Holograph of voice parts (piano-vocal score (12 p.) 37 cm.) laid in.

1. Choruses, Secular (Women's voices, 4 pts.) with orchestra—Scores and parts. I. Title.

ML96.L61   62–66599/M

NL 0442106   DLC

Loeffler, Charles Martin Tornov, 1861–1935.
¡Irish fantasies¡

Five Irish fantasies. ¡192–?¡

score (1 v., various ¡pagings¡) 27 x 34–36 cm.

Holograph sketches, in pencil and ink.
Title from Baker's biog. dict. of musicians, 5th ed.
Published version for tenor and orchestra (New York, G. Schirmer, 1935)

I. Title: Irish fantasies.

ML96.L61   63–33693/M

NL 0442107   DLC

Loeffler, Charles Martin Tornov, 1861–1935.
¡Irish fantasies¡

Five Irish fantasies: for tenor and orchestra. 1920.

score (12, 16, 12, 18, 24 p.) 27 x 36–46 cm.

Holograph of 1st drafts, in ink and pencil (no. 5, incomplete)
At end of no. 1: August, 1920. Medfield, Mass.; no. 2 and 3: July 1920. Medfield, Mass.
Title from complete t. p. for no. 4.
Published: New York, G. Schirmer, 1935.
CONTENTS.—The hosting of the Sidhe.—The host of the air.—The fiddler of Dooney.—Ballad of the foxhunter.—Caitilín ní Uallacháin.

1. Songs (High voice) with orchestra—Scores. 2. Songs, Irish.
I. Title: Irish fantasies.

ML96.L61   63–33701/M

NL 0442108   DLC

VOLUME 338

Loeffler, Charles Martin Tornov, 1861-1935.
Five Irish fantasies. For voice and orchestra or piano. [With accompaniment for the piano.]
— New York. G. Schirmer (Inc.). [1934.] 5 parts in 1 v. 30½ cm.
Contents. — 1-4. The hosting of the Sidhe; The host of the air; The fiddler of Dooney; Ballad of the foxhunter. By William Butler Yeats. 5. Caitilin ni Uallachain. By Heffernan the Blind.

D6240   Songs. With music. Colls.

NL   0442109   MB NBC FTaSU IU

Loeffler, Charles Martin Tornov, 1861-1935.
[Irish fantasies]
... Five Irish fantasies for voice and orchestra ... New York, G. Schirmer, inc. [1935]
2 p. l., 104 p. illus. (facsims.) 22 x 17ᶜᵐ. (*On cover:* G. Schirmer's edition of study scores of orchestral works & chamber music, no. 14)
At head of title: Charles Martin Loeffler.
Publisher's plate no.: 36880.
Miniature score, reproduced from manuscript.
Words of the first four compositions by W. B. Yeats; of the last, by William Heffernan.

CONTENTS.—The hosting of the sidhe (Ceol-shee)—The host of the air (Suantraige)—The fiddler of Dooney (Geantraige)—Ballad of the fox-hunter (Goltraige)—Caitilin Ni Uallachain.

1. Songs (High voice) with orchestra—Scores. 2. Songs, Irish. I. Yeats, William Butler, 1865-1939. The collected poems. II. Heffernan, William, 1720 (ca.)-1803. Caitilin Ni Uallachain.

45-33700

Library of Congress   M1613.L82 I 7 1935 a
                                      [2]   785.22

NN IaU ICN OClW OrU NcU FMU MB ICarbS
NL   0442111   DLC CaBVaU OrU IEdS CLU ICU NIC OU OrU

Loeffler, Charles Martin Tornov, 1861-1935.
For one who fell in battle. Eight-part chorus for mixed voices a cappella. Words by T. W. Parsons. [Music by] Ch. M. Loeffler. [Score with accompaniment for rehearsal only.]
= New York. Schirmer. [1911.] 23 pp. 27 cm.

H7450 — Loeffler, Charles Martin. (M₁) — Parsons, Thomas William. (M2) — Part songs. (1) — Double main card.

NL   0442112   MB MH OO

Loeffler, Charles Martin Tornov, 1861-1935.
[Poems, op. 15]
[Four poems set to music for voice and piano, op. 15. 190-?]
[4], [6], [4], 5 p. 35 cm.
Holograph, in ink.
In caption of 1st song: [To] Mrs. B. C. Child. Of 2d: To Mrs. Gustave Schirmer. Of 3d: To Miss Evelyn Benedict. Of 4th: To Mrs. H. N. Slater.
Published New York, G. Schirmer [*1906]
CONTENTS. — Sudden light (D. G. Rossetti) — A dream within a dream (E. A. Poe) — To Helen (E. A. Poe) — Sonnet (G. C. Lodge)
1. Songs (Medium voice) with piano.

ML96.L61   M 59-755

NL   0442113   DLC

Loeffler, Charles Martin Tornov, 1861-1935.
[Poems, op. 15]
Four poems set to music for voice and piano, op. 15. New York, G. Schirmer [*1906]
4 items.
CONTENTS.—[1] Sudden light (D. G. Rossetti)—[2] A dream within a dream (E. A. Poe)—[3] To Helen (E. A. Poe)—[4] Sonnet (G. C. Lodge)
1. Songs (Medium voice) with piano.

M1621.L   M 59-739

NL   0442114   DLC ViU WaU ICN MH MB NN

Loeffler, Charles Martin Tornov, 1861-1935.
[Songs. Selections]
[Four songs. 19—]
[12] p. 34 cm.
Holograph, in ink, the 4th song incomplete.
CONTENTS.—Marie (A. de Musset)—Madrigal (P. Bourget)—Les hirondelles (A. d'Hotelier)—Rêverie.

1. Songs (Medium voice) with piano.

ML96.L61   M 59-884

NL   0442115   DLC

Loeffler, Charles Martin Tornov, 1861-1935.
[Grave, violin & piano]
Grave. [n. d.]
score ([5] p.) 34 cm.
Holograph, in ink.

1. Violin and piano music. I. Title.

ML96.L61   M 59-1154

NL   0442116   DLC

Loeffler, Charles Martin Tornov, 1861-1935.
Habanera. [n. d.]
score (1 v., various pagings) 35-46 cm.
Holograph sketches of a work for voice and orchestra.

I. Title.

ML96.L61   62-66594/M

NL   0442117   DLC

Loeffler, Charles Martin Tornov, 1861-1935.
Harmonie du soir. [19—]
[15] p. and part. 35 cm.
Copyist's ms., in ink, with additions in pencil and ink by the composer. Page 1 wanting: "Dansons la gigue" (incomplete): p. [14]-[15]
For medium voice, viola d'amore, and piano. The part is for viola d'amore.
Words of the 1st song by Charles Baudelaire; of the 2d, by Paul Verlaine.
1. Songs (Medium voice) with instr. ensemble. I. Loeffler, Charles Martin Tornov, 1861-1935. Poèmes, op. 5. Dansons la gigue. II. Title. III. Title: Dansons la gigue.

ML96.L61   M 59-940

NL   0442118   DLC

ML96
.L61
Case]

Loeffler, Charles Martin Tornov, 1861-1935.
Harmonie du soir. Poésie de Ch. Baudelaire. [19—]
[10] p. 36 cm.
Holograph, in ink, with pencil additions.
For medium voice, viola d'amore, and piano.
"Dansons la gigue" (1st 8 measures only) on p. [10]

1. Songs (Medium voice) with instr. ensemble. I. Loeffler, Charles Martin Tornov, 1861-1935. Poèmes, op. 5. Dansons la gigue. II. Title. III. Title: Dansons la gigue.

ML96.L61   M 59-860

NL   0442119   DLC

Loeffler, Charles Martin Tornov, 1861-1935.
Harmonie du soir (Les fleurs du mal [par] Ch. Baudelaire) [19—]
[10] p. 36 cm.
Holograph, in ink, of 1st draft, with pencil corrections.
For medium voice, viola d'amore, and piano. Words by Baudelaire.

1. Songs (Medium voice) with instr. ensemble. I. Title.

ML96.L61   M 59-861

NL   0442120   DLC

Loeffler, Charles Martin Tornov, 1861-1935.
[The passion of Hilarion. Piano-vocal score. English]
Hilarion. [191-]
161 p. 33 cm.
Holograph of opera, in pencil.
Composer's apograph, in ink, with vocal parts and texts partly omitted (158+ p.) laid in.

1. Operas—Vocal scores with piano. I. Title.

ML96.L61   63-32401/M

NL   0442121   DLC

Loeffler, Charles Martin Tornov, 1861-1935.
[Historiettes]
Historiettes, pour quatuor et harpe. [1922]
score (1 v., various pagings) 23 x 30-41 cm.
Holograph sketches and 1st drafts, in ink and pencil.
For harp, 2 violins, viola, and violoncello.

I. Title.

ML96.L61   62-39424/M

NL   0442122   DLC

Loeffler, Charles Martin Tornov, 1861-1935.
[Historiettes]
Historiettes, pour quatuor et harpe. [1922]
score (4 v.) 23 x 30 cm. (v. 3: 27 x 35 cm.) and parts. 35 cm.
Holographs (score) in ink, and parts (copyist's ms.) The score for Historiette no. 3 is incomplete.
For harp, 2 violins, viola, and violoncello.
CONTENTS.—1. Historiette du mariage de Pierrot Fumiste.—2. Historiette des tribulations conjugales de M. Punch.—3. Historiette de Batyoushka Raspontine.—4. Historiette de la Señorita Conchita Piquer.
1. Quintets (Harp, 2 violins, viola, violoncello) I. Title.

ML96.L61   62-39679/M

NL   0442123   DLC

Loeffler, Charles Martin Tornov, 1861-1935.
[Hora mystica]
Hora mystica. [n. d.]
score ([1] l., [2] p.) 21 x 24-35 cm.
Holograph sketches, in pencil.
Finished version for men's chorus and orchestra.

I. Title.

ML96.L61   62-50624/M

NL   0442124   DLC

Loeffler, Charles Martin Tornov, 1861-1935.
Hymn to our brother the sun
see his
Canticum fratris solis.

Loeffler, Charles Martin Tornov, 1861-1935.
[Hymne d'église]
Hymne d'église. [n. d.]
score (1 v., various pagings) 33-41 cm.
Holograph sketch and 2 1st drafts of the keyboard-vocal score, in ink and pencil.
One of the drafts has title: Hymne à Dieu.
For voice, string orchestra, organ, and piano.

I. Title. II. Title: Hymne à Dieu.

ML96.L61   62-50621/M

Library of Congress   [1]

NL   0442126   DLC

VOLUME 338

Loeffler, Charles Martin Tornov, 1861–1935.
₍Hymne d'église₎

Hymne, pour voix, quintette à cordes, orgue et piano.
₍n. d.₎

score (₍12₎ p.) 46 cm. and parts. 35 cm.
Holograph (score) in ink, and copyist's ms. (parts)
For voice, string orchestra, organ, and piano; French words.

1. Sacred songs (High voice) with string orchestra—Scores and parts. i. Title: Hymne d'église.

ML96.L61   62-50620/M

Library of Congress   ₍t₎

NL 0442127   DLC

₍Loeffler, Charles Martin Tornov₎ 1861–1935.
₍Je te vis₎

₍Je te vis. 19—₎

₍8₎ p. 34 cm.
Holograph, in ink, with revisions in pencil.
On t. p.: Frisch ₍i. e. Povla Frijsh₎
Words by G. Kahn.

1. Songs (High voice) with piano. i. Title.

ML96.L61   M 59–859

NL 0442128   DLC

₍Loeffler, Charles Martin Tornov₎ 1861–1935.

Joe Bibb. ₍19—₎

score (₍7₎ p.) 35 cm.
Holograph sketches, in pencil, of a piece for violin and piano, in part with alternative title: The clown.

1. Violin and piano music. i. Title. ii. Title: The clown.

ML96.L61   M 59–1153

NL 0442129   DLC

Loeffler, Charles Martin Tornov, 1861–1935.
Charles Martin Tornov Loeffler's organ accompaniment to a Mass. 19—.

₍7₎ p. 29 x 29 and 35 cm.
Holograph, in ink, incomplete.
Altered version of the Credo, also incomplete (₍2₎ p.) laid in.
Includes the text, partly superlinear.

1. Chants (Plain, Gregorian, etc.)—Accompaniment.

ML96.L61   M 59–1158
[M14]   rev
Library of Congress   ₍r71b2₎

NL 0442130   DLC

₍Loeffler, Charles Martin Tornov₎ 1861–1935.

The lone prairee; western cowboy song. ₍19—₎

score (₍3₎ p.) and parts. 35 cm.
Holograph, in ink, with pencil corrections (unfinished)
For saxophone, viola d'amore, and piano.

1. Trios (Piano, saxophone, viola d'amore) 2. Cowboys—Songs and music. 3. Folk-songs, American (Instrumental settings) i. Title.

ML96.L61   M 59–1172

NL 0442131   DLC

Loeffler, Charles Martin Tornov, 1861–1935.
₍Quintet, 3 violins, viola & violoncello₎

Lyrisches Kammermusikstück, für 3 Geigen, Bratsche, Violoncell'. ₍1895₎

score (₍27₎ p.) and parts. 35 cm.
Holograph (score) in ink, with corrections in blue and red pencil, and copyist's ms. (parts)
Published: New York, G. Schirmer ₍1938₎

———— Photocopy. Score only.
ML96.5.L82 no. 5
1. String quintets (3 violins, viola, violoncello)

ML96.L61   62–39432

NL 0442132   DLC

Loeffler, Charles Martin Tornov, 1861–
Memories of my childhood (life in a Russian village); poem for modern orchestra, by Ch. M. Loeffler. Score...   New York: G. Schirmer, Inc.₍, cop. 1925.₎ Publ. pl. no. 32027. 51 p. f°.

Full score.
"Awarded the Chicago North Shore Festival Association Prize, 1924. First public performance, May 30, 1924, at Evanston, Ill., by the Chicago Symphony Orchestra."

518934A. 1. Orchestra, Full—   DREXEL MUSICAL FUND.
N. Y. P. L.   Symphonic poems. I. Title.
March 31, 1931

NL 0442133   NN MH MB ICN

Loeffler, Charles Martin Tornov, 1861–1935.
₍Morceau fantastique, violoncello & orchestra₎

Morceau fantastique, pour violoncello avec grand orchestre et harpe. ₍n. d.₎

15 p. 36 cm.
Holograph, in ink, of solo part, with additions and corrections in pencil and ink.
In caption: Alwin Schroeder zugeeignet.

1. Violoncello with orchestra—Parts (Solo) i. Title.

ML96.L61   M 59–1171

NL 0442134   DLC

Loeffler, Charles Martin Tornov, 1861–1935.
₍La mort de Tintagiles₎

La mort de Tintagiles (d'après le drame de M. Maeterlinck) poème symphonique pour grand orchestre et une partie obligé de viole d'amour. ₍n. d.₎

score (1 v., various pagings) 35 cm.
Holograph, in ink, with additions and corrections in pencil and ink.
Published: New York, G. Schirmer, °1905.

1. Symphonic poems—Scores. i. Title.

ML96.L61   62–39429/M

Library of Congress   ₍t₎

NL 0442135   DLC

Loeffler, Charles Martin Tornov, 1861–1935.
₍La mort de Tintagiles₎

La mort de Tintagiles; poème dramatique, d'après le drame de M. Maeterlinck, pour grand orchestre. ₍n. p.₎ G. Schirmer, °1905.

score (97 p.) 35 cm.
Publisher's proof, with composer's corrections in pencil.
The 1st 48 measures of the composer's ms. arrangement in pencil (7 p.) inserted.

1. Symphonic poems—Scores. i. Title.

ML96.L61   M 59–2011

NL 0442136   DLC NN MH MB MiU ICN FTaSU IaU

Loeffler, Charles Martin Tornov, 1861–1935.
₍La mort de Tintagiles; arr.₎

La mort de Tintagiles; poème dramatique, d'après le drame de M. Maeterlinck, pour grand orchestre et viole d'amore. Op. 6. Réduction pour piano à 4 mains par Marcel Labey. New York, G. Schirmer ₍°1908₎

39 p. 34 cm.
For piano, 4 hands.

1. Symphonic poems arranged for piano (4 hands) i. Title.

M209.L83M65   M 56–602

NL 0442137   DLC MB

₍Loeffler, Charles Martin Tornov₎ 1861–1935.

Las moyares corralera; cancion española. ₍n. d.₎

₍3₎ p. 27 cm.
Holograph, in ink.
For voice and piano.

1. Songs (Medium voice) with piano. i. Title.

ML96.L61   62–40774/M

NL 0442138   DLC

Loeffler, Charles Martin Tornov, 1861–1935.
₍Music, string quartet₎

Music for four stringed instruments. New York, G. Schirmer ₍°1923₎

score (37 p.) 27 cm. and parts. 30 cm. (Society for the Publication of American Music. ₍Publication. 4th season₎ 1922–1923 ₍no. 8₎)

1. String quartets—Scores and parts. (Series)

M2.S69A5 1922/23   M 61–1886
———— Copy 2.   M452.L78M9

PP MiU OC1 OO OU MB OrU OrP CSt
NL 0442139   DLC ICU RPB NIC OrU ICN MH CU NcU NN

Loeffler, Charles Martin Tornov, 1861–1935.
₍Music, string quartet₎

Musique pour 2 violons, alto et violoncelle. ₍1917–19₎

score (1 v., various pagings) 23 x 29–46 cm.
Holograph sketches and an incomplete draft for final version, in ink and pencil.

ML96.L61   62–40777/M

NL 0442140   DLC

Loeffler, Charles Martin Tornov, 1861–1935.
₍Une nuit de mai; arr.₎

Une nuit de mai; rapsodie d'après Gogol. ₍189–?₎

score (16 p.) 35 cm.
Holograph, in ink.
For violin and piano; acc. originally for orchestra.

1. Violin with orchestra—Solo with piano. i. Title.

ML96.L61   63–31304/M

NL 0442141   DLC

Loeffler, Charles Martin Tornov, 1861–1935.
₍Une nuit de mai₎

Une nuit de mai; rapsodie d'après Nicolai Gogol, composée pour violon, grand orchestre et harpe. ₍189–?₎

score (42 p.) and part. 35 cm.
Holograph, in ink.
Copyist's ms. of full score, in ink, with composer's additions and corrections in pencil and ink (49 p.) laid in.

1. Violin with orchestra—Scores and parts (solo) i. Title.

ML96.L61   63–31893/M

NL 0442142   DLC

Loeffler, Charles Martin Tornov, 1861–1935.
₍Une nuit de mai₎

Une nuit de mai; rapsodie d'après Nicolai Gogol, pour violon et grand orchestre et harpe. ₍1891₎

score (₍47₎ p.) 35 cm.
Holograph of earliest version, in ink; originally intended by the composer as the 2d movement for his suite Les veillées de l'Ukraine.

1. Violin with orchestra—Scores. i. Title.

ML96.L61   63–31313/M

NL 0442143   DLC

Loeffler, Charles Martin Tornov, 1861–1935.
₍Octet, 2 clarinets, harp & strings₎

Octet. ₍1897₎

score (73 p.) 34 cm.
Holograph, in ink, with additions and corrections in pencil.
For 2 clarinets, harp, 2 violins, viola, violoncello, and double bass.

1. Octets (2 clarinets, harp, 2 violins, viola, violoncello, double bass)

ML96.L61   62–39433/M

NL 0442144   DLC

VOLUME 338

Loeffler, Charles Martin Tornov, 1861–1935.
₍Octet, 2 clarinets, harp & strings₎

Octette. ₍189–?₎

parts. 35 cm.

Copyist's ms., with additions in the hand of the composer.
For 2 clarinets, harp, 2 violins, viola, violoncello, and double bass.
Gift of the South End Music School, Mar. 8, 1948.

1. Octets (2 clarinets, harp, 2 violins, viola, violoncello, double bass)

ML96.L61   M 59–810

NL 0442145   DLC

Loeffler, Charles Martin Tornov, 1861–
...Ode for one who fell in battle; eight-part chorus for mixed voices a cappella. ' Words by T. W. Parsons... New edition revised by the composer. New York: G. Schirmer ₍cop. 1911₎. Publ. pl. no. 22365. 19 p. 4°.

At head of title: G. Schirmer's collections of part-songs and choruses for mixed voices, no. 5536...

1. Choruses (Unaccompanied).   2. Parsons, Thomas William, 1819–92.
3. Title.
N. Y. P. L.   January 17, 1924.

NL 0442146   NN

Loeffler, Charles Martin Tornov, 1861–1935.
Old love song
see his
Vieille chanson d'amour.

₍**Loeffler, Charles Martin Tornov**₎ 1861–1935.

Ouverture pour le T. C. Minstrel entertainment after southern and variety show themes. Pour 2 violons et piano. ₍n. d.₎

score (10 p.) and parts. 35 cm.
Holograph, in ink.

1. Trios (Piano, 2 violins)   I. Title.

ML96.L61   62–66593/M

Library of Congress   ₍₃₎

NL 0442148   DLC

Loeffler, Charles Martin Tornov, 1861–1935.
A pagan poem
For scenario see under Lewisohn, Irene, d. 1944.

Loeffler, Charles Martin Tornov, 1861–1935.
₍A pagan poem₎

A pagan poem (after Virgil) op. 14. Composed for orchestra with piano, English horn and three trumpets obbligato. New York, G. Schirmer ₍ᶜ1909₎.

score (107 p.) and parts. 34 cm.

1. Symphonic poems—Scores and parts.   I. Title.

M1002.L825P3   M 59–814
——— Copy 3. Score.
"This is no. 1 of an edition of fifteen copies printed for the composer on Van Gelder hand-made paper."

OC1 RPB MH MB RPB
NL 0442150   DLC OrP ICN MiU FTaSU NcU OkU IaU MB NN

₍**Loeffler, Charles Martin Tornov**₎ 1861–1935.
₍Partita, violin & piano₎

Partita. ₍1930?₎

score (1 v., various pagings) 37 cm.
Holograph sketches, in pencil and ink.

Title from Baker's biog. dict. of musicians, 5th ed.

ML96.L61   63–34063/M

NL 0442151   DLC

Loeffler, Charles Martin Tornov, 1861–1935.
₍Partita, violin & piano₎

Partita for piano and violin. 1930.

score (1 v., various pagings) 35 cm.

Holograph of 1st and 3d movements, in pencil; copyist's ms. of 4th movement, in ink; 2d movement missing.
On t. p.: 15th Mai–June 1930.
Published: New York, G. Schirmer, ᶜ1937.

1. Suites (Violin and piano)

ML96.L61   63–34062/M

NL 0442152   DLC FTaSU

Loeffler, Charles Martin Tornov, 1861–1935.
₍Partitas. Violin & piano₎
Partita for violin and piano by Ch. M. Loeffler ... New York: G. Schirmer, inc. ₍ᶜ1937₎   Publ. pl. no. 36837.   1 v. 30½cm.

Score (40 p.): violin and piano. Violin part.
"Violin part edited in accordance with the composer's wishes by Jacques Gordon."
CONTENTS.—Intrada.—Sarabande: Variations on a theme by Johann Mattheson.—Divertissement.—Finale des tendres adieux.

           CARNEGIE CORP. OF NEW YORK.
1. Violin and piano—1800–   2. Suites—Violin and piano—1800–
     I. Mattheson, Johann, 1681–   1764. II. Gordon, Jacques, ed.
N. Y. P. L.   September 8, 1938

NL 0442153   NN IaU MB

Loeffler, Charles Martin Tornov, 1861–1935.
₍Sextet, violins, violas & violoncellos. Lento₎

Le passeur d'eau; poëme d'après Verhaeren, pour 2 violons, 2 altos et 2 violoncelles. ₍190–?₎

score (19 p.) 27 x 36 cm.
Copyist's ms., in ink, with composer's corrections and annotations, in ink.
This 2d movement of the string sextet was first performed under new title: Le passeur d'eau, by the Kneisel Quartet at Boston, Dec. 10, 1909.
Incomplete copyist's ms., with measures deleted in composer's (?) hand throughout ₍3–4, 7–18 p.₎ laid in.
1. String sextets (2 violins, 2 violas, 2 violoncellos)   I. Title.

ML96.L61   63–31309/M

NL 0442154   DLC

₍**Loeffler, Charles Martin Tornov**₎ 1861–1935.
₍The passion of Hilarion₎

The passion of Hilarion. ₍191–₎

score (1 v., various pagings) 34 cm.
Holograph sketches of an opera, in ink and pencil.

I. Title.

ML96.L61   63–32411/M

NL 0442155   DLC

M1500
L82P2
Loeffler, Charles Martin Tornov, 1861–1935.
₍The passion of Hilarion₎
The passion of Hilarion; opera in one act and two tableaux, after a play by William Sharp. ₍Boston, C.C. Birchard, c1926₎
278 p. 48ᶜᵐ.
Photocopy of manuscript.

1. Operas. I. Sharp, William, 1855–1905. II. Title.

NL 0442156   CSt

Loeffler, Charles Martin Tornov, 1861–1935.
₍The passion of Hilarion. English₎

The passion of Hilarion; opera in one act and two tableaux after a play by William Sharp. ₍Boston, C. C. Birchard, ᶜ1936₎

score (278 p.) 48 cm.

1. Operas—Scores.   I. Title.

M1500.LS3P3   M 56–728

NL 0442157   DLC MH

KEPT IN
BROWN MUSIC
COLLECTION Loeffler, Charles Martin Tornov, 1861–1935.
•M1500
.L64P3   The passion of Hilarion, opera in one act and two tableaux after a play by William Sharp, by Ch. M. Loeffler. ₍Boston, C. C. Birchard & company, c1939₎
2 p. l., 278 p. 48 x 31 1/2cm.
Score.
Reproduced from manuscript copy.

1. Operas—Scores. I. Sharp, William, 1855–1905. The passion of Hilarion. II. Title. Opera.

NL 0442158   MB

₍**Loeffler, Charles Martin Tornov**₎ 1861–1935.

₍Piece for violin and piano, apparently based on gipsy airs. n. d.₎

score (11₎ p.) 34 cm.
Holograph, in ink.

1. Violin and piano music.

ML96.L61   M 59–1170

NL 0442159   DLC

VM
1002
L 82p
LOEFFLER, CHARLES MARTIN TORNOV, 1861–1935.
Poem, composed for orchestra   Score
New York, G. Schirmer, inc. ₍c1923₎
60p. 33½cm.

First performed in 1902 under the title "Avant que tu ne t'en ailles" from the opening line of the fifth poem in Paul Verlaine's "La bonne chanson". Reorchestrated and performed in 1918 under the title "La bonne chanson" and published for the first time as "Poem".
Plate no.:   31382.

NL 0442160   ICN MH CSt

₍**Loeffler, Charles Martin Tornov**₎ 1861–1935.
₍A pagan poem₎

Poème païen; pour orchestre, piano, cor anglais et trompettes. ₍n. d.₎

score (2 p.) 36 cm.
Holograph sketch of opening bars, in ink.

I. Title.

ML96.L61   62–40785/M

NL 0442161   DLC

Loeffler, Charles Martin Tornov, 1861–1935.
₍Poème, violoncello & piano₎

Poème (Scène dramatique) pour violoncelle solo et piano (ou orchestre) 1916.

score (1 v., unpaged) 34 cm.

Holograph, in ink.
On t. p.: A Pablo Casals. Mars 1916.
Copyist's ms. of score (38 p. 35 cm.) laid in.

1. Violoncello and piano music.   I. Title: Scène dramatique.

ML96.L61   62–50613/M

NL 0442162   DLC

M784
L81
Loeffler, Charles Martin Tornov, 1861–1935
₍Songs₎

Poems set to music for voice and piano; texts by Edgar Allan Poe. Op. 15, no. 2–3. Schirmer, ᶜ1906.

Medium voice.

NL 0442163   OrP

VOLUME 338

Loeffler, Charles Martin Tornov, 1861–1935.
Prayer
see his
Prière.

Loeffler, Charles Martin Tornov, 1861–1935, arr.

Bach, Johann Sebastian, 1685–1750.
[Das wohltemperirte Clavier. Th. 1, no. 8. Prelude; arr.]

Prelude. [n. d.]

Loeffler, Charles Martin Tornov, 1861–1935, arr.

Bach, Johann Sebastian, 1685–1750.
[Das wohltemperirte Clavier. Th. 1, no. 24. Prelude; arr.]

Preludio. [n. d.]

[**Loeffler, Charles Martin Tornov**] 1861–1935.
[Prière]

Prière. [192–]
[1] l. 37 cm.
Holograph, in ink, with sketches on verso, in pencil.
For voice and piano.
French words by Roger Dévigne.
Published: Boston, C. C. Birchard, 1936.
Holograph sketch, in pencil ([2] p. 18 x 27 cm.) laid in.

1. Sacred songs (Medium voice) with piano.   I. Title.

ML96.L61   62–40784/M

NL 0442167   DLC

Loeffler, Charles Martin Tornov, 1861–1935.
[Prière]

Prière; a short prayer for a charming grandmother to
teach her grand-children. 1926.
[3] p. 35 cm.
Holograph, in ink, the music in a copyist's hand.
On t. p.: Mrs. M. Graeme Houghton. Ch. M. Loeffler. Christmas
1926.
For voice and piano. French text by Roger Dévigne, with English
translation by David Stevens.
Published Boston, C. C. Birchard, 1936.
Gift of Mrs. Houghton, Feb. 3, 1954.
1. Sacred songs (Medium voice) with piano.   I. Title.

ML96.L61   M 59–753

NL 0442168   DLC

Loeffler, Charles Martin Tornov, 1861–1935.
[Prière]

Prière. Prayer. [Song for medium voice] Words by
Roger Dévigne; tr. by David Stevens. [Boston] C. C.
Birchard, °1936.
3 p. 31 cm.
Caption title.

1. Sacred songs (Medium voice) with piano.   I. Title. II. Title:
Prayer.

M2113.L   M 59–737

NL 0442169   DLC

Loeffler, Charles Martin Tornov, 1861–1935.
Psalm CXXXVII. (By the rivers of Babylon.) For four-part
chorus of women's voices with accompaniment of organ, harp,
two flutes, and violoncello obbligato. Op. 3. Orchestral score.
— New York. Schirmer. [1907.] (1), 22 pp. 34 cm.
No. 4 of an edition of five copies.

M5895 — T.r. Part song. — Part songs. Female voices. — By the rivers of
Babylon. Part song.

NL 0442170   MB IEN CSt

M783.3   Loeffler, Charles Martin Tornov, 1861–
L825P   1935.
          Psalm CXXXVII [By the rivers of
Op.3   Babylon] for four-part chorus of women's
          voices, with accompaniment of organ,
          harp, two flutes, and violoncello
          obbligato, by Ch. M. Loeffler. Op.3...
          N.Y., G. Schirmer [c1937] Publ.pl.no.
          20079.
            cover-title, 19 p. 26½cm.

            Vocal score with piano accompaniment

NL 0442171   NcD

Loeffler, Charles Martin Tornov, 1861–1935.
[Music, string quartet]

Quartet. [n. p., 192–]
parts. 28 cm.
Reproduced from copyist's ms., containing composer's additions
and corrections.
For 2 violins, viola, and violoncello.
Published: New York, G. Schirmer, °1923.

1. String quartets—Parts.

ML96.5.L82   63–34073/M

NL 0442172   DLC

Loeffler, Charles Martin Tornov, 1861–1935.
[Music, string quartet]

Quartet for two violins, viola, and violoncello [sic. n. p.,
1923]
score (32 p.) 22 x 29 cm.
Reproduced from holograph.
Title from holograph.

1. String quartets—Scores.

ML96.5.L82   63–33688/M

NL 0442173   DLC

Loeffler, Charles Martin Tornov, 1861–1935.
[Music, string quartet]

Quartet for two violins, viola, and violincello [sic] 1917–23.
score (32 p.) 24 x 30 cm.
Holograph, in ink.
On t. p.: May 30, '23. At end, in pencil: Autumn 1917.
Published: New York, G. Schirmer, °1923.

1. String quartets—Scores.

ML96.L61   63–33689/M

NL 0442174   DLC

Loeffler, Charles Martin Tornov, 1861–1935.
[Mélodies, op. 10]

Quatre mélodies pour chant et piano. Poésies de Gustave
Kahn. New York, G. Schirmer [°1903]
4 items. 35 cm.
Words from Kahn's Les palais nomades.

CONTENTS.—Timbres oubliés.—Adieu pour jamais.—Les soirs
d'automne.—Les paons.

1. Songs (Medium voice) with piano.   I. Kahn, Gustave, 1859–
1936. Les palais nomades.

M1621.L   M 59–740

NL 0442175   DLC PP NN ICN MB CSt IU MH

Loeffler, Charles Martin Tornov, 1861–1935.
[Poèmes, op. 5]

Quatre poëmes, pour voix, alto et piano, op. 5. New York,
G. Schirmer [°1904]
4 v. and part. 35 cm.
For alto, viola, and piano.
Text of the 1st song by C. Baudelaire; of the 2d–4th songs, by
P. Verlaine.

CONTENTS.—1. La cloche fêlée.—2. Dansons la gigue.—3. Le son du
cor s'afflige vers les bois.—4. Sérénade.

1. Songs (Low voice) with instr. ensemble.   I. Title: Poèmes.

M1621.3.L   M 59–873

NL 0442176   DLC MB MH NN

Loeffler, Charles Martin Tornov, 1861–1935.
[Quintet, 3 violins, viola & violoncello]

Quintet in one movement, for three violins, viola, and violoncello. [Edited by Adolfo Betti] New York, G. Schirmer
[1938]
score (39 p.) 26 cm. and parts. 30 cm. (G. Schirmer's edition of study scores of orchestral works & chamber music, no. 19)

1. String quintets (3 violins, viola, violoncello)   I. Betti, Adolfo,
1875–1950, ed.

M552.L82Q5   45–34685 rev*/M

     IU FTaSU ICU CLU OrU NcU IEN MiU OC1W
NL 0442177   DLC CaBVaU OrU IaU OC1 PP NN MH MB ICN

ML96   **Loeffler, Charles Martin Tornov,** 1861–1935.
.L61   [Rapsodie russe, violin & orchestra; arr.]
(Case)
         Rapsodie russe, pour violon avec orchestre. [19—]
         score ([15] p.) 34 cm.
         Holograph, in ink, of the composer's reduction for violin and piano,
         with pencil sketches on p. [15]
         Violin part, extensively revised and incomplete ([8] p.) laid in.
         Gift of C. C. Birchard & Co., Feb. 12, 1957.

         1. Violin with orchestra—Solo with piano.   I. Title.

ML96.L61   M 59–752

NL 0442178   DLC

Loeffler, Charles Martin Tornov, 1861–1935.
[The reveller]

The reveller; a Franciscan play by Daniel Sargent. Music
arr. by C. M. L. 1925.
score (6 [i. e. 7] p.) and part. 35 cm.
Holograph, in ink and pencil.
At end: Xmas. 1925.
Incidental music for voice, viola, and piano; part for viola.
Published: New York, Calvert Pub. Corp., °1926.
Copyist's ms. of the score and text of the play (typescript) laid in.
1. Music, Incidental—Scores.   I. Sargent, Daniel, 1890–   The
reveller.   II. Title.

ML96.L61   62–50622/M

NL 0442179   DLC

Loeffler, Charles Martin Tornov, 1861–1935.
[The reveller]

The reveller; by Daniel Sargent. Music arr. by C. M.
Loeffler. New York, Calvert Pub. Corp. [°1926]
score ([11] p.) and part. 24 cm.
Incidental music for the play by Sargent.
For voice, viola, and piano; part for viola.

1. Music, Incidental—Scores.   I. Sargent, Daniel, 1890–   The
reveller.   II. Title.

M1510.L83R5   62–50623/M

NL 0442180   DLC

[**Loeffler, Charles Martin Tornov**] 1861–1935.

Rêverie. [n. d.]
[4] p. 34 cm.
Holograph, in ink.
For voice and piano; French words.
Unidentified holograph sketch, in pencil, on p. 4.

1. Songs (Medium voice) with piano.   I. Title.

ML96.L61   62–50614/M

NL 0442181   DLC

Loeffler, Charles Martin Tornov, 1861–1935.

Rêverie-barcarolle; paraphrase sur des airs nègres pour
violon avec piano. [n. d.]
[6] p. 34 cm.
Holograph (unfinished) in ink, with pencil sketch additions at end.

1. Violin and piano music.   I. Title.

ML96.L61   65–37150/M

Library of Congress

NL 0442182   DLC

VOLUME 338

₍Loeffler, Charles Martin Tornov₎ 1861–1935.

Romance russe. ₍n. d.₎

score (₍6₎ p.) 36 cm.

Holograph, in ink.
In caption of p. ₍1₎: A mon ami W. P. Blake.
For violin and piano.

1. Violin and piano music.　I. Title.

ML96.L61　　　　　　　　62–66590/M

NL 0442183　　　DLC

₍Loeffler, Charles Martin Tornov₎ 1861–1935.

Rondo. ₍n. d.₎

score (₍2₎ l.) 35 cm.

Holograph sketch, in ink.
For viola d'amore and piano.

ML96.L61　　　　　　　　63–31311/M

NL 0442184　　　DLC

ML96
.L61
Case₎　₍Loeffler, Charles Martin Tornov₎ 1861–1935.

Le rossignol. ₍n. d.₎

score (8 p.) 36 cm.

Holograph, in ink.
For medium voice, viola, and piano.
Copyist's ms. of score (8 p. 33 cm.) with unidentified song for
voice, viola, and piano, at end (5 p.: p. 1–3 wanting) laid in.

1. Songs (Medium voice) with instr. ensemble.　I. Title.

ML96.L61　　　　　　　　62–66596/M

NL 0442185　　　DLC

₍Loeffler, Charles Martin Tornov₎ 1861–1935.
₍The Sermon on the Mount₎

The Sermon on the Mount. ₍n. d.₎

score (₍14₎ p.) 36 cm.

Holograph (unfinished) in ink.
For chorus (SSAA), 2 viole d'amore, viola da gamba, harp, and
organ.
Words from St. Matthew 5: 1–12.

1. Choruses, Sacred (Women's voices, 4 pts.) with instr. ensemble.
2. Beatitudes (Music)　I. Title.

ML96.L61　　　　　　　　62–45747/M

NL 0442186　　　DLC

₍Loeffler, Charles Martin Tornov₎ 1861–1935.

₍Set of variations. for violin and piano, comprising the
3d movement of a larger work, apparently based on a Russian folk-song. n. d.₎

score (₍10₎ p.) 34 cm.

Holograph (unfinished) in ink, with pencil additions and corrections.
Acc. originally for orchestra.

1. Variations (Violin with orchestra)—Solo with piano. 2. Folk-
songs, Russian (Instrumental settings)

ML96.L61　　　　　　　　M 59–1169

NL 0442187　　　DLC

Loeffler, Charles Martin Tornov₎ 1861–1935.
₍Sextet, violins, violas & violoncellos₎

Sextuor pour 2 violons, 2 altos ₍et₎ 2 v'celles. ₍19——₎

score (13, 9, 12 p.) 36 cm.

Holograph, in ink, with pencil additions and corrections.
On t. p.: Franz Kneisel in Freundschaft und Verehrung zugeeignet.
Ch. M. Loeffler.　In caption of p. 1, 2d group: (À la mémoire d'un ami
D. B.) Denis Bunker.
Earlier version of the 2d movement "Le passeur d'eau, poème pour
2 violons, 2 altos et 2 v'celles" (score, 15 p.) laid in.

1. String sextets (2 violins, 2 violas, 2 violoncellos)　I. Title: Le
passeur d'eau.

ML96.L61　　　　　　　　M 59–751

NL 0442188　　　DLC

₍Loeffler, **Charles Martin** Tornov₎ 1861–1935.

₍Sketch for a piece for string orchestra and organ. 19——₎

score (₍4₎ p.) and　parts. 34 cm.

Holograph, in ink.　The parts are incomplete.

ML96.L61　　　　　　　　63–35692/M

NL 0442189　　　DLC

ML96
L61
(Case)　₍Loeffler, Charles Martin Tornov₎ 1861–1935.
₍Vassar College song₎

A sketch for a Vassar College song. ₍n. d.₎

₍4₎ p. 20 x 29 cm.

Holograph, in ink and pencil.

I. Title: Vassar College song.

ML96.L61　　　　　　　　62–41348/M

NL 0442190　　　DLC

₍Loeffler, Charles Martin Tornov₎ 1861–1935.

₍Sketchbooks for various works, including a projected
opera The white fox, based on a libretto by Okakura
Kakuzo, Hora mystica, and a symphony. n. d.₎

₍4₎ v. 24–34 cm.

Holograph, in pencil.
Copy of a letter from Kojiro Tomita to Wallace Goodrich, dated
May 28, 1948, concerning The white fox and its libretto (typescript)
laid in v. 3.

ML96.L61　　　　　　　　M 59–1161

NL 0442191　　　DLC

₍Loeffler, Charles Martin Tornov₎ 1861–1935.

₍Sketches for a suite, for voice and dance orchestra. 19——₎

1 v. (various pagings) 24–35 cm.

Holograph, in ink and pencil.
CONTENTS.—Louisiana, tango.—Creole blues.—Old Creole days.—
Mardi Gras in New Orleans.

ML96.L61　　　　　　　　M 59–1138

NL 0442192　　　DLC

Loeffler, Charles Martin Tornov₎ 1861–1935.
₍Poèmes, op. 5. Le son du cor s'afflige vers bois₎

Sonett (P. Verlaine) ₍Serenade (P. Verlaine) 19——₎

₍2₎ l. 35 cm.

Holograph, in ink, of the voice parts only of the songs for alto,
viola, and piano.
German words.
Published: New York, G. Schirmer ₍°1904₎

1. Loeffler, Charles Martin Tornov, 1861–1935. Poèmes, op. 5. Sérénade. II. Title. III. Title: Serenade.

ML96.L61　　　　　　　　M 59–885

NL 0442193　　　DLC

₍Loeffler, Charles Martin Tornov₎ 1861–1935.
₍Spring dance, violin & piano₎

Spring dance (Danse norvégienne) ₍n. d.₎

score (₍8₎ p.) 36 cm.

Holograph, in ink.
In caption: Dedié à mon ami César Thompson.

1. Violin and piano music. 2. Dance music, Norwegian.
I. Title. II. Title: Danse norwégienne.

ML96.L61　　　　　　　　62–66600/M

NL 0442194　　　DLC

ML96
.L61
Case　Loeffler, Charles Martin Tornov, 1861–1935, ar

Albéniz, Isaac Manuel Francisco₎ 1860–1909.
₍Rhapsodie espagnole, piano & orchestra; arr.₎

Spanish rhapsody. ₍Arr. for strings and piano by C. M. T.
Loeffler. n. d.₎

₍Loeffler, Charles Martin Tornov₎ 1861–1935.
₍Quartet, strings, A minor₎

String quartet in A minor. ₍1889?₎

score (23 p.) 27 x 35 cm. and　parts. 34 cm.

Holograph (score) in ink (incomplete: p. 7–12 wanting) and copyist's ms. (parts)
Title from list of unpublished works in Musical Quarterly, vol. 11,
no. 3, July 1925.

1. String quartet—Scores and parts.

ML96.L61　　　　　　　　62–39430/M

NL 0442196　　　DLC

₍Loeffler, Charles Martin Tornov₎ 1861–1935.
₍Tarantella, violin & piano₎

Tarantella. ₍n. d.₎

score (₍13₎ p.) 36 cm.

Holograph, in ink.

1. Tarantellas (Violin and piano)

ML96.L61　　　　　　　　62–66589/M

NL 0442197　　　DLC

ML96
.L6
Case　Loeffler, Charles Martin Tornov, 1861–1935, arr.

Chopin, Fryderyk Franciszek, 1810–1849.
₍Études, piano, op. 10, no. 6–7; arr.₎

₍Three piano pieces, arr. for violin and piano. n. d.₎

---

*
M1
.S444　Loeffler, Charles Martin Tornov, 1861–1935.
v.165
no.49　To Helen. (Edgar Allan Poe). Price, 50
cents. New York, G. Schirmer (Inc.), ₍°1906
Pl. no. 18454.
5 p. 30cm. ₍Sheet music collection, v. 165,
no. 49₎
To Miss Evelyn Benedict.
Four poems set to music for voice and piano,
Op. 15.

1. Songs with piano. I. Poe, Edgar Allen,
1809–1849. To　　Helen. II. Title.

NL 0442199　　　ViU

₍Loeffler, Charles Martin Tornov₎ 1861–1935.
₍La mort de Tintagiles₎

Der Tod des Tintagiles; symphonisches Gedicht nach dem
gleichnamigen Drama von Maurice Mäterlinck. ₍1897?₎

score (89 p.) 36 cm.

Holograph, in ink.
Original, unpublished version for 2 viole d'amore and orchestra.
Holographs, in ink, of solo passages for 2 viole d'amore and orches-
tra (condensed score (₍12₎ p.)) and part for 2d viola d'amore laid in.

1. Symphonic poems—Scores.　I. Title.

ML96.L61　　　　　　　　62–39435/M

NL 0442200　　　DLC

VOLUME 338

⌐Loeffler, Charles Martin Tornov₎ 1861–1935.

Ton souvenir est comme un livre bien aimé. ⌐19—₎

⌐6₎ p. 33 cm.

Copyist's ms., in ink.
In caption of p. ⌐1₎ in composer's hand: à Mme T. S. Fay.
Title from 1st line of text.
For medium voice and piano.

1. Songs (Medium voice) and piano. I. Title.

ML96.L61   M 59–883

NL   0442201   DLC

ML96
.L61   **Loeffler, Charles Martin Tornov, 1861–1935.**
Case
Tartini, Giuseppe, 1692–1770.
⌐Sonata, violin & continuo, G minor₎

Il trillo del diavolo; sonata. ⌐n. d.₎

ML96
.L61   Loeffler, Charles Martin Tornov, 1861–1935, arr

⌐Brahms, Johannes₎ 1833–1897.
⌐Ungarische Tänze, piano, 4 hands. No. 5–6; arr.₎

⌐Ungarische Tänze. n. d.₎

Loeffler, Charles Martin Tornov, 1861–1935.
⌐Les veillées de l'Ukraine₎

Les veillées de l'Ukraine. ⌐189–₎

score ⌐116₎ p.₎ 35 cm.

Holograph of suite for violin and orchestra, in ink.
Omits the 2d movement, Une nuit de mai, later reset as a separate work.
CONTENTS.— Introduction et pastorale.— Chansons russes.— Les parobki s'amusent.

1. Suites (Violin with orchestra)—Scores. I. Title.

ML96.L61   63–33696/M

NL   0442204   DLC

Loeffler, Charles Martin Tornov, 1861–1935.
⌐Les veillées de l'Ukraine₎

Les veillées de l'Ukraine; pour violon avec orchestre, d'après Nicolai Gogol. Violon principal. ⌐189–₎

25 p. 34 cm.

Holograph, in ink.
CONTENTS.—Introduction et pastorale.—Une nuit de mai.—Chansons russes (Doumka)—Les parobki s'amusent.

1. Suites (Violin with orchestra)—Parts (solo) I. Title.

ML96.L61   63–33695/M

NL   0442205   DLC

Loeffler, Charles Martin Tornov, 1861–1935.
⌐Les veillées de l'Ukraine; arr.₎

Les veillées de l'Ukraine; grande suite pour violon solo et grand orchestre, d'après Nicolai Gogol. ⌐1891₎

score ⌐54₎ p.₎ 27 x 36 cm.

Holograph, in ink (incomplete) with 3d movement missing.
Arr. for violin and piano

1. Suite (Violin with orchestra)—Solo with piano. I. Title.

ML96.L61   63–31308/M

NL   0442206   DLC

Loeffler, Charles Martin Tornov, 1861–1935.
⌐Les veillées de l'Ukraine₎

Les veillées de l'Ukraine; pour violon avec orchestre, d'après Nicolai Gogol. ⌐1891₎

parts. 34 cm.

Copyist's ms., in ink; t. p. wrapper in composer's hand, in ink.
Omits the 3d movement, Chansons russes.

CONTENTS.— Introduction et pastorale.— Une nuit de mai.— Les parobki s'amusent.

1. Suites (Violin with orchestra)—Parts. I. Title.

ML96.L61   63–33687/M

NL   0442207   DLC

Loeffler, Charles Martin Tornov, 1861–1935.
⌐Les veillées de l'Ukraine₎

Les veillées de l'Ukraine; suite pour orchestre, violon et hárpe. ⌐1891₎

score ⌐99₎ p.₎ 36 cm.

Holograph of early version, in ink.
Omits the 2d movement, Une nuit de mai, later reset as a separate work.
CONTENTS.—Introduction et pastorale.—Chants russe.—Carnaval russe.

1. Suites (Violin with orchestra)—Scores. I. Title.

ML96.L61   63–33694 M

NL   0442208   DLC

Loeffler, Charles Martin Tornov, 1861–1935.
⌐Vieille chanson d'amour₎

Vieille chanson d'amour (xv. siècle) ⌐Old love song. 1925₎

7 p. 35 cm.

Copyist's ms., in ink, the French title only in composer's hand.
English translation of text added in pencil; typescript of translation (leaf) inserted.
With piano acc.

1. Songs (Medium voice) with piano. I. Title. II. Title: Old love song.

ML96.L61   M 59–863

NL   0442209   DLC

---

fM1002   Loeffler, Charles Martin Tornov, 1861–1935.
L82V5   ⌐La villanelle du diable₎
La villanelle du diable, d'après un poème de M.Rollinat. Fantaisie symphonique pour grand orchestre et orgue. Op.9. Partition d'orchestre. New York, G.Schirmer ⌐1905₎
score (84p.) 24cm.

Text of the poem, in French, English and German, precedes the score.

1. Symphonic   poems – Scores. I. Title.

NL   0442210   IaU NN MH MB MiU FTaSU

Loeffler, Charles Martin, *1861–1935.*
La villanelle du diable. D'après un poème de M. Rollinat. Fantaisie symphonique pour grand orchestre et orgue. Op. 9. Réduction pour piano à 4 mains.
— New York. Schirmer. [1908.] (4), 33 pp. 35 cm.
The original French text with translations into English by Philip Hale, and into German by Stefan Zweig, pp. (4), I.

D9861 — T.r. — Fantaisie symphoniqu. · Pianoforte. Music. Four hands. — Rollinat, Maurice, 1846–1903.

NL   0442211   MB

Loeffler, Charles Martin ⌐Tornov, *1861–1935.*
Violin studies for the development of the left hand.
— New York. G. Schirmer, Inc. [1936.] 20 pp. 30.5 cm.

E2427 — Violin. Music. Left-hand. — Violin. Instruction books.

NL   0442212   MB

Loeffler, Charles Martin Tornov, 1861–
...The wind among the reeds; two poems by W. B. Yeats, set to music for voice and piano, by Ch. M. Loeffler... New York: G. Schirmer₎ cop. 1908₎ Publ. pl. no. 20641. 19 p. f°.

English words precede and accompany music; music for 1 voice with piano acc.
Contents: The hosting of the Sidhe. The host of the air.

1. Songs, American. I. Yeats,   William Butler, 1865– : The wind among the reeds. II. Title.
N. Y. P. L.   February 1, 1932

NL   0442213   NN CLU MH

Loeffler (Christian. Hieronym.) · De febrium natura inflammatoria in nervosas transitu atque decursu. 18 pp., 1 l. 12°. *Tübinga, I. F. Fues,* [1820].
Also, transl. in: WEBER. Samml. mod.-prakt. Diss. [etc.] 8°. *Tübingen,* 1820, v. 70–87.

NL   0442214   DNLM PPC

Loeffler, Dagobert.
Bakterielle versuche ueber die zuverlaessigkeit der taegeschen sterilisierungsmethode des wassers zu injektionen,...
Inaug. diss. Freiburg, 1916. (Leipzig, Wien)
Bibl.

NL   0442215   ICRL CtY DNLM

3781   **Loeffler, Donald Edward.**
S78L   Phase studies in metal-armonia solutions.
⌐Stanford, Calif.₎ 1949.

64 numb. l. plates, tables, diagrs.

Thesis (Ph.D.) - Stanford Univ., 1949.
Bibliography: numb. leaf 62-64.

1. Armonia.

NL   0442216   CSt

Loeffler, E. J.
Plans & Specifications for a Proposed Dynamo Laboratory.
36 p.
Thesis 1938.

NL   0442217   OClW

W 4   LÖFFLER, Eberhard, 1912–
T91   Hämolyse und Blutgerinnung.   Tübingen,
1938   1938.
20 p.
Inaug. -Diss. - Tübingen.
1. Blood coagulation 2. Hemolysis & hemolysins

NL   0442218   DNLM

Pamph.   LOEFFLER, Edmund, 1900–
v. 472   Peter Winter als Kirchenmusiker, ein Beitrag zur Geschichte der Messe. [Aschaffenburg, Druckerei u. Verlagsanstalt Kirsch] 1929.
vi, 94p. front. (port.) music. 21cm.

Inaug.-Diss.--Frankfurt a.M.

NL   0442219   MH-AH NcD

VOLUME 338

Löffler, Eduard.
Die Österreichische Pferde-Ankaufs-Mission
unter dem K.K. Obersten Ritter Rudolf von
Brudermann, in Syrien, Palästina und der Wüste,
in den Jahren 1856 und 1857...   Troppau, 1860.
18.5 cm.

NL 0442220   CtY

LÖFFLER, Eduard, 1858–
. Der comes Theodosius. Inaug.-diss.,
Halle-Wittenberg, Halle a. S., S. Schlesinger, 1885.

pp.40+.
"Vita", atend.

NL 0442221   MH ICRL NjP

617.635
L82   Loeffler, Egbert Theodore
Questions in practical dental therapeutics. With introductory notes on general
& oral hygiene & oral prophylaxis in the
form of questions & answers. By Egbert T.
Loeffler...Ann Arbor, Michigan, Edwards
bros., 1914.
2 p.ℓ.,52 numb.ℓ.   28 x 22 cm.
Mimeographed copy.
Defective copy:ℓ.48 lacking.
Blank leaves for annotation.
Additional questions inserted in ms
on blank leaf preceding ℓ.49.

NL 0442222   MiU

DD 901
U4 L64   Loeffler, Emil von, 1825–
1881   Geschichte der Festung Ulm. Ulm, A.
Kuthe, 1881.
592 p. illus. (part fold.)

1. Ulm – Hist.

NL 0442223   CaBVaU

Löffler, Emil v[on], 1825–
Geschichte der festung Ulm. 2ª aufl. Ulm, Wagner, 1883.
pp. viii, 592. 3 folded plans and other illus.

Ulm, Germany|

NL 0442224   MH DLC-P4 DNW

Loeffler, E[mil] von, 1825–
Das treffen bei Elchingen und die katastrophe von Ulm
im jahre 1805. Von E. v. Loeffler ... Ulm, Druck der
J. Ebner'schen buchdruckerei, 1904.
36 p. fold. plan (in pocket) 28ᶜᵐ. (*On cover:* Ulm, Oberschwaben.
Mitteilungen des Vereins für kunst und altertum in Ulm und Oberschwaben. hft. 11)

1. Elchingen, Battle of, 1805. 2. Ulm—Capitulation, 1805.

Library of Congress   DD801.W6V42   5–38336

NL 0442225   DLC NcD

Löffler, Erich, ed.

PT2613
.I 63J86   **Gillhoff, Johannes,** 1861–1930.
1942   Deutsche Bauern in Amerika. [Auswahl und Durchsicht
dieses Heftes besorgte Erich Löffler. 3. Aufl.] Frankfurt a.
M. M. Diesterweg [1939]

Loeffler, Ernst, 1888–
... Die congenitalen halsfisteln ...   Berlin,
Ebering [1919]
30 p.

Inaug.-diss., Berlin, 1919.
Lebenslauf.
"Literatur": p. [25]-27.

1. Fistula, Cervical.

NL 0442227   NNC DNLM CtY

Löffler, Ernst, 1912–
Lingua nigra. ... Coburg, 1935.   46 p.
Inaug. Diss. - Erlangen, 1935.
Lebenslauf.
Bibliography.

NL 0442228   CtY

Löffler, E[rnst] Conrad Abildgaard] 1835–
Dänemarks natur und volk, eine geographische monographie von Dr. E. Löffler ... Mit 39 illustrationen und
karten. Kopenhagen, Lehmann & Stages, 1905.
4 p. l., 118, [2] p. illus. 23ᶜᵐ.
"Literarischer wegweiser": p. [111]-114.

1. Denmark—Descr. & trav.

Library of Congress   DL118.L7   5–38335

NL 0442229   DLC ICJ NN MB

Løffler, Ernst Conrad Abildgaard, 1835–1911.
Haandbog i Geographien, af Dr. E. Løffler...   Kjøbenhavn:
Gyldendal, 1876.   xii, 610 p.   charts, illus.   22cm.
Bibliography, p. xi–xii.

10337B. 1. Geography—Textbooks,   Danish, 1876.
N.Y.P.L.   February 14, 1940

NL 0442230   NN CU

1835–1911.
Löffler, Ernst [Conrad Abildgaard]. The
Vineland-excursions of the ancient Scandinavians. Extr. fr. Congrès international
des Américanistes. Compte-rendu de la
cinquième session. Copenhague, 1884.
8°. pp. 64–73.   IcB53C748

NL 0442231   NIC

Loeffler, Ernst Rudolf.
De causa probabili diversos vitae aetatum characteres sistente. Dissertatio inauguralis . . . in Academia Lipsiensi . . .
Lipsiae. Staritz. [1838.] 23 pp. 4°.

F9726 — Growth.

NL 0442232   MB DNLM

Loeffler, Ernst Rudolf.
Ph. C. Hartmann's Hypothese über die
assimilativ-blutbereitende Funktion der Leber,
als ein Beitrag zur Physiologie. viii, 64 pp.
12°. Leipzig, W. Laufer, 1848.

NL 0442233   DNLM

LÖFFLER, Eugen, 1883–
Beiträge zur theorie der schnittpunkte
algebraischer kurven. Inaugural-dissertation,
Borna-Leipzig, buchdruckerei R. Noske, 1907.

pp.49.

NL 0442234   MH IU ICRL

Löffler, Eugen, 1883–
Das öffentliche Bildungswesen in Deutschland. Berlin,
E. S. Mittler, 1931.
viii, 144 p. 25 cm.
Bibliography: p. 141–144.

1. Education—Germany.

LA721.8.L63   52–58912

NL 0442235   DLC NcD

Löffler, Eugen, 1883–   tr.

QA565
S4   **Severi, Francesco,** 1879–
... Vorlesungen über algebraische geometrie: geometrie auf
einer kurve, Riemannsche flächen, Abelsche integrale. Berechtigte deutsche übersetzung, von dr. Eugen Löffler ... Mit einem
einführungswort von A. Brill und 20 figuren. Leipzig [etc.]
B. G. Teubner, 1921.

Löffler, Eugen, 1883–
... Ziffern und ziffernsysteme der kulturvölker in alter
und neuer zeit, von dr. Eugen Löffler ... Leipzig und
Berlin, B. G. Teubner, 1912.
iv, 92, [2] p. illus. 18½ᶜᵐ. (Mathematische bibliothek, hrsg. von W.
Lietzmann und A. Witting. 1) M. 0.80
"Literaturverzeichnis": p. [91]–92.

1. Numeration.

Library of Congress   QA141.L7   12–5499

NL 0442237   DLC NjP NcD PBm MiU ICJ NN PU-Mu

QA141
L6   Löffler, Eugen, 1883–
1918   Ziffern und Ziffernsysteme. 2., neubearb. Aufl.
Leipzig, B. G. Teubner, 1918-19
2 v.   (Mathematisch- physikalisch Bibliothek, 34)

Includes bibliography.

Contents.- 1. Die Zahlzeichen der alten Kulturvölker.-
2. Die Z. im Mittelalter und in der Neuzeit.

1. Numeration.

NL 0442238   CU DLC NjP RPB NcD MiU TxHU

QA141
L6   Löffler, Eugen, 1883–
1928   Ziffern und Ziffernsysteme. 3. durchgesehene Aufl. Leipzig, B.G. Teubner, 1928-
v.   illus. (Mathematisch-
Physikalische Bibliothek, 1)

"Literatur": v.1, p.[53]-54.

Contents.- 1.T. Die Zahlzeichen der alten
Kulturvölker.

NL 0442239   CU RPB

VOLUME 338

DD801
B5L82

Löffler, Eugenie.
Landschaft und Stadt in Pfalz und Saar;
Geographische Charakterbilder. Gedruckt mit
Unterstützung der Pfälzischen Gesellschaft
zur Förderung der Wissenschaften. Heidelberg
Westmarkt-Verlag, 1936.
127 p. plates, maps. 26cm.
"Schrifttum": p. 120-124.

1. Palestine - Descr. 2. Saar Valley -
Descr. I. Pfälzi   sche Gesellschaft zur
Forderung der   Wissenschaften. II.
Title.   9

NL 0442240   CSt-H MH

Löffler, Eugenie.
Die Oberflächengestaltung des Pfälzer Stufenlandes.
Stuttgart, J. Engelhorns Nachf., 1929.
78 p. illus. 2 maps (1 fold.) 23 cm. (Forschungen zur deutschen
Landes- und Volkskunde, Bd. 27, Heft 1)
Diss.—Munich.
Without thesis statement.
"Literaturverzeichnis": p. ₁75₎-76.

1. Geology—Palatinate.   I. Title.   (Series: Forschungen zur
deutschen Landeskunde, Bd. 27, Heft 1)
G58.F73 Bd. 27, Heft 1   A 49-2096'

Harvard Univ. Library
for Library of Congress   .2+

NL 0442241   MH MB DLC

Map
G
7432
B6
1890?

Löffler, F
Le Bosphore.   Constantinople, 1890?
col. map 124 x 23 cm. in folder
14 x 25 cm.

Scale 1:33,333.

1. Bosporus--Maps.

NL 0442242   NIC

271.7
L828c1

Löffler, Felipe.
La congregación mariana. Primera versión castellana por Gervasio de Artíñano
de Galdácano, rev. y precedida de un prólogo por Luis Ignacio Fiter. Barcelona,
Librería y Tip. Católica, 1896.
xxviii, 150p. 15cm.

1. Marianists. I. Title.

NL 0442243   CLSU

Loeffler, Felix.
Die gewerbliche private pfandleihe nach geltendem
reichs- und landesrecht. Nebst dem anhange: Die rechtliche natur des pfandscheines. Unter beifügung einer zusammenstellung der wichtigsten bundesstaatlichen gesetze
und verordnungen über die pfandleihe. Von Felix Loeffler ... Berlin, E. Ebering, 1908.
vii, 215, ₍2₎ p. 23ᶜᵐ. (Added t.-p.: Rechts- und staatswissenschaftliche
studien ... hft. xxxiv ...)
"Literaturverzeichnis": p. ₍212₎-215.

8-14963

NL 0442244   DLC NN ICRL CU ICJ

BX2170
.S3L6

Loeffler, Frank Hubert.
Gebet- und gesangbuechlein fuer katholische
kinder zum gebrauch bei der schul-messe.
Cincinnati, O., 1896.

NL 0442245   DLC

₍Loeffler, Frank Hubert₎
Gebet- und gesangbüchlein für katholische kinder, zum gebrauch bei der schul-messe ... Cincinnati, O., Gedruckt von
P. Gfroerer, 1901.
vi, 7-131 p. 13ᶜᵐ.

1. Schools—Prayers. 2. Catholic church—Prayer-books and devotions—German. 3. Catholic church—Hymns. I. Title.
1-16701

Library of Congress   BX2170.S3L6 1901

NL 0442246   DLC

378.76
L930d
1955

Loeffler, Frank Joseph, 1926-
Perception of ambiguous stimuli in motion:
a comparison of schizophrenic and normal
adults with normal children... n.p., 1955.
ix, 107 p. illus., tables. 28 cm.
Thesis (Ph.D.) - Louisiana State University. Baton Rouge, La. 1955.
Vita.
Bibliography: p. ₍67₎-70.
Abstract.
1. Schizophr-   enia. 2. Personality
tests. 3. Pro-   jection (Psychology)
I. Title.

NL 0442247   LU

1882-

Loeffler, Franz, appr. Arzt: Ueber die festen primären
Mesenterialtumoren und einen Fall von Fibro-Sarkoma
mesenterii. Berlin: Lokay ₍1911₎. 28 S. 8°
Leipzig, Med. Diss. v. 20. März 1911, Ref. Marchand
[Geb. 12. April 82 Hilchenbach; Wohnort: Berlin; Staatsangeh.: Preußen;
Vorbildung: Gymn. Arensberg Reife O. 02; Studium: Straßburg 6, Berlin
4 S.; Coll. 25. März 11; Approb. 1. Okt. 08.]   [U 11. 3/56

NL 0442248   ICRL DNLM CtY

Löffler, Franz Adam.
Ueber die gesetzgebung der presse ...
1. th. Leipzig, 1837.
21.5 cm.

NL 0442249   CtY NjP

Bonaparte
Collection
No. 10,023

[Löffler, Franz Adam]

Ut 'n hangbuttenstrukh. Lieder und
gedichte in plattdeutscher mundart, von
Angelus Neomarchicus [pseud.]   Berlin,
1862.

NL 0442250   ICN ICU

Loeffler, Franz Josef 1882-
see Loeffler, Franz, 1882-

879
Ar37
7.6

Loeffler, Franz Joseph.
De Calphurnio Terentii interprete. (In
Dissertationes philologicae argentoraten-
ses selectae. 1879- v.6, p.261-330)

NL 0442252   IU

PA
25
S89
v.6
no.3

Loeffler, Franz Joseph.
De Calphurnio Terentii interprete.
Argentorati, K.J. Truebner, 1882.
70 p. 23cm. (Strasbourg. Université.
Dissertationes philologicae Argentoratenses
selectae. v.6, no.3)

Diss.--Strasbourg.

1. Calphurnius, Joannes, ca. 1443-

NL 0442253   NIC ICRL MH MB CtY

[LOEFFLER, FRIEDERIKE LUISE (HERBORT)] b. 1744
Anweisung zu Frauenzimmer-Arbeiten, zur Behandlung
von Haushaltungs-Sachen und zur Körper-Schönheits-
pflege. Nebst einer Anleitung zur Bereitung von
Speisen und Getränken für Kranke, und zur Anwendung
von Haus-Mitteln. Mit einem Anhange über die Diät
der Wöchnerinnen und über die Erziehung der Kinder
in den ersten Lebens-Jahren. 4. durchaus verb. und
verm. Aufl. Stuttgart, J.F. Steinkopf, 1826.
xii, 916 p. 20cm. (Oekonomisches Handbuch für
Frauenzimmer. 4. durchaus verb. und verm. Aufl. Bd. 2)
1. Domestic economy, to   1850. I. Title.

NL 0442254   NN

Loeffler, Friederike Luise (Herbort), b. 1744.
...Kochbuch für die einfache bürgerliche Küche Hrsg.
von Eugen Bechtel... Ulm: J. Ebner, 1922. xv, 539 p.
col'd front., plates (1 col'd). 2. ed. 8°

58471A. 1. Cookery (German).   2. Bechtel, Eugen, editor.
N. Y. P. L.   September 11, 1922.

NL 0442255   NN

Löffler, Friederike Luise (Herbort) *b.* 1744.
Kochbuch ₍von₎ Löffler ₍und₎ Bechtel. Neubearb. von
Fritz Hauff und Reinhold Schluckebier. Ulm-Donau, J.
Ebner ₍1948₎
352 p. illus. (part col.) 22 cm.

1. Cookery, German.   I. Bechtel, Eugen, joint author. II. Hauff,
Fritz, 1913-   ed.

TX721.L55   641.5943   49-19397*

NL 0442256   DLC NN

₍Löffler, Friederike Luise (Herbort)₎ b. 1744.
Neues Kochbuch; oder, Geprüfte Anweisung zur schmakhaften
Zubereitung der Speisen, des Bakwerks, der Confecturen, des
Gefrornen und Eingemachten.   Stuttgard, J. C. Betulius, 1791.
508 p. 19cm. (Oekonomisches Handbuch für Frauenzimmer.
Bd. 1)

"Vorrede" signed: F. L. Löflerin.

455577. 1. Cookery, German, to   1850. I. Title.   *Card revised*
N. Y. P. L.   *January 25, 1950*

NL 0442257   NN

LOEFFLER, FRIEDERIKE LUISE (HERBORT), b. 1744.
Neues Kochbuch; oder, Geprüfte Anweisung zur
schmackhaften Zubereitung der Speisen, des Backwerks, der Confituren, des Gefrornen und des Eingemachten. 4. durchaus verb. und verm. Aufl. Stuttgart, J.F. Steinkopf, 1825. 1 v. 20cm. (Oekonomisches
Handbuch für Frauenzimmer. 4. sehr verb und verm. Aufl. Bd. 1,
Abth. 2)

Theil 2.
1. Cookery, German. to 1850.   I. Title.

NL 0442258   NN

VOLUME 338

⌈Löffler, Friederike Luise (Herbort)⌉ b. 1744.
　　Neues Kochbuch; oder, Geprüfte Anweisung zur schmackhaften Zubereitung der Speisen, des Backwerks, des Confekts, des Gefrornen und des Eingemachten... 8. verb. und verm. Aufl. Theil 1– Stuttgart, J. F. Steinkopf, 1833– v. 19cm.
　　(Oekonomisches Handbuch für Frauenzimmer. 8. verb. und verm. Aufl. Bd. 1, Abth. 1–)

1. Cookery, German, to 1850.　　　　I. Title.
N. Y. P. L.　　　　　　　　　　　　　　February 24, 1950

NL 0442259　　NN NIC

Löffler, Friedrike Luise(Herbort) b. 1744.
Neues Stuttgarter Kochbuch. Aufl. 18.
Stuttg., Steinkopf, 1887.
513 p.

NL 0442260　　PPG

Löffler, FRIEDRIKE LUISE (Herbort) b. 1744.
Neues Stuttgarter Kochbuch oder bewährte und vollständige Anweisung zur schmackhaften Zubereitung aller Arten von Speisen, Backwerk, Gefrorenem, Eingemachtem u. s. w. Stuttgart: J. F. Steinkopf, 1897. 479 pp. 21. ed. 8°.

NL 0442261　　NN

Löffler, Friederike Luise (Herbort) b. 1744.
Neues Stuttgarter kochbuch...
Stuttgart, Steinkopf, 1902.
522 p.

NL 0442262　　PP

Löffler, Frau Friedrike Luise (Herbort),
　　　　　　　　　　　　1744–181–.
　Neues Stuttgarter Kochbuch, oder, Bewährte und vollständige Anweisung zur schmackhaften Zubereitung aller Arten von Speisen, Backwerk, Gefrorenem, Eingemachtem u. s. w. Von Friedr. Luise Löffler. Sechsundzwanzigte umgearbeitete und vermehrte Auflage mit acht Tafeln in Farbendruck. Stuttgart, J. F. Steinkopf, 1908.
　552 p. illus., VIII col. pl. 21cm.

NL 0442263　　ICJ

Loeffler, Friederike Luise (Herbort), b. 1744.
　Neues Stuttgarter Kochbuch; bewährte und vollständige Anweisung zur schmackhaften Zubereitung aller Arten von Speisen, Backwerk, Gefrorenem, Eingemachtem usw., von Friedr. Luise Löffler; achtunddreissigste, neu durchgesehene und vermehrte Auflage, bearbeitet von Johanna Pölzing. Stuttgart: J. F. Steinkopf, 1930. 428 p. illus. 8°.

517473A. 1. Cooking, German.　　I. Poelzing, Johanna, editor.
N. Y. P. L.　　　　　　　　　　　　March 31, 1931

NL 0442264　　NN CU

Loeffler, Friederike Luise (Herbort) b. 1744.
　Oekonomisches Handbuch für Frauenzimmer. Erster Bd., welcher das Kochbuch enthält.... 7. Aufl.; zweyter Bd., welcher die übrigen dem schönen Geschlechte vorzüglich nützlichen und dessen Berufs-Geschäften angemessenen Kenntnisse enthält. 4. Aufl.
　2 Bde. 12. Stuttgart. Joh. Friedrich Steinkopf. 1824, 1826.

NL 0442265　　PPG

Löffler, Friedrich

Vogel, Johann Heinrich, ed.
　Die keimtötende wirkung des torfmulls. Vier gutachten der herren professor dr. Stutzer ... professor dr. Fränkel ... professor dr. Gärtner ... professor dr. Löffler ... im auftrage der. Dünger-(kainit-)abteilung zusammengestellt und mit erläuterungen versehen von dr. I. H. Vogel ... 2. aufl. Prenzlau, Druck von A. Mieck, 1894.

Löffler, Friedrich, b. 1768.
　Ein Deutscher hilft die welt erobern, 1787–1819; schicksale und abenteuer in österreichischen, holländischen und englischen kriegsdiensten auf drei erdteilen, von sergeant Löffler. Neu herausgegeben und bearbeitet von Otto Dikreiter. Stuttgart, R. Lutz ⌈1937⌉
　330 p. front. (port.) 21cm.

　1. Austria—History, Military. 2. Gt. Brit.—History, Military—1789–1820. 3. Netherlands—History, Military. I. Dikreiter, Otto, ed. II. Title.
　　　　　　　　　　　　　　　38–23137
Library of Congress　　　D304.L6A3 1937
Copyright A—Foreign　　　39225
　　　　　　　　　　　⌈3⌉　　　　　923.5

NL 0442267　　DLC ICarbS ICN

---

*Loeffler, Friedrich, 1885–　　joint author.

Härtel, Fritz, 1877–
　El vendaje; manual de vendajes y apósitos ortopédicos y quirúrgicos, por Fr. Härtel ... y Fr. Loeffler ... Traducido del alemán por el comandante médico dr. A. Vallejo Nágera; con 300 grabados. Madrid, Espasa-Calpe, s. a., 1928.

Loeffler, Friedrich August Johannes, 1852–

Nuttall, George Henry Falkiner, 1862–　　ed.
　The bacteriology of diphtheria including sections on the history, epidemiology and pathology of the disease, the mortality caused by it, the toxins and antitoxins and the serum disease, by F. Loeffler ... Arthur Newsholme ... F. B. Mallory ... G. S. Graham-Smith ... George Dean ... William H. Park ... Charles F. Golduan ... Ed. by G. H. F. Nuttall ... and G. S. Graham-Smith ... Cambridge, University press, 1908.

Loeffler, Friedrich August Johannes, 1852–
[Collected papers on infection, immunity and other questions of public health.]

NL 0442270　　ICJ

Loeffler, Friedrich August Johannes, 1852–
　Die Diphtherie. (In: Soziale Kultur und Volkswohlfahrt während der ersten 25 Regierungsjahre Kaiser Wilhelm II. Berlin, 1913. f°. p. 409–419.)

1. Diphtheria.　　　　　　　MANDEL COLLECTION.
N. Y. P. L.　　　　　　　　　　　　March 27, 1914.

NL 0442271　　NN

Loeffler, Friedrich August Johannes, 1852–
Festschrift gewidmet zum 60. Geburtstage des Herrn Geheimen Medizinalrats Dr. F. Loeffler
　see under title

Löffler, Friedrich, August Johannes, 1852–1915
Die Löffler-Feier, 1952
　see under title

Loeffler (Friedrich August Joh.) [1852–　].
* Ueber den Einfluss der Blutentziehungen auf den Organismus. 30 pp., 1 l. 8°. Berlin, G. Schade, [1874].

NL 0442274　　DNLM ICRL

LOEFFLER, Friedrich August Johannes, 1852–1915.
　Wasserversorgung, Wasseruntersuchung und Wasserbeurteilung. Bearb. von F. Loeffler, G. Oesten, R. Sendtner. (Mit Beiträgen von Th. Weyl. — Jena. Fischer. 1896. (1), viii, (1), 415–782 pp. Illus. [Handbuch der Hygiene. B. 1. Abt. 2.] 8°.
　Contents.—Wasserversorgung, von G. Oesten. — Chemische Untersuchung des Trinkwassers, von R. Sendtner. — Das Wasser und die Mikroorganismen, von F. Loeffler —Die Beurteilung des Trinkwassers, von F. Loeffler, R. Sendtner.

Sheet C 4082　　　　　　　　　September 16, 1896.

NL 0442275　　MB ICJ

Loeffler (Friederich Berthold. * De plexibus choroideis hominum atque animalium vertebratorum. 30 pp. 8°. Regiomonti Prussorum. H. J. Dalkowski. [1852]

NL 0442276　　DNLM

Loeffler, Friedrich Berthold, supposed author.
　General-Bericht über den Gesundheitsdienst im Feldzuge gegen Dänemark, 1864
　　see under Löffler, Friedrich Gottfried Franz, 1815–1874.

W
600
L825p
LOEFFLER, Friedrich Berthold
　Das preussische Physikatsexamen, gerichtlich-medizinischer Leitfaden für Examinanden, Physiker und Juristen. ⌈1.⌉ Aufl. Berlin, Enslin, 1858–
　　v.
　Subtitle varies.

NL 0442278　　DNLM

QR
58
L6
Löffler, Friedrich Berthold.
　Vorlesungen die geschichtliche Entwickelung de Lehre von den Bacterien, für Aerzte und Studirende, von Friedrich Löffler. Leipzig, F.C.W. Vogel, 1887–
　　v. illus., plates.

　1. Bacteriology--Addresses, essays, lectures. I. Title.

　　OCU
NL 0442279　　UU ViU DNLM ICJ PBL KU-M CtY MnU OU MiU

Loeffler, Friedrich Gottfried Franz, 1815–74.
[1815–74]. * De phlebitide uterina. 34 pp., 3 l. 8°. Berolini, typ. Natorfianis, 1837.

NL 0442280　　DNLM

VOLUME 338

LÖFFLER, Friedrich Gottfried Franz,
UH   1815-1874
L825g   General-Bericht über den Gesund-
1867   heitsdienst im Feldzuge gegen Dänemark
1864. 1. Th. Berlin, Hirschwald,
1867.
xvii, 302 p. illus.
No more published?
Attributed by British Museum and
Bibliothèque nationale to Friedrich
Berthold Loeffler.

NL 0442281   DNLM ICJ PPC NN

Löffler, Friedrich Gottfried Franz, 1815-1874.
Grundsätze und Regeln für die Behandlung der Schusswunden im Kriege. Ein Beitrag zur Kriegsbereitschaft, von Dr. F. Löffler ... Erste-[zweite] Abtheilung. ... Berlin, A. Hirschwald, 1859.
2 pt. in 1 vol. 22½ᶜᵐ.
Contents.—1. Abth. Auf dem Schlachtfelde. [4, 3]-100 p.—2. Abth. Im Feldlazareth. [8], 128 p.

NL 0442282   ICN DNLM ICU

LÖFFLER, Friedrich Gottfried Franz,
UH   1815-1874
L825p   Das preussische Militär-Sanitätswesen
1866   und seine Reform nach der Kriegser-
fahrung von 1866. Berlin, Hirschwald,
1868-69.
2 v.
Contents. - 1. Th. Die freiwillige
Krankenpflege und die Genfer Convention
vom 22. August 1864 nach der Kriegser-
fahrung von 1866. - 2. Th. Die Sanitäts-
dienst und seine Organisation.

Erratum slip tipped in, 1. Th.

NL 0442284   DNLM CU-M MB

Loeffler, Friedrich Gottfried Franz, 1815-1874.
——. Rede über die heutige Aufgabe der militairärztlichen Bildungsanstalten zur Feier des Stiftungstages des medicinisch-chirurgischen Friedrich-Wilhelms-Institutes und der medicinisch-chirurgischen Akademie für das Militair am 2. August 1869. 21 pp. 8°. Berlin, G. Lange, [1869?]

NL 0442285   DNLM

Loeffler, Friedrich Karl Georg, 1885-
Experimentelle Untersuchungen über die Bedeutung des Complementes für das Zustandekommen des anaphylaktischen Anfalles... Von Friedrich Karl Georg Loeffler... Jena: G. Fischer, 1910. 2 p.l., 20 p., 1 l. 8°.
Dissertation, Greifswald.
Lebenslauf.
"Literatur." p. 20.

1. Anaphylaxis.
N. Y. P. L.   January 5, 1916.

NL 0442286   NN ICRL DNLM MiU

DS770   Löffler, Friedrich Otto, 1864-
L64   Die China-Expedition, 1900-1901. Unter
besonderer Berücksichtigung der Thätigkeit
des Armee-Oberkommandos und des Deutschen
Expeditionskorps. Berlin, E.S.Mittler,
1902.
48p. 23cm.

1. Boxers. 2. China - Hist. - 1900.

NL 0442287   IaU DLC-P4 ICJ

Löffler, Friedrich Otto, 1864-
Deutschland in China, 1900-1901,
see under title

Löffler, Friedrich Otto, 1864-
... La guerre Russo-Japonaise; enseignements tactiques et stratégiques. Traduit de l'allemand par le Lieutenant C. Olivari ... Paris, Nancy, Berger-Levrault & cie., 1907.
ix, 330 p., 2 l. 10 fold. maps (in pocket) 3 fold. tables. 24ᶜᵐ.

1. Russo-Japanese war, 1904-1905. 2. Tactics. 3. Strategy.   I. Olivari, Henri Charles, tr.

War 9-108

Library, Second Section,   General Staff DS517.L82

NL 0442289   DNW

4DK   Löffler, Friedrich Otto, 1864-
440   Der Russisch-Japanische Krieg in
seinen taktischen und strategischen
Lehren. Berlin, E. S. Mittler,
1905.
2 v. in 1

NL 0442290   DLC-P4 NjP ICJ DNW

Löffler, Friedrich Otto, 1864-
... Strategie, von Löffler ... Leipzig, G. J. Göschen, 1910.
133 p. 16ᶜᵐ. (Sammlung Göschen. [505])

1. Strategy. 2. Military art and science.

11-7776

Library of Congress   U162.L7

NL 0442291   DLC DNW MB MiU

Loeffler, Friedrich Otto, 1864-
...Táctica; manual para la conducción e instrucción de combate, por Löffler ...   Buenos Aires: Ferrari Hnos., 1920. 2 v. maps. 12°. (Biblioteca del oficial.   v. 21, 24.)
"Traducido por los capitanes Abraham Schweizer y Carlos von der Becke."

575498A. 1. Military strategy.   2. Military tactics. I. Schweizer, Abraham, captain, translator.   II. Becke, Carlos von der, translator.
III. Ser.
N. Y. P. L.   July 7, 1932

NL 0442292   NN

Löffler, Friedrich Otto, 1864-
Taktik des truppen-sanitätsdienstes
auf dem schlachfelde, von Löffler...
Berlin, E. S. Mittler und sohn, 1890.
2 p.l., 86 p. 23 cm.

NL 0442293   DNW

Löffler, Friedrich Otto, 1864-
Taktik; ein handbuch für die gefechtsführung und die gefechtsausbildung, von Löffler ... Berlin, E. S. Mittler und sohn, 1912.
xvi, 335, [1] p. maps (2 fold. in pocket) 24½ cm.

1. Tactics.
U165.L79   War 12-146
U. S. Army War College.   Library
for Library of Congress   [a49b1.†]

NL 0442294   DNW DLC

Löffler, Friedrich Otto, 1864-
Taktik des Truppen-Sanitätsdienstes auf dem Schlachtfelde, von Löffler ... Zweite, auf Grund der Kriegs-Sanitätsordnung vom 27. Januar 1907 neu bearbeitete Auflage ... Berlin, E. S. Mittler und Sohn, 1907.
v p., 1 L., 104 p. 2 maps (1 fold.) 23½ᶜᵐ.

NL 0442295   ICJ DNLM DLC-P4 DNW

Loeffler, Friedrich Simon, respondent.
... Disputatio theologica ex Rom. IX, vers. 5
see under Carpzov, Johann Benedict, 1639-
1699, praeses.

LÖFFLER,   Friedrich Simon.
Doppelte nachricht von der romischen kirchen jubel-jahren, deren die erste einehistorische welche ihre ceremonien, jahre und medaillen, und wie sie von 1300 bis 1700 gefeyret worden, vortragt; die andere eine theoretische, welche, /as von denselben uberhaupt, und absonderliche derselben nutzen, welcher der ablass, zu halten, lehret. Nebenst einem anhange, wie dei conduite und das reformiren des ietzigen haupts der ro- ischen kirchen von den evangelischen an- zusehen. Leipzig. 1725.

Fronts.

NL 0442297   MH

AC   Löffler, Fritz, 1892-
831   Die wirtschaftlichkeit eines grossstädtischen
Ruths-Spitzenkraftwerkes mit stadtbeizung.
...1935.
Ineug. Diss. - Techn. Hochschule Berlin, 1935.
Lebenslauf.
Bibliography.

NL 0442298   ICRL

Löffler, Fritz, 1899-
Das alte Dresden; Geschichte seiner Bauten. Dresden, Sachsenverlag, 1955.
411 p. illus., ports., maps (part fold. in pocket) 31 cm. (Deutsche Bauakademie. Schriften des Instituts für Theorie und Geschichte der Baukunst)
Bibliography: p. 377-[380]

1. Architecture—Dresden.   I. Title.   (Series: Deutsche Bauakademie. Schriften des Forschungsinstitutes für Theorie und Geschichte der Baukunst)
NA1086.D7L6   56-28045
CtY
NL 0442299   DLC CLU PSt KyU PU-FA CU NN KU PPT WaU

[Loeffler, Fritz] 1899-   ed.
Die Annenkirche zu Annaberg. [Berlin, Union Verlag
VOB, 1954]
51 p. illus. (Das Christliche Denkmal, 7)

NL 0442300   MH-FA

NA4790   Löffler, Fritz, 1899-   ed.
.C55   Das Christliche Denkmal. Heft 1-
Berlin, Union Verlag, 1953-

VOLUME 338

[Loeffler, Fritz] 1899-   ed.
Der Dom zu Freiberg. [Berlin, Union Verlag VOB, 1953]

30 p. illus. (Das Christliche Denkmal, 3)

NL 0442302   MH-FA

Hkp   **Löffler, Fritz, 1899-**
K523X   Das epische Schaffen Eduard v. Keyserlings.
L82   [n.p.]1928.
    67p. 22cm.
    Inaug.-Diss. - München.
    Bibliography:p.65
    Vita.

    1. Keyserling, Eduard Heinrich Nikolaus, Graf
von, 1855-1918.

NL 0442303   CtY

LÖFFLER, FRITZ, 1899-
    Gottlieb Traugott Bienert. Leipzig, O. Leiner
[194-?] 17 p. port. 21cm. (Sächsische Lebensbilder; hrsg. von
der Sächsischen Kommission für Geschichte)

    Cover title.
    Bibliography, p. 17.

    1. Bienert, Gottlieb Traugott,   1813-1894. I. Sächsische
Lebensbilder.

NL 0442304   NN

Löffler, Fritz, 1899-
    Otto Dix; Maler, Zeichner, Graphiker.
    [Ausstellung. Dresden, 1949]
      see under   Dresden. Staatliche Kunst-
sammlungen.

Löffler, Fritz, 1899-
    Theodor Körner, dichter und freiheits-
held, von Fritz Löffler. Dresden, Verlag
Heimatwerk Sachsen, v. Baensch stiftung,
1938.
    72 p. 18cm. (Grosse Sachsen, diener
des reiches. bd.3)

    "Literatur": p.72.

    1. Körner, Theodor, 1791-1813.

NL 0442306   WU

Loeffler (Georgius). * De hypopyo. 16 pp. 8°.
Monachii, J. Deschler, 1838.

NL 0442307   DNLM

Loeffler, Gisella, 1900-   illus.

Bianco, *Mrs.* **Margery (Williams)** 1880-
    Franzi and Gizi, by Margery Bianco and Gisella Loeffler.
New York, J. Messner inc. [c1941]

PZ7   Loeffler, Gisella, 1900-   ed.
.D3667
L3   **De Huff, Elizabeth (Willis)** 1892-
    Little-Boy-Dance; story by Elizabeth Willis DeHuff, pic-
tures by Gisella Loeffler. Chicago, Wilcox & Follett co. [1946]

Loeffler, Gottfried Friederich Franz
    see   Loeffler, Friedrich Gottfried Franz,
1815-1874.

Loeffler, Gustav
    Die Beschneidung im Lichte der Medizin.
Vier Vorträge gehalten im "Mohalim-Verein"
zu Frankfurt a. M. Frankfurt a.M.: L.
Golde, 1912.
    36 p.

NL 0442311   OCH PPDrop

Loeffler, Gustav
    Wie fördern wir den religiösen Sinn der
jüdischen Jugend? Hischehe, sexualetische
Forderungen. Frühehe und soziale Umschichtung
der jüdischen Jugend Deutschlands. Referat
... erstattet auf der 4. ordentlichen
Delegiertentagung des Verbandes der Jüdischen
Jugendverein Deutschlands am 15. u. 16. Juni
1919 zu Berlin. Berlin: Verband d. Jüd.
Jugendvereine Deutschlands, [1919].
    32 p.

NL 0442312   OCH

Löffler, Gustav, 1879-
    Ueber kleine abgekapselte empyeme im kindesalter ...
Heidelberg, Heidelberger verlagsanstalt und druckerei
(Hörning und Berkenbusch) 1902.
    56 p., 1 l. 22ᶜᵐ.
    Inaug.-diss.—Heidelberg.
    Lebenslauf.
    "Zur arbeit benützte litteraturwerke": p. [55]-56.

    1. Empyema.

Library of Congress   RC751.L8   7-27931†

NL 0442313   DLC DNLM

[LOEFFLER, Gustav Otto]
    Hephata!   Ein ruf Gottes an die menschen
Stuttgart, n. d.

    223 p. 21 cm.
    Author's name appears at end, "Geschrieben
durch Gustav Otto Loeffler."

    The Stuttgart imprint is covered by paster.
"Bietigheim, Würtb., Verlag neuer christlich-
theosophischer schriften".

NL 0442314   MH

Loeffler, Gustav Otto.
    ... Ihr geheimnis. (In trance.) Komödie in drei akten ...
Leipzig-Gohlis, 1910.
    97 p. 20ᶜᵐ.
    "Als unverkäufliches manuskript gedruckt."

    I. Title. II. Title: In trance.

                        43-31843
                        Brief cataloging
Library of Congress   PT2623.O319 I 5

NL 0442315   DLC

Loeffler, H., joint author.

Schwedler, Johann Wilhelm, 1823-1894.
    Der bau der eisenbahnbrücke über die Weichsel bei Thorn.
Nach den entwürfen von J. W. Schwedler ... und H. Loeffler ...
Ausgeführt in den jahren 1870 bis 1873. Mit XVII kupfer-
tafeln und vielen holzschnitten. Berlin, Ernst & Korn, 1876.

Löffler, H
    Über Verschlussvorrichtungen an den Blütenknospen bei
Hemerocallis und einigen anderen Liliaceen, von H. Löffler ...
Mit 2 Tafeln. [Hamburg, L. Friederichsen & Co., 1903]
    11 p. II pl. 27½ᶜᵐ. [In Naturwissenschaftlicher Verein, Hamburg.
Abhandlungen aus dem Gebiete der Naturwissenschaften. XVIII. Bd.]
    Bibliographical foot-notes.

NL 0442317   ICJ

Löffler, Hans.
    Über 19 in der Würzburger geburtshilflichen
Klinik vom Jahre 1889-1899 beobachtete Fälle
von Eklampsie. München, V. Höfling, 1900.
    25 p.
    Inaug.-Diss. - Würzburg, 1900.

NL 0442318   ICRL DNLM

W 4   Löffler, Hans, 1913-
M96   Über den heutigen Stand der
1940   Röntgenbestrahlung des sympathischen
    Nervensystems. München, Mössl, 1940.
    26 p.

    Inaug.-Diss. - Munich.
    Bibliography: p. 25.

NL 0442319   DNLM MnU

W 4   Löffler, Hans, 1916-
296   Zur klinischen Abgrenzung der Hepatitis
1943   epidemica von andern Hepatitisformen. Basel,
    Karger [1943?]
    p. [113]-[140] illus.

    Inaug.-Diss. - Zürich.
    Reprinted from Gastroenterologia, v. 68,
fasc. 3.

NL 0442320   DNLM

Löffler, Hans Eberhard, 1906-
    Wirtschaftliche zusammenhänge maschineller
erfindungen mit kapital und arbeit... [Kirchhain,
N.-L.] 1927.
    36 p.
    Inaug.-Diss. - Hamburg, 1927.

NL 0442321   MiU

W 4   LOEFFLER, Hansgeorg, 1928-
M96   Zum Wirkungsmechanismus des
1953   Kallikreins. [München] 1953.
    49 l. illus.
    Inaug.-Diss. - Munich.
    1. Kallikrein

NL 0442322   DNLM

TX 612   Loeffler, Harold Julius
S4 L6   The quantitave [sic] estimation of inci-
1938   pient decomposition in canned salmon.
    [Stanford, Calif.] Stanford University,
1938.
    315 l. tables.
    Thesis - Stanford University.
    Cover title: The quantitative estimation
of incipient decomposition in canned salmon.
    1. Salmon, Canned. I. Title: The
quantitative   estimation of incipient decom-   position in canned
salmon.

NL 0442323   CaBVaU

VOLUME 338

Löffler, Harry
Die französisch-reformierte gemeinde zu
Königsberg Pr.
Inaug. Diss. Königsberg, 1931.
Bibl. 104p.

NL 0442324   ICRL PU CtY MH-L

Löffler, Heinrich, 1879–
Die deutsche arbeiterschaft und das sachver-
ständigen- gutachten vom 9, april 1924. Berlin,
1924.
39 p. Map.
"Schriften des 'Firn'".
By Heinrich Loeffler and Georg Berger.

NL 0442325   MH-L

OD 94   LÖFFLER, HEINRICH, 1879–
L 82   Der Gewerkschaftliche Separatismus der
Polnisch-Sozialistischen Partei in Deutschland.
Bearb. nach einem Vortrag von Heinrich Löffler-
Kattowitz. Berlin, Verlag der Generalkommis-
sion der Gewerkschaften Deutschlands ₁1914₎
27 p.

1. Polska Partia Socjalistyczna. 2. Poles
in Germany. I. Title.

NL 0442326   InU MH

Loeffler, Heinrich, 1879–
Das Proletariat und die Besetzung des Ruhrgebiets, von
Heinrich Löffler... Berlin: Verlag für Sozialwissenschaft
₁1923₎ 13 p. 8°.
Cover-title.

1. European war, 1914–18.—Repara-   tions. 2. Coal.—Trade and statistics,
Germany: Ruhr valley, 1919–22.
N. Y. P. L.   March 4, 1924.

NL 0442327   NN

Loeffler, Heinrich, 1879–
Russland im Licht englischer Gewerkschafter; kritische Besprechung des Berichts der englischen Gewerkschaftsdelegation
über Russland, von Heinrich Löffler. Berlin: Verlagsgesellschaft des Allgemeinen Deutschen Gewerkschaftsbundes G.m.-
b.H., 1925. 30 p. 8°.

1. British Trades Union Delegation   to Russia and Caucasia, 1924: Russia.
N. Y. P. L.   December 28, 1926.

NL 0442328   NN

Löffler, Heinrich, 1879–
Die staatsbürgerliche erziehung in der knaben- und mäd-
chenfortbildungsschule. Von H. Löffler... Langensalza, H.
Beyer & söhne, 1912.
1 p. l., 53 p. 21½ cm. (Pädagogisches magazin, hft. 478)
"Literatur": p. 53.

1. Political science—Study and teaching.   I. Title.

JA88.G3L6   E33-122
U. S. Office of Education.   Library
for Library of Congress   ₁a50e₎₁†

NL 0442329   DHEW NN DLC

Loeffler, Heinrich, *1879-*
Um Oberschlesien; eine kritische Betrachtung der Entscheidung des Völkerbundrats, von H. Löffler, im Auftrage des Allgemeinen deutschen Gewerkschaftsbundes. Berlin: Verlagsgesellschaft des Allgemeinen deutschen Gewerkschaftsbundes m.b.H.,
1922. 51 p. incl. tables. 8°.

1. Silesia (Upper). 2. Allgemeiner   deutscher Gewerkschaftsbund.
N. Y. P. L.   January 9, 1923.

NL 0442330   NN

1886-
Löffler, Heinrich, appr. Tierarzt, Unterveterinär an d. Mil.-
Vet.-Akad.: Aus d. hyg. Inst. d. Tierärztl. Hochsch. Berlin.
Vorst.: Frosch. Das Formaldehydpräparat 'Autan' als
Desinfektionsmittel für Stallungen, Tierkliniken usw. Berlin
1910: (Mittler). 32 S. 8°
Gießen, Veterinär-Med. Diss. v. 4. Juli 1910, Ref. Geppert
[Geb. 27. Febr. 86 Darmstadt; Wohnort: Berlin; Staatsangeh.: Hessen; Vor-
bildung: Oberrealsch. Darmstadt Reife O. 04; Studium: Berlin Mil.-Vet.-
Akad. 8 S.; Rig. 13. Juni 10.]   [U 10, 1228

NL 0442331   ICRL DNLM PU MH

NB1420   Löffler, Heinz, 1891–
.L8   ... Die grabsteine, grabmäler und epitaphien in den kirchen Alt-Livlands vom 13.–18. jahrhundert. ₁Riga, G. Löffler, 1929₎
₍8₎ 135, ₍3₎ p. xxii pl. on 11 l. 22ᶜᵐ. (On cover: Abhandlungen der Herder-
gesellschaft und des Herder-instituts zu Riga. 3. bd., nr. 2)
Bibliographical foot-notes.

1. Sepulchral monuments—Livonia. 2. Epitaphs—Livonia.

NL 0442332   ICU NN

Löffler, Heinz, 1891–
Kloster Chorin, ein führer. 3. aufl., bearb.
von Carl Dormeyer. Berlin, Deutscher kunst-
verlag, 1932.
39 p. illus.
Folded plan on p. ₍3₎ of cover.

NL 0442333   MiDA

Löffler, Helene (Schwerdtmann).
Schlegel's internationales Kochbuch. Für deutsche Frauen
aller Stände. Populäre Anleitung schmackhafte und wohlfeile
Speisen zu bereiten. Hrsg. von Helene Löffler... 2. Aufl.
Aschersleben, E. Schlegel, 1876. xxix, 600 p. 19cm.

Imperfect: p. 591–600 mutilated.

280746B. 1. Cookery, German.   I. Title.
N. Y. P. L.   December 12, 1944

NL 0442334   NN

Löffler, Hellmut, Referendar, Großschönau: Die rechtliche
Behandlung der Viehmängel beim Kauf. Torgau: Torgauer
Dr.- u. Verlagshaus 1914. VIII, 68 S. 8°
Leipzig, Jur. Diss. v. 28. März 1914
[Geb. 5. März 88 Wurzen; Wohnort: Wurzen; Staatsangeh.: Sachsen; Vor-
bildung: RG. Döbeln Reife 09; Studium: Leipzig 7 S.; Rig. 1. Juli 12.] [U 14, 918

NL 0442335   ICRL

Löffler, Henriette.
Grosses illustrirtes Kochbuch für einfachen Tisch und die
feine Küche. Umgearb. und verm. mit vielen Recepten nach
eigener Erfahrung von Theodor Bechtel. 10. Aufl. Illus.
mit mehreren Hundert Holzschnitten nach Zeichnungen von
W. v. Breitschwert, Julius Schnorr und G. Heyberger. Ulm,
J. Ebner ₁1882₎
xii, 724 p. illus. 21 cm.

1. Cookery, German.   I. Bechtel, Theodor, ed.

TX721.L57 1882   48-39315*

NL 0442336   DLC

Löffler, [Henriette].
Löffler-Bechtel grosses illustriertes Kochbuch. 14 neu bearbeitete, reich illustrierte Ausgabe. Ulm, J. Ebner, ₁1903₎.
₍8₎, xvi, 1280 p. illus., 26 pl. (partly col., partly fold.), 1 diagr. 22ᶜᵐ.
Successive prefaces are signed respectively Henriette Löffler, Theodor Bechtel, Eugen
Bechtel.
4 blank pages for "Notizen und Rezepte".

NL 0442337   ICJ OKentU

Löffler, Henriette.
Neuestes Kochbuch für bürgerliche Haushaltungen. Her-
ausgegeben von Henriette Löffler... Stuttgart: Ebner und
Seubert, 1843. xii, 213 p. 18½cm.

455513. 1. Cookery, German.   *Revised*
N. Y. P. L.   April 17, 1933

NL 0442338   NN

Loeffler, Herman Charles, *1896-*
Costs of venereal disease to St. Louis, by H. C. Loeffler... A
survey undertaken during the months of June to December, 1932.
St. Louis, Mo.: Missouri Social Hygiene Assoc. Inc.₁, 1933.₎
44 p. incl. tables. 23cm.
Cover-title.
Bibliographical footnotes.

739254A. 1. Venereal diseases—U. S.   —Mo.—St. Louis. I. Missouri Social
Hygiene Association, St. Louis.
N. Y. P. L.   January 7, 1935

NL 0442339   NN PU NBuG MBCo OCl

Loeffler, Herman Charles, 1896–
Facts about Pueblo, Colorado
see under Pueblo Commerce Club.

Loeffler, Herman Charles, 1896–
The plan E city charter; legal requirements and procedure;
summary of other standard city charters, prepared by Herman C. Loeffler ... in collaboration with the Massachusetts
federation of taxpayers associations. Boston, Massachusetts
federation of taxpayers associations, inc., 1940.
1 p. l., 18 numb. l. 28 x 21½ᶜᵐ.
Mimeographed.
"Selected plan E bibliography": leaf 8.

1. Municipal government—Massachusetts. 2. Charters. I. Massachusetts federation of taxpayers associations. II. Title.

Library of Congress   JS451.M43L63   41-15564
                               ₍2₎   352.0744

NL 0442341   DLC NN MH-L

JS601
.L6   Loeffler, Herman Charles, 1896–
Plan E city government; legal requirements and
procedure with summary of other standard forms
of city government in Massachusetts. Boston,
Massachusetts Federation of Taxpayers Associa-
tions, 1947.
22 p. facsim. 28cm.
"Revision of ... [his] "The plan E city charter"
"Selected list of Plan E reading material":
p. 12–13.
1. Municipal government—Massachusetts. 2.
Charters.   Massachusetts Federation of
Taxpayers Associa-   tions. II. Title.

NL 0442342   MB

LOEFFLER, Herman Charles, 1896–
Statement presented at budget hearing of City
Council, Committee on Appropriations, by H.C.
Loeffler, secretary, Boston Municipal Research
Bureau, Feb.29,1940. [Boston,1940].

Manifold copy. ff.4.

NL 0442343   MH-PA

VOLUME 338

Loeffler, Hermann, 1880–
Die melanosarkombildung beim menschen und beim pferde
Inaug. Diss. Wuerzburg, 1903. (Mellrichstadt)
Bibl.

NL 0442344   ICRL DNLM

Löffler, Herta, 1911–
Beitrag zur Kenntnis der Ätiologie der Landkartenzunge... [Zeulenroda, 1935]
Inaug.-Diss. - Leipzig.
Lebenslauf.
"Literaturverzeichnis": p. 22-23.

NL 0442345   CtY

Löffler, Hugo, 1909–
...Über Kiefernekrosen, insbesondere über eine geheilte Kiefernekrose bei einem Fall von Leukämischer Lymphadenose... Würzburg, 1937.
Inaug.-Diss. - Heidelberg.
Lebenslauf.
"Schriftennachweis": p. [19] - 20.

NL 0442346   CtY

VK32
L82
Löffler, Immanuel.
Nachrichten von Liederdichtern des Gesangbuchs für die protestantische Gesammtgemeinde des Königreichs Baiern, gesammelt und herausgegeben von Immanuel Löffler...
Sulzbach, J. C. Seidel, 1819.
vi, 144 p.   22 cm.

NL 0442347   NNUT

[Loeffler, J., photographer]
Souvenir of the Catskill mountains.
[Tompkinsville, Staten island, N.Y.? 19-?]
1 p.l., 15 photos. 40½x30cm.
Cover-title.
In portfolio.

1. Catskill mountains - Views. I. Title.

NL 0442348   NRU NN

Loeffler (J. H.) Anweisung zum Gebrauch der Bunsen'schen Batterie für galvanokaustische Zwecke. 8pp. 8°. Berlin, A. Knickmeyer, [s.d.]

NL 0442349   DNLM

Loeffler, J. H.
Gralstrahl... Concertstück für Orgel, componirt von J. H. Löffler... Leipzig: J. Rieter-Biedermann, 1879. Publ. pl. no. 1082. 17 p. f°.
Dedication at head of title.

1. Organ. 2. Title.

April 19, 1918.

NL 0442350   NN

Loeffler, Johann Friedrich, o. 1710.
Dissertatio de mortis causa capionibus.
Lipsiae, n.d.

28,12 p.   8°
Diss. --- [Leipzig],1751.

NL 0442351   MH-L

Löffler, Johann Friedrich, b. 1710, respondent
Dissertatio juridica de mortuis redivivis
see under Joachim, Georg Andreas, 1700-1759, praeses.

Loeffler, Johann Friedrich, b. 1710.
[Tam domino, quam agnatis...]
see under Bauer, Johann Gottfried, 1695-1763.

Löffler, Johann Friedrich, 1768–
Der alte Sergeant. Merkwürdige Begebenheiten und Abenteuer aus dem Leben von Johann Friedrich Löffler von ihm selbst erzählt. Neu bearb. und hrsg. von Jakob Schönholzer. Affoltern a. A., Aehren Verlag [1952]
318 p. illus. 22 cm.

1. Adventure and adventurers.

G530.L82   54-32563 ‡

NL 0442354   DLC

Löffler, Johann Heinrich, 1833-1903.
Martin Bötzinger; ein lebens- und zeitbild aus dem siebzehnten jahrhundert, von J. H. Löffler. Weimar, H. Böhlaus nachfolger, 1925.
2 p. l., 451, [1] p. incl. plates. 20½ᶜᵐ.
"Diese neue ausgabe wurde um etwa ein drittel gekürzt und bearbeitet von dr. H. Lilienfein."
First edition published 1897; 2d edition 1908.

I. Lilienfein, Heinrich, 1879– ed. II. Title.
28-14693
Library of Congress   PT2424.L615M3 1925

NL 0442355   DLC CtY

Loeffler, Johannes, 1900–
Untersuchungen im dreistoffsystem NaO-SiO-ZrO.
Inaug. diss. Berlin, 1930.

NL 0442356   ICRL OU CtY

Löffler, Johannes, 1906–
Die spannungsverteilung in der berührungsfläche gedrückter zylinder auf grund spannungsoptischer messungen. Giessen, W. Herr, 1958.
93 p. illus., diagrs., tables.

Thesis, Technische hochschule, Dresden.
Bibliography: p. 93.

1. Strains and stresses. 2. Photoelasticity.

NL 0442357   NNC

Löffler, Josef, 1872–
Ueber Mortalität und Morbidität bei Müttern und Kindern im Anschluss an Zangen, Wendungen, Extraktionen und Perforationen and der Leipziger Universitäts-Frauenklink vom Jahre 1887-1899...
Leipzig, 1903.
Inaug.-Diss. - Leipzig.
Lebenslauf.
"Literatur": p. [37]

NL 0442358   CtY DNLM ICRL

Löffler, Josef, 1901–
Die Störungen des geschlechtlichen Vermögens in der Literatur der autoritativen Theologie des Mittelalters. Ein Beitrag zur Geschichte der Impotenz und des medizinischen Sachverständigenbeweises im kanonischen Impotenzprozess.
[Mainz? 195–?]
128 l. 29 cm.
Inaug.-Diss.--Mainz.
Vita.
Bibliography: leaves 111-119.

1. Impotence. 2. Impotence (Canon law) I. Title.

56-16791

NL 0442359   DLC

Löffler (Joseph). *Das Resorein, seine therapeutische Verwerthung und seine Giftigkeit.
45 nn. 8°. Würzburg, N. Bauer 1889.

NL 0442360   DNLM

LG43
B641
xL82
Löffler, Josias Friedrich Christian, 1752-1816, ed.
Bonifacius; oder, Feyer des andenkens an die erste christliche kirche in Thüringen, bey Altenberga im herzogthum Gotha. Nebst einer historischen nachricht von seinem leben.
Gotha, Becker, 1812.
xii, 224 p. front. 24 cm.

1. Bonifacius, originally Winfried. Saint, abp. of Mainz,   680-755.

NL 0442361   CtY-D

A30
F72
1784L
Loeffler, Josias Friedrich Christian, 1752-1816, praeses.
Dissertatio ... Ioannis Epistola I. gnosticos inprimis impugnari negans. Traiecti ad Viadrum, 1784.
33 p.
Diss. - Frankfurt a.O. (G.Ph.H.Noeldechen, author and respondent)

I. Noeldechen, Georg Philipp Heinrich author and

NL 0442362   CtY

LÖFFLER, Josias Friedrich Christian, 1752-1816.
Kleine schriften, nach seinem töde gesammelt und herausgegeben. Weimar,1817.

3 v. 13 x 20.

NL 0442363   MH-AH

LOFFLER, Josias Friedrich Christian, 1752-1816.
Predigten. 3e ed. Jena, etc., 1798-1805.

2 v. 13 x 22.

NL 0442364   MH-AH

Loeffler, Julius
Zur geschichte des Culmer gymnasiums waehrend der zweiten 25 jahre seines besiehens.
Culm, Brandt, 1887.
73 p.

NL 0442365   PU

Löffler, J[ulius] B[entley], 1843-1904.
Danske gravstene fra middelalderen. Udgivet med understøttelse af Carlsbergfondet. Kjøbenhavn, C. A. Reitzel, 1889.
f°. pp. (1), viii, 40, viii, vi, (1). 34 plates and other illus.
Added title-page in French.

Denmark-Antiquities   [Sepulchral monuments-Denmark

NL 0442366   MH NN MdBJ

VOLUME 338

Löffler, Julius Bentley, 1843–1904.
Gravenstenene i Roskilde kjøbstad. Ved J. B. Løffler. Med xxxiii lithograferede tavler. Udgivet med understøttelse af Kirkeministeriet ved hjælp af Roskilde domkirkes midler. Kjøbenhavn, C. A. Reitzel, 1885.
3 p. L, xvii p., 1 L, 114 p. 33 pl. (incl. plan) 39½ x 31ᶜᵐ.
Added t.-p. and résumé in French.

1. Roskilde, Denmark—Sepulchral monuments. 2. Roskilde, Denmark. Cathedral. 3. Epitaphs—Roskilde, Denmark.
11–32348
Library of Congress NB1616.R8L8

NL 0442367   DLC NN

Löffler, Julius Bentley, 1843–1904.
Gravmonumenterne i Ringsted Kirke, ved J. B. Løffler. Med xv Tavler efter Tegninger af Magnus Petersen og J. B. Løffler. Udgivet med Understøttelse af den Grevelige Hjelmstjerne-Rosencroneske Stiftelse. Kjøbenhavn: C. A. Reitzel, 1891. 3 p.l., x p., 1 l., 45 p., 15 pl. f°.

With added t.-p. and résumé of introduction in French.

1. Monuments (Sepulchral), Denmark—Churches. 3. Grevelige Hjelmstjerne-Rosencroneske Stiftelse. 5. Title. Ringsted. 2. Ringsted. Denmark. 4. Petersen, Magnus, illustrator. N.Y.P.L.
September 30, 1915.

NL 0442368   NN

Löffler, Julius Bentley, 1843–1904.
Gravmonumenterne i Sorø Kirke. *Kjøbenhavn: C. A. Reitzel,* 1888. 4 p.l., xi, 79 pp., 17 pl. [1 plan.] f°.
Title-page and pref also in French.

NL 0442369   NN

Löffler, Julius Bentley, 1843–1904.
Reliefferne over Korstolene i Roskilde Domkirke. Aftegnede og udgivne af J. B. Løffler. Text af J. Lange. Avec un résumé en français. *Kjøbenhavn: C. A. Reitzel,* 1880. 46 pp., 1l., 25 pl. 8°.

NL 0442370   NN

Löffler, Julius Bentley, 1843–1904.
Udsigt over Danmarks Kirkebygninger fra den tidligere Middelalder (den romanske Periode.) *Kjøbenhavn: C. A. Reitzel,* 1883. 2 p.l, iv, 308 pp. 4°.

NL 0442371   NN CtY

LÖFFLER, KARL.
Ether carboxylic acid esters as plasticizers for igelit synthetic rubber (Acthorcarbonsäureester als weichmacher für igelite) IGF/KF/6–11–43, R 2624 F 1069. Schkopau, Buna-werke G.m.b.h., Nov.1943. tr.by Polamold Research Laboratories, Inc. Wright Field, Dayton, Ohio, Headquarters Air Material Command, 1946.
1l.,13p. tables. 28cm. (Air document index (Tech) IGF 207)

Title taken from verso of title-page.
Translation Report no.F-TS-1036-RE.

NL 0442372   PU-Sc

LÖFFLER, KARL.
Igelit (synthetic rubber) plasticizers containing sulfur atoms (Schwefelatome enthaltende igelit-weichmacher) IGF/KF/4, R 2624, F 1047. Schkopau, Buna-werke G.m.b.h., Sept.1944. tr. by Polamold Research Laboratories, inc. Wright Field, Dayton, Ohio, Headquarters Air Matériel command, 1946.
1l.,34p. 28cm. (Air document index (Tech) IGF 210)

Title taken from verso of title-page.
AAF translation report no.F-TS-1040-

NL 0442373   PU-Sc

Löffler, Karl, mathematician.
Ueber eine algebraische fläche 4. ordnung welche durch die auf ein rechtwinkliges coordinaten-system bezogene gleichung: $c^2z^2=(x^2 \sin^2 \phi - c^2)(y^2 \cos^2 \phi - c^2)$ dargestellt ist ... Darmstadt, Buchdruckerei von G. Otto, 1874.
2 p. l., 19 p. 17½ᶜᵐ.
Inaug.-dis.—Marburg.

1. Surfaces.
4–9510†
Library of Congress QA573.L8

NL 0442374   DLC

Löffler, Karl, writer on chess.
Kurze anleitung zur erlernung des schachspieles. 6., von K. Richter durchgesehene aufl., 51.–60. tausend. 31p. Leipzig, C. Ronniger, 1935.

NL 0442375   OC1

Löffler, Karl, 1872–
see Löffler, Carl, 1872–

Loeffler, K[ar]l 1875–1935, supposed author.
Deutsche klosterbibliotheken...
see under Loeffler, Klemens, 1881–1933.

Löffler, Karl, 1875–1935.
Einführung in die handschriftenkunde, von Karl Löffler ... Leipzig, K. W. Hiersemann, 1929.
xii, 214 p., 1 l. 23½ᶜᵐ.

1. Manuscripts. 2. Paleography. i. Title: Handschriftenkunde, Einführung in die.
32–11142
Library of Congress Z105.L82

NN IU ICU MH DDO OC1W MiU COH PPT PU PPDrop
NL 0442378   DLC NcU CU MU MoSW MdBWA NIC OC1 CtY

Löffler, Karl, 1875–1935.
Einführung in die katalogkunde, von Karl Löffler. Leipzig, K. W. Hiersemann, 1935.
4 p. l., 142 p. illus. (facsim.) 23½ᶜᵐ.

1. Cataloging.
36–3587
Library of Congress Z695.L82
[2] 025.3

NL 0442379   DLC CU NcD CtY OC1W MiU ICJ ICN ICU NN

Löffler, Karl, 1875–1935.
Geschichte der württembergischen landesbibliothek, von prof. Karl Löffler, ober-bibliothekar ... Leipzig, O. Harrassowitz, 1923.
iv p., 2 l., 262 p. 24½ᶜᵐ. (On cover: Beihefte zum Zentralblatt für bibliothekswesen l.)

1. Stuttgart. Landesbibliothek.
24–9705
Library of Congress Z671.C39B no. 50

NL 0442380   DLC MB OC1 OU OCU MiU OU ICJ

Löffler, Karl, 1875–1935.
Weingarten, *Ger. (Benedictine abbey)*
Die handschriften des klosters Weingarten, von prof. dr. Karl Löffler ... unter beihilfe von ... dr. Scherer ... Leipzig, O. Harrassowitz, 1912.

Löffler, Karl, 1875–1935.
Stuttgart. Landesbibliothek.
Die handschriften des klosters Zwiefalten. Von professor dr. K. Löffler ... Linz a. Donau, F. Winkler, verlag "In buchladen", 1931.

Löffler, Karl, 1875–1935.
Columella, Lucius Junius Moderatus.
L. Junius Moderatus Columella De re rustica; uebers. durch Heinrich Oesterreicher, abt von Schussenried. Hrsg. von Karl Löffler ... Tübingen, Gedruckt für den Litterarischen verein in Stuttgart, 1914.

Löffler, Karl, 1875–1935
Der Landgrafenpsalter, eine bilderhandschrift aus dem anfang des xiii. jahrhunderts in der Württembergischen landesbibliothek, mit einleitung von Karl Löffler; mit 28 lichtdrucktafeln, davon 16 farbig. Leipzig, K. W. Hiersemann, 1925.
2 p. L, 62, [2] p., 2 l. xxviii pl. (part col.) 32ᶜᵐ.
Each plate accompanied by leaf with descriptive letterpress not included in the paging.
"Literaturangaben": p. [63]–[64]
1. Illumination of books and manuscripts—Specimens, reproductions, etc. 2. Bible—Pictorial illustrations. 3. Hermann, landgrave of Thuringia. d. 1217. i. Stuttgart. Landesbibliothek. Mss. (H.B. ii, 24) ii. Catholic church. Liturgy and ritual. Psalter. iii. Title.
26–22763
Library of Congress ND3357.L3L6

DDO OCU OC1 MiU PSt
NL 0442384   DLC CLU NN MB MoU NcD PU OC1MA CtY

Löffler, Karl, 1875–1935, ed.
Z118 .L67
Lexikon des gesamten Buchwesens. Hrsg. von Karl Löffler und Joachim Kirchner, unter Mitwirkung von Wilhelm Olbrich. Leipzig, K. W. Hiersemann, 1935 [i. e. 1934]–37.

Löffler, Karl, 1875–1935.
H1d5 41l
Das Passiv bei Otfrid und im Heliand, besonders im Verhältnis zu den lateinischen Quellen. Borna-Leipzig, 1905.
48p. 23cm.
Inaug.-Diss. - Tübingen.
Vita.

NL 0442386   CtY IU MH CU ICRL

Löffler, Karl, 1875–1935.
Romanische zierbuchstaben und ihre vorläufer; mit einführendem text von professor dr. Karl Löffler ... Stuttgart, H. Matthaes, 1927.
4 p. l., 11–46 p., 1 l. 54 col. pl. 35½ᶜᵐ.
Issued in 6 parts, 1926.
"Die initialen stammen alle aus handschriften der Württembergischen landesbibliothek in Stuttgart."—Vorwort.
"Handschriften-beschreibung": p. [21]–46.
Includes bibliographies.
1. Illumination of books and manuscripts—Specimens, reproductions, etc. 2. Initials. 3. Decoration and ornament, Romanesque. 4. Paleography. 5. Stuttgart. Landesbibliothek. Mss. 6. Manuscripts. Germany. i. Title.
27–20990
Library of Congress ND3335.L6

PU OC1 NcGU FMU DDO NN NjF MiU
NL 0442387   DLC MdBWA CLU FTaSU OC1MA WaU GU OU CtY

VOLUME 338

Löffler, Karl, 1875–1935.
Schwäbische buchmalerei in romanischer zeit, von Karl Löffler. Augsburg, B. Filser [*1928]
vii, [1], 84 p. 48 pl. (part col.) 32 x 25½ᶜᵐ.
On spine: Buchmalerei.

1. Illumination of books and manuscripts—Swabia. 2. Miniature painting—Swabia. 3. Illumination of books and manuscripts—Specimens, reproductions, etc. I. Title. II. Title: Buchmalerei.
42–45400

Library of Congress   ND3152.S9L6

NN ICU OC1W OC1 OO PU IaU PSt MiU CU
NL 0442388   DLC OOxM NcU NcD CLU PU DDO CtY MH NjP

Löffler, Karl, 1875–1935, ed.
Weingartner liederhandschrift.
Die Weingartner liederhandschrift in nachbildung, mit begleitwort von prof. dr. Karl Löffler ... Stuttgart, Omnitypie ges. nachf. L. Zechnall, 1927.

WG　**Löffler, Karl,** 1878–
27916　Derivate des α-Picolyl- und α-Picolyl-methylalkins. Breslau, 1903.
70 p.

Inaug.-Diss. - Breslau.

NL 0442390   CtY MH ICRL

LÖFFLER, Karl, 1887–
Untersuchungen über die wachstumsverhältnisse der kopfknochen des pferedes. Giessen, O. Kindt, wwe, 1919.

Plates.   "Lebenslauf", at end.

NL 0442391   MH ICRL CtY DNLM

Bonaparte
Collection   [Löffler, Karl Valentin Immanuel]
No. 9930   1821–1874   ed.
Album plattdeutscher dichtungen.
Leipzig, 1869.

NL 0442392   ICN

Löffler, Karl Valentin Immanuel, 1821–1874.
Der Anbau der Korb- und Bandweide. Eine praktische Anleitung für Landwirthe, aus schlechten Wiesen, Sümpfen ꝛc. den höchsten Ertrag zu erzielen. Von Dr. Karl Löffler, ... Mit 2 Tafeln Abbildungen. Berlin, T. Thiele, 1862.
16 p. II pl. 21½ᶜᵐ.

NL 0442393   ICJ

Löffler, Karl Valentin Immanuel, 1821–1874.
Anbau und ausbeute der industriegewächse für deutsche landwirthe. Von dr. Karl Löffler ... Wittenberg, Reichenbach, 1863–
v. 18½ᶜᵐ.
"1. hft." has also special t-p.
CONTENTS.—1. hft. Die cichorie ...

1. Chicory.
CA 25–461 Unrev'd

Library of Congress   SB351.C5L8

NL 0442394   DLC

Löffler, Karl Valentin Immanuel, 1821–1874.
Anleitung zur maulbeerbaumzucht und zum rationellen seidenbau. Berlin. 1861. sm. 8°. pp. [2], 55+. Illustr.

NL 0442395   MH-A

Löffler, Karl Valentin Immanuel, 1821–1874.
Anleitung zur maulbeerbaumzucht und zum nationellen seidenbau. 2e aufl. Berlin, 1863.
[2] 55 + p.   illustr.   sm. 8°.

NL 0442396   MH-A

Löffler, Karl Valentin Immanuel, 1821–1874.
Aus der Jugend eines preussischen Helden. Lustspiel in fünf Aufzügen. Berlin, F. Hoffschläger, 1859.
74 p.   8°.

NL 0442397   NN

Löffler, Karl Valentin Immanuel, 1821–1874.
Blondel der unschuldig Verurtheilte. Sein qualvolles Leben auf der Galeere, seine nächtliche Flucht und seine grausamen, blutigen Kämpfe mit Indianern in den Urwäldern Amerika's: oder, Die Geheimnisse der Galeere. Ein Criminal-Roman wahren Begebenheiten nacherzählt, von Dr. Carl Tornow [pseud.] ... Dresden, C. G. Lohse, [1873–1874]
3 v. in 1.   col. plates.   21 cm.
Paged continuously.

NL 0442398   CtY

Löffler, Karl Valentin Immanuel, 1821–1874.
Das chinesische zuckerrohr (kao-lien). Ein wundergewächs für agricultur und industrie, in seiner verwendung zur zucker-, alkohol-, farben- und papier-fabrikation etc., sowie als nahrungs-, fütterungs- und düngungsmittel. Nach den neuesten quellen betrachtet von dr. Karl Löffler ... Mit einer colorirten abbildung der pflanze. Braunschweig, F. Vieweg und sohn, 1859.
x p., 1 L., 151 p. col. front. 22½ᶜᵐ.

1. Sorghum.   I. Title.
45–25429

Library of Congress   SB235.L8

NL 0442399   DLC

[Löffler, Karl Valentin Immanuel] 1821–1874, ed.
Conversations-Lexikon des Witzes, Humors und der Satyre. Herausgegeben von einer Gesellschaft Humoristen. Bd.
Altona: Verlags-Bureau [18   v.   19½cm.

[21673–77B.   1. Wit and humor,   German—Collections. I. Title.
N. Y. P. L.   June 26, 1941

NL 0442400   NN CtY

Bonaparte
Collection   [Löffler, Karl Valentin Immanuel]
No. 10,027   1821–1874.
Vör miene un anner' lü's göären. Allergehand nüe vertellnisse för de leewe kingher. Van'n oll'n Nümärker.
Leipzig, 1869.

NL 0442401   ICN

SF   **Löffler, Karl Valentin Immanuel**
488   Die in Deutschland vorkommenden verschiedenen Racen des Haushahn's. Berlin,
G3   J. Springer, 1859.
L82   23 p. col. plate.   17 cm.
Vault

1. Poultry - Germany. 2. Poultry breeds. I. Title.

NL 0442402   NIC

4K   **Löffler, Karl Valentin Immanuel**
9472   Die Justizmorde der Neuzeit aller Länder; interessant und belehrend dem Volke erzählt. Leipzig, C. Minde [1867?]
480 p.

NL 0442403   DLC-P4 NN

Loeffler, Karl Valentin Immanuel, 1821–1874.
Lehre von der landwirthschaft.
Berlin, Thiele, n.d.
179 p.

NL 0442404   PPF

Löffler, Karl Valentin Immanuel, 1821–1874.
Ein Mord; oder, Der falsche Müller. Lustspiel in 3 Akten. Berlin, J. Petsch, [18–?]
68 p.   12°.   (Neuestes Bühnen-Repertoir für Schauspiel, Posse, und Lustspiel. no. 1)

NL 0442405   MH

Loeffler, Karl Valentin Immanuel, 1821–1874.
Die Opfer mangelhafter Justiz...
Jena, Costenoble, 1868.
2 Bde.

NL 0442406   PPG MH

Loeffler, Karl Valentin Immanuel, 1821–1874.
Die opfer mangelhafter justiz; gallerie der interessantesten justizmorde aller völker und zeiten... 2 ausg...
Jena, Coztenoble, 1873.
3 v.

NL 0442407   PBm MH-L CtY

Löffler, Karl Valentin Immanuel, 1821–1874.
Das Pferd. Zucht, Pflege, Veredelung und Geschichte. Encyclopädie für Pferdefreunde...
Berlin, 1866.
4 pts. in 1 v.   23.5 cm.
1. Horses.

NL 0442408   CtY

Loeffler, Karl Valentin Immanuel, 1821–1874.
Das Pferd. Zucht, Pflege, Veredelung und Geschichte. Encyclopädie für Pferdefreunde, ... Theil I. 2. Auflage. Berlin. Grieben. 1868. 64 pp. Plates. 23 cm., in 8s.
Contents. — 1. Zucht, Pflege und Veredelung des Pferdes. I.

H2150 — Horse.

NL 0442409   MB

VOLUME 338

ar V
10994
v.1

Löffler, Karl Valentin Immanuel, 1821-1874.
Die schöne Giesserin; oder, Berlin zu
Joachim's II. Zeit; historischer Roman.
Berlin, H. Kastner, 1862.
iv. 20cm.

NL 0442410   NIC

Löffler, Karl Valentin Immanuel, 1821-1874.
Die schwarze malve. Praktische anleitung zu deren
cultur und benutzung als einträgliches färbemittel. Von
dr. Karl Löffler ... Wittenberg, Reichenbach'sche buchhandlung, 1863.

2 p. l., 30 p. 19cm. (*His* Anbau und ausbeute der industriegewächse
für deutsche landwirthe ... 2. hft.)

1. Dye plants.

Agr 17-209

Library, U. S. Dept. of   Agriculture 77L82

NL 0442411   DNAL

Bonaparte
Collection
No. 10,028

[Löffler, Karl Valentin Immanuel]
1821-1874.
De theerschwöäler. 'ne eenfache
dörpgeschichte ut Mark Brannenborch.
Vam oll'n Nümärker.   Leipzig,1870.

NL 0442412   ICN OCU

Loeffler, Karl Valentin Immanuel, 1821-1874.
Ueber die runkelrübenzucker-fabrikation
Frankreichs.
Berlin, Thiele, 1863.
65 p.

NL 0442413   PPF

[Löffler, Karl Valentin Immanuel, 1821-1874.
Ut min Dischlad. Dit un dat in nige vertellzels. Von'n
oll'n Nümärker *(pseud.)* ... Leipzig, C. A. Koch, 1878-79.
2 v. 18½cm.

1. Title.

45-25590

Library of Congress   PT4848.L6U8

NL 0442414   DLC

Bonaparte
Collection
No. 10,026

[Löffler, Karl Valentin Immanuel]
1821-1874.
Ut 't dörp. Lustege vertellungen.
Van'n oll'n Nümärker.   Jena,1868.

NL 0442415   ICN

[Löffler, Karl Valentin Immanuel, 1821-1874.
Van nienen keenich Willem. Van'n oll'n Nümärker *(pseud.)* ... Jena, H. Costenoble, 1869.
xvi,302 p. 17cm.

1-1a. Wilhelm I, German emperor, 1797-1888.
I. Title. x Nümärker, De olle, pseud.

NL 0442416   CU

Loeffler, Karl Valentin Immanuel, 1821-1874.
Versuch einer Classifikation sämmtlicher Hühnerracen. Von
Dr. Carl Löffler... Berlin: J. Springer, 1859. 27 p. table.
12°.

1. Poultry.
N. Y. P. L.

September 20, 1924

NL 0442417   NN

[Loeffler, Karl Valentin Immanuel,] 1821-1874.
Ein vorsichtiger Mann. Lustspiel in drei Aufzügen. Von
Dr. Tornow [pseud.]... [Leipzig: A. T. Engelhardt,] 1869.
72 p. 8°.

1. Drama (German). 2. Title.
N. Y. P. L.

May 26, 1922.

NL 0442418   NN

Loeffler, Karl Valentin Immanuel, 1821-1874.
Die Zucht der ausländischen Hühner in Deutschland. Anleitung zur Zucht und Pflege sämmtlicher ausländischer Hühnerracen: Der Cochinchina's Malayen, Dorkings, spanischen und
polnischen Hühner, Bantams, Crèvecoeurs, etc. Von Dr. Carl
Löffler... Berlin: J. Springer, 1859. viii, 128 p. 12°.

1. Poultry.—Breeding and raising,   Germany.
N. Y. P. L.

September 20, 1924

NL 0442419   NN

Löffler, Kaspar.
Geschichte des verkehrs in Baden, insbesondere der
nachrichten- und personenbeförderung (boten-, post- und
telegraphenverkehr) von der Römerzeit bis 1872, von K.
Löffler ... mit 5 beilagen, 7 karten und 4 tafeln. Heidelberg, C. Winter, 1910.

xviii, 588 p. plates, fold. maps, facsim., tables (partly fold.) 25cm.

"Benutzte archivalien": p. (xii)
"Literaturverzeichnis": p. (xii)-xviii.

1. Communication and traffic—Baden (Grand duchy) 2. Postal service—Baden (Grand duchy)—Hist.

Library of Congress   HE6996.B2L8

12-12401

NL 0442420   DLC WU CSt CU NcD ICU ICJ

Loeffler, Kenneth.
Ken Loeffler on basketball, by Ken Loeffler, with Ralph
Bernstein. Englewood Cliffs, N. J., Prentice-Hall, 1955.

197 p. illus. 21 cm.

1. Basketball.   I. Bernstein, Ralph, 1921-   joint author.

Full name: Kenneth Dethelm Loeffler.

GV885.L6   796.32   55-12070 ‡

NN MB OU OOxM PPLas
NL 0442421   DLC OrPS OrAshS IdU CaBVaU CaBVa CU PP

Loeffler, Klaus.
...Deutsch-französische Wirtschaftsbeziehungen und die
Probleme einer steigenden wirtschaftlichen Verflechtung. Frei-
burg im Breisgau: J. Waibel, 1934. viii, 154 p. 24½cm.

Bibliography, p. 150-154.

825058A. 1. Germany—Economic   relations with France. 2. France—
Economic relations with Germany.
N. Y. P. L.

May 25, 1936

NL 0442422   NN

Löffler, Klemens, 1881-1933.
Auswärtige politik; ein führer für das deutsche volk,
von prof. dr. Kl. Löffler. Halle (Saale) H. Diekmann,
1920.

3 p. l., 196 p. 23cm.

"Verzeichnis wichtiger quellen": p. 184-189.

1. International law and relations. 2. Germany—For. rel.   I. Title.

Library of Congress   JX1796.L6   25-22221

NL 0442423   DLC NIC NN

Löffler, Klemens, 1881-1933, comp.
Die Bischofschroniken des Mittelalters (Hermanns v.
Lerbeck Catalogus episcoporum Mindensium und seine Ab-
leitungen) kritisch neu herausgegeben. Münster in Westf.,
Aschendorff, 1917.

xlviii, 299 p. 25 cm. (Veröffentlichungen der Historischen Kommission der Provinz Westfalen. Mindener Geschichtsquellen, Bd. 1)

Texts in Latin; introd. and editorial matter in German.
Includes bibliographical references.

PARTIAL CONTENTS.— Einleitung. — Die Chroniken: Nachrichten
aus den Nekrologien. Die "Series episcoporum." Hermanns von
Lerbeck "Catalogus episcoporum Mindensium." Die jüngere Bisch-
ofschronik. Die "Successio episcoporum."

1. Catholic Church. Diocese of Minden. I. Hermannus de Ler-
beke, ca. 1345-ca. 1416. Catalogus episcoporum Mindensium. II.
Title. Series: Münster. Provinzialinstitut für Westfälische
Landes- und Volkskunde. Historische Kommission. Veröffentlichungen. Series: Mindener Geschichtsquellen, Bd. 1)

BX2617.M5L6   70-11080

NL 0442425   DLC CU MH

Loeffler, Klemens, 1881-
Die Corveyer Schlossbibliothek. (In: Westfaelische
Studien. Leipzig, 1928. 4°. p. (287-)296.)

Bibliographical footnotes.

408596A. 1. Libraries, Monastic—   Germany—Korvey.
N. Y. P. L.   June 15, 1929

NL 0442426   NN

DD901
.M58T7
1932

Löffler, Klemens, 1881-1933, ed.

Tribbe, Heinrich, d. 1464.
Des Domherrn Heinrich Tribbe Beschreibung von Stadt
und Stift Minden (um 1460). Hrsg. von Klemens Löffler.
Münster in Westf., Verlag der Aschendorffschen Buchhandlung, 1932.

Löffler, Klemens, 1881-
Deutsche Klosterbibliotheken. Köln, J.P.
Bachem, 1918.
72 p. (Gorresgesellschaft (zur Pflege der
Wissenschaft im katholischen Deutschland) 1.
Vereinsschrift (für) 1918)

Includes bibliography.

NL 0442428   CU MH IU PLatS

Löffler, Klemens, 1881-1933.
Deutsche klosterbibliotheken, von prof. dr. Kl. Löffler. 2.,
stark verm. und verb. aufl. Bonn und Leipzig, K. Schroeder, 1922.

310 p. 19½ cm. (*Added t.-p.:* Bücherei der kultur und geschichte
... bd. 27)

1. Monastic libraries—Germany. 2. Libraries—Hist.—400-1400.
I. Title.

Z801.L82   23—16436

NL 0442429   DLC PP PU NjP NN OCU OO

VOLUME 338

micro- Löffler, Klemens, 1881-1933.
film   Deutsche Klosterbibliotheken   2. stark verm.
Z   und vorb. Aufl. Bonn, K. Schroeder, 1922.
100   (Bücherei der Kultur und Geschichte; hrsg. von
Dr. Sebastian Hausmann, Bd. 27)
Negative; original in possession of Pierce
Butler, University of Chicago.

NL 0442430   ICU

Loeffler, Klemens, 1881-   , editor.
Deutschlands Zukunft im Urteil führender Männer; Beiträge
von Reichspräsident Ebert ¡u. a.₎...hrsg. von Prof. Dr. Kl. Löffler. Halle-Saale: H. Diekmann ¡1921₎. 136 p. 8°.

Contents: Zur Einführung. EBERT, F. Geleitwort. FEHRENBACH, K. Geleitwort. BERNSTORFF, J. H., Graf von. Gedanken über die Zukunft Deutschlands.
BRAUN, F., Edler von. Wege zu Deutschlands Wiederaufbau. DERNBURG, B.
Deutschlands Zukunft. ENGELBRECHT, K. Unsere Kulturnot. FESTER, R. Hat das
deutsche Volk noch eine Zukunft? GRASSL, J. Die biologisch-soziologischen Grund-
lagen des Wiederaufbaues. HAAS, L. Gedanken zur Politik des Wiederaufbaues.
KERN, F. Solidarität als Grundlage des Wiederaufbaues. MÜLLER, A. Der Wieder-
aufbau Deutschlands. MÜLLER, K. Landwirtschaft und Ernährungspolitik. PLENGE,
J. Deutschlands Zukunft im Lichte der staatswissenschaftlichen Erneuerung. RADE,
M. Deutschlands Zukunft. ROHRBACH, P. Deutschlands Zukunft.

24121A. 1. European war, 1914-   —Reconstruction, Germany.
N. Y. P. L.   November 5, 1921.

NL 0442431   NN MH IU NjP MiU CSt-H CU

Löffler, Klemens, 1881-
Elsass-Lothringen, von dr. Klemens Löffler. Köln, J. P.
Bachem, 1918.

103 p. 24ᶜᵐ. (*Added t.-p.:* Zeit- und streitfragen der gegenwart; eine
sammlung von schriften zur politischen und kulturellen tagesgeschichte,
hrsg. von dr. K. Hoeber. 11. bd.)

1. Alsace-Lorraine question.

Library of Congress   DD801.A55L6   20-17442

NL 0442432   DLC NjP MH ICJ KyLoU

Löffler, Klemens, 1881-
Geschichte der katholischen Presse Deutschlands, von Professor
Dr. Kl. Löffler ... M. Gladbach, Volksvereins-Verlag GmbH.,
1924.

112 p. 24ᶜᵐ. (*In* Soziale Tagesfragen, Heft 50.)
"Literatur," p. ¡100₎-103.

NL 0442433   ICJ MH-AH NN

Loeffler, Klemens, 1881-
The great fraud; some further evidences on the origins of
the war by Dr. Clemens Loeffler, Dr. Jean Lulvès, and others.
Münich, Knorr & Hirth, ltd. ¡1922₎.

57 p. incl. facsim. 22ᶜᵐ.

1. European war, 1914-1918—Causes.   I. Lulvès, Jean, 1866-
II. Title.

Library of Congress   D511.L62   27-22082

NL 0442434   DLC OClW NN

Löffler, Klemens, 1881-1933.
Griechenland und die Neugriechen. Hamm (Westf.)
Breer & Thiemann, 1917.

36 p. 25 cm. (Frankfurter zeitgemässe Broschüren, Bd. 37, Heft 2)
Cover title.

1. Greece, Modern—Hist.—1821—   (Series)

DF803.L6   56-54449

NL 0442435   DLC

947.2   Löffler, Klemens, *1881-1933.*
L82g   Gross-Nowgorod und sein Peterhof.
Gotha, 1918.
p. ¡49₎-57.   (Deutsche geschichts-
blätter. bd. XIX. 4/6 hft.)

NL 0442436   IU

DD491   Löffler, Klemens, 1881-1933, ed.
.W468H3   Hamelmannus, Hermannus, 1526-1595.
Hermann Hamelmanns Geschichtliche Werke, kritisch
neu hrsg. von Heinrich Detmer. Münster i. W., Aschendorff, 1902-13.

LÖFFLER, K[lemens], 1881-
Kolnische bibliotheksgeschichte im ulmriss
Mit einer nachweisung kölnischer handschriften
und einem beitrage von Goswin Frenken über
den katalog der Dombibliothek von 833. Köln,
Rheinland-verlag, 1923.

4°. pp. (2). 85†

NL 0442438   MH

FILM   Löffler, Klemens, 1881-1933.
15006   Kölnische Bibliotheksgeschichte im Umriss; mit einer Nach-
Z   weisung kölnischer Handschriften und ein Beitrage von Goswin
Library   Frenken über den Katalog der Dombibliothek von 833.   Köln,
School   Rheinland Verlag, 1923.
85 p. On film (positive)

Microfilm.   Original in Harvard Univ. Library.

1. Cologne (City) - Libraries.   2. Cologne (City) Dom.
Bibliothek. I. Frenken, Goswin, 1887-   II. Title.

NL 0442439   CU MH NNC

Z   Löffler, Klemens, 1881-
801   Kölnische Bibliotheksgeschichte im
L82   Umriss, von Kl. Löffler. Mit einer
K7++   Nachweisung kölnischer Handschriften
1923a   und einem Beitrage von Goswin Frenken
über den Katalog der Dombibliothek von
833. Köln, Rheinland-Verlag, 1923.
85 p. 28cm.
Photocopy. Cambridge, Harvard University Library, Microreproduction Dept.
[1969]   [45] l. 28 x 47cm.
Each leaf of the photocopy represents
approximately   2 pages of the original.
1. Cologne   --Libraries. I. Title.

NL 0442440   NIC

Löffler, Klemens, 1881-1933, ed.
Lyrische übersetzung der Psalmen 78-150
von Friedrich Leopold Grafen zu Stolberg
see under   Bible. O. T.
Psalms. German. Paraphrases. 1918.
Stolberg.

LÖFFLER, Klemens, *1881-1933, ed.*
Mindene geschichtsquellen. Kritisch neu
herausgegeben. Bd. I. Munster in Westf.
verlag der Aschendorffschen buchhandlung, 1917.

Added title-page reads: Veroffentlichungen
der historischen kommission der provinz Westfalen.   Ger 6630.15.16

NL 0442442   MH

                 Löffler, Klemens, 1881-1933.
                 FOR OTHER EDITIONS
                 SEE MAIN ENTRY
BX955   Seppelt, Franz Xaver, 1883-
.S37   Papstgeschichte von den Anfängen bis zur Gegenwart
1940   ¡von₎ Franz Xaver Seppelt ¡und₎ Klemens Löffler. Neue
verb. und ergänzte Aufl. München, Kösel-Pustet ¡1940₎

NL 0442436   IU

Löffler, Klemens, 1881-1933.
Papstgeschichte von der französischen Revolution bis zur Gegenwart.   Kempten und München,
Jos. Kösel, 1911.
199 p. 17 cm.

NL 0442444   MnCS

KH38   Löffler, Klemens, 1881-
L825   Papstgeschichte von der französischen
Revolution bis zur Gegenwart. Von Prof. Dr.
Klemens Löffler. Zweite, fortgeführte Auflage.
München, J. Kösel & F. Pustet ¡c1923₎
3p.l.,220p. 17.5cm. (On cover: Sammlung
Kösel)

NL 0442445   NNUT

Loeffler, Klemens, 1881-   ed.
Quellen zur Geschichte des Augustinerchorherrenstifts
Frenswegen, Windesheimer Kongregation. Soest, 1930

xliv, 347 p. (Veröffentlichungen der Historischen
Kommission des Provinzialinstitutes für Westfälische
Landes- und Volkskunde)

NL 0442446   MH NNC

Löffler, Klemens, 1881-1933.

Seppelt, Franz Xaver, 1883-
A short history of the popes, based on the latest researches,
by Professor Francis X. Seppelt, D. D. and Professor Clement
Löffler, PH. D.; authorized adaptation from the German by
Horace A. Frommelt, edited by Arthur Preuss. St. Louis,
Mo. and London. B. Herder book co., 1932.

Löffler, Klemens, 1881-*1933.*
Die westfälischen bischöfe im investiturstreit und in
den Sachsenkriegen unter Heinrich IV. und Heinrich V. ...
Halle, 1903.
54 p., 1 l. 21ᶜᵐ.
Inaug.-dis.—Halle.
Lebenslauf.
"Erscheint vollständig als 2. heft der 'Neuen folge' der Münsterschen
beiträge zur geschichtsforschung."

                                5-1899†

NL 0442448   DLC MH CtY PU OO

Löffler, Klemens, 1881-*1933.*
Die Wiedertäufer zu Münster 1534/35; berichte, aus-
sagen und aktenstücke von augenzeugen und zeitgenossen
... Mit 4 tafeln und 5 abbildungen im text. Ausgewählt
und übers. von Klemens Löffler. Jena, E. Diederichs,
1923.

2 p. l., 3-269 p., 1 l. front., illus., 2 port., fold. plan. 22ᶜᵐ. (Das alte
reich)
"1. bis 3. tausend."

1. Anabaptists. 2. Münster—Hist.—Sources. 3. Germany—Hist.—1517-
1648. I. Title.

Library of Congress   BX4933.G3L6   25-1304

OB1C
NL 0442449   DLC ViHarEM NIC TNJ-R NjPT IaU InGo OU

Lfj75   Löffler, Lambert,
G2   Das deutsche Fortbildungs- (Berufs-)
1   Schulwesen nach Reichs- und Landesrecht ...
1928   Düsseldorf[1928]

Inaug.-Diss. - Würzburg.
Bibliography: p. vii-viii.

NL 0442450   CtY ICRL MH PU

VOLUME 338

Löffler, Lambert.
Das deutsche Fortbildungs- (Berufs-) Schulwesen nach Reichs- und Landesrecht. Düsseldorf, Verlag der Katholischen Schulorganisation Deutschlands, 1928.
ix, 167 p. 24 cm. (Schulpolitik und Erziehung. Zeitfragen, Heft 34)
"Literaturverzeichnis": p. v. "Rechtsquellen": p. vi.

1. Vocational education—Germany.　I. Title.　(Series)

49–43470*

NL 0442451　DLC DCU IaU

Löffler, Leonhard, 1906–
Die Arteriographie der Lunge und die Kontrastdarstellung der Herzhöhlen am lebenden Menschen; eine klinische und tierexperimentelle Studie. Leipzig, G. Thieme, 1946.
74 p. illus.
"Schrifttum": p. [72]–74.

NL 0442452　ICJ DNLM

Löffler, Leonhard, 1906–
Die Arteriographie der Lunge und die Kontrastdarstellung der Herzhöhlen am lebenden Menschen, unter Mitarbeit von Helmut Roth. 2., völlig umgearb. Aufl. Leipzig, G. Thieme, 1955.
158 p. illus.

I. Roth, Helmut, joint author.　612.2158
616.07851　616.07852　616.24

NL 0442453　ICJ DNLM

PD
1576
L49
B5
Läffler, Leopold Fredrik Alexander, 1847–1921.
Bidrag till läran om i-omljudet, med särskild hänsyn till tiden för den germaniska sprakenheten. [Kjobenhavn, 1876]
144 p. 22 cm.
Reprinted from Tidskrift for philologi og paedagogik, ny raekke 2 (1875–1876) p. 1–19, 146–180, 231–320.
Bound with author's Om v-omljudet af i, i oc ei i de nordiska spraken. Upsala, 1877.
1. Scandinavian languages - Phonology. I. Tidskrift for philologi og paedagogik. II. Title.

NL 0442454　DCU

PD
1576
L49
B5
Läffler, Leopold Fredrik Alexander, 1847–1921.
Om v-omljudet af i, i och ei i de nordisk spraken. I. Om v-omljudet af i framför nasal. Upsala, E. Edquists (boktryckori) 1877.
xv, 95 p. 23 cm.
Bound with author's Bidrag till läran om i-omljudet. Kjöbenhavn, 1876.

1. Scandinavian languages - Phonology. I Title.

NL 0442455　DCU NdU

Löffler, Leopold Fredrik Alexander, 1847–1921.
Två kväden i fornnordisk ton. Särtryck ur Ny Svensk Tidskrift.　Upsala, 1886.
(2) f.　8°.

NL 0442456　NIC

Löffler, Lorenz Georg, 1930–
Zur sakralen Bedeutung des Büffels und Gajals für Ahnenkult, Ernteriten und soziale Feste im Gebiet Südostasiens. [Mainz? 1954?]
247 l. mounted illus., maps. 20 cm.
Inaug.-Diss.—Mainz.
Vita.
Bibliography : leaves 235–247.

1. Animal lore. 2. Folk-lore—Asia, Southeastern.　I. Title.

GR705.L6

57–37747

NL 0442457　DLC

Mason
Film
1338
Löffler, Lorenz Georg, 1930–
Zur sakralen Bedeutung des Büffels und Gajals für Ahnenkult, Ernteriten und soziale Feste im Gebiet Südostasiens. [Mainz] 1954.
247 l. illus., maps.

Inaug.-Diss.—Mainz.
Microfilm (negative) 1 reel. 35mm.

1. Animal lore. 2. Folk-lore—Asia, Southeastern.

NL 0442458　NIC CtY

Loeffler, Lothar, ed.
Arbeit, Freizeit und Familie im Hinblick auf die Ehe, das Alter und die Jugend
see under Deutsche Arbeitsgemeinschaft für Jugend- und Eheberatung.

GN62
.L82
LOEFFLER, LOTHAR.
...Tabellen zur berechnung der ohrhöhe des kopfes, von dr. Lothar Loeffler. Jena, G. Fischer, 1932.
[4]p. V tab. 32½cm.
At head of title: Aus dem Anthropologischen institut der Universität Kiel.

1. Ear.　2. Anthropometry.

NL 0442460　ICU CU

Loeffler, Ludwig, 1819–1876, illus.

Jerrold, Douglas William, 1803–1857.
Madame Kaudel's gardinenpredigten, von Douglas Jerrold. Bearb. von Friedrich Gerstäcker. Mit illustrationen von Ludwig Loeffler. 3. aufl. Leipzig, O. Wigand, 1864.

Löffler, Ludwig, 1819–1876, illus.
Schiller's Lied an die Freude
see under Schiller, Johann Christoph Friedrich von, 1759–1805.

Löffler, Ludwig, 1819–1876, illus.
Zwei lustige Soldaten-Lieder
see under title

GER
969HA
LOE
Loeffler, Ludwig, 1906–
Selbstverwaltung und Staatsaufsicht im hamburgischen Gemeinderecht ... vorgelegt von Ludwig Loeffler ... Hamburg, 1932.
x, 99 p., [1] l. 22cm.
Diss. - Hamburg.
"Lebenslauf": leaf at end.
"Benutztes Schrifttum": p. [v]–ix.

NL 0442464　MH-L MiU

V
4
H46
1939
Löffler, Ludwig, 1915–
Maligne Nierentumoren im Kindesalter. Erlangen, Krahl, 1939.
17, [2] p.
Inaug.-Diss. - Heidelberg.
Bibliography: p. [18]

NL 0442465　DNLM

Loeffler, Manuel John, 1918–
Phases in the development of the land-water resource in an irrigated river valley, Colorado. Ann Arbor, University Microfilms [1953]
([University Microfilms, Ann Arbor, Mich.) Publication 5903)
Microfilm copy of typescript. Positive.
Collation of the original: ix, 201 l. illus., fold. maps (1 in pocket)
Thesis—University of Washington.
Abstracted in Dissertation abstracts, v. 13 (1953) no. 5, p. 758.
Vita.
Bibliography : leaves [195]–201.

1. Irrigation—Colorado. 2. Arkansas Valley. 3. Water resources development—Colorado.　I. Title.

Microfilm AC-1　　no. 5903　　Mic A 53–141f
Washington. Univ.　Seattle. Library
for Library of Congress　[1]†

NL 0442466　WaU CoU DLC

Löffler, Marianne, 1910–
Beiträge zur Volkskunde und Mundart von Ustou (Ariège) Tübingen, 1942.
111 p. 21 cm.
Inaug.-Diss.—Tübingen.
Vita.
Bibliography: p. 6–8.

1. Folk-lore—France—Ariège (Dept.)

GR162.A72L6

52–59175

NL 0442467　DLC MH CU CtY

Loeffler, Marie (Gronewaldt) 1887–
Uber Ursache und Behandlung der Nachgeburtsblutungen (an Hand der geburtshilflichen Fälle der Göttinger Frauenklinik aus der Zeit vom 1. Januar bis 31. Dezember 1924) ... Göttingen, 1926.
Inaug.-Diss. - Göttingen.
Lebenslauf.
"Literatur": p. [45]

NL 0442468　CtY

Law
Löffler, Martin, ed.

Germany (*Federal Republic, 1949–*) *Laws, statutes, etc.*
Presserecht. Kommentar zum Reichsgesetz über die Presse und zum Presserecht der Länder sowie zu den sonstigen die Presse betreffenden Vorschriften, von Martin Löffler. München, Beck, 1955.

Löffler, Martin.
Vereinigte Staaten von Amerika, Versailler vertrag und Völkerbund; ein beitrag zur Europa-politik der U. S. A., von dr. jur. Martin Löffler. Berlin-Grunewald, W. Rothschild, 1932.
xvi, 143, [1] p. 24½cm. (*Added t.-p.:* Politische wissenschaft ... hft. 11)
"Verzeichnis der hauptsächlich benutzten literatur": p. [xii]–xvi.

1. U. S.—For. rel. 2. Versailles, Treaty of, June 28, 1919 (Germany) 3. League of nations. 4. Monroe doctrine.　I. Title.　II. Title: Europapolitik der U. S. A.; Ein beitrag zur.

Library of Congress　　E183.7.L76　　32–29592
[3]　　　327.73

NL 0442470　DLC MiU NN

Loeffler, Mary Constance.
Thermochemistry of normal decylcyclopentane, normal decylcyclohexane, 1-hexadecene, normal decylbenzene, and related compounds. Pittsburgh, 1954.
28 l. diagr., tables. 29 cm.
Cover title.
Thesis—Carnegie Institute of Technology.
Bibliography: leaves 27–28.

1. Thermochemistry. 2. Hydrocarbons.

QD511.L7

55–38626

NL 0442471　DLC NN

VOLUME 338

Löffler, Max
Beiträge zur casuistik der lidoperationen ...
Neuburg a. D., Griessmayer ₁188-?₁
21 p.

Inaug.-diss., Munich.

1. Eyelids - Surgery.

NL 0442472   NNC

Loeffler, Max.
Deutsche Heimat-Landschaften; Süddeutschland. ₁1.
Aufl.₁ Bühl-Baden, Verlag Konkordia ₁1951₁
94 p. illus. 21 cm.

1. Germany, Southern—Descr. & trav.   I. Title.

DD784.L6   55-35916 ‡

NL 0442473   DLC

Loeffler, Max
Rachitis im allgemeinen und die durch rachitis
bedingten veraenderungen am gebiss.
Inaug. Diss.   Leipzig, 1924

NL 0442474   ICRL DNLM

NK7150   Löffler, Max, of Stuttgart, ed.
V4
Verein zur Förderung Deutscher Kultur, insbesondere zur
Hebung des Verständnisses Kunsthandwerklichen Schaf-
fens.
Neue Goldschmiedekunst in Baden-Württemberg. ₁Ge-
samtbearbeitung Max Löffler. Stuttgart₁ W. Kohlhammer
₁*1955₁

Loeffler (Moritz). *Ueber Gifte und Gegen-
gifte. 26 pp. 8°. München, F. S. Hübschmann,
1848.

NL 0442476   DNLM PPC

LOEFFLER, Norbert.
Verzeichnis der in der umgegend von Rheine
wachsenden. Phanerog. Pflanzen,
[Progr]. Rheine, Weigel, Lagerkat,139.
1887.

NL 0442477   MH-G

Löffler, Otto, 1908–
Der Inseratenmarkt der illustrierten Zeitung... von Diplom-
Kaufmann Otto Löffler... ₁Mannheim: Industrie-Druckerei,
1935₁ 83 p. incl. forms, tables.   illus. (charts.)   21cm.

Dissertation — Heidelberg, 1935.
Lebenslauf.
"Literaturverzeichnis," p. 5–7.

872227A. 1. Advertising—Mediums—   Newspapers and periodicals.
N.Y.P.L.   April 7, 1937

NL 0442478   NN CtY

Loeffler, Paul.
Einwirkung von Kalkhydrat auf Milchzucker, Konstitution von Parasaccharin.   Freiburg in Baden, Buchdr.
E. Kuttruff, 1904.
35 p. 23 cm.

Inaug.-Diss.—Freiburg i. B.
Bibliographical footnotes.

1. Lactose. 2. Saccharin. 3. Lime.   I. Title.

QD321.L82   73-231111

NL 0442479   DLC MH CtY PU

LÖFFLER,Paul,1903–
Das gemischte Werk;ein Beitrag zur Kombina-
tionsbewegung. Tübingen,A.Becht,1938.

21 cm.
Inaugural-Dissertation - Tübingen.
"Lebenslauf",p.119.

NL 0442480   MH CtY

LOEFFLER, Peter.
Ueber das phenmorpholin. Inaugural-dissertation. Jena, A. Kampfe, 1894.

pp. 52-.

NL 0442481   MH-C ICRL PU

Löffler, Philip, S.J., 1834-1902.
Festpredigt bei Gelegenheit der feierlichen
Weihe der Diözese Regensburg an das heiligste
Herz Jesu. Regensburg, Fr. Pustet, 1872.
28p 21cm

NL 0442482   MnCS

Loeffler, Rebecca Wells, *comp.*
Our country is India, by young Indians and their leaders,
compiled by Rebecca Wells Loeffler; decorations by Jeanne
McLavy. New York, Friendship press ₁1946₁
xii, 180 p. fold. map. 18¼ᵐ.
"A selected reading list": p. 175–178.

1. Missions—India. 2. Youth—India. 3. India—Soc. condit.
I. Title.   46–4429

Library of Congress   BV3265.L57
₁10₁   [266] 275.4

NL 0442483   DLC ICU KyU KyLxCB CaBVaU Or NcD

Löffler, Reinhold, 1902–
Untersuchung uber besondere arten von silber-
zinn-amalgamen. [1933?]
Inaug.-Diss.-Tübingen.

NL 0442484   OU CtY

Löffler, Richard, 1884– Die Zusammensetzung des
Grundgebirges im Ries. Stuttgart 1912: (Grüninger). S. 107
—154. 1 Taf. 8° [Umschlagt.] ¶ (Aus: Jahreshefte d. Ver.
f. vaterl. Naturkunde in Württemberg. Jg. 68.)
Tübingen, Naturwiss. Diss. v. 1. Juni 1910, Ref. v. Koken
[Geb. 2. März 86 Weinsberg; Wohnort: Tübingen; Staatsangeh.: Württemberg;
Vorbildung: Karls-Gymn. Stuttgart Reife Juli 04; Studium: Stuttgart Techn.
Hochsch. 7, Tübingen 4 S.; Rig. 1. Juni 10.] [U 11. 4508]

NL 0442485   ICRL PU

Löffler, Richard, 1910–
Kraftfahrzeugversicherung und Autoabsatz-
finanzierung... Hamburg, 1937.
Diss. - Hamburg.

NL 0442486   CtY

Loeffler, Samuel,
Ueber den einfluss der magnetisierung auf die
torsionselastizitaet des eisens. Zuerich,1901.
In. Diss.

NL 0442487   ICRL NN

Löffler, Siegfried, 1929–
Die Presse des Regierungsbezirks Kassel von 1866–1919.
München, 1954.
viii, 313 l. 30 cm.
Typescript (carbon copy)
Inaug.-Diss.—Munich.
Vita.
Bibliography : leaves ii–vii.

1. Journalism—Kassel (Regierungsbezirk)

PN5217.K3L6   58–32048

NL 0442488   DLC

Loeffler, St₁ephan₁
Mechanische Triebwerke und Bremsen...   München: R.
Oldenbourg, 1912. vi, 132 p.   illus.   8°.

1. Brakes. 2. Power.—Transmis-   sion.
N.Y.P.L.   August 7, 1912.

NL 0442489   NN MiU ICJ

Löffler, Stephan.
Oelmaschinen. Wissenschaftliche und praktische Grundlagen
für Bau und Betrieb der Verbrennungsmaschinen. Von St. Löffler, ... ₁und₁ A. Riedler, ... Mit 288 Textabbildungen.
Berlin, J. Springer, 1916.
xvi, 516 p. illus., diagrs. 23½ᵐ.

NL 0442490   ICJ NN NNCoCi OU MiU N

Löffler, Stephan.
Reibungstriebwerke und ihre missdeutung durch theo-
retiker, von St. Löffler und A. Riedler. München und
Berlin, R. Oldenbourg, 1921.
22 p. 24½ᵐ.

CONTENTS.—I. Erledigung der angriffe gegen die dynamische erfassung de
reibung. Von St. Löffler.—II. Erledigung der angreifer der dynamischen rei
bungserfassung. Von A. Riedler.

1. Gearing.   I. Riedler, Alois, 1850–

NL 0442491   MiU

Löffler, Susi, 1920–
Johann Peter Hebel, wesen und wurzeln seiner dichterischen
welt ... von Susi Löffler ... Frauenfeld/Leipzig, Huber & co.
aktiengesellschaft, 1944.
111, ₁1₁ p. 23ᵐ.
Thesis—Zürich.
"Teildruck. Die vollständige arbeit erscheint als band 44 der samm-
lung 'Wege zur dichtung.'"
Lebenslauf.
"Literaturverzeichnis": p. ₁110₁–111.

1. Hebel, Johann Peter, 1760–1826.

Library of Congress   PT2298.H3Z63   46–19018
.0.

NL 0442492   DLC OrU IU CaBVaU OrU CtY NNC ICU

Löffler, Susi, 1920–
Johann Peter Hebel; wesen und wurzeln seiner dichterischen
welt, von Susi Löffler. Frauenfeld, Leipzig, Huber & co. aktiengesellschaft, 1944.
212 p. 24ᵐ. (Added t.-p.: Wege zur dichtung; Zürcher schriften zur
literaturwissenschaft, hrsg. von Emil Ermatinger. Bd. XLIV)
Issued also in part (111 p.) as thesis, Zürich.
"Literaturverzeichnis": p. ₁211₁–212.

1. Hebel, Johann Peter, 1760–1826.

A 46–4328
Harvard univ. Library
for Library of Congress   ₁2₁

RPB NNC NRU PPT ViU NcU MU MnU CSt FTaSU MoU
NL 0442493   MH NIC NjP WU GU CU-I OU TxU ICU CtY PU

Löffler, Valerie
see Kropp, Valerie (Löffler) 1900–

VOLUME 338

R
565
Z8L6
Löffler, W
    Die medizinische Klinik Zürich 1833-1950.
Zürich,Regierungsrat des Kantons Zürich,1951.
236p. ports. 25cm.

    Cover title.
    "Separatdruck aus der Zürcher Spital-
geschichte."

    1. Medicine - Switzerland - Zürich.
2. Physicians, Swiss. I. Title.

NL 0442495   MU

Loeffler, Walter, *of Germany.*
    Planen und zeichnen, herausgegeben von Walter Loeffler ...
Stuttgart, Julius Hoffmann ₁1935₎
    v. illus., plans (part fold.) tables, diagrs. 25 x 34ᶜᵐ.
    CONTENTS.—bd. 1. Kleines wohnhaus.

    1. Architecture, Domestic—Designs and plans.   I. Title.

New York. Public library
for Library of Congress   ₍r46c2₎
                                   A C 35–2706 rev

NL 0442496   NN

Loeffler, Walter, *1909–*
    Die haftung des arztes aus ärztlicher behandlung, von dr. iur.
Walter Loeffler. Aarau, H. R. Sauerländer, 1945.
    x, 116 p. 23½ᶜᵐ. (Zürcher beiträge zur rechtswissenschaft ... n. f.,
hft. 114)
    "Abdruck der der Rechts- und staatswissenschaftlichen fakultät der
Universität Zürich vorgelegten dissertation."
    Bibliography: p. ₍ix₎–x.

    1. Malpractice.   2. Medical laws and legislation—Switzerland.

                                   46–13556

NL 0442497   DLC MH

Löffler, Walter, *1909-*
    Die strafrechtliche unverantwortlichkeit der
abgeordneten und ihre künftige gestaltung. ...
Urach, 1933. 72 p.
    Inaug. Diss. -Tübingen, 1933.
    Lebenslauf.
    Bibliography.

NL 0442498   ICRL

Loeffler, Werner.
    Die moderne Konzernierung; das Konzentrationsproblem
in der deutschen Grossunternehmung unter besonderer Berücksichtigung der Spät- und Nachinflationszeit, von Dr. jur., Dr. rer.
pol. Werner Löffler...   Frankenstein i. Schles.: E. Philipp's
Buchhandlung, G.m.b.H., 1926. 142 p. 12°.

    Bibliography, p. 139-142.

273595A. 1. Cartels.
N.Y.P.L.   December 16, 1926

NL 0442499   NN PU CtY CSt-H

Loeffler, Wilhelm.
    ... Respirationsversuche am Menschen im
nüchternen Zustand und nach Zufuhr verschiedener
Eiweisskörper... [n.p.] 1912.
    Inaug.-Diss. - Basel.

NL 0442500   CtY DNLM MiU

848
850
L82
Löffler,Wilhelm,1885-
    Die literarischen Urteile der Frau von Sévigné
nach ihren Briefen; ein Beitrag zur Geschichte
des literarischen Geschmacks in Frankreich.
Darmstadt, 1912.
    127 p. 23 cm.
    Inaug.-Diss.--Heidelberg.
    Vita.

    1.Sévigné,Marie (de Rabutin-Chantal) marquise
de,1626-1696.

NL 0442501   MiU ICRL CtY MH PU IU ICN

Löffler, Wilhelm, 1887–
    Die Brucellose als Anthropo-Zoonose. Febris undulans.
Eine zusammenfassende Darstellung für Ärzte und Tier-
ärzte, von W. Löffler, D. L. Moroni ₍und₎ W. Frei. Berlin,
Springer, 1955.
    xii, 198 p. illus. (part col.) 25 cm.
    Bibliography: p. 143–166.

    1. Brucellosis in animals. 2. Undulant fever.   I. Title.

SF871.6   A 55–4504
Iowa.   State Coll. Libr.
for Library of Congress   ₍1₎†

NL 0442502   IaAS DNLM DLC PU-V NNC MiU GU IU DNAL

Löffler, Wilhelm, 1887-
    Festschrift zur feier des 60. geburtstages
herrn prof. dr. Wilhelm Löffler gewidmet von
freunden und schülern, sommer 1947
    see under title

Loeffler, X   W.
    Industrial and railroad averages: chronological
news, 1922-1938.   Westwood, N.J. [1938]
    chart. 38 x 86 cm. fold. to 29 x 28 cm.
    1. Securities - U.S.

NL 0442504   CU

Loeffler-Delachaux, Marguerite.
    Le cercle, un symbole. ₍Genève₎ Éditions du Mont-Blanc
₍1947₎
    207 p. illus. 20 cm. (Collection Action et pensée, 38)
    Includes bibliography.

    1. Symbolism. 2. Circle.

BL603.L6   58–47777 ‡

NL 0442505   DLC NN ICU CLSU

Loeffler-Delachaux, Marguerite.
    Le symbolisme des contes de fées. Paris, Arche ₍1949₎
    248 p. 19 cm. (Action et pensée)

    1. Symbolism. 2. Fairy tales—Hist. & crit.

GR550.L6   50–30278

NL 0442506   DLC OrU NBuU LU CLU NcD CtY IU

Loeffler-Delachaux, Marguerite.
    Le symbolisme des légendes. Paris, Arche ₍1950₎
    146 p. 19 cm.

    1. Symbolism. 2. Legends—Hist. & crit.   I. Title.

                                              A 51–2255
Illinois. Univ. Library
for Library of Congress

NL 0442507   IU LU OU NN CU CtY NcD

Löffler-Herzog, Anna.
    Ein beispiel von vererbung musikalischer begabung, von A.
Löffler-Herzog. Mit einer deszendenztafel ... Zürich, Orell
Füssli ₍1939₎
    cover-title, ₍195₎–198 p. geneal. tab. 24½ᶜᵐ.
    "Separatabdruck aus: Archiv der Julius Klaus-stiftung für verer-
bungsforschung, sozialanthropologie und rassenhygiene, band XIV, 1989,
heft 1/2."
    "Deszendenztafel der familie Friedli": p. 198.

    1. Friedli, Emanuel, 1846–1939. 2. Friedli family. 3. Heredity.
4. Musical ability.   I. Title.
                                              43–40673
Library of Congress   ML3838.L63B3

NL 0442508   DLC

Löffler-Kattowitz, Heinrich
    see Löffler, Heinrich, 1879-

W 1
AR192
Bd. 6
1952
Beiheft
    Die LOEFFLER-FEIER, 1952. Leipzig,
    Hirzel, 1952.
        iv, 124 p. illus., ports. (Archiv für
    experimentelle Veterinärmedizin, Bd. 6,
    Beiheft)
        1. Löffler, Friedrich, 1852-1915
    Series

NL 0442510   DNLM

Loefflerin, A.
    Neuestes Kochbuch für die Küche aller Stände; oder, An-
weisung zur schmackhaften Zubereitung von Speisen, Backwerk,
Eingemachtem, Getränken etc., über 650 Rezepte enthaltend.
Hrsg. von A. Löfflerin.   Reutlingen: R. Bardtenschlager ₍1922₎.
vi, 8–224 p. 25. ed. 24°.

68568A. 1. Cookery (German).
N.Y.P.L.   January 23, 1923.

NL 0442511   NN

TX
721
L6
    Löfflerin, Charlotte, ed.
    Neuestes Kochbuch für Haushaltungen aller
Stände, oder Anweisung nach mehr denn 650
Recepten... Stereotyp-Ausgabe. Reutlingen,
Ensslin u. Laiblin ₍n.d.₎
    224 p.

    COOKERY, GERMAN
    Neuestes Kochbuch

NL 0442512   KMK

Löfflerin, F.L.
    see Löffler, Friederike Luise (Herbort)
b. 1744.

Mhc9
L823
So8
    Loeffs, Isaac
    The souls ascension in the state of
separation. ... preached at Shenly in the
county of Hertford the 21. of November, 1660.
at the funeral solemnities of Mrs. Mary
Jessop, late wife of William Jessop Esq; and
since enlarged and publish'd for common
benefit... London,Printed for N.Ranew and J.
Robinson,1670.
    7p.ℓ.,142p. 15cm.
    T.p. mutilated; ₱art of title wanting
and supplied in   manuscript.

NL 0442514   CtY NNG

W 4
M96
1951
    LOEFFTZ, Renate, 1923-
    Abbau des Blutfarbstoffes zu Mesobili-
fuscinen durch Pneumokokken. München,
1951.
    20 ℓ. illus.
    Inaug.-Diss. - Munich.
    1. Hemoglobin 2. Pneumococcus

NL 0442515   DNLM

VOLUME 338

Löfgren, Albert.
Det svenska tenngjutarehantverkets historia. Stockholm, Nordiska museets förlag, 1925–

v. illus., plates. 28 cm.

At head of title: Nordiska museet.
Includes bibliographies.

CONTENTS.—del 1. bd. 1–2. Stockholms kanngjutareskrå intill år 1720. bd. 1. Organisation, närings- och sociala förhållanden. bd. 2. Biografier, stämplar och arbeten. bd. 3. Stockholms kanngjutareskrå 1720–1850.

1. Pewter. 2. Stockholms kanngjutareskrå. 3. Hall-marks. I. Stockholm. Nordiska museet. II. Title.

NK8415.S8L6   52–27139

NL 0442516   DLC OrU NN MnU

LÖFGREN, Alberto, 1854-1918.
Analysis de plantas; ensaio para uma botanica descriptiva das especies mais frequentes en São Paulo e outros estados de Brazil. By A. Löfgren, and H.L.Everett. São Paulo, 1905.

Port. of Dr. Löfgren and other illustr.

NL 0442517   MH RPB CtY

LOEFGREN, Alberto.
Contribucao para a flora Pulista Regiãeo campestre. [S.Paulo,] Max Weg. Antq. Kat. 108. [1890].

NL 0442518   MH-G

Löfgren, Albert, 1854–

São Paulo, *Brazil (State) Secretaria da agricultura, commercio e obras publicas.*

... Contribuições para a algologia paulista. Familia *Oedogoniaceae,* por Alberto Löfgren ... São Paulo, Red. da "Revista agricola," 1906.

Löfgren, Alberto, 1854–1918.
... Contribuições para a archeologia paulista. Os sambaquis de S. Paulo, por Alberto Löfgren. S. Paulo, Typ. a vapor de Vanorden & comp., 1893.

2 p. l., v p., 2 l., [13]–91 (i. e. 93) [1] p. XVII pl., maps (incl. fold. front.) 23ᶜᵐ. (São Paulo, Brazil (State) [Instituto geografico e geologico, Boletim n. 9)

"Nota sobre os craneos dos sambaquis de Santos (Passa-Mirim) por dr. J. B. de Lacerda": p. 89–01 (i. e. 91–93)
"Obras consultadas" : p. l–v.

1. São Paulo, Brazil (State)—Antiq.   I. Lacerda, João Baptista de, 1846–
                                                 G S 11–378 Revised 2
U. S. Geol. survey. Library
for Library of Congress   F2510.1.S2L6

NL 0442520   DI-GS DLC NIC FU LU-NO CU MH-P ViU MH

[Löfgren, Alberto] 1854–1918.
... Contribuições para a botanica paulista. Região campestre. Memoria das excursões botanicas de 1887, 1888 e 1889. S. Paulo, L. King Bookwalter, typographia King, 1890.

51 p. 23ᶜᵐ. (São Paulo, Brazil (State) [Instituto geografico e geologico] Boletim n. 5)

By Alberto Loefgren. cf. p. [3]

1. Botany—Brazil—São Paulo (State)   I. Title.
                                                 G S 11–376 Revised 3 †
U. S. Geol. survey. Library
for Library of Congress   QK263.L6

NL 0442521   DI-GS DLC MH-A MiU ViU NNBG

Löfgren, Albert, 1854–
... Contribuições para a questão florestal da região do nordéste do Brazil, por Alberto Löfgren ... Rio de Janeiro, 1912.

124 p., 1 l. illus. 27ᶜᵐ. (Brazil. Ministerio da viação e obras publicas. Inspectoria de obras contra as seccas. Publicação n. 18. Ser. I, A—Investigações botanicas)

1. Botany—Brazil. [1. Brazil—Botany]

                                                         Agr 15–415
Library, U. S. Dept. of   Agriculture 9.2B73 no. 18

NL 0442522   DNAL ICJ NN

QK263   **Löfgren, Alberto, 1854–1918.**
L64   Contribuições para a questão florestal da região do nordéste do
1923   Brazil. 2. ed. [Rio de Janeiro] Imprensa Ingleza, 1923.
Biology   xiii, 131 p. illus. ([Brazil] Ministerio da Viação e Obras
Library   Publicas. Inspectoria Federal de Obras Contra as Seccas.
             Publicação n. 18. Ser. I, A: Investigações botanicas)

             Bound with: His Notas botanicas (Ceará) 1923.
             Bibliographical footnotes.

             1. Botany - Brazil.   I. Title.

NL 0442523   CU

Löfgren, Alberto, joint author.

Vieira Souto, Luiz Raphael, 1849–
... O córte das mattas e a exportação das madeiras brasileiras. Exposição redigida pela Commissão composta dos Drs. L. R. Vieira Souto (relator), Alberto Löfgren e Hannibal Porto, e apresentada, depois de unanimemente approvada em sessão de 9 de março de 1917, ao exmo. Sr. ministro da agricultura. Rio de Janeiro, Typ. do Jornal do commercio, de Rodrigues &c., 1917.

Löfgren, Alberto, 1854–1918.
Da colheita e do preparo das plantas para herbarios, especialmente dos phanerogamos, por Alberto Loefgren ... Impresso por conta do governo do estado do São Paulo e illustrado pelo autor. S. Paulo, Typ. de "Diario official", 1897.

25 p. illus. 23½ᶜᵐ.

1. Plants—Collection and preservation. 2. Herbaria.
                                                         22–24067
Library of Congress   QK61.L77

NL 0442525   DLC DPU NN

[Löfgren, Alberto] 1854–1918.
... Ensaio para uma distribuição dos vegetaes nos diversos grupos floristicos do estado de S. Paulo. Indice das plantas do herbario da Commissão seguido por uma relação das plantas cultivadas no jardim da Commissão. São Paulo, Typographia a vap. de Hennies irmãos, 1896.

230 p., 1 l. 23ᶜᵐ. (São Paulo, Brazil (State) [Instituto geografico e geologico] Boletim n. 11)
At head of title : ... Commissão geographica e geologica ...
Part I signed: Alberto Löfgren ; pt. 2 : Gustavo Edwall.

1. Botany—São Paulo, Brazil (State)   I. Edwall, Gustavo, 1862–
                                                 G S 11–380 Revised
U. S. Geol. survey. Library
for Library of Congress
                           [f 45b2]

NL 0442526   DI-GS MH

[Löfgren, Alberto] 1854–1918.
Ensaio para uma distribuição dos vegetaes nos diversos grupos floristicos no estado de São Paulo. [São Paulo, Typographia a vapor de Vanorden & cia., 1898]

50 p. diagr. 23 cm. [São Paulo, Brazil (State) Instituto geografico e geologico. Boletim. n.º 11. 2. ed.]
Caption title.
Signed : Alberto Löfgren.

1. Botany —Brazil—São Paulo (State)   [1. São Paulo, Brazil. Botany] 2. Phytogeography.   I. Title.

TN42.S3A3 no. 11, 1898   Agr 11—1926
U. S. Dept. of Agr. Libr.   455L82E
for Library of Congress   [a56r45d½]†

NL 0442527   DNAL ViU DLC

Löfgren, Alberto, 1854–1918.
... Ensaio para uma synonimia dos nomes populares das plantas indigenas do estado de S. Paulo por Alberto Löfgren. S. Paulo, Typ. Hennies irmãos, 1894–1906.

2 v. 25 cm. (São Paulo, Brazil (State) [Instituto geografico e geologico, Boletim no. 10, 16)
Part 2, by Gustavo Edwall, has imprint: São Paulo, Typographia e papelaria de Vanorden & cia.

1. Botany—Brazil—São Paulo (State) 2. Plant names, Popular—Brazil—São Paulo (State)   I. Edwall, Gustavo, 1862–   II. Title: Synonimia dos nomes populares das plantas indigenas do estado de S. Paulo.
QK263.L64   G S 11—379
U. S. Geol. Survey. Libr.
for Library of Congress   [a56r45d½]†

NL 0442528   DI-GS TxU ViU MiU DLC

QK265   **Löfgren, Alberto, 1854–1918.**
.L6   Ensaio para uma synonimia dos nomes populares
             das plantas indigenas do estado de S. Paulo.
             [1ª parte] S. Paulo, Typ. H. Irmãos, 1895.
             115 p. 23 cm. (Boletim. Commissão geographica
             e geologica do Estado de São Paulo, no. 10)

             Part 2. by Gustavo Edwall, Bulletin no. 16.

             1. Botany - Brazil - São Paulo.   i.t.   ii.s.

NL 0442529   NNBG NIC MH-A

[Löfgren, Alberto] 1854–1918.
... Flora paulista I–IV ... São Paulo, Typographia e papelaria de Vanorden & cia, 1897–1905.
4 v. 23ᶜᵐ. (São Paulo, Brazil (State) [Instituto geografico e geologico Boletim n.º 12–15)
At head of title : Commissão geographica e geologica de São Paulo.
Imprint varies slightly.
CONTENTS.—I. Familia Compositae, por Alberto Löfgren. 1897.—II. Familias Solanaceae e Scrophulariaceae, por Gustavo Edwall. 1897.—III. Familias Campannulaceae, Cucurbitaceae e Calyceraceae. Serie aggregatae família Valerianaceae, por Alberto Löfgren. 1897.—IV. Familia Myrsinaceae, por Gustavo Edwall. 1905.
1. Botany—Brazil—São Paulo (State)   I. Edwall, Gustavo, 1862–   II. Title.
                                                 G S 11–381 Revised 3 †
U. S. Geol. survey. Libra.
for Library of Congress   QK263.L66
                           [r45f2]†

NL 0442530   DI-GS DPU MH-A PPAN MiU ViU DLC

Löfgren, Albert, 1854–
... A fructicultura em Argentina. Observações feitas numa excursão á Buenos Ayres em commissão do governo do estado de S. Paulo por Alberto Löfgren ... S. Paulo, Duprat & comp., 1904.

1 p. l., 43 p., 1 l. 8 pl. 23ᶜᵐ.

At head of title: Secretaria da agricultura, commercio e obras publicas do Estado de São Paulo.

1. Fruit-culture—Argentine Republic. [1. Argentine Republic—Pomology]   I. São Paulo, Brazil (State) Secretaria da agricultura, commercio e obras publicas.
                                                         Agr 10–732 Revised
Library, U. S. Dept. of   Agriculture 93L82

NL 0442531   DNAL

Löfgren, Albert, 1854–
... O genero *Rhipsalis,* por Alberto Löfgren ... Rio de Janeiro, Typ. da Directoria geral de estatistica, 1915.

48 p. 25 pl. 24½ᶜᵐ.

At head of title: Jardim botanico do Rio de Janeiro. (Dos "Archivos do Jardim botanico")

1. Rhipsalis. 2. Rio de Janeiro. Jardim botanico.
                                                         Agr 16–1091
Library, U. S. Dept. of   Agriculture 452.3L822

NL 0442532   DNAL

Loefgren, Alberto.
Géographie botanique de la flore de S. Paul. (In: Congresso Scientifico Latino-Americano, III. Rio de Janeiro, 1905. Relatorio geral. Rio de Janeiro, 1909. 8°. (Tomo 3, livro A. p. 471–501, 2 diagr.)

1. Botany, Brazil: São Paulo.
N. Y. P. L.   December 4, 1911.

NL 0442533   NN

VOLUME 338

Löfgren, Alberto, 1854–1918.
... Manual das familias naturaes phanerogamas, con chaves dichotomicas das familias e dos generos brasileiros ... Rio de Janeiro, Impresa nacional, 1917.
xviii, 611 p. 24½ᶜᵐ.

1. Botany. 2. Botany—Brazil. ₍2. Brazil—Botany₎

Agr 28–440 Revised

U. S. Dept. of agr. Library 452L82
for Library of Congress ₍r42b2₎

NL 0442534 DNAL

Löfgren, Albert, 1854–1918.
... Notas botanicas (Ceará) por Alberto Loefgren. Rio de Janeiro, 1910.
5 p. l., ₍3₎–39 p. plates. 27½ᶜᵐ. (Brazil. Ministerio da viação e obras publicas. Inspectoria de obras contra as seccas. Publicação n. 2. ser. 1, A—Investigações botanicas)
"Obras consultadas" : p. ₍36₎–39.

1. Botany—Ceará, Brazil (State) ₍1. Ceará—Botany₎

Agr 16–275

Library, U. S. Dept. of Agriculture 9.2B73 no. 2

NL 0442535 DNAL DCU NNBG ICJ

G581.9813
L823n **Löfgren, Albert,** 1854–1918.
1923 Notas botanicas (Ceará) 2. ed. Rio de Ja-neiro, 1923.
35p. plates. 27cm. (Ministerio da viação e Obras Publicas. Inspectoria de Obras contra as Seccas. Publicação n.2. Ser.1, A - In-vestigações botanicas)
Bibliography: p.[32]-35.
1. Botany - Ceará. I. Series: Brazil. De-partamento Nacional de Obras contra as Sêcas. Publicações. 2.

NL 0442536 TxU CU

Löfgren, Albert, 1854–

São Paulo, *Brazil (State) Secretaría da agricultura, commercio e obras publicas.*
... Notas sobre as plantas exoticas introduzidas no estado de S. Paulo. Por Alberto Löfgren ... São Paulo, Red. da "Revista agricola," 1906.

Loefgren, Alberto, 1854–1918.
Phytographia com indicação sobre o modo de colleccionar e preparar as plantas paro o herbario para uso das escolas no curso de botanica. ed. 2. São Paulo, 1914.
120 p. Illus. 16°.

NL 0442538 MH-G

Löfgren, Alberto, 1854–1918.
Serviço florestal de particulares, por Alberto Löfgren ... São Paulo, Typographia do "Diario official," 1903.
83 p., 1 l. illus., plates. 22½ᶜᵐ.

₍1. Arboriculture₎ ₍2. Brazil—Forestry₎ 1, 2. Forests and forestry—Brazil.

Agr 3–1229 Revised 2

U. S. Dept. of agr. Library 99.65L82
for Library of Congress ₍r40b2₎

NL 0442539 DNAL ICJ

99.65
L82 **Löfgren, Alberto,** 1854–1918.
Ed.2 Serviço florestal de particulares. 2. ed., rev. por Bento José Pickel. São Paulo, 1947
40 p.

NL 0442540 DNAL

Löfgren, Albert, 1854–*1918,*
... A tamareira e seu cultivo, por Alberto Löfgren ... Rio de Janeiro, Inspectoria de obras contra as seccas, 1912.
1 p. l., 9 p. illus. 27ᶜᵐ. (Brazil. Ministerio da viação e obras publicas. Inspectoria de obras contra as seccas. Publicação n. 13. ser. 1–A)

1. Date-₍palm₎

Agr 16–924

Library, U. S. Dept. of Agriculture 9.2B73 no. 13

NL 0442541 DNAL NN

Löfgren, Alberto, 1854–1918, tr.

Lindman, Carl Axel Magnus, 1856–1928.
A vegetação no Rio Grande do Sul (Brasil austral) pelo prof. dʳ. C. A. M. Lindman ... Obra publicada em Sueco com sub-sidio da Real academia das sciencias do fundo Regnelliano. Traducção portugueza por Alberto Löfgren ... Porto Alegre, Typographia da "Livraria universal" de E. Irmãos & cia., 1906.

Löfgren, Alberto, 1854–1918, tr.

Staden, Hans, *16th cent.*
... Viagem ao Brasil; versão do texto de Marpurgo, de 1557, por Alberto Löfgren; revista e anotada por Theodoro Sampaio. Rio de Janeiro, Officina industrial graphica, 1930.

Löfgren, Axel.
... Fosseis cretaceos de Aracajú Sergipe (sondagem em Ponta da Atalaia) por Axel Löfgren, Paulo Erichsen de Oliveira. ₍Rio de Janeiro₎ 1943.
54 p. illus., plates, maps. 23ᶜᵐ. (Brazil. Departamento nacional da produção mineral. Divisão de geologia e mineralogia. Boletim n. 106)
At head of title : Ministerio da agricultura. Departamento nacional da produção mineral. Divisão de geologia e mineralogia. Anibal Alves Bastos, diretor.
"Bibliografia" : p. 53–54.
Plates I–VI each accompanied by leaf with descriptive letter-press.
1. Paleontology — Brazil — Sergipe. 2. Paleontology — Cretaceous. I. Erichsen de Oliveira, Paulo, joint author. II. Title.

G S 44–69

U. S. Geol. survey. Library
for Library of Congress [QE235.A2 no. 106]
₍3₎ (558.1)

NL 0442544 DI-GS

Löfgren, Axel, joint author.

Erichsen, Alberto Ildefonso.
... Geologia de Goiaz a Cuiabá, por Alberto I. Erichsen e Axel Löfgren. Rio de Janeiro, Brasil, Serviço de informação agrícola, Ministério da agricultura, 1940.

Löfgren, Axel.
... Reconhecimento geologico nos rios Tocantins e Araguaya, por Axel Löfgren. Rio de Janeiro, Papelaria Mendes, 1936.
60, ₍1₎ p. plates, 2 fold. maps, profiles (1 fold.) diagr. 27½ᶜᵐ. ₍¹Brazil₎ Serviço geologico e mineralogico. Boletim n. 80)
At head of title : Ministerio da agricultura.
"Bibliographia" : p. ₍61₎

1. Geology—Brazil. 2. Tocantins river, Brazil. 3. Araguaya river, Brazil. I. Title.

G S 36–328

U. S. Geol. survey. Library (410) B no. 80
for Library of Congress QE235.A2 no. 80

NL 0442546 DI-GS ViU DLC

Loefgren, Bo, 1866–
Släkten Löfgren från Högsby, anteckningar. Stockholm, Iduns tryckeri, 1925.
62 p. illus., 8 plates.

NL 0442547 MH

Löfgren, Börje.
The electrical impedance of a complex tissue and its rela-tion to changes in volume and fluid distribution; a study on rat kidneys. Uppsala, 1951.
51 p. illus. 23 cm. (Acta physiologica Scandinavica, v. 23. Sup-plementum 81)
Akademisk avhandling—Uppsala.
Extra t. p., with thesis note, inserted.
"From the Institute of Physiology, University of Uppsala, Sweden." Bibliography : p. ₍50₎–51.

1. Electrophysiology. I. Title. (Series)

QP341.L73 612.01442 51–7581

NL 0442548 DLC CoU ViU TxU

Löfgren (Carolus)
*De ratione, virtutes animi excitandi et excolendi, naturæ congrua. Lundæ, 1795. 16 pp. 4°.
In: YFH p. v. 1.

NL 0442549 NN

Löfgren, *Fru* Ebba Maria Lovisa (Leche) 1878–
... Ellen Key; hennes liv och verk. Illustrerad med 24 planscher. Stockholm, Bokförlaget Natur och kultur ₍1930₎
224 p. front., 1 illus., plates, ports. 22ᶜᵐ.
At head of title : Mia Leche-Löfgren.
"Bibliografi" : p. ₍214₎–220.

1. Key, Ellen Karolina Sofia, 1849–1926.

33–19509

Library of Congress HQ1687.K4L6 928.397

NL 0442550 DLC MB NN CtY ICU MnU OrP CtY IU IEN

940.931485
L823 **Löfgren, Ebba Maria Lovisa (Leche),** 1878–
Hård tid ₍av₎ Mia Leche Löfgren. Stockholm, L. Hökerberg ₍1946₎
315 p. illus., ports. 23 cm.

1. World War 1939–1945. Sweden.
2. Segerstedt, Torgny Karl, 1876–1945.
3. Ossietzky, Carl von, 1887–1938.
I. Title.

NL 0442551 MnU NN OC1

CT1328
.L6A3 **Löfgren, Ebba Maria Lovisa (Leche)** 1878–
Ideal och människor ₍av₎ Mia Leche Löfgren. Stockholm, Hökerberg ₍1952₎
319 p. ports. 22 cm.

I. Title.

A 53–4984

Minnesota. Univ. Libr
for Library of Congress ₍1₎

NL 0442552 MnU OC1 NN DLC

Löfgren, Ebba Maria Lovisa (Leche) 1878–
Så var det då 1900–1940 [by] Mia Leche Löfgren. Stockholm, L. Hökerberg [1941]
399 p. illus.

NL 0442553 MH OC1 MnU

VOLUME 338

Löfgren, Ebba Maria Lovisa (Leche) 1878–
Vara föräldrars värld. Stockholm, L.Hökerberg
[1934]

NL 0442554   MH

[Löfgren, Eliel] *1872–*
Högbroforsmålet mot Torsten Kreuger. [Stock-
holm, Centraltryckeriet, 1933]
xv, 722 p.

NL 0442555   MH-BA

Löfgren, Eliel, 1872–
Klockorna i Östervåla. Stockholm, A. Bonnier [1934]
358 p. plates, ports., fold. map. 21 cm.

An account of the murder of Johan Åkerlund, in Östervåla, 1896; the trial and acquittal of Eriksson ("Börstil") 1897; the trial and acquittal of Blomberg, 1905, and the confession of Karl Karlgren-Bäck, 1928.

1. Åkerlund, Johan, d. 1896. 2. Blomberg, ———, 1860– 3. Eriksson, Erik. 4. Karlgren-Bäck, Karl, 1858–1928. I. Title.

Full name: Jonas Eliel Löfgren.

50–53550

NL 0442556   DLC

Löfgren, Eliel, 1872–
Kort framställning av prisrättsförfarandet i England; föredrag vid exportföreningens årsstämma 29 april 1916, av Advokaten Eliel Löfgren. Stockholm: P. Palmquist, 1916. 24 p. 12°.
(Sveriges allmänna exportförening. Publ. no. 2.)

1. European war, 1914– —Prizes.   2. Naval prizes.—Jurisprudence,
Gt. Br. 3. Series.
N. Y. P. L.   April 19, 1920.

NL 0442557   NN

[Löfgren, Eliel,] 1872–
De nordiska förliknings- och skiljedomsavtalen; i deras ställning till det internationella rättssystemet. Utarbetad i anslutning till anförande vid Sveriges Advokatsamfunds årsmöte den 5 juni 1926. Stockholm: P. A. Norstedt & söner, 1927. 102 p. 8°.

1. Arbitration, International.   2. Title.
N. Y. P. L.   January 20, 1928

NL 0442558   NN

---

*Löfgren, Eliel, 1872–   ed.

Grundtvig, Ludvig August, 1869–1913.
De nordiske sølove, med domsreferat og sagregister, efter planlægning af dr. L. A. Grundtvig ... udgivne af Jac. Winther ... Olaf Sparre ... Eliel Löfgren ... som redaktører for Danmark, Norge, Sverige. Kjøbenhavn, A/s J. H. Schultz forlagsboghandel, 1914.

NL 0442560   ICJ

Löfgren, Emil.
Folktro, sed och sägen från Njurunda socken i Medelpad, av Emil Löfgren. Malmö, Maiander, 1918.
88, [4] p. 16½ x 10 cm.

Formler och tabeller över cirkulära, hyperboliska och Besselska funktioner samt gammafunktionen. Stockholm, Nordisk rotogravyr, 1954. 51 p. illus. 21cm.
(Forskning och teknik. Häfte 5)

Bibliography, p. 6.

1. Trigonometrical functions. 2. Functions, Exponential. 3. Functions, Bessel's, 1954. 4. Functions.   Gamma. I. Series. t. 1954.

NL 0442561   NN

Löfgren, Erik.
...Om ansvarighetsförsäkring, av Erik Löfgren... [Stockholm: I. Hæggströms boktryckeri a. b., 1936] 111 p. 22cm.
(Svenska försäkringsföreningens studiehandböcker. [nr.] 3.)

"Litteraturanvisningar," p. 102.

912222A.   1. Insurance, Liability—   Sweden. I. Ser.
N. Y. P. L.   January 25, 1938

NL 0442562   NN

Löfgren, Erik O.
Sverige-Norge och danska frågan 1848–49 från stilleståndet i Malmö till den svensk-danska konventionen augusti 1849 ... Uppsala, Wretmans boktryckeri, 1921.
3 p. l., [ix]–xiv, 285 p. fold. map. 22½ cm.

Akademisk avhandling—Upsala.
"I viss mån en fortsättning av d:r Hj. Haralds gradualavhandling, Sveriges utrikespolitik 1848 [Uppsala, 1912]"
"Källor och litteratur": p. [xii]–xiv.

1. Schleswig-Holstein question. 2. Sweden—For. rel.—Denmark. 3. Denmark—For. rel.—Sweden. 4. Norway—For. rel.—Denmark. 5. Denmark—For. rel.—Norway. I. Title.

Library of Congress   DL218.L6   24–13189

NL 0442563   DLC PU CtY WaU ICU

Löfgren, Folke, joint author.

AS284
.L82
bd. 45,
nr. 9

Lindegård, Bengt.
Anthropologische Untersuchung mittelalterlicher Skelettfunde aus dem Aussätzigenspital St. Jörgen in Åhus, von Bengt Lindegård und Folke Löfgren. Lund, C. W. K. Gleerup [1949]

Löfgren, Folke.
Das topographische System der Malpighischen Pyramiden der Menschenniere. Lund, H. Ohlssons boktr., 1949.
200 p. illus. 25 cm.

Akademisk avhandling—Lund.
Extra t. p., with thesis note, inserted.
At head of title: Aus dem Anatomischen Institut der Universität Lund. Aus dem Tornblad-Institut für Vergleichende Embryologie der Universität Lund.
Summaries in English and French.
Bibliography : p. [196]–200.

1. Kidneys.

QM404.L6   611.61   50–20390

NL 0442565   DLC NIC DNLM ICU CtY NNC-M

Löfgren, Gunnel.
Étude sur les prépositions françaises od, atout, avec, depuis les origines jusqu'au xvi° siècle. Uppsala, Almqvist & Wiksells boktr., 1944.
191 p. 24 cm.

Thèse—Université d'Upsal.
Bibliography : p. [176]–189.

1. French language—Old French—Prepositions. I. Title.

PC2867.L6   57–56922

InU
NL 0442566   DLC PU MiU NNC NjP CU MH ICU CtY LU CLU

Löfgren, Ivan, *ed.*
Ärtemark; en Dalslandssocken. [Ärtemark, 1955]
381 p. illus., ports., map. 23 cm.

1. Artemark, Sweden—Hist.

DL991.A518L6   A 57–3726
Minnesota. Univ. Libr.
for Library of Congress   [3]†

NL 0442567   MnU DLC

Löfgren, Jonas Eliel

see

Löfgren, Eliel, 1872–

R96
.A6
v.32

Löfgren, L
Experimental gastric histamine erosions and ulcers, with special reference to the effect of somatotropic hormone on their frequency. Helsinki, 1954.
20 p. illus. (Annales medicinae experimentalis et biologiae Fenniae, v.32, supplementum 6)

NL 0442569   ICU

Löfgren, L
Über die Anthropologie der Bewohner von Uusimaa; akademische Abhandlung. Helsinki, Suomalainen Tiedeakatemia, 1937.
219 p. illus., map. 25 cm.

1. Anthropometry - Finland - Uusimaa.

NL 0442570   DSI OrU CtY OU

Löfgren, Luiz.
... Estudo sobre descarga dos rios brasileiros avaliação do potencial hydraulico do Brasil, pelos engenheiros Luiz Löfgren e Ruchdi Salhab. Rio de Janeiro, Pap. Americana, 1930.
1 p. l., 8 p. incl. tables. 26½ cm.

At head of title: Ministerio da agricultura, industria e commercio. Serviço geologico e mineralogico do Brasil.

1. Water-power—Brazil.   I. Salhab, Ruchdi, joint author. II. Brazil. Serviço geologico e mineralogico. III. Title.

G S 30—269
U. S. Geol. Survey. Libr.
for Library of Congress   [a56c]

NL 0442571   DI-GS TxU MiU CtY

Löfgren, Luiz

Brazil. *Serviço geologico e mineralogico.*
... Forcas hydraulicas (Trabalhos de 1920–1923)—
Rio de Janeiro, 1925–

Löfgren, Nils.
Studies on local anesthetics. Xylocaine, a new synthetic drug. [Translation prepared by L. Wilson] Stockholm, 1948.
151, [1] p. diagrs. 25 cm.

Inaug. diss.—Stockholm.
Extra t. p., with thesis statement, inserted.
"References": p. 147–[152]

1. Xylocaine. I. Wilson, L., tr.

RD86.X8L6   615.781   50–37662

MiU IaU PSt IU NjR DNLM TxU NIC
NL 0442573   DLC PRaW OrU-M CaBVaU IParkA CLSU OU OU

VOLUME 338

Löfgren, Nils Isak, 1797–1881
Kalmar och dess stift i Smaland, landskaps-
beskrivning ... Calmar, P. Ahlquist, 1828–30.
2 v. in 1. 22½ cm.

DL991
K28
L64

1. Kalmar, Sweden.

NL 0442574 CtY

AS284
.L82
bd. 36,
nr. 6

Löfgren, Olov, 1917–   joint author.

Linell, Folke, 1913–
... Verlauf der lungengefässe besonders des lobulus beim
menschen und bei einigen säugetieren, von Folke Linell und
Olov Löfgren ... Lund, C. W. K. Gleerup; ₍etc., etc.,₎ 1940₎

Löfgren, Oscar, 1898–   ed.
Die äthiopische Übersetzung des Propheten
Daniel... Paris, 1927
            see under   Bible. O. T.
            1927.

Löfgren, Oscar, 1898–
Ambrosian fragments of an illuminated manuscript containing the Zoology of Al-Gâḥiẓ. 24 facsim. plates ed. with
an introd. and philological notes, by Oscar Löfgren. With
a contribution: The miniatures: their origin and style, by
Carl Johan Lamm. Uppsala, Lundequistska bokhandeln
₍1946₎
38 p. plates. 25 cm. (Uppsala universitets årsskrift 1946: 5)
Bibliographical footnotes.
1. 'Amr ibn Baḥr, Abū 'Uthmān, al-Jāḥiẓ, 799?–869? Kitāb al-
ḥayawān. 2. Milan. Biblioteca ambrosiana. Mss. (Ar. A. F. D 140
inf.) 3. Miniature painting.   i. Lamm, Carl Johan, 1902–
The miniatures: their origin and style.   ii. Title.   (Series: Uppsala.
Universitet. Årsskrift,   1946: 5)
            Full name: Oscar Anders Valfrid Löfgren₎
AS284.U7 1946,   no. 5 (378.745) A 48–2658 rev*
Minnesota Univ. Libr.
for Library of Congress   ₍r49c1₎†

NL 0442577 MnU OC1 PU DDO DLC NSyU MoSW MoU UU

Löfgren, Oscar, 1898–
Arabische Texte zur Kenntnis der Stadt Aden
            see under
Abū Makhramah, al-Ṭayyib ibn 'Abd Allāh,
1465–1540.

BX101
.O7
num. 85

Löfgren, Oscar, 1898–   ed.
YaʾItyoP̄yä ʾortodoks tawäḥedo béta kerestiyän. **Liturgy
and ritual.**
₍Akotéta qurbän zaqedus Gorgoreyos za'Armänyä₎ German &
Ethiopic.
Die beiden gewöhnlichen äthiopischen Gregorius-Ana-
phoren, nach 5 bzw. 3 Handschriften hrsg. von Oscar Löf-
gren. Übers. und mit Anmerkungen versehen von Sebastian
Euringer. Roma, Pont. Institutum Orientalium Studi-
orum, 1933.

DS206
.I2

Löfgren, Oscar, 1898–   ed.

Ibn al-Mujāwir, Yūsuf ibn Ya'qūb, d. 1291.
Descriptio Arabiae meridionalis, praemissis capitulis de
Mecca et parte regionis Ḥiḡāz, qui liber inscribitur: Ta'rīḫ
al-mustabṣir, secundum codicem Constantinopolitanum
Hagiae Sophiae 3080, collato codice Leidensi Or. 5572, cum
adnotatione critica edidit Oscar Löfgren. Leiden, E. J.
Brill, 1951–54.

Löfgren, Oscar, 1898–
... Ein Hamdāni-fund; über das Berliner unicum der beiden
ersten bücher des Iklil, von Oscar Löfgren. Uppsala, A.-b.
Lundequistska bokhandeln ₍1935₎
32 p. facsim. 24½ᶜᵐ. (Uppsala universitets årsskrift 1935: 7)
Series title also in French.
"Abkürzungen" : p. ₍2₎

1. al-Hamdāni, al-Ḥasan ibn Aḥmad, called Ibn al-Ḥā'ik, d. 945. a.
Iklil.
                                                    ₍Full name: Oscar Anders Valfrid Löfgren₎
                                                              A C 38–1358
Minnesota. Univ. Library
for Library of Congress   [AS284.U7 1935]
                                                      (378.485)

NL 0442581 MnU MoU DLC

DS247
Y47H3

Löfgren, Oscar, 1898–   ed.

al-Hamdāni, al-Ḥasan ibn Aḥmad, *called* Ibn al-Ḥā'ik, d. 945.
Al-Iklil, erstes Buch. In der Rezension von Muḥammed
bin Naŝwān bin Sa'īd al-Ḥimyarī. Nach der einzigen Berliner Handschrift Or. oct. 968 zum ersten Male hrsg. von
Oscar Löfgren. Uppsala, Almqvist & Wiksells boktr. ₍1954–

Löfgren, Oscar, 1898–   ed.

Bible. *O. T. Minor prophets. Ethiopic.* 1930.
Jona, Nahum, Habakuk, Zephanja, Haggai, Sacharja und
Maleachi äthiopisch unter zugrundelegung des Oxforder ms.
Huntington 625 nach mehreren handschriften herausgegeben
von Oscar Löfgren ... Uppsala, Almqvist & Wiksells; ₍etc.,
etc.₎ 1930.

Löfgren, Oscar, 1898–
... Studien zu den arabischen Danielübersetzungen mit beson-
derer berücksichtigung der christlichen texte. Nebst einem
beitrag zur kritik des Peschittatextes, von Oscar Löfgren.
Uppsala, Almqvist & Wiksells boktryckeri-a.-b., 1936.
xvi, 103 p. 24ᶜᵐ. (Uppsala universitets årsskrift 1936:4)
Series title also in French.
"Literatur" : p. ₍xi₎–xiv.
1. Bible. O. T. Daniel. Arabic—Versions. 2. Bible. O. T. Daniel.
Syriac—Criticism, Textual. 3. Bible. Arabic—Versions—O. T. Daniel.
4. Bible. Syriac—Criticism, Textual—O. T. Daniel. i. Bible. O. T.
Daniel. Arabic. Selections. 1936. ii. Bible. Arabic. Selections. O. T.
Daniel.
                                ₍Full name: Oscar Anders Valfrid Löfgren₎
                                                              A C 39–2908
Minnesota. Univ. Library
for Library of Congress   [AS284.U7 1936]
                                        ₍3₎   (378.485)

NL 0442584 MnU MoU PU PPDrop

CS1126
.H35

Löfgren, Oscar, 1898–   ed.

al-Hamdāni, al-Ḥasan ibn Aḥmad, *called* Ibn al-Ḥā'ik, d. 945.
Südarabisches Muŝtabih. Verzeichnis Homonymer und
homographer Eigennamen, aus dem Berliner Unikum des
Iklil. Hrsg. von Oscar Löfgren. Uppsala, Almqvist &
Wiksells boktr. ₍1953₎

890
L825
eng
1947

Löfgren, Rudolf
Engelsk grammatik för skolor och självstudium.   2. uppl.
Stockholm, Natur och kultur [1947]
vii, 212 p.

1. English language – Grammar – 1870–

NL 0442586 CU

WY
58
L825s
1955

LÖFGREN, Signe
Silmätautioppi. 5. painos. Helsinki,
Söderström ₍1955₎
62 p. illus. ₍Sairaanhoitajien koulu-
tussäätiön julkaisema₎
Bound with Werner, Rakel. Silmätau-
tien sairaanhoito. Helsinki ₍1955₎
1. Ophthalmology

NL 0442587 DNLM

Löfgren, Stig.
The fibrogram; investigations on the influence of fibre
length and its distribution, on the working progress in Paul's
draw field, and on the properties of yarn and fabric. Gothenburg, 1950.
144 p. illus. 25 cm. (Doktorsavhandlingar vid Chalmers tekniska
högskola, nr. 5)
Akademisk avhandling—Chalmers tekniska högskola, Gothenburg.
Extra t. p., with thesis statement, inserted.
Bibliography: p. ₍139₎–144.
1. Textile fibers.   (Series: Gothenburg, Sweden. Chalmers tekniska högskola. Doktorsavhandlingar, nr. 5)
TS1540.L6   677.028   50–36881

NL 0442588 DLC NN NNC NcRS DNAL

UA646
.M8

Löfgren, Stig, joint author.

Murray, Malcolm, 1904– -
För Nordens frihet; synpunkter på ett tidsenligt försvar,
av Malcolm Murray och Stig Löfgren. Stockholm, Norstedt
₍1949₎

CT275
E8L6

Löfgren, Svante Emanuel, 1882–1951.
Barth Ar-Kell (The White Bear)   Seattle,
Wash., Publications press, 1949.
208 p. plates, port., map.

NL 0442590 CU PPAmSwM CaBVa CaBViP WaU Wa WaS WaT

Lofgren, Svante Emanuel, 1882–1951.
The early Swedish settlements of
Washington; The Swedes of Oregon, by
William Carlson Smith. ₍36₎ p. Amer.
Swedish historical museum, 1946.
Excerpts from American Swedish histori-
cal museum yearbook, 1946.

NL 0442591 OrP

Löfgren, Svante Emanuel, 1882–1951.
I fjarran Västern. Med förord af Ernst
Skarstedt. Seattle, Wash. ₍Washington
Printing co., 1921₎
175 p.

NL 0442592 WaU WaS Wa

LÖFGREN, Svante Emanuel, 1882–1951.
I urskogen.
[1923]

NL 0442593 WaS

LÖFGREN, Svante Emanuel, 1882–1951.
Jorden runt genom luften.
1928.

NL 0442594 WaS

Löfgren, Svante Emanuel, 1882–1951.
Poverty and golden dreams. A biography of
K₍nute₎ O. Erickson.
Manuscript.

NL 0442595 PPAmSwM

Löfgren, Svante Emanuel, 1882–1951.
Röda flodens delta. Stockholm, H. Geber ₍1951₎
220 p. illus. 21 cm.

1. East (Far East)—Soc. condit. 2. East (Far East)—Descr. &
trav.   i. Title.
DS518.1.L6   52–23972 ‡

NL 0442596 DLC NN CU

VOLUME 338

Löfgren, Svante Emanuel, 1882-1951.
...Soliga Spanien välkomnar; iberiska halvön i dag.
Stockholm [etc.] Ljus [1945] 269 p. illus. 22cm.

574330B. 1. Spain—Descr. and trav., 1910-

NL 0442597   NN MnU NjP

LÖFGREN, Svante Emanuel, 1882-1951.
    Vita Björnen.
      Seattle. Publications pr. 1949,c48.
225p. illus. map.

NL 0442598   WaS CaBViPA PPAmSwM

Löfgren, Sven.
    Apoteket Pantern; roman av Sven Löfgren. Tredje upplagan.
Stockholm: A. Bonnier ₁1935₎ 357 p. 19½cm.

786578A. 1. Fiction, Swedish.   I. Title.
N. Y. P. L.   November 14, 1935

NL 0442599   NN

Löfgren, Sven
    Mellan hakkorset och trikoloren. Stockholm,
H.Schildt [1935]

NL 0442600   MH

Löfgren, Sven Halvar, 1910-
    Erythema nodosum; studies on etiology and pathogenesis
in 185 adult cases. ₁Tr. by Grace Lundberg₎ Stockholm,
Kungl. boktryckeriet, P. A. Norstedt, 1946.
    197 p. illus. 24 cm. (Acta medica scandinavica. Supplementum 174)
    At head of title: From the Medical Service of St. Göran's Hospital
and the State Bacteriologic Laboratory, Stockholm, Sweden.
    Errata slip inserted.
    "Bibliography": p. ₁181₎-197.

    1. ₁Erythema nodosum₎ I. Lundberg, Grace, tr.   (Series)
                           A 48-8271*

John Crerar Library
for Library of Congress   ₁3₎

NL 0442601   ICJ ViU OU

Löfgren, Sven Halvar, 1910-
    ... Erythema nodosum; studies on etiology and patho-
genesis in 185 adult cases ... Stockholm, Norstedt, 1946.
    197 p. illus. 23 cm.
    Also published as Acta medica scandinavica, v. 124, suppl. 174.
    Translated by Grace Lundberg.

    1. ₁Erythema nodosum₎
                            Med 47-1484 rev
U. S. Army Medical Libr.   [WE847L825e 1946]
for Library of Congress   ₁r48c1₎

NL 0442602   DNLM

Loefgren, Ture Fr.
    Talets teori i enlighet med nyare aasigter.
    Inaug. diss. Upsala, 1881.

NL 0442603   ICRL NjP RPB PU

Löfgrén, Anton, 18th cent., respondent.

Burman, Erik, 1692-1729, praeses.
    ... Dissertatio musica, De basso fundamentali ... Up-
saliæ, literis Wernerianis ₁1728₎

Löfke, Heinz.
    Kanadas Wirtschaft zwischen USA. und dem Empire.
Bad Oeynhausen (Westf.) A. Lutzeyer ₁1942₎
    79 p. illus. 21 cm. (Wirtschaftsschlaglichter, Bd. 4)

    1. Canada—Econ. condit.   I. Title.

HC115.L63   53-50351 ‡

CtY
NL 0442605   DLC IEN MH CU NN IaU IU MH IU NNC NcD

Löfke, Heinz, 1913-
    Versuch einer begriffsbestimmung der mensch-
lichen gesellschaft ... von Heinz Löfke ...
Düren, Spezial-dissertations-buchdruckerei, 1938.
    2 p. l., 40 p., 1 l. 21½ᶜᵐ.

    Thesis, Giessen, 1938.
    Bibliography on verso of 2d prelim. leaf.

    1. Anthropology.
    2. Sociology.

NL 0442606   NNC MB ICRL DLC CtY

W 4
M22
1954
    LÖFKE, Margot, 1928-
       Über die Resorptionszeit von Hyaluroni-
dasequaddeln bei verschiedenen Derma-
tosen. ₁Mainz₎ 1954.
       30 ℓ.
       Inaug.-Diss. - Mainz.
       1. Hyaluronidase 2. Skin - Diseases

NL 0442607   DNLM

Löfken, Alexander, 1891-
    ... Baulicher luftschutz zur sicherung von stadt und land,
wirtschaft und industrie gegen luftangriffe, von dr.-ing. Alexander Löfken ... 3. neubearb. aufl. Berlin, W. Ernst & sohn,
1940.
    3 p. l., 72 p. incl. illus. 21ᶜᵐ. (Baulicher luftschutz, hft. 2)

    1. Air defenses. 2. Germany—Air defenses.   I. Title.
                            44-44361
    Library of Congress   UG630.L65 1940
            ₁2₎   623.38

NL 0442608   DLC

Löfken, Alexander, 1891-
    Über den baulichen luftschutz zur sicherung
von stadt und land, wirtschaft und industrie
gegen luftangriffe... ₁Berlin,Buchdruckerei
Gebrüder Ernst₎ 1937.
    3 p.l., 62 p. 21ᶜᵐ
    Diss.- Berlin.
    Lebenslauf.
    Published also without dissertation note with
title: Baulicher luftschutz zur sicherung von
stadt und land, wirtschaft und industrie gegen
luftangriffe as heft 2 of the series "Baulicher
luftschutz."
    "Quellenverze ichnis": p.62.
    1.Air defenses.   2.Building.3.Cities and
towns - Planning.   I.Title: Baulicher luftschutz zur sicherung von stadt und land.

NL 0442609   CSt-H NNC

Loefler, Adam Ludwig
    Dissertatio inavgvralis jvridica de jvre
venandi ex generali investitvra in svbfevdvm
valide concesso, sed defectv svbinfevdantis
extincto, qvam ... subjicit M. Adam
Lvdovicvs Loefler ... Altdorfi,Literis
Henrici Meyeri,Vniversit.typogr.[1706]
    26p. 20cm. [Dissertationes de venatione
... Vol. III]
    Diss.- Altorf.
    Signatures: A-C⁴D¹.

Uznl2
610
3

NL 0442610   CtY

Löfler, Adam Ludwig.
    Meditationes probabiles de puella Zittaniensi incantata,
earumque sectionem primam, submittit. 13 l
4°. Lipsiæ, excud. J. H. Richterus, [1706]

NL 0442611   DNLM CtY

W 4
E69
1955
    LÖFLER, Imre, 1929-
       Diskussion über die Pseudotabes
an Hand eines Falles. ₁Erlangen,
1955₎
       30 p. illus.
       Inaug.-Diss. - Erlangen.
       1. Pseudotabes

NL 0442612   DNLM

Löflerin, F.L.
    see Löffler, Friederike Luise (Herbort)
b. 1744.

Löfling, Per, 1729-1756.
    An abstract of the most useful and necessary articles
mentioned by Peter Loefling, botanist to His Catholic
Majesty, in his travels through Spain, and that part of
South America called Cumana, consisting in his life, and
in systematical descriptions of the plants of both countries, referred to the pages of the original Swedish edition.
    (In Bossu, N. Travels through that part of North America formerly
called Louisiana. London, 1771. 20ᶜᵐ. v. 2, p. 69-422)
    A translation of the greater part of the author's "Iter hispanicum" ex-
clusive of the journal.

    1. Botany—Spain. 2. Botany—South America.
                            10-14402
    Library of Congress   F373.B73 vol. 2

NL 0442614   DLC TxU OC1 MH-A MiU-C

Löfling, Per, 1729-1756, respondent.

Linné, Carl von, 1707-1778, praeses.
    ... Gemmae arborum ... Upsaliæ ₁1749₎

Löfling, Per, 1729-1756.
    ... Iter hispanicum, eller, Resa til spanska länderna uti
Europa och America, förrättad ifrån år 1751 til år 1756,
med beskrifningar och rön öfver de märkvärdigaste väx-
ter, utgifven efter dess frånfälle af Carl Linnæus. Stockholm, Tryckt på Direct. L. Salvii kostnad, 1758.
    10 p. l., 316 p. 19ᶜᵐ.

    1. Botany—Spain. 2. Botany—America.   I. Linné, Carl von, 1707-
1778, ed.
                            5-36430†
    Library of Congress   QK5.L7

            CU NN MiU
NL 0442616   DLC NNBG OkU PPC PPAN MH-A CtY RPJCB

Löfling, Per, 1729-1756.
    Peter Loeflings ... reise, nach den spanischen ländern
in Europa und America in den jahren 1751 bis 1756,
nebst beobachtungen und anmerkungen über die merkwürdigen gewächse herausgegeben von herrn Carl von
Linné ... aus dem schwedischen übersetzt durch d.
Alexander Bernhard Kölpin ... Berlin und Stralsund, G.
A. Lange, 1766.
    16 p. l., 406 p. 2 fold. pl. 21ᶜᵐ.

    1. Botany—Spain. 2. Botany—America.   I. Linné, Karl von, 1707-
1778, ed. II. Kölpin, Alexander Bernhard, 1739-1801, tr.
                            2—17726
    Library of Congress   QK5.L78

NL 0442617   DLC ICJ PPL MH-A KMK NNBG CtY RPJCB

VOLUME 338

Löfling, Per, 1729–1756.
... Reisebeschreibung nach den spanischen ländern in Europa und America in den jahren 1751 bis 1756 nebst beobachtungen und anmerkungen über die merkwürdigen gewächse, hrsg. von Herrn Carl von Linné ... Aus dem schwedischen übersetzt durch D. Alexander Bernhard Kölpin ... 2. aufl. Berlin, G. A. Lange, 1776.
16, ₍16₎, 406, ₍2₎ p. ₁₁ fold. pl. 20ᶜᵐ.

1. Botany—Spain. 2. Botany—America. ɪ. Linné, Carl von, 1707–1778, ed. ɪɪ. Kölpin, Alexander Bernhard, 1739–1801, tr.

Library of Congress   QK5.L8   5–38065†

NL 0442618   DLC RPJCB CU

Löflund, Arthur.
Mot fjärran horisont. Helsingfors, Söderström ₍1955₎
281 p. illus., ports. 22 cm.

ɪ. Title.

Minnesota. Univ. Libr.
for Library of Congress   ₍8₎   A 57–5538

NL 0442619   MnU NN

Löflund, Christian Wilhelm.

Enslin, Theodor Christian Friedrich, 1787–1851.
Bibliotheca theologica oder verzeichniss aller brauchbaren ... bis zum schluss des jahres 1831 in Deutschland erschienenen werke über alle theile der ... protestantischen theologie. Nach dem "Handbuch der theologischen literatur des herrn prof. Winer" mit zuziehung anderer zuverlässiger literarischer hülfsmittel zuerst bearbeitet und herausgegeben von Th. Chr. Fr. Enslin ... von neuem durchgesehen und fortgesetzt von Christian Wilhelm Löflund ... Zweite vermehrte und verbesserte auflage. Stuttgart, F. C. Löflund und sohn, 1833.

Löflund, Fritz
WO   Ueber algebraische Raumkurven. Tübingen,
3735   1912.
44 p.

Inaug.-Diss. - Tübingen.

NL 0442621   CtY NjP ICRL NIC

LÖFLUND & COMPAGNIE G. m. b. H., Grunbach, Germany
75 Jahre Löflund's Malz Extrakt. [Grunbach b. Stuttgart, 1939?] 45 p. illus., ports. 30cm.

ɪ. [Title] Fünfundsiebzig.

NL 0442622   NN

Löfman (Johannes Benjamin)
*De sepultura Romanorum. Upsaliae [1728]. 2 p.l., 32 pp. 8°.

NL 0442623   NN

Löfman, Nils, joint author.
Hägglund, Erik, 1887–
... Ueber azetylcellulose aus holzzellstoffen, von prof. dr. Erik Hägglund, mag. phil. Nils Löfman und dr. Eduard Färber. Åbo, Åbo akademi, 1921.

Löfmarck, Ellen.
PS1541
.A57L8

Dickinson, Emily, 1830–1886.
Emily Dickinson, en introduktion med lyriska tolkningar av Ellen Löfmarck. Stockholm, Natur och kultur ₍1950₎

Löfmarck (Joh. Matthiae). Examen diversarum methodorum, quae ad determinandum corporum solidorum et liquidorum calorem specificum adhibitae fuere. Pta. i & ii. ₍59 pp. 4°. Londini Gothorum, typ. Berlingiar; 1831.

NL 0442626   DNLM

Law   **Löfmark, Ernst,** 1890–   ed.

Sweden. *Laws, statutes, etc.*
Försäkring för olycksfall i arbete och yrkessjukdom; ersättning för skada under militär- och civilförsvarstjänstgöring m. m., av Ernst Löfmark. 6. uppl. Stockholm, Norstedt ₍1952₎

FOR OTHER EDITIONS
SEE MAIN ENTRY

Law   **Löfmark, Ernst,** 1890–   joint ed.

Eisen, Albert, 1878–   ed.
Lag om försäkring för olycksfall i arbete den 17 juni 1916 med däri senast år 1928 vidtagna ändringar m. m.; med historik, kommentar och sakregister utgiven av Albert Eisen ... och Ernst Löfmark ... 3. uppl. Stockholm, P. A. Norstedt & söner ₍1929₎

S(100)   **Löfquist, Bertil**
N21tt   Lifting force and bearing capacity of an
no.164   ice sheet (Lyftkraft och bärförmåga hos ett
         istäcke) Translated by H.A.G. Nathan.
         Ottawa, 1951.
27 ℓ. illus. 28 cm. (National Research Council, Canada. Technical translation TT–164)
Translation of Teknisk tidskrift, no.25, Stockholm, 1944.
Bibliography: leaf 20.

1.Ice. ɪ.Title.

NL 0442629   DI-GS DAS

Löfquist, Bertil.
Temperatureffekter i härdnande betong; undersökning av några faktorer som påverka sprickbildningen i grövre konstruktioner, jämförelse mellan två svenska cement. Stockholm, 1946.
195 p. illus. 24 cm. (Doktorsavhandlingar vid Chalmers tekniska högskola, nr. 3)
Akademisk avhandling—Chalmers tekniska högskola, Gothenburg.
Extra t. p., with thesis statement, inserted.
Summary in English.
Bibliography: p. ₍188₎–191.
1. Concrete construction—Testing. ɪ. Title. (Series: Gothenburg, Sweden. Chalmers tekniska högskola. Doktorsavhandlingar, nr. 3)

TA681.L75   52–24109

NL 0442630   DLC NN MiU

Löfquist, Helge, 1896–   joint author.

Benedicks, Carl Axel Fredrik, 1875–
Non-metallic inclusions in iron and steel, by Dr. Carl Benedicks ... and Helge Löfquist ... ₍London₎ Chapman & Hall, 1930.

Löfquist, Helge, 1896–
... Det stora nordenskiöldska järnblocket från Ovifak: mikrostruktur och bildningssätt, av H. Löfquist och C. Benedicks. Med 64 figurer, varav 5 å vikt plansch och en färgbild. With an English summary ... Stockholm, Almqvist & Wiksells boktryckeri-a.-b., 1941.
96 p. illus. ₁₁ pl. (1 fold. 1 col.) diagrs. 28ᶜᵐ. (Kungl. svenska vetenskapsakademiens handlingar. 3. ser., bd. 19, n:o 3)
"Litteratur rörande ovifakjärnet (och bühljärnet)": p. 94.
1. Iron ores—Greenland—Disko island. 2. Iron ores—Analysis. ɪ. Benedicks, Carl Axel Fredrik, 1875–   joint author.
₍Full name: Karl Helge Sigfrid Löfquist₎
A 42–1021

Chicago. Univ. Library
for Library of Congress   [Q64.S85   ser. 3, bd. 19, no. 3]
                           ₍2₎   ₍508₎

NL 0442632   ICU NcD

Löfqvist, Eero Gunnar, 1897–
... Klinisch-statistische untersuchungen über frühgeburten ... von Eero Löfqvist ... Helsingfors, 1931.
1 p. l., 165 p. incl. tables, diagrs. 24ᶜᵐ. (Half-title: Supplementum ad Acta obstetricia et gynaecologica scandinavica. vol. xi, suppl. ɪɪ)
At head of title: Aus der Univ.-frauenklinik zu Lund.
Thesis—Helsingfors.
Translated by Fru Lilli Löfqvist. cf. Vorwort.
Summaries in German, French and English.
"Literaturverzeichnis": p. ₍154₎–158.

1. Labor (Obstetrics), ₍Premature₎ ɪ. Löfqvist, Fru Lilli, tr.
A C 33–3441

Title from John Crerar   Libr. Printed by L. C.

NL 0442633   ICJ MoU NNC

Löfqvist, Karl Erik, 1907–
Jämtlands och Härjedalens diplomatarium
see under   Jaemtland, Bibliotek.
Diplomatariekommitté.

Löfqvist, Karl-Erik, 1907–
Om riddarväsen och frälse i nordisk medeltid; studier rörande adelsståndets uppkomst och tidigare utformning ... av Karl-Erik Löfqvist. Lund, H. Ohlssons boktryckeri, 1935.
xv, 279 p. 24ᶜᵐ.
Akademisk avhandling—Lund.
Extra t-p., with thesis note in full, inserted.
"Källor och litteratur": p. ₍vii₎–xv.

1. Knights and knighthood—Scandinavia. 2. Sweden—Nobility. 3. Chivalry. ɪ. Title.
36–31578

Library of Congress   CR5745.L6
                       ₍2₎   929.78

NL 0442635   DLC ICU CtY NjP MH MnU

Löfqvist, Karl Erik, 1907–
Svensk historia i bild. För läroverk och självstudium. Stockholm, Natur och kultur ₍1950–
v. illus. 23 cm.

1. Sweden—Hist.—Pictorial works. ɪ. Title.

DL650.L64   52–39668 ‡

NL 0442636   DLC OCl MH

Löfqvist, Fru Lilli, tr.
Klinisch-statistische untersuchungen...

See under

Löfqvist, Eero Gunnar, 1897–

Löfqvist, Recuel.
.. Zur pathologie der mucosa corporis uteri ... Berlin, Gedruckt bei S. Karger, 1903.
4 p. l., 238 p. 2 pl. 24ᶜᵐ.
Akademisk afhandling—Helsingfors.
"Litteraturverzeichnis": p. 219–237.

1. Uterus—Diseases.
7–31054†

Library of Congress   RG301.L82

NL 0442638   DLC DNLM

Löfs, pseud.

See

Löwendorf, Heinz.

VOLUME 338

Löfstedt, Annie, *ed.*
  Barnen, livet och vi; en bok om barnets värld och
föräldrarnas uppgifter. ¡Redaktion: Annie Löfstedt, Nore
Bäckmark¡ Stockholm, Natur och kultur ¡1951–53¡
  5 v. illus. (part col.) 24 cm.
  CONTENTS.—del 1. Vård och trygghet.—del 2. Upptäcktsfärden börjar.—del 3. Fråga och lära.—del 4. I naturen.—del 5. Hem och samhälle.

  1. Encyclopedias and dictionaries, Swedish.   I. Bäckmark, Nore,
joint ed.   II. Title.
  AG45.L6   A 54–4077
Harvard Univ. Library
for Library of Congress   ¡1¡†

NL 0442640   MH DLC

PN   **Löfstedt, Annie**
776   Figurer mot mörk botten. Stockholm, A.
L6   Bonnier ¡1943¡
          174p. 20cm.
          Critical essays, first published in Göte-
        borgs Handels- och Sjöfartstidning.

          1. Literature, Modern – 20th cent. – Hist.
        & crit. I.   Title

NL 0442641   WU WaU CU

PZ59   **Löfstedt, Annie,** comp.
.T58P7 **Topelius, Zakarias,** 1818–1898.
1953   Prinsessan Lindagull och andra sagor. I urval av Annie
        Löfstedt. Illus. och omslag av Per Silfverhjelm. Stock-
        holm, Natur och kultur ¡1953¡

Löfstedt, Einar, 1831–1889.
    1571 års skolordning. En kort reckning.
  Upsala, E. Edquist, 1878.
    xvi p.   8°.
    Repr.: Nisbethska flickskolans i Upsala
  examensprogram. 1877–1878.

NL 0442643   NN

Loefstedt, Einar, *1831–1889.*
  Grekisk grammatik.
  Stockholm, Norstedt, 1868.
  238 p.

NL 0442644   PU PBm

Löfstedt, Einar, 1831–1889.
  Grekisk grammatik, utgifven af Einar Löfstedt ... 2. öfversedda uppl. Stockholm, I. Hæggströms boktryckeri, 1873.
  xv, ¡1¡ 243 p. 24½ᵐ.

  1. Greek language—Grammar—1870–
          ¡Full name: Nor Einar Ansgarius Löfstedt¡
                                          35–29586
Library of Congress   PA258.L6 1873   485

NL 0442645   DLC

PA258 **Löfstedt, Einar,** 1831–1889.
.L6   Grekisk grammatik, af Einar Löfstedt ...
1885   3. öfversedda och förkortade uppl. utg. af
        Julius af Sillén ...   Stockholm, I. Hægg-
        ströms boktryckeri, 1885.
          2 v. in 1. 24½cm.

          1. Greek language—Grammar—1870–
        I.* Sillén, Julius af, 1854–1924.
        [Full name: Nor Einar Ansgarius Löfstedt]

NL 0442646   DLC WaU

Löfstedt, Einar, *1831–1889.*
  In illa Demosthenis et Aeschinis de Philocra-
tea pace contentione uter utrum melioribus rationibus impugnaverit. Upsaliae, typis descripserunt Edquist, 1860–61.
  2 v. in 1.

  Vol. 1, author's thesis, Upsala.
  Bibliographical footnotes.

  1. Demosthenes.   2. Aeschines.

NL 0442647   NNC ICRL PU

Löfstedt, Einar, 1831–1889.
  Sveriges skolor före år 1571... Upsala, E.
Edquist, 1876.
  xxv p.   8°.
  Repr.: Nisbethska flickskolans i Upsala exa-
mens-program för läsårek 1875–1876.

NL 0442648   NN

*****Löfstedt, Einar,** *1831–1889.*
Sweden. *Kommittén för undersökning av högre flickskolor.*
  **Undersökning af Sveriges högre flickskolor. Underdånigt
utlåtande afgifvet den 19 januari 1888 af utsedde komiterade.**
Stockholm, I. Hæggströms boktryckeri, 1888.

Löfstedt, Einar, 1880–*1955.*
  ... Arnobiana. Textkritische und sprachliche studien zu
Arnobius von Einar Löfstedt. Lund, C. W. K. Gleerup; ¡etc.,
etc., 1917¡
  105, ¡2¡ p. 25ᶜᵐ. (Lunds universitets årsskrift. n. f., avd. 1, bd. 12,
nr. 5)
  "Litteratur": p. ¡3¡

  1. Arnobius, Afer, fl. 284–305.
                            ¡Full name: Haimon Einar Harald Löfstedt¡
                                                     A 28–645
Chicago. Univ. Library   AS284.L96 n. f., avd. 1, bd. 12
for Library of Congress   [AS284.L8 n. f., avd. 1, bd. 12]

NL 0442650   ICU ViU NN NcU

Löfstedt, Einar, 1880–*1955,*
  Beiträge zur kenntnis der späteren latinität; inaugural-
dissertation von Einar Löfstedt. Stockholm, O. L. Svanbäcks
buchdr., 1907.
  3 p. l., ¡3¡–128, ¡2¡ p. 24½ᵐ. ¡Upsala universitets årsskrift, 1907¡

  1. Latin language—Hist.
                            ¡Full name: Haimon Einar Harald Löfstedt¡
                                                     8–17313
Library of Congress   AS284.U7

NL 0442651   DLC CU TxU NcD NjP NN PU PBm

Löfstedt, Einar, 1880–*1955.*
  Coniectanea. Untersuchungen auf dem Gebiete der
antiken und mittelalterlichen Latinität. Uppsala, Almqvist
& Wiksells boktr. ¡1950–
  v. 24 cm.
  Bibliography: v. 1, p. 143–¡145¡

  1. Latin language—Syntax. 2. Latin language—Semantics.
                  Full name: Haimon Einar Harald Löfstedt.
  PA2289.L6   A 51–7718
Chicago. Univ. Libr.
for Library of Congress   ¡a53r58c¡†

             NN TxU NcU CU OCU DLC
NL 0442652   ICU CBPac MH NBuU PBm PU PHC PPLT CtY

Loefstedt, Einar, 1880–*1955.*
  Eranos Loefstedtianus
  see under title

Löfstedt, Einar, 1880–*1955.*
  ... Kritische bemerkungen zu Tertullians Apologeticum, von
Einar Löfstedt. Lund, C. W. K. Gleerup; ¡etc., etc., 1918¡
  119. ¡1¡ p. 25ᵐ. (Lunds universitets årsskrift. n. f., avd. 1, bd. 1.
nr. 36)

  1. Tertullianus, Quintus Septimius Florens. Apologeticus.
                            ¡Full name: Haimon Einar Harald Löfstedt¡
                                                     A 28–672
Chicago. Univ. Library   AS284.L96 n. f., avd. 1, bd. 14²
for Library of Congress   [AS284.L8 n. f., avd. 1, bd. 14]

NL 0442654   ICU CtY–D MoU ViU NN

Löfstedt, Einar, 1880–*1955.*
  Minnesord över Carl Magnus Zander, av Einar Lotstedt och
Martin P:n Nilsson.
  (In Humanistiska vetenskapssamfundet i Lund. Årsberättelse
1922–1923. Lund, 1923. 23¼ᵐ. p. ¡15¡–24)

  1. Zander, Carl Magnus, 1845–1923.   I. *Nilsson, Martin Persson,
1874–   joint author.
                  ¡Full name: Haimon Einar Harald Löfstedt¡
                                                     A 44–5071
Cincinnati. Univ. Libr.
for Library of Congress   AS284.L85 1922/23
                  ¡2¡†   (068.485)

NL 0442655   OCU DLC

Löfstedt, Einar, *1880–1955.*
  Philologischer kommentar zur Peregrinatio Aetheriae,
untersuchungen zur geschichte der lateinischen sprache,
von Einar Löfstedt. Hrsg. mit unterstützung des Vilh.
Ekman'schen universitätsfonds. Uppsala, Almqvist &
Wiksell; ¡etc., etc., 1911¡
  2 p. l., 359, ¡1¡ p. 25½ᵐ. (On cover: Arbeten utgifna med understöd
af Vilhelm Ekmans universitetsfond, Uppsala. 9)

                                                     11–31204

NL 0442656   DLC N NjP CU PU DDO

230.6 **Löfstedt, Einar,** *1880–1955.*
6174   Philologischer kommentar zur peregrinatio
L825   Aetheriae; untersuchugen zur geschichte der
        Lateinischen sprache, von ... Leipzig,
        Otto Harrassowitz, 1936.

          360p. 26cm.

          (Unaltered reprint of the 1911 edition)

          I.Title. 1.PEREGRINATIO AETHERIAE.

NL 0442657   OWorP

Löfstedt, Einar, 1880–*1955.*
  Philologischer kommentar zur Peregrinatio Aetheriae;
untersuchungen zur geschichte der lateinischen sprache, von
Einar Löfstedt ... Oxford, B. H. Blackwell ltd.; Uppsala,
Almqvist & Wiksell; ¡etc., etc., 1936¡
  3 p. l., ¡3¡–359, ¡1¡ p. 25½ᵐ.
  "Unveränderter anastatischer neudruck nach der auflage von 1911."
  "Litteratur": p. ¡20¡–23.

  1. Peregrinatio Aetheriae. 2. Latin language, Vulgar.
                  ¡Full name: Haimon Einar Harald Löfstedt¡
                                                     37–6034
Library of Congress   PA6554.P8L6 1936

NL 0442658   DLC OrU NcU NcD TxU PHC ICU NCH

AS   **Löfstedt, Einar,** 1880–*1955.*
284   Spätlateinische Studien. Uppsala,
H91286 Akademiska Bokhandeln ¡1908¡
v.12   95 p. 24cm. (Skrifter utg. af K.
no.4   Humanistiska vetenskaps-samfundet i Uppsala,
        XII, 4)

          1. Latin language, Postclassical.
          2. Latin language, Postclassical—Particles.

NL 0442659   NIC NNC NjP PU ICN MB DCU NcD MH

VOLUME 338

Löfstedt, Einar, 1880-*1955*.
Syntactica; studien und beiträge zur historischen syntax des
lateins, von Einar Löfstedt ... Lund, C. W. K. Gleerup; ₍etc.,
etc.₎ 1928-33.
2 v. 24½ᶜᵐ. (Half-title; Skrifter utg. av Kungl. humanistiska
vetenskapssamfundet i Lund ... x: 1-2)
"Literatur": v. 1, p. ₍xl₎-xx; v. 2, p. ₍ix₎-xiii.
Contents.—1. t. Über einige grundfragen der lateinischen nominal-
syntax. 1928.—2. t. Syntaktisch-stilistische gesichtspunkte und probleme. 1933.
1. Latin language—Syntax.   I. Title.
₍Full name: Haimon Einar Harald Löfstedt₎
35-34201 Revised

Library of Congress   PA2285.L6
                           ₍r42c2₎   475.2

NcD MH
NL 0442660   DLC CaQMM CU TxU CSt ICU IU OCU PU CtY

Löfstedt, Einar, 1880-*1955*.
Syntactica; Studien und Beiträge zur historischen Syntax des Lateins. 2., erweiterte Aufl. Lund, C. W. K.
Gleerup, 1942-
     v. 25 cm. (Skrifter utg. av Kungl. Humanistiska vetenskaps-
samfundet i Lund, x: 1-
     Bibliography: v. 1, p. ₍xiii₎-xxv.

     1. Latin language—Syntax.   I. Title.   (Series: Humanistiska
vetenskapssamfundet i Lund. Skrifter, x: 1-
                    Full name: Haimon Einar Harald Löfstedt.

PA2285.L62   56-2711

MoU
NL 0442661   DLC ICU NcU IU MH CU LU MiDW InU PSt

Löfstedt, Einar, 1880-1955.
Tertullians Apologeticum, textkritisch unter-
sucht
          see under   Tertullianus, Quintus Septimius
Florens.

475   Löfstedt, Einar, 1880-1955.
L82v Vermischte beiträge zur lateinischen
      sprachkunde.   Upsaliae, 1903.
      cover-title, 85-116p.

      "Ex Erani vol.VIII.   Seorsum expr."
      Presentation copy.

NL 0442663   IU NcD

Löfstedt, Einar, 1880-*1955*.
Vermischte studien zur lateinischen sprachkunde und syntax, von Einar Löfstedt. Lund, C. W. K. Gleerup; London,
H. Milford, Oxford university press; ₍etc., etc.₎ 1936.
xiii, 282 p. 24½ᶜᵐ. (Half-title; Skrifter utg. av Kungl. humanistiska
vetenskapssamfundet i Lund ... XXIII)
"Vorliegendes buch ist dazu bestimmt, mein ... werk 'Syntactica' ...
zu ergänzen. Zugleich soll es meine ... 'Spätlateinische studien' durch
eine erneute und vertiefte behandlung derselben probleme und einiger
verwandten erscheinungen ersetzen. Geplant und begonnen wurde es
zunächst als eine zweite, gänzlich umgearbeitete und sehr vermehrte
ausgabe dieser letztgenannten schrift."—Vorwort.
"Literatur": p. ₍x₎-xiii.
     1. Latin language—Syntax. 2. Latin language—Semantics.   I. Title.
                    ₍Full name: Haimon Einar Harald Löfstedt₎
                                                     37-6009

Library of Congress   PA2285.L63
                           ₍2₎   475.2

MoU IaU WU PU NN
NL 0442664   DLC CU MU FU OrU UU CaBVaU NBuU TNJ

Löfstedt, Einar, 1880-1955.
Zum ursprung und gebrauch der partikel dum..
[Uppsala, Berling, 1922]
cont. p.   O.

NL 0442665   NcD

Löfstedt, Einar, 1880-*1955*.
... Zur sprache Tertullians, von Einar Löfstedt. Lund,
C. W. K. Gleerup; ₍etc., etc., 1920₎
     vi, 117 p. 24½ᶜᵐ. (Lunds universitets årsskrift. n. f., avd. 1, bd. 16,
nr. 2)
"Literatur": p. ₍v₎-vi.

     1. Tertullianus, Quintus Septimius Florens.
                    ₍Full name: Haimon Einar Harald Löfstedt₎
                                                     A 28-688

Chicago. Univ. Library   A8284.L96 n. f., avd. 1, bd. 16
for Library of Congress   [A8284.L8 n. f. avd. 1, bd. 16]

NL 0442666   ICU NBuU MoU ViU NN

Löfstedt, Ernst, 1893-
... Beiträge zur nordfriesischen mundartenforschung, von
Ernst Löfstedt. Lund, H. Ohlssons buchdruckerei, 1933.
     98, ₍2₎ p. maps (1 fold.) fold. tables. 26ᶜᵐ. (Lunds universitets
årsskrift. n. f., avd. 1, bd. 29, nr. 2)
     Bibliography: p. ₍97₎-98.

     1. Friesian language—Dialects.
                                                     A 35-814

Title from Univ. of Chi-   cago A8284.L96 n. f., avd. 1, bd. 29
Library of Congress   [A8284.L8 n. f., avd. 1, bd. 29]

NL 0442667   ICU LU WU

Löfstedt, Ernest, 1893-   *ed.*
... Ein mittelostfälisches gebetbuch im auszug herausgegeben von Ernst Löfstedt. Lund, C. W. K. Gleerup ₍1935₎
     141, ₍2₎ p. illus. (facsims.) 25½ᶜᵐ. (Lunds universitets årsskrift.
n. f., avd. 1, bd. 30, nr. 5)
     "Die ... texte finden sich in dem Kodex Helmst. 1318 der Herzog
August-bibliothek in Wolfenbüttel."—Einleitung.
     "Literaturverzeichnis": p. ₍135₎-138.

     1. Catholic church—Prayer-books and devotions—Low German (East-
phalian)   I. Wolfenbüttel. Herzog-August-bibliothek. Mss. (Cod.
Helmst. 1318)
                                                     A 35-1242

Title from Univ. of Chi   cago A8284.L96 n. f., avd. 1, bd. 30
Library of Congress   [A8284.L8 n. f., avd. 1, bd. 30]

NL 0442668   ICU TxU GU

Löfstedt, Ernst, 1893-
... Nordfriesische dialektstudien, von Ernst Löfstedt. Lund,
C. W. K. Gleerup; ₍etc., etc., 1931₎
     ₍3₎, 310 p. 25ᶜᵐ. (Lunds universitets årsskrift. n. f., avd. 1, bd. 26,
nr. 4)
     "Bildet den 2. teil meiner 1928 erschienenen dissertation Die nord-
friesische mundart des dorfes Ockholm und der Halligen I."—Vorwort.

     1. Friesian language—Dialects.   I. Title.
                                                     A 32-13

Title from Univ. of Chi-   cago A8284.L96 n. f., avd. 1, bd. 26
Library of Congress   [A8284.L8 n. f., avd. 1, bd. 26]

NL 0442669   ICU CLU MU CSt OrU CU

Löfstedt, Ernst, 1893-
Die nordfriesische Mundart des Dorfes Ockholm und der Halligen. I... Von Ernst Löfstedt.   Lund, 1928.   xxiv, 254 p.
map. 23cm.

     Akademische Abhandlung — Lund.
     Continued by his Nordfriesische Dialektstudien.
     "Literaturverzeichnis," p. 248-252.

524914B. 1. German language—   Dialects.
N. Y. P. L.   July 7, 1950

NL 0442670   NN CU ICRL CtY ICN MH ICU

Löfstedt, Ernst, 1893-
... Ostfälische studien ... von Ernst Löfstedt. Lund, H.
Ohlssons buchdruckerei, 1933-
     v. 26ᶜᵐ. (Lunds universitets årsskrift. n. f., avd. 1, bd. 29,
nr. 7
     Contents.—L. Grammatik der mundart von Lesse im kreise Wolfen-
büttel (Braunschweig)

     1. Low German language—Dialects.   I. Title.
                                                     A 35-818

Title from Univ. of Chi-   cago A8284.L96 n. f., avd. 1, bd. 29
Library of Congress   [A8284.L8 n. f., avd. 1, bd. 29   ]

NL 0442671   ICU NNU-W GU

Löfstedt, Ernst, 1893-
... Zwei beiträge zur friesischen sprachgeschichte, von Ernst
Löfstedt. Lund, H. Ohlssons buchdruckerei, 1932.
     65, ₍1₎ p. 25½ᶜᵐ. (Lunds universitets årsskrift. n. f., avd. 1, bd. 28,
nr. 2)
     "Literaturverzeichnis und abkürzungen": p. ₍63₎-65.

     1. Friesian language — Dialects — Sylt. 2. Friesian language — Dia-
lects—Wangeroog.
                                                     A 33-2072

Title from Univ. of Chi-   cago A8284.L96 n. f., avd. 1, bd. 28
Library of Congress   [A8284.L8 n. f., avd. 1, bd. 28]

NL 0442672   ICU LU

Löfstedt, Haimon Einar Harald
         see
Löfstedt, Einar, 1880-1955.

Löfstedt, Inga Birgit Maria, 1910-
Zum sekundärumlaut von germ. *a* im bairischen, von Inga
Löfstedt. Lund, C. W. K. Gleerup; ₍etc., etc., 1944₎
     xix, 361 p. 24ᶜᵐ. (Half-title: Lunder germanistische forschungen,
hrsg. von Erik Rooth. 15)
     "Literaturverzeichnis": p. ₍vii₎-xix.

     1. German language — Dialects — Bavarian. 2. German language—
Middle High German—Vowels.   I. Title.
                                                     45-20410

Library of Congress   PF3838.B3L6
                           ₍3₎   437.3

OU OCU
NL 0442674   DLC KyU CSt GU TxU CLSU MU CU-S PU ViU

Löfstedt, Nor Einar Ansgarius
         see
Löfstedt, Einar, 1831-1889.

Löfstedt, Sigrid.
Veliga Johanna i tre akter skriven för Damk-
lubben E.Q.V.   [Boston, c1919]
[31] p.   18 cm.

NL 0442676   RPB

Löfstrand, G.
Om apatitens förekomstsätt i Norrbottens län jemfördt
med dess uppträdande i Norge, af G. Löfstrand ... Stockholm, Kongl. boktryckeriet, P. A. Norstedt & söner, 1890.
     2 p. l., 48, 2 p. 2 fold. maps. 22½ᶜᵐ.
     Published by the Geological survey of Sweden.

     1. Apatite.   I. Sweden. Sveriges geologiska undersökning.

Library, U. S. Geol.   survey   G S 7-1524

NL 0442677   DI-GS PPWI ICJ PPAN

           Löfstrand, Nils, joint author.
GV722
1956
L45   Lehman, Martin.
      Toppkvartett inför Melbournespelen: Bertil Antonsson,
      Gert Fredriksson, Bengt Nilsson, Björn Thofelt. ₍Av₎
      Martin Lehman ₍och₎ Nils Löfstrand. Stockholm, O.
      Eklund, 1955.

           Löfstrand, Nils, joint author.
GV842
1956
L42   Lehman, Martin.
      Tre ess inför winterolympiaden: Sixten Jernberg, Sigge
      Ericsson, 'Stöveln' Öberg. ₍Af₎ Martin Lehman ₍och₎ Nils
      Löfstrand. Stockholm, O. Eklund, 1955.

VOLUME 338

FL8
87.9
L825v
1947

Löfstrand, Victor
... Växel- och checklära: ny edition
omarbetad och utgiven av Sune Kellgren ...
Stockholm, Svenska bokförlaget Norstedts
[1947]
vi, 131 p.   facsims., plates (1 fold.) forms.
22cm.

NL 0442680   MiU-L

Löfstrand, Victor
Växel- och checklära; ny ed. omarb. och utg. av Sune
Kellgren. 2. uppl. Stockholm, Norstedt [1952]
150 p. 22 cm.

1. Bills of exchange—Sweden. 2. Checks—Sweden.   i. Kellgren,
Sune, ed. ii. Title.

53-36391 ‡

NL 0442681   DLC

DK459
L825

Löfström, Ernst Berthold, 1865–
—Ledningen av Ostarméns operationer i Karelen
1918. Helsingfors [Lindbergs tryckeri aktie-
bolag] 1931.
94 p.   illus.(plans)   23ᵐ.

1.Finland - History - Revolution, 1917-1918.
2. Finland - Army. 3. Karelia.

NL 0442682   CSt-H InU

Löfström, Frans, 1888–1946.
Kring Sandhammaren, av Frans Löfström.   Lund, C. W. K.
Gleerup [1946] 275 p.   illus. 21cm.

448829B.   1. Sandhammaren, Sweden.
N. Y. P. L.   February 24, 1949

NL 0442683   NN

Löfström, Gunnar, 1907–
... Nonspecific capsular swelling in pneumococci; a sero-
logic and clinical study by Gunnar Löfström. Translated by
Helen Frey ... Stockholm, P. A. Norstedt & söner, 1943.
98 p. incl. tables, diagrs. 24 cm.

"From the Fourth medical service of St. Erik's hospital ... and the
State bacteriologic laboratory ... Stockholm, Sweden."
"Also published as a supplement to Acta medica scandinavica,
1943."
Bibliography : p. 93-98.

1. Pneumococcus. 2. Antigens and antibodies.   i. Frey, Helen D.,
1907–   tr.

                                                A 44–4432 rev
William H. Welch Med.   Library QR201.P7L82
for Library of Congress   [r48d1]

NL 0442684   MdBJ-Q IdPI PU-Med OU

Löfström, Gunnar, 1907–
... Nonspecific capsular swelling in pneumococci; a sero-
logic and clinical study, by Gunnar Löfström. Translated
by Helen Frey. Stockholm, P. A. Norstedt & söner, 1943.
98 p. incl. tables, diagrs. 23½ cm. (On cover: Acta medica scandinavica. Supplementum cxli)
"From the Fourth medical service of St. Erik's hospital ... and the
State bacteriologic laboratory ... Stockholm, Sweden."
Imprint on cover: Helsingfors, Mercators tryckeri, 1943.
Akademisk avhandling—K. Karolinska medikokirurgiska institutet, Stockholm. Without thesis note.
Errata slip inserted.
Bibliography : p. 93-98.
1. Serum. 2. Pneumococcus. 3. Antigens and antibodies.
i. Frey, Helen D.,   1907–   tr.
                                                A 48—1231
John Crerar Library
for Library of Congress   [48b3]

NL 0442685   ICJ

Ecd
955L

Löfström, Inge
Jorden runt som Skeppspräst; reseminnen
från HMS Älvsnabbens världsomsegling 1954–
1955. 2. uppl. Stockholm, Svenska Kyrkans
Diakonistyrelses Bokförlag [1955]
230p. illus., maps. 21cm.

1. Voyages around the world - 1950-1975.
I. Title(1)

NL 0442686   CtY MH

Löfström, Johan Gustav.
De conformatione arti-
culorum corporis humani ossea, generatim spec-
tata, ejusque vi et efficacia in motus, quorum
ipsi sunt potentes, et luxationes quibus sunt ob-
noxii. 1 p. l., 34 pp. 8°. Londini Gothorum,
ex off. Berlingiana, 1829.

NL 0442687   DNLM

Löfström, Johan Gustav, respondent.
De fatis messenici populi...
see under   Höijer, Joseph Otto, 1775-1833,
praeses.

Löfström, K   G
Maa- ja ilmakuvamittaus. Helsinki, 1949.
188 p. illus., diagrs. 21 cm. (Teknillinen Korkeakoulu. Moniste
n:o 88)

1. Photogrammetry.   i. Title.   (Series: Helsingfors. Suomen
Teknillinen Korkeakoulu. Moniste n:o 88)

TR693.L6   58–46265

NL 0442689   DLC

Löfström, K   G
Saksalais-suomalainen fotogrammetrian sanasto. Helsinki, 1943.
44 p. 25 cm. (Maanmittaustieteiden seuran julkaisu n:o 5)

1. Photogrammetry.   i. Title.   (Series : Maanmittaustieteiden
Seura, Helsingfors. Julkaisut, n:o 5)

TA504.M2 no. 5   48–40839 rev*

NL 0442690   DLC

Löfström, Karl August, 1881–
Äskagsslakten. En varmlandskts Bergsmansslakts
historia.
Stockholm, Nordisk Rotogravyr, 1931.
235 p.

NL 0442691   PPAmSwM

948.5
K181Yl

Löfström, Karl August, 1881–
Karl Johans pommerska donationer.
[Stockholm, Nordisk rotogravyr, 1943]
121p. 22cm.

1. Karl XIV Johan, King of Sweden and
Norway. 1763-1844.

NL 0442692   IEN MnU

Löfström, Karl August, 1881–
Sveriges riddarordnar. [Under redaktion av Carl Gustav
Lantz och Dag W. Scharp] Stockholm, Steinsvik [1948]
659 p. illus., ports., col. plates, coats of arms. 27 cm.

1. Heraldry—Sweden. 2. Knights and knighthood—Sweden.
i. Title.

CR5787.L6   51–30994

NL 0442693   DLC

Löfström, S.A.
Swedish catalogue
see under   Chicago. World's Columbian
Exposition, 1893.

Loefstroem, Seth Axel.
Ueber die zusammensetzungen im plattdeutschen.
Inaug. diss. Upsala, 1875.

NL 0442695   ICRL NjP CU

Loefstroem (Theodor). *Zur Kenntniss der Di-
gestibilität der gewöhnlichsten in Finnland ein-
heimischen Getreidearten. 43 pp. 8°. Helsingfors, Päivälahti, 1892.

NL 0442696   DNLM

Løfting, Johan Christian Lund Levinsen, 1867–

Johansen, Anders Cornelius Jacob, 1867–
Randers fjords naturhistorie, ved A. C. Johansen;
under medvirkning af Hj. Ditlevsen, F. Heerfordt, J. P.
Jacobsen, A. Jessen, Knud Jessen, M. Klinge, P. Kramp,
J. Chr. Løfting, C. H. Ostenfeld, K. Stephensen og Hj.
Ussing. Med 236 figurer i teksten og 5 tavler. Udgivel-
sen bekostet af Carlsbergfondet. København, I kommis-
sion hos C. A. Reitzel, 1918.

Löfvall, *Mme.* J   H.
How to cut, fit, and finish a dress. By Mdme. Löfvall ...
Boston, A. Mudge & son, printers, 1892.
3 p. l., [5–67 p. diagrs. 17ᵐ.

1. Dressmaking.
                                                8-31419†
Library of Congress   T515.L82

NL 0442698   DLC

Löfvén, Andreas.
De jure imputandi dissertatio...
see under   Boëthius, Daniel.

Löfvenberg, Joh. Christoph, respondent.
Om folk-rättens princip...
see under   Dellden, Carl Olof, 1800-1854,
praeses.

VOLUME 338

Löfvenberg, Mattias Teodor, 1907–
Contributions to Middle English lexicography and etymology. Lund, C. W. K. Gleerup [1946]
xxiii, 110 p. 25 cm. (Lunds universitets årsskrift, n. f., avd. 1, bd. 41, nr. 8)
Bibliography: p. [v]–xii.

1. English language — Middle English (1100–1500) — Glossaries, vocabularies, etc. 2. English language—Middle English (1100–1500)— Etymology. (Series: Lund. Universitet. Acta Universitatis Lundensis. n. s. Lunds universitets årsskrift, n. f., avd. 1, bd. 41, nr. 8)
AS284.L8 n. f., avd. 1, bd. 41, nr. 8   A 48–4409*

Chicago. Univ. Libr.
for Library of Congress   [2]†

TxU OC1 OC1W PU ViU DLC GU MeU MsU WU
NL 0442701   ICU CSt NRU FU TNJ FMU MoSU NcU CoU

Löfvenberg, Mattias Teodor, 1907–
On the syncope of the Old English present endings. Upsala, Lundequist; Cambridge, Harvard University Press [1949]
52 p. 25 cm. (The English Institute in the University of Upsala. Essays and studies on English language and literature, 1)
Bibliography: p. 51–52.

1. Anglo-Saxon language—Verb.   (Series: Uppsala. Universitet. Engelska seminariet. Essays and studies on English language and literature, 1)
PE197.L6   429.58   49–11156*

NL 0442702   DLC OrU MU KU NN PPT NNC NjR MH NIC CtY

Löfvenberg, Mattias Teodor, 1907–
... Studies on Middle English local surnames, by Mattias T. Löfvenberg. Lund, C. W. K. Gleerup; London, Williams & Norgate; [etc., etc., 1942]
xiv, [2], 255 p. 23½ᶜᵐ. (Lund studies in English. xi. Professor Eilert Ekwall, editor)
Thesis—Lund.
Extra title-page, with thesis note, inserted.
Bibliography: p. [ix]–xvi.

1. Names, Personal—English. 2. English language—Etymology—Names. 3. English language—Middle English (1100–1500)—Etymology. i. Title: Middle English local surnames.
CS2505.L57   929.4   46–45136

MH ICU PPT NcU OU OC1JC CU MB TxU PU AAP MU
NL 0442703   DLC WaS CaBVaU OrU MoU OOxM ViU IaU NjP

Loefvenius, Carl Abraham, respondent.
Konst-theoreirnas historia...
see under   Lenstroem, Carl Julius, 1811–1893, praeses.

Löfvenius, Daniel, respondent.
Vita Mag. Jacobi Boëthu...
see under   Fant, Erik Mikael, 1754–1817, praeses.

Löfvenius, Ericus, respondent.
Acta Dalecarlica an. 1503–1511...
see under   Fant, Erik Nikael, 1754–1817, praeses.

Löfvenius, Ericus, respondent.
D. D. Diss. moralitate polyganiae...
see under   Boudrie, Gustavo Anton, praeses.

LÖFVENMARK, GUNNAR, tr.
Non kantiki por la deala servo e la kunsidi dil Internacona supra lojio dil Bontemplani.   Uppsala, K. W. Appelbergs boktryckeri i kommission Ido-editerio, Lüsslingen. 1914.   15 p.   17cm.   (Por exerco e plezuro sueda Ido-biblioteko. 4.)

Without music.

1. Ido—Books in. L. Series.   Mrs. Dave H. Morris collection.
i. Lofvenmark.

NL 0442708   NN

Löfvenskjöld, Salomon, *friherre,* 1764–1850.
Presidenten, frih. Löfvenskjölds yttrade serskildta mening uti Kongl. komitén till organiserandet af rikets styrelseverk. Stockholm, Ecksteinska boktryckeriet, 1823.
1 p. l., 205 p. fold. tab. 20 x 12½ᶜᵐ.

1. Sweden—Pol. & govt. 2. Sweden—Executive departments.   i. Sweden. Kommittén för reglering av rikets styrelseverk, 1819. Comiterades till reglering af rikets styrelse-verk underdåniga betänkande.
34–39844
Library of Congress   JN7877.A5 1823 b   354.48504

NL 0442709   DLC

Löfving, Börje
Murre Katt.   Techningar av Ilon Wikland [Stockholm] Geber [*1955]
unpaged.   (De roliga böckerna, 17)

NL 0442710   PP

Löfving, Concordia, tr.
Hartelius, Truls Johan, 1818–1896.
Home gymnastics for the preservation and restoration of health in children and young and old people of both sexes.   With a short method of acquiring the art of swimming.   By Professor T. J. Hartelius ...   Tr. and adapted from the Swedish original by special permission of the author.   By C. Löfving.   With thirty-one illustrations.   Philadelphia, J. B. Lippincott & co., 1883.

LŒFVING, Concordia.
Jeannot l'Intrépide. Illus. Pls.
(Nouvelles suédoises. Pp. 179–211. Paris. [1892.])

NL 0442712   MB

Löfving, Concordia.
On physical education, and its place in a rational system of education. A lecture by Concordia Löfving. With a portrait. London, W. S. Sonnenschein & co. [1882]
viii, 67 p. front. (port.) 18½ᶜᵐ.
"This lecture was first delivered in March, 1881, before the Birmingham teacher's association."

1. Physical education.   E 10–1005
Library, U. S. Bur. of   [E]ducation GV345.L83
—— Copy 2.

NL 0442713   DHEW

Löfving, Concordia.
Så vann han stolts jungfrun. Lyriskt sagospel i fem akter med prolog.   Stockholm, Loostrom & Komp., [1890]
vii (1), 117 (1) p.   8°.

NL 0442714   NN

Löfving, Isidor.
Svensk bok-katalog för åren 1866–
Stockholm [1878]–19

Löfving, Stefan, 1690–1777.
923.5471
L825   En spanare under stora ofreden; Stefan Löfvings dagbok över hans äventyr i Finland och Sverige 1710–1720. Med inledning och förklaringar av Eirik Hornborg. Helsingfors, H. Schildt [1926]
200 p.   illus.   24 cm.

1. Löfving, Stefan, 1690–1777. i. Hornborg, Eirik, 1879–   ed. ii. Title.

NL 0442716   NcD IEN InU

LÖFVING, Stefan, *1690–1777.*
En spanare under Stora ofreden; dagbok över hans äventyr i Finland och Sverige 1710–1720. Med inledning och förklaringar av Eirik Hornborg. 2ᵃ upplagan.   Stockholm, Almqvist & Wiksells Förlag, [1927].
22 cm.   Ports and other illustr.

NL 0442717   MH

Loefwander, Petrus, respondent.
... Dissertatio philologica, de Voce...
see under   Aurivillius, Karl, praeses.

Löfwenskiöld, Salomon, friherre
see
Löfvenskjöld, Salomon, friherre, 1764–1850.

Lög-þingis booken, iñihalldandi þad sem giørdist of framfoor fyrir lög-þingis-rettinum ...
see under   Iceland. Alþingi.

Lögberg. L.–XXV. ár.   Winnipeg Man., 1888–1912.   25 *vols.* fol.   IcR5L782
Weekly. No t.-p.   The first three vols. (to no. 96 of vol. iii.) were published by a board consisting of Sigtryggur Jónasson, Bergvin Jónsson, Árni Friðriksson, Einar Hjörleifsson, Ólafur Þorgeirsson and Sigurður J. Jóhannesson. After that, to the end of vol. iii., the editors were Einar Hjörleifsson and Jón Ólafsson; [v]ol. iv. nos. 1–3 were ed. by Jón Ólafsson; vol. iv. no. 4. to vol. viii. no. 9 by Einar Hjörleifsson; vol. viii. no. 10 to vol. xiv. no. 28 by Sigtryggur Jónasson; vol. xiv. no. 29 to vol. xviii. no. 41 by Magnús Paulson, and since by Stefán Björnsson.   The paper was published by the Lögberg Printing and Publishing Co., later by the Columbia Press Co.

NL 0442721   NIC

Lögberg. XXVI.–XXXVIII. ár.   Winnipeg, Man., 1913–25.   13 *vols.* fol.   IcR5L781
Stefán Björnsson continued as editor to vol. XXVII, No. 14 (April 2, 1914), being succeeded by Sig. Júl. Jóhannesson, who edited Nos. 15–35 of Vol. XXVII (April 9–Aug. 27, 1914). From Sept. 3, 1914 (Vol. XXVII, No. 36) to Sept. 30, 1915 (Vol. XXVIII, No. 40), the paper was however, edited by Kristján Sigurðsson.   With No. 41 of Vol. XXVIII (Oct. 7, 1915) Sig. Júl. Jóhannesson resumed the editorship, and continued to Vol. XXXI, No. 43 (Nov. 1, 1917); J. J. Vopni was temporary editor from Nov. 8 to Dec. 20, 1917 (Nos. 44–50); Jón J. Bíldfell edited Vols. XXXII.–XXXVIII.

NL 0442722   NIC

Lögberg. XXXIX.–LIV. ár.   Winnipeg, Man., 1926–41.   16 *vols.* fol.   IcR5L781
Publ. by the Columbia Press Ltd.; ed. by Jón J. Bíldfell (vols. xxxix–xl, nos. 1–5); Einar P. Jónsson (vols. xl, nos. 6–52, –liv).

NL 0442723   NIC

VOLUME 338

Loegberg.
—— Almanak "Lögbergs" um ár eptir Krists burð 1888, 1889. Reiknað eptir aðstöðu Winnipeg í Manitoba. Winnipeg, Man., n. d. 2 *pts.* 8°. IcMSA255

NL 0442724   NIC

Lögbirtingablað. Gefið út samkvæmt lögum 16. nóvember 1907. I.–V. ár 1908–1912. Útgefandi fyrir hönd landstjórnarinnar og ábyrgðarmaður: G. Sveinbjörnsson. Reykjavík. 5 *vols.* fol. IcR3L789
    Weekly. No t-p.

NL 0442725   NIC

Lögbirtingablað. Gefið út samkvæmt lögum 16. nóvember 1907. VI.–XVIII. ár. Reykjavík, 1913–25. 12 *vols.* sm. fol. IcR3L789
    Weekly. No t-p. Vols. VI–VII and vol. VIII, Nos. 1–41, were ed. by Guðm. Sveinbjörnsson, thereafter by Gísli Ísleifsson, vols. IX–XV, and Pétur Hjaltested vols. XVI–XVIII.

NL 0442726   NIC

Lögbirtingablað. Gefið út samkvæmt lögum 16. nóvember 1907. XIX.–XXXIII. ár. Reykjavík, 1926–40. 15 *vols.* sm. fol. IcR3L789
    Vols. xix–xxix, ed. by Pétur Hjaltested; vols. xxix–xxxiii, by Einar Bjarnason.

NL 0442727   NIC

Lögbók Íslendinga ...
    see under   Jónsbók.

Lögdberg, Åke, 1913–
    Spörsmål angående rembours. Uppsala, Almqvist & Wiksells boktr., 1950.
    116 p. forms. 25 cm.
    Summary in English.
    Bibliography: p. 93–97.

    1. Bills of exchange.   I. Title.
        Full name: Bror Åke Asmund Lögdberg.
                A 51–2486
    Yale Univ. Library
    for Library of Congress   (2)

NL 0442729   CtY NNC

Lögdberg, Åke, 1913–
    Studier över förlagsinteckningsinstitutet. Uppsala, Almquist & Wiksells boktr., 1947.
    317 p. 25 cm.
    Akademisk avhandling—Uppsala.
    Extra t-p. with thesis statement, inserted.
    "Rättelser": leaf inserted.
    "Litteratur": p. 305–311.

    1. Chattel mortgages. 2. Chattel mortgages—Sweden. 3. Security (Law)
        Full name: Bror Åke Asmund Lögdberg.
                49–13074*

NL 0442730   DLC MH

Lögdberg, Åke, 1913–
    The title to copyright in moving pictures; general report at the International Academy of Comparative Law, 4th International Congress, Paris, 1954. Lund, Gleerupska universitetsbokhandeln (1955)
    15 p. 24 cm.

    1. Copyright—Moving-pictures. I. Title.
        Full name: Bror Åke Asmund Lögdberg.
                56–21666

NL 0442731   DLC MH-L

Lögdberg, Bror Åke Asmund
    see Lögdberg, Åke, 1913–

Lögdberg, Gunnar, 1902–
    In Macrobii Saturnalia adnotationes. Commentatio academica. Scripsit Gunnar Lögdberg. Upsaliae, Almqvist & Wiksell soc., 1936.
    xii, 149 p. 24ᶜᵐ.
    Issued also as the author's thesis, Uppsala.
    Bibliographical foot-notes.

    1. Macrobius, Ambrosius Aurelius Theodosius. Saturnalia.
        (*Full name: Erik Gunnar Lögdberg*)
                A 40–2231
    Fordham univ. Library   PA6499.L7
    for Library of Congress   (2)

NL 0442733   NNF NIC NcU NNU-W IU NcU CtY PBm

Lögdberg, Gustaf Adolf, 1904–
    De nordiska konungarna och Tyska orden 1441–1457 ... av Gustaf Adolf Lögdberg ... Uppsala, Appelbergs boktryckeriaktiebolag, 1935.
    xvi p., 1 l., 326 p., 1 l. 25ᶜᵐ.
    Akademisk avhandling—Uppsala.
    "Källor och litteratur": p. (xi)–xvi.

    1. Scandinavia—For. rel.—Teutonic knights. 2. Teutonic knights—For. rel.—Scandinavia. 3. Christopher III, king of Denmark, 1418–1448. 4. Christian I, king of Denmark, 1426–1481. I. Title.
                36–31502
    Library of Congress   DL59.L6 1935
              (2)   948.03

NL 0442734   DLC MnU PU CtY NjP

293dg   **Lögdberg, L**   E
L825   Animadversiones de actione $\pi\alpha\rho\alpha\nu\mu\omega\nu$.
Law   Upsaliae, typis descripserunt Almqvist & Wiksell, 1898.
Library   79 p.
    Diss. - Upsala.

NL 0442735   CU NjP NBuU MH CtY PU ICRL

Loegel, Oscar.
    Die bischofswahlen zu Münster, Osnabrück, Paderborn, 1256–1389. Paderborn, F. Schöningh, 1883.
    pp. (90). (Münsterische beiträge zur geschichtsforschung, 6.)

    Bishops||.

NL 0442736   MH

DD140.7   **Löger, A**
L6   Heinrich II, der Heilige, und Joseph II in ihrem Verhältniss zur Kirche, dargestellt von A. Löger. Wien, R. Lechner, 1869.
    45 p. 24ᶜᵐ
    Bibliographical footnotes.

    1. Heinrich II, Emperor of Germany, 972–1024. 2. Joseph II, Emperor of Germany, 1741–1790. 3. Church and state in Germany I. Title.

NL 0442737   CSt NIC MH

Löger, Albert.
    Aphorismen und Wahrnehmungen den geographischen Unterricht betreffend. (Waidhofen a. d. Ybbs, 1877)
    46 p.
AC831   Programmschrift - Niederöster. Landes-Unter-
W34   real- und Gewerbe-Schule, Waidhofen a. d. Ybbs.
1877   Caption title.
Stack   Accompanies Schulnachrichten.

    1. Geography - Study and teaching.

NL 0442738   CSt

PK 2501   **Lögfræðingur.** Tímarit um lögfræði, löggja-
.L 82   farmál og þjóðhagsfræði. Útgefandi Páll Briem. 1.–5. árgangur; 1897–1901. Akureyri, Prentsmiðja Bjarnar Jónssonar, 1897–1901.
    5 v. 18½ cm.

    No more published.

NL 0442739   MdBJ MH NIC

Lögfraeðislegur leiðarvísir Ísafoldar ... Reykjavík, Ísafoldarprentsmiðja, 1892–94.
    3 v. 12½ cm.
    "Sjerprentun úr Ísafold 5. jan 1888 til 27. okt. 1894."

NL 0442740   MH-L MH

Lögler, Benedikt, 1790–1820.
    Die Edelfrau von Bosenstein; oder, Das Urtheil über sich selbst. Ein Gemälde der Barbarei des 13ten Jahrhunderts, in fünf Aufzügen. Nach einer Volksage bearbeitet. Augsburg u. Leipzig, n. d.
    17.5 cm. [In Deutsche Schaubühne...; 1811, etc.; Bd. 13]

NL 0442741   CtY

833L828   **Lögler, Benedikt,** 1790–1820.
Og   Die Grafen von Hohengeroldseck; oder, Rache für Weibermord. Ein Gemählde der vaterländischen Vorzeit in vier Aufzügen. (Nach wahren historischen Angaben) (Mit einem Titel-Kupfer. Augsburg, In Kommission in der Stageschen Buchhandlung, 1811.
    128p. front. 18cm. (Deutsche Schaubühne; oder, Dramatische Bibliothek der neuesten Lust-, Schau-, Sing- und Trauerspiele, 7. Bd.)
    Half title.

NL 0442742   IU CtY

Lögler, Benedikt, 1790–1820.
    Kaiser Heinrich der Vogler. Ein Schauspiel in einem Aufzuge. Augsburg u. Leipzig, n. d.
    17.5 cm. [In Deutsche Schaubühne...; 1811, etc.; Bd. 23]

NL 0442743   CtY

Lögler, Benedikt, 1790–1820.
    Die Wallfahrt. Ein Schauspiel in drey Aufzügen aus den Zeiten der Vehmgerichte. Augsburg u. Leipzig, n. d.
    17.5 cm. [In Deutsche Schaubühne...; 1811, etc.; Bd. 24]

NL 0442744   CtY

Lögmál og náð
    see under [Cox, Charles H   ]

VOLUME 338

Lögmálið
see under   Jochumsson, Einar, 1842-1923.

Lögmannsannáll.
Annálar og nafnaskrá
see under
Annálar íslenzkir.

Loegr, Eglwys Gweinidog o, pseud.
see   Jones, Griffith, 1683-1761.

Lögreglan í Reykjavik
see under   [Jonsson, Gudbrandur] 1888-

Lögrjetta.
— Ritsafn Lögrjettu. I. bindi. 1.
hefti. Reykjavik, Prentsmiðjan Rún,
1915. 8°. pp. 80. IcF85L821
Covertitle. Contents: Jón Þorláksson, Járn-
brautir á Íslandi;—Suðurlands undirlendið;—
Rúnure, K., Rétagróts, saga, þýdd af P. G.;—Sig.
Þórðlássson Um værðrstunes á Ísl.;—B. Björnson,
Bernlíót, kvæði, þýtt af P. G.

NL 0442750   NIC

Lögsögumannskjör a althingi 930 synt a þingvöllum
1930
see under   Iceland. Althingi.

Løgstrup, Knud Ejler Christian, 1905-
Den erkendelsesteoretiske konflikt mellem den transcen-
dental-filosofiske idealisme og teologien. København, Sam-
lerens forlag, 1942.
156 p. 26 cm.
Thesis—Københavns universitet.
Bibliographical footnotes.

1. Knowledge, Theory of.   I. Title.

BD168.D4L6   54-52651

NL 0442752   DLC MH ICU NIC NjP CtY NNC PPDrop

Løgstrup, Knud Ejler Christian, 1905-
Die Freiheit des Evangeliums und die Ordnung
der Gesellschaft
see under   Gesellschaft für Evangelische
Theologie. Tagung, Bad Boll, 1951.

4B   Løgstrup, Knud Ejler Christian, 1905-
996   Kants filosofi. København, G. E. C.
Gad, 1952-
v. 1-

(Bidrag til filosofiens historie)

NL 0442754   DLC-P4 ICRL

B 4377   Løgstrup, Knud Ejler Christian, 1905-
.L 7   ... Kierkegaards und Heideggers Existenz-
1950   analyse, und ihr Verhältnis zur Verkündigung,
von K. E. Løgstrup ... Berlin, E. Blaschker
Verlag, 1950.
127, [1] p. 17cm. (Breviarium litterarum)

"Erste bis dritte Auflage".

1. Kierkegaard, Søren Aabye, 1813-1855.
2. Heidegger,   Martin, 1889-
3. Existentialism.

NL 0442755   MdBJ CtY ICU IEN NNC MH MnU NjPT CU

Løgstrup, Theodor, 1853-
Danmarks ældste Præstegaard og Bidrag til Nyborg Bys
Historie i 500 Aar, ved T. Løgstrup.   Nyborg: C. Schønemann,
1925. 162 p. illus. 8°.

1. Parsonages—Denmark—Nyborg.
N.Y.P.L.   March 31, 1928

NL 0442756   NN

Løgstrup, Theodor, 1853-
Det Danske Bibelselskabs ordbog til det Gamle
Testament
see under   Danske Bibelselskab.

Løgstrup, Theodor, 1853-   , ed.
Det Danske Bibelselskab Ordbog til det Nye
Testament (den reviderede Oversættelse af 1907)
see under title

Løgstrup, Theodor, 1853-
Det danske missionsselskab, 1821-1917...
København, 1917.
76 p. maps. 23 cm.

NL 0442759   CtY

Løgstrup, Theodor, 1853-
Det danske missionsselskab historie. Ny
adgave... Kjøbenhavn, 1907.
4 p.l., 593 [1] p. illus., maps (part fold.)
21 cm.

NL 0442760   CtY

Mkb36   Løgstrup, Theodor, 1853-   ed.
L82   Nordisk missionshaandbog, samlet og udgivet
af T. Løgstrup ... Kjøbenhavn, I kommission
hos Indre-Missions boghandel (C.Christiansen),
1889.
344p.,incl.tables. ports. 21cm.
"Nordens missionsblade": p.273-276; "Missions
skrifter": p.276-294; "Missionskort": p.294-
295

NL 0442761   CtY

Løgstrup, Theodor, 1853-
Den nyere danske mission blandt
Tamulerne. Historisk fremstillet ved T.
Løgstrup... Kjøbenhavn, C. Christiansen,
1885.
240 [1] p.   20 1-2 cm.

NL 0442762   NNG CtY

Løgstrup, Theodor, 1853-
Vor mission. En skildring af det Danske
missionsselskab og dets arbejde... Kjøbenhavn,
1895.
104 [2] p., 1 l. incl. illus. 21 cm.

NL 0442763   CtY

Løgtingssøga Føroya
see under   Faroe Islands. Løgting.ð.

Löhbach, Rudolph
Bemerkungen zu Valerius Flaccus.
n.p. 1876

NL 0442765   NjP PU

LÖHBACH, Rudolph.
Geschichte der Höheren stadtschule zu Andernach. [Progr.] Neuwied,G.Höhn,1861.
4°. pp.(2),13+

NL 0442766   MH

870.8   Löhbach, Rudolph.
L825h   Handbuch der römischen Nationalliteratur;
Prosaiker und Dichter. Mit kurzen biographischen
und anderen Erläuterungen. Ein Lesebuch.
Braunschweig, G.Westermann, 1868.
xiii,656p. 22cm.

1. Latin literature. Collections.

NL 0442767   IEN

ar X   Löhbach, Rudolph.
2968   Observationes criticae in C. Valerii
no.22   Flacci Argonautica.   Neuwied, Strüder,
1869.
16 p. 26cm.

Separate from "Programm" (Jahresbericht)--
Progymnasium, Andernach, 1868/69.
No. 22 in a vol. lettered: Programmes:
Latin literature. II.

1. Valerius   Flaccus, C.

NL 0442768   NIC NjP

Loehbach, Rudolph
Quaestionum Sophoclearum decas. Dissertatio...
Neoviidii, 1865.
1 pam. 8° S

NL 0442769   NjP

ar X   Löhbach, Rudolph.
2968   Studien zu Valerius Flaccus.   Neuwied,
no. 23 Strüder, 1872.
17 p. 26cm.

Separate from "Programm" (Jahresbericht)--
Progymnasium, Andernach, 1871/72.
No. 23 in a vol. lettered: Programmes:
Latin literature. II.

1. Valerius Flaccus, C.

NL 0442770   NIC

VOLUME 338

Loehbach, Rudolph.
Zur kritik des Aristodemos. (1868. Aus Jahrb.
f. class. phil. Bd. 97 p. 242)

NL 0442771   PBm

Löhde, Hermann, 1904–
Giambattista Vico und das Problem der Bildung... Erlan-
gen-Bruck: M. Krahl, 1932.   ix, 204 p.   22cm.

Inaugural-Dissertation — Erlangen, 1931.
Vita.
"Quellen," p. 201–204.

688720A. 1. Vico, Giovanni Battista,   1668–1743. 2. Education—Theory
and systems—Vico.
N. Y. P. L.   March 6, 1934

NL 0442772   NN PU MdBJ ICN MiU CtY

Löhde, Walter, 1890–

BL2780
.L79   Ludendorff, Erich, 1865–1937.
Abgeblitzt! Antworten auf Theologengestammel, hrsg.
von General Ludendorff. München, Ludendorffs Verlag,
1937

Löhde, Walter, 1890–
Erich Ludendorffs Kindheit und Elternhaus. München,
Ludendorff, 1938.
133 p. plate, ports. 19 cm.

1. Ludendorff, Erich, 1865–1937.
DD231.L8L6   A F 48–3191*
New York. Public Libr.
for Library of Congress   (1)†

NL 0442774   NN NcD DLC

BL 2710
L6
1934   Löhde, Walter, 1890–   ed.
Für gewissens- und glaubensfreiheit;
das christentum im urteil grosser
dichter, denker und staatsmänner, ausgewählt und herausgegeben von Walter
Löhde. Berlin, Nordland verlag,1934.
185 p. 22 cm.

1. Free thought. 2. Christianity -
Controversial literature. I. Title.

NL 0442775   CaBVaU

Löhde, Walter, 1890–
Für Gewissens- und Glaubensfreiheit; das
Christentum im Urteil grosser Dichter, Denker
und Staatsmänner. Berlin, Nordland-Verlag, 1940.

115 p. 23 cm. (Nordland-Buchreihe, 1)
"3. Aufl."

NL 0442776   MH MiU

Löhde, Walter, 1890–   ed.
Für gewissens- und glaubensfreiheit; das christentum im
urteil grosser dichter, denker und staatsmänner, ausgewählt
und herausgegeben von Walter Löhde. Berlin, Nordland verlag (1941)
185 p., 1 l. 21½ᶜᵐ.
"4. auflage, 16. bis 35. tausend, 1941."

1. Free thought. 2. Christianity—Controversial literature.
BL2710.L6   211   47–34160

TNJ
NL 0442777   DLC IaU MH NNC PU IU OU NcD WU MH CoD

Löhde, Walter, 1890–
... Ein kaiserschwindel der "hohen" politik; abschnitte aus
dem ringen um die weltherrschaft zwischen dem jesuitismus
und der freimaurerei. München, Ludendorff (1941)
418 p. plates, ports. 22ᶜᵐ.
"Benutzte werke, bücher und schriften" : p. 414(–418.

CONTENTS.—Ein "kaiserschwindel"?—Wer war Napoleon III.?—Was
ging in Mexiko vor?—Der schwindel wird hoffähig.—Die "zwei schwer-
ter" in Mexiko vor?—Der bischof grollt–der kaiser greift ein–bruch mit
Rom.—Der freimaurer ging–der jesuit kam.—Der wahnsinn im Vati-
kan.—Schüsse in Queretaro.—Wetterleuchten auf der Pariser weltausstellung.
1. Mexico—Hist.—European intervention, 1861–1867. I. Title.
F1233.L8   972.07   A F 46–944
Michigan. Univ. Library
for Library of Congress   (4)†

NL 0442778   MiU CaBVaU CU NN NjP DLC CU

Löhde, Walter, 1890–
Ludendorffs gerader Weg, ein Gang durch die Werke und
Schriften des Feldherrn. Zum 75. Geburttag des Feldherrn. München, Ludendorffs Verlag (194–)
82 p. 21 cm.

1. Ludendorff, Erich, 1865–1937.   I. Title.

DD231.L8L62   53–32438 ‡

NL 0442779   DLC

Löhde, Walter, 1890–
... Der papst amüsiert sich ...   München,
Ludendorff, 1939.
172 p. plates, ports. 21 cm.

NL 0442780   NcD

Löhde, Walter, 1890–
... Der papst amüsiert sich ... München, Ludendorff, 1939.
Film copy made in 1943 by the Library of Congress. Negative.
Collation of the original, as determined from the film: 172 p. plates,
ports.
"Benützte werke; bücher und schriften": p. (170(–172.

1. Papacy.   I. Title.
                                                        43–21067
Library of Congress   Film DD–1 reel 25, no. 10

NL 0442781   DLC MiU NNUT CtY NN

PT
2482   Löhde, Walter, 1890–
Z8   Schiller, ein deutscher
L6   Revolutionär. München, Ludendorffs
Verlag, 1935.
26p. 23cm. (Ludendorffs Verlag,
München. Schriftenreihe 1, Heft. 10)

1. Schiller, Johann Christoph
Friedrich von, 1759–1805 I. Title.

NL 0442782   MU

B29
.L6   Löhde, Walter, 1890–
Von Tacitus bis Nietzsche; die
gedanklichen Grundlagen des Kulturkampfes
in Aussprüchen und Meinungen aus zwei
Jahrtausenden, zusammengestellt von
W. V. D. Cammer.   Düsseldorf, Nordland
(1934)
116 p. 23 cm.

1. Philosophy--Addresses, essays,
lectures.   I. Title. (x) Cammer,
W. v. d.

NL 0442783   TU

Löhde, Walter, 1890–   , ed.
Wider Kreuz und Krummstab; die gedanklichen Grundlagen
des Kulturkampfes in Aussprüchen und Meinungen aus zwei
Jahrtausenden, von W. v.d. Cammer.   Magdeburg, Nordland-
Verlag (c1934) 122 p. 21cm.

¹ Christianity. Anti.

NL 0442784   NN MH

Loehdefink, August.
Die Entwicklung der Brauergilde der Stadt Hannover zur
heutigen Erwerbsgesellschaft (ein Beitrag zur Lehre von den Unternehmungen)...von Diplom-Volkswirt August Löhdefink...
Hannover, 1925.   194 p.   8°.

Dissertation, Göttingen.

507479A. 1. Gilds, Brewers'—Ger-   many—Hannover.
N. Y. P. L.   December 26, 1930

NL 0442785   NN ICRL MH MiU CtY

---

ar W
53090   Löhe, Conrad.
no.2   Die Rechtsstellung des Agenten einer
Versicherungs-Gesellschaft auf Aktien.
Köln (Kölner Verlags-Anstalt und Druckerei)
1897.
52 p. 23cm.

Inaug.-Diss.--Erlangen.

NL 0442786   NIC ICRL

Löhe, Eugen: Ueber den Wert der Weiss'schen Suffizienzprüfung
für das Studium der peripheren Zirkulation in der Geburtshilfe.
(Maschinenschrift.) 16 S. 4°. — Auszug: (Lindlar (1923): Sülz-
taler Bote). 2 Bl. 8°
Bonn, Med. Diss. v. 30. April 1923   (U 23. 964)

NL 0442787   ICRL

LÖHE, Fritz.
Über den Bau des Mammaadenoms. Bonn.
Georgi, 1913.

Bonn, Med. Diss.

NL 0442788   MBCo DNLM ICRL CtY

Löhe, Hans
Das Vertragsangebot nach dem Bürger-
lichen Gesetzbuch ... von Hans Löhe ...
Fürth, A. Schröder, 1899.

35 p. 22cm.

Inaug.-Diss. - Erlangen.

NL 0442789   MH-L ICRL

Löhe, Hans, 1879–   ed.   FOR OTHER EDITIONS
                                          SEE MAIN ENTRY
Be dömes dæge.
Be dömes dæge; hrsg. und erläutert von dr. Hans Löhe.
Bonn, P. Hanstein, 1907.

Löhe, Heinrich, 1877–
Die Dermatologen deutscher Sprache; bio-bibliographi-
sches Verzeichnis; hrsg. von H. Löhe (und) E. Langer. Leipzig, J. A. Barth, 1955.

391 p. 25 cm.

1. Dermatologists—Bio-bibl. 2. Dermatology—Bibl. I. Langer,
Erich, 1891–   joint author. II. Title.

Z6670.L6   56–26075

NL 0442791   DLC CaBVaU NNC DNLM

VOLUME 338

WC LÖHE, Heinrich, 1877–
140 Die Geschlechtskrankheiten; Leitfaden
L883g für Studierende und Ärzte. Berlin,
1926 Karger, 1926.
viii, 213 p. illus.
1. Venereal diseases

NL 0442792 DNLM ICRL

Löhe, Heinrich, 1877–
Über den Einfluss Körperlicher Bewegungen
auf Pulsfrequenz und Blutdruck beim Soldaten.
Berlin, Mittler, 1907.
26 p.
Inaug. Diss. - Berlin, 1907.

NL 0442793 ICRL MBCo DNLM

Löhe, Johann Conrad, respondent.
Dissertatio inauguralis de Columnis Herculis
see under Schwarz, Christian Gottlieb
1675-1761, praeses.

Löhe, Johann Joseph
see
Löhe, Hans, 1879–

Loehe, Johann Konrad Wilhelm
see
Loehe, Wilnelm, 1808-1872

Löhe, W. *ed.*
Der Landwirtschaftliche fortschritt. *1878.*
see under title

Löhe (Wilhelm). "Ueber sichtbare Lymph-
bahnen der Retina. 13 pp., 2 pl. 8°. München,
Kastner & Lossen, 1882.

NL 0442798 DNLM

Löhe, Wilhelm, 1808-1872.
Gesammelte Werke. Hrsg. im Auftrage der Gesellschaft
für Innere und Äussere Mission im Sinne der Lutherischen
Kirche e. V. von Klaus Ganzert. Neuendettelsau, Freimund-
Verlag, 19
v. in 24 cm.
CONTENTS:—
3. Bd. Die Kirche in Gemeinde, Schule und Haus. v.
5. Bd. Die Kirche im Ringen um Wesen und Gestalt. v.
6. Bd. Die Kirche in der Verkündigung. v. —7. Bd. Die Kirche
in der Anbetung. v.
1. Lutheran Church—Collected works. 2. Theology—Collected
works—19th cent. I. Ganzert, Klaus, ed.
BX8011.L6 65-41601

MH-AH NjPT ICU MH CSaT
NL 0442799 DLC IaU NcD IEG PPL MoSCS MH-AH CtY-D

BX 8067
.A2 L6 Löhe, Wilhelm, 1808-1872.
1844 Agende für christliche Gemeinden des
lutherischen Bekenntnisses. Hrsg. von
Wilhelm Löhe ... Nördlingen, C. H.
Beck, 1844.
10 p.l., 252, [4] p. 26cm.

I. Lutheran Church. Liturgy and
ritual. II. Title.

NL 0442800 MdBJ PPLT

YAR Lohe, Wilhelm, 1808-1872.
177 Agende für christliche gemeinden des
Lutherischen bekenntnisses. 2. verm.
aufl. Nördlingen, 1859.
2 v.

NL 0442801 DLC PPLT NBuG

Löhe, Wilhelm, 1808-1872.
Agende fur christliche gemeinded des Lutherischen bekenntnisses, von ... 3. aufl. besorgt von
J. Deinzer. Nordlingen, Beck, 1884.
2v. in 1.

NL 0442802 PPLT

*Löhe, Wilhelm, 1808-1872, ed.
Olearius, Gottfried, 1672-1715.
... Anweisung zur krankenseelsorge. Mit einigen einleiten-
den sätzen und zwei anhängen versehen. Für junge geistliche,
krankenpfleger und krankenpflegerinnen herausgegeben von
Wilhelm Löhe ... 2. aufl. Nürnberg, G. Löhe, 1871.

Löhe, Wilhelm, 1808-1872.
Mra32 Aphorismen über die neutestamentlichen
L82 Aemter und ihr Verhältnis zur Gemeinde. Zur
Verfassungsfrage der Kirche ... Nürnberg, J.P.
Raw, 1849.
vi, 140p. 20½cm.

1. Church polity - Early church.

NL 0442804 CtY PPLT MH-L

BX8073 LÖHE, WILHELM, 1808-1872.
.L8B4 Beicht- und communionbuch für evangelische christen.
1871 Zum gebrauch sowol in, als ausserhalb des Gotteshauses.
Von Wilhelm Löhe ... 5. verm. und verb. aufl. Nürnberg,
G. Löhe, 1871.
xi, 391 p. incl. front. 18cm.
Added t.-p.: Prüfungstafel und gebete.

1. Confession. 2. Lord's supper.

NL 0442805 ICU

RARE BOOK Löhe, Wilhelm, 1808-1872.
BV
4870 Betbüchlein für Kinder. Stuttgart, S.
L6 G. Liesching, 1846.
xvi, 55p.
Appeared first in W. Löhe's Haus-, Schul-
und Kirchenbuch, part 1. Stuttgart, 1846.

NL 0442806 MoSCS

Löhe, Wilhelm, 1808-1872.
Conrad; eine gabe fur Confirmanded, by ... i.e.
Johann Konrad Wilhelm Löhe. 2. verm. aufl.
Dresden, Naumann, 1851.
71 p.

NL 0442807 PPLT

Löhe, Wilhelm, 1808-1872.
Conrad; eine gabe für confirmanden, by ...
3. verm. aufl. Dresden, Naumann, 1852.
79 p.

NL 0442808 PPLT

YAR Löhe, Wilhelm, 1808-1872.
186 Conrad. Eine gabe für confirmanden.
Amerikanische ausg. New York, 1887.
60 p.

NL 0442809 DLC

BX8065 Löhe, Wilhelm, 1808-1872.
L64 Drei Bücher von der Kirche, den Freunden
der lutherischen Kirche zur Ueberlegung und
Besprechung dargeboten. Stuttgart, S.G.
Liesching, 1845.
154 p.

1. Church. 2. Lutheran church -
Doctrinal and controversial works.

NL 0442810 CU MoSCS MH PPLT MH-AH

Löhe, Wilhelm, 1808-1872.
Drei Bücher von der Kirche; den Freunden der
lutherischen Kirche zur Überlegung und Besprechung dargeboten von Wilhelm Löhe. Berlin,
Christlicher Zeitschriftenverlag, 1947.

184 p. (Hilfe für's Amt, 9)

NL 0442811 MH IaU NN CtY

Löhe, Wilhelm, 1808-1872
Einfaltiger beichtunterricht fur Christen
Evangelisch-Luth. bekenntnisses, by ... 3. aufl.
Kropp i. Schleswig, Kropper kirchlanzeiger,
1881
76 p.

NL 0442812 PPLT

Löhe, Wilhelm, 1808-1872.
Erinnerungen aus der reformationsgeschichte von Franken,
insonderheit der stadt und dem burggraftum Nürnberg ober-
und unterhalb des gebirgs. Von Wilhelm Löhe ... Mit dem
bildnis des markgrafen Georg von Brandenburg, in stahl gestochen von Enzing-Müller. Nürnberg, J. P. Raw, 1847.
viii, 189, [1] p. front. (port.) fold. tab. 23cm.

1. Reformation—Germany. 2. Franconia—Church history.
3. Nuremburg—Hist.
[Full name: Johann Konrad Wilhelm Löhe]

33-11035
Library of Congress BR358.F7L6 274.33

NL 0442813 DLC CSt CtY NcD PPLT MH PPeSchw

RARE BOOK Löhe, Wilhelm, 1808-1872.
BV
4424 Etwas aus der Geschichte des Diaconissen-
L8 hauses Neuendettelsau. Nürnberg, G. Löhe,
L6 1870.
136p.

NL 0442814 MoSCS PPLT

610.2 LOEHE, Wilhelm, 1808-1872.
L825.4e Etwas aus der Geschichte des Diaconissen-
hauses Neuendettelsau. Guetersloh,
Bertelsmann, 1907.
138p. 18cm.

3. Auflage.

NL 0442815 MH-AH

VOLUME 338

⌈Löhe, Wilhelm⌉ 1808–1872.
Etwas über die deutsch-lutherischen niederlassungen in der
grafschaft Saginaw, staat Michigan. Mit einem kärtchen der
niederlassungen. (Manuscript.) Erlangen, Gedruckt bei P.
A. Junge & sohn, 1849.
cover-title, 29 p. fold. map, fold. facsim. 21ᶜᵐ.
Signed: Wilhelm Löhe, pfr.
1. Germans in Saginaw co., Mich. 2. Saginaw co., Mich.—Descr. &
trav. 3. Lutheran church in Michigan. I. Title.
⌈Full name: Johann Konrad Wilhelm Löhe⌉
1–13502 Revised
Library of Congress　　F572.S17L8

NL 0442816　　DLC MiU-C

BX8066 **LOEHE, WILHELM, 1808–1872.**
.L8L8 **Evangelien-postille für die sonn- und festtage des**
1859 **kirchenjahres. Von Wilhelm Löhe... 3.verm.aufl. ...**
Stuttgart, S.G.Liesching, 1859.
2 v. in 1. 25x20cm.
Each part has also special t.-p.

1.Sermons, German. 2.Bible. N.T. Epistles and
Gospels, Liturgical—Criticism, interpretation, etc.

NL 0442817　　ICU PPLT

Löhe, Wilhelm, 1808–1872.

Evangelien-Postille für die Sonn- und Festtage des Kirchenjahres. 4., unv. Aufl.
Gütersloh, C. Bertelsmann, 1874.
2v. In 1. 24cm.

1. Lutheran Church - Sermons. 2. Church
year sermons. 3. Bible. N. T. Gospels -
Sermons. i. Title.

NL 0442818　　MoSCS

610.2 **LOEHE, Wilhelm, 1808–1872.**
L825.4ev **Der evangelische Geistliche. Dem nun**
1872 **folgenden Geschlechte evangelischer**
Geistlichen. 4., mit der 3. gleichlautende
Aufl. Guetersloeh, Bertelsmann, 1872–
1876.
2v. 19cm.

Mixed set: v.2. is "3., mit der 2.
gleichlautende Aufl."
Note on　　title page v.2.:

"Ansichten aus den verschiedenen Arbeits-
gebieten des geistlichen Amtes."

NL 0442820　　MH-AH

Löhe, Wilhelm, 1808–1872.
Den evangeliske presten. Ett stycke pastoral-theologi, af
Wilhelm Löhe. Öfwersättning med tillämpning på svenska
förhållanden af C. J. Lénström ... Stockholm, A. Bonnier,
1853.
2 p. l., 266 p. 19½ᶜᵐ.
1. Theology, Pastoral. I. Lénström, Carl Julius, 1811–1893, tr.
II. Title.
⌈Full name: Johann Konrad Wilhelm Löhe⌉
35–29628
Library of Congress　　BV4010.J63　　　　250

NL 0442821　　DLC

Löhe, Wilhelm, 1808–1872
Fragen und antworten zu den fünf hauptstücken
des kleinen katechismus M. Luthers; hrsg. von der
Ev. Luth. Synode von Iowa u.a. staten by ....
Waverly (Ia.) Wartburg Pub. house, 1887.
142 p.

NL 0442822　　PPLT

Löhe, Wilhelm, 1808–1872, 1808–1872.
Wilhelm Loehe's⌐Fragen und antworten zu den fünf hauptstücken des Kleinen katechismus dr. Martin Luther's. Herausgegeben von der Evangel.-luth. synode von Iowa u. a. staaten.
2. aufl. Waverly, Ia., Wartburg publishing house, 1890.
x, 142 p. 17½ᶜᵐ.

1. Luther, Martin. Catechismus, Kleiner.　1. Evangelical Lutheran
synod of Iowa and other states.
⌈Full name: Johann Konrad Wilhelm Löhe⌉
40–21887
Library of Congress　　BX8070.L8L6 1890
⌈2⌉　　　　238.41

NL 0442823　　DLC

BX **Löhe, Wilhelm, 1808–1872.**
8074 **Gåfva för konfirmander. Efter andra, tyska**
.C7L6 **upplagan af N. J. Cervin-Stenhoff. Chicago,**
Enander & Bohmans boktr., 1878.
80 p. 20 cm.

1. Confirmation—Lutheran Church. I.
Cervin-Steenhoff, Nicolaus Johan, 1805–1879.
II. Title.

NL 0442824　　MnHi

Loehe, Wilhelm, 1808–1872.
Wilhelm Löhe's Gebete für Kriegszeiten, zeitgemäss verän-
dert. Mit einem Anhang... Neuendettelsau: Buchhandlung der
Diakonissenanstalt, 1914. 19 p. 12°.
1. European war, 1914– —Reli-　　gious life, etc.: Prayerbooks,
hymnbooks, etc.　　　　　　August 15, 1916.
N. Y. P. L.

NL 0442825　　NN

Löhe, Wilhelm, 1808–1872.
Gutachten in sachen der abendmahlsgemeinschaft. Vor
einigen freunden gelesen von pfarrer Löhe ... Nördlingen,
Beck, 1868.
40 p. 19½ᶜᵐ.

1. Close and open communion.　I. Title.
⌈Full name: Johann Konrad Wilhelm Löhe⌉
38–5194
Library of Congress　　BV828.L6
⌈2⌉　　　　265.3

NL 0442826　　DLC

Löhe, Wilhelm, 1808–1872.
Haus-, Schul & Kirchenbuch...erster Theil...
Aufl.2. 336 S.12. Stutt. Liesching, 1851.

NL 0442827　　PPG

Löhe, Wilhelm, 1808–1872.
Haus-, schul- und kirchenbuch für
christen des Lutherischen bekenntnisses
hrsg. von Wilhelm Löhe. 3 ... verm. aufl.
Stuttgart, Liesching, 1858.
3 v.

NL 0442828　　PPLT

Löhe, Wilhelm, 1808–1872.
Haus-, Schul- und Kirchenbuch... Stuttgart,
S. G. Liesching, 1859.
v.

NL 0442829　　ICRL

Loehe, Wilhelm, 1808–1872.
...Im Dienst der Kirche. Quellen und Urkunden zum Ver-
ständnis Neuendettelsauer Art und Geschichte; gesammelt von
Pfarrer J. Götz. Neuendettelsau: Buchhandlung der Diakonis-
senanstalt, 1925. 116 p. 22½cm.
"Verzeichnis der benützten Schriften Löhes in zeitlicher Folge," 1 p. at end.

1. Evangelical Lutheran Church—　　Govt. and discipline. 2. Deaconesses
—Evangelical Lutheran Church.　　I. Götz, Justus, 1869– , editor.
N. Y. P. L.　　　　　　　May 18, 1933

NL 0442830　　NN

Div.S. Löhe, Wilhelm, 1808–1872.
264.041
L825I　　Im Dienst der Kirche. Quellen und Urkunden
zum Verständnis Neuendettelsauer Art und Geschichte, gesammelt von J. Götz. 2. Aufl.
Neuendettelsau, Verlag der Buchhandlung der
Diakonissenanstalt, 1933.
116 p. 23 cm.

1. Worship. 2. Lutheran Church. Liturgy
and ritual. I. Götz, J. II. Title.

NL 0442831　　NcD

⌈Löhe, Wilhelm⌉ 1808–1872.
Käsi-kirja, jossa, wanhemmille ohjeeksi ja nuoru-
kaisille neuwoksi toht. M. Lutheruksen lyhy katekismus
yksinkertaisesti selitetään. Suomen kansalle hyödyksi
suomensi ja walmisti G.Dahlberg. 2.oikastu painos.
Turussa, Granlund, 1861.

144 p.

NL 0442832　　MH

Loehe, Wilhelm, 1808–1872.
Die Kirche im Ringen um Wesen und Gestalt.
Neuendettelsau, Freimund-Verlag, 1954–56

2 v. (His Gesammelte Werke, 5)

NL 0442833　　MH

Loehe, Wilhelm, 1808–72
Die Kirche in der Anbetung. Neuendettelsau,
Freimund-Verlag, 1953

v. (His Gesammelte Werke, 7)

NL 0442834　　MH

Loehe, Wilhelm, 1808–1872.
Die Kirche in Gemeinde, Schule und Haus.
Neuendettelsau, Freimund-Verlag, 1951

2 v. (His Gesammelte Werke, 3)

NL 0442835　　MH

BX8072 **LÖHE, WILHELM, 1808–1872.**
.L8 **Klein-sacramentale für tauf-, beicht- und abend-**
mahls-tage. Von Wilhelm Löhe ... Nürnberg, U.E.
Sebald, 1859.
xi, ⌈1⌉, 163, ⌈1⌉p. front. 12cm.

1.Sacraments.

NL 0442836　　ICU PPLT

VOLUME 338

Löhe, Wilhelm, 1808-1872.
Lebenslauf einer heiligen magd gottes aus
dem pfarrstande.. by ... 3. aufl. Nurnberg,
Löhe, 1867.
51 p.

NL 0442837 PPLT

BX8080 Löhe, Wilhelm, 1808-1872.
.L8A3 ₍Letters to Adam Ernst and other papers.
Rare bk 1842-54₎
19 items (₍75₎ l.) in envelope. 28cm.
Typewritten transcripts, in German.

I. Ernst, Adam, d.1895.

NL 0442838 ICU

Micro- Löhe, Wilhelm, 1808-1872.
film ₍Letters to Johann Friedrich Wucherer, 1840-
BX 1860₎
149
Manuscript.
Positive; original mss. in the Minnesota Historical Society.

NL 0442839 ICU

Löhe, Wilhelm, 1808-1872.
Liturgy for Christian congregations of the Lutheran faith,
by William Loehe. 3d ed.. edited by J. Deinzer ... Translated
by the Rev. F. C. Longaker. A. M. With an introduction by
the Rev. Edward T. Horn. D. D. Newport, Ky., 1902.
3 p. l., ix-xvi, 157 p. 16½ᶜᵐ.

1. Lutheran church. Liturgy and ritual.   I. Deinzer, Johannes,
1842-1897, ed.   II. Longaker, Frank Carroll, tr.
₍Full name: Johann Konrad Wilhelm Löhe₎
2-8122 Revised
Library of Congress   BX8067.A3L7

NL 0442840 DLC PPT NNUT MH-AH

Löhe, Wilhelm, 1808-1872.
Martyrologium. Zur Erklärung der herkömmlichen Kalendernamen. Nürnberg,
G. Löhe, 1868.
247 p., 15ᶜᵐ.

NL 0442841 NjPT PPLT

Löhe, Wilhelm, 1808-1872.
Martyrologium, zur erklärung der herkömmlichen kalendernamen, von Wilhelm Löhe. 2. aufl. Gütersloh, C. Bertelsmann, 1913.
247 p. 20ᶜᵐ.

1. Saints. 2. Church calendar.   I. Title.
₍Full name: Johann Konrad Wilhelm Löhe₎
38-15709
Library of Congress   BR1710.L6 1913
₍2₎   922

NL 0442842 DLC

Löhe, Wilhelm, 1808-1872.
Meine Suspension im Jahre 1860; acht
Wochen aus dem Leben eines landeskirch-
lichen Pfarrers... Nördlingen, C.H.
Beck, 1862.
iv, 48 p. 23ᶜᵐ.

NL 0442843 NjPT

---

17 Löhe, Wilhelm, 1808-1872.
1736a Questions and answers to the six parts of
the small catechism of dr. Martin Luther.
Translated from the 4th ed. of the House-school-
and church-book for Christians of the Lutheran
faith, of Wilhelm Loehe, by Edward T. Horn.
Columbia, S. C., W. J. Duffie [1893]
198p.   18°.

NL 0442844 DLC ScU PPLT

Löhe, Wilhelm, 1808-1872.
Raphael; ein Evangelischen betuchlein fur
reisende, by ₎₎₎ .Nurnberg, Sebald, 1872.
236 p.

NL 0442845 PPLT

Löhe, Wilhelm, 1808-1872.
Rauchopfer für kranke und sterbende und deren freunde.
Von Wilhelm Löhe. 3. aufl. Nördlingen, Beck, 1863.
vii, ₍1₎, 368 p. 14½ᶜᵐ.

1. Sick—Prayer-books and devotions—German.   I. Title.
₍Full name: Johann Konrad Wilhelm Löhe₎
37-37047
Library of Congress   BV270.L6 1863
₍2₎   242

NL 0442846 DLC PPLT

BX Loehe, Wilhelm, 1808-1872.
8041
L6 Rechenschaftsbericht der Redactoren
der kirch. Mittheilungen aus und über
Nordamerika über das was seit 1841 ge-
scheben ist. n.p., 1847.
23p.

1. Lutheran Church in the U. S. I.
Title.

NL 0442847 MoSCS

Loehe, Wilhelm, 1808-1872.
Samenkörner des Gebetes; ein Taschenbüchlein für evangelische Christen, von Wilhelm Löhe... Amerikanische Ausgabe
nach der 33. Auflage der Original-Ausgabe. Chicago: Wartburg
Pub. House ₍18—₎. vii, 492 p., 1 l. 24°.

1. Prayer-books.—Lutheran (Evan-   gelical) Church. 2. Title.
N.Y. P. L.   October 21, 1919.

NL 0442848 NN

248.3 Löhe, Wilhelm, 1808-1872.
L83s Samenkörner des Gebetes. Ein Taschenbüch-
1854 lein für evangelische Christen. Vollständige,
dem Originale gleichkommende Ausg. Konstanz,
C. Hirsch ₍1854?₎
viii, 487p. plate, port. 15cm.

"Vorwort zur sechsten Ausgabe" dated: 1854.

1. Prayers.   I. Title.

NL 0442849 IU

LÖHE, Wilhelm, 1808-1872.
Samenkorner des gebetes. Ein taschenbuch-
ounde evangelische Christen. 15e Nördlingen,
1862.

10 x 14.

NL 0442850 MH-AH

Löhe, Wilhelm, 1808-1872.
Samenkörner des gebetes; ein taschenbuchlein
fur Evengelische Christen by ₎₎₎₎ 36. aufl.
Nordlingen, Beck, 1869.
515 p.

NL 0442851 PPLT

---

264 Löhe, Wilhelm, 1808-1872.
L825e Samenkörner des Gebetes; ein Taschenbüchlein für evangelische Christen. 5. Abdruck.
Reading, Pa., Pilger, 1899.
viii,487p. illus.,port. 15cm.

1. Prayer-books. I. Title.

NL 0442852 IEN

YAR Löhe, Wilhelm, 1808-1872, comp.
178 Sammlung liturgischer formulare der
Evangelisch-lutherischen kirche.
Nördlingen, 1839.
3 v. in 1

NL 0442853 DLC

Löhe, Wilhelm, 1808-1872, comp.
Sammlung liturgischer formulare der Evangelisch-
Lutherischen kirche, von Wilhelm Löhe. Nördlingen,
Beck, 1839-42.

3 v. in 1

NL 0442854 PPLT

Loehe, Wilhelm, 1808-1872.
Seed grains of prayer. Chicago, Wartburg
Pub. House, 1912.

NL 0442855 PG1adM

Loehe, Wilhelm, 1808-1872.
Seed-grains of prayer; a manual for evangelical Christians,
by William Loehe. Translated from the original German 36th
edition by H. A. Weller... With an introduction by Henry
Eyster Jacobs... Chicago: Wartburg Pub. House, 1914. x,
640 p., 1 l. 16°.

1. Prayer-books. 2. Weller, H. A.,   translator. 3. Jacobs, Henry
Eyster, 1844-   4. Title.
N. Y. P. L.   June 7, 1915.

NL 0442856 NN PPLT

RARE BOOK Loehe, Wilhelm, 1808-1872.
BT
455 Sieben Vorträge über die Worte Jesu Christi
L7 vom Kreuze. Stuttgart, C. G. Liesching,
1859.
viii,132p.

NL 0442857 MoSCS

RARE BOOK Löhe, Wilhelm, 1808-1872.
BT
455 Sieben Vorträge über die Worte Jesu
L7 Christi vom Kreuze. 2. mit vier kleinen
1868 Anhängen verm. Aufl. Stuttgart, C. G.
Liesching, 1868.
xiii,148p.

NL 0442858 MoSCS

VOLUME 338

Löhe, Wilhelm, *1808-1872*
Sieben vortrage uber die worte Jesu Christi vom
kreutze, by .... 4. aufl. Gutersloh, Bertelsmann,
1908.
160 p.

NL 0442859   PPLT

Löhe, Wilhelm, *1808-1872*.
Siebzehn lectionen für die Passionszeit,
nebst einigen kurzeren vortragen uber Evangelische
texte des kirchen-jahres; aus der 2. aufl der
Evangelienpostille...abgedruckt, by ....Stutt-
gart, Liesching, 1854.
201 p.

NL 0442860   PPLT

Löhe, Wilhelm, 1808-1872.
Siebzehn lectionen für die passionszeit, nebst einigen kürze-
ren vorträgen über evangelische texte des kirchenjahres. Von
Wilhelm Löhe ... 2. aufl. Gütersloh, C. Bertelsmann, 1877.
176 p. 19ᶜᵐ.
"Aus der Evangelienpostille besonders abgedruckt."
"Kurze vorträge über nachbenannte kirchliche feste": p. ₍101₎-176.

1. Jesus Christ—Passion—Sermons. 2. Lutheran church—Sermons.
3. Sermons, German. I. Title.
₍Full name: Johann Konrad Wilhelm Löhe₎
37-33336
Library of Congress   BT430.L57 1877
₍2₎   232.96

NL 0442861   DLC MoSCS

Loehe, Wilhelm, 1808-1872.
Syv prædikener over Jesu Christi ord paa korset af
Wilhelm Løhe ... Oversat. Med forord af pastor J. N.
Skaar. Skien, G. O. Ulleberg, 1867.
2 p. l., 136 p. 19ᶜᵐ.
"Nærmest ... udgivet for at hjælpe til ved in diakonisseanstalts grund-
læggelse."—Pref.
Translation of Sieben vorträge über die worte Jesu Christi am kreuze.
₍Full name: Johann Konrad Wilhelm Loehe₎
17-6062

NL 0442862   DLC

Löhe, Wilhelm, 1808-1872.
Three books concerning the church, offered to friends of the
Lutheran church, for consideration and discussion, by Wilhelm
Loehe ... translated from the German by Edward T. Horn ...
Reading, Pa., Pilger publishing house, 1908.
xiii p., 2 l., ₍3₎-202 p. 18½ᶜᵐ.

1. Church. 2. Lutheran church—Doctrinal and controversial works.
I. Horn, Edward Traill, 1850-1915, tr.
₍Full name: Johann Konrad Wilhelm Löhe₎
8-37069 Revised
Library of Congress   BX8065.L7

NL 0442863   DLC MoSCS PGladM PPLT

BV
150
L6   Loehe, Wilhelm, 1808-1872.
Vom Schmuck der heiligen Orte. ₍Hrsg.
von Arnold Rickert₎   Kassel, J. Stauda,
1949.
77p.
Bibliographical references.

NL 0442864   MoSCS

Löhe, Wilhelm, *1808-1872*,
Von der barmherzigkeit; sachs kapitel fur
jedermann zuletzt ein siebentes fur dienerinnen der
barmherzigkeit, by .... 1860.
181 p.

NL 0442865   PPLT

W
HQ
1223   Löhe, Wilhelm, 1808-1872.
L53V6   Von der weiblichen Einfalt. Von Wilhelm
1853   Löhe.   Stuttgart, Verlag von G. O. Liesching,
1853.
108 p. 13 cm.

1. Wives. 2. Woman-Psychology. I. Title.

NL 0442866   NcGU

Löhe, Wilhelm, 1808-1872.
Von der weiblichen Einfalt. 11. Aufl. Gütersloh, Bertelsmann, 1891.
142 p.   T.

NL 0442867   PPLT

Loehe, Wilhelm, *1808-1872*.
Von der weiblichen Einfalt.
Gutersloh, C. Bertelsmann, 1908.
100p.

NL 0442868   PGladM

Loehe, Wilhelm, 1808-*1872*.
Wilhelm Löhe: der Mensch, das Werk.   Stuttgart [1949]

NL 0442869   MH

Loehe, Wilhelm, 1808-1872.
Wilhelm Löhe's Leben; aus seimen schriftlichen Nachsass zusammengestellt.   Nürnberg,
Verlag von Gottfr. Löhe, 1874.
2 v.

NL 0442870   PGladM

LOEHE, Wilhelm, 1808-1872.
Wilhelm Löhes leben; aus seinem schriftlichen
nachlass zusammengestellt.   Gutersloh, C.
Bertelsmann, etc., etc., 1901, 1877-92.
3 vol. Port. and plates.
Vol. i, 3e aufl. -ii, 1 Nurnberg, G.Löhe,
1877.   C 1279.11
Ed. by Johannes Deinzer.

NL 0442871   MH NcD DLC PPLT

BX8041   ₍Loehe, Wilhelm₎ 1808-1872.
.L8   Zuruf aus der heimat an die Deutschlutherische kirche
Nordamericas. Stuttgart, S. G. Liesching, 1845.
2 pt. in 1 v. 20½ᶜᵐ.
Signed at end of pt. 1: Wilhelm Löhe.
Pt. 2 contains "Beistimmende unterschriften."
With this is bound a reprint of the first part issued by the Wartburg pub.
house, Chicago.

1. Lutheran church in the U. S.

NL 0442872   ICU PPLT

ar W   Löhe, Wilhelm, 1880-
53884   Bericht über einen Fall von Verschluss des
no.16   Ureters durch massenhafte Einschwemmung linsen-
förmiger Nierenbeckensteine.   Erlangen,
Buchdr. von Junge & Sohn, 1905.
22 p. plate. 23cm.

Inaug.-Diss.--Erlangen.

NL 0442873   NIC NN DNLM ICRL

RC81   Loeheim, Julius.
903ℓ   Das goldene Buch der Gesundheit; aerztlicher
Ratgeber für Gesunde und Kranke. Berlin, Hirschberg, 1903.
512p. illus. 24cm.

1. Medicine - Popular works.

NL 0442874   CtY-M DNLM

Loeher, Bernard Charles, 1895-   *comp.*
Following Christ through the mass; an explanation of the
mystical meaning of the ceremonies of the mass, which represent the events in the life of Our Lord Jesus Christ under the
form of a continuous allegory, and which constitute the sacred
drama of the mass. Compiled and adapted from approved
sources by Rev. Bernard A. Loeher. Milwaukee, The Bruce
publishing company ₍ᶜ1935₎
94 p. 16½ᶜᵐ.
Bibliography: p. 93-94.
1. Mass. I. Title.
Library of Congress   BX2230.L6   35-5130
Copyright A 80652   ₍2₎   265.3

NL 0442875   DLC

Löher, Ernst Theodor, 1888-
...Ueber einen Fall von Quadrantenhemianopsie
nach Schussverletzung des Hinterhauptes im Felde
...   Berlin [1918]
38 [2] p.   23 cm.
Inaug.-Diss. - Berlin.
Lebenslauf.

NL 0442876   CtY DNLM

Löher, Franz von, 1818-1892, ed.
Archivalische zeitschrift. Herausgegeben durch das bayerische Hauptstaatsarchiv in München. 1.-13. bd., 1876-88;
neue folge, 1.-20. bd., 1890-1914; 3. folge, 1.— bd. 1915-
Stuttgart, W. Spemann, 1876-80; München, T. Ackermann,
1881-19

Löher, Franz von, *1818-1892*.
Archivlehre. Grundzüge der geschichte, aufgaben
und einrichtung unserer archive, von Franz v. Löher
... Paderborn, F. Schöningh, 1890.
xii, 400 pp. 24ᶜᵐ.
Subject entries: Archives.   1-27809—M 2
Library of Congress, no. Z6626.L82.

NL 0442878   DLC PLatS NN ICJ MH MB

943.44
L825a   Löher, Franz von, 1818-1892
Aus Natur und Geschichte von Elsass-Lothringen. Leipzig, Duncker und Humblot, 1871.
vi, 228p. 22cm.

1. Alsace-Lorraine. I. Title.

NL 0442879   TNJ PPGi MH CtY

VOLUME 338

Löher, Franz von, 1818–1892.
Aussichten für gebildete Deutsche in Nordamerika
... Berlin, Julius Springer, 1853.
vi, 3–91 p., 1 l. 19cm. (Travels in the Old
South III, 348)

1. U.S.-Descr. & trav.   I. Title.

NL 0442880   MsU NjP MiD NN MH

Löher, Franz von, 1818–1892.
Aussichten für gebildete Deutsche in Nordamerika ... Berlin, J. Springer, 1853.
vi, ₃3₃–91 p. 19cm. (Clark. Travels in the
Old South)

Micro-opaque copy of the original at University of Wisconsin. Louisville, Ky., Lost Cause
Press, 1963. 2 cards. 7.5 x 12.5cm.

1. U. S. - Description and travel - 1848–1865.

NL 0442881   NNC ICRL CSt MoU TxFTC

Loeher, Franz von, 1818–1892.
Beiträge zur Geschichte der Jakobäa von Bayern.
(In Koeniglich-bayerische Akademie der Wissenschaften, Munich. Historische Classe. Abhandlungen. Band 10, pp. 1–112,
205–336. München. 1867.)

K7114 — Jacqueline, Countess of Holland, 1401–1436.

NL 0442882   MB RPB NIC MdBP

Löher, Franz von, 1818–1892.
Beiträge zur geschichte und völkerkunde, von Frank von
Löher ... Frankfurt a/M., Rütten & Loening, 1885–86.
2 v. 22½ᵐ.

1. History—Addresses, essays, lectures.   I. Title.

Library of Congress   D7.L7   41–26851
                          ₍2₎   904

NL 0442883   DLC NN OCU MH CtY PPGi

Löher, Franz von, 1818–1892
Cypern in der geschichte. 48p. Berlin,
C. Habel, 1878. (Sammlung gemeinverständlicher
wissenschaftlicher vorträge, hft. 307)

NL 0442884   OCl NjP MH NN CtY NIC

Loeher, Franz von, 1818–1892.
Cypern. Reiseberichte über Natur und
Landschaft. Volk und Geschichte.
Stuttgart: J. G. Cotta, 1878. 2.ed
376 p.

NL 0442885   OCH NjP NN CtY

DS
54
.L64
1879
Löher, Franz von, 1818–1892
Cypern. Reiseberichte über Natur und Landschaft, Volk und Geschichte. Dritte um Vorwort und Karte vermehrte Auflage. Stuttgart,
J. G. Cotta, 1879.
x, 376p. map. 19cm.

1. Cyprus - Descr. & trav.   I. Title.

NL 0442886   TNJ NN

DS54
.L8
Löher, Franz von, 1818–1892.
Cyprus: historical and descriptive. Adapted
from the German of Franz von Löher, with much
additional matter by Mrs. A. Batson Joyner ...
London, W. H. Allen & co., 1878.
xvi, 308 p. 2 maps (incl. front.) 19 1/2ᶜᵐ.

1. Cyprus—Descr. & trav. 2. Cyprus—Hist.
I. Joyner, Mary Anne, "Mrs. A. Batson Joyner,"
ed. and tr.

NL 0442887   MB MH PPL CtY DN

Löher, Franz von, 1818–1892.
Cyprus: historical and descriptive. From the earliest
times to the present day. Adapted from the German of
Franz von Löher, with much additional matter by Mrs.
A. Batson Joyner ... New York, R. Worthington, 1878.
xvi p., 1 L, 324 p. 15 pl., 2 maps (incl. front.) 21ᶜᵐ.

1. Cyprus—Descr. & trav. 2. Cyprus—Hist. I. Joyner, Mary Anne,
"Mrs. A. Batson Joyner," ed. and tr.

Library of Congress   DS54.L8   5—7099

NN
NL 0442888   DLC WaTC MdBP DCU-H CU NjP PU ViU PPA

[Löher, Franz von] 1818–1892.
Dante in Deutschland. (In Beilage zur Allge-
meinen Zeitung. 28, 29, 30 Sept. 1865)
Reviews Witte's translation of the commedia.

NL 0442889   NIC

Löher, Franz von, 1818–1892.
Des deutschen volks. Bedeutung in der weltgeschichte. Vorträge gehalten in Cincinnati,
Anfang 1847. Cincinnati, Verlag von Eggers
und Wulkop, 1847.
109 p.

Contents. - I. Eroberung und bildung des
reichs. - II. Handel und geisteskraft im mittelalter. - III. Staatliche entwicklung. - IV.
Wissenschaft und kunst. - V. Auswanderung. -
Gegenwart.
1. Germany - History - Addresses, essays, lectures. I. Title.

NL 0442890   MdU NN ICN OCU PV NNC PPGi PHi

Löher, Franz ₍von₎, 1818–1892.
Die deutsche politik König Heinrich I; festrede vorgetragen in
der K. Akademie der Wissenschaften. München, J. G. Weiss,
1857.
4°. pp. 27.

Heinrich I, king of Germany₎|

NL 0442891   MH

Loeher, Franz von, 1818–1892.
Deutsche Rechtsbildung.
(In Koeniglich-bayerische Akademie der Wissenschaften,
Munich. Philosophisch-philologische und historische Classe.
Sitzungsberichte. 1886, pp. 516–569. München. 1886.)

K6566 — Germany. Juris.

NL 0442892   MB

Löher, Franz von, 1818–1892.
Dolmenbauten und hünengräber. Von Franz v. Löher.
₍Braunschweig, G. Westermann, 1890₎
₍540₎–563 p. illus. (incl. map) 26ᶜᵐ.
Caption title.
Separate from Westermann's illustrierte deutsche monats-hefte, 34.
jahrg., heft 406, juli 1890.

1. Dolmens. 2. Mounds.

Library of Congress   GN791.L82   4–34155

NL 0442893   DLC

DB 919
.L82
LÖHER, FRANZ VON, 1818–1892
Das Erwürgen der deutschen Nationalität in
Ungarn; Denkschrift aus Siebenbürgen mit Vor-
wort. München, A. Ackermann, 1874.
59 p.

1. Germans in Hungary. I. Title.

NL 0442894   InU

Loeher, Franz von, 1818–1892.
Fürsten und Städte zur Zeit der Hohenstaufen dargestellt an den
Reichsgesetzen Kaiser Friedrich II.
Halle. Anton. 1846. x, 118 pp. 21 cm., in 8s.

M4367 — T.r. — Germany. Pol. hist. — Hohenstaufen Dynasty.

NL 0442895   MB MH-L

LOEHER, Franz von, 1818–1892,
Fürstenromantik in 15 Jahrhundert.
(In Historisches Taschenbuch. Jahrgang 36, pp. 217–307. Leipzig,
1865)

NL 0442896   MB

DP
302
C4
L56
Loeher, Franz von, 1818–1892.
Los germanos en las Islas Canarias. Madrid,
Impr. Central à Cargo de V. Saiz ₍1886?₎
140 p. 19 cm.

Traducción del alemán.

1. Ethnology - Canary Islands. 2. Germanic
tribes in the Canary Islands. 3. Canary Islands
- Hist.

NL 0442897   CU-S CU MiU

Löher, Franz von, 1818–1892.
Geschichte des kampfes um Paderborn 1597 bis 1604. Berlin,
A. Hofmann & co. 1874.
pp. xvi, 372. (Allgemeiner verein für deutsche literatur.)

Paderborn, Germ.||Series₎

NL 0442898   MH IU PBm NIC CtY CSt OU

Löher, Franz von, 1818–1892.
Geschichte und zustände der Deutschen in Amerika.
Von Frank Löher. Cincinnati, Eggers und Wulkop; ₍etc.,
etc.₎ 1847.
2 p. L, xii, 544 p. 21½ᵐ.

1. Germans in the U. S.

Library of Congress   E184.G3L8   2—8099

PPLT PSt MB NN IaU CSt MoU KMK MsU NcD OBiC-M PPL
NL 0442899   DLC ViU TxU NcU KyU OHi NIC CtY ScU PU

Löher, Franz von, 1818–1892.
Geschichte und Zustände der Deutschen in
Amerika. Cincinnati, Verlag von Eggers und
Wulkop, 1847.
Microcard edition (7 cards) (Travels in
the Old South III, 349) microprinted by the
Lost Cause Press, Louisville, 1961.

1. Germans in the U. S. I. Title. II. Ser.

NL 0442900   ViU ICRL UU

VOLUME 338

Löher, Franz von, 1818–1892.
Geschichte und zustände der Deutschen in Amerika.
Von Franz Löher. 2. ausg. Göttingen, G. H. Wigand,
1855.
iv p., 1 l., x, 544 p. 21½ᶜᵐ.

1. Germans in the U. S.

2–8100

Library of Congress　　E184.G3L82

NL 0442901　　DLC TxU CtY PPL PPGi NN ICN

Löher, Franz von, 1818–1892.
Griechische küstenfahrten, von dr. Franz v. Löher ... Bielefeld und Leipzig, Velhagen & Klasing, 1876.
vi, 378 p. 17ᶜᵐ.

1. Islands of the Ægean.　ɪ. Title.

34–31320

Library of Congress　　D852.L75　　914.99

NL 0442902　　DLC MH

Löher, Franz von, 1818–1892.
Hrotsvitha und ihre zeit, von Franz Löher.
(Braunschweig, F. Vieweg & sohn, 1858)
1 p.l., p. (487)–630. 21cm.
Extracted from: Wissenschaftliche vorträge gehalten zu München, 1858.

NL 0442903　　CU

Löher, Franz von, 1818–1892.
Jacoba van Beijeren en haar tijd. Uit het hoog-duitsch van Franz Löher...'s Gravenhage, Van Stockum, 1863–71.
3 v. in 1. 24cm.

NL 0442904　　CU

Löher, Franz von, 1818–1892.
Jakobäa von Bayern und ihre zeit. Acht bücher niederländischer geschichte, von Franz Löher ... Nördlingen, Beck, 1862–69.
2 v. 21½ᶜᵐ.
"Quellen, literatur und noten": v. 1, p. (401)–472.

1. Jacoba, countess of Hainaut and Holland, 1401–1436. 2. Netherlands—Hist.—House of Burgundy, 1384–1477. 3. Belgium—Hist.—To 1555.

32–7088

Library of Congress　　DJ401.H665J18　　949.201

NL 0442905　　DLC IU NIC PPLT

Löher, Franz von, 1818–1892.
Jakobäa von Bayern und ihre zeit. Acht bücher niederländischer geschichte von Franz v. Löher ... Auf veranlassung und mit unterstützung Seiner Majestät des königs von Bayern Maximilian ɪɪ. Nördlingen, C. H. Beck, 1869.
2 v. in 1. 21½ᶜᵐ.
Vol. 1, 2. ausg.
"Quellenliteratur": v. 1, p. (401)–430.

1. Jacoba, countess of Hainault and Holland, 1401–1436. 2. Netherlands—Hist.—House of Burgundy, 1384–1477.

NL 0442906　　ICU MB CtY

956.4
L826
LÖHER, FRANZ VON, 1818–1892.
Kaiser Friedrich II. kampf um Cypern. Von
Franz v. Löher... München, Verlag der k. Akademie, in commission bei G. Franz, 1878.
72 p. 28½cm.

"Aus den abhandlungen der k. bayer. Akademie der wiss. III. cl. XIV. Bd. II. abth."

NL 0442907　　PU

Loeher, Franz von, 1818–1892.
Kaiser Friedrich II. Kampf um Cypern.
(In Koeniglich-bayerische Akademie der Wissenschaften, Munich. Historische Classe. Abhandlungen. Band 14, Abtheilung 2, pp. 109–180. München. 1879.)

K7112 — Frederick II., of Germany, 1194–1250. — Cyprus. Hist.

NL 0442908　　MB NIC RPB MH

Löher, Franz von, 1818–1892, ed.

Viana, Antonio de, b. 1578.
Der kampf um Teneriffa, dichtung und geschichte von Antonio de Viana, hrsg. von Franz von Löher. Tübingen, Litterarischer verein in Stuttgart, 1883.

Löher, Franz von, 1818–1892.
Das Kanarierbuch; geschichte und gesittung der Germanen auf den Kanarischen Inseln. Aus dem nachlasse herausgegeben. München, J. Schweitzer, 1895.
pp. (4), 603.

Canary Islands||

NL 0442910　　MH IEN

Löher, Franz von, 1818–1892.
Karl Witte. (In Beilage zur Allgemeinen Zeitung. 23, 24 Dec. 1884)

NL 0442911　　NIC

AS
182
M9624+
v.8
no.7
Löher, Franz von, 1818–1892.
König Konrad I. und Herzog Heinrich von Sachsen; ein Beitrag zur deutschen Reichsgeschichte, von Franz Löher.
(In Akademie der Wissenschaften, Munich. Historische Classe. Abhandlungen. München. 27cm. 8. Bd., 2. Abth. (1857) p. (489)–655)

1. Konrad I, King of Germany, d. 918. 2. Heinrich I, Emperor of Germany, 876 (ca.)– 936. 3. Germany—Hist.—843–1273. I. Title.

NL 0442912　　NIC RPB

4DF
198
Löher, Franz von 1818–1892.
Kretische Gestade. Bielefeld,
Velhagen & Klasing, 1877.
363 p.

NL 0442913　　DLC ICJ

CB
214
.L63
Löher, Franz von, 1818–1892
Kulturgeschichte der Deutschen im Mittelalter von Franz v. Löher. München, C. Mehrlich, 1891–1894.
3 v. in 4 pts. 22cm.

vol. 3: "Aus dem Nachlasse hrsg." published by Schweitzer.
Contents.— 1. Bd. Germanenzeit und Wanderzeit.— 2. Bd. Frankenzeit.— 3. Bd. Kaiserzeit.

1. Civilization, Germanic. 2. Civilization, Medieval.

NL 0442914　　MA MB MH TNJ

F
4711
.52
Löher, Franz von, 1818–1892.
Kulturgeschichte der Deutschen im mittelalter... 2. ausg. München, 1896.
3 v. in 1.

Contents.—1. bd. Germanenzeit und wanderzeit.—2. bd. Frankenzeit.—3. bd. Kaiserzeit.

NL 0442915　　ICN PU MU CU

Löher, Franz von, 1818–1892.
Land und Leute, in der Alten und Neuen Welt.
Reisekizzen... Göttingen, George H. Wigand,
1858. New York, L. W. Schmidt, 1855.
3 v. in 2.
Microcard edition.

NL 0442916　　ICRL ViU MoU

Loner, Franz von, 1818–1892.
Land und leute in der Alten und Neuen welt. Reiseskizzen von Franz Löher ... Göttingen, G. H. Wigand; New York, L. W. Schmidt, 1855–58.
3 v. in 2. 17½ᶜᵐ.
v. 3 published only at Göttingen.
Includes brief sketches of England, Provence, northern Italy, etc.

1. U. S.—Descr. & trav.　ɪ. Title.

2—2859

Library of Congress　　E166.L82

NL 0442917　　DLC NcU MsU NN PPGi PU

Löher, Franz von, 1818–1892.
Die Magyaren und andere Ungarn, von Franz von Löher. Leipzig, Fues's verlag (R. Reisland) 1874.
xvi, 451, (1) p. 22½ᶜᵐ.

1. Hungary—Descr. & trav. 2. Magyars.

4—7059

Library of Congress　　DB914.L8

NL 0442918　　DLC PBm CtY PHC InU ICJ CU–S

Löher, Franz von, 1818–1892.
Nach den glücklichen Inseln; canarische Reisetage. Bielefeld, Velhagen & Klasing, 1876.
viii, 385 p. col. map.

1. Canary Islands – Descr. & trav.

NL 0442919　　NNC CU PPGi NjP

Löher, Franz v(on), 1818–1892.
Das neue Italien. Berlin, C. Habel, 1882.
pp. 44. (Deutsche zeit- und streit fragen, xi. 175.)
Cover dated "1883."

NL 0442920　　MH WU

VOLUME 338

G
85
.52

Löher, Franz von, 1818-1892.

Reiseskizzen... 2.ausgabe. Berlin
n.d.

From his Land und leute in der alten
und neuen welt, published 1855-58.

NL 0442921 ICN

LÖHER, Franz von, 1818-1892.
Ritterschaft und adel im späteren
mittelalter. München, J.G.Weiss,1861.

pp.54.
"Abdruck aus den Sitzungsberichten der k.
Akademie der Wissenschaften 1861. Bd. 1.
Heft. IV".

NL 0442922 MH

Löher, Franz von, 1818-1892.
Russlands Werden und Wollen. München, T. Ackermann, 1881.

3 v. in 1. 19 cm.

1. Russia—Description and travel. 2. Russia—Social conditions
I. Title.

DK26.L8   70-235139

NL 0442923 DLC CtY NjP PPGi InU

DG864 Löher, Franz von, 1818-1892.
.L8   Sizilien und Neapel, von Franz Löher ... München, E.
A. Fleischmann. (A. Rohsold) 1864.

2 v. in 1. 18½ᶜᵐ.
Paged continuously.

1. Sicily—Descr. & trav. 2. Naples—Descr. 3. Sicily—Hist.

NL 0442924 ICU NcD

Loeher, Franz von, 1818-1892.
Stellung der canarischen Inseln in der Entdeckungsgeschichte.
(In Koeniglich-bayerische Akademie der Wissenschaften,
Munich. Philosophisch-philologische und historische Classe
Sitzungsberichte. 1880, pp. 77-105. München. 1880.)

K6566 — Canary Islands. Geog.

NL 0442925 MB

Loeher, Franz von, 1818-1892.
Ueber Alter, Herkunft und Verwandtschaft der Germanen.
(In Koeniglich-bayerische Akademie der Wissenschaften,
Munich. Philosophisch-philologische und historische Classe.
Sitzungsberichte. 1883, pp. 593-633. München. 1883.)

K6565 — Teutonic races. Ethnology.

NL 0442926 MB

Loeher, Franz von, 1818-1892.
Über angebliche Menschenopfer bei den Germanen.
(In Koeniglich-bayerische Akademie der Wissenschaften,
Munich. Philosophisch-philologische und historische Classe.
Sitzungsberichte. 1882, Band I, pp. 373-390. München. 1882.)

K6570 — Human sacrifices. — Teutonic races. Manners & customs.

NL 0442927 MB CU

Löher, Franz von, 1818-1892.
Ueber Deutschlands weltstellung. Rede gehalten in
der öffentlichen sitzung der K. Akademie der wissenschaften am 25. juli 1874 zur vorfeier des allerhöchsten
geburts- und namens-festes Sr. Majestät des königs Ludwig II. von Bayern, von Franz von Löher. München, Königl. akademie, 1874.

1 p. L, 48 p. 21½ᶜᵐ.

1. Germany—Pol. & govt. 2. Germany—For. rel.

13-17807

Library of Congress   DD117.L7

NL 0442928 DLC CtY CU

LÖHER, Franz [von], 1818-1892.
Ueber die kulturhistorische bedeutung unserer städte. München, J.G.Weiss,1858.

pp.18.

NL 0442929 MH NN

Loeher, Franz von, 1818-1892.
Über die Quellen und Literatur zur Geschichte der Jakobaea von
Bayern-Holland.
(In Koeniglich-bayerische Akademie der Wissenschaften, Mu-
nich. Sitzungsberichte. 1861, Band I, pp. 152-163. München.
1861.)

K6565 — Jacqueline, Countess of Holland, 1401-1436.

NL 0442930 MB

Löher, Franz von, 1818-1892.
... Ueber handschriftliche annalen und berichte der Jesuiten.
(In Akademie der wissenschaften, Munich. Philosophisch-philologi-
sche und historische classe. Sitzungsberichte. München, 1874. 22ᶜᵐ.
jahrg. 1874, bd. II, p. (155)-184)
At head of title: ... v. Löher.

1. Jesuits. Letters from missions (Bavaria) 2. Bavaria—History—
Sources.
Hamilton college. Library   A C 39-8598
for Library of Congress   [AS182.M823 1874, bd. 2]
,2,   (063)

NL 0442931 NCH MB DLC

Loeher, Franz von, 1818-1892.
Über Ritterschaft und Adel im späteren Mittelalter.
(In Koeniglich-bayerische Akademie der Wissenschaften, Munich. Sitzungsberichte. 1861, Band I, pp. 365-416. München.
1861.)

K6581 — Knighthood. — Nobility. — Middle Ages. Heraldic and social dis-
tinctions.

NL 0442932 MB

LÖHER, Franz von, 1818-1892.
Vom sprach- und volkerstreit in Ungarn.
Hermannstadt, S.Filtsch's buchdruckerei,
1873.

1.8°. pp.16.
"Die obige abhandlung die durch die
Augsburger (Allgemeiner zeitung) zum erstenmal veroffentlicht, wird als bestand-
theil einer umfangreichern verker desselben
verfassers Die Magyaren und anderen Ungarn."

NL 0442933 MH

Loeher, Franz von, 1818-1892.
Zur Geschichte des Archivwesens im Mittelalter.
(In Koeniglich-bayerische Akademie der Wissenschaften,
Munich. Philosophisch-philologische und historische Classe.
Sitzungsberichte. 1889, Band 2, pp. 278-314. München. 1889.)

K6570 — Middle Ages Archives. — Documents and archives.

NL 0442934 MB

Löherer, Andor, 1846-
Az amerikai kivándorlás és a visszavándorlás, írta Löherer Andor... Budapest: "Pátria" irod. váll. és nyomdai részvénytársaság, 1908. 263 p. incl. tables. 24cm.

868133A. 1. Emigration and immi-   gration—U. S., 1908.
N. Y. P. L.   December 23, 1937

NL 0442935 NN

Löhers, Franz, mi - Zur forensischen Beurteilung der Imbe-
zilität. Aus d. Psychiatr. u. Nervenkl. d. Univ. Kiel. Kiel
1919: Schmidt & Klaunig. 26 S. 8°
Kiel, Med. Diss. v. 26. April 1919, Ref. Siemerling
[Geb. 5. April 88 Geszke; Wohnort: Kiel; Staatsangeh.: Preußen; Vorbildung:
G. Brilon Reife 09; Studium: München 3, Kiel 3, Berlin 2, Kiel 2 S.; Coll.
20. März 19; Approb. 12. Nov. 14.]   [U 19. 1721]

NL 0442936 ICRL DNLM CtY

Löhers (Heinrich) [1861-] J. *Ueber den Einfluss des Bromäthyls auf Atmung und Kreislauf.
31 pp., 1 diag. 8°. Berlin, G. Schade, 1890.

NL 0442937 DNLM

Löhle, Anton.
Predigten für das Landvolk an alle Sonntage.
Breslau, Korn, 1794.
2 parts.

NL 0442938 OC1StM

Löhle, August.
[Herz-Jesu-Messe]

Herz-Jesu-Messe (sehr leicht ausführbar) für Sopran, Alt,
Tenor u. Bass. Partitur u. 4 Singstimmen. Augsburg, A.
Böhm [19—] Pl. no. 4904.

close score (11 p.) and   parts. 29 cm.
At head of title: Missa in honorem SS. Cordis Jesu.
Previously published without the Credo.
For chorus (SATB)

1. Masses—Vocal scores.   I. Title. II. Title: Missa in honorem
SS. Cordis Jesu.

M2011.L74H4   M 53-1014

NL 0442939 DLC

Löhle, August.
Missa in honorem st. Annae, für vierstimmigen gemischten
chor komponiert von A. Löhle. Op. VI. Ravensburg, Dorn
[1900]

11 p. 31 x 24½ᶜᵐ.
Publisher's plate no.: D. B. 3.
Close score: SATB.

1. Masses—Vocal scores.

Library of Congress   M2011.L74 op. 6   45-50972

NL 0442940 DLC

---

ar W   Löhle, Bernhard, 1886-
54392   Die Bildung des Gaumens bei Cavia cobaya.
no.8   Leipzig und Berlin, W. Engelmann, 1913.
[595]-654 p. illus., plates. 22cm.

Inaug.-Diss.—Erlangen.
Imperfect: plates lacking.
"Sonderdruck aus 'Morphologisches Jahr-
buch.' 46. Bd. 3./4. Heft."

NL 0442941 NIC ICRL MH PU CtY DNLM

VOLUME 338

Zg19 Löhle, Franz
8e413 Theater-Catechismus; oder, Humoristische
845ℓ Erläuterung verschiedener vorzüglich im
Bühnenleben üblicher Fremdwörter. Eine
Toilettengabe für Freundinnen des Theaters,
von Franz Löhle. Mit Illustrationen, componirt
und auf Stein gezeichnet von Franz Seitz.
München, Piloty & Löhle [1845]
105p., 1ℓ. 11 plates. 21½cm.

NL 0442942   CtY

LOEHLE, FRANZ XAVER, 1792-1837.
Liebesklage; von König Ludwig von Bayern. Für
vier Maennerstimmen (und Clavierbegleitung ad
libitum) In Partitur u. ausgeschriebenen Stimmen.
München, Falter und Sohn [ca. 1829] Pl. no. 131.
score (6 p.) and 4 parts.   28x36cm.

From the collection of music performed before Ludwig I, in Munich,

May 25, 1829, and published under the title: Gedichte Seiner Majestaet
des Koenigs Ludwig von Bayern, in Musik gesetzt und gesangen von den
Mitgliedern des Liederkranzes. —cf. Fétis, Biogr. univ., 6:153.

1. Choral music, Secular (Men, 4 pt.)--Unacc. 2. Choral music, Secular
(Men, 4 pt.)--Keyboard acc. I. Louis I, king of Bavaria, 1786-1868.

NL 0442944   NN

8A
408 LÖHLE, FRANZ XAVER, 1792-1837.
[Messe No. 1 in C Dur] [Messe] No.1
in D Dur.   München, Falter und Sohn [18--]
5 parts.   36cm.

At head of title: Drey lateinische Messen
für vier Singstimmen und Orgel..."
Pub. no. 415.
Lithographed.

NL 0442945   ICN

Löhle, Friedrich.
Sichtbeobachtungen vom meteorologischen standpunkt, von
Friedrich Löhle. Mit 45 abbildungen. Berlin, J. Springer,
1941.
2 p. l., 119, [1] p. illus., diagrs. 24cm.
"Literaturverzeichnis": p. [107]-114.

1. Meteorological optics.   I. Title.
41-24383
Library of Congress   QC975.L6
[2]
551.5

NL 0442946   DLC NN CoU TxHR NN ICU MCM

PA Löhle, J   B
4494 Der Character des Cyrus nach
.C9 Xenophons Cyropädie, von Professor
.L6 Löhle. Tauberbischofsheim, J.
Lang [1874?-
v.
#Xenophon.
Cyropaedia.
#Cyrus, the Great, King of Persia,
d. 529 B. C.
(A) Der Character des Cyrus nach
Xenophons Cyropädie.

NL 0442947   MoU NjP

Pa
371.3ХSci LÖHLE, M
L826 Der naturgeschichtsunterricht an volksschulen und unterklassen von bürger- und
mittelschulen. In methodischer bearbeitung
für den lehrer, mit über 600 aufgaben zu na-
turbeobachtungen, zum zeichnen, sowie zur
mündlichen und schriftlichen lösung. 2. verb.
und verm. aufl.   Gera, T. Hofmann, 1889.
viii, 175p. illus. 23cm.

NL 0442948   PU

LOEHLE, S.
De Aristophanis fabula, quae in scribitur
Aves. [Progr]. Heidelbergae, 1865.

pp. 88.

NL 0442949   MH ViU NjP PU MiU PBm CtY

Löhlein, A
See
Löhlein, Herbert Andreas

Löhlein, Anton, 1906-
Schädigung der Zähne durch Gifte... Würz-
burg, 1930.
Inaug.-Diss. - Würzburg.
Lebenslauf.
"Literatur": p. [22]

NL 0442951   CtY

Löhlein, Christian Adolph Hermann
see Löhlein, Hermann, 1847-1901.

Div.S. Loehlein, Conradus Ludovicus Ernestus.
227.5 Syrus, epistolae ad Ephesios inter-
L825S pres, in causa critica denuo examinatus.
Erlangae, Apud C. Heyderum, 1835.
63 p.   22 cm.

Photocopy.   Durham, N.C., Duke University Library, 1963.

1. Bible. N. T Ephesians. Criticism,
interpretation,   etc.

NL 0442953   NcD MH

Loehlein (Ernestus Ludovicus Carolus) [1831-
]. * De tensionis gasorum in pneumothorace
rationibus. 28 pp., 2 l. 8°. Berolini, B. Schlesinger. [1855].

NL 0442954   DNLM

Löhlein, Georg.
Die Alpen- und Italienpolitik der Merowinger im VI. jahrhundert, von Georg Löhlein. Erlangen, Palm & Enke, 1932.
viii, 81 p. 25½cm. (Added t.-p.: Erlanger abhandlungen zur mittleren
und neueren geschichte ... 17. bd.)
"Quellen und literatur": p. 78-81.

1. Franks—History—To 768. 2. Merovingians. 3. Italy—History—
476-1268.   A C 33-2002
Title from Princeton   Univ. Printed by L. C.

NL 0442955   NjP MH WU CtY NN

Löhlein, Georg Simon, 1725-1781.
Anweisung zum violinspielen, mit pracktischen beyspielen und zur uebung mit vier und zwanzig kleinen duetten erläutert, von George Simon Löhlein. Leipzig und
Züllichau, Auf kosten der Waysenhaus- und Frommanischen buchhandlung, 1774.
6 p. l., 136 p. 18 x 21½cm.
Title vignette.

1. Violin—Instruction and study.
9-5277
Library of Congress   MT262.A2L62

NL 0442956   DLC

Löhlein, Georg Simon, 1725-1781.
Anweisung zum Violinspielen, mit praktischen Beyspielen und zur Uebung mit vier und
zwanzig kleinen Duetten erläutert. 2. verb.
Aufl. Leipzig und Züllichau, auf Kosten der
Waisenhaus- und Frommannischen Buchhandlung,
1781.
140 p. 19 x 23cm.
Autograph of Jos. Verlage, 1814, signed on title-
page.
1. Violin—In   struction and study.

NL 0442957   ViU

Löhlein, Georg Simon, 1725-1781.
George Simon Löhlein's Anweisung zum violinspielen, mit
praktischen beyspielen und zur übung mit zwölf kleinen
duetten erläutert, zum dritten mahl mit verbesserungen und
zusätzen, auch mit zwölf balletstücken aus der oper An-
dromeda und der oper Brenno verm. hrsg. von Johann Friederich Reichardt. Leipzig und Züllichau, F. Frommann,
1797.
2 p. l., 128 p. illus. 18¼ x 22 cm.

1. Violin—Instruction and study—To 1800. I. Reichardt, Johann
Friedrich, 1752-1814.

MT262.L85 1797   8-16368 rev

NL 0442958   DLC

LOEHLEIN, GEORG SIMON, 1725-1781.
Anweisung zum Violinspielen. Zum dritten Mahl mit
Verbesserungen und Zusätzen vermehrt hrsg. von J.F.
Reichardt.   Leipzig, F. Frommann, 1797.   123 p.

Microfilm (master negative)

NL 0442959   NN CaBVaU

Löhlein, Georg Simon, 1725-1781.
[Clavier-Schule]
Clavier-Schule; oder, Kurze und gründliche Anweisung
zur Melodie und Harmonie, durchgehends mit practischen
Beyspielen erkläret. Leipzig, Auf Kosten der Waisenhaus-
und Frommanischen Buchhandlung, 1765.
188 p. 18 x 23 cm.

1. Piano—Instruction and study—To 1800. 2. Thorough bass.

MT224.L72 1765   12-18598 rev 2*

NL 0442960   DLC

Löhlein, Georg Simon, 1725-1781.
[Clavier-Schule]
Clavier-Schule; oder, Kurze und gründliche Anweisung
zur Melodie und Harmonie, durchgehends mit practischen
Beyspielen erkläret. 2. und verm. Aufl. Leipzig, Auf
Kosten der Waisenhaus- und Frommannischen Buchhand-
lung, 1773.
190 p. illus. 18 x 23 cm.

1. Piano—Instruction and study—To 1800. 2. Thorough bass.

MT224.L72 1773   62-57027 ‡

NL 0442961   DLC

Film Löhlein, Georg Simon, 1727-1781.
11926 Georg Simon Löhleins Clavier-Schule, oder
kurze und gründliche Anweisung zur Melodie und
Harmonie, durchgehends mit practischen Beyspielen
erkläret. 3. und verb. Aufl.   Leipzig, auf
Kosten der Waisenhaus- und Frommannischen
Buchhandlung, 1779.
190p. music.

Microfilm. New York, New York Public
Library, 1968. 1 reel.

1. Piano - Methods. 2. Thorough bass.

NL 0442962   IaU

VOLUME 338

MT224
L65
779
Music
Library

Löhlein, Georg Simon, 1725-1781.
 [Clavier-Schule]
  Clavier-schule; oder, Kurze und gründliche Anweisung zur Melodie und Harmonie, durchgehends mit practischen Beyspielen erkläret. Leipzig, Auf Kosten der Waisenhaus- und Frommannischen Buchhandlung, 1779- [81]
  2 v. music.

  Vol. [1]: 3. und verb. Aufl.
  Vol.2 imperfect: t. p. wanting. Vol.2. published under title: Clavier-Schule, worinnen eine vollständige Anweisung zur Begleitung der unbezifferten Bässe und andern im ersten Bande fehlenden Harmonien gegeben wird, durch sechs Sonaten mit Begleitung einer Violin erkläret. Nebst   einem Zusatze vom Recitativ.

NL 0442963   CU NcU NcRS NcU

Löhlein, Georg Simon, 1725-1781.
 [Clavier-Schule]

  Clavier-Schule; oder, Kurze und gründliche Anweisung zur Melodie und Harmonie, durchgehends mit practischen Beyspielen erkläret. Leipzig, Auf Kosten der Waissenhaus- und Frommannischen Buchhandlung, 1781-82.
  2 v. in 1. 18 x 23 cm.
  Vol. 2 has title: Clavier-Schule, worinnen eine vollständige Anweisung zur Begleitung der unbezifferten Bässe und andern im ersten Bande fehlenden Harmonien gegeben wird, durch sechs Sonaten mit Begleitung einer Violine erkläret. Nebst einem Zusatze vom Recitativ.
  Principally exercises.
  1. Piano—Instruction   and study—To 1800. 2. Thorough bass.

MT224.L72 1781   9-11063 rev*

NL 0442964   DLC ViU NN

AW 1
R4015

Löhlein, Georg Simon, 1727-1781.
  Georg Simon Löhleins Clavier-schule, oder Kurze und gründlich anweisung zur melodie und harmonie, durchgehends mit practischen beyspielen erkläret... Leipzig und Züllichau, Auf kosten der Waisenhaus- und Frommannischen buchhandlung, 1782.
  2 v. in 1. music.
  Microfilm. New York Public Library. 1 — reel. 35 mm.
  Vol. 1:4.   und verb. aufl., 1782.

  Vol. 2 has title: Georg Simon Löhleins Clavier-schule, zweyter band. Worinnen eine vollständige anweisung zur begleitung der unbezifferten bässe / und andern im ersten bande fehlenden harmonien gegeben wird: durch sechs sonaten / mit begleitung einer violine   erkläret. Nebst einem zusatze vom   recitativ.

  1. Pianoforte - Instruction and study.
  2. Musical accompaniment. I. Title.

NL 0442967   CaBVaU

Löhlein, Georg Simon, 1725-1781.

  Clavier-Schule: oder, Kurze und gründliche Anweisung zur Melodie und Harmonie, durch geh ends mit practischen Beyspielen erkläret. 2. Aufl. Züllichau und Freystadt, N. S. Frommann, 1788.
  2v. 18x22cm.

  1. Piano—Instruction and study. · 2. Thorough-bass.

NL 0442968   ViU

Loehlein, Georg Simon, 1727-1781.
  —. Bericht über die Verhandlungen der Georg Simon Löhleins Clavier-Schule, oder kurze Anweisung zum Clavierspielen und dem Generalbasse, mit practischen Bey-spielen. Fünfte Auflage, umgearbeitet und vermehrt von Johann Georg Witthauer. Theil 1-2. Leipzig: N. S. Frommanns Erben, 1791. 188 p. ob. 12°.

  Paging continuous.

98824A. 1. Piano.—Methods.   2. Witthauer, Johann Georg,
1750-1802, editor.
N.Y.P.L.   October 26, 1923.

NL 0442969   NN

MT224
L65
1779

Löhlein, Georg Simon, 1725-1781.
  Klavier-Schule, oder Kurze und gründliche Anweisung zur Melodie und Harmonie, durchgehends mit practischen Beyspielen erkläret., 3. und verbessarte Aufl. Leipzig, Auf Kosten der Waisenhaus- und Frommannischen Buchhandlung, 1779.
  190 p. music.

  Title vignette.

NL 0442970   CU

Löhlein, Georg Simon, 1725-1781.
  George Simon Löhleins Klavier-Schule. Zweyter Band. Worinnen eine vollständige Anweisung zur Begleitung der unbezifferten Bässe, und andern im ersten Bande fehlenden Harmonien gegeben wird: durch Sechs Sonaten, mit Begleitung einer Violine erkläret. Nebst einem Zusatze vom Recitativ. Zweyte Auflage. Züllichau und Freystadt, bei Nathanael Sigismund Frommanns Erben, 1788.
  188 p. 8.1/2 x 6 3/4 cm.

NL 0442971   NcWsMM

Löhlein, Georg Simon, 1725-1781.
 [Clavier-Schule]

  Klavierschule; oder, Anweisung zum Klavier- und Fortepiano-Spiel nebst vielen praktischen Beyspielen und einem Anhange vom Generalbasse. 6. Aufl., ganz umgearb. und sehr vermehrt von A. E. Müller. Jena, F. Frommann, 1804.
  viii, 372 p. diagr. 22 x 27 cm.
  Added t. p.: A. E. Müllers Klavier- und Fortepiano-Schule; oder, Anweisung zur richtigen und geschmackvollen Spielart beyder Instrumente nebst einem Anhang vom Generalbass.
  Principally exercises.
  1. Piano—Instruction and study—To 1800. 2. Thorough bass.
  I. Müller, August Eberhard, 1767-1817.

MT224.L72 1804   57-50633

NL 0442972   DLC CSt ICN InU

Löhlein, Georg Simon, 1725-1781.
  Konzert für Cembalo (Klavier) 2 Violinen und Bass. [Hrsg. von F. von Glasenapp] Leipzig, Breitkopf & Härtel [1953?]
  Score (25 p.) (Collegium musicum, 80)
  Breitkopf & Härtels Kammermusik-Bibliothek, 1981a/b

NL 0442973   MH

Löhlein, Georg Simon, 1725-1781.
  ...Neujahrslied, 1768. Gedicht von Goethe. [Von] Georg Simon Löhlein... [München, 1949] 1 l. 30cm.

  For one voice with piano accompaniment.
  First line: Wer kommt? Wer kauft von meiner Waar?
  Supplement to Neue Musikzeitschrift, 1949, no. 12.

  1. Songs, German. 2. New Year   I. Goethe, Johann Wolfgang von.
  Poems. I. Song index (2).
  N.Y.P.L.

NL 0442974   NN

Löhlein, Georg Simon, 1725-1781.
 [Concertos, harpsichord & string orchestra, op. 7]

  Trois concertos, pour la clavecin, ou piano-forte. Avec accompagnement de deux violons, & basse. Œuvre 7. Lyon, Guera [1770?]
  parts. 33 cm.

  L. C. set imperfect.

  1. Concertos (Harpsichord with string orchestra)—To 1800—Parts.

M1105.L83 op. 7   46-34483 rev/M

NL 0442975   DLC

LÖHLEIN, GEORG SIMON, 172 5-1781.
  [TRIOS, OP. 4]
  III trio pour le clavecin avec accompagnement de violon ou flute et base ad libitum, composés par G.S. Löhlein. Œuvre IV... Leipsic, Chez l'auteur et Breitkopff [1769?] 1 v. 32cm.

  Collection 1.
  Part for harpsichord only
  "Gravé par l'auteur."
  1. Chamber music, 18th cent. --   Trios. 2. Harpsichord--To 1800.
  3. Piano--To 1800.

NL 0442976   NN

M785.72
L825d

Löhlein, George Simon, 1727-1781.
 [Duets, violins]
  Vierundzwanzig Duos für Geigen oder andere Instrumente. Hrsg. von Gotthold Frotscher. Wolfenbüttel, Möseler, 1950.
  39p. 27cm.

NL 0442977   IEN

Löhlein, Herbert Andreas.
  Charakterkunde, leicht verständlich; eine praktische Methode, mittels Klapptafeln den Charakter seiner Mitmenschen zu erkennen. Mit 67 Textabbildungen und 6 Darstellungen auf Klapptafeln. Stuttgart, Mundus-Verlag [1955]
  147 p. illus. 21 cm.

  1. Physiognomy. I. Title.

BF853.L6   55-35430 ‡

NL 0442978   DLC NN MH NcD

Löhlein, Herbert Andreas.
  Die Gezeiten des Schicksals; die moderne kosmo-psychologische Prognostik. Auswertung des Individual-Horoskopes auf empirisch-statistisch gewonnenen Grundlagen. Die zeitliche Vorhersage. Zürich, Schweizer Druck- und Verlagshaus [1951]
  159 p. illus. 21 cm.
  "Literatur-Hinweise": p. 157.

  1. Astrology. I. Title.

Harvard Univ. Library   A 52-5942
for Library of Congress   [2]

NL 0442979   MH NN

WB
24237

Löhlein, Herbert Andreas.
  Piraten, Perlen, Panzertaucher; ein Tatsachenbericht von tollkühnen Abenteuern am Grunde der Meere, Flüsse und Seen. Zürich, Schweizer Druck- und Verlagshaus [195-]
  288p. illus.

  1. Diving, Submarine. I. Title (1)

NL 0442980   CtY

Loehlein, Hermann 1847-1901.
  —. Bericht über die Verhandlungen der Gesellschaft für Geburtshilfe und Gynäkologie zu Berlin. [From Jan. 11 to Dec. 13, 1881.] 9, 17 m. 8°. [Berlin, 1881.]

NL 0442981   DNLM

Löhlein, Hermann, 1847-1901.
  [Collected papers on gynecology and obstetrics.]

NL 0442982   ICJ

VOLUME 338

Loehlein, Hermann 1847-1901.
— Der gegenwärtige Stand und die Ziele der Gynäkologie und des gynäkologischen Unterrichts. Academische Antrittsrede gehalten am 15. December 1888 zu Giessen. 16 pp. 8°. Wiesbaden, J. F. Bergmann, 1889.

NL 0442983   DNLM

Löhlein, Hermann 1847-1901.
Gynäkologische Tagesfragen, nach Beobachtungen in der Giessener Universitäts-Frauenklinik besprochen von Dr. med. H. Löhlein, ... Erstes-[v] Heft. Wiesbaden, J. F. Bergmann, 1890-1898.
5 vol. in 1. 25ᶜᵐ.
Contents.— 1. Heft. 1. Zur Kaiserschnittsfrage. 2. Die Versorgung des Stumpfes bei Laparohysterektomien. 3. Fruchtaustritt und Dammschutz. 1890. [4], 78 p. incl. 4 illus., tables. 11 pl.—2. Heft. 4. Über Häufigkeit, Prognose und Behandlung der puerperalen Eklampsie. 5. Die geburtshülfliche Therapie bei osteomalacischer Bekkenenge. 6. Die Bedeutung von Hautabgängen bei der Menstruation nebst Bemerkungen über pränenstruale Congestion. 1891. p. [79]-157 incl. 6 illus., tables. — 3. Heft. 7. Zur Diagnose und Therapie des Gebärmutterkrebses. 8. Zur Ventrifixation der Gebärmutter. 9. Die Verhütung Fieberhafter Erkrankung im Wochenbett. 1893. p. [159]-264. pl. III-IV.— 4. Heft. Ovarialtumoren und Ovariotomie in Schwangerschaft, Geburt und Wochenbett. Meningocele sacralis anterior als schwere Geburts- und Wochenbettscomplication. Die Symphyseotomie und ihr Verhältniss zum Kaiserschnitt und zur künstlichen Frühgeburt. 1895. [2], 75 p.—5. Heft. Erfahrungen über vaginale Bauchschnitt-Operationen. Die manuelle Beckenschätzung. Wann sind Falschlagen der Gebärmutter Gegenstand der Behandlung? 1898. p. [76]-156.

NL 0442985   ICJ N PPC DNLM

Loehlein, Hermann 1847-1901.
— . Die Indication der Ovariotomie und der Myomotomie. 16 pp. 8°. Berlin, Fischer, 1888. Forms 2. Hft. of: Berl. Klinik.

NL 0442986   DNLM

Loehlein, Hermann 1847-1901.
— . Leistungen und Aufgaben der geburtshülflichen Institute im Dienste der Humanität. Akademische Festrede. 31 pp. 4°. Giessen, von München, 1869.

NL 0442987   DNLM ICRL MH

Loehlein, Hermann, 1847-1901.
— . Ueber das Verhalten des Herzens bei Schwangern und Wöchnerinnen. Nach Beobachtungen in der geburtshülflichen Klinik der Berliner Universität. 35 pp., 1 tab. 8°. Stuttgart, F. Enke. 1876.

NL 0442988   DNLM

Löhlein (Hermann) 1847-1901.
Ueber die Bedeutung subperitonealen (anteuterinen) Euphysems während der Geburt. 12 pp. 8°. [Stuttgart, 1875.] Repr. from: Ztschr. f. Geburtsh. u. Frauenkr., Stuttg. 1875-6, I.

NL 0442989   DNLM

Loehlein Hermann, 1847-1901.
* Ueber die Kunsthülfe bei der durch allgemeine Beckenenge erschwerten Geburt. 36 pp., 1 l. 8°. Berlin, G. Schade. [1870].

NL 0442990   DNLM

LÖHLEIN, Johann Baptist Andreas, d. 1765.
Actionem pignoratitiam personalem in rem scriptam esse, et sic dari contra tertium quemcunque possessoren ad illustrandam legem 27. ff. de actione pignoratitia demonstrat. Wirceburgi, n. d. [1762].
27 p.

NL 0442991   MH-L

Löhlein, Johann Baptist Andreas, d. 1765.
Actorem in actione negatoria, possessione etiam penes reum existente, a probatione immunem esse demonstrat ... Joannes Baptista Andreas Löhlein ... Wirceburgi, Typis Viduae J.J.C.Kleyer, 1759.
26 p   20ᵐ.

FL6
D613
v.14
no.29
Vol.14, no.29 of a collection with binder's title: Dissertationes juridicae.

1. Parties to actions.

NL 0442992   MiU-L

Löhlein, Johann Baptist Andreas, d. 1765, respondent.
Canonica episcoporum Germaniae constitutio... celebrata...
see under   Barthel, Johann Kaspar, 1697-1771, praeses.

Löhlein, Johann Baptist Andreas, d. 1765.
Causam juramento delato, judiciali voluntario aeque ac extrajudiciali, ac insimul praestito praetextu perjurii, retractari posse, ad illustrandam legem fin. C. De reb. credit. demonstrat ... Joannes Baptista Andreas Löhlein ... Wirceburgi, Typis Viduae J.J.C. Kleyer, 1760.
[24] p. 20ᵐ.

FL6
D613
v.14
no.31
Vol.14, no.31 of a collection with binder's title: Dissertationes juridicae.

1. Oaths.

NL 0442994   MiU-L

Löhlein, Johann Baptist Andreas, d. 1765.
Communem opinionem de ordinaria praescriptione servitutum sine titulo currente legibus & rationi repugnare demonstrat ... Joannes Baptista Andreas Löhlein ... Wirceburgi, Typis J.J.C.Kleyer, 1753.
[27] p. 20ᵐ.

FL6
D613
v.14
no.30
Vol.14, no.30 of a collection with binder's title: Dissertationes juridicae.

1. Servitudes. I.Title: De ordinaria praescriptione servitutum.

NL 0442995   MiU-L

FLGZ
84
no.7
Löhlein, Johann Baptist Andreas, d. 1765, praeses
... De dominio eminente ... Wirceburgi, typis viduae J.J.C. Kleyer, 1762.
9 p. l., [5]-50, [6] p. 20½cm.
(Foreign law pamphlet collection, v.84, no.7)

Inaug.-diss. - Wurzburg (J.S. Fabris)

NL 0442996   CtY-L

Löhlein, Johann Baptist Andreas, d. 1765, respondent.
... De rebus ecclesiae non alienandis...
see under   Barthel, Johann Kaspar, 1697-1771, praeses.

Löhlein, Johann Baptist Andreas, d. 1765.
Possessorium summariissimum duntaxat locum tenere in remedio retinendae possessionis demonstrat ... Joannes Baptista Andreas Löhlein ... Wirceburgi, Typis Viduae J.J.C.Kleyer, 1757.
[16] p. 20ᵐ.

FL6
D613
v.14
no.28
Vol.14, no.28 of a collection with binder's title: Dissertationes juridicae.

1. Possession - Germany. I.Title.

NL 0442998   MiU-L

Löhlein, Johann Baptist Andreas, d. 1765.
Privilegia titulo oneroso etiam extraneo quaesita revocari posse demonstrat ... Joannes Baptista Andreas Löhlein ... Wirceburgi, Typis Viduae J.J.C.Kleyer, 1756.
[22] p. 20ᵐ.

FL6
D613
v.14
no.26
Vol.14, no.26 of a collection with binder's title: Dissertationes juridicae.

1. Revocation - Germany. I.Title.

NL 0442999   MiU-L

Löhlein, Johann Baptist Andreas, d. 1765
Specimen juris civilis de otio clausulae codicillaris, quo clausula codicillaris contra dissertationem inauguralem juridicam sub praesidio Francisci Aleff ... desuper expositam ab imputato otio tum vindicatur, tum nullitates testamentorum clausula codicillari insanabiles, casusque varii, quibus eadem inefficax est, insimul determinantur ... [Wirceburgi] Typis J. J.C.Kleyer, 1750.

FL6
D613
v.42
no.36
[16], 56 p. 20cm.
Vol.42, no.36 of a collection with binder's title: Dissertatione[s] [j]uridicae.

NL 0443000   MiU-L

Löhlein, Johann Baptist Andreas, d. 174[?]
Specimen juris civilis, de otio clausulae salutaris, quo clausulae salutaris origo investigatur, effectus a DD.eidem attribui consüeti enumerantur, otium denique ejusdem in quovis libello demonstratur ... Wirceburgi, Typis J.J.C.Kleyer, 1752.
[16], 51 p. 20ᵐ.

FL6
D613
v.14
no.22
Vol.14, no.22 of a collection with binder's title: Dissertationes juridicae.

1. Pleading. I.Title: Clausula salutaris.

NL 0443001   MiU-L

Löhlein, Johann Baptist Andreas, d. 1765.
Testamenta sola voluntate contraria verbis, solemniter tamen, declarata, facto nullo concurrente, neque lapsu decennii accedente infirmari demonstrat ... Joannes Baptista Andreas Löhlein. Wirceburgi, Typis J.J.C.Kleyer, 1754.
[24] p. 20ᵐ.

FL6
D613
v.14
no.23
Vol.14, no.23 of a collection with binder's title: Dissertationes juridicae.

1. Wills.

NL 0443002   MiU-L

Löhlein, Ludwig, comp.
Campaign of 1870-1. The operations of the corps of General v. Werder. Comp. from the official documents, by Ludwig Löhlein ... tr. by Lieut. Fred T. Maxwell ... Chatham, Printed by J. Gale [1876?]
1 p. l., ix, 171, xxiv p. fold. maps. 22ᵐ.

1. Franco-German war, 1870-1871. 2. Werder, August, graf von, 1808-1887. I. Maxwell, Frederick Thomson, tr. II. Title.

15-22360

Library of Congress   DC297.C14th.L6

NL 0443003   DLC

LÖHLEIN, Ludwig, compiler.
Feldzug 1870-71. Die operationen des korps des generals von Werder. Nach den akten des general-kommandos dargestellt. Berlin, E.S.Mittler, und sohn, 1874.
Maps.

NL 0443004   MH

VOLUME 338

Löhlein, Max, 1877-1921.
Beiträge zur pathologie der eingeborenen
von Kamerun. Leipzig, Barth, 1912.
110 p. illus., 4 plates (part col.) tables
(Deutsche medizinische zeitschrift, bd. 16,
beiheft 9)

1. Camerons, Africa - Sanitary affairs.

NL 0443005   NNC DNLM

Loehlein, Max, 1877-1921.
— Die Gesetze der Leukozytentätigkeit bei
entzündlichen Progressen. iv, 25 pp. 8°.
Jena. G. Fischer, 1913.

NL 0443006   DNLM

Loehlein, Max, 1877-1921.
... Die krankheiterregenden bakterien; entstehung, heilung und bekämpfung der bakteriellen infektionskrankheiten des menschen, gemeinverständlich dargestellt von
dr. med. M. Loehlein ... mit 33 abbildungen im text.
Leipzig, B. G. Teubner, 1910.
vi, 120 p. illus. 18½ᶜᵐ. (Aus natur und geistes welt; sammlung wissenschaftlich-gemeinverständlicher darstellungen. 307. bdchen.)   M. 1.25

1. Bacteria, Pathogenic. 2. Contagion and contagious diseases.

Library of Congress   QR56.L8   10-16112

NL 0443007   DLC DNLM MiU

Loehlein, Max, 1877-1921.
... Die krankheiterregenden bakterien; grundtatsachen der
entstehung, heilung und verhütung der bakteriellen infektionskrankheiten des menschen, gemeinverständlich dargestellt von
dr. med. M. Loehlein ... 2., verb. aufl. Mit 33 abbildungen im
text. Leipzig und Berlin, B. G. Teubner, 1919.
110 p. illus. 18½ᶜᵐ. (Aus natur und geistes welt; sammlung wissenschaftlich-gemeinverständlicher darstellungen. 307. bdchen.)

1. Bacteria, Pathogenic. 2. Contagion and contagious diseases.
43-43943

Library of Congress   QR56.L8 1919

NL 0443008   DLC

Löhlein, Max, 1877-1921.
Über die entzündlichen Veränderungen der Glomeruli der
menschlichen Nieren und ihre Bedeutung für die Nephritis,
von Dr. med. M. Löhlein ... Mit 2 Tafeln. Leipzig, S. Hirzel,
1907.
(4, 98 p. II double col. pl. 26ᶜᵐ. (Added t.-p.: Arbeiten aus dem pathologischen Institute zu Leipzig ... (1. Bd.) Heft 4)
"Literaturverzeichnis": p. (95)-96.

NL 0443009   ICJ DNLM NcD IU-M

Loehlein, Max, 1877-1921.
Ueber die sogenannte follikuläre Ruhr, von M. Löhlein...
Jena: G. Fischer, 1923. 50 p. illus. 4°. (Veröffentlich-
ungen aus der Kriegs- und Konstitutionspathologie. Bd. 3,
Heft 4.)

Bibliography, p. 45-50.

1. Dysentery. 2. Series.
N. Y. P. L.   June 7; 1924

NL 0443010   NN DNLM

Löhlein, Max, 1877-1921.
Über die sogenannte follikuläre Ruhr, von M.
Löhlein. Jena, G. Fischer, 1923.
50 p. illus. 26 cm. (Veröffentlichungen
aus der Kriegs- und Konstitutionspathologie,
Heft 13)

RB6
V546
no.13
1923

Bibliography: p. 45-50.

1. Dysentery.   I. Title.   (Series)

NL 0443011   CU-M DNLM ICU ICJ

Loehlein, Max, 1877-1921.
Ueber kugelthromben des herzens.
Inaug. diss. Giessen, 1900.

NL 0443012   ICRL MH DNLM

Löhlein, Roland.
Der Schutz des Kunstwerks vor Entstellung...
Erlangen, 1929.
Inaug.-Diss. - München.

NL 0443013   CtY MH-L

Löhlein, Roland, ed.
Studien zum kausalen Rechtsdenken; eine Festgabe zum
80. Geburtstag von Rudolf Müller-Erzbach überreicht von
Freunden und Schülern. Hrsg. von Roland Löhlein und
Erwin Seidl, unter Mitarbeit von Emilio Betti (et al.)
München-Pasing, Filser-Verlag (°1954)
127 p. 21 cm.
CONTENTS.—Der Grundsatz von Treu und Glauben in rechtsge-
schichtlicher und -vergleichender Betrachtung, von E. Betti.—Rechtli-
che Fragen aus der Konkurrenz zwischen Bundesbahn, Bundespost
und privaten Verkehrsunternehmen im Linienverkehr, von D. Gogos.—
Zur geistigen Situation der deutschen Rechtswissenschaft, von R.
Löhlein.—Nozione dogmatica della società per azioni nella storia, di
L. Mossa.—Die Machtlage bei den römischen Juristen, von E. Seidl.—
Acceptkredit und Gefälligkeitsaccept, von H. Würdinger.

1. Law—Germany (Federal Republic, 1949-   )—Addresses, essays, lectures. 2. Law—Addresses, essays, lectures. 3. Müller-
Erzbach, Rudolf, 1874-   I. Seidl, Erwin, 1905-   joint ed.
II. Title.
57-46464

NL 0443015   DLC MH-L CtY-L ICU

Löhlein, Theodor, 1829-1915.
C. F. Drollinger. Von prof. dr. Theodor Löhlein ... Karlsruhe, G. Braun'sche hofbuchdr., 1873.
2 p. l., 40 p. 20ᶜᵐ.
"Beilage zu dem Programm des Grossh. gymnasiums zu Karlsruhe für
1873."

1. Drollinger, Carl Friedrich, 1688-1742.
29-11943

Library of Congress   PT1846.D9Z7

NL 0443016   DLC

Löhlein, Walther, 1882-
... Bindehaut. Von Walther Löhlein ... Mit 114 Abbil-
dungen ...
(In Handbuch der speziellen pathologischen Anatomie und Histologie. Ber-
lin, 1928. 26½ᶜᵐ. Bd. 11, Teil 1, p. 1-215. illus. (part col.))
"Literatur": p. 202-215.

NL 0443017   ICJ DNLM

LÖHLEIN, Walther, 1882-
Die Entwicklung des Sehens. Jena,
Fischer, 1931.
30 p. (Jenaer akademische Reden,
Heft 13)
Lecture delivered at the Feier der
akademischen Preisverteilung, Jena
Univ., June 20, 1931.
1. Vision - Physiology   Title

WW
103
L825e
1931

NL 0443018   DNLM IEN CtY

Loehlein, Walther, 1882-
— Glaukom. 30 pp. 8°. Würzburg, C
Kabitzsch, 1912.
Forms Heft 6, v. 12, of Würzb. Abhandl. a. d. Gesamtgeb
d. prakt. Med.

NL 0443019   DNLM

Loehlein, Walther, 1882-
— Hygiene des Auges. 62 pp. 8°. Würzburg, A. Stuber, 1911.
Forms Heft 3 & 4, v. 11, of Würzb. Abhandl. a. d. Gesamt
geb. d. prakt. Med.

NL 0443020   DNLM

Löhlein, Walther, 1882-
— Intraokularer Flüssigkeits-
wechsel und intraokular Druck; Glaukom;
Hypotonie. p.501-45. 8° Jena. 1945.
In Lehrb. Augenh. (Axenfeld, T.) Jena, 1945.

NL 0443021   DNLM

Löhlein, Walther, 1882-
... Über die Volhardsche methode der quantitativen
pepsin- und trypsinbestimmung durch titration ...
Braunschweig, F. Vieweg und sohn, 1905.
28 p., 1 l. 23½ᶜᵐ.
Inaug.-diss.—Giessen.
Lebenslauf.
Beiträge zur chemischen physiologie und pathologie ... Sonder-abdruck
aus band VII, heft 1/3.

1. Pepsin. 2. Trypsin.
7-40900†

Library of Congress   QP193.L5

NL 0443022   DLC DNLM NN

LÖHLEIN, Walther, 1882-   ed.
Zeitfragen der Augenheilkunde;
Vorträge vom augenärztlichen Fort-
bildungskurs, Berlin 1938. Stuttgart,
Enke, 1938.
vii, 428 p. illus.
1. Ophthalmology   Title

WW
100
L825z
1938

NL 0443023   DNLM MoSU

Löhlein, Walther, 1882-   ed.
ZEITFRAGEN DER AUGENHEILKUNDE; VORTRÄGE UND
demonstrationen vom augenärztlichen Fortbildungs-
skurs, Berlin, 4.Bis 9, August 1952. Zusammen
mit W.Hoffmann und H.Gasteiger. Hrsg. von W.
Löhlein. Leipzig,G.Thieme,1954.
11+474 p. illus.

RE 940
.A3 Z4

1. Optometry--Addresses,essays,lectures,etc.
2. Optometry--Congresses.   I. Hoffmann,W

NL 0443024   InU DNLM

Löhlein, Wilhelm, Oberarzt b. Jäger-Reg. zu Pferde No. 6:
Aus d. Univ.-Augenkl. zu Marburg. Zur Physiologie der
Irisbewegung. Marburg 1911: Hamel. 61 S. 8°
Marburg, Med. Diss. v. 8. Jan. 1912, Ref. Bach
[Geb. 6. Sept. 82 Ansbach; Wohnort: Erfurt; Staatsangeh.: Bayern; Vor-
bildung: Luisen-Gymn. Berlin Reife M. 01; Studium: Berlin K. W. A. 10 S.;
Coll. 11. Dez. 11; Approb. 22. Febr. 08.]   [U 12.3487]

NL 0443025   ICRL DNLM CtY DLC

VOLUME 338

Loehlin, Clinton Herbert, 1897-   , ed.
Self-support in village churches of
India; ed. by C.H. Loehlin and B.L.
Hamilton; introduction by... J.W. Robinson...
Bangalore, Scripture literature press,
1931.
viii, 50 p. map. 19ᵐ.

NL 0443026   NjPT

Loehlin, Clinton Herbert, 1897-
The Sikhs and their book. Lucknow, Lucknow Pub.
House, 1946.
109, viii p. plates. 19 cm.
Bibliography : p. (107)-109.

1. Sikhs—Religion. 2. Ādi-Granth.   I. Title.

BL2020.S5L59   294.553   60-22414

NL 0443027   DLC IEN NjP ICU

Löhmann,
Zur frage der canalverbindung Leipzigs mit der Elbe.
(Leipzig, Gedruckt bei E. Polz, 1872)
(6) p., 1 l. 31ᵐ.
Caption title.
Signed : Baurath Löhmann.

1. Leipzig-Wallwitzhafen canal (projected)

Library of Congress   TC674.L5L8   6-6542†

NL 0443028   DLC

Löhmann, Erich, 1883-
Studien über den Verlauf der Sandmeyerschen
Reaktion bei Bromamidochinolinen. Freiburg,
Speyer & Kaerner, 1908.
40 p.
Inaug.-Diss. - Freiburg, 1908.

NL 0443029   ICRL NN PU

Löhmann, Friedrich, 1787-1835.
Die Fahrstrasse unter dem Wasser
see under Brunel, Sir Marc Isambard,
1769-1849.

Löhmann, Friedrich, 1787-1835.
Handbuch für juridische und staatswirthschaftliche
rechnungen ... nebst dreizehn bogen tabellen über die
höhere interessen-berechnung ... Von Friedrich Löhmann
... Leipzig, J. A. Barth, 1829.
lvi, 392 p. incl. tables. 21½ᶜᵐ.
Bound with this is his Tafeln der höhern und niedern zinsrechnung ...
1829.

1. Accounting—Early works to 1900.

NL 0443031   MiU

Löhmann, Friedrich, 1787-1835.
Tafeln der höhern und niedern zinsrechnung ...Ent-
worfen und auf das genauste berechnet von Friedrich
Löhmann ... Leipzig, J. A. Barth, 1829.
208 p. tables. 21½ᶜᵐ.
With his Handbuch für juridische und staatswirthschaftliche rechnungen
... 1829.

1. Interest and usury—Tables, etc.

NL 0443032   MiU

QV
716
qL825t
1832
LÖHMANN, Friedrich 1787-1835.
Tafeln der Medicinal- und Apotheker-
gewichte aller Länder und freien Städte in
Europa. Poids médicaux et pharmaceuti-
ques de tous les états et villes-libres de
l'Europe. Leipzig, Barth, 1832.
xxvi, 73, 172 p. (His Tafeln zur
Verwandlung des Längen- und Hohl-
Maasses. 5. Bd., 1.-2. Abth.)

NL 0443033   DNLM

HG219 Löhmann, Friedrich, 1787-1835.
.L8'   Tafeln der rechnungsmünzen; oder, Verwandlung, einthei-
lung, gewicht und wahrer werth derjenigen münzen, nach
welchen sowohl bei öffentlichen cassen, als im handel gerech-
net wird ...   Tables de monnaies de compte, ou Réduction,
division, poids et valeur effective des monnaies d'après les-
quelles on compte soit dans les caisses publiques, soit dans le
commerce ... Calculés avec soin pour la première fois, par
Frédéric Löhmann ... Leipzig, J. A. Barth, 1826.
xvi, 482 p. fold. tables. 25¼x21½ᵐ. (Added t.-p.: Tafeln zur verwandlung
des längen- und hohl-masses ... von Friedrich Löhmann ... 4. abt.)
German and French in parallel columns.

1. Money—Tables, etc.   2. Foreign exchange—Tables, etc.

NL 0443034   ICU RPB

Loehmann, Georg Heinrich, respondent.
... Circa lvctvm pvblicvm
see under Böhmer, Just Henning, 1674-
1749, praeses.

Löhmann (H.) Ueber die Wendung und Ex-
traction bei engem Becken.
In : Kameradschaft (Der). 8°. Stuttgart, 1888, 33-76.

NL 0443036   DNLM

Löhmann (Heinrich). *Beiträge zur Kenntniss der chronischen Hirnabscesse. 28 pp., 2 l.,
1 pl. 8°. Kiel, Schmidt u. Klaunig, 1883.

NL 0443037   DNLM

LÖHMANN, Heinrich.
Beitrage zur kenntniss der chronischen
hirnabscesse. Diss. Kiel, 1886.

NL 0443038   MBCo ICRL

Löhmann (Karl) [1878-   ]. *Der Einfluss
digitaler Untersuchung interpartum auf die
Wochenbettsmorbilität bei strenger Anwendung der Heisswasser-Seife-Alkoholhändedes-
infection. 43 pp. 8°. Marburg, John Hamel, 1906.

NL 0443039   DNLM ICRL CtY

AC
831
Löhmann, Otto, 1908-
Die rahmenerzählung des Decameron ...
Halle, 1935.   46 p.
Inaug. Diss. - Halle-Wittenberg, 1935.
Lebenslauf.

NL 0443040   ICRL MiU

Löhmann, Otto, 1908-
Die rahmenerzählung des Decameron, ihre quellen und nach-
wirkungen; ein beitrag zur geschichte der rahmenerzählung,
von Otto Löhmann. Halle (Saale) M. Niemeyer, 1935.
vii, 232 p. 23½ᶜᵐ. (Added t.-p.: Romanistische arbeiten, hrsg. von dr.
K. Voretzsch ... xxII)

1. Boccaccio, Giovanni. Il Decamerone. 2. Frame-stories. I. Title.

35-15793

Library of Congress   PN3383.F7L6
(3)   808.8

NL 0443041   DLC CoU CtY PU NN

Löhmann, Otto, 1908-
... Die sage von Gawain und dem Grünen ritter, von Otto
Löhmann. Königsberg (Pr) und Berlin, Ost-Europa-verlag,
1938.
iv, 97 p. diagrs. 22½ᵐ. (Schriften der Albertus-universität, hrsg.
vom Königsberger universitätsbund. Geisteswissenschaftliche reihe,
bd. 17)

1. Gawain and the Grene knight. I. Title.

A C 39-3066

Princeton univ. Library
for Library of Congress   (2)

NL 0443042   NjP CtY MiU ICN

Löhmer, Alfred.
Geschichte des Häringer Kohlenbergbaues; Werk und
Menschen. Mit einem Nachtrag von Otto Sykora. (n. p.)
1953(?)
252, 9 p. 20 cm.
Bibliography : p. 7 (1st group of foliation)

1. Coal mines and mining—Häring, Austria.   I. Title.

HD9555.A83H36   56-37285

NL 0443043   DLC

W 4
M96
1953
LÖHMER, Helmut, 1926-
Aortenrupturen und deren Begut-
achtung in der Unfallversicherung.
(München) 1953.
25 ℓ.
Inaug. -Diss. - Munich.
Typewritten copy.
1. Aorta

NL 0443044   DNLM

Loehn, Anna
see Loehn-Siegel, Maria Anna, 1830-
1902.

Löhn, Eduard Wilhelm.
Dr. Caspar Creutziger oder Cruciger,
der Schüler, Freund und Amtsgenosse
Luther's und Melanchthon's, nach ungedruckten und gedruckten Quellen... 2.
neubearb. und vermehrte Aufl.   Leipzig,
J. Naumann, 1859.
iv, 62 p. 23ᵐ.

1 Cruciger, Caspar, 1504-1548

NL 0443046   NjPT

Löhn, Eduard Wilhelm.
Encyclopädie der Bibelkunde
see under Gemmerll, Gottf. Alb.

VOLUME 338

Loehn (Joannes Godofredus) [1765–]. *De apoplexia.* 2 p. l., 31 pp. 4°. *Lipsiæ, Tauchnitz, 1862.*

NL 0443048   DNLM

Löhn (P.). Das Lampenfieber; ein Ratgeber für Redner, Deklamatoren, Amateur- und Berufsschauspieler, angehende Künstler, Dilettanten sowie für Gelegenheitsvortragende jeden Genres. 37 pp. 8°. Oranienburg [190?].

NL 0443049   DNLM

Loehn-Siegel, *Frau Maria Anna,* 1830–1902.
Aus der alten coulissenwelt. Mein engagement am Leipziger und Madgeburger stadttheater in den jahren 1847 und 1848. Von Anna Löhn-Siegel. Leipzig, W. Friedrich, 1883.
1 p. L, [v]–viii p., 1 L, 461 p. 20ᶜᵐ.

1. Actors—Correspondence, reminiscences, etc. 2. Theater—Leipzig. 3. Theater—Magdeburg. ɪ. Title. · LC

32–6060

Library of Congress   PN2658.L6A3   927.92

NL 0443050   DLC CLSU

PT2424
.L62D4
1872
Loehn-Siegel, Maria Anna, 1830–1902.
Ein deutscher Schulmeister; eine Dorfgeschichte in Versen, von Anna Löhn. Leipzig, H. Matthes, 1872.
99 p. 14 cm.

NL 0443051   ViU

DG426
L64
1871
Loehn-Siegel, Maria Anna, 1830–1902.
Innerhalb zehn Jahren. Reiseerlebnisse und Reiseeindrücke aus den Jahren 1857 bis 1867. 2. ergänzte und verm. Aufl. Gera, Issleib & Rietzschel, 1871.
viii,448 p.

NL 0443052   CU

Loehn-Siegel, Maria Anna, 1830–1902.
Odowalsky. Schauspiel in 5 Akten. Mit freier Benutzung des Romans: "Die Schweden vor Prag" von Caroline Pichler, geb. von Greiner. Dresden, H. Henkler, [18–?]
1 p.l., 66 p. 8°.

NL 0443053   NN

Loehn-Siegel, Maria Anna, 1830–1902.
Reisetagebuch einer alleinreisenden Dame in Italien. Leipzig, J.A. Bergson-Sonenberg, 1861.
1 p.l., 124 p. 16°. (Bergson's Eisenbahnbücher, 41)

NL 0443054   NN

Loehn-Siegel, *Frau Maria Anna,* 1830–1902.
Theatererinnerungen und vermischtes, von Anna Löhn. Leipzig, J. A. Bergson-Sonenberg [1861]
126 p. 17½ᶜᵐ. (*On cover:* Bergson's eisenbahnbücher. no. 55)

ɪ. Title.

22–25035

Library of Congress   PT2424.L62T5 1861

NL 0443055   DLC

PN2658
L6A5
Löhn-Siegel, Maria Anna, 1830–1902.
Vom Oldenburger Hoftheater zum Dresdner; letzte Theatertagebuchblätter, von Anna Löhn-Siegel. Oldenburg, Schulzesche Hof-Buchhandlung und Hof-Buchdruckerei [Vorwort 1885]
vi, 268 p. 19 cm.

1. Actors, German - Correspondence, reminiscences, etc. 2. Theater - Germany - Hist. I. Title.

NL 0443056   OU IEN

Loehnberg, Alfred.
הנגב הרחוק [תירגם מכתב־יד. י. מאן] תל־אביב. עם עובד. [Tel-Aviv, 1952/53] תשי״ב.
191 p. illus. maps (1 fold. in pocket) 23 cm.

1. Negeb.   *Title transliterated:* ha-Negev ha-raḥoḳ.

DS110.N4L6   54–54065 rev

NL 0443057   DLC MiU

Loehnberg, Alfred.
Zur Hydrographie des Cerkniško Polje; ein Beitrag zur Karstforschung. Beograd, Impr. "Mlada Srbija," 1934.
114 p. illus. 25 cm. (Mémoires de la Société de géographie de Beograd, v. 3)
Includes bibliography.

1. Karst. 2. Physical geography—Yugoslavia. 3. Water, Underground—Yugoslavia. ɪ. Title.

GB608.67.L6   64–58800 ‡

NL 0443058   DLC MiU NN NIC DI-GS

Loehnberg, Alfred.
Zur Hydrographie des Cerkniško Polje; ein Beitrag zur Karstforschung. Beograd, Impr. "Mlada Srbija," 1934.
114 p. illus. 25 cm. (Mémoires de la Société de géographie de Beograd, v. 3)
Includes bibliography.
Microfilm copy.

NL 0443059   DI-GS

AC
831
Löhmberg, Erhart, 1903–
Die typen der nachahmung bei den primitiven völkern ...
Inaug. Diss. –Berlin, [1933]
Lebenslauf.

(Archiv für die gesamte psychologie Bd. 88, 1933)

NL 0443060   ICRL CtY PU

Löhnberg, Ernst, 1885–
Über Lupus erythematodes mit besonderer Berücksichtigung der Aetiologie und der neueren Therapie vorzüglich der Radiotherapie und der Kohlensäurevereisung. Bonn 1911: Ludwig. 62 S. 8°
Bonn, Med. Diss. v. 7. Juli 1911, Ref. Doutrelepont
[Geb. 9. Jan. 85 Warstein; Wohnort: Cöln; Staatsangeh.: Preußen; Vorbildung: Marzellen-Gymn. Cöln Reife O. 05; Studium: München 2, Bonn 8 S.; Coll. 6. Mai 10; Approb. 15. Mai 11.]   [U 11.419]

NL 0443061   ICRL MH DNLM

Löhndorff, Ernst Friedrich, 1899–
Ägyptische nächte. Schloss Bleckede an der Elbe, O. Meissner [1952]
246 p. 20 cm. ([R]ot[w]eiss[R]omane)

ɪ. Title.

PT2623.O33A67   833.91   53–15104 ‡

NL 0443062   DLC

916.5
L825xlD
Löhndorff, Ernst Friedrich, 1899–
Afrika græder. [Autoriseret oversætte se for Danmark og Norge ved Otto Wadstet] København, Jespersen, 1930.
216p. plates. 25cm.

Translation of Afrika weint.

1. Sahara. Descr. & trav. 2. France. Armée. Légion étrangère. I. Title.

NL 0443063   IEN

Löhndorff, Ernst Friedrich, 1899–
Afrika weint; Tagebuch eines Legionärs. Zürich: Grethlein & Co. [cop. 1930.] 360 p. fold. map. 12°.

1. France—Army. 2. Title.
N. Y. P. L.   November 16, 1933

NL 0443064   NN MiD MH

PT
2623
.O33
A55
Löhndorff, Ernst Friedrich, 1899–
Amineh. Die zehntausend Gesichter Indiens. Bremen, Carl Schünemann [c1930]
295p. 20cm.

NL 0443065   TNJ MiD PPT NN

Löhndorff, Ernst Friedrich, 1899–
... Bestie ich in Mexiko. 1. aufl. Stuttgart, Dieck & co. [1927]
522, [1] p. 20ᶜᵐ. (*Half-title:* Heimat und weltbücher)

ɪ. Title.

Library of Congress   PT2623.O33B4 1927   29–14086

NL 0443066   DLC PPT

G833
L825b
1927r
LÖHNDORFF, ERNST FRIEDRICH, 1899–
... Bestie ich in Mexiko, wahre erlebnisse. Bremen, C. Schünemann verlag [c1927]
397,[1]p. fold. map. 20cm.

At head of title: Ernst F. Löhndorff.
"61.–80. tausend."

NL 0443067   TxU IaU OU

Loehndorff, Ernst Friedrich, 1899–
...Bestie Ich in Mexiko. Stuttgart: Dieck & Co. [cop. 1927.] 522 p. 4. ed. 12°. (Heimat und Weltbücher.)

383488A. 1. Fiction, German. 2. Mexico—Hist., 1910— — Fiction. 3. Indians, Mexican—Yaqui. 4. Title.
N. Y. P. L.   November 30, 1928

NL 0443068   NN

Löhndorff, Ernst Friedrich, 1899–
... Bestie ich in Mexiko, wahre erlebnisse. Bremen, C. Schünemann [194–]
397, [1] p. fold. map. 20ᶜᵐ.
At head of title: Ernst F. Löhndorff.
"91.–105. tausend."

ɪ. Title.

PT2623.O33B4   833.91   A F 46–1396
Princeton univ. Library
for Library of Congress   [4]†

NL 0443069   DLC ViU   NjP ScU ICRL RPB NRU MnU TxU IaU RPB

VOLUME 338

Löhndorff, Ernst Friedrich, 1899–
Bestie Ich; Jugendbiographie und Beichte.
Bremen, C. Schünemann [1952, c1927] 411 p.
(map on lining paper) 19cm.

1. Mexico—Hist., 1910– , Fiction. 2. Indians,
Mexican—Tribes—Yaqui—Fiction. I. Title.

NL 0443070   NN

Löhndorff, Ernst Friedrich, 1899–
... Blumenhölle am Jacinto; urwalderlebnis. Bremen, C.
Schünemann [1932]
252, [1] p. 20ᶜᵐ.
At head of title: Ernst F. Löhndorff.

I. Title.

Library of Congress   PT2623.O33B5 1932   41–22625
[2]   833.91

NL 0443071   DLC WU PPG PPT

Löhndorff, Ernst Friedrich, 1899–
Blumenhölle am Jacinto; Urwalderlebnis. Leipzig: Grethlein & Co. [, cop. 1932] 266 p. 12°.

NL 0443072   NN

Löhndorff, Ernst Friedrich, 1899–
Chasseur d'orchidées. Texte français de G. Duchet-
Suchaux. Illustrations de Jean Reschofsky. [Paris] Ha-
chette [1955]
187 p. illus. 21 cm.
Translation of Blumenhölle am Jacinto.

I. Title.

PT2623.O33B55   55–32476 ‡

NL 0443073   DLC

Löhndorff, Ernst Friedrich, 1899–
... Die frau von Hawai, roman. Bremen, C. Schünemann
[*1938]
291, [1] p. 20ᶜᵐ.
At head of title: Ernst F. Löhndorff.
"Erstes bis zehntes tausend."

I. Title.

Library of Congress   PT2623.O33F7 1938   39–3506

NL 0443074   DLC NN CU CtY

Löhndorff, Ernst Friedrich, 1899–
... Die frau von Hawai, roman. Bremen, C. Schünemann
[194–?]
291, [1] p. 20ᶜᵐ.
At head of title: Ernst F. Löhndorff.
"41.- 50. tausend."

NL 0443075   CtY

Löhndorff, Ernst Friedrich, 1899–
... Gloria und der Teddyboy, amerikanisches sittenbild.
Bremen, C. Schünemann [1943]
303, [1] p. 19½ᶜᵐ.
At head of title: Ernst F. Löhndorff.
"Erstes bis fünfundzwanzigstes tausend."

I. Title.

PT2623.O33G5   A F 47–891
California. Univ. Libr.
for Library of Congress   [4]†

NL 0443076   CU IaU ICU OCU CtY TNV RPB MB DLC

Löhndorff, Ernst Friedrich, 1899–
... Gold, whisky und frauen in Nordland, roman. Bremen,
C. Schünemann [*1935]
253, [1] p. 20ᶜᵐ.
At head of title: Ernst F. Löhndorff.
"Sechstes bis zehntes tausend."

I. Title.

Library of Congress   PT2623.O33G6 1935 a   36–10002
Copyright A—Foreign   30827
[2]   833.91

NL 0443077   DLC WU CtY CU NN

Loehndorff, Ernst Friedrich, 1899–
Hell in the Foreign legion, by Ernst F. Löhndorff; translated
by Gerard Shelley. London: G. Allen & Unwin, Ltd. [, 1931.]
349 p. 8°.
"The German original, 'Afrika Weint', was published in 1930."

531632A. 1. Foreign legion, French.   I. Shelley, Gerard, translator.
I. Title.
N. Y. P. L.   June 22, 1931

NL 0443078   NN MH

Löhndorff, Ernst Friedrich, 1899–
Hell in the Foreign legion, by Ernst F. Löhndorff; trans-
lated by Gerard Shelley. New York, Greenberg, 1932.
349 p. 20ᶜᵐ.
"Printed in Great Britain."
"The German original, 'Afrika weint', was published in 1930."

1. France—Army—Infantry—Légion étrangère.   I. Shelley, Gerard,
tr. II. Title.

Library of Congress   UA703.L5L6   32–10554
[5]   356.160944

NL 0443079   DLC MB NN NcD ViU

Löhndorff, Ernst Friedrich, 1899–
Khaiberpass, Roman. Bremen, C. Schünemann [1941]
287 p. 20 cm.

I. Title.

PT2623.O33K5   833.91   A F 48–3792*
California. Univ. Libr.
for Library of Congress   [2]†

     ViU IaU MiU DLC
NL 0443080   CU OrU MB TxU NcU MH CtY EPB CLU OCl

Löhndorff, Ernst Friedrich, 1899–
... Der narr und die mandelblüte, roman. Bremen, C. Schü-
nemann [*1935]
295, [1] p. 20ᶜᵐ.
At head of title: Ernst F. Löhndorff.
"Erstes bis zehntes tausend."

I. Title.

Library of Congress   PT2623.O33N3 1935   35–19463
Copyright A—Foreign   29143
                 833.91

NL 0443081   DLC NN ICRL NjP WU NN CtY

PT   Löhndorff, Ernst Friedrich, 1899–
2623   Noahs Arche; eine Saga von Mensch und Wal
O33   [von] Ernst F. Löhndorff. Leipzig, Grethlein
N6   [c1932]
      263p. 20cm.

NL 0443082   WU NN PPG MiD

Old Jamaica Rum; historischer Roman. Berlin, Gebr.
Weiss [1955] 502 p. 21cm.

Bibliography, p. 502.

1. Pirates—Fiction. 2. Exquemelin, Alexandre Olivier—Fiction. I. Title.

NL 0443083   NN

Löhndorff, Ernst Friedrich, 1899–
... Satan Ozean, von eisernen männern und schiffen. Mit
vier karten. Bremen, C. Schünemann [*1930]
287, [1] p. front., maps. 19½ᶜᵐ.
At head of title: Ernst F. Löhndorff.
"21.-30. tausend."

I. Title.

Library of Congress   PT2623.O33S3   46–38109
[2]   833.91

NL 0443084   DLC NNC CtY MiD

Löhndorff, Ernst Friedrich, 1899–
Satan Ozean; von Schnapspiraten, Trampfahrern und Wal-
fängern. Leipzig: Grethlein & Co. [cop. 1930] 299 p. maps.
12°.

I. Title. 2. Travel. 3. Tramps.   4. Adventures.
N. Y. P. L.   April 2, 1936

NL 0443085   NN

Löhndorff, Ernst Friedrich, 1899–
... Seltsame pfade, auf 10 grad süd. Bremen, C. Schüne-
mann [*1937]
330, [1] p. 20ᶜᵐ.
At head of title: Ernst F. Löhndorff.
"Erstes bis zehntes tausend."

I. Title.

Library of Congress   PT2623.O33S4 1937   38–21606
Copyright A—Foreign   38388
[2]   833.91

NL 0443086   DLC NcD

Löhndorff, Ernst Friedrich, 1899–
Stimme aus der Wüste: Muhamed ibn Abd'Allah ibn Abd
el Mottalib ibn Hadschim el Emin; Roman. [1. Aufl.] Bremen, C. Schünemann [1953]
225 p. 20 cm.

1. Muhammad, the prophet—Fiction. I. Title.

PT2623.O33S7   54–34879 ‡

NL 0443087   DLC CtY

Löhndorff, Ernst Friedrich, 1899–
... Südwest-nordost, erlebnisschilderungen. Bremen, C.
Schünemann [1936]
105, [1] p. 20ᶜᵐ.
At head of title: Ernst F. Löhndorff.
Illustration on t.-p.
"Erstes bis zehntes tausend."
Contents.—Bimbo.—Light o' morn.—"Amalia."—Heiah.

I. Title.

Library of Congress   PT2623.O33S8 1936   36–31275
Copyright A—Foreign   33000
[2]   833.91

NL 0443088   DLC CtY

VOLUME 338

Löhndorff, Ernst Friedrich, 1899–
... Trommle, Piet! Deutsche landsknechte im urwald, roman. Bremen, C. Schünemann ₁*1934₁
370, ₁2₁ p. 19½ᵐ.
At head of title: Ernst F. Löhndorff.
"Erstes bis zehntes tausend."

ɪ. Title.
Library of Congress   PT2623.O33T7 1934   34–35513
Copyright A—Foreign   25822
                                                   ₁2₁   833.91

NL 0443089   DLC NN

Löhndorff, Ernst Friedrich, 1899–
... Tropensymphonie; roman. Bremen, C. Schünemann ₁*1936₁
262 p. ₁1₁ p. 20ᵐ.
At head of title: Ernst F. Löhndorff.
"Erstes bis zehntes tausend."

ɪ. Title.
                                                   37–6337
Library of Congress   PT2623.O33T75 1936
Copyright A—Foreign   34934
                                                   ₁2₁   833.91

NL 0443090   DLC

LÖHNDORFF, ERNST FRIEDRICH, 1899–
Tropensymphonie; Roman.   Bremen, C.
Schünemann [1955, c1936] 222 p. 20cm.

NL 0443091   NN

PT   Löhndorff, Ernst Friedrich, 1899–
2623   Ultima esperanza; Aufstieg und Ende des
O33   "Königs von Feuerland" ₁von₁ Ernst F.
U4   Löhndorff. Bremen, C. Schünemann [1953,
           c1950₁
           238p. 19cm.

NL 0443092   WU

DS   Löhndorff, Ernst Friedrich, 1899–
710   Unheimliches China; ein reisebericht.   Bremen,
L82u   C. Schünemann [1939]
           262 p., [2] p. 20cm.

1. China – Description and travel. I. Title.

NL 0443093   CLU ICU NNC

Löhndorff, Ernst Friedrich, 1899–
Unheimliches China, ein Reisebericht. Bremen, C.
Schünemann ₁1940, *1939₁
262 p. 20 cm.

1. China—Descr. & trav.   ɪ. Title.
DS710.L82   915.1   A F 50–37
Columbia Univ.   Libraries
for Library of Congress   ₁3₁†

NL 0443094   NNC WU DLC

Löhndorff, Ernst Friedrich, 1899–
...Unheimliches China; ein Reisebericht.
Bremen, C. Schünemann [1951] 211 p. 19cm.

1. China—Descr. and trav., 1910–

NL 0443095   NN OU

Löhndorff, Ernst Friedrich, 1899–
Wen die Götter streicheln; indischer Tatsachen-
roman.   Berlin, Gebr. Weiss [c1954] 404 p.
21cm.

NL 0443096   NN

Löhndorff, Ernst Friedrich, 1899–
Yangtsekiang; ein Chinaroman. Bremen, C. Schünemann
₁*1940₁
851 p. 20 cm.

ɪ. Title.

PT2623.O33Y3   56–51427 ‡

NL 0443097   DLC NN MH NjP WU CU CtY MH

HD5022   Löhne der oberösterreichischen Arbeiterschaft.
.U6A83
             Linz, a. D.
             v. 30 cm. annual. (Statistische Veröffentlichung der Oberö-
             sterreichischen Kammer für Arbeiter und Angestellte)
             "Herausgegeben von der Kammer für Arbeiter und Angestellte in
             Linz a. D." 19

             1. Wages — Austria, Upper.   ɪ. Kammer für
             Arbeiter und Angestellte ... Oberösterreich in Linz.
             HD5022.U6A83   56–49080 ‡

NL 0443098   DLC

Loehneissen, Georg Engelhard von
  See
Loehneyss, Georg Engelhard, 1552–1622.

Loehner, Ermanno von
  see Löhner, Hermann von, 1841–1902.

Kress   Löhner, F
Room   Beytrag zur verbreitung der kenntniss der
            wechselwirthschaft und ihrer unwendbarkeit in
            Böhmen ... Hrsg. von dem Privatverein zur
            unterstützung der prager hausarmen. Prag,
            Gedruckt bey G.Haase, 1813.
              iii[i.e.iv], 86 p. fold. table. 17.5 cm.

              1.Rotation of crops. I.Privatverein zur
            unterstützung der prager hausarmen, ed.
            II.Title.

NL 0443101   MH–BA

ML50   Löhner, Fritz, 1883–1942.
.A127B61
1951   Ábrahám, Pál, 1892–
            ₁Die Blume von Hawaii. Libretto. German₁

            Die Blume von Hawaii; Operette in drei Akten, von Alfred
            Grünwald, Fritz Löhner-Beda und Emmerich Földes.
            Musik von Paul Abraham. Zürich, Apollo-Verlag ₁1951₁

₁Löhner, Fritz₁ 1883– 1942.
Ecce ego! Lieder und Gedichte, von Beda ₁pseud.₁ Wien,
R. Löwit, 1920.
66 p. illus. 20 cm.

ɪ. Title.

PT2623.O335E35   49–41639*

NL 0443103   DLC TxU

M1503   Löhner, Fritz, 1883–1942.
.L518F33   FOR OTHER EDITIONS
            Lehár, Ferenc, 1870–1948.   SEE MAIN ENTRY
            ₁Friederike. Piano-vocal score. German₁

            Friederike; Singspiel in drei Akten von Ludwig Herzer
            und Fritz Löhner. Musik von Franz Lehár. Klavierauszug
            mit Text. Wien, Glocken-Verlag, *1936.

Löhner, Fritz, 1883–
Der fromme Silvanus
  see under Ascher, Leo, 1880–1942.

Löhner, Fritz, 1883–1942.
Der Gerüchterstatter und anderes ₁von₁ Beda. Wien, R.
Löwit, 1915.
31 p. 19 cm.
Poems.
CONTENTS: Den Griesgrimigen ins Stammbuch. — Die Gerüch-
terstatter. — Kaffeehaus-Moltke. — Herr Unke. — Die Lords. — Herr
Zappelig. — Die Jubeltrompete. — Der Mann mit dem Fragezeichen. —
Die Suffragetten kommen. — Herr Schofel. — Der Schaukelmann. —
Die Schwägerin. — Der Nörgelmayer. — Der traurige Dichter. — Die
Fabel vom Schwein. — Mädchens Frühlingslied. — Die Ehrenaffäre. —
Impression. — Die Tugend und der Teufel. — Der Radschah von
Khandapur.
ɪ. Title.

PT2623.O335G4   73–200218

NL 0443106   DLC

₁Löhner, Fritz₁ 1883–1942.
Getaufte und Baldgetaufte, von Beda, Umschlag-Zeichnung von C. Josef, Wien: [The
auth.] by M. Frisch, 1908.
63(1)p. 3 ed.

NL 0443107   OCH

₁Loehner, Fritz,₁ 1883–
Getaufte und Baldgetaufte, von Beda ₁pseud.₁. Umschlag-
zeichnung von Carl Josef. Wien: Huber & Lahme Nachfg.,
1909. 68 p. 16°.

1. Poetry, German. 2. Satire, Ger-   man. 3. Jews in poetry. 4. Title.
N. Y. P. L.   May 3, 1927

NL 0443108   NN

₁Löhner, Fritz₁ 1883–1942.
Getaufte und Baldgetaufte, von Beda. Wien;
Wiener Boheme-Verlag, 1925. new ed.
12.(Boheme-Bibliothek.)
59p.

NL 0443109   OCH

Löhner, Fritz, 1883–1942.

Lehár, Ferenc, 1870–

... Giuditta. Leipzig, New York ₁etc.₁ W. Karczag ₁*1933₁

VOLUME 338

₍Loehner, Fritz,₎ 1883–
Israeliten und andere Antisemiten, von Beda ₍pseud.₎. Umschlag-Zeichnung von Carl Josef. Wien: Huber & Lahme Nachfg., 1909. 60 p. 16°.

1. Poetry, German. 2. Satire, German. 3. Jews in poetry. 4. Title.
N. Y. P. L.   May 3, 1927

NL 0443111   NN OCH

Löhner, Fritz, 1883–1942.
Israeliten und andere Antisemiten, von Beda. Wien, R. Löwit, 1919.
47 p. 18 cm.
Poems.

1. Jews in Austria—Anecdotes, facetiae, satire, etc.   I. Title.
PT2623.O335 I 8   73–202357

NL 0443112   DLC

M1503
.L518L32
1937
Löhner, Fritz, 1883–1942.   FOR OTHER EDITIONS SEE MAIN ENTRY
Lehár, Ferenc, 1870–1948.
₍Das Land des Lächelns. Piano-vocal score. German₎

Das Land des Lächelns: romantische Operette in drei Akten nach Viktor Léon ₍pseud.₎ von Ludwig Herzer und Fritz Löhner. Klavierauszug mit Text. Originalausg. des Komponisten. ₍4. Aufl.₎ Wien, Glocken-Verlag, °1937.

ML50
.L518L22
1954
Löhner, Fritz, 1883–1942.   FOR OTHER EDITIONS SEE MAIN ENTRY
Lehár, Ferenc, 1870–1948.
₍Das Land des Lächelns. Libretto. English₎

The land of smiles; a musical play in three acts, by Ludwig Herzer and Fritz Löhner. English version by Harry Graham. New book and additional lyrics by Conrad Carter and Fred S. Tysh; adapted by Hans May. ₍Libretto, London, Glocken Verlag ₍1954₎

₍Loehner, Fritz,₎ 1883–
Neue Satiren, von Beda ₍pseud.₎... Wien: Adria-Verlag, 1912. 57 p. sq. 16°.

1. Poetry, German. 2. Satire, German.
N. Y. P. L.   September 11, 1926

NL 0443115   NN

Löhner, Fritz, 1883–1942.
Lehár, Ferenc, 1870–

Schön ist die welt! Operette in 3 akten von Ludwig Herzer und Fritz Löhner. Musik von Franz Lehár. Klavierauszug mit text. Originalausgabe des komponisten ... Inszenierung von Hubert Marischka ... Leipzig ₍etc.₎, W. Karczag, °1930.

Löhner, Fritz, 1883–1942, joint author.

Warden, Bruno.
... Schwester Chrysantheme (Die englischen fräulein) Schauspiel in einem vorspiel und drei akten, von Bruno Warden und Friedrich Löhner ... Wien ₍etc.₎ °1919.

Löhner, Fritz, 1883–1942.
Lehár, Ferenc, 1870–

Der sterngucker, operette in 3 akten von d⁰ Fritz Löhner. Musik von Franz Lehár ... Klavierauszug mit text ... Leipzig, Wien, W. Karczag; New-York, Karczag publishing co., °1916.

₍Löhner, Fritz₎ 1883–
Tanz der millionen, ein spiel in 3 akten, von Beda ₍pseud.₎ und Klemens ₍pseud.₎ Wien ₍etc.₎ °1930₎
28 p. 20ᶜᵐ.
"Als unverkäufliches manuskript gedruckt."

I. Klemens, pseud., joint author. II. Title.
                                                 48–28592
Library of Congress   PT2623.O335T3   Brief cataloging

NL 0443119   DLC

Löhner, Fritz, 1883–1942.
Wie man sich trefft im Ampezzotal. Altes und Neues von Beda. Wien, R. Löwit, 1916.
30 p. 19 cm.
Poems.
CONTENTS: Doktor Finks Brautfahrt.—Im Ampezzotal.—Der Markomanne.—Die Nase des Ladislaus.—Jüdisch.—Der Jour.—Die wahre Liebe.—Tante Sophie.—Ghetto.—Nikolofest.—Mährischer Wahlkreis Göding.—Der Fall Back.

I. Title.
PT2623.O335W5   73–202377

NL 0443120   DLC

Loehner, Helmut, 1903–
Ueber den quantenhaften geschwindigkeitsverlust langsamer elektronen in verduennten gasen.
Inaug. diss. Danzig, Techn.Hoch., 1930 ₍Leipzig₎

NL 0443121   ICRL

LÖHNER, Hermann von, 1841–1902.
Carlo Goldoni e le sue Memorie; frammenti [Venezia, tip. del commercio di M. Visentini, 1882]

Mounted in 4°. vol. pp.23–.
"Extratto dall'Archivio veneto, t. xxiv, p.1.₎1882".

NL 0443122   MH

Löhner, Hermann von, 1841–1902.
La divina commedia
see under Dante Alighieri, 1265–1321.
Divina commedia. German. 1905.

Löhner, Hermann von, 1841–1902, ed.

Goldoni, Carlo, 1707–1793.
Mémoires de m. Goldoni, pour servir à l'histoire de sa vie et à celle de son théâtre, dédiés au roi. Tome premier ... Ristampate sull'edizione originale di Parigi (MDCCLXXXVII) e corredate con annotazioni da Ermanno von Loehner. Venezia, Stab. tip. dei Fratelli Visentini, 1883.

Löhner, Hermann von, 1841–1902.
Unterwegs. Lustspiel in einem Act. Wien, Wallishausser, 1876.
17 p. 8°. (Wiener Theater-Repertoir. No. 317)

NL 0443125   NN

Loehner, J.
Die musik als human-erziehliches bildungsmittel. Ein beitrag zu den reformbestrebungen unserer zeit auf dem gebiet der musikalischen unterrichtslehre, von J. Loehner. Leipzig, Breitkopf und Härtel, 1886.
iv p., 1 l., 54 p. 22½ᶜᵐ.

1. Music—Instruction and study—Germany.
                                                 10–9363
Library of Congress   MT1.L74

NL 0443126   DLC MH

Z
245
.L323g
Löhner, Johann, 1645–1705.
Der Geistlichen Erquickstunden des Fürtrefflichen Theologi H. Doct. Heinrich Müllers Post. und Profess. Publ. bey der löbl. Universität Rostock Poetischer Andachtsklang. Von denen Pegnitz-Blumengenossen verfasset und in Arien gesetzet durch Johann Löhner, der Sing-Kunst beflissenen. Nürnberg, Verlegt von W.E. Felseckern, 1673.
[20],295,[7]p. illus.,plate, music. 15cm.

NL 0443127   TxU

FILM
4333
PT
Reel
131
Löhner, Johann, 1645–1705.
₍Der geistlichen Erquickstunden des...Doct. Heinrich Müllers...poetischer Andacht-Klang: von denen Pegnitz-Blumengenossen verfasset; und in Arien gesetzet durch Johann Löhner...Nürnberg, Verlegt von W.E. Felseckern, 1673.
10p.♪.,292,[10]p. 14cm.
Bled.
Melodies for one voice, with thorough bass accompaniment.
(German Baroque Literature, No.570, reel No. 131 Research Publications, Inc.)
Microfilm.

NL 0443128   CU

Zg17
1817
691
[**Löhner, Johann**] 1645–1705
Der geistlichen Erquick-Stunden des ... Doctor Heinrich Müllers ..., poetischer Andacht-Klang von denen Blumgenossen verfasset, anjetzo mit 60. Liedern vermehret und von unterschiedlichen Ton-Künstlern in Arien gesetzet. Nürnberg, druckt und verlegts J.J.Felsecker, 1691.
6p.♪.,620,[19]p. double front. 18cm.
Melodies for one voice, with thorough bass accompaniment.
Preface signed, Myrtillus [pseud. of Martin Limburger]

NL 0443129   CtY

FILM
4333
PT
Reel
132
[**Löhner, Johann**] 1645–1705
₍Der geistlichen Erquick-Stunden des...Doctor Heinrich Müllers...poetischer Andacht-Klang von denen Blumgenossen verfasset, anjetzo mit 60. Liedern vermehret und von unterschiedlichen Tonkünstlern in Arien gesetzet. Nürnberg, druckt und verlegts J.J. Felsecker, 1691.
6p.♪.,620,[19]p. double front. 18cm.
Melodies for one voice, with thorough bass accompaniment.
Preface signed, Myrtillus [pseud. of Martin Limburger]
(German Baroque Literature, No.571, reel No. 132 Research Publications, Inc.)
Microfilm.

NL 0443130   CU

Zg17p
L52
680
Löhner, Johann, 1645–1705.
Keusche Liebs-und Tugend-Gedancken/in zwölff Arien/mit einer Sing-Stimm und zwey Violinen verfasst von Johann Löhner.Cantus. Nürnberg, C.Gerhard,1680.
[19]p. 6x20cm.

NL 0443131   CtY

VOLUME 338

Löhner, Johann, 1645-1705.
Keusche Liebs- und Tugend-Gedancken/in zwölff
Arien/mit einer Sing-Stimm und zway Violinen ver-
fasst von Johann Löhner Cantus. Nürnberg, C. Ger-
hard, 1680.
[19]p.   6x20cm.
Signatures:)(²A-B⁴.
(German Baroque Literature, No.569, reel No. 131
Research Publications, Inc.)
Microfilm.

FILM
4333
PT
Reel
131

NL 0443132   CU

Löhner, Johann, 1645-1705.
XLIV [i.e. Vier und vierzig] Arien, aus der
Opera von Theseus. In die Music gebracht durch
Johann Löhnern. Org. in der Kirche zum H.
Geist.   Nürnberg, Gedruckt bey Wolfgang Moritz
Endtern, 1688.
87 p.   15 x 20.5 cm.
Airs with accompaniment, unfigured bass.
Text by the composer, translated from an
Italian libretto by Aureli, Teseo tra le rivali.
cf. Loewenberg.
Music printed from type.

NL 0443133   CtY-Mus

338.198
L823   [Löhner, Joseph, Edler von]
Fragmente über Schafzucht, Wollhandel und
Wollmärkte in Böhmen. Von einem Gutsbesitzer
Prag, J. G. Calve'sche Buchhandlung, 1828.

48 p.   fold. tab.   21 cm.

1. Wool trade and industry in Bohemia.

NL 0443134   MnU

Löhner, Karl.
Das Landjahr in seiner Bedeutung für die Berufsnach-
wuchslenkung der männlichen Schulabgänger.   Leipzig,
Akademische Verlagsgesellschaft Becker & Erler, 1941.
[537]-436 p. forms. 24 cm.
Cover title.
"Sonderdruck aus 'Archiv für die gesamte Psychologie' 109 (1941)"
Bibliography: p. 482-436.

1. Labor, Compulsory non-military—Prussia. 2. Youth—Prussia.
I. Title.
HD4869.L6   50-49394

NL 0443135   DLC

Löhner, Kurt Eugen, 1900-
Die Brennkraftmaschine, Innenvorgänge und Gestaltung.
Düsseldorf, Deutscher Ingenieur-Verlag [1953]
328 p. illus. 22 cm.

1. Gas and oil engines.   I. Title.
TJ785.L7   621.43   53-31419 ‡

NL 0443136   DLC MiU

Löhner, Leopold Robert Josef, 1884-   ed.

Biologia generalis. International journal of general biology.
Archives internationales de biologie générale. Internationale zeitschrift für allgemeine biologie. Archivio in-
ternazionale di biologie generale ... v. 1-
1925-
Vienna, E. Haim & co.; Baltimore, Md., The Johns Hopkins press, 1925-

Löhner, Leopold Robert Josef, 1884-
... Die exkretionsvorgaenge im lichte ver-
gleichend-physiologischer forschung, von Dr. med. et
phil. Leopold Löhner ... Nach einem in der Gesellschaft fuer morphologie und physiologie zu Graz
gehaltenen vortrage.   Jena, 1916.

QP 1   (Sammlung anatomischer und physiologischer
.S 18   vortraege und aufsaetze ... Hft. 28. (3. bd.,
Hft.28. Hft.4.)
3. bd., Hft.4

NL 0443138   MdBP

Löhner, Leopold Robert Josef, 1884-
... Die inzucht, eine monographische skizze ihres wesens und
ihrer erscheinungen, von dr. med. et phil. Leopold Löhner ...
mit 27 abbildungen und 11 tabellen im texte. Freising-Mün-
chen, Dr. F. P. Datterer & cie., 1929.
146 p. illus., diagrs. 25ᶜᵐ. (Added t.-p.: Naturwissenschaft und
landwirtschaft; abhandlungen und vorträge über grundlagen und
probleme der naturwissenschaft und landwirtschaft ... [hft. 15])
"Literatur-übersicht": p. 124-146.
1. Breeding. 2. Heredity.   I. Title.
Library of Congress   8494.L6   30-21096
Copyright A—Foreign   6605
[2]   636.08241

NL 0443139   DLC DNAL

Löhner, Leopold Robert Josef, 1884-
Die sehschärfe des menschen und ihre prüfung.
Eine physiologisch-ophthalmologische studie von
Leopold Löhner ...   Leipzig und Wien, F. Deuticke,
1912.
iv, 136 p. illus. 22½cm.

"Literaturübersicht": p. [104]-136.

1. Sight. 2. Eye—Examination.

NL 0443140   MiU DNLM CU

Loehner, Otto.
Die Ansiedlung von Kriegsbeschädigten in der Landwirt-
schaft. Gesetz vom 15. Juli 1916. Nebst den hierzu ergangenen
Ausführungsbestimmungen. In gemeinverständlicher Form dar-
gestellt, von Dr. oec. publ. Otto Löhner.   München: Bayer.
Kommunalschriften-Verlag, G.m.b.H., 1918.   83 p.   12°.

Bibliography, p. 81.

1. Land settlement, Germany, 1916.   2. Soldiers.—Civil employment,
Germany, 1916.   Germany, 1916.
N. Y. P. L.   October 3, 1924

NL 0443141   NN

HD7269 Löhner, Otto.
.B9G32   Bauarbeiterschutz und baupolizei in Bayern ... Stuttgart,
Druck der Union Deutsche verlagsgesellschaft, 1907.
vi, [2], 140 p. 23½ᶜᵐ.
Inaug.-diss.—München.
"Literatur": 1 p. preceding p. 1.

NL 0443142   ICU

Löhner, Otto.
Bauarbeiterschutz und baupolizei in Bayern, von Otto
Löhner ... Stuttgart und Berlin, J. A. Cotta'sche buchhandlung nachfolger, 1907.
viii, [2], 140 p. 23½ᶜᵐ. (Added t.-p.: Münchener volkswirtschaftliche
studien; hrsg. von L. Brentano und W. Lotz. 84. stück)
"Literatur": 1 page preceding p. 1.

1. Building trades—Bavaria. 2. Labor laws and legislation—Bavaria.
3. Labor and laboring classes—Accidents.
8—3656
Library of Congress   HD7269.B9G33

NL 0443143   DLC ICJ NN

PT   Löhner, Rudolf.
1501   Beiträge zu Alpharts Tod.   Kremsier,
A62L82   H. Gusek, 1885.
24 p. 24cm.

1. Alpharts Tod.

NL 0443144   NIC CU

Löhnert (Carl). Graphisches A B C-Buch für
Impffreunde. 26 pp., 1 l., 3 tab. 8°. Chemnitz,
O. Krüger, 1876.
Bound with: Ortmann (H.) Nach Canossa! [etc.].
8°. Chemnitz, 1876.

NL 0443145   DNLM

Löhnert, Carl.
Die impffrage ist gelöst!
[In Meyner, n.d., Hilferuf an den hohen
deutschen reichstag um aufhebung des impfzwanges.
[N. 2] 8°. Berlin, T. Grieben, 1877. p. 56-
60]

NL 0443146   DLC

Löhnert, Carl.
Kritische bemerkungen zu der chronologischen
zusammenstellung aller constatirten fälle von
vaccinaler syphilis.   [n.p., 188-?]

NL 0443147   MiU

Löhnert, Hans.
Intonation und Lautgebung in der Aussprache von Ramsay
Macdonald. Berlin, W. de Gruyter, 1939.
21 p. 83 plates. 25 cm. (Lebendige Sprache, experimental-
phonetische Untersuchungen, Heft 8)
Issued also as inaug. diss., Berlin.

1. English language—Pronunciation. 2. English language—Intonation. 3. MacDonald, James Ramsay, 1866-1937. I. Title. (Series)
PE1137.L65 1939   50-44991

NL 0443148   DLC NNC FU CtY MH TxU IaU RPB ICU NN

Löhnert, Karl, 1910-
Die Bechterew'sche Erkrankung und ihre
Beziehung zum Kiefergelenk ... Leipzig, 1936.
Inaug.-Diss. - Leipzig.
Lebenslauf.
Full name: Karl Gustav Richard Löhnert.

NL 0443149   CtY

LÖHNERT, Kurt, 1884-
. Personal- und amtsdaten der trierer erzbis-
chöfe des 10—15. jahrhunderts. Inaug.-
diss., Greifswald, 1908.

NL 0443150   MH PU NN ICRL

Loehneysen, Georg Engelhard von
see
Loehneyss, Georg Engelhard von, 1552-1622.

Löhneysen, Hilbert.
Der fall Löhneysen nach den gerichtlichen
verhandlungen
see under Löhr, H.

VOLUME 338

Löhneyss, Georg Engelhard von, 1552-1622.
Aulico politica; darin gehandelt wird, 1.
von erziehung und information junger herrn;
2. vom ampt tugent und qualitet der fürsten und
bestellung derselben raht und officirer; 3. von
bestellung der concilien, die ein fürst in seinen
lande haben mus... [30],677,[2]p. il. plates
(part fold.) Remlingen, 1622.

NL 0443153   OC1

LÖHNEYSS, GEORG ENGELHARD VON, 1552-1622.
Bericht, vom Bergkwerck, wie man dieselben Bawen,
vnd in guten Wolstandt bringen sol, sampt allen darzu
gehörigen Arbeiten, Ordnung vnd rechtlichen Process.
Beschrieben durch G. E. Löhneyss... [Zellerfeldt,
Gedruckt] 1617.   12 p.l., 343 [i.e. 364] p.   16 double plates.
34cm.(f°.)

For description, cf. Prandtl, W. Die erste Ausgabe von Georg Engel-
hard Löhneyss' Bericht vom Bergkwerck. (In: Zeitschrift für Bücherfreunde.
Leipzig. 1935. p. 15-22)
First leaf, blank, wanting.
Some leaves numbered as folios, most as pages.
Printed at the author's private press which was moved to Zellerfeld from
his Remlingen estate to print this book.

In the second state.--cf. Prandtl.
Woodcuts by Moses Thym.

110283A. 1. Mines and mining. 2. Metallurgy, 1617.   t. 1617.

NL 0443156   NN CtY PBL NjP

Löhneyss, Georg Engelhard von, 1552-1622.
Bericht vom Bergwerck wie man dieselben bawen
vnd in guten Wolstande bringen sol. Sampt allen
dazu gehörigen Arbeiten, Ordnung und rechtlichen
Processen. Beschrieben durch G.E.Löhneyss.
[Zellerfeldt?1619?]
11p.l.,343p. 16 double plates. 32½cm.

NL 0443157   CtY

Löhneyss, Georg Engelhard von, 1552-1622.
Bericht vom bergwerck, wie man dieselben
bawen vnd in güten wolstande bringen sol,
sampt allen dazü gehörigen arbeiten, ordnüng
und rechtlichen processen. Beschrieben dürch
G.E.Löhneijss.   [n.p., ca.1620?]
11 p.l., 343 (i.e.363) p.incl.tables.
16 fold.pl. 31 cm.

Part of pages numbered as leaves; p.75
numbered 71, no.76 duplicated.
First edition 1617.

NL 0443158   MH-BA

Löhneyss, Georg Engelhard von, 1552-1622.
Bericht vom bergwerck, wie man dieselben bawen vnd
in güten wolstande bringen sol, sampt allen dazü
gehörigen arbeiten, ordnüng und rechtlichen processen
...[n.p., 1690?]
11 p.l., 343 (i.e. 363) p. incl. tables. (part fold.)
fold. plates. 31 cm.
First edition, 1617.

NL 0443159   MH-BA

LÖHNEYSS, GEORG ENGELHARD VON, 1552-1622.
Della Caualleria. Das ist: Gründlicher vnd ausz-
führlicher Bericht, von allem was zu der löblichen
Reuterey gehörig, vnd einem Cavallier zu wissen vn
nöhten: Jnsonderheit von Turnier- vnd Ritterspielen,
Erkentnis... auch Cur vnd Wartung der Pferde, vnd wie
man dieselben auff allerley Manier abrichten vnd zeumen sol. Allen Liebhabern solcher Künste...beschrie-
ben, durch...Georg Engelhard Löhnesz... Jtzo aber

Continued in next column

Continued from preceding column

auffs newe mit nützlichem gutem Bericht, auch...Fi-
guren, allenthalben vermehrt, verbessert vnd zum
dritten Mal gedruckt.   Remlingen, 1624.   8 p.l.,
614 p.   illus., port.   45cm.(f°.)

Grasse, IV, 246. See: Lipperheide: Kat. der... Kostümbibliothek,
2905. Archiv für die zeichnenden Künste. Leipzig. Jahrg. 2 (1856)
p. 253-254.

Printed at the author's private press at his Remlingen estate.--cf.
Prandtl, W. Die erste Ausgabe von Georg Engelhard Löhneyss' Bericht vom
Bergwerck. (In: Zeitschrift für Bücherfreunde. Leipzig. 1935. p. 16-18)
Previously published at Gruningen in 1588 and at Remlingen in 1609-10.
--cf. pref. by the editor, Michael Bömerus.
Includes music. p. 74-82.
Illustrations: numerous woodcuts and engravings, many full-page or
double, depicting tournaments, processions, horses (many with views of

Lüneburg in the background), harness, etc., and an engraved portrait of
the author. A few of the large woodcuts have the monograms LG and VW.
With bookplate (silhouette portrait) of J. H. Anderhub, 1937.
Binding of brown leather, gilt; rebacked.

1. Horsemanship. 2. Harness. 3. Festival books, German, 17th cent.
4. Engravings, German, 17th cent. 5. Wood engravings, German, 17th
cent. I. Bömerus, Michael, ed.

NL 0443163   NN

---

qTN144
.L825b
1690a
Hist
of
Sci

Löhneyss, Georg Engelhard, 1552-1622.
... Gründlicher und aussführlicher bericht
von bergwercken. Wie man dieselbigen nützlich
und fruchtbarlich bauen, in glückliches auffneh-
men bringen, und in guten wolstand beständig
erhalten; insonderheit die ertze und metallen,
als gold, silber, kupffer, zien, bley, wissmuht,
spiessglass, stahl-stein, magneten und eisen-
stein, ein jedes nach seiner rechten natur, art
und eigenschafft auffs nützlichste bearbeiten,
rösten, waschen, puchen, seigern, auff mancherle

weise in kleinem feuer probiren, cimentiren, und
scheiden, auch im grossen feuer ohne abgang
schmeltzen und zu nutze machen soll. Nebenst
vielen kunstlichen abbildungen allerhand darzu
nöhtigen ofen und werckzeuge; wie auch vor-
theyliche anweisung von schwefel machen, vitriol
alaun, salpeter und saltzsieden. Sampt beyge-

fügter nützlicher berg-ordnung, und bericht von
der bergleute verrichtung und freyheiten. Allen
denen, so bergwercke bauen, und dabey interessir
sind, zu dienst und gefallen auffs neue wiederumb an den tag gegeben.   Stockholm und Hamburg, In verlegung Gottfried Liebezeits
buchhändlers, gedruckt in Leipzig bey Christopff

Günthern, 1690.
12p.l.,343 (i.e. 363)p. 16 fold. plates.
32½cm.
At head of title: Georg Engelhard von
Löhneyss ...
Added t.-p., engraved.
Pagination partly by leaves.

First ed. published under title: Bericht vom
bergwerck.
Eight pages of ms. notes withdrawn.
Armorial bookplate of Count Gustav von Chorin-
sky.
Wilhelm Prandtl Collection.
With this is bound: Rössler, Balthasar, Speculum metallurgiae politissimum. Dresden,
1700.

NL 0443168   TxU MeB NNE NNC CtY TxDaM DeU PBa MH-BA

---

xq172.2
L82a
1679

Löhneyss, Georg Engelhard von, 1552-1622.
Hof- staats- und regier-kunst/ bestehend in
dreyen buchern/ deren erstes handelt von erziehung und information junger herren/ Das
andre, vom ambt/ tugenden und qualitaten regie-
render fursten ... Das dritte, von verschiednen
rahts-collegiis/ so ein furst/ gestalten sachen
nach/ in seinem lande haben muss; das religion-
policy- justitz- cammer- berg- und kriegs-wesen
betreffend. Allen regenten/ furstlichen rahten/
hof- land- und kriegs-officirern/ auch denen
unterthanen und iedermanniglichen zu nutz und gut

Continued in next column

Continued from preceding column

beschrieben von Georg Engelhard von Lohneys ...
Itzo mit fleiss durchsehn/ auch an einigen orten
vermehret. Benebenst einem angefugten discurs
von denen zweyen der H. Romischen reichs hochsten
gerichten/ dem kayserl. reichs-hofrath und cam-
mer-gericht zu Speyr.   Franckfurt am Meyn/
In verlegung G. V. R. in Henning Grossens buchladen, 1679.
24 p.l., 777, [25]p. 36cm.

Title in red and black: head and tail-pieces.
Many errors in paging.
Dedicatory epistle signed: Joh. Andreas Gerhard.
First published, 1622, under title: Aulico-po-
litica; oder Hof- staats- und regierungskunst.

1. Political ethics. 2. Education of princes.
I. Gerhard, Johann Andreas, 1634-1680. ed.

NL 0443171   IU ICN MH-L OkU

Löhneyss, Georg Engelhard von, 1552-1622.
Georg Engelhard von Löhneisen...neu-eröffnete Hof- Kriegs-
und Reit-Schul, das ist: Gründlicher Bericht della Cavalleria, oder
von allen, was zur Reuterey gehörig und einem Cavalier davon
zu wissen gebühret, nach den ersten Titul dieses überaus rar-
wordenen Buches, welches aber anjetzo in einen gantz andern
Stand gesetzet, verneuert, und mit ausführlichen schönen Noten,
auch gantzen Capiteln vermehret und verbessert worden...von
Valentin Trichter.   Nürnberg: P. Lochner, 1729.   6 parts
in 1 v.   illus.   41cm.

Each part has separate paging.
With bookplate of Carl Friedrich, Sohn, Freyherr von Elfz Rodendorff.

232019B. 1. Cavalry. 2. Horse-   manship. I. Trichter, Valentius,
fl. 1715, ed.
N.Y.P.L.   June 21, 1943

NL 0443173   NN

SF
309.9
f. L8

Löhneyss, Georg Engelhard von, 1552-1622.
Von Zeumen; gründlicher Bericht des Zeumens vnd ordentliche
Ausstellung der Mündstück vnd Stangen, wie dieselben nach
eines jeden Pferdts Arth vnd Eigenschafft sollen gebrauchtt
werden ... [Groningen?] 1588.
[1b, 122 l. illus. 42 cm.

Dedication signed Georg Engelhart Löneyssen.
On cover: L H T. Tabvlae geographicae, 1627.
MS. notes.
Leaf 9 torn and mended with some loss of text.
Leaves 36-38 wanting supplied in facsim. from British
Museum copy.

1. Bridle. 2. Horsemanship. 3. Horses. I. Title.

NL 0443174   MiEM CtY

Löhneyss, Georg Engelhard, 1552-1622.
Zwey gute und sehr nutzliche Bücher von
Stangen und Mundstücken...
see under title

Löhning (Bernhard) [1858-   ] *Ein Fall
von Explosionsverletzung des Auges. [Heidel-
berg.] 29 pp., 1 l. 8°. Dülmen, J. Sievert,
1917.

NL 0443176   DNLM CtY ICRL

Löhning, Ernst Carl Hugo, 1884-
Die Voraussetzungen des Versäumnis-verfahrens.
Leipzig, Veit, 1909.
iv, 40 p.
Inaug.-Diss. - Leipzig, 1909.

NL 0443177   ICRL

VOLUME 338

Löhninger, Klemens, 1886–
Angina und Sepsis... Bielefeld, 1913.
Inaug.-Diss. - München.
Lebenslauf.
"Literatur": p. [30]–31.
Full name: Klemens Wilhelm Löhninger.

NL 0443178   DNLM CtY

Löhnis, Eduard
Desertie van schepelingen. Artt.
390-393 S. W. B. ... door Eduard
Löhnis ... Leiden, P. Somerwil,
1887.
3 p.l., 63 p. 22½cm.
Proefschrift - Leiden.

NL 0443179   MH-L

LÖHNIS, F.B.
Arbeiders-kolonies als middel tot wering
van bedelarij. [Amsterdam? 1887]
pp.(10).
A review of Edouard Robin's Hospitalité
et travail.
De economist, 1887 pp. 593-602.

NL 0443180   MH

Loehnis, F. B., and D. A. de Jong.
Import and export of meat in various countries and the answer
to the question: Is the import of frozen and chilled meat from
abroad desirable for the Netherlands. (In: International Congress of Refrigeration, II. Vienna, 1910. Reports and proceedings. English edition. Vienna, 1911. 4°. p. 550-564.)

1. Meat.—Trade and statistics.   2. Jong, D. A. de.
N. Y. P. L.   October 23, 1912.

NL 0443181   NN

Löhnis, F. B.
Land-, tuin- en boschbouw, veeteelt. door F. B. Löhnis...
(In: Nederland in den aanvang der twintigste eeuw. Leiden.
1910. 4°. p. 496-537.)

1. Agriculture, Netherlands. 2. For-   estry, Netherlands. 3. Cattle.—
Breeding, etc., Netherlands.
N. Y. P. L.   December 30, 1914.

NL 0443182   NN

Löhnis, Felix, 1874–1930.
Ein Beitrag zur Frage der Rotkleedüngung.
Merseburg, Stollberg, 1901.
63 p.
Inaug.-Diss. - Leipzig, 1901.

NL 0443183   ICRL CtY PU

Löhnis, Felix, 1874–1930.
Boden-bakterien und boden-fruchtbarkeit; von dr. F.
Löhnis ... Berlin, Gebrüder Borntraeger, 1914.
vi p. 1 l., 70 p. 23½ᵐᵐ.

1. Soils—Bacteriology. (1. Soil bacteria)
                                        Agr 14-1106
Library, U. S. Dept. of   Agriculture 57L83

NL 0443184   DNAL OrCS CU PPAN

Löhnis, Felix, 1874–
Einführung in die bakteriologie. Für landwirte.
Verfasst von priv.-doc. dʳ F. Löhnis ... Leipzig, H.
Voigt, 1906.
141 p. 20½ᵐᵐ.

1. Bacteriology, Agricultural.

                                        Agr 6-914 Revised
Library, U. S. Dept. of   Agriculture 448.2L83

NL 0443185   DNAL NjR ICJ

Löhnis, Felix, 1874–
Feldversuche über brache. Berichterstatter: professor dr.
F. Löhnis ... dr. E. Hiltner ... professor dr. August Rippel ...
dr. B. Heinze ... Berlin, Deutsche landwirtschafts-gesell-
schaft, 1928.
90 p. diagr. 24½ᵐᵐ. (Added t.-p.: Arbeiten der Deutschen landwirt-
schafts-gesellschaft ... hft. 364 ..)

1. (Fallowing) I. Heinze, Berthold. II. Hiltner, Erhard. III. Rippel, August, 1888–
                                        Agr 29-820
Library, U. S. Dept. of   Agriculture 18D48 hft. 364

NL 0443186   DNAL ICJ

Löhnis, Felix, 1874–1930.
Grundriss der gesetzes- und verwaltungskunde. Verfasst von Dr. F. Löhnis ... Leipzig, H. Voigt, 1903.
viii, 102 p. 22ᵐᵐ.
                                        4-917

NL 0443187   DLC ICJ

Löhnis, Felix, 1874–
Handbuch der landwirtschaftlichen bakteriologie, von dr.
F. Löhnis ... Berlin, Gebrüder Borntraeger, 1910.
xii, 907 p. 26ᵐᵐ.

1. Bacteriology, Agricultural.
Library of Congress   QR51.L8   10-13588 Revised

NL 0443188   DLC NN NBuG ICJ UU CU OrCS NcRS

Löhnis, Felix, 1874–1930.
... Handbuch der landwirtschaftlichen bakteriologie.
Zweite, neu bearbeitete auflage ... Berlin, Gebrüder Borntrae-
ger [1933–
v. 26½ᵐᵐ.
Bibliographical foot-notes.

1. Bacteriology, Agricultural.
                                        Agr 33-801
Library, U. S. Dept. of   Agriculture 448.2L83H
Library of Congress   [QR51.L   ]

NL 0443189   DNAL

Löhnis, Felix, 1874–

Müller-Lenhartz, Wilhelm H   O   1873–
Hygienische milchgewinnung mit besonderer berücksichtigung der vitamine und mineralbestandteile des fut-
ters, von hofrat dr. W. Müller-Lenhartz ... und dr. phil.
et med. G. von Wendt ... in verbindung mit prof. dr.
F. Löhnis ... Berlin, P. Parey, 1925.

Löhnis, Felix, 1874–
... Inoculation of legumes and nonlegumes with nitro-
gen-fixing and other bacteria. [By F. Löhnis and L. T.
Leonard] [Washington, Govt. print. off., 1926]
ii, 28 p. illus. 23ᵐᵐ. (U. S. Dept. of agriculture. Farmers' bulletin
no. 1496)
Contribution from Bureau of plant industry.

1. Bacteria, Nitrifying. (1. Nitrifying bacteria) 2. Soil-inoculation.
I. Leonard, Lewis Thompson, 1885– joint author. II. Title.
                                        Agr 26-1154
Library, U. S. Dept. of   Agriculture 1Ag84F no. 1496

NL 0443191   DLC WaWW

Löhnis, Felix, 1874–1930.
Laboratory methods in agricultural bacteriology: by F.
Löhnis ... Tr. by William Stevenson ... and J. Hunter Smith
... and rev. by the author. With three plates and forty figures
in the text. London, C. Griffin and company, limited; Philadelphia, J. B. Lippincott company [1913]
xi, 136 p. front., illus., diagr. 20ᵐᵐ.

1. Bacteriology, Agricultural. I. Stevenson, William, tr. II. Smith,
J. Hunter, tr. III. Title.
                                        A 14-822
Title from St. Paul Pub.   Libr.   Printed by L. C.

NL 0443192   MnS NcRS OrPR IdPI IdU ICJ NjR

Löhnis, Felix, 1874–
Landwirtschaftlich-bakteriologisches praktikum; anleitung zur ausführung von landwirtschaftlich-bakteriologi-
schen untersuchungen und demonstrations-experimenten,
von dr. F. Löhnis ... Mit 3 tafeln und 40 abbildungen im
text. Berlin, Gebrüder Borntraeger, 1911.
vii, 156 p. illus., III pl. (incl. front.) 19ᵐᵐ.   M. 3.40

1. Bacteriology, Agricultural.
                                        11-14741
Library of Congress   QR51.L85

NL 0443193   DLC NcRS OrCS DNLM ICJ

Löhnis, Felix, 1874–1930.
Life cycles of the bacteria. ⟨Preliminary communica-
tion⟩ By F. Löhnis and N. R. Smith.
(In U. S. Dept. of agriculture. Journal of agricultural research. vol.
VI, no. 18, p. 675-702 incl. tables, diagrs. 7 pl. 26ᵐᵐ. Washington, 1916)
Contribution from the Bureau of plant industry.
"Literature cited": p. 701-702.

1. Bacteria—(Biology, etc.) I. Smith, Nathan Raymond, joint author.
II. Title.
                                        Agr 16-1007
Library, U. S. Dept. of   Agriculture 1Ag84J vol. 6

NL 0443194   DNAL

Löhnis, Felix, 1874–
Nodule bacteria of leguminous plants. By F. Löhnis
... and Roy Hansen ...
(In U. S. Dept. of agriculture. Journal of agricultural research. vol.
XX, no. 7, p. 543-556. pl. 68-69 on 1 l. 26ᵐᵐ. Washington, 1921)
Contribution from Bureau of plant industry and Illinois agricultural ex-
periment station (G—215)
"Literature cited": p. 554-555.

1. Bacteria, Nitrifying. (1. Nitrifying bacteria) I. Hansen, Roy, joint
author.
                                        Agr 21-283 Revised
Library, U. S. Dept. of   Agriculture 1Ag84J vol. 20

NL 0443195   DNAL

VOLUME 338

Löhnis, Felix, 1874–
... Studies upon the life cycles of the bacteria ...
by F. Löhnis. [Washington, Govt. print. off., 1921–
> v. plates. 31 x 24½ᶜᵐ. (National academy of sciences. vol. xvi, 2d memoir)
> Bibliography: v. 1, p. 213–246.

1. Bacteria.   i. Title: Life cycles of the bacteria.
21-26713

Library of Congress   Q11.N2 vol. xvi, 2d mem.

NL 0443196   DLC CaBVaU MB NcU ICJ

QR75   Löhnis, Felix, 1874-1930
L6   Studies upon the life cycles of the bacteria. [Washington,
Biology   Govt. Print. Off., 1921]-23.
Library   2 v. illus.

> Part 2 has cover title only.
> Part 1 issued as Memoirs of the National Academy of Sciences;
> v.16, no.2; part 2 reprinted from the Journal of agricultural
> research; v.23, no.6, Feb.10, 1923.
> Includes bibliographies.

> Contents. – Pt.1. Review of the literature, 1838-1918. – Pt.2.
> Life history of Azotobacter, by F. Löhnis and N.R. Smith.

NL 0443197   CU NIC

Löhnis, Felix, 1874–
Studies upon the life cycles of the bacteria—pt. ii:
Life history of azotobacter. By F. Löhnis ... and N. R.
Smith ...
> (*In* U. S. Dept. of agriculture. Journal of agricultural research. vol.
> xxiii, no. 6, p. 401-432. 9 pl. on 5 l. 25ᶜᵐ. Washington, 1923)
> Contribution from the Bureau of plant industry (G—278)
> "Literature cited": p. 430-432.
> Pt. 1 published in Memoirs of National academy of sciences, vol. xvi, pt. 2.

1. Azotobacter.   i. Smith, Nathan Raymond, 1888–   joint author.
ii. Title: Life cycles of the bacteria.
Agr 23-499

Library, U. S. Dept. of   Agriculture 1Ag84J vol. 23

NL 0443198   DNAL

Loehnis, Felix, *1874–* , and Edwin Brown Fred, *1847–*
Textbook of agricultural bacteriology. 1st edition.
— London. McGraw-Hill Book Co., Inc. 1923. ix, 283 pp. Illus.
Plates, some colored. Diagrams. Tables. [Agricultural and
biological publications.] 23 cm.

M6380 — Jt. auth. — S.r. — Bacteria. — Agriculture.

NL 0443199   MB TU

Löhnis, Felix, 1874-1930.
Textbook of agricultural bacteriology, by F. Löhnis ...
and E. B. Fred ... 1st ed. New York [etc.] McGraw-Hill
book company, inc., 1923.
> ix. 283 p. illus., x pl. (part col.) diagrs. 23½ᶜᵐ. (Half-title: Agricultural
> and biological publications, C. V. Piper, consulting editor) $3.00
> "Most of the material ... was collected ... by the senior author while teach-
> ing at the University of Leipzig ... and under the title 'Vorlesungen über
> landwirtschaftliche bakteriologie' was published in 1913."—Pref.

1. Bacteriology, Agricultural.   i. Fred, Edwin Broun, 1887–   joint
author.
23—7215

Library of Congress   QR51.L87

NL 0443200   DLC CU NN ViU MsU NcD ICRL NcRS CaBVaU
ICJ Or IdU-SB OrCS

Löhnis, F[elix], 1874–
Untersuchungen über den verlauf der stickstoffum-
setzungen in der ackererde ... Langensalza, Druck von
H. Beyer & söhne (Beyer & Mann) 1905.
> 2 p. l., 103 p. incl. tables. diagr. 24½ᶜᵐ.
> Habilitationsschrift—Leipzig.

1. Nitrogen. 2. Soils.
12-12973

Library of Congress   S651.L83

NL 0443201   DLC CtY

Löhnis, Felix, 1874–
Vorlesungen über landwirtschaftliche bakteriologie,
von dr. F. Löhnis ... Mit 10 tafeln und 60 abbildungen im
text. Berlin, Gebrüder Borntraeger, 1913.
> viii, 398 p. illus., x pl. (part col.) diagrs. 25½ᶜᵐ. M. 16

1. Bacteriology, Agricultural.
13-26745

Library of Congress   QR51.L86

NL 0443202   DLC TU ICJ OrCS NcRS

Löhnis, Felix, 1874–
Vorlesungen über landwirtschaftliche bakteriologie, von
dr. F. Löhnis ... 2., neubearb. aufl. Mit 10 tafeln und 66
abbildungen im text. Berlin, Gebrüder Borntraeger, 1926.
> viii, 400 p. illus., x pl. (part col.) diagrs. 25½ᶜᵐ.

1. Bacteriology, Agricultural.
28-7413

Library of Congress   QR51.L86 1926

NL 0443203   DLC IU ICJ CtY CU

Löhnis, Felix, 1874-1930.
...Welche mehrarbeit und mehrkosten
entstehen durch die gesteigerten anforderung
an die güte der milch?   (1908).

NL 0443204   DNAL

Löhnis, Felix, 1874-1930.
Ziele und wege der bakteriologischen bodenforschung.
> Landw. jahrb. bd. 42, p. 751-765.   Berlin, 1912.

1. Soil bacteriology.
Agr 13-1599

Library, U. S. Dept. of   Agriculture

NL 0443205   DNAL

Loehnis, H[erman], editor.
Beiträge zur kenntnis der Levante, mai 1882. Leipzig, O.
Wigand, 1882.
> pp. ix, (1), 153 +. Map and 12 plans. (Deutscher handels-
> verein.)

Levant-Descr. 1878-1908]

NL 0443206   MH

PT2424   LOEHNIS, Hermann
.L62Z8A3   Briefe meines vaters. Hrsg. von Ch.A.Loehnis.
London,Trübner u.co.;[etc.,etc.]1880.
[6],373,[2]p. 23cm.

NL 0443207   ICU

Loehnis, Hermann.
Die europäischen kolonieen. Beiträge zur kritik der
deutschen kolonialprojekte. Von H. Loehnis. Bonn,
E. Strauss, 1881.
> vii (i. e. ix), [1], 103, [1] p. 2 fold. maps. 22½ᶜᵐ.

1. Colonies. 2. Germany—Colonies.
1-18578

Library of Congress   JV175.L7

NL 0443208   DLC CtY NcD

Microfilm   Loehnis, Hermann.
81119   Der Marasmus in Handel und Industrie, 1877.
London, Trübner, 1877.
240,56 p. 1 fold. illus.

> "Anhang": p.1-56 at end.
> Microfilm (negative) London, British Museum,
> Photographic Service, 1967. 1 reel. 35mm.

> 1. Economic history - 1750-1918. 2. Europe -
> Economic conditions. 3. U.S. - Economic
> conditions - 1865-1918. I. T.

NL 0443209   MiDW

Loehnis, Hermann.
Unterricht, Erziehung und Fortbildung. London, Siegle, 1875.
3 v.

NL 0443210   WaSpG

Loehnis, Hermann
Die Vereinigten Staaten von Nord-Amerika. Mit besonderer berücksichtigung ihrer finanziellen verhältnisse,
von H. Loehnis. Bonn, M. Cohen & sohn, 1863.
> 2 p. l., 97, [1] p. fold. tab. 21½ᶜᵐ.
> [Miscellaneous pamphlets, v. 17, no. 4]

1. U. S.—Hist.—Civil war—Foreign public opinion.
19-12194

Library of Congress   AC901.M5 vol. 17

NL 0443211   DLC

Loehnis, Hermann
Die Vereinigten Staaten von Amerika. Deren vergangenheit und gegenwart in socialer, politischer und finanzieller
beziehung. Von H. Loehnis. Leipzig, E. H. Mayer [etc.]
1864.
> x p., 1 l., xxxi, 352 p. tables (part fold.) 22ᶜᵐ.

1. U. S.—Pol. & govt. 2. Finance—U. S. 3. Slavery in the U. S.
2-4114

Library of Congress   E167.L82

NL 0443212   DLC CtY ICU MiU OClWHi MB

---

*A
1869   Loehnis, Hermann
.L64
Die Vereinigten Staaten von Amerika.
Deren Vergangenheit und Gegenwart in
socialer, politischer und finanzieller
beziehung. Zweite, mit einer Einleitung
vermehrte ausgabe. Leipzig, Verlag von
Eduard Heinrich Mayer, 1869.
xxxi, 352 p. 5 fold. tab. 22cm.

> 1. U. S.—Hist.—Civil war—Foreign public
> opinion. 2. U. S.—Pol. & govt. I. Title.

NL 0443213   ViU NN PU CtY

UG33   Löhnis, Jonathan Michael Athananasius,
L825   1788-1855.
De praenunciato novi foederis seu
missae sacrificio in priscis vatibus.
Dissertatio exegetico-dogmatica ...
Francofurti a/M.,typis Andreaeanis,
1836.
68p. 21cm.

NL 0443214   NNUT ICRL

VOLUME 338

Löhnis, Jonathan Michael Athanasius
Grundzüge der biblischen Hermeneutik und
Kritik entworfen von Jonath.Mich.Athanas.
Loehnis ... Giessen,B.C.Ferber,1839.
xxp.,XI.,435,[1]p. 23cm.

NL 0443215   NNUT PLatS NjPT

Loehnis, Jonathan Michael Athanasius, 1788-1855.
Das Land und Volk der Alten Hebräer nach den
in der Bibel angegebenen Zuständen. Ein Beitrag
zum bessern Verstandniss und Genuss der heiligen
Schriften des Alten und Neuen Testamentes.
Regensburg, G. Joseph Manz, 1844.

xxiv, 447p. 22cm.

NL 0443216   PLatS InU CtY OCH

Loehnis, [Johathan] Michael [Anthanasius].
Ueber den Nutzen des Studiums der mit
der hebräischen Sprache verwandten
Mundarten ... Aschaffenburg: A. J.
Weitlandt's Wittib u. Sohn, [1833]
32 p.

NL 0443217   OCH

ar W
12036   Löhnis, Jonathan Michael Athanasius, 1788-1855.
Ueber den Nutzen des Studiums der mit
der hebräischen Sprache verwandten Mundarten; ein Programm zum Schlusse des Studien-
jahres 1832-33. Aschaffenburg, M. J.
Wailandt's Wittib [1834]
32 p.   24cm.

1. Semitic philology--Study and teaching.

NL 0443218   NIC

Löhnis, Marie Petronella, 1888-
Histology of boron deficiency in plants.
Wageningen, H. Veenman & Zonen, 1940.
36 p. tables, plates. 25 cm. (Mededeelingen
van de Landbouwhoogeschool te Wageningen, deel
44, verhandeling 3)

XM
.E289   Bibliography: p.33.
deel
44-3   1. Plants, Effect of boron on. 2. Deficiency
diseases in plants. i.t. ii.s: Mededelingen
Landbouwhogeschool Wageningen, Nederland, 44-3.
iii.t: Boron defi-   ciency in plants.

NL 0443219   NNBG

Löhnis, Marie Petronella, 1888-
Plant development in the absence of boron.
Wageningen, H. Veenman & Zonen, 1937.
36 p. tables, plates. 25 cm. (Mededeelingen
van de Landbouwhoogeschool, deel 41, verhandeling 3)

XM
.E289   Bibliography: p.34-36.
deel
41-3   1. Plants, Effect of boron on. i.t. ii.s:
Mededelingen Landbouwhogeschool Wageningen,
Nederland, 41-3.

NL 0443220   NNBG

Löhnis, Maria Petronella, 1888-
... Onderzoek naar het verband tusschen de weersge-
steldheid en de aardappelziekte (*Phytophthora infestans*)
en naar de eigenschappen, die de vatbaarheid der knollen
voor deze ziekte bepalen. With a summary in English.
Door Dr. Maria P. Löhnis ... [Scheveningen, 1924]
iv, 139 p. plates, diagrs. (part fold.) 27cm.
At head of title: Mededeeling van de Wetenschappelijke commissie voor
advies en onderzoek in het belang van de volkswelvaart en weerbaarheid.
"Litteratuurlijst": p. [109]-110.
1. Phytophthora infestans. 2. [Potato blight] 3. Botany—Pathology. [3.
Weather influences—Effect on plant diseases] i. Netherlands. Wetenschappelijke commissie voor advies en onderzoek in het belang van de volkswelvaart en weerbaarheid.

Agr 25-1318

Library, U. S. Dept. of   Agriculture 464.04L83On

NL 0443221   DNAL NIC CU LU

Löhnis, Maria Petronella, 1888-
Onderzoek over *Phytophthora infestans* (Mont.) de By.
op de aardappelplant ... door Maria Petronella Löhnis ...
Wageningen, H. Veenman, 1922.
96 p. vi pl., diagrs. 24½cm.
Proefschrift—Utrecht.
"Summary": p. [84]-90.
"Litteratuurlijst": p. [91]-92.

1. Phytophthora infestans. 2. Potatoes—Diseases and pests.

Library of Congress   SB608.P8L6   1922   36-36350
[2]   632.452

NL 0443222   DLC CtY MH ICU DNAL

Löhnis, Maria Petronella, 1888-
Plantenvoeding, door Dr. Marie P. Löhnis.   Gorinchem, 1946.
81 p.   19cm.   (Noorduijn's wetenschappelijke reeks. no. 26)
"Litteratuurverwijzing," p. [82]

1. Plants—Nutrition.
N. Y. P. L.   February 24, 1950

NL 0443223   NN

Löhnis, Maria Petronella, 1888-
Rol der micro-organismen in het dagelijks leven. Gorinchem, J. Noorduijn, 1948.
96 p.   19 cm.

1. Micro-organisms. 2. Food—Bacteriology.   i. Title.

QR56.L82   589.95   49-27159*

NL 0443224   DLC

Loehnis, Michael
see Loehnis, Jonathan Michael Athanasius,
1788-1855.

Loehr, Adalbert.
Bühnen-almanach des St. Louis Opern hauses (mit beiträgen
der herren Otto Ruppius, Georg Hillgärtner, Heinrich
Börnstein, A. Loehr, u. a.) Herausgegeben von F. Kreuter
& C. Börnstein. 1. jahrg.; 1. jan. 1861. St. Louis, 1861.

Loehr, Adalbert.
Gedichte, von Adalbert Loehr. Augsburg und
St. Louis, Gedruckt auf kosten des verfassers,
1855.
vi, 218 p., 1 l.   18 cm.

NL 0443227   CU

F863
.6
L5   Loehr, Adeline M   plaintiff-respondent.
(Board of Education, et al., defendants-appellants)
Action for reinstatement of plaintiff to her position of teacher
in the School Dept. of the City and County of San Francisco.
Cover title.
Percy V. Long, John T. Nourse, attorneys for appellant.
C. M. Fickert, L. F. Chapman, attorneys for respondent.
In the District Court of Appeal of the State of California.
Provenance: Adolphus E. Graupner papers.
[1] Transcript on appeal. June, 1909. (46 p.)
[2] S.F. no. 870. Appellants' opening brief. July, 1909.
(17 p.)

1. Teachers - Legal status, laws, etc. - San Francisco. L
San Francisco. Board of Education, defendant-appellant. II.
Long, Percy Vincent, 1876-   III. Nourse, John T
IV. Fickert, Charles M   V. Chapman, L   F
VI. California. District Court of Appeal (1st District)

NL 0443229   CU-B

Löhr, Adolf, 1889-
Auf froher Fahrt, Erzählungen von A. Frohmut [pseud.]
Mit Bildern von Liesel Lauterborn. Reutlingen, R. Bardtenschlager [1942]
63 p. illus. 20 cm.

i. Title.

PZ33.L527   54-47882 ‡

NL 0443230   DLC

Löhr, Adolf, 1889-
Die blaue Glocke, eine Erzählung für Mädchen von Adolf
Frohmut [pseud.] Reutlingen, R. Bardtenschlager [1942]
59 p. illus. 20 cm.

i. Title.

PZ33.L528   54-47883 ‡

NL 0443231   DLC

Löhr, Adolf, 1889-
Käthe aus dem Klingengrund, ein Geheimnis um einen
Stammbaum von A. Frohmut [pseud.] Reutlingen, R.
Bardtenschlager [1943]
127 p. illus. 22 cm.

i. Title.

PZ33.L529   54-47872 ‡

NL 0443232   DLC

Löhr, Adolf, 1889-
Kasperle wird Schlaraffenkönig, eine lustige Kasperlege-
schichte. Reutlingen, R. Bardtenschlager [1943]
240 p. illus. 18 cm.

i. Title.

PZ33.L53   52-47591

NL 0443233   DLC

Löhr, Adolf, 1889-
Kleeblatt auf Wanderfahrt, eine Erzählung für Mädchen.
Reutlingen, R. Bardtenschlager [1942]
119 p. illus., col. plates. 21 cm.

i. Title.

PZ33.L533   52-47578

NL 0443234   DLC

VOLUME 338

Löhr, Adolf, 1889–
Das Kleeblatt im Märchenland, eine Erzählung für Mädchen. Reutlingen, R. Bardtenschlager ₁1941₎
112 p. col. plates. 21 cm.

ɪ. Title.

PZ33.L535   52–47580

NL 0443235   DLC

Löhr, Adolf, 1889–
Kleeblatt im Wochenende, eine Erzählung für Mädchen.
Reutlingen, R. Bardtenschlager ₁1941₎
108 p. col. plates. 21 cm.

ɪ. Title.

PZ33.L536   52–47614

NL 0443236   DLC

Löhr, Adolf, 1889–
Die Kleeblattmädel; eine Erzählung für junge Mädchen.
Reutlingen, R. Bardtenschlager ₁1940₎
63 p. col. front. 19 cm.

ɪ. Title.

PZ33.L537   52–47630

NL 0443237   DLC

Löhr, Adolf, 1889–
Die Mädels vom Erlenhof, eine Mädchengeschichte.
Reutlingen, R. Bardtenschlager ₁1941₎
144 p. 18 cm.

ɪ. Title.

PZ33.L539   52–47603

NL 0443238   DLC

Löhr, Adolf, 1889–
Rosen am Rhein; Jungmädchen-Roman, von A. Frohmut
₁pseud.₎ Reutlingen, R. Bardtenschlager ₁1947, ᶜ1946₎
188 p. 18 cm.

ɪ. Title.

PZ33.L54   A 51–1338
New York. Public Libr.
for Library of Congress   ₁3₎†

NL 0443239   NN IU DLC

Löhr, Adolf, 1889–
Vier Mädel fahren ins Blaue, eine heitere Erzählung **für**
Mädchen. Reutlingen, R. Bardtenschlager ₁1941₎
111 p. front. 21 cm.

ɪ. Title.

PZ33.L543   52–47620

NL 0443240   DLC

Löhr, Adolf, 1909–
Die veränderung der schwingungsfetigkeit und
der dämpfungsfähigkeit infolge hydraulischen
drückens. Bau einer hydraulischen druckanlage.
... Braunschweig, 1936.
Inaug. Diss. - Techn. Hochschule Braunschweig,
1936.
Lebenslauf.
Schrifttum.

NL 0443241   ICRL

NL 0443242   DNLM

Löhr, Aemiliana.
Abend und Morgen ein Tag; die Hymnen der Herrentage
und Wochentage im Stundengebet. Regensburg, F. Pustet
₁1955₎
710 p. 20 cm.

"Den Grundstock dieses Buches bildet eine Aufsatzreihe über die
Ferialhymnen des monastischen Breviers, die während der Jahre
1928–1931 in der Klosterneuburger Zeitschrift 'Bibel und Liturgie'
veröffentlicht wurde."

1. Catholic Church—Hymns—Hist. & crit. 2. Hymns, Latin—Hist.
& crit.   ɪ. Title.

BV468.L6   56–17484 ‡

NL 0443243   DLC DCU PLatS InStme ICU

263.36   **Löhr, Aemiliana**
L825a   L'année du Seigneur; le mystère du
            Christ au cours de l'année liturgique.
            Bruges, C. Beyaert ₁1946₎
            2 v. (Collection Renaissance et
            tradition)

            Bibliographical footnotes.

            1. Church year - Meditations.
            I. Title.

NL 0443244   CaQML KAS OWorP MdBJ

Löhr, Aemiliana.
Das Herrenjahr; des Mysterium Christi im
Jahreskreis der Kirche ... Regensburg,
Friedrich Pustet [1951]
2 v. 21 cm.
Fünfte verbesserte Auflage.
1. Church year. I. Title.

NL 0443245   MnCS

Löhr, Aemiliana
Des Endes Ende. Zwei Gesprache. Regensburg,
Pustet, 1948.
71 p., front., illus., 19 cm.

NL 0443245-1   OrStbM

Löhr, Aemiliana.
Jahr des Herrn; das mysterium Christi im jahreskreis der
kirche, von Aemiliana Löhr ... Regensburg, F. Pustet, 1934.
3 p. l., ₁ix₎-xvi, 292 p. 20½ᵐᵐ.

1. Church year.   ɪ. Title.

Library of Congress   BV30.L6
                               ₁2₎   264

NL 0443246   DLC

Löhr, Aemiliana.
The year of Our Lord; the mystery of Christ in the
liturgical year, by Emiliana Loehr ... translated by a monk
of Saint Benedict. New York, P. J. Kenedy & sons ₁ᶜ1937₎
xxxii, 393 p. 21 cm.

1. Church year—Meditations. ɪ. Ducey, Michael, father, 1897–
tr. ɪɪ. Title.
                              Secular name: Maria Löhr.

BX2184.L62   264   37–6354

NL 0443247   DLC OrStbM

Loehr, August,
Ueber einige Phenolphentriazole. Giessen: J. Weinert,
1910. 46 p., 1 l. 8°.
Dissertation, Giessen.

1. Phenolphenyltriazols.
N. Y. P. L.   May 16, 1911.

NL 0443248   NN DNLM ICRL PU MH

Loehr, August, *ritter von,* 1847–
Wiener medailleure, 1899. Von A. r. v. Loehr. Illustrationen nach photographien der Herren Ph. r. v. Schoeller, A. r. v. Loehr u. a.—22 heliogravure-tafeln von Blechinger & Leykauf.—3 autotypie-tafeln und 67 autotypien
im texte von Angerer & Göschl. Wien, A. Schroll &
co., 1899.
1 p. L., 42 p. illus., xxv pl. incl. col. front. 35½ x 26ᵐᵐ.
—— Wiener medailleure. Nachtrag 1901. Von A. r. v.
Loehr. Mit 2 heliogravuren, 10 zinkotypie-tafeln und 18
illustrationen im texte. Wien, A. Schroll & co., 1902.
2 p. l., 47–61, [1] p. illus., pl. 35½ x 26ᵐᵐ. [*With his Wiener medailleure,*
1899. Wien, 1899]
                                             3–8256–7

NL 0443249   DLC DSI ICJ MB

Löhr, August, *1878–*
Beiträge zur würdigung der akkordlohnmethode im
rheinisch-westfälischen maschinenbau, von August Löhr
... M. Gladbach, Volksvereins-verlag, gmbh., 1912.
105 p. 23ᵐᵐ.
"Literaturverzeichnis": p. 5–7.

1. Piece work. 2. Machinery—Trade and manufacture—Germany.
3. Wages—Westphalia.
                                             L 13–24
Library, U. S. Bur. of   Labor HD4928.P5L8

NL 0443250   DL

Löhr, August, 1878–

Hönigschmid-Grossich, Rüdiger.
Zwangsschiedsspruch und schlichtungswesen; drei abhandlungen, von dr. oec. publ. Rüdiger Hönigschmid-Grossich, dr.
oec. publ. Emanuel Leidig ... ₁und₎ dr. oec. publ. August Löhr
... Jena, G. Fischer, 1929.

Loehr, August Oktav, *ritter von,* 1882–
Catalog der Sammlung von Mittelalter- und
modernnen Münzen und Medaillen des ...
Hauptmann v. Lohr ...
see under Hamburger, L. & L.,
Frankfurt-am-Main.

CJ43   **Loehr, August Oktav,** *ritter von,* 1882–
.V52
           Vienna. *Kunsthistorisches museum. Sammlung von me*
           daillen, münzen und geldzeichen.
           ... Führer durch die ausstellung der bundessammlung von
           medaillen, münzen und geldzeichen, von August Loehr.
           Wien, Verlag der Kunsthistorischen sammlungen, 1935.

VOLUME 338

Loehr, August, Oktav, Ritter von, 1882–
...Geldwesen, von A. Loehr. Wien: Kunsthistorisches
Museum, 1933?. 20 p. 4 pl. on 2 l. 18cm. (Vienna.
Kunsthistorisches Museum. Führer durch die kunsthistorischen
Sammlungen in Wien. Heft 24.)

1, Money. I. Ser.
N.Y.P.L.   October 2, 1934

NL 0443254   NN

Loehr, August Oktav, Ritter von, 1882–
Hofrat Univ.-Prof.Dr.Hermann Julius Hermann, erster
Direktor des Kunsthistorischen Museums. [Wien] 1955

10 p. port. (Veröffentlichungen des Verbandes Österreichischer Geschichtsvereine, 9)

NL 0443255   MH

Loehr, August Oktav, Ritter von, 1882–
In memoriam Hans Hirsch. [Wien] 1953

9 p. port. (Veröffentlichungen des Verbandes Österreichischer Geschichtsvereine, 3)
Biographien österreichischer Historiker, 1

NL 0443256   MH

LOEHR, August Octav Ritter von, 1882–
Karl Domanig. Wien,   F. Tempsky, etc.,
etc., 1925.

f°. Illustr.
"Jahrbuch der Kunsthistorischen sammlungen
des allerhöchsten   Kaiserhauses, Bd. XXXII,
Heft, 5." pp.417-423.

NL 0443257   MH

Loehr, August Oktav, Ritter von, 1882–
Die Medaille in Österreich, von A. O. Loehr und F. Dworschak. Wien: E. Hölzel & Co., Ges. m.b.H., 1933, 29 p.
incl. plates. 18½cm. (Vienna. Kunsthistorisches Museum.
Führer durch die kunsthistorischen Sammlungen in Wien. Heft
23.)

"Literatur," p. 12–13.

1. Medals, Austrian. I. Dworschak,   Friedrich, jt. au. II. Ser.
N.Y.P.L.   October 2, 1934

NL 0443258   NN

Loehr, August Oktav, Ritter von, 1882–
Die niederländische Medaille des 17.Jahr-
hunderts. Wien, Österr. Verlagsgesellschaft,
E.Hölzel & Co., G.m.b.H. [1921]

20 p. 10 mounted plates, illus. 20 cm.
"Kunst in Holland, 11."

NL 0443259   MH

NB1268 Loehr, August Oktav, Ritter von, 1882–
L76   Die niederländische Medaille des 17.
(SA)   Jahrhunderts. Wien, Hölzel [1930]
          20 p. illus.,10 pl.(in pocket) 20 cm
          (Kunst in Holland, 11)

          Bibliography: p.18

          1. MEDALS – HOLLAND I. T

NL 0443260   NjP

Loehr, August Oktav, Ritter von, 1882–
... Numismatik und Geldgeschichte, von August Loehr.
Wien, Kunsthistorisches Museum [etc., etc.] 1944. 47 p. 16 pl.
22cm. (Vienna. Kunsthistorisches Museums. Führer durch
die kunsthistorischen Sammlungen in Wien. Heft 30)

1. Numismatic—Hist. 2. Money   —Hist. I. Ser.
N.Y.P.L.   December 6, 1951

NL 0443261   NN CLU

Loehr, August Oktav, *Ritter* von, 1882–
Österreichische Geldgeschichte. Wien, Universum, 1946.

89 p. illus. (part mount. col.) port. 21 cm. (Veröffentlichungen
des Instituts für Österreichische Geschichtsforschung, Bd. 4)

1. Money—Austria—Hist. 2. Numismatics—Austria.   I. Title.
(Series: Vienna. Institut für Oesterreichische Geschichtsforschung.
Veröffentlichungen, Bd. 4)

                                              A 48–10139*

Harvard Univ. Library
for Library of Congress   [1]

NL 0443262   MH CLU DSI CU

Löhr, Beda.
Die Bedeutung der motiva credibilitatis für die
fides theologica mit besonderer Berücksichtigung
der Controverse zwischen Lugo und Suarez über
das Glaubensmotiv. Würzburg, F.X. Bucher,
1891.
81 p., 1 l.
Inaug.-Diss. – Würzburg, 1891.

NL 0443263   ICRL

Loehr (Benedictus Henricus).   * De lethargo. 2
p. l., 42 pp. 4°. Gottingæ, typ. J. C. L. Schultzii,
[1752].

NL 0443264   DNLM

U
24
L825   Loehr, Carl Adolf
         Grosses kriegswörterbuch, oder Encyclop-
         ädie aller in das gebiet der kriegswissen-
         schaften einschlagenden wörter und materien.
         bearb. von Carl Ed. Loehr. Mannheim, J.
         Bensheimer, 1851.
         2 v. XII pl. (part fold.) tables (1 fold.)
         22 cm.
         Pages 1-16 of vol. 2, including plate IX,
         are wanting in Patent office copy; pages 17-
         32 are repeated.
         1. Military art and science - Dictionaries

NL 0443265   DP

U29   Löhr, Carl Adolf.
        Ueber die Taktik und das Kriegswesen der
        Griechen und Römer nach den Quellen bearbeitet
        ... Mit lithographirten Plänen und Tafeln.
        Kempten, J. Kösel, 1825.
        xii, 332 p. [5 l.] x p. fold. tables, fold.
        plates. 21 cm.

        1. Military art and science.

NL 0443266   NWM

Loehr, Charles T.
War history of the old First Virginia infantry regiment,
Army of Northern Virginia, by Charles T. Loehr. Published
by request of the Old First Virginia infantry association.
Richmond, W. E. Jones. printer. 1884.

87 p. 22½ᶜᵐ.

Vi
NL 0443267   ViU NcD DNW OClWHi NjP NN NIC WaS CU

        Loehr, Charles T.
        War history of the old First Virginia infantry regiment,
        Army of Northern Virginia, by Charles T. Loehr. Published
        by request of the Old First Virginia infantry association.
        Richmond, W. E. Jones, printer. 1884.

        87 p. 22½ᶜᵐ.
        L. C. Copy Replaced by Microfilm

        1. U. S.—Hist.—Civil war—Regimental histories—Va. Inf.—1st. 2.
        Virginia infantry. 1st regt., 1861–1865.   I. Title: First Virginia in-
        fantry regiment.

                                              2–17933 rev.

        Library of Congress   [E581.5.1st]

NL 0443268   DLC LU

Loehr, E.L., ed.
Inspiring recitations for the school and home.
Comprising four hundred and fifty choice selections for Christmas, New Years, Easter, Thanksgiving. Chicago, [c1909]
160 p. 20 cm.

NL 0443269   RPB CSmH

Loehr, E   L   ed.
Paramount Sunday school recitations comprising three
hundred choice selections for Sunday school anniversa-
ries, Easter, children's day, patriotic, flag day, rally day,
harvest home, Thanksgiving, Christmas, little folks, temperance, missionary and miscellaneous. Ed. by E. L.
Loehr ... Chicago, Ill., Meyer & brother, 1902.
114 p. 20ᶜᵐ.

1. Readers and speakers—1870–   I. Title.

Library of Congress   PN4231.L6   12–36293

NL 0443270   DLC OCl

Löhr, Egid Valentin Johann Felix Nepomuk Ferdinand von,
1784–1851.
Beyträge   zur der theorie der culpa.
Giessen.und Darmstadt, 1808.

NL 0443271   MH-L CtY-L

Löhr, Egid Valentin Johann Felix Nepomuk Ferdinand von,
1784–1851.
Die theorie der culpa. Eine civilistische abhandlung von
Egid von Löhr. Giessen, Heyer, 1806.
4 p. l., 200 p. 19½ᶜᵐ.

1. Negligence (Roman law) 2. Criminal intent (Roman law)
I. Title: Culpa, Die theorie der.

                                              40–20141

NL 0443272   DLC CtY MH PU-L

Löhr, Egid Valentin Johann Felix Nepomuk Ferdinand von, 1784–1851
Ueber die römischen Begriffe von
Tutel und Curatel. Eine Einladungs-
schrift zu den auf der Rechtsschule
zu Wetzlar im Winter 1809 zu halten-
den Vorlesungen vom Justizrath von
Löhr. [Wetzlar] Gedruckt mit
Wincklerischen Schriften [1809]
1 p.l., 74 p. 16½ᶜᵐ.

Bibliographical footnotes.

NL 0443273   MH-L

VOLUME 338

LÖHR, Egid Valentin Johann Felix Nepomuk
Ferdinand von, 1784-1851.
Uebersicht der das privatrecht betreffenden
constitutionen der romischen kaiser von
Constantin I bis auf Theodos II u. Valentinian
III. [Wetzlar,1811]

Programm.
Uebersicht der das privatrecht betreffenden constitutionen der romischen kaiser-
von Theodos II und Valentinian III bis auf
Justinian. [Wetzlar,1 12].

NL 0443274   MH CLL

Löhr, Egid von.
Beiträge zur genaueren kenntniss der hülsenfrüchte und
insbesondere der bohne ... Giessen, Buchdruckerei von
G. D. Brühl, 1848.
19 p. fold. pl. 25ᶜᵐ.
[Botanical pamphlets, v. 2, no. 10]
Inaug.-diss.—Giessen.

1. Seeds—Anatomy. 2. Beans.

Library of Congress   QK3.B77   5-37009†

NL 0443275   DLC

Loehr, Ernst Georg
Vereins-zolltarif der königreiche Preusen,
Bayern, Würtenberg, Sachsen dann des churfürstenthums und grossherzogthums Hessen und
der übrigen vereins-staaten ... für das
gesamtgebiet des Zollvereins ... Nürnberg,
Riegel und Wiessner, 1834.
138 p.

NL 0443276   MiU

Löhr, Eugen.
Kuczynski, Robert René, 1876–
... Die hülfenfrüchte in der deutschen ernährungswirtschaft,
von direktor dr. R. Kuczynski und bezirksamtmann E. Löhr.
Berlin, Verlag der Beiträge, R. Hobbing, 1917.

389
183af   Löhr, F
L'homme et les fléaux.   Paris, La table
ronde [1954]
318 p.

Translation of Die grosse Plague.

1. Famines. 2. Food supply. 3. Pests.
I. Löhr, F   Die grosse Plague.

NL 0443278   DNAL

Löhr, [Franz Emil] Oscar
see Löhr, Oscar, 1854–

Löhr, Franz von
see Löher, Franz von, 1818-1892.

Loehr, Frederic Nicholls, 1844-1888.
Ave Maria, for solo & chorus.   London, [187-?]

NL 0443281   MB

8A
1835   LÖHR, FREDERIC Nicholls, 1844-1888.
Margarita, song, the words by F.E.Weatherly,
the music by Frederic N. Löhr.   London,
Boosey & Co. [189-?]
7p. 35cm.

For voice and piano.

NL 0443282   ICN

Loehr, Frederic Nicholls, 1844-1888.
"Out on the deep". [Song with piano acc.]
New York, S. T. Gordon, [18-   ]
5 p.   f°.   (Latest and most popular English
ballads. Fifth series)

NL 0443283   NN

Loehr, Frederic Nicholls, 1844-1888.
School exercises... By Frederic N. Löhr...   London:
Forsyth Bros. [pref. 1881.]   3 books in 1 v.   4°.
Dedication at head of title.
Contents: Book 1. Elementary music. Book 2. Sight singing. Book 3. Sol-
feggi in two parts (Concone).

1. School music.—Instruction.
N. Y. P. L.   July 17, 1917.

NL 0443284   NN

Loehr, Frederic Nicholls, 1844-1888.
Swing song. [Two-part chorus for women's voices with accom-
paniment for the pianoforte.] Words by G. Clifton Bingham.
[Music by] Frederic N. Löhr.
= New York. Franklin. [188-?] 8 pp. [The Schumann Club
collection of quartetts and choruses for female and mixed voices.
No. 19.] 27 cm.

D3612 — Double main card. — L: Frederic Nicholls. (M1) — Bingham,
Clifton, 1858-1913. (M2) — T.r. Chorus. (1) — Part songs. Female voices. (1)

NL 0443285   MB

BX
3534   Löhr, Gabriel M., Father, 1877-
Q3   Beiträge zur Geschichte des Kölner Do-
no.15-17   minikanerklosters im Mittelalter.   Leip-
sig, O. Harrassowitz, 1920-22.
2 v. illus. 24 cm. (Quellen und Forschungen zur Geschichte des Dominikanerordens in Deutschland, 15.-17. Heft)

Contents--T. 1. Darstellung--
T. 2. Quellen.

NL 0443286   NIC NN MH

Löhr, Gabriel M   1877-
Die Dominikaner an der Leipziger universität, von p. Gabriel M. Löhr, o. p. Vechta, Albertus-Magnus-verlag, 1934.
116 p. 24ᶜᵐ. (Added t.-p.: Quellen und forschungen zur geschichte
des Dominikanerordens in Deutschland ... 30. heft)
"Verzeichnis mehrfach zitierter werke": p. [7]-8.

1. Dominicans in Leipzig. 2. Leipzig. Universität.

Title from Cornell Univ.   A C 34-4034
Library of Congress   [BX3534.A4 hft. 30]

NL 0443287   NIC PU

Loehr, Gabriel M., 1877-
Die Kapitel der Provinz Saxonia im Zeitalter der Kirchen-
spaltung, 1513-1540, von P. Gabriel M. Löhr...   Vechta: Albertus-Magnus-Verlag, 1930. xii, 260 p.   8°.   (Quellen
und Forschungen zur Geschichte des Dominikanerordens in
Deutschland. Heft 26.)
Bibliography, p. vii-xii.

1. Dominicans—Germany—Saxony.
N. Y. P. L.   December 3, 1930

NL 0443288   NN MH NIC CtY PU IMunS

Löhr, Gabriel M., Father, 1877-
Die Kölner Dominikanerschule vom 14. bis zum 16. Jahrhundert, mit einer Übersicht über die Gesamtentwicklung.
Freiburg, Paulusdruckerei, 1946.
92 p. 20 cm.

NL 0443289   CU InStmeS

Löhr, Gabriel M., Father, 1877-
Die Kölner Dominikanerschule vom 14. bis zum 16. Jahr-
hundert, mit einer Übersicht über die Gesamtentwicklung.
[Köln] Kölner Universitätsverlag, 1948.
119 p. 20 cm.
"Verzeichnis der wichtigsten in abgekürzter Form zitierten
Werke": p. 116.

1. Cologne. Universität—Hist. 2. Dominicans in Germany.
I. Title.
                                      A 52-482
New York. Public Libr.
for Library of Congress   [1]

NL 0443290   NN NjPT DCU ICN

Löhr, Gabriel M., Father, 1877- ed.
Registrum litterarum pro provincia Saxoniae,
Joachimi Turriani, 1487-1500, Vincentii Bandelli,
1501-1506, Thomae de Vio Caietani, 1507-1513
see under Dominicans. Master general,
1487-1500 (Joachimus Turrianus)

Löhr, Gabriel M., Father, 1877- ed.
Dominicans. Master general, 1474-1480 (Leonardus Man-
suetus)
Registrum litterarum pro provincia Saxoniae, Leonardi de
Mansuetis, 1474-1480, Salvi Cassettae, 1481-1483, Barnabae
Saxoni, 1486; herausgegeben von p. Gabriel M. Löhr, o. p.
Köln-Rhein, Albertus-Magnus-verlag, in kommission bei O.
Harrassowitz, Leipzig, 1939.

Loehr, Gabriel M., Father, 1877-
Die Teutonia im 15. Jahrhundert; Studien und Texte vor-
nehmlich zur Geschichte ihrer Reform, von P. Gabriel M. Löhr...
Leipzig: O. Harrassowitz, 1924. xi, 190 p. 8°. (Quellen
und Forschungen zur Geschichte des Dominikanerordens in
Deutschland. Heft 19.)
Bibliography, p. [ix]-xi.

1. Dominicans—Germany, 15th cent. 3. Ser.   2. Dominicans—Switzerland, 15th
N. Y. P. L.   cent.
                                                  May 3, 1926

NL 0443293   NN NIC MH IMunS

Loehr, Gabriel M., Father, 1877-
Die theologischen Disputationen und Promotionen an der
Universität Köln im ausgehenden 15. Jahrhundert, nach den An-
gaben des P. Servatius Fanckel...von P. Gabriel M. Löhr...
Leipzig: O. Harrassowitz, 1926. 124 p. 8°. (Quellen und
Forschungen zur Geschichte des Dominikanerordens in Deutsch-
land. Heft 21.)

1. Dominicans—Germany. 2. Dis-   sertations, Academic—Germany.
Bibl. 3. Fanckel, Servatius, d. 1508.   4. Ser.
N. Y. P. L.   October 27, 1926

NL 0443294   NN NIC WU CU

Löhr, Georg, 1836-
Das Allgemeine deutsche Handelsgesetzbuch. Erläutert
aus den Materialien, der Rechtslehre und den Entscheidungen der deutschen Gerichte, unter genauer Berücksichtigung der Einführungsgesetze sämmtlicher deutschen
Staaten. Elberfeld, R. L. Friedrichs, 1868.
557 p. 22 cm.
Includes text of the Allgemeine deutsche Handelsgesetzbuch,
drafted by a commission of the German Confederation as a model
for its member states and adopted by the Bundesversammlung of the
German Confederation in 1861. Cf. Gareis, C. Das Allg. deut.
Handelsgesetzbuch. 1891. p. [vii]-viii.
Includes bibliographical references.

Continued in next column

VOLUME 338

Continued from preceding column

NL 0443296   DLC

Löhr, Georg, ed.
1836–
Central-organ für das deutsche handels- und wechselrecht. Hrsg. von dr. jur. Georg Löhr ... Neue folge ... Elberfeld, R. L. Friderichs, 1865–73.

Löhr, Georg, 1836–
De ficticiis actionibus ex jure romano ... quam ... publice defendet auctor Georgius Loehr ... Adversariorum partes suscipient Ferd. Eich ... Otto Kroenitz ... Wilh. Treitz ... Coloniae ad Rhenum, typis M. Dumont-Schauberg, ₁1858₎

64 p. 21½cm.
Inaug.-diss.-Bonn.
"Theses": p. ₍63₎–64.
Bibliographical footnotes.

NL 0443298   MH-L DLC

Loehr, George Robert.
... Giuseppe Castiglione (1688–1766) pittore di corte di Ch'ien-Lung, imperatore della Cina. Roma, Istituto italiano per il Medio ed Estremo Oriente, 1940.
126, ₍2₎ p. 28 pl. (1 fold.) on 12 l. 24½ᶜᵐ.
"Conferenza tenuta all' Istituto italiano per il Medio ed Estremo Oriente il 23 maggio 1938, xvi."
"Bibliografia": p. ₍119₎–123.

1. Castiglione, Giuseppe, 1688–1766.
ND623.C485L6   A F 47–3840
Columbia univ. Libraries
for Library of Congress   ₍2₎†

ICU
NL 0443299   NNC TxU MH NN CtY IaU MiU NcD ICRL DLC

LÖHR, Godo, 1901–
Die azoester-reaktion der ein-und mehwertigen Phenole und die deutung des reaktionsverlaufes. Inaug.-diss., Kiel, 1925.

pp. (7), 32+.
"Lebenslauf", at end.
"Cover:-Aus dem Chemischen institut der Universitat, Kiel.

NL 0443300   MH-C ICRL CtY

Loehr, Godo, 1901–
Ueber das verhalten der plazenta bei cholesteringe speicherten kaninchen.
Inaug. Diss.   Kiel, 1926, (Leipzig)
Bibl.

NL 0443301   ICRL CtY

LÖHR, H.
Der fall Löhneysen nach den gerichtlichen verhandlungen bearbeitet, von A. Baumgarten. Braunschweig, 1873.
H. Löhr versus Hilbert Löhneysen.
60 p.

NL 0443302   MH-L

Löhr, H
Über die Selbstbiographie Kaiser Karls IV. Rostock, C. Boldt, 1886.

62 p. 22.5 cm.
Inaugural-Dissertation - Rostock.

NL 0443303   MH

GR880   LÖHR, HANNS, 1891–
.L82   Aberglauben und medizin, von professor dr. Hanns Löhr ... Leipzig, J. A. Barth, 1940.
vi, 106 p. 20½cm.
Bibliographical foot-notes.

1. Medicine, Magic, mystic and spagiric. 2. Superstition.

NL 0443304   ICU ViU

Löhr, Hanns, 1891–
Hist.   Aberglauben und Medizin. 7.-16. Tausend.
R133   Leipzig, Barth, 1942.
942ℓ   vi, 132p. 21cm.
Bibliographical foot-notes.

1. Medicine, Magic, mystic and spagiric.
2. Medical delusions.

NL 0443305   CtY-M

Löhr, Hanns, 1891–
Aberglauben und medizin, von professor dr. Hanns Löhr ... 17.-30. tausend. Leipzig, J. A. Barth, 1943.
vi, 132 p. 21ᶜᵐ.
Bibliographical foot-notes.

1. Medicine, Magic mystic and spagiric. I. Title.
44–47403
Library of Congress   R133.L73
₍2₎   615.85

NL 0443306   DLC OkU DNLM NNC IU MnU

Löhr, Hanns, 1891–
... Naturwissenschaft und theologie; eine zweitausendjährige auseinandersetzung. Dortmund, Volkschaft-verlag ₍1944₎
viii, 268 p. front. (port.) 22ᶜᵐ.
Bibliographical references in "Anmerkungen" (p. 251–260)

1. Religion and science—History of controversy. I. Title.
BL245.L6   215   A F 46–564
Union theol. sem. Library
for Library of Congress   ₍3₎†

NL 0443307   NNUT IaU FU CU TxHR DNLM ICU ViU DLC

W   Löhr, Hanns, 1891–
9   Ueber die Stellung und Bedeutung der
L825u   Heilkunde im nationalsozialistischen
1935   Staate. Berlin, "Die Medizinische Welt"
₍1935₎
36 p.

Bibliography: p. 35–36.

1. Medicine - Germany

NL 0443308   DNLM

Löhr, Hanns, 1891–   joint ed.
LF2879
.5   Ritterbusch, Paul, 1900–   ed.
.R5   Die Universität Kiel und Schleswig-Holstein; Reden und Vorträge zur "Woche der Universität Kiel," 14. bis 21. Juni 1937. Hrsg. von Paul Ritterbusch ₍und₎ Hanns Löhr. Neumünster in Holstein, K. Wachholtz, 1937.

Löhr, Hanns, 1891–
Eine verbesserte methodik zur ununterbrochenen registrierung der atmung isolierter säugetierlungen in wechselnden gasgemischen nach Hanns Löhr und Cornelis de Lind van Wijngaarden. Von Hanns Löhr ... (Mit 5 abbildungen.)
(*In* Abderhalden, Emil, ed. Handbuch der biologischen arbeitsmethoden ... Berlin, 1920–   25ᶜᵐ. abt. v. Methoden zum studium der funktionen der einzelnen organe des tierischen organismus. t. 4, II (1927) p. ₍1705₎–1714. illus., diagrs.)
Bibliographical foot-notes.

1. Lungs. 2. Respiration.
Title from Ohio State   Univ.   A C 36–3759
Library of Congress   ₍QH324.A3 1920 abt. 5, t. 4, II₎
(574.072)

NL 0443310   OU

Löhr, Hanns, 1891–   ed.
Wissenschaftliche Akademie des NSD.-Dozentenbundes der Christian-Albrechts-Universität Kiel, 1938.
see under Nationalsozialistischer Deutscher Dozentenbund. Kiel (Universität) Wissenschaftliche Akademie.

Löhr, Hans.
Geschichte der Städtischen höheren mädchenschule zu Quedlinburg. Ein beitrag zur geschichte Quedlinburgs und zur entwickelung des höheren mädchen-schulwesens, von dem direktor dr. Hans Löhr. ₍Quedlinburg? 1899?₎
2 p. l., 71 p. 21ᶜᵐ.

1. Quedlinburg. Städtische höhere mädchenschule. 2. Education of women—Germany. ₍2. Woman—Education—Germany₎
E 15–1444
Library, U. S. Bur. of   Education LF3197.Q3S8

NL 0443312   DHEW

W 4   LÖHR, Hans, 1915–
F82   Ueber Bakteriologie der Frauenmilch.
1942   ₍Frankfurt a. M.₎ 1942.
30 p.
Inaug. -Diss. - Frankfurt.
1. Milk - Bacteriology 2. Milk - Human

NL 0443313   DNLM

Löhr, Harvey, 1856–   ed.
The London chant book. Edited by Harvey Löhr and Howard B. Humphery. London, Weekes & co. [pref. 1886]

NL 0443314   MH

Löhr, Harvey, 1856–
Principia of music. A complete explanation of the rudiments of music, specially designed for preparing candidates for the Royal academy of music, Royal college of music, Cambridge, and other examinations: together with a brief account of instruments, harmony, composition, and form, and the most common terms in connection. By Harvey Löhr ... London ₍etc.₎ Forsyth brothers ₍1890₎
93 p. illus. (music) 25ᶜᵐ.
1. Music—Manuals, text-books, etc. I. Title.
₍Full name: Richard Harvey Löhr₎
20–14659
Library of Congress   MT7.L84

NL 0443315   DLC CtY

VOLUME 338

W 4
F86
1937

Löhr, Hermann, 1912–
Die Verwendung von Octimum als Mydria-
ticum. Freiburg i. Br., Rebholz, 1937.
12, ₍3₎ p.

Inaug.-Diss. – Freiburg.
Bibliography: p. ₍14₎

NL 0443316   DNLM

LÖHR, HERMANN FREDERIC, 1872–

Album. London, New York, Chappell [191-]
Pl. no. 25864. 1 v. port. 31cm. (The Portrait series)

Vol. 2.
For voice and piano.
CONTENTS. --v. 2. For baritone voice.
1. Songs, English.   I. The Portrait series.

NL 0443317   NN

---

*M1620
L65

Löhr, Hermann Frederic, 1872–
. Four Indian songs from "The garden of Kama",
by Laurence Hope ₍pseud.₎ Music by Hermann
Löhr ... London, New York ₍etc., etc.₎
Chappell & co., ltd., c1914.

2p.ℓ.,17p.   31cm.

Medium voice.

Contents: Starlight.--Just in the hush before
the dawn.--This passion is but an ember.--On the
city wall.

NL 0443318   NBuG NN

Löhr, Hermann Frederic, 1872–
A garland of song. The words by Harold Boulton, the
music by Hermann Löhr ... London, W. Chappell & co. ltd.;
New York, Boosey & co., *1901.

2 p. l., 49 p. 31cm.

Publishers' plate no.: 21, 232.
Pianoforte accompaniment.

I. Boulton, Sir Harold Edwin, bart., 1859–   II. Title.

         Music-336 Revised
Library of Congress   M1620.L82G3

NL 0443319   DLC NN

---

qM784.312
L83L2

Löhr, Hermann Frederic, 1872–
₍Little grey home in the West₎
Little grey home in the West; song, words
by Eardley-Wilmot. New York, Chappell,
c1911.
5p. 34cm.

Cover title.
For voice and piano.
Words printed also as text: p.₍1₎

NL 0443320   IU OrP

Löhr, Hermann Frederic, 1872–
Little grey home in the West: song. New York,
Chappell, c1916.
5p. 35½cm.

NL 0443321   OrU

Löhr, Hermann Frederic, 1872–
The little Irish girl, song; words by Edward
Teschemacher. Chappell, c1903.
High voice.

NL 0443322   OrP

A784.94
L826

LÖHR, HERMANN FREDERIC, 1872–
₍The little sunbonnet₎
...The little sunbonnet; a song-cycle for
four solo voices with pianoforte accompaniment.
The words by Edward Teschemacher and Arthur
Cleveland. The music composed by Hermann Löhr.
London and New York, Boosey & co., c1904.
4ℓ.,50p. 30½cm.

English text with piano acc.
Publ.plate no.H.4316.

NL 0443323   PP OrP

Löhr, Hermann Frederic, 1872–
₍Our little Cinderella. With piano.₎
Our little Cinderella; a play with music in three acts.
By Leo Trevor. Lyrics by Arthur Wimperis. Music by Hermann Löhr
... London₍, etc.₎: Chappell & Co., Ltd., cop. 1911. Publ. pl.
no. 24617. 155 p. 28cm.

Vocal score. English words.

737125A. 1. Operas, Comic—Piano   and voice. I. Trevor, Leo, 1865?–
1927: Our little Cinderella. II. Wim-   peris, Arthur Harold, 1875– :
N.Y.P.L.   Our little Cinderella.
                              December 14, 1934

NL 0443324   NN CU

Loehr, Hermann **Frederic**, 1872–
...Romany songs. Words by Edward Teschemacher and
Arthur Cleveland, music by Hermann Löhr...   London: Chap-
pell & Co., Ltd., cop. 1909.   Publ. pl. no. 24537.   30 p.   f°.

For low voice.
English words with music for 1 voice with piano acc.

1. Songs (English). 2. Tesche-   macher, Edward, 1876–
3. Cleveland, Arthur Rackham.   4. Title.
N.Y.P.L.   December 2, 1921.

NL 0443325   NN IEN

Löhr, Hermann Frederic, 1872–

Russian love songs. Words by Katerina Bogosoff. Music by
Hermann Löhr...   London ₍etc.₎ Chappell & co. ltd., c1921.
Publ. pl. no. 27314.   27 p.   31cm.

For 1 voice with piano acc. English words.
CONTENTS.--The brown eyes of my dushka.—Throb of the passionate day.—In
the path thro' the dark arbutus.—Lifeless and grey the sea lies.—A Black sea song.
—Russian snow song.

1. Songs, English. I. Bogo-   soff, Katerina. II. Title.
N.Y.P.L.   March 25, 1940

NL 0443326   NN OrP

M1503
L567S86

Löhr, Hermann Frederic, 1872-1943.
₍Sarenna, acc. arr. piano₎
Sarenna, an episode at the cross roads; lyric drama in one act.
Book by Avon Marsh. London, New York, Chappell, c1907.
138 p.

English words.

NL 0443327   CU

LÖHR, HERMANN FREDERIC. 1872–

Songs in exile. Words by Arthur Stringer. London,
New York, Chappell, c1908.   Pl. no. 23558. 23 p. 31cm.

For low voice and piano; accompaniment originally for orchestra.
CONTENTS. --The philanderer. --Soft ways. --Whistlin' Dannie. --Exile.
--Ould Doctor Ma'ginn.

1. Songs, English.   I. Stringer, Arthur John Arbuthnott. 1874-1950.
II. Title.

NL 0443328   NN

LÖHR, HERMANN FREDERIC, 1872–
[SONGS OF ITALY]
Songs of Italy. Words by Edward Lockton. Music
by Hermann Löhr.   London, New York, Chappell,
c1919.   24 p. 30cm.

For voice and piano.
CONTENTS.--Italian boat song.--The hills at Asolo.--Golden
stars that shone in Lombardy.--   Festal song.
1. Songs, English. I. Lockton,   Edward. II. Title.

NL 0443329   NN

Loehr, Hermann Frederic, 1872–
Songs of Roumania. Words by Edward Teschemacher.
Music by Hermann Löhr...   London: Chappell & Co., Ltd.,
cop. 1911.   Publ. pl. no. 25035.   14 p.   f°.

For medium voice.
English words; music for 1 voice with piano acc.
Contents: 1. The Roumanian mountains. 2. Life has sent me many roses.
3. Roumanian night song.

1. Songs, English. 2. Teschemacher,   Edward, 1876–   3. Title.
N.Y.P.L.   September 29, 1928

NL 0443330   NN

LÖHR, HERMANN FREDERIC, 1872–
[SONGS OF THE NORSELAND]
Songs of the Norseland. Words from the Danish and
Norwegian by Edward Teschemacher. Music by Hermann
Löhr. London, New York, Chappell, c1906. 33 p.
30cm.

For voice and piano.
CONTENTS. --My ships that went a-sailing. --Love is an ocean. --You
loved the time of violets. --Time was I roved the mountains. --Eyes that
used to gaze in mine. --Youth   has a happy tread.
1. Songs, English. I. Title.

NL 0443331   NN RPB

LÖHR, HERMANN FREDERIC, 1872–
[SONGS OF THE SOUTHERN ISLES]
Songs of the southern isles. Words by Edward
Teschemacher. Music by Hermann Löhr. London,
New York, Chappell, c1913.   17 p.   31cm.

For low voice and piano.
CONTENTS. --Star of the south. --I dream of a garden of sunshine.
--Cyprian night song. --When spring comes to the islands.

1. Songs, English. 2. Song   cycles. I. Teschemacher,
Edward. 1876–   II. Title.

NL 0443332   NN OrP OrU NBuG

Loehr, Hermann Frederic, 1872–
...Three little Spanish songs... Words from the Spanish
by Comfort Parry. Music by Hermann Löhr...   London:
Chappell & Co., Ltd., cop. 1919. Publ. pl. no. 27009.   8 p.   f°.

For low voice.
English words; music for 1 voice with piano acc.
Cover-title.
Contents: 1. My love, the swallow. 2. Lola (habanera). 3. Ah! though the
silver moon were mine.

1. Songs, English. 2. Parry,   Comfort, translator.
N.Y.P.L.   November 30, 1928

NL 0443333   NN

Löhr, Hermann Frederic, 1872–
Where my caravan has rested; song from "Romany songs."
New York, Chappell, c1910.
5p. 35½cm.

NL 0443334   OrU

Löhr, Hermann Frederic, 1872–

Where my caravan has rested, from
Romany songs, words by Edward Teschemacher
with violin or violoncello obbligato.
Chappell, c1917.

Violin and cello parts in pocket.

NL 0443335   OrP

VOLUME 338

PT2424
L627D4 Löhr, J   poet.
        Drei Blümcher aus Frankfurt. Hanau,
        F. König, 1857.
        16 p.

NL 0443336   CU

PS3527
.E117 Loehr, Jeska, tr.
E23   Neagoe, Peter.
        ... Ileana aus Aciliu, roman. Leipzig [etc.] Zinnen-verlag
        [1936]

Loehr (Joannes Josephus). *De partium corporis humani situ abnormi cum animi aliena-
tione. 2 p. l., 30 pp., 1 l. 4°. Bonnæ, H. Kni-
rrenschild [1826]

NL 0443338   DNLM PPC

Löhr, Johann.
    Anleitung zur erteilung des schreibunterrichtes in der
volksschule. Für seminaristen und lehrer, bearb. von
Johann Löhr ... Trier, H. Stephanus, 1889.
    48 p. 3 pl. (2 fold.) 19½ᶜᵐ.

    1. Writing.
                                        E 14–1174
    Library, U. S. Bur. of   Education LB1590.L82

NL 0443339   DHEW

Löhr, Johann Andreas Christian, 1764–1823.
    ABC und Bilderbuch, nebst einer Anweisung Kinder leicht
lesen zu lehren, zunächst zum Gebrauch beim häuslichen Unterricht, von J. A. C. Löhr. Dritte verbesserte Auflage. Leipzig:
Bei G. Fleischer dem Jüngern, 1807. 214 p. 6 col'd pl. 18cm.
(His: Erste Vorbereitungen für Kinder. Bdchn. 1.)

    649455A. 1. Primers, German.
    N. Y. P. L.   July 5, 1933

NL 0443340   NN

[Löhr, Johann Andreas Christian] 1764–1823.
    Anweisung zur zweckmässigen behandlung des obst- und
gemüsegartens, nebst einem anhang von blumen, von J. C. F.
Müller [pseud.] Wien, J. Stabel und compagnie, 1796.
    2 v. in 1. 21ᶜᵐ.

    1. Fruit-culture. 2. Gardening. [1, 2. Horticulture]
                                        Agr 16—977
    U. S. Dept. of agr. Library   90L83A
    for Library of Congress   [a41b1]

NL 0443341   DNAL

[Löhr, Johann Andreas Christian] 1764–1823.
    Der aufrichtige baumgärtner; oder, Kurze und deutliche an-
weisung wie man auf eine zweckmässige art bäume erziehen,
veredeln und versetzen soll. Zunächst für den bürger und
landmann, und für gärtner auf dem lande, aber auch für gutsbesitzer, landprediger und schullehrer, welche sich mit der
baumzucht beschäftigen wollen. Von einem freunde der baumzucht. Halle, 1798.
    2 p. l., 92 p. 18½ᶜᵐ.
    Authority for author's name: Kayser, C. G. Voll. büch.-lex.
    1. Fruit-culture. [1. Pomology] I. Title.
                                        Agr 14—1276
    U. S. Dept. of agr. Library   93Au3
    for Library of Congress   [a38d1]

NL 0443342   DNAL

Loehr, Johann Andreas Christian, 1764–1823.
    Die bewohner der erde oder beschreibung der
voelker der erde. Leipzig, 1823.
    12°

NL 0443343   NN

Loehr, Johann Andreas Christian
    Die bewohner der erde; oder, beschreibung der
volker der erde. 2 aufl. Leipzig, 1832

NL 0443344   NN

Löhr, Johann Andreas Christian, 1764–1823.
    Das Buch der Bilder, Geschichten und Lehren für Kindheit
und Jugend. Von J. A. C. Löhr. Mit 12 illum. Kupfern. Leipzig: G. Fleischer[, 1819]. 364 p. col'd plates. 18 x 11cm.

    649446A. 1. Juvenile literature—Fic-   tion, German. I. Title.
    N. Y. P. L.   November 13, 1933

NL 0443345   NN

PT921
.L6   Löhr, Johann Andreas Christian, 1764–1823.
        Das Buch der Maehrchen, für Kindheit und
Jugend, nebst etzlichen Schnaken und Schnur-
ren, anmuthig und lehrhaftig. Leipzig, G.
Fleischer [1819–20]
        2 v. illus. 16cm.

        1. Fairy tales. 2. Folk-lore - German.
3. Tales, German. I. Title.

NL 0443346   OCU

Löhr, Johann Andreas Christian, 1764–1823.
    Des D. Martinus Katz- und Wachtelbüchlein, mit mancher-
lei anmuthig-ergötzlichen Begebenheiten, Historien, und lehr-
reichen sowohl, als gut gemeinten Betrachtungen zur Lehre, Warnung und Ermahnung für das junge Volk in Deutschland, d. i., für
unsere hochgelahrte, gebildete Jugend. Von J. A. C. Löhr. Ein
schlecht gering Büchlein, das niemand wird lesen wollen. Mit
bunten Kupfern. Leipzig: F. A. Brockhaus, 1823. xxxxii,
393 p. col'd front., col'd plates. 16 x 12½cm.

    Purported to be the work of Martin Luther.

    646974A. 1. Juvenile literature—Fic-   tion, German. 2. Cat—Legends and
    stories. 3. Dogs—Legends and stories. I. Luther, Martin, 1483–1546, sup-
    posed au. II. Title.
    N. Y. P. L.   November 16, 1933

NL 0443348   NN

LÖHR, Johann Andreas Christian.
    Deutsche märchen. Neu geordnet von
Gustav Harrer. Stuttg., 1876.
    sm.8° Front. and illustr.

NL 0443349   MH

Löhr, Johann Andreas Christian, 1764–1823.
    Elementarbegriffe; oder, Entwickelung vieler Begriffe zur Be-
stimmtheit im Denken und zum Verständniss vielgebrauchter
Wörter. Ein Handbuch beim öffentlichen und häuslichen Unterricht und ein Nachtrag zu seinen Vorbereitungen, von J. A. C.
Löhr... Zweite mit Zusätzen vermehrte Auflage. Frankfurt
am Mayn: P. H. Guilhauman, 1809–11. 2 v. in 1. 18½cm.
(His: Denkübungen in Entwickelung vieler wichtigen Begriffe
und Erklärung häufig gebrauchter Wörter. Theil 1–2.)

    761811A. 1. Encyclopedias, German.   I. Title.
    N. Y. P. L.   August 23, 1935

NL 0443350   NN

Löhr, Johann Andreas Christian, 1764–1823.
    Erste Lese- und Erzählungs-Blätter. Bildungsstoff für Herz
und Kopf. Von J. A. C. Löhr. Mit illuminirten Kupfern. Leipzig: E. Fleischer, 1823. xii, 284 p. col'd front., col'd plates.
16cm.

    649868A. 1. Juvenile literature,   German.
    N. Y. P. L.   July 5, 1933

NL 0443351   NN

Löhr, Johann Andreas Christian, 1764–1823.
    Erwekkungen für das Herz der Kinder, von J. A. C. Löhr.
Zweite durchgesehene Auflage. Mit 30 Kupfern. Leipzig: G.
Fleischer[, pref. 1810]. vi, 233 p. 30 col'd pl. 20cm.
(His: Erste Lehren und Bilder zunächst für Kinder. Abt. 2.)

    Title vignette.

    646968A. 1. Juvenile literature—   Fiction, German. 2. Juvenile litera-
    ture—Picture books, German.   I. Title.
    N. Y. P. L.   March 23, 1934

NL 0443352   NN

Löhr, Johann Andreas Christian, 1764–1823.
    Erzählungen für das Herz der Kinder, nach J. A. C. Löhr.
Von Leopold Klette. Grätz: J. A. Kienreich, 1807. vi, 188 p.
16½cm.

    764927A. 1. Juvenile literature—   Fiction, German. I. Klette,
    Leopold, ed.
    N. Y. P. L.   August 23, 1935

NL 0443353   NN

Loehr, Johann Andreas Christian, 1764–1823.
    Erzählungen für Kinder, von J. A. C. Löhr. In neuer Aus-
wahl... Stuttgart: Loewe [1902]. 2 parts in 1 v. pl. (part
col'd, incl. front.), illus. 3. ed. 16°.

    1. Juvenile literature (German).
    N. Y. P. L.   April 22, 1916.

NL 0443354   NN

Löhr, Johann Andreas Christian, 1764–1823.
    Erzählungen für Kinder. In neuer Auswahl. Mit
3 Bunt-, 3 Ton- und 16 Textbildern nach Originalen
bewährter Künstler. 6. Aufl. Stuttgart, Loewes
Verlag Ferdinand Carl [191-?]
    [4], 111 p. illus., plates (part col.) 18ᶜᵐ.

    1. Children's stories, German. I. Title.

NL 0443355   ViU

LÖHR, JOHANN ANDREAS CHRISTIAN, 1764–1823.
    Erzählungen und Geschichten für Herz und Gemüth der Kind-
heit und Jugend... Ein Nachtrag zu mehrern seiner Schriften,
insonderheit zu den Erwekkungen für's Herz und zu der Familie
Oswald, von J. A. C. Löhr... Leipzig: G. Fleischer [1822]
    2 v. in 1. front. (v. 1.) 16½x13cm.

    Frontispiece by Ramberg.

    764970A. 1. Juvenile literature—Fiction, German.

NL 0443356   NN

VOLUME 338

LÖHR, JOHANN ANDREAS CHRISTIAN, 1764–1823.
Die Familie Oswald; oder, Erweckungen des religiösen
Sinnes der Kindheit. Deutschlands Müttern und Kindern
gewidmet, von J.A.C.Löhr... Leipzig: G. Fleischer der
Jung., 1819. 3 v. front. (v. 1.) 16½cm.

759108–10A. 1. Juvenile literature—Fiction, German.
I. Title.

NL 0443357   NN

Loehr, J₍ohann₎ A₍ndreas₎ C₍hristian₎.
Gemeinnützige und vollständige Naturgeschichte für Liebhaber und Lehrer. Bd.   Leipzig: G. Fleischer, der Jüngere,
18   v.   8°.

Bd. 5: Das Mineralreich. Nebst Register über das ganze Werk.

1. Natural history. 2. Mineralogy.
N.Y.P.L.   August 9, 1911.

NL 0443358   NN NcD

Löhr, Johann Andreas Christian, 1764–1823.
Geographie; oder, Beschreibung der länder aller erdtheile für den frühen unterricht. Von J. A. C. Löhr.
Leipzig, G. Fleischer d. jüng., 1819.
xii, 298 p., 1 l. 18ᵐᵐ.

1. Geography—Text-books—1800-1870.

NL 0443359   MiU

---

220   Löhr, Johann Andreas Christian, 1764–1823.
L82g   Die geschichten der Bibel zum gebrauch für
lehrer und schüler von J. A. C. Löhr ...   Leipzig, Bei G. Fleischer dem jüngern, 1810.
190p. front.   (Added t.-p.: Der erste lehrmeister ... l.t.)

With this is bound: Schellenberg, J. A. P. Der
fleissige rechenschüler. Leipzig, 1810.

1. Bible stories.

NL 0443360   IU

D21   LÖHR, JOHANN ANDREAS CHRISTIAN, 1764–1823.
.L82   Grössere weltgeschichte für leser aus allen stän-
den, von J.A.C.Löhr... Leipzig, G.Fleischer, 1811.
2 v. in 1. front. 19cm.

1. History, Universal.

NL 0443361   ICU KyU

Löhr, Johann Andreas Christian, 1764–1823.
...Grosses marchenbuch. Neu geordnet von
Gustav Harrer. 2. aufl. mit kolorirtem titelbild.
Leipzig, E. Berndt, 1880.
v, 481 p. col. front. 20 cm.
1. Folk-lore - Germany.

NL 0443362   CU

BS   Löhr, Johann Andreas Christian, 1764–1823.
558   Las historias della Bibla per adoever
R13L82 dellas scolas romanschas. Vertidas our del
1821   tudaisc. Cuoira, stampo traes A.T. Otto,
1821.
170 p. 20cm.

1. Bible stories, Raeto-Romance. I. Title.

NL 0443363   NIC

Löhr, Johann Andreas Christian, 1764–1823.
Kleine Erzählungen. Zum Vorlesen und zur Leseübung für
kleine Kinder. Von J. A. C. Löhr. Mit vier farbigen Bildern
nach Aquarellen von L. v. Kramer. 4. Aufl. Stuttgart: K.
Thienemann ₍18—?₎ 184 p. illus. 21cm.

NL 0443364   NN OrU ICU

PZ 32 Löhr, Johann Andreas Christian, 1764–1823.
L6   Kleine Geschichten und Erzählungen für Kinder
zur Bildung des sittlichen Gefühls zunächst zum
Gebrauch beim häuslichen Unterricht, von J. A. C.
Löhr ... Leipzig, bei Gerhard Fleischer dem
Jüngern, 1799.
xviii, 312 p. 17 cm.

NL 0443365   OU

Löhr, Johann Andreas Christian, 1764–1823.
Kleine Geschichten und Erzählungen für Kinder,
zur Bildung des sittlichen Gefühls und Urtheils
sowohl zum Gebrauch beim öffentlichen als häuslichen Unterricht. 3.verbesserte Aufl. Leipzig,
G.Fleischer, 1811.

NL 0443366   MH

LÖHR, JOHANN ANDREAS CHRISTIAN, 1764–1823.
Kleine Weltgeschichte für den ersten Anfang beim Haus-
und Schulunterricht. Von J.A.C.Löhr... Leipzig: G. Fleischer der Jüngere, 1811. xxxvi, 224 p. 17cm.

762245A. 1. History, General, Juvenile.

NL 0443367   NN

Löhr, Johann Andreas Christian, 1764–1823.
Kleinigkeiten für unsere Kinder. Von J. A. C. Löhr. Zweite
Ausgabe, mit sechs Tafeln colorirter Abbildungen. Leipzig:
H. Fritzsche₍, 1829₎. vi, 294 p. col'd front., col'd plates.
16½cm.

646632A. 1. Juvenile literature—   Fiction, German. I. Title.
N.Y.P.L.   September 19, 1933

NL 0443368   NN

Löhr, J₍ohann₎ A₍ndreas₎ C₍hristian₎ 1764–1823.
Die länder und völker der erde, oder vollständige
beschreibung aller fünf erdtheile und deren bewohner.
Von J. A. C. Löhr ... 3. nach dem jetzigen politischen
stand der dinge neu umgearb. aufl. Leipzig, G. Fleischer
der jüngere, 1818–19.
4 v. fronts. (3 col.) plates (partly col.) 5 fold. maps. 20ᵐᵐ.
CONTENTS.—I. bd. Europa.—2. bd. Asien.—3. bd. Afrika.—4. bd. Amerika und Australien.

Subject entries: 1. Geography. 2. Ethnology.
3-18586

Library of Congress, no.   GN310.L8.

NL 0443369   DLC TU NN

Löhr, Johann Andreas Christian, 1764–1823.
Ea   Die Länder und Völker der Erde, oder
822L   vollständige Beschreibung aller fünf Erdtheile
und deren Bewohner ... 4.nach dem jetzigen
politischen Stand der Dinge bearb. Aufl.
Stuttgart, A.F.Macklot,1822.
4v. col.fronts.,plates(part.col.) 19½cm.
1st edition published with title: Bildergeo-
graphie, 1810.
Contents. - 1.T. Europa. - 2.T. Asien. -
3.T. Afrika. - 4.T. Amerika und Australien.

NL 0443370   CtY

Löhr, Johann Andreas Christian, 1764–1823.
Ludewig und seine Gespielen; oder, Leichte Uebungen für
Verstand und Herz in Erzählungen, Geschichten von Thieren und
Aufgaben für das frühere Alter, von J. A. C. Löhr... Leipzig:
G. Fleischer der Jüngere ₍1810₎ vii, 198 p. front. 17cm.

Frontispiece by H. Ramberg.

762944A. 1. Juvenile literature,   German. I. Title.
N.Y.P.L.   November 8, 1935

NL 0443371   NN

LB1507 LÖHR,JOHANN ANDREAS CHRISTIAN,1764–1823.
.L8   Materialien zur erweckung und uebung des verstandes
und der urtheilskraft der kinder,sowohl zum gebrauch
beim öffentlichen als häuslichen unterricht,von J.A.
C.Löhr. 3.verm.aufl. Leipzig,Bei G.Fleischer dem
jüngern,1810.
xvi,253 p. 19cm. (Added t.-p.:Erste vorbereitung
für kinder sowohl zum gebrauch beim öffentlichen als
häuslichen unterricht. 3.bdchen.)
1.Education of children.

NL 0443372   ICU

Löhr, Johann Andreas Christian, 1764–1823.
570   Merkwürdigkeiten aus dem Reiche der Thiere
L825   und Pflanzen, oder ausführliche Beschreibung
ed.3   der merkwürdigsten Thiere und Pflanzen für
Freunde und Liebhaber der Natur. 3. Aufl.
Frankfurt am Main, P.H.Guilhauman, 1827.
x, 458 p. 18ᵐᵐ.

1.Biology - Curiosa and miscellany. I.
Title.

NL 0443373   CSt

LÖHR, Johann Andreas Christian, 1764–1823.
Morgenländische   märchen. Neu geordnet
von Gustav Harrer. [With an appendix.
Kalmuckische marchen.] Stuttg., 1876.

sm.8°. Front. and illustr.
The cover has Leipzig in the imprint.

NL 0443374   MH

9-NASZ
Löhr, Johann Andreas Christian, 1764–1823.
Tändeleyen und Scherze für unsere Kinder, von J. A. C. Löhr
... Bdchn. 1- Leipzig: G. Fleischer₍, 1805-   v.
plates.   24½ x 20½cm.

Imperfect: text of v. 1 wanting.
Title vignette.
Plates engraved by Rosmäsler.

1. Juvenile literature—Picture books,   German. I. Title.
N.Y.P.L.   March 23, 1934

NL 0443375   NN

VOLUME 338

Loehr Johann Andreas Christian. 1764–1823.
Voedsel voor het kinderlijk hart, of zedekunde voor kinderen, in leerrijke voorbeelden en verhalen, vrij gevolgd naar het Hoogduitsch van J. A. C. L...
2 p. l., iii–xiv, 366 pp. *Leyden : D. Dumortier & Zoon,* 1810. 8°.
Also publ. as v. 2 under title: Voedsel voor het kinderlijk verstand en hart.

NL 0443376 NN

ₗLöhr, Johann Andreas Christianₗ 1764–1823.
Der vollständige monatsgärtner, oder, Deutliche und vollständige anweisung zu allen geschäften im baumküchen- und blumengarten für alle monate des jahres. Von J. C. F. Müller ₗpseud.ₗ 2. verb. aufl. Frankfurt am Mayn, P. H. Guilhauman, 1798.
207 p. 19ᵐ.

1. Fruit-culture. ₗ1. Pomologyₗ 2. Vegetables. ɪ. Title.
Agr 22—329

U. S. Dept. of agr. Library 90L83
for Library of Congress ₗa41b1ₗ

NL 0443377 DNAL

Löhr, Johann Andreas Christian, 1764–1823.
Der vollständige monatsgärtner; oder, Deutliche und vollständige anweisung für die kultur der pflanzen und zu allen geschäften bei dem obst- und gemüsebau, dann in der blumenzucht, so wie im weinberge und hopfengarten, für alle monate des jahres. Mit einem anhange die kunst alle arten gärten anzulegen, von J. C. F. Müller ₗpseud.ₗ 6. aufl. gänzlich umgearb. und verm. von Jakob Ernst von Reider ... Frankfurt am Main, F. Wilmans, 1837.
254 p. 18ᵐ.
1. Fruit-culture. ₗ1. Pomologyₗ 2. Vegetables. ɪ. Reider, Jacob Ernst von, ed.
Agr 12–5 Revised

Library, U. S. Dept. of Agriculture 90L83

NL 0443378 DNAL

ₗLöhr, Johann Andreas Christianₗ 1764–1823.
Vollständiger und gründlicher gartenunterricht oder Anweisung für den obst- küchen- und blumengarten, mit drei anhängen vom aufbewahren und erhalten der früchte und gewächse von obstwein und obstessig und mit einem monatsgärtner versehen, von Carl Friedrich Schmidt ₗpseud.ₗ 8. aufl. Leipzig, Bei G. Fleischer dem jüngern, 1816.
xx, 372 p. 18¼ᵐ.

1. Gardening. ₗ1. Horticultureₗ
Agr 21–834

Library, U. S. Dept. of Agriculture 90L83V

NL 0443379 DNAL

Löhr, Johann Friedrich Werner, respondent.
Actio utilis de recepto
  see under Harpprecht, Ferdinand Christoph, 1650–1714, praeses.

ₗLoehr, Johann Josephₗ
An essay on the theory and practice of tuning in general, and on Scheibler's invention of tuning pianofortes and organs by the metronome in particular. For the use of musicians, tuners, and organ builders. ₗ2d ed.ₗ London, R. Cocks and co., 1853.
64 p. tables., diagrs. 18¼ᵐ.
On cover : Translated from the German by Augustus Wehrhan.

1. Tuning. 2. Scheibler, Johann Heinrich, 1777–1838. ɪ. Wehrhan, August Heinrich, tr.

Library of Congress MT165.L82 6–3219

NL 0443381 DLC NN MB

1891–
Löhr, Johannes. Ein Versuch zur therapeutischen Anwendung von Kupfersalzlösungen (Gräfin von Linden) bei der Behandlung von Typhus abdominalis. Aus d. Med. Universitätskl. zu Kiel. [In Maschinenschrift.] 18 S. 4°(2°). — Auszug: (Kiel 1920: Schmidt & Klaunig). 1 Bl. 8°
Kiel, Med. Diss. v. 15. April 1920, Ref. Schittenhelm
[Geb. 10. Sept. 91 Hohensolms; Wohnort: Kiel; Staatsangeh : Preußen; Vorbildung: G. Elberfeld Reife 11; Studium: Gießen 2, Bonn 4, Kiel 1, Bonn 2, Kiel 1 S.; Coll. 14. Febr. 20; Approb. 26. Juli 19.] [U 20. 2488]

NL 0443382 ICRL

Loehr, Josef.
...Abraham und Isaak auf der Jagd; Schwank in zwei Akten, von Josef Löhr... Bonn am Rhein: A. Heidelmann, 1927₎ 24 p. 7.–8. ed. 12°. (A. Heidelmann's Theaterbibliothek. ₗNr.ₗ 153.)

1. Drama, German. 2. Title.
N. Y. P. L. February 6, 1928

NL 0443383 NN

Loehr, Josef.
Der laestige Zimmernachbar; oder, Wurst wider Wurst. Posse in zwei Akten, von Jos. Löhr... Bonn am Rhein: A. Heidelmannₗ, 1927₎ 44 p. 2. ed. 12°. (Theaterbibliothek. Nr. 162.)

1. Drama, German. 2. Title.
N. Y. P. L. September 4, 1928

NL 0443384 NN

Loehr, Josef.
Die Mehlspeise; oder, Meier in tausend Aengsten. Komische Szene in einem Akt, von Josef Löhr... Bonn am Rhein: A. Heidelmannₗ, 1927₎ 12 p. 2. ed. 12°. (Theaterbibliothek. Nr. 74.)

1. Drama, German. 2. Title.
N. Y. P. L. September 4, 1928

NL 0443385 NN

Loehr, Josef.
Die neue Feuerwehr; Schwank in einem Akt, von Jos. Löhr... Bonn am Rhein: A. Heidelmannₗ, 1927₎ 16 p. 2. ed. 12°. (Theaterbibliothek. ₗNr.ₗ 103.)

1. Drama, German. 2. Title
N. Y. P. L. June 27, 1928

NL 0443386 NN

Loehr, Josef.
Der pfiffige Bauer. Posse in 1 Akt. Bonn a. Rh.: A. Heidelmann ₗ1911₎ 13 p. 3. ed. 12°. (A. Heidelmann Theaterbibliothek. Heft 54.)

1. Drama (German). 2. Title.
N. Y. P. L. August 4, 1911.

NL 0443387 NN

Loehr, Josef.
Die Rache des Lehrlings; oder, Schneidermeister Zwirn als Wunderdoktor. Bonn a. Rh.: A. Heidelmann, [1909]
18 p. 12°. (A. Heidelmann's Theaterbibliothek. 137.)
4. ed.

NL 0443388 NN

Loehr, Josef.
Rot oder Schwarz; Posse in einem Akt, von Josef Löhr... Bonn am Rhein: A. Heidelmannₗ, 1927₎ 11 p. 3. ed. 12°. (Theaterbibliothek. Nr. 70.)

1. Drama, German. 2. Title.
N. Y. P. L. September 4, 1928

NL 0443389 NN

Loehr, Josef.
Der schlaue Polizist. Posse in zwei Akten, von Jos. Löhr... Bonn am Rhein: A. Heidelmannₗ, 1926₎ 24 p. 4. ed. 12°. (A. Heidelmann's Theaterbibliothek. ₗNr.ₗ 86.)

1. Drama, German. 2. Title.
N. Y. P. L. January 18, 1927

NL 0443390 NN

Loehr, Josef.
Ein Stuendchen Kasernenleben; Militärischer Schwank in 1 Akt. Bonn a. Rh.: A. Heidelmannₗ 1911₎ 36 p. 2. ed. 12°. (Heidelmann's Theaterbibliothek. ₗno.ₗ 85.)

1. Drama (German). 2. Military life in drama. 3. Title.
N. Y. P. L. October 5, 1911.

NL 0443391 NN

Loehr, Josef.
Die verhaengnisvolle Wurst; Posse in einem Akt, von Josef Löhr... Bonn am Rhein: A. Heidelmannₗ, 1927₎ 13 p. 4. ed. 12°. (Theaterbibliothek. ₗNr.ₗ 113.)

1. Drama, German. 2. Title.
N. Y. P. L. June 27, 1928

NL 0443392 NN

Löhr, Josef.
Die verhexten Pantoffeln. Posse in 2 Akten. Bonn a. Rh. : A. Heidelmann [1908]
26 p. 12°. (A. Heidelmann's Theaterbibliothek. Heft. 53)

NL 0443393 NN

Loehr, Josef, writer on banking.
Das deutsche Bankwesen, von Dr. Joseph Loehr... München: J. Schweitzer, 1921. 171 p. 8°.

29225A. 1. Banks and banking, Germany.
N. Y. P. L. December 7, 1921.

NL 0443394 NN CtY NjP MH

Löhr, Josef, writer on banking, ed.

Germany. *Laws, statutes, etc.*
Das Hypothekenbankgesetz vom 13. juli 1899, hrsg. mit kurzen erläuternden anmerkungen und einem anhang: Das recht der hypothekenpfandbriefe, von dr. jur. Joseph Löhr ... Leipzig, A. Deichert nachf. (G. Böhme) 1906.

VOLUME 338

Löhr, Josef, writer on banking.
Die volkswirtschaftliche bedeutung der hypotheken-banken, von dr. Josef Löhr ... Leipzig, A. Deichert nachf. (G. Böhme) 1908.
53, ₁1₁ p. 21ᶜᵐ.

1. Mortgage banks—Germany.   1. Title.

16–7834

Library of Congress   HG2051.G4L65

NL 0443396   DLC

Löhr, Josef, 1878–
... Beiträge zum missionsrecht. Missionsobere, missionare und missionsfakultäten, von dr. theol. et iur. et phil. Joseph Löhr ... Paderborn, F. Schöningh, 1916.
vi, ₍2₎, 174 p. 23½ᶜᵐ. (Görres-gesellschaft zur pflege der wissenschaft im katholischen Deutschland. Veröffentlichungen der Sektion für rechts- und sozialwissenschaft ... 29. hft.)
"Quellen und wiederholt zitierte literatur": p. ₍viii₎

1. Catholic church—Missions. 2. Missions. 3. Sponsors (Canon law) 1. Title.

35–21129 rev.

Library of Congress   BV2180.L6

₍r36b2₎   266.2

NL 0443397   DLC CtY MH-L NN

Löhr, Josef, 1878–
... Ist eine staatliche "kirchenhoheit" und eine besondere staatsaufsicht über die kirche mit der deutschen reichsverfassung vereinbar? Von dr. theol. dr. iur. dr. phil. Joseph Löhr ... Paderborn, F. Schöningh, 1927.
2 p. l., 60 p. 23½ᶜᵐ. (Görres-gesellschaft zur pflege der wissenschaft im katholischen Deutschland. Veröffentlichungen der Sektion für rechts- und sozialwissenschaft ... 47. hft.)
"Literaturverzeichnis": p. ₍56₎–57.
1. Church and state in Germany. 2. Ecclesiastical law—Germany. 3. Germany—Constitutional law.   1. Title: Kirchenhoheit.

36–2648

Library of Congress   BR856.L6

₍2₎   261.70943

NL 0443398   DLC NN MH-L

Löhr, Josef, 1878– Die katholische Kirchengesellschaft und ihre Oberen nach dem Preußischen Allgemeinen Landrecht. Paderborn 1917: Schöningh. 46 S. 8° ¶ Vollst. als: Veröffentlichungen d. Sektion f. Rechts- u. Sozialwissensch. d. Görresgesellsch. H. 31 u. d. T.: Das Preuß. Allg. Landrecht u. die kath. Kirchengesellschaften.
Münster, Rechts- u. staatswiss. Diss. v. 7. Aug. 1917, Ref. Rosenfeld, Lucas
₍Geb. 21. Jan. 78 Kornelimünster; Staatsangeh.: Preußen; Vorbildung: G. Münstereifel Reife 98; Studium: Bonn Phil. 6, Theol. 8, Jura 12 S.; Rig. 5. Dez. 12.₎   ₍U 17. 525₎

NL 0443399   ICRL

Löhr, Josef, 1878–
Der krieg und das schicksal der kirchen Frankreichs, eine deutsche antwort auf französische anklagen. Von Joseph Löhr ... Köln, J. P. Bachem, 1915.
44 p. 23½ᶜᵐ. (Added t.-p.: Zeit- und streitfragen der gegenwart. 5. bd.)

1. European war, 1914–1918—Religious aspects.   1. Title.

25–15342

Library of Congress   D639.R4L6

NL 0443400   DLC CSt

Löhr, Josef, 1878–
Methodisch-kritische Beiträge zur Geschichte der Sittlichkeit des Klerus, besonders der Erzdiözese Köln, am Ausgang des Mittelalters. Münster i. W., Aschendorff, 1910.
viii, 120 p. 23cm. (Reformationsgeschichtliche Studien und Texte, Heft 17)

BR
302
R33
v.17

1. Clergy—Germany. 2. Cologne (Archdiocese)—Hist.

NcD

NL 0443401   NIC TxDaM MH-AH NNUT CtY MH IMunS NjPT

Löhr, Josef, 1878–
... Das preussische Allgemeine landrecht und die katholischen kirchengesellschaften. Von dr. theol. et iur. et phil. Joseph Löhr ... Paderborn, F. Schöningh, 1917.
x, 152 p. 23½ᶜᵐ. (Görres-gesellschaft zur pflege der wissenschaft im katholischen Deutschland. Veröffentlichungen der Sektion für rechts- und sozialwissenschaft ... 31. hft.)
"Benutzte literatur": p. ₍viii₎–x.

1. Church and state in Prussia. 2. Catholic church in Prussia. 3. Ecclesiastical law—Prussia. 4. Civil law—Prussia.   1. Title.

36–1993 rev.

NL 0443402   DLC NN MH-L

Löhr, Josef, 1878– Studien zur Geschichte der Verfassung und Verwaltung der Kölnischen Archidiakonate zu Ausgang des Mittelalters. Stuttgart 1909: Union. 38 S. 8° ¶(Ersch. vollst. u. d. T.: Die Verwaltung d. kölnischen Großarchidiakonats Xanten zu Ausgang d. Mittelalt., als: Kirchenrechtl. Abhandlungen. H. 59–60.)
Bonn, Phil. Diss. v. 14. Aug. 1909, Ref. Schulte
₍Geb. 21. Jan. 78 Cornelimünster; Wohnort: Preußen; Vorbildung: Gymn. Münstereifel Reife O. 98; Studium: Bonn Theol. 8, Jura u. Phil. 12 S.; Rig. 27. Mai 08.₎   ₍U 09. 411₎

NL 0443403   ICRL PU CtY MH

Löhr, Josef, 1878–
Die verwaltung des kölnischen grossarchidiakonates Xanten am ausgange des mittelalters. Von dr. phil. Joseph Löhr ... Stuttgart, F. Enke, 1909.
xvi, 202 p. incl. tables. 22½ᶜᵐ. (Added t.-p.: Kirchenrechtliche abhandlungen. Hrsg. von dr. Ulrich Stutz ... 59. und 60. hft.)
Issued also in part as the author's dissertation, Bonn, 1909.
"Verzeichnis der abgekürzten literatur": p. ₍xi₎–xvi.

1. Xanten, Ger. (Archdiaconate)—History. 2. Germany—Church history—Middle ages.

A C 38–4235

Chicago. Univ. Library   BV759.A1K6   vol. 59–60
for Library of Congress   ₍2₎

NL 0443404   ICU PPPD ICU MH CtY

Löhr, Joseph, 1878–

see

Löhr, Josef, 1878–

Löhr, Joseph, 1914–
Die verwaltung der aktiengesellschaft, insbesondere unter berücksichtigung der durchführung des führerprinzips ... von Joseph Löhr ... Tauberbischofsheim, "Tauber- und Frankenbote," 1940.
viii, 60 p., 1 l. 21ᶜᵐ.
Inaug.-diss.—Heidelberg.
Lebenslauf.
"Literaturverzeichnis": p. v–vi.

1. Directors of corporations—Germany.

47–37042

NL 0443406   DLC MH IEN

Löhr, Karl, 1889–
Otto Ludwig's jugendwerke "Die rechte des herzens" und "Die torgauer heide". (Quellenkritische untersuchungen.) ... Borna-Leipzig, R. Noske, 1913.
cover-title, 2 l., ₍vii₎–viii, 100 p., 1 l. 23ᶜᵐ.
Inaug.-diss.—Münster i. W.
"Mein leben."
"Literaturverzeichnis": p. ₍vii₎–viii.

1. Ludwig, Otto, 1813–1865.

NL 0443407   MiU PU IU MH NNU-W NNU CtY

Löhr, Karl, 1889–
Otto Ludwigs Jugendwerke "Die Rechte des Herzens" und "Die Torgauer Heide" Münster, R. Noske, 1913.
100 p. 23cm.

PT
2426
Z5
L6

"Inaugural-Dissertation" (Ph.D.)

1. Ludwig, Otto, 1813–1865.

NL 0443408   CU-I

Löhr, Karl Adolf
see   Löhr, Carl Adolf.

Löhr, Kurt Ida
Der anwaltsgehilfe; anleitung zur ausbildung von Kurt Ida Löhr ... unter juristischer mitarbeit von ... Gerhard Triebel. 1. aufl. Limburg/Lahn, Limburger vereinsdruckerei ₍1955₎
xii, 308 p. forms. 23cm.

NL 0443410   MH-L

Loehr (Ladovicus). *De febre intermittente.*
1 p. l., 20 pp. 4°. *Lipsia, typ. Brockhausii,*
1843.

NL 0443411   DNLM PPC

Löhr, Ludwig.
Faustzahlen für den Landwirt.
Graz, Stocker, 1952.
223 p.

33.29
L83

1. Austria. Agriculture. 2. Agriculture. Tables and ready-reckoners.

NL 0443412   DNAL

Löhr, Ludwig.
Faustzahlen für den Landwirt.   2. verb. Aufl. Graz, Stocker ₍1953₎
257 p.

33.29
L83
Bd.2

1. Austria. Agriculture. 2. Agriculture. Tables and ready-reckoners.

NL 0443413   DNAL

VOLUME 338

58
L83
Löhr, Ludwig.
Der Seilzug im Bergbauernbetrieb; eine
Anleitung zu allen Feldarbeiten am Steilhang
im Fallinienseilzug.   Graz, Stocker
[1951]
104 p.

1. Cableways.   2. Mountain farming.
Implements and machinery.

NL 0443414   DNAL RU

Löhr, Ludwig.
Der Seilzug im Bergbauernbetrieb; eine Anleitung zu
allen Feldarbeiten am Steilhang im Fallinienseilzug. 2.,
überarb. Aufl. Graz, L. Stocker [1952]
120 p. (p. 115–120 advertisements) illus. 23 cm.
Bibliographical footnotes.

1. Tillage. 2. Field crops—Austria. 3. Agricultural machinery.
I. Title.
S604.L6 1952   60–28720

NL 0443415   DLC DNAL

Löhr, Ludwig.
Die variabilität des rechnungsmässigen betriebserfolges der
landgutswirtschaft unter dem einfluss der abschlusstermine.
diagrs.
Landw. jahrb. bd. 70, p. 637–726.   Berlin, 1929.

1. Agriculture—Accounting.
                                 [87.L27 bd. 70]   Agr 30–809
Library, U. S. Dept. of   Agriculture 18L23 bd. 70

NL 0443416   DNAL

Löhr, Ludwig.
Die zusammenfassende buchführung mit vollkommenem in-
ventar. Rechnungsmethodische vorschläge zur vermeidung
der reinertragsvariabilität in der zusammenfassenden buchführung.
Landw. jahrb. bd. 77, p. 1–68.   Berlin, 1933.

1. Agriculture—Accounting.
                                                Agr 33–607
Library, U. S. Dept. of   Agriculture 18L23 bd. 77
Library of Congress   [87.L27 bd. 77]

NL 0443417   DNAL

                                 KF 24143
Loehr, Maja, 1888–
Leoben; Werden und Wesen einer Stadt. Baden bei
Wien, Rohrer [c1934]
200p.

NL 0443418   MH ICarbS

                                 KE 31784
Loehr, Maja, 1888–
Die Radmeister am steirischen Erzberg bis 1625 [by]
M.Loehr. Aus dem Werfener Schichten des Dachstein-
gebietes bei Schladming [by] Ernst Ehrlich. Graz, Moser
[1947]
207 p. (Mitteilungen des Museums für Bergbau, Geologie
und Technik am Landesmuseum Joanneum in Graz, 5)

NL 0443419   MH

Loehr, Maja, 1888–
Schönbrunn.   [Wien, Steffel-Verlag, 19]
32 p.   (Kleinbuchreihe "Österreich," Nr. 2)

NL 0443420   MH NN

Loehr, Maja, 1888–

Der steirische Reimchronist--ein österreichischer Geschichtsschreiber des Mittelalters.
Wien, Bindenschild-Verlag, 1945.

44 p. 21 cm. (Der Bindenschild; Darstellungen aus dem Kultur- und Geistesleben Österreichs,
Heft, 2).

1. Ottokar, Austrian chronicler, d. ca. 1309.
I. Title. (Series).

NL 0443421   CaBVaU

Loehr, Maja, 1888–
Der steirische reimchronist -- ein österreichischer geschichtsschreiber des mittelalters. Wien, Bindenschild-verlag, 1946.
44 p. (Der bindenschild; darstellungen
aus dem kultur- und geistesleben Österreichs,
hft 2)

1. Ottokar, Austrian chronicler, d. ca. 1309.
Österreichische reimchronik.

NL 0443422   NNC

Loehr, Maja, 1888–
Thörl; Geschichte eines steirischen Eisenwerkes vom
vierzehnten Jahrhundert bis zur Gegenwart. Wien, Verlag
für Geschichte und Politik, 1952.
176 p. illus. 25 cm.

1. Iron industry and trade—Thörl, Austria (Styria) 2. Steel industry and trade—Thörl, Austria (Styria)
HD9525.A83T456   338.47672   53–25786 ‡

NL 0443423   DLC NN ICU NIC

PT
2623
O337T7
Loehr, Maja, 1888–
Tristans Tod; Tragödie in fünf Aufzügen.   Wien, H.Heller, 1919.
116p.   21cm.

NL 0443424   CLSU   IEN OC1 CtU

Löhr, Maria
see
Löhr, Aemiliana.

Löhr, Matthias Joseph, 1800–1864.
Botanischer führer zur flora von
Köln; oder, Beschreibung der in den weiteren umgebungen
von Köln wildwachsenden und am häufigsten cultivirten
pflanzen, mit angabe ihrer fundorte, blüthezeit und dauer.
Köln. 1860. sm. 8°. pp. xv, 323.
Works consulted, p. xiv.

NL 0443426   MH-A MH RPB

Löhr, Matthias Joseph, 1800–1864.
Enumeratio der flora von Deutschland und der angren-
zenden länder im ganzen umfange von Reichenbach's
Flora germanica excursoria, vom Mittelländischen meere
bis zur Nord- und Ost-See ... Bearb. von Math. Jos. Löhr
... Braunschweig, F. Vieweg und sohn, 1852.
xxi, 820 p. 16°·.
"Bei der arbeit benutzte werke und litteratur": p. ⸤xviii–xxi.

1. Botany—Germany.

Library of Congress   QK314.L8   5–25568†

NL 0443427   DLC OkU

Löhr, Matthias Joseph, 1800–1864.
Flora von Coblenz; oder, Systematische zusammenstellung und beschreibung der in jener gegend des mit-
telrheines wildwachsenden und gebauten phanerogamischen
pflanzen, nach dem natürlichen systeme geordnet. Cöln.
1838. sm. 8°. pp. xxvi, 319 ·⸀·.

NL 0443428   MH-A

Löhr, Matthias Joseph, 1800–1864.
Taschenbuch der flora von Trier und Luxemburg,
mit berücksichtigung der nahe- und glan-gegenden. Trier.
1844. 16°. pp. lxvi, 318 +.
"Benutzte werke und literatur," p. xvii.

NL 0443429   MH-A

LÖHR, Matthias Joseph, 1800–1864.
Zur kenntniss der rheinischen saginarten
vorgetragen bei der General-versam des.
naturhist. ver in Munster, 1852. [Bonn],
[1852].

NL 0443430   MH-G

LÖHR, Matthias Joseph, 1800–1864.
Zusammenstellung der phanerogamischer
pflanzen aus der grafschaft Meisenheim nach
fruheren aufnahmen. [Bonn], Kat.107.
O.Weigel, [1872].

NL 0443431   MH-G

Loehr, Max.
Beiträge zur chronologie der älteren
chinesischen bronzen. [Berlin, 1936?]
41 p. illus., 6 plates. 28 cm.
The author's dissertation, Munich.
"Sonderabzur aus Ostasiatische zeitschrift, Neue
folge XII, hft 5".
Bibliographical footnotes.

NL 0443432   PU-Mu

Fv
2082
L824
Loehr, Max.
Bronzentexte der Chou-Zeit. Peking, Deutsch-
land-Institut, 1944.
30,91p. illus. 26cm.
Reprinted from Sinologische Arbeiten, 2.
Cover title.
At head of title: 漢學集刊

1. Inscriptions, Chinese. 2. China - Antiq.

NL 0443433   CtY MiU

NK5750
.M5
Loehr, Max.

Michigan. University. *Museum of Art.*
Early Chinese jades. A loan exhibition presented by the
Museum of Art, University of Michigan, Alumni Memorial
Hall, Ann Arbor, March 22 through April 22, 1953. ⸤Ann
Arbor, 1953⸣

VOLUME 338

NK
4165
.L82
Loehr, Max.
Neue Typen grauer Shang-Keramik. Peking,
Deutschland-Institut, 1943.
54-86 p. illus. 26 cm. (Sinologische
Arbeiten. Sonderabdruck ₍₁₎)
Chung Tê Hsüeh Chih 5.Jahrg.Nr.1/2. Beiheft.

1.Pottery,Chinese.

NL 0443435　　MiU

Loehr, Max.
Das rollteir in China. (Sonderabzug aus
Ostasiatische zeitschrift, neue folge 14. hft. 4. 5.
p. [137]-142. plates. 28 cm.)

NL 0443436　　PU-Mu

ND
1049
.W25
L82
Loehr,Max.
Studie über Wang Mong (die datierten Werke)
Frankfurt am Main, Verlag des China-Instituts
₍1939₎
₍273₎-290 p. plates. 28 cm.
Cover title.
"Sonderdruck aus Sinica,XIV.Jahrgang,Heft
5/6 ₍1939₎"

1.Wang Mong,d.1385.

NL 0443437　　MiU

BS412
L6
Löhr, Max Richard Hermann, 1864-1931, ed.
Das Alte Testament; die Literatur des
Jahres 1913. Tübingen, J.C.B. Mohr
(P. Siebeck); New York, G.E. Stechert,
1914.
37 p. (Theologischer Jahresbericht, 33.
Jahrgang 1913, 1.Bd.,2.Abt.)

1. Bible. O.T. - Bibl. 2. Bibl. O.T. -
Criticism, interpretation, etc. - Bibl.

NL 0443438　　CU

Löhr, Max Richard Hermann, 1864-1931.
... Alttestamentliche religions-geschichte, von d. dr. Max
Löhr ... Leipzig, G. J. Göschen, 1906.
147 p. 15¹ᶜᵐ. (Sammlung Göschen. ₍292₎)
"Literatur": p. ₍5₎

1. Bible. O.T.—Theology. 2. Bible—Theology—O. T.

Library of Congress　　BS1197.L7

6-36068 Revised

NL 0443439　　DLC ViU MB PPWe PPiPT ViRUT

Löhr, Max Richard Hermann, 1864-1931.
... Alttestamentliche religions-geschichte, von d. dr. Max
Löhr ... 2., neubearb. aufl. Berlin und Leipzig, W. de Gruyter
& co., 1919.
146 p. 16ᶜᵐ. (Sammlung Göschen. ₍292₎)
"Literatur": p. 5.

1. Bible. O.T.—Theology. 2. Bible—Theology—O. T.

Library of Congress　　BS1197.L7 1919

43-43360

NL 0443440　　DLC OCH

Löhr, Max Richard Hermann, 1864-1931.
... Das asylwesen im Alten Testament, von Max Löhr.
Halle (Saale) Max Niemeyer verlag, 1930.
4 p. l., p. ₍177₎-217. 26ᵐ. (Schriften der Königsberger gelehrten gesellschaft. Geisteswissenschaftliche klasse. 7. jahr, hft. 3)
"1. auflage."
"Literatur": 4th prelim. leaf.

1. Asylum, Right of. 2. Bible. O. T.—Antiquities. 3. Bible—Antiquities—O. T. I. Title.

A C 36-4340

Title from Univ. of Cin-　　cinnati AS182.K7　jahr 7, hft. 3
Library of Congress　　[AS182.K7　jahr 7, hft.3]
₍2₎　　(063)

IaU MoU
NL 0443441　　OCU ICU NjPT PPLT PU CSaT CtY-D KyLoS

Loehr, Max Richard Hermann, 1864-1931.
Babel und die biblische Urgeschichte.
Vortrag, gehalten in der Schlesischen
Gesellschaft für Vaterländische Kultur am
28. Februar,1903. Mit ... Abbildungen.
Breslau: G. P. Aderholz, 1903.
28 p.

NL 0443442　　OCH

Judaica
BM198
.L825b
Löhr, Max Richard Hermann, 1864-1931.
Beiträge zur Geschichte des Chassidismus.
Leipzig, Kaufmann, 1925-
v.

CONTENTS: 1. Begriff und Wesen des
Chassidismus.

1. Hasidism. I. Title. II. Title: Begriff
und Wesen des　　Chassidismus.

NL 0443443　　TNJ-R MoSCS DLC-P4 NN OCH PU PPDrop

Löhr, Max Richard Hermann,
1864-1931.
... Das buch Jeremia und die Klagelieder Jeremia übersetzt und erklärt.
Göttingen, Vandenhoeck und Ruprecht
[1906-07]
　　see under Bible. O.T.
Jeremiah. German. 1906-07. Giesebrecht.

Löhr, Max Richard Hermann, 1864-1931.
Das Buch Judith... Tübingen, 1900
　　see under Bible. O.T. Apocrypha.
Judith. German. 1900. Loehr.

Loehr, Max Richard Hermann, 1864-1931.
Das Buch Tobit... Tübingen, 1900
　　see under Bible. O.T. Apocrypha.
Tobit. German. 1900. Loehr.

Loehr, Max Richard Hermann, 1864-1931.
Die bücher Samuels erklärt von O.
Thenius... Leipzig, 1898
　　see under Thenius, Otto, 1801-1876.

Loehr, Max Richard Hermann, 1864-1931.
De libir qui inscribitur ... nomine et de
loco, quem in canone habet.

NL 0443448　　DCU-H

Löhr, Max Richard Hermann, 1864-1931.
... Das Deuteronomium ... von Max Löhr. Berlin, Deutsche
verlagsgesellschaft für politik und geschichte m. b. h., 1925.
2 p. L., ₍163₎-206 p., 1 L. 26ᵐ. (H4 Untersuchungen zum Hexateuchproblem II)
Schriften der Königsberger gelehrten gesellschaft. Geisteswissenschaftliche klasse. 1. jahr, hft. 6.
"1. auflage."
"Literatur": leaf at end.

1. Bible. O. T. Deuteronomy—Criticism, interpretation, etc.
2. Bible—Criticism, interpretation, etc.—O. T. Deuteronomy.

A C 36-4367

Title from Univ. of Cin-　　cinnati AS182.K7　jahr 1, hft. 6
Library of Congress　　[AS182.K7　jahr 1, hft. 6]
₍3₎　　(063)

CtY MH
NL 0443449　　OCU CtY NcD MH OCH PPiPT CtY-D MoU NN

Loehr, Max Richard Hermann, 1864-1931.
...Einführung in das Alte Testament, von Dr. theol. et phil.
Max Löhr... Leipzig: Quelle & Meyer, 1912. 125 p. illus.
12°. (Wissenschaft und Bildung. ₍Bd.₎ 102.)

Bibliography, p. 122.

167117A. 1. Bible. O. T.—Intro-　　duction. 2. Ser.
N. Y. P. L.　　January 21. 1926

NL 0443450　　NN NNUT MH OCH CU CtY ViRUT

BS1225
L6
Löhr, Max Richard Hermann, 1864-1931.
The five books of Moses and the question of
their origin, by Max Loehr. Nashville, Publishing House of the M. E. Church, South, 1924.
333-382 p. 20 cm. (The Aftermath series, 8)

1. Bible. O.T. Pentateuch--Criticism, interpretation, etc. I. Title.

NL 0443451　　PPiPT GEU NN

4DS
Pales.-
36
Löhr, Max Richard Hermann, 1864-1931.
Geschichte des Volkes Israel in acht Vorträgen
dargestellt. Strassburg, K. J. Trübner, 1900.
168 p.

NL 0443452　　DLC-P4 ICU PU MH OCH NjPT CtY MiDW

Loehr, Max Richard Hermann, 1864-1931.
A history of religion in the Old Testament, by Max Loehr
... London, I. Nicholson and Watson limited, 1936.
ix p., 1 L, 13-192 p. 20½ᵐ. (Half-title: The International library of
Christian knowledge, ed. by W. A. Brown and B. L. Woolf)
Bibliography: p. 189.

1. Bible. O. T.—Theology. 2. Bible—Theology—O. T.

Library of Congress　　BM605.L62

37-3816

₍3₎　　296

NL 0443453　　DLC OrU MiU NcD OCU OC1Tem

LOEHR, MAX RICHARD HERMANN, 1864- ₍1931₎
A history of religion in the Old Testament, by Max Loehr
... New York: C.Scribner's Sons, 1936. ix, 13-192 p.
20cm. (International library of Christian knowledge.)

871228A. 1. Bible—O.T.—Hist. of events. 2. Judaism,
Ancient.

OKentU
NL 0443454　　NN PBL OC1W OCU OOxM MH KyLxCB KyU IEG

VOLUME 338

Löhr, Max Richard Hermann, 1864–1931.
Introductionis ad commentarium de
Threnis Jeremiae capita nonnulla.
Regimonti, Ex officina Hartungiana
₍1890?₎
30 ₍2₎ p. 23ᶜᵐ.

Inaug.-Diss. – Königsberg i. Pr.
"Vita": p. ₍31–32₎

NL 0443455   NjPT CU ICRL

4DS
Jews-
28
Löhr, Max Richard Hermann, 1864–1931.
Israels Kulturentwickelung. Strassburg, K. J.
Trübner, 1911.
147 p.

TxDaM-P NjPT CtHC NjP TNJ-R
NL 0443456   DLC-P4 ICU PP OCH PPDrop MH CtY NNC

Löhr, Max Richard Hermann, 1864–1931.
... Die Klagelieder des Jeremia ...
see under Bible. O. T. Lamentations.
German. 1891. Löhr.   (also with dates 1893 and
1906)

BV
2073
L6
Löhr, Max Richard Hermann, 1864–1931.

Der Missionsgedanke im Alten Testament.
Ein Beitrag zur alttestamentlichen
Religionsgeschichte.   Freiburg, J.
C. B. Mohr, 1896.
40p.

1. Missions - Biblical teaching.

NL 0443458   MoSCS CtY-D OCH PU PPDrop NNUT

Löhr, Max Richard Hermann, 1864–1931.
... Der priesterkodex in der Genesis. Giessen, A. Töpelmann, 1924.
2 p. l., 82 p. 22¹⁄₂ᶜᵐ. (Untersuchungen zum Hexateuchproblem, von
Max Löhr ... 1)
On cover: Beihefte zur Zeitschrift für die alttestamentliche wissenschaft. 38.

1. Bible. O. T. Genesis—Criticism, interpretation, etc. 2. Bible—
Criticism, interpretation, etc.—O. T. Genesis.

Library of Congress   BS410.Z5 vol. 38
₍37g2₎   (221.082) 222.11   27–6692 Revised

NL 0443459   DLC PCC PU NN CSaT NjPT TNJ-R MoSCS

BS1433 Löhr, Max Richard Hermann, 1864– 1931.
.L8   Psalmenstudien, von d. dr. Max Löhr ... Berlin ₍etc.₎
W. Kohlhammer, 1922.
₍3₎, 53 p. 24ᶜᵐ. (On verso of t.-p.: Beiträge zur wissenschaft vom Alten Testament ... 2. l., hft. 3)

1. Bible. O. T. Psalms—Criticism, Textual.

NL 0443460   ICU MH NN OCH NcD CtY CU NjPT CBPac

Löhr, Max Richard Hermann, 1864–1931.
... Das räucheropfer im Alten Testament; eine archäolo-
gische untersuchung, von Max Löhr. Halle (Saale) Max Niemeyer verlag, 1927.
viii, ₍155₎–191 p. 4 pl. 29ᶜᵐ. (Schriften der Königsberger gelehrten
gesellschaft. Geisteswissenschaftliche klasse. 4. jahr, hft. 4)
"1. auflage."
"Literatur": p. ₍vii₎–viii.

1. Sacrifice. 2. Bible. O. T.—Antiquities. 3. Bible—Antiquities—
O. T.   I. Title.   A C 36–4380

Title from Univ. of Cin-   cinnati   AS182.K7 jahr 4, hft. 4
cinnati Library of Congress   [AS182.K7 jahr 4, hft. 4]
₍3₎   (063)

NjPT ICU KyLoS
NL 0443461   OCU DDO OCH IEG MoU CtY-D NN PPDrop PPLT

Löhr, Max Richard Hermann, 1864–1931.
... Das ritual von Lev. 16 ... von Max Löhr. Berlin, Deutsche verlagsgesellschaft für politik und geschichte m. b. h.,
1925.
2 p. l., 18 p., 1 l. 29ᶜᵐ. (His Untersuchungen zum Hexateuchproblem
III)
Schriften der Königsberger gelehrten gesellschaft. Geisteswissenschaftliche klasse. 2. jahr, hft. 1.
"1. auflage."
"Literatur": leaf at end.

1. Bible. O. T. Leviticus XVI — Criticism, interpretation, etc. 2.
Bible—Criticism, interpretation, etc.—O. T. Leviticus XVI.   I. Title.
A C 36–4369

Title from Univ. of Cin-   cinnati AS182.K7 jahr 2, hft. 1
cinnati Library of Congress   [AS182.K7 jahr 2, hft. 1]
₍2₎   (063)

NL 0443462   OCU OCH MoU CtY-D MnU MH NN

BL25
.R4
II Reihe
pt. 1
Löhr, Max Richard Hermann, 1864–1931.
Seelenkämpfe und Glaubensnöte vor
2000 Jahren. Halle, Gebauer-Schwetschke,
1904.
48p. (Religionsgeschichtliche
Volksbücher für die deutsche christliche
Gegenwart, II Reihe, 1 Hft)

1. Belief and doubt.   I. Title.

NL 0443463   TNJ-R MH CtY-D

Löhr, Max Richard Hermann, 1864–1931.
Seelenkämpfe und glaubensnöte vor 2000 jahren, von
prof. d. dr. Max Löhr ... 1.–10. tausend. Tübingen,
J. C. B. Mohr (P. Siebeck) 1906.
2 p. l., 48 p., 1 l. 20ᶜᵐ. (Half-title: Religionsgeschichtliche volksbücher
für die deutsche christliche gegenwart ... ₍II. reihe. 14. hft.₎)

13–19696

NL 0443464   DLC NcD OCH

Loehr, Max ₍Richard Hermann₎ 1864–1931.
Sind Thr. IV und V makkabäisch? Eine
Prüfung der von S. A. Fries zu Upsala
aufgestellten Behauptung. n.t.–p.
₍Giessen, 1894.₎ p. 51–59.
Title from first page.
Extr.: Zeitschr. f. d. altt. wiss. Jhrg.
15, 1894.
Bd. with: Gaster, M₍oses₎. – The Hebrew
text of one of the testaments of the twelve
patriarchs. ₍London, 1894?₎

NL 0443465   OCH

Löhr, Max Richard Hermann, 1864–1931.
Sozialismus und individualismus im Alten Testament; ein
beitrag zur alttestamentlichen religionsgeschichte, von d. dr.
Max Löhr ... Giessen, A. Töpelmann, 1906.
2 p. l., 36 p. 22ᶜᵐ. (Added t.-p.: Beihefte zur Zeitschrift für die alttestamentliche wissenschaft. x)

1. Socialism. 2. Individualism. 3. Bible. O. T.—Criticism, interpretation, etc. 4. Bible—Criticism, interpretation, etc.—O. T.
6–39752
Library of Congress   BS410.Z5 vol. 10

NL 0443466   DLC PU PPPD OCH ICJ OU IEG PPiPT TNJ-R

BS1199 Löhr, Max Richard Hermann, 1864– 1931.
.W8L8   Die stellung des weibes zu Jahwe-religion und -kult,
untersucht von d. dr. Max Löhr ... Leipzig, J. C. Hinrichs,
1908.
₍4₎, 56 p. 22¹⁄₂ᶜᵐ. (On verso of t.-p.: Beiträge zur wissenschaft vom Alten Testament ... hft. 6)
"Literatur": p. 3–4.

1. Women in the Bible. 2. Women, Jewish.

NjPT
NL 0443467   ICU MB MH OCH PU NNC CtY NjP CU IEG

Löhr, Max Richard Hermann, 1864–1931.
Untersuchungen zum buch Amos, von dr. theol. et phil. Max
Löhr ... Giessen, Ricker, 1901.
4 p. l., 67, ₍1₎ p. 23ᶜᵐ. (Added t.-p.: Beihefte zur Zeitschrift für die
alttestamentliche wissenschaft. IV)
CONTENTS.—A. Der text des Amos-buches.—B. Der theologische gehalt
des Amos-buches.—C. Jahve Zebaoth.

1. Bible. O. T. Amos—Criticism, interpretation, etc. 2. Bible—
Criticism, interpretation, etc.—O. T. Amos.
6–41356
Library of Congress   BS410.Z5 vol. 4

NL 0443468   DLC OCH MH OU PLatS ICMcC IEG TNJ-R

BS410
Z5
v.38
Löhr, Max Richard Hermann, 1864–1931.
Untersuchungen zum Hexateuchproblem. Der
Priesterkodex in der Genesis. Giessen, A.
Töpelmann, 1924.
32 p. 23 cm. (Zeitschrift für die alttes-
tamentliche wissenschaft. Beihefte, 38)

1. Bible. O.T. Genesis—Criticism, interpretation, etc. I. Title: Der priesterkodex
in der Genesis. (Series)

NL 0443469   PPiPT PLatS OU IEG

Löhr, Max Richard Hermann, 1864–1931.
... Volksleben im lande der Bibel, von Max Löhr ... Leipzig,
Quelle & Meyer, 1907.
2 p. l., 134 p. illus. 19ᶜᵐ. (Wissenschaft und bildung, einzeldarstel-
lungen aus allen gebieten des wissens, hrsg. von privatdozent dr. Paul
Herre. 7)

1. Palestine—Descr. & trav. 2. Palestine—Soc. life & cust.   I. Title.
44–32169
Library of Congress   DS107.3.L754

NL 0443470   DLC CtY CU OCH ICU MoSW TNJ-R

PJ6808 Löhr, Max Richard Hermann, 1864– 1931.
.5   Der vulgärarabische dialekt von Jerusalem nebst texten
.J5L8   und wörterverzeichnis, dargestellt von d. dr. Max Löhr ...
Giessen, A. Töpelmann, 1905.
viii, 144 p. 22¹⁄₂ᶜᵐ.

1. Arabic language—Dialects—Jerusalem.

RPB NIC TxU NRCR
NL 0443471   ICU OC1 MH NN OCH PU PPDrop CtY MiU CU

Löhr, Oscar, 1854–
Zwei fälle von complicirter luxation, ein
beitrag zur conservativen behandlung complicirter luxationen ... Berlin, Hermann ₍1880₎
30 p., 1 l.

Inaug.-diss., Berlin, 1880.
Vita.

1. Dislocations.

NL 0443472   NNC DNLM

Loehr, Oskar, 1899–
Untersuchungen ueber diphenauccindandion -9.12.
Inaug. diss. Giessen, 1923. ₍Auszug₎

NL 0443473   ICRL

DD801
.P4L8
Löhr, Otto, ed.
Saarpfälzische abhandlungen zur landes- und volksforschung.
1–   bd.; 1937–
₍Kaiserslautern₎ Pfälz. gesellschaft zur förderung der wissen-
schaften ₍1937–

VOLUME 338

Löhr (Otto). *Studien über die quantitative Bestimmung und Trennung des Wismutes.* [Erlangen.] 30 pp. 8°. *München, M. Ernst,* 1893.

NL 0443475   DNLM ICRL

Löhr, Otto, 1901-
Ueber die vergasung von steinkohlen-halbkoksen und koksen und von holzkohle mittels wasserdampf. ... Berlin, 1933. (Auszug)
Inaug. Diss. -Techn. Hochsch. Berlin, 1933.
Lebenslauf.

NL 0443476   ICRL

Löhr, Paul
Beiträge zur Kenntniss der Inhaltsverhält-nisse der Blütenblätter. Göttingen, Druck der Dieterich'schen Univ.-Buchdruckerei (Kästner), 1903.

100 p.
Inaug.-Diss.- Georg-Augusts-Universität zu Göttingen.

NL 0443477   MH-A CtY

Löhr (Paul) [1864-]. *Ueber die Behandlung acuter innerer Einklemmungen.* 31 pp. 8°. *Berlin, G. Schade,* [1887].

NL 0443478   DNLM

QD411 **Loehr, Philipp.**
.L83 Ueber die einwirkung von alkyljodiden auf cadmium und magnesium.
Tuebingen, 1889.
83p.
Inaug. diss. Tuebingen.

NL 0443479   DLC

Löhr (Pipin Carl) [1865-]. *Beitrag zur Behandlung der Otitis media purulenta.* 27 pp., 2 l. 8°. *Königsberg, M. Liedtke,* 1891.

NL 0443480   DNLM

Löhr, Richard, 1908-
Munich   ... Über traubenförmige sarkome der cervix
diss.   uteri ... München, 1931.
1931

NL 0443481   MiU CtY DNLM

Loehr, Richard Harvey

see

Loehr, Harvey, 1856-

---

*F602 **Loehr, Rodney C**
.M69L8 Business history material in the Min-nesota historical society, by Rodney C. Loehr. [Boston, Mass., 1940,
p.21-28.   facsim.   23cm.

Extracted from the Bulletin of the Business historical society, vol.12, no.2, April, 1940.

NL 0443483   MnHi

---

*HD9757 **Loehr, Rodney C.**
.M6L82 Caleb D. Dorr and the early Minnesota lumber industry, by Rodney C. Loehr. [St. Paul, Minnesota historical society, 1943.
cover-title, p.125-141, [2] p.   port. 23cm.
*F601.5 "Reprinted from Minnesota history,
.M66   June, 1943."
v.24   "The Caleb D. Dorr fund [by] E.M. Freeman:" [2] p. at end.

NL 0443484   MnHi

Loehr, Rodney C   *ed.*
Minnesota farmers' diaries: William R. Brown, 1845-46, Mitchell Y. Jackson, 1852-63. With an introduction and notes by Rodney C. Loehr. Saint Paul, The Minnesota historical society, 1939.
ix p., 1 l., 247 p., ports., fold. map, facsims. 20½ᵐ. *(Half-title:* Publications of the Minnesota historical society, ed. by T. C. Blegen ... Narratives and documents. vol. III)

1. Minnesota—Hist.—Sources. 2. Agriculture—Minnesota. 3. Farm life. ɪ. Brown, William Reynolds, 1816-1874. ɪɪ. Jackson, Mitchell Young, 1816-1900.

Library of Congress   F601.M68 vol. 3   39-32510
———— Copy 2.   F605.L74
Copyright A 134342   [10]   (977.60062) 926.3

PHC CU NcD ViU OU OCU OOxM
NL 0443485   DLC CaBVaU WaWW UU FU DAU Wa IdPI OrU

HG3048 **Loehr, Rodney C**
1825   The West German banking system. [Bad Godes-berg] Historical Division, Office of the Execu-tive Secretary, Office of the U.S. High Commis-sioner for Germany, 1952.
vii,126 p.   21cm.
At head of title:Restricted; covered by stamp: Unclassified.
Bibliografical footnotes.

1. Banks and banking - Germany (Federal Repub-lic, 1949-   ) 2. Banks and banking - Germany (Territory under Allied occupation, 1945-   ) I. U.S. Office of   High Commissioner for Germany. Historic   cal Division. II. Title.

NL 0443486   CSt-H

Loehr, Theodor, 1883-
Beobachtungen und untersuchungen an...
Inaug. diss. Bonn,1908.
Bibl.

NL 0443487   ICRL CtY MH

Löhr, Wilhelm, joint author.

Schulte, Gottfried.
Markscheidekunde für bergschulen und den praktischen ge-brauch, von G. Schulte und W. Löhr ... mit 186 abbildungen im text und 4 farbigen tafeln. Berlin, J. Springer, 1932.

Löhr, Wilhelm, *of Elberfeld.*   G504-L
Gottes Herrlichkeit in der deutschen Natur; in zwölf Monats-bildern dargestellt von Wilhelm Löhr. Elberfeld: "Die Aue," 1929. 104 p.   12°.

1. Nature. 2. Title.
N. Y. P. L.   April 13, 1934

NL 0443489   NN

Löhr, Wilhelm, *of Elberfeld.*   G504-L
Traute Heimat; durchwandert und geschaut von Wilhelm Löhr; Buchschmuck von Heinz Schoen. Elberfeld: "Die Aue," 1929. 184 p.   illus., port.   12°.

1. Title. 2. Nature.
N. Y. P. L.   April 13, 1934

NL 0443490   NN

Loehr, Wilhelm, 1886-
Der selbsthuelfeverkauf nach dem rechte des deutschen buergerlichen gesetzbuchs...
Inaug. diss. Leipzig,1910.
Bibl.

NL 0443491   ICRL

Löhr, Wilhelm, 1889-   L616.03
... Die Arteriographie der Hirngefässe, von Prof. Dr. W. Löhr ...   S800 v.14

(In Neue deutsche Klinik. Berlin, 1937. 26ᵐ. Bd. 14 (Erg. Bd. 4) p. [653]-694. illus.)

At head of title: Aus der Chirurgischen Klinik des Städtischen Kranken-hauses Magdeburg-Altstadt.

NL 0443492   ICJ

Löhr, Wilhelm, 1889-
Die bakteriologie der wurmfortsatzentzündung und der ap-pendikulären peritonitis, von W. Löhr ... und L. Rassfeld ... Mit 46 abbildungen auf 11 tafeln. Leipzig, G. Thieme, 1931.
vi p., 1 l., 94, [1] p. xi pl. 26ᵐ.
Bibliographical foot-notes.

1. Appendicitis. 2. Peritonitis. 3. Intestines—Bacteriology.
ɪ. Rassfeld, Lissie, joint author. ɪɪ. Title.
                                         A 32-36
Title from John Crerar   Libr. 616.34   Printed by L. C.

NL 0443493   ICJ

Löhr, Wilhelm, 1889-
Dauerresultate operativ behandelter Magenulcera. Leipzig: Vogel 1916. 90 S. 8°
Kiel, Med. Diss. v. 26. Aug. 1916, Ref. Anschütz
[Geb. 15. März 89 Hohensolms; Staatsangeh.: Preußen; Vorbildung: G. Barmen Reife 08; Studium: Gießen 4, Berlin 1, München 1, Bonn 1, Kiel 3 S.; Coll. 11. Juli 13; Approb. 19. Aug. 14.]   [U 16. 1086]

NL 0443494   ICRL CtY NNC DNLM

Löhr, Wilhelm, 1889-   L616.03
Furunkel und Karbunkel, von Prof. Dr. W. Löhr ...   S800 v.3

(In Neue deutsche Klinik. Berlin, 1929. 26ᵐ. Bd. 3, p. 524-539. col. illus.)
"Literatur:" p. 538-539.

NL 0443495   ICJ

Löhr, Wilhelm, 1889-
... Die kombinierte enzephal-arteriographie, von W. Löhr und W. Jacobi ... Leipzig, Thieme, 1933.
83 p. incl. illus., plate. 30ᵐ. (Fort-schritte auf dem gebiete der röntgenstrahlen, Ergänzungsband 44)

At head of title: Aus der Chirurgischen klinik des städt. krankenhauses Magdeburg-Alstadt (direktor prof. Löhr) und aus der städt. nervenklinik Magdeburg-Sudenburg (direktor prof. Jacobi)

NL 0443496   NNC MBCo

VOLUME 338

Löhr, Wilhelm, 1889-   joint author.
Jacobi, Walter, 1889-
    Über die darstellung des zentralen und peripheren nerven-
systems im röntgenbild, von prof. dr. Walter Jacobi ... prof. dr.
Wilhelm Löhr ... und priv.-doz. dr. Otto Wustmann ... mit
einem pathologisch-anatomischen beitrag von dr. Julius Hal-
lervorden ... Mit 34 abbildungen. Leipzig, J. A. Barth, 1934.

Löhr, Wilhelm, 1889-
    Wundheilung, von prof. dr. Wilhelm Löhr ... mit 141 abbil-
dungen im text. Leipzig, J. A. Barth, 1937.
    vi, 234 p. illus. 27½ᵐ.
    Includes bibliographies.

    1. Wounds—Treatment. 2. Vitamin therapy. 3. Bones—Diseases.
I. Title.
                                                    38–14356
Library of Congress   RD131.L6
                           ₍a10c1₎   617.1

NL 0443498   DLC ICJ

Löhr, Willi, 1900-
    Die erhöhung des grundkapitals der aktien
gesellschaften durch ausgabe neuer aktien
Inaug. Diss. Würzburg, 1927
Bibl.

NL 0443499   ICRL CtY MH-L PU

Löhr vom Wachendorf, F., pseud.
    see
Ettighoffer, Paul Cölestin, 1896-

X   ₍LÖHRBACH,   Graf VON₎   ed.
975   Die theoretischen Brüder, oder Zweite Stuffe
.517   der Rosenkreutzer und ihrer Instruktion das er-
          stemahl ans Licht herausgegeben von einem Pro-
          phanen, nebst einem Anhang aus dem dritten und
          fünften Grad, als Probe.   Athen,1785.
             278p. 2 fold.pl. 18cm.

NL 0443500   ICN DLC MH

BF   ₍Löhrbach,   Graf von₎
1623   Die theoretischen Brüder oder zweite
R7L82   Stuffe der Rosenkreutzer und ihrer Instruk-
1785   tion das erstemahl ans Licht herausgegeben
          von einem Prophanen nebst einem Anhang aus
          dem dritten und fünften Grad, als Probe.
          Athen, zur Zeit der Aufklärung ₍Regensburg,
          Montag & Weiss₎ 1785.
             278 p. 2 fold. plates. 18cm.

             1. Rosicrucians.   I. Title.

NL 0443501   NIC

Löhre, Nels Johnson, 1873-
    Addresses to young men and young women, delivered to the
St. Paul's congregation, Minneapolis, Minn. by Rev. N. J.
Löhre, a. l., on the Bible ... some economic factors of a young
man's life ... the young lady ... Minneapolis, Minn. ₍Press of
the Ungdommens ven₎ 1902.
    272 p. front. (port.) 20ᵐ.
    "Bibliography": p. 270-271.

    1. Young men—Religious life. 2. Young women—Religious life.

    BV4310.L6   2–16087 rev

NL 0443502   DLC NN

Löhre, Nels Johnson, 1873-   ed.
Norwegian Lutheran church of America.
    Report, district conventions of the Norwegian Lutheran
church of America, 19   ... with messages and reports from officers and boards ... complete statistics from congregations by counties; clerical roster ... Minneapolis, Minn.,
Printed by Augsburg publishing house ₍19

Löhren, Alfred.
    Beiträge zur geschichte des gesandtschaftlichen ver-
kehrs im mittelalter. 1. Die zeit vom vierten bis zum ende
des neunten jahrhunderts ... ₍Marburg, Universitäts-
buchdruckerei (R. Friedrich) 1884₎
    2 p. l., ₍vii-viii, 116 p. 21½ᵐ.
    Inaug.-diss.—Heidelberg.

    1. Diplomacy—Hist.

Library of Congress   JX1641.L7,   10–16775

NL 0443504   DLC NcD

Löhrer, Alfred, 1895-
    Swinburne als kritiker der literatur. Mit besonderer be-
rücksichtigung seiner unveröffentlichten schriften ... Weida
i. Thür., Druck von Thomas & Hubert, 1925.
    184 p., 1 l. 23ᵐ.
    Abhandlung—Zürich.
    Lebenslauf.
    "Bibliographische einleitung": p. ₍7₎-8; "Bibliographie": p. ₍182₎-183.

    1. Swinburne, Algernon Charles, 1837-1909. 2. Criticism. 3. Litera-
ture—Hist. & crit.   I. Title.

Library of Congress   PR5514.L6   27–4223

NL 0443505   DLC CtY

Loehrer, Alfred, 1895-
    Swinburne al kritiker der literatur.
Zuerich, 1925.
    Inaug.-Diss. - Zuerich.
    Bibl.

NL 0443506   ICRL

Löhrer, Edwin, 1906-
    Die Messen von Ludwig Senfl; stilkritischer Beitrag zur Ge-
schichte des polyphonen Messordinariums um 1500. . .von Edwin
Löhrer. . .   Lichtensteig: A. Maeder Söhne, 1938. vii, 71 p.
24cm.
    Abhandlung — Zürich, 1938?
    Lebenslauf.
    "Die Messen Ludwig Senfls: Bibliographie," p. 12-16.

    1. Senfl, Ludwig, ca. 1492–   ca. 1555.
N. Y. P. L.   December 12, 1939

NL 0443507   NN CU CtY ICRL ICU

M2   Löhrer, Edwin, 1906—
.E66
bd. 5   Senfl, Ludwig, 1492 (ca.)-1555.
         ₍Masses. Selected₎

             ... Sieben messen zu vier bis sechs stimmen. Herausgegeben
         von Edwin Löhrer und Otto Ursprung. Leipzig, F. Kistner
         & C. F. W. Siegel, 1936.

Löhrer, Fidelis
    Ein altprovenzalischer traktat aus dem 14.
jahrhundert über die heilige messe ... 1924.
Inaug. Diss. - Freiburg, 1924.

NL 0443508   ICRL

Löhrer, Fr   J.   Ger 6914.95-3
    Geschichte der stadt Neuss. Neuss, L. Schwann, 1840.
    pp. xv, 447, (1), viii.

    Neuss, Germ.||AcS 25054

NL 0443509   MH

WC   Löhrer, Frieda, 1906-
12409   Bei Lupe und Lyra: A. E. W. O'Shaughnessy.
          ₍Teufen/App.₎ 1955.

             1. O'Shaughessy, Arthur William Edgar, 1844-
          1881.

NL 0443510   CtY NN

Hky   Löhrer, Frieda, 1906-
2   Margarete Babenberg; Drama. [n.p.]1955.
L824   Pamphlet

NL 0443511   CtY NN

LÖHRER,Frieda,1906-
    Die mystik und ihre quellen in Thomas
Traherne;abhandlung zur erlangung der doktor-
würde der PhilosophischenFakultät I der Universität Zürich. Angenommen von B.Fehr. n.p.,
Buchdruckerei Rheintaler Volksfreund Au,1930.

    pp.69+.
    "Lebenslauf",at end.
                        14456.63.15

NL 0443512   MH CtY NjP ICRL

Löhrer, Frieda, 1906-
    Die Mystik und ihre Quellen in Thomas
Traherne. ₍n.p., 1930₎
    68 p. 23ᵐ.

    "Literatur-Angabe": p. 65-68.

    1 Traherne, Thomas, d. 1674

NL 0443513   NjPT

LÖHRER, FRIEDA, 1906 -
    Puer Apuliae: Friedrich II; Drama.   Teufen, Im
Selbstverlag, 1955. 110, [1]p. 21cm.

    Bibliography, p. [111]

    1. Frederick II, emperor of   Germany, 1194-1250--Drama.
    2. Drama, Swiss-German.   I. Title.

NL 0443514   NN CtY DLC-P4

LÖHRER, FRIEDA, 1906-
    Roger Williams; Drama.   [Teufen?] Im Selbstverlag.
1954. 102 p. 21cm.

    1. Williams, Roger, 1604?-1683--Drama. 2. Drama, Swiss-German.

NL 0443515   NN MH CtY

VOLUME 338

Löhrer, Frieda, 1906–
Hky   Thomas Otway, drama. [Teufen]Selbstverlag,
L82&1   1953.
T56   83p. 21cm.

1. Otway, Thomas, 1652–1685 – Drama.

NL 0443516   CtY NN

Löhrer, Frieda, 1906–
Tile Kolup; Drama. [Teufen?] Im Selbstverlag, 1954.   85 p.
21cm.

Bibliography, p. 84.

1. Holzschuh, Dietrich, d. 1285—   Drama. 2. Frederick II, emperor
of Germany, 1194–1250—Drama.   3. Drama, Germany. I. Title.

NL 0443517   NN CtY

Löhrer, Hans.
Die Schweiz im Spiegel englischer Literatur 1849–1875.
Zürich, Juris-Verlag, 1952.
147 p. 28 cm. (Zürcher Beiträge zur vergleichenden Literaturge-
schichte, Bd. 1)
Issued also in part, as thesis, Zürich.
Bibliography: p. 141–145.

1. Switzerland in literature. 2. Switzerland—Relations (general)
with Gt. Brit. 3. Gt. Brit.—Relations (general) with Switzerland.
(Series)

PR129.S9L6 1952   55–21507
ICU
NL 0443518   DLC CaBVaU NcD GU CU–S NcU NN OU ICN

Löhrer (Hermann) [1877–   ]. "Ueber Verletzungen der Lider und Thränenorgane mit besonderer Berücksichtigung der Thränensackver-
letzungen. 38 pp., 1 l. 8°. Giessen, O. Kindt,
1901.

NL 0443519   DNLM ICRL MH

Löhrer, Josef, 1914–
Uzfm18   ... Wundbehandlung und Wundnaht in der
Z64   Veterinärchirurgie ... Zürich,1944.
1944   Inaug.-Diss. - Zürich.

NL 0443520   CtY DNLM

Löhrer, Magnus.
Der Glaubensbegriff des hl. Augustinus in seinen ersten
Schriften bis zu den Confessiones. Einsiedeln, Benziger
[1955]
280 p. 21 cm.
Diss.—Pontificio Ateneo di S. Anselmo, Rome.
Bibliography: p. 273–280.

1. Augustinus, Aurelius, Saint, Bp. of Hippo.

A 56–2273
Harvard Univ. Library
for Library of Congress   [1]

NL 0443521   MH IEG IaU ICMcC CtY–D DCU NjPT

---

792   **Löhrer,** Robert.
L83b   Beiträge zur kenntnis der beziehungen
von mienenspiel und maske in der griechischen tragödie... Paderborn, 1927.
36p.

Inaug.-diss.--Freiburg.
"Die vollständige arbeit erscheint
gleichzeitig in den 'Studien zur geschichte und kultur des altertums' bd.
14., hft.4. und 5. (Schöningh, Pader- .

born) unter dem titel: 'Mienenspiel und
maske in der griechischen tragödie'."

NL 0443523   IU

PA3657 **Löhrer,** Robert,   comp. and tr.
.F8L8   Freundschaft in der Antike, ausgewählt, übers.
und eingeleitet von Robert Löhrer. Luzern, Rex-
Verlag [1949]
58 p. (Verpflichtendes Erbe, Bd.16/17)

1. Classical literature—Translations into
German.   2. Friendship.

NL 0443524   ICU DDO OU

Löhrer, Robert.
Mienenspiel und maske in der griechischen tragödie, von
dr. p. Robert Löhrer ... Paderborn, F. Schöningh, 1927.
xvi, 192 p. 24ᶜᵐ. (Added t.-p.: Studien zur geschichte und kultur
des altertums ... 14. bd. 4. und 5. hft.)
"Literaturverzeichnis": p. [xi]–xiv.

1. Greek drama (Tragedy)—Hist. & crit. 2. Masks. 3. Actors, Greek.
4. Acting.   I. Title.

Library of Congress   PA3203.L6   27–25635

NL 0443525   DLC ViMiM CtY DDO NcD IU

B7   **Löhrer,** Robert,   , 1893–   ed.
2293   Priestertum im Zeugnis der Kirchenväter; aus-
.L83   gewählt und übertragen von Dr. P. Robert Löhrer
OSB. Luzern, Rex-Verlag [c1951]
95 p. 18cm. (Verpflichtendes Erbe, Bd.
21/23)
"Bibliographische Hinweise": p. 93–94.

1. Priesthood. I. Title.

NL 0443526   DCU DDO NNUT

Loehrich, Rolf Rudolf, 1913–
Oneirics and psychosomatics; an introductory treatise concerning a new theory of psychoanalysis, its logic and
methodology. McHenry, Ill., Compass Press [1953]
157 p. 24 cm.

1. Dreams. 2. Psychotherapy.   I. Title.

BF1078.L55   135.383   53–2339 †

NcD NN PPT
NL 0443527   DLC CaBVaU DNLM CaBVa OrU UU ICU CU

Loehrich, Rolf Rudolf, 1913–
The secret of Ulysses; an analysis of James Joyce's
Ulysses. McHenry, Ill., Compass Press [1953]
viii, 200 p. 24 cm.

1. Joyce, James, 1882–1941. Ulysses.   I. Title.

PR6019.O9U68   823.91   53–13389

IU MB OC1 PBm PPT OO OC1W OCU OU GDecA KAS RPB MeB
FTaSU NcD IEN PSt PBL PHC TxU NN CU TU ICN NIC ViU
NL 0443528   DLC Or WaS WaSpG MeWC OrU CaBVaU CaBVa

Loehrich, Rolf Rudolf, 1913–
The secret of Ulysses; an analysis of James
Joyce's Ulysses. London, P. Owen [1955]

1. Joyce, James, 1882–1941. Ulysses.

NL 0443529   NN MH IEN ViU

Löhrig, Alfred: Ueber die Färbung der Zähne. [Maschinenschrift.]
49 S. 4° [Lag nicht vor.] — Auszug: (Roding) 1923: (Witt-
mann). 4 Bl. 8°
Leipzig, Med. Diss. v. 11. Mai 1923   [U 23. 8017

NL 0443530   ICRL

Löhrke, Mrs. Arline, joint author.

Löhrke, Eugene William, 1897–
... The long watch in England. New York, H. Holt and
company [1940]

Löhrke, Arline, joint author.

Löhrke, Eugene William, 1897–
... Night over England; a report. New York, Harrison-
Hilton books [1939]

Löhrke, Eugene William, 1897–   ed.
Armageddon; the world war in literature, edited by Eugene
Löhrke. New York, J. Cape and H. Smith [1930]
xiii p., 2 l., 820 p. 23½ᵐ.
Maps on lining-papers.
Bibliography: p. 805–813.

1. European war, 1914–1918—Literature and the war.   I. Title.
II. Title: The world war in literature.

Library of Congress   D509.L6   30—14902
———— Copy 2.
Copyright A 23676   [a36n1]   940.49

WaT WaSp WaS WaTC NcD ViU MiHM NN
NL 0443533   DLC MoSW CaBVaU NIC MB ICarbS NcU WaE

Löhrke, Eugene William 1897–   ed.

Lange, Johannes, 1891–
Crime and destiny [by] Johannes Lange, translated by Charlotte Haldane. New York, C. Boni, 1930.

Löhrke, Eugene William, 1897–
Deep evening [by] Eugene Löhrke. New York, J. Cape &
H. Smith [1931]
5 p. l., 3–270 p. 19ᵐ.

I. Title.

Library of Congress   PZ3.L8239De   31–11381

NL 0443535   DLC WaT WaS NN PSt ViU CtY

Löhrke, Eugene William, 189–
The first bus out, by Eugene Löhrke ... New York, London,
D. Appleton-Century company, incorporated, 1935.
5 p. l., 3–231 p. 19½ᵐ.

I. Title.

Library of Congress   PZ3.L8239Fi   35–8978

NL 0443536   DLC OrCS

VOLUME 338

Löhrke, Eugene William, 1897–   ed.
Von Hoffman, Carl, 1889–
   Jungle gods, by Carl Von Hoffman; edited by Eugene Löhrke; illustrated by Baroness Katharina Dombrowski (κ. ο. s.) and with photographs by the author. New York, H. Holt and company [*1929]

Löhrke, Eugene William, tr.
   1897–
Rolland, Romain, 1866–
   ... Les léonides, by Romain Rolland, translated from the French by Eugene Löhrke. New York, H. Holt and company [*1929]
   xii, 201 p. 19½ᵐ.

Löhrke, Eugene William, 1897–
   The long exile, by Eugene Löhrke. New York, London, D. Appleton-Century company, incorporated, 1936.
   5 p. l., 3–263 p. 19½ᵐ.

   ɪ. Title.   36–6474
   Library of Congress   PZ3.L8239Lo

NL 0443539   DLC MB IU WaT

Löhrke, Eugene William, 1897–
   ... The long watch in England. New York, H. Holt and company [*1940]
   6 p. l., 3–243 p. front. 22½ᵐ.
   At head of title: Eugene and Arline Lohrke.

   1. Gt. Brit.—Civilization.   ɪ. Löhrke, Mrs. Arline, joint author.
   Library of Congress   DA110.L64   40–9344
   ——— Copy 2.
   Copyright   [20]   914.2

NL 0443540   MnU WaE NcRS ViU CU–I CaBVaU
             DLC DAU OrP WaSp WaS IdU OrU Or WaTC

DA586   LÖHRKE, EUGENE WILLIAM, 1897–
.L8   Night over England, by Eugéne and Arline Löhrke. London, Putnam [1939]
           191 p. 19cm.

           1.Gt.Brit.--For.rel.--1936--   2.Europe--Poli-
           tics--1938--   3.Gt.Brit.--Civilization.

NL 0443541   ICU

Löhrke, Eugene William, 1897–
   ... Night over England; a report. New York, Harrison-Hilton books [*1939]
   192 p. 21ᵐ.
   At head of title: Eugene and Arline Löhrke.

   1. Gt. Brit. — For. rel — 1936–   2. Europe — Politics — 1938–
   3. Gt. Brit.—Civilization.   ɪ. Löhrke, Arline, joint author.   ɪɪ. Title.
   Library of Congress   DA586.L6   39–15283
   ——— Copy 2.
   Copyright A 128884   [395]   942.084

NL 0443542   DLC CaBVa WaE OrPR WaS NN FMU ViU

Löhrke, Eugene William, 1897–
   ... Night raid. New York, H. Holt and company [*1941]
   5 p. l., 3–229 p. 19½ᵐ.
   At head of title: Eugene Lohrke.

   1. European war, 1939–   —Fiction.   ɪ. Title.   41–5879
   Library of Congress   PZ3.L8239Ni

NL 0443543   DLC ViU WaT WaS

Löhrke, Eugene William, 1897–
   Overshadowed, by Eugene Löhrke. New York, J. Cape & H. Smith [*1929]
   5 p. l., 3–235 p. 20ᵐ.

   1. European war, 1914–1918—Fiction.   ɪ. Title.
   Library of Congress   PZ3.L8239Ov   29–15289

NL 0443544   DLC CoU

Löhrke, Eugene William, tr.

Rolland, Romain, 1866–
   Palm Sunday, by Romain Rolland; translated from the French by Eugene Lohrke. New York, H. Holt and company [*1928]

NL 0443546   DLC

Loehrke, Eugene William, 1897–
   The unmaking of the American. [n.p., 1926]
   79p.   YA23079.

NL 0443546   DLC

Loehrke, Leah Marie
   An evaluation of the Rorschach method for the study of brain injury.
   viii, 213, 4 l.
   Thesis. – Ph. D. degree. – Western Reserve University. – Dept. of Psychology. – June, 1952.
   Subjects for the study were trainees in the Psychology Dept. of the Veterans Administration Hospital, Cleveland.

NL 0443547   OClW

Loehrke, Otto Friedrich Robert, 1888– Die künstlerische Bedeutung des Fremd-wortes bei Gottfried Keller. Greifswald 1911: Adler. 68 S. 8°
   Greifswald, Phil. Diss. v. 7. April 1911, Ref. Ehrismann
   [Geb. 8. April 88 Kempen i. P.; Wohnort: Stargard i. Pom.; Staatsangeh.: Preußcu; Vorbildung: Gymn. Stargard Reife O. 08; Studium: Leipzig 3 Berlin 1, Greifswald 2 S.; Rig. 2. März 11.]   [U 11. 1697

NL 0443548   ICRL TxU NNU PU CtY IU MH NN MiU

LOEHRKE, OTTO FRIEDRICH ROBERT, 1888–
   Die künstlerische Bedeutung des Fremwortes bei Gottfried Keller. Greifswald, H. Adler, 1911.   68 p. 24cm.

   Microfiche (neg.) 2 sheets. 11 x 15cm. (NYPL FSN 14,134)
   Diss. --Greifswald.
   Vita.

   1. Keller, Gottfried, 1819–   1890.

NL 0443549   NN

Loehrl, August.
   Ueber konforme und äquilonge Transformationen im Raum. Ein Beitrag zur Geometrie der Kugeln.   Würzburg: H. Stürtz, A. G., 1910. 66 p., 1 l. 8°.

   Dissertation, München.

   1. Transformations [math.]
   N.Y.P.L.   February 1, 1912

NL 0443550   NN NjP MH IU

Löhrl, Elsbet.
   Kinder leben ihre Welt; Geschichten aus meinem Kindergarten. Mit Bildern von Marigard Bantzer. Ravensburg, O. Maier [1952]
   71 p. illus. 20 cm.

   1. Kindergarten.   ɪ. Title.
   LB1169.L64   372.2   52–65511 ‡

NL 0443551   DLC

Loehrl (Fritz). * Ueber das Vorkommen von Angeoerkrankungen bei Gicht [harnsaure Diathese]. 37 pp., 1 pl. 8°. *Erlangen, E. T. Jacob*, 1909.

NL 0443552   DNLM ICRL

Loehrl (Hermann). * Die Neurotomie des Ramus lingualis trigemini. 28 pp. 8°. *Tübingen, H. Laupp*, 1863.

NL 0443553   DNLM

Löhrl, Hermann.
   ... Schiffahrt und schiffahrtspolitik der USA seit dem weltkrieg. Hamburg, A. Preilipper, 1938.
   150, [1] p. 23ᵐ.
   "Die abhandlung entstand im sozialökonomischen seminar der Hansischen universität ... Sie ist von der rechts- und staatswissenschaftlichen fakultät der Hansischen universität zu Hamburg als dissertation anerkannt."—Vorwort, foot-note.
   "Literatur": p. 150–[160]

   1. Shipping—U. S. 2. Merchant marine—U. S. 3. Shipping bounties and subsidies—U. S.   ɪ. Title.
   Library of Congress   HE745.L6   41–19081
   [2]   387.50973

NL 0443554   DLC ICN MH–BA

Loehrl (Joannes C. C.) * De morbis ossium in genere. 3 p. l., 40 pp. 8°. *Erlange, S. Hilpert*, 1790, v. 146.

NL 0443555   DNLM

Loehwing, Walter Ferdinand.
   Bohumil Shimek. Iowa City, Univ. of Iowa Press, 1947.
   36 p. port. 24 cm. (Centennial memoirs)

   1. Shimek, Bohumil, 1861–1937.   ɪ. Series: Iowa. University. Centennial memoirs.
   QH31.S5L6   925.7   48–2304*

NL 0443556   DLC MiEM MiU NcGU MH OrU CU OO InU TxU

Loehwing, Walter Ferdinand.
   Effects of lime and potash fertilizers on certain muck soils. 1925.
   30 l. 29 cm.
   Typescript (carbon copy)
   Thesis—Chicago.
   Bibliography: leaves 29–30.

   1. Liming of soils. 2. Potassium fertilizers. 3. Humus.   ɪ. Title.
   S643.L63   72–202670

NL 0443557   DLC ICU

There are no cards for numbers
NL 0443558 to NL 0444000

VOLUME 338

Loeillot,
Nouveaux élémens de grammaire russe à l'usage
des commerçans ...   St. Pétersbourg: Pluchart
et comp., 1812.
175 p.   8°.

NL 0444001   NN

Loeillet, Jean Baptiste.
*Contributors to the National Union
Catalog have frequently identified Jean
Baptiste Loeillet de Gant, b. 1688, with
John Loeillet, 1680-1730.
Works whose authorship cannot at present
be determined are here entered under
Loeillet, Jean Baptiste [without dates]
Works whose authorship has been deter-
mined are entered as established under:
1) Loeillet, Jean Baptiste, b. 1688.
2) Loeillet, John, 1680-1730.*

NL 0444002

Loeillet, Jean Baptiste

Airs & dances for descant and treble
recorders; arr. by Audrey Abbott and Theo
Wyatt. London, Schott [c1951]
score (15 p.)

1.Recorder music (2 recorders)

NL 0444003   OrP

[Loeillet, Jean Baptiste]
...Gavotte et menuet...   Paris: A. Durand & fils, c1910.
Publ. pl. no. D. & F. 7506.   1 v.   35cm.   (Les vieux maîtres
du violon. 3.)

Score (5 p.): violin and piano. Violin part.
"Révision par Alfred Moffat."
At head of title: 2me série... J.-B. Lulli [i.e. Loeillet]

1. Violin and piano—To 1800.
3. Minuets—Violin and piano.
supposed composer. II. Moffat,
N.Y.P.L.

2. Gavottes—Violin and piano.
I. Lully, Jean Baptiste de, 1632-1687,
Alfred Edward, 1866-   , ed.

CARNEGIE CORP. OF NEW YORK.

February 4, 1938

NL 0444004   NN

---

qM788.51 Loeillet, Jean Baptiste,
L82l
Largo in C minor for treble recorder &
harpsichord or pianoforte. The recorder part
edited by Edgar H. Hunt, realization of the
figured bass by Jules de Swert. London,
Schott, c1940.
score (3p.) and part. 31cm. (Schott's
recorder series, 9)

1. Recorder and harpsichord music—To 1800.

NL 0444005   IU CLSU MeB

Lœillet, Jean Baptiste,
Quintett H-moll, für zwei Querflöten, zwei Blockflöten
und Basso continuo. Hrsg. von Rolf Ermeler. Aussetzung
des Generalbasses: Engelhard Barthe. Kassel, Bärenreiter-
Verlag [1955]
score (15 p.) and   parts. 29 cm. (Hortus musicus, 133)
For 2 flutes, 2 recorders, and unfigured bass realized for keyboard
instrument; includes part for double bass.

1. Quintets (Harpsichord, 2 flutes, 2 recorders)—To 1800.
(Series)

M517.L64Q54   M 58-1627

NN NcU CSt NBC MB ICN
NL 0444006   DLC OrSaW IaU AU ICU LU MiU MH NcD IU

Loeillet, Jean Baptiste,
[Sonata, flute & continuo]
Sonata V for flute and bass. Uitwerking
van de becijferde Bas door Joh. Feltkamp.
Amsterdam, Van Broekman [19--]
score (8 p.) & part.

For flute and piano.

1.Sonatas (Flute & piano)

NL 0444007   OrP

Loeillet, Jean Baptiste,
...Suite in G min...   London: Augener, Ltd. [, 1895.]
Publ. pl. no. 10493.   2 parts in 1 v.   f°.
Violoncello and piano (realization of basso continuo) in score, and violoncello part.
At head of title: Augener's edition. Classical violoncello music by celebrated
masters of the 17th and 18th centuries; arranged for violoncello with pianoforte ac-
companiment by Carl Schroeder. ser. 1. [Book 13.] no. 5513. J. B. Loeillet.

DREXEL MUSICAL FUND.

1. Violoncello and piano. 2. Violon-
Karl, 1848-   , arranger.
N.Y.P.L.

cello and basso continuo. I. Schroeder,
January 4, 1932

NL 0444008   NN

---

qM786.49 Loeillet, Jean Baptiste,
L82s
Suite of three pieces for pianoforte, four
hands. Transcribed by Georg Eggeling.
Boston, A. P. Schmidt c1911.
17p. 31cm. (Schmidt's Education series,
no.407)

1. Suites (Piano, 4 hands)

NL 0444009   IU IEN

Loeillet, Jean Baptiste, 1680-1730.
see Loeillet, John, 1680-1730.

FILM   Loeillet, Jean Baptiste, b. 1688
A1027   [Sonatas, flute & continuo, op.3 (Priestman III)]
M   XII [i.e. Douze] sonates à une flûte & bass continue, par
Jean Baptiste L'Oeillet de Gant. Troisième ouvrage.
Amsterdam, E Roger [ca. 1715]
score (51 p.) On film (positive)

Microfilm. Original in the Bibliothèque nationale, Paris.
Contents.- 1. C major.- 2. Bb major.- 3. G minor.- 4. G
major.- 5. C minor.- 6. E minor.- 7. Eb major.- 8. F major.-
9. Bb major.- 10. D minor.- 11. A major.- 12. E minor.

On same reel:
(1) Caix d'Hervelois, L. de, Pièces, flute & continuo (1726)
(2) Caix d'Hervelois, L. de, Pièces, flute & continuo (1731)
(3) Caix d'Hervelois, L. de, Suites, op. 6. 1736.
(4) Corrette, M. Sonatas, op. 13. [ca. 1735]

NL 0444012   CU

Loeillet, Jean Baptiste, b. 1688.
[Sonatas. Flute & piano. Op. 1, no.]
...Drei Sonaten für Flöte (Geige, Oboe) und Generalbass; herausgegeben von W. Hinnenthal nach der im Besitz Sr. Durch-
laucht des Fürsten zu Bentheim-Tecklenburg befindlichen Kupferstich-Ausgabe...   Kassel: Bärenreiter-Verlag, 1936.   3 parts
in 1 v.   29cm.   (Bärenreiter-Ausgabe 957.)

Score (28 p.) including realized figured bass. 2 parts. Violoncello doubles bass.
"Die vorliegenden 3 Sonaten stammen aus der bei Roger-Amsterdam unter dem Titel
'XII sonates à une flute & basse continue' als Op. 1 erschienenen Kupferstich-Ausgabe."

1. Flute and piano—To 1800.
3. Oboe and piano—To 1800.
1800. I. Hinnenthal, W., ed.
N.Y.P.L.

2. Violin and piano—To 1800.
4. Sonatas—Flute and piano—To

September 9, 1937

NL 0444013   NN

Lœillet, Jean Baptiste, b. 1688.
[Sonatas, recorder & continuo. Selections.]
Drei Sonaten für Flöte (Geige, Oboe) und Generalbass.
Hrsg. von Joh. Philipp Hinnenthal. Kassel, Bärenreiter-
Verlag, [1952]
score (v.) and   parts. 29 cm. (Hortus musicus, 42, 162, [etc.]
Vols. 2-   Sonaten für Flöte (Geige, Oboe) und
Generalbass.
Figured bass realized for harpsichord or piano. Parts for flute,
violin, or oboe, and violoncello.
CONTENTS.—Heft 1, Op. 1, no. 1-3 (Priestman I)—Heft 2. Op. 3,
no. 9 (Priestman III) Op. 4, no. 9-10 (Priestman IV)—
1. Sonatas (Recorder and harpsichord)—To 1800. I. Hinnen-
thal, Johann Philipp,   1883-   , ed. (Series)

M241.L6S64   M 57-1130 rev

MiDW IU NcD AU ICN
NL 0444014   DLC OrSaW OU MiU MB CLU NBC NcD IaU MH

LOEILLET, JEAN BAPTISTE, b. 1688
[SONATA, FLUTE & CONTINUO, OP. 3, NO. 5 (PRIESTMAN III).
POCO ALLEGRO]
Poco allegro, for treble recorder and pianoforte or
harpsichord, from Sonata in C minor. Ornamentation,
phrasing and accompaniment from the figured bass by
Carl F. Dolmetsch. London, Schott, c1941.
score (4 p.) and part. 31cm. (Schott's recorder series. Recorder with
piano accompaniment. 12)

Caption title.

1. Recorder and harpsichord—To 1800. 2. Flute and piano—To 1800.
I. Dolmetsch, Carl, ed.

NL 0444016   NN

M   Loeillet, Jean Baptiste, b. 1688
289   [Sonatas, 2 flutes, op. 5, book II] Six
L8249 sonatas of two parts made on purpose for two
Op. 5.Bk.2 German flutes. Compos'd by Jean Baptiste
Loeillet de Gant. London, I. Walsh... and Ioseph
Hare [1715?]
31cm.

Separate parts.
Engraved.

NL 0444017   NRU-Mus

Lœillet, Jean Baptiste, b. 1688.
[Sonatas, 2 flutes, op. 5, livre 2 (Priestman VI)]
Six sonatas of two parts, made on purpose for two
German flutes; compos'd by Jean Baptiste Lœillet de Gant.
London, Printed for and sold by I. Walsh and I. Hare
[172-?]
parts. 33 cm.

1. Sonatas (2 flutes)—To 1800.

ML30.4c no. 1187 Miller
[M289]   71-216164

NL 0444018   DLC

VOLUME 338

Film 11973   Loeillet, Jean Baptiste. b. 1688
      ₍Sonatas, 2 flutes, op.5, book 2₎
    VI sonates à deux flutes traversières, hautbois ou violons. Cinquième ouvrage, livre second.   Amsterdam, Jeanne Roger ₍1725?₎
    2 parts (15p. each)
    Microfilm (negative) London, British Museum, 1968. 1 reel.
    On reel with Blavet, Michel. Sonatas or duets for two German flutes or violins. London, 1760.

NL 0444019   IaU

Lœillet, Jean Baptiste, b. 1688
    ₍Sonatas, flute & continuo, op. 5, livre 1 (Priestman v)₎
    VI sonates à une flute traversiére, un haubois ou violon & basse continue ... par Jean Baptiste L'Oeillet de Gant. Cinquiéme ouvrage, livre premier. Amsterdam, Jeanne Roger ₍1717₎
    score (28 p.)   30 cm.
    Publisher's plate no.: 427.

    1. Sonatas (Flute and harpsichord)—To 1800.

M242.L   46–30920 rev

NL 0444020   DLC

Film 11973   Loeillet, Jean Baptiste, b. 1688.
    ₍Sonatas, flute & continuo, op.5, book 1₎
    VI sonates à une flute traversiere, un hautbois ou violon & basse continue. Cinquième ouvrage, livre premier. Amsterdam, Jeanne Roger ₍1720?₎
    score (28p.)
    Microfilm (negative) London, British Museum, 1968. 1 reel.
    On reel with Blavet, Michel. Sonatas or duets for two German flutes or violins. London, 1760.

NL 0444021   IaU

M242 L8 op.3 no.11   Loeillet, Jean Baptiste, 1688–
    [Sonata, flute & continuo, op. 3, no. 11, A major]
    Sonata XI in A major for flute or alto recorder and piano. Edited by Reba Paeff Mirsky. New York, Hargail Music Press, 1946.
    score (9 p.) and part. 31 cm. (Flute and recorder music)
    1. Sonatas (Flute & harpsichord)—To 1800. 2. Sonatas (Recorder & harpsichord)—To 1800. I. Mirsky, Reba Paeff, ed.

NL 0444022   MB

LOEILLET, JEAN BAPTISTE, 1688–
    [SONATA, FLUTE & CONTINUO, OP. 3, NO. 5 (PRIESTMAN III). ARR. FOR VIOLONCELLO & PIANO]
    Sonata in G min. Arranged for violoncello with pianoforte accompaniment by Carl Schroeder. London, Augener ₍193–?₎ Pl. no. 10360. score (10 p.) and part. 31cm. (Classical violoncello music by celebrated masters of the 17th and 18th centuries. First series. Book 7)

    Augener's edition. no. 5507.

    1. Violoncello and piano--Arr. I. Classical violoncello music by celebrated masters of the 17th and 18th centuries. II. Schroeder, Carl, arr. III. Schroeder, Carl.

NL 0444024   NN

Loeillet, Jean Baptiste. b. 1688
    ₍Sonatas. Flute & piano. Op. 3, no. 11₎
    ...Sonata XI en la majeur (d'après l'édition de la bibliothèque du Conservatoire royal de Bruxelles.) Édition J. Jongen et Joseph Debroux. Paris: H. Lemoine & cie., cop. 1912. Publ. pl. no. 21566 P. 1277 H. L.   2 parts in 1 v.   35½cm. (L'école du violon au XVIIme et au XVIIIme siècle: Les maitres français du violon au XVIIIe siècle.)

    Flute and piano (realized from basso continuo) in score and flute part.

    With reproduction of early t-p.: XII sonatas or solos for a flute with a through bass for the harpsicord or bass violin. Opera terza. London: Printed for I. Walsh & I. Hare ₍ca. 1725₎
    Caption-title.
    "Collection Joseph Debroux." "Panthéon. no. 1277.

    1. Flute and piano. 2. Sonatas—Flute and piano. I. Jongen, Joseph, 1873– ed. II. Debroux, Joseph, ed.
N.Y. P. L.   CARNEGIE CORPORATION OF NEW YORK.   January 10, 1936

NL 0444026   NN

Lœillet, Jean Baptiste, b. 1688.
    ₍Sonata, recorder & continuo, op. 3, no. 11 (Priestman III) A major; arr.₎
    Sonata XI, en la majeur (d'après l'édition de la Bibliothèque du Conservatoire royal de Bruxelles) ₍Opera terza₎ Édition: J. Jongen et Joseph Debroux. Paris, M. Senart, B. Roudanez, ᶜ1912.
    score (9 p.) and part. 35 cm. (L'École du violon au XVIIᵐᵉ et au XVIIIᵐᵉ siècle. Les Maîtres du violon au XVIIIᵉ siècle)
    Caption title.
    For violin and piano.
    1. Sonatas (Violin and piano), Arranged.

M223.L   M 56–336

NL 0444027   DLC

---

qM788.5343 L82s3 1956   Loeillet, Jean Baptiste. b. 1688.
    ₍Sonatas, 2 flutes (Priestman VII) No.3₎
    Sonata III in F, 2 treble recorders. From 6 sonatas of 2 parts fitted and contrived for 2 flutes, Walsh and Hare, London, 1728. Ed. Carl Dometsch. London₎ Universal Edition ₍ᶜ1956₎
    score (7p.) 31cm. (Il Flauto dolce)
    "Dolmetsch recorder series."

NL 0444028   IU

Lœillet, Jean Baptiste. b. 1688.
    ₍Sonatas, recorder & continuo, op. 1 (Priestman I)₎
    Sonatas or solos for a flute, with a through bass for the harpsicord or bass violin. Compos'd by Jean Luly of Gant. Parte prima. London, J. Walsh servᵗ to her Britanick Majesty ... & J. Hare ₍171–?₎
    score (53 p.) 37 cm.

    1. Sonatas (Recorder and harpsichord)—To 1800.

M242.L   46–42464 rev*

NL 0444029   DLC

M 242 L82 S71 171-a   Loeillet, Jean Baptiste. b. 1688
    ₍Sonatas, recorder & continuo, op.1 (Priestman I)₎
    Sonatas or solos for a flute with a through bass for the harpsicord or bass violin. Compos'd by Jean Luly of Gant. Parte prima. London, Printed for J. Walsh servᵗ to his Britanick Majesty ... & J. Hare ₍171–?₎
    ₍14₎l. 36 cm.
    Photocopy (negative) of original in Brussels, Conservatoire royal de musique, Bibliothèque (Wotquenne 5574) Mounted in an album.
    Collation of original as determined by photocopy: 1 p.l. score   (53 p.) 18 cm.
    1. Sonatas (Recorder and harpsichord)--To 1800.

NL 0444030   MiU

M242 L85 op.1 1730 Case X   Loeillet, Jean Baptiste. 1688–
    [Sonatas, recorder & continuo, op.1 (Priestman I)]
    Sonatas or solos for a flute with a through bass for the harpsicon or bass violin. Compos'd by Jean Luly of Gant. Parte prima. London. Printed for J. Walsh. servᵗ to his Britanick Majesty ... & J. Hare [ca. 1730]
    score (53 p.)

    Plate number is in ms.
    J. Hare, in imprint, partly deleted.
    Has bound in the composer's
    (1) XII sonatas. Op. 2. ca. 1730.
    (2) XII sonatas. Op. 3. ca. 1730.
MUSIC LIB. ₍3₎ XII sonatas. Op. 4 ca. 1730.

NL 0444031   CU

M178 M693 v.28   Loeillet, Jean Baptiste. b. 1688
    ₍Sonatas, recorder & continuo, op.1 (Priestman I) No.1₎
    Sonate, A-moll, für Alt-Blockflöte (Querflöte, Obe, Violine) und Cembalo (Klavier); Violoncello (Gambe) ad lib., oder für 2 Alt-Blockflöten allein. Op.1, Nr.1. ₍Bass ausgesetzt von Helmut Mönkemeyer₎ Celle, H. Moeck ₍ᶜ1943₎
    score (11 p.) & 3 pts. 31cm. (Moecks Kammermusik, 28)
    Edition Moeck,   Nr. 1028.
    1. Sonatas (Recorder and harpsichord)

NL 0444032   CSt ICU MH NN IU

Loeillet, Jean Baptiste, 1688–
    Sonatas, recorder & continuo, op.3, no.2
    Sonate B-Dur für Altblockflöte in f' (Querflöte, Oboe, Violine) und Cembalo (Klavier): Gambe (Violoncello) ad lib. Op.3 Nr.2. [Hrsg. von P.F.] Scherber [und A.] Kutz. [Mainz, Schott, c1949] Pl.no.B.S.S 37083
    Score (15 p.) & 2 pts. (Originalmusik für die Blockflöte)
    Edition Schott, 4076
    Cover title
    Figured bass realized   for keyboard instrument

NL 0444033   MH

M242 .L82S3   Loeillet, Jean Baptiste. b. 1688
    ₍Sonatas, recorder & continuo, op.1 (Priestman I) No.6₎
    Sonate, C-Dur, op.1, Nr.6, für Alt-Blockflöte (Querflöte, Oboe, Violine) und Cembalo (Klavier) Violoncello (Gambe) ad lib. ₍Bass ausgesetzt von Helmut Mönkemeyer₎ Celle, H. Moeck ₍ᶜ1948₎
    score (11 p.) and 2 parts. (Moecks Kammermusik, Nr.30)
    Edition Moeck, Nr.1030.

    1. Sonatas (Recorder and harpsichord)

NL 0444034   ICU CSt IU NN MH

Loeillet, Jean Baptiste, 1688–
    Sonatas, recorder & continuo, op.3, no.5
    Sonate c-Moll für Altblockflöte in f' (Querflöte, Oboe, Violine) und Cembalo (Klavier); Gambe (Violoncello) ad lib. Op.3 Nr.5. [Hrsg. von A.] Scherber [und A.] Kutz. [Mainz, Schott, c1949] Pl.no.B.S.S 37086
    Score (11 p.) & 2 pts. (Originalmusik für die Blockflöte)
    Edition Schott, 4079
    Cover title
    Figured bass realized   for keyboard instrument

NL 0444035   MH IEN

VOLUME 338

Loeillet, Jean Baptiste, 1688-
Sonatas, recorder & continuo, op.3, no.10
Sonate d-Moll für Altblockflöte in f' (Querflöte,
Oboe, Violine) und Cembalo (Klavier); Gambe (Violoncello) ad lib. Op.3 Kr.10. [Hrsg. von P.F.] Scherber
[und A.] Kutz. [Mainz, Schott, c1949] Pl.no.B.S.S
37088

Score (11 p.) & 2 pts. (Originalmusik für die
Blockflöte)
Edition Schott, 4081
(Figured bass realized
Cover title   for keyboard instrument

NL 0444036   MH

Loeillet, Jean Baptiste, 1688-
Sonatas, recorder & continuo, op.1, no.8
Sonate d-moll, Op.1 Nr.8, für Alt-Blockflöte (Querflöte, Oboe, Violine) und Cembalo (Klavier); Violoncello (Gambe) ad lib. Celle, Moeck [c1948]

1. Score (11 p.) & 2 pts. (Moecks Kammermusik, 31)
Edition Moeck, 1031
Figured bass realized for keyboard instrument

NL 0444037   MH CSt IU NN ICU

Loeillet, Jean Baptiste, b. 1688.
Sonate [E moll] von Jean Baptiste Loeillet. Bearbeitung von A.
Moffat. [Berlin: N. Simrock, G.m.b.H., 1899] Publ. pl. no.
11234. 2 parts in 1 v.   34cm. (Meister-Schule der alten
Zeit: Sammlung klassischer Violin-Sonaten berühmter Kom-
ponisten des 17. u. 18. Jahrhunderts. 21.)
Score (7 p.) : violin and piano (realized from basso continuo). Violin part.
Caption-title.

                              CARNEGIE CORPORATION OF NEW YORK.
1. Violin and piano—To 1800.   2. Sonatas—Violin and piano—
To 1800. I. Moffat, Alfred Edward,   1800—
N.Y.P.L.   September 21, 1936

NL 0444038   NN

Loeillet, Jean Baptiste, 1688-
Sonatas, recorder & continuo, op.2, no.7. Selections.
Arr.
Sonate, E moll. Nach den Original-Ausgaben für Violine
mit beziffertem Bass bearb. mit Vertragszeichen versehen
und hrsg. von A. Moffat. Berlin, Simrock [19 –]
Score (7 p.) & 1 pt. (Meister-Schule der alten Zeit;
Sammlung klassischer Violin-Sonaten berühmter Komponisten
des 17. u. 18. Jahrhunderts, 21)
Simrock's classical violin music, 80
The 4th movement is arr. from the Giga in Sonata, op.
1, no.12

NL 0444039   MH-Mu

Loeillet, Jean Baptiste, 1688-
Sonatas, recorder & continuo, op.3, no.6
Sonate e-Moll für Altblockflöte in f' (Querflöte,
Oboe, Violine) und Cembalo (Klavier); Gambe (Violoncello) ad lib. Op.3 Nr.6. [Hrsg. von P.F.] Scherber
[und A.] Kutz. [Mainz, Schott, c1949] Pl.no.B.S.S
37087

Score (15 p.) & 2 pts. (Originalmusik für die
Blockflöte)
Edition Schott, 4080
Cover title
Figured bass realized
                        for keyboard instrument

NL 0444040   MH

M178   Loeillet, Jean Baptiste, 1688-
M693   [Sonatas, recorder & continuo, op.1 (Priest-
v.29   man I) No. 4]
       Sonate, F-dur, für Alt-Blockflöte (Querflöte,
       Oboe, Violine) und Cembalo (Klavier);
       Violoncello (Gambe) ad lib. oder für 2 Alt-
       Blockflöten allein. Bass ausgesetzt von Hel-
       mut Mönkemeyer. Celle, Moeck [c1948]
       score (11 p.) & 3 pts. 31cm. (Moecks
       Kammermusik, 29)
       Edition Moeck, Nr. 1029.
       1. Sonatas. (Rec   order and harpsichord)

NL 0444041   CSt

Loeillet, Jean Baptiste, 1688-
Sonatas, recorder & continuo, op.1, no.4
Sonate F-Dur, Op.1 Nr.4, für Alt-Blockflöte (Querflöte, Oboe, Violine) und Cembalo (Klavier); Violoncello (Gambe) ad lib., oder für 2 Alt-Blockflöten allein. Celle, Moeck [c1948]

Score (11 p.) & 3 pts. (Moecks Kammermusik, 29)
Edition Moeck, 1029
Pts. for Alt-Blockflöte (Querflöte,Oboe,Violine),
2.Alt-Blockflöte (Querflöte,Oboe,Violine) & Violon-
cello (Gambe)
Figured bass realized   for keyboard instrument

NL 0444042   MH ICU NN

Loeillet, Jean Baptiste, b. 1688.
[Sonata, recorder & continuo, op. 3, no. 8 (Priestman III) F major]
Sonate für Blockflöte u. Generalbass. Berlin, J. P. Hinnenthal, 1945.
score (11 p.) and part. 30 cm.

1. Sonatas (Recorder and harpsichord)—To 1800.

M242.L   M 56-314

NL 0444043   DLC IaU IU NBuG PU PU-FA

Loeillet, Jean Baptiste, b. 1688
Sonatas, recorder & continuo, op.3, no.4
Sonate G-Dur für Altblockflöte in f' (Querflöte,
Oboe, Violine) und Cembalo (Klavier); Gambe (Violoncello) ad lib. Op.3 Nr.4. [Hrsg. von P.F.] Scherber
[und A.] Kutz. [Mainz, Schott, c1949] Pl.no.B.S.S
37085

Score (8 p.) & 2 pts. (Originalmusik für die
Blockflöte)
Edition Schott, 4078
Cover title
Figured bass realized   for keyboard instrument

NL 0444044   MH

Loeillet, Jean Baptiste, b. 1688
[Sonata, recorder & continuo, op. 3, no. 5 (Priestman III) C minor:
arr.]
Sonate, G moll. [Bearb. von Carl Schroeder] Mainz, B.
Schott's Söhne [1911]
score (10 p.) and part. 31 cm. (Klassische Violoncell-Musik,
Heft 7)
Edition Schott, S-2640g.
For violoncello and piano.

1. Sonatas (Violoncello and piano), Arranged.

M236.L   M 56-335

NL 0444045   DLC

Loeillet, Jean Baptiste, b. 1688.
Sonatas, recorder & continuo, op.3, no.3
Sonate g-Moll für Altblockflöte in f' (Querflöte,
Oboe, Violine) und Cembalo (Klavier); Gambe (Violon-
cello) ad lib. Op.3 Nr.3. [Hrsg. von] P.F.Scherber und
A.Kutz. [Mainz, Schott, c1949] Pl.no.B.S.S 37084

Score (11 p.) & 2 pts. (Originalmusik für die
Blockflöte)
Edition Schott, 4077
Cover title
Figured bass realized   for keyboard instrument

NL 0444046   MH IEN

W.C.L. Loeillet, Jean Baptiste, 1680-1730.
M785.73 A [Trio-sonata, op. 2 (Priestman x) No. 6; arr.]
L826S
         Sonate à trois en si mineur pour violon,
op.2   violoncelle et piano, Harmonisées par Alexandre
no.6   Béon. [Paris, H. Lemoine, c1912]
         score (15 p.) and 2 parts. 28 cm. (His
         Sonates pour instruments divers et piano har-
         monisées par A. Béon, 2)
         Caption title.
         Edition Nationale Française.
         Originally for flute, oboe, and continuo.
         1. Piano   trios, Arranged. [I.]
Béon, Alexandre,   arr.

NL 0444046-1   NcD

Loeillet, Jean Baptiste, b. 1688
[Sonata, recorder & continuo, op. 1, no. 11 (Priestman I) G major.
Selections; arr.]
Sonate in D dur, für Violine mit beziffertem Bass. Bearbeitung für Violine & Klavier von Alfred Moffat. Sonata
in D major, for violin with figured bass. Arrangement for
violin and piano by Alfred Moffat. Berlin, N. Simrock
[1929]
score (11 p.) and part. 31 cm. (Edition Simrock, No. 1066)
The 1st and 2d movements are arr. from the 2d and 3d, respectively,
of the original; the 3d, from the Gavotta, op. 1, no. 3.
1. Sonatas (Violin and piano), Arranged.   I. Loeillet, Jean Baptiste, 1680-1730. Sonata,   recorder & continuo, op. 1, no. 3
(Priestman I) G major.   Gavotte.
M223.L   M 56-276

NL 0444047   DLC IU

M223   Loeillet, Jean Baptiste, b. 1688
.L82S83   [Sonatas, recorder & continuo, op.1 (Priest-
         man I) Selections; arr.]
         Sonate in D-dur für Violine mit beziffertem
         Bass. Bearb. für Violine & Klavier von Alfred
         Moffat [und] Hans Mlynarczyk. Hamburg, N.
         Simrock [c1929]
         score (11 p.) and part.
         The 2d and 3d movements of no.11, and the 4th
         of no.3, respectively; originally for recorder
         and continuo.
         1. Sonatas (Violin and piano), Arranged.

NL 0444048   ICU

Loeillet, Jean Baptiste, 1688-
[Sonata, recorder & continuo, op. 2, no. 7 (Priestman II) E minor.
Selections; arr.]
Sonate in E moll, für Violine mit beziffertem Bass. Bearbeitung für Violine und Klavier von Alfred Moffat. Sonata
in E minor, for violin with figured bass. Arrangement for
violin and piano by Alfred Moffat. Berlin, N. Simrock
[1929]
score (7 p.) and part. 31 cm. (Edition Simrock, No. 1094)
The 4th movement is arr. from the Giga in Sonata, op. 1, no. 12.
CONTENTS.—Largo.—Corrente.—Sarabanda.—Giga.
1. Sonatas (Violin and piano), Arranged.   I. Loeillet, Jean Baptiste, 1680-1730. So-   nata, recorder & continuo, op. 1, no.
12 (Priestman I)   E minor. Gigue.
M223.L   M 56-270

NL 0444049   DLC

Loeillet, Jean Baptiste, b. 1688
[Sonata, recorder & continuo, op. 3, no. 5 (Priestman III) C minor:
arr.]
Sonate, la mineur, arrangée pour violon avec accompagnement de piano par J. Salmon. Paris, Ricordi, [1918.
score (16 p.) and part. 35 cm.
Cover title.

1. Sonatas (Violin and piano), Arranged.

M223.L   M 56-345

NL 0444050   DLC NIC IU

Loeillet, Jean Baptiste, b. 1688
[Sonata, recorder & continuo, op. 3, no. 5 (Priestman III) C minor:
arr.]
Sonate, la mineur, arrangée pour violoncelle avec accompagnement de piano par J. Salmon. Paris, Ricordi, [1918.
score (16 p.) and part. 35 cm.
Cover title.

1. Sonatas (Violoncello and piano), Arranged.

M236.L   M 56-343

NL 0444051   DLC IU NIC ICU

VOLUME 338

M219 Loeillet, Jean Baptiste, b. 1688
.L75 ₍Sonata, violin & piano, no. 3, D major₎
no. 3
    Sonate pour violon et piano ₍ou viole d'amour et
clavecin₎ ₍en ré majeur₎ Harmonisation A. Béon.
Paris, H. Lemoine ₍c1911₎
    score (12 p.) and part.   31 cm.   (Edition na-
tionale française. Panthéon des pianistes, no. 931)

    On cover-title: J.-B. Loeillet (1653-1728)

    1. Sonatas (Violin and piano) – To 1800.
    2. Sonatas (Viola   d'amore and piano) – To 1800

NL 0444052   NjR

M219 Loeillet, Jean Baptiste, b. 1688
.L75 ₍Sonata, violin & piano, no. 9, G minor₎
no. 9
    ₍Sonate₎ pour violon et piano, ou viole d'amour
et clavecin, en sol mineur ₍no. 9₎ Harmonisé par
A. Béon.   Paris, H. Lemoine, c1912.
    score (8 p.) and part.   31 cm.   (Edition na-
tionale française. Panthéon des pianistes, no. 932)

    On cover-title: J.-B. Loeillet (1653-1728)

    1. Sonatas (Violin and piano) – To 1800.
    2. Sonatas (Viola   d'amore and piano) – To
1800.

NL 0444053   NjR

---

*M223 Loeillet, Jean Baptiste, b. 1688
.L6486
no. 9   Sonate pour violon et piano ou viole d'amour
et clavecin en sol mineur [no. 9] Paris,
H. Lemoine ₍c1912₎
    score (11 p.) and part.   31 cm.   (His
Sonates pour instruments divers et piano)
Pantheon des pianistes, no. 932.

    1. Sonatas (Violin and piano),
Arranged.

NL 0444054   MB

Lœillet, Jean Baptiste, b. 1688
₍Sonata, recorder & continuo, op. 3, no. 11 (Priestman III) A major;
arr.₎

    Sonate, sol majeur, arrangée pour violon avec accompagne-
ment de piano par J. Salmon.   Paris, Ricordi, ₍1918.
    score (11 p.) and part.   35 cm.

    Cover title.

    1. Sonatas (Violin and piano), Arranged.

M223.L   M 56-346

NL 0444055   DLC IU NIC

Lœillet, Jean Baptiste, b. 1688
₍Sonata, recorder & continuo, op. 3, no. 11 (Priestman III) A major; arr.₎

    Sonate, sol majeur, arrangée pour violoncelle avec accom-
pagnement de piano par J. Salmon.   Paris, Ricordi, ₍1918.
    score (11 p.) and part.   35 cm.

    Cover title.

    1. Sonatas (Violoncello and piano), Arranged.

M236.L   M 56-344

NL 0444056   DLC OrP OO NN NIC IU

LOEILLET, JEAN BAPTISTE, 1688–
    [SONATA, FLUTE & CONTINUO, OP. 4, NO. 11 (PRIESTMAN IV)]
    Sonate voor fluit [en klavier van] Jan-Baptist
Loeillet. Sonate voor fluit [en klavier, Fasciculus
musicus Amsterdam 1710, van] Elias Broennemuller.
Met klavierbegeleiding volgens basso-continuo door
Julius van Etsen.   Antwerpen, "De Ring" [c1952]
    score (16 p.) and part.   34cm.

    For flute and piano.

    1. Flute and piano--To 1800.   I. Broennemuller, Elias, 1666-1762.
Sonata, flute and continuo.

NL 0444058   NN

QM785.72 Loeillet, Jean Baptiste, b. 1688.
L825sr   ₍Sonatas, recorder & continuo. Selections₎

    ₍Sonaten₎ für Alt- Blockflute (Querflöte,
Oboe, Violine) und Cembalo (Klavier); Violoncello (Gambe) ad. lib. oder für 2 Alt-
Blockflöten allein.   Celle, H. Moeck ₍c1943₎
    scores (5v.) and parts.   Moeck, Nr. 1028-1032)
    Moeck's Kammermusik, Nr. 28-32.
    Contents.--cv.1₎ Op. 1, Nr. 1.--cv.2₎ Op. 1, Nr. 4.--
cv.3₎ Op. 1, Nr. 6.--cv.4₎ Op. 1, Nr. 8.--cv.5₎ Op. 2, Nr.
5; Op. 4, Nr. 6.

    1. Sonatas (Recor-   der and piano)

NL 0444059   ICarbS

M   Loeillet, Jean Baptiste, b. 1688.
242   ₍Sonatas, recorder & continuo, op. 1
L821++ (Priestman I) Selections₎
Pr.1
    Sonate₍n₎ für Alt-Blockflöte (Querflöte,
Oboe, Violine) und Cembalo (Klavier); Violon-
cello (Gambe) ad lib.   Celle, H. Moeck
₍c1943-48₎
    score (4 v.) and 3 parts.   31cm.   (Moecks
Kammermusik, Nr. 28-31)

    Edition Moeck   1028-1031.

    Sonatas no. 1 and 4 have second recorder
part, taken from Walsh & Hare ed. (1728?).
    Figured bass realized for harpsichord; in-
cludes part for violoncello or gamba.
    Contents.--₍1₎ No. 1, A minor.--₍2₎ No. 4,
F major.--₍3₎ No. 6, C major.--₍4₎ No. 8, D
minor.

NL 0444061   NIC

M242 Loeillet, Jean Baptiste, 1688–
.L82585   ₍Sonatas, recorder & continuo, op.3 (Priest-
man III) Selections₎
    Sonaten fur Altblockflöte (Querflöte, Oboe,
Violine) und Basso continuo ₍embalo (Piano-
forte), Violoncello (Viola da gamba) ad lib.
Op.3, Nr.2-6, 10. Hrsg. von Paul Friedrich
Scherber und Adalbert Kutz. Mainz, B. Schott's
Sohne; New York, Schott Music Corp. (Associated
Music Publishers) ₍c1949₎
    score (6 v.) and 12 parts.   (Originalmusik für
die Blockflöte)
    Edition Schott,   4076-4081.

NL 0444062   ICU

LOEILLET, JEAN BAPTISTE, 1688–
    [SONATA, FLUTE & CONTINUO, OP. 3, NO. 2 (PRIESTMAN III)]
    Sonaten für Altblockflöte in F (Querflöte, Oboe,
Violine) und Cembalo (Klavier), Gambe (Violoncello)
ad lib. Hrsg. von Paul Friedrich Scherber und Adalbert
Kutz. Op. 3, Nr. 2, B-dur.   Mainz, B. Schott's
Söhne; New-York, Associated music publishers [c1949]
    score (15 p.) and 2 parts.   31cm.   (Originalmusik für die Blockflöte)

    Edition Schott 4076.

Continued in next column

Continued from preceding column

    For recorder (flute, oboe, violin) and figured bass realized for
keyboard instrument. Includes part for violoncello.

    1. Recorded and harpsichord--To 1800.   2. Flute and piano--To 1800.
    3. Oboe and piano--To 1800.   4. Violin and piano--To 1800.
    I. Scherber, Paul Friedrich, ed.   II. Kutz, Adalbert, ed.
    III. Scherber, Paul Friedrich.   IV. Kutz, Adalbert.

NL 0444064   NN NBC

LOEILLET, JEAN BAPTISTE, 1688–
    [SONATA, FLUTE & CONTINUO, OP. 3, NO. 3 (PRIESTMAN III)]
    Sonaten für Altblockflöte in F (Querflöte, Oboe,
Violine) und Cembalo (Klavier), Gambe (Violoncello)
ad lib. Hrsg. von Paul Friedrich Scherber und Adalbert
Kutz. Op. 3, Nr. 3, g-moll.   Mainz, B. Schott's
Söhne; New-York, Associated music publishers [c1949]
    score (11 p.) and 2 parts.   31cm.   (Originalmusik für die Blockflöte)

    Edition Schott 4077.

    For recorder (flute oboe, violin) and figured bass realized for keyboard
instrument.
    Includes part for violoncello.

    1. Recorder and harpsichord-- To 1800.   2. Flute and piano--To 1800.
    3. Oboe and piano--To 1800.   4. Violin and piano--To 1800.
    I. Scherber, Paul Friedrich, ed.   II. Kutz, Adalbert, ed.

NL 0444066   NN

LOEILLET, JEAN BAPTISTE, 1688–
    [SONATA, FLUTE & CONTINUO, OP. 3, NO. 4 (PRIESTMAN III)]
    Sonaten für Altblockflöte in F (Querflöte, Oboe,
Violine) und Cembalo (Klavier), Gambe (Violoncello)
ad lib. Hrsg. von Paul Friedrich Scherber und Adalbert Kutz. Op. 3, Nr. 4, G-dur.   Mainz, B. Schott's
Söhne; New-York, Associated music publishers [c1949]
    score (8 p.) and 2 parts.   31cm.   (Originalmusik für die Blockflöte)

    Edition Schott 4078.

    For recorder (flute, oboe, violin) and figured bass realized for key-
board instrument. Includes part for violoncello.

    1. Recorder and harpsichord --To 1800.   2. Flute and piano--To 1800.
    3. Oboe and piano--To 1800.   4. Violin and piano--To 1800.
    I. Scherber, Paul Friedrich, ed.   II. Kutz, Adalbert, ed.

NL 0444068   NN

LOEILLET, JEAN BAPTISTE, 1688–
    [SONATA, FLUTE & CONTINUO, OP. 3, NO. 5 (PRIESTMAN III)]
    Sonaten für Altblockflöte in F (Querflöte, Oboe,
Violine) und Cembalo (Klavier), Gambe (Violoncello)
ad lib. Hrsg. von Paul Friedrich Scherber und Adalbert Kutz. Op. 3, Nr. 5, c-moll.   Mainz, B. Schott's
Söhne; New-York, Associated music publishers [c1949]
    score (11 p.) and 2 parts.   31cm.   (Originalmusik für die Blockflöte)

    Edition Schott 4079.

    For recorder (flute, oboe, violin) and figured bass realized for key-
board instrument. Includes part for violoncello.

    1. Recorder and harpsichord--To 1800.   2. Flute and piano--To 1800.
    3. Oboe and piano--To 1800.   4. Violin and piano--To 1800.
    I. Scherber, Paul Friedrich, ed.   II. Kutz, Adalbert, ed.

NL 0444070   NN

VOLUME 338

LOEILLET, JEAN BAPTISTE. 1688–
[SONATA, FLUTE & CONTINUO, OP. 3, NO. 6 (PRIESTMAN III)]
Sonaten für Altblockflöte in F (Querflöte, Oboe,
Violine) und Cembalo (Klavier), Gambe (Violoncello)
ad lib. Hrsg. von Paul Friedrich Scherber und Adalbert
Kutz, Op. 3, Nr. 6, e-moll. Mainz, B. Schott's
Söhne; New-York, Associated music publishers [c1949]
score (15 p.) and 2 parts.   31cm. (Originalmusik für die Blockflöte)
    Edition Schott 4080.

For recorder (flue, oboe, violin) and figured bass realized for keyboard
instrument. Includes part for violoncello.

1. Recorder and harpsichord'--To 1800.   2. Flute and piano--To 1800.
3. Oboe and piano--To 1800.   4. Violin and piano--To 1800.
I. Scherber Paul Friedrich, ed.   II. Kutz, Adalbert, ed.

NL 0444072   NN

LOEILLET, JEAN BAPTISTE. 1688–
[SONATA, FLUTE & CONTINUO, OP. 3, NO. 10 (PRIESTMAN III)]
Sonaten, für Altblockflöte in F (Querflöte, Oboe,
Violine) und Cembalo (Klavier). Gambe (Violoncello)
ad lib. Hrsg. von Paul Friedrich Scherber und Adalbert
Kutz, Op. 3, Nr.10, d-moll. Mainz, B. Schott's
Söhne; New-York, Associated music publishers [c1949]
score (11 p.) and 2 parts.   31cm. (Originalmusik für die Blockflöte)
    Edition Schott 4081.

For recorder (flute, oboe, violin) and figured bass realized for keyboard
instrument. Includes part for violoncello.

1. Recorder and harpsichord--To 1800.   2. Flute and piano--To 1800.
3. Oboe and piano--To 1800.   4. Violin and piano--To 1800.
I. Scherber, Paul Friedrich, ed.   II. Kutz, Adalbert, ed.

NL 0444074   NN IU NIC

Loeillet, Jean Baptiste, b. 1688
[Sonatas, recorder & continuo, op. 3 (Priestman III) Selections]
    Sonaten, Op. 3, für Altblockflöte in f' (Querflöte, Oboe,
Violine) und Cembalo (Klavier) Gambe (Violoncello) ad
lib., hrsg. von Paul Friedrich Scherber und Adalbert Kutz.
Mainz, B. Schott's Söhne; New York, Associated Music
Publishers [1949]
    score (6 v.) and part. 30 cm. (Originalmusik für die Blockflöte)
    Edition Schott, 4076–4081.
    Figured bass realized for harpsichord by Adalbert Kutz. Without
a violoncello part.

Some movements of Sonatas no. 2, 4, 5, 6, and 10 include ornamentation by one of the editors.
    Contents.—[1], No. 2, Bb major.—[2], No. 3, G minor.—[3], No. 4,
G major.—[4], No. 5, C minor.—[5], No. 6, E minor.—[6], No. 10, D
minor.

1. Sonatas (Recorder and harpsichord)—To 1800.

M242.L   51–17305 rev

NL 0444076   DLC NcU

f788.5   Loeillet, Jean Baptiste, 1688–
L825s   [Sonatas, flute, op.4, no.9 & 10]
    Twee sonaten voor fluit en klavier met
klavierbegeleiding volgens basso-continuo door
Julius van Etsen.   Berchem-Antwerpen, "De
Ring," n.d.
    2 pts. in 1v. F. (Vereeniging voor
musiekgeschiedenis te Antwerpen)

    Score and part.

NL 0444077   IaU

Loeillet, Jean Baptiste, 1688–
[Sonatas. Flute & piano. Op. 4, no. 9–10]
    ...Twee sonaten voor fluit en klavier; met klavierbegeleiding
volgens basso-continuo door Julius van Etsen. Berchem-
Antwerpen: "De Ring" v. z. w. [193–]   Publ. pl. no. 7876a.
1 v.   36cm.

    Score (16 p.) and flute part.
    At head of title: Vereeniging voor muziekgeschiedenis te Antwerpen.
    No. 279 of 300 copies printed.
    With reproduction of t.-p. of his Op. 4 published by J. Walsh, London.

1. Flute and piano--To 1800.   2. Sonatas—Flute and piano—To
1800. I. Etsen, Julius van.   II. Vereeniging voor muziekge-
schiedenis te Antwerpen.   N.Y.P.L.
                                                September 16, 1943

NL 0444078   NN MH

fM242   Loeillet, Jean Baptiste, 1688–
L61   [Sonatas, recorder & continuo, op.4 (Priest-
P.IV   man IV) No.9-10]
no.9-10   Twee sonaten voor fluit en klavier, met
    klavierbegeleiding volgens basso-continuo, door
    Julius van Etsen. Berchem-Antwerpen, "De
    Ring" [1932?] Pl.no.7876-b.
    score (16p.) and pt.in 1v. 32cm. (Vereeni-
    ging voor muziekgeschiedenis te Antwerpen)

    1. Sonatas (Flute and harpsichord) — To 1800.
    I. Vereeniging voor muziekgeschiednis, Antwerp.

NL 0444079   IaU

Loeillet, Jean Baptiste, b. 1688
[Sonatas, recorder & continuo, op. 2 (Priestman II)]
    XII sonatas or solos for a flute, with a thorough bass for
the harpsicord or bass violin. Compos'd by Jean Baptiste
Loeillet de Gant. Opera [2d] London, I. Walsh ... & I.
Hare ... [171–?]
    score (46 p.) 37 cm.
    Opus number supplied in manuscript on t. p.

1. Sonatas (Recorder and harpsichord)—To 1800.

M242.L   46–42462 rev*

NL 0444080   DLC

LOEILLET, JEAN BAPTISTE, 1688–
[SONATAS, FLUTE & CONTINUO, OP. 2 (PRIESTMAN II)]
    XII sonatas or solos for a flute with a thorough base
for the harpsicord or bass violin. Compos'd by Jean
Baptiste Loeillet de Gant. Opera secunda. London,
Printed for J. Walsh and J. Hare [1715] score (46 p.)
33cm.

    Imprint covered by label: Sold by Iohn Young, musical instrument
seller.
1. Flute and piano--To 1800.

NL 0444081   NN

M242   Loeillet, Jean Baptiste, 1688–
L65   [Sonatas, recorder & continuo, op. 2 (Priestman II)]
op.1   XII sonatas or solos for a flute with a thorough bass for the
1730   harpsicord or bass violin, compos'd by Jean Baptiste Loeillet de
Case   Gant. Opera Seconda. London, Printed for I: Walsh, servant
X   in ordinary to his Majesty ... and I:Hare [ca. 1730] No. 117.
    score (46 p.)   [Bound with the composer's Sonatas or
    solos for a flute with a through bass for the harpsicord or bass
    violin. Op.1. ca. 1730]

    Plate number is in ms.

NL 0444082   CU

Loeillet, Jean Baptiste, b. 1688
[Sonatas, recorder & continuo, op. 3 (Priestman III)]
    XII sonatas or solos for a flute, with a through bass for the
harpsicord or bass violin. Compos'd by Jean Baptiste
Loeillett de Gant. Opera terza. London, I. Walsh ... in
Catherine Street ... & I. Hare ... [171–?]
    score (51 p.) 37 cm.

1. Sonatas (Recorder and harpsichord)—To 1800.

M242.L   45–31416 rev*

NL 0444083   DLC ViU

Loeillet, Jean Baptiste, b. 1688
[Sonatas, recorder & continuo, op. 3 (Priestman III)]
    XII sonatas or solos for a flute, with a through bass for the
harpsicord or bass violin. Compos'd by Jean Baptiste
Loeillet de Gant. Opera terza. London, I. Walsh ... in
Catherine Street ... & I. Hare ... [172–?]
    score (51 p.) 37 cm.

    Univ. of Mich. copy formerly in the Wagener
collection.

NL 0444084   MiU

M242   Loeillet, Jean Baptiste, 1688–
L65   [Sonatas, recorder & continuo, op. 3 (Priestman III)]
op.1   XII sonatas or solos for a flute with a through bass by Jean Baptiste Loeillet de
1730   Gant. Opera terza. London. Printed for I: Walsh, serv'd in
Case   ordinary to his Majesty ... & I:Hare [ca. 1730] No. 118.
X   score (51 p.)   [Bound with the composer's Sonatas or
    solos for a flute a through bass for the harpsicord or bass
    violin. Op.1. ca. 1730]

    Plate number is in ms.

NL 0444085   CU

Loeillet, Jean Baptiste, b. 1688
[Sonatas, recorder & continuo, op. 4 (Priesman IV)]
    XII sonatas or solos for a flute, with a thorough bass for
the harpsicord or bass violin. Compos'd by Jean Baptiste
Loeillett de Gant. Opera quarta. London, I. Walsh ...
and In° & Ioseph Hare ... [171–?]
    score (45 p.) 37 cm.

1. Sonatas (Recorder and harpsichord)—To 1800.

M242.L   46–42465 rev*

NL 0444086   DLC

M   Loeillet, Jean Baptiste, 1688–
242   [Sonatas, recorder & continuo, op.4 (Priestman
.L82   IV)]
S74   XII sonatas or solos for a flute with a thor-
172-a   ough bass for the harpsicord or bass violin.
    Compos'd by Jean Baptiste Loeillett de Gant.
    Opera quarta. London, Printed for & sold by I:
    Walsh ... and In° & Ioseph Hare [172–?]
    [12]l.   36 cm.
    Photocopy (negative) of original in Brussels,
    Conservatoire royal de musique, Bibliothèque (Wot-
    quenne 5574) Mounted in an album.
    Collation of original as determined from photo-
    copy: 1 p.l.   score (45 p.)   18 cm
    1. Sonatas (Re-   corder and harpsichord)
    --To 1800.

NL 0444087   MiU

M242   Loeillet, Jean Baptiste, 1688–
L65   [Sonatas, recorder & continuo, op. 4 (Priestman IV)]
op.1   XII sonatas or solos for a flute with a thorough bass for the
1730   harpsicord or bass violin, compos'd by Jean Baptiste Loeillett de
Case   Gant. Opera Quarta. London, Printed for & sold by I:Walsh,
X   serv'd to his Majesty ... and In° & Ioseph Hare [ca. 1730] No. 119.
    score (45 p.)   [Bound with the composer's Sonatas or solos
    for a flute with a through bass for the harpsicord or bass violin.
    Op.1. ca. 1730]

    Plate number is in ms.

NL 0444088   CU

M242   Loeillet, Jean Baptiste, b. 1688
.L825S35   [Sonatas, recorder & continuo, op.2 (Priest-
    man II) No.5]
    Zwei Sonaten. Sonate, c-moll, Op.2, Nr.5
    [und] Sonate g-moll, Op.4, Nr.6, für Alt-Block-
    flöte (Querflöte, Oboe, Violine) und Cembalo
    (Klavier); Violoncello (Gambe) ad lib. Celle,
    H. Moeck [c1948]
    score (15 p.) and 2 parts. (Moecks Kammer-
    musik, Nr.32)
    Edition Moeck, Nr.1032.
    1. Sonatas (Recorder and harpsichord)

NL 0444089   ICU MH NIC CSt IU NN

VOLUME 338

₍Loeillet, John ₎ 1680–1730.
₍Sonatas. Fl. & pf. Op. 3, no. 11. Allemande. Ed. for vln & pf.₎
...Allemande (Lully)... Berlin: N. Simrock, G.m.b.H.
₍etc., etc., cop. 1899₎ Publ. pl. no. 11142. 2 parts in 1 v.
34cm.

Violin and piano (realized from basso continuo) in score, and violin part.
From his: XII sonatas or solos for a flute with a through bass for the harpsicord
or bass violin... Opera terza. London: Printed for I. Walsh & I. Hare ₍ca. 1725₎
Erroneously ascribed to Lully.
At head of title: Compositionen und Arrangements von Alfred Moffat... 12 Violin-
stücke klassischer Meister des 17. u. 18. Jahrhunderts... Op. 43, No. 5.

1. Violin and piano—Arr.   CARNEGIE CORPORATION OF NEW YORK.
for violin and piano. I. Lully, Jean   2. Sonatas—Flute and piano—Arr.
composer. II. Moffat, Alfred   Baptiste de, 1632–1687, supposed
N.Y.P.L.   Edward, 1866–
                                                          July 8, 1936

NL 0444090   NN

M303 Loeillet, John.   1680–1730.
L8   ₍Sonata, recorder, oboe, violoncello₎
       Baroque trio sonatas: Loeillet and
       Telemann. ₍New York? Technicord, c1947₎

       32p. 15cm.

NL 0444091   NBuG

Loeillet, John, 1680–1730.
Jig for clavecin, by Jean Baptiste Loeilly... Transcribed for
the pianoforte by Edward MacDowell. ₍Opera secunda₎ Editor₎ Fritz Rikko. New
cop. 1900. Publ. pl. no. A. P. S. 5185. 5 p. f°.

Caption-title.
t.-p. reads: Piano compositions, edited by Edward MacDowell...
Binder's title: MacDowell. Piano compositions edited by MacDowell. no. 20.

1. Piano. 2. MacDowell, Edward   Alexander, 1861–1908, editor.
N.Y.P.L.   June 7, 1923.

NL 0444092   NN

M   Loeillet, J ohn,   1680–1730.
30   ₍Lessons for the harpsichord (Priestman XI)₎
.L82   Lessons for the harpsichord or spinet, viz₎ al-
L4   mands, corants, sarabands, airs, minuets & jiggs,
171-a compos'd by Mr Baptist Lully. London, Printed
       and sold by D. Wright ₍171–₎
       ₍8₎ ℓ. 36 cm.
       Photocopy (negative) of original in Brussels,
       Conservatoire royal de musique, Bibliothèque
       (Wotquenne 14337) Mounted in an album.
       Collation of original as determined from photo-
       copy: 1 p.ℓ., 15 p.   15 x 23 cm.
       1. Harpsichord   music—To 1800.

NL 0444093   MiU

Loeillet, John, 1680–1730.
...Sarabande... Boston: A. P. Schmidt ₍cop. 1902₎. Publ.
pl. no. A. P. S. 5934. 3 p. f°.

At head of title: From the XVIII century. Harpsichord and clavichord pieces
transcribed for the pianoforte by Edward MacDowell...
Binder's title: MacDowell. Piano compositions edited by MacDowell. no. 21.

1. Piano. 2. MacDowell, Edward   Alexander, 1861–1908, editor.
N.Y.P.L.   June 7, 1923.

NL 0444094   NN

Lœillet, John.   1680–1730.
₍Trio-sonatas, op. 2 (Priestman x) Selections₎

Six sonatas for two violins and figured bass (piano and
optional 'cello) ₍Opera secunda₎ Editor₎ Fritz Rikko. New
York ₍Weaner-Levant Publications, c1945–
       score (v.) and   parts. 31 cm.
       Cover title.
       Figured bass realized for piano. Violoncello part included.
       No. 1, 3, 5,   of the original ed. (London, J. Walsh and Jno.
       and Joseph Hare ₍172–₎
       CONTENTS.—v. 1. No. 1, Bb major. No. 2, F major. No. 3, G minor.
       1. Trio-sonatas.   I. Rikko, Fritz, ed.
M312.4.L83 Pr.10.W4   M 56–339

NL 0444095   DLC MB ICU   NcD NcU NIC IEN ICN OrU

Lœillet, John,   1680–1730.
₍Trio-sonatas, op. 2 (Priestman x) Selections₎

Six sonatas for two violins with a thorough bass for the
harpsicord or violoncello. Compos'd by Mr John Loeillet.
Opera 2da London, I. Walsh ₍174–?₎

       parts. 33 cm.

       No. 1, 3, 5, 7, 9, and 11 of the original ed. (London, J. Walsh and
       Jno. and Joseph Hare ₍172–₎
       Parts : violino 1, violino 2, basso continuo.

1. Trio-sonatas.

M312.4.L83 Pr. 10   49–36818 rev*

NL 0444096   DLC

Lœillet, John,   1680–1730.
₍Suits of lessons, harpsichord (Priestman XII)₎

Six suits of lessons for the harpsicord or spinnet in most of
the key's with variety of passages and variations throughout
the work. Compos'd by Mr: Iohn Loeillet. London, Printed
and sold by I. Walsh ... and I₉ & Ioseph Hare ... ₍172–?₎

       55 p. 32 cm.

       CONTENTS.—G minor.—A major.—C minor.—D major.—F major.—
       Eb major.
       1. Suites (Harpsichord)—To 1800.   I. Title: Suits of lessons for
       the harpsichord or spinet.

M24.L8255 Pr.12   M 56–240

NL 0444097   DLC

M   Loeillet, John,   1680–1730.
24   ₍Suits of lessons, harpsichord (Priestman XII)₎
.L82   Six suits of lessons for the harpsicord or
S8   spinnet in the most of the key's with variety of
1730a passages and variations throughout the work.
       Compos'd by Mr: Iohn Loeillet. London, Printed
       and sold by I: Walsh ₍ca. 1730₎ pub. no.: 188.
       ₍29₎ℓ. 36 cm.
       Photocopy (negative) of original in Brussels,
       Conservatoire royal de musique, Bibliothèque.
       Mounted in an album.
       Collation of original as determined from
       photocopy: 1 p.ℓ.   55 p.   22 cm.

       CONTENTS.—G minor.—A major.—C minor.—
       D major.—F major.—E major.

       1. Suites (Harpsichord)—To 1800. I. Title:
       Suits of lessons for the harpsichord or spinet.

NL 0444099   MiU

---

fM242 Loeillet, John   1680–1730.
L6hW7 ₍Sonata, recorder & continuo, op. 2
op. 2   (Priestman XI) no. 11; arr.₎
no. 11 Sonata c-dur für Sopran-blockflöte
       (Violine) oder Alt-blockflöte und Klavier.
       ₍edited by₎ Thomas F. Wood. Wilhelmshaven,
       Otto Heinrich Noetzel Verlag ₍1955₎
       score (7p.) and part in 1v. 30cm.

       1. Sonatas (Recorder and harpsichord)—
       To 1800.

NL 0444100   IaU

LX42 Loeillet, John, 1680–1730.
       ₍Trio-sonata, flute, oboe & continuo, op. 2,
       no. 4, D minor₎
       Sonata for flute, oboe and continuo. Allegro
       AL 69 ₍1950?₎
       2/3 s. 10 in. 33 1/3 rpm. microgroove.

       Phillip Kaplan, flute; John Holmes, oboe; Samuel
       Mayes, violoncello; Erwin Bodky, harpsichord.
       Program notes on slipcase.
       With the composer's Trio-sonata, flute, oboe &
       continuo, op. 1, no. 1, F major; arr.; and his Trio-
       sonata, violins & continuo, op. 2, no. 9, G minor.
       1. Trio-sonatas. 2. Quartets (Harpsichord,
       flute, oboe, violoncello)—To 1800. I. Kaplan,
       Phillip. II.   Holmes, John. III. Mayes,
       Samuel. IV. Bodky,   Erwin, 1896–

NL 0444101   CU

M787.3 Loeillet, John,   1680–1730.
L825t3 ₍Trio-Sonatas, op. 2, (Priestman)
        no. 3; arr. violoncello & piano₎
        Sonata, in B flat major for cello
        and piano. [Realization of the figured
        bass by Alexandre Beon₎ New York,
        International Music Co. [195–]
        score (7p.) and part.   31cm.

        Cover title.

NL 0444102   IEN

787.2 Loeillet, John,   1680–1730.
L82t3 ₍Trio-sonatas, op. 2 (Priestman X) No. 3;
       arr.₎
       Sonata in B flat major for viola and piano.
       (Vieland) New York, International Music
       Co. ₍n.d₎ Pl. no. 1895.
       score (7 p.) and part. 31 cm.

       Realization of the figured bass by Alex-
       andre Beon.
       Originally for 2 violins and continuo.

       1. Sonatas (Vi-   ola and piano) Arr.
       I. Beon, Alexandre.

NL 0444103   LU

Lœillet, John,   1680–1730.
₍Trio-sonatas, op. 2 (Priestman x) No. 8; arr.₎

Sonata in B minor, for violin, viola, cello, and piano.
₍Harmonized by₎ A. Béon. New York, International Music
Co. ₍1947₎
       score (15 p.) and   parts. 31 cm.
       Originally for 2 flutes and continuo.

       1. Piano quartets. Arranged.
M414.L6 op. 2, no. 8 Pr. 10   51–31079 rev

NL 0444104   DLC Or

Lœillet, John,   1680–1730.
₍Solos, op. 3 (Priestman VIII) No. 1₎

Sonata in C-major, for alto recorder with accompaniment
for harpsichord or piano, realized from the original figured-
bass by Edith Weiss-Mann. Boston, E. C. Schirmer ₍1945₎
       score (11 p.) and part. 31 cm. (Earls court repertory for recorder,
       2046)

       1. Sonatas (Recorder and harpsichord)—To 1800.

M242.L   46–6782 rev*

NL 0444105   DLC MB

Lœillet, John,   , 1680–1730.
₍Solos, op. 3 (Priestman VIII) Selections; arr.₎

Sonata in C major, for oboe and piano. Edited and arr.
by Evelyn Rothwell. Figured bass realized by A. Gibilaro.
London, J. & W. Chester, c1947.
       score (11 p.) and part. 31 cm.
       The 1st movement of Sonata no. 1, the 2d of no. 10, the 1st of no.
       4, and the 2d of no. 1, respectively. The 1st, 3d, and 4th movements
       originally for recorder and continuo; the 2d, for flute and continuo.

       1. Sonatas (Oboe and piano), Arranged.
M247.L   M 56–775

NL 0444106   DLC NIC IU MH LU

Lœillet, John,   1680–1730.
₍Sonatas for variety of instruments, op. 1 (Priestman IX) No. 5₎

Sonata in C minor, for flute, oboe, and piano. ₍Realization
of figured bass by₎ A. Béon. New York, International Music
Co. ₍1949₎
       score (11 p.) and   parts. 31 cm.
       For recorder, oboe, and continuo in the original ed.

       1. Trio-sonatas.
M317.L78 op. 1, no. 5.B4   M 56–560

NL 0444107   DLC NIC MH ViU NIC FTaSU

VOLUME 338

Lœillet, John,   1680–1730.
  ₍Sonatas for variety of instruments, op. 1 (Priestman ɪx) No. 4;
  arr.₎

  Sonata in D major, for two violins and piano. ₍Harmonized by₎ A. Béon. New York, International Music Co.
  ₍1944₎

  score (11 p.) and   parts. 31 cm.

  Originally for 2 flutes and continuo.

  1. Trios (Piano, 2 violins) Arranged.
  M314.L   45–15230 rev*

NL 0444108   DLC CtY-Mus

Lœillet, John,   1680–1730.
  ₍Trio-sonatas, op. 2 (Priestman x) No. 4₎

  Sonata in D minor, for flute, oboe, and piano. ₍Realization of figured bass by₎ A. Béon. New York, International Music Co. ₍ᶜ1949₎

  score (18 p.) and   parts. 31 cm.

  1. Trio-sonatas.
  M317.L78 op.2, no.4 B4   M 58–1863

NL 0444109   DLC ICU MH IU NIC FTaSU NIC

M
242
L82++
Pr.8   Lœillet, John,   1680–1730.
no.7   ₍Solos, op. 3 (Priestman VIII) No. 7₎

        Sonata in E minor, for flute and piano.
        Edited by M. Lovering. London, Rudall,
        Carte ₍ᶜ1936₎
          score (8 p.) and part. 32cm.

        Figured bass realized for piano.

        1. Sonatas (Flute and harpsichord)--To
        1800.

NL 0444110   NIC IU MH ICU

Lœillet, John,   1680–1730.
  ₍Sonatas for variety of instruments, op. 1 (Priestman ɪx) No. 6₎

  Sonata in E minor, for two flutes and piano. ₍Harmonized by Alexandre₎ Béon. New York, International Music Co. ₍195–?₎ Pl. no. 1511.

  score (15 p.) and   parts. 31 cm.
  Originally a trio-sonata for flutes and continuo.

  1. Trio-sonatas.
  M317.L78 op. 1, no. 6   M 56–812 rev

NL 0444111   DLC ViU

Lœillet, John,   1680–1730.
  ₍Sonatas for variety of instruments, op. 1 (Priestman ɪx) No. 1;
  arr.₎

  Sonata in F major, for flute and piano. ₍Realization of the figured bass by Alexandre₎ Béon. New York, International Music Co. ₍195–?₎ Pl. no. 1490.

  score (10 p.) and part. 31 cm.
  Title from flute part.
  Originally for recorder, oboe, and continuo.

  1. Sonatas (Flute and piano), Arranged.

  M244.L   M 56–813

NL 0444112   DLC LU

M787.3
L825t10   Lœillet, John,   1680–1730.
          ₍Trio-sonatas, op. 2, (Priestman) F
          no. 10; arr. violoncello & piano₎
          Sonata, in F sharp minor, for cello
          and piano. ₍Realization of the figured
          bass by Alexandre Beon₎ New York,
          International Music Co. ₍n.d.₎
            score (8p.) and part. 31cm.

NL 0444113   IEN

787.2
L82t10   Lœillet, John,   1680–1730.
          ₍Trio-sonatas, op. 2 (Priestman X) No. 10;
          arr.₎
          Sonata in F sharp minor for viola and
          piano (Vieland)   New York, International
          Music Co. ₍n.d.₎ Pl. no. 1897.
            score (8 p.) and part. 31 cm.

          Realization of the figured bass by Alex-
          andre Beon.
          Originally for 2 flutes and continuo.

          1. Sonatas (Vi-   ola and piano) Arr.
          I. Beon, Alexandre.

NL 0444114   LU

M
788.7   Lœillet, John,   1680–1730.
L825s   ₍Sonatas for variety of instruments, op. 1 (Priestmann IX)
Op.1xo2   no. 2; arr.₎
 1   Sonata in G major for oboe and piano. ₍Realization
          of the figured bass by Alexandre₎ Beon. New York,
          International Music Co. ₍n.d.₎ Pl. no. 1422.
            score (12p.) and part.

          Cover title.
          Originally for two flutes and continuo.

          1. Sonatas (Oboe and piano), Arranged.

NL 0444115   FTaSU

M
312.4   Lœillet, John,   1680–1730.
L86
3 maj.   Sonata in G major for two violins and piano.
[(A Beon)   New York, International Music Co.
          ₍n.d.₎ Pl. no. 735.
            Score (14p.) and 2 parts.

          "Realization of figured bass by Alexandre
          Beon."

          1. Trios (Harpsichord, 2 violins) - To 1800.
          I. Béon, Alexandre,   arr.

NL 0444116   FTaSU

Lœillet, John,   1680–1730.
  ₍Trio-sonatas, op. 2 (Priestman x) No. 12; arr.₎

  Sonata in G major, for two violins and piano. ₍Harmonized by₎ A. Béon. New York, International Music Co. ₍1944₎

  score (14 p.) and   parts. 31 cm.
  Originally for 2 flutes and continuo.

  1. Trios (Piano, 2 violins), Arranged.

  M314.L   45–15231 rev*

NL 0444117   DLC CtY-Mus

Lœillet, John,   1680–1730.
  ₍Trio-sonatas, op. 2 (Priestman x) No. 2; arr.₎

  Sonata, in G major, for violin, cello, and piano. ₍Realization of the figured bass by Alexandre Beon₎ New York, International Music Co. ₍195–?₎

  score (16 p.) and   parts. 31 cm.
  Originally for recorder, oboe, and continuo.

  1. Piano trios, Arranged.

  M314.L   M 57–488

NL 0444118   DLC OrP

788.5
L82s   Lœillet, John.   1680–1730.

          Sonata in G minor, for flute and piano.
          ₍Realization of the figured bass by
          Alexandre₎ Béon. New York, International
          Music Company ₍195–?₎ Pl. no. 1491.
            score (12 p.) and part. 31 cm.

          M1. Sonatas (Flute and piano)

NL 0444119   LU IaU

Lœillet, John,   1680–1730.
  ₍Trio-sonatas, op. 2 (Priestman x) No. 9; arr.₎

  Sonata in G minor, for two flutes and piano. ₍Harmonized by Alexandre₎ Béon. New York, International Music Co. ₍195–?₎ Pl. no. 1265.

  score (12 p.) and   parts. 31 cm.
  Originally for 2 violins and continuo.

  1. Trio-sonatas.

  M319.L   M 56–800

NL 0444120   DLC ViU

Lœillet, John,   1680–1730.
  ₍Solos, op. 3 (Priestman VIII) No. 7₎

  Sonata no. 7, for flute and pianoforte. Edited & the pianoforte acc. arr. from the figured bass by M. Lovering. London, Rudall, Carte ₍ᶜ1936₎

  score (8 p.) and part. 31 cm. (Flute player's journal)

  1. Sonatas (Flute and harpsichord)--To 1800.

  M242.L   M 56–340

NL 0444121   DLC

Lœillet, John,   1680–1730.
  ₍Trio-sonatas, op. 2 (Priestman x) No. 8; arr.₎

  Sonate à quatre en si mineur ₍pour₎ violon, alto, violoncelle et piano ou 2 violes d'amour, viole de gambe et clavecin. Paris, H. Lemoine ₍ᶜ1912₎

  score (15 p.) and   parts. 31 cm. (*His* Sonates pour instruments divers et piano harmonisées par A. Béon, 18)

  For violin, viola, violoncello, and piano; originally for 2 flutes and continuo.

  1. Piano quartets, Arranged.

  M3.1.L64 vol. 18   M 56–284

NL 0444122   DLC PSC CtY MeB

Lœillet, ₎ John, ₎ 1680–1730.
  Sonate à quatre ₍Si mineur₎ pour violon, alto, violoncelle et piano ₍par₎ J. B. Lœillet...harmonisée par Alexandre Béon. ₍Paris₎ H. Lemoine & Cie., cop. 1912.   Publ. pl. no. 20912 HL.
  4 parts.   f°.   (Panthéon des pianistes. no. 948.)

  Score and 3 string parts.
  Caption-title. t.-p. reads: J.-B. Lœillet... Sonates pour instruments divers et piano, harmonisées par A. Béon...

                                        DREXEL MUSICAL FUND.
  1. Quartets—Piano, violin, viola and   violoncello. 2. Béon, Alexandre,
  d. 1912, arranger.   June 27, 1929
  N. Y. P. L.

NL 0444123   NN

VOLUME 338

Loeillet, John,   1680–1730.

Sonate à trois ₍en mi mineur₎ pour deux flûtes et piano ₍par₎ J. B. Loeillet... Harmonisée par Alexandre Béon.   ₍Paris₎ H. Lemoine & cie., 1911.   Publ. pl. no. 20780. HL. P. 942.   3 parts in 1 v.   30cm.

Score (including realized basso continuo) and 2 flute parts.
Caption-title; t.-p. reads: ...J.-B. Loeillet... Sonates pour instruments divers et piano... Pour 2 flûtes et piano...
"Édition nationale française." "Panthéon. no. 942."

1. Chamber music, 18th cent.—   CARNEGIE CORPORATION OF NEW YORK.
wind—To 1800. 3. Flute—Trios—To   Trios. 2. Piano—Trios—Piano and
N.Y.P.L.   1800. I. Béon, Alexandre, d. 1912.
    August 14, 1936

NL 0444124   NN

Loeillet, John,   , 1680–1730.
₍Sonatas for variety of instruments, op. 1 (Priestman IX) No. 4₎ arr.₎

Sonate à trois en ré majeur, pour 2 violons et piano ou 2 violes d'amour et clavecin. Paris, H. Lemoine ₍c1912₎

score (11 p.) and parts. 31 cm. (*His* Sonates pour instruments divers et piano harmonisées par A. Béon, 11)
Originally for 2 flutes and continuo.

1. Trios (Piano, 2 violins), Arranged.

M3.1.L64 vol. 11   M 56–269

NL 0444125   DLC PSC

Loeillet, John,   1680–1730.
₍Trio-sonatas, op. 2 (Priestman x) No. 4₎

Sonate à trois en ré mineur, pour flûte, hautbois et piano. Paris, H. Lemoine ₍c1912₎

score (16 p.) and parts. 31 cm. (*His* Sonates pour instruments divers harmonisées par A. Béon, 16)
For flute, oboe, and piano, the latter realized from figured bass.

1. Trio-sonatas.

M3.1.L64 vol. 16   M 56–282

NL 0444126   DLC PSC 00

Loeillet, John,   , 1680–1730.
₍Sonatas. Op. 2, no. 6. Arr. for vln, vlc. & pf.₎
Sonate à trois en si mineur pour violon, violoncelle et piano ₍par₎ J. B. Loeillet... Harmonisée par Alexandre Béon. no. 2. ₍Paris₎ H. Lemoine & cie., cop. 1911. Publ. pl. no. 20771 HL. P. 944. 3 parts in 1 v. 31cm.

Score (including realized basso continuo) and violin and violoncello parts.
Composed for flute, oboe and bass.
From his: XII sonatas in three parts... Opera secunda. London: Printed for and sold by I. Walsh and I. and J. Hare ₍171–?₎

Caption-title; t.-p. reads: ...J.-B. Loeillet. Sonates pour instruments divers et piano... Pour violon, violoncelle ou, viole d'amour, viole de gambe et clavecin
"Édition nationale française." "Panthéon no. 944."

1. Chamber music, 18th cent.—Trios.   CARNEGIE CORPORATION OF NEW YORK.
and violoncello—Arr. 3. Viola d'amore   2. Piano—Trios—Piano, violin
Trios—Arr. 5. Sonatas—Trios—   —Trios—Arr. 4. Viola da gamba—
cello. I. Béon, Alexandre, d. 1912,   Arr. for piano, violin and violon-
N.Y.P.L.   arr.
    April 2, 1936

NL 0444128   NN FTaSU

785.7   Loeillet, John, 1680–1739.
L825s.B
...Sonate à trois en si mineur pour violon, violoncelle et piano. No.2. Harmonisée par Alexandre Béon... ₍Paris₎ Lemoine ₍c1912₎
3 pts.in 1v. Q. (On cover: Édition nationale française, 944)
Caption title.
On cover: His Sonates pour instruments divers et piano, harmonisées par A. Béon.
Score and parts.

NL 0444129   IaU MB

M312   Loeillet, John,   1680–1730.
.L58B4   ₍Sonata, violin, violoncello, no. 2, B minor; arr.₎
no.2
1912   Sonate à trois en Si mineur pour violon, violoncelle et piano. No. 2. Harmonisée par Alexandre Béon. Paris, H. Lemoine, ₍e₎1912.
score (15 p.) and 2 parts. 31cm. (Édition national française. Pantheon des pianistes. 944)
Caption title.
Score and parts: vl., cello.
1. Piano trios—To 1800—Scores and parts.

NL 0444130   ViU

M787   Loeillet, John,   1680–1730.
L82so
194-   Sonate à trois en si mineur pour violon, celle et piano, no.2; harmonisée par Alexandre Béon. ₍Paris, H. Lemoine, 194-? c1911₎
score (15p.) and 2 parts. 28cm. (Édition nationale française, 944)

Caption title

1. Trio-sonatas. 2. Piano trios—To 1800—Scores and parts. I. Béon, Alexandre.

NL 0444131   IU NcD

Loeillet, John,   1680–1730.
₍Trio-sonatas, op. 2 (Priestman x) No. 9; arr.₎
Sonate à trois en sol mineur ₍pour₎ 2 flûtes et p₍ian₎o. Paris, H. Lemoine ₍c1912₎
score (11 p.) and parts. 31 cm. (*His* Sonates pour instruments divers et piano harmonisées par A. Béon, 17)
Originally for 2 violins and continuo.

1. Trios (Piano, 2 flutes), Arranged.

M3.1.L64 vol. 17   M 56–283

NL 0444132   DLC NN PSC MB

Loeillet, John, 1680–1730.   8051 1024.5
Sonate à trois pour flûte, hautbois et piano. [Partition et parties.] Harmonisée par Alexandre Béon.
Paris. Lemoine & cie. 1911. 3 v. [Sonates pour instruments divers et piano. 5.] 31cm.
Contents.—[1.] Partition. [2.] Flute. [3.] Hautbois.

L9056 — No main card. — Ed. ref. ₍..₎ ₍..₎e. — S.r.c. — Sonatas. Flute, oboe and pianoforte. — Chamber music. Trios. Pianoforte and woodwind.

NL 0444133   MB

---

f785.7   Loeillet, John,   1680–1730.
L825so.B
Sonate a trois pour flûte, hautbois et piano. No.5. Harmonisée par Alexandre Béon... ₍Paris, Lemoine, c1912₎
3 pts.in 1v. F. (On cover: Édition nationale française, 946)
Caption title.
On cover: His Sonates pour instruments divers et piano, harmonisées par A. Béon.
Score and parts.

NL 0444134   IaU

M317   Loeillet, John,   1680–1730.
L82S6   ₍Sonatas for variety of instruments, op.1 (Priestman IX) no.5₎
op.1:5   Sonate à trois, pour flûte, hautbois et piano. Paris, H. Lemoine, 1912. Pl. no. 20778. P. 946. H.
score(11 p.) & 2 pts. 30cm. (*His* Sonates pour instruments divers et piano harmonisées par A. Béon, 5)
Originally for recorder, oboe, and continuo.
1. Trios (Piano, flute, oboe), arranged.
I. Béon, Alexandre,   re, arr

NL 0444135   CSt IU

Loeillet, John,   1680–1730.
Sonate à trois ₍en ut mineur₎ pour flûte, hautbois et piano ₍par₎ J. B. Loeillet... Harmonisée par Alexandre Béon. no. 5. ₍Paris₎ H. Lemoine & cie., cop. 1912₎ Publ. pl. no. 20778 P. 946 HL. 3 parts in 1 v. 31cm.

Score (including realized basso continuo) and flute and oboe parts.
Caption-title; t.-p. reads: ...J.-B. Loeillet... Sonates pour instruments divers et piano... Pour flûte, hautbois et piano...
"Édition nationale française." "Panthéon. no. 946."

1. Chamber music, 18th cent.—   CARNEGIE CORPORATION OF NEW YORK.
wind—to 1800. 3. Flute—Trios—To   Trios. 2. Piano—Trios—Piano and
I. Béon, Alexandre, d. 1912.   1800. 4. Oboe—Trios—To 1800.
N.Y.P.L.   August 14, 1936

NL 0444136   NN

M   Loeillet, John,   1680–1730.
785.73851   ₍Sonatas for variety of instruments,
L825   op.1, no. 6 op. 1 (Priestman IX) No. 6₎
Lm   Sonate à trois, pour deux flûtes et piano. Harmonisée par Alexandre Béon. Paris, ₍H.₎ Lemoine, ₍c₎1912. Pl. no. 20780. H.P.942.
score (4p.) and 2 parts. (Édition nationale française)

Originally a Trio-sonata for 2 flutes and continuo.
1. Trio-sonatas.

NL 0444137   FTaSU

M   Loeillet, John,   1680–1730.
319
L78S6   Sonate a trois, pour deux flûtes et piano. Harmonisée par Alexandre Béon. [Paris, H. Lemoine, c1912]
score (15p.) and 2 parts. 31cm. (Édition nationale française)

Caption title.

1. Trio-sonatas.

NL 0444138   CLSU

Loeillet, John,   1680–1730.
₍Sonatas for variety of instruments, op.1 (Priestman IX) No. 3; arr.₎
Sonate à trois, pour deux flûtes et piano. Harmonisée par Alexandre Béon. Paris, ₍H.₎ Lemoine, ₍c₎1912. Pl. no. 20911.H.
score (11p.) and 2 parts. (Édition nationale française)

Originally for recorder, oboe, and continuo.

1. Sonatas (2 flutes and piano), Arranged.

NL 0444139   FTaSU

Loeillet, John,   1680–1730 (2)
Trio-sonatas, op.2, no.9
Sonate à trois pour deux flûtes et piano [en sol mineur] Harmonisée par A.Béon. [Paris] Lemoine, c1912 [1950] Pl.no.20911.H., pub.no.943

Score (11 p.) & 2 pts. (Edition nationale française. Panthéon des pianistes)
His Sonates pour instruments divers et piano, harmonisées par A.Béon

NL 0444140   MH

Loeillet, John,   1680–1730.
₍Trio-sonatas, op. 2 (Priestman x) No. 10; arr.₎

Sonate en fa dièse mineur, pour violoncelle et piano ou viole de gambe et clavecin. ₍Paris, H. Lemoine ₍c1912₎
score (8 p.) and part. 31 cm. (*His* Sonates pour instruments divers et piano harmonisées par A. Béon, 12)
Originally for 2 flutes and continuo.

1. Sonatas (Violoncello and piano), Arranged.

M3.1.L64 vol. 12   M 56–280

NL 0444141   DLC 00

VOLUME 338

Lœillet, John,   1680–1730.
⟨Sonatas for variety of instruments, op. 1 (Priestman IX) No. 1; arr.⟩

Sonate en fa majeur, pour flûte et piano. Paris, H. Lemoine, ⁰1911.

score (11 p.) and part. 31 cm. (*His* Sonates pour instruments divers et piano harmonisées par A. Béon, 7)

Originally for recorder, oboe, and continuo.

1. Sonatas (Flute and piano), Arranged.

M3.1.L64 vol. 7   M 56–265
————Copy 2.   ML30.4c no. 1264 Miller

NL 0444142   DLC NN OO PSC

Loeillet, John,   1680–1730.
⟨Sonatas. Op. 2, no. 10. Arr. for vlc. & pf.⟩

Sonate ⟨en fa♯ mineur⟩ pour violoncelle et piano ⟨par⟩ J. B. Loeillet... Harmonisée par Alexandre Béon. no. 12. ⟨Paris⟩ H. Lemoine & cie., cop. 1911.   Publ. pl. no. 20864 HL. P. 935. 2 parts in 1 v.   31cm.

Score (including realized basso continuo) and violoncello part.
Composed for 2 flutes and bass.

From his: XII sonatas in three parts... Opera secunda. London: Printed for and sold by I. Walsh and I. and J. Hare ⟨171–?⟩
Caption-title; t.-p. reads: ...J.-B. Loeillet... Sonates pour instruments divers et piano... Pour violoncelle et piano, ou viole de gambe et clavecin... "Édition nationale française." "Panthéon. no. 935."

1. Violoncello and piano—Arr.   DREXEL MUSICAL FUND.
3. Sonatas—Trios—Arr. for   2. Viola da gamba and piano—Arr.
Alexandre, d. 1912, arr.   violoncello and piano. I. Béon,
N. Y. P. L.   March 27, 1936

NL 0444144   NN

M247   Loeillet, John,   1680–1730.
.L825s6 ⟨Trio-sonatas, op.2 (Priestman X) No.7; arr.⟩
Sonate, en mi majeur, pour hautbois et piano. ⟨Harmonisée par Alexandre Béon. Paris, H. Lemoine, 1911.
score and part. (*His* Sonates pour instruments divers et piano, no.6)
Édition nationale française, 938.
Originally for 2 violins and continuo.

1. Sonatas (Oboe and piano), Arranged.

NL 0444145   ICU

788.7   Loeillet, John,   1680–1730
L825s   ⟨Sonatas, oboe, no.6, E maj.⟩
Sonate en mi majeur pour hautbois et piano, no.6, harmonisée par Alexandre Béon. ⟨Paris⟩ Lemoine ⟨1912⟩
2 pts. in 1v. Q. (Édition nationale française)

1.Sonatas. Scores. 2.Oboe music. Scores. 3.Piano music. Scores.

NL 0444146   IaU

Lœillet, John,   . 1680–1730.
⟨Sonatas for variety of instruments, op. 1 (Priestman IX) No. 6⟩

Sonate en mi mineur, pour deux flûtes et piano. Paris, H. Lemoine, ⁰1911.

score (15 p.)   and   parts. 31 cm. (*His* Sonates pour instruments divers et piano harmonisées par A. Béon, 8)

Originally a Trio-sonata for 2 flutes and continuo.

1. Trio-sonatas.

M3.1.L64 vol. 8   M 56–266

NL 0444147   DLC OO OOxM PSC KEmT

Lœillet, John,   1680–1730.
⟨Trio-sonatas, op. 2 (Priestman x) No. 11; arr.⟩

Sonate en ré majeur, pour violon et piano ou viole d'amour et clavecin. Paris, H. Lemoine, ⁰1911.

score (12 p.) and part. 31 cm. (*His* Sonates pour instruments divers et piano harmonisées par A. Béon, 3)

Originally for 2 violins and continuo.

1. Sonatas (Violin and piano), Arranged.

M3.1.L64 vol. 3   M 56–273

NL 0444148   DLC PSC NN

Loeillet, John,   1680–1730.
⟨Sonatas. Op. 2, no. 4⟩

Sonate ⟨en ré mineur⟩ pour flûte, hautbois et piano ⟨par⟩ J. B. Loeillet... Harmonisée par Alexandre Béon. no. 16. ⟨Paris⟩ H. Lemoine & cie., cop. 1912. Publ. pl. no. 20892 HL. P. 947. 3 parts in 1 v.   31cm.

Score (including realized basso continuo) and flute and oboe parts.
From his: XII sonatas in three parts. Opera secunda. London: Printed for and sold by I. Walsh and I. and J. Hare ⟨171–?⟩
Caption-title; t.-p. reads: ...J.-B. Loeillet. Sonates pour instruments divers et piano...
"Édition nationale française." "Panthéon. no. 947."

1. Chamber music, 18th cent.—Trios. 2. Piano—Trios—Piano and wind
—To 1800. 3. Flute—Trios—To   1800. 4. Oboe—Trios—To 1800.
5. Sonatas—Trios—To 1800. I. Béon,   Alexandre, d. 1912
N. Y. P. L.   April 2, 1936

NL 0444149   NN KEmT

Loeillet, John,   1680–1730.
⟨Sonatas. Op. 2, no. 1. Arr. for vln & pf.⟩

Sonate ⟨en si♭ majeur⟩ pour violon et piano ⟨par⟩ J. B. Loeillet... Harmonisée par Alexandre Béon. no. 10. ⟨Paris⟩ H. Lemoine & cie., cop. 1911. Publ. pl. no. 20856 HL. P. 933. 2 parts in 1 v.   31cm.

Score (including realized basso continuo) and violin part.
Composed for 2 violins and bass.
From his: XII sonatas in three parts. Opera secunda.   London: Printed for and sold by I. Walsh and I. and J. Hare ⟨171–?⟩
Caption-title; t.-p. reads: ...J.-B. Loeillet... Sonates pour instruments divers... "Édition nationale française." "Panthéon. no. 933."

1. Violin and piano—Arr. 2. Viola   d'amore and piano—Arr. 3. Sonatas
—Trios—Arr. for violin and piano.   I. Béon, Alexandre, d. 1912, arr.
N. Y. P. L.   April 2, 1936

NL 0444150   NN

Lœillet, John,   1680–1730.
⟨Trio-sonatas, op. 2 (Priestman x) No. 1; arr.⟩

Sonate en si ♭ majeur, pour violon et piano ou viole d'amour et clavecin. Paris, H. Lemoine ⟨1912⟩

score (8 p.) and part. 31 cm. (*His* Sonates pour instruments divers et piano harmonisées par A. Béon, 10)

Originally for 2 violins and continuo.

1. Sonatas (Violin and piano), Arranged.

M3.1.L64 vol. 10   M 56–268

NL 0444151   DLC PSC

M   Loeillet, John,   1680–1730.
231   ⟨Sonata, violoncello & continuo, B♭ major⟩
L6S6   Sonate en si♭ majeur, pour violoncelle et
B♭maj.   piano. ⟨Paris⟩ H. Lemoine, c1911.
score (7 p.) and part. 31cm. (Pantheon des pianistes, 935)
Caption title.

1. Sonatas (Violoncello and harpsichord)—To 1800.

NL 0444152   CoU

Lœillet, John,   1680–1730.
⟨Trio-sonatas, op. 2 (Priestman x) No. 3; arr.⟩

Sonate en si bémol majeur, pour violoncelle et piano. Paris, H. Lemoine, ⁰1911.

score (7 p.) and part. 31 cm. (*His* Sonates pour instruments divers et piano harmonisées par A. Béon, 4)

Originally for 2 violins and continuo.

1. Sonatas (Violoncello and piano), Arranged.

M3.1.L64 vol. 4   M 56–274

NL 0444153   DLC NN MB

Lœillet, John,   1680–1730.
⟨Trio-sonatas, op. 2 (Priestman x) No. 6; arr.⟩

Sonate en si mineur, pour violon, violoncelle et piano ou viole d'amour, viole de gambe et clavecin. Paris, H. Lemoine, ⁰1911.

score (15 p.) and   parts. 31 cm. (*His* Sonates pour instruments divers et piano harmonisées par A. Béon, 2)

Originally for flute, oboe, and continuo.

1. Piano trios, Arranged.

M3.1.L64 vol. 2   M 56–272

NL 0444154   DLC CaBVa PSC OO CoU

Loeillet, John,   1680–1730.
⟨Sonatas. Op. 2, no. 12. Ed. for 2 vln & pf.⟩

Sonate ⟨en sol majeur⟩ pour deux violons et piano, par J. B. Loeillet... Harmonisée par Alexandre Béon. no. 1. Paris: H. Lemoine et cie., cop. 1911. Publ. pl. no. 20743 HL. P. 940. 3 parts in 1 v.   31cm.

Score (including realized basso continuo) and violin I-II parts.
Composed for 2 flutes and bass.
From his: XII sonatas in three parts. Opera secunda. London: Printed for and sold by I. Walsh and I. and J. Hare ⟨171–?⟩

Caption-title; t.-p. reads: ...J.-B. Loeillet. Sonates pour instruments divers et piano... Pour 2 violons et piano, ou 2 violes d'amour et clavecin... "Édition nationale française." "Panthéon. no. 940."

1. Chamber music, 18th cent.—   CARNEGIE CORPORATION OF NEW YORK.
and 2 violins—To 1800. 2. Piano   Trios. 2. Piano—Trios—Piano
4. Flute—Trios—To 1800. 3. Piano   and wind—To 1800.
—Trios—To 1800. I. Béon, Alex-   5. Viola d'amore—Trios. 6. Sonatas
N. Y. P. L.   andre, d. 1912.
                                         March 31, 1936

NL 0444156   NN

Lœillet, John,   1680–1730.
⟨Trio-sonatas, op. 2 (Priestman x) No. 12; arr.⟩

Sonate en sol majeur, pour deux violons et piano ou deux violes d'amour et clavecin. Paris, H. Lemoine, ⁰1911.

score (12 p.)   and   parts. 31 cm. (*His* Sonates pour instruments divers et piano harmonisées par A. Béon, 1)

Originally for 2 flutes and continuo.

1. Trios (Piano, 2 violins), Arranged.

M3.1.L64 vol. 1   M 56–271

NL 0444157   DLC OO PSC

Loeillet, John, 1680–1730.
⟨Trio-sonatas, op.2 (Priestman X) No.12; arr.⟩
Sonate ⟨en sol majeur⟩ pour deux violons et piano. Harmonisée par Alexandre Béon. Paris, Lemoine, ⁰1911 ⟨i.e.1952 ⁰11⟩ score(12p.) and parts. (Pantheon des pianistes, 940)

Caption title.
Originally for 2 flutes and continuo.

NL 0444158   CaBVa

VOLUME 338

Lœillet, John, 1680–1730.
₍Sonatas for variety of instruments, op. 1 (Priestman ɪx) No. 2; arr.₎
Sonate en sol majeur, pour hautbois et piano. Paris, H. Lemoine ₍ᵉ1912₎
score (12 p.) and part. 31 cm. (*His* Sonates pour instruments divers et piano harmonisées par A. Béon, 15)
Originally for 2 flutes and continuo.

1. Sonatas (Oboe and piano), Arranged.

M3.1.L64 vol. 15   M 56–304

NL 0444159   DLC NN MH PSC LU

Lœillet, John, 1680–1730.
₍Sonatas. Op. 2, no. 2. Arr. for vln, vlc. & pf.₎
Sonate ₍en sol majeur₎ pour violon, violoncelle et piano ₍par₎ J. B. Lœillet... Harmonisée par Alexandre Béon. no. 13. ₍Paris₎ H. Lemoine et cie., cop. 1911. Publ. pl. no. 20865 HL. P. 945. 3 parts in 1 v. 30½cm.
Score (including realized basso continuo) and violin and violoncello parts.
Composed for flute, oboe and bass.
From his: XII sonatas in three parts... Opera secunda. London: Printed for and sold by I. Walsh and I. and J. Hare ₍171–?₎

Caption-title: t.-p. reads: ...J.-B. Lœillet. Sonates pour instruments divers et piano... Pour violon, violoncelle et piano, ou viole d'amour, viole de gambe et clavecin...
"Edition nationale française." "Panthéon. no. 945."

1. Chamber music, 18th cent.—Trios. and violoncello.—Arr. 3. Viola gamba—Trios—Arr. 5. Sonatas—violoncello. I. Béon, Alexandre, d. N. Y. P. L.	Carnegie Corporation of New York. 2. Piano—Trios—Piano, violin d'amore—Trios—Arr. 4. Viola da Trios—Arr. for piano, violin and 1912, arr.
	April 2, 1936

NL 0444161   NN

785.73
L82s17
Lœillet, John, 1680–1730.
₍Sonatas for variety of instruments, op. 1 (Priestman ɪx) No. 17₎
Sonate en sol mineur pour deux flûtes et piano. Paris, H. Lemoine ₍c1912₎
score (11 p.) and parts. (His Sonates pour instruments divers et piano harmonisée par A. Béon, 17)

Cover title. Caption title: Sonate a trois. Pantheon des pianistes. Edition nationale Française, no. 943.
1. Trio-sonatas

NL 0444162   KEmT

Lœillet, John, 1680–1730.
₍Sonatas for variety of instruments, op. 1 (Priestman ɪx) No. 8; arr.₎
Sonate en sol mineur, pour flûte et piano. Paris, H. Lemoine ₍ᵉ1912₎
score (10 p.) and part. 31 cm. (*His* Sonates pour instruments divers et piano harmonisées par A. Béon, 14)
Originally for recorder, oboe, and continuo.

1. Sonatas (Flute and piano), Arranged.

M3.1.L64 vol. 14   M 56–281

NL 0444163   DLC ViU OO PSC

Lœillet, John, 1680–1730.
₍Sonatas. Op. 2, no. 5. Arr. for vln & pf.₎
Sonate ₍en sol mineur₎ pour violon et piano ₍par₎ J. B. Lœillet... Harmonisée par Alexandre Béon. no. 9. ₍Paris₎ H. Lemoine et cie., cop. 1911. Publ. pl. no. 20857 HL. P. 932. 2 parts in 1 v. 31cm.
Score (including realized basso continuo) and violin part.
Composed for 2 violins and bass.
From his: XII sonatas in three parts... Opera secunda. London: Printed for and sold by I. Walsh and I. and J. Hare ₍171–?₎
Caption-title; t.-p. reads: ...J.-B. Lœillet... Sonates pour instruments divers et piano... Pour violon et piano, ou viole d'amour et clavecin...
"Edition nationale française." "Panthéon. no. 932."

1. Violin and piano—Arr. 2. Viola —Trios—Arr. for violin and piano. N. Y. P. L.	d'amore and piano—Arr. 3. Sonatas I. Béon, Alexandre, d. 1912. arr.
	March 27, 1936

NL 0444164   NN MB

Lœillet, John, 1680–1730.
₍Trio-sonatas, op. 2 (Priestman x) No. 5; arr.₎
Sonate en sol mineur, pour violon et piano ou viole d'amour et clavecin. Paris, H. Lemoine ₍ᵉ1912₎
score (8 p.) and part. 31 cm. (*His* Sonates pour instruments divers et piano harmonisées par A. Béon, 9)
Originally for 2 violins and continuo.

1. Sonatas (Violin and piano), Arranged.

M3.1.L64 vol. 9   M 56–267

NL 0444165   DLC PSC

Lœillet, John, 1680–1730.   8051.1024.8
Sonate en trois en mi mineur pour deux flûtes et piano. [Partition et parties.] Harmonisée par Alexandre Béon.
— Paris. Lemoine & cie. 1911. 3 v. [Sonates pour instruments divers et piano.] 8.] 31 cm.
Contents. — [1.] Partition. [2.] 1re flûte. [3.] 2e flûte.

NL 0444166   MB

Lœillet, John, 1680–1730.
₍Sonatas for variety of instruments, op. 1 (Priestman ɪx) No. 5₎
Sonate en ut mineur, pour flûte, hautbois et piano. Paris, H. Lemoine, ᵉ1911.
score (11 p.) and parts. 31 cm. (*His* Sonates pour instruments divers et piano harmonisées par A. Béon, 5)
Originally for recorder, oboe, and continuo.

1. Trios (Piano, flute, oboe), Arranged.

M3.1.L64 vol. 5   M 56–296

NL 0444167   DLC PSC

Lœillet, John, 1680–1730.
₍Trio-sonatas, op. 2 (Priestman x) No. 7; arr.₎
Sonate in mi majeur, pour hautbois et piano. Paris, H. Lemoine, ᵉ1911.
score (8 p.) and part. 31 cm. (*His* Sonates pour instruments divers et piano harmonisées par A. Béon, 6)
Originally for 2 violins and continuo.

1. Sonatas (Oboe and piano), Arranged.

M3.1.L64 vol. 6   M 56–295

NL 0444168   DLC PSC CSt NN NcD

M244
.L64
op.2
no.7
.B4
1912
Lœillet, John, 1680–1730.
₍Trio-sonatas, op. 2 (Priestman X) No. 7; arr.₎
Sonate in mi majeur, pour hautbois et piano. Paris, H. Lemoine, 1912.
score (8 p.) and part. 31cm. (*His* Sonates pour instruments divers et piano harmonisées par A. Béon, 6)
"Edition nationale française. Pantheon des pianistes. No. 938."
Originally for 2 violins and continuo.
1. Sonatas (Oboe and piano), Arranged.

NL 0444169   ViU

Lœillet, John, 1680–1730.
... [Sonata for two violins and piano, D major] [Sonate] pour 2 violons et piano, ou 2 violes d'amour et clavecin. En re majeur ... Paris [etc.] Henry Lemoine & cie., c1911.
1 p.l., 11 p. & 2 parts. 30 cm. (*His* Sonates pour instruments divers et piano, harmonisées par A. Béon ...)
Edition nationale française .. 941.
Parts for first and second violin in pocket in back cover

NL 0444170   CtY-Mus

---

*X314
.L64S6
no. 11
Lœillet, John, 1680–1730.
[Sonatas for variety of instruments, op. 1 (Priestman IX) No. 3; arr.]
Sonate pour 2 violons et piano ou 2 violes d'amour et clavecin, en re majeur [no. 11] Paris, H. Lemoine, c1912.
score (11 p.) and 2 parts. 31 cm. (*His* Sonates pour instruments divers et piano)
Pantheon des pianistes, no. 932.

1. Trios (Piⁱ no, 2 violins), Arranged.

NL 0444171   MB

Lœillet, John, 1680–1730.
... [Sonate] pour 2 violons et piano, ou 2 violes d'amour et clavecin. En sol majeur ... Paris [etc.] Henry Lemoine & cie., c1911.
1 p.l., 12 p. & 2 parts. 30 cm. (*His* Sonates pour instruments divers et piano, harmonisées par A Béon ...)
Edition nationale française ... 940.
Parts for first and second violin in pocket in back cover.

NL 0444172   CtY-Mus

M244
.L64
op.1
no.1
.B4
1954
Lœillet, John, 1680–1730.
₍Sonatas for variety of instruments, op. 1 (Priestman IX) No. 1; arr.₎
Sonate pour flûte et piano en fa majeur.
Paris, H. Lemoine ₍1954₎
score (11 p.) and part. 30cm. ₍His Sonates pour instruments divers et piano harmonisées par A. Béon, 7₎
"Edition nationale française. Pantheon des pianistes. No. 936."
Originally for recorder, oboe, and continuo.
1. Sonatas (Flute and piano), Arranged.

NL 0444173   ViU

MUSIC
M
242
L63S7
Lœillet, John, 1680–1730. · Pr. IX; 1; arr.
Sonate pour flûte et piano, no.7. Harmonisée par Alexandre Béon. [Paris, H. Lemoine, c1912]
score (11p.) and part. 31cm. (Édition nationale française)

Caption title.

₍1.Sonatas (Flute and piano), Arranged.

NL 0444174   CLSU

---

fM244
L6
1912
Lœillet, John, 1680–1730.
₍Sonatas for variety of instruments, op.1. (Priestman IX) No.3; arr.₎
Sonate pour flûte et piano, no.14. Harmonisée par Alexander Béon. ₍Paris₎ H. Lemoine, 1912.
piano score (10p.) and pt. in 1v. 31cm. (Edition nationale française)

Caption title.
Originally for recorder, oboe, and continuo
Preface by Ernest Closson.
1. Sonatas (Flute and piano) Arranged.

NL 0444175   IaU CLSU

M317
L82T8
op.2:4
Lœillet, John, 1680–1730.
₍Trio-sonatas, op.2 (Priestman X) no.4₎
Sonate pour flute, hautbois et piano, en re mineur. Paris, H. Lemoine, 1912. Pl. no. 20892 H.
score(16 p.) & 2 pts. 30₍. (*His* Sonates pour instruments divers et piano harmonisées par A. Béon, 16)
For flute, oboe, and piano, the later realized from figured bass.
1.Trio-sonatas. I.Béon, Alexandre, arr.

NL 0444176   CSt

VOLUME 338

qM785.7   Loeillet, John,   1680-1730.
L82so16   ₍Sonata, flute, oboe, & piano, no.16, D
1912   minor₎
     Sonate pour flûte, hautbois et piano. No.
16 ₍en ré mineur₎ Harmonisée par Alexandre
Béon. ₍Paris, H. Lemoine, c1912₎
     score (16p.) and 2 parts. 31cm. (Édition
nationale française, 947)

     Caption title.
     Introductory   biographical sketch signed
Ernest Closson.

NL 0444177   IaU

M785.72   Loeillet, John,   1680-1730.
L825sl.2   ₍Sonatas for variety of instruments, op.1
Music   (Priestman IX) no.2; arr.₎
lib.   Sonate pour hautbois et piano, no.15.
₍Paris₎ H. Lemoine, ᶜ1912.
     score (12p.) and part. 32cm. (His:
Sonates pour instruments divers et piano
harmonisées par A. Béon)

     Caption title.
     For oboe and piano; originally for 2
flutes and continuo.

NL 0444178   NcU

Loeillet, John,   1680-1730.
    ₍Sonatas. Op. 2, no. 11. Arr. for vln & pf.₎
    ...Sonate pour piano et violon (ou clavecin et viole d'amour);
harmonisée par Alexandre Béon... Répertoire de la Société de
musique ancienne de Bruxelles. Paris: Costallat & cie., cop.
1907.   2 parts in 1 v.   34½cm.

    Score (including realized basso continuo) and violin part.
    Composed for 2 violins and bass.
    From his: XII sonatas in three parts... Opera secunda. London: Printed
for and sold by I. Walsh and I. and J. Hare ₍171-?₎

    JUILLIARD FOUNDATION FUND.
1. Violin and piano—Arr.   2. Viola   d'amore and piano—Arr.   3. Sonatas
—Trios—Arr. for violin and piano.   I. Béon, Alexandre, d. 1912, arr.
N. Y. P. L.   March 27, 1936

NL 0444179   NN

Loeillet, John, 1680-1730.   8051.1024.10
    Sonate pour violon et piano. En si♭ majeur. [Partition et partie
de violon.] Harmonisée par Alexandre Béon.
— Paris. Lemoine & cie. 1911.   2 v. [Sonates pour instruments
divers et piano. 10.]   31 cm.
    Contents.—[1.] Partition. [2.] Partie de violon.

NL 0444180   MB

M
785.737   Loeillet, John,   1680-1730.
L825t   ₍Trio-sonatas, op. 2 (Priestman x) no. 2;
Op.2,no.2   arr.₎
La   Sonate pour violin, violoncelle et piano.
Harmonisée par Alexandre Béon.   Paris, H.
Lemoine, ᶜ1911. Pl. no. 20865. H.P.945.
     score (15p.) and 2 parts.   (His, Sonates
pour instruments divers et piano harmonisées
par A. Béon, 13)

     Caption title.
     1. Trio-sonatas.

NL 0444181   FTaSU OO

qM787.0436   Loeillet, John,   1680-1730.
L82s2   ₍Trio-sonatas, op.2 (Priestman X) No.2;
arr.₎
     Sonate pour violon, violoncelle et piano.
Harmonisée par Alexandre Béon.   ₍Paris₎
Lemoine, c1911 ₍i.e.1912₎
     score(15p.) and 2 parts. 32cm. (Édition
nationale française)

     Caption title.
     Originally for recorder, oboe and continuo.

NL 0444182   IU ViU

M   Loeillet, John,   1680-1730.
231   ₍Sonata, violoncello & continuo, F minor₎
L6S6   Sonate, pour violoncelle et piano, no. 12.
Fmin.   ₍Paris₎ H. Lemoine, c1911.
     score (8 p.) and part. 31cm. (Pantheon
des pianistes, 935)
     Caption title.

     1. Sonatas (Violoncello and harpsichord) –
TO 1800.

NL 0444183   CoU

Loeillet, John,   1680-1730.
    ₍Trio-sonatas, op. 2 (Priestman x) no. 7; arr.₎
     Sonate, ré majeur, harmonisée pour violon avec accom-
pagnement de piano par J. Salmon. Paris, Ricordi, ᶜ1921.
     score (7 p.) and part. 35 cm.
     Cover title.
     Originally for 2 violins and continuo.

     1. Sonatas (Violin and piano), Arranged.

M223.L   M 56-341

NL 0444184   DLC IU NIC

Loeillet, John,   1680-1730.
    ₍Trio-sonatas, op. 2 (Priestman x) No. 7; arr.₎
     Sonate, ré majeur, harmonisée pour violoncelle avec ac-
compagnement de piano par J. Salmon. Paris, Ricordi,
ᶜ1921.
     score (7 p.) 35 cm.
     Cover title.
     Originally for 2 violins and continuo.

     1. Sonatas (Violoncello and piano), Arranged.

M236.L   M 56-347

NL 0444185   DLC NN

Loeillet, John,   1680-1730.
    ₍Sonatas for variety of instruments, op. 1 (Priestman IX) No. 2;
arr.₎
     Sonate, sol majeur, harmonisée pour violon avec accom-
pagnement de piano par J. Salmon. Paris, Ricordi, ᶜ1921.
     score (10 p.) and part. 35 cm.
     Cover title.
     Originally for 2 flutes and continuo.

     1. Sonatas (Violin and piano), Arranged.

M223.L   M 56-358

NL 0444186   DLC NN

Loeillet, John,   1680-1730.
    ₍Sonatas for variety of instruments, op. 1 (Priestman IX) No. 2;
arr.₎
     Sonate, sol majeur, harmonisée pour violoncelle avec
accompagnement de piano par J. Salmon. Paris, Ricordi,
ᶜ1921.
     score (10 p.) and part. 35 cm.
     Cover title.
     Originally for 2 flutes and continuo.

     1. Sonatas (Violoncello and piano), Arranged.

M236.L   M 56-338

NL 0444187   DLC NIC OO

Loeillet, John,   1680-1730.   ₍Pr. IX + X₎
    ₍Works, chamber music. Selections; arr.₎
     Sonates pour instruments divers et piano harmonisées par
A. Béon. Paris, H. Lemoine, ᶜ1911-12.
     score (18 v.) and   parts. 31 cm.
     L. C. set incomplete: v. 13 wanting.
     Identical introductory note by Ernest Closson in each vol.
     For various solo instruments and piano.

     1. Chamber music.   I. Béon, Alexandre, arr.

M3.1.L64   M 56-275

NL 0444188   DLC MB IaU

Loeillet, John,   1680-1730.
    ₍Suits of lessons, harpsichord (Priestman XII) No. 1₎
     Suite for harpsichord. Edited for piano by Leo Podolsky.
₍Chicago, C. F. Summy Co., ᶜ1952₎
     16 p. 31 cm.

     1. Suites (Harpsichord)—To 1800.

M24.L8255 no. 1   M 56-709

NL 0444189   DLC IEN OU MB

Loeillet, John,   1680-1730.
    ₍Suits of lessons, harpsichord (Priestman XII) No. 1. **Selections;**
arr.₎
     Suite, G moll. ₍Bearb. von Carl Schroeder₎ Mainz, B.
Schott's Söhne ₍1911₎
     score (13 p.) and part. 31 cm. (Klassische Violoncell-Musik,
Heft 13)
     Edition Schott, S-2640n.
     For violoncello and piano.

     1. Suites (Violoncello and piano), Arranged.

M236.L   M 56-342

NL 0444190   DLC

fM24   Loeillet, John.   1680-1730.
L8255D9   Suite in D for piano solo. Rev. and
edited by Leonard Duck.   London, Francis,
Day & Hunter ₍1954₎
     8p. 31cm.

     1. Suites (Piano) To 1800.

NL 0444191   IaU

Loeillet, John,   1680-1730.
    ₍Trio-sonatas, op. 2 (Priestman x) No. 4₎
     Trio sonata in D minor, for recorder, oboe, and keyboard,
or flute, oboe, and keyboard, or two violins and keyboard,
with violoncello (bassoon) ad lib. Op. 2, no. 4. Edited by
Alfred Mann. New York, Music Press ₍1947₎
     score (12 p.) 31 cm.
     Cover title.
     For flute, oboe, and continuo in the original ed.
     1. Trio-sonatas.   I. Mann, Alfred, 1917–   ed.

M317.L78 op. 2, no. 4   48-16177 rev*

NL 0444192   DLC OOxM NcU

Loeillet, John,   1680-1730.
    ₍Sonatas for variety of instruments, op. 1 (Priestman IX) No. 1₎
     Trio sonata no. 1, op. 1, no. 1, for treble recorder (or flute)
oboe (or tenor recorder or violin) and piano. Arr. and
adapted by Walter Bergmann & Max Champion. London,
Schott ₍1946₎
     score (10 p.) and   parts. 32 cm. (Edition Schott, 10055)
     Cover title.
     Figured bass realized for piano. Violoncello part not included in
parts.
     1. Trio-sonatas.

M317.L78 op.1, no.1   M 56-333

NL 0444193   DLC IU NN NIC MH

Société   Loeillet, John,   1680-1730.
Francaise   ₍Trio-sonatas. Selections₎ Phonodisc
du Son   Trio sonatas for two violins and harpsi-
174.141   chord. Société Francaise du Son. 174.141.
     2 s. 33 1/3 rpm.

NL 0444194   KMK

VOLUME 338

Brown
M2
.H77
no. 176

Loeillet, John, 1680-1730.
[Trios-sonatas op. 2 (Priestman x) no. 6]
Triosonate C-moll, für Alt Blockflöte (Querflöte), Oboe (Violine) und Basso continuo. Trio sonate in C minor for treble recorder (flute), oboe (violin) and basso continuo. Edited by Hugo Ruf. op. II/6. Kassel, New York, Bärenreiter.
score (16 p.) and 3 parts. 29 cm.

(Hortus musicus, 176)
Figured bass realized for harpsichord.
Includes continuo part for violoncello or viola da gamba or bassoon.
1. Trio-sonatas. I. Series.

NL 0444196   MB

Brown
M2
.H77
no.166

Loeillet, John, 1680-1730.
[Trio-sonatas, op. 2 (Priestman x) no. 2]
Triosonate F-dur für Alt-Blockflöte (oder Querflöte), Oboe (oder Violine) und Basso continuo, op. II/2. Hrsg. von Hugo Ruf. Trio sonata in F major, for treble recorder (flute), oboe (violin) and basso continuo. Edited by [Hugo Ruf] Kassel, New York, Bärenreiter [c1961]
score (12 p.) and 3 parts. 29 cm. (Hortus musicus, 166)
Figured bass realized for harpsichord; includes continuo part for violoncello, viola da gamba or bassoon.
1. Trio-sonatas. I. Ruf, Hugo, ed. II. Series.

NL 0444198   MB

Loeillet, John, 1680-1730.
[Sonatas, flute & bass, op.3]
XII solos, six for a common flute and six for a German flute with a thorough bass for the harpsichord or bass violin ... By ... Iohn Loeillet. Opera terza. London, Printed for and sold by I: Walsh ... and Ios: Hare [1725?]
49p. 38cm.
Flute and figured bass, in score.
In side titles, Sonata I to XII.

NL 0444199   CtY

LOEILLET, JOHN, 1680-1730.
[SOLOS, OP. 3 (PRIESTMAN VIII)]
XII solos, six for a common flute and six for a German flute, with a thorough bass for the harpsichord or bass violin... By... Iohn Loeillet. Opera terza. London, Printed for and sold by I: Walsh and Ios: Hare [1729] score (49 p.) 31cm.
Imperfect: t.p. slightly mutilated.

1. Recorder and harpsichord-- To 1800. 2. Flute and piano-- To 1800.

J.S. Billings Mem. Coll.

NL 0444200   NN

Film
8847

L'oeillet, John, 1680-1730.
[Solos, op. 3, (Priestman VIII).
XII [i.e. Twelve] solos: Six for a common flute and six for a German flute, with a thorough bass for the harpsichord or bass violin...by John L.'oeillet. Opera terza. London, J.Walsh...and Jos. Hare [ca.1730?]
score (49p.)

The bass is figured.
Microfilm (negative) made in 1961 of the original in the Rowe Music Library,

King's College, Cambridge.
On reel with Bréval, J.B., Simphonie concertante, op.38, Paris, Richomme [n.d.]

1. Sonatas (Recorder and harpsichord) -- To 1800. 2. Sonatas (Flute and harpsichord) -- To 1800.

NL 0444202   IaU

Loeillet, John, 1680-1730.
[Sonatas]
XII sonatas in three parts, six of which are for two violins and a bass, three for two German flutes and three for a hautboy & common flute with a bass for the violoncello and a thorough bass for the harpsichord, compos'd by Mr John Loeillet. Opera secunda. London, Printed for and sold by I: Walsh, and In° and Ioseph Hare [ca. 1722] 1 v. in 4. 32cm.

Parts for violin I (flute, recorder), violin II (flute II, oboe) and bass, figured (2 copies).

With bookplate of John, lord St. John, barron St. John of Bletsoe.

535491-4B. 1. Chamber music, 18th (Piano, 2 violins) --To 1800. --To 1800. 4. Piano in trios (Piano, in trios--To 1800. N. Y. P. L.

cent.--Trios. 2. Piano in trios 3. Piano in trios (Piano, 2 flutes) flute, oboe)--To 1800. 5. Recorder

December 13, 1951

NL 0444204   NN

Loeillet, John, 1680-1730.
[Trio-sonatas, op. 2 (Priestman x)]
XII sonatas in three parts, six of which are for two violins and a bass, three for two German flutes, and three for a hautboy & common flute, with a bass for the violoncello and a thorough bass for the harpsichord. Compos'd by John Loeillet. Opera secunda. London, Printed for and sold by I. Walsh and I. and I. Hare [ca. 1725]
parts. 33 cm.
1. Trio-sonatas.

ML30.4c no. 2552 Miller
[M312.4]   75-204403

NL 0444205   DLC MiU ViU

Loeillet, John, 1680-1730.
[Works, harpsichord]
Werken voor clavicimbel, uitgegeven door Jos. Watelet, met een inleiding door Paul Bergmans. Berchem-Antwerpen, De Ring, 1932.
xviii, 71 p. facsims. 35 cm. (Monumenta musicae belgicae. 1. jaarg.)
Text in Dutch, French, English, and German.
"An exact reproduction of the two volumes of suites for the harpsichord published in London, the Lessons for the harpsichord or spinet, printed by Daniel Wright and the Six suits or [i. e. of] lessons for the harpsichord or spinet, printed by John Walsh, John and Joseph Hare."--p. xii.

300 copies printed. "25 luxe-exemplaren op simili-japon in half perkamenten band en genummerd van 1 tot 25, 275 exemplaren op genummeerd papier alfa Lafuma genummerd van 26 tot 300. 183."

CONTENTS.--Brief account concerning John Baptiste Loeillet and his works for the harpsichord, by Paul Bergmans.--Lessons for the harpsichord or spinet, viz?. almands, corants, sarabands, airs, minnets, jiggs.--Six suits of lessons for the harpsichord or spinet.

1. Suites (Harpsichord)--To 1800. I. Watelet, Jos., ed. II. Bergmans, Paul, 1868-1935. (Series)

M2.M482 1. jaarg.   786.4   36-14946 rev*

IaU NIC
NL 0444207   DLC NIC ICarbD MU MB NcU NN NcD MU CLU

M
2
M482
v.1

Loeillet, John, 1680-1730.
[Works, harpsichord]
Werken voor clavicembel, uitgegeven door Jos. Watelet, met een inleiding door Paul Bergmans. [2e druk.] Berchem-Antwerpen, De Ring [1951]
xviii, 71 p. facsims. 35 cm. (Monumental musicae belgicae, 1. Jaarg.)

Text in Dutch, French, English & German.

"An exact reproduction of the two volumes of suites for the harpsichord published in London, the Lessons for the harpsichord or spinet, printed by Daniel Wright, and the Six suits or [i.e., of] lessons for the harpsichord or spinet, printed by John Walsh, John and Joseph Hare" -- p. xii.

NL 0444209   NcGU CLU OU CoU NSyU

Loeillot, Karl
see Loeillot-Hartwig, Karl, b. 1798.

Loeillet de Mars (G.) [1845-]. * Ueber die mit Fieber verbundenen Genitalerkrankungen der Wöchnerinnen. 34 pp. 8°. Berlin, G. Lange. [1889]

NL 0444211   DNLM

Loeillot-Hartwig, Charles Henri, b. 1798
see Loeillot-Hartwig, Karl, b. 1798.

Loeillot-Hartwig, Karl, b.1798.
Begleitungen zu Schiller's Wallenstein. Skizzen nach des Dichter's Schilderungen, entworfen und auf Stein gezeichnet von K. Loeillot. Accompagnements au Drame de Wallenstein, par Schiller, Scènes esquissées et lithographiées par K. Loeillot. Paris, Rittner & Goupil, etc., [18-]

NL 0444213   MH

Loeillot-Hartwig, Karl, b. 1798.
Les nouvelles voitures publiques de Paris, dessinées d'après nature par Karl Loeillot. [Paris] Chez Gihaut frères [183-?]
16 col'd pl. 19 x 40cm.
Cover-title.
Illustrations: 16 full page colored lithographs designed by K. Loeillot-Hartwig and printed by Gihaut frères.
Binding of full green cloth with black leather labels lettered in gilt on spine and front cover. Original paper covers bound in.

1. Cab and omnibus service--
N.Y.P.L.

France--Paris. 2. Lithographs, German.

July 10, 1942

NL 0444214   NN

R684.9
L824n

Loeillot-Hartwig, Karl, b.1798.
Les nouvelles voitures publiques de Paris; seize lithographies polychromes d'après nature, par Loeillot vers 1830. Offert par la S. N. T. R. Calberson à l'occasion de son cinquantenaire. [Paris, S. N. T. R. Calberson, 1954?]
16 plates

1. Carriages   I. T.

NL 0444215   MiD

VOLUME 338

Løjmand, Hans, 1873–
... I magsvejr og modvind; roman fra opgangsaarene. København, Bernhard E. Kleins forlag, 1938.
227 p. 21ᶜᵐ.

I. Title.   A C 39–1781

New York. Public library
for Library of Congress

NL 0444216   NN

PT8175 Løjmand, Hans, 1873–
L58Z514   Den lange vandring, livsbilleder. København, Jespersen og Pios, 1949.
1949   184 p.

1. Løjmand, Hans, 1873–   I. Title.

NL 0444217   CU DLC-P4 MnU NN

Løjmand, Hans, 1873–
... Naar vi gaar vejen—folkets ledere; roman. København, Gyldendal, 1932.
415 p. 22ᶜᵐ.

I. Title.
Library of Congress   PT8175.L58N3 1932   32–20758
Copyright A—Foreign   17296
                                            839.8136

NL 0444218   DLC

Löke, Karl, 1908–
... Über Grösse und Ausdehnung der analgetischen Zone bei Injektion anästhetischer Lösungen in das Foramen incisivum und über das Ergebnis der Untersuchungen an 306 mazerierten Schädeln ... Marburg (Lahn), 1935.
Inaug. -Diss. - Marburg.
Lebenslauf.
"Literaturangabe": p. [22]–23.

NL 0444219   CtY DNLM

W.4   LÖKE, Karl Heinrich Friedrich, 1907–
M31   Ergebnisse der Behandlung der kindlichen
1938   supracondylaeren Humerusfrakturen an der Marburger Chirurgischen Klinik in den letzen 10 Jahren, 1924-1934. Marburg, Bauer, 1938.
47 p. illus.
Cover title.
Inaug. -Diss. - Marburg.
1. Humerus - Fracture

NL 0444220   DNLM

Løken, Astrid
574.92   ... Observations of bumble bee activity
B495P   during the solar eclipse June 30., 1954 ...
no.13   Bergen, John Griegs [1954]
6 p. illus. 25 cm. (Universitetet i Bergen. Årbok, 1954. Naturvitenskapelig rekke, nr. 18. Publications from the Biological Station, 13)

1. Bumblebees.

NL 0444221   NcD NNBG

Løken, Haakon, 1859–1923
Laurin, Carl Gustaf Johannes, 1868–
Alla ha rätt, samt andra uppsatser med anledning av världskriget, av Carl G. Laurin. Stockholm, P. A. Norstedt & söner, 1917.

Løken, Haakon, 1859-1923.
... Anne Kathrines ungdom, hverdagsbilleder fra 1830-40-aarene. Kristiania, H. Aschehoug & co. (W. Nygaard) 1910.
2 p. l., 228 p. 20ᶜᵐ.   kr. 3.40

                                            10–29423

NL 0444223   DLC IU

DL 519 LØKEN, HAAKON, 1859-1923
.L825   For uafhaengighed og stemmeret ... tale den 17de Mai, 1896 i Trondhjem ved Venstres tog for uafhaengighet og stemmeret. ₙn. p., 1896.
8 p.

"Efter Dagspostens referat."

1. Norway--Pol. & govt.--1814-1905. I. Tc.

NL 0444224   InU

Løken, Haakon, 1859-1923.
Fra Fjordnes til Sjøvinn, billeder og minder fra 1870-aarene. Kristiania, H. Aschehoug & co. (W. Nygaard) 1912.
4 p. l., 232 p. 19½ᶜᵐ.   kr. 3.25

I. Title.
Library of Congress   13–2138

NL 0444225   DLC MnU NN

Løken, Haakon, 1859-1923.
Ibsen og kjærligheten, en grunntanke gjennem Ibsens verker; en essay av Håkon Løken. Kristiania [etc.] Gyldendal, 1923.
110 p. 20ᶜᵐ.

1. Ibsen, Henrik, 1828-1906. I. Title.
Library of Congress   PT8895.L56   24–4887

NL 0444226   DLC NIC NcU TxU

Løken, Haakon, 1859-1923.
... Landsens liv, billeder fra 1850-60-aarene. Kristiania, H. Aschehoug & co. (W. Nygaard) 1911.
4 p. l., 240 p. 20ᶜᵐ.   kr. 3.60

                                            11–32261

Library of Congress

NL 0444227   DLC NN

Løken, Haakon, 1859-1923.
... Urolige tider; billeder og minner fra ungdoms- og studentertiden 1875-1881. Kristiania, H. Aschehoug & co. (W. Nygaard) 1923.
4 p. l., 151 p. 20ᶜᵐ.

I. Title.
Library of Congress   PT8950.L7Z52   24–4927

NL 0444228   DLC WaU

Løken, Haakon, 1859-1923
Världens förenade stater; ingen utopi utan en logisk konsekvens av rättshistorien, av Haakon Löken... Stockholm: Svenska andelsförlaget [1916]. 31 p. 12°.

1. League of nations to enforce peace. 2. Title.
N. Y. P. L.   May 10, 1918.

NL 0444229   NN MH

Løken, Haakon, 1859-1923.
Verdens forenede stater, en verdensdomstol med makt bak retten ingen utopi men en logisk konsekvens av retshistorien, av Haakon Løken. Kristiania, J. W. Cappelen [1916]
30 p. 20½ᶜᵐ.

1. League of nations. 2. Arbitration, International. I. Title.
Library of Congress   JX1975.L84   23–1586

NL 0444230   DLC

Løken, Johan.
Forsikringskravet; grenser og tapsregler. Oslo, J. G. Tanum, 1952.
167 p. 23 cm.
Bibliography : p. [8]

1. Insurance law—Norway.
                                            A 53–6697
New York Univ.   Libraries
for Library of Congress   [2]†

NL 0444231   NNU DLC

Løken, Olaus
Kokebok, lærebok for almindelige husholdninger. 7th omarbeidede og økede utgave. Oslo, H. Aschehoug & co. (W. Nygaard), 1944.
330 p.

NL 0444232   OCl

Løken, Per.
Om ansvar i naboforhold. [Oslo, Norsk forsikringsjuridisk forening, 1955]
32 p. 23 cm. (Norsk forsikringsjuridisk forenings publikasjoner, nr. 35)

1. Adjoining landowners—Norway.
                                            59–45593 ‡

NL 0444233   DLC MH ICU

VOLUME 338

BX
8070
.L7515
1899

Løkensgaard, Knute Olson, 1860–
　　Haandbog for søndagsskolelaerere; veiledning i katekismeundervisningen, af K. Løkensgaard. Om søndagsskolens ordning og drift, af O. G. Belsheim. Minneapolis, Den Forenede kirkes forlag, 1899.
　　118 p. 20 cm.

"Udgivet af forlagskomiteen."

NL　0444234　　MnHi

Løkensgaard, Knute Olson, 1860–
　　Lærebog i kateketik af K. Løkensgaard ... Minneapolis, Minn., Augsburg publishing house, 1913.
　　151 p. 20ᶜᵐ.　$0.80

ɪ. Title.

13–17990

NL　0444235　　DLC

Løkensgaard, Knute Olson, 1860–
　　Læsebog for børn ... Minneapolis, Minn., Forenede kirkes forlag, 1896–1910.

Løkensgaard, Knute Olson, 1860–
　　Outlines of the catechism as a guide for Sunday school teachers, by Prof. K. Lokensgaard. Canton, S. D., 1923.
　　70 p., 1 l. 19½ᶜᵐ.

ɪ. Title.

Library of Congress　　BX8070.L4

23–9801

NL　0444237　　DLC

Løkensgaard, Knute Olson, 1860–
　　Outlines of the catechism as a guide for Sunday school teachers, by Prof. K. Lokensgard. (Rev. ed.) Minneapolis, Minn., Printed by Augsburg publishing house ₁1928₎
　　75 p. 19ᶜᵐ.

ɪ. Title.

Library of Congress　　BX8070.L4 1928

28–10201

NL　0444238　　DLC NcD

Löker, Erhan
　　Beşerî âlemin rasadhânesi olarak Türkiye. Ankara [Güven Matbaası] 1955

　　15 p. (Ankara İçtimaiyat Enstitüsü yayınları, 3)
　　Cover title

　　1. Turkey–Soc. policy

NL　0444239　　MH

HM
19
L82k

Löker, Erhan
　　Dünya sosyolojisi. Ankara, Örnek Matbaası, 1953–
　　　　v. (Ankara İçtimaiyat Enstitüsü Yayınları, 2

　　Added titles: World sociologie (sic) Sociologie mondiale. Welt Soziologie.

　　1. Sociology – Hist. I. Title.

NL　0444240　　CLU

Loekianos
　　see Lucianus *Samosatensis.*

Loekisan doenia. Medan.
　　1, 1936–

NL　0444242　　NIC

Løkke, Jakob Olaus, 1829–1881, ed.

Dickens, Charles, 1812–1870.
　　Dickens' skizzer i udvalg. Med oplysende anmærkninger, udg. af Jakob Løkke. Christiania, J. W. Cappelen, 1881.

Løkke, Jakob Olaus, 1829–1881.
　　Engelsk grammatikk; ny utg. ved Kristian Smidt. 10. oppl. Oslo, Cappelen ₍1946₎
　　87 p. 20 cm.

　　1. English language—Text-books for foreigners—Norwegian.
　　PE1129.S2L49 1946　　52–37558 ‡

NL　0444244　　DLC

420.7
L836e

Løkke, Jakob Olaus, 1829–1881
　　Engelsk grammatikk. Ny utg. ved Kristian Smidt. 11. oppl. Oslo, J. W. Cappelens ₍1948₎
　　87 ₍1₎ p.

　　1. English language – For foreigners – Norwegian I. Smidt, Kristian

NL　0444245　　MiD

Løkke, Jakob Olaus, 1829–1881.
　　Engelsk læsebog for begyndere af Jakob Løkke ... Kjøbenhavn, Gyldendal (F. Hegel & søn) 1878.
　　4 p. l., 175 p. 20ᶜᵐ.

　　1. Readers and speakers.

14–9720

Library of Congress　　PE1129.S2L5

NL　0444246　　DLC

Løkke, Jakob Olaus, 1829–1881, ed.
　　Engelsk læsebog for mellemklasserne. Med oplysende anmærkninger udg. af Jakob Løkke ... Kjøbenhavn, Gyldendalske boghandel (F. Hegel), 1876.
　　4 p. l., 295, ₍1₎ p. 20½ᶜᵐ.

　　1. Readers and speakers.

10–25436

Library of Congress　　PE1129.S2L6

NL　0444247　　DLC

Løkke, Jakob Olaus, 1829–1881, ed.
　　Engelske forfattere i udvalg. Med biografiske indledninger og oplysende anmærkninger af Jakob Løkke ... Kjøbenhavn, Gyldendal (F. Hegel) 1875.
　　1 p. l., viii, 532 p., 1 l. fold. plan. 21ᶜᵐ.

　　1. English literature (Selections: Extracts, etc.)

16–210

Library of Congress　　PR1109.L6

NL　0444248　　DLC

Løkke, Jakob Olaus, 1829–1881.
　　Kortfattet Engelsk grammatik. Ny utgave ved Sigurd Røst. 2.opl. Kristiania. 1908. 72p.

NL　0444249　　WaS

Løkke, Jakob Olaus, 1829–1881, ed.
　　Læsebog i modersmaalet for middelskolen. Af Jakob Løkke og Chr. Schive ... Christiania, J. W. Cappelen, 1879.
　　2 v. 21ᶜᵐ.
　　Contents.—1. afd. For de lavere klasser.—2. afd. For de høiere klasser.

　　1. Norwegian language—Chrestomathies and readers. ɪ. Schive, Christopher i. e. Jens Christopher Delphin, 1839– joint ed.

13–12217

Library of Congress　　PD2625.L7

NL　0444250　　DLC

Bonaparte
Collection LØKKE, JAKOB OLAUS, 1829–1881.
No.8652
　　Modersmaalets formlaere i udførlig fremstilling. Kristiania, J. Dahl, 1855.
　　208p. 20cm.

NL　0444251　　ICN IU

Løkke, Jakob Olaus, 1829–1881.
　　Modersmaalets grammatik til skolebrug. 5te udg. Cappelen, 1874.

NL　0444252　　NdU

Løkke, Jakob Olaus, 1829–1881.
　　Modersmaalets grammatik til skolebrug. 7. udg. Christiania, Cappelen, 1879.
　　18.5 cm.

NL　0444253　　CtY NdU

VOLUME 338

839.85
L825nn
1946
Løkke, Jakob Olaus, 1829-1881.
Norsk grammatikk, med oversyn over bøygningslaera i nynorsk; ny utg. ved Geirmund Vislie.
32.oppl. Oslo, J.W.Cappelen ₁1946₎
64 p. 20 cm.

1.Norwegian language--Grammar. I.Vislie,
Geirmund,1895- ed

NL 0444254   MiU

439.85
L82n
Løkke, Jakob Olaus, 1829-1881.
Norsk grammatikk, med oversyn over
bøygningslaera i nynorsk; ny utg. ved
Geirmund Vislie. 33. oppl.   Oslo,
J.W. Cappelen ₁1952₎

64 p.   20cm.

1. Norwegian language. Grammar. I.
Vislie, Geirmund, 1895-   ed.

NL 0444255   MnU

Løkke, Jakob Olaus, 1829-1881.
Tydsk syntax til skolebrug..
Kristiania, Feilberg, 1863.
6,134 p.   19½ ᶜᵐ.

1.German language-Syntax.

NL 0444256   NjP

Løkke, Jakob Olaus, 1829-1881.
Tysk grammatik til skolebrug, 5.
udgave af Tysk formlaere og tysk
syntax.   Kristiania, Feilberg &
Landmark, 1876.

210 p.   20cm.

1.German language. Grammar.

NL 0444257   MnU

Løkkegaard, Christian Frederik.

Prior, William Wain.
... Den militære situation ved krigens udbrud: Hærene,
af W. W. Prior og C. F. Løkkegaard ... Udg. af det
Krigsvidenskabelige selskab. København, I kommission
hos V. Tryde, 1918.

Løkkegaard, Frede.
Islamic taxation in the classic period, with special refer-
ence to circumstances in Iraq. Copenhagen, Branner &
Korch, 1950.

266 p. 22 cm.

Thesis—Copenhagen.
Summary in Danish.
Bibliography: p. 266-272.

1. Taxation, Mohammedan. 2. Taxation—Mesopotamia.   I. Title.

HJ233.L6   336.2   50-35296

CtY PU DDO NN MH NNC
NL 0444259   DLC CaBVaU OrPS MH-AH WaSpG MiU OC1

DL256
.5
.A9
Lökken, Jacob Olesen, joint author.

Auning, Mogens.
Efter vår seger ₁av₎ Mogens Auning ₁och₎ Jacob Olesen
Lökken. Stockholm, Block ₁1944₎

Lökken, Jacob Olesen.
Terror, sabotage och annat; dagligt liv i Danmark.
Stockholm, Blocks förlag [1943]
111 p.   22 cm.
By Holger Danske, pseud.

NL 0444261   IEN MH

Lökken, Jacob Olesen.
Terror, sabotage och annat dagligt liv i Danmark ₁av₎
Holger Danske ₁pseud.₎ 3. uppl. Stockholm, Blocks förlag
₁1944₎
111 p.   22 cm.

1. World War, 1939-1945—Denmark.   I. Title.

D763.D4L6 1944   63-56003 ‡

NL 0444262   DLC

Lökken, Thomas Olesen, 1877-
Bjørn Strand, en roman om en havn. ₁København₎ S. Hasselbalch, 1940.
216 p.   20ᶜᵐ.
Sequel to En ny baad i hav.

I. Title.

Library of Congress   PT8175.L6B5   42-43807
                                                   839.8136

NL 0444263   DLC

Lökken, Thomas Olesen, 1877 -
...Bonden Niels Hald; en Roman om en moderne Bonde.
København: S. Hasselbalchs Forlag ₁cop. 1921₎. 255 p. 3. ed.
8°.

1. Fiction (Danish). 2. Title.
N.Y.P.L.   April 4, 1923.

NL 0444264   NN

Løkken, Thomas Olesen, 1877-
Bonden Niels Hald; en roman om en
moderne bonde.   København, S. Hasselbalch, 1924.

256 p.   20cm.

Sequels: Niels Halds hustru; Niels
Halds hjem.

NL 0444265   MnU

PT8175
.L887
1942
Løkken, Thomas Olesen, 1877-
Bonden Niels Hald; en roman om en moderne bonde.
₁København₎ S. Hasselbach, 1942.
448 p.

NL 0444266   ICU

PT8175
L6B6
1943
Lökken, Thomas Olesen, 1877-
Bonden Niels Hald, en roman om en moderne
bonde.   København, P. Branner, 1943.
212 p.

NL 0444267   CU WaS

Lökken, Thomas Olesen, 1877-
Danmark i Amerika. Omslagstegning af Einar Gross.
København, Uhlmanske forlag, 1950.
296 p. fold. map. 23 cm.

1. Danes in the U. S. 2. Danes in Canada. 3. U. S.—Descr. &
trav.—1940-   4. Canada—Descr. & trav.   I. Title.

E184.S19L8   52-22292

NL 0444268   DLC MH MnU NN NNC

Lökken, Thomas Olesen, 1877-
Den danske Arv. ₁København₎ S. Hasselbalch, 1941.
232 p. 21 cm.
A novel.

I. Title.
PT8175.L6D3   839.8136   47-39805*

NL 0444269   DLC FMU

Lökken, Thomas Olesen, 1877-
...Drømmen om et Rige. ₁København₎ S. Hasselbalch, 1935.
379 p.   20½cm.   (His: Folket ved Stormosen. ₁Bind₎ 4.)

834065A. 1. Fiction, Danish.   I. Title.
N. Y. P. L.   August 24, 1936

NL 0444270   NN MnU MiU

Lökken, Thomas Olesen, 1877-
Familien ved havet. København, H. Hirschsprung, 1955.
331 p. illus. 20 cm.

I. Title.
                                                   A 56-2424
Minnesota. Univ. Libr.
for Library of Congress   ₁3₎

NL 0444271   MnU NN

Lökken, Thomas Olesen, 1877-
...Fra Marehalmens Rige. ₁Hjørring:₎ Vendsyssel Tid-
ende₁, 1926₎.   29 p. illus. sq. 8°.

1. Dunes—Denmark.
N. Y. P. L.   August 5, 1928

NL 0444272   NN

Lökken, Thomas Olesen, 1877-
... Fra vildmosens land. København, E.V.
Olsen, 1934.

171 p.   22ᶜᵐ.
Illustrated cover.
CONTENTS.—Pigen fra vildmosen.—Sejren.—Mølleren.—
Hjemløs.—Slaegten spanner.—Den mørke Jul.—Kun en lille
pige.—Sognets mor.—Brønden.—Kaerlighedsgaven.

NL 0444273   MiU

VOLUME 338

Løkken, Thomas Olesen, 1877-
... Guds venner; billeder fra mosefolkets liv. [København] S. Hasselbalch, 1930.
336 p. 20½cm.
A novel.

I. Title.
Library of Congress PT8175.L6G8 1930 31-13079
Copyright A—Foreign 11882
[2] 839.8136

NL 0444274 DLC MnU

PT8175 .L6K53 Løkken, Thomas Olesen, 1877-
Harmaan särkän uudisasukkaat; romaani. [Tekijän luvalla tanskasta suomentanut Siiri Hannikainen. [Porvoo, W. Söderström [1928]
499 p. 18 cm.
Translation of Klavs Bjerg og Bodel, billeder fra den gra klit.

NL 0444275 MB OCl OrP

Løkken, Thomas Olesen, 1877-
... Hilsen fra Hannes hus, Ved den yderste kyst. Julen 1923. [Aalborg, Gyldendal, Nordisk forlag, 1923]
25, [1] p., 1 l. illus. 23cm.
Prose sketch and poem.
Title vignette; illustration on cover.
"200 salgseksemplarer, hvoraf dette er nr. 118."—Colophon.

NL 0444276 MiU

Løkken, Thomas Olesen, 1877-
...Hilsen fra Hannes Hus. Ved den yderste Kyst. [Holstebro: N. P. Thomsen,] 1923. 25 p. illus. 8°.
no. 101 of 200 copies printed.

1. Poetry, Danish. 2. Title.
N. Y. P. L. April 13, 1927

NL 0444277 NN

PT8175 L6J4 1943 Løkken, Thomas Olesen, 1877-
... Jesper spillemand og andre historier fra gammel tid. København, P. Branner, 1943.
200 p.

Contents.- Jesper spillemand.- Vesterude.- Moderen.- Jørgen.- Offerlammet.- Møllermarens penge.- Kviksand.- Grethe fiskerkone og dronningen.- Navnet paa ruden.- Den gamle spillemands jul.

NL 0444278 CU

Løkken, Thomas Olesen, 1877-
... Jesper spillemand og seks andre historier fra gammel tid. Illustreret af Lars Nielsen. [København] S. Hasselbalch [1925]
131 p., 1 l. illus. 20cm.
Contents.—Jesper spillemand.—Vesterude.—Moderen.—Jørgen.—Offerlammet.—Kviksand.—Møllermarens penge.

I. Title.
Library of Congress PT8175.L6J4 1925 25-21064

NL 0444279 DLC MnU NN

Løkken, Thomas Olesen, 1877-
... Den jydske kamp mod hav og braending. [n.p.] Egen udgivelse [Pandrup bogtrykkeri, V. Christensen, 1928]
47 p. illus. 22½cm.
Title vignette.
Prose and poetry.
Each illustration in the text covered by a corresponding mounted illustration apparently clipped from a periodical.
Author's autograph presentation copy.
CONTENTS.—Den gamle kvinde.—Den jydske kamp mod hav og braending.—Foraar ved havet.—Fra redningsvaesenets journaler.—Personlige oplevelser.—Fra fiskernes liv og faerden.—Ved de fire blokhusfiskeres sidste faerd.—Fiskerens sang.
1. Coast guard (Denmark) I. Title.
DL151.L52

NL 0444280 MiU

Løkken, Thomas Olesen, 1877-
... Klavs Bjerg og Bodil, billeder fra den graa klit. København, S. Hasselbalch, 1923.
393, [1] p., 1 l. 21cm.

I. Title.
Library of Congress PT8175.L6K5 1923 24-3526

NL 0444281 DLC CaBVa PP

Løkken, Thomas Olesen, 1877-
Klavs Bjerg og Bodil; billeder fra den graa klit. København, S. Hasselbalch, 1928.
395 p. 19cm.

NL 0444282 MnU

PT8175 L6K5 1943 Løkken, Thomas Olesen, 1877-
... Klavs Bjerg og Bodil, billeder fra den graa klit. København, P. Branner, 1943.
2 v.

NL 0444283 CU

PT 8175 .L6 K6 1948 LØKKEN, THOMAS OLESEN, 1877-
Klavs Bjerg og Bodil. København, A. Sørensen, 1948.
306 p. illus.

NL 0444284 InU PU

PT8175 .L6K54
Løkken, Thomas Olesen, 1877-
Klavs Bjergs søn. København, Hirschsprung, 1953.
358 p. 20 cm.

I. Title. A 54-2557

Minnesota. Univ. Libr. for Library of Congress [1]

NL 0444285 MnU DLC NN

Løkken, Thomas Olesen, 1877-
...Kongevej og Kirkevej. Motiv fra Hammer Bjerge. [Blokkus,] Egen Udgivelse [1930] 18 p. 22½cm.
No. 147 of 200 copies printed.

761717A. 1. Poetry, Danish. I. Title.
N. Y. P. L. June 14, 1935

NL 0444286 NN

Løkken, Thomas Olesen, 1877-
... Mosepigens søn; en roman om ungdom. [København] S. Hasselbalch, 1931.
359 p. 20½cm.
Sequel to Stormosen.

I. Title.
Library of Congress PT8175.L6M7 1931 32-7933
Copyright A—Foreign 15478
839.8136

NL 0444287 DLC MnU

Løkken, Thomas Olesen, 1877-
... Niels Halds hjem. 1.-6. tusinde. [København] S. Hasselbalch [1924]
275 p. 20½cm.
Preceded by Bonden Niels Hald and Niels Halds hustru.

I. Title.
Library of Congress PT8175.L6N47 1924 25-5018
Copyright A—Foreign 26187

NL 0444288 DLC MnU

PT8175 L6N5 1943 Løkken, Thomas Olesen, 1877-
... Niels Halds hjem; en roman om en moderne bonde. København, P. Branner, 1943.
223 p.

Preceded by Bonden Niels Hald and Niels Halds hustru.

NL 0444289 CU WaS

Løkken, Thomas Olesen, 1877-
... Niels Halds hustru, en roman om en kvinde. 4. tusinde. [København] S. Hasselbalch [1922]
229 p. 20½cm.
Preceded by Bonden Niels Hald.

I. Title.
Library of Congress PT8175.L6N5 1922 23-7142

NL 0444290 DLC MnU NN

PT8175 L6N6 1943 Løkken, Thomas Olesen, 1877-
... Niels Halds hustru, en roman om en moderne bonde. København, P. Branner, 1943.
183 p.

Preceded by Bonden Niels Hald.

NL 0444291 CU WaS

Løkken, Thomas Olesen, 1877-
... En ny baad i hav. [København] S. Hasselbalch, 1932.
288 p. 20½cm.

I. Title.
Library of Congress PT8175.L6N8 1932 33-10577
Copyright A—Foreign 20166
839.8136

NL 0444292 DLC NN

VOLUME 338

839.8136
L82nl   Løkken, Thomas Olesen, 1877–
Ny båd i hav.   København, Fremad ₍1953₎
283,₍1₎p.   20cm.   (Fremads folkebibliotek

"Uforkortede udgave"

NL 0444293   KU MH

Løkken, Thomas Olesen, 1877–
... Østergaard og Vestergaard; lystspil med
sange i 3 akter. For dilettanter. ₍København₎
S.Hasselbalch, 1927.
113 p.,₍1₎ l.   21ᶜᵐ.

NL 0444294   MiU NN

Løkken, Thomas Olesen, 1877–
... Pensionatet Havørnen. Lystspil med sange
i 4 akter. For dilettanter. ₍Pandrup₎ Egen
udgivelse, 1931.
139 p.   21½ᶜᵐ.

NL 0444295   MiU

Løkken, Thomas Olesen, 1877–
Pigen fra Vildmosen. ₍København₎ S. Hasselbalch, 1940.
231 p.   21 cm.

ɪ. Title.
PT8175.L6P5   47–40527*

NL 0444296   DLC

PT8175   Løkken, Thomas Olesen, 1877–
L6P5   Pigen fra Vildmosen.   ₍2.opl.₎ København,
1943   havn, P. Branner, 1943.
228 p.

NL 0444297   CU

Løkken, Thomas Olesen, 1877–
...Poul Dam; Kampaar. ₍København:₎ S. Hasselbalchs
Forlag₍,₎ 1926₎.   250 p.   8°.

1. Fiction, Danish.   2. Title.
N. Y. P. L.   May 9, 1927

NL 0444298   NN

Løkken, Thomas Olesen, 1877–
Povl Dam. ₍København₎ S. Hasselvalch
₍c1925–c1927₎
3 v.

NL 0444299   WaU MiU

PT8175   Løkken, Thomas Olesen, 1877–
L6P7   ... Povl Dam ...   København, P. Branner,
1943   1943.
3 v.

Contents.– 1. Ungdom.– 2. Kampaar.–
3. Sejren.

NL 0444300   CU

Løkken, Thomas Olesen, 1877–
...Povl Dam, Sejren. ₍København:₎ S. Hasselbalchs Forlag₍,₎ 1927₎.   277 p.   8°.

1. Fiction, Danish.   2. Title.
N. Y. P. L.   December 29, 1927

NL 0444301   NN

Løkken, Thomas Olesen, 1877–
... Povl Dam, ungdom. ₍København₎ S. Hasselbalch
₍1925₎
216 p., 1 l.   20½ᶜᵐ.

ɪ. Title.
                                                26–8328 Revised
Library of Congress   PT8175.L6P6 1925

NL 0444302   DLC

Løkken, Thomas Olesen, 1877–
... Rejsebreve fra Holland. ₍København₎ S. Hasselbalch,
1927.
142, ₍1₎ p. plates (incl. port.) 20ᶜᵐ.
Title vignette.

1. Netherlands—Descr. & trav.
Library of Congress   DJ39.L6   29–3255

NL 0444303   DLC

Løkken, Thomas Olesen, 1877–
... En Rejsefærd til Løkken Aar 1886. ₍København: S.
Hasselbalch₍,₎ 1924₎.   27 p. illus. 8°.
Tegningerne af Maleren Lars Nielsen Løkken.
no. 221 of 400 numbered copies.

1. Jutland—Descr. and trav.
N. Y. P. L.   September 14, 1925

NL 0444304   NN MiU

Løkken, Thomas Olesen, 1877–
...Sagfører Sigerslet; en levnedsskildring.   København, P.
Branner, 1943. 313 p. 21cm.
Novel.

NL 0444305   NN MnU

Løkken, Thomas Olesen, ₍1877–
... Sange fra Vendsyssel. København, E.V.
Olsen, 1934.
95 p. 26ᶜᵐ.
CONTENTS.—Stedmoderblomsten.—Sange til havet.—Naturen holder pinsefest.—Fra Hammer Bjerge.—Vendsyssel.
—Livets spil.

NL 0444306   MiU

Slavic   Løkken, Thomas Olesen, 1877–
Coll.   Sedlák Niels Hald; román o moderním sedláku.
420.91   Z dánského originálu přeložila Marie Polívková.
D3   Praha, Sfinx, Bohumil Janda, 1948.
L653
553 p. 21 cm. (Evropská knihovna; svazek
35, nové cíle; svazek 1049)

English translation of title: The peasant
Nields Hald; a novel on a modern peasant.
From Danish original translated by Marie
Polívková.

NL 0444307   IEdS

Løkken, Thomas Olesen, 1877–
...Skæbner bag en strand. Tolv bekendelser og een daares
drøm.   København, P. Branner, 1947.   223 p.   20cm.

NL 0444308   NN MnU

Løkken, Thomas Olesen, 1877–
...Den skæve Linie; Lystspil i 3 Afsnit. For Dilettanter.
Aalborg: Gyldendalske Boghandel, 1922. 68 p.   8°.

1. Drama (Danish). 2. Amateur   theatricals. 3. Title.
N. Y. P. L.   July 8, 1924

NL 0444309   NN MiU

Løkken, Thomas Olesen, 1877–
... Stormosen; billeder fra mosens brune land. København,
S. Hasselbalch ₍²1929₎
365 p. 20½ᶜᵐ.
Novel.

ɪ. Title.
Library of Congress   PT8175.L6S8 1929   30–16984

NL 0444310   DLC MnU

PT8175   LØKKEN, THOMAS OLESEN, 1877–
L6Z57
Bailum, Henry.
Thomas Olesen Løkken; besøg hos forfatteren på Kancelligården. ₍Holstebro, 1954₎

Løkken, Thomas Olesen, 1877–
... Ungdom gaar i gang ... ₍København₎ S. Hasselbalch,
1938.
2 v. 20½ᶜᵐ.

ɪ. Title.
Library of Congress   PT8175.L6U5 1938   40–17877
Copyright A—Foreign   42270
                                        ₍2₎   839.8136

NL 0444312   DLC MiU NN

Løkken verk
see
Orkla grube-aktiebolag.

Loel, Wayne, 1888–
The Vaqueros formation, Lower Miocene of California.
ɪ. Paleontology, by Wayne Loel and W. H. Corey ... Berkeley, Calif., University of California press, 1932.
cover-title, 1 p. l., ₍3₎–410 p. 2 fold. maps, pl. 4–65, tables (1 fold.)
27 cm. (University of California publications. Bulletin of the Department of geological sciences. v. 22, no. 3)
Bibliography: p. 281–286.

1. Paleontology—California. 2. Paleontology—Miocene.
ɪ. Corey, William Henry, 1901–   joint author. ɪɪ. Title.
                                                A 33—611
California. Univ. Libr.
for Library of Congress   ₍a56b1₎

NL 0444314   CU OrU MtBuM MU MiU OU OCl

VOLUME 338

Loel, Wayne, and W. H. Corey.   *3862.133.22
The Vaqueros formation, lower Miocene of California.
(*In* University of California. Publications in geological sciences.
Vol. 22, pp. (2), 31-410. Plates. Map. Berkeley, Cal. 1934.)
Bibliography, pp. 281-286.

D7848 — Jt. auth. — Miocene fossils. — Vaqueros formation.

NL 0444315   MB

839.83 Løland, Rasmus, 1861-1907.
L83   [Løland's varker.   Kristiania,
            1895-1902]
          4v.

          Binder's title; each work has special
          t.-p.

NL 0444316   IU

Løland, Rasmus, 1861-1907.
    Aasmund Aarak

NL 0444317   NdU

Løland, Rasmus, 1861-1907.
    Blodstyng

NL 0444318   NdU

Løland, Rasmus, 1861-1907.
    Blodstyng og andre sogor. Kristiania,
  Bertrand Jensen, 1895.
    94 p.

NL 0444319   WaU MnU

Løland, Rasmus, 1861-1907.
    Emne

NL 0444320   NdU

PT   Løland, Rasmus, 1861-1907
8915   Emne; sogor. Kristiania, B. Jensen, 1896.
L6   255p. 18cm.
E4

NL 0444321   WU

PT   Løland, Rasmus, 1861-1907
8915   Folkeliv. Bergen, M. Litleré, 1891.
L6   165p. 17cm.
F6   Bound with the author's Ungar. Kristiania,
           1897; and Smaagutar. Kristiania, 1897.

NL 0444322   WU

PT9077 Løland, Rasmus, 1861-1907.
.H3   Hans og Margreta. Ei soga av Rasmus Løland.
1898   2.utgaava.   Oslo, Bokreidar: B.Jensen, 1898.
          46 p. 17½ᶜᵐ.

          "Denne soga vart fyrste gongen prenta i "Lauv-
          duskar" for 1887. Er no umvøltog avstutta."

NL 0444323   ICU

Løland, Rasmus, 1861-1907.
    Hugtekne. Kristiania, Bertrand Jensens
  Forlag, 1897.
    255 p.

NL 0444324   WaU MnU NdU

PT   Løland, Rasmus, 1861-1907
8915   Hundrad aar; forteljingar; etterlate arbeid.
L6   Oslo, Norske samlaget [1910]
P3   160p. 19cm.
          Bound with the author's Paa skuggesida. Oslo,
          1908.

NL 0444325   WU

Løland, Rasmus, 1861-1907.
    Jordvend

NL 0444326   NdU

Løland, Rasmus, 1861-1907.
    Kvar vart det av jola?

NL 0444327   NdU

Løland, Rasmus, 1861-1907.
    Kvar vart det av jola? 2. utg.   Oslo,
  Oslo prenteverk, 1900.
    54 p. 19cm.

NL 0444328   MnU

Løland, Rasmus, 1861-1907.
    Nervesliten; forteljing. Kristiania,
  B. Jensen, 1896.
    64 p. 19cm.

NL 0444329   MnU

Løland, Rasmus, 1861-1907.
    Norsk eventyrbok; 1. bundelen etter uppskrifter
  av Hans Ross, Anders Eivindson Vang, Knut Laupar-
  dalen, Ivar Mortensson og fleire. 156p.
  Oslo, 1904.

    Cover-title.

NL 0444330   OC1 OC1W

B   LØLAND, RASMUS, 1861-1907.
8551   Norsk eventyrbok, etter uppskrifter paa
.517   folkemaalet, utgjevne av det Norske samlaget.
         Oslo, Johansen & Nielsen, 1905.
           viii, 372p. 18cm.

           Bibliography: p.[368]-372.

NL 0444331   ICN

PT8625   LØLAND, RASMUS, 1861-1907, comp.
.L8   Norsk eventyrbok etter uppskrifter paa folkemaa-
           let utgjevne av det Norske samlaget ved Rasmus Lø-
           land. Oslo, 1906, '05.
             viii, 372 p. 19cm.
             "Største parten av eventyri i denne boki er etter
           uppskrifter av Hans Ross og Andres Eivindson Vang.
           --Fyreord.
             Issued in 2 parts; pt.2,2.uppl.
             1.Fairy tales. 2.Folk-lore--Norway.

NL 0444332   ICU IU WaS

Løland, Rasmus, 1861-1907.
    Paa sjølvstyr 2 dreutg.

NL 0444333   NdU

PT   Løland, Rasmus, 1861-1907
8915   Paa skuggesida; forteljingar. Arne Garborg:
L6   eit ettermæle. Oslo, Norske samlaget, 1908.
P3   135p. 19cm.
           Bound with the author's Hundred aar. Oslo
         [1910]

NL 0444334   WU NIC

Løland, Rasmus, 1861-1907.
    Skattegravaren

NL 0444335   NdU

Løland, Rasmus, 1861-1907.
    Smaagutar

NL 0444336   NdU

PT   Løland, Rasmus, 1861-1907
8915   Smaagutar; sogor. Kristiania, B. Jensen,
L6   1897.
F6   138p. 17cm.
           Bound with the author's Folkeliv. Bergen,
         1891.

NL 0444337   WU MnU

Løland, Rasmus, 1861-1907.
    (Det) store nashorne

NL 0444338   NdU

VOLUME 338

839.8L82
O8t   Løland, Rasmus, 1861-1907.
       Det store nashorne; minne fraa gutedagarne.
       Oslo, O. Husebys prenteverk, 1900.

         135 p.   19cm.

NL 0444339   MnU

PT   Løland, Rasmus, 1861-1907
8915   Ungar; sogor for born. 2. utg. Kristiana,
L6   B. Jensen, 1897.
F6   78p.   17cm.
          Bound with the author's Folkeliv. Bergen,
        1891.

NL 0444340   WU NdU

LØLAND, Rasmus, 1861-1907.
   Ungar: forteljingar. 3. utg.
     Oslo. 1905. 79p.

   Contents: Hunden og katten. Guten og
grisen. Nils som gjekk til skogs.

NL 0444341   WaS

Løland, Rasmus, 1861-1907.
   Ute og heime

NL 0444342   NdU

Loele, August Walter
    see Loele, Walter, 1875-

PT 2623 LOELE, KONRAD
.O34 Z4   Züllinger und seine Zucht. Zeichnungen von
1920   Hans Albert Förster. Leipzig, Pandora-Verlag
        1920.
          104 p.   illus.

NL 0444344   InU

Loele, Kurt: Beiträge zur Kenntnis der Histologie und Funk-
tion des Hymenopterendarmes. Jena: Fischer 1913. 36 S.,
1 Taf. 8° ¶Aus: Zeitschrift f. allg. Physiol. Bd 16.
Leipzig, Phil. Diss. v. 17. Jan. 1914, Ref. Chun, Pfeffer
[Geb. 28. Sept. 88 Döschnitz; Wohnort: Leipzig; Staatsangeh.: Schwarzburg-
Rudolstadt; Vorbildung: G. Rudolstadt Reife 08; Studium: Leipzig 3, Jena 2,
Leipzig 5 S.; Rig. 8. Juli 13.]   [U 14. 4226

NL 0444345   ICRL OCU CtY PU MH

Loele, Kurt.
   Das Bücher-Schaufenster; mit einem Anhang: Innenauslagen
und Innenausstattung, Ausstellungen; eine Anleitung für die
Praxis, von Kurt Loele und Otto Bruère...   Berlin: Oldenburg
& Co. [pref. 1919.]   105 p.   plates.   8°.

3303A. 1. Show windows.   2. Bruère, Otto, jt. au.
N. Y. P. L.   March 11, 1921.

NL 0444346   NN

Loele, Kurt.
   Der sieg des deutschen buches im weltkriege, von Kurt
Loele. Leipzig, Schulze & co., 1915.
   48 p. 19½ᶜᵐ.   (On cover: Kriegs-zeitfragen ... 4. hft.)

   1. European war, 1914-1918—Germany. 2. European war, 1914-1918—
Public opinion.   I. Title.

Library of Congress   D515.L65   27-22077

NL 0444347   DLC NjP NN IU

Loele (Paul).   *Ein Fall von Orbitalphlegmone
bei Schädelsyphilis. 31 pp. 8°. Jena, H. Pohle,
1900.

NL 0444348   DNLM ICRL MH

Loele, W   591.104 8001
   Die Phenolreaktion (Aldaminreaktion) und ihre Bedeutung für
die Biologie, von W. Loele, ... Mit 2 Textfiguren und 24
Photogrammen. Leipzig, W. Klinkhardt, 1920.
   viii, 58, [2] p. illus., xII pl. 23½ᶜᵐ.

NL 0444349   ICJ CU

Loele (Walter) [1875-   ]. *Versuche
über den Einfluss des Alcohol auf Fremdkör-
per-Entzündungen. 24 pp., 2 l. 8°. Leipzig,
B. Georgi. 1900.
Full name: August Walter Loele.

NL 0444350   DNLM ICRL CtY

Loelgen, Carl August, 1896-
   Koerperbau und geschlecht.
   Inaug. diss. Bonn, 1924.
   Bibl.

NL 0444351   ICRL

[Loelgen, Carl August]
   Sire; die einunddreissig Sendschreiben an den Wirt-
schaftsführer. Eingeleitet von Siegfried Behn. Berlin,
Dümmler, 1928

   149 p.
   "Den Teilnehmern der Herbstversammlung 1928 des
Börsenvereins der deutschen Buchhändler gewidmet vom
Verlag anlässlich seines 120jährigen Bestehens"

NL 0444352   MH

Lölhöffel, Edith von.
   Hopsa-Tralla; ein Lieder- und Spielheft. Vierzehn neue
Bewegungsspiele für Kinder. Potsdam, L. Voggenreiter
[19—] Pub. no. 601c.
   16 p. 12 x 20 cm.
   "Der 'Langen, langen Reihe' 3. Folge."
   Singing games.
   Unacc. melodies, each followed by directions for the game.

   1. Games with music.   I. Title.

   M1993.L8H6   51-26625

NL 0444353   DLC NRU NN

Lölhöffel, Edith von.
   Lange, lange Reihe; ein Lieder- und Spielheft. Neue Bewegungsspiele für Kinder, 1. Folge. Potsdam, L. Voggenreiter [19—] Pub. no. MRV Nr. 601a.
   16 p. 12 x 20 cm.
   Singing games.
   Unacc. melodies, each followed by directions for the game.

   1. Games with music.   I. Title.

   M1993.L8L3   51-26624

NL 0444354   DLC NRU NN IaU

LÖLHÖFFEL, Edith von.
   Lange, lange Reihe; ein Lieder- u. Spielheft. Neue
Bewegungsspiele für Kinder. Potsdam, L. Voggenreiter
[194-?] 3 v. in 1. 12 x 20cm.
   Tunes, with directions for the games.
   CONTENTS. Folge 1. Lange, lange Reihe.--Folge 2. Mühle, mahle!
--Folge 3. Hopsa-Tralla.
   1. Singing games, German.   2. Children's music--Songs,
German. I. Title.

NL 0444355   NN

Lölhöffel, Edith von.
   Mühle, mahle! Ein Lieder- und Spielheft. Neue Be-
wegungsspiele für kleine Kinder. Potsdam, L. Voggen-
reiter [19—] Pub. no. MRV NR. 601b.
   16 p. 12 x 20 cm.
   "Der Langen, langen, Reihe, 2. Folge."
   Singing games.
   Unacc. melodies, each followed by directions for the game.

   1. Games with music.   I. Title.

   M1993.L8M8   51-26676

NL 0444356   DLC NRU NN

Lölhöffel, Edith von
   Report on the effects of physical education
on the development, structure and functions
of the female body...[Bayeux, Impr.
R. P. Colas, 1934?]
   25p. illus.
   At head of title: 3d Quinquennial Congress
Medical Women's International Association.
Stockholm--August 7-12, 1934.

NL 0444357   ICRL

Lölhöffel, Erich von, ed.

Umbehr, Heinz.
   ... Der schmalfilm tönt, von Heinz Umbehr; mit 22 abbildungen. Halle (Saale) W. Knapp, 1938.

Lölhöffel, Erich von.
   ... Wie ein Tonfilm entsteht, von Dr. E. v. Lölhöffel. Mit 26
Abbildungen.   Halle (Saale) W. Knapp [1933?].   47 p.   illus.
21cm. (Die Bücher des Lichtspielvorführers. [Nr.] 12.)

   1. Moving pictures, Sound. I. Ser.
N. Y. P. L.   March 12, 1934

NL 0444359   NN

W 4   LOELHOEFFEL, Heinrich
L68   Dissertatio medica inauguralis. De frictione ... Lugduni
1732   Batavorum, Apud Conradum Wishoff [1732]
L.1   45 p. illus. 22 cm.
           Diss. - Leyden.

NL 0444360   DNLM

VOLUME 338

Lölhöffel von Löwensprung, Erich

see

Lölhöffel, Erich von.

W 4 LOELIGER, Alfred, 1924-
Z96 Über den Nachweis eines neuen
1952 Blutgerinnungsfaktors: Faktor VII.
ͺWien, Spiesͺ 1952.
p. ͺ169ͺ-180. illus.
Inaug.-Diss. - Zürich.
Reprinted from Wiener Zeitschrift
für innere Medizin, Jahrg. 33, Heft 5,
1952.
1. Blood - Coagulation

NL 0444362 DNLM

LÖLIGER, Emil.
Kritik der todesfalle nach gynäkologischen
eingriffen im Basler Frauenspital während
der jahre 1901-1911. Inaugural-dissertation,
Basel. Stuttgart, druck der Union deutsche
Verlagsgesellschaft,1913.

NL 0444363 MBCo CtY DNLM MiU

RS125 Loeliger, Emil, joint author.
L83
Ludwig, Herbert.
Repertorium pharmazeutischer Spezialpräparate, Sera und
Impfstoffe, hrsg. von ... Herbert Ludwig ... unter Mitarbeit
von ... L. V. Furlan und ... E. Loeliger. 1. Ausg. ... Basel,
Verlagsgesellschaft Beobachter, 1946.

Loeliger, Hans Robert, 1923–
Kernspin und magnetisches Moment des Arsens und
Titans. Zürich, 1952.
55 p. diagrs. 25 cm.
Inaug.-Diss.—Zürich.
Vita.
Bibliography: p. 54-55.

1. Nuclear moments. 2. Arsenic. 3. Titanium. I. Title.

QC794.L6   57-22054

NL 0444365 DLC CtY NN

W 4 Loeliger, Hans Theodor, 1913–
Z96 Beitrag zum quantitativen Nirvanolnachweis
1943 im Harn und zur Nirvanolausscheidung beim
Tier. Zürich, Leeman, 1943.
41, ͺ1ͺ p. illus.

Inaug.-Diss. - Zürich.

NL 0444366 DNLM

Loeliger, Karl.
Der Installateur im Gas- und Wasserfach. Berufsbild.
Hrsg. vom Schweizerischen Verband für Berufsberatung
und Lehrlingsfürsorge in Verbindung mit dem Schweizer-
ischen Spenglermeister- und Installateurverband. Zürich,
Zu beziehen beim Zentralsekretariat für Berufsberatung,
1951.
44 p. illus. 21 cm.
Bibliography: p. 43-44.
1. Plumbers. 2. Plumbing. 3. Gas-fitting. 4. Vocational guidance.
I. Schweizerischer Verband für Berufsberatung und Lehrlingsfürsorge.
II. Title.

A 53-1637

Illinois. Univ. Library
for Library of Congress

NL 0444367 IU

Loeliger, Robert.
Streifzüge ins Reich der Insekten; Erlebnisse und Beobachtungen aus der Welt der Insekten, von Dr. R. Loeliger... Zürich, Verlag Pro Juventute ͺ194–?ͺ 31 p. illus. 21cm.
(Schweizer Freizeit-Wegleitungen. Nr. 28)

1. Insects. I. Ser.
N. Y. P. L.   October 1, 1951

NL 0444368 NN

Loeliger, Robert.
Untersuchung des druck- und stroemungsverlaufs,...
Inaug. diss. Zuerich, tehhn. hochs., 1915

NL 0444369 ICRL

Loelius ͺ Joh. Laurentius ͺ [1641-1700]. De
sanguine. 29 l. 4°. *Wittebergæ, lit. J. Röhneri,*
ͺ1664ͺ.

NL 0444370 DNLM

Loelius, Joh. Laurentius, 1641-1700.
——. *De scorbuto.* 98 pp., 3 l. sm. 4°. *Jenæ,
e chalcographo J. Nisi.* [1668].

NL 0444371 DNLM

Loelius, Johann Elias, praeses
... De monarchiae eminentia, subjecto,
& adipiscendae medio ... Jenae, J.
Nisius, 1656.
ͺ24ͺ p. 18cm.
Diss. - Jena (J.S. Hartlaub, respondent)

NL 0444372 MH-L

W 4 LOELIUS, Johann Lorenz Ludwig
L68 Disputatio medica inauguralis. De hydrope anasarca ...
1713 Lugduni Batavorum, Apud Conradum Wishof, 1713.
L 1 18 p. 22 cm.
Diss. - Leyden.

NL 0444373 DNLM

Loelius, Lucius.   1893.
(Sonnet.)

NL 0444374 NIC

Löll, Louis, 1823–1899.
Der getreide-schutzzoll, eine nothwendigkeit für
Deutschland, von dr. L. Löll ... mit zwei tabellen durch-
schnittspreise, sowie ein- und ausfuhr enthaltend. Würzburg, A. Stuber, 1885.
38 p. incl. tables. 21½ᶜᵐ.

1. Grain trade—Germany. 2. Tariff—Germany.

15-25619

Library of Congress   HF2651.G849L6

NL 0444375 DLC

Loell, Louis, 1823-1899.
Die Goldwährung; eine für jeden unterrichteten Geschäfts-
mann verständliche Belehrung über den Werth, das Geld, die Goldwährung und deren Folgen für Landwirthschaft und Kleingewerbe,
von Dr. L. Löll... Würzburg: G. Hertz, 1885. iv, 96 p. 8°.

60284A. 1. Gold (Money), Germany,   1885.
N. Y. P. L.   October 6, 1922.

NL 0444376 NN

HJ4353 Löll, Louis, 1823-1899.
L7 Die Grundrente, die preussische und
bayerische Grundsteuer. Würzburg, A.Stuber,
1872.
173p. 23cm.

1. Land - Taxation - Prussia. 2. Land -
Taxation - Bavaria I. Title.

NL 0444377 IaU ICJ

Löll, Louis, 1823-1899.
... Das Klima und der Boden, von Ökonomierat Dr. Löll ...
Stuttgart, E. Ulmer, 1888.
iv, 149 p. illus., diagrs. 17ᶜᵐ.   (Des Landmanns Winterabende.
38. Bändchen)

NL 0444378 ICJ

DD 801 Loell, Louis, 1823-1899
.83483 Landwirthschaft [in Unterfranken]

(In Bavaria. Landes-und volkskunde Muenchen, 1866
8°. v. 4, part 1. p. 286-294)

NL 0444379 DLC

Löll, Louis, 1823-1899.
Die währungsfrage. Ein hilfsmittel zum verständnisse derselben von dr. L. Löll ... 2., verb. ausg. Nebst einem referate:
Die nachtheile der goldwährung von Carl freiherrn von Thüngen-Rossbach. Würzburg, G. Hertz, 1889.
iv, 96, 31 p. 22½ᶜᵐ.

1. Currency question—Germany. I. Thüngen-Rossbach, Karl Ernst,
freiherr von.

Library of Congress   HG999.L82   1—20706

NL 0444380 DLC ICJ

Löll, Louis, 1823-1899.
Eine währungs-rede des Reichstags-abgeordneten
herrn. dr. L. Bamberger im lichte der thatsachen. Von
dr. L. Löll ... Eine ergänzung der beiden schriften: Die
goldwährung von dr. L. Löll. Die nachtheile der goldwährung von Frhr. v. Thüngen-Rossbach. Worms, P.
Reiss, 1886.
97, ͺ1ͺ p. 24ᶜᵐ.

1. Currency question—Germany. I. Bamberger, Ludwig, 1823-1899.

1—20705

Library of Congress   HG999.L81

NL 0444381 DLC

Löllmann, Theodor, 1907-
... Über Bromoderma Tuberosum ... Bonn,
1937.
Inaug. -Diss. - Bonn.
Lebenslauf.
"Literatur": p. 31

NL 0444382 CtY

VOLUME 338

LÜLOFF, Carl.
Über - p-trianisyl-und p-triphenetylstibin
und einige ihrer derivate. Rostok, 1897.

NL 0444383   MH-C

Loeltz, Omar Joseph, 1914–
Geology and water resources of Smith Valley, Lyon and
Douglas Counties, Nevada, by O. J. Loeltz and T. E. Eakin,
prepared in cooperation with the Office of the State Engi-
neer, State of Nevada. Washington, U. S. Govt. Print. Off.,
1953.
iv, 89 p. illus., maps (3 fold., 1 col., in pocket) 24 cm. ([U. S.]
Geological Survey. Water-supply paper 1228)
"Literature cited": p. 88.
1. Geology—Nevada—Smith Valley. 2. Water-supply—Nevada—
Smith Valley. 3. Water, Underground—Nevada—Smith Valley. 4.
Borings—Nevada—Smith Valley. i. Eakin, Thomas Emery, 1914–
joint author.   (Series)
TC801.U2 no. 1228   G S 54–286
——— Copy 2.   GB705.N3L6
U. S. Geol. Survey. Libr.
for Library of Congress   [5]†

NL 0444384   DI-GS PP DLC

GB705
N3A3   Loeltz, Omar Joseph, 1914–
no.10   Ground water in Paradise Valley, Humboldt
County, Nevada, by Omar J. Loeltz, David A.
Phoenix and Thomas W. Robinson. [Carson City,
Nev.] 1949.
61 p. illus., maps (1 in pocket) tables
(1 fold.) 23 cm. (Nevada. Office of State
Engineer. Water resources bulletin no. 10)
Prepared in cooperation with the U.S. Geolo-
gical Survey.
1. Water, Underground - Nevada. I. U.S.
Geological Survey   (Series)

NL 0444385   DI

Loemban Toroean, M   S
see
Lumban Toruan, M   S

Loembantobing, Arsenius
Nkd72   Angka Toeritoerian ni Halak Batak. Leiden,
I61   S. C. van Doesburgh, 1919.
B3e   35 p. 23 cm. (Bataksch Instituut, Leyden.
16   Uitgaven no. 16)

NL 0444387   CtY

4PL-4   Loembantobing, Arsenius.
Pingkiran ni halak Batak sipelebegoe taringot toe
tondi ni djolma doeng mate. Leiden, S. C. van
Doesburgh, 1920.
56 p. (Uitgaven van het Bataksch Instituut,
no. 17 [?])

NL 0444388   DLC-P4 CtY

Loemke, Heinrich, 1902 –
Messungen mit optischen pyrometern
Inaug. Diss. Darmstadt, 1931

NL 0444389   ICRL

Film
no.
385   Loemker, Kenneth Karl, 1906–
Factors in visual localization, by
Kenneth Loemker. [Chicago, Ill.] The
University of Chicago library, Dept of
photographic reproduction [1947]
1 reel.

Thesis (Ph. D.) - University of Chicago,
1941.
Film reproduction (positive) of the original
type-written dissertation.

NL 0444390   MdBJ

BF1999   Loemker, Kenneth Karl, 1906 –
The influence of certain visual and somesthetic factors on the manual localization of a
visual object. 1941.
44 numb.l.

Typewritten.
Thesis(Ph.D.)--University of Chicago.

NL 0444391   ICU

Loemker, Kenneth Karl, 1906–
The influence of certain visual and somesthetic factors on
the manual localization of a visual object. Chicago [Univ.
of Chicago Library, Dept. of Photographic Reproduction]
1947.
Microfilm copy of typewritten manuscript. Positive.
Collation of the original: 44 l. diagrs., tables.
Thesis—Univ. of Chicago.

1. Space-perception.
Microfilm QP–4   Mic A 48–250*
Chicago. Univ. Libr.
for Library of Congress   [2]†

NL 0444392   ICU ViU OU NjP NNC MH NN DLC

Loemongga Haroen, Ida
see Haroen, Ida Loemongga.

NA
2880   Lämpel, Heinrich.
.L82   Die monumentale Tonne in der Architektur.
München, Piloty & Loehle, 1913.
75 p. illus.,plans. 33 cm.
Diss.--K.Technische Hochschule,Munich.
Bibliography: p.73.

1.Vaults. I.Title.

NL 0444394   MiU NNC NN CU ICRL CtY

Loën, A   de Villenfagne
see Villenfagne de Loën, A   de.

Loen, Arnoldus Ewout, 1896–
Inleiding tot de wijsbegeerte. 's-Gravenhage, Boekencen
trum,1947.
192 p. 23 cm.

1. Philosophy.
BD28.L6   49–13932*

NL 0444396   DLC ICU NN

Loen, Arnoldus Ewout, 1896–
De vaste grond. Amsterdam, H. J. Paris, 1946.
vii, 332 p. 25 cm.

1. Ontology. 2. Knowledge, Theory of. 3. Christianity—Philosophy.
BD331.L82   A F 47–5997*
Chicago. Univ. Library
for Library of Congress   [2]†

NL 0444397   ICU ICMcC DLC NNC

BD161 Loen, Arnoldus Ewout, 1896 –
.L82   Wijsbegeerte en werkelijkheid; een inleiding tot een onder-
zoek van het geloof ... Utrecht, H. Honig, 1927.
x, 333 p. diagrs. 24½ cm.
Proefschrift—Leyden.
"Stellingen" (3 p.) laid in.

1. Knowledge, Theory of.

NL 0444398   ICU MB

Loën, August, Freiherr von, 1828–1887.   6898.203
Bühne und Leben. Roman.
Leipzig. Brockhaus. 1864. 309 pp. 18 cm., in 8s.

K8677 — T.r. — Theatre. Fiction.

NL 0444399   MB

4DD-   Loën, August, Freiherr von, 1828–1887.
841   Die Kriegsverfassung des deutschen Reiches und
des deutschen Bundes (1668–1860) Dessau, Aue,
1860.
98 p.

NL 0444400   DLC-P4

No. 8 in **G.3910.9=No. 19 in **G.3910.17
Loën, August, Freiherr von, 1828–1887.
Die Shakespeare-Kenntniss im heutigen Frankreich. (Mit beson-
derem Bezug auf die Shakespeare-Forschungen von A. Mézières.
[Wien, 1866.] 21 pp. 8°.
Cut from the Internationale Revue, July, 1866.

[This work is kept on the Special Libraries Floor.]

E9327 — Shakespeare, William. Shakespeare in France. — Mézières, Alfred
Jean François.

NL 0444401   MB

Loen, H   von, supposed author.
Die Auerstädter schlacht auf meiner kammer
see under title

Loen, Jean Michel de
see Loen, Johann Michael, Freiherr
von, 1694–1776.

838
L8225ad Loen,Johann Michael,Freiherr von,1694–1776.
1752a   Der Adel. Ulm,J.F.Baum,1752.
520 p.
Photocopy. Ann Arbor,Mich.,University
Microfilms,1970. 520 p.(on double leaves).

NL 0444404   MiU

VOLUME 338

Loën, Johann Michael, *freiherr von*, 1694–1775.
The analysis of nobility, in its origin; as military, mercantile, and literary; proofs, privileges, duties, acquisition, and forfeiture thereof, interspersed with several curious monuments of history, relating to laws of chivalry, creations, degradations, justs, tournaments, combats, &c. Tr. from the original German of Baron von Lowhen. With notes collected from the best English antiquarians, and other authors ... London, Printed and sold by J. Robinson, 1754.
1 p. l., iv, 16, 317, ɪ7ɪ p. 17ᵐᵐ.
1. Nobility. 2. England—Nobility. ɪ. Title.

Library of Congress   CR3505.L6

15-18501

NL 0444405   DLC MdBP

Loen, Johann Michael, freiherr von, 1694–1775.
Bedencken von der Schädlichkeit der Festungen
see under title

Loen, Johann Michael, Freiherr von, 1694–1776,
ed.
Rusdorf, Johann Joachim von, 1589–1640.
Consilia et negotia politica, ubi diversi tractatus et consilia, diverso tempore, prout res in deliberationem cadebant, aut proponebantur, scripta & rerumpublicarum in Europa statum concernentia, continentur. Accedit Epistolarum familiarum ipsius autoris, ad viros illustres & amicos scriptarum, collectio. Francofurti ad Moenum, Apud J. M. a Sande, 1725.

D221
.P8R8
Rare Bk
Coll

611
L825e
1750

[LOEN, Johann Michael von] 1694–1776.
Die einzige wahre Religion, allgemein in ihren Grund=Saetzen, verwirrt durch die Zaenkereyen der Schriftgelehrten, zertheilet in aller hand Secten, vereiniget in Christo. Franckfurt und Leipzig, Fleischer, 1750.
2pts. in 1v. front. 17.5cm.

NL 0444408   MH-AH

Loen, Johann Michael, Freiherr von, 1694–1776
Die einzige wahre Religion. Frankfurt, Fleischer, 1751.
2 v.

NL 0444409   MH InGo

4JC
618

Loen, Johann Michael, Freiherr von, 1694–1776.
Entwurf einer Staats-Kunst, worinn die natürlichste Mittel endecket werden ein Land mächtig, reich, und glücklich zu machen. 3. Aufl. Frankfurt, J. F. Fleischer, 1751.
[200] p.

NL 0444410   DLC-P4 MH MH-BA

304
L825f

[Loën, Johann Michael, freiherr von] 1694–1776.
Freie gedancken zur verbesserung der menschlichen gesellschafft ... Franckfurt [etc.] J. F. Fleischer, 1746-48.
4v. in 1. fold.plan.

1. Sociology--Addresses, essays, lectures. I. Title.

NL 0444411   IU

Loen, Johann Michael, freiherr von, 1694–1776.
Des herrn von Loen freie gedancken zur verbesserung der menschlichen gesellschafft. Andere und verb. ausg.   Franckfurt und Leipzig, J.F.Fleischer, 1750.
4 pts. in 1 v. fold. plan. 17.5 cm.

1.Wealth. 2.Political science - Addresses, essays, lectures. 3.Crime and criminals. 4.Cities and towns. I.Title. II.Title: Freie gedancken   zur verbesserung der 'menschlichen ges-   ellschafft.

NL 0444412   MH-BA MH

41

Loen, Johann Michael von, 1694–1775.
Des herrn von Loen freie gedanken zur verbesserung der menschlichen gesellschaft. Frankfurt & Leipzig, 1752.

NL 0444413   DLC NjP

4BR
1119

[Loen, Johann Michael, Freiherr von] 1694–1776.
סוד רימבה ושרפה i. e. Das Geheimnuss der Verwesung und Verbrennung aller Dinge, nach seinen Wundern im Reich der Natur und Gnade, Macro et microcosmice, als die Schlüssel, dadurch der Weeg zur Verbesserung eröffnet, das verborgene der Creaturen entdecket, und die Verklärung des sterblichen Leibes gründlich erkant wird. 3. und mit vielen curiösen, observationibus. verm. Aufl. Franckfurt am Mayn, in der Fleischerischen Buchhandlung, 1758.
169 p.

Title Transliterated: Sood rikvah u-serefah.

NL 0444414   DLC-P4 WU CtY

[Loen, Johann Michael von] 1694–1776.
Das Geheimnuss der Verwesung und Verbrennung aller Dinge, nach seinen Wundern im Reich der Natur und Gnade. Vierte und mit vielen Observationibus vermehrte Auflage. Franckfurt am Mayn, 1771.

DION

NL 0444415   WU

PT2424
L63
1749a

Loen, Johann Michael, freiherr von, 1694–1776.
Gesammelte kleine Schriften (1749-1752) Besorgt und hrsg. von J.C.Schneider. [n.d.]
4v. illus. 19cm.

Vol. 4 edited by J.B.Müller.
Reprint of the 1749-1752 edition.

I. Schneider, J   C   ed.
II. Müller, J   B   ed.

NL 0444416   IaU

Zgl8
L810
749
v.1 only

Loën, Johann Michael, Freiherr von, 1694–1776
Des Herrn von Loen Gesammlete kleine Schrifften. Besorgt und herausgegeben von J. C. Schneidern. Frankfurt und Leipzig,Zu finden bey Philipp Heinrich Huttern[1749]
4v. front.(port.,v.1) 18cm.

NL 0444417   CtY CU

Loen, Johann Michael, Freiherr von, 1694–1776
Gesammlete kleine Schrifften. Besorgt und hrsg. von J.C.Schneidern. Franckfurt, Bey Huttern, 1750-52
4 v.
Vol.4: hrsg. von J.B.Müllern
Imprint of v.4: Franckfurt, Brönner

NL 0444418   MH

PT2424
L63A1
1750

Loen, Johann Michael, Freiherr von, 1694–1776.
Gesammlete kleine Schriften; besorgt und heraus gegeben von J.C. Schneidern. Franckfurt, H. Huttern, 1750-51 [v.1, 1751]
2 v. in 1. port.

Vol. 1, 3. Aufl.

NL 0444419   CU

Zg17
L818
751

Loën, Johann Michael, freiherr von, 1694–1776
... Gesammlete kleine Schrifften: besorgt und heraus gegeben von J.C.Schneidern ... Franckfurt und Leipzig,Zu finden bey P. H.Huttern,1751,'50.
2v.in 1. fronts.(incl.port.) 18cm.

NL 0444420   CtY

Ca5
L81
751

Loën, Johann Michael, Freiherr von, 1694–1776.
Des Herrn von Loen Gesammlete kleine Schrifften: besorgt und heraus gegeben von J.C. Schneidern ... Franckfurt und Leipzig, Zu finden bey P.H.Huttern,1751-52.
4v. fronts.(v.1,port.) 17cm.
Vol.1, 3. Auflage; vol.2, 2. Auflage; vol.3-4 without edition-note.
Vol.4, "Besorgt und heraus gegeben von J.B. Müllern ... Franckfurt und Leipzig,Bey H.L.Bronner,1752."

NL 0444421   CtY MH CU

AC33
.L82

Loen, Johann Michael, Freiherr von, 1694–1776.
Des Herrn von Loen gesammlete kleine Schriften, besorgt und heraus gegeben von J. C. Schneidern. Franckfurt und Leipzig, H. L. Brönner, 1751-56.
4 v. port.
Erster Th., 4. Aufl., 1753; 2. Th., 3. Aufl. 1756. 4. Th. besorgt und herausgegeben von J. B. Müller.

NL 0444422   ICU

BR
75
L6

Loen, Johann Michael von, 1694–1776.
Des Herrn von Loen gesammlete kleine Schrifften von Kirchen- und Religions-Sachen Zur Erläuterung der bey seiner einzigen wahren Religion ihm angedichteten ungleichen Meynungen eines unlauteren Syncretismi, besorget und hrsg. von Osterländer. Franckfurt, Philipp Heinrich Hutter, 1751.
[30,420[25,p.
1. Theology - Collected works - 18th cent. 2. Enlig   htenment.

NL 0444423   MoSCS

Loën, Johann Michael, *freiherr von*, 1694–1776.
Johann Michael von Loen, Goethes grossoheim (1694–1776), sein leben, sein wirken und eine auswahl aus seinen schriften, von dr. Siegfried Sieber. Mit einem bildnis. Leipzig, P. Schraepler, 1922.
237 p. front. (port.) 18⅓ᵐᵐ.
CONTENTS.—Loens leben.—Loen und Goethe.—Loens schriften.—Auswahl aus Loens werken (p. 175)–233)—Verzeichnis von Loens werken p. (234)–237).
1. Goethe, Johann Wolfgang von, 1749-1832. ɪ. Sieber, Siegfried, 1885- ed.

24-5082

Library of Congress   PT2424.L63 1922

NL 0444424   DLC CU CtY

VOLUME 338

A85.2l [Loën, Johann Michael, Freiherr von] 1694-1776.
Lettres curieuses d'un gentilhomme allemand, pour l'année 1741[-1742] touchant les moeurs & les afaires du tems. t.1-3. A Francfort sur le Mayn,Chez Jean Frederic Fleischer[etc., 1741-42]
3v. in 1. 17cm.

Imprint varies: t.1, A Franckfort sur le M., Chez Jean Friederic Fleischer; t.2, A Francfort sur le Mayn,Chez Antoine Heinscheit imprimeur; t.3, A Francfort sur le Mayn,Chez Jean Frederic Fleischer.

Contents: Tome I, Lettre I-XXII, 1741.- Tome II, Lettre I-XVII, 1741.- Tome III, Lettre I-IX, 1742.

NL 0444426   CtY

Loen, Johann Michael,Freiherr von, 1694-1776.
Moralische gedichte; hrsg. von Naumann.
Franckfurt, 1751.

NL 0444427   NjP

Loen, Johann Michael, *Freiherr* von, 1694-1776.
Разсужденіе объ истлѣніи и сожженіи всѣхъ вещей, по чудесамъ онаго въ царствѣ натуры и благодати, относительно къ большому и малому міру. Переводъ съ 4. изд. на нѣмецкомъ языкѣ печатаннаго. Москва, Въ Тип. Н. С. Всеволожскаго, 1816.
177 p. 21 cm.
Title in Hebrew precedes Russian title.

1. Microcosm and macrocosm.   I. Title.
Title transliterated: Razsuzhdenie ob istlienii i sozhzhenii vsiekh veshchei.

BD508.R8L65 1816   55-52427

NL 0444428   DLC

[Loen, Johan Michael, Freiherr von, 1694-1775]
Der redliche Mann am Hofe, oder die Begebenheiten des Grafens von Rivera....Vorgestellt von dem Herrn von*** Frankfurth am Mayn, Jung, 1742

NL 0444429   MH

Loen, Johann Michael, Freiherr von, 1694-1776
Der redliche Mann am Hofe, oder Die Begebenheiten des Grafens von Rivera. Verb.Ausg. Mit einer critischen Beurtheilung von dem Herren von Loen. Franckfurt a.M., Jung, 1751
552 p.

NL 0444430   MH

Loen, Johann Michael, Freiherr von, 1694-1776.
Sod riḳvah u-serefah
see his   Das Geheimnuss der Verwesung und Verbrennung aller Dinge.

U O .517 [LOEN, JOHANN MICHAEL, Freiherr VON] 1694-1776.
Le soldat, ou Le metier de la guerre considéré comme le metier d'honneur. Avec un essai de bibliotheque militaire par Monsieur de**. Francfort sur le Mayn,J.F.Fleischer,1743.
310,167p. front. 17cm.

"Bibliotheque militaire" has special t.-p. and separate pagination.

NL 0444432   ICN N

Loen, Johann Michael, Freiherr von, 1694-1776
Der Soldat, oder Abhandlung vom Kriegs-Stand. Aus dem Französischen. Neue verb.und verm.Aufl. Frankfurt, Fleischer, 1752
460 p. front.

NL 0444433   MH

LOEN, Johann Michael, Freiherr von, 1694-1776.
Systeme de la religion universelle pour la reuion des chretiens. n.p., 1753.
nar.16°. pp. 32.   C 1279.10

NL 0444434   MH

Me65 L824 V4 [Loën, Johann Michael, Freiherr von] 1694-1776.
La véritable religion, unique dans son espèce, universelle dans ses principes, corrompue par les disputes des théologiens, divisée en plusieurs sectes, réunies en Christ. Francfort, J. F. Fleischer, 1751.
2 v. in 1. 18 cm.

NL 0444435   CtY

[Loen, Johann Michael, Freiherr von, 1694-1776]
Vorläuffige Gedancken über die Religion zur Vereinigung der Christen. Aus dem Französischen übers. np, 1749
32 p.

NL 0444436   MH

LOEN, Justus Abraham van.
Aanmerkingen op den brief des heeren D. van Lennep.. Amsterdam, etc., [1804?]

NL 0444437   MH

Wason Film 3160 no.5 Loen, Justus Abraham van.
Aanmerkingen op den brief des heeren D. van Lennep. Amsterdam, Schalekamp en Schooneveld [1804]
36 p.

Microfilm. 1 reel. 35mm.
Filmed with: Huysers, A. Beknopte beschryving der Oostindische etablissementen. [Amsterdam, 1792]
1. Lennep, David van. Brief. I. Title.

NL 0444438   NIC

Loën, S.   **M.442.28
L'imère. L'imera. Scène lyrique de salon. Scena lirica per salotto. Paroles et musique de S. Loën. Partition piano, chant, violon.
— [Paris. Pfister. 1911.] (4), 31 pp. 27½ cm.
The words are in French and Italian.

K4002 — T.r. — Operas.

NL 0444439   MB

Loën, S.   **M.417-43
Irénis. Irenide. Scène lyrique de salon. Scena lirica per salotto. Paroles et musique de S. Loën. Partition piano, chant, violon.
— Paris. Pfister. 1911. (4), 32 pp. 27½ cm.

K4134 — T.r. — Operas.

NL 0444440   MB

Loën, S.   **M.442.40
Sur l'Euryale. Scène lyrique de salon. Paroles et musique de S. Loën. Partition piano, chant, violon (et harpe ad libitum).
= Paris. Pfister. [190-?] (4), 64 pp. 28 cm.

K4306 — T.r. — Operas.

NL 0444441   MB

Loën, Waldemar, Freiherr von, 1884-
Das Erfordernis der ministeriellen Gegenzeichnung nach dem Staatsrecht Preussens und des Deutschen Reichs ... von Waldemar Freiherrn von Loën ... Borna-Leipzig, R. Noske, 1907.
1 p.l., [v]-x, 68, [1] p. 22cm.
Inaug.-diss. - Breslau.
"Lebenslauf": p.[69]
"Literaturverzeichnis": p.[vii]-x.

NL 0444442   MH-L NN ICRL

Løn og virke.
København, Samvirkende fagforbund i Danmark.
v. in   illus. 30 cm. semimonthly.
Title varies: -1956, Arbejderen.
Began publication in 1904. Cf. Union list of serials.
1942-44, microfilm copy (positive) made by the Library of Congress (Microfilm 0235 HD)

1. Labor and laboring classes—Denmark—Period.   I. Samvirkende fagforbund i Danmark.

HD8542.A68   53-35518 rev

NL 0444443   DLC NN DL

Loenartz, Alois
see Loenartz, Friedrich Aloys.

Loenartz, Friedrich Aloys.
Obstbau im Haus- und Kleingarten. 1. Aufl. Essen, W. Girardet, 1948.
111 p. illus. 21 cm.

1. Fruit-culture—Germany.

SB359.L58   634   51-15850

NL 0444445   DLC

Loenartz, Friedrich Aloys.
Der praktikus; handbuch für den praktischen landwirt, das ergebnis jahrelanger praktischer erfahrungen und beobachtungen hervorragender fachmänner zusammengestellt und mitbearb. von diplom-landwirt Al. Loenartz. 2., verm. und verb. aufl. Essen, W. Girardet [1925]

VOLUME 338

Loenartz (Michael). *De sudore sanguineo.*
20 pp. 8°. *Bonna, lit. L. Anachelii,* 1850. [*Also,
in* • P v. 579]
C.

NL 0444447   DNLM

BT
1946
.L82
Loenartz, Peter Josef
Die restitutionspflicht des besitzers
fremden gutes. Eine theologische-
juristische abhandlung, von Peter
Josef Loenartz... Trier, Paulinus-
Druckerei, 1885.
xii,295p. 23cm.

NL 0444448   DCU MH

Loenartz, Theresia, *schwester.*
... Mutter Rita Scheuer. Kirnach-Villingen, Baden, **Verlag**
der Schulbrüder, 1935.
xi p., 2 l., 3–336 p. front. (port.) 19½ᵐ.
"Verzeichnis der quellen und der literatur": p. xi.

1. Scheuer, Rita, mutter, 1880–1925.

Library of Congress   BX4705.S513L6   35–17216
Copyright A—Foreign   27705
                                  922.243

NL 0444449   DLC OrStbM

Lönarz, Alois, Referendar: Die polizeiliche Auflösung von
Versammlungen nach dem Reichsvereinsgesetz vom 19. April
1908. Greifswald 1913: Abel. 77 S. 8°
Greifswald, Jur. Diss. v. 7. Mai 1913, Ref. Hubrich
[Geb. 27. Okt. 86 Bruttig; Wohnort: Godesberg; Staatsangeh.: Preußen;
Vorbildung: G. Hadamar Reife 08; Studium: Freiburg 1, München 2, Bonn
4 S.; Rig. 28. Jan. 13.]   [U 13.653]

NL 0444450   ICRL MH-L NN

Loenartz (Franciscus) [1867–]. *De sensu
rei futurae praesagiendi.* 2 p. l., 34 pp., 1 l. 4°.
Bonna, ex off. Neusseriana, [1833].

NL 0444451   DNLM PPC

Lönberg, Erik Gustav, respondent.
De siti febrili
see under   Acrel, Johan Gustaf, praeses.

Lönberg, Erik Gustav, respondent.
Ratio plantas in sedecim classes disponendi ...
see under   Liljeblad, Samuel, 1761–1815,
praeses.

WU
101
L825c
1951
LÖNBERG, Pontus
Changes in the size of the lower jaw
on account of age and loss of teeth.
[Tr. from the Swedish] Stockholm, 1951.
90 p. illus.
Contains errata slip.
1. Jaws 2. Old age

NL 0444454   DNLM MiU OC1W CLSU OU PU-D ICU NNC

Lönberg-Holm, Knud, 1895–
Catalog design, by K. Lönberg-Holm and **Ladislav Sutnar.**
[New York] Sweet's catalog service [1944]
[71] p. illus. (part col.) diagrs. (part col.) 21ᵐ.
"Published 1944 by Sweet's catalog service—division of F. W. Dodge
corporation."

1. Catalogs, Commercial.   I. Sutnar, Ladislav, joint author.
II. Sweet's catalog service.   III. Title.
                                        45–365
Library of Congress °   HF5862.L6
                                        659.13

NL 0444455   DLC CaBVa OrU WaS NIC OCU

Lönberg-Holm, Knud, 1895–
Catalog design progress, by K. Lönberg-Holm and Ladislav Sutnar. [New York] Sweet's Catalog Service [1950]
1 v. (unpaged) illus. (part col.) 25 x 32 cm.

1. Catalogs, Commercial.   I. Sutnar, Ladislav, joint author.
II. Title.
HF5862.L6 1950   659.13   50–11091

        IdU OrU WaS MtBC   CaBVaU OrMonO WaS
NL 0444456   DLC ViU MB TxU CU NN FMU FTaSU AAP CoU

NC
997
.L84
Lönberg-Holm, Knud, 1895–
Designing information by K. Lönberg-Holm and
Ladislav Sutnar. [New York, Whitney publications,
inc., 1947]
cover-title, [20] l. illus. (part col.) 30½ᶜᵐ.
"Reprinted from Interiors, February, March, April,
1947."

1. Commercial art. 2. Design. I. Sutnar, Ladislav,
joint author. II. Title.

NL 0444457   MiU OrU

Lönberg-Holm, Knud, 1895–
Development index; a proposed pattern for organizing and
facilitating the flow of information needed by man in fur-
thering his own development, with particular reference to
the development of buildings and communities and other
forms of environmental control [by K. Lönberg-Holm and
C. Theodore Larson. Ann Arbor, University of Michigan
Press, 1953]
unpaged. illus. 29 cm. (Architecture and planning series)

1. Methodology.   I. Larson, Carl Theodore, 1906–   joint author.
II. Title.
BD241.L72   720.1   53–19118 ‡

    NIC PU-FA NbU Wa NN
NL 0444458   DLC OrU NcRS TxU OU NSyU AU OkU KyU

Lönberg-Holm, Knud, 1895–
Planning for productivity, by K. Lönberg-Holm and C.
Theodore Larson. [New York city, N. Y., International industrial relations institute, 1940]
cover-title, 43, [1] p. incl. fold. tables. 25 x 19ᵐ. [International industrial relations institute. Technical series. no. 1]
"Printed in the Netherlands."

1. Industry—Organization, control, etc. 2. Efficiency, Industrial. 3.
Building trades.   I. Larson, Carl Theodore, 1908–   joint author.
II. Title.   III. Title: Productivity.
                                    A 40–2399
Virginia. Univ. Library
for Library of Congress

NL 0444459   ViU MH NIC NN MoS

Loenbom, Johannes Fredericus, respondent.
Dissertatio symbolico-theologica sententiam
ecclesiae romano-catholicae
see under   Butsch, Johanne Albertus,
praeses.

[LOENBOM, Samuel, 1725–1776.]
Anecdoter om namnkunniga och märkwärdiga
swenska män. Stockholm, J.A.Carlbohm, 1770–75.

3 vol.
                      Scan 3361.18

NL 0444461   MH NN

4DL
Swed.
516
Loenbom, Samuel, 1725–1776.
Handlingar til Konung Carl XI:tes
historia. Stockholm, Tryckte pa
L. Salvii kostnad, 1763–
v..1–4

NL 0444462   DLC-P4 NN IU CU

Loenbom, Samuel, 1725–1776, comp.
Historiska märkwärdigheter, til uplysning af swenska
häfder. [2. uppl.] Stockholm, Tryckt i Kongl. Finska
boktryckeriet, 1768–1781.
4 v. in 2. 19 cm.
Vol. 2: Tryckt hos Wennberg & Nordström; v. 3: Tryckt hos L.
Kumblins änka; v. 4: Hos J. C. Holmberg.
"Konunga- och andra märkwärdiga bref, korta berättelser, histo-
riska utdrag och anmärkningar, m. m."
Includes bibliographical references.
L. C. copy replaced by microfilm.

1. Sweden—History—Sources.   I. Title.
[DL603.L642]   77–265446
Microfilm 28521 DL

NL 0444463   DLC

Lönbom, Samuel, 1725–1776.
Historiskt archivum.
Stockholm, 1774.
6 vols. 8vo.

NL 0444464   NN

Lönbom, Samuel, 1725–1776.
Observationes philologicae in linguam suigothicam
versionis scripturae canonicae veteris testamenti.
Upsaliae, 1755.
4to.

NL 0444465   NN

Lönbom, Samuel, 1725–1776.
Uplysninger i Swenska historien.
Stockholm, 1773–74.
8vo.

NL 0444466   NN

[Lönborg, Augusta]
Convolvler; dikter af Aster, [pseud.]
Uppsala, Tidn. Barnavännens förlag, [1901]
Port.

NL 0444467   MH

Lønborg, Hans Johansen, 1653–1727.
To beretninger fra Skanderborgegnen. Udg. af Hjem-
stavnsforeningen for Skanderborg og omegn i København.
Skanderborg, A. Møller, 1948.
48 p. 19 cm.
"Efterskrifter og kommentarer er udarbejdet af ... Chr. Holtet."
"300 nummererede eksemplarer hvoraf dette er nummer 108.
Includes the author's Beretning om Scanderborrig slott, 1727, and
Beretning om en graeselig orm, 1722.

1. Skanderborg, Denmark.   I. Hjemstavnsforeningen for Skanderborg og omegn, Copenhagen.   II. Title.
DL991.S545L6   57–3339

NL 0444468   DLC

VOLUME 338

Lönborg, Sven Erik, 1871–
Adam af Bremen och hans skildring af Nordeuropas
länder och folk ... Uppsala, H. Wretman, 1897.
v p., 1 l., 181, [1] p. 23ᶜᵐ.
Inaug.-dis.—Upsala.

1. Adamus Bremensis, 11th century.   4-4437

Library of Congress   G94.A2L8

NL 0444469   DLC CtY ICRL NIC PU

938
L824d
    LÖNBORG, SVEN ERIK, 1871–
    Dike och Eros, människor och makter i
    forntiden Aten. Stockholm, Svenska Andels-
    förlaget, 1920.
    2v. illus.,maps. 22cm.

    CONTENTS.—v.1. Staden. Statsmannen.
    Diktaren.—v.2. Den vise.

    1. Athens - Hist. 2. Greece - Biog. 3.
    Mythology, Greek I. Title.

NL 0444470   TxU

184
P71
XLon
1924
    Lönborg, Sven Erik, 1871–
    Dike und Eros; Menschen und Mächte
    im alten Athen. [Einzig autorisier-
    te Übertragung aus dem Schwedischen
    von Marie Franzos] München, C.H.
    Beck, 1924.
    471p. 23cm.

    CONTENTS.-Die Stadt.-Der Staats-
    mann.-Der Dichter.-Der Weise.

NL 0444471   CLSU ICU NRU LU CU MH NcD NjP

Lönborg, Sven Erik, 1871–
    ...Dike och Eros; människor och makter i forntidens Aten
... Stockholm: Svenska andelsförlaget, 1927.   2 v. in 1.
plates, ports.   8°.
    Contents: Del 1. Staden, statsmannen, diktaren. Del 2. Den vise.

1. Athens—Social life. 2. Euripides.   3. Socrates.
N. Y. P. L.   September 11, 1928

NL 0444472   NN

LÖNBORG, Sven, 1871–
Dike och Eros; människor och makter i forntidens aten. Uppsala och Stockholm, Almqvist & Wiksells boktryckeri-A.-B., [1932-37].

3 pt. 22 cm. Plates and maps.
Vol.I and II are "2ª tillökade upplagan".
Contents: 1.Staden,statsmannen,diktaren.-
ii.Den vise.- iii.Filosofen.

NL 0444473   MH

Lönborg, Sven Erik, 1871–
Ekkehart; ur mystikens tankevärld. Föreläsningar hållna vid Uppsala universitet på inbjudan av Olaus Petri-stiftelsen i november 1930, av Sven Lönborg. Stockholm: Wahlström & Widstrand[, 1931]. 206 p. 22½cm.

589761A. 1. Mysticism. 2. Eckhart,   Meister, ca. 1260-1327.
N. Y. P. L.   October 5, 1933

NL 0444474   NN

Lönborg, Sven Erik, 1871–
Från Viktor Rydbergs Göteborgstid. Göteborg, Elanders
boktr., 1934.
    110 p. 26 cm. (Göteborgs kungl. vetenskaps- och vitterhets-
samhälles handlingar, 5. följden, ser. A, bd. 4, n:o 2)
    "Inlämnad den 13 november 1933."

    1. Rydberg, Viktor, 1828-1895.   i. Series: Göteborgs kungl.
vetenskaps- och vitterhets-samhälle. Handlingar, 5. följden, ser. A,
bd. 4, no. 2.
    AS284.G7   föl. 5, ser. A, bd. 4, no. 2   A 48–3246*

Illinois. Univ. Library
for Library of Congress   [2]†

NL 0444475   IU PU CtY TxU DLC

Lönborg, Sven Erik, 1871–
Göteborgs högre Samskola, 1901-1911
see under Gothenburg, Sweden. Högre
samaskola.

Lönborg, Sven Erik, 1871–
Jésu de Nazara; traduit du suédois avec l'autorisation de l'auteur, par Fritiof Palmér.   Paris: M. Giard & É. Brière, 1915.
2 p.l., 257 p., 1 l.   8°.
    Author's name at head of title.

1. Jesus Christ. 2. Palmér, Fritiof,   1879-   , jt. translator.
N. Y. P. L.   April 10, 1917.

NL 0444477   NN

GN492 Lönborg, Sven Erik, 1871–
.L8   ... Der klan. Jena, E. Diederichs, 1921.
    [2], 40, [1] p. 20[ᶜᵐ].
    At head of title: Sven Lönborg.
    "Autorisierte übertragung aus dem schwedischen von Marie Franzos."

    1. Clans and clan system. 2. Family.

NL 0444478   ICU NN

Lönborg, Sven Erik, 1871–
Mellan Påsk och Pingst; det äldsta
evangeliet och Lukastraditionen-
Stockholm, P.A. Norstedt & söners
förlag [1945]
    162 p., 22½cm.

    Bibliographical references in "Tillägg
och anmärkningar": p. [153]-162.

NL 0444479   NjPT MH-AH

B
360
L82
    Lönborg, Sven Erik, 1871–
    Platons Eros; det sjunde brevet och
    Symposion. Stockholm, P. A. Norstedt
    [1939]
    78 p. 23cm. (Svenska humanistiska
    förbundet. [Skrifter] 49)

    1. Plato. Phaedrus. 2. Plato. Symposium.
    I. Title. II. Series.

NL 0444480   NIC

Lönborg, Sven Erik, 1871–
Den primitiva familjen. Stockholm, P.A.
Norstedt & Söners Förlag, (1916)
    40 p.   25 cm. (Populära etnologiska skrifter
    ... 13)
    Summary in English p. 39-40.

NL 0444481   MH-P

Lönborg, Sven Erik, 1871–
Religion och vetenskap, av Sven Lönborg. Stockholm, H. Gebers
förlag, [1914].
    [10, 3]-143 p. 21¼ᶜᵐ.
    "De här samlade artiklarna ha förut varit offentliggjorda i handelstidningen
och dagens nyheter."—Pref.
    Contents.—Religion och vetenskap (1911).—Det religiösa problemet (1913).
—Historisk religionsundervisning (1904; 1911).—Hädelse (1908).—Religions-
lärares lärofrihet (1912).—Lärofrihet och statskyrka (1912).—Biskopspetitionen
(1913).—Till Göteborgs studenter (1911).

NL 0444482   ICJ MH

Lönborg, Sven Erik, 1871–
Sveriges karta, tiden till omkring 1850, af Sven Lönborg. Utg. med understöd från Vilhelm Ekmans universitetsfond. Uppsala, I distribution hos Almqvist & Wiksells boktryckeri-a.-b. [1903]
    vi, 242 p. 25ᶜᵐ. [Arbeten utgifna med understöd af Vilhelm Ekmans
universitetsfond, Uppsala, 2]

1. Cartography—Sweden—Hist. 2. Sweden—Descr. & trav.—Maps.
                                                         3-27706
Library of Congress   GA991.L84

NL 0444483   DLC CtY ICJ NjP

Lönborg, Sven Erik, 1871– *ed.*
Swedish maps. First series. Stockholm, Generalstabens
litografiska anstalt [1907]
    8 p., 15 maps (in portfolio) 51 cm.
    Text describing these maps published in the author's "Sveriges
karta," 1908.
    No more published?

    1. Sweden—Maps.

                                                    Map 49–953*

NL 0444484   DLC

PT9788
.Z5L6
    Lönborg, Sven Erik, 1871–
    Viktor Rydbergs kärlekssaga. [Malmö] Gleerup [1950]
    217 p. illus., ports. (1 col.) facsims. 22 cm.

    1. Rydberg, Viktor, 1828-1895.
                                                         A 51–6225
    Minnesota. Univ. Libr.
    for Library of Congress   [2]

NL 0444485   MnU NN WaU ICU NcD DLC

Lönd og lýðir. 1.–   bd.
Reykjavík, Bókaútgáfa menningarsjóðs, 1949–
    v. illus. 22 cm.

1. Geography—Collections.
    G58.L6   55-24091

NL 0444486   DLC

Löndahl, Hjalmar, 1859–
Bidrag till kännedomen om platinasulfinbasernas konstitution, af Hjalmar Löndahl. Lund: Berlingska boktryckeri- och
stilgjuteri-Aktiebolaget, 1892. 47 p. 4°. (Lund. Universitet. Acta Universitatis Lundensis. Lunds universitets årsskrift.
Tomus 27, afdelning 2[, no. 3].)
    Bibliographical footnotes.

1. Platinum—Salts.
N. Y. P. L.   December 28, 1925

NL 0444487   NN

VOLUME 338

Löndahl, Hjalmar, 1859–
Inverkan af alkoholiskt natriumetylat på ättikester och benzaldehyd, af Hjalmar Löndahl.   Lund: Berlingska boktryckeri- och stilgjuteri-aktiebolaget, 1893.   8 p.   4°.   (Lund. Universitet. Acta Universitatis Lundensis. Lunds universitets årsskrift. Tomus 29, afdelning 2(, no. 3).)

Bibliographical footnotes.

1. Acetone.   2. Benzaldehyde.
N. Y. P. L.   December 29, 1925

NL 0444488 NN

Löndahl, Hjalmar, 1859–
Platinasulfinföreningar af normalbutyl, isobutyl och benzyl, af Hjalmar Löndahl.   Lund: C. W. K. Gleerup, 1887–1888.   51 p. 4°.   (Lund. Universitet. Acta Universitatis Lundensis. Lunds universitets årsskrift. Tomus 24, afdelning 2(, no. 4).)

Bibliographical footnotes.

1. Platinum—Salts.
N. Y. P. L.   December 28, 1925

NL 0444489 NN

Loendahl, Hjalmar, 1859 –
Platinasulfinfoereningar af normalbutyl, isobutyl
och benzyl. Lund, 1888.
In. Diss.

NL 0444490 ICRL

Loenderdon, J
De emigrant te Hoboken. Tweede vertoog;
behelzende: De onverwagte wederkomst van
Loenderdon. Klugtspel. Waarin de schryver
zig zelve bedoeld. Antwerpen, bij J. Strembuch,
MDCCLXXXIX/ (1789)
40 p.

NL 0444491 MiU-C

Löne- och verkstadsreglemente [för möbelsnickare]. Stockholm, 189–.
Caption title, [48] p. 15½ᶜᵐ.
[45] p. blank.

NL 0444492 ICJ

Lönegren, Ernst, bp.
Johan Christoffer Bring, en föregångsman inom diakonien Sveriges kyrka, av Ernst Lönegren... Stockholm, Svenska kyrkans diakonistyrelses bokförlag (1926) 268 p. illus. 20cm.

1. Bring, Iohan Christofer,   1829–1898.

NL 0444493 NN

QH9
.T6
no. 176
Rare bk.
Lönegren, Fredric Isaac, 1781–1852, respondent.
Thunberg, Karl Peter, 1743–1828, præses.
Dissertatio de ricino ... Upsaliæ, excudebant Zeipel et Palmblad (1815)

Lönegren, Holger, 1901–
Genealogia Caroli Frederici Björnbergi, curavit Holger Lönegren. (Ekenäs) Ekenäs tryckeri aktiebolags förlag, 1948. 159 p.   illus.   25cm.

Half-title in Swedish and Finnish: Carl Fredrik Björnberg, släktbok — sukukirja.
Bibliography, p. 136–137.

574357B.   1. Björnberg family.
N. Y. P. L.   November 27, 1951

NL 0444495 NN

Lönegren (Johan   Per)
Momenta quædam terminorum usum spectantia. Upsaliæ, 1806. 1 p.l., 8 pp. 4°.

NL 0444496 NN

Lönegren (Johan Per)
Om slåttertiden. Upsala, 1803.   1 p.l., 8 pp.   4°.

NL 0444497 NN

Lönegren, Karin.
Svenska folkvisor; arrangement för piano med text av K. Lönegren. Stockholm: Elkan & Schildknecht, E. Carelius (cop. 1922). Publ. pl. no. E. C. 321.   35 p.   f°.

Arranged for piano with superlinear Swedish words.
t.-p. illustrated in color.

Juilliard Foundation Fund.

1. Folk songs (Swedish).
N. Y. P. L.   April 29, 1924.

NL 0444498 NN

Loenen, Dirk.
De Atheense democratie, drogbeeld of historie? Amsterdam, Noord-Hollandsche Uitg. Mij., 1946.
28 p. 25 cm.
Bibliographical footnotes.

1. Athens—Pol. & govt.   I. Title.

JC79.A8L6   54–25528

NL 0444499 DLC MH

Loenen, Dirk.
Athene, Hellas van Hellas. Amsterdam, Noord-Hollandsche Uitgeversmij., 1947.
155 p. 22 cm.   (Uit leven en wetenschap, 13)

1. Philosophy, Ancient.   2. Greece—Civilization.   I. Title.
(Series)
B178.L6   55–36408

NL 0444500 DLC MH-L NNC

Loenen, Dirk.
Basileia; oud-Griekse opvattingen over het koningschap. Amsterdam, Noord-Hollandsche Uitg. Mij., 1950.
42 p. 23 cm.
Rede—Amsterdam (aanvaarding van het ambt van bijzonder hoogleraar) 1950.
Bibliographical references included in "Aanteekeningen" (p. 34–42)

1. Divine right of kings.   2. Greece—Kings and rulers.   I. Title.
JC379.L6   A 52–6769
Princeton Univ. Libr.
for Library of Congress   (3)†

NL 0444501 NjP DLC NN

Loenen, Dirk.
Het conservatief-aristocratisch karakter van Plato's staatsphilosophie ... Leiden, S. C. van Doesburgh, 1923.
4, 82 p., 1 l. 25ᶜᵐ.
Proefschrift—Amsterdam.

1. Plato. Respublica.
24–28040

Library of Congress   JC71.P6L6 1923

NL 0444502 DLC IU

Loenen, Dirk.
Het cultuur-ideaal van Aristoteles, door dr D. Loenen ... Assen, Van Gorcum & comp. n. v., 1940.
20 p. 24½ᶜᵐ. (Vragen-van-nu, nr 33)
"Overdruk uit 'Tijdschrift voor wijsbegeerte,' jrg. 33 afl. 4 april 1940."
Bibliographical foot-notes.

1. Aristoteles.
46–40252
Library of Congress   B485.L6
185.1

NL 0444503 DLC ICRL NNC ICU

Loenen, Dirk.
Diké, een historisch-semantische analyse van het Griekse gerechtigheidsbegrip. Amsterdam. Noord-Hollandsche Uitg. Mij., 1948.
101 p. 24 cm. (Mededelingen der Koninklijke Nederlandsche Akademie van Wetenschappen. Afd. Letterkunde. Nieuwe reeks, deel 11, no. 6)
Cover title.
Pages also numbered 159–259.
Bibliographical footnotes.
1. Diké (The word)   2. Law, Greek.   3. Law—Philosophy.   (Series: Akademie van Wetenschappen, Amsterdam. Afdeeling voor de Taal-, Letter-, Geschiedkundige en Wijsgeerige Wetenschappen. Verslagen en mededeelingen. Nieuwe reeks, deel 11, no. 6)
AS244.A51 n. r.,   deel 11, no. 6   A 52–7442
———— Copy 2.
Chicago. Univ. Libr.
for Library of Congress   (3)†

NL 0444504 ICU DLC

4JC-
143
Loenen, Dirk.
De Grieksche grondslagen van de vrijheid.
Assen, Van Gorcum, 1938.
32 p. (Waakzaamheid, 2 reeks, brochure nr. 5)

NL 0444505 DLC-P4 NN CSt-H

Gfs63
y949ℓ
Loenen, Dirk
Het Griekse geweten; Socrates en Athene.
Arnhem, Van Loghum Slaterus, 1949.
62p. plate, port. 22cm. (Gastmaal der
eeuwen)

1. Socrates.

NL 0444506 CtY NNC ICU

Loenen, Dirk.
Helleense vormingsidealen uit de 5e en 4e eeuw voor Christus. Purmerend, J. Muusses, 1948.
36 p. 16 x 16 cm.

NL 0444507 OU

Loenen, Dirk.
Mens en maatschappij in Plato's
"Republiek"... Assen, 1935.
23 p. ("Vragen-van-nu." 16)

NL 0444508 NjP CU

VOLUME 338

PA4456
.D8A5
1939

Loenen, Dirk, tr.

Thucydides.
De ondergang der Meliërs, een gesprek tusschen gevolmachtigden van een grooten en een kleinen staat en het jaar 416 vóór Christus naar de berichtgeving van Thucydides in zijn boek over den Peloponnesischen oorlog; vertaald door D. Loenen. Amsterdam, Wereldbibliotheek-Vereeniging, 1939.

NL 0444510　　NN MH NNC

LOENEN, DIRK.
Plato's reserve tegenover het actieve staatsleven. Amsterdam, De Beuk [1955] 30 p. 19cm. (Serie A van De Beuk. [no.] 3, deel 1)

1. Plato. I. Serie A van De　　　　　Beuk.

NL 0444510　　NN MH NNC

AS244
.A51
n. r.,
deel 16,
no. °

Loenen, Dirk.
Polemos, een studie over oorlog in de Griekse oudheid. Amsterdam, Noord-Hollandsche Uitg. Mij., 1953.
97 p. 24 cm. (Mededelingen der Koninklijke Nederlandsche Akademie van Wetenschappen. Afd. Letterkunde. Nieuwe reeks, deel 16, no. 3)
Pages also numbered ₍71₎–167.
Bibliographical footnotes.
1. Military art and science—Greece. I. Title.　(Series: Akademie van Wetenschappen, Amsterdam. Afdeeling voor de Taal, Letter-, Geschiedkundige en Wijsgeerige Wetenschappen. Verslagen en mededeelingen. Nieuwe reeks, deel 16, no. 3)
[AS244.A51　n. r., deel 16, no. 3]　　A 53-8190

Chicago. Univ. Libr.
for Library of Congress　　　　₍2₎

NL 0444511　　ICU DLC

Loenen, Dirk.
Protagoras and the Greek community, by Dr. D. Loenen. Amsterdam, N. v. noord-hollandsche uitgevers maatschappij ₍1941₎
4 p. l., 129 p. 22½ᶜᵐ.
Bibliographical foot-notes.

1. Protagoras, the Sophist, 5th cent. B. C.　2. Political science.

Library of Congress　　　B305.P84L6
42-1292
188.1

CaBVaU OU CLU NcD MB PU NcU
NL 0444512　　DLC ICU NNC TNJ NIC NBuU NBC MoU CtY

DF82
.5
.L65

Loenen, Dirk.
Stasis; enige aspecten van de begrippen partij- en klassenstrijd in Oud-Griekenland. Amsterdam, Noord-Hollandsche Uitg. Mij., 1953.
48 p. 24 cm.
Rede—Amsterdam (aanvaarding van het ambt van gewoon hoogleraar) 1953.
Bibliographical references included in "Aantekeningen" (p. 39-48)

1. Greece—Pol. & govt.　I. Title.

A 54-320

Cincinnati. Univ. Libr.
for Library of Congress

NL 0444513　　OCU DLC NN

PA4275
.D8L6

Loenen, Dirk, tr.

Pindarus.
De vierde pythische ode van Pindaros, behelzende het oudste verhaal over den tocht der Argonauten, vertaald door dr D. Loenen. Amsterdam, Wereldbibliotheek-vereeniging, 1940.

Loenen, Dirk
... Vrijheid en gelijkheid in Athene, een onderzoek naar de geschiedenis, den inhoud en de functi van de begrippen vrijheid en gelijkheid in Athene tijdens de 5ᵉ en 4e eeuw voor Christus. Amsterdam, Seyffardt, 1930.
324 p. 23½ cm.

At head of title: Dr. D. Loenen.
Bibliography: p. ₍325₎

1. Athens - History　　2. Greece - Civilization.

NL 0444515　　NNC NIC CLU ICU

BS3650
.Z7L8

Loenen, Jacobus van.
Het evangelie van Paulus ... Groningen, F. Wilkens, 1863.
₍iii₎-xvi, 152, ₍8₎ p. 22½ᶜᵐ.
Proefschrift—Groningen.

1. Paul, Saint, apostle—Theology.

NL 0444516　　ICU

Loenen, Jacques Cornelis van
De Haarlemse brouwindustrie vóór 1600. Amsterdam, Jasonpers, Universiteitspers ₍1950₎
159 p. illus., tables.

Thesis, Amsterdam.
Bibliography: p. 152-159.

1. Brewing industries - Haarlem.

NL 0444517　　NNC MH CtY ICU IEN

Loenen, Janus Everardus van
... De testium fide in inquisitione praevia criminali jurejurando firmanda ... submittit Janus Everardus van Loenen ... Trajecti ad Rhenum, C. Bielevelt, 1846.
2 p.l., ₍vii₎-ix, 62 p. 22cm.
Diss.- Utrecht.
Bibliographical footnotes.

NL 0444518　　MH-L

Loenen, Johan Willem Adriaan Cornelis van, 1867–
De gemeentewet en hare toepassing, door J. W. A. C. van Loenen ... met medewerking van mr. S. J. Blaupot ten Cate ... Alphen (Z.-H.) N. Samsom, 1911-19.
3 v. 25ᶜᵐ.
Originally issued in parts.
Vol. 3, "met medewerking van mrs. Blaupot ten Cate."
Bibliography precedes text of each volume.
Contents.—1. deel. Artikelen 1-119.—2. deel. Artikelen 120-202.—3. deel. Artikelen 203-294.
JS5934.L6

—————— Eerste vervolg. Alphen a. d. Rijn, N. Samsom, 1922.
xl, 204 p. 25ᶜᵐ.

1. Municipal corporations—Netherlands.　2. Municipal government—Netherlands.　I. Netherlands (Kingdom, 1815–　) Laws, statutes, etc.　II. Blaupot ten Cate, Steven Jan, 1867–　III. Blaupot ten Cate, Herman, 1875–　IV. Title.
36-31483
Library of Congress　　　JS5934.L6　1. vervolg
352.0492

NL 0444520　　DLC

4JS
80

Loenen, Johan Willem Adriaan Cornelis van, 1867-
De gemeentewet en haar toepassing. 2., geheel herziene, druk. Alphen aan den Rijn, N. Samsom, 1934.
2 v. (1403 p.)

————— Eerste vervolg. 2., geheel herziene, druk. Alphen aan den Rijn, N. Samsom, 1938.
136 p.

NL 0444521　　DLC-P4

K8.P70
z951L

Loenen, Johannes Hubertus Mathias Marie
De nous in het systeem van Plato's philosophie; onderzoekingen betreffende de verhouding nous-psyche, de ontwikkeling der teleologische natuurverklaring en haar plaats in het systeem. Amsterdam, [1951]
viii,297p. 24cm.
Academisch proefschrift - Amsterdam.
Summary in English and French.
"Stellingen": [4]p.,inserted.
Bibliography: p.293-297.

OrU DLC-P4
NL 0444522　　CtY ICU IU NNC IEN NIC OCU MH MiU NcD

W 4
G87
1797
L.1

LOENEN, Reinhardus van
Dissertatio medico-practica inauguralis, de dolore faciei convulsivo ... Groningae, Apud Joannem Oomkens [1797]
50 p. 20 cm.
Diss. - Groningen.

NL 0444523　　DNLM

Loenen Martinet, J. van.
Over "den normalen arbeidsdag." Rede uitgensproken op de Mei-meeting te Haarlem. [Haarlem?: 1891?]
15 p.　12°.
n. t. p.
Repr.: Herrorming, 16 Mei, 1891.

NL 0444524　　NN

Loenen. Nederlandsch hervormde Kerk.
Kerkgeschiedenis van Loenen en Silven. Gedenkboek...
　see under　Burgt, G　　J　　van der.

741.9
M997ch
1589

LOENER, Josua, 1535-1595.
Eine christliche Predigt/uber das Sprüchlein aus dem siebenzehenden Psalm dess Königlichen Propheten Dauids...Gehalten zu Wittenberg inn der Schlosskirchen/bey der Visitation dess Churfürstenthums Sachsen/dem 19.Julij/ Anno 92. Durch M.Josua Lonern ... Gedruckt zu Leipzig/ bey Johann:Beyer/Im Jahr: M.D.XCij.
₍19₎p.　20.5cm.
Signatures: A-B，　C².
No. 18 in bound　　volume of 16th century tracts.

NL 0444526　　MH-AH

608.2
M97.4dre
1592

LOENER, Josua, 1535-1595.
Eine Predigt/ welche geschehen ist zu Weissenfels den 6. Septembris, Anno 1592 ...Gedruckt zu Leipzig/ bey Johan: Beyer. M.D.XCij.
[22]p.　20cm.

Signatures: A-C⁴, last leaf blank.
Colophon with printer's mark.
Title vignette.
No.8 in a　　　volume of 16th century　　　works.

NL 0444527　　MH-AH

VOLUME 338

Loener, Josua, 1535-1595.
*GC5 Zwo christliche, lehr vnd trosthafftige
A100 Predigten: eine am Sontag Reminiscere, die
B598p andere desz Dienstages hernach den 22.
Februarij dieses 1592. Jahrs, zum Anfang desz
angestelten Landtages zu Torgaw, inn grosser
Versamlung, geschehen durch M. Josua Lonern ...
Leipzig, bey Johan:Beyer, jm Jahr:M.D.XCij.
4°. [39]p. 1 illus. 20cm.
Signatures: A-E⁴.
Printer's marks on t.-p. & recto of last leaf.
No.11 in a   volume of 16th-century
tracts.

NL 0444528   MH

Loenertz, Paul.
Die Formen der Gewinn- und Verlust-Rechnung, von Dr.
Paul Loenertz ...   Leipzig: G. A. Gloeckner, 1926.   x, 138 p.
incl. tables.   8°.   (Zeitschrift für handelswissenschaftliche
Forschung. Ergänzungsbände. Bd. 9.)

Bibliography, p. [vii]-[viii.

1. Accounting—Balance sheet.   2. Ser.
N.Y.P.L.   April 22, 1927

NL 0444529   NN CU IU

Loenertz, Raymond Joseph, 1900-
The Apocalypse of Saint John [tr. of Loenertz'
commentary]
see under Bible. N.T. Revelation. English.
1947. Reims. (also 1948)

Loenertz, Raymond Joseph, 1900 —
BX4705
.K25A4 Kalekas, Manouël, d. 1410.
Correspondance, publiée par Raymond-J. Loenertz. Città
del Vaticano, Biblioteca apostolica vaticana, 1950.

Loenertz, Raymond Joseph, 1900 -
922.22 La légende parisienne de S. Denys l'Aréo-
D395L pagite; sa genèse et son premier témoin. Brux-
elles, Société des Bollandistes, 1951.
237 p.   25cm.
Cover title.
Extract from Analecta Bollandiana, vol.
LXIX.
Bibliographical footnotes.

NL 0444532   NcD

Loenertz, Raymond Joseph, 1900-
L'Oridine di San Domenico e la chiesa di S.
Giorgio di Pera in Constantinopoli.
Extracts from Memorie domenicane; rivista di
religione, storia, aria, arte, Anno 56, Fasc. 4-5,
1939, & Anno 57, Fasc. 1, 1940.

NL 0444533   DDO

Loenertz, Raymond Joseph, 1900 —
PA5310
.D4A83
Demetrius Cydonius.   FOR OTHER EDITIONS
                                   SEE MAIN ENTRY
Les recueils de lettres de Démétrius Cydonès [éd. par] Ray-
mond J. Loenertz. Città del Vaticano, Biblioteca aposto-
lica vaticana, 1947.

Loenertz, Raymond Joseph, 1900-
... La Société des frères pérégrinants; étude sur l'Orient
dominicain ...   Romae ad S. Sabinae, 1937-

v.   25 cm.   (Added t.-p.: Institutum historicum ff. praedicatorum.
Romae ad S. Sabinae.   Dissertationes historicae.   fasc. VII)

At head of title: R. Loenertz o. p.
Imprint on cover: Roma, Istituto storico dominicano, 1937-
"On se propose de pousser l'étude de la société jusqu'en 1500 ...
Dans ce premier volume l'histoire générale de la société ... sera
conduite jusqu'en 1374."—Préf.
"Ouvrages cités en abrégé": v. 1, p. [ix]-xii.

1. Societas fratrum peregrinantium propter Christum.   2. Dominicans in the East.

BX3546.A1L6   271.2   A C 38-2427 rev

Princeton Univ. Library
for Library of Congress   [r67c2]†

NL 0444535   NjP CtY NN OU CtY-D MH DLC

LOENERTZ, RAYMOND Joseph, 1900 —
Théodore Métochite et son père.

[184]-194.
In: Istituto storico Santa Sabina, Rome.
Archivum fratrum praedicatorum. v. 23, 1953.
Appears as an appendix to Deux nouveaux
ouvrages de Fr. Philippe Incontri de Péra O. P.,
by Thomas Kaeppeli.

NL 0444536   DDO

Löng, Schöng-Hang, 1910-
... Arbeitsversuche über den toten Punkt in
normalem Zustand und in künstlicher Alkalose und
Acidose ...   Charlottenburg [1937]
Inaug.-Diss. - Berlin.
Lebenslauf.
"Literaturnachweis": p. [23]

NL 0444537   CtY

Löng, Schöng-Nung, 1910-
... Die Aetiologie der Blasensteinkrankheit und
ihre Bedeutung für das endemische Vorkommen
derselben in der Kanton-Provinz in Südchina ...
Charlottenburg [1936]
Inaug.-Diss. - Berlin.
Lebenslauf.
"Literatur": p. [46]-55.

NL 0444538   CtY

W 4 Löng, Tsun-Yöng, 1913-
B51 Selbstversuche über Veränderungen
1940 des Blutes bei langdauernder künstlicher
Alkalose und Acidose. Charlottenburg,
Hoffmann, 1940.
21, [3] p. illus.

Inaug.-Diss. - Berlin.
Bibliography: p. [23]

NL 0444539   DNLM

Löngfeldt, E   , pseud.
see Fischer, Elise (Lieungh)

Löngodsfabrikanternas förening
see
Svenska löngodsfabrikanternas förening.

4TL Lönholdt, Franz
264 Betrachtungen über Fahrten und
Havarien der Zeppelin-Luftkreuzer
sowie Vorschläge zum Bau und Betrieb
von Motor-Luftschiffen starren Systems. Frankfurt am Main, Gebr.
Knauer [1911]
36 p.

NL 0444542   DLC-P4

HD Loenholdt, Fritz.
1827 The agricultural economy of El Salvador.
L82 Report for the United Nations Technical
Assistance Mission to El Salvador. San
Salvador, 1953.
102, 8, 9, 10 p.   diagrs., maps, tables.
28 cm.

1. Agriculture - Economic aspects -
Salvador. I. United Nations. Mission of
Technical Assista   nce to El Salvador.
II. Title.

NL 0444543   NIC

q
HD Loenholdt, Fritz.
1486 Informe sobre la Cooperativa Lechera de
S1 Oriente, Ltda., por Fritz Loenholdt y
L64 Angel Roberto Vaquero. San Salvador,
LAC Ministerio de Agricultura y Ganadería,
Oficina del Area de Demostración Agrícola,
1954.
25l. 33cm.
1. Cooperativa Lechera de Oriente, Ltda. 2.
Dairy plants - Salvador. 3. Agriculture, Co-
operative - Salvador. I. Vaquero, Angel
Roberto, joint   author. II. Title.

NL 0444544   TxU

Lönholm, Ludwig Hermann, 1854-   ed.

Japan.   *Laws, statutes, etc.*
Das Bürgerliche gesetzbuch für Japan.   Übers. von dr. iur.
L. Lönholm ...   2. aufl.   Tokyo, Selbstverlag des verfassers;
[etc., etc.,] 1897-98.

Lönholm, Ludwig Hermann, 1854-   ed.
                                   FOR OTHER EDITIONS
Japan.   *Laws, statutes, etc.*   SEE MAIN ENTRY
The Civil code of Japan ...   Translated by
L. H. Loenholm ... and R. H. Loenholm ... 4th ed. Tokyo
and Yokohama; Los Angeles, Calif., Maruya & co. [pref. 1906]

Loenholm, Ludwig Hermann, 1854-   tr.

Japan.   *Laws, statutes, etc.*
Code civil de l'empire du Japon. Livres IV et v. (Famille
et successions). Traduction par L. K. [1] Loenholm ... et
Jules Adam ... Tokyo, Maruya & co.; Paris, Société du Recueil général des lois et des arrêts, 1902.

Law Lönholm, Ludwig Hermann, 1854-   tr.
                                   FOR OTHER EDITIONS
Japan. *Laws, statutes, etc.*   SEE MAIN ENTRY
Code de commerce de l'empire du Japon. Traduction par
L. Loenholm ... Tokyo et Yokohama, Maruya, et cie; Paris,
Librairie de la société du recueil général des lois et des arrêts,
1899.

VOLUME 338

Lönholm, Ludwig Hermann, 1854-　tr.
Japan. *Laws, statutes, etc.*
　Code pénal de l'empire du Japon. Tr. par L. H. Loen-
holm ... Yokohama, Impr. du "Japan mail office," 1907.

Lönholm, Ludwig Hermann, 1854-　ed. and tr.
Japan. *Laws, statutes, etc.*
　The Commercial code of Japan and laws and ordinances
relating thereto. Translated by L. H. Loenholm ... and R. H.
Loenholm ...　6th ed.　Tokyo and Yokohama, Maruya & co.;
Gelsenkirchen, Printed by Stueck & Lohde [191-]

Lönholm, Ludwig Hermann, 1854-　tr.
Japan. *Laws, statutes, etc.*　　FOR OTHER EDITIONS
　　　　　　　　　　　　　　　SEE MAIN ENTRY
　The commercial code of Japan and the law concerning
its operation. Tr. by Dr. L. H. Loenholm ... 3d ed.
Tokyo and Yokohama, Maruya & co.; London, P. S. King
& son; [etc., etc., 1901]

Lönholm, Ludwig Hermann, 1854-
　The condition of foreigners under the new treaties. A
digest written for the International committee of Yokohama, by Dr. L. Lönholm ... Printed as manuscript ...
Tokyo, Printed by the Kokubunsha [1898]
　ii, 54 p., 1 l.　22½ᶜᵐ.
　Japanese title at end.
　——— Supplement to the Digest on the condition of foreigners under the new treaties. Written for the International committee of Yokohama, by Dr. L. Lönholm ...
Printed as manuscript ... Tokyo, Printed by the Kokubunsha [1899]
　1 p. l., ii, 41 p., 1 l.
　Japanese title at end.　　22½ᶜᵐ.
　1. Law—Japan. 2.
of Yokohama.　II. Title.　Aliens.　I. International committee
　Library of Congress　[a25c1]　7-16912-3

NL 0444552　DLC NjP

Lönholm, Ludwig Hermann, 1854-　tr.
　Entwurf des japanischen Handelsgesetzbuchs,
in der vom Oberhaus angenommenen Form
　　see under　Japan. Laws, statutes, etc.

LÖNHOLM, Ludwig Hermann, 1854 –
　Das handelsrecht, wechselrecht, konkursrecht
und seerecht Japans.　Berlin, n. d.

In HANDELSGESETZE des erdballs, v.6.
'Japanese and German.

NL 0444554　MH-L

Lönholm, Ludwig Hermann, 1854-　tr.
Japan. *Laws, statutes, etc.*
　Japanisches handelsgesetzbuch nebst einführungsge-
setz. Übers. von d. Ludwig Lönholm ... Bremen, M.
Nössler; [etc., etc., 1899]

LÖNHOLM, LUDWIG HERMANN, 1854-
　Japans moderne Civilisation; ein Beitrag zur ost-
asiatischen Frage.　Tokyo, Verfasser, 1896.　94 p.
19cm.

NL 0444556　NN

LÖNHOLM, LUDWIG HERMANN, 1854-
Japans moderne Civilisation; ein Beitrag zur ost-
asiatischen Frage.　Tokyo, Verfasser, 1896.　94 p.
19cm.

Film reproduction. Negative.

1. Japan—Descr. and trav., 1875-1900.

NL 0444557　NN

Loenholm, Ludwig Hermann, 1854-　tr.
　Law concerning the registration of immovables and ordinances and rules relating thereto. Translated by Dr. L. Loenholm ... Published by the author.　Tokyo and Yokohama,
Maruya & co.; [etc., etc.] 1899.
　1 p. l., vi, 2, 103 p., 1 l.　forms.　22ᶜᵐ.

　1. Land titles—Registration and transfer—Japan. 2. Real property—
Japan.　I. Japan.　Laws, statutes, etc.　II. Title: Registration of
immovables.
　　　　　　　　　　　　　　　　　42-26906

NL 0444558　DLC

Loenholm, Ludwig Hermann, 1854-
　Das neue japanische strafgesetzbuch
　　see under　Japan. Laws, statutes, etc.

Lönholm, Ludwig Hermann, 1854-　tr.
Japan. *Laws, statutes, etc.*
　Die neuen japanischen gesetze über patent, handels-
marken, muster und gebrauchsmuster. Übers. von dr.
jur. L. H. Lönholm ... Yokohama, Selbstverlag des verfassers, druckerei der "Japan mail", 1909.

Lönholm, Ludwig Hermann, 1854-　tr.
Japan. *Laws, statutes, etc.*
　The new Criminal code of Japan. Translated by L. H.
Loenholm ... 1st ed. Tokyo & Yokohama, Maruya & co.;
[etc., etc., 190-]

LÖNHOLM, Ludwig Hermann, 1854-
　The new Japanese civil code; a short explanation of its provisions and of those parts of
the new treaties relating to it.　Tokyo, published by the author, printed by the Kokubunsha,
1896.

　22 cm.　pp.(2),31.

NL 0444562　MH

Lönholm, Ludwig Hermann, 1854-　tr.
Japan. *Laws, statutes, etc.*
　The new Japanese laws concerning patents, trade
marks, designs and utility models, with all ordinances &
regulations relating thereto. Tr. by L. H. Loenholm ...
2d ed. Tokyo, Maruya & co.; [etc., etc., 1910]

Lönholm, Ludwig Hermann, 1854-　tr.
Japan. *Laws, statutes, etc.*
　New Japanese laws supplementary to the codes. Tr.
by Dr. Ludwig Lönholm ... With an appendix containing a glossary of commercial terms.　Pub. by the author.
Bremen, M. Nössler; Tokyo and Yokohama, Maruya &
co. [1898]

Loening, Edgar, 1843-1919.
　Die autonomie der standesherrlichen häuser
Deutschlands nach dem rechte der gegenwart;
denkschrift im auftrage des Vereins der deutschen
standesherren verfasst.　Halle a. S., 1905.

NL 0444565　MH-L

HT
761　　Loening, Edgar, 1843-1919.
L82　　Die Befreiung des Bauernstandes in Deutschland und in Livland.　Riga, Moskau, Deubner,
1880.
　41 p.　25cm.

　"Sonder-Abdruck aus der Baltischen Monatsschrift, Band XXVII, Heft 2."

　1. Serfdom—Germany. 2. Serfdom—Livonia.
3. Peasantry—Germany. 4. Peasantry—Livonia.

NL 0444566　NIC

Loening, Edgar, 1843-1919, ed.
Bluntschli, Johann Kaspar, 1808-1881, ed.
　Bluntschli's staatswörterbuch in drei bänden auf grundlage des Deutschen staatswörterbuchs von Bluntschli und
Brater in elf bänden, in verbindung mit mehreren gelehrten bearb. und hrsg. von dr. Löning. Zürich, F. Schulthess, 1871-72.

Loening, Edgar, 1843-1919
　De pace domestica ...
　Inaug. Diss. Bonn, 1865

NL 0444568　ICRL

Loening, Edgar, 1843-1919.
Bole, John Archibald, 1869-　　ed.
　Deutsche wirtschaft; selections from Loening's Grundzüge
der verfassung des Deutschen Reiches and from Arndt's
Deutschlands stellung in der weltwirtschaft, ed. with notes and
vocabulary, by John A. Bole ... New York, H. Holt and
company, 1910.

Loening, Edgar, 1843-1919
　Die Entwicklung des Genossenschaftswesens in Deutschland.
Halle a. S.: Buchdruckerei des Waisenhauses, 1911.　23 p.　4°.
(Halle. Universität. Bekanntmachung der Ergebnisse der Aka-
demischen Preisbewerbung vom Jahre 1910...)

1. Companies (Commercial), Ger-　　　many. 2. Colleges, etc., Germany:
Halle University.　　　　　　　　　　　　　
N. Y. P. L.
　　　　　　　　　　　　　　　　　　September 23, 1912.

NL 0444570　NN ICRL CtY

VOLUME 338

Loening, Edgar, 1843–1919.
Die erbverbrüderungen zwischen den häusern Sachsen und Hessen und Sachsen, Brandenburg und Hessen ... Frankfurt a. M., Literarische anstalt (Rütten und Löning) 1867.

3 p. l., ₍₃₎–108 p. 24ᶜᵐ.
Habilitationsschrift.

1. Saxony—Kings and rulers—Sources. 2. Hesse—Kings and rulers—Sources. 3. Brandenburg—Kings and rulers—Sources.

8–30981†

Library of Congress   DD801.S357.L7

NL 0444571   DLC CtY MiU

Loening, Edgar, 1843–1919.
——. Festrede zur Jahresfeier der Stiftung der Universität Dorpat am 12. December 1879. Nebst den Mittheilungen über die Preisaufgaben, sowie dem Universitäts-Jahresbericht für das Jahr 1879. Hrsg. von der kaiserlichen Universität Dorpat. 50 pp. 4°. *Dorpat, Schnakenburg, 1880.*

NL 0444572   DNLM

Loening, Edgar, 1843–1919.
Die gemeindeverfassung des urchristenthums. Eine kirchenrechtliche untersuchung. Festschrift von dr. Edgar Loening ... Halle, M. Niemeyer, 1888.

4 p. l., 154 p., 1 l. 23½ᶜᵐ.
"Herrn dr. Rudolf von Gneist ... zur feier des fünfzigjährigen doctor-jubiläums am xx. november MDCCCLXXXVIII, die juristische facultät der Vereinigten Friedrichs-universität Halle-Wittenberg."

1. Church polity—Early church. 2. Gneist, Rudolf von, 1816–1895.

3–13778

Library of Congress   BR165.L8

NL 0444573   DLC CtY OO OCH OC1W MB PPPD

4K
Ger.
2490
Loening, Edgar, 1843–1919.
Gerichte und Verwaltungsbehörden in Brandenburg-Preussen; ein Beitrag zur preussischen Rechts- und Verfassungsgeschichte. Halle a. d. S., Verlag der Buchhandlung des Waisenhauses, 1914.
326 p.

(His Abhandlungen und Aufsätze, Bd. 1)

NL 0444574   DLC-P4 WU

Loening, Edgar, 1843–1919.
Die gerichtsbarkeit über fremde staaten und souveräne. Von dr. Edgar Loening ... Halle a. S., M. Niemeyer, 1903.

2 p. l., 163 p. 24½ᶜᵐ.
"Sonderabdrug aus: Festgabe der Juristischen fakultät der Vereinigten Friedrichs-universität Halle-Wittenberg für Hermann Fitting."

9–1854

Library of Congress   JX4003.L6

NL 0444575   DLC NcD CtY-L

Loening, Edgar, 1843–1919.
Geschichte des deutschen kirchenrechts, von dr. Edgar Loening ... Strassburg, K. J. Trübner, 1878.

2 v. 23ᶜᵐ.
Each volume has also special t.-p.
CONTENTS.—v. 1. Das kirchenrecht in Gallien von Constantin bis Chlodovech.—v. 2. Das kirchenrecht im reiche der Merowinger.

1. Ecclesiastical law—Germany. 2. Ecclesiastical law—France.

G–262 Revised

Library of Congress
———— Copy 2.   BX1937.G3L7

NN MH NcD NjNbS CtY MdBP NIC
NL 0444576   DLC CU-L DCU MdBP CtY OU OO PPPD CU

LOENING, Edgar, 1843–1919.
Grundzüge der verfassung der Deutschen Reichs, sechs vorträge. Leipzig, 1901.

NL 0444577   MH-L MiU

342.43
L824
Loening, Edgar, 1843–1919.
Grundzüge der Verfassung des Deutschen Reiches; sechs Vorträge gehalten von Edgar Loening. 2.aufl. Leipzig, B.G. Teubner, 1906.
iv,140p. 19cm. (Aus natur und geisteswelt, 34. bdchen.)

1. Germany. Constitution. I. Series.

NL 0444578   OrU

Loening, Edgar, 1843–1919.
... Grundzüge der verfassung des Deutschen Reiches: sechs vorträge gehalten von dr. Edgar Loening ... 3. aufl. Leipzig, B. G. Teubner, 1909.

2 p. l., 134 p. 18½ᶜᵐ. (Aus natur und geisteswelt. Sammlung wissenschaftlich-gemeinverständlicher darstellungen. 34. bdchen.)
"Literatur": p. 134.

1. Germany. Constitution.

9–30392

Library of Congress   JN3425.L7

NL 0444579   DLC NNC

4JN
Ger.
198
Loening, Edgar, 1843–1919
Grundzüge der Verfassung des Deutschen Reiches; sechs Vorträge. 4. Aufl. Leipzig, Teubner, 1913.
132 p.

(Aus Natur und Geisteswelt; Sammlung wissenschaftlich-gemeinverständlicher Darstellungen, 34. Bändchen)

NL 0444580   DLC-P4

Loening, Edgar, 1843–1919.
Die haftung des staats aus rechtswidrigen handlungen seiner beamten nach deutschem privat- und staatsrecht. Eine festschrift, von dr. Edgar Loening ... Dorpat, 1879.

4 p. l., 135 p. 26ᶜᵐ.
Dedication: Herrn J. C. Bluntschli ... zur feier des tages, an welchem derselbe vor fünfzig jahren die würde eines doctor der rechte erlangt hat, glückwünschend dargebracht von der Juristen-facultät der Kaiserlichen universität Dorpat, den 3. august 1879.
"Gedruckt auf verfügung der Juristen-facultät der Kaiserlichen universität Dorpat."

1. Administrative responsibility—Germany. 2. Bluntschli, Johann Kaspar, 1808–1881. I. Tartu. Ülikool. Öigusteaduskond.

46–38458

NL 0444581   DLC

Loening, Edgar, 1843–1919.
Die haftung des staats aus rechtswidrigen handlungen seiner beamten nach deutschem privat- und staatsrecht. Eine festschrift, von dʳ Edgar Loening ... Frankfurt a/M., Rütten & Loening, 1879.

4 p. l., 135 p. 26½ᶜᵐ.
Dedication: Herrn J. C. Bluntschli ... zur feier des tages, an welchem derselbe vor fünfzig jahren die würde eines doctor der rechte erlangt hat, glückwünschend dargebracht von der Juristen-facultät der Kaiserlichen universität Dorpat, den 3. august 1879.

1. Administrative responsibility—Germany. 2. Bluntschli, Johann Kaspar, 1808–1881. I. Tartu. Ülikool. Öigusteaduskond.

9–22543 Revised

NL 0444582   DLC CtY-L ICU

Loening, Edgar, 1843–1919.
Handbuch der politischen oekonomie
see under title

Loening, Edgar, 1843–1919, ed.
Handwörterbuch der staatswissenschaften. Hrsg. von dr. J. Conrad ... dr. L. Elster ... dr. W. Lexis ... dr. Edg. Loening. 3. gänzlich umgearb. aufl. ... Jena, G. Fischer, 1909–11.

FOR OTHER EDITIONS SEE MAIN ENTRY

Loening, Edgar, 1843–1919, ed.
Jahrbücher für nationalökonomie und statistik. 1.–34. bd., 1863–79; 35.–55. bd. (neue folge 1.–21. bd.) 1880–90; 56.– bd. (3. folge 1.– bd.) 1891–19   Jena, F. Mauke ₍etc.₎ 1863–19

[Loening, Edgar] 1843–1919.
Juvenile criminality in Germany. Washington, 1905.
Pamphlet.
Cover serves as title-page.
At head of title: Advance sheets. U. S. Bureau of Education. Chapter from the Report of the Commissioner of Education for 1904. Chapter IX, p. 703–713.

NL 0444586   MH DL

Loening, Edgar, 1843–1919.
Kaiser und reich, 1888–1913; festrede gehalten in der aula der Königlichen Friedrichs-universität, Halle-Wittenberg, am 16. juni, 1913, von dr. Edgar Loening ... Halle a. d. S., Buchhandlung des Waisenhauses, 1913.

33, ₍1₎ p. 23ᶜᵐ.

1. Wilhelm II, German emperor, 1859– 2. Germany—Pol. & govt.—William II, 1888– I. Halle. Universität. II. Title.

15–6464

Library of Congress   DD229.5.L6

NL 0444587   DLC CtY ICRL

Loening, Edgar, 1843–1919.
Lehrbuch des deutschen verwaltungsrechts, von dr. Edgar Loening ... Leipzig, Breitkopf und Härtel, 1884.

xvi, 859 p. 23½ᶜᵐ.

1. Administrative law—Germany.

8–36162

Library of Congress   JN3551.L7

NL 0444588   DLC CtY

Loening, Edgar, 1843–1919.
Bluntschli, Johann Kaspar, 1808–1881. ed.
Lehre vom modernen staat. Bearbeitet von J. C. Bluntschli. Stuttgart, J. G. Cotta, 1885–86.

Loening (Édgar). Oratio. Subjecta sunt G. Loeschli de basi quadam prope Spartam reperta observationes archeologicae. (Ueber die Reliefs der altspartanischen Basis.) 16 pp., 1 pl. 4°. *Dorpati Livon., Schnakenburg, ₍1879₎*

NL 0444590   DNLM

VOLUME 338

Loening, Edgar, 1843–1919.
Die repräsentativverfassung im XIX. jahrhundert ... von
Edgar Loening. Halle a. S., M. Niemeyer ₁1899₎
32 p. 24½ᵐ. *(On cover: Hallesche rektorreden. I)*
Rektoratsrede—Univ. Halle.

1. Representative government and representation. I. Halle. Universität.

Library of Congress   JF1051.L7   2-1025

NL 0444591   DLC MiU

B   Loening, Edgar, 1843–1919
qG571   Rudolf v. Gneist.   Mün. 1895.
v.p.

In Beilage zur Allgemeinen zeitung,
6–7 Ag., 1895.

NL 0444592   IU

Löning, Edgar, 1843–1919.

Die verwaltung des generalgouvernements im
Elsass. Ein beitrag zur geschichte des völkerrechts, von Edgar Löning. Strassburg, K. J.
Trübner, 1874.
265 p. 18cm.

1. Alsace. Politics and government.1. International law and relations.

NL 0444593   NcD MH MiU

Loening, Fritz *i. e.* Friedrich Karl Rudolf, 1879–
... Ueber oxydation von eiweiss mit übermangansauren
salzen ... Jena, Frommannsche hof-buchdr. (H. Pohle)
1903.
42 p. 22½ᵐ.
Inaug.-diss.—Jena.
Lebenslauf.

1. Albumin. 2. Manganese, Physiological effect of.
8-22765

Library of Congress   QP551.L82

NL 0444594   DLC DNLM

LÖNING, G.E.
Unser Denken und Leben in Gott. Bremen,
1854.
pp. 37.   Phil 2998.1

NL 0444595   MH

Löning, G   E
Unsere Kindesstellung zu Gott, von G.E.
Löning. Bremen, Löning & Comp., 1856.
21 p.

NL 0444596   TxDaM

Löning, George Anton, 1900–
Festschrift Justus Wilhelm Hedemann zum sechzigsten geburtstag am 24. april 1938. Herausgeber: Roland Freisler ... George Anton Löning ... ₍und₎ Hans Carl Nipperdey ... Jena, Frommannsche buchhandlung, W. Biedermann, 1938.

Löning, George Anton, 1900–
Die Grundstücksmiete als dingliches Recht. Jena,
G. Fischer, 1930.
xxvi, 378 p.   25ᵐ.   (Schriften des Instituts
für Wirtschaftsrecht an der Universität Jena ...
Nr. 9)
"Verzeichnis der benutzten Schriften": p. 318–
341.

1. Rent - Germany. I. Title.   Series.

NL 0444598   MiU-L MH-L NN

Löning, George Anton, 1900–
Das münzrecht im erzbistum Bremen, von George A.
Löning ... Weimar, H. Böhlaus, 1937.
xv, 231 p. 23½ᵐ.   *(Half-title:* Quellen und studien zur verfassungsgeschichte des Deutschen reiches in mittelalter und neuzeit ... bd. VII, hft. 3)

1. Coinage—Bremen.   I. Title.
38-17705
Library of Congress   HG1010.B7L6
332.4943525

NL 0444599   DLC CaBVaU WU WaU NcD

Loening, George M
Elegy on the death of Lt. Col. Chas. Dreux.   Words by
James R. Randall.   New Orleans, Published by the author,
96. Canal St. ₍ᵒ1861₎
5 p. 33 cm.
For voice and piano.

1. U. S.—Hist.—Civil War—Songs and music—Confederate. 2.
Dreux, Charles Didier, 1832–1861—Songs and music.   I. Title.

M1642.L   52-52682

NL 0444600   DLC

Loening, Grover Cleveland, 1888 –
Amphibian-airplane development... n.p.,
1926.

NL 0444601   DAL

Loening, Grover Cleveland, 1888–
Aviation and banking.   Prepared for
confidential use of the Chase national bank
...   New York, Chase national bank ₍1939₎
1 p.f., 50 p.incl.tables, mounted colored
charts.

NL 0444602   MH-BA

Loening, Grover Cleveland, 1888–
Fifty years of flying progress.
(*In* Smithsonian Institution.   Annual report, 1954.   Washington,
1955.   24 cm.   p. 201–216.   illus.)
"Reprinted, with some revisions ... from the Journal of the Franklin Institute, vol. 256, no. 6, December 1953."

1. Aeronautics—Hist.   I. Title.

Q11.S66 1955   56-2361

NL 0444603   DLC

Loening, Grover Cleveland, 1888–
Military aeroplanes; an explanatory consideration of their
characteristics, performances, construction, maintenance and
operation, for the use of aviators, by Grover C. Loening ...
Prepared for Signal corps aviation school, San Diego, California. ₍San Diego, Calif., Printed by Frye & Smith, 1915₎
3 p. l., ₍3₎–169 p.   front., illus., diagrs.   26½ cm.

1. Aeroplanes. 2. Aeronautics, Military.   I. Title.

TL670.L55 1915   15–14684

NL 0444604   DLC OrP OCl MiU NN DN-Ob

Loening, Grover Cleveland, 1888 –
Military aeroplanes; an explanatory consideration of their
characteristics, performances, construction, maintenance and operation, for the use of aviators, by Grover C. Loening... ₍Boston:
W. S. Best Prtg. Co., 1916.₎   3 p. l., (1)10–182 p., front.   illus.
(incl. diagr.), tables. 2. ed.   4°.

NL 0444605   NN OU ICJ NjP DN

Loening, Grover Cleveland, 1888–
Military aeroplanes; an explanatory consideration of their
characteristics, performances, construction, maintenance and
operation, for the use of aviators, by Grover C. Loening ...
3d ed. ₍Boston, W. S. Best printing company, ᵒ1916₎
182 p. incl. front., illus., diagrs.   26½ᵐ.

1. Aeroplanes. 2. Aeronautics, Military.   I. Title.
16—22580
Library of Congress   TL670.L55 1916

NL 0444606   DLC CaBVa ICJ NcD CoU

Loening, Grover Cleveland, 1888–
Military aeroplanes; an explanatory
consideration of their characteristics,
performances, construction, maintenance
and operation, for the use of aviators,
by Grover C. Loening ... 4th ed.
₍Boston, W. S. Best printing company,
1917₎
182 p.   illus.   27 cm.

NL 0444607   OKentU NjP MWA

Loening, Grover Cleveland, 1888 –
Military aeroplanes; an explanatory consideration of their
characteristics, performances, construction, maintenance and operation, for the use of aviators.   ₍Boston: W. S. Best Prtg. Co.,
1917.₎   182 p.   Charts, diagr., illus.   5. ed.   8°.

NL 0444608   NN ICRL OCU OClW

Loening, Grover Cleveland, 1888 –
Military aeroplanes; an explanatory consideration of
their characteristics, performances, construction, maintenance and operation, for the use of aviators, by Grover
C. Loening ... 6th ed.   Boston, W. S. Best printing company, ᵒ1917₎
182 p. incl. front., illus., diagrs.   26½ᵐ.

1. Aeroplanes. 2. Aeronautics, Military.   I. Title.   17—29030
Library of Congress   UG650.L7 1917 b

NL 0444609   DLC

Loening, Grover Cleveland, 1888 –
Military aeroplanes; an explanatory consideration of their characteristics, performances, construction, maintenance and operation, for the use
of aviators, by Grover C. Loening... 6th ed.
₍San Diego, Cal., Printed by Frye & Smith, 1918.
182 p. front., illus., diagrs.

NL 0444610   MiD

VOLUME 338

Loening, Grover Cleveland, 1888–
  Military aeroplanes, simplified, enlarged; an explanatory consideration of their characteristics, performances, construction, maintenance, and operation, specially arranged for the use of aviators and students, by Grover C. Loening ... Ed. for year 1918. ¡Boston, W. S. Best printing company¡ 1918.
  3 p. l., 202 p. front., illus., plates (1 double, part fold.) fold. diagr. 26½ᶜᵐ.

  1. Aeroplanes. 2. Aeronautics, Military.   ɪ. Title.

  Library of Congress   TL670.L55 1918
                                                18—9683

  ICJ NN IU OCl OClW OU ViU NcD KMK NIC
  NL 0444611 DLC NNC NjP MH OO MiU WaS Or DAL DN-Ob

Loening, Grover Cleveland, 1888 —
  Military aviation, by Grover C. Loening ... Prepared for Signal corps aviation school, San Diego, Cal. ¡San Diego, Cal., Frye & Smith, 1915¡
  17 p. illus. 26ᶜᵐ.

  1. Aeronautics, Military.   ɪ. Title.

  Library of Congress   UG630.L7
                                                15—2650

  NL 0444612 DLC

Loening, Grover Cleveland, 1888–
  Monoplanes and biplanes, their design, construction and operation; the application of aerodynamic theory with a complete description and comparison of the notable types, by Grover Cleveland Loening ... 278 illustrations. New York, Munn & company, inc., 1911.
  1 p. l., ¡vii¡–xiv p., 1 l., 331 p. front., illus., diagrs. 21½ᶜᵐ.
  Contains References.
  "Much of the work involved in the writing of this book was done in fulfilment of the requirements for the degree of master of arts at Columbia university."—Pref.
  1. Aeroplanes.   ɪ. Title.
                                                11—11198
  Library of Congress   TL670.L6

  DN-Ob CoD I ICJ MB NN DNW
  NL 0444613 DLC WaS OrP CaBVa CU OU OCl OU MiU DAL

Loening, Grover Cleveland, 1888–
  Our wings grow faster. In these personal episodes of a lifetime in aviation may be found an historical and pictorial record showing how we so quickly stepped into this air age— and through what kinds of difficulties and developments we had to pass to get there. By Grover Loening ... Garden City, N. Y., Doubleday, Doran & co., inc., 1935.
  vi, 203 p. illus. 27½ cm.
  Illustrated title on two leaves.

  1. Aeronautics—U. S.—Hist. 2. Aeroplane industry and trade— U. S.   ɪ. Title.

  TL521.L6   629.130973   35—27196

  OClh NcRS CU IU OrP WaS OrU
  NL 0444614 DLC OrU Or WaS MB DAL OCl OLak OEac

Löning, Hans: Geldentwertung und Rechtsfindung. ¡Maschinenschrift.¡ ɪv, 88 S. 4°. — Auszug: (Bremen ¡1923¡: Gutbe). 2 Bl. 8°
Marburg, Jur. Diss. v. 10. Okt. 1922 ¡1924¡   ¡U 24. 7098¡

  NL 0444615 ICRL

Loening, Helmuth: Ref.: Der Eigentumserwerb an beweglichen Sachen durch Abtretung des Herausgabeanspruchs des Nichteigentümers. Jena ¡1919¡: Frommann. 34 S. 8°
Jena, Jur. Diss. v. 1. Okt. 1919 ¡1920¡, Ref. Fischer
¡Geb. 6. Juli 91 Jena; Wohnort: Jena; Staatsangeh.: Sachsen-Weimar; Vorbildung: G. Jena ¡Reife 09; Studium: Heidelberg 3, Berlin 1, Jena 3 S.; Rig. 1. Okt. 19.¡   ¡U 20. 723¡

  NL 0444616 ICRL

Loening, Hellmuth, ed.   FOR OTHER EDITIONS
                                                    SEE MAIN ENTRY
  Thuringia (1919–   ) *Constitution.*
  Die verfassung des landes Thüringen, erläutert von dr. Hellmuth Loening ... 3., erweiterte aufl. Weimar, Panses verlag, g. m. b. h. ¡1926?¡

Loening, Karl, 1877–
  Die behandlung der schussverletzungen des abdomen im frieden und im felde.
  Inaug. diss. Halle, 1902.
  Bibl.

  NL 0444618 ICRL MH DNLM

1877–
Loening (Karl) ∧ *Experimentelle und klinische Untersuchungen über den Eiweisstoffwechsel im Fieber.* ¡Habilitationsschrift. Halle-Wittenberg.¡ 1 p. l., 86 pp., 8 tab. 8°. Jena, G. Fischer, 1907.

  NL 0444619 DNLM MH ICRL

Loening, Karl, 1877–   , ed.
  Medizinische Essays. Herausgegeben von Karl Loening, Erster–¡zweiter¡ Band, ¡erster Teil¡. Leipzig, B. Konegen, 1910-1911.
  2v. in 1. illus.

  NL 0444620 ICRL ICJ

Z6660   **Loening, Karl,** 1877–   ed.
.R4   **Reichsmedizinal-anzeiger.**
              –30. jahrg., nr. 1   –1930. Stuttgart, Montanaverlag, a. g., Medizinische abteilung Benno Konegen; ¡etc., etc., 19 –30¡

Loening, Kurt Leopold, 1924–
  Esterification of some hindered aliphatic acids 1951.
  93 l.
  Thesis - Ohio state university.

  NL 0444622 OU

Loening, Lilli, 1898–
  Das chorgestühl im dom zu Erfurt ... von Lilli Loening ... Erfurt, 1925.
  43 p., 1 l. Illus. (incl. plans) 22½ᶜᵐ.
  Thesis, Marburg.
  "Teildruck."

  1. Choir-stalls. 2. Erfurt. Cathedral.

  NL 0444623 NNC IU MH PU CtY ICRL

771
63
  Loening, Louise Susanne Ernestine.
  A bibliography of the status of South-west Africa up to June 30th, 1951, by L. S. E. Loening. Rondebosch¡ University of Cape Town, School of Librarianship, 1951.
  32 l. 26 cm. (University of Cape Town. School of Librarianship. Bibliographical series)

  1. Africa, Southwest—History—Bibliography.

  Z3771.L63   016.9688   53–19612 ‡

  DSI CLSU
  NL 0444624 DLC CoU MiU FU CSt-H CaBVaU CSt NcD

A.W.   Loening, Otto, 1880–   ed.

  Germany. *Laws, statutes, etc.*
  ... Bürgerliches gesetzbuch nebst einführungsgesetz erläutert von dr. Otto Loening ... James Basch und Ernst Strassmann ... (Stand vom 1. juli 1931) Berlin, O. Liebmann, 1931.

DD901   **Loening, Otto,** 1880–
.D283L82 Danzig, sein Verhältnis zu Polen und seine Verfassung. Mit Anhang: Der Danzig-polnische Vertrag vom 9. November 1920. Berlin, H. R. Engelmann, 1921.
              50 p. (Das Selbstbestimmungsrecht der Deutschen, Heft 3)
              Bibliographical footnotes.

  1. Danzig—For. rel.—Poland. 2. Poland— For. rel.—Danzig. 3. Danzig. Treaties, etc., 1920. 4. Poland. Treaties, etc., 1919-1922 (Piłsudski)   Series.

  NL 0444626 ICU NN NjP MH CSt CSt-H

Loening, Otto, 1880–
  Danziger staats-und völkerrechtliche Schriften
  see under title

LOENING, Otto, 1880 —
  Deutsche rechtsgeschichte. Leipzig, 1929.

  NL 0444628 MH-L

Loening, Otto, 1880–
  ... Deutsche rechtsgeschichte von dr. Otto Loening ... 16. bis. 20. durchgesehene aufl. Düsseldorf, Schwann ¡1949¡
  136 p. 22½cm. (Schaeffers grundriss des rechts und der wirtschaft; abt. I: Privat- und prozessrecht, 22. bd., 1. t.)

  NL 0444629 MH-L

Loening, Otto, 1880–
  Grunderwerb und treuhand in Lübeck, von Dr. jur. Otto Loening. Breslau, M. & H. Marcus, 1907.
  4 p. l., 87 p. 23½ᶜᵐ. (Added t.-p.: Untersuchungen zur deutschen staats- und rechtsgeschichte ... 93. hft.)
                                                8-3266

  NL 0444630 DLC MB NN

Loening, Otto, 1880–
  ... Internationales übereinkommen über den eisenbahnfrachtverkehr (I. Ü. G.) vom 23. oktober 1924; kommentar von dr. Otto Loening ... Berlin, G. Stilke, 1927.
  xvi, 1081 p. 18½ᶜᵐ. (Stilkes rechtsbibliothek nr. 63)
  Text of the convention in German and French.
  Contains bibliographies.

  1. Railroads—Freight. 2. Railroads—Europe. 3. Transportation— Laws and regulations.   ɪ. Convention internationale concernant le transport de marchandises par chemins de fer, Bern, 1904.
                                                30–23464

  NL 0444631 DLC

VOLUME 338

Loening, Otto, 1880–
    ... Die rechtsstellung der Freien Stadt Danzig, von dr. Otto
Loening ... Berlin, F. Dümmler, 1928.
    34 p. 24ᶜᵐ. (Völkerrechtsfragen; eine sammlung von vorträgen und
studien ... 22. hft.)

    Published in 1927.
    "Literaturangaben": p. ₍33₎–34.

    1. Danzig.   I. Title.

    Library of Congress   DD901.D283L6   27–23750

NL 0444632   DLC CtY OCIW NN CSt-H

Loening, Otto , 1880–
    Staatsrechtliche Betrachtungen zu einer künftigen Verfassung
von Danzig, von Dr. Otto Loening...   Danzig: A. W. Kafemann, G.m.b.H., 1919. 51 p. 12°.

    1. Constitutions, Danzig.
    N. Y. P. L.   September 19, 1924

NL 0444633   NN

Loening, Otto, 1880–
    Das testament im gebiet des Magdeburger stadtrechtes,
von dr. Otto Loening. Breslau, M. & H. Marcus, 1906.
    4 p. l., 157 p. 24ᶜᵐ. (Added t.-p.: Untersuchungen zur deutschen staats-
und rechtsgeschichte, hrsg. von dr. O. Gierke ... 82. hft.)

    1. Wills—Magdeburg.   I. Title.

                                                      6–23310

NL 0444634   DLC ICRL MH-L MH MB

4K   Loening, Richard, 1848–1913.
4822   Geschichte der strafrechtlichen
        Zurechnungslehre. Jena, G. Fischer,
        1903–
            v. 1

NL 0444635   DLC-P4 ICJ PU NN NIC

4K   Loening, Richard, 1848–1913.
Ger.   Grundriss zu Vorlesungen über
1934   deutsches Strafrecht. Frankfurt
        am Main, Literarische Anstalt Rütten
        & Loening, 1885.
            147 p.

NL 0444636   DLC-P4 MH PU-L

PR   Loening, Richard, 1848–1913.
2807   Die Hamlet-tragödie Shakespeares, von Richard
.L82   Loening ... Stuttgart, J.G.Cotta'schen buch-
        handlung nachfolger, 1893.
            x,418 p. 24ᶜᵐ.

    "Die deutsche Hamlet-kritik": p.1–142.
    "Litteratur-verzeichnis": p.₍401₎–408.

    1.Shakespeare,William. Hamlet. 2.Shakespeare,William
--Criticism and interpretation--Hist.

        OCIW OU MH
NL 0444637   MiU ICU NjP MB OCl PU-F NcD CLU NcU

4K   Loening, Richard, 1848–1913.
Ger.   Der Reinigungseid bei Ungerichts-
1335   klagen im deutschen Mittelalter.
        Heidelberg, C. Winter's Universitäts-
        buchhandlung, 1880.
            316 p.

NL 0444638   DLC-P4 MH NNC MiU-L

Loening, Richard, 1848–1913.
    Die strafrechtliche haftung des verantwortlichen redakteurs,
von dr. Richard Loening ... Jena, G. Fischer, 1889.
    2 p. l., 305, ₍1₎ p. 25ᶜᵐ.

    "Aus der Festgabe der Juristischen facultät in Jena zum 50jährigen
doctorjubiläum Rudolf von Gneist's."

    1. Press law—Germany.   I. Title.

                                                    42–30163

NL 0444639   DLC MH

Loening, Richard, 1848–1913.
    Über ältere rechts- und kulturzustände an der Fürstlich
sächsischen gesammt-universität zu Jena. Rede gehalten bei
der akademischen preisvertheilung am 19. juni 1897 in der Kol-
legienkirche zu Jena, von Richard Loening ... Jena, Universi-
täts-buchdr. G. Neuenhahn, 1897.
    88 p. 28ᶜᵐ.

    1. Jena. Universität.   E 15—1445

    U. S. Off. of educ. Library   LF2833.A3L8
    for Library of Congress   ₍a41b1₎

NL 0444640   DHEW CtY

Loening, Richard   1848–. Ueber censur
und preszfreiheit. 24 pp. (Deutsch. rundschau, v. 66,
1891, p. 441.)

NL 0444641   MdBP MH-L

LOENING, Richard, 1848–1913.
    Ueber die begründung des strafrechts;
rede gehalten bei der akademischen preisvertheilung zu Jena 2m 22. Juni 1889.
Jena,1889.
    32 p.

NL 0444642   MH-L

Loening, Richard, 1848–1913.
    Über wurzel und wesen des rechts; rede gehalten bei der
akademischen preisverteilung am 15. juni 1907 in der Kolle-
gienkirche zu Jena, von Richard Loening ... Jena, G. Fischer,
1907.
    48 p. 28ᶜᵐ.

    1. Law—Philosophy.   I. Title.

                                                    8–498

NL 0444643   DLC NN ICRL NcD CtY-L

Loening, Richard, 1848–1913.
    Die Verjährung (§§ 66–72 RStGB.) Bearb.
von ... Dr. Richard Loening ... ₍Berlin,
Otto Liebmann, 1907₎
    ₍379₎–471 p. 26cm.
    Caption title.
    On cover: Sonderabdruck aus der Vergleich-
enden Darstellung des deutschen und ausländischen Strafrechts ... Herausgegeben ...
von ... Dr. Karl Birkmeyer, Dr. Fritz van

NL 0444644   MH-L

Löning, Richard, 1848–1913.
    Der vertragsbruch im deutschen recht. Von dr. Richard
Löning. Mit einem anhang: Ueber ursprung und rechtliche
bedeutung der in den alt-deutschen urkunden enthaltenen
strafklauseln. Strassburg, K. J. Trübner, 1876.
    xx, 604 p. 22ᶜᵐ. (Added t.-p.: Der vertragsbruch und seine rechts-
folgen ... 1. bd.)

    1. Contracts (Germanic law) 2. Debtor and creditor (Germanic law)
3. Punishment (Germanic law)   I. Title.

                                                    36–5292

NL 0444645   DLC NN CtY

4 K   Loening, Richard, 1848–1913.
Ger. –   Die Widerklage im Reichs-Civilprozess.
199   Berlin, C. Heymann, 1881.
            190 p.

NL 0444646   DLC-P4

LOENING, Richard, 1848 – 1913.
    Zu dem preussischen entwurf eines gesetzes,
betreffend die erschwerung des vertragsbruches
landwirtschaftlicher arbeiter und des gesindes.
n. t. p.
    "Sonderabdruck aus ZEITSCHRIFT für die
gesamte strafrechtswissenschaft", 25. p.453–
475.

NL 0444647   MH-L

Loening, Richard, 1848– 1913.   171 Q310 v.1
Die Zurechnungslehre des Aristoteles. Von Richard Loening,
... . Jena, G. Fischer, 1903.
    xx, 359. ₍1₎ p. 25ᶜᵐ. (In his Geschichte der strafrechtlichen Zurechnungslehre,
erster Band)

NL 0444648   ICJ NjP GU-L CaBVaU

Loening, Sarah Elizabeth (Larkin)
    see Larkin, Sarah, 1896–

LOENING aeronautical engineering corporation,
New York.
    Loening monoplane: Model M-8-0: instruction
    N.Y. Author. n.d. ₍19₎p. diagrs.
    Loose-leaf.

NL 0444650   WaS

VOLUME 338

LOENIUS, Joannes.
　Decisien en observantien . . . met byvoe-
ginge van eenige aanteekeningen; midsgaders
resolutien, placaaten, handvesten. . . het romse,
oude en heedendaagse regt en de practyk betreffende, door Tobias Boel, junior. 2de druk.
's-Gravenhage,1735.

NL 0444651　　MH-L

Z9644
.S8L6
　Lönn, Klas.
　　Att samla Stockholmiana. Stockholm, Sällskapet bok-
vännerna ₁1950₎
　　62 p. 20 cm. (Bokvännens småskrifter, 3)

　　1. Book collecting. 2. Stockholm—Bibl.　(Series: Sällskapet
Bokvännerna, Stockholm. Bokvännens småskrifter, 3)

　　Minnesota. Univ. Libr.　　　　　　　　　　　　A 51-4646
　　for Library of Congress　　　　₁3₎

NL 0444652　　MnU NN DLC

　Lønn, Leo, pseud.
　　　see
　Mathiesen, Sigurd, 1871-

　Lønnå, Finn, 1909-
　　Norsk dental depot gjennom 50 år, 1903-1953. Oslo, Fa-
britius boktr., 1953.
　　55 p. illus. 27 cm.

　　1. Norsk dental depot a/s, Oslo.

　RK11.N6L6　　　　　　　　　　　62-29994 ‡

NL 0444654　　DLC CaBVaU DNLM

Lönnbeck, Albin Alexander, b.1856.
　Poetisk läsebok för skolans lägre klasser, utgifven af A. Lönnbeck. Helsingfors: K. E. Holm ₁1892₎. viii, 137 p.　12°.

1. Poetry (Swedish).—Collections.　　　　2. Title.
N. Y. P. L.　　　　　　　　　　　　　　　August 24, 1917.

NL 0444655　　NN

　Loennbeck, Albin Alexander, b. 1856.
　　Studier i den arkaiska konsten i Grekland ...
Helsingfors, 1888.
　　Diss. - Helsingfors.

NL 0444656　　ICRL

839.709
L825S
　Lönnbeck, Albin Alexander, b.1856.
　Studier i finska vitterheten efter 1830.
Helsingfors, P. H. Beijer, 1883.
　82 p. 23 cm.

　　1. Swedish literature. Finnish authors.
History and criticism.

NL 0444657　　NcD

Loennbeck, Gustaf Ferdinand
　Folkskoleidens utveckling i Finland...
inaug. diss. Helsingfors, 1887.

NL 0444658　　ICRL

LÖNNBECK, Gustaf Ferdinand
　Om "Åskådningen" hos Pestalozzi; akademisk
afhandlung. Helsingfors, Weilin & Göö
1886.
　pp. vi, 98.　　　　　　　　Educ 206.1.130

NL 0444659　　MH ICRL

4LB
763
　Lönnbeck, Gustaf Ferdinand.
　Uno Cygnaeus, 'finska folkskolans
fader". Helsingfors. Weilin & Göös,
1890.
　132 p.

NL 0444660　　DLC-P4 NcD MH

923.7471
C995L
　Lönnbeck, Gustaf Ferdinand
　Uno Cygnaeus, "Finska folkskolans
fader" ... Jubileumsupplaga ... Helsingfors, Söderström, 1910.
　191 p. illus. 23 cm.

　　1. Cygnaeus, Uno, 1810-1888.

NL 0444661　　NcD

　Loennberg, Axel Johan Einar
　　see　Loennberg, Einar, 1865-

　Lönnberg, Carl Johan Leonhard, 1828-1905,
　　respondent.
　Fries, Elias Magnus, 1794-1878, praeses.
　　Conspectus floræ ostrogothicæ, dissertatio academica ... p. l.
Upsaliæ, C. A. Leffler ₁1854₎

[Lönnberg, Carl Johan Leonhard] tr.
　Fornnordiska sagor; [från fornnordiskan af
C. J. L. Lönnberg] Norrköping, M. W. Wallberg
[1870-73]
　2v. in 1. fold.map.

　Vol.2 has imprint: Stockholm, A. L. Norman.
Contents.-v.1. Vatnsdalingarnes saga.-v.2.
Eyrbyggarnes saga.

NL 0444664　　OC1 CtY MH NIC

　Lönnberg, Egil　　　　　ed.
　En bok om Nydala kloster. [Jönköping,
Lundgrenska boktryckeriet,1943]
　157p. illus.,facsims. 23cm.

　　1. Nydala, Sweden (Cistercian abbey)

NL 0444665　　CtY

QL
731
L82++
　Lönnberg, Einar, 1865-
　Anatomical notes on mammals obtained
in British East Africa by the Swedish
zoological expedition 1911.　Uppsala,
Almqvist & Wiksell, 1912.
　33 p. illus. 32cm. (Svenska vetenskapsakademiens, Stockholm. Handlingar.
Band 49, no. 7)

　Bound with his: "Mammals collected by
the Swedish zoological expedition to
British East　Africa 1911", 1912.

NL 0444666　　NIC NN

Lönnberg, Einar, 1865-
　... Anatomische studien über skandinavische cestoden, von
Einar Lönnberg ... Stockholm, P. A. Norstedt & söner,
1891-92.
　2 v. plates. 31ᶜᵐ. (Kongl. svenska vetenskaps-akademiens handlingar. ₁Ny följd₎ bd. 24, n:o 6, 16)
　"Verzeichniss der wichtigsten benutzten litteratur": v. 1, p. 106-109.

　1. Cestoda. 2. Worms—Norway. 3. Worms—Sweden. 4. Parasites—
Fishes.
　　　　　　　　　₁Full name: Axel Johan Einar Lönnberg₎
　　　　　　　　　　　　　　　　　　A 43-181
　Chicago. Univ. Library
　for Library of Congress　　Q64.S85 bd. 24, no. 6, 16

NL 0444667　　ICU CU ICRL MU NN DLC

Lönnberg, Einar, 1865-
　...Birds collected by the Swedish Zoological Expedition to
British East Africa, 1911, by Einar Lönnberg... Uppsala: Almqvist & Wiksell, 1911. 131 p. incl. tables. illus., plates (part
col'd). fᵒ. (Kungliga svenska Vetenskapsakademien. Handlingar. Ny följd, bd. 47, no. 5.)

　1. Birds, Africa (East), British.　　2. Svenska zoologiska Expeditionen
　till Britisk Öst Afrika, 1911.　　　　3. Series.
　N. Y. P. L.　　　　　　　　　　　　　　　January 15, 1923.

NL 0444668　　NN NIC ICarbS

Loennberg, Einar, 1865-
　Björnen i Sverige, 1856-1928, av Einar Lönnberg.
Uppsala och Stockholm, Almquist & Wiksells boktryck
erei - A.- B [1929]
　31p. 21 1/2 cm.

NL 0444669　　DSI

Lönnberg, Einar. Carl von Linné und die lehre von den
wirbeltieren. Jena. 1909. pp. 48. (In KONGLIGA SVEN-
SKA VETENSKAPS-AKADEMIEN. Carl von Linné's bedeutung
als naturforscher und arzt, 1909.)

NL 0444670　　MH-A

✱Lönnberg, Einar, 1865-

K. Svenska vetenskapsakademien, Stockholm, ed.
　Carl von Linnés betydelse såsom naturforskare och
läkare. Skildringar utgifna af Kungl. vetenskapsakademien i anledning af tvåhundraårsdagen af Linnés födelse. Uppsala, Almqvist & Wiksells boktryckeri-a.-b.,
1907.

✱Lönnberg, Einar, 1865-　　ed.

Linné, Carl von, 1707-1778.
　Caroli Linnæi ... Methodus avium sveticarum, utgifven af
Einar Lönnberg. Uppsala, Almqvist & Wiksells boktryckeri-
a.-b., 1907.

VOLUME 338

Lönnberg, Einar, 1865–
...Cestoden... Hamburg, L. Friederichsen & Co., 1896.
9, [1] p.   plate.   28.5 cm.   (Ergebnisse der Hamburger magalhaensischen Sammelreise 1892/93. Hamburg, 1896-1907. Bd. III, [no. 11])
At head of title: Hamburger magalhaensische Sammelreise.
Issued as l. Leif., 5.
"Litteratur-Verzeichnis": p. [10]

NL 0444673   CtY PPAN

QL
252
.S73   Lönnberg, Einar, 1865–
L82   Contributions to the fauna of South Georgia.
        I. Taxonomic and biological notes on vertebrates.
        With 12 plates and 7 figures in the text. Uppsala,
        Almqvist & Wiksell, 1906.
        104 p.   illus., 12 plates (2 col.) 32 x 26 cm.
        (K. Svenska vetenskapsakademien. Handlingar. Ny
        följd, bd. 40, no. 5)

        1. Craniata—South Georgia (Island)

NL 0444674   MiU MU MH

QL691   Lönnberg, Einar, 1865–
S15   Contributions to the ornis of Saghalin.
L6   [Tōkyō, University, 1908]
           69 p. 27 cm. (Journal of the College of
           Science, Imperial University of Tōkyō, Japan,
           v. 23, article 14)
           Caption title.

           1. Birds - Sakhalin.

NL 0444675   CtY

Lönnberg, Einar, 1865–   ed.
Fauna och flora. Populär tidskrift för biologi ... 1.–
    årgång;
1906–
Uppsala & Stockholm, Almqvist & Wiksell [1906–

Lönnberg, Einar, 1865–
Fische.
— Hamburg. Friederichsen & Co. 1907. 16 pp. Plate. [Hamburger magalhaensische Sammelreise.] L. 8°.

G7538 — S.r. — Ichthyology.

NL 0444677   MB PPAN

Lönnberg, Einar, 1865–
The fishes of the Swedish South polar expedition, by Einar Lönnberg... Stockholm: Lithographisches Institut des Generalstabs, 1905.   69(1) p., 1 l. illus., plates (part col'd).   4°.
(Svenska Sydpolar-Expeditionen, 1901–1903. Wissenschaftliche Ergebnisse. Bd. 5, Lief. 6.)

Cover-title.

1. Fish, Antarctic regions.
N.Y.P.L.   2. Series.
                                    September 16, 1920.

NL 0444678   NN

Lönnberg, Einar, 1865–   *2261.134.5.Lief.6
The fishes of the Swedish South Polar Expedition. By Einar Lönnberg.
    (*In* Nordenskiöld, Nils Otto Gustaf, editor. Wissenschaftliche Ergebnisse der schwedischen Südpolar-Expedition 1901–1903. Band 5, Lief. 6. 69, (3) pp. Illus. 5 plates. Tables. Stockholm. 1908.)

D5008 — Antarctic Regions. Ichthyology. — Ichthyology.

NL 0444679   MB

Lönnberg, Einar, 1865–
Is the Florida box tortoise a distinct species? By Einar Lönnberg.
    (*In* U. S. National museum. Proceedings. Washington, 1897. 23½ᶜᵐ. v. 19, p. 253–254)
Issued December 30, 1896.

1. Tortoises.
                            [Full name: Axel Johan Einar Lönnberg]
                                                S 33–505
Library, Smithsonian   Institution
Library of Congress   [Q11.U55 vol. 19]

NL 0444680   DSI

Lönnberg, Einar, 1865–
Linnean type-specimens of birds, reptiles, batrachians and fishes in the Zoological Museum of the R. University in Upsala
    see under Uppsala. Universitet. Zoologiska Museet.

---

*Lönnberg, Einar, 1865–

Linné, Carl von, 1707–1778.
Linnés föreläsningar öfver djurriket, med understöd af Svenska staten för Uppsala universitet utg. och försedda med förklarande anmärkningar af Einar Lönnberg. Uppsala, A.-b. Akademiska bokhandeln i kommission; [etc., etc., 1913]

Lönnberg, Einar, 1865–
...Lizards, by Einar Lönnberg... Batrachians, by Lars Gabriel Andersson... Stockholm: Almqvist & Wiksell, 1916.
17 p.   illus.   f°.   (Kungliga svenska Vetenskapsakademien. Handlingar. Ny följd, bd. 55, no. 4.)
Svenska zoologiska Expeditionerna till Siam, 1911–1912 & 1914–1915. Zoological results. [v.] II–III.

1. Lizard, Siam. 2. Frog, Siam.   3. Anderson, Lars Gabriel,
1868–   . 4. Series.
N.Y.P.L.   January 10, 1923.

NL 0444683   NN

Lönnberg, Einar, 1865–
... Mammals, by Prof. Dr. Einar Lönnberg. With 7 plates. Uppsala, Almqvist & Wiksells boktryckeri-a.-b., 1908.
    cover-title, 58 p.   7 pl. (1 col.)   30½ x 24½ᵐᵐ.   (Wissenschaftliche Ergebnisse der schwedischen zoologischen Expedition nach dem Kilimandjaro, dem Meru und den umgebenden Massaisteppen Deutsch-Ostafrikas 1905-1906, unter leitung von prof. dr. Yngve Sjöstedt. Hrsg. von der Königl. schwedischen akademie der wissenschaften. 2)
    Each plate preceded by leaf with descriptive letter-press not included in paging.
    1. Mammals—Africa, German East.
                            [Full name: Axel Johann Einar Lönnberg]

NL 0444684   MiU

Lönnberg, Einar, 1865–
...Mammals, by Einar Lönnberg...   Uppsala: Almqvist & Wiksell, 1913.   10 p. illus. f°. (Kungliga svenska Vetenskapsakademien. Handlingar. Ny följd, bd. 52, no. 1.)
Mjöbergs svenska vetenskapliga Expeditionerna till Australien, 1910–1913.
I.

1. Mammalia, Australia.   2. Series.
N.Y.P.L.   January 15, 1923.

NL 0444685   NN

Lönnberg, Einar, 1865–
...Mammals collected by the Swedish Zoological Expedition to British East Africa, 1911, by Einar Lönnberg... Uppsala: Almqvist & Wiksell, 1912.   188 p. incl. tables.   illus., plates (part col'd).   f°.   (Kungliga svenska Vetenskapsakademien. Handlingar. Ny följd, bd. 48, no. 5.)

1. Mammalia, Africa (East)   British. 2. Svenska zoologiska
Expeditionen till Britisk Öst Afrika,   1911. 3. Series.
N.Y.P.L.   January 15, 1923.

NL 0444686   NN NIC

Lönnberg, Einar, 1865–
... Mammals collected in Central Africa by Capt. E. Arrhenius, by Einar Lönnberg ... Stockholm, Almqvist & Wiksells boktryckeri-a.-b., 1917.
110 p. illus., 12 pl. 31½ᶜᵐ. (Kungl. svenska vetenskapsakademiens handlingar. bd. 58, n:o 2)

1. Mammals—Africa, Central. I. *Arrhenius, Elias, 1883–
                            [Full name: Axel Johan Einar Lönnberg]
                                                A 28–2116
Title from Univ. of Chi-   cago Q64.8828 vol. 58, no. 2
                                Printed by L. C.

NL 0444687   ICU NIC NN

Lönnberg, Einar, 1865–   , and E. G. Mjöberg.
...Mammals from Queensland, by Einar Lönnberg and Eric Mjöberg...   Stockholm: Almqvist & Wiksell, 1916.   20 p. incl. tables.   illus., col'd.pl.   f°.   (Kungliga svenska Vetenskapsakademien. Handlingar. Ny följd, bd. 52, no. 2.)
Mjöbergs svenska vetenskapliga Expeditionerna till Australien, 1910–1913.
II.

1. Mammalia, Australia: Queens-   land. 2. Mjöberg, Eric Georg,
1882–   , jt au. 3. Series.
N.Y.P.L.   January 16, 1923.

NL 0444688   NN

LÖNNBERG, Einar, 1865–
Material for the study of ruminants.
Upsala, 1903.

NL 0444689   MH

Lönnberg, Einar, 1865–
Notes on reptiles and batrachians collected in Florida in 1892 and 1893. By Einar Lœnnberg ...
    (*In* U. S. National museum. Proceedings. Washington, 1895. 23½ᶜᵐ. v. 17, 1894, p. 317–339. illus.)
Issued November 15, 1894.

1. Batrachia—Florida. 2. Reptiles—Florida.
                            [Full name: Axel Johan Einar Lönnberg]
                                                S 33–405
Library, Smithsonian   Institution
Library of Congress   [Q11.U55 vol. 17]

NL 0444690   DSI

VOLUME 338

Lönnberg, Einar, 1865–
... Om renarne och deras lefnadsvanor, af Einar Lönnberg. Uppsala, Almqvist & Wiksells boktryckeri-A.B., 1909.
2 p.l., 197, ₍2₎ p. illus., fold.maps, fold. tab. 24 cm.
(At head of title: Bilaga till "Forhandlingarne inför skiljedomstolen af 1909 i renbetesfrågan, afdelning I, svensk inlaga n:r 3")

1. Reindeer.

NL 0444691   DSI

Lönnberg, Einar, 1865–
... On a new fossil porcupine from Honan with some remarks about the development of the *Hystridae*, by Einar Lönnberg, Stockholm ... Peking, Geological survey of China, 1924.
1 p. l., 15 p., 2 l. pl. 29ᶜᵐ. (China. Geological survey. Palæontologia sinica, ser. c, v. 1, fasc. 3)

1. Porcupines, Fossil. 2. Paleontology—China—Honan (Province)
₍Full name: Axel Johan Einar Lönnberg₎
G S 25–277
U. S. Geol. survey. Library for Library of Congress   QE756.C6A3 ser. c, vol. 1, fasc. 3

NL 0444692   DI-GS MiU OU DLC CU

LÖNNBERG, Einar, 1865–
On the adaptations to a molluscivorus diet in Varanus miloticus. Stockholm,1903.

NL 0444693   MH

LÖNNBERG, Einar, 1865–
On the homologies of the different pieces of the compound rhamphoteca of birds. Stockholm, 1904.

NL 0444694   MH

Lönnberg, Einar , 1865–
Peter Artedi. A bicentenary memoir written on behalf of the Swedish royal academy of science by Einar Lönnberg. Tr. by W. E. Harlock. Uppsala & Stockholm, Almqvist & Wiksells boktryckeri-a.-b.; ₍etc., etc.₎ 1905.
44 p. 22½ᶜᵐ.

1. Artedi, Peter, 1705–1735. i. Harlock, Walter Ernest, 1866– tr.
6—805
Library of Congress   QL31.A7L8

NL 0444695   DLC CtY CU WU ICJ

Lönnberg, Einar, 1865–
... *Pisces* (Fische). I. Buch: Einleitendes. *Leptocardii* und *Cyclostomi*. Bearbeitet von E.Lönnberg, G.Favaro, B.Mozejko und M.Rauther ... Leipzig,Akademische Verlagsgesellschaft m.b.H.,1924.
v,710p. illus.XXXIIpl.(partly double) 26cm.
(Dr.H.G.Bronn's Klassen und Ordnungen des Tier-Reichs, 6.Bd.,1.Abt.,1.Buch)
Issued in parts, 1901-1924.
Includes bibliographies.

Sᴸᴮ
336
6

NL 0444696   CtY PPAN

Lönnberg, Einar, 1865–
...Reptiles, by Einar Lönnberg and L. G. Andersson... Uppsala: Almqvist & Wiksell, 1913. 17 p. illus. f°. (Kungliga svenska Vetenskapsakademien. Handlingar. Ny följd, bd. 52, no. 3.)
Mjöbergs svenska vetenskapliga Expeditionerna till Australien, 1910–1913.
III.

1. Reptilia, Australia. 2. Anders-   son, Lars Gabriel, 1868–
jt. au. 3. Series.
N. Y. P. L.   January 22, 1923.

NL 0444697   NN

Lönnberg, Einar, 1865–
...Reptiles, batrachians and fishes collected by the Swedish Zoological Expedition to British East Africa, 1911. Reptiles and fishes, by Einar Lönnberg. Batrachians, by Lars Gabriel Andersson ... Uppsala: Almqvist & Wiksell, 1911. 42 p. illus., plates. f°. (Kungliga svenska Vetenskapsakademien. Handlingar. Ny följd, bd. 47, no. 6.)

1. Reptilia, Africa (East). British.   2. Fish, Africa (East), British.
3. Batrachia, Africa (East), British.   4. Svenska zoologiska Expeditionen
till Britisk Öst Afrika, 1911. 5. An-   dersson, Lars Gabriel, 1868–
6. Series.
N. Y. P. L.   January 15, 1923.

NL 0444698   NN

Lönnberg, Einar, 1865–
...Reptiles collected in northern Queensland, by Einar Lönnberg and L. G. Andersson, read May 12th, 1915. Stockholm: Almqvist & Wiksell, 1915. 9 p. f°. (Kungliga svenska Vetenskapsakademien. Handlingar. Ny följd, bd. 52, no. 7.)
Mjöbergs svenska vetenskapliga Expeditionerna till Australien, 1910–1913.
VII.

1. Reptilia, Australia: Queensland.   2. Andersson, Lars Gabriel, 1868–
jt. au. 3. Series.
N. Y. P. L.   January 22, 1923.

NL 0444699   NN

LÖNNBERG, Einar, 1865–
A second contribution to the mammalogy of Eucador with some remarks on Caenolestes. Stockholm, etc., Almquist & Wiksells etc., 1921.

104 pp. ills.

NL 0444700   MH-Z

LÖNNBERG, Einar, 1865–
Short notes on a collection of birds from Tianshan. Stockholm,1905.

NL 0444701   MH

Lönnberg, Einar, 1865–
... Some speculations on the origin of the North American ornithic fauna, by Einar Lönnberg. Communicated April 13ᵗʰ 1927. Stockholm, Almqvist & Wiksells boktryckeri-a.-b., 1927.
24 p. 28½ᶜᵐ. (Kungl. svenska vetenskapsakademiens handlingar. 3. ser., bd. 4, n:o 6)

1. Birds—Geographical distribution. 2. Birds—North America.
₍Full name: Axel Johan Einar Lönnberg₎
A 29–54
Title from Univ. of Chi-   cago Q64.8828 3. ser., vol. 4, no. 6
Printed by L. C.

NL 0444702   ICU

Lönnberg, Einar, 1865–
Studies on ruminants. I and II. Stockholm: P. A. Norstedt & Söner, 1901. 58 p., 3 pl. illus. f°. (Kongliga Svenska Vetenskaps-Akademien. Handlingar. Ny följd. Bd. 35, no. 3.)

1. Ruminants. 2. Horns. 3. Gnu.
N. Y. P. L.   January 4, 1912.

NL 0444703   NN

Lönnberg, Einar, 1865–
Svenska fåglar efter naturen och på sten ritade, af M., W. och F. von Wright, med text af professor Einar Lönnberg. Stockholm, I. Baarsen ₍1924–29₎
3 v. illus, 364 col. pl. 39ᶜᵐ.
Vol. 2–3, Förlaget svenska fåglar, Stockholm.
Paged consecutively.

1. Birds—Sweden. ₍1. Sweden—Ornithology₎ i. Wright, Magnus von, 1805–1868, illus. ii. Wright, Wilhelm von, 1810–1887, illus. iii. Wright, Ferdinand von, 1822–1906, illus.
₍Full name: Axel Johan Einar Lönnberg₎
Agr 30–1422
Library, U. S. Dept. of   Agriculture 413L862

NL 0444704   DNAL PPAN DI ICF CtY

Lönnberg, Einar, 1865– , ed.
Svenska jaktboken; utgiven av prof. Einar Lönnberg. ₍Stockholm₎ A. Bonnier ₍1923–25₎ 2 v. illus. (incl. music), col'd plates. 26½cm. (Half-title: Svenska jordbrukets bok; illustrerad handbok för jordbruket och dess binäringar.)
Issued in 17 parts.
Title from cover of parts.
Each volume has special and general t.-p.
General : ₍p. of v. 1: Svenska jordbrukets bok. Sveriges jaktbara djur; v. 2: Svenska jordbrukets bok. Jakt och jaktvård.
Bibliographies included.
CONTENTS.—₍Del 1₎ Sveriges jaktbara djur av Einar Lönnberg —₍Del 2₎ Jakt och jaktvård, av Einar Lönnberg under medverkan av Arvid M. Bergman ... Hj. Dahlström... Pelle Falk ₍och andra₎
791751–2A. 1. Hunting—Sweden.   I. Title.
N. Y. P. L.   November 22, 1938

NL 0444705   NN

Lönnberg, Einar, 1865–
De svenska ryggradsdjurens vetenskapliga namn, af Einar Lönnberg. Uppsala & Stockholm, Almqvist & Wiksells boktryckeri-A.-B., [1908].
[4], 159, [1] p. 25ᶜᵐ.

NL 0444706   ICJ

639.1
L824   LÖNNBERG, Einar, 1865–
Sveriges jaktbara djur... Stockholm, A. Bonniers förlag ₍1923–1925₎
2v. illus. (incl. diagrs., music) col. plates (1 fold.) 26cm. (Svenska jordbrukets bok; illustrerad handbok för jordbruket och dess binäringar. ₍N₎)
Vol.2 has title: Jakt och jaktvård.
Vol.2 "Under medverkan av: Arvid M. Bergman... Hj. Dahlström... Pelle Falk... ₍m.fl.₎"
Each volume issued in parts with title: Svenska jakt-   boken.
"Förteckning   över en del använd litteratur": v.l.,   1 l. at end.

1. Game and game-birds in Sweden. 2. Hunting. Implements and appliances. 3. Dogs. 4. Hunting. I. Title. II. Title: Jakt och jaktvård.

NL 0444708   MnU NN

Lönnberg, Einar, 1865–
Nyström, J₍ohan₎ F₍redrik₎ 1855– ed.
Sveriges rike; handbok för det svenska folket, utgifven under redaktion af D:r J. F. Nyström ... Stockholm, Expeditionen af Ljus, 1899–1902.

VOLUME 338

Lönnberg, Einar, 1865–
Sveriges ryggradsdjur. 1–[III]. ... Av Einar Lönnberg. Stockholm, P. A. Norstedt & söner, [1914–1915].
3 vol. illus. 24ᶜᵐ.
Contents.—1. Däggdjuren. [1914.] [4, II]–iv, 100 p.—2. Fåglarna. [1915.] viii, 367 p.—3. Kräldjur. Groddjur. Fiskar. [1915.] [4], 331 p.

NL 0444710   ICJ

Lönnberg, Einar, 1865–
Die Vögel der schwedischen Südpolar-Expedition, von Einar Lönnberg. Stockholm: Lithographisches Institut des Generalstabs, 1905. 9 p. 4°. (Svenska Sydpolar-Expeditionen, 1901–1903. Wissenschaftliche Ergebnisse. Bd. 5, Lief. 5.)
Cover-title.

1. Birds, Antarctic regions.   2. Series.
N.Y.P.L.   September 16, 1920.

NL 0444711   NN MB

WQ   **LÖNNBERG, Ingolf**
L825s   Studien über das Nabelbläschen an der
1901   Nachgeburt des ausgetragenen Kindes.
Stockholm, Central-tryckeriet, 1901.
118 p.

NL 0444712   DNLM PPC ICJ

Lönnberg, Matilda Lovisa Jakobina, 1837–1907.
Ragnfast Mårsson; en forntidsbild/tecknad af -th- [pseud.] Stockholm, Ivar Haeggström, 1873.
206 p. (Skönliteratur, 3)

NL 0444713   WaU

Lönnbohm, Anders Oskar Ferdinand
Taikanuotta eli opas taikojen kerääjille, toimittanut O.A.F. Mustonsn...
Helsinki, Suomalaisen kirjallisuuden seura [1936]
48 p. 20 cm.

NL 0444714   DSI NN

[Loennbohm, Anders Oskar Ferdinand]
Tietoja Kajaanin kihlakunnasta ja etenkin Paltamon pitäjäästä, [by] O.A.F. Mustonen[pseud.]
Hämeenlinnassa, Hämeen sanomain osakeyhtiön kirjapainossa, 1885
272 p.

NL 0444715   MH

[Lönnbohm, Anders Oskar Ferdinand.]   27252.23.?
Virolaisia kansanrunoja. Vihukene eesti rahva laulusid. Helsingissä, Suomalaisen kirjallisuuden seuran kirjapainossa, 1893.
pp. (1), 101.
At head of title: "O. A. F. Mustonen" pseud.

Ballads-Esthonian||Title°|.

NL 0444716   MH

Lönnbohm, Armas Eino Leopold
see   Leino, Eino, 1878–1926.

Lönnbohm, Eino.
See
Leino, Eino, 1878– 1926.

Lönnbohm, Kasimir Agathon
see   Leino, Kasimir, 1866-1919.

LÖNNE, Franz, 1887–
Ueber die reinigende wirkung der galle.
Inaug.-diss., Giessen. Hövel, J. Teitfeld, 1919.

Giessen, "Lebenslauf", p.15.
At head of title-page: Aus dem Pharmakologischen institut des universität.

NL 0444720   MH PU ICRL DNLM

Lönne, Friedrich, 1891–   Die Bedeutung der Wohnungsinspektion für die moderne Wohnungsfrage erläutert an den in Hessen gemachten Erfahrungen. Wiesbaden: Bergmann 1914. 52 S. 8° ¶Im Buchh. ebd.
Gießen, Phil. Diss. v. 16. Nov. 1914, Ref. Skalweit
[Geb. 17. Febr. 91 Katernberg; Wohnort: Gießen; Staatsangeh.: Preußen; Vorbildung: Rf-G. Wiesbaden Reife 11; Studium: Med. u. Phil. Straßburg 2, Heidelberg 1, Gießen 4 S.; Rig. 24. Juni 14.]   [U 14. 3494

NL 0444721   ICRL NN CtY DNLM MH PU

Loenne, Friedrich, 1891–
Deutschlands Volksvermehrung und Bevölkerungspolitik vom nationalökonomisch-medizinischen Standpunkt, von Friedrich Lönne... Wiesbaden: J. F. Bergmann, 1917.   3 p.l., 67 p. incl. tables. 4°.

1. Birth rate, Germany. 2. Birth   control, Germany.
N.Y.P.L.   January 20, 1921.

NL 0444722   NN CU MdBJ DNW

LÖNNE, Friedrich, 1891–
Das problem der fruchtabtreibung vom medizinischen, juristischen und nationalökonomischen standpunkt. Berlin,1924.
42 p.

NL 0444723   MH-L

Loenne, Friedrich, 1891–
—— *Ueber Kriegsverletzungen des peripheren Nervensystems an der Hand von 60 Beobachtungen in der chirurgischen Universitätsklinik zu Giessen. 46 pp., 2 l. 8°.
Giessen, O. Kindt. 1916.

NL 0444724   DNLM

QZ   **LÖNNE, Friedrich,** 1891–
200   Was jede Frau und jeder Mann vom
L825w   Krebs wissen muss! Krebskrankheit
1951   und Krebsheilung. Kevelaer, Butzon &
Bercker [1951]
160 p.
1. Cancer - Popular works

NL 0444725   DNLM ICJ

W   Lönne, Friedrich, 1891–
1   Was muss jeder Mann und jede Frau
RE175   vom Krebs wissen? Berlin, Reichsgesund-
Heft 29   heitsverlag [1941]
1941   11 p. illus. (Schriftenreihe des
Reichsausschusses für Volksgesundheitsdienst. Heft 29)

1. Cancer - Popular works Series:
Reichsausschuss für Volksgesundheitsdienst.
Schriftenreihe. Heft 29

NL 0444726   DNLM

Lönne, Martha, 1903–
Wirkung von Schwermetallen auf Pflanzen ...
Würzburg, 1930.
Inaug.-Diss. - Würzburg.
Lebenslauf.
"Literaturverzeichnis": p. v–vii.

NL 0444727   CtY

HF5835   Lönnecke, Günther.
.L82   Reklamesteuer? Das Für und Wider einer Besteuerung der Werbung. Berlin, Duncker & Humblot [1954]
88 p. (Finanzwissenschaftliche Forschungsarbeiten. N. F., Heft 7)
Includes bibliography.

1. Taxation of advertising. I. Title.

NL 0444728   ICU NIC MH IU CtY

Lönnegren, A   V   , 1842-1904.
Nordisk svampbok, med beskrifning öfver sveriges och norra europas allmännaste. Ätliga och giftiga svampar, de ätligas insamling, förvaring, anrättning, odling och veredning for afsättning i handeln. Lättfattlig framställning af A. V. Lönnegren... Med 60 nya bilder i färgtryck å 4 planscher. Femte tillökade upplagan. Stockholm, C. A. V. Lundholm A.-B [1916]
85 [1] p. 4 col. fronts., illus. 21.5 cm.

NL 0444729   PSt

Lönnegren,A   V   1842-1904
Svampbok,innehållande beskrifning öfver sveriges allmännaste ätliga och giftiga svamper,jemte de ätligas insamling,förvaring,tillredning och odling,tillika med uppgifter om deras beredning för afsättning i handeln. Lättfattligt försök af A.V.Lönnegren.... Stockholm, C.A.V.Lundholms förlag [1883]
70 p.,1 l. IV col.front.,illus. 19ᶜᵐ.
Each frontispiece has descriptive letterpress mounted on blank leaf,not included in paging.
With this is bound Fröléen & comp.,publishers,Stockholm Fröléens svampbok [1917]; and Strömbom,N.G. Våra vanligaste svenska svampar. 1896.
1.Mushrooms—Sweden. Title.
QX608.S85L83

NL 0444730   MiU

Loennegren, August Valfrid.
Carmen musaei grammatici, quod "HP Kai Deandpos insoribitur, latinis versibus expressit.
Inaug. diss. Upsala, 1869.

NL 0444731   ICRL

VOLUME 338

Loennegren, August Valfrid.
De syntaxi sulpicii severi.
Inaug. diss. Upsala, 1882.

NL 0444732   ICRL MH NIC NjP MiU

Loennegren, Aug. Valfrid.
Quid sacra scriptura de immortalitate, quid de
aeterna beatitudine et infelicitate doceat?.
Inaug. diss. Upsala, 1881.
Bibl.

NL 0444733   ICRL

Lönnegren, John,   1878-
Anders Berch und der schwedische
Merkantilismus ...   Berlin, 1916.
Inaug.-diss. - Greifswald.
Lebenslauf.
Full name: John Alexander Lönnegren.

NL 0444734   CtY MiU PU KU

Lönnegren, John, 1878-
Ryssland och Europa. Bemyndigad bearbetning efter
dr. Paul Rohrbachs Russland und wir, av John Lönnegren. Stockholm, Ahlén & Akerlund ₁1915₁
159 p. 19¹ᵐ.
Errata slip inserted.

1. Russia—Pol. & govt.—1894-1917. 2. European war, 1914-1918—Russia.
I. Rohrbach, Paul, 1869-   Russland und wir. II. Title.

Library of Congress   D514.L⁶   22-4866

NL 0444735   DLC MH NjP

Lönner (Carolus). ° De cognitione aberrantium
praecipue arteriarum medico necessaria, et ex-
emplis notabilioribus in theatro anatomico etiam
nostro observatis illustrata. 1 p. l., 16 pp. 8°.
Lundae, C. F. Berling, 1830.

NL 0444736   DNLM

Loenner, Ferdinand Alexander, respondent.
De expositione fidei orthodoxae...
see under Lenstroem, Carl Julius, 1811-
1893, praeses.

Loenner, Ferdinand Alexander
De paroecia eds capell in Smolandia; dissertatio
historicò-topographica...Upsaliae (1845)

NL 0444738   NN

Loenner, Fredericus Adolphus, respondent.
Dissertatio de stilo historico... apud Romanos
see under Geijer, Erik Gustaf, 1783-1847,
praeses.

Lönner, Laurentius, respondent.
... Dissertationis de legatis nuntiis que papelibus
in sveciam missis...
see under   Ekerman, Petrus, 1696(7)-1783,
praeses.

Lönnerberg, Rob. Guil., respondent.
Remarques sur l'instruction publique en Suede...
see under Egnell, Andre J., praeses.

Lönnerblad, Georg.
... Über den sauerstoffhaushalt der dystrophen seen, von
Georg Lönnerblad. Lund, C. W. K. Gleerup; ₁etc., etc., 1931₁
53 p. incl. tables, diagrs. 26ᶜᵐ. (Lunds universitets årsskrift. n. f.,
avd. 2, bd. 27, nr. 14)
Kungl. fysiografiska sällskapets handlingar. n. f., bd. 42, nr. 14.
"Literatur": p. ₁52₁-53.

1. Water—Analysis. 2. Lakes—Sweden.   I. Title.

                                                  A 32-2305
Title from Univ. of Chi-   cago AS284.L96 n. f., avd. 2, bd. 27
Library of Congress   [AS284.L8 n. f., avd. 2, bd. 27]

NL 0444742   ICU OU

Lönnerblad, Lars Viktor, 1902-
Transit time through the small intestine : a roentgenologic
study on normal variability. ₁Translated by Klas M. Lind-
skog₁ Stockholm, 1951.
85 p. illus., diagrs., tables. 25 cm. (Acta radiologica. Supple-
mentum 88)
Akademisk avhandling—Karolinska institutet, Stockholm.
Without thesis statement.
Summaries in English, French and German.
Errata leaf inserted.
Bibliography: p. ₁83₁-85.

1. Intestines. 2. Diagnosis, Radioscopic.   I. Title.   (Series)
                                                  A 51-9948
Michigan. Univ. Libr.
for Library of Congress   ₁2₁

NL 0444743   MiU MoU PPT-M ViU

QL
858   **Lönnerblad, Tore.**
.L82   Vergleichende anatomische Studien über das
Kauorgan einiger Säugetiere. Stockholm, 1955.
78 p. 25 cm.

NL 0444744   MiU PU-D

WU
101   **Lönnerblad, Tore.**
L86lv   Vergleichende anatomische Studien über
das Kauorgan einiger Säugetiere. Stockholm, 1955.
109p. plates. 25cm.

Bibliography: p.76-78.

1.Jaws. 2.Mammals. I.Title.

NL 0444745   CLSU IaU OU

Lönnerstrand, Sture
Den oupphörliga (Incestrala) Blodsym-
fonien.   Stockholm, Litteraturförlaget,
1951.
72p. 19ᶜᵐ.

NL 0444746   KU MnU

Lönnerstrand, Sture.
Psykoanalys och erotik; tre artiklar. Stockholm, Bokförlaget Indigo ₁1953₁
39 p. 21 cm.

1. Sex (Psychology) 2. Psychoanalysis.   I. Title.

BF692.L57   56-45060 ‡

NL 0444747   DLC

Lönnerstrand, Sture.
Rymdhunden, en resa till Jupiter. Stockholm, Bonnier
₁1954₁
178 p. 19 cm. (Planetböckerna 3)

I. Title.

PT9875.L59R9   55-18092 ‡

NL 0444748   DLC

Lönnerstrand, Sture.
...Ung mans gåtor; dikter.   Lund: Sundqvist & Edmond
₁1939₁ 93 p. 20½cm.

1. Poetry, Swedish. I. Title.
N. Y. P. L.   February 7, 1941

NL 0444749   NN MH

Lönne, Friedrich.
Deutschlands volksvermehrung und bevolkerungspolitik
vom nationalokonomisch-medizinichen standpunk von
Friedrich Lönne...Wiesbaden, J.F. Bergmann, 1917
3 p.l., 67 p. incl. tables. 25 cm

NL 0444750   DNW

Lönnfors, Frans.
... Beiträge zur morphologie der analginen, von Frans Lönnfors (mit 22 tafeln und 12 textabbildungen) Helsingforsiae
₁Akademische buchhandlung₁ 1930.
4 p. l., 7-81 p., 1 l. incl. illus., tables. 22 pl. 28ᶜᵐ. (Added t.-p.: Societas pro fauna et flora fennica. Acta zoologica fennica. 8)

"Literaturverzeichnis": p. ₁69₁-73.

1. Mites.
                                                  A C 33-894
Title from Ohio State   Univ.
Library of Congress   [QH7.S78 no. 8]

PPAmP ViU OU ICJ
NL 0444751   OU MoU AAP MU MiU ICRL ViU CtY PU NcU

Lonnfors, Frans.
Vesimääränmittaukset Soumessa
see under   Finland. Hydrologinen toimisto.

Lönnfors, Frans.
Wassermengenmessungen in Finnland bis Jahr 1936.
Helsinki. 1936. Helsingfors. 1936.
65 p. 24½ cm.
Text in Finnish, Swedish & German.

NL 0444753   DAS

VOLUME 338

4PT
Swed.-
233

Lönnhammar, Isse Reinhold.
Min son var icke min; roman. Stockholm,
Morgondagens förlag [1950]
200 p.

NL 0444754   DLC-P4

Loennies, Hermann.
Ueber die a-und y-sulfoisophtalsaeure...
Inaug. diss. Rostock,1881.

NL 0444755   ICRL

Loennies, Richard,1875–
Der vergleich nach deutschem buergerlichem...
Inaug. diss. Greifswald,1898.
Bibl.

NL 0444756   ICRL

Lönning, Josef M., tr.
... Horazens Epistel an die Pisonen ...
see under Horatius Flaccus, Quintus.

Lønning, Mikkjell.
Paa vidderne; spelstykke i tvo bolkar. Bergen: K. Madsen,
1910. 39 p. 12°.

1. Drama (Norwegian). 2. Title.
N. Y. P. L.   June 14, 1912.

NL 0444758   NN

Lønning, Per.
Hva er kristendom? ₁Oslo₁ Forlaget Land og kirke ₁1955₁
181 p. 21 cm.
Bibliography: p. ₁180₁-181.
——————Studieplan, ved forfatteren i samarbeid med
Norsk kristelig studieråd. ₁Oslo₁ Forlaget Land og kirke
₁1955₁
15 p. 18 cm.
Bibliography: p. 3.
           BX8015.L63 Suppl.
1. Religious education—Textbooks—Lutheran.   I. Norsk kriste-
lig studieråd.   II. Title.
BX8015.L63   76-405414

NL 0444759   DLC NcD

BX4827
.K5L58

Lønning, Per.
"Samtidighedens situation"; en studie i Søren Kierkegaards kristendomsforståelse. Mit einer deutschen Zusammenfassung. Oslo, Land og kirke, 1954.
328 p. 24 cm.
"Litteraturfortegnelse": p. 315–325.

1. Kierkegaard, Søren Aabye, 1813–1855. 2. Christianity—Philosophy.
           A 54–7715
Chicago. Univ. Libr.
for Library of Congress   ₁†₁

NL 0444760   ICU NcD CU WU IaU MnU CtY-D MH-AH DLC

Lønning, Per, ed.
Søren Kierkegaard
see under Kierkegaard, Søren Aabye,
1813–1855.

Lönning, Thor Jacob Grell, 1919–
Über den Einfluss von Lösungsmittel und Temperatur auf
die Stärke von Aminosäuren. Basel, Buchdr. E. Birk-
häuser, 1945.
₁1057₁-1079 p. illus. 23 cm.
Promotionsarbeit—Eidgenössische Technische Hochschule, Zürich.
"Sonderabdruck aus Helvetica chimica acta, volumen XXVIII,
fasciculus sextus, 1945."
Lebenslauf.

1. Amino acids. 2. Dissociation.
QD305.A7L77   A F 48–2546*
Illinois. Univ. Library
for Library of Congress

NL 0444762   IU DLC

Lönnkvist, Frederick.
Allt-omfattande svensk-amerikansk uppslagsbok
see his Hjelpreda och sälskap för hvarje hem

PD5640
L64

Lönnkvist, Frederick
Engelsk-svensk och svensk-engelsk ordbok med fullständig
uttalsbeteckning. Ordlista öfver amerikanska ord, fraser,
förkortningar, samtalsöfningar och ordspråk, tillsammans med
utförliga underrättelser rörande brefskrifning omfattande affärsbref,
umgängesbref, rekommendationsbref, o.s.v., med formulär både
på svenska och engelska. Utarbetad af Fred. Lönnkvist. [n. p.,
W. E. Scull? c1901]
342 p. illus.   (Nordstjernans premium)

1. English language - Dictionaries - Swedish. 2. Swedish
language - Dictionaries - English.

NL 0444764   CU NN ICU

Lönnkvist, Frederick, tr.
₁Stretton, Hesba₁ 1832–1911.
Från Betlehem till Golgata, en enkel och liflig framställning
af Jesu underfulla lif. Med valda stycken af religiös poesi af
C. D., af Virsén, J. L. Runeberg m. fl. Jemte evangelisternas
och apostlarnes lif, lidanden och martyrdöd. Bearbetad för
svenska läsare af Fred Lönnkvist ... Philadelphia, Chicago,
J. C. Winston & co., 1893.

Lönnkvist, Fred₁erick₁
Hjelpreda och sälskap för hvarje hem. Allt-omfattande svensk-amerikansk uppslagsbok innehållande engelsk-svensk ordbok och svensk-engelsk ordbok, engelska samtalsöfningar, anvisningar för välskrifning . . .
och ett stort antal andra allmännyttiga underrättelser för
alla klasser. Af Fred. Lönnkvist . . . Philadelphia och
Chicago, J. C. Winston & co., 1894.
1 p. l., [9]–791 pp. incl. illus., pl. front. (map) pl. 26½ᶜᵐ.
         2–3612—M 2

NL 0444766   DLC MnHi WaU

Loennkvist, Frederick
Laettfattlig biblish ordbok [1890]
see under Nystroem, Erik.

Lönnkvist, Frederick.
Livre des enfants. Le règne animal; histoire naturelle
pour les enfants ... par Frederic Lonnkvist ... ₁Philadelphia?₁ 1901₁
1 p. l., vii–xvi, 17–256 p. col. front. illus. (partly col.) plates (partly
col.) 24½ᶜᵐ.

1. Animals, Habits and behavior of. 2. Zoology—Juvenile and popular
literature
         1–27381 Additions
Library of Congress   QL49.L86

NL 0444768   DLC

₁Lönnkvist, Frederick₁
Et mindeværk om Norge og Amerika. De hjem vi forlod
og de hjem vi fandt ... Det maleriske Norge og det maleriske
Amerika ... Chicago, Philadelphia, J. C. Winston & co., 1892.
xxii, 1 l., 17–496 p. incl. front. (port.) illus. 27ᶜᵐ.
The portion of this work which treats of America is almost identical
with that contained in "Ett minnesverk öfver Sverige och Amerika."

1. U. S.—Descr. & trav. 2. Norway—Descr. & trav.   I. Title.
II. Title: De hjem vi forlod og de hjem vi fandt.
Library of Congress   E168.L82   2—3348

NL 0444769   DLC

Lönnkvist, Frederick.
Ett minnesverk öfver Sverige och Amerika. De hem vi
lemnade och de hem vi funno. Det pittoreska Sverige och
det pittoreska Amerika ... Bearbetad af Fred. Lönnkvist, PH. D.
... Philadelphia, Chicago, J. C. Winston & co., 1893.
xxx, 31–500 p. incl. front. (port.) illus., pl. 2 pl. 26½ᶜᵐ.
Illustrated title-page added.
The portion of this work which treats of America is nearly identical
with that contained in "Et mindeværk om Norge og Amerika."

1. U. S.—Descr. & trav. 2. Sweden—Descr. & trav.   I. Title.
         2—3347
Library of Congress   E168.L83

NL 0444770   DLC PPAmSwM MnHi

Lönnkvist, Frederick, tr.
Morris, Charles, 1833–
Ny och fullständig Förenta Staternas historia; omfattande detta lands födelse och tillväxt från tidigaste dagar
af dess upptäckt och bebyggande intill närvarande hän-
delserika år ... Af Charles Morris ... bearbetad på
svenska ... af Fredrik Lönnkvist ... ₁Philadelphia? 1902₁

₁591.5
L868w

Lönnkvist, Frederick
₁Wild animals of forest and jungle. Philadelphia, John C. Winston, n.d.₁
240 p. illus. (Standard series)
Title-page and pages 1–31, 65–6, and 240–250
lacking.

NL 0444772   WaPS

17
1187

Loennkvist, Frederick
Veiledning ved loesningen af den hellige skrifts
boger, ... aspasset soerskilt for denne
bibeludgave eften den .... beibel-haandbog af pastor
Joh. Aug. Bert. Rigt illustreret. [Phila., A. J.
Hohnan & co., 1889]
1 p. l., 48 p. 4°.

NL 0444773   DLC

VOLUME 338

Lönnquist, Carl Adolph, 1869-1937.
Efter fyrtio år, 1876-1916; stycken ur en församlingshistoria med anledning av Sv. Ev. Luth. Bethania-församlingens i Kearney Co., Nebr., jubileum, av C. A. Lönnquist... ₍Rock Island, Ill., Augustana Book Concerns tryckeri, 1916₎
99, 2-16 p. illus., music, ports. 23 cm.

"Var är mitt hem?": p.2-16 (2d group)

NL 0444774   MnHi

Lönnquist, Carl Adolph, 1869-1937.
Sundet vid treskär, och andra dikter, af C. A. Lönnquist. Malmö, Förlags-aktiebolagets boktr., 1913.
199 p. port. 23 cm.

NL 0444775   MnHi NcD ICLT

Lönnquist, Carl Adolph, 1869-1937.
... Vildros; ett nytt knippe. Rock Island, Ill., Augustana book concern ₍1916₎
112 p. 19½ᶜᵐ. $0.75
Poems.

I. Title.

Library of Congress   PT9995.L6V5   16-24831

NL 0444776   DLC ICLT MnHi WaU TxU

Lönnqvist, Bernt.
Bidrag till kännedom om magsaftafsöndringen ... Helsingfors, Helsingfors centraltryckeri och bokbinderi aktiebolag, 1906.
2 p. l., 97 p. 23ᶜᵐ.
Akademisk afhandling—Helsingfors.
"Litteratur-förteckning": p. 92-97.

1. Stomach—Secretions.

Library of Congress   QP193.L6   8-9335

NL 0444777   DLC CtY DI-GS

Lönnqvist, Conrad, 1889-
... Måste jordens kärna antagas vara av hög temperatur? av Conrad Lönnqvist. Med 7 figurer i texten ... ₍Uppsala, Almqvist & Wiksells boktryckeri-a.-b., 1920₎
26 p. diagrs. 23ᶜᵐ. (Arkiv för matematik, astronomi och fysik. bd. 14, n:o 26)
Caption title.
Bibliographical foot-notes.

NL 0444778   ICJ

Lönnqvist, Conrad, 1889-
Människan på världsteatern. Stockholm, Ljus ₍1947₎
218 p. illus. 20 cm.

1. Astronomy. 2. Physics. 3. Plurality of worlds. I. Title.
Full name: Conrad Leopold Lönnqvist.

QB44.L76   52-43889 ‡

NL 0444779   DLC NN

Lönnqvist, Conrad, 1889-
On the evolution of the stars with mass reduction; a theoretical investigation on the basis of Eddington's theory of radiative equilibrium ... Uppsala, Almqvist & Wiksells boktryckeri-a.-b., 1927.
2 p. l., 104 p. incl. tables, diagrs. 22½ᶜᵐ.
Inaug.-diss.—Upsala.
On cover: Arkiv för matematik, astronomi och fysik, utg. av K. Svenska vetenskapsakademien, bd. 20 A. n:o 21.
Bibliographical foot-notes.
1. Stars. 2. Stars—Radiation. 3. Cosmogony. I. Arkiv för matematik, astronomi och fysik. II. Title: Evolution of the stars with mass reduction.
₍Full name: Conrad Leopold Lönnqvist₎

Library of Congress   QB801.L7   29-10860

NL 0444780   DLC CtY ICJ

Lönnqvist, Conrad, 1889-
... Versuch einer Deduktion der Frequenz der Meteoriten, von Conrad Lönnqvist. Mit 13 Figuren im Texte ... ₍Uppsala, Almqvist & Wiksells boktryckeri-a.-b., 1924₎
39, ₍1₎ p. diagrs. 23ᶜᵐ. (Arkiv för matematik, astronomi och fysik. bd. 18, n:o 25)
Caption title.
Bibliographical foot-notes.

NL 0444781   ICJ

Lönnqvist, Olov
Förenkling av höjduträkningen vid radiosondering. A new method for simplifying aerological height computation. (With a summary in English) Stockholm, Kungl. Boktryckeriet, 1947.
11 p. 26 cm. (Sveriges Meteorologiska och Hydrologiska Institut. Meddelanden, ser. B, nr.4)

NL 0444782   CtY

Lönnqvist, Olov.
On the estimation of long-wave effective radiation. Uppsala, Almqvist & Wiksell, 1955.   8 p.   25 cm.
Inaug.-diss. — Uppsala.

1 Radiation, Atmospheric.   I. 1955.

NL 0444783   NN CtY

Lönnrot (Elias) [1802-84]. *Afhandling om Finnarnes magiska medicin. 16 pp. 8°. Helsingfors, J. C. Finckel & Son, 1832.*

NL 0444784   DNLM

Lönnrot, Elias, 1802-1884.
Kanteletar.
Alku-Kanteletar. Elias Lönnrotin käsikirjoituksen mukaan painosta julkaisut O. Relander. Helsinki, 1929.

Lönnrot, Elias, 1802-1884.
Kanteletar.
Alku-Kantelettaren korjaukset ja lisäykset. Elias Lönnrotin käsikirjoituksen mukaan painosta julkaisut O. Relander. Helsinki, 1929.

Lönnrot, Elias, 1802-1884.
Elias Lönnrotin matkat. Helsingissä, Suomal. Kirjallis. Seura, 1902-
v. port. 26 cm. (Suomalaisen Kirjallisuuden Seuran toimituksia, 98. osa)
CONTENTS.—1. osa. Vuosina 1828-1839.

1. Finland — Description and travel. (Series: Suomalaisen Kirjallisuuden Seura. Toimituksia, 98. osa)

PH117.L6A3   77-205378

NL 0444787   DLC InU MnU

Lönnrot, Elias, 1802-1884.
Elias Lönnrotin muistolle hänen syntymänsä 150-vuotispäivhä omistaa tämän vuosikirjansa 9. 4. 1952
see under   Kalevalaseura.

Loennrot, Elias, 1802-84
Elias Lönnrotin nuoruuden ajoilta laukon kartanossa; muistoja kokoillut E. Nervander. Suomennos. Helsingissä, Kustannusosakeyhtiö Otava, 1893
112 p.

NL 0444789   MH

Lönnrot, Elias, 1802-1884.
Finskt-svenskt lexikon, af Elias Lönnrot ... Helsingfors, Finska litteratur-sällskapets tryckeri, 1874-80.
2 v. 25½ cm. (Half-title: Suomalaisen kirjallisuuden seuran toimituksia. 50 osa. I-II)
Added t.-p.: Suomalais-ruotsalainen sana kirja ...   PH281.S8L7
——— Supplementhäfte. Utarbetadt af A. H. Kallio. Helsingfors, Finska litteratur-sällskapets tryckeri, 1886.
3 p. l., 212 p. 25¼ cm. (Half-title: Suomalaisen kirjallisuuden seuran toimituksia. 50. osa)
Added t.-p.: Lisävihko Elias Lönnrotin Suomalais-ruotsalaiseen sanakirjaan. Toimittanut A. H. Kallio.
1. Finnish language—Dictionaries—Swedish. 2. Swedish language—Dictionaries—Finnish. I. Kallio, Aukusti Herman.
PH281.S8L7   Suppl.   2-1559 rev 2

NL 0444790   DLC ICN MB CU

Bonaparte
Collection LÖNNROT, ELIAS, 1802-1884.
No.192   Flora fennica. Suomen kasvio. Uusi parannettu laitos, jonka toimittivat E.L. ja Th. Soelan.   Helsingissä, Suomalaisen kirjallisuuden seuran kirjapainossa, 1866.
xx,425p. iii fold.pl. 21½cm. (Suomalaisen kirjallisuuden seuran toimituksia. 24.osa)

NL 0444791   ICN MH

Bonaparte
Collection ₍LÖNNROT, ELIAS₎ 1802-1884.
No.191   Flora fennica. Suomen kasvisto. Koelma. Helsingissä, Suomalaisen kirjallisuuden seuran kirjapainossa, 1860.
L,376p. iii fold.pl. 20½cm. (Suomalaisen kirjallisuuden seuran toimituksia. 24.osa)

"Alkulause" signed: E.L. ₍i.e. Elias Lönnrot₎

NL 0444792   ICN MH-A

Lönnrot, Elias, 1802-1884.   FOR OTHER EDITIONS SEE MAIN ENTRY
Kalevala.
Kalevala. Uuden Kalevalan 23. painos. Helsingissä, Suomalaisen Kirjallisuuden Seura, 1951.

VOLUME 338

Lönnrot, Elias, 1802-1884.

PH329
.K355
1882   **Kanteletar.**
Kanteletar, die volkslyrik der Finnen. In's deutsche übertragen von Hermann Paul. Helsingfors, G. W. Edlund,
1882.

Lönnrot, Elias, 1802-1884.

PH329   FOR OTHER EDITIONS
.L8   SEE MAIN ENTRY
1937   **Kanteletar.**
Kanteletar; elikkä, Suomen kansan vanhoja lauluja ja
virsiä. 9. painos. Helsinki, Suomalaisen Kirjallisuuden
Seura, 1937.

[Lönnrot, Elias] 1802-1884, *ed.*
Kanteletar taikka suomen kansan, etc.
see under Kanteletar.

Lönnrot, Elias, 1802-1884.
Kutsumuskirja Suomen Keisarillisen Alek-
santerin Yliopiston muistojuhlaan kanslianeuvos
Elias Lönnrot'in kuoleman
see under Helsinki. Yliopisto.

4PH   Lönnrot, Elias, 1802-1884.
Fin-   Loihtoja; loitsujen ensimmäinen laitos.
181   Esipuheella varustanut Aarne Anttila. Helsinki,
Suomalaisen Kirjallisuuden Seura, 1932.
94 p. (Suomalaisen Kirjallisuuden Seuran
toimituksia, 194 osa)

NL   0444798   DLC-P4 NNC ICU MH InU

Bonaparte
Collection LÖNNROT, ELIAS, 1802-1884.
No.8842   Minnes-tal öfver akademikern d:r Anders Johan
Sjögren, hållet vid Finska vetenskaps-societetens
årshögtid den 29 april 1855, af Elias Lönnrot.
₍Helsingfors,H.C.Friis,1856₎
63p. 6½x21cm.

"Förteckning öfver akademikern A.J.Sjögrens
under åren 1821-1854 tryckta skrifter och uppsatser": p.41-63.

NL   0444799   ICN NIC

Bonaparte
Collection LÖNNROT, ELIAS, 1802-1884.
No.273   Om det nord-tschudiska språket... Helsingfors,J.C.Frenckell & son,1853.
53p. 24½x19cm.

Akademisk afhandling—Helsingfors.

NL   0444800   ICN CLU OCl NN MH

PH316 Lönnrot, Elias, 1802-1884, *praeses.*
.L8   Om Finnarnes folkdikt i obunden berättande form ...
Helsingfors, J. C. Frenckell & son, 1857.
₍1₎, 70 p. 19ᶜᵐ.
Akademisk afhandling—Helsingfors (Erik Rudbeck, respondent and author)

1. Folk-literature—Finland.

NL   0444801   ICU

Q   Lönnrot, Elias, 1802-1884.
60   Om ursprunget till finnarnes hiisi.
F508+   Föredr. d. 8 febr. 1858.
v.5   (In Finska vetenskaps-societeten, Helsing-
no.12   fors. Acta Societatis Scientiarum Fennicae.
Helsingforsiae. 29cm. t.5 (1858) p. ₍569₎-
578)

1. Finnish language—Words—Hist.
2. Mythology, F   inno-Ugrian.

NL   0444802   NIC

Lönnrot, Elias, 1802-1884.
Suomalais-Ruotsalainen sanakirja . . .
Helsingissä. Suomalaisen Kirjallisuuden Seuran Kirjapainossa.
1874-86. 3 v. [Suomalaisen Kirjallisuuden Seura. Toimituksia.
Osa 50.] 8°.
Contents. — 1. A—M. 2. N—Ö. Supplement. Lisävihko . . . Toimittanut
A. H. Kallio.
The title is repeated in Swedish.

G7872 — S.r. — Finland. Lang. Dict. — Kallio, Aukusti Herman, continuator.

NL   0444803   MB MH ICN

PN6505 Lönnrot, Elias, 1802-1884, *ed.*
.F5L8   ... Suomalaisia sananlaskuja. Selittänyt Elias Lönnrot.
Porvoossa, W. Söderström, 1892.
vii, ₍9₎-42 p. 18ᶜᵐ. (Tuhansille kodeille tuhat järvien maassa. n:o 2)
Finnish proverbs.

1. Proverbs, Finnish.

NL   0444804   ICU OCl

Bonaparte
Collection LÖNNROT, ELIAS, 1802-1884, *ed.*
No. 236   Suomen kansan arvoituksia ynnä 135 wiron
arvoituksen kanssa. Helsingissä,J.Simeliuksen
perillisten tykona,1844.
xviii,184p. 20cm. (Suomalaisen kirjallisuuden seuran toimituksia. 5.osa)

"Alkulause" signed: Elias Lönnrot.
A collection of Finnish and Estonian riddles.

NL   0444805   ICN CtY

PH333 ₍Lönnrot, Elias₎ 1802-1884, *ed.*
.L8   Suomen kansan arvoituksia ynnä 189 Wiron arvoituksen
kanssa. 2. lisännetty painos. Helsingissä, Suomal. kirjall.
seuran kirjapainossa, 1851.
₍4₎, xvi. 221 p. 20ᶜᵐ. (*Half-title:* Suomalaisen kirjallisuuden seuran Toimituksia. 5. osa)
A collection of Finnish and Estonian riddles.

1. Riddles, Finnish. 2. Riddles, Esthonian.

NL   0444806   ICU OCl MH NIC

---

4 PH   Lönnrot, Elias, 1802-1884.
Fin. -   Suomen kansan muinaisia loitsurunoja.
180   Helsingissä, Suomalaisen Kirjallisuuden Seuran
Kirjapainossa, 1880.
373 p. (Suomalaisen Kirjallisuuden Seuran
Toimituksia, 62. osa)

NL   0444807   DLC-P4 MH NN NIC

Y   ₍LÖNNROT, ELIAS₎ 1802-1884.
0534   Suomen kansan sanalaskuja. Helsingissä,I.
52   Silemiusken lesken tykönä,1842.
576p. ₍Suomalaisen kirjallisuuden seura,
Helsingfors. Toimituksia. 4.osa₎

Imperfect: series t.-p. wanting.
"Alkulause" signed: Elias Lönnrot.

NL   0444808   ICN CtY NcU MH

Lönnrot, Elias, 1802-1884.

PH117
.L8S9   **Suomen** ylioppilaskunnan albumi Elias Lönnrotin kunniaksi,
hänen täyttäessään kahdeksankymmentä vuotta, 9. IV, 1882.
Helsingissä, Suomalaisen Kirjallisuuden Seuran Kirjapainossa, 1882.

Bonaparte
Collection ₍LÖNNROT, ELIAS₎ 1802-1884, comp.
No.1722   Svensk, finsk, och tysk tolk. Ruotsin,
suomen ja saksan tulkki. Schwedisch-finnisch-
deutsches wörter- und gespräch-buch. Helsingfors,Tryckt hos J.Semelii arfvingar,pa A.C.
Öhmans förlag,1847.
232p. 23cm.

"Förord" signed: E.L.

NL   0444810   ICN

GR 71   Lönnrot, Elias, 1802-1884.
L84   Svenska skrifter; utg. af Jenny af Forselles.
Helsingfors, 1908-11.
2 v. 24 cm. (Skrifter utg. af Svenska
litteratursällskapet i Finland, 87, 99)

Contents. - I. Uppsatser och öfversättningar.
II. Bref, anteckningar och reseskildringar.

NL   0444811   OU GU DLC-P4 NIC NN MdBP MoU MH NcD

Q   Lönnrot, Elias, 1802-1884.
60   Ueber den enare-lappischen Dialekt.
F508+   Vorgetr. d. 23 Oktob. 1854.
v.4   (In Finska vetenskaps-societeten, Helsing-
no.10   fors. Acta Societatis Scientiarum Fennicae.
Helsingforsiae. 29cm. t.4 (1856) p. ₍133₎-
279)

1. Lappish language—Dialects—Inari.

NL   0444812   NIC

Bonaparte
Collection LÖNNROT, ELIAS, 1802-1884.
No.376   Ueber den enare-lappischen dialekt... ₍Hel-
singforsiae,H.C.Friis,1856₎
p.₍133₎-279. 26x21cm.

Caption title.
"Vorgetr. d. 23 oktob. 1854."
"An den herrn pastor N.V.Stockfleth."
Extract from Acta Societatis scientiarum fen-
nicae. t.IV.

NL   0444813   ICN

4DK   Lönnrot, Elias, 1802-1884.
Fin   Vaeltaja; muistelmia jalkamatkal-
279   ta Hämeestä, Savosta ja Karjalasta
1828. Helsinki, Suomalaisen Kirjallisuuden Seura, 1952.
161 p.

NL   0444814   DLC-P4 InU MH

VOLUME 338

Lönnrot, Elias, 1802–1884.

PH329
.A2S3
1950

Kanteletar.
Valikoima Kantelettaren runoja. Toimittanut E. A. Saarimaa. 3. painos. Helsinki, Suomalaisen Kirjallisuuden Seura, 1950.

LÖNNROTH, ARVO, 1881–
Parikkalan-Onkamon radan kannattavaisuuslaskelma. Laatinut: Arvo Lönnroth, arvio metsävaroista: Yrjö Ilvessalo, kustannusarvio ja suuntatutkimus: Unto Riihä. [n. p.] Tohmajärven-Parikkalan rautatietoimikunta [1954] 91 p. illus., maps. 22cm.

I. Railways--Finland--Projected roads. I. Ilvessalo, Yrjö, 1892– II. Tohmajärven-Parikkalan   rautatietoimikunta.

NL 0444816   NN

Lönnroth, Emil Fredrik, respondent.
Kritisk skärskädning af Schillers...
see under Böttiger, Carl Wilhelm, 1807–1878, praeses.

Lönnroth, Erik, 1910–
En annan uppfattning; essayer. Stockholm, Bonnier [1949]
206 p. 20 cm.
CONTENTS.—Epik och historia.—Historikern Geijer.—En banbrytare.—Om vikingar.—De äkta folkungarnas program.—Medeltidskrönikornas värld.—Kalmarunionen.—Engelbrekt.—Den Svenska riksdagens uppkomst.—Gustav Vasa.—En reflexion över Tysklands kris.—Thomas Edward Lawrence.

1. Sweden—Hist.—Addresses, essays, lectures.   I. Title.
Full name: Nils Erik Magnus Lönnroth.
DL651.L6   A 50–1182
Minnesota. Univ. Libr.
for Library of Congress   [3]†

NL 0444818   MnU DLC MH NN

D802
.A2F6

Lönnroth, Erik, 1910–
För humanitet mot förtryck; inlägg av Erik Lönnroth [et al. Stockholm, Studentföreningen Verdandi [1942]

B166
.622l

Lönnroth, Erik, 1910–
Lawrence av Arabien; ökenkrigaren och politikern. Stockholm, A.Bonnier[1945]
100p. fold.map. 20cm. (Göteborgs Högskola. Forskningar och föreläsningar)
"Föreläsningar vid Göteborgs Högskola den 31 oktober och 4 november 1941."

NL 0444820   CtY WU

Lönnroth, Erik, 1910–
... Medeltidskrönikornas värld, en politisk miljöstudie av Erik Lönnroth. Göteborg, Elanders boktryckeri aktiebolag, 1941.
27 p. 25ᶜᵐ. (Göteborgs högskolas årsskrift XLVII, 1941: 18)
Summary in French.

1. Political science—Literary history. 2. Political science—Hist.—Sweden. 3. Swedish literature—Hist. & crit.   I. Title.
[Full name: Nils Erik Magnus Lönnroth]
A 46–5206
Michigan. Univ. Library
for Library of Congress   AS284.G6 vol. 47, no. 18

NL 0444821   MiU DLC ViU

AP48
.S3

Lönnroth, Erik, 1910–   ed.

Samtid och framtid [tidskrift för] idépolitik och kultur. 1.–årg., jan. 1944–
[Stockholm] Natur och kultur [1944–

Lönnroth, Erik, 1910–
... Statsmakt och statsfinans i det medeltida Sverige; studier över skatteväsen och länsförvaltning, av Erik Lönnroth. Göteborg, Elanders boktryckeri aktiebolag, 1940.
280 p., 1 l. 25ᶜᵐ. (Göteborgs högskolas årsskrift XLVI, 1940: 3)
"Zusammenfassung" (in German): p. [277]–280.

1. Finance—Sweden—Hist. 2. Sweden—Pol. & govt.   I. Title.
[Full name: Nils Erik Magnus Lönnroth]
A 41–3265
Michigan. Univ. Library
for Library of Congress   AS284.G6 vol. 46, no. 3
(082)

NL 0444823   MiU DLC NcD ViU PU TxU

Lönnroth, Erik, 1910–
Sverige och Kalmar-unionen, 1397–1457, av Erik Lönnroth. Göteborg, Elanders boktryckeri aktiebolag, 1934.
387, [1] p. 25ᶜᵐ.
Akademisk avhandling—Göteborgs högskola.
Extra t.-p. with thesis note, laid in.
"Källor och litteratur": p. [376]–387.

1. Kalmar, Union of, 1397. 2. Sweden—Hist.—1397–1523. 3. Sweden—Pol. & govt.—1397–1523. 4. Karl Knutsson, king of Sweden, 1408 (ca.)–1470.   I. Title.
[Full name: Nils Erik Magnus Lönnroth]
41–30869
Library of Congress   DL694.L6
948.03

NL 0444824   DLC MnU MiU IU NN CtY

Lönnroth, Erik Johannes, 1883–
Ein Dendrometer. Helsinki, n. p., 1926.
17 p. fold. plates tables O.
Sonderabdruck aus den Acta Forestalia Fennica, 30.

NL 0444825   NcD

Lönnroth, Erik Johannes, 1883–
Der Stereometrische Bestandesmittelstamm. Helsinki, n. p., 1926.
35 p. diagrs. O.
Sonderabdruck aus den Acta Forestalia Fennica, 30.

NL 0444826   NcD

Lönnroth, Erik Johannes, 1883–
Über Stammkubierungsformeln. Helsinki, n. p., 1927.
56 p. tables, diagrs. O.
Reprinted from Acta forestalia Fennica, 31.

NL 0444827   NcD

Lönnroth, Erik Johannes, 1883–
Untersuchungen über die innere struktur und entwicklung gleichaltriger naturnormaler kiefernbestände basiert auf material aus der südhälfte Finnlands ... von Erik Lönnroth ... Helsinki [Druckerei der Suomal.kirjall.seuran kirjapaino o.y.] 1925.
3 p.l.,269,[44] p. tables,diagrs. 25ᶜᵐ.
Akademische abhandlung--Helsingfors,1925.
Transparent sheet of co-ordinate paper laid in.
"Graphische tafeln 2–60": [44] p.at end.
"Literaturverzeichnis": p.[241]–269.

1.Pine. 2.Forests and forestry--Finland.

NL 0444828   MiU NcD MH-A NN NcD WaU ICRL MH

Lönnroth, Erik Johannes, 1883–
—— Die waldtypen und die innere bestandesentwicklung. [Finnland-buch. Wendisch-Wilmersdorf. 1926.] l. 8°. Diagrs.
"Sonder-abdruck aus Mitteilungen der Deutschen dendrologischen gesellschaft," 1926, xxxvi, 133–152.

NL 0444829   MH-A

Lönnroth, Erik Johannes, 1883–
Zur Frage der Waldbetriebsregelung mit besonderer Berücksichtigung der Waldverhältnisse Finnlands. Helsinki, n. p., 1927.
61 p. O.
Reprinted from Acta forestalia Fennica, 32.

NL 0444830   NcD

Lönnroth, Knut Johan, 1826–1885, respondent.
Fries, Elias Magnus, 1794–1878, *praeses.*
Observationes criticæ plantas suecicas illustrantes ... [Decas prima] Upsaliæ, Wahlström & c. [1854]

Lönnroth, Knut Johan, *b.* 1826.
Vexternas metamorphoser i korthet skildrade, af K. J. Lönnroth. Helsingfors, J. C. Frenckell & son, 1859.
1 p. l., 42 p. 19ᶜᵐ. bound 21ᶜᵐ.

NL 0444832   ICJ

Lönnroth, Nils Erik Magnus
see
Lönnroth, Erik, 1910–

Lönnström, Carl Jacob. Förespråk öfver nordiska mythologien samt om skapelsen och Asarnes första idrotter. Linköping, Petre och Abrahamsson, 1819. 8°. pp. (2) + 22.
IcD1LS61

NL 0444834   NIC

574.92
B495P

Lönöy, Norvald
... A comparative anatomical study on Phoronis ovalis Wright from Norwegian, Swedish, and Brazilian waters ... Bergen, John Griegs [1953]
23 p. illus. 25 cm. (Universitetet i Bergen. Årbok, 1953. Naturvitenskapelig rekke, nr. 2. Publications from the Biological Station, 8)

no.8

Includes bibliography.
1. Phoronis   ovalis.

NL 0444835   NcD

[Lönroth, Ebba Eleonora (Lundgren).]
Svensk rimkrönika. En liten lärobok i fäderneslandets historia, utgifven af En Lärarinna. Stockholm, 1864. 8°. pp. 76.
IcB35L861
See especially the poems no. 1–21, pp. 5–26.

NL 0444836   NIC

VOLUME 338

Lönroth, Elisabet.
　　Arne Bindt; eller Gud, ödet och jag själv. Roman, av Elisabet Lönroth. Del 1–2.　Göteborg: N. J. Gumperts bokhandel₍.
1926₎. 2 v.　12°.

1. Fiction, Swedish. 2. Title.
N. Y. P. L.　　　　　　　　　　　　　　　　October 11. 1927

NL 0444837　NN

PT
2623
.O36
Z83

Löns, Elisabet
　　Meine Erinnerungen an Hermann Löns ₍von₎
Elisabet Löns-Erbeck. Dortmund, Gebr.
Lensing ₍1924₎
　　94 p.　illus.　20 cm.

1. Löns, Hermann. 1866–1914.

NL 0444838　WU

LOENS, Emil, 1863–
　　Ein fall von typhus abdominalis kombiniert
mit miliatuberkulose, etc., Inaug.-diss.,
Rostock, 1905.

NL 0444839　MBCo ICRL DNLM

Löns, Ernst, 1886–
　　Hermann Löns, eines dichters leben, erzählt von seinem
bruder Ernst Löns. Mit 6 kunstdrucktafeln und einem titelbild. Minden (Westf.) W. Köhler ₍1942₎
　　220 p. front., 12 pl. (incl. ports., facsim.) on 6 l.　20ᵐ.

1. Löns, Hermann, 1866–1914.
Illinois. Univ. Library　　　　　　　　　A F 46–107
for Library of Congress　　　PT2623.O36Z73
　　　　　　　　　　　　　　　　　　　928.3

NL 0444840　IU NcU CtY CU DLC

B
L825

Löns, Ernst　1886–
　　Hermann Löns' Jugendzeit, erzählt von seinem
Bruder.　Minden, Ger.，W.Köhler ₍1927₎
　　239p.　illus.　port.(front.) 21cm.

1. Löns, Hermann, 1866–1914.

NL 0444841　NcU TxU ViU CtY WU OCl

PT
2623
.O36
Z84

Löns, Ernst, 1886–
　　Hermann Löns' Mannesjahre. Sein Leben und
Schaffen bis zum tragischen Ende; erzählt
von seinem Bruder. Minden in Westfalen, W.
Köhler ₍c1930₎
　　247 p.　illus.　21 cm.

1. Löns, Hermann, 1866–1914.

NL 0444842　WU OCl IU NcU

---

ar X
2878

Löns, Friedrich.
　　Die Vorfahren Hugo Capets im Kampfe mit
den letzen karolingern um den westfränki-
schen Thron.　Deutsch-Crone, 1870.
　　14 p.　26cm.

"Programm"—K. K. Gymnasium, Deutsch-Crone.
No. 1 in vol. lettered: Programme;
French history.

1. Hugues Capet, King of France, 941–996.

NL 0444843　NIC

4DD 178

Löns, Georg G.
　　"Bruder, weisst du, dass ich lebe?" Die
Auswanderung aus der Provinz Hessen-Nassau, ihre
Ursachen, Wirkungen und die Möglichkeiten für die
Zukunft.　Kassel, Druck, Bärenreiter-Verlag [193]
　　63 p.

NL 0444844　DLC-P4

Löns (Heinrich) [1869–]. * Beiträge zur
Hämophilie. 27 pp., 2 l. 8°. Halle a. S., F.
Rode, 1895.

NL 0444845　DNLM MH

PT
2623
.O36
1923

Löns, Hermann, 1866–1914.
　　Sämtliche Werke in acht Bänden; hrsg. von
Friedrich Castelle. Leipzig, Hesse &
Becker, 1923–
　　8 v. front. (port.).

　　Contents.– 1. Bd. Geleitwort. Leben und
Schaffen. Junglaub. Mein goldenes Buch.
Mein blaues Buch. Der kleine Rosengarten.
Ulenspiegels Ausgewählte Lieder. Sagen und
Märchen.– 2. Bd. Da draussen vor dem Tore.
Mein buntes Buch.　Heidbilder.– 3. Bd.

　　Aus Forst und Flur. Wasserjungfern.– 4. Bd.
Mümmelmann. Widu. Mein grünes Buch. Kleine
Jagdgeschichten.– 5. Bd. Kraut und Lot. Auf
der Wildbahn. Hoh Rüdhoh!– 6. Bd. Der
zweckmässige Meyer. Frau Döllmer. Was da
kreucht und fleugt. Niedersächsisches
Skizzenbuch.– 7. Bd. Kleine Erzählungen.
Dahinten in der Heide.　Das zweite gesicht.–
8. Bd. Die　　　　　Häuser von Ohlenhof.
Der letzte Hans　　bur. Der Wehrwolf. Worterklärungen.

NL 0444847　NBuU RPB OO

Löns, Hermann, 1866–1914.
　　... Sämtliche werke in acht bänden, herausgegeben von
Friedrich Castelle ... Leipzig, Hesse & Becker, 1924.
　　8 v. front. (port.) 19½ ᶜᵐ₎
　　"Achtes bis einundzwanzigstes tausend."
　　CONTENTS.–1. bd. Geleitwort. Leben und schaffen. Junglaub.
Mein goldenes buch. Mein blaues buch. Der kleine rosengarten.
Ulenspiegels ausgewählte lieder. Sagen und märchen.–2. bd. Da
draussen vor dem tore. Mein buntes buch. Heidbilder.–3. bd. Aus
forst und flur. Wasserjungfern.–4. bd. Mümmelmann. Widu. Mein
grünes buch. Kleine jagdgeschichten.–5. bd. Kraut und lot. Auf
der wildbahn. Hoh Rüdhoh!–6. bd. Der zweckmässige Meyer.
Frau Döllmer. Was da kreucht und fleugt. Niedersächsisches skizzenbuch.–7. bd. Kleine erzählungen. Dahinten in der heide. Das
zweite gesicht.–8. bd. Die häuser von Ohlenhof. Der letzte Hansbur.
Der wehrwolf.　　　　　　　Worterklärungen.
　　1. Castelle, Fried-　　　rich, 1879–　　　ed.
PT2623.O36 1924　　　　　　　　　　　25–21630

PU NcU ViU TU
NL 0444848　DLC CU CaBVaU MU NcD OCl OCU OClW PPT

833.9
L825

Löns, Hermann, 1866–1914.
　　Sämtliche Werke. Hrsg. von Friedrich
Castelle.　Leipzig, Hesse & Becker,
1924–25.
　　8v. port. 20cm.

I. Castelle, Friedrich, 1879–　　ed.

NL 0444849　IEN

　　Sämtliche Werke. Herausgegeben von Friedrich Castelle.
—　Leipzig. Hesse & Becker. 1930. 8 v. 19 cm., in 8s.
　　Contents. – 1. Geleitwort. — Leben und Schaffen. — Junglaub. — Mein
goldenes Buch. — Mein blaues Buch. — Der kleine Rosengarten. — Ulenspeigels Ausgewählte Lieder. — Sagen und Märchen. 2. Da draussen vor
dem Tore. — Mein buntes Buch. — Heidbilder. 3. Aus Forst und Flur. —
Wasserjungfern. 4. Mümmelmann. — Widu. — Mein grünes Buch. — Kleine
Jagdgeschichten. 5. Kraut und Lot.— Auf der Wildbahn.— Ho Rüd' hoh!
6. Der zweckmässige Meyer. — Frau Döllmer. — Was da kreucht und
fleugt. — Niedersächsisches Skizzenbuch. 7. Kleine Erzählungen. — Dahinten in der Heide.— Das zweite Geschicht. 8. Die Häuser von Ohlenhof.
— Der letzte Hans' — Der Wehrwolf. — Worterklärungen.

NL 0444850　MB

M1538
.E7A2

Löns, Hermann, 1866–1914.

Erdlen, Hermann Christian Georg, 1893–
　　₍Aber dies, aber das. German₎

　　Aber dies, aber das; ein Löns-Liederspiel für Sopran-,
Bariton- und Tenorsolo, Männerchor und Orchester. Heidelberg, Hochstein ₍193–?₎　Pl. no. H. 3618 H.

NL 0444852　CtY WU

Löns, Hermann, 1866–
　　... Auf der wildbahn: jagdschilderungen.
Hannover, A. Sponholtz verlag, g. m. b. h. ₍c1912₎
　　2 p.l., [5]–254, [2] p.　21 cm.
　　"63.–67. Tausend".

NL 0444852　CtY WU

Löns, Hermann, 1866–1914.
　　... Auf der wildbahn: jagdschilderungen. 2. aufl. Hannover, A. Sponholtz verlag g. m. b. h. ₍1912₎
　　3 p.l., 216 p. 21 cm.

1. Hunting—Germany.　I. Title.

SK201.L67 1912　　　　　　　　13–13558 rev

NL 0444853　DLC

Löns, Hermann, 1866–1914.
　　... Auf der wildbahn: jagdschilderungen. 8. aufl.
Hannover, A. Sponholtz verlag, g. m. b. h. [c1912]
　　3 p.l., 216 p.　21 cm.

NL 0444854　NcD

Löns, Hermann, 1866–1914.
　　... Auf der wildbahn, jagdschilderungen. Hannover, A.
Sponholtz ₍1942₎
　　253, ₍1₎ p.　19ᵐ.

1. Hunting—Germany.　I. Title.
　　　　　　　　　　　　₍Full name: Hermann Fritz Moritz Löns₎
Library of Congress　　SK201.L67 1942　　45–32524
　　　　　　　　　　　　　　　　　　　790.2943

NL 0444855　DLC MnU

NE1217
P25L6

Löns, Hermann, 1866–1914.

Pape, Hans, 1894–
　　Aus der Bauernchronik, Der Wehrwolf, von Hermann
Löns; eine Holzschnittfolge. Hrsg. vom Sonderreferat,
Truppenbetreuung beim Reichskommissar für die Besetzten
Niederländischen Gebiete. Jena, E. Diederichs ₍194–?₎

VOLUME 338

833　Löns, Hermann, 1866-1914.
L862A　　Aus Forst und Flur; Tiernovellen. [n.p.]
　　　Verlag Deutsche Volksbücher [c1916]
　　　245p. plates. 23cm.

1. Animals, Legends and stories of I. Title.

NL 0444857　　NBC KU

Löns, Hermann, 1866-1914.
　Aus Forst und Flur, 40 Tiernovellen.Mit einer
Einleitung von Karl Soffel. 11. Aufl. Leipzig, R. Voigtländer [1916]
　xvi,319p. illus., port. 21cm.

NL 0444858　　IEN

833　Löns, Hermann, 1866-1914.
L825a　　Aus Forst und Flur; vierzig Tiernovellen.
　　Mit einer Einleitung von Karl Soffel.
　24. Aufl. Leipzig, R. Voigtländer ₁1916₁
　319p. illus.,front. (port.) 21cm.

NL 0444859　　NcU OCU MiD

Löns, Hermann, 1866-1914.
　Aus forst und flur; vierzig tiernovellen von
Hermann Löns, mit einer einleitung von Karl
Soffel ... 38. aufl. Leipzig, R. Voigtländer
[pref. 1916]
　xv, [1], 319 p.　front. (port.) plates.　21 cm.
　1. Animals, Legends and stories of.

NL 0444860　　CU

QL791　Löns,Hermann, 1866-1914.
.L92　　Aus forst und flur;vierzig tier-
　　novellen,von Hermann Löns. 56.aufl.
　Leipzig,R.Voigtlanders ₁1916₁
　xv,₁1₁,319p. illus. 20cm.
　Preface signed Karl Soffel,1916.

1.Animals,Habits and behavior of.2.Birds

NL 0444861　　NNU-W OrPR

Loens, Hermann, 1866-1914.
　Aus Forst und Flur; vierzig Tiernovellen, von Hermann Löns
... Leipzig: R. Voigtländer₁, 1916₁.　xv, 319 p.　front.
(port.), plates.　63. ed.　12°.

312748A. 1. Fiction, German.　　　　　　2. Animals—Legends and
N. Y. P. L.　　　　　　　　stories. 3. Title.
　　　　　　　　　　　　　　　　　　August 24, 1927

NL 0444862　　NN MBU NNiaU OCU

833.1x　Löns, Hermann, 1866-1914.
920ℓ　　Aus Forst und Flur; vierzig Tiernovellen.
　　65.Aufl. Leipzig,R.Voigtländer[192-?]
　xv,319p. illus.,port. 20cm.

1. Animals, Legends and stories of.

NL 0444863　　CtY

PT　Löns, Hermann, 1866-1914.
2623　　Aus Forst und Flur; Tiernovellen. Leipzig,
036　　Koehler & Voigtländer [1940, c16]
A73　　375p. illus. 20cm.
1940

1. Animals, Legends and stories of

NL 0444864　　WU

PT　Löns, Hermann, 1866-1914.
2623　　Aus Wald und Heide; Geschichten und
.036A6　　Schilderungen. Hameln, A. Sponholtz [n.d.]
　　131 p. illus.

NL 0444865　　NBuU

PT2623 Löns, Hermann, 1866-
.O5A92　Aus wald und heide; geschichten und schilderungen von
1909　Hermann Löns, für die jugend ausgewählt vom jugend-
　schriften—ausschuss des Lehrervereins Hannover-Linden.
　Hannover, A. Sponholtz ₁1909 ?₁
　　110 p. illus. 19½ᵗᵐ.

NL 0444866　　ICU IU PSt NcD

PT　Löns, Hermann, 1866-1914
2623　　Aus Wald und Heide; Geschichten und
036　　Schilderungen. Hannover, A. Sponholtz
A74　　[193-?]
　　175p. illus. 21cm.

NL 0444867　　WU MiD

Löns, Hermann, 1866-1914.
　... Aus wald und heide; sagen, erzählungen, tiergeschichten,
gedichte, edited by Erwin Gustav Gudde ... Chicago, Ill.,
The University of Chicago press ₁1930₁
　xv, 154, ₁1₁ p.　front. (port.) illus. 21ᶜᵐ.　(Half-title: The University
of Chicago Junior college series. German. Peter Hagboldt, editor)

　1. Gudde, Erwin Gustav, 1889-　　ed.　ɪɪ. Title.
　　　　　　　　　　　　　₍Full name: Hermann Fritz Moritz Löns₎
　Library of Congress　　　　PT2623.O36A6 1930　　　30-14686
　————— Copy 2.
　Copyright A 24104　　　　　　　　　　　　　　833.9₁

NL 0444868　　DLC OKentU NN PSC NBC OC1W OC1 OCX

Löns, Hermann, 1866-1914.
　Aus Wald und Heide, Geschichten und Schilderungen.
10. Aufl. Hannover, A. Sponholtz ₁1941?₁
　110 p. illus. 19 cm.

　ɪ. Title.　　　　　　　Full name: Hermann Fritz Moritz Löns
　PT2623.O36A6 1941　　　833.91　　　51-51523

NL 0444869　　DLC

833.91　Löns, Hermann, 1866-1914.
L824a71　　Aus Wald und Heide; Geschichten und
1951　　Schilderungen.　Hannover, A. Sponholtz
　　₁1951?₁
　　131p. illus. 21cm.

1. Animals,　　　　　Legends and stories
of. I. Title.

NL 0444870　　KU

Löns, Hermann, 1866-1914.
　Ausgewählte Tiergeschichten. Mit einem
Nachwort von Wilhelm Deimann. Stuttgart, Reclam
c1951₃
　80p. 16cm. (Reclams Universal-Bibliothek,
Nr. 7701)

　Selections from his "Mümmelmann" und "Widu."

NL 0444871　　FMU

Löns, Hermann, 1866-1914
　... Da draussen vor dem tore; heimatliche
naturbilder. Auswahl. Hanover, Adolf Sponholtz[19--?]
　78 p. 18 1/2 cm.

　Illustration on cover.
　Foreword signed: Friedrich Castelle.

　I. Castelle, Friedrich, 1879-

NL 0444872　　MdBP DLC-P4

Löns, Hermann, 1866-1914
　Da draussen vor dem tore; heimatliche
naturbilder. Hannover, A. Sponholtz ₁c1911₁
　186 ₁1₁ p.

NL 0444873　　MiD

Löns, Hermann, 1866-
　Da draussen vor dem tore, heimatliche naturbilder. Warendorf 1911. 195p.19cm.

NL 0444874　　CU

Löns,Hermann,1866-1914.
　... Da draussen vor dem tore; heimatliche naturbilder. 22.-35.tausend ... Hannover, A.Spon-
holtz verlag,g.m.b.h., 1913.
　190 p.,1 ℓ. 20½ᵗᵐ.

NL 0444875　　MiU CtY

PT　Löns, Hermann, 1866-1914
2623　　Da draussen vor dem Tore; heimatliche
036　　Naturbilder. Hannover, A. Sponholtz, 1923.
D27　　₁c1911₁
　　190p. 21cm.

NL 0444876　　WU NN

Löns, Hermann, 1866-1914.
　Dahinten in der Haide, Roman...Hannover, R. Sponholtz
₁c1910₁
　219 p. 19 cm.
　"2.Auflage."

NL 0444877　　PPT

Löns,Hermann,1866-1914.
　... Dahinten in der heide,roman. Hannover,
A.Sponholtz verlag,g.m.b.h. ₁c1912₁
　2 p.ℓ.,218,₁1₁ p. 18½ᵗᵐ.

NL 0444878　　MiU WU NcU NN CtY IU ICU OC1 OrU

VOLUME 338

Löns, Hermann, 1866–1914.
Dahinten in der Haide, Roman. Hannover, R. Sponholtz
₁*1912₎
210 p. 19 cm.

1. Title.

PT2623.O36D3   49–33473*‡

NL 0444879   DLC MH NcGU LU

833.91 Löns, Hermann, 1866–1914.
L824d   Dahinten in der Haide; Roman.
1912   ₁Sonderausgabe₎ Hannover, A. Sponholtz
₁1912₎
159p. 18cm.

NL 0444880   KU

Loens, Hermann, 1866–1914.
...Dahinten in der Haide; Roman...   Hanover: A. Sponholtz Verlag, G.m.b.H., 1922. 210 p. 12°.

312699A. 1. Fiction, German.   2. Title.
N.Y.P.L.   September 8, 1927

NL 0444881   NN MH OOxM

Löns, Hermann, 1866–1914.
...Das deutsche Buch; eine Auswahl aus seinen Werken,
eingeleitet von Wilhelm Deimann.   Hannover: A. Sponholtz
Verlag G.m.b.H., 1933.₎ 285 p. 19cm.

670594A. 1. German literature—   Misc. I. Deimann, Wilhelm, 1889–
N.Y.P.L.   editor.   October 11, 1933

NL 0444882   NN OrPR

Löns, Hermann, 1866–1914.
Eine Dichterstunde; zusammengestellt von Hans Wagner.
Hamburg, Hanseatische Verlagsanstalt ₁*1938₎
31 p. 24 cm.
Prose and verse.

1. Title.
                        Full name: Hermann Fritz Moritz Löns.

PT2623.O363D5   54–55255 ‡

NL 0444883   DLC

PT   Löns, Hermann, 1866–1914
2623   Einsame Heidfahrt; bisher "Tal der Lieder."
O36   Bad Pyrmont, Hannover, F. Gersbach, 1925.
E38   102p. 21cm.
        Bound with the author's Junglaub. Bad
Pyrmont, Hannover, 1925.

NL 0444884   WU

Löns, Hermann
Einsame Heidfahrt. Bad Pyrmont, F. Gersbach,
1926.
102 ₁1₎ p.

Formerly pub. with title: Das Tal der Lieder.

NL 0444885   MiD WaWW OC

Löns, Hermann, 1866–1914.
... Einsame heidfahrt (bisher "Das tal der
lieder")... Hannover, F. Gersbach, 1928.
1 p. l., 102 p., 1 l. 18.5 cm.

NL 0444886   MtU

Löns, Hermann, 1866–1914
Eulenspiegeleien; eingeleitet und hrsg. von
Traugott Pilf. Wiesbaden, H. Staadt ₁1917₎
67 p. col. illus. port.

NL 0444887   MiD WaS

837.912 Löns, Hermann, 1866–1914.
L824f   Frau Döllmer; humoristisch-satirische
19--   Plaudereien von Fritz von der Leine
        (Hermann Löns)   Hannover, F. Gersbach
₁19--₎
73p. illus. 18cm.

NL 0444888   KU

G
837   Löns, Hermann, 1866–1914.
L869f   Frau Döllmer; humoristisch-satirische plauder-
        eien von Fritz von der Leine (Hermann Löns).
        Buchschmuck von Richard Schlösser ... Hanover, F.
Gersbach ₁19--?₎
93 p., 1 l.

NL 0444889   WaPS

PT   Löns, Hermann, 1866–1914
2623   Frau Döllmer; humoristisch-satirische
O36   Plaudereien von Fritz von der Leine.
F7   Buchschmuck von Richard Schlösser. Bad
Pyrmont, F. Gersbach, 1925.
91p. illus. 21cm.
        Bound with the author's Ulenspiegels und
Fritz von der Leines ausgewählte Lieder.
Bad Pyrmont, 1925.

NL 0444890   WU LU

Löns, Hermann, 1866–1914.
... Frau Döllmer; humoristisch-satirische
Plaudereien von Fritz von der Leine. Buchschmuck
von Richard Schlösser. 49. bis 53. Tausend.
Bad Pyrmont, Hannover, F. Gersbach, 1926. 1p. l.,
91pp., 1 l. illus. 20cm.
At head of title: Hermann Löns.

NL 0444891   CtY

Löns, Hermann, 1866–1914.
... Frau Döllmer, humoristische satirische
plaudereien von Fritz von der Leine. Buchschmuck
von Richard Schlösser ... Hannover, F. Gersbach,
1928.
1 p. l., 91 p., 1 l. 18.5cm.

NL 0444892   MtU WaWW

Löns, Hermann, 1866–1914.
Für Sippe und Sitte, aus dem Nachlasse hrsg. von Wilhelm Deimann. Hannover, A. Sponholtz, 1924.
xv, 121 p. 21 cm.

1. Natural history—Germany. 2. Farmers—Germany. I. Deimann, Wilhelm, 1889–   ed. II. Title.
                        Full name: Hermann Fritz Moritz Löns.

QH149.L58   57–55746

NL 0444893   DLC KU NcD NN

Löns, Hermann, 1866–1914.
Für Sippe und Sitte; aus dem Nachlasse hrsg. von Wilhelm Deimann. Hannover, A. Sponholtz ₁1941, *1924₎
139 p. 19 cm.

1. Deimann, Wilhelm, 1889–   ed. II. Title.
                        Full name: Hermann Fritz Moritz Löns.

PT2623.O36F8   A F 49–137*
Yale Univ. Library
for Library of Congress   ₁1₎†

NL 0444894   CtY IU CU NcD IU DLC

Löns, Hermann, 1866–1914.
... Gedanken und gestalten, aus dem nachlasse
hrsg. von Wilhelm Deimann. Hannover, A. Sponholtz verlag, g.m.b.h., 1924.
ix, 119, ₁1₎ p. 20cm.
"1.–10. tausend."
"Studien über kunst und geisteswesen, über kunstlertum
und menschentum."--Vorwort.
14 biographical sketches, all but 3 of German authors,
artists, etc.

I. Deimann, Wilhelm, 1889– ed.

NL 0444895   MiU OCU OOxM LU MU CtY PBm VtMiM

833.91 Löns, Hermann, 1866–1914.
L824A2d   Geschichten und Sagen: Mein braunes Buch.-
1913   Haidbilder.- Da draussen vor dem Tore.
Mit einem Geleitwort von W. Deimann.
Hannover, A. Sponholtz ₁1913₎
338p. 20cm.
        "Den vollständigen Titel "Der letzte
Hansbur" schrieb Hermann Löns zu dem
Manuskript dieses Romans, das sich im
Besitz des Städtischen Löns-Archives,
Hannover, befindet.
        I. Title. II.   Title: Mein braunes
Buch. III. Title.   Haidbilder. IV. Da
draussen vor dem   Tore.

NL 0444896   KU

834L86 Löns, Hermann, 1866–1914.
Og   ... Goldhals; ein tierbuch für die jugend aus-
        gewählt vom Jugendschriftenausschuss des Lehrer-
        vereins Hannover-Linden.   Hannover, A. Sponholtz
₁1918₎
141p. illus.

NL 0444897   IU FMU PU

PZ   Löns, Hermann, 1866–1914
36.3   Goldhals; ein Tierbuch für die Jugend
L57   ausgewählt vom Jugendschriften-Ausschuss des
Go   Lehrervereins Hannover-Linden. Hannover, A.
Sponholtz ₁1925?₎
141p. illus. 20cm.

1. Animals, Legends and stories of I. Title

NL 0444898   WU

VOLUME 338

838
L823gn
1947
Löns,Hermann,1866-1914.
  Goldhals; ein Tierbuch. Bilder von Karl
Reinecke-Altenau. Hannover, S.Sponholtz
₍1947₎
  109 p. illus. 21 cm.

  1.Animals,Legends and stories of.

NL 0444899   MiU

PT2623 Löns, Hermann, 1866-1914.
.036G7   Grün ist die Heide. Eine Auswahl von 25
  der besten Novellen, Jagd-, Tier- und Naturschilderungen des Dichters. Mit 112 Licht-
  bildern aus dem gleichnamigen Film und nach
  Aufnahmen...und einem Vorwort von Friedrich
  Castelle.   Hannover, A. Sponholtz ₍1932₎
  240 p. illus. 24 cm.

NL 0444900   NcRS MBU GEU OrPR

833.91
L824h
1917
Löns, Hermann, 1866-1914.
  Die Häuser von Ohlenhof; der Roman eines
Dorfes.   Hannover, A. Sponholtz ₍c1917₎
  242p. 20cm.

NL 0444901   KU

Loens, Hermann, 1866-1914.
  ...Die Haeuser von Ohlenhof; der Roman eines Dorfes.
Hannover: A. Sponholtz, G.m.b.H.₍, cop. 1917.₎ 238 p. 12°.

NL 0444902   NN CtY PSt ICU

Löns, Hermann, 1866-1914.
  ... Die häuser von Ohlenhof; der roman lines dorfes. 21.-
30. tausend. Hannover, A. Sponholtz verlag, g. m. b. h.,
1917.
  2 p. l., 148 p. 20½ cm.

  I. Title.
                        Full name: Hermann Fritz Moritz Löns.

  PT2623.O36H27 1917   22-23334

NL 0444903   DLC NcU

Löns, Hermann, 1866-1914.
  ... Die häuser von Ohlenhof, der roman eines dorfes, edited
by Ewald P. Appelt ... New York, H. Holt and company
₍*1930₎
  xii, 90 p. front. (port.) 17½ᵐ.

  I. Appelt, Ewald Paul, ed.   II. Title.
                  ₍*Full name:* Hermann Fritz Moritz Löns₎
                                          30-19305 Revised
  Library of Congress   PT2623.O36H27 1930
  Copyright A 25512   ₍r39c2₎   833.91

NL 0444904   DLC ICarbS WaTC ViU NBC OC1 OC1W

Löns, Hermann, 1866-1914
  ... Haidbilder; neue folge von Mein braunes buch.
1. aufl. Hannover, A. Sponholtz verlag, g. m. b. h. ₍1913₎
  2 p. l., 180 p. 21ᵐ. M. 3.50

  I. Title.
                                          13-26716
  Library of Congress   PT2623.O36H3 1913

NL 0444905   DLC CtY

LÖNS,Hermann,1866-1914.
  Haidbilder;neue Folge von Mein braunes Buch.
Hannover,A.Sponholtz Verlag,G.m.b.H.,[1918].

  18.5 cm. pp.(2),176.

NL 0444906   MH WU

Löns, Hermann, 1866-1914.
  Harm Wulf, a peasant chronicle; translated by
Marion Saunders. London, J. Lane ₍1931₎
  309p. 19cm.

NL 0444907   NcU KyLoU

Löns, Hermann, 1866-1914.
  Harm Wulf, a peasant chronicle, by Hermann Löns; translated by Marion Saunders. New York, Minton, Balch & company, 1931.
  v. 291 p. 20ᵐ.

  I. Saunders, Marion, tr. II. Title.   *Translation of* Der wehr-
wolf.
  Library of Congress   PZ3.L82395Har   31-26802
  ———— Copy 2.
  Copyright A 38234   ₍5₎   833.91

          OEac ViU MB OrU CoU
NL 0444908   DLC OC1h CU NBuU ICU NcD OC1 OCU MiU

M1620
.M724H4
Möller, Emil, *musician.*

  Das Hederitt; neue Weisen, aus Hermann Löns' Kleinem
Rosengarten, für Gesang und Klavier. Mit einem Vorwort
von Konrad Kölle. Berlin, Deutsche Landbuchhandlung
₍*1922₎

Löns, Hermann, 1866-1914.
  Hermann Löns, bearb. von Friedrich Andreas Schmidt.
₍Giessen, K. Christ, 1940₎
  55 p. illus. 21 cm. (Feierstunden deutscher Meister. Bd. 2)
  "Werke von Hermann Löns" : p. 54-55.

  I. Schmidt, Friedrich Andreas, ed.   (Series)
                        Full name: Hermann Fritz Moritz Löns.

  PT2623.O36Z515   57-53470

NL 0444910   DLC

PT2623
.O36Z66
1941
Löns, Hermann, 1866-1914.
                        FOR OTHER EDITIONS
                        SEE MAIN ENTRY
Deimann, Wilhelm, 1889-
  Hermann Löns, ein soldatisches vermächtnis, von Wilhelm
Deimann. ₍Berlin-Dahlem₎ Ahnenerbe-stiftung verlag ₍*1941₎

Löns, Hermann, 1866-1914.
  Hermann-Löns-kassette ...
    see his Kassette.

PT2623
.05
1920
Löns,Hermann,1866-1914.
  Hermann Löns,sein leben,sein schaffen und seine
  werke,von dr.Heinrich Schauerte. 2.aufl. ...
  Dortmund,Gebrüder Lensing,1920.
    107,272,240 p. port. 20cm. (Added t.-p.:Lebens
  bilder aus Westfalen und Niedersachsen. bd.1)

    "Das zweite gesicht" and "Der wehrwolf" have
  special title-pages and separate pagination.

NL 0444913   ICU

873
L825
h
Löns, Hermann,1866-1914.
  Hermann Löns und seine heide. Eine wanderung
  in bildern durch die stätten seiner werke, von
  Ernst Ludwig v. Aster, Ernst Barkemeyer ₍u.a.₎
  mit skizzen und handschriftdrucken aus dem nach-
  lass von Hermann Löns ... hrsg. von Friedrich
  Castelle. 3. aufl./ 15. tausend. Berlin,
  F. Zillessen, 1925.
    213,₍1₎p. front.(port.) illus., col.
  plates, facsim. 24cm.

NL 0444914   CU

Löns, Hermann, 1866-1914.
  ... Ho Rüd'hoh! 1.-20. tausend. Hannover, A. Sponholtz, g. m. b. h., 1918.
  3 p. l., 190 p. 21ᵐ.
  "Jagderlebnisse."

  1. Hunting—Germany. I. Title.
  Library of Congress   SK201.L68   22-24568

NL 0444915   DLC KU NcU WU OU

Löns, Hermann, 1866-1914.
  Ho Rüd'hoh! Hannover: Adolf Sponholtz, 1923. 190 p.
8°.

NL 0444916   NN

Löns, Hermann, 1866-1914.
  ... Im flammenden morgenrot, tier-, jagd- und na
turschilderungen; erzählungen aus wald und heide,
dichtungen, ausgewählt und mit vorwort versehen vor
Heinrich Sohnrey ... Mit 114 teils vielfarbigen
kunstbeilagen nach originalen, sowie einfarbigen ab
bildungen nach aufnahmen bekannter photographen.
Bad Pyrmont/ Hannover, Friedrich Gersbach, 1934.
  237 p. incl. plates, facsim. 23½ cm.

  1. Nature in literature. I. Title. II. Sohnrey,
Heinrich, 1859-   ed.

NL 0444917   NNC WU

Löns, Hermann, 1866-1914.
  Im Wald und auf der Heide. Tiernovellen, mit 106 Fotos
auf Kupfertiefdrucktafeln von Hermann Fischer. Berlin,
Safari-Verlag ₍19-₎
  207 p. plates. 24 cm.

  1. Animals, Legends and stories of. I. Title.
                        Full name: Hermann Fritz Moritz Löns.

  PT2623.O36 I 5   838.91   49-42773*

NL 0444918   DLC NNC

VOLUME 338

Löns, Hermann, 1866–1914.
 Im Wald und auf der Heide, Tiernovellen. Mit 138 Fotos
auf Kupfertiefdrucktafeln von Hermann Fischer. Berlin,
Safari-Verlag ₍19—₎
  126 p. plates. 24 cm.

  1. Animals, Legends and stories of.   I. Title.
                    Full name: Hermann Fritz Moritz Löns.

 PT2623.O36 I 5   54–50482

  NL 0444919   DLC

---

833   Löns, Hermann, 1866–1914.
L861 4   Im Wald und auf der Heide; ein Buch vom
        deutschen Wald und deutschen Wild, mit 138
        Photos und einem Nachwort von Hermann
        Fischer-Braunschweig, und 14 Tiernovellen,
        ₍4.Aufl.₎ Berlin, Safari ₍1932?₎
         139 p. plates.

  1. Animals. Legends and stories of.   I.

  NL 0444920   WaU CtY AAP CU

---

838   Löns,Hermann,1866–1914.
L823im   Im Wald und auf der Heide. Mit Zeich-
1947   nungen von Fritz Jaspert. Berlin, Safari-
        Verlag ₍1947₎
         134 p. illus. 24 cm.
         "Die Tiernovellen entstammen der Samm-
        lung 'Aus Forst und Flur.'"

  1.Animals,Legends and stories of.

  NL 0444921   MiU

Löns, Hermann, 1866–1914.
 ...Im Wald und auf der Heide. Mit 61 Zeichnungen von Fritz
Jaspert und 82 Abbildungen auf Kupfertiefdrucktafeln. Berlin,
Safari-Verlag ₍1950₎ 216 p. illus. 22cm.

 "Die Tiernovellen entstammen der Sammlung 'Aus Forst und Flur'."

  1. Animals—Legends and stories.   2. Photography of animals—Specimens, reproductions, etc.
N. Y. P. L.   January 22, 1952

  NL 0444922   NN

Löns, Hermann, 1866–1914
 ... Im Wald und auf der Heide. Mit 61
Zeichnungen von Fritz Jaspert und 82 Abbildungen auf Kupfertiefdrucktafeln nach Fotos
von Hermann Fischer. Berlin, Safari-Verlag
₍1954₎
  214 p. illus., plates. 24 cm.

  NL 0444923   NcD

PT 2623
036   Löns, Hermann, 1866–1914.
I53   In Heide und Wald. Berlin, Deutsche
       Buch-Gemeinschaft [19--]
        358 p.

  NL 0444924   CaBVaU

Löns, Hermann, 1866–1914.
 In Heide und Wald.   Berlin: Deutsche Buch-Gemeinschaft₍,₎
192–?₎. 360 p. port. 12°.

  1. Animals. 2. Title.
N. Y. P. L.   November 28, 1928

  NL 0444925   NN

Löns, Hermann, 1866–1914.
 ...In Heide und Wald; 26 Tiergeschichten mit einer Einleitung. Berlin: Deutsche Buch-Gemeinschaft G.m.b.H.₍,₎ 1931.₎
358 p. front. (port.) 19cm.
 "Dieses Werk ist ein für die Mitglieder der Deutschen Buch-Gemeinschaft heraus-
gegebener Auswahlband von Hermann Löns Aus Forst und Flur."

 657189A. 1. Natural history—Essays   and misc.
N. Y. P. L.   September 1, 1933

  NL 0444926   NN MnCS

4QL 15   Löns, Hermann, 1866–1914.
         Isegrimms Irrgang, Tier- und Jagdgeschichten.
        Köln a. Rh., H. Schaffstein.
         55 p.   (9. der Blauen Bändchen)

  NL 0444927   DLC-P4

Löns, Hermann, 1866–1914.
 Jagdgeschichten von Hermann Löns u.a. Mit
Federzeichnungen von Max Bernuth.   Köln am
Rhein, H. Schaffstein, 1922.
 70 p.   (Schaffsteins blaue Bändchen, 137)

  NL 0444928   DLC-P4

Löns, Hermann, 1866–1914.
 Junglaub; Lieder und Gedichte. Hannover, F. Gersbach
₍1920?₎
  xv, 96 p. facsim. 21 cm.
  "Aus der Werdezeit von Hermann Löns" (p. vii-xv) signed: Friedrich Castelle.

  I. Castelle, Friedrich, 1879–
                  Full name: Hermann Fritz Moritz Löns.

 PT2623.O36J8   48–43698*

  NL 0444929   DLC WU

PT   Löns, Hermann, 1866–1914
2623   Junglaub; Lieder und Gedichte. Bearb.
036   und mit einer Einleitung versehen von
E38   Friedrich Castelle. Bad Pyrmont, Hannover,
       F. Gersbach, 1925.
        88p. 21cm.
        Bound with the author's Einsame Heidfahrt.
       Bad Pyrmont, Hannover, 1925.

  I. Castelle, Friedrich, ed. II. Title

  NL 0444930   WU CtY CU

Löns, Hermann, 1866–1914.
 Junglaub, Lieder und Gedichte, bearbeitet und mit Einleitung versehen von Friedrich Castelle. Volksausg. Bad
Pyrmont, F. Gersbach, 1928.
  88 p. 19 cm.

  I. Title.
                  Full name: Hermann Fritz Moritz Löns.
 PT2623.O36J8 1928   55–54625 ‡

  NL 0444931   DLC MtU

Löns, Hermann, 1866–1914.
 Kassette. Volksausgabe. Bad Pyrmont,
Friedrich Gersbach ₍c1927₎
 3v.

  Contents: Band 1. Das Lönsbuch; mein grünes
Buch.– Band 2. Junglaub mein goldenes Buch;
Ulenspiegel; Frau Döllmer.– Band 3. Einsame
Seidfahrt; Löns-Gedenkbuch, von Dr. Friedrich
Castelle.

  NL 0444932   ScU IaU

---

838   Löns, Hermann, 1866–1914.
L824   Kassette; 8 Werke in 4 Bände gebunden;
        farbig illustrierte Auswhal. Bad
       Pyrmont (Hannover), F. Gersbach ₍194–?₎
        4 v. illus. 21 cm.

  Each work has separate t.p., and is
paged separately.

  Contents:- 1.Bd. Mein grünes Buch; Jagd- und
Tiergeschichten. Junglaub; Balladen und
Dichtungen aus Löns Jugendzeit; gesammelt und
mit Einleitung versehen von Dr. Friedrich
Castelle.- 2.Bd. Mein goldenes Buch; die
Geschichte einer Liebe. Dichtungen. Das
Lönsbuch. Erzählungen, Tier- und
Jagdgeschichten, Naturschilderungen,
Tiermärchen, mit den Kriesschilderungen: Mein

                   Kamerad Löns, von Max
A. Tönjes.- 3.Bd. Einsame Heidfahrt.
Erzählungen und Schilderungen (Letztes Werk
Löns). Frau Döllmer; humoristische Erzählungen
und Schilderungen. Buchschmuck von Richard
Schlösser. Ulenspiegel, humoristisch,
satirische Dichtungen, Nebst Schulaussätzen von
Aadje Ziesenis und Ulenspiegels
Selbstbiographie .- 4.Bd. Friedrich Castelle

                   Löns-Gedenkbuch; neue
Bearb. mit 15 Abbildungen.

  1. Hunting. 2. Eulenspiegel--Poetry. I.
Tönjes, Max A. II. Castelle, Friedrich, 1879–
Löns-Gedenkbuch. III. Castelle, Friedrich,
1879–

  NL 0444936   LU

Löns, Hermann, 1866–1914.
 Der kleine Rosengarten; Volkslieder. Jens, E. Diederichs
₍1940, *1922₎
  86 p. 19 cm. (Deutsche Reihe, Bd. 13)

  I. Title. (Series)
                  Full name: Hermann Fritz Moritz Löns.
 PT2623.O36K5   A F 48–4310*
 Yale Univ. Library
 for Library of Congress   ₍1₎†

  NL 0444937   CtY CU IU DLC

M1734   Löns, Hermann, 1866–1914.
.J612K5
        Jöde, Fritz, 1887–

         Der kleine Rosengarten; Volkslieder von Hermann Löns
        zur Laute gesungen von Fritz Jöde. Jena, L. Diederichs,
        1917.

Löns, Hermann, 1866–1914.
 Der kleine Rosengarten ... 32 Volkslieder zur
Laute gesetzt von Karl Kühn
    see under   Kühn, Karl, musician.

VOLUME 338

Löns, Hermann, 1866–
... Kraut und lot, ein buch für jäger und heger. 2. aufl.
Hannover, Adolf Sponholtz verlag g. m. b. h. ₍1911₎
4 p. l., 231 p. 21ᶜᵐ.   M. 4.20

1. Hunting.

Library of Congress   SK201.L7   11–23308

NL 0444940   DLC

SK   Löns, Hermann, 1866–1914
201   Kraut und Lot; ein Buch für Jäger und Heger.
L7   Hannover, A. Sponholtz, 1918 ₍c1911₎
231p. 21cm.

1. Hunting I. Title

NL 0444941   WU

Löns, Hermann, 1866–
... Kraut und lot, ein buch für jäger und heger.
Hannover, Adolf Sponholtz verlag g. m. b. h., 1922.
4 p. l., 231 p.   20 cm.
39.–58. Tausend.

NL 0444942   CtY

Löns, Hermann, 1866–1914.
Kraut und Lot; ein Buch für Jäger und Heger. Radebeul,
Neumann Verlag ₍1955₎
298 p. plates, port. 25 cm.

1. Hunting. I. Title.
                        Full name: Hermann Fritz Moritz Löns.

SK201.L7 1955   56–29753

NL 0444943   DLC MoU

Löns, Hermann, 1866–1914.

Deimann, Wilhelm, 1889–
... Der künstler und kämpfer, eine Lönsbiographie und
briefausgabe. Hannover, A. Sponholz ₍1935₎

Löns, Hermann, 1866–1914.
... De laatste Hansboer, roman van de Lüneburgerheide.
2. druk. Vertaald door R. J. de Stoppelaar. Amsterdam,
Uitgeverij Westland, 1942.
149, ₍1₎ p. 20ᶜᵐ. (*His* Meesterwerken)

I. Stoppelaar, Reinder Jacobus, 1873– tr. II. Title.
                        ₍*Full name:* Hermann Fritz Moritz Löns₎

PT2623.O36L42   833.91   46–44871

NL 0444945   DLC

Löns, Hermann, 1866–1914.
... Der letzte Hansbur; ein bauernroman aus der Lüneburger haide. Hannover, A. Sponholtz verlag, g. m. b. h., 1909.
3 p. l., 3–292 p. 20ᶜᵐ.
Advertising matter: p. 289–292.

I. Title.
                        ₍Full name: Hermann Fritz Moritz Löns₎
                                   9–28724 Revised
Library of Congress   PT2623.O36L4 1909
Copyright A—Foreign   476

NL 0444946   DLC CtY PP

Loens, Hermann, 1866–1914.
Der letzte Hansbur, ein bauernroman aus der
Luenenburger haide. Ed. 5. Hannover, Sponholtz,
1910.
288 p.

NL 0444947   PU

---

tPT2623 Löns, Hermann, 1866–1914.
Lo36L4   ... Der letzte Hansbur; ein bauernroman aus
1910   der Lüneburger haide. Hannover, A. Sponholtz
        verlag ₍c1910₎
        232 p. 13cm.

        "7. Auflage der Feldausgabe."

NL 0444948   CU CtY

LÖNS, Hermann, 1866–1914.
Der letzte Hansbur; ein Bauernroman aus der
Lüneberger Heide. Hannover, A. Sponholtz, G. m. b. H.
[1917?]

14 cm. pp. 247, (1).

NL 0444949   MH

Löns, Hermann, 1866–1914.
... Der letzte Hansbur; ein bauernroman aus der Lüneburger Heide. Hannover, A. Sponholtz ₍1920₎
247 p. 20cm.

NL 0444950   NIC

833.91 Löns, Hermann, 1866–1914.
L824f   Der letzte Hansbur; ein Bauernroman
1922   aus der Lüneburger Heide. Hannover,
        A. Sponholtz ₍1922₎
        288p. 18cm.

NL 0444951   KU CSt PPT

Löns, Hermann, 1866–1914.
Der letzte Hansbur; ein bauernroman aus der Lüneburger
heide, von Hermann Löns. Hannover, A. Sponholtz ₍1941?₎
255 p. 19ᶜᵐ.

I. Title.
                        ₍Full name: Hermann Fritz Moritz Löns₎
                                   46–38107
Library of Congress   PT2623.O36L4 1941
                                   833.91

NL 0444952   DLC

Löns, Hermann, 1866–1914.
... Der letzte Hansbur, ein bauernroman aus der Lüneburger
heide. 6. aufl. der feldausgabe. Hannover, A. Sponholtz
₍1942?₎
232 p. 14ᶜᵐ.

I. Title.
                        ₍Full name: Hermann Fritz Moritz Löns₎
                                   46–38108
Library of Congress   PT2623.O36L4 1942
                                   833.91

NL 0444953   DLC

Löns, Hermann, 1866–1914.
... Das Lönsbuch; erzählungen, natur- und
jagdschilderungen, heidebilder, märchen, tiergeschichten. Volksausgabe. Hannover, F.
Gersbach, 1928.
3 p. l., 5–197 p. 1 l. facsim.   18.5 cm.
"Hermann Löns", a biographical and critical
sketch, signed Max A. Tönjes, p. 5–26.

NL 0444954   MtU

Löns, Hermann, 1866–1914.
... Das Lönsbuch; erzählungen, tier- und jagdgeschichten,
naturschilderungen, tiermärchen. Mit den kriegsschilderungen: Mein kamerad Löns, von Max A. Tönjes. Bad Pyrmont
(Hannover) F. Gersbach ₍1942₎
197 p., 1 l. facsim. 20½ᶜᵐ.

I. Tönjes, Max A. II. Title.
                        ₍Full name: Hermann Fritz Moritz Löns₎

PT2623.O36L6 1942   838.91   47–34527

NL 0444955   DLC ICRL NNC PU IU MdBJ TNJ

Löns, Hermann, 1866–1914.
... Das Lönsbuch; erzählungen, tier- und jagdgeschichten,
heideheimlichkeiten. Mit den kriegsschilderungen: Mein kamerad Löns, von Max A. Tönjes. Bad Pyrmont (Hannover)
F. Gersbach, 1943.
3 p. l., 5–197 p. illus. (facsim.) 20½ᶜᵐ.

I. Tönjes, Max A. II. Title.
                        ₍Full name: Hermann Fritz Moritz Löns₎
PT2623.O36L6 1943   838.91   A F 47–1280
California. Univ. Libr.
for Library of Congress

NL 0444956   CU NbU OO FU CtY DLC

Löns, Hermann, 1866–1914.
Das Lönsbuch; novellen, natur- und jagdschilderungen,
heidebilder, märchen und tiergeschichten, mit einem
lebensbild des dichters ... 1. tausend. Hannover, F.
Gersbach ₍1916₎
2 p. l., 3–169, ₍1₎ p. front. (port.) illus., facsim. 20½ᶜᵐ.   M. 3.60
"Lebensbild" signed: Max A. Tönjes.

I. Tönjes, Max A., ed.

Library of Congress   PT2623.O36 1916   17–891

NL 0444957   DLC KU LU

PT   Löns, Hermann, 1866–1914.
2623   Das Lönsbuch; Novellen, Natur- und
.O36   Jagdschilderungen, Heidebilder, Märchen
1916   und Tiergeschichten, mit einem Lebensbild
        des Dichters. Hannover, F. Gersbach [c1916]
        171 p.   front. (port.) illus., facsim.
        "57. Tousend."
        "Lebensbild" signed: Max A. Tönjes.

        1. Tönjes, Max A.,   ed.

NL 0444958   NBuU

VOLUME 338

Löns, Hermann, 1866-1914.
Das Lönsbuch; novellen, natur- y.
jagdschilderungen, heidebilder, marchen,
tiergeschichten. Mit einem lebensbild
des dichters ... Bad Pyrmont,Hannover
₍etc.₎F.Gersbach,1923.
3p.ℓ.,3-171₍1₎p. illus.,facsim.
20½cm.

NL 0444959   PSt

PT2623 Löns, Hermann, 1866-
.05M4   ... Mein blaues buch, balladen. ₍Hannover₎ A. Sponholtz
1912 ₍1912₎
₍4₎, 175 p. 18½ᶜᵐ.
At head of title: Hermann Löns.

NL 0444960   ICU PPT OCU MiD

Löns, Hermann, 1866-1914.
...Mein blaues Buch, Balladen...   Hannover: A. Sponholtz,
1916. 175 p. front. 18cm.

NL 0444961   NN OCU

PT   Löns, Hermann, 1866-1914.
2623   Mein blaues Buch; Balladen.   Hannover,
.036   A. Sponholtz, 1921.
M38   175 p. 18 cm.

NL 0444962   WU CtY

Löns, Hermann, 1866-1914.
Mein blaues Buch; Balladen. Umschlagzeichnung von
Fritz Eggers. Hannover, A. Sponholtz, 1922 ₍1912₎
175 p. 20 cm.

I. Title.
Full name: Hermann Fritz Moritz Löns.

PT2623.O363M4   54-50490 ‡

NL 0444963   DLC NcU NNC

Löns, Hermann, 1866-1914.
... Mein braunes buch; heidbilder ... Hannover, A. Sponholtz, 1907.
3 p. l., 178 p. 23ᶜᵐ.

I. Title.
₍Full name: Hermann Fritz Moritz Löns₎
7-20847 Revised
Library of Congress   PT2623.O36M4 1907

NL 0444964   DLC

Loens, Hermann, 1866-   .
Mein braunes Buch; Heidbilder...   Hannover: A. Spon-
holtz Verlag, G. m. b. H., 1910. 4 p.l., 181 p. 7. ed. 8°.
Author's name at head of title.

NL 0444965   NN NcD

Löns, Hermann, 1866-1914.
Mein braunes buch; Heidbilder. 8. Aufl.
Hannover, A. Sponholtz ₍c1910₎
181 p.

NL 0444966   WaU

Löns, Hermann, 1866-1914.
Mein braunes Buch; Heidbilder. Berlin,
Büchergilde Gutenberg ₍c1912₎
184 p.

NL 0444967   WaU

Löns, Hermann, 1866-1914.
Mein braunes Buch; Heidbilder.   Hannover: Adolf Spon-
holtz₍, cop. 1912₎.   223 p.   12°.

1. Nature. 2. Title.
N. Y. P. L.   October 16, 1928

NL 0444968   NN CtY

834L86 Löns, Hermann, 1866-1914.
Om1915   Mein braunes buch; haidbilder. 16.aufl
Hannover, 1915.
181p.

NL 0444969   IU

Löns,Hermann,1866-1914.
... Mein braunes buch; haidbilder. 110.-130.
tausend.   Hannover, A.Sponholtz verlag g.m.b.h.,
1923.
2 p.ℓ.,176 p. 20½ᶜᵐ   (His Werke)

NL 0444970   MiU PPT MH

Löns, Hermann, 1866-1914.
... Mein buntes buch, naturschilderungen ... 1. tausend.
Hannover, A. Sponholtz verlag, g. m. b. h., 1913.
163 p. 21½ cm.

1. Natural history—Germany.   I. Title.

QH149.L6 1913   13-26715

NL 0444971   DLC InU

Löns, Hermann, 1866-1914.
Mein buntes Buch; Naturschilderungen.   Hannover: Adolf
Sponholtz, 1924. 164 p. 8°.

NL 0444972   NN CtY

Löns, Hermann, 1866-1914.
... Mein buntes buch, naturschilderungen. Mit 155 natur-
aufnahmen von Hermann Fischer-Braunschweig. Hannover,
A. Sponholtz verlag, g. m. b. h. ₍1935₎
207 p. incl. plates. 23½ᶜᵐ.
First edition 1913.

1. Natural history—Germany.   I. Title.
₍Full name: Hermann Fritz Moritz Löns₎
36-8180
Library of Congress   QH149.L6 1935
Copyright A—Foreign   30351

574

NL 0444973   DLC WU

PT   Löns, Hermann, 1866-1914
2623   Mein goldenes Buch, Lieder.   Hannover, F.
.036   Gersbach ₍n. d.₎
M5   64 ℓ. 21 cm.

NL 0444974   WU DLC-P4 CSt

Loens, Hermann, 1866-1914
Mein goldenes Buch; Lieder. Bad Pyrmont, Gersbach, 1922₍

NL 0444975   MH

Löns, Hermann
Mein goldenes Buch; Lieder. Hannover, F.
Gersbach, 1922.
64 ℓ.

Printed on one side of leaf only.

NL 0444976   MiD

Löns, Hermann, 1866-1914.
Mein goldenes buch; lieder... Leipzig,
Gersbach, 1923.
64 numb.ℓ. 20 ᶜᵐ.

NL 0444977   NjP

Löns, Hermann, 1866-1914.
... Mein goldenes buch; lieder. 61.bis 70.
tausend. Bad Pyrmont - Hannover, F. Gersbach,
1925.
1 p.l.,63 numb.l. 21cm.

NL 0444978   CU

Löns, Hermann, 1866-1914.
... Mein goldenes Buch; Lieder. 71. bis 78.
Tausend.
Bad Pyrmont,Hannover,F.Gersbach,1926. 1p.ℓ.,
63 numb.ℓ. 20½cm.
Text on recto of leaves only.

NL 0444979   CtY PPLas

Löns, Hermann, 1866-1914.
Mein goldenes Buch, Lieder. Volksausg.
Bad Pyrmont/Hannover, F. Gersbach ₍c1928₎
63 L.

NL 0444980   WaU MtU

VOLUME 338

LÖNS, HERMANN, 1866-1914.
Mein grünes Buch. Jagdschilderungen. 3. Aufl.
Hannover, E. Geibel, 1908. 184 p. 22cm.

NL 0444981 NN

Löns, Hermann, 1866-1914.
Mein grünes Buch, Jagdschilderungen.
5. Aufl. Hannover, E. Geibel, 1911.
204 p. 21cm.

NL 0444982 FU

LÖNS, Hermann, 1866-1914.
Mein grünes Buch; Jagdschilderungen. Hannover,
F. Gersbach, [1918?].

21 cm.

NL 0444983 MH

Löns, Hermann, 1866-1914.
... Mein grünes buch. Jagdschilderungen. 101.
bis 110. tausend. Bad Pyrmont, Hannover, F.
Gersbach, 1925.
1 p. l., 216 p., 1 l. 21 cm.

NL 0444984 CU

Löns, Hermann, 1866-1914.
... Mein grünes Buch, Jagdschilderungen.
Volksausgabe. Hannover, F. Gersbach, 1928.
1 p. l., 215 p., 1 l. 18.5 cm.

NL 0444985 MtU WaWW

GERMAN
799   Löns, Hermann, 1866-1914
L8m   Mein grünes Buch; das klassische
         Löns-Werk, Tier- und Jagdgeschichten,
         Naturschilderungen. Bad Pyrmont/
         Hannover, F. Gersbach [°1936]
           256 p. illus.

NL 0444986 MiD

Löns, Hermann, 1866-1914.
... Mein grünes buch, jagd- und tiergeschichten. Bad Pyrmont (Hannover) F. Gersbach [194-?]
1 p. l., 215, [1] p. 21ᵐ.

1. Hunting. I. Title.
[Full name: Hermann Fritz Moritz Löns]
Library of Congress   SK35.L6
                                    45-32526
                                         799.2

NL 0444987 DLC MiU PSt CU CtY

Löns, Hermann, 1866-1914.
... Mein grünes buch, tier- und jagdgeschichten. Feldausgabe. Gütersloh, C. Bertelsmann [1942]
221, [1] p. 18ᵐ.
"2. auflage der feldausgabe."
"Lizenzausgabe."

1. Hunting. I. Title.
[Full name: Hermann Fritz Moritz Löns]
Library of Congress   SK35.L6 1942
                                    45-32525
                                         799.2

NL 0444988 DLC

Löns, Hermann, 1866-1914.
... Mein grünes buch, jagd- und tiergeschichten, schilderungen. Sonder-ausgabe. Bad Pyrmont (Hannover) F. Gersbach, 1944.
218 p., 1 l. 17ᵐ.

1. Hunting. I. Title.
[Full name: Hermann Fritz Moritz Löns]
SK35.L6 1944   799.2   A F 47-62
Yale univ. Library
for Library of Congress

NL 0444989 CtY WU NN CU DLC

834.91   Löns, Hermann, 1866-1914.
L824m   Mein grünes Buch; das klassische Löns-
.1953   Werk; Tier- und Jagdgeschichten; Natur-
         schilderungen. Berlin, Safari-Verlag
         [1953]
           214p. illus. 25cm.

"Die Fotos aus der Natur stammen von
Hermann Fischer, ..."

1. Natural   history. Essays.

NL 0444990 KU

PT   Löns, Hermann, 1866-1914
2623   Mein grünes Revier. Mit Zeichnungen
036   von Fritz Jaspert. Berlin, Safari [1949]
M53   148p. illus. 24cm.
           Die Tiernovellen entstammen der sammlung
         "Aus Forst und Flur."

1. Animals, Legends and stories of

NL 0444991 WU

834.91   Löns, Hermann, 1866-1914.
L824me   Mein grünes Revier. Berlin, Safari-
1950   Verlag [1950]
           228p. illus. 25cm.

"Federzeichnungen von Fritz Jaspert."
"Die Tiernovellen entstammen der
Sammlung "Aus Forst und Flur."

1. Natural history. Essays. I. Title.

NL 0444992 KU NN

PT2623   Löns, Hermann, 1866-1914.
036M4   Mein niedersächsisches Skizzenbuch. Aus dem
1924   Nachlasse, hrsg. von Wilhelm Deimann. Hanover,
         A. Sponholz, 1924.
           325 p. 21 cm.

I. Deimann, Wilhelm, ed. II. Title.

NL 0444993 NcRS TxU WU InU

Löns, Hermann, 1866-1914.
Met den helm geboren, de roman van een liefde. Vertaald
door J. van Wageningen. Amsterdam, Volksche Uitgeverij
Westland, 1943.
347 p. port. 20 cm. (His Meesterwerken)
Translation of Das zweite Gesicht.

I. Wageningen, J. van, tr. II. Title.
Full name: Hermann Fritz Moritz Löns.
PT2623.036Z43   A F 48-2572*
California. Univ. Libr.
for Library of Congress   [1]†

NL 0444994 CU CtY DLC

Löns, Hermann, 1866-1914.
... Mümmelmann; ein tierbuch. Auswahl.
Hannover, A. Sponholtz verlag g. m. b. h. [19]
80 p. 18cm.

NL 0444995 NcD WaS

PT2623   Löns, Hermann, 1866-1914.
.036M8   Mümmelmann; ein Tierbuch. Hannover, A.
1910   Sponholtz [191-?]
           167 p. 21cm.

NL 0444996 ViU NIC

Löns, Hermann, 1866-1914.
Mümmelmann, ein Tierbuch. Hannover, A. Sponholtz
[°1911]
179 p. 21 cm.

1. Animals, Legends and stories of.
Full name: Hermann Fritz Moritz Löns.
PZ36.3.L57   54-47925 ‡

NL 0444997 DLC MiD

Löns, Hermann, 1866-1914.
Mümmelmann; ein tierbuch. Hannover, Sponholtz
[c1911]
187 p.

NL 0444998 NNC OrP WaTC

Löns, Hermann, 1866-1914.
... Mümmelmann, ein tierbuch. 15. aufl. ...
Hannover, A. Sponholtz verlag g.m.b.h., 1914.
163 p. 21ᶜᵐ.
Cover-title has subtitle: Tiergeschichten.
"20 tier- u. jagdnovellen."--Publisher's notice laid in.

NL 0444999 MiU

Löns, Hermann, 1866-1914.
...Mümmelmann; ein tierbuch, 2. feldausg.
... Hannover, A. Sponholtz, 1917.
167 p.

NL 0445000 OCU

VOLUME 338

Loens, Hermann, 1866–1914.
...Muemmelmann; ein Tierbuch. Hannover: A. Sponholtz Verlag, G.m.b.H., 1926?, 179 p. 8°.
Contents.—Muemmelmann. Murkerichs Minnefahrt. Krähengespräch. Sein letztes Lied. Goldhals. Der letzte seines Stammes. Achtracks Ende. Böbchen. Der Zaunigel. Jakob. Hausfriedensbruch. Mein Dachs und meine Dackel. Die Zeit der schweren Not. Des Rätsels Lösung. Das Eichhörnchen. Hasendämmerung. Der Mörder. Der Alte vom Berge. Die Einwanderer. Ein Hauptschwein.

NL 0445001　　　NN OCU

Löns, Hermann, 1866–1914.
Mümmelmann. ,Bilder von Carl Lindeberg, Leipzig, E. Skacel ,1944,
184 p. col. plates. 22 cm. (Lagerbücherei der Kinderlandverschickung. 13. Bd.)

1. Animals, Legends and stories of.　I. Title.　(Series)
Full name: Hermann Fritz Moritz Löns.
A 48–6244*
Harvard Univ. Library
for Library of Congress　　,1,

NL 0445002　　　MH

Löns, Hermann, 1866–1914.
Mummelman, een dierenboek. Vertaald naar een exemplaar van het 149ste duizendtal der oorspronkelijke uitg. door C. v. d. Tonge-Koster. Met een inleiding van A. B. Wigman. Amsterdam, Uitgeverij Westland, 1942.
203 p. 19 cm. (*His* Meesterwerken)

I. Tonge-Koster, C. van der, tr.　II. Title.
Full name: Hermann Fritz Moritz Löns.
PZ16.3.L6　　　A F 48–2681*
California. Univ. Libr.
for Library of Congress　　,1,†

NL 0445003　　　CU CtY DLC

838
L823
D32
Löns, Hermann, 1866–1914.
... Nachgelassene schriften, hrsg. von Wilhelm Deimann ... Leipzig, Hesse & Becker; ,etc., etc., 1928.
2 v. plates (part col.) 19½cm.
CONTENTS.—1.bd. Mein niedersächsisches skizzenbuch. Reisebilder. Für sippe und sitte.—2.bd. Naturwissenschaftliche aufsätze und plaudereien. Gedanken und gestalten. Eulenspiegeleien.

I. Deimann, Wilhelm, 1889–　ed.

NL 0445004　　　MiU IEN OO OC1 NRU

Löns, Hermann, 1866–1914.
...Die rote Beeke. Hannover: A. Sponholtz ,1927, 16 p. illus. 24½cm.
With woodcuts by Erich Feyerabend.

19619B.　I. Fiction, German.　　I. Title.
N. Y. P. L.　　　October 20, 1939

NL 0445005　　　NN CtY OC1 NNC CU CSt

PT
2623
.O3682
Löns, Hermann, 1866–1914.
Sagen und Märchen. Hrsg. von Wilhelm Deimann. Hameln, A. Sponholtz [n.d.]
120 p. illus.

I. Deimann, Wilhelm, ed. II. Title.

NL 0445006　　　NBuU

Löns, Hermann, 1866–1914.
Sein letztes Lied; eine Auswahl der schönsten Jagdgeschichten. Mit 128 Naturaufnahmen ausgewaehlt von Hermann Fischer-Braunschweig. Berlin, Deutsche Buch-Gemeinschaft ,°1924,
190 p. illus. 23 cm.

1. Hunting—Germany.　I. Title.

SK201.L72　　　68–127263

NL 0445007　　　DLC WaWW WaS

Löns, Hermann, 1866–1914.
Das Tal der Lieder, und andere Schilderungen, von Hermann Löns. Mit Buchschmuck von W. Kirsch... Hannover: F. Gersbach ,1916, 84 p. illus. 18½cm. (Hannoversche Volksbücher. Bd. 8.)
The illustrations are head- and tailpieces.

996383A.　1. Germany—Descr. and　　　trav., 1900–1914.　I. Title.
N. Y. P. L.　　　December 12, 1939

NL 0445008　　　NN MiD NNC

872
L835
t
Löns, Hermann, 1866–1914.
... Das tal der lieder, und andere schilderungen 73. bis 80. tausend. Bad Pyrmont – Hannover, F. Gersbach, 1925.
1 p.l. ,102p., 1 l. 21cm.

NL 0445009　　　CU CtY

834L86
Ot1934
Löns, Hermann, 1866–1914.
Tier- und jagdgeschichten ... Frankfurt am Main, M. Diesterweg ,1934?,
31p. illus. (Kranz-bücherei. hft.7)
"Achte auflage."

NL 0445010　　　IU

Löns, Hermann, 1866–1914.
... Tiergeschichten. Leipzig, Im Insel-Verlag [1932?]
71 p. 18½cm. (On cover: Insel-Bücherei Nr. 425)

NL 0445011　　　NcD CoFS MiD

PT2623
.O36A6
1917
Löns, Hermann, 1866–1914.
Tiergeschichten. Mümmelman. Widu. Was da kreucht und fleugt. Geleitwort von Dr. W. Deimann. Hannover, A. Sponholtz ,1917,
344 p. 20 cm.

. 1. Animals, Legends and stories of. I. Title. II. Title: Mümmelman. III. Title: Widu. IV. Title: Was da kreucht und fleugt.

NL 0445012　　　NcRS

837.912
L824u
19--
Löns, Hermann, 1866–1914.
Ulenspegel ,humoristisch, satirische Dichtungen, nebst Schulaufsätzen von Aadje Ziesenis und Ulenspeigels Selbstbiographie. Bad Pyrmont, F. Gersbach ,19--,
110p. 20cm.
Cover title: Ulenspeigels Lieder.

NL 0445013　　　KU

PT
2623
036
F7
Löns, Hermann, 1866–1914
Ulenspeigels und Fritz von der Leines ausgewählte Lieder; nebst Schulaufsätzen von Aadje Ziesenis und Ulenspeigels Selbstbiographie. Bad Pyrmont, F. Gersbach, 1925.
113p. 21cm.
Bound with the author's Frau Döllmer. Bad Pyrmont, 1925.

NL 0445014　　　WU CtY

Löns, Hermann, 1866–1914.
Von ost nach west; Selbstbiographie Berlin, Verlag der Schriftenvertriebsanstalt g.m.b.h. [1921]
32 p.
"Die seit jahren vergriffenen biographie wird den Lönsfreunden hiermit aufs neue vorgelegt." – p.4.

NL 0445015　　　MH CU

Löns, Hermann, 1866–1914.
Was da kreucht und fleugt; ein tierbuch.. Leipzig, Hesse ,c1922,
189 p. incl. plates. front. 24 cm.

NL 0445016　　　NjP DLC-P4 NN

Löns, Hermann, 1866–1914.
Was da kreucht und fleugt; ein Tierbuch. Vollständige Ausg. mit Holzschnitten von Emil Bröckl. Berlin, Gebr. Paetel ,°1924,
156 p. illus. 19 cm. (Paetels Roman-Reihe, 17)

1. Animals, Legends and stories of.　I. Title.
Full name: Hermann Fritz Moritz Löns.
PT2623.O36W3　　　50–48425

NL 0445017　　　DLC WU

Loens, Hermann, 1866–1914.
Was da kreucht und fleugt; ein Tierbuch, von Hermann Löns ... Berlin: H. Paetel, G.m.b.H., cop. 1924., 151 p. front., plates. 8. ed. 12°. (Sammlung belehrender Unterhaltungsschriften. Bd. 31.)

319428A.　1. Animals, Wild.　　　2. Title.
N. Y. P. L.　　　August 20, 1927

NL 0445018　　　NN

Löns, Hermann, 1866–1914.
Was ich unter tieren erlauschte, geschichten aus forst und flur, von Hermann Löns. Mit 40 bildern nach naturaufnahmen. 66. bis 80. tausend. Leipzig, Hesse & Becker ,1935,
871. ,1, p. front., plates. 19 cm.

1. Animals, Legends and stories of.　I. Title.
45–26550
Library of Congress　　　QL791.L79
,2,　　　591.5

NL 0445019　　　DLC WU PPT NcD

PT
2623
036
W33
Löns, Hermann, 1866–1914
Wasserjungfern; Geschichten von Sommerboten und Sonnenkündern. 6. Aufl. Leipzig, Voigtländer, 1919.
122p. 20cm.

NL 0445020　　　WU

VOLUME 338

Löns, Hermann, 1866–1914.
Wasserjungfern; Geschichten von Sommerboten und Sonnenkündern ... 7. Aufl. Leipzig, 1919.
19.5 cm.

NL 0445021　CtY

Löns, Hermann, 1866–1914.
Wasserjungfern; Geschichten von Sommerboten und Sonnenkündern. 8.Aufl. Leipzig, R. Voigtländers Verlag, 1919.

NL 0445022　MH

Löns, Hermann, 1866–1914.
Wasserjungfern: geschichten von sommerboten und sonnenkündern. Von ... 11. aufl. Leipzig, R. Voigtländer, ₍1920?₎
122 p.

NL 0445023　OU

595.733　Löns, Hermann.
L824w　Wasserjungfern; Geschichten von Sommerboten und Sonnenkünden. Stuttgart, 1953　Deutsche Volksbücher ₍1953₎
111p. mounted col. illus. 23cm.

1. Dragon-flies. I. Title.

NL 0445024　KU NIC

PT 2623 LÖNS, HERMANN, 1866–1914.
.O36 W4 ...Der Wehrwolf; eine bauernchronik. 1–5.Tausend. Jena, E. Diederichs, 1910.
1910　2 p. l., 248, ₍1₎ p. 20 1/2ᶜᵐ.

NL 0445025　InU

Loens, Hermann, 1866–1914.
Der Wehrwolf; eine Bauernchronik. Jena: E. Diederichs, 1913. 1 p.l., 243(1) p. 12°.
Author's name at head of title.
Titelzeichnung by F. H. E. Schneidler.

1. Fiction (German). 2. Schneidler. F. H. Ernst, illustrator. 3. Title.
N. Y. P. L.　November 11, 1914.

NL 0445026　NN

Loens, Herman, 1866–1914.
Der Wehrwolf. Eine Bauernchronik von Hermann Löns. Wolfenbüttel: Heckner₍, 1915₎. 111 p. 8°.

In shorthand.
Suppl. to Deutsche Stenographien-Zeitung.

1. Shorthand—Books in.
N. Y. P. L.　June 29, 1925

NL 0445027　NN

Löns, Hermann, 1866–
833.91　Der Wehrwolf; eine Bauernchronik. Jena,
L825HC　E. Diederichs, 1918.
243 p. 19 cm.

NL 0445028　NcD OCU

PT2623 Löns, Hermann, 1866–
.O5W4　... Der wehrwolf, eine bauernchronik. 121–140. tausend.
1921　Jena, E. Diederichs, 1921.
₍4₎, 243, ₍1₎ p. 19½ᶜᵐ.
T.-p. illus.
At head of title: Hermann Löns.

NL 0445029　ICU NcU CaBVaU WaSp

Löns, Hermann, 1866–1914.
... Der wehrwolf; eine bauernchronik. 141.–155. tausend.
Jena, E. Diederichs, 1922.
2 p. l., 243, ₍1₎ p. 20½ᵐ.

I. Title.
₍Full name: Hermann Fritz Moritz Löns₎
23–6992 Revised
Library of Congress　PT2623.O36W4 1922

NL 0445030　DLC OrU WaWW OrPR OrP NcU CtY ScU OO

PT　Löns, Hermann, 1866–1914.
2623　Der Wehrwolf; eine Bauernchronik. Jena,
.O36 W4　E. Diederichs, 1923.
1923　241 p. 20 cm.

NL 0445031　VtMiM NIC PV CU OrU

Löns, Hermann, 1866–1914.
...Der wehrwolf; eine bauernchronik.
₍406–420 tausend₎ Jena, E. Diederichs
₍c1923₎
241, ₍1₎ p.

NL 0445032　MiU

Löns, Hermann, 1866–1914.
... Der wehrwolf; eine bauernchronik.
421–440 tausend. Jena, E. Diederichs,
₍c1923₎
2 p. l., 243, ₍1₎ p.

NL 0445033　ODW

PT　Löns, Hermann, 1866–1914.
2623　... Der wehrwolf; eine Bauernchronik.
.O36　[481.–499. tausend] Jena, E. Diederichs
W4　[c1923]
1923　245 p.

NL 0445034　DGU OOxM

Löns, Hermann, 1866–1914.
...Der wehrwolf; eine bauernchronik.
Jena, Ed. Diederichs, 1925.
243 p.

NL 0445035　OClW OU

Löns, Hermann, 1866–1914.
Der Wehrwolf; eine Bauernchronik. Jena: Eugen Diedrichs, 1926. 244 p. 12°.

NL 0445036　NN

LÖNS, HERMANN, 1866–1914.
... Der wehrwolf; eine bauernchronok. Jena, E. Diederichs, 1930.
2 p. l., 243 [1] p. 20½ cm.

NL 0445037　PPCS

Löns, Hermann, 1866–1914.
Der wehrwolf, eine bauernchronik. Jena, Diederichs, 1930.
241 p.

NL 0445038　NNC

Löns, Hermann, 1866–1914.
Der Wehrwolf, eine Bauernchronik. Jena, E. Diederichs ₍1942₎
253 p. 20 cm.

I. Title.
Full name: Hermann Fritz Moritz Löns.
PT2623.O36W4 1942　A F 48–3663*

California. Univ. Libr.
for Library of Congress　₍1₎†

NL 0445039　CU ICU TxU TNJ CtY MH DLC

Löns, Hermann, 1866–1914.
Der Wehrwolf, eine Bauernchronik ₍646.–655. tausend₎ Jena, E. Diederichs ₍1943₎
253 p. 20ᶜᵐ.

NL 0445040　ViU

Löns, Hermann, 1866–1914.
Der Wehrwolf. Leipzig, B. Tauchnitz, 1943.
263 p. 18 cm. (Der Deutsche Tauchnitz, Bd. 107)

I. Title.
Full name: Hermann Fritz Moritz Löns.
PT2623.O36W4 19—　48–36088*

NL 0445041　DLC

Löns, Hermann, 1866–1914.
Der Wehrwolf, eine Bauernchronik. Jena, E. Diederichs [1944, c1923]
253p. 20cm.

NL 0445042　TxU MH MB

Löns, Hermann, 1866–1914.
... Widu; ein neues tierbuch. 1.–10. tausend. Hannover, A. Sponholtz verlag, g. m. b. h., 1917.
2 p. l., 165, ₍1₎ p. 21ᵐ.

I. Title.
Library of Congress　PT2623.O36W5 1917　22–23825

NL 0445043　DLC OCl

VOLUME 338

PT2623 Löns, Hermann, 1866–
.O5W6   ... Widu, ein neues tierbuch. Hannover, A. Sponholtz
1917 ₁1917₎
     ₍4₎, 165, ₍1₎ p.   20½ᶜᵐ.
     At head of title: Hermann Löns.

NL 0445044   ICU WU

LÖNS, Hermann, *1866-1914.*
     Widu; ein *neues* tierbuch. *51-60* tausend.
Hannover, A. Sponholtz, g. m. b. h. [cop.
1917].

NL 0445045   MH

833.91   Löns, Hermann, 1866-1914.
L824wi   Widu; Tiergeschichten; mit 14 Zeichnungen
1952   von Paul Haase ₍et al.₎   Hannover, A.
     Sponholtz ₍1952₎
     160p. illus. 18cm.   (Grüne Reihe, Bd.2

     1. Animals, Stories and legends of.
     I. Haase, Paul,   illus.

NL 0445046   KU

     Löns, Hermann, 1866-1914.
     ... Der zweckmässige Meyer; ein schnurriges buch.   1.-4.
tausend. Hannover, A. Sponholtz verlag, g. m. b. h. ₍1911₎
     3 p. l., 148 p. 21½ᵐ.

     I. Title.   ₍Full name: Hermann Fritz Moritz Löns₎
                                  12—1806
     Library of Congress   PT2623.O36Z3 1911

NL 0445047   DLC

834L86   Löns, Hermann, 1866-1914.
Ozw1922   Der zweckmässige Meyer; ein schnurriges buch.
     49.-67. tausend.   Hannover, A. Sponholtz verlag
     g.m.b.h., 1922.
     153p.

NL 0445048   IU

833.91   Löns, Hermann, 1866-1914.
L824z   Das zweite Gesicht; eine Liebesgeschichte.
1912   Jena, E. Diederichs, 1912.
     272p. 20cm.

NL 0445049   KU OC1

PT   Löns, Hermann, 1866-1914
2623   Das zweite Gesicht; eine Liebesgeschichte.
O36   Jena, E. Diederichs, 1918.
Z4   272p. 20cm.

NL 0445050   WU

PT2623   Löns, Hermann, 1866-1914.
.O 36   Das Zweite Gesicht; eine Liebesgeschichte.
Z4   24 bis 153. tausend. Jena, E. Diederichs,
1920   1920.
        272p. 20cm.

NL 0445051   NcU

Löns, Hermann, 1866-1914.
     ... Das zweite gesicht; ein liebesgeschichte.   84. bis 103.
tausend. Jena, E. Diederichs, 1920·
     2 p. l., 272 p., 1 l. 20½ᵐ.

NL 0445052   NcRS MH DLC

Löns, Hermann, 1866-1914.
     ... Das zweite gesicht; ein liebesgeschichte.   124. bis
153. tausend.   Jena, E. Diederichs, 1921.
     2 p. l., 272 p., 1 l. 20½ᵐ.

     I. Title.   23–1863
     Library of Congress   PT2623.O36Z4 1921

NL 0445053   DLC NcGU OrPR MoSU NcD NcU WU

Löns, Hermann, 1866-1914.
     ...Das zweite gesicht; roman. Jena,
E. Diederichs ₍c1923₎
     3-203 p.

     "387.-400. tausend."

NL 0445054   OCU ODW WaWW

Löns, Hermann, 1866-1914.
     ... Das zweite gesicht; ein liebesgeschichte.   272.bis
290. tausend.   Jena, E. Diederichs,   1926.
     2 p. l., 272 p., 1 l. 20½ᵐ.

NL 0445055   CU

Loens, Hermann, 1866-1914.
     ...Das zweite Gesicht; eine Liebesgeschichte...   Jena: E.
Diederichs, 1927.   271 p.   12°.

     Contents: Vorspuk. Die Sektflasche. Das Stapelienbild. Der Vollmond. Der
eiserne Ritter. Das Seelenhaus. Der Mohnblumenkranz. Der Platzhirsch. Die Wund-
fährte. Der graue Engel. Der weisse Garten. Der Sarg. Die Panne. Nachspuk.

     312706A. 1. Fiction, German.   2. Title.
     N. Y. P. L.   July 11, 1927

NL 0445056   NN Mi

Löns, Hermann, 1866-1914.
     ... Das zweite gesicht; ein liebesgeschichte.
316. bis 325. tausend.   Jena, E. Diederichs, 1929.
     1 p. l., 271, [1] p., 1 l. 19.5 cm.

NL 0445057   CtY

Löns, Hermann, 1866-1914.
     Das zweite Gesicht, Roman. Düsseldorf, E. Diederichs
₍1935₎
     298 p. 20 cm.

     I. Title.   *Full name: Herman Fritz Moritz Löns.*
     PT2623.O36Z4 1935   54–50173 ‡

NL 0445058   DLC

Löns, Hermann Fritz Moritz
     see   Löns, Hermann, 1866-1914.

Löns, J., ed.
     Gesetz zur Regelung der Rechtsverhältnisse der
unter Artikel 131 des Grundgesetzes fallenden
Personen
        see under   Germany (Federal Republic,
1949-   ) Laws, statutes, etc.

Loens, Konrad.
     Die Rentabilität der Oelpalme, von Konrad Loens...   Ber-
lin: W. Süsserott ₍1914₎.   21 p. incl. diagrs., tables.   8°.
(Koloniale Abhandlungen. Heft 71.)

     1. Palms (Oil). Africa. 2. Series.
     N. Y. P. L.   July 23, 1924

NL 0445061   NN

     Löns, Lisa H., 1871-   tr.

     Brinig, Myron, 1900-
     ... Die Singermanns, roman. Hannover, A. Sponholtz ver-
lag, g. m. b. h. ₍1930₎

Loens, Max, 1886–
     Ueber die Ausscheidung des Jods in der Frauenmilch nach
Verabreichung von Jodkalium und Lipojodin...von Max Löns...
Göttingen: L. Hofer, 1912.   16 p., 1 l.   Tables.   8°.

     Cover-title.
     Dissertation, Göttingen.
     Lebenslauf.
     "Literatur." 1 p. at end of volume.

     1. Milk (Human).
     N. Y. P. L.   October 23, 1915

NL 0445063   NN MiU DNLM

Pamph.   LOENS, Pieter
v.500   Regtelyke aanmerkingen, omtrent eenige
     poincten, concernerende de execrable
     sonde tegens de natuur, veroorzaakt
     wegens het treurenswaardig geval van
     Andreas Klink ... achter dit werk vindt
     men het uitgesprooke vonnis over denzel-
     ven, door Pieter Loens. Rotterdam, Joost
     van de Laan, 1760.
     3 p. l., 58p. 19cm.

NL 0445064   MH-AH

LOENS, Richard Emil, 1863-

     See LOENS, Emil, 1863-

PT   Löns, Rudolf.
2623   Der Dilwel; Taubengeschichten.   Eberbach
.638D8   am Neckar, H. Kahlsdorf ₍1920₎
     71 p. 20cm.

NL 0445066   KyLoU

     Lons, Rudolf.
     ... Die Erziehung des jungen Hundes im
ersten Lebensjahre; als Grundlage seiner
Eignung zum Haushund, Begleithund und Dienst-
hund aller Art. Eberbach a. Neckar, Heinrich
Kahlsdorf Verlag, 1920.
     126 p., 1 l. illus. 20½cm.
     Author's name at head of title.

     1. Dogs - Training. I. Title.

     SF431.L6

NL 0445067   ViW CaBVaU

VOLUME 338

PT
921
L824¦ₛ
Löns, Rudolf, *ed.*
Geheimes Raunen in alten Märchen. Gedeutet von Rudolf Löns. Eberbach am Neckar, H. Kahlsdorf, 1920.
91 p.

1. Fairy tales, German. 2. Folk-lore, German. I. Title.

NL 0445068   CLU OCl

4PT
Ger.
8011
Löns, Rudolf
Die Löns'sche Art. [Hannover,
F. Gersbach]
79 p.

NL 0445069   DLC-P4

Löns, Rudolf.
Vagtelhunden; jagtspaniels, deres Opdraet og Føring. Af Rud. Löns og E. v. Otto. Paa Dansk ved Jens F. Israelsen ... Odense, Miloske Boghandels Forlag, 1910.
53 p. illus. 21½ cm.

1. Spaniels. 2. Bird dogs. I. Otto, E. von, jt. auth. II. Israelsen, Jens F.

SF429.S7L6

NL 0445070   ViW

Loens (Wilhelm Georg). *Ueber Pneumatose in Beckenabcessen.* 31 pp. 8°. *Halle, Lipke,* 1873.
c.

NL 0445071   DNLM

Löns-Erbeck, Elisabet
see Löns, Elisabet.

Loenser, Carl William.
Gottes heilsplan in den verschiedenen zeitaltern; mit anhang von einer zeitalter-karte, herausgegeben von C. W. Loenser ... [Milwaukee, Wis., Word & witness publishing co., ᵃ1937]
55 p. fold. diagr. 22ᶜᵐ.

1. Covenants (Theology)   I. Title.
Library of Congress   BT155.L6   37-33393
———— Copy 2.
Copyright A 110675   [3]   238

NL 0445073   DLC

Loenser, Carl William, *ed.*
Heilslieder; eine Sammlung von bewährten, geistlichen Liedern für alle kirchlichen und festlichen Gelegenheiten. Cleveland, Ohio, Branch Publishing House [ᵃ1945]
1 v. (unpaged) 22 cm.
Hymns, with music.

1. Hymns, German.   I. Title.
M2132.G3L8   52-17318

NL 0445074   DLC

W 6
P3
v. 1931
no. 17
LOENSMA, Ludovicus
Dissertatio medica inauguralis, de cerebro et nervis ...
Franequerae, Apud Gulielmum Coulon, 1775.
22 p. 24 cm.
Diss. - Franeker.

NL 0445075   DNLM

BR937
.B2L8
Lööralt, W.
Baltenhetze. Die verfolgung von glauben, sprache und recht in den ostseeprovinzen Russlands. Von W. Lööralt ... Leipzig, Duncker & Humblot, 1890.
[3], 154 p. 22½ᶜᵐ.
CONTENTS.—Entstehung der Baltenhetze und versuch sie zu erklären.—Zu den kontroversen gegen pastor Daltons "Offenes sen/lschreiben."

1. Baltic provinces—Church history.

NL 0445076   ICU NN MB InU CU

M2140
.S8A5
Lööw, Anton, *joint ed.*

Åmark, Mats, *ed.*
Julvisor och cantilenor. Samlade och utgivna av Mats Åmark och Anton Lööw. Stockholm, Svenska kyrkans diakonistyrelses bokforlag [ᵃ1951]

Loepelmann, Fritz, 1896–
Ueber die mechanischen eigenschaften des tempergusses, unter besonderer berücksichtigung seiner korngrösse... Düsseldorf, 1932. 12 p.
Inaug. Diss. –Techn. Hochsch. Berlin, 1932.
Lebenslauf.

NL 0445078   ICRL

Loepelmann, Hans, *ed.*
Das Volksschulfinanzgesetz vom 2. dezember 1936 (GS. s. 161) textausgabe mit systematischer darstellung und vordruckmuster, bearbeitet von stadtobersekretär Loepelmann ... Neuwied, J. Meincke, 1937.
viii, 185 p. 21½ᶜᵐ.
"Literatur-nachweis": p. 183.

1. Public schools—Prussia—Finance. 2. Educational law and legislation—Prussia.   I. Prussia. Laws, statutes, etc.   II. Title.
Library of Congress   LB2911.L6   41-15841
[2]   379.1109431

NL 0445079   DLC

Löpelmann, Martin, 1891–
Abriss einer vergleichenden lautlehre des deutschen, englischen, französischen und italienischen nebst darstellung der menschlichen sprechwerkzeuge, von dr. phil. M. Löpelmann und dr. med. W. Minnigerode. Mit 3 figuren im text und einer doppeltafel. Berlin und Bonn, F. Dümmler, 1929.
vii, [1], 104 p. fold. plate, tables, diagrs. 22½ᶜᵐ.
1. Phonetics. 2. Languages, Modern—Phonetics.   I. Minnigerode, Wilhelm, 188—   , joint author.

NL 0445080   ViU CU NBC MnU NNC

858.08
L88a
Löpelmann, Martin, 1891–
Aus der Volksdichtung der macedonischen Rumänen. Leipzig, Armanen-Verlag, 1934.
132p. 23cm.
"Die Märchen sind der umfangreichen Sammlung von Per. Papahagi, Basme Aromâne (Bukarest, 1905) entnommen und — übertragen — Die Volkslieder sind der Sammlung von M. G. Obedanaru, Texte Macedoromâne (Bukarest, 1891) entnommen — Diese Lieder habe ich — übertragen."

NL 0445081   IU OCl DLC-P4 NjP

Löpelmann, Martin, 1891–
... Choix de poésies politiques et satiriques du temps de la Fronde, publiées d'après quelques vieux imprimés et trois manuscrits de la Bibliothèque royale de Berlin. Strasbourg, Heitz; New-York, G. E. Stechert & co.; [etc., etc., 1916]
2 p. l., 12 p., 1 l., [13]–146, [1] p. 15ᶜᵐ. (Bibliotheca romanica. 237. 238. Bibliothèque française)
All but two of the pieces are Mazarinades of 1649. The two exceptions are "L'ombre du grand Armand", by Georges de Scudéry, 1643, and the anonymous "Chapeau vergeté", about the end of the 17th century. *cf.* Notice.
1. Mazarinades. 2. Political ballads and songs, French.   I. Title.   II. Title: Le chapeau vergeté.

Library of Congress   PQ1175.L6   21-16361

NL 0445082   DLC OCl

PF5002
.L8
LÖPELMANN, MARTIN, 1891–   *ed.*
..Die deutschen mundarten;eine sammlung von textproben hrsg.von dr.Martin Löpelmann. Dresden, L. Ehlermann[1927]
173,[1] p.incl.map. 18cm. (Deutsche schulausgaben...nr.133)
"Literatur":p.25.

1.German language—Dialects—Texts. 2.Low German language—Dialects—Texts.

NL 0445083   ICU IU

PQ1590
.A2
1942
Löpelmann, Martin, 1891–   *tr.*
Villon, François, *b.* 1431.
Dichtungen; französisch und deutsch, übertragen mit Einleitung und Anmerkungen von Martin Löpelmann. [3. abermals verb. Aufl.] München, G. D. W. Callwey [1942]

Löpelmann, Martin, 1891–
Erinn, alte irische Märchen und Geschichten. Brünn, R. M. Rohrer [1944]
522 p. 22 cm.
Includes unacc. melodies.

1. Folk-lore—Ireland. 2. Legends—Ireland. 3. Fairy tales.
I. Title.
GR147.L6   50-48323

NL 0445085   DLC

Löpelmann, Martin, 1891–
Frau Venus und die spielleute; tolldreiste geschichten aus dem frühen mittelalter, erzählt von Martin Löpelmann. Mit zeichnungen von Hans Fronius. Berlin, P. Neff, 1943.
270, [1] p. illus. 19ᶜᵐ.
CONTENTS.—Abend am Hörselberg.—Die dreisten verschwüre kaiser Karls und seiner paladine.—Gautier, der Wolf.—Traubenlese in der Champagne.—Falstaffs uruhn.—Literarischer nachweis (p. [265]–[271])

1. Tales, German. 2. Troubadours.   I. Title.
PT915.L6   A F 47–4352
Harvard univ. Library
for Library of Congress   [2]†

NL 0445086   MH CSt NcU DLC OCl

892.78
L825ge
Löpelmann, Martin, 1891–   *ed.*
Das Gesetz der Wüste; vormuhammedanische Kampf- und Liebeslieder. Aus dem Arabischen übertragen und nachgedichtet. Genf-Zürich, Arena Verlag, 1950.
94 p. 19 cm.

1.Arabic poetry (Collections) 2.Arabic poetry—Trans-   lations into German.

NL 0445087   MiU DLC-P4 OCl ICU

VOLUME 338

Löpelmann, Martin, 1891–
... Der goldene teufel, miniaturen und schattenbilder; mit 8 zeichnungen und stichen alter meister. Berlin, Universitas, Deutsche verlags-aktiengesellschaft (°1938)
138, (2) p. front., 7 pl. 19ᶜᵐ.

1. Devil in literature. I. Title.
Library of Congress   PT2623.O37G6 1938   39–17124
Copyright A—Foreign   40165
                        (2)   833.91

NL 0445088   DLC OrP OCl

Löpelmann, Martin, 1891–
Der Granatapfelgarten; Jaap de Knippers komische Liebesgeschichten aus dem Orient. Wien, Paul Neff Verlag [c1948]
371 p. illus. 21 cm.
Includes bibliography.
1. German wit and humor.

NL 0445089   NB

808.1
L825h   Löpelmann, Martin, 1891–   comp.
Himmel und Hölle der Fahrenden; Dichtungen der grossen Vaganten aller Zeiten und Länder. Stuttgart, Klett [pref. 1950]
394p. 19cm.

1. German poetry. Translations from foreign literature. I. Title.

NL 0445090   IEN CaBVaU

Löpelmann, Martin, 1891–
Der junge Diderot ... von dr. Martin Löpelmann. Berlin, Weidmann, 1934.
viii, 146 p., 1 l. fold. geneal. tab. 21ᶜᵐ.
Title vignette: Familiensiegel der Diderots.
"Bibliographie": p. v–viii.

1. Diderot, Denis, 1713–1784.
                                A 41–872
Ohio state univ. Library
for Library of Congress   (2)

NL 0445091   OU NjP CtY OU

Löpelmann, Martin, 1891–

Berlin. Prussische staatsbibliothek.
... Kurzes verzeichnis der romanischen handschriften. Berlin, Weidmann, 1918.

Löpelmann, Martin, 1891–
Legenden der Liebe. Berlin, P. Neff (°1941)
246 p. 19 cm.
Contents.—Tristan in der Kutte.—Der Wolkensteiner und Sabina.—Estrella.

PT2623.O37L4   52–47704

NL 0445093   DLC

Löpelmann, Martin, 1891–   ed.
... Die **Liederhandschrift** des cardinals de Rohan (xv. jahrh.) Nach der Berliner hs. Hamilton 674, hrsg. von Martin Löpelmann. Göttingen, Gedruckt für die Gesellschaft für romanische literatur, 1923.

138
L824m   **Löpelmann, Martin, 1891–**
1941   **Menschliche Mimik**; psychologische Betrachtungen mimischer Vorgänge in der Natur und in der Kunst, von M. Löpelmann unter Mitwirkung von Th. Wohlrath. Berlin, Holle (1941)
232p. illus. 25cm.

Includes bibliographies.

1. Physiognomy. 2. Expression. 3. Gesture
II. Title.   I. Wohlrath, Th
jt.auth.

NL 0445095   KU

RC489
P7L6   Löpelmann, Martin, 1891–
Menschliche Mimik; psychologische Betrachtungen mimischer Vorgänge in der Natur und in der Kunst, von Martin Löpelmann unter mitwirkung von Th. Wohlrath. Berlin, Holle (1943)
232 p. illus. 25cm.

1. Psychodrama. 2. Mime. I. Title.

NL 0445096   GU

Löpelmann, Martin, ed.
... La **petite** bovrgeoize, poème satirique de l'an 1610. Strasbourg, J. H. E. Heitz (Heitz & Mündel); New-York, G. E. Stechert & co; (etc., etc., 1914?)

398.21
L88r   Löpelmann, Martin, 1891–
Russische Märchen nach den Einzelausgaben der Kaiserlichen Druckerei in St. Petersburg aus den Jahren 1901–03. Mit farbigen Zeichnungen von Iwan J. Bilibin. Hrsg. von Martin Löpelmann.   Berlin, Deutsche Buchgemeinschaft (1937?)
159p. mounted col.illus. 25cm.

1. Fairy tales. 2. Tales, Russian.

NL 0445098   IU

398.209498
L825s   Löpelmann, Martin, 1891–
Sagen und Märchen der Rumänen. Leipzig Armanen, 1937.
132 p. 23 cm.
Contents.—Märchen und Sagen.—Lieder.
Anmerkungen: p. 128–(133)
On spine and cover: Aus der Volksdischtung der Macedonischen Rumänen.
1. Folklore - Macedonia. 2. Folklore - Rumania. 3. Legends Macedonia. 4. Legends Rumania. 5. Folk tales. I. Title.

NL 0445099   TNJ DLC-P4 WaU

Löpelmann, Martin, 1891–   ed.
Wege und Ziele der Kindererziehung unserer Zeit. In Verbindung mit berufenen Fachleuten des Erziehungswesens hrsg. Mit 28 Bildern und 2 Zeichnungen. Leipzig, Hesse & Becker (1936)
340 p. illus., plates. 25 cm.

1. Education of children. 2. Educational psychology. 3. Children, Abnormal and backward. I. Title.
LB1025.L83 1936   372   A F 48–2130*
Teachers College Library   Columbia Univ.
for Library of Congress   (1)†

NL 0445100   NNC-T MH DLC

Löpelmann, Martin, 1891–   ed.
Wege und ziele der kindererziehung unserer zeit; in verbindung mit berufenen fachleuten des erziehungswesens herausgegeben von dr. Martin Löpelmann ... Mit 28 bildern und 2 zeichnungen. Leipzig, Hesse & Becker (1936)
340 p., 1 l. incl. plates, diagrs. 25ᶜᵐ.
"2. auflage."

1. Education of children. 2. Education—Germany. I. Title.
Library of Congress   LA724.L6   42–5845
                        (2)   372

NL 0445101   DLC MH CU CoFS NbU

LB1025   **Löpelmann, Martin, 1891–**   ed.
L68   **Wege und Ziele der Kindererziehung unserer Zeit, in Verbindung mit berufenen Fachleuten des Erziehungswesens.** (3. Aufl.) Leipzig, Hesse & Becker (194–)
340 p. illus.,plates. 25 cm.

1. Education of children. 2. Educational psychology. 3. Children, Abnormal and backward.

NL 0445102   CU IaU

Löpelmann, Martin, 1891–   ed.
Wege und Ziele der Kindererziehung unserer Zeit, in Verbindung mit berufenen Fachleuten des Erziehungswesens hrsg. (2., veränderte Aufl.) Leipzig, Hesse & Becker (1943)
330 p. illus., plates. 25 cm.

1. Education of children. 2. Educational psychology. 3. Children, Abnormal and backward. I. Title.
LB1025.L83 1943   372   48–33609*

NL 0445103   DLC OCU CtY IaU

LÖPELMANN, Martin, 1891–
. Das weichnachtslied der Franzosen und der übrigen romanischen völker. Inaug.-diss., Berlin, [Erlangen? Junge & sohn, 1913?]

"Bibliographie", pp. [5]–17.
"Lebenslauf", at end.
"Sonderabdruck aus Romanische forschungen, Bd. XXXIII, 2".

NL 0445104   MH CtY

Loepelmann, Martin, 1861–   *4682.6.33
Das Weihnachtslied der Franzosen und der übrigen romanischen Völker.
(In Romanische Forschungen. Band 33, pp. 489-616. Erlangen. 1914.)
Bibliographie, pp. 602–614.

—175 — France. Lit. Hist. — Romance .iterature. Hist. — Christmas carols and hymns.

NL 0445105   MB

VOLUME 338

Loeper, Alfhild von, 1911–
Königshorst im havelländischen Luch, der Aufbau eines Neubauerndorfes. Würzburg, 1941.

74 p. 21 cm.

Inaug.-Diss.—Berlin.
Vita.

1. Konigshorst, Ger.

HD660.K6L6   50–49957

NL   0445106   DLC CtY NIC

Löper, C. F., respondent.
De iure reluendi feudum legitime oppignoratum
see under   Böhmer, Georg Ludwig, 1715–1797, praeses.

Löper, Carl.
Die Rheinschifffahrt Strassburgs in früherer Zeit und die Strassburger Schiffleut-Zunft. Nach archivalischen und anderen Quellen bearbeitet von Carl Löper. . . . Nebst einer einleitenden Abhandlung: Das Zunftwesen und die Stadtverfassung der alten Reichsstadt Strassburg von E. Trauttwein von Belle, . . . Strassburg, K. J. Trübner, 1877.
viii, 310 p. 21½cm.

NL   0445108   ICJ

Löper, Carl.
Zur Geschichte des Verkehrs in Elsass-Lothringen mit besonderer Berücksichtigung der Schifffahrt, des Post-, Eisenbahn- und Telegraphenwesens nach archivalischen und anderen Quellen nebst 32 auf das Verkehrsleben bezüglichen Urkunden aus der Zeit von 1350 bis 1779, von Carl Löper. Strassburg, K. J. Trübner, 1873.
[4], 288 p. 20½cm.

NL   0445109   ICJ

Loeper (Carolus Gustavus). *De tracheotomia.
16 pp. 8°. Halis Sax., typ. Ploetzianis, 1857.

NL   0445110   DNLM

Loeper (F.) *Beiträge zür pathologischen Anatomie der Lymphdrüsen. 39 pp. 8°. Würzburg, C. J. Becker, 1856.

NL   0445111   DNLM

Loeper (Fr. Guilelmus). *De ovariorum morbis. 2 p. l., 27 pp., 1 l. 8°. Bonna, Baaden, 1840. [P., v. 579.]

NL   0445112   DNLM

HD9013
.5
.D6
Loeper, H. F. von, joint comp.

Dommaschk, Heinz, comp.
Kriegsernährungswirtschaft; systematisches erläuterungswerk der verbrauchsregelungsvorschriften, von oberreigierungsrat dr. Heinz Dommaschk ... unter mitwirkung von regierungsrat von Loeper ... Berlin, Deutsche verlagsgesellschaft m. b. h. [1942–

PT
2424
.L634
A87
Loeper, Hermann von
Aus den Tagen der Jungend; Gedichte.
Landsberg, Volger u. Klein, 1850.
vii, 132p. 14cm.

NL   0445114   TNJ

Loeper, Hugo von.
Die aufbringung der mittel der deutschen invalidenversicherung ... München, J. Schweitzer (A. Sellier) 1903.
2 p. l., 50 p. incl. tables. 25ᶜᵐ.

Inaug.-diss.—Tübingen.

1. Insurance, State and compulsory—Germany. 2. Insurance, Health. I. Title: Invalidenversicherung.
6–11775
Library of Congress   HD7106.G3L7

NL   0445115   DLC

Loeper, Hugo von.
Die Versicherung der Arbeiter-Witwen und -Waisen in Deutschland. Von Dr. H. von Loeper ... Berlin, C. Heymann, 1907.
vii, 176 p. 25½ᶜᵐ.
Bibliographical foot-notes.

NL   0445116   ICJ IU MH NN

Loeper, Jacques, 1913–
... Les sécretions internes du cancer du sein ... Paris, Jouve & cⁱᵉ, 1943.
156 p. vi pl., diagrs. 24ᶜᵐ.
Thèse—Univ. de Paris.
"Bibliographie": p. [149]–156.

1. Breast—Cancer.
RG498.L6   618.19   Med 46–102

NL   0445117   DLC MnU NNC DNLM

Loeper, Jacques, 1913–
Traitement de l'athérosclérose; bases physiopathologiques et expérimentales. Paris, G. Doin, 1955.
184 p. illus. 25 cm. (Bibliothèque de thérapeutique médicale)
Includes bibliography.

1. Arteriosclerosis.
RC692.L6   55–41324 ‡

NL   0445118   DLC ICJ DNLM

Löper, Joachim Wilhelm, respondent.
... De jure nocendi aliis ...
see under   Cocceji, Heinrich von, 1644–1719, praeses.

Loeper, Johann Daniel, respondent
... De privilegiis miserabilium personarum ratione fori...
see under   Beier, Adrian, 1634–1712, praeses.

Loeper, Johann Ludwig Gustav von, 1822–1891.
Briefe Goethe's an Sophie von La Roche und Bettina Brentano ...
see under   Goethe, Johann Wolfgang von, 1749–1832.
Correspondence.

Loeper, Johann Ludwig Gustav von, 1822–1891.
Faust. Eine Tragödie
see under   Goethe, Johann Wolfgang von, 1749–1832. Faust. Parts I and II.

Loeper, Johann Ludwig Gustav von, 1822–1891.
Gesang der lieblichen Geister in der Wüste
see under   Goethe, Johann Wolfgang von, 1749–1832.
Miscellany

Loeper, Johann Ludwig Gustav von, 1822–1891, ed.

Goethe, Johann Wolfgang von, 1749–1832.
Goethe's werke. Nach den vorzüglichsten quellen rev. ausg. ... Berlin, G. Hempel [1879]

Loeper, Johann Ludwig Gustav von, 1822–1891.
West-östlicher divan
see under   Goethe, Johann Wolfgang von, 1749–1832.

Loeper, Johann Ludwig Gustav von, 1822–1891.
Zu den Quellen Goethischer Gedichte und Sprüche.
(*In* Archiv für Litteraturgeschichte. Vol. 3, pp. 488–494. Leipzig. 1874.)

E1898 — Goethe, Johann Wolfgang von, 1749–1832.

NL   0445126   MB

Loeper, Johann Ludwig Gustav von, 1822–1891.
Zu Goethe's Gedichten.
(*In* Archiv für Litteraturgeschichte. Vol. 2, pp. 520–525. Leipzig. 1872.)

E1898 — Goethe, Johann Wolfgang von, 1749–1832.

NL   0445127   MB

Loeper, Johann Ludwig Gustav von, 1822–1891.
Zu Goethe's Uebersetzungen aus fremden Sprachen.
(*In* Archiv für Litteraturgeschichte. Vol. 2, pp. 525–527. Leipzig. 1872.)

E1898 — Goethe, Johann Wolfgang von, 1749–1832.

NL   0445128   MB

Loeper, Karl Friedrich, respondent.
De iure reluendi feudum legitime oppignoratum ...
see under   Böhmer, Georg Ludwig, 1715–1797, praeses.

VOLUME 338

Loeper, Maurice, 1875–
　　Aux confins de la dyspepsie, par Maurice Loeper ... Paris, Masson et cᴵᵉ, 1940.
　　vi, 307, ₁1₎ p. illus., diagrs. 24ᵐᵐ.

　　1. Dyspepsia. ɪ. Title.
　　　　　　　　　　　　　　　　　　　　　　45–26606
　　Library of Congress　　　RC826.L6
　　　　₍2₎　　　　　　　　　　　　　　　　　　　616.33

NL 0445130　　DLC DNLM IU ICJ

RM663
.C45
　　Loeper, Maurice, 1875–
　　　... Chimiothérapie; sous la direction de M. Loeper, par R. Hazard, L. Justin-Besançon, R. Legroux ₍etc.₎ ... Paris, Masson et cᵉ, 1942.

Loeper, Maurice, 1875–
　　... De la sémiologie à la thérapeutique. Paris, Doin & cᴵᵉ, 1938.
　　2 p. l., ₍9₎–806, ₍2₎ p. 25½ᵐᵐ.
　　Illustration on t.-p.

　　1. Semiology. 2. Therapeutics. ɪ. Title.
　　Library of Congress　　　RC69.L64　　　39–12756
　　Copyright A—Foreign　　　40082
　　　　₍2₎　　　　　　　　　　　　　　　　　　　616.075

NL 0445132　　DLC

Loeper, Maurice, 1875–
　　Dujardin. Formulario práctico de terapéutica y de farmacología, por M. Loeper ₍y₎ Ch. Michel. 33. ed. española del antiguo formulario de Dujardin, Yvon y Gilbert Michel, corr. por Angel Ortega Díez. Madrid, Bailly-Bailliere, 1941.
　　1089 p. 15 cm.
　　1. Medicine—Formulae, receipts, prescriptions. 2. Pharmacy. 3. Pharmacology. ɪ. Michel, Charles H., joint author. ɪɪ. Dujardin-Beaumetz, Georges Octave, 1833–1895. ɪɪɪ. Ortega y Díez, Angel.
　　　　　　　　　　　　　Full name: Maurice René Loeper.
　　RS125.L7515　1941　　615.13　　　49–32179*

NL 0445133　　DLC

Loeper, Maurice, 1875–
　　Dujardin Formulario práctico de terapéutica y de farmacología, por M. Loeper ... ₍y₎ Ch. Michel ... 34. ed. española del antiguo formulario de Dujardin, Yvon et Gilbert, Michel, corr. por ... Angel Ortega Díez. Madrid, Bailly-Baillière, 1944.
　　24, 1089 p. 15½ᵐ.
　　Translation of: Formulaire pratique de thérapeutique et de pharmacologie.
　　1. Medicine—Formulae, receipts, prescriptions. ₍1. Formularies₎ 2. Therapeutics. ɪ. Michel, Charles H., joint author. ɪɪ. Dujardin-Beaumetz, George Octave, 1833–1895. ɪɪɪ. Yvon, Paul, 1848– ɪᵥ. Gilbert, Augustin Nicolas, 1858–1927. ᵥ. Ortega y Díez, Angel.
　　　　　　　　　　　　　　　　　　　　Med 46–137
　　U. S. Army medical library　　[WB742L825f 1944]
　　　for Library of Congress

NL 0445134　　DNLM

Loeper, Maurice, 1875–
　　Foie, glandes endocrines et nutrition. Paris, Masson, 1931.
　　377p. illus.　　(Thérapeutique médicale, iii)

NL 0445135　　ICRL DLC

Loeper, Maurice, 1875–
　　Formulaire pratique de thérapeutique et de pharmacologie, par M. Loeper ... et Ch. Michel ... Ancien formulaire de Dujardin-Beaumetz—Yvon et Gilbert—Michel. 34. éd., conforme au Codex 1937 et aux récents décrets ministériels. Paris, G. Doin & cᴵᵉ, 1938.
　　2 p. l., 2 p., 2 l., xlviii, 1030 p. 16ᵐ.
　　1. Medicine—Formulae, receipts, prescriptions. 2. Pharmacy. 3. Pharmacology. ɪ. Michel, Charles H., joint author. ɪɪ. Dujardin-Beaumetz, Georges Octave, 1833–1895. ɪɪɪ. Yvon, Paul, 1848– ɪᵥ. Gilbert, Augustin Nicolas, 1858–1927. ᵥ. Title.
　　　　　　　　　　　　　₍Full name: Maurice René Loeper₎
　　　　　　　　　　　　　　　　　　　　　39–12757
　　Library of Congress　　　RS125.L75　1938
　　Copyright A—Foreign　　　39061
　　　　₍2₎　　　　　　　　　　　　　　　　　　615.13

NL 0445136　　DLC

Loeper, Maurice, 1875–
　　Formulaire pratique de thérapeutique et de pharmacologie, par M. Loeper ... et A. Lesure ... Ancien formulaire de Dujardin-Beaumetz—Yvon et Gilbert—Michel. 35. éd., conforme au Codex 1937 et aux récentes lois et décrets ministériels. Paris, Doin, 1945.
　　lxix, 1098 p. 16ᵐ.
　　1. Medicine—Formulae, receipts, prescriptions. ₍1. Formularies₎ 2. ₍Therapeutics₎ 3. ₍Pharmacy₎ 4. ₍Pharmacology₎ ɪ. Lesure, André, joint author. ɪɪ. Michel, Charles H., joint author. ɪɪɪ. Dujardin-Beaumetz, Georges Octave, 1833–1895. ɪᵥ. Yvon, Paul, 1848– ᵥ. Gilbert, Augustin Nicolas, 1858–1927.
　　RS125.L75　1945　　　615.13　　　Med 46–181
　　U. S. Army medical library　　[WB742L825f 1945]
　　　for Library of Congress　　₍3₎†

NL 0445137　　DNLM DLC

Loeper, Maurice, 1875–
　　Formulaire pratique de thérapeutique et de pharmacologie, par M. Loeper et A. Lesure. Ancien formulaire de Dujardin-Beaumetz, Yvon et Gilbert—Michel. 36. éd., conforme au Codex 1937 et aux récents lois et décrets ministériels. Paris, G. Doin, 1948.
　　lxxv, 1109 p. 16 cm.
　　1. Medicine—Formulae, receipts, prescriptions. 2. Pharmacy. 3. Pharmacology. ɪ. Lesure, André, 1878– joint author. ɪɪ. Dujardin-Beaumetz, Georges Octave, 1833–1895. ɪɪɪ. Title.
　　　　　　　　　　　　　Full name: Maurice René Loeper.
　　RS125.L75　1948　　　615.13　　　48–25538*

NL 0445138　　DLC

Loeper, Maurice, 1875–
　　Formulaire pratique de thérapeutique et de pharmacologie, par M. Loeper et J. Lesure. Ancien formulaire de Dujardin-Beaumetz. 37. éd., conforme au Codex 1949 et aux récents lois et décrets ministériels. Paris, G. Doin, 1955.
　　1360 p. 17 cm.
　　1. Medicine—Formulae, receipts, prescriptions. 2. Pharmacy. 3. Pharmacology. ɪ. Lesure, Jean, 1911– joint author. ɪɪ. Dujardin-Beaumetz, Georges Octave, 1833–1895. ɪɪɪ. Title.
　　　　　　　　　　　　　Full name: Maurice René Loeper.
　　RS125.L75　1955　　　　　　　55–41332

NL 0445139　　DLC ICJ DNLM

Loeper, Maurice, 1875–
　　... La goutte et sa cure hydro-minérale
　　see under title

Loeper, Maurice, 1875–
　　Les hépatites. Paris, Masson, 1937.
　　vi, 262 p. illus. 25cm.

　　Bibliographical footnotes.

　　1. Hepatitis, Infectious. 2. Liver-Diseases. ɪ. Title.

NL 0445141　　NNC-M DNLM

Loeper, Maurice, 1875–
　　Hépatites rares ... Paris, Masson, 1946.
　　214, ₍1₎ p. illus. 24½ᵐ.

　　1. Liver—Diseases. ɪ. Title.
　　　　　　　　　　　　　　　　　　　Med 47–874
　　U. S. Army medical library　　[WI 940L825h 1946]
　　　for Library of Congress　　₍2₎

NL 0445142　　DNLM ICJ ICU

Loeper, Maurice, 1875–
　　Histoire de la sécrétion gastrique. Paris, Masson, 1924.
　　120, 47, ₍1₎ p. (p. ₍1₎ advertisement) illus. (incl. ports.) 23cm.

　　1. Gastric juice. 2. Digestion - Physiology.

NL 0445143　　KU-M CtY

Loeper, Maurice, 1875–　　ed.
　　Intoxications et carences alimentaires, par Maurice Loeper ... Paris, Masson et cᴵᵉ, 1938.
　　viii, 259, ₍1₎ p. illus., diagr. 25ᵐᵐ.
　　Includes bibliographies.
　　Contents.—Loeper, M. L'hypersensibilité digestive.—Bioy, E. Insuffisances sécrétoires et résidus alimentaires.—Marchal, G. La défense et la protection du tube digestif.—Perrault, M. Les corps toxiques du milieu intestinal.—Duchon, L. Les microbes du tube digestif, leur élimination urinaire.—Lesure, A. Polypeptides et acides aminés de l'organisme (caractérisation et méthodes de dosages)—Gilbrin, E. Les défaillances hépatiques.—Cottet, J. Le foie malade
　　et la carence en vitamine C.—Lemaire, A. & Parrot, J. L. Le milieu humoral et les troubles digestifs.—Varay, A. L'oxalurie et l'oxalémie.—Parrot, J. L. L'équivalent histaminique des milieux organiques.—Soulié, P. Les anémies des entéritiques.—Garcin, R. Troubles vasculaires et nerveux d'origine digestive.—Degos, R. Les réactions cutanées d'origine digestive.—Turpin, R. Les effets des avitaminoses sur l'appareil digestif.—Debray, M. Traitement local et général de l'insuffisance digestive.

NL 0445145　　ICJ DNLM

Loeper, Maurice, 1875–
　　Leçons de pathologie digestive. ... Par M. Loeper, ... Paris, Masson et cᴵᵉ, 1912–1919.
　　Library has vol. 2, 4. 23ᵐᵐ.
　　Bibliographical foot-notes.

NL 0445146　　ICJ PPC

Loeper, Maurice, 1875–
　　Leçons de pathologie digestive ... par M. Loeper ... Paris, Masson et cᴵᵉ, 1922–
　　v. illus., tables, charts. 23ᵐᵐ.

　　1. Digestive organs—Diseases.　　　22–20359
　　Library of Congress　　　RC801.L6

NL 0445147　　DLC MiU

WI
100
L825L
1914
　　LOEPER, Maurice, 1875–
　　　Leçons de pathologie digestive. 3. sér. Paris, Masson, 1914.
　　　vi, 317 p. illus.

NL 0445148　　DNLM

VOLUME 338

WI
100
L825L
1919
LOEPER, Maurice, 1875–
Leçons de pathologie digestive. 4. sér.
Paris, Masson, 1919.
vii, 298 p. illus.

NL 0445149   DNLM ICJ

Loeper, Maurice, 1875–
Maladies du tube digestif. Avec la collaboration
du André Lemaire.   Paris, Masson, 1930.
vii, 369 p.   Illus.   25 cm.   (Thérapeutique
Médical, No. 1)

NL 0445150   MBCo DNLM

Loeper, Maurice, 1875–
... Maladies infectieuses et parasitaires, par M. Loeper avec
la collaboration de R. Turpin et de mm. Abrami, Bazy ... ₁et
autres₎   Paris, Masson & cⁱᵉ, 1935.
2 p. L. 414⁴⁵⁷⁄₈ diagrs. 25ᵐ.   (Thérapeutique médicale, IX)
At head of title: Chaire de thérapeutique de la Faculté de médecine
de Paris (pr. M. Loeper)
Bibliographical foot-notes.
1. Contagion and contagious diseases. ₁1. Infectious diseases₎
2. Parasites.   I. Turpin, Raymond Alexandre, 1895–
₁Full name: Maurice René Loeper₎
Agr 36–703
Library, U. S. Dept. of   Agriculture 448L82
Library of Congress   [RM101.T5   no.9]

NL 0445151   DNAL ICJ

Loeper (Maurice) [1875–   ].   * Mécanisme
régulateur de la composition du sang. 174 pp.
8°. Paris. 1902. No 191.

NL 0445152   DNLM

Loeper, Maurice, 1875–   ed.
Les médications du jour, sous la direction de
M. Loeper ₁et al.₎ Paris, Masson, 1949.
vi, 310 p.
At head of title: Institut de thérapeutique de
la faculté de médecine de Paris.
Includes bibliographies.

I. Title. 1. Drugs.

NL 0445153   ICJ DNLM PPSKF PPC

Loeper, Maurice, 1875–   ed.
... Peau, syphilis et cancer, par M. Loeper, G. Milian, L. Bory
... ₁et d'autres₎ Paris, Masson et cie., 1932.
vii, 408 p. 25ᵐ.   (Thérapeutique médicale. v)

I. Milian, Gaston, 1871–

NL 0445154   ICJ

Loeper, Maurice, 1875–
... Poumons et tuberculose par mm. M. Loeper,
L. Tanon, R. Turpin [et autres] ...   Paris, Masson
& cie, 1932.
2 p. l., 378 p.   incl. illus., plates, diagrs.
25.5 cm.   (Thérapeutique médicale, IV)
At head of title: Chaire de thérapeutique de la
Faculté de médecine de Paris (pr. M. Loeper)

NL 0445155   CtY-M

Loeper, Maurice, 1875–
... Précis d'anatomie pathologique...
see under
Achard, Charles, 1860–

RM666
.S9S6
Loeper, Maurice, 1875–
... Le Soufre, sous la direction de M. Loeper, par P.
Ameuille ₁etc.₎ ... Paris, Masson & cⁱᵉ, 1943.

Loeper, Maurice, 1875–
Le soufre en biologie et en thérapeutique, par M. Loeper ... &
L. Bory ... avec 4 figures dans le texte. Paris, G. Doin & cⁱᵉ,
1932.
3 p. l., ll, 341 p. illus., pl., diagrs. 24ᵐ.
Published 1931.
Bibliographical foot-notes.
1. Sulphur in the body. 2. Sulphur—Therapeutic use. 3. Mineral
waters, Sulphurous.   ı. *Bory, Louis, 1880–   joint author. ıı. Title.
₁Full name: Maurice René Loeper₎
32–4500
Library of Congress   QP535.S1L6
₁a45c₁   ₁612.014469₁   615.7

NL 0445158   DLC CtY NcD

Loeper, Maurice, 1875–
La spécificité chimique en sémiologie, par M. Loeper, A.
Lemaire, A. Lesure ₁etc.₎ ... Paris, Masson et cⁱᵉ, 1944.
2 p. l., 187, ₁2₁ p. 24½ᵐ.
"Bibliographie": p. ₁133₁–137. Bibliography at end of some of the
chapters.
1. Semiology. 2. Chemistry, Medical and pharmaceutical. ı. Lemaire, André, 1898–   joint author. ıı. Lesure, André, joint author.
ııı. Title.
RC69.L642   616.0756   Med 47–481

NL 0445159   DLC DNLM IU NN CtY

RM666
.S84S8
Loeper, Maurice, 1875–
... Sulfamidothérapie; sous la direction de M. Loeper ... ₁par₁
J. Cottet ₁et d'autres₁ Paris, Masson, 1944.

Loeper, Maurice, 1875–
... Thérapeutique médicale ...
Paris, Masson & cⁱᵉ, 1930–

RM103
.T45
Loeper, Maurice, 1875–
... Thérapeutiques associées (auxothérapie) sous la direction
de M. Loeper, par H. Bénard, H. Claude, A. Dognon ₁etc.₁ ...
Préface de A. Baudouin. Paris, Masson et cⁱᵉ, 1942.

Loeper, Maurice, 1875–
Traitement des lithiases renales, par Maurice Loeper et
Jean Cottet. Paris, G. Doin, 1955.
208 p. illus. 25 cm. (Bibliothèque de thérapeutique médicale)
Includes bibliography.
1. Calculi, Urinary. ı. Cottet, Jean Marie, 1905–   joint author.
ıı. Title.
Full name: Maurice René Loeper.
RC916.L6   55–43484 ‡

NL 0445163   DLC ICJ DNLM

Loeper, Maurice René
see
Loeper, Maurice, 1875–

Loeper (Mauritius). * De vitiis fabricæ primi-
tivæ intestini recti et orificii ani. vi, 7–36 pp.,
2 pl. 4°. Wirceburci, C. G. Becker, 1859.

NL 0445165   DNLM

Loeper, R.   No. 14 in *Cab.29.32.1
Das alte Athen.
— Leipzig. Koehler. 1905. 1 v. and 2 colored plates. Text: 26
pp. Illus. Plate. Map. 27 cm., in 8s. Colored plates: size, 21⅞
× 28½, 23 × 28¾ inches. Plans. Maps. [Tabulae quibus antiquitates Graecae et Romanae illustrantur. Tafel 14a, 14b.]

H6653 — Athens, Greece. Antiq. — Antiquities.

NL 0445166   MB

Loeper-Housselle, Frau Marie, 1837–1916, ed.
Die Lehrerin ... 1.–   jahrg.; ₁okt. 1884₁–
Leipzig und Berlin, B. G. Teubner; ₁etc., etc.₁ 1885–19

Loeper-Housselle, Marie, 1837– 1916.
Der Mattenbauer. Eine historische Erzählung aus dem
Elsass. Von Marie Loeper-Housselle. Gera: T. Hofmann, 1890.
101 p. 8°.

57285A. 1. Fiction (German).   2. Title.
N. Y. P. L.   October 6, 1922.

NL 0445168   NN InGo

Loepert, Arthur
Der eigentumsvorbehalt beim kauf nach gemeinem
recht und dem buergerlichen gesetzbuch.
Inaug. diss. Heidelberg, 1904 (Berlin)
Bibl.

NL 0445169   ICRL

Loepert, John: Das Plasma im Schmelz und seine Bedeutung für
den Zahn m. kurzer Berücks. d. Kariestheorie [Maschinenschrift.]
38, ııı S. m. Abb. 4°. — Auszug: Greifswald 1922: Adler. 4 S. 8°
Greifswald, Med. Diss. v. 31. Aug. 1922   [U 22.2815

NL 0445170   ICRL

Löpfe, Adolf.
... Über Rorschach'sche Formdeutversuche mit
10–13 järigen Knaben ... Zürich, 1925.
23 cm.
Inaug.-Diss. - Zürich.
"Zonderabdruck aus der Zeitschrift für angewandte
Psychologie, Bd. 26 (1925)"

NL 0445171   CtY DNLM

VOLUME 338

LOEPFE, Alfred.
Das (deutsche) aufgebot und die (schweizerische) verkundung; ein beitrag zum
eherecht. Borna-Leipzig,1907.

9+(1)+69+(1) p.
Inaug.-diss.,---Leipzig,

NL 0445172   MH-L ICRL

Loepfe, Alfred.
Die wortstellung im griechischen sprechsatz, erklärt an
stücken aus Platon und Menander ... von Alfred Loepfe.
Freiburg in der Schweiz, Paulusdruckerei, 1940.
1 p. l., v–vii, 147 p. 23ᶜᵐ.
Diss.—Fribourg.
"Literaturangaben": p. 145–147.

1. Greek language—Word order. 2. Plato. 3. Menander, of Athens.

Library of Congress   PA373.L6

42–31012

NL 0445173   DLC CtY NIC IU ICU

Löpfe, Dominikus, 1916–
Die Tugendlehre des heiligen Ambrosius. Sarnen
(Schweiz) Benediktiner Kollegium, 1951.
xi, 175 p. 24 cm.
Diss.—Fribourg.
"Literaturverzeichnis": p. viii–x.

1. Ambrosius, Saint, Bp. of Milan. 2. Virtue.   I. Title.

Catholic Univ. of   America. Library
for Library of Congress   (2)

A 52–5918

NL 0445174   DCU MH PLatS DLC-P4 NIC

Loepfe, Rolf, 1923–
Ungehorsam gegen amtliche Verfügungen, schweizerisches
Strafgesetzbuch Art. 292. Zürich, E. Lang, 1947.
111 p. 22 cm.
Diss.—Zürich.
"Literaturverzeichnis": p. 8–11.

1. Administrative law—Switzerland. 2. Criminal law—Switzerland.
I. Title.

48–26352*

NL 0445175   DLC CU-L

Löpfelmeyer (Joh. Nicolaus). *Docetur quod
medice vivere sit optime vivere, contra vulgarem
canonem: medice vivere est misere vivere. 36
pp., 2 l. sm. 4°. Hala Magdeb., typ. J. C. Hen-
delii, (1743)

NL 0445176   DNLM

Loepffé, Raymonde, tr.
PR6007
.E25R62
Deeping, Warwick, 1877–
... L'impasse des cordiers; roman traduit de l'anglais par
R. L. Genève, J.-H. Jeheber, s. a. (1942)

Loepke, Zillah Marshall.
The unseen commander, a novel by Zillah Marshall Loepke.
Moorestown, N. J., Zionsville, Ind., The Marshall company
(*1933)
vi, 295 p. 21ᶜᵐ.

I. Title.

Library of Congress   PZ3.L82397Un

33–21929

NL 0445178   DLC 00

Loepman, Carolus Petrus, respondent.
C. Jul. Caesaris de bello gallico...
see under Frigell, Anders, 1820–1897,
praeses.

Loepp (Hermann). * Ueber Einleitung der
künstlichen Frühgeburt. 29 pp. 8°. Tübingen,
H. Laupp, jr., 1886.

NL 0445180   DNLM

Loepp, Willy.
... Gegenseitige auswertung der augen- und röntgensymp-
tome bei der tumordiagnostik im sellabereich, von dr. Willy
Loepp. Mit 28 abbildungen auf 8 tafeln. Berlin, Verlag von
S. Karger, 1936.
2 p. l., 58 p. viii (2) 25½ᶜᵐ. (Abhandlungen aus der augenheilkunde
und ihren grenzgebieten. Beihefte zur Zeitschrift für augenheilkunde,
hrsg. von C. Behr und J. Meller. hft. 23)
"Aus der Röntgenabteilung der Krankenhauses der barmherzigkeit zu
Königsberg i. Pr. ... und der Augenklinik der Universität Königsberg
i. Pr."
1. Eye—Diseases and defects. 2. Brain—Tumors. 3. Pituitary fossa.
4. Diagnosis, Radioscopic.   I. Title.

A C 37–1152

Iowa. Univ. Library
for Library of Congress   (3)

NL 0445181   IaU

Loepp, Willy.
Röntgendiagnostik des Schädels, von Willy Loepp und
Reinhold Lorenz. Stuttgart, G. Thieme, 1954.
579 p. illus. 27 cm.
Includes bibliography.

1. Skull—Radiography.   I. Lorenz, Reinhold, 1908– joint
author. II. Title.
Full name: Willy Hermann Loepp.

RC386.5.L6

55–28557 ‡

NL 0445182   DLC CtY-M ICU PPC DNLM

Loepp, Willy Hermann,
Luxatio femoris centralis traumatica. Berlin 1913: Schu-
macher. 15 S. 8° ¶ Aus: Archiv f. klin. Chirurgie. Bd 102.
Halle, Med. Diss. v. 2. Dez. 1913, Ref. Beneke
(Geb. 22. Okt. 85 Jungfer; Wohnort: Tiegenhof; Staatsangeh.: Preußen; Vor-
bildung: G. Marienburg Reife 04; Studium: Greifswald 5, Leipzig 1, Frei-
burg 1, Halle 1, Freiburg 2 S.; Coll. 21. Juni 13; Approb. 1. Sept. 10.)
[U 13. 2051]

NL 0445183   ICRL MBCo MiU DNLM

RC815
K81
1918
Loeppen, Karl, 1888–
Beiträge zur diagnose und therapie gutartiger
oesophagusstrikturen. Fürstenwalde, Germany,
Richter, 1918.
32 p.

Inaug.-diss., Berlin.
"Literatur": p. 32.

1. Esophagus - Diseases.

NL 0445184   NNC-M

Løppenthin, Bernt Hartvig Ove Fabricius, 1904–
Fortegnelse over Danmarks fugle. Udg. af Dansk orni-
thologisk forening. København, B. Lunos bogtr., 1946.
121 p. 25 cm.

1. Birds—Denmark.

QL690.D3L6

53–16013 ‡

NL 0445185   DLC DI NIC LU PPAN CtY CU MnU MiU

Løppenthin, Bernt Hartvig Ove Fabricius, 1904–
... Systematic and biologic notes on the long-tailed skua,
Stercorarius longicaudus Vieill., by Bernt Løppenthin; with a
Danish summary. With 4 figures in the text. København,
C. A. Reitzel, 1943.
26 p. illus. (incl. diagr.) 28ᶜᵐ. (Meddelelser om Grønland, udgivne
af Kommissionen for videnskabelige undersøgelser i Grønland. Bd. 131,
nr. 12)
"Literature": p. (24)–26.

1. Stercorarius longicaudus.
Q115.D39 bd. 131,   nr. 12
(508) 599.42

Yale univ. Library
for Library of Congress   (3)†

A 46–5762

NL 0445186   CtY DLC MB PU-BZ TxU ViU

Løppenthin, Bernt Hartvig Ove Fabricius, 1904–
... Die vögel Nordostgrönlands zwischen 73° 00' und 75° 30'
N. br. Samt beobachtungsergebnissen von der dänischen God-
thaab-expedition 1930, von Bernt Løppenthin. Mit einer englischen zusammenfassung und übersicht über die vögel des
gebietes. 26 textfiguren und 1 karte. København, C. A. Reitzel, 1932.
127, (1) p. incl. illus., tables. fold. map. 28ᶜᵐ. (Meddelelser om Grønland, udgivne af Kommissionen for videnskabelige undersøgelser i Grønland, bd. 91, nr. 6)
"Literaturverzeichnis": p. (112)–116.
1. Birds—Greenland.   I. "Godthaab" expedition, 1930.

A 45–234

Yale univ. Library
for Library of Congress   (3)

NL 0445187   CtY MB ViU OCU

Loepper, Alfred.
Das Studium der Chemie nebst einem Anhange, enthaltend im
Auszuge die Prüfungsordnungen für Chemiker auf schweizer und
österreichischen Hochschulen mit deutscher Unterrichtssprache
und ein Verzeichnis der Universitäten und technischen Hochschulen des Deutschen Reichs, der deutschen Schweiz und
Deutsch-Österreichs. Von Alfred Loepper. Wien, Leipzig,
(etc.), A. Hartleben, 1903.
[8], 70 p. 19½ᶜᵐ. (On cover: Chemisch-technische Bibliothek, Band 262.)

NL 0445188   ICJ

Loeppert, Adam John, 1873–
Modernism and the Vatican, by Adam J. Loeppert, D. D.;
with an introduction by Bishop William F. McDowell, D. D.
Cincinnati, Jennings and Graham; New York, Eaton and
Mains (*1912)
324 p. 19½ᶜᵐ.

1. Modernism—Catholic church.   I. Title.

12–20650

Library of Congress   BX1396.L6

NL 0445189   DLC TxU OrSaW MnU PU IU

Loeppert, Richard Henry, 1914–
The activation of ammonia synthesis by means of alkali ions
... by Richard H. Loeppert ... (n. p., 1941)
cover-title, 221–234 p. diagrs. 22½ᶜᵐ.
Based on thesis (PH. D.)—University of Minnesota, 1940.
"By Geo. Glockler and R. H. Loeppert.
A reprint from Transactions of the Electrochemical society, v. 80, 1941,
with addition of cover having thesis note and Vita on p. (3)

1. Ammonia. 2. Alkalies. 3. Ions—Migration and velocity. 4. Electric discharges through gases.   I. Glockler, George, 1890– joint
author.

Library of Congress   QC711.L77

43–47790

NL 0445190   DLC

VOLUME 338

Loeppert, Theodor Arthur, 1903–
Die fortentwicklung der Bábí-bahá'í im
Westen ... Würzburg, K.Triltsch, 1933.
v.146 p.,1 ł.   3 pl.(incl.ports.) 22½cm.
Inaug.-diss.—Leipzig.
Lebenslauf.
"Literatur": p.137–146.

1.Bahaism.   2.'Abd al-Bahā ibn Bahā Allāh,1844–1921.

NL 0445191   MiU PU

Loeppert, Theodor Arthur, 1903–
Die Fortentwicklung der Bábí-Bahá'í im
Westen ... Würzburg, K. Triltsch, 1933.
v, 146 p.   illus., ports.   22.5 cm.
Bibliography: p. 137–146.

NL 0445192   NcD

Löpping, Josef,
Zur Symptomatologie und forensischen Be-
deutung der Amentia. Kiel 1916: Fiencke. 21 S. 8°
Kiel, Med. Diss. v. 10. April 1916, Ref. Siemerling
[Geb. 20. März 81 Legden i. W.; Wohnort: Kiel; Staatsangeh.: Preußen; Vor-
bildung: G. Koesfeld Reife 04; Studjum: Münster 6, Leipzig 3, Gießen 2 S.;
Coll. 12. Des. 13; Approb. 30. Febr. 11.]   [U 16. 1087

NL 0445193   ICRL CtY DNLM

Loepthien, Walter, editor.
Neuer Reisefuehrer durch die Schweiz, mit einem Verzeichnis der christlichen Hospize und Pensionen, sowie vieler alkohol-
freier Häuser. Meiringen: W. Loepthien Verlag, 1929.   280 p.
incl. tables.   illus., map, plates.   16°.

Most plates printed on both sides.
Preface signed: W. Loepthien.
Based upon "Führer durch die Schweiz für das christliche Publikum," edited by
Friedrich Ruch.— cf. Pref.

459771A. 1. Switzerland—Guidebooks,   1929.
N.Y.P.L.   April 18, 1930

NL 0445194   NN

[Loër, Dirk, d.1554]
*NC5   D Dionysii Carthvsiani, doctoris extatici
L824ó   vita, simul & operum eius fidissimus catalogus.
532d   Coloniae excudebat Iaspar Gennepius.
M.D.XXXII.
8°.   [104]p. 1 illus.   14.5cm.
Signatures: A-F⁸,G⁴.
Title within ornamental border.

NL 0445195   MH

Loera, Juan de Luna

see

Luna Loera, Juan de.

Loera y Chávez, Agustín, 1895–
Estampas provincianas. Ilus. de Alberto Beltrán. México, Editorial Cultura, 1953.
57 p. illus. 24 cm.
Contents.—La Calle del Obrador.—El tío Esteban.—Los Alato-
rres.—El mesón de don Romualdo.—La tía Marianita.—Don Trinidad.

I. Title.

PQ7297.L583E8   54–36807 ‡

NL 0445197   DLC PPiU CU NN TxU

Loera y Chávez, Agustín, 1895–
El Maestro; revista de cultura nacional ... t. 1–3; abril 1921–
1923. Mexico, Universidad nacional [1921–23]

G917.2   [LOERA Y CHÁVEZ, AGUSTÍN] 1895–
L824s   Spanish antecedents of Mexican culture in
the colonial period.   [n.p., 19--]
7 numb l. 28cm.

Caption title.
Reproduced from type-written copy.
Signed at end: Agustín Loera y Chávez.

1. Mexico - Civilization.

NL 0445199   TxU

Loera y Chávez, Agustín, 1895–
El viajero alucinado, crónicas de España ... Prólogo de
Alfonso Cravioto, maderas originales de Francisco Díaz de
León. México, Editorial Cultura, 1945.
187 p. 21 cm.
Impresiones de viaje que escribí hace veinte años y que fueron publi-
cadas en 'El Universal' de México, en 'La Prensa' de Santiago de Chile
y en 'Social' de la Habana."—p. 3.

1. Spain—Descr. & trav.   I. Title.

DP42.L6   914.6   47–26362*

NL 0445200   DLC IU PU

Loera y Chávez, Agustín, 1895–
Viñetas ilustres. Prólogo de J. M. González de Mendoza.
Litografías de Alberto Beltrán. México, Editorial Cultura,
1951.
xvi, 148 p. ports. 24 cm.
Contents.—Alfonso Cravioto.—Luis Cabrera.—Manuel M. Ponce.—
Pedro de Alba.—Juan Manuel Ruiz Esparza.—Luis R. Alarcón.—Al-
berto Garduño.—Alfonso Caso.—Alejandro Quijano.—Jorge Enciso.—
Lorenzo L. Hernández. — Ignacio López Bancalari. — Juvencio
Ramírez.—Manuel Toussaint.

1. Mexico—Biog.   I. Title.

CT556.L6   920.072   51–30926

NL 0445201   DLC CU-B GU NN CU TxU

Lörch, Ph   Jakob.
Die Flora des Hohenzollers und seiner nächsten Umgebung,
von Ph. J. Lörch. I.–III. Teil ... Hechingen, Ribler'sche Hofbuchdruckerei, R. Kleinmaier, 1890–1892.
3 vol. in 1. 20½cm.
Paged continuously.
Programm—Königl. Höhere Bürgerschule zu Hechingen.

NL 0445202   ICJ MH

Loereh (Wilhelm) [1877–   ]. *Die Tuberku-
lose des Harn- und Geschlechtsapparates beim
Weibe. 88 pp. 8°. München, Kastner &
Callwey, 1904.

NL 0445203   DNLM

Lörcher, Adolf, 1878–
Bericht über die literatur zu Ciceros philosophischen schriften aus den jahren 1902–1911, von A. Lörcher ...
(In Jahresbericht über die fortschritte der klassischen altertumswissenschaft ... 1913. Leipzig, 1913. 22ᶜᵐ. 162. bd. (41. jahrg., 2. abt.)
p. [1]–153)

1. Cicero, Marcus Tullius. Opera philosophica—Bibl.
A 42–2560
Rochester. Univ. Library
for Library of Congress   [PA3.J3 bd. 162]
[2]   (880.5)

NL 0445204   NRU

Lörcher, Adolf, 1878–
Bericht über die literatur zu Ciceros philosophischen
schriften aus den jahren 1912–1921. Von A. Lörcher ...
(In Jahresbericht über die fortschritte der klassischen altertumswissenschaft ... 1924, 1926. Leipzig, 1924–26. 23ᶜᵐ. 200. bd. (50.
jahrg., 2. abt.) p. [71]–165; 204. bd. (51. jahrg., 2. abt.) p. [59]–154;
208. bd. (52. jahrg., 2. abt.) p. [23]–66)

1. Cicero, Marcus Tullius. Opera philosophica—Bibl.
A 42–2683
Rochester. Univ. Library
for Library of Congress   [PA3.J3 bd. 200, etc.]
[2]   (880.5)

NL 0445205   NRU

Lörcher, Adolf, 1878–
Bericht über die literatur zu Ciceros philosophischen
schriften aus den jahren 1922–1926. Von Adolf Lörcher ...
(In Jahresbericht über die fortschritte der klassischen altertumswissenschaft ... 1932. Leipzig, 1932. 22ᶜᵐ. 235. bd. (58. jahrg.,
2. abt.) p. [1]–98)

1. Cicero, Marcus Tullius. Opera philosophica—Bibl.
A 42–2788
Rochester. Univ. Library
for Library of Congress   [PA3.J3 bd. 235]
(880.5)

NL 0445206   NRU

Lörcher, Adolf, 1878–
De compositione et fonte libri Ciceronis, qui est
De fato ... Halis Saxonum, E. Karras, 1907.
2 p. l., 50 p. 22 cm.
Dissertatio inauguralis - Halle.
Vita.
Published also in Dissertationes philologicae
halenses ... vol. XVIII.

NL 0445207   CtY ICRL PU MH MiU NjP MdBJ

Lörcher, Adolf, 1878–
... De compositione et fonte libri Ciceronis, qui est De fato.
(In Halle. Universität. Dissertationes philologicae halenses ...
Halis Saxonum, 1907. 22½ᶜᵐ. vol. XVII. 2 l., p. [337]–384)
At head of title: Adolphus Loercher.
Issued also, in part, as the author's thesis, Halle.

1. Cicero, Marcus Tullius. De fato.
A C 37–1948
Yale univ. Library
for Library of Congress   [2]

NL 0445208   CtY NIC InU

Lörcher, Adolf, 1878–
878.5   Das Fremde und das Eigene in Ciceros Büchern
DL825 De finibus bonorum et malorum und den Academica.
Halle a. S., M. Niemeyer, 1911.
vii, 327 p. 25ᶜᵐ.
Includes bibliographical references.

1. Cicero, Marcus Tullius. De finibus bonorum et malorum. 2. Cicero, Marcus Tullius.
Academica.

NjR NNC NcU
NL 0445209   CSt MH IU CtY ICN ICU NIC WaU TxU CU

PA4037 Lörcher, Adolf, 1878–
.L8   Wie, wo, wann ist die Ilias entstanden? Von dr. Adolf
Lörcher. Halle (Saale) M. Niemeyer, 1920.
iv, 131, [1] p. 22½ᶜᵐ.

1. Homerus. Iliad.

NL 0445210   ICU NjP IU OU OCU PSt CU MnCS

VOLUME 338

Lörcher, Alfred.
Alfred Lörcher zum 80. Geburtstag gewidmet von seinen Freunden. ₁Stuttgart₁ W. Kohlhammer, 1955.
1 v. (chiefly plates, part col.) 41 cm.
Reproductions of Lörcher's drawings and sculptures.

I. Title.
NB588.L6K6   56-39288

NL 0445211   DLC MiDA NN MH

Lörcher, Alfred.
Der bildhauer Alfred Lörcher; einleitender text von P.O.Heim. Stuttgart, Krais, 1935.
23 p. 54 pl.

-I.Heim,P   - O

NL 0445212   NjP WaS NN

Lörcher, Alfred.
Der grabstein, von Alfred Lörcher ... Hrsg. im auftrag des Württembergischen landesgewerbeamts von der Staatlichen beratungsstelle für das baugewerbe in Stuttgart. 48 tafeln. Stuttgart, K. Wittwer, 1927.
₍7₎ p. illus., 48 pl., diagrs. 30½ᶜᵐ.
In portfolio.

1. Sepulchral monuments.   I. Württemberg. Beratungsstelle für das baugewerbe.
28-15105
Library of Congress   NB1870.L6

NL 0445213   DLC

Lörcher, Alfred.
Das Grabzeichen aus Holz. Stuttgart, J. Hoffmann ₍1941₎
₍1₎ l., 36 plates, diagrs. 30 cm.
Issued in portfolio.

1. Sepulchral monuments—Germany. I. Title.
NB1830.L6   48-41493*

NL 0445214   DLC

LÖRCHER, Christian Friedrich Eberhard.
Die wichtigsten Giftpflauzen Deutschlands. in Illumnirten Abbildugn.   mit Text. 3. Aufl. Ulm 1857.

NL 0445215   MH-G

Lörcher,   Erica (Grupe) 1875–
Drei bräute finden ihren weg; roman von Erica Grupe-Lörcher. Berlin, A. Weichert ₍1934₎
318 p. 19ᶜᵐ.

I. Title.
Library of Congress   PT2623.O38D7 1934   34-41097
Copyright A—Foreign   26084
₍2₎   833.91

NL 0445216   DLC

Lörcher, *Frau* **Erica (Grupe) 1875–**
Die drei rosen im Süden; eine erzählung für junge mädchen, von Erica Grupe-Lörcher; mit bildern von C. Benedek. Berlin, Meidinger's jugendschriften verlag g. m. b. h. ₍1935₎
189, ₍1₎ p. col. front., illus., col. plates. 20½ᶜᵐ.
"1.–5. tausend."

I. Title.
37-343
Library of Congress   PT2623.O38D75 1935
Copyright A—Foreign   33336
₍2₎   833.91

NL 0445217   DLC

Lörcher, Frau Erica (Gruppe) 1875–
Die ewige schmach! ein geiselnroman aus dem Elsass. Leipzig, Reclam [1919]
541 p. S. (Reclams universal bibliothek, nr. 5876–5880a)

NL 0445218   NcU

Lörcher, Erica(Grupe) [1875–
Der falsche Herzog. Leipzig: Friedrich Rothbarth₁, 19—?₁.
256 p. 12°.

NL 0445219   NN

Lörcher, Erica (Grupe) 1875–
Fern im Süd das schöne Spanien. Roman von Erica Grupe-Lörcher. Reutlingen, Ensslin & Laiblin [n.d.]
316p. 16cm. (Ensslins Romane; eine Sammlung guter Haus- und Familienromane. 98)

NL 0445220   IEN

Lörcher, *Frau* **Erica (Grupe) 1875–**
Die flucht ins glück; roman von Erica Grupe-Lörcher. Berlin, A. Weichert ₍*1934₎
317 p. 18½ᶜᵐ.

I. Title.
35-2118
Library of Congress   PT2623.O38F6 1934
Copyright A—Foreign   26475
₍2₎   833.91

NL 0445221   DLC

Lörcher, Erica (Grupe) 1875–
Das hohe Ziel, Roman. Dresden, F. Müller, 1943.
271 p. 21 cm.

I. Title.
PT2623.O38H6   A F 48-5303*
Wisconsin. Univ. Libr.
for Library of Congress   ₍1₎†

NL 0445222   WU IU NN CU DLC

4PT   **Lörcher, Erica (Grupe), 1875–**
Ger.   Im Schatten des Strassburger Münsters;
6532   geschichtliche Erzählungen. Buchschmuck und Deckenzeichnung von Fr. Greiner. 1. und 2. Aufl. Lahr in Baden, M. Schauenburg, 1918.
164 p.

(Deutsche Jugendbücherei "Heim und Herd", Bd. 27)

NL 0445223   DLC-P4

834L883 **Lörcher, Erica (Grupe) 1875–**
Op1909   Prinzessin Flunkerli. Originalmärchen in 5 Bildern. ₍Strassburg i. Els., Elsass-Lothringische Druckerei, 1909?₁
86p. 20cm.

NL 0445224   IU

Lörcher, Erica (Grupe) 1875–
Unter der Trikolore, aus den letzten Tagen des deutschen Strassburg. Roman von E. Grupe-Lörcher. Leipzig, P. List [1922]
303p. 18cm.

NL 0445225   IEN PPG

Wason   **Lörcher, Frau Erica (Gruppe) 1875–**
DS655   4000 Inseln im Ozean. Die
G89   Philippinen, das Land der Zukunft. Kassel, Karl Winter, 1949.
167 p. illus. 19cm.

1. Philippine Islands. I. Title.
II. Title: Die Philippinen, das Land der Zukunft.

NL 0445226   NIC

Lörcher, Erica (Gruppe) 1875–
Der Weg über den Vulkan, Roman. Dresden, F. Müller, 1944.
200 p. 21 cm.

I. Title.
PT2623.O38W4   A F 48-5304*
Wisconsin. Univ. Libr.
for Library of Congress   ₍1₎†

NL 0445227   WU ICU NbU MH OCl MB DLC

Lörcher,   Erica (Gruppe) 1875–
Der weg über den Vulkan, roman. Dresden, Muller, 1944. 200 p. 21cm.

Film reproduction. Negative.

NL 0445228   NN DLC CtY NNC

Lörcher (Gotthold) [1872–   ]. * Ueber den Einfluss von Salzen auf die Labwirkung. 32 pp. 8°. Tübingen. 1897.

NL 0445229   DNLM ICRL

Wason   **Lörcher, Jakob G.**
BV3415   Die Basler Mission in China. Von Jakob
E94   Lörcher. Basel, Verlag der Missionsbuchhandlung, 1882.
48 p. illus., map. 21cm.

No. 8 in vol. lettered Basel – Missionsgesellschaft (12 pamphlets)

1. Evangelische Missionsgesellschaft, Basel.

NL 0445230   NIC CtY

VOLUME 338

Loercher, Ulrich
Die Familie Lavenstein; ein Bild aus der Zeit der Gegenreformation. Calw, Verlag der Vereinsbuchhandlung, 1894

283 p. (Calwer Familienbibliothek, 32)

NL 0445231   MH

4PT   **Lörcher, Ulrich**
Ger-   Im Kampf ums Elsass; Erzählung.   Herborn,
2536   Buchhandlung des Nassauischen Colportagevereins,
1911.
206 p.

NL 0445232   DLC-P4

Lörcher, Ulrich.
Treu im Glauben; die Leiden der Evangelischen im Elsass,
nach alten Urkunden erzählt. Stuttgart, Quell-Verlag
[1929]
191 p. 20 cm. (Volks- und Heimatbücher)

1. Protestants in Alsace—Fiction.   I. Title.

PT2623.O383T7   53-51954 ‡

NL 0445233   DLC

4PT-   **Lörcher, Ulrich.**
47   Vogesenhelden; Volkserzählungen.   Stuttgart,
Holland und Josenhans, 1917.
190 p.

NL 0445234   DLC-P4

Lörcher, Ulrich.
Weihnachtslichter im Erdendunkel; Erzählungen. Mit
4 Originalbildern von Carl Schmauk. Stuttgart, Quell-Verlag [1928]
162 p. illus. 20 cm. (Volks- und Heimatbücher)

I. Title.

PT2623.O383W4   54-54398 ‡

NL 0445235   DLC OrP

LOERCIO, Clibeo, pseud.
Un sermón de Ipandro Acaico,[pseud.for Ignacio
Montes de Oca y Obregón.] n.p.,[187-?]

20 cm. pp.24.
Paper cover serves as title-page.
Signed:Clibeo Loercio.

NL 0445236   MH

Lördags-aftenblad for arbeidsklassen.
A87   1.-   aarg., 7. jan. 1860-
+L824   Christiania, J.C. Abelsted.
29 cm. weekly.

"Udgivet af Anthon Bang."
Ceased publication with 7. aarg., 1866?

1. Periodicals - Norway.   I. Bang, Anthon,
1809-1870.   ed.

NL 0445237   CtY

Lörenthey, Emerich,

    SEE

Lörenthey, Imré.

565.38   **Lörenthey, Imré.**
L88b   Beiträge zur Decapodenfauna des ungarischen
Tertiärs. Über die Brachyuren der palaeontologischen Sammlung des bayerischen Staates.
[Von] Emerich Lörenthey. [Budapest, 1898]
152p. 11 plates. 26cm.

Title from label mounted on cover.
"Editio separata e Természetrajzi füzetek,
vol. XXI, 1898."
In ms. on cover: Hommage de l'auteur.
Bibliographical footnotes.

NL 0445239   IU

Lörenthey, Imré.
Beiträge zur entwicklung des Eozäns und seiner fauna in
Nordalbanien, von Emerich Lörenthey. [Budapest, Buchdruckerei der Stadium a.-g., 1926.
20 p., 2 l. incl. illus., diagrs. 2 pl. 29ᶜᵐ. (Hungary. Földtani intézet; Mitteilungen aus dem jahrbuche der Kgl. ungarischen geologischen anstalt. xxv. bd., 1. hft.)
Bibliographical foot-notes.

1. Paleontology—Albania. 2. Paleontology—Eocene.   I. Title.
                                  G S 29-368
                [QE1.H95 bd. 25, hft. 1]
Library, U. S. Geological   Survey (534) B vol. 25, hft. 1

NL 0445240   DI-GS

Loerenthey, Imre.
Beiträge zur Fauna und stratigraphischen Lage der pannonischen Schichten in der Umgebung des Balatonsees. (Magyar
Földrajzi Társaság-Balaton Bizottsága. Resultate der wissenschaftlichen Erforschung des Balatonsees.   Wien, 1911.   4°.
Bd. 1, Teil 1.   Palæontologischer Anhang, Bd. 4, [part] 3.
215(1) p., 3 l., 3 pl.   illus.)

1. Palaeontology, Austria-Hungary.
N. Y. P. L.   November 5, 1913.

NL 0445241   NN

Lörenthey, Imré.
... Die fossilen dekapoden der länder der Ungarischen
krone. Budapestini, Edidit Institutum regni Hungariae geologicum, 1929.
[3]-420 p., 16 l. incl. illus. xvi pl., xii tab. (1 fold.) 31ᶜᵐ. (Geologica hungarica; fasciculi ad illustrandam notionem geologicam et palaeontologicam regni Hungariae. Ser. palaeontologica, fasc. 3)
At head of title: E. Lorenthey, K. Beurlen.
"Literaturverzeichnis": p. 19-25.

1. Crustacea, Fossil.   I. Beurlen, Karl, joint author.   II. Title.
                                    G S 30-207
Library, U. S. Geological   Survey (534) qG36 ser. Pal. fasc. 3

NL 0445242   DI-GS LU CU CLSU

Lörenthey, Imré.
563.12   Mikroskopische Untersuchungen der paleo-
L825   zoischen Gesteine.   [Wien, 189-]
1 p.l., [239]-304 p. illus. 28ᶜᵐ
"Separatabdruck aus dem Werke: 'Wissenschaftliche Ergebnisse der Reise des Grafen Béla
Széchenyi ir Ostasien.' III.Band. 'Die
Beschreibung des gesammelten Materials', IV.
Abtheilung."
Bibliographical footnotes.

1.Foraminifera, Fossil. 2.Paleontology -
China.

NL 0445243   CSt

Lörenthey, Imré.
... Die oberen pontischen sedimente und deren fauna
bei Szegzárd, Nagy-Mányok und Arpád. Von dr. Emerich Lörenthey. (Mit tafel iii-v.) [Budapest, Druck des
Franklin-verein, 1894]
90 p. 3 pl. 25½ᶜᵐ. (On cover: Mittheilungen aus dem Jahrbuche der
Kön. ungarischen geologischen anstalt. x. bd., 4. hft.)
"Edirt im januar 1894."
Each plate accompanied by leaf with descriptive letterpress.
"Literatur": p. 4-5.

1. Paleontology—Hungary.
                                  G S 12-468
Library, U. S. Geol.   survev   (534) B bd. 10, hft. 4

NL 0445244   DI-GS

Lörenthey, Imré.
... Die pontische stufe und deren fauna bei Nagy-Mányok im comitate Tolna, von dr. Emerich Lörenthey. Mit
tafel I.   Budapest, Buchdr. des Franklin-verein, 1890.
cover-title, 18 p., 1 l. pl., diagr. 25½ᶜᵐ. (Mittheilungen aus dem Jahrbuche der Kön. ungarischen geologischen anstalt. ix. bd., 2. hft.)
"Edirt im oktober 1890."
Numbered 4 in Inhalt to Mittheilungen, bd. IX.

1. Paleobotany—Hungary.
                                  G S 12-469
Library, U. S. Geol.   survey   (534) B bd. 9, hft. 2

NL 0445245   DI-GS

Lörer, Johann.
Novum instrumentum geometricum perfectum. Das
ist / Vollkomner vnd grundlicher bericht / alle weite /
breite / höhe vnnd tieffe / mit sonderbarem vortheil / als
mit einem eintzigen instrument / ohne ziffer vnd rechnung / gantz gewiss abzumessen. Mit 13. nohwendigen
[!] kupfferstucken / sampt einem register geziert vnd
erklärt. Allen liebhabern diser kunst zu sonderem gefallen / jetzund erstlich an tag gegeben. Durch Johann
Lörer / Burger vnd klein Vhrenmacher zu Basel. Getruckt zu Zürich / bey Johann Hardmeyer / 1616.
2 v. in 1. plates. 14½ x 18ᶜᵐ.
Titles within wide illustrated borders.
All plates except one have text on one side of leaf.
Date of imprint of v. 1 blurred. Prefaces dated 1616.
Vol. 2 has title: Planemetrische Beschreibung. Wie man mit vorbemelten
Instrument ... alle Statt / Gärten / Weyher vnd Landschafften ... in grund
legen soll. Mit ix, nothwendigen kupfferstucken ...
Bound in fragment of illuminated manuscript.
1. Mathematical instruments.

NL 0445247   MiU

---

838   **Lörges, Karl Robert, 1904-**
G860   Mimische Studien zu Franz Grillparzers Dramen,
L83   mit besonderer Berücksichtigung der Beziehungen
zwischen Wort und Gebärde. [Köln, 1929?]
32 p.
Inaug.-Diss.(Teildruck)--Cologne.
Vita.
"Die ganze Arbeit erscheint gleichzeitig als
Band 3 der Sammlung: Die Schaubühne,herausgegeben von Dr.Carl Niessen ... 1929."
1.Grillparzer,Franz,1791-1872.

NL 0445248   MiU OrU TxU NcD

PT   **Lörges, Karl Robert, 1904-**
2273   Mimische studien zu Franz Grillparzers
L82m   dramen, mit besonderer berücksichtigung
der beziehungen zwischen wort und gebärde ... Bonn, F.Klopp verlag g.m.b.h.,
1929.
114p. 23cm. (On verso of t.-p.: Die schaubühne; quellen und forschungen zur theatergeschichte, hrsg. von Carl Niessen. bd.3)
Imprint on cover: Emsdetten, H.u.J.Lechte.
"Literaturverzeichnis": p.[111]-114.
1.Grillparzer, Franz.   2. Drama - Technique.
3. Gesture. 4. Expression.   I. Title.

NL 0445249   NRU

VOLUME 338

Löri, Eduard.
Die durch anderweitige Erkrankungen bedingben Veranderungen des Rachens, des Kehlkopes und der Luftrohre. Stuttgart, Enke, 1885.
23ý p.

NL 0445250   PPC

894/5113   Lörinc, Péter
L872h   Hétköznapok, regény. Moviszad [sic]
            Testvériség-Egység, 1950.
            480 p. 21cm.

            1. Hungarian language--Text. I. Title.

NL 0445251   C DLC-P4 NN OC1

4DB   Lörinc, Péter.
Hung.-   A nagy pöri pör; birtok-kisajátitás és
75   aratósztrajkok Vajdaságban. Noviszad,
           Testvériség-Egység Könyvkiadóvállalat, 1950.
           103 p.

NL 0445252   DLC-P4

Lörincz, Alois Aladar de, 1901-
Ueber einen Fall von traumatischer subcutaner Berstungsruptur des Magens ... Würzburg, 1929.
Inaug.-Diss. - Würzburg.
Lebenslauf.
"Literaturverzeichnis": p. 19.

NL 0445253   CtY

Lörincz, Ferenc.
Adatok a tartósított hazai húskészitmények minőségi értékléséhez. ₍Budapest₎ Könnyüipari Kiadó, 1951.
118 p. diagr. 21 cm. (Az Országos Mezőgazdasági Ipari Kisérleti Intézet közleményei, 1.)
Includes bibliographies.

1. Food industry and trade—Hungary.   (Series: Hungary.
Országos Mezőgazdasági Ipari Kisérleti Intézet.   Az Országos Mezőgazdasági Ipari Kisérleti Intézet közleményei, 1)

HD9015.H82L6   65–56851

NL 0445254   DLC

Lörincz, Ferenc.
Az ancylostomiasis (bányász-aszály) kérdésének mai ál-lása Magyarországon (The ancylostomiasis problem in Hun-gary) Ács László ₍et al.₎ közreműködésével. Pécsett, Dunántúl Pécsi Egyetemi Könyvkiadó és Nyomda, 1935.
90 p. illus. 24 cm. (A M. Kir. Országos Közegészségügyi Intézet közleményei, 6, 1935)
Summary in English.
Includes bibliographies.

1. Hookworm disease. 2. Miners—Hungary.   (Series: Hungary.
Országos Közegészségügyi Intézet.   A. M. Kir. Országos Közegészségügyi Intézet közleményei, 6)

RC199.95.L6   61–55628

NL 0445255   DLC

Lörincz, Gyula, 1862-
A vegyes házasságok. Különös tekin-tettel Magyarországra. Irta Lörincz Gyula ... Nagyszombat, Winter Zs., 1890.

175, ₍1₎ p. 24½cm.

Bibliographical footnotes.

NL 0445256   MH-L

Lörincze, Lajos.
Földrajzineveink élete. Budapest, Néptudományi Intézet, 1947.
32 p. 23 cm. (A Magyar táj- és népismeret könyvtára, 9)
"Jegyzetek" (bibliographical) : p. 30–32.

1. Names, Geographical — Hungary.   2. Hungarian language—
Etymology—Names.   I. Title.   II. Series.

DB904.L6   79–287260

NL 0445257   DLC NNC CLU

PH   Lörincze, Lajos.
2745   A Magyar nyelvatlasz anyaggyüjtésének
L64   módszere. Budapest, Akadémiai Kiadó, 1955.
           81 p. illus., 1 fold. map. 24 cm.
           (A Magyar Nyelvtudományi Társaság kiadványai, 90. szám)
           Summary in German.

           1. Hungarian language - Dialects. I. Title.

NL 0445258   NBuU TxU InU

Lörincze, Lajos.
Nyelv és élet. Budapest, Müvelt Nép Könyvkiadó, 1953.
173 p. 21 cm.

1. Hungarian language—Idioms, corrections, errors.   I. Title.

PH2810.L6   55–19752 ‡

NL 0445259   DLC CLU NNC NN

Lörincze, Lajos   ed.
Nyelvmüvelésünk főbb kérdései; tanulmány-gyüjtemény. Szerkesztette Lörincze Lajos, munkatársak Deme László ₍et al.₎ Budapest, Akadémia Kiadó, 1953.
294 p. illus.

1. Hungarian language - Addresses, essays, lectures. I. Title.

NL 0445260   NNC DLC-P4 MH

302.9439   Lörincze, Lajos
N355   A Tolna-baranyal (volt bukovinai) székelyek
sz.3   névadási szokásaihoz. Budapest, Néptudományi
           Intézet, 1949.
           16 p. (Néprajzi tanulmányok 3)

           Reprint from Ethnographia-Népélet v. 59.
           Bibliographical footnotes.
           Summary in French: p. 15-16.

NL 0445261   NNC

WA   **LÖRINCZI, Ferencz, ed.**
L872v   Vezérkönyv a közegészségügyi
1882   szolgálat terén; orvosok gyógyszerészek,
           szülésznök, megyei, városi, községi
           tisztviselők, közegészségügyi bizottsági
           tagok használatára. Az 1876. XIV. t. cz.
           és a vele kapcsolatos kormányrendeletek
           alapján. Budapest ₍Neuer₎ 1882.
           332, vi p.

NL 0445262   DNLM

Lörinczy, Éva B
A Königsbergi töredék és szalagjai mint nyelvi emlék, irta B. Lörinczy Éva. Budapest, Akadémiai Kiadó, 1953.
224 p. illus. 21 cm. (Nyelvészeti tanulmányok, 3)

1. Königsberg. Staats- und Universitätsbibithek. Mss. (1194/a)
2. Hungarian language—Glossaries, vocabularies, etc.   I. Title.
(Series)

PH3194.K6L6   65–58021

NL 0445263   DLC CU NNC IU TxU NIC MH NN

Lörinczy, György, 1860-1941.
Aranykarikak; elbeszelesek a serdültebb ifjusag ssamara. Budapest, Singer, 1907.
₍144 ₎p.

NL 0445264   OC1

Lörinczy, György, 1860-
...A boldogság császárja. Falu Tamás. Nyolcvanas évek. Budapest: Singer és Wolfner irodalmi intézet r.-t., 1926. ₎ viii, 183, 144 p. illus. (ports.) 12°. (Magyar irómesterek; a Petőfi társaság jubiláris könyvei.)

467382A. I. Fiction, Hungarian.   I. Falu, Tamás, 1881-   : Nyolcvanas évek. II. Title: A boldogság   császárja.
N. Y. P. L.   May 7, 1930

NL 0445265   NN

Lörinczy, György, 1860-1941.
A boldogság császárja; regény. Budapest, Singer és Wolfner ₍c1927₎
viii, 185 p. port. (Magyar irómesterek; a Petőfi Társaság jubiláris könyvei)

NL 0445266   NNC WaS CLU

Lörinczy, György, 1860-1941.
Falusi potentatok.

NL 0445267   OC1

Lörinczy, György, 1860-1941.
Fekete rossak. Budapest, Singer es Wolfner, 1912.
[124p.]

NL 0445268   OC1

Lörinczy, György, 1860-1941,
Az igmándi bég. Budapest : Singer és Wolfner, 1911.   186 (1) p. illus. sq. 8°.

NL 0445269   NN

Lörinczy, György, 1860-1941.
A kók ember meg egyeb novellak. Budapest, Singer, 1918.
[143 p.]

NL 0445270   OC1

VOLUME 338

Lőrinczy, György, 1810-1941
A magam földjén.   Budapest: Singer es Wolfner, 1898.
189(1) p.   16°.

Az útszélről. Öt hold homok. Ivúr. A templom felé. Tíz rőf kanavász.
Konota szomszédék. A lepkék. A vasút. Vihar után. Az uri ember. Radnót.
Az utolsó áldozás. A fűzfavesszszők. A Virőkné tyúkjai. Felhők, sugarak.

NL 0445271   NN OC1

LŐRINCZY, GYÖRGY, 1860- 1941.
Utitarsaim   Budapest, Singer és Wolfner, 1912.
203 p.   20cm.

Film reproduction. Positive.

1. Essays, Hungarian.   I. Title.

NL 0445272   NN

W 4   LŐRINCZY, József
B89   A' vörhenyről.   Pesten, 1847.
1847   23 p.
         Ertekezés - Budapest.
         Added title page in Latin: De scarla-
         tina.

NL 0445273   DNLM

Lőringhoff, Bruno, baron von Freytag

see

Freytag-Lőringhoff, Bruno, baron von,
1912-

Loerke, Georg, 1888-
...Das Laecheln im Spiegel; Roman von Kopernikulus.
Riga: Baltischer Verlag, 1929.   162 p.   12°.   ("Riga am
Sonntag." Romanbibliothek. Bd. 10.)

512414A. 1. Fiction, German.   I. Title.
N. Y. P. L.   January 19, 1931

NL 0445275   NN

[Loerke, Georg] 1888-
Weltuntergang, Roman einer Menschheit, von Kopernikulus [pseud.] Leipzig, Koehler & Amelang [1928]
240 p. 19 cm.

I. Title.

PT2623.O385W4   28-24860 rev*

NL 0445276   DLC NN CtY

Loerke, Günther
Die geschichte der pfarrwitwenversorgung in
der evangelischen kirche der altpreussischen
union. ... Düsseldorf, 1936.   63 p.
     Inaug. Diss. - Erlangen, 1936.
     Literatur-Verzeichnis.

NL 0445277   ICRL

Loerke,   John J.
Bulman, A   D.
     Bulman-Loerke debate, Clintonville, Wisconsin. [An-
tigo, Wis., Berner bros. pub. co., '1914]

Loerke,   John J.
Bulman, A   D.
     The great debate (2d ed.) between A. D. Bulman ...
and Rev. J. J. Loerke ... [Portland, Or., The Arcady
press, 1917]

Loerke, Oskar, 1884-1941.
     Die Abschiedshand, letzte Gedichte.   [Berlin]
Suhrkamp, 1949.
     151 p.   21cm.

          InU TU NBuU WU OU MiU NRU IU
NL 0445280   CSt NcU IEN OCU NN CU CtY MH IU PBm

Loerke, Oskar, 1884-
Döblin, Alfred, 1878-
     Alfred Döblin im buch, zu haus, auf der strasse, vorgestellt
von Alfred Döblin und Oskar Loerke. Berlin, S. Fischer,
1928.

Loerke, Oskar, 1884-
Anton Bruckner, ein charakterbild von Oskar Loerke. Berlin, S. Fischer [1938]
     3 p. l., 9-292, [1] p., 1 l. 20ᶜᵐ.
     "Erste bis dritte auflage."
     "Notiz über die benutzte literatur": p. 291-[296]

     1. Bruckner, Anton, 1824-1896.
     Library of Congress   ML410.B88L52   39-296
     Copyright A—Foreign   40105
                                 [2]   927.8

NL 0445282   DLC INS ICU NjP

ML 410   LOERKE, OSKAR, 1884-1941
.B85 L8   Anton Bruckner; ein Charakterbild.   Berlin,
           Suhrkamp [1943]
           292 p.

           1. Bruckner, Anton, 1824-1896.

NL 0445283   InU

Loerke, Oskar, 1884-
     Atem der Erde; sieben Gedichtkreise.   Berlin: S. Fischer,
1930.   140 p.   8°.

NL 0445284   NN

PT   Loerke, Oskar, 1884-1941
2623   Atem der Erde; sieben Gedichtkreise.
.O39   Berlin, S. Fischer, 1930.
A9   135 p.   21 cm.

NL 0445285   WU NcU NN OC1 RPB MH IU

PT   Loerke, Oskar, 1884-1941
2623   Chimärenreiter; Novellen.   München,
O39   Roland-Verlag, 1919.
C5   58 p.   20cm.   (Die neue Reihe, Bd. 20)

NL 0445286   WU IEN MH OU

AC30   Loerke, Oskar, 1884-1941, ed.
D38
1953   Deutscher Geist; ein Lesebuch aus zwei Jahrhunderten.
             [Neue erweiterte Ausg.] Berlin, Suhrkamp Verlag [1953]

Hky   Loerke, Oskar, 1889-1941. Berlin, G.
L826   Franz Pfinz; Erzählung. Berlin, G.
F6   Fischer, 1909.
             141 p. 19 cm.

NL 0445288   CtY PU NNC MH

PT 2623   LOERKE, OSKAR, 1884-1941
.O39 A17   Gedichte. Berlin, S. Fischer, 1916.
1916   179 p.

NL 0445289   InU IU NNC MH

PT2623   Loerke, Oskar, 1884-1941.
.O39A17   Gedichte. [Auswahl und Nachwort von Hermann Kasack.
1954   Berlin, S. Fischer, 1954.
           119 p. 33 cm.

                                        A55-6064

Rochester. Univ. Libr.   PT2623
for Library of Congress   [a50b1]

          CU IEN OO PU OC1 TU DLC
NL 0445290   NRU TxU NBC OC1W OCU OU CtY MH NN IU

Loerke, Oskar, 1884-1941.
     Gedichte und Prosa. [Frankfurt, a.M.] Suhr-
kamp Verlag [n.d.]
     2v. 21cm.

NL 0445291   NcU

Loerke, Oskar, 1884-
... Das goldbergwerk, eine novelle. München
[etc.] Dreiländerverlag, 1919.
     36,[1] p. 16½cm. (Die pforte, bd.2)

NL 0445292   MiU NN InU

Loerke, Oskar, 1884-
Hausfreunde; charakterbilder, von Oskar Loerke. Berlin,
S. Fischer [1939]
     3 p. l., 9-434, [1] p., 2 l. 19ᶜᵐ.
     "Erste bis dritte auflage 1939."
     "Von Oskar Loerke erschienen früher": leaf at end.

     CONTENTS.—Vorbemerkung.—Hausfreunde.—Herders weltgebäude.—
Wächterin am tierparadies.—Renée Sintenis.—Adalbert Stifter.—Das
brennende opfer.—Hugo Wolf.—Von der unermüdlichen freude.—E. R.
Weiss.—Jean Paul.—Der Goethe des Westöstlichen divans.—Friedrich
Rückert.—Vom reimen.

     I. Title.   40-9485
     Library of Congress   PT2623.O39H3 1939
     Copyright A—Foreign   45638
                                 [2]

NL 0445293   DLC OC1W MH NcU CaBVaU IEN

VOLUME 338

Loerke, Oskar, 1884-1941.
Die heimliche Stadt; Gedichte. Berlin,
S. Fischer, 1921.
159p. 19cm.

NL 0445294   IEN OU MH CU IU NNC OCU WU

Loerke, Oskar, 1884-1941.
Johann Sebastian Bach; zwei Aufsätze. ₍Berlin₎ Suhrkamp Verlag, 1950 ₍*1925/1935₎
187 p. 19 cm.
CONTENTS.— Geleitwort, von H. Kasack.— Wandlungen eines Ge-
dankens über die Musik und ihren Gegenstand.— Das unsichtbare
Reich.

1. Bach, Johann Sebastian, 1685-1750.

ML410.B1L6 1950   780.81   51-15971

NL 0445295   DLC NSyU CU NjP OC1 OU NN

LOERKE, OSKAR, 1884-
...Der längste Tag. Berlin: S.Fischer, 1926. 140 p.
20½cm.

Poems.

811717A. 1. Poetry, German. I. Title.

NL 0445296   NN InU OU MH NcU OC1 IaU MiU NjP RPB

Loerke, Oskar, 1884-1941.
Magische Verse. Berlin, S. Fischer ₍193-?₎
38 p. 19 cm.

I. Title.

PT2623.039M3   55-48951 ‡

NL 0445297   DLC IU InU NcU MH

Loerke, Oskar, 1884-   ed.

Heimann, Moritz, 1868-1925.
Nachgelassene schriften, von Moritz Heimann. Berlin, S.
Fischer ₍*1926₎

NL 0445299   MiU NN CtY IEN MH OC1 OC1W

Loerke,Oskar,1884-
Der oger,roman von Oskar Loerke. Hamburg,
Berlin, Hoffmann und Campe, 1921.
344 p. 19cm. (Half-title: Die junge welt; gegen-
warts-dichtungen aller völker. 4)

NL 0445299   MiU NN CtY IEN MH OC1 OC1W

Loerke, Oskar, 1884-
... Pansmusik. Berlin, S. Fischer, 1929.
4 p. l., ₍11₎-179, ₍2₎ p. 22cm.
"Zweite auflage der 'Gedichte' von 1916".
"Bücher von Oskar Loerke": p. ₍180₎
CONTENTS.— Pansmusik.— Übersetzungen.— Berlin.— Ländliche rondelle.—
Meer.— Südliche insel.— Morgenland.

NL 0445300   MiU CU IEN WU MiU NNC OC1 MH NN

Loerke, Oskar, 1884-
... Pompeji; eine gedicht-reihe.
Potsdam, G. Kiepenheuer, 1921.
20, ₍2₎ p. 24½cm.

NL 0445301   MShM MH InU

PT 2623   LOERKE,OSKAR,1884-1941.
.039 P8   Der Prinz und der Tiger;Erzählung von Oskar
Loerke. Berlin, S. Fischer, 1920.
181 p.

NL 0445302   InU MA NNC OC1 MH

PT2623   Loerke,Oskar,1884-
.05585   ...Der silberdistelwald;gedichte. Berlin,S.
1934   Fischer,1934.
155,₍8₎ p. 20½cm.

NL 0445303   ICU NcU InU RPB NN NjP

PT2623   Loerke,Oskar,1884-
.05587   Der steinpfad; dichtung von Oskar Loerke.
1941   Leipzig,J.Asmus₍1941₎
35,₍1₎ p. 20cm.
"Gedruckt für die zeitschrift 'Philobiblon',
Leipzig,im jahre 1941."
"Geschrieben im juni und juli 1938."

NL 0445304   ICU NIC OC1W CtY WU NcD

Loerke, Oskar, 1884-1941.
Tagebücher, 1903-1939; hrsg. von Hermann Kasack.
Heidelberg, L. Schneider, 1955.
376 p. illus., ports. 24 cm. (Veröffentlichungen der Deutschen
Akademie für Sprache und Dichtung, Darmstadt. 5. Veröffentli-
chung)

I. Kasack, Hermann, 1896-   ed.   (Series: Deutsche Akademie
für Sprache und Dichtung. Veröffentlichungen, 5)
                                                    A 57-204
New York Univ.   Libraries PT2623
for Library of Congress   ₍2₎

IaU ICU InU NcU NcD MWelC MH CtY VtMiM DLC
NL 0445305   NNU LU OU CLSU NN ViU MdBJ IEdS MiU

Loerke, Oskar, 1884-
Der turmbau; roman von Oskar Loerke. Berlin, S.
Fischer, 1910.
312 p., 1 l. 18½cm. M. 4.00

                                                    11-876

NL 0445306   DLC

ML   Loerke, Oskar, 1884-1941.
410
B1   Das unsichtbare Reich. Johann Sebastian
L8   Bach. Berlin, S. Fischer Verlag [1935]
37₍2₎p.
"Sonderdruck aus der Zeitschrift 'Die Neue
Rundschau'."
Includes bibliography.

NL 0445307   MoSCS NcD IEN

Loerke, Oskar, 1884--1914.
Vineta; erzählung von Oskar Loerke. Berlin, S. Fischer, 1907.
179, ₍1₎ p. 18cm.

PT2623.039V5 1907   8-13297

Library of Congress   (Copyright 1907 Res. no. 800)

NL 0445308   DLC MH NjP

Loerke, Oskar, 1884-
... Der wald der welt; gedichte. Berlin,
S. Fischer, 1936.
3 p. l., 9-147 ₍5₎ p., 1 l. 20½ cm.

Contents.—Der wald der welt.—Die grundmächte.
—Unterwelt.—Tröstungen.—Bemalte vasen von At-
lantis.—Das alte dasein.

NL 0445309   NNC OU InU

Loerke, Oskar, 1884-1941.
Wanderschaft, gedichte ... Berlin, S.
Fischer, 1911.
5 p. l., 13-164 p., 2 l. 17 cm.
Author's autographed presentation copy.

NL 0445310   PU RPB MH NNC NcU InU IEN WU OCU

Loerke, Oskar, 1884-1941.
... Zeitgenossen aus vielen zeiten. Berlin, S. Fischer, 1925.
3 p. l., 13-239, ₍1₎ p., 1 l. 21½cm.
CONTENTS.—J. S. Bach.—Jean Paul. Der Goethe des Westöstlichen
divans. Kurze begegnungen.—Buddho von Westen. Das indische mär-
chenmeer. Besessene.—G. Hauptmann. H. Stehr. A. Mombert. M. Heimann. W. Lehmann. Gedenken an Max Dauthendey.

I. Title.
Library of Congress   PT2623.039Z3 1925
                                                    27-2285

OOxM NN PPT
NL 0445311   DLC IU IEN WU PU CtY CU OU MiU OCU OC1

Lörn, Chr. Jacobi
see Orn, Christen Jacobi Larsen.

Lörner, Alfred.
Bremen im welthandel; handbuch der Zweigstelle des Aus-
wärtigen amtes für aussenhandel, Bremen, bearb. von dr. Alfred Lörner. Bremen, F. Leuwer, 1927.
1 p. l., viii, 268 p. front. (map) illus. (incl. mounted facsim.) fold.
plans. 22½cm.
German, English and Spanish.

1. Bremen—Comm. 2. Bremen—Comm.—Direct.   I. Germany
(1918-   ) Auswärtiges amt. Zweigstelle für aussenhandel, Bremen.
II. Title.

Library of Congress   HF3570.B8L6
                                                    28-23722

NL 0445313   DLC OrU ICU MH WaS MH NN

MICROFILM
F4691   Lörrach, Paulinus von
v.6   Grammatik der Yap-Sprache in Mikronesien.
₍195-?₎
427 l.

Microfilm (positive) of manuscript and typescript. 'Posieux, Schweiz, Anthropos-Institut,
1953. 1 reel. 35mm. (Micro-bibliotheca An-
thropos, v. 6)

NL 0445314   NNC

VOLUME 338

Lörrach, Ger. (City) Gewerbeschule.
Jahres-Bericht.
Lörrach.
v. 23 cm.

T173.L82A2   63-56922 ‡

NL 0445315   DLC

Lörrach, Ger. (City) Städtische Handelsschule.
Jahres-Bericht.
Lörrach.
y. 22 cm.

HF1148.L7S7   63-57204 ‡

NL 0445316   DLC

184
P71m
XL

Loers, Vitus.
Quae ratio inter Platonis Menexenum et
Lysiae laudationem sive epitaphium interce-
dat, disputatio. Trier, F.Lintz, 1846.
39p. 26cm.
Cover-title.
At head of title: Programm womit zu der öffentlichen Prüfung u.Redeübung der Schüler des Gymnasiums zu Trier den 26. und 27.August und zu der Schlussfeierlichkeit den 28.August 1846 ganz ergebenst einladet die Direction.
"Schulnachrichten über das Jahr von Herbste 1845 bis zum Herbste 1846"L p.c19=39.

1.Plato. Menexenus. 2.Lysias. Oratio
funebris. I.Treves Gymnasium.

NL 0445317   CLSU

K
L818

Loersch, Hugo, 1840-1907, ed.
Achener Rechtsdenkmäler aus dem 13., 14.
und 15. Jahrhundert. Nebst einem Anhange,
Regesten der Achener Vögte, Untervögte, Schul-
theissen, Meier, Richter und Bürgermeister
enthaltend. Bonn, A. Marcus, 1871.
x, 288 p. 23cm.

1. Law—Germany (Middle Ages) 2. Aachen—
History.

NL 0445318   NIC CU MH-L

Loersch, Hugo, 1840-1907, ed.

France. *Laws, statutes, etc.*
Der Code civil französisch und deutsch (verbesserte Cramer'sche uebersetzung) nebst den ihn abändernden und ergänzenden preussischen und reichs-gesetzen. Leipzig, K. Bae-
deker, 1879.

Loersch, Hugo, 1840-1907.
... Das falsche diplom Karls des Grossen und Friedrichs I.
privileg für Aachen vom 8. januar 1166. Von Hugo Loersch.
Leipzig, Duncker & Humblot, 1890.
1 p. l., 151-223, 1 p. 23cm.
"Sonderabdruck des anhangs zur VII. publication des Gesellschaft für rheinische geschichtskunde."

1. Aix-la-Chapelle — Charters, grants, privileges. 2. Charlemagne,
742-814. 3. Friedrich I, Barbarossa, emperor of Germany, 1121-1190.
Full name: Konrad Hubert Hugo Loersch.

33-22106

Library of Congress   DD901.A25L6   943.42

NL 0445320   DLC

4K
Fr
731

Loersch, Hugo, 1840-1907.
Das französische Gesetz vom 30. März
1887. Ein Beitrag zum Recht der
Denkmalpflege. Bonn, Druck von
C. Georgi, 1897.
35 p.

(Bonn. Universität. Programm zur
Feier des Dedächtnisses des Stifters
der Universität Königs Friedrich
Wilhelm III, zugleich mit dem Bericht

über die Akademische Preisverteilung
am 3. August ...)

NL 0445322   DLC-P4 CU PU MH-L

Loersch, Hugo, 1840-1907.   Ger 6995.2
Der Ingelheimer oberhof. Bonn, A. Marcus, 1885.
pp. (10), vi, ccxii, (1), 560. Map and diagrs.

Ingelheim

NL 0445323   MH

Loersch, Hugo, 1840-1907.
Die Legende Karls des Grossen
see under Charlemagne. Vita Karoli Magni
sec. XII.

LOERSCH, Hugo, 1840-1901.
Rheinische weistümer und verwandte urkunden im kölner stadtarchiv. Köln, 1895.

(2) + 23 p.
Sonderabdruck aus der mevissen-festschrift
dargebracht von dem archiv der stadt Köln.

NL 0445325   MH-L

Loersch, Hugo, 1840-1907.
Sechs Urkunden aus der Bonner Kreisbib-
liothek, von Hugo Loersch ... Bonn, Carl
Georgi, 1905.
20 p. 22cm.
"Sonderabdruck aus Heft LXXIX der Annalen
des historischen Vereins für den Niederrhein."
Bibliographical footnotes.

NL 0445326   MH-L

LOERSCH, Hugo, 1840-1901.
Ueber die älteste datirte handschrift
des Sachsenspiegels. n.p., n. d.

32 p.

NL 0445327   MH-L

Loersch, Hugo, 1840-1907.
Die Urkunden der Bonner Kreisbibliothek,
von Hugo Loersch ... Bonn, Carl Georgi,
1898.
1 p.l., 54 p. 23cm.
"Sonderabdruck aus Heft LXVI der Annalen
des historischen Vereins für den Niederrhein."
Bibliographical footnotes.

NL 0445328   MH-L

Loersch, Hugo, 1840-1907, ed.
Urkunden zur Geschichte des deutschen Privatrechtes, für
den Gebrauch bei Vorlesungen und Übungen, hrsg. von Hugo
Loersch und Richard Schröder, unter Mitwirkung von
Alexander Reifferscheid. 2. verm. und verb. Aufl. Bonn, A.
Marcus, 1881.
xii, 274 p. 22 cm. (*Their* Urkunden zur Geschichte des deut-
schen Rechtes, für den Gebrauch bei Vorlesungen und Übungen, 1)
Latin or German.
Includes bibliographies.
1. Civil law—Germany—Sources. I. Schroeder, Richard, 1838-
1917, joint ed. II. Title. (Series: Urkunden zur Geschichte des
deutschen Rechtes, 1)
Full name: Konrad Hubert Hugo Loersch.

58-54537

NL 0445329   DLC NcD MH-L MoU MH ICU

Loersch, Hugo, 1840-1907, *ed.*
Urkunden zur geschichte des deutschen privatrechtes.
Für den gebrauch bei vorlesungen und übungen, hrsg. von
Hugo Loersch und Richard Schröder. 3., neu bearb. aufl,
von dr. Richard Schröder ... und dr. Leopold Perels ...
Bonn, A. Marcus und E. Weber, 1912.
xxxii, 250, (2), p. 23 cm.
"Abkürzungen": p. (xxxi)-xxxii.
1. Civil law—Germany—Sources. I. Schroeder, Richard, 1838-
1917, joint ed. II. Perels, Leopold, 1875- III. Title.
Full name: Konrad Hubert Hugo Loersch.

12—23150

NL 0445330   DLC CtY MH-L WaU-L

LOERSCH, Hugo, 1860-1901.
Ein verschollenes achener stadtrechts-
buch. Bonn, 1878.

14 p.

NL 0445331   MH-L

---

*Loersch, Hugo, 1840-1907, ed.
Die weistümer der Rheinprovinz.
Hrsg. von Hugo Loersch. Bonn, H. Behrendt. 1900-

PT
1206
L82

Loersch, Hugo, 1840-1907, *ed.*
Zwei achener historische Gedichte des
15. und 16. Jahrhunderts; hrsg. von H.
Loersch und A. Reifferscheid. Achen, J.
Kaatzer, 1874.
iv, 98 p. 22cm.

I. Reifferscheid, August, 1835-1887, joint
ed.

NL 0445333   NIC CU

Loersch, Hugo, 1840-1907.
Zwei urkunden zum streit des Mainzer
Stephansstiftes mit Ritter Emercho von
Ingelheim (1320-1322) ... von Hugo
Loersch. n.p., n.d.
14 p. 21½cm.
Caption title.
Bibliographical footnotes.

NL 0445334   MH-L

Loersch, Konrad Hubert Hugo, 1840-1907.
See
Loersch, Hugo, 1840-1907.

VOLUME 338

Loersch, Philip U   ed.
Hand-buch der Deutschen evangelisch-
lutherischen und protestantischen Kirchen
zu Detroit, Mich. Detroit, J. Bornman,
1896.
58 ₍1₎ p. illus.

1. Detroit - Churches

NL 0445336   MiD

Loertscher, Gottlieb, 1914–
Die romanische Stiftskirche von Schönenwerd; ein Bei-
trag zur Frage der Doppelturmfassade im 11. Jahrhundert.
Basel, 1952.
xi, 124 p. illus., plates, plans. 24 cm.
Inauguraldiss.—Basel.
Vita.
"Die vorliegende Arbeit erscheint gleichzeitig als Band v der Schrif-
tenreihe 'Basler Studien zur Kunstgeschichte.'"
Bibliography: p. 119–122.
1. Schönenwerd, Switzerland. Stiftskirche. 2. Architecture, Ro-
manesque. 3. Towers.   I. Title.

NA5851.S37L6   57-39934

         NIC NjP CtY ViU MoU
NL 0445337   DLC CSt CLU MiU MH NN InU CU MH DDO NNC

Lörtscher, Hans, 1908–
Variationsstatistische untersuchungen an
leistungserhebungen in einer British-Friesian
Herde. ... Berlin, 1937.   108 p.
Inaug. Diss. - Techn. Hochschule Zürich, 1937.
Lebenslauf.
Literatur.

NL 0445338   ICRL CtY

Lörtscher, Marie.
... Eine vergleichende Untersuchung der
Tonometer von Fick-Livschitz und Schiötz ...
Stuttgart, 1931.
Inaug. -Diss. - Basel.
"Zugleich erschienen in Klinische Monatsblätter
für Augenheilkunde, Bd. 86, 1831, Seite 753–769."
"Literatur": p. 17.

NL 0445339   CtY DNLM MiU

ar X   Loertzer, Brigitte, 1923–
601   Weitere Untersuchungen zur selektiven
Befruchtung II.   Essen, W. Witzel, 1954.
vi, 55 p. illus. 30cm.

Diss.--Erlangen.

1. Fertilization of plants. 2. Hybridization, Vegetable. I. Title.

NL 0445340   NIC CtY

Loertzer, Erika, 1908–
... Über die Gründe der Narbenrezidive nach
Antrotomien ...   Berlin, 1936.
Inaug. -Diss. - Berlin.
Lebenslauf.

NL 0445341   CtY

Lörz (Adolf Ludwig) [1882–   ]. *Beitrag zur
Behandlung der penetrierenden Bauchschuss-
verletzungen. 31 pp. 8". Freiburg i. Br.,
Speyer & Kaerner. 1910.

NL 0445342   DNLM

Lörz, Kurt, 1904–
... Über Darmlipome ...   München, 1929.
Inaug. -Diss. - München.
Lebenslauf.

NL 0445343   CtY

Loes, A   de, b. 1840.
Louis Fabre; souvenirs de sa vie avec des
fragments de ses discours et un portrait.
Lausanne, F. Rouge, 1900.
306 p.   illus.   23 cm.
I. Fabre, Louis, 1797-1871.

NL 0445344   NcD

FL8   Loës, Charles de.
89.9   Der Hausfriedensbruch auf der Grundlage des
L825h   Entwurfes zu einem schweizerischen Straf-
1920   gesetzbuch und unter Berücksichtigung der
kantonalen Gesetzgebung. Frankfurt a.M.,
Druck A. Weisbrod, 1920.
63 p.   22cm.
Inaug. -Diss. - Bern.
Bibliography: p. 61-63.

1. Unlawful entry - Switzerland. I. Title.

NL 0445345   MiU-L ICRL

Loës, Elisabeth, 1908–
Die Emission der Lenardphosphore im Roten und
Ultraroten ...   [n. p., 1934]
[3] p.   22.5 cm.
Inaug. -Diss. - Heidelberg.
Lebenslauf.
Title-page, Lebenslauf and Inhaltsangabe only.
"Erschienen in Annalen der Physik. 5. Folge,
Bd. 19, Heft 5 1934."

NL 0445346   CtY

Loës, F   T.
Exports and imports from and to the port of Philadelphia during the last 52 years, from 1821 to 1872, included,
prepared for the Commercial exchange of Philadelphia,
by F. T. Loës, statistical clerk.   Philadelphia; A. L.
Weise, lith., ₍1873₎.
diagr. 43½ x 58½ᶜᵐ.
Caption title.

1. Philadelphia—Comm.—Stat.

Library of Congress   HF3163.P5L7   CA 9-5186 Unrev'd

NL 0445347   DLC

Loës, F   T.
Neuester zolltarif der Vereinigten Staaten von Amerika. Bearb. und vervollständigt bis zum 3. März, 1875.
Von F. T. Loës ...   Philadelphia und Leipzig, Schäfer
und Koradi, 1875.
58 p. 23ᶜᵐ.

1. Tariff—U. S.—Law.   I. U. S. Laws, statutes, etc.

Library of Congress   H 16086.A6 1875 v   8-33387†

NL 0445348   DLC NjP

Loes, Harry Dixon, comp.
Challenging songs and choruses. Wheaton, Ill., Van
Kampen Press ₍1955†₎
close score (1 v., unpaged) 23 cm.
Caption title.

1. Hymns, English.   I. Title.

M2198.L7966C5   M 55-767

NL 0445349   DLC NN

M1999   Loes, Harry Dixon.
.S38G6
Schuler, George S

Gospel songs for the Easter season ₍by₎ George S. Schuler
and Harry Dixon Loes. A compilation of solos, duets and
trios on Easter themes ... ₍Chicago, Moody press, 1945₎

Loes, Harry Dixon.
Immanuel victorious, Easter story cantata for women's
voices; music by Harry Dixon Loes, story by Avis B. Christiansen ... Kansas City, Mo., Lillenas publishing company,
°1944.
16 p. 22½".
Score: solo voices, chorus and piano.

1. Cantatas, Sacred (Women's voices)—Vocal scores with piano.
2. Easter music.   I. Christiansen, Avis B. Immanuel victorious.
II. Title.

Library of Congress   M2034.L83 I 5   45-14471

NL 0445351   DLC

Loes, Harry Dixon, comp. and arr.
Let youth sing; a junior-intermediate hymnal for all purposes. Wheaton, Ill., Van Kampen Press ₍1953, °1952₎
1 v. (unpaged) 24 cm.

1. Hymns, English. 2. Sunday-schools—Hymns.

M2193.L83L4   M 53-379

NL 0445352   DLC

LOES, HARRY DIXON, comp.
Tell the story with a song; gospel solos & duets.
[Wheaton, Ill., Van Kampen press, c1948]   close score
(33 p.) 23cm.

1. Sacred songs, English--   Collections, 20th cent.
2. Vocal duos, Sacred--   Collections. I. Title.

NL 0445353   NN

Loesberg, Jacob Paul.
Gems of German literature; ed., with introduction, by
J. P. Loesberg ... containing some of the choicest selections for memorizing, from Goethe, Schiller, Heine, Körner and Lessing. New York and Boston, The Morse
company, 1896.
ix, 83 p. 2 port. (incl. front.) 18ᶜᵐ.

1. German language—Chrestomathies and readers.

Library of Congress   PT1105.L6   12-36444

NL 0445354   DLC PP NIC PSC

VOLUME 338

PT1105
.L6
1898

Loesberg, Jacob Paul.
 Gems of German literature; ed., with
introd. by J. P. Loesberg, containing some
of the choicest selections for memorizing,
from Goethe, Schiller, Heine, Körner and
Lessing ₂2d ed.₎ New York, Morse Co.,
1898.
 ix, 83 p. 2 ports. 20cm.

NL 0445355   ViU

Loesberg, Jacob Paul.
 Sprache und gespräch; German reader founded on the
natural method ... ₂Ed. by C. F. Kolbe₎ New York,
The Morse co., 1898.
 vii, 205 p. illus. 12°.

 June 22, 99-55

NL 0445356   DLC PP OU

Lösch (Alexander). *Ueber die Einwirkung des
Ammoniaks auf Quecksilberoxydulsalze, mit
besonderer Berücksichtigung des Hahnemann-
schen Salzes; eine Abhandlung. 48 pp. 8°.
Dorpat, E. J. Karow, 1862.

NL 0445357   DNLM

Loesch, Alfred
 ... La monnaie de compte en droit inter-
national privé ... Luxembourg, Joseph
Beffort, 1936.
 44 p. 22cm. (Etudes juridiques et
economiques de l'Echo de l'Industrie")
 Bibliographical foot-notes.
 "Conférence prononcée le 26 juin 1936 sous
les auspices de la Conférence du Jeune
Barreau de Luxembourg."

NL 0445358   MH-L

W 4
M961
1951

LOESCH, Annemarie Margarete Karoline,
1926-
 Über die Abwasserreinigung in
Fischteichen. ₂München₎ 1951.
 36 ℓ.
 Inaug.-Diss. - Munich.
 1. Water - Purification

NL 0445359   DNLM

Lösch, August, 1906-1945.
 Bevölkerungswellen und wechsellagen, von dr. August
Lösch ... Mit 8 kurven im text. Jena, G. Fischer, 1936.
 x, 124 p. tables, diagrs. 23½ᶜᵐ. (Added t.-p.: Beiträge zur erforschung der wirtschaftlichen wechsellagen, aufschwung, krise, stockung,
hrsg. von Arthur Spiethoff ... hft. 13)
 "Benutzte schriften": p. ₂123₎-124.

 1. Demography. 2. Business cycles. 3. Economic conditions.
 I. Title.
             A C 37-2475
 Iowa. State coll. Library
 for Library of Congress   ₂2₎

NL 0445360   IaAS KMK CU IdU NN

Lösch, August, 1906-1945.
 The economics of location. Translated from the 2d rev.
ed. by William H. Woglom with the assistance of Wolfgang
F. Stolper. New Haven, Yale University Press, 1954.
 xxviii, 520 p. illus. maps. 25 cm.
 Translation of Die räumliche Ordnung der Wirtschaft.
Bibliographical footnotes.

 1. Industry. 2. Industries, Location of. 3. Commerce.
 I. Title.
 HD35.L6513   338   52-9268

 OCU OC1 OU PBL CoU MB ViU-L CaBVa MtBC MtU CaBViP
 NcRS MiU NIC DNAL MB OC1W PHC PSt OrCS OrU WaT OrP
NL 0445361   DLC WaTC PP PPT TxU ViU PU-W NcD NN TU

Lösch, August, 1906-
 Die räumliche ordnung der wirtschaft; eine untersuchung
über standort, wirtschaftsgebiete und internationalen handel,
von dr. habil. August Lösch, mit 94 abbildungen im text. Jena,
G. Fischer, 1940.
 viii, 348 p. diagrs. 24½ᶜᵐ.
 "Schrifttum": p. ₂341₎-348.

 1. Industries, Location of. 2. Commerce. I. Title.
                          41-21853
 Library of Congress   T56.L67
                                        338

NL 0445362   DLC NIC CU CtY NcU WaU NN OU IEN

Lösch, August, 1906-
 Die räumliche ordnung der wirtschaft, von dr. habil. August
Lösch. 2., neu durchgearb. aufl. Mit 100 abbildungen im text.
Jena, G. Fischer, 1944.
 viii, 380 p. diagrs. 24ᶜᵐ.
 "Schrifttum": p. ₂365₎-374.

 1. Industry. 2. Industries, Location of. 3. Commerce. I. Title.
                          46-12525
 Library of Congress   HD35.L65 1944
                                        ₂2₎

NL 0445363   DLC NN TxU NcD LU IU MH NjP WaSpG

Micro-
film
T
4

Lösch, August, 1906-
 Die räumliche ordnung der wirtschaft, von dr. habil. August
Lösch. 2., neu durchgearb. aufl. Mit 100 abbildungen im text.
Jena, G. Fischer, 1944.
 viii, 380 p. diagrs. 24ᶜᵐ.
 "Schrifttum": p. ₂365₎-374.   Library of Congress.
 Negative; original in

NL 0445364   ICU

Lösch, August, 1906-
Görzel, Ida.
 Technische umwälzungen, internationale standortsverschie-
bungen und protektionismus in der nachkriegszeit, von dr.
Ida Görzel. dr. Hellmut Gottschalk ₂und₎ dr. August Lösch.
Berlin, Junker und Dünnhaupt, 1934.

Lösch, August, 1906-1945.
 ... Was ist vom geburtenrückgang zu halten? ... Heiden-
heim (Württemberg) Im eigenen verlag. 1932.
 2 v. illus. (maps) diagrs. 23ᶜᵐ.
 "Eine frühere fassung erhielt den Helfferich-preis von 1930."
 "Zitierte schriften": v. 2, p. 94-95.

 1. Population. 2. Germany—Population. I. Title.
                                       33-19895
 Library of Congress   HB3595.L6 1932
 Copyright A—Foreign   20805
                                ₂2₎   312

NL 0445366   DLC NN CU

Lösch (Carl). *Vergleichung der Wirkungen
des Schwefeläthers und des Chloroforms. 19 pp.
8°. Erlangen. C. H. Kunstmann. 1848.

NL 0445367   DNLM

Loesch, Charles F.
Loesch, Frank Joseph, 1852-
 ... The Pennsylvania railroad company, appellant, vs.
United States Railroad labor board, R. . Barton ₂and
others₎ ... appellees. Appeal from the ₂ nited States
Circuit court of appeals for the Seventh circuit. Frank
J. Loesch, Timothy J. Scofield, Charles F. Loesch, Rob-
ert W. Richards, attorneys for appellant. C. B. Heiser-
man, E. H. Seneff, F. D. McKenney, of counsel. Chicago,
Gunthorp-Warren printing company ₂1922?₎

Loesch, Ernst, 1882-
 Der Versuch im geltenden deutschen
Strafrecht und in den drei Vorent-
würfen deutscher Sprache ... von Ernst
Loesch ... Traunstein, E. Leopoldseder,
1912.
 80 p. 22½cm.
 Inaug.-Diss. - Erlangen.
 "Literaturverzeichnis": p. 76-78.

NL 0445369   MH-L NN DLC NIC

Loesch, Ferdi, tr.

Tolten, Hans, 1888-
 ... Enchanting wilderness, adventures in darkest South
America; translated from the German by Ferdi Loesch. With
23 illustrations and a map. London, Selwyn & Blount ₂1936₎

Loesch Fr   Wilhelm Max

see

Loesch, Wilhelm Max, 1905-

Loesch, Frank Joseph, 1852-

Building a moral reserve; or, The civic responsibilities of the
Christian citizen. The following persons have co-operated
in the preparation of this course: Shailer Mathews, Andrew
C. McLaughlin, Harold D. Lasswell ₂and others₎ ... Chicago, The American institute of sacred literature ₂ᶜ1930₎

fY
245
.L 82

LOESCH, FRANK JOSEPH, 1852-
 Gleams from Glimmerglass... Read before the
Chicago literary club, Chicago, Illinois. November twenty ninth, 1937. ₂Chicago, 1937₎
 62 numb. leaves. 28cm.

 Type-written (carbon copy)

NL 0445373   ICN

VOLUME 338

Loesch, Frank Joseph, 1852–
... The Pennsylvania railroad company, appellant, *vs.* United States Railroad labor board, R. M. Barton [and others] ... appellees. Appeal from the United States Circuit court of appeals for the Seventh circuit. Frank J. Loesch, Timothy J. Scofield, Charles F. Loesch, Robert W. Richards, attorneys for appellant. C. B. Heiserman, E. H. Seneff, F. D. McKenney, of counsel. Chicago, Gunthorp-Warren printing company [1922?]
cover-title, vii, 84 p. 23½ᶜᵐ.

In the Supreme court of the United States. October term, 1922. No. 585.

1. Railroads — U. S. — Employees. 2. Arbitration, Industrial — U. S. 3. Transportation act, 1920. Section III. 4. [Railroads—Employees—Representation] I. Scofield, Timothy J. II. Loesch, Charles F. III. Richards, Robert W. IV. Heiserman, Clarence Benjamin, 1862– v. Seneff, Edward H., 1867– VI. McKenney, Frederic Duncan, 1863– VII. Pennsylvania railroad company. VIII. U. S. Railroad labor board.

A 23–521 [.]

Title from Bureau of   Railway Economics. Printed by L. C.

NL 0445375   DBRE

Loesch, Frank Joseph, 1852–
Personal experiences during the Chicago fire, 1871, by Frank J. Loesch ... Chicago, Priv. print., 1925.
25 p. 22ᶜᵐ.

1. Chicago—Fire, 1871.   I. Title.

Library of Congress   F548.42.L82
27–2430

NL 0445376   DLC ICJ ICN

Loesch, Frank Joseph, 1852–
Railroads from a legal aspect. Address of Frank J. Loesch, esq. Annual meeting of the Society of railway financial officers, Highland Park, Illinois, September 24, 1913. [n. p., 1913]
cover-title, 8 p. 23ᶜᵐ.

1. Railroads and state—U. S.   I. Title.

A 14–562

Title from Bureau of   Railway Economics. Printed by L. C.

NL 0445377   DBRE

Lösch, Friedrich, 1903–
Die Fakultät (Gammafunktion) und verwandte Funktionen, mit besonderer Berücksichtigung ihrer Anwendungen [von] Lösch-Schoblik. Bearb. von Friedrich Lösch. Leipzig, Teubner, 1951.
205 p. illus. 22 cm.

1. Functions, Gamma.   I. Title.

QA351.L77
52—26040 ‡

NcD TU NBC
NL 0445378   DLC NBuU IEN OCU NcU OU NjPT TxU ODW

Lösch, Friedrich, 1903–
Siebenstellige Tafeln der elementaren transzendenten Funktionen. Berlin, Springer, 1954.
335 p. 28 cm.

1. Functions, Transcendental.   I. Title.

QA351.L773
55–15162 ‡

NcD IEN PU-Math NN CSt OrCS OrU
NL 0445379   DLC MoU ViU OCIW ViU CU MH OU IU NjP NN

Loesch, Friedrich, 1903–
Eine verallgemeinerung der eulerschen reihentransformation mit funktionentheoretischen anwendungen.
Inaug. diss. Tuebingen, 1929. (Berlin)

NL 0445380   ICRL

Loesch, Fritz, 1908–
... Klinische Beobachtungen über Blasenmolenschwangerschaften und Chorionepitheliome (1913–1934) ... Speyer a. Rh., 1937.
Inaug.-Diss. - Heidelberg.
Lebenslauf.
"Literaturverzeichnis": p. 39.

NL 0445381   CtY

---

ar W
54517
no.17

Loesch, Georg, 1890–
Die impressionistische Syntax der Goncourt. (Eine syntaktisch-stilistische Untersuchung) Nürnberg, Buchdr. B. Hilz, 1919.
xvi, 124 p. 23cm.

Inaug.-Diss.--Erlangen.

1. Goncourt, Edmond Louis Antoine Huot de, 1822–1896. 2. Goncourt, Jules Alfred Huot de, 1833–1870.

NL 0445382   NIC ICRL WaU MiU MH CtY CaBVaU

W 4
F82
1955

LÖSCH, Hans Walter, 1931–
Veränderungen im Blutgerinnungssystem nach Myokardinfarkt. Frankfurt a. M., [1955?]
80 ℓ. illus.
Inaug.-Diss. - Frankfurt.
1. Coronary vessels - Diseases

NL 0445383   DNLM

Loesch, Harald Hermann v., 1902–
Die mir-verfassung ihre entstehung, ausbildung und ihr abbau, unter besonderer berücksichtigung der umteilungsgemeinde. ... Berlin, 1931.
Inaug. Diss. - Berlin, 1931.
Lebenslauf.
Literaturverzeichnis.

NL 0445384   ICRL InU NNC

Loesch, Heinrich von.
Die Kölner kaufmannsgilde im zwölften jahrhundert ... Trier, Buchdruckerei von J. Lintz, 1904.
3 p. l., 61 p. 22½ᶜᵐ.
Inaug.-diss.—Marburg.
"Die ... arbeit erscheint gleichzeitig als Ergänzungsheft XII der Westdeutschen zeitschrift für geschichte und kunst."

1. Cologne—Gilds.

Library of Congress   HD6469.C7L7
5—8935

NL 0445385   DLC CU ICJ

Loesch, Heinrich von, *ed.*
Die Kölner zunfturkunden nebst anderen Kölner gewerbeurkunden bis zum jahre 1500, bearb. von Heinrich von Loesch ... Bonn, P. Hanstein, 1907.
2 v. 25½ᶜᵐ. (Added t.-p.: Publikationen der Gesellschaft für rheinische geschichtskunde. XXII)
"Stifter und patrone," "Satzungen," and "Publikationen der Gesellschaft": v. 1, p. v–xxi.
CONTENTS.—1. bd. Allgemeiner teil.—2. bd. Spezieller teil.

1. Cologne—Gilds. 2. Cologne—Indus.   I. Title.

13–23985

Library of Congress   HD6469.C6L6

NL 0445386   DLC MB NN

Lösch, Hildegard.
... Die bäuerlichen familiennamen des habsburgischen urbars, von Hildegard Lösch. Giessen, von Münchowsche universitäts-druckerei O. Kindt, 1936.
82 p. 24½ᶜᵐ. (Giessener beiträge zur deutschen philologie ... XLV)
"Verzeichnis der benützten werke": p. [4]–6.

1. Names, Personal — German. 2. German language — Etymology — Names. 3. Habsburg, House of.

A C 36–1529

Univ. of Chicago   PF3025.G5 no. 45   Printed by L. C.

NL 0445387   ICU INS MoU PBm PU NN

W 4
W95
1954

LOESCH, Ingeborg (Trappen) 1927–
Zur Bedeutung der dezidualen Umwandlung des Endometriums. Würzburg, 1954.
35 p.
Inaug.-Diss. - Würzburg.
1. Uterus - Pregnant

NL 0445388   DNLM

N6886
.N9L8
(8A)

Lösch, Johann Christoph Ernst.
Geschichte und Beschreibung der Kirche zu St. Jakob in Nürnberg nach ihrer Erneuerung im Jahr 1824/25. Nürnberg, Riegel, 1825.
48 p. plates. 21 cm.

I. Nuremberg. St. Jakobskirche.

NL 0445389   NjP

D965
.L7

Loesch, Karl Christian von, 1880–
Das antlitz der grenzlande ... von Karl C. von Loesch. München, F. Bruckmann a.g. [c193]
v.   illus., fold. map.   29½x22½cm.

1. Europe—Descr. & trav.—Views.   2. Germany—Bound.   I. Title.

NL 0445390   DLC NcD NN ICU IEN CtY MH CU

Loesch, Karl Christian von, 1880–
Die aussenpolitischen wirkungen des geburtenrückganges, dargelegt am beispiel der Franzosen; von dr. Karl C. von Loesch ... Berlin, Junker und Dünnhaupt, 1938.
40 p. incl. tables. 23ᶜᵐ. (Added t.-p.: Schriften der Deutschen hochschule für politik, hrsg. von Paul Meier-Benneckenstein. I. Idee und gestalt des nationalsozialismus. hft. 31)
"Schrifttum": p. 38–40.

1. France—Population.   I. Title.

38–22846

Library of Congress   JA44.B37 I, hft. 31
[3]   (320.82)   312.0944

NL 0445391   DLC NNC CU NN CtY MH CU

DK412
.B6

Loesch, Karl Christian von, 1880–   *joint ed.*

Boehm, Max Hildebert, 1891–   *ed.*
Der befreite Osten, eine volkspolitische und wirtschaftliche Darstellung mit zahlreichen Kartenskizzen und Diagrammen, im Auftrage des Institute für Grenz- und Auslandstudien hrsg. von M. H. Boehm und Karl C. von Loesch. Berlin-Steglitz, K. Hofmeier [1940]

VOLUME 338

Loesch, Karl Christian von, 1880–

DB205
.G53

Gierach, Erich, 1881–1943.
Böhmen und Mähren im Deutschen Reich, von Erich Gierach und Karl C. von Loesch. München, F. Bruckmann ₁1939₁

Loesch, Karl Christian von, 1880–   *ed.*
Bücher des Deutschtums. Für den Deutschen Schutzbund hrsg. in Zusammenarbeit mit A. Hillen Ziegfeld. Breslau, F. Hirt, 1925–26.
2 v. maps (part fold.) diagrs. 27 cm.
Vol. 2 has imprint: Berlin, Deutscher Schutzbund Verlag.
No more published?
Bibliography: v. 1, p. ₁415₁–429.; v. 2, p. 789–798.
CONTENTS.—Bd. 1. Volk unter Völkern, unter Mitwirkung von G. Berka ₁et al.₁—Bd. 2. Staat und Volkstum.
   1. Germans. 2. Nationalism—Germany. 3. Germany—Civilization. I. Title.

DD76.L6   26–7595 rev*

NL 0445394   DLC MiU FU NN

DD237
.H45

Loesch, Karl Christian von, 1880–

Heiss, Friedrich, 1897–   *ed.*
Deutsche revolution: die wende eines volkes; in zusammenarbeit mit A. Hillen Ziegfeld und K. C. von Loesch herausgegeben von Friedrich Heiss. Berlin, Volk und reich verlag, 1933.

Loesch, Karl Christian von, 1880–   *ed.*
Das deutsche volk, sein boden und seine verteidigung; herausgegeben von dr. Karl C. von Loesch ₁und₁ generalmajor a. d. Ludwig Vogt. Berlin, Volk und reich verlag, 1937.
470 p. incl. illus. (incl. maps, facsim.) tables, diagrs. 23½ᶜᵐ.
"Für die ... abteilung, 'Die deutsche volksgemeinschaft', ist ... Karl C. von Loesch verantwortlich; gemeinsam mit Alfred Petran verfasste er diesen abschnitt."—p. 8.
CONTENTS.—Blomberg, Generalfeldmarschall v. Geleitwort.—Vogt, Ludwig. Einleitung.—Fischer, Rudolf. Geschichte der Deutschen.—Bade, Wilfrid. Das dritte reich.—Vogt, Ludwig. Die Hitler-jugend.—Loesch, K. C. von. Die deutsche volksgemeinschaft.—Vogt, Ludwig. Die deutsche wehrmacht.—Vogt, Ludwig. Nachwort.
   1. Germany—History. 2. Germans. 3. Germany—Army. I. Vogt, Ludwig, joint ed. II. Title.

New York. Public library   A C 37–2721
for Library of Congress   ₁3₁

NL 0445396   NN CaBVaU

Loesch, Karl Christian von, 1880–   *ed.*
Das deutsche volk, sein boden und seine verteidigung; herausgegeben von dr. Karl C. von Loesch ₁und₁ generalmajor a. d. Ludwig Vogt. 2. aufl. Berlin, Volk und reich verlag, 1938.
408 p. illus. (maps, plans) diagrs. 23½ᶜᵐ.
"11.–28. tausend."
CONTENTS.—Fischer, Rudolf. Geschichte der Deutschen bis 1933.—Bade, Wilfrid. Das dritte reich.—Vogt, Ludwig. Die Hitler-jugend.—Loesch, K. C. von. Die deutsche volksgemeinschaft.—Vogt, Ludwig. Die deutsche wehrmacht.
   1. Germany—Hist. 2. Germany—Hist.—1933–1945. 3. Germans. 4. Germany. Heer. I. Vogt, Ludwig, 1873–   joint ed. II. Title.

Library of Congress   DD4.L6 1938   45–32838
                         ₁2₁   943.0082

NL 0445397   DLC NIC CtY IaU OU

Loesch, Karl Christian von, 1880–
Deutsche Züge im Antlitz der Erde; Deutsches Siedeln, deutsche Leistung. Hrsg. unter Mitarbeit des Deutschen Ausland-Institutes, Stuttgart. München, F. Bruckmann ₁1935₁
306 p. (chiefly illus., maps) 30 cm.

   1. Germans in foreign countries. I. Title.

DD119.3.L6   54–51915

DGU NN PPCS OCl IEN
NL 0445398   DLC ICU IU CSt-H NNC RPB CU IaU OU CtY

Loesch, Karl Christian von, 1880–
Frankreich, ein schrei von der westgrenze, von dr. Karl C. von Loesch. Berlin, Zentralverlag, g. m. b. h., 1923.
31, ₁1₁ p. illus. (maps) 16ᶜᵐ.

   1. Germany—Hist.—Allied occupation, 1918–   2. European war, 1914–1918—Territorial questions—Germany. I. Title.

Library of Congress   D650.M5L6   26–17049

NL 0445399   DLC

DD119.3
L826

Loesch, Karl Christian von, 1880–
Die Gliederung der deutschen Volksgrenze, mit einer Tabelle und einer Übersichtskarte. Berlin, Volk und Reich Verlag, 1937.
24 p. maps (part fold.), tables. 24ᶜᵐ.
(Mitteleuropäische Schriftenreihe, Bd. 4)

   1. Germans in Europe. 2. Germany – Boundaries.

NL 0445400   CSt-H MH DLC-P4

Loesch, Karl Christian von, 1880–   *ed.*
Grenzdeutschland seit Versailles; die grenz- und volkspolitischen folgen des friedensschlusses, hrsg. von Karl C. v. Loesch und Max Hildebert Boehm. Berlin, Brückenverlag, 1930.
vii, 450 p. illus. (maps) 24½ᶜᵐ.
Includes bibliographies.
CONTENTS.—Die gegnerischen gebietsforderungen und ihre vorgeschichte: Die Franzosen, von P. Wentscke. Die Belgier, von P. Osswald. Die Dänen, von F. Hähnsen. Die Polen, von W. Recke. Die Litauer, von E. Röhn. Die Tschechen, von G. Peters.—Gebietsbesetzung: Saargebiet, von H. Röchling. Rhein-, Main- und Ruhrgebiet, von K. Mehrmann.—Gefährdung und gebietsverlust durch abstimmung: Nordschleswig, von F. Hähnsen. Marienwerder und Masuren, von M. Worgitzki.

Oberschlesien, von J. P. Wardernoit. Eupen-Malmedy, von W. Wirths.—Gebietsverlust durch erzwungene abtretung oder verselbständigung: Elsass-Lothringen, von H. Knecht. Posen und Westpreussen, von O. Kaestner. Memel, von F. Borchardt. Hultschin, von R. Weigel. Die Freie Stadt Danzig, von T. Rudolph. Deutsch-Österreich und seine grenzgebiete, von K. G. Hugelmann. Sudetendeutsche gebiete, von F. Jesser.—Volkszerreissung: Grenzverengung und verletztes selbstbestimmungsrecht, von K. C. von Loesch. Volkszerreissung und minderheitennot, von M. H. Boehm.
   1. European war, 1914–1918— Territorial questions — Germany. 2. Europe—Politics—1914–   3. Germany—Bound. I. Boehm, Max Hildebert, 1891–   joint ed. II. Title.

Library of Congress   D651.G3L6
                         ₁3₁   31–400
                                               940.31424

NL 0445402   DLC CSt

Loesch, Karl Christian von, 1880–   *joint author.*

Fenner, Gerhard.
... Die neuen agrargesetze der ost- und südosteuropäischen staaten. Von Gerhard Fenner und dr. von Loesch ... Berlin, H. R. Engelmann, 1923

Loesch, Karl Christian von, 1880–
Der polnische volkscharakter, urteile und selbstzeugnisse aus vier jahrhunderten, von dr. Karl C. v. Loesch. Berlin, Junker und Dünnhaupt, 1940.
100 p. 23½ᶜᵐ. (Half-title: Schriften für politik und auslandkunde, hrsg. von prof. dr. F. A. Six ... hft. 67/69)

   1. Poles. 2. National characteristics, Polish. I. Title.

Library of Congress   JA44.B37 I, hft. 67/69   41–19222
                                               (320.82) 914.38

NL 0445404   DLC OU CU MH NNC TxU

Loesch, Karl Christian von, 1880–
Staat und volkstum ... für den Deutschen schutzbund hrsg. von dr. K. C. v. Loesch, in zusammenarbeit mit A. Hillen Ziegfeld. Berlin, Deutscher schutzbund verlag, 1926.
798 p. maps, tables. 26½ cm. (Added t.-p.: Bücher des Deutschtums, bd. 2)

   1. Germany – Nationality. 2. Germany - Civilization. 3. Minorities. 4. Germans. I. Ziegfeld, Arnold Hillen, jt.au. II. Deutscher schutzbund für das grenz- und auslanddeutschtum, Berlin.

NL 0445405   NNC CU-I OCl NN MH CU CtY

Loesch, Karl Christian von, 1880–   *ed.*
Taschenbuch des grenz- u. ausland-deutschtums
see under title

LOESCH, Karl C[hristian] von, 188?-
Ueber einige Nautiliden des weissen Jura. München 1912. 42 W.

München. Phil. Diss.

NL 0445407   MH PU

Loesch, Karl Christian von, 1880–
Die verlustliste des deutschtums in Polen, von dr. Karl C. von Loesch. Berlin, Junker und Dünnhaupt, 1940.
80 p. 23ᶜᵐ. (Half-title: Forschungen des Deutschen auslandswissenschaftlichen instituts, hrsg. von prof. F. A. Six. Abt.: Volkstumskunde, bd. 2)

   1. Germans in Poland. 2. Germany—For. rel.—Poland. 3. Poland—For. rel.—Germany. I. Title.

DD241.P6L6   325.24309438   47–35452

NL 0445408   DLC MiU IU MH NN NcD CtY

BR856
L826
f

Loesch, Karl Christian von, 1880–
Verteilung und Gliederung der Evangelischen im Grenz- und Aussendeutschtum. Hrsg. vom Institut für Grenz- und Auslandstudien, Berlin-Steglitz. Bearb. von Karl C. von Loesch und Paul Ullrich. ₁Berlin, 1939-
v. maps (part fold.) 26x34cm.
"Als Handschrift für den Dienstgebrauch gedruckt."
In portfolio.
Contents.- 1. Tl. Europa. (26 p., 9 maps)
   1. Evangelische   Kirche in Deutschland.
2. Germans in for   eign countries. I.
Ullrich, Paul, 1908-   II. Institut für
Grenz- und Auslandstudien, Berlin. III. Title.

NL 0445409   CSt-H

Loesch, Karl Christian von, 1880–
... Die völker und rassen Südosteuropas. Mit 96 aufnahmen und einem reisebericht von Gustav Adolf Küppers. Berlin ₁etc.₁ Volk und reich verlag, 1943.
104 p. incl. plates (incl. maps) 20¼ x 16¼ᶜᵐ. (On cover: Kleine Volk und reich bücherei)
At head of title: Karl C. von Loesch und Wilhelm E. Mühlmann.
CONTENTS.—Loesch, K. C. von. Die völker Südosteuropas.—Mühlmann, W. E. Die rassische bild.—Bildteil.—Küppers, G. A. Völkerkundliche bilder von fünf Balkanreisen.
   1. Ethnology—Europe. I. Mühlmann, Wilhelm Emil, 1904–   II. Küppers, Gustav Adolf, 1894–   III. Title.

Library of Congress   GN575.L6   44–20823
                         ₁2₁   572.9496

NL 0445410   DLC ICU ICRL LU CtY NNM ICU CaBVaU

VOLUME 338

Loesch, Karl Christian von, 1880–
Volk unter völkern; bücher des deutschtums ...
Für den Deutschen schutzbund unter mitwirkung von
Günther Berka ,u. a., ... hrsg. von dr. K. C. v. Loesch
in zusammenarbeit mit A. Hillen Ziegfeld. Breslau, F.
Hirt, 1925–

v. maps (part fold.) diagrs. 26½ᵐ.

1. Germans. 2. Germany—Nationality. 3. Germany—Civilization. I.
Ziegfeld, Arnold Hillen. II. Deutscher schutzbund für das grenz- und auslanddeutschtum, Berlin. III. Title.

Library of Congress   DD76.L6   26-7595

NL 0445411   DLC WU MH NN CSt-H CaBVaU

Loesch, Karl Christian von, 1880–   *ed.*
Volkwerdung und Volkstumswandel. Leipzig, Schwarz-
häupter-Verlag ,1943,

216 p. maps, diagrs., tables. 21 cm. (Volkskundliche Untersuchungen des Instituts für Grenz- und Auslandstudien zum europäischen Problem, 2. Folge)

"Herausgegeben von Carl C. von Loesch."—Label mounted on t.-p.

1. Ethnology—Addresses, essays, lectures. I. Title. (Series:
Institut für Grenz- und Auslandstudien, Berlin. Volkskundliche
Untersuchungen zum europäischen Problem, 2. Folge)

GN325.L62   48-43063*

NL 0445412   DLC

D651
.G3S33

Loesch, Karl Christian von, 1880–

Schnee, Heinrich, 1871–1949, *ed.*
Zehn Jahre Versailles ,1919–1929, Hrsg. von Heinrich
Schnee ,und, Hans Draeger. Berlin, Brückenverlag, 1929–
30.

Lösch, Kurt, 1905–
Der Begriff der "amtlichen Funktion"
... von ... Kurt Lösch ... Bochum-
Langendreer, H. Pöppinghaus, 1934.

viii, 41, ₍1₎ p. 21cm.

Inaug.-Diss. - Jena.
"Mein Lebenslauf": p. ₍42₎
"Literaturverzeichnis": p. v-vi.

NL 0445414   MH-L ICRL CtY

Lösch, L   F.
Vollständige anleitung zur einrichtung und führung des
cameralrechnungswesens was sowohl die rechnungsstell selbst,
als auch die rechnungs-probation oder revision, und rechnungs-
justificatur betrifft, nach grundsätzen theoretisch entworfen und
mit verschiedenen beyspielen practisch erläutert, von L. F.
Lösch. 2. ausg. Heilbronn am Neckar u. Rothenburg ob der
Tauber, J. D. Class, 1798.

xx p., 5 l., 218, ₍610₎ p. incl. tables. 19ᵐ.

First published 1793.

1. Municipal finance—Germany—Accounting. I. Title.

42-33408

Library of Congress   HJ9779.G3L6 1798

NL 0445415   DLC

536
L896v

Lösch, L   F
Vollständige einleitung in das cameral-
rechnungs-wesen was sowohl die rechnungsstell selbst, als auch die rechnungs-probation oder revision, und rechnungs-justi-
ficatur betrifft, nach grundsätzen theoretisch entworfen, und mit verschiedenen
beyspielen praktisch erläutert. Heilbronn am Neckar, 1793.
v.p.

NL 0445416   IU

Loesch, M.
... Bestimmung der Intensität der schwerkraft
auf zwanzig stationen an der westafrikanischen
küste von Rio Del Rey ...
see under Germany. Marineleitung.

Loesch, M.
... Mass in honor of St. Michael. For soprano, alto,
tenor, and bass, with organ accompaniment ... New
York, J. Fischer & bro. ₍1901₎

35 p. 28½ᵐ. (Fischer's ed., no. 1898)   2-16782

NL 0445418   DLC

Loesch, Maria von, 1905–
Ueber einige neue hydrazine und isomere stoffe.
... Breslau, 1933. 43 p.
Inaug. Diss. -Breslau, 1933.
Lebenslauf.

NL 0445419   ICRL MiU CtY PU

Loesch, Max, 1905–
see Loesch, Wilhelm Max, 1905–

Lösch, Olga, 1898–
Das naturgefühl bei George Eliot und Thomas Hardy, von
Olga Lösch.

(*In* Beiträge zur erforschung der sprache und kultur Englands und
Nordamerikas ... Breslau, 1928. 21½ᵐᵐ. bd. v, p. ₍88₎–180)

"Literaturverzeichnis": p. ₍88₎

1. Eliot, George, pseud., i. e. Marian Evans, afterwards Cross, 1819–
1880. 2. Hardy, Thomas, 1840–1928. 3. Nature in literature.

A C 33–1399

Title from Stanford Univ.
Library of Congress   ₍PE25.G5 bd. 5₎

NL 0445421   CSt NcU OCU

Ip
B44
S928l

Lösch, Olga, 1898–
Das Naturgefühl bei George Eliot und Thomas
Hardy ... Giessen, J. Christ, 1928.
2p.l., p.89-180,1l. 23cm.
Diss - Giessen.
Text of thesis edition reprinted from:
Beiträge zur Erforschung der Sprache und
Kultur Englands und Nordamerikas ... 1928.
Lebenslauf.
"Literaturverzeichnis": p.₍88₎

NL 0445422   CtY

Loesch (R.). *Ueber* Urticaria perstans
papulosa. 8°. München. 1926.

NL 0445423   DNLM PPWI

---

ar W
2090

Lösch, Reinhard.
Die intrauterine Anwendung des Sulfones Balu-
don bei puerperalen Erkrankungen des Rindes.
Hannover, 1950.
35 p. 21cm.

Diss.--Tierärztliche Hochschule Hannover,
1950.

NL 0445424   NIC

D
15
B81
Z99
1948

Loesch, Ronald.
Jacob Burckhardt (1818-1897); Persönlichkeit,
Werke und Wirkungen, von Ronald Loesch.
(Detached from Europa-Archiv.   Frankfurt
a.M. 31cm. 3.Jg.(April,1948),p.1293-1304.)
Caption title: Kultur-Archiv.

1. Burckhardt, Jakob Christoph, 1818-1897.
2. Burckhardt, Jakob Christoph, 1818-1897--Bibl.
I. Europa-Archiv.

NL 0445425   NSyU

WB
405
L826j
1951

LÖSCH, Senta
Jung! Gesund! Schlank! Das
Geheimnis der kochsalz- und harnsäure-
freien Diät. ₍Bad Wörishofen, Bernhard,
1951?₎
212 p.
1. Diet - Salt-free 2. Cookery

NL 0445426   DNLM

W 4
M96
1953

LÖSCH, Siglinde (Kropf)
Über die Beeinträchtigung des geistigen Reaktionsvermögens nach
Blutspenden. München, 1953.
21 ℓ.
Inaug.-Diss. - Munich.
1. Blood donors

NL 0445427   DNLM

Lösch, Stephan, 1881–
Die anfänge der Tübinger Theologischen quartalschrift
(1819-1831) Gedenkgabe zum 100. todestag Joh. Ad. Möhlers,
von d. dr. Stephan Lösch ... Rottenburg a. N., Bader, 1938.

viii, 180, ₍1₎ p. 23ᵐ.

1. Theologische quartalschrift. 2. Möhler, Johann Adam, 1796–1838.
I. Title.

Library of Congress   BR4.T452L6   39-5567

₍2₎   205

NL 0445428   DLC CSt

Lösch, Stephan, 1881–
Deitas Jesu und antike apotheose; ein beitrag zur exegese
und religionsgeschichte, von Stephan Lösch. Rottenburg a. N.
(Württ.) Bader, 1933.

xv, 137 p. 24ᵐ.

"Literatur-verzeichnis": p. vii-xv.

1. Jesus Christ—Divinity. 2. Church history—Primitive and early
church. 3. Religious thought—Ancient period. I. Title.

35-13847

Library of Congress   BT215.L6

₍2₎   232.8

NL 0445429   DLC DDO CtY ICU OC1W NjP

BS2310   **Lösch, Stephan,** 1881–
.L77
Diatagma kaisaros; die inschrift von Nazareth und das
Neue Testament; eine untersuchung zur neutestamentlichen
zeitgeschichte, mit 1 bild der inschrift, von d. dr. Stephan
Lösch ... Freiburg im Breisgau, Herder & co., 1936.

xiii, 99, ₍1₎ p. pl. 25ᵐ.

"Literatur zur Nazareth-inschrift": p. xi-xiii.

1. Inscriptions, Greek—Nazareth. 2. Jesus Christ—Resurrection. 3. Bible.
N. T.—History of New Testament times. 4. Tombs.

NL 0445430   ICU NNC NjP IU NjPT OCU TxFTC

VOLUME 338

Lösch, Stephan, 1881–
Döllinger und Frankreich, eine geistige Allianz, 1823–1871. Im Lichte von 56 bisher meist unbekannten Briefen, mit zwei Döllingerbildnissen nebst Döllinger-Bibliographie. München, Beck, 1955.

xi, 568 p. ports. 25 cm. (Schriftenreihe zur bayerischen Landesgeschichte, Bd. 51)

1. Döllinger, Johann Joseph Ignaz von, 1799–1890. 2. Döllinger, Johann Joseph Ignaz von, 1799–1890—Bibl.   (Series)

DD801.B322S4 Bd. 51   57–22313

NL 0445431   DNAL NcD NjPT CaBVaU MsSM TU PU OCU PPiU
DLC CtY ViU NNC TxU MiU NIC NN MH IaU

Lösch, Stephan, 1881–
Epistula Claudiana, der neuentdeckte brief des kaisers Claudius vom jahre 41 n. Chr. und das urchristentum; eine exegetisch-historische untersuchung, von Stephan Lösch. Rottenburg a. N. (Württ.), Bader, 1930.

48 p. 24½ᶜᵐ.

Text and translation of the part of the letter relating to the Jewish question: p. 8–11.
"Literatur zum Claudius-brief": p. 45–47.

1. Church history—Primitive and early church. 2. Jews in Alexandria. 3. Greeks in Alexandria. 4. Claudius, emperor of Rome, B. C. 10–A. D. 54.   I. Title.

Library of Congress   BR170.L6   32–16356
                         (2)   270.1

NL 0445432   DLC NcD CU DDO CtY MH OCU IU MiU PBm

Loesch, Vilma von.
... Variationen über Berlin; liebevolle kritik einer stadt. Stuttgart, Berlin, Deutsche verlags-anstalt, 1932.

192 p. 18ᶜᵐ.

1. Berlin.   I. Title.

Library of Congress   DD866.L6   32–2244
Copyright A—Foreign   14806
                         (2)   914.315

NL 0445433   DLC NN

Lösch, Waldo, 1923–
Leitung, Mitbestimmung und Arbeitnehmerhaftung. (Hamburg, 1951?)

71 p. 21 cm.

Inaug.-Diss.—Wirtschaftshochschule, Mannheim.
Vita.
Bibliography: p. 70–71.

1. Employees' representation in management—Germany.   I. Title.

HD5660.G4L6   56–18008

NL 0445434   DLC

41.2
1895

Lösch, Wilhelm.
Ermittlungen über die klinische Seite, die Verluste und Schäden der Maul- und Klauenseuche im Jahre 1951/52. Hannover, Eberlein, 1952.

23 p.

Inaug.-Diss. – Tierärztliche Hochschule, Hannover.

1. Foot-and-mouth disease.

NL 0445435   DNAL

Lösch (Wilhelm). Untersuchungen über den Flusschwamm (Spongia fluviatilis). Eine zur öffentlichen Vertheidigung bearbeitete Abhandlung. 23 pp. 8°. *St. Petersburg, k. Akad. d. Wissensch.,* 1854.

NL 0445436   DNLM

Loesch, Wilhelm Max, 1905–
Gk13.44   Die Einführung der direkten Rede bei den epischen Dichtern der Römer bis zur domitianischen Zeit ... Erlangen, Buchdruckerei K. Döres, 1927.

2p.ℓ.,102[i.e.101]p. 21½cm.
Inaug.-Diss. – Erlangen.
Lebenslauf.
"Literaturverzeichnis": p.100.

1. Latin poetry language – Syn-   Hist. & crit. 2. Latin tax.

NL 0445437   CtY PU MiU MH IU NN OCU ICRL NIC

Löschardt, F(erdinand)
... Ein vorschlag zur bestimmung der Venusrotation, von F. Löschardt ... Wien, Aus der K.-K. Hof- und staatsdruckerei, 1904.

cover-title, 6 p. 24½ᶜᵐ.

Aus den Sitzungsberichten der K. Akademie der wissenschaften in Wien. Mathem.-naturw. klasse; bd. CXIII. abt. IIa. mai 1904.

1. Venus (Planet)

Library of Congress   QB621.L82   5–25707†

NL 0445438   DLC

Loeschbrandt, F
Bleaching of sulphate pulp, by F. Loeschbrandt, translated by E. Martin. (New York, The Technical association of the pulp and paper industry, 1941)

71 p. diagrs. 23ᶜᵐ.

"Presented at the annual meeting of the Technical association of the pulp and paper industry ... New York, N. Y., Feb. 17–20, 1941. The translation was sponsored by the Technical association ... through its Pulp purification committee."
Bibliography: p. 70–71.

1. Wood-pulp. 2. Bleaching.   I. Martin, Euterpe, tr. II. Technical association of the pulp and paper industry. III. Title: Sulphate pulp.

Library of Congress   TS1176.L6   43–48023
                         (3)   676

NL 0445439   DLC NcRS MB OU OCl OrCS OrP Wa WaS

Löschburg, Herbert, 1897–
Zahnärztliches aus den consilien des Thaddäus aus Florenz ... vorgelegt von Herbert Löschburg ... Leipzig, Lehmann, 1922.

54 p. 22ᶜᵐ.

Thesis, Leipzig, 1922.
"Literatur": p. 53.

1. Thaddaeus Florentinus, 1223?–1303? 2. Dentistry – Early works. 3. Medicine, Medieval

NL 0445440   NNC DNLM ICRL CtY

Loeschcke, Georg, 1852–1915.
Altattische grabstelen.

(In Archäologisches institut des Deutschen reichs. Athenische zweiganstalt. Mitteilungen. Athen, 1879. 24½ᶜᵐ. 4. jahrg. p. (36,–44, (289,–306. plates (part col.))

Signed: Georg Loeschcke.

1. Stele (Archaeology) 2. Sepulchral monuments—Greece. 3. Painting, Greek.

Hamilton college. Library for Library of Congress   A 44–8718
                    DE2.D44 jahrg. 4

NL 0445441   NCH DLC

Loeschcke, Georg, 1852–1915.
Archaische Niobidenvase. (Hierzu Antike denkmäler I, taf. 22)

(In Archäologisches institut des Deutschen reichs. Jahrbuch. Berlin, 1888. 27½ᶜᵐ. bd. II (1887) p. (275,–279)

Signed: G. Loeschcke.

1. Vases, Greek. 2. Niobe.   I. Title. II. Title: Niobidenvase.

Hamilton college. Library for Library of Congress   A C 39–263
                    (DE2.D5 bd. 2)
                    (2)   (913.3)

NL 0445442   NCH OCU DLC

Loeschcke, Georg, 1852–
... Aus der unterwelt; (on a painting on an ancient Greek sarcophagus from Clazmenae in the British Museum). Dorpati Livonorum (1888).

12p. illus. 27cm.

Sollemne Caesareae Universitatis Dorpatensis, 1888.

NL 0445443   CU CtY

Loeschcke, Georg, 1852–1915.
... Boreas und Oreithyia am Kypseloskasten. Dorpati Livonorum (1886)

Pamphlet
Programm – Univ. of Dorpat (announcement of prizes)
Title without border.

NL 0445444   CtY MH

LOESCHCKE, Georg, 1852–
(A collection of pamphlets on archaeological subjects, with dates ranging from 1876 to 1904).

Plates.

NL 0445445   MH

Loeschcke, Georg, 1852–1915.
... De basi quadam prope spartam reperta observationes archaeologicae ... Dorpati Livonorum [1879]

Programm – Dorpat.
Text in German
Caption title: Ueber die Reliefs der altspartanischen Basis. Ein Beitrag zur Geschichte der bildlichen Tradition.
"Anhang. Vasen aus der Fabrik der Arkesilasschale": p. 12–16.

NL 0445446   CtY

Löschcke, Georg, 1852–
De Pausaniae descriptione urbis Athenarum quaestiones. (In Univ. Programma, 1883) Dorpati Livonorum.

26 p. 4°. [In "Greek geography", v. 3]

NL 0445447   CtY NjP

VOLUME 338

Loeschcke, Georg, 1852–1915.
De titvlis aliqvot atticis, qvaestiones historicae. Bonnae, typis C. Georgi, 1876.
2 p. L, 86 p. 21½ᶜᵐ.
Inaug.-diss.—Bonn.
Vita.

1. Inscriptions, Greek. 2. Athens—Hist.

Library of Congress   DF82.5.L7   4–34258

NL 0445448   DLC CtY PU NBuU

LÖSCHCKE, Georg, 1852–
Die Enneakrunosepisode bei Pausanias. Ein beitrag zur topographie und geschichte. Athens. [Progr. Dorpati Livonorum, 1883.]
4°. pp. 26.
Also with the title:–"De Pausaniae de scriptione urbis Athenarum questiones."

NL 0445449   MH PU

Loeschcke, Georg, 1852–1915.
Die enthauptung der Medusa, ein beitrag zur geschichte der griechischen malerei, von dr. Georg Loeschcke ... Bonn, F. Cohen, 1894.
16 p. illus., pl. 32½ x 24½ᶜᵐ.
On verso of t.-p.: Festschrift zur feier des fünfzigjährigen doctorjubiläums von Heinrich von Brunn am 20. märz 1896, herausgegeben von der Philosophischen facultät der ... Universität zu Bonn.

1. Painting, Greek. 2. Medusa. I. Bonn. Universität. Philosophische fakultät. II. Title.

Library of Congress   ND110.L6   34–21621
759.938

NL 0445450   DLC MH PU

Loeschcke, Georg, 1852.
Ephoros-Stricken. - I. Die schlacht bei Salamis. (From Jahrbücher für class. Philos., Bd. 115. Leipzig, 1877)
8 p. 8°. [In "Greek History, v. 3]

NL 0445451   CtY

Loeschcke, Georg, 1852–
Helbig, Wolfgang, 1839–1915.
Die Italiker in der Poebene, von Wolfgang Helbig ... Leipzig, Breitkopf & Härtel, 1879.

Loeschcke, Georg, 1852–1915.
Kopf der Athena Parthenos des Pheidias. (Festschrift des Ver. v. Alterthumsfr. im Rhein zum 50-jährigen Jubileum 1891)
22 p. + pl. 4°. (In "Greek art," 3)

NL 0445453   CtY

NK4646
.F8
folio
Loeschcke, Georg, 1852–1915, joint author.
Furtwängler, Adolf, 1853–1907.
Mykenische thongefaesse. Festschrift zur feier des fünfzigjährigen bestehens des Deutschen archaeologischen institutes in Rom, im auftrage des Institutes in Athen herausgegeben von Adolf Furtwaengler und Georg Loeschcke. Berlin, In commission bei A. Asher und co., 1879.

NK4646
.F85
folio
Loeschcke, Georg, 1852–1915, joint author.
Furtwängler, Adolf, 1853–1907.
Mykenische vasen; vorhellenische thongefässe aus dem gebiete des Mittelmeeres. Im auftrage des Kaiserlich deutschen archaeologischen instituts in Athen gesammelt und hrsg. von Adolf Furtwaengler und Georg Loeschcke. Mit einem atlas von 44 tafeln. Berlin, A. Asher & co., 1886.

Loeschcke, Georg, 1852–1915.
Observationes archaeologicae. Dorpati Livonorum [1880]
12 p. 28 cm.
Separate from programm—Dorpat (Anniversary of founding)
In German.
Bibliographical footnotes.

1. Classical antiquities—Addresses, essays, lectures.

DE60.L6   48–32623*

NL 0445456   DLC CtY

Loeschcke, Georg, 1852–1915.
... Die oestliche Giebelgruppe am Zeustempel zu Olympia ... Dorpati Livonorum [1885]
Programm - Dorpat.

NL 0445457   CtY NjP

Loeschcke, Georg, 1852–
Phidias Tod und die Chronologie des olympischen Zeus. (Sep. Abdr. ....) Bonn, 1882.
25–46 p. 8°. (In "Greek sculpture," 2)

NL 0445458   CtY

Loeschcke, Georg, 1852–1915.
Relief aus Messene.
(In Archäologisches institut des Deutschen reichs. Jahrbuch. Berlin, 1889. 27½ᶜᵐ. bd. III (1888) p. [189]–193. 1 illus., pl. 7)
Signed: G. Loeschcke.

1. Relief (Sculpture) 2. Sculpture—Paris. 3. Messene—Antiq. 4. Sculpture, Greek.

Hamilton college. Library
for Library of Congress   DE2.D5 bd. 3   A C 39–275
[a44c1]†   (913.8)

NL 0445459   NCH OCU DLC

Loeschcke, Georg, 1852–1915.
Stele aus Amyklä.
(In Archäologisches institut des Deutschen reichs. Athenische zweiganstalt. Mitteilungen. Athen, 1878. 24½ᶜᵐ. 3. jahrg., p. [164]–171. 1 illus.)
Signed: Georg Löschcke.

1. Stele (Archaeology) 2. Inscriptions, Greek—Amyclae, Greece.

Hamilton college. Library
for Library of Congress   DE2.D44 jahrg. 3   A 44–3708

NL 0445460   NCH DLC

Loeschcke, Georg, 1852–1915.
Vasenbilder aus Kameiros.
(In Archäologisches institut des Deutschen reichs. Athenische zweiganstalt. Mitteilungen. Athen, 1880. 24½ᶜᵐ. 5. jahrg., p. [380]–383. pl. XIII–XIV.)
Signed: G. Loeschcke.

1. Vases, Greek. 2. Vases—London. 3. Vase-painting, Greek.

Hamilton college. Library
for Library of Congress   DE2.D44 jahrg. 5   A 44–3776

NL 0445461   NCH DLC

Loeschcke, George, 1852–
Vermutungen zur griechischen kunstgeschichte und zur topographie Athens. (In univ. programm, 1884.)
Dorpati Livonorum, 1884.

NL 0445462   NjP CtY

Loeschcke, George, 1852–1915.
... Die westliche Giebelgruppe am Zeustempel zu Olympia ... Dorpati Livonorum [1887]
Programm - Dorpat.

NL 0445463   CtY NjP

Loeschcke, Georg, 1852–1915.
Zur datierung des Hermes des Alkamenes.
(In Archäologisches institut des Deutschen reichs. Jahrbuch. Berlin, 1904. 27½ᶜᵐ. bd. XIX (1904) p. 22–25)
Signed: Georg Loeschcke.

1. Alcamenes. 2. Mercurius.

Hamilton college. Library
for Library of Congress   DE2.D5 bd. 19   A 44–3873
(913.3)

NL 0445464   NCH DLC

BR60
.G7
Bd. 28
Loeschcke, Gerhard, 1880–1912, ed.
Gelasius of Cyzicus, fl. 475.
Gelasius Kirchengeschichte, hrsg. im auftrage der Kirchenväter-commission der Königl. preussischen akademie der wissenschaften, auf grund der nachgelassenen papiere von prof. lic. Gerhard Loeschcke, durch dr. Margret Heinemann. Leipzig, J. C. Hinrichs, 1918.

BR129
.J8L7
(Ha)
Loeschcke, Gerhard, 1880–1912.
Jüdisches und heidnisches im christlichen kult. Eine vorlesung von Gerhard Loeschcke. Bonn, A. Marcus und E. Weber, 1910.
[3], 36 p. 19ᶜᵐ.

1. Christianity and other religions.

NL 0445466   ICU IU NN CU MH PPDrop MiU OCH CtY CU

BR160
.G3S8SL8
LOESCHCKE, GERHARD, 1880–1912.
Das Syntagma des Gelasius Cyzicenus... von Gerhard Loeschcke... Bonn, C. Georgi, 1906.
71 p. 21½ cm.
Inaug.--diss.--Bonn.
Lebenslauf.
Separatabdruck aus dem Rhein.mus. LX 594 LXI 34.

1. Gelasius of Cyzicus, fl. ca. 475. Syntagma.

NL 0445467   ICU PU CtY MH DDO

Loeschcke, Gerhard, 1880–1912.
Die Vaterunser-erklärung des Theophilus von Antiochien; eine quellenuntersuchung zu den Vaterunser-erklärungen des Tertullian, Cyprian, Chromatius und Hieronymus, von Gerhard Loeschcke ... Berlin, Trowitzsch & sohn, 1908.
2 p. L., 51 p. 24ᶜᵐ. (Added t.-p.: Neue studien zur geschichte der theologie und der kirche, hrsg. von N. Bonwetsch ... und R. Seeberg ... 4. stück)

1. Theophilus, Saint, bp. of Antioch, 2d cent. 2. Lord's prayer.

Library of Congress   BR141.S82 stück 4   8–19782

NL 0445468   DLC OO NNUT PCC

VOLUME 338

BR162
.L82 Loeschcke, Gerhard, 1880-1912.
Zwei kirchengeschichtliche entwürfe,
von Gerhard Loeschcke. Tübingen, J. C. B.
Mohr (Paul Siebeck) 1913.
78p.

CONTENTS.- Die alte kirche und das
evangelium.- Quellenkunde der alten kirchengeschichte.

1. Church history - Primitive and early
church. 2. Fathers of the church. I. Title.

NL 0445469   TNJ-R CLU OO MH-AH

Loeschcke, Hermann, 1882-
Methoden der morphologischen untersuchung des ver-
dauungsapparates, pancreas. Von H. Loeschcke ... und R.
Otto ...
(*In* Abderhalden, Emil. ed. Handbuch der biologischen arbeitsmethoden ... Berlin, 1926.   25ᶜᵐ. abt. VIII, Methoden der
experimentellen morphologischen forschung. t. 1, 1. hälfte (1924)
p. [661]-674)
Bibliographical foot-notes; "Literatur": p. 665.

1. Digestive organs. 2. Pancreas.   I. Otto, Richard Ernst Wilhelm,
1872-   joint author.

Title from Ohio State   Univ.   A C 36-3229
Library of Congress   [QH324.A3 1920 abt. 8, t. 1]

NL 0445470   OU

Loeschcke, Hermann, 1882-
Methoden zur morphologischen untersuchung der lunge. Von
H. Loeschcke ...
(*In* Abderhalden, Emil. ed. Handbuch der biologischen arbeitsmethoden ... Berlin, 1926.   25ᶜᵐ. abt. VIII, Methoden der
experimentellen morphologischen forschung. t. 1, 1. hälfte (1924)
p. [575]-598. illus.)

1. Lungs.
Title from Ohio State   Univ.   A C 36-3225
Library of Congress   [QH324.A3 1920 abt. 8, t. 1]

NL 0445471   OU

Loeschcke, Hermann, 1882-
Methoden zur morphologischen untersuchung des genital-
apparates, nebennieren. Von H. Loeschcke ... und H. Weinnoldt ...
(*In* Abderhalden, Emil. ed. Handbuch der biologischen arbeitsmethoden ... Berlin, 1926.   25ᶜᵐ. abt. VIII, Methoden der
experimentellen morphologischen forschung. t. 1, 1. hälfte (1924)
p. [651]-660)
Bibliographical foot-notes.

1. Generative organs. 2. Suprarenal bodies.   I. Weinnoldt, H., joint
author.

Title from Ohio State   Univ.   A C 36-3228
Library of Congress   [QH324.A3 1920 abt. 8, t. 1]

NL 0445472   OU

L616.078 v.3
8491 pt.1
Loeschcke, Hermann, 1882-
... Störungen des Luftgehalts. Von H. Loeschcke ... Mit 67
Textabbildungen ...
(*In* Handbuch der speziellen pathologischen Anatomie und Histologie. Ber-
lin, 1928.   26¼ᶜᵐ. Bd. 3, Teil 1, p. [599]-700. illus., diagrs.)
"Literatur": p. 695-700.

NL 0445473   ICJ

LOESCHCKE, Hermann, 1882-
Über die berechtigung der annahme dass das
glykogen in den etc. Inaug.-diss. Bonn, 1907.

NL 0445474   MBCo

Loeschcke (Moritz) [1871-   ]. *Primäre Gal-
lengangcarcinome mit einem kasuistischen
Beitrag. 24 pp. 8° München, Kastner &
Callwey, 1907.

NL 0445475   DNLM

Loeschcke, Siegfried, 1883-1956.
Antike laternen und lichthäuschen. Von Siegfried Loeschcke.
(*In* Bonner jahrbücher. Jahrbücher des Vereins von altertumsfreunden im Rheinlande. Bonn, 1909. 27½ᶜᵐ. hft. 118, p. [370]-430.
illus., pl. XXVIII-XXXVI (part fold.))
Bibliographical foot-notes.

1. Lanterns.
                                           A 42-3098
Metropolitan mus. of art,   N. Y. Library
for Library of Congress   [DD491.R4B7 hft. 118]
                                                      (948.42)

NL 0445476   NNMM

Loeschcke, Siegrfried, 1883-1956.
Bedeutung und Gefährdung der grossen Tempelgrabung in Trier.   Trier, 1930.
cover-title, 149-166 p.   illus., 4 plates., plan.
27 cm.
"Sonderdruck aus Trierer Zeitschrift, IV, 1929;
Druck und Verlag von Jacob Lintz, Trier."

NL 0445477   NNC-A MH

Loeschcke, Siegfried, 1883-

Niessen, Carl Anton, 1850-
Beschreibung römischer altertümer gesammelt von Carl An-
ton Niessen ... 3. bearbeitung ...   Cöln a. Rh., Druck von
Greven & Bechtold, 1911.

Gt31
09   Loeschcke, Siegfried, 1883-
Denkmäler vom Weinbau aus der Zeit der
Römerherrschaft an Mosel, Saar und Ruwer, vom
Leiter der Römischen Abteilung des Deutschen
Weinmuseums der Stadt Trier, Dr. Siegfried
Loeschcke ... Mit 15 Tafeln und 33 Textab-
bildungen.   Trier, Selbstverlag der Römischen
Abteilung des Deutschen Weinmuseums[1933]
vii,60,ix-xiip.,1ℓ. front.,illus.,plates.
29cm.

"In erster Bearbeitung erschien diese Ab-
handlung i. J. 1930 in "Rheinlands Weine:
Mosel-, Saar- und Ruwerweine", 4.Heft der
Schriftenfolge "Rheinlands Weine" her. v.
Propagandaverband preussischer Weinbaugebiete,
Bonn".
Bibliographical foot-notes.

NL 0445480   CtY PU-Mu DDO NjP

915.45
L82e   Loeschcke, Siegfried, 1883-
Die Erforschung des Tempelbezirkes im Altbachtale zu Trier vom Ausgrabungsleiter der
Kommission zur Erforschung der Römischen Kai-
serresidenz und Frühchristlichen Bischofstadt
Trier.   Berlin, E. S. Mittler Buchdruckerei, 1928.
vii, 46p. illus., 29 plates(1 fold.) fold.
plan in pocket. 27cm.

1. Treves--Antiquities, Roman. 2. Excavations (Archaeological)--Treves.

NL 0445481   IU PBm MdBJ CtY OCU ICU MH

BR 133
.F83 T8   LOESCHCKE, SIEGFRIED, 1883-
Frühchristliche Denkmäler aus Trier.
[Düsseldorf, Druck von L. Schwann, 1936?]
91-145 p. illus.

Reprinted from Rheinischer Verein für
Denkmalpflege und Heimatschütz. Zeitschrift,
v. 29, 1936, no.1.

1. Christian--Antiquities--Treves. I. Title.

NL 0445482   InU

NK5107
F86d   Loeschcke, Siegfried, 1893-
Gefässe in Bronze, Glas, und Ton zur Rö-
merzeit. Trier, 1925. 5 p. illus. 40 cm.

Photocopy (negative)
Bound with: Fremersdorf, Fritz. A great
discovery of Roman glass ... 1930.

4484. 1. Art industries and trade--Roman
Empire. 2. Glassware, Roman. I. Title.

NL 0445483   NCorniC

Jh5
88   Loeschcke, Siegfried, 1883-
Keramische Funde in Haltern. Ein Beitrag zur
Geschichte der augusteischen Kultur in Deutsch-
land ... Münster i.W.,1909.
2p.ℓ.,[103]-190,[2]p. illus.,pl. X-XV.
23½cm.
Inaug.-Diss. - Bonn.
Lebenslauf.
Published in full as Mitteilungen der
Altertumskommission für Westfalen, Heft 5.

NL 0445484   CtY CU DLC MH CU PU NjP ICRL

Loeschcke, Siegfried, 1883-
Lampen aus Vindonissa. Ein beitrag zur geschichte
von Vindonissa und des antiken belenchtungswesens, von
Siegfried Loeschcke ...   Zürich, In kommission bei Beer &
cie. [etc.] 1919.
358 p., 1 l. illus., xxiii pl. 33ᶜᵐ.
Double paging (193-546) with reference to "Mitteilungen der Antiqua-
rischen gesellschaft," v. 27, in which it was originally intended to include
this work.

1. Lamps. 2. Windisch, Switzerland—Antiquities, Roman.   I. Title.

Library of Congress   NK4680.L6
                                                        19-18898

NL 0445485   DLC ICU CaBVaU NjP

DD491
.W46A7   Loeschcke, Siegfried, 1883-

Albrecht, Christoph, 1898-   ed.
... Das Römerlager in Oberaden und das uferkastell in
Beckinghausen an der Lippe, herausgegeben von Christoph Al-
brecht.   Dortmund, Verlag Fr. Wilh. Ruhfus, 1938-

Loeschcke, Siegfried, 1883-   ed.
... Der tempelbezirk im Altbachtale zu Trier, herausgegeben
von Siegfried Loeschcke ...   Berlin, Reichsverlag, 1938-
v. illus. 31½ x 23½ᶜᵐ. and portfolio of plates, plans. 36 x 27½ᶜᵐ.
At head of title: Archäologisches institut des Deutschen reiches, Rö-
misch-germanische kommission, Frankfurt a. M.
Each volume has also special t.-p.
Label mounted over publisher's name in imprint: Reichsverlagsamt.
CONTENTS.—hft. I. Planausschnitt Ritonatempel und umgebung, bearb.
von E. Gose, L. Hussong, W. Jovy und S. Loeschcke.

1. Germanic antiquities. 2. Treves—Antiquities, Roman. 3. Cultus,
Germanic. 4. Excavations (Archaeology)—Treves.   I. Archäologisches
institut des Deutschen reichs. Römisch-germanische kommission. II.
Title.

Library of Congress   DD901.T85L6   41-38018

                                                        913.4342

NL 0445487   DLC MH NNC CtY NN

VOLUME 338

Loeschck, Siegfried, 1883-1956.
Von den Ausgrabungen im grossen Tempelbezirk
in Trier. [1930]
7 p. illus. 23 cm.
"Durch Abbildung S. 5 erweiterter Sonderdruck
aus 'Heimat', Blätter des Vereins für Mosel,
Hochwald und Hunsrück, Nr. 5, Berncastel-Cues,
Mai 1930."
Bound with the author's Bedeutung und Gefährdung
der grossen Tempelgrabung in Trier.

NL 0445488   NNC-A

NK5107
L82   Loeschcke, Siegfried, 1883-1956.
Zur angeblich römischen Glashütte auf der
Hochmark b. Cordel. Römische Glasfabrikation
in Trier. Trier, 1915 49-57 p. illus.
30 cm.

Photocopy (negative)
Detached from Römisch-germanisches Korres-
pondenzblatt, Jg. 8, nr. 4.
Bound with: no. 2.Behrens, Gustav. Römisches
Grab aus Oberingelheim. 1925.-no. 3.Behrens,
Gustav. Früher   manische Funde aus der

Friedberger Gegend.1931.-no.4.Haberey, Waldemar. Wandnischen in spätromischen Erdgräben
zu Köln. 1934.

4499. 1. Glassware, Roman. 2. Manufacture of
glass—Roman Empire. I. Title. II. Title:
Römische Glasfabrikation in Trier.

NL 0445490   NCOrniC

Loesche, Adolf, 1883-   comp.

Jahresbericht über die leistungen der chemischen technologie
... 1.–   jahrg., 1855-19
Leipzig, O. Wigand, 1856-1909; J. A. Barth. 1910–

Loesche, Adolf, 1883-   comp.

Jahresbericht über die leistungen der chemischen technologie
(Indexes)
Patentregister zum Jahresbericht über die leistungen der
chemischen technologie, 1925-1935; bearbeitet von dr. Adolf
Loesche ... Leipzig, J. A. Barth, 1936.

Loesche, Adolf, 1883-
1. Untersuchung in der Sesquiterpenreihe:
über Caryophyllen. 2. Über Verbindungen von Eisen und
Chrom mit Fluorwasserstoffsäure. Weida i. Th. 1909:
Thomas & Hubert. 78 S. 8°
Leipzig, Phil. Diss. v. 21. Juni 1909, Ref. Beckmann, Hantzsch
Geb. 18. Okt. 83 Magdeburg; Wohnort: Magdeburg; Staatsangeh.: Preussen;
Vorbildung: Guericke-Realgymn. Magdeburg; Studium: Karlsruhe Techn.
Hochsch. 2, Rostock 4, Leipzig 7 S.; Rig. 26. Mai 09.]   [U 09. 3013

NL 0445493   ICRL OCU MH-C PU

Lösche, Bernhard, 1860-
Du stolzes England – schäme dich! Ein deutsches
Wort dem lebenden Geschlecht zur Erstarkung dem
kommenden zur Beherzigung ... 2. Aufl. Leipzig,
1914.
24 p. 23 cm.

NL 0445494   CtY NjP

Loesche, Bernhard, 1860-
Du stolzes England — schäme dich! Ein deutsches Wort
dem lebenden Geschlecht zur Erstarkung, dem kommenden zur
Beherzigung, von Bernhard Lösche... Leipzig: Serig, 1915.
24 p. 3. ed. 8°.

1. European war, 1914–   –Ad-   dresses, sermons, etc. 2. Character
N. Y. P. L.   (National), Gt. Br. 3. Title.   May 18, 1916.

NL 0445495   NN IU

Loesche, Bernhard, 1860-
Gewehr in Ruh! Bilder aus dem Stilleben des
Lazaretts, erlebt und erzählt von Pastor Bernhard
Loesche ... Leipzig, 1914.
31, [1] p. 20 cm.

NL 0445496   NjP CtY

Lösche, Bernhard, 1860-
...Die verschwundenen Bücklinge; oder, Das Spirituswunder.
Schwank in einem Aufzug für Mädchenrollen, von B. Lösche.
Leipzig: A. Strauch [190-?] 32 p. 22cm. (Jugendvereins-
Bühne.)

1. Juvenile literature—Drama,   German. I. Title.
N. Y. P. L.   February 17, 1939

NL 0445497   NN

Lösche, Eduard
    see Lösche, Gustav Eduard, 1821-1879.

Loesche, Georg, 1855-1932, ed.
Luther, Martin, 1483-1546.
Analecta Lutherana et Melanthoniana. Tischreden Luthers
und aussprüche Melanthons, hauptsächlich nach aufzeichnun-
gen des Johannes Mathesius. Aus der Nürnberger hand-
schrift des Germanischen museums, mit benutzung von d. Joh.
Karl Seidemanns vorarbeiten herausgegeben und erläutert von
Georg Loesche ... Gotha, F. A. Perthes, 1892.

Loesche, Georg, 1855-1932.
Archivalische Beiträge zur Geschichte des
Täufertums und des Protestantismus in Tirol und
Vorarlberg. Wien, Manz'sche Verlags- und
Universitäts- Buchhandlung, 1926.

xii, 156p. 23 1/2cm. (Jahrbuch der
Gesellschaft für die Geschichte des Protestantismus im ehemaligen und im neuen Österreich.
47. Jahrgang).

NL 0445500   ViHarEM

BX4841 Loesche, Georg, 1855-1932.
.A2G4   Die böhmischen Exulanten in Sachsen; ein
v.42-   Beitrag zur Geschichte des dreissigjährigen
44   Krieges und der Gegenreformation auf archivalischer Grundlage. Mit archivalischen
Beigaben. Wien, Mainz'sche Verlags- und
Universitäts-Buchhandlung, 1923.
xii, 585 p. (Jahrbuch der Gesellschaft für
die Geschichte des Protestantismus im ehemaligen Österreich. 42.-44.Jahrg.)
Includes bibliography.
"Archivalische   Beilagen": p.[291]-542.
1. Czechs in   Saxony. 2. Counter-Ref-
ormation--Bohemia.

NL 0445501   ICU OO NN

Loesche, Georg, 1855-1932.
De Augustino Plotinizante, in doctrina
de Deo disserenda... Jenae, 1880.
68 p. 23ᵐ.

Inaug.-Diss. - Jena.
Bibliographical footnotes.

1 Augustinus, Aurelius, Saint, Bp. of
Hippo - Theology

NL 0445502   NjPT NNC NcD ICRL NNUT

LOESCHE, Georg, 1855-1932.
Deutsch-evangelische kultur in Österreich-
Ungarn. Leipzig, A. Strauch, 1915.
34 p.

NL 0445503   MH OO

PT
1807   Loesche, Georg, 1855-1932.
Z5L82   Ernst Moritz Arndt; der deutsche
Reichsherold. Biographie und Charakteristik.
Gotha, F. A. Perthes, 1884.
74 p. 22cm.

1. Arndt, Ernst Moritz, 1769-1860.

NL 0445504   NIC OClW NNUT PU TU

Loesche, Georg, 1855-1932.
Die evangelischen fürstinnen im hause
Habsburg. Eine historisch-psychologische
studie. Mit benutzung archivalischer
quellen ... Wien, Manz'sche k.u.k. hofverlags-
und universitäts buchhandlung (J. Klinkhardt
& co) Leipzig, J. Klinkhardt, 1904.
71 p. plates (ports., facsim.) O.

NL 0445505   OO PPLT CaBVaU

Loesche, Georg, 1855-1932.
Geschichte des protestantismus im vormaligen und im neuen
Österreich, von Georg Loesche ... 3., verb., verm., mit drei
karten und einer notenbeilage versehene aufl. ... Wien, Manz;
[etc., etc.,] 1930.
xvi, 811 p. fold. pl. (music) fold. maps. 24ᵐ.
"Bücherwelt": p. 747-784.

1. Protestant churches—Austria. 2. Protestants in Austria. 3. Austria—Church history.
                                         34-23702
Library of Congress   BX4841.L6 1930   284.09436

NL 0445506   DLC NcD CU WU IU IaU CtY MH

Loesche, Georg, 1855-1932.
Geschichte des protestantismus in Oesterreich. In umrissen.
Im auftrag der "Gesellschaft für die geschichte des protestan-
tismus in Oesterreich." Von Georg Loesche. Tübingen und
Leipzig, Mohr, 1902.
4 p. l., 251 p. 19ᵐ.
"Ausgewählte quellen": p. 246-251.

1. Protestants in Austria.   I. Gesellschaft für die geschichte des
protestantismus in Österreich.
                                         42-34905
Library of Congress   BX4841.L62

        PPLT CaBVaU
NL 0445507   DLC CU-L OU NjPT ViU CSt MH ICU CLU

Loesche, Georg, 1855-
Inneres Leben der österreichischen Toleranzkirche. Archivalische Beiträge zur Kirchen- und Sittengeschichte des Protestantismus in Österreich 1781-1861. Von Georg Loesche. Wien:
J. Klinkhardt & Co., 1915. xii, 531 p. 8°. (Gesellschaft
für die Geschichte des Protestantismus in Österreich. Jahrb.
Jahrg. 36.)

1. Protestant church, Austria, 1781-   1861.
N. Y. P. L.   May 29, 1916.

NL 0445508   NN OO

VOLUME 338

Loesche, Georg, 1855–
Johannes Mathesius. Ein lebens- und sitten-bild aus der reformationszeit. Von Georg Loeschè ... Gotha, F. A. Perthes, 1895.
2 v. front. (port.) facsim. 22ᶜᵐ.
"Verzeichnis der sigla": 1. bd., p. ₍xiii₎–xv.

1. Mathesius, Johann, 1504–1565. 2. Reformation.

28–1477

Library of Congress   BR350.M3L6

NL 0445509   DLC NcD PPLT MH IU

Loesche, G₍eorg₎, 1855–1932.
Literarische Rundschau über die den Protestantismus in Österreich betreffenden Veröffentlichungen des Jahres 1910. Nebst einem Anhange: Proff. DDr. Bidlo und Kvačala über "Brüderunität und Luthertum." Wien: J. Klinkhardt & Co., 1911. 91 p. 8°. (Gesellschaft für die Geschichte des Protestantismus in Österreich. Nachtrag zum Jahrbuch. Jahrgang 32.)

1. Protestantism.—History, Austria,   1910. 2. Skalský, Gustaf Adolf.
3. Bidlo, Jaroslav. 4. Kvačala,   Johannes.
N.Y.P.L.   May 16, 1912.

NL 0445510   NN CtY-D MH

274.36
L824ℓ
Loesche, Georg, 1855–
Luther, Melanthon und Calvin in Österreich-Ungarn. Zu Calvins vierter Jahrhundertfeier. Mit archivalischen Beilagen. Tübingen, J. C.B. Mohr, 1909.
xvi,371 p. 25cm.

Bibliographical footnotes. "Schriften Luthers, Melanthons, Zwinglis, Calvins in tschechischer, polnischer, slowenischer und magyarischer Übersetzung": p. ₍345₎–359.

NL 0445511   MiDW CLU ICU InU CSt MnU

Loesche, Georg, 1855–1932.
Luther, Melanthon und Calvin in Österreich-Ungarn. Zu Calvins vierter Jahrhundertfeier. Mit archivalischen Beilagen. Tübingen, J. C. B. Mohr, 1909.
xvi, 371 [1] p. 8°. (Gesellschaft für die Geschichte des Protestantismus in Oesterreich. Jahrbuch. [Ergänzungsband zu Jahrg. 30])

NL 0445512   NN

₍Loesche, Georg₎ 1855–1932
₍Minucius Felix' verhältniss zu Athenagoras, von Dr. Georg Loesche. ...₎
N.p., n.p., n.d.
p. ₍168₎–178. 22½cm. (With this is bound: Kühn, Richard Furchtegott. Der Octavius des Minucius Felix; Wöfflin, E. Minucius Felix.)

NL 0445514   NcD

BX 4841 **LOESCHE, GEORG,** 1855–1932
.L82   Neues über die Ausrottung des Protestantismus in Salzburg 1731/32, zur zweihundertjahr-Erinnerung. Auf Grund des handschriftlichen Nachlasses des Gustav Rohrer. Wien, Manz, 1929.
217 p. (Gesellschaft für die Geschichte des Protestantismus im ehemaligen und im neuen Österreich. Jahrbuch, 50)
1. Protestants—Salzburg (Province)—History. 2. Salzburg (Province)—History.
I. Rohrer, Gustav. II. Title.

NL 0445515   InU MH-AH

Loesche, Georg, 1855–1932,
Der Protestantismus in der österreichisch-ungarischen Monarchie. Illus. Portraits. Plate. Fac-similes.
(In Werckshagen. Der Protestantismus am Ende des XIX. Jahrhunderts. Band 2, pp. 865–896. Berlin. [1902.])

F68 — Austria. Hist. Relig.

NL 0445516   MB

Loesche, Georg, 1855–1932.
Die reformatorischen kirchenordnungen Ober- und Innerösterreichs. ₍I₎–₍IV₎ Mitgeteilt, eingeleitet und erläutert von Georg Loesche.
(In Archiv für reformationsgeschichte ... Leipzig, 1920–21. 23ᶜᵐ. nr. 67. 17. jahrg. p. ₍209₎–230; nr. 68. 17. jahrg. p. ₍277₎–300; nr. 69/70. XVIII. jahrg. p. ₍35₎–55; nr. 71/72. XVIII. jahrg. p. ₍121₎–154)

1. Ecclesiastical law—Austria. 2. Lutheran church. Liturgy and ritual—History. 3. Reformation—Austria. 4. Lutheran church in Austria—Government.
A C 34–2103
Title from Union Theol.   Sem.
Library of Congress   [BR300.A5 jahrg. 17–18]

NL 0445517   NNUT OCl

BX4841 **Loesche, Georg,** 1855–
.L82   ... Von der duldung zur gleichberechtigung. Archivalische beiträge zur geschichte des Protestantismus in Österreich 1781–1861. Zur 50jährigen erinnerung an das Protestantenpatent. Von prof. dr. Georg Loesche. Wien, Manz, ₍etc., etc.₎ 1911.
lii, 812 p. front., 1 illus. 23ᶜᵐ. (Jahrbuch der Gesellschaft für die geschichte des Protestantismus in Österreich ... 32. und 33. jahrgang)
"Belege und erläuterungen": p. ₍667₎–799.

1. Protestants in Austria. 2. Protestant churches—Austria. 3. Church and state in Austria.

NL 0445518   ICU OO NcD NN NjP MiU WU CLU CtY-D CU

943.6
L824   **Loesche, Georg,** 1855–1932.
Von der toleranz zur parität in Österreich, 1781–1861, zur halbjahrhundertfeier des Protestantenpatentes. Leipzig, J.C. Hinrichs'sche Buchhandlung, 1911.
96 p.   illus.   24cm.

1. Austria. Church history. 2. Tolerance. 3. Protestants in Austria.

NL 0445519   MnU MH NIC

Loesche, Georg, 1855–1932.
Zur gegenreformation im Salzkammergut. Von Georg Loesche.
(In Archiv für reformationsgeschichte ... Berlin, 1906. 23½ᶜᵐ. nr. 11. 3. jahrg. p. ₍292₎–306)

1. Counter-reformation. 2. Protestants in Austria.
A C 34–1976
Title from Union Theol.   Sem.
Library of Congress   [BR300.A5 jahrg. 3]

NL 0445520   NNUT

Loesche, Georg, 1855–
Zur gegenreformation in Schlesien, Troppau, Jägerndorf, Leobschütz. Neue archivalische aufschlüsse von d. dr. Georg Loesche ... Leipzig, Verein für reformationsgeschichte, 1915–16.
2 v. 23 cm. (On cover: Schriften des Vereins für reformationsgeschichte. 32. jahrg., 1–2. stück, nr. 117/118; 33. jahrg. 3. stück, nr. 123)
CONTENTS.—1. Troppau—Jägerndorf.—II. Leobschütz.
1. Counter-reformation. 2. Catholic church in Silesia. 3. Jägerndorf, Austria—Church history. 4. Leobschütz, Ger.—Church history. 5. Silesia—Church history. 6. Troppau, Austria—Church history.
[BR300.V5 no. 117/118, 123]   A C 33—3030

Union Theol. Sem. Libr.
for Library of Congress   ₍a55d½₎

TxU CU ICMcC MoSCS KU MH-AH
NL 0445521   NNUT NN MH MiU OCU OU NcD CtY TNJ-R MU

Loesche, Georg, 1855–1932, ed.
Zwei Wiener evangelische stammbücher aus der zeit der gegenreformation. Mitgeteilt, eingeleitet und erläutert von Georg Loesche.
(In Archiv für reformationsgeschichte ... Leipzig, 1926. 23ᶜᵐ. nr. 91/92. XXIII. jahrg. p. ₍161₎–212)

1. Autograph albums.
A C 34–2147
Title from Union Theol.   Sem.
Library of Congress   [BR300.A5 jahrg. 23]

NL 0445522   NNUT OCl

LÖSCHE, Gustav Eduard, 1821–1879.
De causis nature chemicae et efficaciae plantarum. Dissertatio inauguralis botanico-chemica et pharmacodynamica. Lipsiae, [1843].
4°. pp. 31.   Bot 7158.43

NL 0445523   MH PPC DNLM

Lösche, Gustav Eduard, 1821–1879.
Ueber periodische Veränderungen des Windes an der Erdoberfläche Nach Beobachtungen zu Dresden von 1853 bis 1858. Dresden, Meinhold, 1865.

NL 0445524   DAS

Lösche, Gustav Eduard, 1821–1879.   581.105 K400
Das vegetabilische Leben und die chemische Affinität in ihren gegenseitigen Beziehungen, dargestellt von Dr. Eduard Lösche. Leipzig, L. Voss, 1844.
iv, 132 p. 22½ᶜᵐ.

NL 0445525   ICJ MH

Loesche, H   C
... Electronic mine-shaft signal system at Magma copper co., Superior, Ariz., by H. C. Loesche. ₍Washington, 1945₎
cover-title, 4 p. diagrs. 27ᶜᵐ. (U. S. Bureau of mines. Information circular 7318)
At head of title: April 1945. United States Dept. of the interior ... Bureau of mines ...
Reproduced from type-written copy.

1. Mining engineering—Safety measures. 2. Magma copper company. 3. Signals and signaling.   I. Title.
45–8566
Library of Congress   TN295.U4 no. 7318
——— Copy 2.   TN295.L6
(622.06173)   622.8

NL 0445526   DLC

Lösche, Haldor.
VM147
.F8   Fachkunde für Stahlschiffbauer. ₍Bearb. von dem Autorenkollektiv: Haldor Lösche, Erwin Bieber und Alfred Helms₎ Berlin, Volk und Wissen Volkseigener Verlag, 1953–

VOLUME 338

Loesche, Heinrich.
...Lassen sich die diluvialen Breitenkreise aus klimabeding-
ten, diluvialen Vorzeitformen rekonstruieren? Von Dr. Heinrich
Lösche... Hamburg, 1930. 39 p. charts, pl. 4°.
(Germany. Seewarte, Direktion der. Aus dem Archiv der deut-
schen Seewarte. Bd. 48, Nr. 7.)

Author's doctoral dissertation, Hamburg, 1929?
Bibliography, p. 36-39.

1. Earth—Surface. I. Ser.
N. Y. P. L.   March 27, 1931

NL 0445528   NN

Y   LOESCHE, JOHANNES, 1884-
7675   Die abfassung der Faits des Romains...   Halle
.F 186   a.S.,.C.A.Kaemmerer & co.,1907.
78p.

Inaug.-diss.—Halle-Wittenberg.
Lebenslauf.

NL 0445529   ICN MH MiU ICRL NjP PU CtY

Loesche, Martin.
Gedanken Goethes in der neuzeitlichen Biologie. Bremen,
J. Storm, 1949.
26 p. 21 cm.
"Vortrag, gehalten als Auftakt des Goethejahres am 2. Januar 1949
für die Goethegesellschaft. Ortsvereinigung Bremen und den Naturwissenschaftlichen Verein Bremen im Festsaale des Rathauses."

1. Goethe, Johann Wolfgang von—Knowledge—Biology. I. Title.
                                                        A 50-5458
Yale Univ. Library
for Library of Congress

NL 0445530   CtY NcD MH

Loesche, Martin.
Gestalt im Formlosen; ein Beitrag zur
Einführung in Goethes naturwissenschaft-
liches Denken.   Leipzig. Goethe-
Gesselschaft ₍n.d.₎
9 p. 21 cm.

"Nach einem Vortrag, gehalten in der
hamburger Goethe-Gesellschaft, kriegs-
winter 1942/43."

NL 0445531   IU

833Q55   Loesche, Martin.
DL82gi   Gibt es einen Mythos bei Goethe?
Leipzig, Goethe-Gesellschaft, 1944.
20p. 29cm.

"Vortrag, gehalten am 14. Oktober 1944 vor
der Goethe-Gesellschaft in Bremen ... und am
15. Oktober 1944 vor der Goethe-Gesellschaft
in Leipzig."

1. Goethe, Johann Wolfgang von, 1749-1832.
I. Title.

NL 0445532   IU InU

Loesche, Martin.
Goethes geistige Welt. Stuttgart, S. Hirzel, 1948.
379 p. 21 cm. (Welt und Genius)
Bibliographical references included in "Anmerkungen" (p. 345-
360)

1. Goethe, Johann Wolfgang von, 1749-1832.   (Series)

PT2177.L57   832.62   49-54190*

NNC CtY OrU GU UU MU
NL 0445533   DLC OrU NBuU N TU FTaSU PU NcD OU ICU

Loesche, Martin.
... Grundbegriffe in Goethes naturwissenschaft (und ihr
niederschlag im Faust) Leipzig, E. A. Seemann ₍1944₎
181 p. 19ᵐ. ₍Kleine bücherei zur geistesgeschichte, bd. 12₎

1. Goethe, Johann Wolfgang von—Knowledge—Science. 2. Goethe,
Johann Wolfgang von. Faust. I. Title.

PT2206.L6   A F 47-290
Yale univ. Library
for Library of Congress

WaU CLSU MoU CoU
NL 0445534   CtY NcD TU TxU IaU NN WaU PU MB WU DLC

PT2193   Loesche, Martin
L6   ... Tod und Ur.sterblichkeit in
1944   Goethes Weltbild, nach einem Vortrag
gehalten im Oktober 1943 in der Goethe-
Gesellschaft ... 3. Aufl. Leipzig,
Goethe-Gesellschaft, 1944.
16p. 21cm.

NL 0445535   RPB

Loesche, Paul.
Beitraege zur kenntnis der chinolin-ana-sulfon-
saeure und einiger ihrer derivate.   Breisgau, 1888
Inaug. diss. - Breisgau.

NL 0445536   ICRL

Loeschebrand-Horn, Hans Joachim von, ed.
...Heimatführer...hrsg. von Hans Joachim von
Loeschebrand-Horn und Walter Hüsing. Berlin,
Touristik-Verlag ₍1935₎
v.1, illus. maps (Die deutschen Heimatführer)

I. Hüsing, Walter, ed.

NL 0445537   MiD

Loeschebrand-Horn, Hans Joachim von.
Kartenlesen. 7. Aufl. Berlin, Bernard &
Graefe, 1940.
117p. illus.

NL 0445538   ICRL

Loeschebrand-Horn, Hans Joachim von.
Kartenlesen, von Hans-Joachim v. Loeschebrand-Horn ...
8. aufl.   Berlin, Bernard & Graefe, 1941.
117, ₍1₎ p., 1 l. illus., 2 fold. pl. (incl. maps) diagrs. 17ᵐ.

1. Maps.   I. Title.

Library of Congress   G151.L6 1941   43-17796
                         ₍2₎   526.99

NL 0445539   DLC NN MH ICU

Loeschebrand-Horn, Hans Joachim von, ed.
Saarpfalz. Berlin, Verlag der Deutschen
Heimatführer [1937]

260 p. (Die deutschen Heimatführer, 3)

NL 0445540   MH

Loeschebrand-Horn, Hans Joachim von,   ed.
Südbayern. Berlin, Deutschen Heimatführer
Touristik-Verlag ₍1938?₎
263 p. illus. 22ᵐ. ₍Die deutschen Heimatführer,
Bd. 6₎
1. Bavaria - Descr. & trav. - Guide-books.

NL 0445541   ViU

Loeschebrand-Horn, Hans Joachim von, ed.
Württemberg, Hohenzollern. Berlin, Verlag der
Deutschen Heimatführer [1937]

299 p. (Die Deutschen Heimatführer, 5)

NL 0445542   MH

D810   Löschenkohl, Bernhard.
.P7G755   Kessemeier, Heinrich, 1876-   ed.
Der feldzug mit der andern waffe. Herausgeber: Heinrich
Kessemeier ... 1.-5. tausend. Hamburg, Falken-verlag ₍1940₎

Löschenkohl, Bernhard.
Hamburg. Berlin, Junker und Dünnhaupt, 1941.
45 p. map. 21 cm. (Die Deutschen Gaue seit der Machtergrei-
fung)

1. Nationalsozialistische Deutsche Arbeiter-Partei. Gau Hamburg.
(Series)

DD253.4.H3L68   52-54142

NL 0445544   DLC IU WU NcD NN IU MH

*NK4749   ₍Löschenkohl, Hieron₎
L7   ₍Album mit 108 eingeklebten kostüm- u. mode-
bildern kopfputz, haartrachten.   Aquarellierte
bleistiftzeichnungen ... aus de zeit 1790.
No imprint, 1790?₎

col.plates mounted on 54 l.   25x33cm.

Original drawings.
Title from sales catalog: Gilhofer &
Ranschburg catalog no. 222.
1. Costume.-France.

NL 0445545   NBuG

Löschenkohl, ₍Johann₎.   Carl 106*
Schema aller uniform der kaiserl. königl. kriegsvölkern. Wienn,
H. Löschenkohl, ₍17--?₎
7 ports. and 138 engraved and colored plates.
The title-page is engraved.
Formerly owned by Thomas Carlyle. With the book-plates of William Henry,
duke of Clarence, afterwards William IV king of England, and of Thomas Carlyle.

Austria-Army-Uniforms‖

NL 0445546   MH

Loescher, Abraham, 1520-1575.
Threni; seu, Lamentationes Ieremiae
Prophetae; elegiaco carmine redditae per
Abrahamum Laescherum...   Basileae, 1551
see under   Bible. O.T.
Lamentations. Latin. Paraphrases. 1551.
Loescher.

VOLUME 338

LOESCHER, Albert.
Doctrine de Jean Huss sur l'église. Thèse.
Strasbourg, G. Silbermann, 1865.

At head of title: Université de France.
Faculté de théologie protestante de Strasbourg.

NL 0445548   MH

Löscher (Bochumil Josef) [1886-]. *Die
Knorpelkappen der Brustwirbeldornfortsätze
des Pferdes. Ein Beitrag zur Operation der
Widerristfistel. [Leipzig.] 28 pp., 1 pl. 8°.
Dresden. 1919.

NL 0445549   DNLM ICRL

Loescher, Burt Garfield.
The history of Rogers' rangers ... By Burt Garfield
Loescher, with colored plates by Helene Loescher. San Francisco, 1946-
   v. illus. (part col.; incl. facsim.) col. fold. pl., maps (1 fold.)
18½ᶜᵐ.
   Contents.—I. The beginnings, Jan. 1755–April 6, 1758.

   1. Rogers' rangers. 2. U. S.—Hist.—French and Indian war, 1755–
1763—Regimental histories—Rogers' rangers.
                        46–20688
   Library of Congress   E190.L8
                                 973.2ⁱ

    ICN NN
NL 0445550   DLC CU MH MU NcU NcD MB ICU MiU-C PPT

Loescher, Carl, 1861-
Ueber magnetische folgepunkte.
Inaug. diss. Halle, 1884

NL 0445551   ICRL

Loescher, Carl Friedrich Heinrich, b. 1828.
   * De Lusatiae inferioris in curandis parturientibus
praestantia. Berolini, G. Schade, 1853.
   31 p. 1 tab. 8°.

NL 0445552   DNLM

Löscher, Carl Immanuel, 1750-1814.
   Der Bergmaschinenmeister, oder kurze
Uebersicht alles dessen, was einer wissen
und beobachten muss, wenn er hier den Mann
machen will, den er soll. Dem bergmännischen Publiko gewidmet. Dresden, In der
Arnoldischen Buchhandlung, 1805.
   viii,64p. diagrs. 22cm.

NL 0445553   OkU

Egleston
D622.14
Z
v.1   Löscher, Carl Immanuel, 1750-1814.
   Erfindung eines bergmännischen instruments
wodurch beim ueberfahren der gänge auf stölln
und strecken, und beim durchsinken derselben
in schächten, nicht allein ihr wahres strei-
chen, sondern auch ihr recht und widersinnige
fallen genau bestimmt werden kann. Leipzig,
S. L. Crusius, 1803.
   64 p. illus.

    Bibliography: p. 63-64.
    Volume of   phlets.

NL 0445554   NNC

TN 74
F7 L6   Löscher, Carl Immanuel, 1750-1814.
   Historisch bergmännische Briefe über verschie-
dene Gegenstände des Freybergischen Bergbaues.
Leipzig, S. L. Crusius, 1786.
   viii, 160 p. fold. diagrs. 19 cm.

NL 0445555   OU PPAN

QD904
L6   Löscher, Carl Immanuel, 1750-1814.
Earth   Uibergangsordnung bei der Kristallisation der Fossilien, wie
Sciences   sie aus einander entspringen und in einander übergehen.
Library   Leipzig, S. L. Crusius, 1796.
   vi, 61 p. plates.

    1. Crystallography - To 1800.

NL 0445556   CU IU

Loescher, Carolus Fridericus Henricus
     see   Loescher, Carl Friedrich Heinrich,
         b. 1828.

Loescher, Caspar, 1636-1718.
   Casparis Loescheri...Amoenitates evangelicæ, LXII. dis-
put. inclusæ, & studiis æqvè academicis, atqve ecclesiasticis con-
secratæ... Wittenbergæ: C. Schrödterus, 1696. 248 p.
4°.

558556A. 1. Bible. N. T.: Gospels.
N. Y. P. L.   November 18, 1931

NL 0445558   NN

Loescher, Caspar, 1636-1718, praeses.
   ... Dissertatio historico-theologica, de Saule per musicam
curato ... ex I. Sam. xvi, 14. seqq. ... Wittenbergæ, typis
Christiani Schrödteri [1688]
   78, [2] p. 19ᶜᵐ.
   Diss.—Wittenberg (Heinrich Pipping, respondent and author)

   1. Bible. O. T. 1 Samuel, xvi—Criticism, interpretation, etc. 2. Saul,
king of Israel. 3. Music. Influence of. I. Pipping, Heinrich, 1670-
1722, respondent.
                           8-27851 Revised
   Library of Congress   ML3920.A2L8

NL 0445559   DLC

Loescher, Caspar, d. 1718
   Der ehrwürdige Priester...Zum Druck
befördert von M. Johann. Andr. Gleichen.
Torgau, David Lötsch, 1691. 170 pp. Several
pages of text badly mutilated

NL 0445560   OSW

Löscher, Caspar, 1636-1718.
   ... Neue Absolutions-Formulen, aus allen
Sonn-und Fest-Tags Evangelien genommen, so
wohl Beicht-Vättern als Beicht-Kindern, nicht
weniger Lehrern und Zuhörern ... verfertiget.
Leipzig, Verlegts Johann Herbordt Kloss, 1692.
3 pts. in 1 v. front. 14 cm.
   At head of title: D. Caspar Löschers ...

NL 0445561   NNUT PPLT

A30
W7
1694L   Loescher, Caspar, 1636-1718, praeses.
   Scylla et Charybdis, interpretibus aeque
ac concionatoribus vitandae. Wittebergae,
1694.
   32 p.
   Diss. - Wittenberg (M.Maneken, respondent)

   I. Maneken, Martin   respondent.

NL 0445562   CtY

Loescher (Christian Immanuel.) * De morbo
coeliaco singulari a Cornelio Celso descripto.
xix pp. 4°. Wittebergae, lit. Dürrii, 1765.

NL 0445563   DNLM

A30
W7
1694L   Loescher, Christian Wilhelm   praeses.
   De Epistolis Pauli ad Senecam Hypobolimaeis. Wittenbergae, 1694.
   Diss. - Wittenberg (J.Ch.Weidner, respondent)

   I. Weidner, Johann Christian
respondent.

NL 0445564   CtY

Loescher, Christian Wilhelm, respondent and author
   De epistolis Senecae ad Paulum hypobolimaeis ...
     see under   Kirchmayer, Georg Kaspar,
       1635-1700, praeses.

Loescher, E., pub.
   Guida igienica di Roma
     see under title

LOESCHER Eduard.
   Die königliche wasserlilie victoria regia;
ihre geschichte ihr wesen und ihre kultur,
nebst einem anhange über wasserpflanzen der
warmeren zonen. Hamburg, Perthes -Besser &
Mauke, 1852.

   Colored plates.   Herb.Lib.

NL 0445567   MH

Loescher, Ernst,
      SEE
Loescher, Valentin Ernst, 1673-1749.

AC
901
H34
no.15   Loescher, Frank Samuel
   Pathways to understanding; overcoming
community barriers to international cultural
cooperation. [Haddam, Conn.,Edward W. Hazen
Foundation]1946.
   20p. 23cm. (Hazen pamphlets, no. 15)

     1. International cooperation - Addresses,
essays, lectures. I. Title. (Series)

NL 0445569   MU CaBVaU OrU IU ViU NN

VOLUME 338

Loescher, Frank Samuel.
The Protestant church and the negro ₍by₎ ...
Philadelphia, 1948.
159 p.

Thesis - Univ. of Pennsylvania.

NL 0445570   OCU PU

Loescher, Frank Samuel.
The Protestant church and the Negro. Philadelphia,
1948.
159 p.   21 cm.
Essential portion of thesis—University of Pennsylvania.
Published also without thesis statement.
Bibliographical footnotes.

1. U. S.—Race question. 2. Protestant churches—U. S.
3. Negroes.   I. Title.
BR563.N4L6 1948a   261   A 50-1332

Pennsylvania. Univ.   Library
for Library of Congress   ₍1₎

NL 0445571   PU NcD CLSU ViU MH OClW CU OU PSt DLC

Loescher, Frank Samuel.
The Protestant church and the Negro, a pattern of segre-
gation; with a foreword by Bishop William Scarlett. New
York, Association Press, 1948.
159 p. 21 cm.
Bibliographical footnotes.

1. U. S.—Race question. 2. Protestant churches—U. S. 3. Negroes.
I. Title.
BR563.N4L6   261   48-7076
                    ₍25₎

IdPI Or OrCS OrP OrU WaS WaTC
OO OU ICU Mi PLF PSt OCICC PHC PSC-Hi PBL PPEB PCC
NL 0445572   DLC KyU KyLxCB MiU NcRS NBC MB ViHaI

Loescher, Friedrich Gottl.
... Paradoxon praxeos victorem in
expensas condemnatum ... offert Frider.
Gottl. Loescher ... Erffordiae, Typis
Groschianis ₍1708₎
₍36₎+ p. 20cm.
Diss. - Erfurt.
Imperfect: p. ₍37₎+ lacking.

NL 0445573   MH-L

Löscher, Friedrich Hermann.
... Schule, kirche und obrigkeit im reformations-jahrhun-
dert; ein beitrag zur geschichte des sächsischen kirchschulle-
hens, von Friedrich Hermann Löscher ... Leipzig, M. Hein-
sius nachfolger, Eger & Sievers, 1925.
175 p. 23½ᶜᵐ. (Schriften des Vereins für reformationsgeschichte. jahrg.
43 (nr. 138))

1. Church and education in Saxony. 2. Education—Saxony—History.
3. Church finance. 4. Reformation—Saxony.

Title from Union Theol.   Sem.   A C 33-3044
Library of Congress   ₍BR300.V5 no. 138₎

ICMcC MoSCS
NL 0445574   NNUT NcD MH-AH MU CtY MiU OCU OU PU NN

Loescher, Fritz, 1873-   778.225 L82
Die Bildnis-Photographie. Ein Wegweiser für Fachmänner und
Liebhaber von Fritz Loescher. Zweite umgearbeitete und erweiterte Auflage mit 133 Abbildungen. Berlin, G. Schmidt
(vorm. R. Oppenheim), 1907.
xii, 220 p. illus. 24 x 18ᶜᵐ.

NL 0445575   ICJ NN CtY

Loescher, Fritz, 1873-
Die Bildnis-Photographie; ein Wegweiser für Fachmänner
und Liebhaber, von Fritz Loescher; dritte erweiterte Auflage,
bearbeitet von Otto Ewel... Berlin: G. Schmidt, 1910. xi,
235 p. illus. 8°.

212746A. 1. Photography, Portrait.   2. Ewel, Otto, editor.
N. Y. P. L.   June 4, 1926

NL 0445576   NN NNC

Loescher, Fritz, 1873-1908.
Leitfaden der Landschafts-Photographie.
— Berlin. Schmidt. 1901. v, (3), 162 pp. Plates. Diagrams. 8°.

NL 0445577   MB ICJ

Loescher, Fritz, 1873-
Leitfaden der Landschafts-Photographie. Von Fritz Loescher.
Zweite neu bearbeitete und erweiterte Auflage. Mit 27 erläuternden Tafeln nach Aufnahmen des Verfassers. Berlin, G. Schmidt,
1904.
xii, 183, [1] p. diagrs., 27 pl. 204ᵐᵐ.

NL 0445578   ICJ

Loescher, Fritz, 1873-1908.
Leitfaden der Landschaftsphotographie, von Fritz Loescher;
neu bearbeitet und erweitert von Karl Weiss... 116 Abbildungen.
7. Auflage.   Berlin: Union Deutsche Verlagsgesellschaft₍, 1929₎.
vii, 194 p. illus. 23½cm.

690999A. 1. Photography, Landscape.   I. Weiss, Karl, editor.
N. Y. P. L.   February 20, 1934

NL 0445579   NN

Loescher, Fritz, 1873-
Vergrössern und Kopieren auf Bromsilber- und Gaslichtpapieren,
von Fritz Loescher. Fünfte Auflage, neu bearbeitet und erweitert
von Karl Weiss. Mit 31 Figuren im Text. Berlin, Union
Deutsche Verlagsgesellschaft, 1922.
[5], 106 p. illus. 20ᶜᵐ.   (Half-title: Photographische Bibliothek, Band 15.)

NL 0445580   ICJ

Loescher, Fritz, 1873-
Vergrössern und Kopieren auf Bromsilberpapier. Von Fritz
Loescher. Mit einer Tafel in Bromsilberdruck und 19 Abbildungen im Text. Berlin, G. Schmidt, 1902.
ix, 105 p. front. (phot.), 19 illus. incl. diagrs. 21ᶜᵐ.   (Added t.-p.: Photographische Bibliothek. Bd. 15.)

NL 0445581   ICJ NN

Löscher, Hans, 1881-1946.
... Alles getrennte findet sich wieder; ein buch vom wahren
leben. Tübingen, R. Wunderlich ₍1937₎
2 p. l., 7-462, ₍1₎ p. 21ᶜᵐ.
A novel.

I. Title.
                                              45-46913
Library of Congress   PT2623.O4A7 1937 a

NL 0445582   DLC OCl NN MtBC

Löscher, Hans, 1881-1946.
Alles Getrennte findet sich wieder. Ein Buch vom wahren
Leben. Stuttgart, R. Wunderlich Verlag ₍1948₎
584 p. 20 cm.

I. Title.
PT2623.O4A7 1948   49-29582*

NL 0445583   DLC TNJ

Löscher, Hans, 1881-
... Das befreite herz. Tübingen, R. Wunderlich (H. Leins)
₍1939₎
3 p. l., ₍9₎-221, ₍1₎ p. 19ᶜᵐ.

I. Title.
                                              A 42-2905
Wellesley college. Library
for Library of Congress   ₍2₎

NL 0445584   MWelC CSt CtY

Loescher, Hans, 1881-1946
Das befreite Herz. [12.Aufl.] Stuttgart, Wunderlich
[1949]
181 p.

NL 0445585   MH DLC-P4

Loescher, Hans Ludwig, 1910-
Die norddeutsche lederindustrie, ihre entwick-
lung und ihre stellung in der gesamtdeutschen
lederindustrie ... von Hans-Ludwig Loescher ...
Hamburg, 1936.
viii, 96 p., ₍1₎ s. 22½ᶜᵐ.
Dissertation--Hamburg.
Lebenslauf.
"Literatur-verzeichnis": p. iii-v.

1. Leather industry and trade--Germany.
                                  HD9780.G32L83

NL 0445586   MiU CtY NN

Loescher (Henricus Theoph.) [1796-   ]. *De
judicationibus in morbis chronicis. 28 pp. 8°.
₍Berolini, formis Brüschke, [1819]₎

NL 0445587   DNLM MBCo

BT1313   Loescher, Johann Kasper, 1677-1752.
.P54   De patrvm Africanorvm meritis singularibus
libri II. Rochlitii, Impensis haeredum Miethi-
anorum Dresdens, 1722.
191 p.
Bound with Philastrius, Saint, Bp. of Brescia.
De haeresibus. Hamburgi, 1721.
Title on two leaves.
Contains "liber I" only; no more published?

1. Fathers of the church. 2. Christians in
Africa.

NL 0445588   ICU

A30   Loescher, Johann Kaspar, 1677-1752, praeses.
W7   Memoria Christiani Daumii, magni nominis
1701L   critici, & philologi. Wittebergae, 1701.
Diss. - Wittenberg (M.G.Loescher, respondent)

1. Daum, Christian, 1612-1687.
2. Loescher, Martin Gotthelf, d.1735,
respondent.

NL 0445589   CtY

VOLUME 338

BR75
.L8O2
1703

LÖSCHER,JOHANN KASPAR,1677-1752.
M.J.C.Loescheri ... Observationum selectarum ad
theologiam sacramqve et eccles.historiam spectantium,
fasciculus I.-[II]... Lipsiæ,impensis hæred.Grossian,
1703-06.
2 v.in 1. 16½cm.
Vol.2 has imprint:Altenburgii,sumt.& typis J.L.
Richteri,1706.

1.Theology--Addresses,essays,lectures.

NL 0445590   ICU

BR75
.L8O2
1703

LÖSCHER,JOHANN KASPAR,1677-1752.
Theatrvm montivm sacrorum,das ist Schauplatz heiliger und heilig gehaltener berge ... aus der Heil.
Schrifft, antiqvität, geographie und historie eröffnet
...von Johann Casparo Löschern. Rochljtz,Gedruckt
mit Langischen schrifften,1728-30.
2 v.in 1. [With his Observationum selectarum ad
theologiam sacram. Lipsiæ,1703-06]
Vol.2 has title:Anderer theil des schauplatzes heiliger...berge.
1.Bible--Geography.

NL 0445591   ICU

Loescher, Karl Gustav, 1861-
Ueber magnetische folgepunkte ... Halle a/S., Druck
von E. Karras, 1884.
2 p. l., 43, [1] p., 1 l. diagrs. 19½cm.
Inaug.-diss.--Halle.
Vita.

1. Magnetism.
9-20729

Library of Congress   QC757.L8

NL 0445592   DLC

Löscher, Karl Immanuel, 1750-1814.
see Löscher, Carl Immanuel, 1750-1814.

W 4
M96
1953

LÖSCHER, Lisa (Grosse-Darrelmann)
1919-
Über das Papilloma fibroepitheliale
der freien Bulbusbindehaut. München,
1953.
26 l. illus.
Inaug.-Diss. - Munich.
1. Conjunctiva - Neoplasms
2. Papilloma

NL 0445594   DNLM

Adelmann
BT
870
L82

Loescher, Martin Gotthelff, d.1735, praeses.
Disputatio prior De corporis humani palingenesia, p.p. praeside Martino Gotthelff
Loeschero...a Esdra Henrico Edzardo autore
et respondente... Vitembergae, Literis
Viduae Gerdesiae [1722]
16 p. 21cm.

Diss.--Wittenberg (E. H. Edzardi, re-
spondent and author)
With this is bound: Edzardi, Esdras
Heinrich, prae   ses. Disputatio

posterior De corporis humani palingenesia.
1722.

1. Resurrection--Early works to 1800.
I. Edzardi, Esdras Heinrich, respondent.

NL 0445596   NIC

W 4
W82
1712
L 1

LOESCHER, Martin Gotthelff, d. 1735, praeses
... Disertationem medicam de anima hominis materiali
insensibili simul data disserendi occasione, causam morborum
contagiosorum hactenus grassantium naturalem reddentem, p. p.
praeses Mart. Gotth. Loescherus ... et respondens Augustinus
Christianus Gilbertus ... Vittembergae, Literis Christiani
Gerdesii [1712]
40 p. 20 cm.
Diss. - Wittenberg (A. C. Gilbert, respondent)

L Gilbert, Augustin Christian, respondent

NL 0445597   DNLM

Loescher, Martin Gotthelf, d. 1735, respondent.
Memoria Christiani Daumii
see under Loescher, Johann Kaspar, 1677-
1752, praeses.

Löscher, Martin Gotthelff, d.1735.
Physica theoretica et experimententalis compen-
losa in usum juventutis academicae, adornata et
novissimis rationibus et experimentis illustrata.
Editio altera eademque auctior et emendatior.
Vitembergae, Apud haeredes Godofr. Zimmermanni,
1728.
4 p.l., 278, [7] p. 19 cm.

NL 0445599   OkU

Loescher, Otto Ernst,1881.
Ueber rezidivierende augenmuskellaehmungen.
Inaug. diss. Leipzig,1906.
Bibl.

NL 0445600   ICRL DNLM CtY

QD341
.A5L3

Loescher, Paul Emil, 1870-
Ueber n-alkyI-aIdoxime und deren spaltungs-
produkte.
Leipzig. 1899.
31p.
Inaug. diss. Erlangen.

NL 0445601   DLC NN PU

Loescher, Samuel Megaw.
Imperfect collusion in the portland cement
industry; basing-point pricing and the Cement
Institute case.

Thesis - Harvard, 1950.

NL 0445602   MH

W 4
M22
1952

LÖSCHER, Ursula Charlotte, 1922-
Ursache, Prophylaxe und Behandlung
der Nachgeburtsblutungen; eine Untersuchung am Material der Universitäts-
Frauenklinik Mainz. [Mainz, 1952]
37 l.
Inaug.-Diss. - Mainz.
Typewritten copy.
1. Labor - Complicated
2. Uterus - Hemorrhage

NL 0445603   DNLM

f882
Box 1

LOESCHER, V   A
A Funeral service for Arthur Lincoln
Robinson, February 14, 1946./ West Roxbury, Mass., West Roxbury Congregational Church, 1946.
4 l. 28cm.

Mimeographed.

NL 0445604   MH-AH

919.47
D773s
H655vom
1728
no.2

LOESCHER, Valentin Ernst, 1674-1749.
Abgewiesener Demas, zur Uberzeugung
der Paebstler und der den Abfall befoer-
dernden Frey-Geister: nebst angehengten
Documenten von einigen paebstischen Dingen,
...Leipzig, Johann Grossens Erben, 1713.
278, [12]p. 17cm.

No.2 in a bound volume.

NL 0445605   MH-AH

BT900
.L8

Löscher,Valentin Ernst,1674-1749,comp.
Auserlesene sammlung der besten und neuern
schrifften vom zustand der seele nach dem tod
...an das licht gestellt auch mit einem vorbe-
richt und besonderer ausführung vermehrt,von Val.
Ernst Löschern. Dressden,R.C.Saueressig,1735.
[62],700,[120]p. front.(port.) 17½cm.
Contents.-- Der zustand der abgeschiedenen
seelen,von Joh.Meisnero.--Das leben der seelen
im todte,durch Theodorum Reinoking.--Schrifft-
mässige gedancken vom zustande der abgeschie-

denen seelen,von Gottlieb Wernsdorffen.--Val.
Ernst Löschers Wiederhohlung der lehre vom zustand der abgeschiedenen seelen.

1.Future life.

NL 0445607   ICU NNUT PPLT

RARE BOOK
BX
8064
L82

Loescher, Valentin Ernst, 1674-1749.
Aussführliche Historia Motuum zwischen den
Evangelisch Lutherischen und Reformirten...
[Nebst einer Friedfertigen Anrede An die Reformirten Gemeinden in Teutschland] Franckfurt, J. Grossens seel. Erben, 1707-24.
3v. in 2.
v.3 includes the author's Heilsame Worte,
Oder Friedfertige Anrede...an die Reformirten

Gemeinden in Teutschland, and Supplementa.
With v.2 are bound Odelem, Johann Philipp.
Unpartheyische Gedancken, Welche über die so
genandte Unterthänigste Addresse An Ein Hohes
Durchlauchtiges Haupt im Heil. Römischen
Reiche. 1722. [Klemm, Johann Christian]

Vertheidigte Glaubens-Einigkeit Der Protestan-
tischen Kirche. 1722. Die Pflicht Eines
Geistlichen Lehrers...1721. Odelem, Johann
Philipp. Reliqviae Papo-Caesariae Rom...1722.

NL 0445610   MoSCS MdBP NNUT

BR301
.L8

Loescher, Valentin Ernst, 1674-1749.
Ausführliche historia motuum zwischen den Evangelisch-
Lutherischen und Reformirten. In welcher der gantze lauff
der streitigkeiten bisz auf jetzige zeit acten-mäszig erzehlet,
und fast alle diszfalls hin und wieder gewechselte schrifften
excerpiret ... Und demnach unter andern Lavateri historia
sacramentaria, Hospiniani historia sacramentaria ... Nebst
andern noch nicht refutirten historischen streit-schrifften der
Reformirten nicht weniger was aus Gottfried Arnolds kätzer-
historie hieher gehöret, widerleget worden von Valentin
Ernst Löschern ... Franckfurt und Leipzig, J. Grossens seel.

erben, 1723-24.
3 v. in 1. 22x17½cm. [With his Vollständige reformations-acta ... Leipzig,
1720-29]
Vol. 1: 2. und verm. aufl. Nebst kurzer vertheidigung der allerunterthänigsten
addresse. v. 3: Nebst einer friedfertigen anrede an die reformirten gemeinden in
Teutschland.

—— Supplementa zu der Ausführlichen historia motuum
... Leipzig, J. Grossens seel. erben, 1722.
71 p. 22x17½cm. [With the preceding]

1. Lutheran church--Doctrinal and controversial works. 2. Reformation--
Germany. 3. Calvinism

NL 0445612   ICU NjR CtY PPLT NcD

VOLUME 338

RARE BOOK   Loescher, Valentin Ernst, 1674-1749.
BX
8064   Ausführliche Historia Motuum zwischen den
L82   Evangelisch-Lutherischen und Reformirten...
1723   Nebst kurzer Vertheidigung der Allerunter-
            thänigsten Addresse. [Nebst einer Friedfertigen
            Anrede An die Reformirten Gemeinden in Teutsch-
            land] 2. und verm. Aufl.   Franckfurt, J.
            Grossens seel. Erben, 1723-1770.
            4v.

            v.3 includes the author's Heilsame Worte,
            Oder Friedfertige Anrede...an die Reformirten
            Gemeinden in Teutschland, and Supplementa.
            v.4: Fortsetzung der Historia Motuum des
            Wohlseeligen Herrn D. Valentin Ernst Löschers,
            zwischen den Evangelisch-Lutherischen, und

            Reformirten, da sie mit dem Jahre 1580. aufhör-
            et. Zur Ergänzung bis auf das Jahr 1601. da
            diese Crypto-Calvinistischen Unruhen in Chur-
            sachsen geendiget worden sind. (Beylagen) Von
            Johann Rudolph Kiesling. Schwabach, J. G.
            Mizler, 1770.

NL 0445615   MoSCS

Loescher, Valentin Ernst, 1674-1749.
    Breviarium oratoriae sacrae in academia
witebergensi olim privatis lectionibus dicatum
...Lipsiae, [etc.,] Gaarmanni, 1713.
    94 p.

NL 0445616   PPLT

BS   Loescher, Valentin Ernst, 1674-1749.
476
L6   Breviarium oratoriae sacrae, in Academia
            Wittebergensi olim privatis lectionibus
            dicatum...   Francofurt, Christian Gott-
            hold Gaarmann, 1715.
            94p.
            Bound with his Breviarium theologiae
            exegeticae... 1715.
            1. Preaching. I. Title.

NL 0445617   MoSCS

BS   Loescher, Valentin Ernst, 1674-1749.
476
L6   Breviarium theologiae exegeticae, regulas
            de legitima scripturae sacrae interpreta-
            tione succincte atque solide tradens.
            Francofurt, Christian Gotthold Gaarmann,
            1715.
            202p.
            With this is bound his Breviarium
            oratoriae sacrae... 1715.
            1. Bible -   Hermeneutics.

NL 0445618   MoSCS

BS647   Loescher, Valentin Ernst, 1674-1749.
.A2L8   ... Breviarivm theologiae propheticae, brevem
            institvtionem monitaqve salvberrima ad illivs
            stvdivm rite sobrieqve instivendvm continens,
            lvci pvblicae exposvit et praefatvs est Ioan.
            Dietericvs Wincklervs ... Hambvrgi, typis N. C.
            Woermeri, 1766.
            x, [2,] 60 p.

            1. Bible--Prophecies.

NL 0445619   ICU

Z   LOESCHER, VALENTIN ERNST, 1674-1749.
491   Catalogvs bibliothecae cvivs pars I-[III,]
.L82   hastae pvblicae svbiicietvr [1750-1751,] in aedi-
            bvs vidvae B.Hermanni Poligraphi.   Dresdae, In
            commissis apvd Harpetervm[1749-51,]
            3v. 17cm.

            Contents.--pars I continens bibliothecam
            theologicam.--pars II continens bibliothecam
            historicam.--pars III continens bibliothecam
            philologicam, philosophicam, mathematicam,
            ivridicam et   medicam, cvm qvincvpli-
            ci appendice.

NL 0445620   ICN ICU

PA6277 LOESCHER,VALENTIN ERNST,1674-1749.
.C4A1G6   D.Val.Ernest.Loescheri Chrestomathia theologica,
1742   sive,De apparatv praestantiore atqve et ordine librorvm
            opervmqve theologicorvm commentatio svccincta. Accv-
            rante Io.Christophoro Colero. Vitembergae,svmptv S.
            Hannaveri,typis Crevsigianis,1720.
            [12,]52 p. 17cm. [With Censorinus. De die natali
            Altorphii,1742]

            1.Theology--Bibl.

NL 0445621   ICU

PJ4543   Loescher,Valentin Ernst,1674-1749.
.L8   Val.Ern.Loescheri...De cavsis lingvae ebraeae
            libri III... Francofurti & Lipsiae,sumtibus hae-
            redum J.Grossii,1706.
            [16,],496,[10,] p. double pl. 21x17cm.
            Title vignette;head and tail pieces;initials.

            1.Hebrew language.

NL 0445622   ICU PPiPT PPLT OCH PU CtY IU

A30   Loescher, Valentin Ernst, 1674-1749.
L4   De noviter tentatis in ebraea literatura
1704L   disserit, ac rationem operis de causis lin-
            gune ebraeae. Lipsiae,1704.
            14 p.
            Diss. - Leipzig (Dedicated to C.Loescher)

NL 0445623   CtY

Div.S. Löscher, Valentin Ernst, 1674-1749.
252.041
L826D   Drey Predigten von der Erkänntniss und
            Ehre des Sohnes Gottes ... Welches aus den
            evangelischen Texten am 8., 9. und 10. Sonntage
            post Trinit. ... vorgestellet worden. Dressden,
            G. C. Hilscher, 1733.
            84 p. 21 cm.

            1. Sermons, German. 2. Lutheran Church.
            Sermons.

NL 0445624   NcD

RARE BOOK Loescher, Valentin Ernst, 1674-1749.
BS
1565   Epistolae de theologia et illuminatione
O59   impiorum, nec non de veritate carnis Christi
            cum responsoriis Ioannis Olearii.
            Lipsiae, Brandenburger, 1710.
            112p.
            Bound with Olearius, Gottfried, 1672-
            1715. Redemtionem ex inferno et liberationem
            a morte...1707.

NL 0445625   MoSCS ICU

Löscher, Valentin Ernst, 1674-1749.
    D. Val. Ernst Löschers Evangelische predigt von unter-
schiedlichen hörern der göttlichen rede, so zu erst in der
neu-erbauten Frauen-kirche, domin. sexagesima 1734, als
dieselbe zum Gottesdienst der nothdurfft nach fertig war,
gehalten worden. Dressden, C. Robring [1734?]
    1 p. L, 37 p. 19 x 15½ cm.

    1. Lutheran Church--Sermons. 2. Sermons, German.

BX8066.L592E9   38-31683 rev

NL 0445626   DLC

GT6   Löscher, Valentin Ernst, 1674-1749.
M994g   ... Exercitatio theologica de Claudii
            Pajonii ... Accedit Lectionum sacrarum ...
            farrago ... Lipsiae, Apud J.H. Klosium, 1692.
            10 p.L., 245 p. 14½ cm.

            Bound with Mylius, Georg. Gründlicher
            Beweiss, dass Doct. Martin Luther. [n.p.,]
            Gedruckt im Jahr 1725.

            1. Pajon, Claude, 1626-1685.

NL 0445627   CtY-D

Löscher, Valentin Ernst, 1674-1749.
    Die geheimen Gerichte Gottes über das römische
Pabsthum ... Anbey auch der unlängst edirte
wolffenbüttelische Tractat, Beantwortung der Frage
ob jemand von der Evangelische-Lutherischen
Religion zur Catholischen übertrend dadurch die
Seeligkeit verliebte? Leipzig, C. Seidel, 1706.
    109 p. 21 cm.
    Bound with Löscher, V.E. Praenotiones
theologicae contra natvralistarvm. Vittembergae,
1708.
    1. Lutheran Church. 2. Papacy.

NL 0445628   MdBP

F   LOESCHER, VALENTIN ERNST, 1674-1749.
093   Die Historie der mittlern Zeiten, als ein
.518   Licht aus der Finsternüss.   Leipzig, F.Lancki-
            schens sel.Erben,1725.
            16,354p. fold.maps.geneal.tables. 21cm.

            Contents.--Historie des römischen Huren-
            Regiments.--Römische Intriguen.--Einleitung zur
            historia media, und denen scriptoribus der bar-
            barischen Zeiten.

NL 0445629   ICN PCC

Löscher, Valentin Ernst, 1674-1749.
    Historie des römischen Huren-Regiments der
Theodorae und Maroziae; in welcher die Begebenheiten des zehenden Seculi und Intriguen des
römischen Stuhls ausgeführet werden, nebst einer
längst verlangten Einleitung zur Histor. Medii Aevi,
verschiedenen neuen geographischen und genealogischen Tabellen, und einer Anzahl historischer
Beweissthümer wieder das Pabstthum. Leipzig,
Lanckischens Erben, 1705.
    354 p. maps, tables. 21 cm.
    Bound with his Ausführliche Historia. Frankfurt,
1708-24 [v. 1, 1723]

NL 0445630   MdBP

Löscher, Valentin Ernst, 1674-1749
    Kurtze Rettung der ersten Reformationswahrheiten gegen die
Melodischen Einwürffe.   Leipzig, J. Grossens Erben, 1729.
48 p. 19cm.

1. Bernd, Adam, 1676-1748.   Einfluss der Göttlichen Wahrheiten
in den Willen. 2. Theology. Ger-   man, 18th cent.

NL 0445631   NN MdBP

VOLUME 338

678
8587*lez*
1762
LOESCHER, Valentin Ernst, 1674-1749.
... Kurzgefasste Erklärung der Offenbarung St. Johannis. ₍n.p.₎ 1770.
29p. 17cm.

At head of title: Des hochberühmten ehemaligen Sächsischen Gottesgelehrten, Herrn D. Valentin Ernst Löschers ...
Translation of Meditationes Apocalypticae.
No. 3 in a bound volume.

NL 0445632   MH-AH

Löscher, Valentin Ernst, 1674-1749.
... Letzte und getreue Worte an seine geliebteste Gemeine zu Delitzsch bey gehaltener Abschieds-Predigt am Sönntag Miser. Dom. A. 1707 ... Leipzig, in Verlag Jo. Grossens sel. Erben, [1707]
19, [4] p.   22.5 cm.
At head of title: Valentin Ernst Löschers ...
Bound with: Neumann, Johann Georg, 1661-1709. Prodromus Anti-Spenerianus ... 1695.
No. 14 of a volume of pamphlets.

NL 0445633   NNUT

P
561
L6
Loescher, Valentin Ernst, 1674-1749.
Literator celta, seu de ex colenda literatura Europaea, occidentali et septentrionali consilium et conatus. Curante Joanne Augustin Egenolf.   Lipsiae, Jo. Christian Martin, 1726.
₍8₎120p.
With this is bound Jan, Johann Hermann. De B. Luthero studii biblici instauratore...
1. Europe - Languages - Study & teaching.

NL 0445634   MoSCS MH ICU

Löscher, Valentin Ernst, 1674-1749.
Die merckwürdigen Wercke Gottes in denen Reichen der Natur, der Kunst, und des Glückes ... im Jahr 1722. geprediget ... Von Val. Ernst Löschern ...   Dressden, C. Robring, 1724.
10p.*l.*,994,₍24₎p. front., illus. 17cm.

NL 0445635   NNUT InU

BX8066
L6
Löscher, Valentin Ernst, 1674-174y.
Merkwürdige Werke Gottes in den Reichen der Natur, der Kunst, und des Glücks ... ehemals im Jahre 1722 gepredigt, und Auszugsweise ans Licht gestellt, auch mit Sinn-Bildern geziert. Jezo aber von neuem ... durchgegangen ... auch mit einem besondern Vorberichte und zwiefachem Register versehen von Adam Grenz.   Dresden, J. W. Harpeter, 1753.
956 p.   illus.

1. Lutheran Church - Sermons.   2. Sermons, German.

NL 0445636   CU ICN

Loescher, Valentin Ernst, 1674-1749, praeses.
... Th. Munzeri doctrinam et facta ex idoneis monvmentis denvo examinata sistit atqve G. Arnoldi admissos hac etiam in parte lapsvs exponit .... Habita ex Cathedra Lvtheri 1708. Vittembergae, Literis Christiani Gerdesii, 1708.
23p. 19.5cm.
Respondent: G. N. Kiessling.
Dispvtatione pvblica.

NL 0445637   MH-AH CtY

P636
Sch6.2
Loescher, Valentin Ernst, 1674-1749.
Nöthige Reflexiones über das Anno 1722. zum Vorschein gebrachte Buch Pensées libres sur la religion &c. oder Freye Bedancken von der Religion. Nebst wohlgemeynter Warnung vor dergleichen Büchern abgefasst ...   Wittenberg, bey Samuel Hannauern, 1724.
38 p.   17 cm.

NL 0445638   CtHC OSW

Löscher, Valentin Ernst, 1674-1749.
Praenotiones theologicae contra natvralistarvm et fanaticorvm omne genvs atheos, deistas, indifferentistas, antiscripturarios & c. Crassos aeqve ac svbtiles cvstodiendae ...   Vittembergae, typ. et svmtibvs C. Gerdesii, 1708.
259 p.   21 cm.

NL 0445639   MdBP

Löscher, Valentin Ernst, 1674-1749.
Praenotiones theologicae ...   Wittemberg, 1713.

NL 0445640   NjNbS

BX
8066
.L592
P73
1719
Loescher, Valentin Ernst, 1674-1749
Praenotiones theologicae contra naturalistarum et fanaticorum, omne genus, atheos, deistas, indifferentistas, antiscripturarios, etc. Crassos aeque ac subtiles nec non suspectos doctores, custodiendae. Editio tertia emendata et aucta indiceque locupletiori instructa. Wittemberg, Samuelem Hannaverum, 1719.
₍xx₎, 208p. 17cm.

NL 0445641   TNJ NNUT

BT
1100
L6
Loescher, Valentin Ernst, 1674-1749.
Praenotiones theologicae contra naturalistarum et fanaticorum omne genus atheos, deistas, indifferentistas, antiscripturarios, etc. Editio quinta emendata. Vitembergae, Gottlib. Henricum Schwartz, 1752.
₍22₎364₍19₎p.
With this is bound his Theologia pretiosa. 1750.
1. Apologe   cics - 18th cent. 2.
Lutheran Chur   ch - Doctrinal & contro-
versial works.   I. Title.

NL 0445642   MoSCS

W30
W7
1698L
Loescher, Valentin Ernst, 1674-1749, praeses.
... Racemationes orientales de Babylonica Medica Phrygica, aliisque ignotis linguis orientalibus. Vitembergae, 1698.
[14] p.
Diss. - Wittenberg (J.Ch.Eyring, respondent)
Title in Hebrew precedes Latin.

I. Eyring, Johann Christian   respondent.

NL 0445643   CtY

Löscher, Valentin Ernst, 1674-1749, ed.
Räuchwerck der heiligen; oder, Vollständiges Gesangbuch worinnen ... Delitzsch u. Leipzig, Vogelgesang [170-?]
see under title

609.2
L826.4ro
1717
LOESCHER, Valentin Ernst, 1674-1749.
Roemisch=Catholische Discurse, vom Evangel. Lutherischen Jubel-Jahr zur christlichen Anleitung wie man bey diesen boesen Zeiten geuebte Sinnen zum Unterscheid des Boesen und Guten erlangen solle. Leipzig, Johann Friedrich Braun, 1717.
6p.*l.*, 556p. front. 17cm.

NL 0445645   MH-AH

Löscher, Valentin Ernst, 1674-1749.
... Stromateus; sive, Dissertationes sacri et literarii argumenti ineditae partim hactenus partim editae olim sed revisae nunc et loculpetatae; accedit Der servando in controversiis theologicis modo commentatio ad— Henr. Muhlium nec non Pachomii Sermo contre impietatem sui seculi et provinciale romenum— Vittembergae apud Saxones, Sumptibus S. Hannaveri, 1724.
₍8₎ 520, 207 p₍.₎ 20cm.

NL 0445646   NjPT TxDaM

BT
1100
L6
Loescher, Valentin Ernst, 1674-1749.
Theologia pretiosa variis cum illustramentis ideo ex msc. in Lucem edita... Hamburgi, n.p., 1750.
₍16₎110p.
Bound with his Praenotiones theologicae. ... 1752.
1. Theology - Collected works - 18th cent
2. Lutheran Church - Doctrinal and controversial works.   I. Title.

NL 0445647   MoSCS

628.47
U59n
1710th
LOESCHER, Valentin Ernst, 1674-1749
Theologische annales, das erste Decennium des 18. Seculi; oder Begriff der Unschuldigen Nachrichten von theologischen Sachen von anno 1710. biss 1710. nebst darzu gehoerigen Supplementis, Vertheidigung und Verbesserungen obgedachter zehen Jahre der Unschuldigen Nachrichten, auch einer Haupt-Einleitung zur Chrestomathia Theologica, oder zum voelligern Studio

und Apparatu Theologico, sowohl auch zu dem Wercke der Unschuldigen Nachrichten: mit einiger Christlichen Personen Beyhuelffe ausgefertiget von Valentin Ernst Loeschern. Leipzig, verlegts Johann Friedrich Braun, 1715.
15p.*l.*, 919, 77p. front. (engr.) 17cm.
Stamped   on cover: Cancell:
Martisb: 1715.

NL 0445649   MH-AH OSW

Löscher, Valentin Ernst, 1674-1749
Übung der Gottseeligkeit, als der im Jahr 1720, von Ihm gepredigte Jahr-Gang. So wohl von Ihm selbst kurtz entworffen, als auch, so gut es seyn kennen, hernach zusammen getragen. Worinnen alles, was zum thetigen Christenthum nethig. Sonderlich Busse, Glaube, Liebe, Hoffnung, Gebet, Creutzes-und Todes-Uberwindung gezeiget wird. Nebst einem Anhange von denen Jubel-Predigten 1730.

Andere Aufl. gedruckt in dem Evangelischen Jubel-Jahr. Dressden und Leipzig, 1730.
3 v. in 1.

NL 0445651   WU

Löscher, Valentin Ernst, 1674-1749, ed.
Unschuldige Nachrichten von alten und neuen theologischen Sachen
see under title

VOLUME 338

BR301   Loescher, Valentin Ernst, 1674-1749.
.L8   Vollständige reformations-acta und documenta; oder, Umständliche vorstellung des evangelischen reformations-wercks,
mit einrückung der darzu dienlichen, theils noch nie gedruckten, nachrichten, so dass dieses werck zugleich vor theologische annales dienen kan. Ausgefertiget von Valentin Ernst
Löschern ... Leipzig, J. Grossens erben, 1720-29.
   3 v. in 2. front. 22x17½ᵐ.
   CONTENTS.—1. t. Auf das jahr 1517. Nebst angefügten 5. jubel-predigten.—

   2. t. Auf das jahr 1518. Nebst angefügter neuer, allerklärster und theils mathe
matischer uberzeugung des pabstthums.—3. t. Auf das jahr 1519. Welcher son
derlich die geschichte der berühmten Leipziger disputation enthält, sammt einer
kurtzen rettung der ersten reformations-wahrheiten.

      1. Reformation—Hist.—Sources. 2. Reformation—Germany.

   MH-AH NNG MdBP PPLT
NL 0445654   ICU MH NNUT NcD PPeSchw NjNbS NjPT NIC

────────────────────

BX8080   LOESCHER, VALENTIN ERNST, 1674-1749.
.H15L8   Von dem wohlredenden blute eines unschuldig-ge-
tödteten Abels musste am 6.junii des 1726sten jahres,
als am tage der leich-bestattung des...herrn m.Herr-
mann Joachim Hahns...reden Valentin.Ernst Löscher...
Dresden,J.C.Stössel[1727]
   [4],92,[78]p. 21x18cm.
   Head and tail pieces.
   Contains also: "Lebens-lauff" and "Epicedia."
   1.Hahn,Herrmann Joachim,1679-1726.

NL 0445655   ICU CtY

────────────────────

ar W   Löscher, Werner.
53:83   Über die in den letzten Jahren in der
no.2   Erlanger chirurgischen Klinik zur Beobachtung gelangten Fälle von Schilddrüsenge-
schwülsten. Erlangen, Hofbuchdruckerei
A. Vollrath, 1898.
   45 p. 22cm.
   Inaug.-Diss.--Erlangen.

NL 0445656   NIC MiDW DNLM

────────────────────

Löscher, Wilhelm: Die Westfälischen Galeritenschichten mit
besonderer Berücksichtigung ihrer Seeigelfauna. Stuttgart:
Schweizerbart 1910. S. 269—312. 8° ¶(Aus: Neues Jahr-
buch f. Mineral. Beil.-Bd 30.)
Münster, Phil. Diss. v. 20. Sept. 1910, Ref. Busz
[Geb. 1. Mai 81 Dortmund; Wohnort: Lippstadt; Staatsangeh.: Preußen;
Vorbildung: Realgymn. Münster Reife O. 01; Studium: Münster 10 S.;
Rig. 4. Aug. 09.]   [U 11. 3971]

NL 0445657   ICRL MH CtY PU

────────────────────

Loescher & co., publishers, Rome.

Bibliographia archaeologica, donnant une liste très complète
des ouvrages d'archéologie, d'histoire antique, etc. ... en vente
chez la Librairie Loescher & co. ... nr. 1—   mai 1906—
                                          Rome, 1906—

────────────────────

Loescher & co., publishers, Rome.

Roma; a pictorial description of Rome. 245 illustrations.
With explanatory text. Rome, Loescher & co. [1913?]

────────────────────

Loescheri, Val Ernesti,

      SEE

Loescher, Valentin Ernst, 1673-1749.

────────────────────

Loeschheimer; ein Journal in zwanglosen Heften. Kiel
Heft 1-6; 1807-08
   "Hrsg. von H.v. L——n" (edited by C.F. von Both,
   according to Kirchner)
   No more published

   I. Both, C.F. von

NL 0445661   MH

────────────────────

Löschhorn, Albert.
   Christus in uns; die Lehre von der Einwohnung Christi.
Gütersloh, Rufer-Verlag, 1954.
   133 p. 19 cm. (Sammlung Lebendige Gemeinde)

   1. Mystical union. 2. Luther, Martin, 1483-1546. 3. Calvin, Jean,
1509-1564.   I. Title.
   BT769.L6   54-24163 ‡

NL 0445662   DLC CtY-D MH-AH

────────────────────

Löschhorn, Albert.
   Gerhard Tersteegen, sein Leben, seine Persönlichkeit,
Einführung in seine Lieder. Zürich, Zwingli-Verlag [ᶜ1946]
   112 p. 18 cm. (Zwingli-Bücherei, 50)
   "Anmerkungen": p. 110-112.

   1. Tersteegen, Gerhard, 1697-1769.
   BV5095.T4L6   49-58259*

NL 0445663   DLC NN MH-AH

────────────────────

BV5095   Löschhorn, Albert.
.T4L6   Ich bete an die Macht der Liebe; Gerhard
Tersteegens christliche Mystik. Mit einem
Geleitwort von Erich Schick. Basel,
Brunnen Verlag [1948]
   223 p. 23 cm.

   Includes bibliography.

   1. Tersteegen, Gerhard, 1697-1769.
   2. Mysticism.   I. Title.

NL 0445664   TU CU NjPT InU TxU CaBVaU MB ICU NNUT

────────────────────

Loeschhorn, Albert, 1819-1905.
   Abendruhe (Aus der kinderwelt) für
streich-quartett, glockenspiel und harfe.
[15 parts in portfolio] Berlin, C. A.
Challier & co., n.d.

NL 0445665   OCl

────────────────────

LÖSCHHORN, Albert, 1819-1905.
   Album für die Jugend. Opus 80. Für pianoforte. Heft 2. n.p., [18-].

NL 0445666   MH

────────────────────

LOESCHHORN, Albert, 1819-
   Arabesken.Sechs Klavierstücke. Op.90. n.p.,
[18-].

NL 0445667   MH

────────────────────

VM   LOESCHHORN, ALBERT, 1819-1905.
1060   La belle Amazone, componirt von A.Löschhorn,
L 82b   instr. von G.Michaelis. [n.p.,n.d.]
   24 pt.in 1v. 34½cm.

   Op.25.
   Manuscript copy by an unknown hand.
   Parts for 1st and 2d violin, viola, violoncello, bass, 1st and 2d flute, 1st and 2d oboe,
1st and 2d clarinet, 1st and 2d bassoon, 1st to
4th horn, 1st to 3d trombone, 1st and 2d trumpet,
and 2 drums.

NL 0445668   ICN IdU

────────────────────

Loeschhorn, Albert, 1819-1905.
   Charakteristische Studien für das
Pianoforte zur Förderung des Vortrags
und der höheren Technik componirt und
mit fingersatz bezeichnet. Berlin,
Challier, n.d.
   3v. scores, 34cm.

NL 0445669   IdU

────────────────────

Loeschhorn, Albert, 1819-1905.
   Etuden fur piano in fortschreitender
ordnung, zur beforderung der technik und
des vortrage ... Theil 1: Fur anfanger ...
Boston, Arthur P. Schmidt, n.d.

   Op. 65.
   Cover title: Progressive studies.

NL 0445670   OCl

────────────────────

Loeschhorn, Albert, 1819-1905.
   Etuden für piano in fortschreitender
ordnung, zur beforderung der technik und
des vortrage ... Theil 2: Fur fortgeschrittene
... Boston, Arthur P. Schmidt, n.d.
   3 v. in 1.

   Op. 66.
   Cover title: Progressive studies.

NL 0445671   OCl ICN

────────────────────

8A   LOESCHHORN, ALBERT, 1819-1905.
869   Etuden für Piano in fortschreitender Ordnung zur Beförderung der Technik und des Vortrags, mit Fingersatz, von A. Loeschhorn.
Theil III. Für Geübtere. Op.67. Heft 1[-3]
Berlin, J.Weiss[1861-62]
   3v. 35cm.

   Pl.no.: J.W.206-208.

NL 0445672   ICN

────────────────────

8A   LOESCHHORN, ALBERT, 1819-1905.
870   Etudes for piano in progressive order with
special reference to the acquirement of a perfect execution and a brilliant style with complete fingering. By A. Loeschhorn. Part 2.
Op.66. Progressive (to form the execution)
Bk.2. New-York,W.A.Pond & Co.[187-?]
   23p. 36cm.

NL 0445673   ICN

────────────────────

LOESCHHORN, ALBERT, 1819-1905.
   [UNIVERSAL-ETÜDEN, OP. 169-171]
   Études universelles. Universal-Etüden. Pour piano,
par A. Loeschhorn. Paris, A. Leduc [1882?]
Pl. no. A.L. 6594-6596. 3 v. in 1. 35cm.

   CONTENTS. --livre 1, op. 169. --livre 2, op. 170. --livre 3, op. 171.

   I. Piano.

NL 0445674   NN

VOLUME 338

R016.785 Loeschhorn, Albert, 1819-1905
L824f   Führer durch die Klavier—Literatur.
    ₍Leipzig, C. G. Röder, 1886?₎
    vi, 80 p.

    1. Piano music — Bibliography I. T.

NL 0445675   MiD

Löschhorn, A₍lbert₎ 1819-
    Führer durch die klavier-literatur, hrsg. von A. Loesch-
horn. 2. verm. aufl. ₍Berlin, E. Bote & G. Bock, 1895₎
    viii, 118 p. 13ᶜᵐ.
    p. 101-118, advertising matter.
    First edition, by A. Löschhorn and J. Weiss appeared in 1862, under title:
Wegweiser in der pianoforte-literatur.

    Subject entries: Pianoforte music—Bibl.

                      8-13671

    Library of Congress, no.   ML128.P3L4.

NL 0445676   DLC

M1
.S444 Loeschorn, Albert, 1819-1905.
v.64
no.11   Good night; Gute nacht. A. Loeschhorn₍sic₎
    op. 96 ₍Price 30. n. p., 18—?₎ Pl. no.
    678.
      3 p.   34cm. ₍Sheet music collection, v. 64,
    no. 11₎
      Caption title.
      Select gems for the piano forte.

    1. Piano music. I. Title.

NL 0445677   ViU

Loeschhorn, Albert, 1819-1905.
    Kinder-etuden für pianoforte ...
    Leipzig, Peters, n.d.
    23 p.

    Op. 181.

NL 0445678   OC1 MH

Löschhorn, Albert, 1819-1905.
    ₍Die Klavier-Technik₎

    Die Klavier-Technik; tägliche Uebungen. Leipzig, C. F.
Peters ₍n. d.₎ Pl. no. 5908.
    51 p. 31 cm.
    For piano.

    1. Piano—Studies and exercises.   I. Title.

    MT225.L82   52-20052

NL 0445679   DLC OC1

LOESCHHORN,Albert,1819-
Liebes-Lust und Lied. 10 Charact-Clav.No.6
Denke mein.No.7 Herzeleid.8 Soldaten-lied.
n.p.,₍18-₎.

NL 0445680   MH

---

sVM   LOESCHHORN, ALBERT, 1819-1905.
1145   _Menuet. Für streichinstrumente_   Berlin,
L 82m E.Bote & G.Bock₍c1897₎
    3p.

    Op.199, no.1.
    Full score.
    Plate no.: 14500.

NL 0445681   ICN OU

Löschhorn, Albert, 1819-1905.
    ... Modern school of velocity. Thirty-three
studies for attaining strength, independence and
dexterity of fingers ... bk. 1-2. New York, G.
Schirmer ₍c1889₎
    v. 33 cm. (G. Schirmer's standard edition of
pianoforte studies)
    At head of title: A. Löschhorn ... op. 136.
    Publisher's numbers: 7690-
    "Edited by A. R. Parson."
    I. Parsons, Albert Ross, 1847-   ed.
    [Full name: Carl Albert Löschhorn]

NL 0445682   CU

VMT   LOESCHHORN, ALBERT, 1819-1905.
229   Octavenschule für pianoforte_ Op.176_
L 82o Leipzig,C.F.Peters₍n.d.₎
    74p. 31cm. (Edition Peters, no.2083)

    "Verzeichniss von octaven-etüden verschie-
dener schwierigkeit": p.74.
    Plate no.: 6524.

NL 0445683   ICN OC1

---

q786.4 Loeschhorn, Albert, 1819-1905.
L824p   Piano studies to form execution.
    Parts I, II, III. Op.66.   Boston,
    White-Smith music pub. co., n.d.
    23p.

NL 0445684   IU OrU

Loeschhorn, Albert, 1819-1905.
    Pianoforte etudes in progressive order
for the development of technic and
expression, with fingering ... Part II...
for intermediate grade ... Boston, B. F.
Wood music no. n.d.
    67 p.

    (Edition Wood, no. 629)
    Op. 66. Books 1, 2, 3.

NL 0445685   OC1

Loeschhorn, Albert, 1819-1905.
    Pianoforte studies in progressive order
for the development of technic and expression,
with fingering by A. Loeschhorn. Part I,
For beginners, Op. 65, Book 1, 2, 3...
Boston, The B. F. Wood music co., n.d.
    3 v.

    (Edition Wood no. 10 a,)

    Lacking: Books 2 & 3

NL 0445686   OC1

Loeschhorn, Albert, 1819-1905.
    Pianoforte studies in progressive order
for the development of technic and
expression, with fingering ... Part 3: For
advanced pupils. Bk 3. Boston, The B. F.
Wood music co., n.d.

    Op 67.

NL 0445687   OC1

Löschhorn, Albert, 1819-1905.
    ₍Die Klavier-Technik₎

    Pianoforte-technics; daily exercises. Translations by Th.
Baker. New York, G. Schirmer, ℅1900.
    51 p. 30 cm. (Schirmer's library of musical classics, v. 254)

    1. Piano—Studies and exercises.

    MT225.L84   51-55242

NL 0445688   DLC

MT225 Löschhorn, Albert, 1819-1905.
L64
1905   Progressive piano studies, for advanced grades [by] Carl Albert
Music Loeschhorn. Op. 67, book 2. Edited by Thomas Tapper.
Library Boston, O. Ditson, c1905.
    20 p. (Ditson edition, no. 34)

    1. Piano - Studies and exercises.

NL 0445689   CU MWA

LOESCHHORN,Albert,1819-
    Romance-Étude pour piano. Op.76. n.p.,
₍18-₎.

NL 0445690   MH

M1
.S444 Löschhorn, Albert, 1819-1905.
v.33   ₍Fleurs du sud. Salterello; arr.₎
no.10
    Salterello, no. 2. ₍op. 108₎ Pour piano.
    Braunschweig, Henry Litolff ₍not after 1892₎
    Pl. no. 4160.
      9 p. 34cm. ₍Sheet music collection, v.33,no.10₎
      Stamp of Edw. Schuberth & Co., 23 Union Square,
New York, on cover.

    1. Piano music. I. Title. II. Title: Fleurs du
sud.

NL 0445691   ViU

VMT   LOESCHHORN, ALBERT, 1819-1905.
225   _Studies for the pianoforte for development
L 82s of technique and expression_ Op.65₍-67₎ New
    York,Schirmer,n.d.
      3v. (Schirmer's library of musical
    classics. vol.966-968)

      Plate nos.: 21135-37.
      Contents.—pt.I. For beginners.—pt.II.
For the intermediate degree.—pt.III. For more
advanced pupils.

NL 0445692   ICN IEN OC1

---

fMT225 Loeschhorn, Albert, 1819-1905.
L6
op.66   Studies for the pianoforte for development
    of technique and expression. For the inter-
    mediate degree in three books. Op.66.
    New York, G.Schirmer, 1895.
      3v. 31cm. (Schirmer's library of musical
    classics, v.313-315)

      1. Piano - Studies and exercises.

NL 0445693   IaU

---

q784.3 Loeschhorn, Albert, 1819-1905.
Sh37   Tarantelle, par A. Loeschorn₍!₎   Chicago,
v.3   Root & Cady, c1863.
no.13   7p.

    ₍Sheet music printed in Chicago prior to 1871.
    v.3,no.13₎
    Plate no.: 327.6.

    1. Pianoforte music. I. Title.

NL 0445694   IU ICN

Loeschhorn, Albert, 1819-
    30 melodious studies. Op.52. Boston [etc.,
etc.] G.D.Russell & co. [18-?]

    pt.2. 36 cm.
    Piano score.
    Contents. - Pt.2. No.11-20.

NL 0445695   MH

VOLUME 338

Loeschhorn, Albert, 1819-1905.
　Der Triller. Vierzehn Etuden ueber die gebräuchlichsten Arten des Trillers mit genauer Bezeichnung der Ausführung und des Fingersatzes füir Pianoforte componirt von A. Loeschorn. Op. 165, Heft 2, Nos 9-14. Leipzig, Rob. Forberg. [18-　]
　15 p. f.

NL　0445696　　NN

M786.4
L826u　Löschhorn, Albert, 1819-1905.
　[Studies, piano, op.169-170]
　...Universal piano studies for medium grade, edited and revised by A.R. Parsons. N.Y., G. Schirmer [n.d.]
　45p. 31cm. (Schirmer's library of musical classics, vol.1615)

　　Publ.no.: 39662.

　　1. Piano. Studies & exercises.

NL　0445697　　IEN

LOESCHHORN, Albert, 1819-
　Valse brillante. Op.37. [Partitur for the piano]. Boston, [18-].

NL　0445698　　MH

LOESCHHORN, Albert, 1819-
　Volkslieder-Album für pianoforte, Op.89. Heft II. Nos.6,7,9. Heft I. No.9. n.p., [18-].

NL　0445699　　MH

LOESCHHORN, ALBERT, 1819-1905.
　Wegweiser in der Pianoforte-Literatur. Verzeichniss von mustergültigen und anerkannten Pianoforte-Werken älterer und neuerer Zeit, in stufenweiser Schwierigkeitsfolge geordnet und hrsg. von A. Loeschhorn und Jul. Weiss. Berlin, J. Weiss, 1862. 101 p. 16cm.

　　1. Piano music—Bibl. 2. Chamber music—Bibl. I. Weiss, Julius, 1814-1898, joint author.

NL　0445700　　NN

M204
L6
op.51　Löschhorn, Albert, 1819-1905.

　　Zwölf vierhändige Klavierstücke zum Unterricht für Anfänger; eine Reihe melodiöser und charakteristischer Tonbilder in fortschreitender Ordnung komponiert, op. 51. Leipzig, C.F. Peters [n.d.] Pl. no. 6899.
　　score (51 p.) 23x31cm. (Edition Peters, Nr. 1011)

　　　For piano, 4 hands.
　　　1. Piano music (4 hands)

NL　0445701　　IaAS OrP

Loeschhorn, Carl Albert.
　See
Loeschhorn, Albert, 1819-1905.

PT1383　LÖSCHHORN, HANS, 1850-　　comp.
.L8　Anthologie mittelalterlicher gedichte. Mit benutzung der von Gustav Legerlotz veranstalteten ausgaben für den schulgebrauch zusammengestellt von prof. dr. H. Löschhorn. Bielefeld und Leipzig, Velhagen & Klasing, 1906.
　xiii, [1], 172 p. 17cm. (On cover: Velhagen & Klasings Sammlung deutscher schulausgaben, 118. lfg.)

　　1. German poetry—Collections.

NL　0445703　　ICU

Löschhorn, Hans, 1850-　　ed.
　Anthologie mittelalterlicher gedichte, mit benutzung der von Gustav Legerlotz veranstalteten ausgaben für den schulgebrauch zusammengestellt. Bielefeld, Velhagen & Klasing, 1934.
　172 p. S. (Deutsche ausgaben, bd. 118)

NL　0445704　　NcU

Loeschhorn, Hans, 1850-
　Deutsche Litteratur: Allgemeines.
　(In Ergebnisse und Fortschritte der germanistischen Wissenschaft im letzten Vierteljahrhundert ... Pp. 191-200. Leipzig. 1902.)

F8185 — Germany. Lit. Hist.

NL　0445705　　MB

Löschhorn, Hans, 1850-
　Museumsgänge, eine einführung in kunstbetrachtung und kunstgeschichte, von Hans Löschhorn; mit 262 abbildungen im text, einem titelbild und einem einschaltbild. 2. aufl. Bielefeld und Leipzig, Velhagen & Klasing, 1905.
　vi, 268 p. front., illus., double pl. 28cm.

First published 1908.

　　1. Art—Hist. 2. Art criticism. I. Title.
　　　　　　　　　　　　　　　　　　　　43-33793
Library of Congress　　N5303.L62 1905

NL　0445706　　DLC NIC OrCS

Löschhorn, Hans, 1850-
　Museumsgänge; eine Einführung in Kunstbetrachtung und Kunstgeschichte. 4. Aufl. Bielefeld, Velhagen & Klasing, 1920.

NL　0445707　　MH

PP3064　Löschhorn, Hans, 1850-
.G8L7　Rede auf Jacob Grimm zu seiner säcularfeier 1885, in der Gesellschaft für deutsche philologie zu Berlin gehalten von Hans Löschhorn. Berlin, W. Weber, 1885.
　31 p. 20cm.

　　1. Grimm, Jacob Ludwig Karl, 1785-1863.

NL　0445708　　ICU MH NjP NIC

Loeschhorn, Hans, 1850-
　Zum normannischen Rolandsliede ... Leipzig, Druck von Breitkopf und Härtel, 1873.
　35 p. 18½cm.
Inaug.-diss.—Göttingen.

　　1. Chanson de Roland. I. Title.
　　　　　　　　　　　　　　　　22-17704
Library of Congress　　PQ1525.L6

NL　0445709　　DLC OCl NjP TNJ NN CtY NcD

Loeschhorn, Karl,
　SEE
Loeschhorn, Karl Friedrich Wilhelm, 1851-

---

arX　Löschhorn, Karl Friedrich Wilhelm, 1851-
3427　Kritische Studien zur Platonischen und christlichen Ethik. Wittenberg, 1880.
　40 p. 26cm.

　　1. Plato.

NL　0445711　　NIC NjP

Loeschhorn, Karl Friedrich Wilhelm, 1851-1920.
　Quaestiones metricae ... Magdeburgi, typis E. Baenschii, 1873.
　2 p. l., 34 p. 22½cm.
Inaug.-diss.—Rostock.
Vita.

　　1. Greek language—Metrics and rhythmics.
　　　　　　　　　　　　　　　　10—28930
Library of Congress　　PA411.L7

NL　0445712　　DLC CtY NjP

4DD　Löschin, Gotthilf
4124　Geschichte Danzigs von der ältesten bis zur neuesten Zeit. Mit beständiger Rücksicht auf Cultur der Sitten, Wissenschaften, Künste, Gewerbe und Handelszweige, zum 2. Male bearb. Danzig F. W. Ewert, 1822-23.
　2 v.

NL　0445713　　DLC-P4 IU

Loeschke, Adalbert, 1903-
　Aneurysma dissecans auf luetischer grundlage. Inaug. diss. Berlin, [1927]
　Bibl.

NL　0445714　　ICRL CtY OU

Loeschke, Johann Traugott
　Denkschrift über Gräfin Ludoämilia Elisabetha aus dem nun Fürstlichen Hause Schwarzburg-Rudolstadt, und über Hochderselben in Gemeinschaft mit zwei Hochgräflichen Schwestern vor 200 Jahren im Frühling des Jahres 1672 erfolgtes christ-seliges Ende. Leipzig, Löschke, 1872
　xiii, 86 p. illus.

NL　0445715　　MH

---

ar V　Löschke, Karl Julius.
14862　Leben und Wirken des Valentin Friedland, genannt Trozendorf; ein Beitrag zur Geschichte der schlesischen Schulen im sechzehnten Jahrhundert. Neisse und Leipzig, T. Hennings, 1842.
　112 p. 19cm.

　　1. Trotzendorf, Valentin, 1490-1556.

NL　0445716　　NIC

VOLUME 338

377.1
L89r
Löschke, Karl Julius.
Die religiöse bildung der jugend und der sitt-
liche zustand der schulen im sechzehnten jahrhun-
dert. Ein beitrag zur geschichte der pädagogik
Breslau, Grass, Barth und comp., 1846.
244p.

Bibliographical foot-notes.

1. Religius education--Germany. 2. Education--
Germany--Hist.

NL 0445717   IU ICU

B
T858ℓ
Löschke, Karl Julius.
Valentin Trotzendorf nach seinem leben und wirken. Zur erinnerung an seinen todestag, den 26.
april 1556 ... Breslau, Grass, Barth und comp.,
1856.
viii, 95p.

"Quellenschriften": p.iv; bibliographical foot-
notes.

1. Trotzendorf, Valentin, 1490-1556.

NL 0445718   IU CtY PPSchw

Loeschmann, Emil, 1866-
Beiträge zur hydrographie der oberen oder.
Inaug. diss. Breslau,1892.

NL 0445719   ICRL DNLM CU

Löschmann, Johann, compiler.
Kurtzer Auszug etlicher Sprüche Herrn Lutheri,
wie auch des Corporis Julij, und der Lüneburg.
Artickeln wieder den neuen Majoristen zu Helmstäd
über der Lehre: Gute wercke sind nöthig zur Seligkeit
... n.p., 1648.
[28] p.   19 x 16 cm.   In vol. lettered
Löschmann, Sprüche Herrn Lutheri.

NL 0445720   NIC

Löschner, Hans, 1874-1956
Einführung in die erdbildmessung (terrestrische photo-
grammetrie) von dr Hans Löschner ... mit 121 figuren im text
und 2 tafeln. Leipzig und Wien, F. Deuticke, 1930.
vi, 218 p. illus. (incl. map) pl., diagrs. (1 fold.) 24½ᶜᵐ.
Plate attached to p. 161.
"Einiges aus der literatur": p. 214-215.

1. Photographic surveying.

33-34871

Library of Congress   TA593.L6   526.91

NL 0445721   DLC CU ICJ NN

Loeschner, Hans, 1874-
Genauigkeitsuntersuchungen fuer Laengenmes-
sungen, mit besonderer Beruecksichtigung einer
neuen Vorrichtung fuer Praecisions-Stahlband-
messung. Hannover, 1902.
56 p.   15 x 22 cm.

NL 0445722   DBS

Löschner, Hans, 1874-
Instrumente der praktischen geometrie, von dr. H. Löschner ... Mit 50 figuren im text und 70 instrumentenbildern.
Wien-Leipzig, Österreichischer bundesverlag für unterricht,
wissenschaft und kunst, 1926.
145 p. illus. diagrs. 20ᶜᵐ. (Added t.-p.: Die landkarte; fachbücherei
für jedermann in länderaufnahme und kartenwesen)

1. Surveying--Instruments.   I. Title.

31-24203

Library of Congress   TA562.L57   526.91

NL 0445723   DLC

*GC9
L8247
905u
Löschner, Hans, 1874-1956.
Über Sonnenuhren; Beiträge zu ihrer Geschicht
und Konstruktion, nebst Aufstellung einer
Fehlertheorie, von Dr Hans Löschner ... Mit
59 Abbildungen im Texte.
Graz,Leuschner & Lubensky's Universitäts-
buchhandlung,1905.
154p.,1ℓ. illus. 23.5cm.,in case 25cm.
"Berichtigung" on leaf at end.
Original printed stiffened blue-gray wrapper
in cloth case.

NL 0445724   MH

Löschner, Hans, 1874-1956.
Über sonnenuhren; beiträge zu ihrer geschichte und konstruktion, nebst aufstellung einer fehlertheorie, von dr Hans
Löschner ... mit 72 abbildungen im texte. 2. umgearb. und
verm. ausg. Graz, Leuschner & Lubensky, 1906.
165 p. illus. diagrs. 22½ᶜᵐ.
"Zusammenstellung der für den historischen teil benützten quellen":
p. [10]-13.
"Ueber sonnenuhr-konstruktionen, von prof. Jos. Adamczik" (reprint
from "Zeitschrift für vermessungswesen, bd. xxxvi, hft. 11, april 11,
1907", p. 265-278) attached to front lining-paper.
1. Sun-dials.   I. Adamczik, Josef, 1863-1919.   II. Title.

35-23743

Library of Congress   QB215.L8 1906   529.78

NL 0445725   DLC ICJ PU

Loeschner, Harald, 1926-
August Bebels politische Entwicklung während seiner
Leipziger Jahre; ein Beitrag zur neueren sächsischen
Landesgeschichte. [Leipzig, 1952]

Inaug. Diss. - Leipzig

NL 0445726   MH

WS
100
L826a
1860
LÖSCHNER, Joseph Wilhelm, Freiherr von,
1809-1888
Aus dem Franz Josef-Kinder-Spitale
in Prag. Beobachtungen und Erfahrungen
aus dem Gebiete der Medicin überhaupt
und der Paediatrik insbesondere, hrsg.
von Löschner und Lambl. Prag, Tempsky
1860-68.
2 v. illus.

I. Lambl, D   F
II. Praha. Franz Josef-Kinderspital

NL 0445728   DNLM CtY

Löschner, Joseph Wilhelm, freiherr von, 1809-
1888.
Carlsbad, Marienbad, Franzensbad, und ihre
umgebung vom naturhistorischen, medicinisch-
geschichtlichen und therapeutischen standpunkte,
hrsg. unter der redaction des landesmedicinal-
rathes dr. Löschner ... Prag & Carlsbad, H.
Dominicus, 1863.
5 p. l., 340, [2] p. incl. tables. col.
fold. map. 25½ᶜᵐ. (Added t.-p.: Beiträge zur
balenologie ... I. bd.)

"Literatur [von Carlsbad]": p. [173]-176.

NL 0445729   NNC

WBI
L827c
1889
LÖSCHNER, Joseph Wilhelm, Freiherr von,
1809-1888
Der Curort Giesshübl-Puchstein in
Böhmen, mit vorzugsweiser Berücksichtigung des Nutzens und Gebrauches
von Mattoni's Giesshübler Sauerbrunn.
12. verm. Aufl. Wien, Braumüller,
1889.
132 p. illus. (Braumüller's Bade-
Bibliothek, Nr. 13)

NL 0445730   DNLM

Loeschner, Joseph Wilhelm, 1809-
---- Der Curort Puchstein in Böhmen, mit be-
sonderer Berücksichtigung des Nutzens und Ge-
brauches seiner verwendeten Mineralwässer vor-
zugsweise der König Otto-Quelle (Giesshübler
Sauerbrunn). 8. Aufl. 87 pp., 1 map. 8°.
Carlsbad, [Franieck u. Comp.], 1875.
Also, Co-Editor of: Archiv für Balneologie, Neuwied.

NL 0445731   DNLM

RC66
834ℓ
Löschner, Joseph Wilhelm, 1809-
Dissertatio ... sistens conspectum morborum
in clinico medico Pragensi altero semestri anni
schol. 1831 tractatorum. Pragae, J. Spurny[1834]
xiv, 68, [2]p. 22cm.

1. Medicine - Cases, clinical reports, statistics.

NL 0445732   CtY-M DNLM

WS
100
L826e
1868
LÖSCHNER, Joseph Wilhelm, Freiherr von,
1809-1888
Epidemiologische und klinische Studien
aus dem Gebiete der Paediatrik. Prag,
Tempsky, 1868.
xii, 383 p.
Many of the papers were read at the
Franz-Josef Kinderspitale in Prague,
1858-1861.

NL 0445733   DNLM ICJ MiU

Loeschner, Joseph Wilhelm, 1809-
---- Der Giesshübler Sauerbrunn in Böhmen,
die König Otto Quelle. 5. Aufl. 78 pp., 1 l., 3
pl. 8°. Carlsbad, G. Feyerick, 1869.

NL 0445734   DNLM

RA
887
.C9
L83
1857
Löschner, Joseph Wilhelm, Freiherr von, 1809-1888.
Der Sauerbrunn von Giesshübl in Böhmen, die
König Otto-Quelle genannt. Von Prof. Dr.
Löschner. 4., mit einer neuen chemischen Analyse
von Göttl verm.Aufl. Karlsbad, Buchdr. der
Gebrüder Franieck, 1857.
44 p. col.front. 21 cm.
With this is bound Franieck,F. Album der
König Otto's Quelle bei Giesshübl. 1857.
1. Mineral waters--Kysibl-Kyselka,
Czechoslovak   Republic. I.Göttl, Hugo.
II.Title.   III.Title: König Otto-
Quelle.

NL 0445735   MiU DNLM

WC
262
L826s
1854
LÖSCHNER, Joseph Wilhelm, Freiherr von,
1809-1888
Schlussbericht über die vom 21. Mai
1849 bis Ende Dezember 1851 in Prag
beobachtete Cholera-Epidemie nebst einer
Abhandlung: die Cholera der Kinder.
Prag, Calve, 1854.
90 p.

NL 0445736   DNLM

VOLUME 338

Loeschner, Joseph Wilhelm, Freiherr von, 1809-1888.
— Die Wirkungen des Saidschitzer Bitter-
wassers. Theoretisch und praktisch erläutert.
34 pp. 8°. Prag, J. G. Calve, 1853.

NL 0445737   DNLM

Loeschner, Siegmund.
Balkenbrücken als räumliche Gebilde, Beitrag mit besonderer
Berücksichtigung der Förderbrücken.   Wittenberg: A. Ziem-
sen, 1913. x, 181 p.   8°.

1. Bridges.—Construction. 1913.
N. Y. P. L.   February 2, 1914.

NL 0445738   NN

390.1   Löschnig, Josef.
L89A   Anleitung zur Herstellung und Behandlung
Ed. 6   der Obstweine (Gärmoste) und Süssmoste.
6. verm. und verb. Aufl.   Wien, Scholle,
1947.
64 p.   (Scholle-Bücherei, Bd. 119)

1. Cider.   2. Fruit wines. I. Scholle-
Bücherei. Bd. 119.

NL 0445739   DNAL

93   Löschnig, Josef.
L89B   Die Bewertung der Obstgehölze.   Wien,
Frick [1947]
115 p.

1. Fruit.   Estimating of crop.

NL 0445740   DNAL

Löschnig, Josef.
Empfehleswerte Obstsorten (Normalsortiment
für Nieder-Österreich)
see under   Landes-Obstbauverein für
Niederösterreich.

Löschnig, Josef.
Der frischverkauf des obstes. Anleitung zur ernte,
zum sortieren, verpacken und aufbewahren des obstes,
von Josef Löschnig ... Mit 48 abbildungen. Stuttgart,
E. Ulmer, 1907.
iv, 52 p. illus. 21ᶜᵐ.

1. Fruit.   2. Fruit trade.

13-12104

Library of Congress   SB360.L7

NL 0445742   DLC ICJ

390.1   Löschnig, Josef.
L89   Frucht-Branntweine und ihre Bereitung ...
Ed. 4   mit einem Anhang: Aus den Vorschriften
über die Branntweinerzeugung von E. Hartmann.
4. erweiterte Aufl.   Wien, 1948.
88 p.   (Scholle-Bücherei, 118. Bdchn.)

NL 0445743   DNLM

SB   Löschnig, Josef.
379   Die Marille (Aprikose) und ihre Kultur,
A7   von Josef Löschnig and Fritz Passecker.
L82   Wien, Österreichischer Agrarverlag [c1954]
363 p. illus. 25 cm.

1. Apricot. I. Title. II. Passecker,
Fritz.

NL 0445744   NIC InLP DNAL MiEM

Löschnig, Josef.
Pflanzung und Pflege der Obstbäume und Beerensträucher,
praktische Anleitung zur Durchführung der wichtigsten Arbeiten im Obstbau. 15. Aufl. Wien, Scholle-Verlag, 1948.
106 p. illus. 28 cm.   (Scholle-Bücherei, 113. Bdchn.)

1. Fruit-culture—Austria.   I. Title.

SB359.L6 1948   634   50-17000

NL 0445745   DLC DNAL

Löschnig, Josef
Praktische anleitung zum rationellen betriebe
des obstbaues. Wien, Hrsg. vom Landes-obstbau-
vereine für Niederösterreich, 1901.
150 p.

NL 0445746   CU-A

465.62   Löschnig, Josef.
L89   Verbesserung der Obstsorten; Bastarde,
Mutationen, Zwillingsfrüchte, Chimären,
Xenien, Luther Burbanks und J.W. Mitscourins
Erkenntnisse. Wien, 1948.
88 p.   (Scholle-Bücherei, 187. Bdchn.)

1. Austria. Pomology. 2. Fruit.
Breeding. I. Scholle-Bücherei. Bd. 187.

NL 0445747   DNAL

389   Löschnig, Josef.
L893   Die Verwertung von Obst und Gemüse im
Haushalte. Wien, Hartleben [1947?]
192 p.

1. Food. Nutritive value. 2. Food.
Preservation. 3. Fruit. 4. Vegetables.

NL 0445748   DNAL

Löschnig, Josef.
40 tage Nordamerika; wahrnehmungen und eindrücke einer
studienreise nach U. S. A., von hofrat Josef Löschnig ... 2.
aufl. Wien [Hauptverband der weinbautreibenden Österreichs
und gemeinschaft österreichischer obstzüchter] 1935.
208 p. illus. (incl. ports., maps) diagrs. 23ᶜᵐ.
Advertising matter: p. 175-208.

1. U. S.—Descr. & trav. 2. Fruit-culture—U. S.   I. Title.

35-15346

Library of Congress   E169.L82
[2]   917.3

NL 0445749   DLC

Loeschnigg, Hélène de, 1908-
... La transfusion sanguine dans les hemoptysies
tuberculeuses ...   Paris, 1934.
Thèse - Univ. de Paris.
"Bibliographie": p. [67]-68.

NL 0445750   CtY

Loesdau, Bruno, 1883-
Der Besitz von Sachteilen nach dem
Bürgerlichen Gesetzbuche ... von Bruno
Loesdau ... Borna-Leipzig, R. Noske,
1908.
vi, 55 p.   21½cm.
Inaug.-diss. - Erlangen.
"Literaturverzeichnis": p. [v]-vi.

NL 0445751   MH-L NIC ICRL

Lösecke, A   von.
Deutschlands verbreiteste pilze; oder, Anleitung zur bestimmung der wichtigsten pilze Deutschlands und der angrenzenden länder, zugleich als
commentar der fortgesetzten prof. Büchner'schen
pilznachbildungen. Von A. v. Lösecke und F.A. Bösemann. 1. bändchen. Die hautpilze. Berlin, T.
Grieben, 1872.
xlv p., 1 l., 185, [2] p.   18ᶜᵐ.
No more published?

1. Mushrooms—Germany. I. Büchner, Eduard Wilhelm Gottlieb, 1805-1867. II. Bösemann, F.A., joint author. III.
Title.   QK608.03L83

NL 0445752   MiU MH

Loesecke, Harry Willard von
see
Von Loesecke, Harry Willard, 1898-1958.

Lösecke, Helene von.
... Über supravitale Färbung von Eiterkörperchen
... Berlin, 1926.
Inaug.-Diss. - Göttingen.
"Sonder-Abdruck aus 'Bruns' Beiträge zur
klinischen Chirurgie', Band 135, Heft 4."
Bibliographical foot-notes.

NL 0445754   CtY MiU

W 4   Lösecke, Helmut von, 1915-
B51   Calcinosis. Berlin, Linke [1940]
1940   47 p.

Inaug.-Diss. - Berlin.
Bibliography: p. 43-47.

NL 0445755   DNLM

238   Löseke, Christoph Albrecht, 1676-1753.
L89c   Catechetische Anleitung die Haushaltung und
1729   Wege Gottes mit dem Menschen zu betrachten,
darin Lehre von den Bündnissen Gottes mit den
Menschen verhandelt, die Ordnung des Heyls, wie
alle Glaubens-Artickel in biblischer Folge
ketten-weise an einander hangen, gezeiget, und
die Kirchen-Historie von Anbegin der Welt bis
an gegenwärtige Zeit kurz und deutlich vorgestellet wird, von Christoph Albrecht Lösecken.

2.Ed.   Halle, Verlegung des Wäysen-Hauses,
1729.
72p. 18ᶜᵐ.

NL 0445757   IU

VOLUME 338

Löseke, Christoph Albrecht, 1676–1753.
Kurtzer Begriff der Fest-Lehren, oder, Einfältige Betrachtung der göttlichen Wohlthaten, die an den Fest-Tagen durchs gantze Jahr in der christlichen Kirche betrachtet werden; Tabellenweise, in Fragen u. Antworten verfasset, und mit Sprüchen Heiliger Schrift bewiesen, der Jugend zum Besten aufgesetzet. 2.Aufl. Verb., und mit einigen Festtagen vermehret, von Christoph Albrecht Lösecken. Magdeburg, C. Seidels sel.

Wittwe, 1734.
64p. 18cm.

Manuscript notes in margins.

NL 0445759 IU

Löseke, Christoph Albrecht, 1676–1753.
Der wohl unterrichtete schul-lehrer, oder, Anweisung, wie die anvertraute jugend in den niedrigen schulen zur gottseligkeit, singen, beten, lesen, schreiben, rechnen, guten sitten, betrachtung der naturlehre, gebrauch des calenders, und andern den leuten in den städten und auf dem lande nöthigen häuslichen wissenschaften gründlich und nützlich kan angeführet werden, allen schul-lehrern zu ihrem eigenen nutzen ... heraus gegeben von C. A. Löseke ... Züllichau,

In der Waysenhaus- und Frommannischen buchhandlung, 1774.
278p. incl.fold.tab. front.(diagrs.)

1. Education of children. 2. Teaching.

NL 0445761 IU

Löseke (Johann Ludwig Leberecht) [1724–57.]
Abhandlung der auserlesensten Arzney-Mittel, nach derselben Ursprung, Güte, Bestandtheilen, Maasse und Art zu wirken, ingleichen wie dieselben aus der Apotheke zu verschreiben sind; Zum Nutzen seiner Zuhörer abgefasst. Mit Anmerkungen versehen, und mit einer Tabelle vermehrt von A. H. Gumpertz. 2. Aufl. 14 p. l., 656t pp., 18 l. 16°. Berlin, G. W. Nicolai, 1756.

NL 0445762 DNLM

Löseke, Johann Ludwig Leberecht, 1724–1757.
Abhandlung der auserlesensten Arzneymittel nach derselben Ursprung, Güte, Bestandtheilen, Maasse und Art zu wirken, ingleichen wie dieselben aus der Apotheke zu verschreiben sind ... 3. verb. Aufl.Mit Anmerkungen versehen... von A. S. Gumperz. Berlin, Nicolai, 1763.
15p.ℓ.,658p.,16ℓ. 19cm.

1. Materia medica. I. Title.

NL 0445763 CtY-M NNNAM ICJ

Loeseke (Joh. Ludovicus Leberecht.) [1724–57]
De motu sanguinis intestino. 56 pp., 1 l. sm. 4°. Halae Magdeb., ex off. Schneideriana, [1745]. [Also, in: P., v. 58.]

NL 0445764 DNLM

Löseke, Johann Ludwig Leberecht, 1724–1757.
... Materia medica concentrata; oder, Verzeichnis von den vorzüglichsten inn- und äuserlichen Artzeneymitteln, und ihren nöthigsten Dosibus, zur klugen Wahl und nützlichen Gebrauch in der Praxi clinica, unter ihre gehörige Classen gebracht, nebst einem Anhang von Nahrungs-Mitteln, Giften und Gegengiften, aus allen 3. Reichen der Natur, und einem Dispensatorio privato, herausgegeben von Georg Ludewig Rumpelt ... Dresden, Bey M. Gröll, 1758.
[24], 320 p. 17cm.

At head of title: Dr. Joh. Ludw. Leberecht Lösecke.

NL 0445765 ICJ

Löseke, Johann Ludwig Leberecht, 1724–1757.
Dr. Joh. Ludw. Leberecht Lösecke, Materia medica concentrata; oder, Verzeichnis von den vorzüglichsten inn- und äuserlichen arzeneymitteln, und ihren nöthigsten dosibus, zur klugen wahl und nützlichem gebrauch, in der praxi clinica, unter ihre gehörige classen gebracht. Nebst einem anhang von nahrungs-mitteln, giften und gegengiften, aus allen drey reichen der natur, und einem dispensatorio privato, heraus gegeben von Georg Ludewig Rumpelt. 2. und vorm. aufl. ... Dressden, bey Michael Gröll, 1761.
[16], 336 p. 17½ cm.

Bound with his Neue und seltene anatomisch-chirurgisch-medicinische wahrnehmungen ... 1761.

1. Materia medica - Early works. 2. Drugs. Rumpelt, Georg Ludewig, ed.

NL 0445767 NNC

Loeseke, Joh. Ludovicus Leberecht, 1724–57.
Materia medica concentrata, oder Verzeichnis von den vorzüglichsten inn- und äusserlichen Arzneymitteln, und ihren nöthigsten Dosibus, zur klugen Wahl und nützlichen Gebrauch, in der Praxi clinica, unter ihre gehörige Classen gebracht, nebst einem Anhang von Nahrungs-Mitteln, Giften und Gegengiften, aus allen drey Reichen der Natur, und einem Dispensatorio privato, herausgegeben von Georg Ludewig Rumpelt. 3. Aufl. 7 p. l., 336 pp. 8°. Dresda u. Warschau. M. Gröll, 1764.

NL 0445768 DNLM

Loeseke, Joh. Ludovicus Leberecht, 1724–57.
Materia medica, oder Abhandlung von den auserlesenen Arzneymitteln nach derselben Ursprung, Güte, Bestandtheilen, Maasse und Art zu wirken, nebst Vorschriften wie dieselben aus der Apotheke zu verschreiben sind. 4. Aufl., verbessert von D. Johann Friedrich Zückert. 7 p. l., 614. pp., 9 l. 8°. Lucern, B. Hautt, 1776.

NL 0445769 DNLM

Loeseke, Johann Ludwig Leberecht, 1724–1757.
... Materia medica oder abhandlung von den auserlesenen arzneymitteln ... 5. aufl. durchgangig verbessert und mit den neuern entdeckungen bereichert von d. Johann Friedrich Gmelin ... Berlin und Stettin, F. Nicolai, 1795.
567 p.

NL 0445770 MiU

Löseke, Johann Ludwig Leberecht, 1724–1757
Materia medica; oder, Abhandlung von den auserlesenen arzneymitteln nach derselben ursprung, güte, bestandtheilen, maase und art zu wirken, nebst vorschriften wie dieselben aus der apotheke zu verordnen sind. Siebente aufl., durchgängig verbessert und mit den neuern entdeckungen bereichert von D. Johann Friedrich Gmelin... Berlin und Stettin, F. Nicolai, 1800.
16 p., 600 p., 11 ℓ.

NL 0445771 MiDW DNLM

Löseke, Johann Ludwig Leberecht, 1724–1757.
Johann Ludwig Leberecht Löseke ... Neue und seltene anatomisch-chirurgisch-medicinische wahrnehmungen mit kupferstichen erläutert. Berlin, bey Gottlieb August Lange, 1761.
[16], 79 p. III fold. plates. 17½ cm.

1. Medicine - Early works. 2. Surgery - Early works. I. Title.

NL 0445772 NNC DNLM

Löseke, Johann Ludwig Leberecht, 1724–1757.
... Neue und seltene anatomisch-chirurgisch-medicinische Wahrnehmungen mit Kupferstichen erläutert. Zweyte verbesserte Auflage. Berlin und Stralsund, G. A. Lange, 1767.
[16], 78 p. III pl. 17cm.
At head of title: Joh. Ludwig Löseke, ...

NL 0445773 ICJ

Loescke, Joh. Ludovisus Leberecht, 1725–57.
Observationes anatomico-chirurgico-medicae novae et rariores, accurate descriptae iconibusque illustratae. 47 pp., 3 pl. 4°. Berolini, apud J. J. Schatzii vid., 1754.

NL 0445774 DNLM NNNAM

Loeseke, Johann Ludwig Leberecht, 1724–1757.
Observations nouvelles et rares, d'anatomie, de chirurgie, et de medecine; décrites avec exactitude, & enrichies de figures en taille-douce; traduites du latin de Jean Louis Le Berecht Loeseke ... sur l'edition de Berlin, 1754. [1757]
70 p. III fold. plates. 17 cm. (In Warner, Joseph. Observations de chirurgie. 1757. [pt. 2.])

NL 0445775 NNC

Löseke, Johann Ludwig Leberecht, 1724–1757.
Joh. Ludwig Leberecht Lösekens ... Pathologie; oder, Lehre von den Krankheiten des menschlichen Körpers ... Dresden und Warschau, Gröllische Buchhandlung, 1762.
[16], 128 p. 17½cm.

Bound with his Semiotik; oder, Lehre von den Zeichen der Krankheiten. 1762.

NL 0445776 ICJ

Löseke, Johann Ludwig Lebrecht, 1724–1757.
Pathologie, oder Lehre von den Krankheiten des menschlichen Körpers. 3. Aufl. Dresden, Gröll, 1775.
8p.ℓ.,128p. 18cm.

1. Pathology. I. Title.
Bound with his: Semiotik. 3. A. 1775. Phisiologie. Neue A. 1782.

NL 0445777 CtY-M

Löseke, Johann Ludwig Leberecht, 1724–1757.
Phisiologie, oder Lehre von dem gesunden Zustande des menschlichen Körpers, nebst einem Unterricht, denselben zu erhalten. Mit einer Vorrede von Christian Gotthold Schwenken. Neue Aufl. Dresden, Gröll, 1771.
12p.ℓ.,348p.,2ℓ. 18cm. (Bound with his Pathologie. 1775).

NL 0445778 CtY-M

612.04
L895
Löseke, Johann Ludwig Leberecht, 1724–1757.
Joh. Ludwig Leberecht Lösekens ... Physiologie; oder, Lehre von dem gesunden Zustande des menschlichen Körpers, nebst einem Unterricht, denselben zu erhalten. Mit einer Vorrede von D. Christian Gotthold Schwenken ... Dresden und Warschau, Gröllische Buchhandlung, 1762.
[24], 328 p. 17½cm.

NL 0445779 ICJ

VOLUME 338

Löseke, Johann Ludwig Leberecht, 1724-1757.
Joh. Ludw. Leberecht Lösekens ... Semiotik; oder, Lehre von den Zeichen der Krankheiten ... Dresden und Warschau, Gröllische Buchhandlung, 1762.

196 p. 17¼ᶜᵐ.

NL 0445780   ICJ

Löseke, Johann Ludwig Lebrecht, 1724-1757.
Semiotik, oder Lehre von den Zeichen der Krankheiten. 2. Aufl. Dresden, Gröll, 1768.
128p. 18cm. (Bound with his Pathologie. 1775).

1. Semiology.   I. Title.

NL 0445781   CtY-M

Loeseke, Johann Ludwig Leberecht, 1724-57.
Therapia specialis interna, oder gründliche Anweisung zur Erkenntnis und Cur der innerlichen Krankheiten des menschlichen Körpers. Nebst einem Anhange und einem Register über sämtliche Theile dieser Therapie. 3. & 4. Theil. 2. Aufl. 364 pp.; 352 pp., 7 l. 12°. Dresden & Leipzig, Gröll, 1763.

NL 0445782   DNLM

Löseke, Johann Ludwig Leberecht, 1724-1757.
Therapia specialis interna, oder gründliche Anweisung zur Erkenntnis und Cur der innerlichen Krankheiten des menschlichen Körpers. 3. Aufl. Dresden, Gröll, 1775-76.
4v. in 2. 19cm.

1. Internal medicine.   I. Title.

NL 0445783   CtY-M

Lösekrug, F   ed.
Der Fahrzeuggenerator; Einbau und Betrieb, hrsg. von F. Lösekrug und G. Riedel, unter Mitarbeit der Fachleute der Generatoren-, Motoren- und Kraftstoffindustrie sowie des Ingenieurstabes der Zentralbüro für Mineralöl G. m. b. H. Berlin, Verlag der Allgemeinen Automobil-Zeitung ₁1943-

1 v. (loose-leaf) diagrs. 31 cm.

1. Gas producers. 2. Automobiles—Motors.   I. Riedel, G., joint ed.
TL229.G3L6   629.25144   A 48-8530*
Columbia Univ.   Libraries
for Library of Congress   ₁1₎†

NL 0445784   NNC DLC

Lösel, Emilie.
Rex-Kochbuch; mit gründlicher Anleitung zur Bereitung sämtlicher Hauskonserven in verlässlichster und erfolgreichster Art in Obst, Gemüse, Kompott, Marmelade, Säfte, Moste, Pilze, Suppen, Fleisch, Fisch, Puddings u. s. w. verfasst von Frau Emilie Lösel...herausgegeben von der Generalrepräsentanz der Rex-Conservenglas-Gesellschaft A. Bräuer...   Aussig: Rex-Conservenglas-Gesellschaft₁ 1933₎.   208 p. illus. 21½cm.

691435A. 1. Canning and preserving.   I. Bräuer, Adolf, editor. II. Rex-Conservenglas-Gesellschaft, Usti,   Czecho-Slovakia.
N. Y. P. L.   June 15, 1934

NL 0445785   NN

Lösel, Franz. tr.
Thulin, Josef Gottfrid, 1855-
Kleinkinderturnen, mit übungsschatz und stundenbildern für das 6. bis 8. lebensjahr, von major J. G. Thulin ... Deutsche ausgabe, bearbeitet nach der ersten und zweiten schwedischen aufl. von Franz Lösel ... Leipzig, P. Eberhardt, 1925.

Loesel, J. C.
The violin, by J. C. Loesel...   Pittsburg, Pa.: J. C. Loesel₁, 19—?₎₎ 80 p. pl. 24°.

1. Violin—Construction.
N. Y. P. L.   November 17, 1927

NL 0445787   NN 00

---

610   **Loeselius, Johannes,** 1607-1655.
L82d   Ioh. Loseli ... De podagra tractatus ... Editio secunda locupletata. ₌Accessit insuper Hieronymi Cardani ... Podagræ encomium₎ Lugduni Batavorum, Ex officina Ioannis Maire, 1639.

382p., 1l. illus. 13ᵐ

Another title page: 1l. at end. "Hieronymi Cardani ... Podagræ encomium": p.₌341-379₎

NL 0445788   PCarlD PPC CtY-M DNLM

Loeselius, Johannes, 1607-1655.
Flora prussica; sive, Plantae in regno Prussie sponte nascentes. Quarum catalogum & nomina Johannes Loeselius ... olim disseruit, nunc additis nitidissimis iconibus rariorum partim ab aliis nondum delineatarum plerarumque Prussie propriarum & inqvilinarum plantarum, earundemque accurata descriptione nec non adjectis synonymiis veterum botanicorum, interspersisque observationibus historico-philologico-criticis & medio-practicis noviter efflorescentes curante Johanne Gottsched ... Regiomonti, sumptibus typographiae Georgianae, 1703.
8 p. l., 294, ₌80₎ p. 85 (i. e. 83) pl. 19 x 14½ᵐ
Added t-p., engr.
1. Prussia. Botany.   I. Gottsched, Johannes, 1668-1704, ed.
                                                Agr 11-1053
Library, U. S. Dept. of   Agriculture   459L82

NL 0445789   DNAL MH-A MoSB

Loesell, Clarence Michal, 1892-
Size of plat and number of replications necessary for varietal trials with white pea beans ₌by₎ C. M. Loesell ... ₌Geneva, N. Y., 1936.
cover-title, ₌1₎, 534-547 p. incl. tables. 23ᵐ
Thesis (PH. D.)—Michigan state college of agriculture and applied science, 1936.
Thesis note on p. 534.
Running title: Plat technic with pea beans.
"Published as Journal article no. 260 n. s. of the Michigan Agricultural experiment station."
"Reprinted from Journal of the American society of agronomy, vol. 28, no. 7, July 1936."
"Literature cited": p. 547.
1. Beans. 2. Agriculture—Experimentation.   I. Title: Plat technic with pea beans.
                                                       37-10783
Library of Congress   SB205.B3L6 1936
Michigan State College of
——— Copy 2.   ₌2₎   633.3
Agriculture and Applied Science Libr.

NL 0445790   MiEM DLC

Lösener, Bernhard.
... Grundriss des deutschen zollrechts, von dr. jur. B. Lösener ... und W. Lottner ... 4. völlig neubearb. und verb. aufl. 7. tausend. Hamburg-Leipzig, R. Hermes, 1938.
196 p. 18½ᵐ. (Zoll- und steuer-juristische bücherei)
Pages 193-196, advertising matter.
Errata (1 fold. leaf, mimeographed) laid in.

1. Tariff—Germany—Law. 2. Customs administration—Germany.
I. Lottner, Walter, joint author.
                                                   41-21829
Library of Congress   HJ6921.L6
                         ₌2₎   336.260043

NL 0445791   DLC MH

Lösener, Bernhard, ed.
                                   FOR OTHER EDITIONS
                                   SEE MAIN ENTRY
Germany. *Laws, statutes, etc.*
Die Nürnberger gesetze, mit den durchführungsverordnungen und den sonstigen einschlägigen vorschriften, herausgegeben und erläutert von dr. Bernhard Lösener ... ₌und₎ dr. Friedrich A. Knost ... 5. aufl. (14./15. tausend) Berlin, F. Vahlen, 1942.

Lösener, Bernhard, ed.
Die Nürnberger gesetze über das reichsbürgerrecht und den schutz des deutschen blutes und der deutschen ehre, nebst den durchführungsverordnungen sowie sämtlichen einschlägigen bestimmungen (insbesondere über den abstammungsnachweis) und den gebührenvorschriften; im rahmen der nationalsozialistischen gesetzgebung dargestellt und erläutert von dr. jur. Bernhard Lösener ... ₌und₎ dr. jur. Friedrich A. Knost ... mit nachtrag enthaltend die neuesten vorschriften. 6. tausend. Berlin, F. Vahlen, 1936.
107, 19 p. 18½ᵐ. (On cover: Sammlung Vahlen. 23)
1. Citizenship—Germany. 2. Marriage law—Germany. 3. Jews—Legal status, laws, etc.—Germany. 4. Flags—Germany.   I. Knost, Friedrich August,   joint ed. II. Germany. Laws, statutes, etc. III. Title.
                                                   40-18304
NL 0445793   DLC

K   **Lösener, Bernhard,** ed.
L833   Die Nürnberger gesetze über das reichsbürgerrecht und den schutz den deutschen blutes und der deutschen ehre, nebst den durchführungsverordnungen sowie sämtlichen einschlägigen bestimmungen (insbesondere über den abstammungsnachweis) und den gebührenvorschriften; im rahmen der national-sozialistischen gesetzgebung dargestellt und erläutert von Bernhard Lösener [und] Friedrich A. Knost. 2. neubearb. und erweiterte aufl. Berlin, F. Vahlen, 1937.
1937

168p. 19cm. (Sammlung Vahlen, 23)
1. National socialism 2. Citizenship – Germany 3. Jews in Germany 4. Marriage law – Germany I Knost, Friedrich August, ed. II. Germany. Laws, statutes, etc. III. Title.

NL 0445795   MU

Loesener, Max
Die Grundzüge der Kredithypothek nach preussischem, österreichischem und französischem Rechte ... von Max Loesener ... Halle a.S., Druck der Buchdruckerei des Waisenhauses, 1894.

3 p.l., 29 p. 21cm.

Inaug.-Diss. - Göttingen.

NL 0445796   MH-L

Loesener, Otto
Studien über die Gattung Veratrum und ihre Verbreitung. Herrnhut i. Sachsen, Gustav Vinter, 1926.

65 p., illus.

Thesis - Friedrich-Wilhelms-Universität Berlin, 1926.

NL 0445797   MH-A ICRL MH CtY

Loesener, Theodor, 1865-1941.
Kronfeld, Ernst Moriz, 1865-
Aquifoliaceae, von M. Kronfeld. Mit 23 einzelbildern in 4 fig.
(In Die natürlichen pflanzenfamilien, begr. von A. Engler und K. Prantl. Leipzig, 1887-1909. 25ᵐ. III. teil, 5. abt. (1896) p. 183-189)

VOLUME 338

Loesener, Theodor, 1865–
Celastraceae, von Th. Loesener. Mit 63 einzelbildern in 12
fig.
(*In* Die natürlichen pflanzenfamilien. begr. von A. Engler und K.
Prantl. Leipzig, 1887–1909. 25ᶜᵐ. III. teil, 5. abt. (1896) p. 189–222,
459)
"Gedruckt im august, 1892": p. 189–222.
Supplement, *in* Nachträge z. II.–IV. t. (1897) p. 221–225, *in* Ergän-
zungsheft I: Nachträge II z. II.–IV. t. (1900) p. 39–40, and *in* Ergänzungs-
heft II: Nachträge III z. II.–IV. t. (1908) p. 198–202.
Classed under ₍haupt₎abt. IV, Embryophyta siphonogama.

1. Celastraceae.
                                                                3–30239 Revised
Library of Congress   QK97.E6

NL 0445799   DLC PPAN OU

Loesener, Th₍eodor₎ 1865–
Hippocrateaceae, von Th. Loesener. Mit 30 einzelbildern in 3 fig. (*In* Die natürlichen pflanzenfamilien,
begr. von A. Engler und K. Prantl. Leipzig, 1887–
25ᶜᵐ. III. teil, 5. abt. (1896) p. 222–230)
"Gedruckt im november 1892."
Supplement, *in* Nachträge z. II.–IV. t. (1897) p. 225, and *in* Ergänzungsheft I (1900) p. 40.
Classed under ₍haupt₎abt. IV, Embryophyta siphonogama.

Subject entries: Hippocrateaceae.
                                                                3–30240
Library of Congress, no.   QK97.E6.

NL 0445800   DLC PPAN PPT OU

583.2781   Loesener, Theodor, 1865–
L826   Monographia Aquifoliacearum. Halle, Für
f   die Akademie in Commission bei W. Engelmann
            in Leipzig, 1901–1908.
            2 pt. illus., 15 plates (1 double) 3 fold.
            maps. 33ᶜ. (In Nova acta. Abh. der Kaiserl.
            Leop.-Carol. deutschen Akademie der Natur-
            forscher. Bd. 78, 89, nr. 1)
            Bibliographical footnotes.

            1. Aquifolia   ceae.

NL 0445801   CSt ICF MiU MB MBH MH–A

Loesener, Theodor, 1865–1941.
Die Pflanzenwelt des Kiautschou-Gebietes
    see his Prodromus florae Tsingtauensis.

QK   Loesener, Theodor, 1865–
211   Plantae Selerianae die von Eduard Seler und
L64   Cæcilie Seler in Mexico gesammelten Pflanzen
        unter Mitwirkung von Fachmännern veröffentlicht
        von Th. Loesener. Genève, Imp. Romet, 1894.
        533–566 p. illus. 24 cm.
        Extrait du Bulletin de l'Herbier Boissier,
        v.2, no. 8, Août 1894.
        1. Botany--Mexico. I. Seler, Eduard. II. Se-
        ler, Cæcilie. I. T.

NL 0445803   CtU MH–A

QK   Loesener, Theodor, 1865–
211   Plantae Selerianae die von Eduard Seler und
L643   Cæcilie Seler in Mexico und Central America
        gesammelten Pflanzen unter Mitwirkung von
        Fachmännern veröffentlicht von Th. Loesener.
        Genève, Imp. Romet, 1899.
        1 v. (various pagings) illus. 24 cm.
        Extrait du Bulletin de l'Herbier Boissier,
        v.7, nos. 7 et 8, 1899.
        1. Botany--Mexico. 2. Botany--Central Ameri-
        ca. I. Seler, Eduard. II. Seler, Cæcilie.

NL 0445804   CtU

Loesener, Theodor, 1865–
Prodromus florae tsingtauensis. Die pflanzenwelt des Kiautschou-gebietes; mit unterstützung
des Deutsch-chinesischen verbandes veröffentlicht von Th. Loesener. Mit tafel I–X. Dresden-
N., C. Heinrich ₍1918₎
1 p.ℓ.,206 p. X pl. 24ᶜᵐ.
Reprinted from Beihefte zum Botanischen centralblatt,
bd.37,abt.2,hft.1,1919. cf.Vorwort.

1. Botany--Kiao-chou.

NL 0445805   MiU DLC–P4

Loesener, Theodor, 1865–
—— Rudolf Schlechters leben und wirken. [Berlin-
Dahlem. 1926.] 8°.
"Sonderdruck aus Notizblatt des Bot. gart. u. mus. Berlin-Dahlem."
1926, ix, 913–958.

NL 0445806   MH–A

LOESENER, Theodor, 1865–
Ueber einige neue pflanzenarten aus
Brasilien. [Marb.],[1889].

NL 0445807   MH–G

Loesener, Willibald Edmund Julius, 1863–
—— Die Trinkwasserversorgung der Truppe
unter besonderer Berücksichtigung der bei den
örtlichen Prüfungen von Wassergewinnungs-
anlagen in Betracht kommenden Gesichtspunkte für Sanitätsoffiziere. Militär-, Medi-
zinal- und Verwaltungsbehörde. 3 p.l., 56 pp.
8°. Berlin, A. Hirschwald, 1909

NL 0445809   DNLM

QL183   Loesener, Theodor, 1865–1941.
.A1   Vorstudien zu einer Monographie der Aqui-
L6   foliaceen. Berlin, Druck von Mesch & Lichten-
        feld, 1890.
        45 p. 1 plate. 26 cm.

        Inaug.-Diss. - Berlin.
        Vita.
        Bibliographical footnotes.
        Copy 1 inscribed: Monsieur Alph. de Can-
        dolle hommage à l'auteur.
        1. Aquifoliaceae. i.t. a. b. Candolle,
        Alphonse de.

NL 0445808   NNBG MH–A ICRL

Lösener (Willibald Edmund Julius) [1863–].
*Ueber Trinkwasser und Wasserversorgungs-
anlagen. 61 pp., 1 l. 8°. Königsberg i. Pr.,
O. Kümmel. 1905.

NL 0445810   DNLM ICRL MH CtY CU

Loeser (Alfred) [1887–]. *Ueber die End-
resultate der wegen chronischen Appendizitis
und im Intervall ausgeführten Appendekto-
mien. 46 pp. 8°. Breslau, 1913.

NL 0445811   DNLM ICRL

W 1   LOESER, Arnold, 1902–
BE186   Hormontherapie, von Arnold Loeser
Bd. 2   und Hellmut Marx. 2. verb. Aufl.
1944   Leipzig, Hirzel, 1944.
        xi, 151 p. illus. (Beiträge zur
        Arzneimitteltherapie, Bd. 2)
        1. Hormones - Therapeutic use
        I. Marx, Hellmut, 1901–1945   Series

NL 0445812   DNLM

W 1   LOESER, Arnold
BE186   Hormontherapie, von Arnold Loeser und
Bd. 2   Hellmut Marx. 3. verb. Aufl. Leipzig,
1947   Hirzel, 1947.
        xi, 152 p. illus. (Beiträge zur
        Arzneimitteltherapie, Bd. 2)
        1. Hormones - Therapeutic use
        I. Marx, Hellmut, 1901–1945   Series

NL 0445813   DNLM ICJ

Loeser, Arnold.
Hormontherapie, von Arnold Loeser und Hellmut Marx.
2. verb. Aufl. Leipzig, S. Hirzel, 1944. ₍Ann Arbor, J. W.
Edwards,1948₎
xi, 151 p. diagrs. 21 cm. (Beiträge zur Arzneimitteltherapie,
Bd. 2)
"Lithoprinted by Edwards Brothers, inc., Ann Arbor, Michigan."
"Schrifttum": p. 67–68, 148–151.
CONTENTS.—Pharmakologische Grundlagen der Hormontherapie,
von Arnold Loeser.—Klinische Hormontherapie, von Hellmut Marx.
1. Hormones—Therapeutic use. I. Marx, Hellmuth, 1901–
(Series)
RM799.L6 1944   50–20526

NL 0445814   DLC CU

Loeser, Arnold, 1902–
Pharmakologische methode zur wertbestimmung der
hypophysen vorderlappenwirkung. ... Berlin, 1931.
Inaug. Diss. - Freiburg i. Br., 1931.
Lebenslauf.

NL 0445815   MiU

Löser, Benno, 1878–1944.
Behälter, maste, schornsteine, rohrleitungen
see under title

693.5   Löser, Benno, 1878–
L89b7   Bemessungsverfahren. Zahlentafeln und zahlen-
        beispiele zu den Bestimmungen des Deutschen aus-
        schusses für eisenbeton 1932 ... 7.verb.aufl. ...
        Berlin, W. Ernst & sohn, 1938.
        214p. incl.tables, diagrs.

        1. Concrete, Reinforced. I. Deutscher ausschuss
        für eisenbeton. Bestimmungen des Deutschen aus-
        schusses für eisenbeton 1932.

NL 0445817   IU

Löser, Benno, 1878–
Bemessungsverfahren; zahlentafeln und zahlenbeispiele zu
den bestimmungen des Deutschen ausschusses für eisenbeton
1932, von B. Löser ... 8. aufl, 32. bis 34. tausend. Mit 217
textabbildungen. Berlin, W. Ernst & sohn, 1942.
viii, 214 p. illus. diagrs. 24ᶜᵐ.
1. Structures, Theory of. 2. Concrete construction. 3. Concrete, Reinforced. I. Title.
                                                    46–32948
Library of Congress   TH845.L6 1942
                                                    620.136

NL 0445818   DLC

Löser, Benno, 1878–
Bemessungsverfahren, zahlentafeln und zahlenbeispiele zu
den deutschen stahlbeton-bestimmungen vom märz 1943, von
Benno Löser ... 9. vollkommen neu bearb. und erweiterte aufl.
(35. bis 39. tausend) Mit 290 textabbildungen. Berlin, W.
Ernst & sohn, 1943.
xi, 288 p. illus. diagrs. 24ᶜᵐ.
1. Structures, Theory of. 2. Concrete, construction. 3. Concrete,
Reinforced. I. Title.
                                                    46–43153
Library of Congress   TH845.L6 1943
                                                    620.136

NL 0445819   DLC NNE

VOLUME 338

Egleston
D691
L897

Löser, Benno, 1878–1944.
Bemessungsverfahren; zahlentafeln und zahlenbeispiele zu den deutschen stahlbeton-bestimmungen von märz 1943. 10., überarbeitete aufl., mit einem anhang, hrsg. von Erhard Löser. Berlin, W. Ernst, 1948.
xi, 300 p. illus., diagrs., tables.

NL 0445820   NNC

Löser, Benno, 1878–1944.
Bemessungsverfahren, Zahlentafeln und Zahlenbeispiele zu den deutschen Stahlbeton-Bestimmungen vom März 1943. 11., berichtigte Aufl, mit einem Anhang. Hrsg. von Erhard Löser. Berlin, W. Ernst, 1949.
xii, 300 p. illus. 24 cm.

1. Structures, Theory of. 2. Reinforced concrete construction.
I. Title.

TH845.L6 1949   620.136   50–17721

NL 0445821   DLC

Löser, Benno, 1878–1944.
Bemessungsverfahren, Zahlentafeln und Zahlenbeispiele zu den deutschen Stahlbeton-Bestimmungen vom März 1943 (Stand Mai 1949) 12., von Gottfried Brendel überarbeitete Aufl. Hrsg. von Helmut Löser und Erhard Löser. Berlin, W. Ernst, 1950.
xi, 300 p. illus. 26 cm.

1. Structures, Theory of. 2. Reinforced concrete construction—Tables, calculations, etc.   I. Title.

TH845.L6 1950   693.5083   51–15645

NL 0445822   DLC CU

Löser, Benno, 1878–1944.
Bemessungsverfahren; Zahlentafeln und Zahlenbeispiele zu den Bestimmungen des Deutschen Ausschusses für Stahlbeton. 13. ergänzte Aufl. in der Überarbeitung von Gottfried Brendel. Hrsg. von Helmut Löser und Erhard Löser. Berlin, W. Ernst, 1951.
300 p. illus. 25 cm.

1. Structures, Theory of. 2. Reinforced concrete construction—Tables, calculations, etc.   I. Title.

TH845.L6 1951   693.5083   51–6683 †

NL 0445823   DLC

Löser, Benno, 1878–1944.
Bemessungsverfahren; Zahlentafeln und Zahlenbeispiele zu den Bestimmungen des Deutschen Ausschusses für Stahlbeton. 14. Aufl. ergänzt von Helmut Löser. Berlin, W. Ernst, 1953 ¡i. e. 1952¡
304 p. illus. 25 cm.

1. Structures, Theory of. 2. Reinforced concrete construction—Tables, calculations, etc.   I. Title.

TH845.L6 1952   693.5083   53–399 †

NL 0445824   DLC NN IU ICJ

Löser, Benno, 1878–1944.
Bemessungsverfahren; Zahlentafeln und Zahlenbeispiele zu den Bestimmungen des Deutschen Ausschusses für Stahlbeton. 15., ergänzte Aufl. bearb. von Helmut Löser. Berlin, W. Ernst, 1955.
314 p. illus. 24 cm.

1. Structures, Theory of. 2. Reinforced concrete construction—Tables, calculations, etc.   I. Title.

TH845.L6 1955   55–35936 †

NL 0445825   DLC IU

Löser, Benno, 1878–   joint author.

Grün, Richard, 1883–
Flüssigkeitsbehälter, röhren, kanäle ... bearbeitet von dr. phil. R. Grün, dr. ing. dr. Lewe, B. Löser, F. Lorey. Mit 743 textabbildungen. Berlin, W. Ernst & sohn, 1923.

TH
845
.L614

Löser, Benno, 1878–1944.
Méthodes pratiques de dimensionnement des ouvrages en béton armé, avec tableaux et exemples numériques. Trad. d'après la 14. éd. allemande et adapté aux règlements français, par Pierre Charon. Paris, Éditions Eyrolles, 1955.
418 p. illus.

1. Structures, theory of. 2. Concrete construction. 3. Concrete, Reinforced. I. Title.

NL 0445827   MiEM NN

E
464
C585
v.89
no.2

Loeser, C   defendant.
Judicial proceeding against C. Loeser. Philadelphia, King & Baird, printers [1863]
14 p. 25cm.   4

At head of title: Schuylkill County.
Common pleas.

I. Schuylkill Co., Pa. Court of Common Pleas. II. Title.

NL 0445828   NIC

LOESER, CARL,
Gefahren der Kapitalflucht. (Nachdruck). Ueberreicht von Carl Loeser... Berlin[, cop. 1930]. 63 p. incl. tables. 20½cm.

656908A. 1. Investments, German, in foreign countries. 2. Investments, Foreign.

NL 0445829   NN

Loeser, Carl, 1870–
Abgase, technik ihrer entrussung, entstaubung und entgiftung, von dr.-ing. Carl Loeser ... Mit 45 abbildungen und 67 zahlentafeln im text. Berlin, Gebrüder Borntraeger, 1940.
xxxii, 554 p. incl. illus., tables. 23½ᵐ.

1. Gases, Asphyxiating and poisonous. 2. Soot. 3. Dust—Removal.
I. Title.

Library of Congress   TP149.L6   42–752
                            ¡2¡   628.5

NL 0445830   DLC CtY NN

Loeser, Carl, 1870–
Abgase; Technik ihrer Entrussung, Enstaubung und Entgiftung, von Dr.-Ing. Carl Loeser... Berlin, Gebrüder Borntraeger, 1940 ¡repr.¡ Ann Arbor, Edwards bros., 1946¡ xxxii, 554 p. illus. 22cm.

355405B. 1. Gases—Purification.   2. Smoke—Prevention.
N. Y. P. L.   December 4, 1946

NL 0445831   NN ICJ

---

ar W
50691

Loeser, Carl, 1870–
Handbücher der keramischen Industrie für Studierende und Praktiker. Halle, L. Hofstetter, 1901–04.
2 v. in 1. illus. 24cm.

NL 0445832   NIC NjR ICJ

666.4
L82k

Loeser, Carl, 1870–
Kalkhaltige tone, ihre eigenschaften, verhalten und färbungen im feuer. ... Halle a.S., 1906.
63p. tables(1 fold.) diagrs.

Inaug.-diss.--K. Technische hochschule zu Hannover.

NL 0445833   IU

Loeser, Carl, 1870–
Zur chemischen und physikalischen Konstitution der Kaoline und Tone. [Von] Carl Loeser ... Halle a. S., L. Nebert's Verlag, 1906.
50 p. 23ᵐᵐ.

NL 0445834   ICJ

Loeser (Carolus Otto Guilielmus) [1801–   ].
"Nonnulla circa scirrham cancromque melete-mata, seu uncineta gravissimorum argumentorum expositio cum brevi horum addita consideratione quibus et illorum morborum indoles minime localis, eorumemque ad scrophulosam maxime accedens propinquitas demonstrari et confirmari videntur. 40 pp. 4°. Rostochii, typ. Adlerianis, 1826.

NL 0445835   DNLM

Loeser, Charles.
La collection Beckerath au cabinet des estampes de Berlin.
Illus.
Gazette des beaux-arts, ser. 3, v. 28, p. 471–482.   Paris, 1902
To be continued.

1. Italian drawings 2. Berlin. Königliche Museen   ALA 203–239

NL 0445836   MB

Loeser, Charles.
Käthe Kollwitz.
= Berlin, 1902. 7 pp. 8°.
Reprint from the Socialistische Monatsheft, February, 1902.

F3636 — Kollwitz, Käthe.

NL 0445837   MB

Loeser, D.
The Colloidal nature of iron scale salts.

Reprinted from the Journal of the American Pharmaceutical Association. Vol. XVIII, no. 2, February, 1929.

NL 0445838   OCIW

Loeser, Edgar, 1909–
... Eheschwierigkeiten der erblichen Veitstanz-Kranken ... Gütersloh i. Westf., 1937.
Inaug.-Diss. - Münster.
Lebenslauf.

NL 0445839   CtY

Loeser, Erich F   1908–
Die tätigkeit des völkerbundes auf dem gebiete der hygiene ... Berlin [1931?]
Diss. - Göttingen, 1931.

NL 0445840   MiU

VOLUME 338

W 4
F86
1937
Löser, Ernst Ludwig, 1910–
Über die brunsterregenden Stoffe der menschlichen Placenta. Freiburg i[m] Br[eis-gau] Weis, Mühlhans & Räpple, [1937?]
28, [3] p. illus.

Inaug.-Diss. - Freiburg in Breisgau.
Bibliography: p. [30]

NL 0445841   DNLM

JS5431
.L82
LÖSER, EWALD, 1888–   ed.
...Reformen in den städtischen verwaltungen; material sammlung hrsg. auf veranlassung des Deutschen städte-tages und des Reichsstädtebundes...von dr. Löser...[und] dr. Couvé... Berlin, C. Heymann [1930]
vi, [1], 171, [1] p. illus., forms, diagrs. 29cm.
(Schriftenreihe des Diwiv. Deutsches institut für wirt-schaftliche arbeit in der öffentlichen verwaltung. bd. V)

1. Municipal government—Germany.

NL 0445842   ICU

Loeser, Ewald, 1888–
Verfassungsänderung nach Art. 78, Abs. 1 der Verfassung des Deutschen Reiches vom 16. 4. 1871. Eine Uebersicht der Streitfragen. Berlin: E. Ebering, 1911. 91 p. 8°.

Dissertation, Göttingen. Bibliography, p. 7-10.

1. Constitutions, Germany, 1871.
N. Y. P. L.   February 7, 1912.

NL 0445843   NN MH-L NcD MH

Loeser, Felix, Referendar: Unterliegt die nach der Zahlungs-einstellung des Ehemannes erfolgte hypothekarische Sicher-stellung des eingebrachten Vermögens der Frau nach Er-öffnung des Konkurses über das Vermögen des Mannes der Anfechtung auf Grund des § 30 der deutschen Konkurs-ordnung? Breslau 1909: Breslauer Genoss.-Buchdr. VIII, 39 S. 8°
Rostock, Jur. Diss. v. 10. Aug. 1909, Ref. Wachenfeld
[Geb. 21. Nov. 86 Breslau; Wohnort: Jauer; Staatsangeh.: Preußen; Vor-bildung: Johannes-Gymn. Breslau Reife M. 05; Studium: Breslau 1, München 1, Breslau 4 S.; Rig. 1c. Juni 09.]   [U 09. 3671]

NL 0445844   ICRL MH

Loeser (Frans). *Ueber Epithelwucherungen an den Lymphgefässen der Lunge im Anschluss an Pneumonie. [Wurtzburg.] 18 pp., 1 l. 8°. Würzburg: B. Cramer, 1899.

NL 0445845   DNLM ICRL

833.9
L8262b
Löser, Frans, 1889–
Der Bergherr von Gastain. Zürich, Amalthea-Verlag [1930]
238p. 20cm.

NL 0445846   IEN

Löser, Franz, 1889–
... 's borstige Lies'l; Bauernschwank in 1 Akt, von Franz Löser. Mühlhausen in Thüringen: G. Danner [, 1932] 31 p. illus. 19½cm. (Vereinstheater. Nr. 298.)

Music of incidental song, p. [32]

1. Drama, German. I. Title. II. Ser.
N. Y. P. L.   October 18, 1933

NL 0445847   NN

Löser, Franz, 1889–
Erben der Erde. Wien: Stephan Szabo [, cop. 1932]. 294 p. 12°.

NL 0445848   NN

Löser, Franz, 1889–
... Ein mann geht seinen weg, roman. Niedersedlitz (Sa.) Das Vaterhaus verlags-gesellschaft [*1937]
282 p. 19½ᶜᵐ.

1. Title.

Library of Congress   PT2623.O42M3 1937   38-7020
Copyright A—Foreign   37161
                                       [2]   833.91

NL 0445849   DLC

832.9
L826n
Löser, Franz, 1889–
Der Nazarener; 16 Szenen (von der Bergpredigt bis zum Abschied von Maria) aus den Lehrjahren des Meisters. Der Heiligen Schrift und alten Werken frei nachgedichtet. Salzburg, Mayris-che Buchhandlung, 1926.
72p. 17cm.

NL 0445850   IEN

Hky
L8274
P61
Löser, Franz, 1889–
Pierres de Strass; das Geheimnis der Wiener Brillanten. Roman. Salzburg, "Das Bergland-Buch", [1952]
294p. 20cm.

NL 0445851   CtY

M51
L826c
Loeser, G
Comparison of the possibilities for measuring turbulence in the free atmosphere. (Vergleich der Moeglichkeiten zur Messung der Turbulenz in der freien Atmosphaere) Translated by: Charles A. Meyer & Co., Inc. Upper Nyack-on-th-Hudson, Nyack, N.Y., [1948?]
16 numb. [. 25cm.

M(05)
Z48
From: "Zeitschrift fuer Meteorologie" (Meteorological Journal) Vol. 2, No. 9, Sept.

1948, pp. 275–279.
Photostat.

NL 0445853   DAS

Loeser, Georg.
Das problem der wehrsteuer in der praxis, von Georg Loeser ... Stuttgart und Berlin, Cotta, 1916.
x, 105, [1] p. 23ᶜᵐ. (Added t.-p.: Münchener volkswirtschaftliche stu-dien ... 138. stück)
"Literatur": p. [ix]-x.

1. Military service, Compulsory. 2. Taxation—Germany.   I. Title: Wehrsteuer in der praxis.

                                                         21-263
Library of Congress   UB345.G3L6

NL 0445854   DLC CtY MH ICJ NN

Loéser, Gertrude, 1884–
... Le pronostic de la tuberculose chez les femmes enceintes ... Paris, 1914.
58 p., 1 l. 24.5 cm.
Thèse - Univ. de Paris.

NL 0445855   CtY DNLM

231.6
L89a
Löser, Hans, 1653?-1715.
Die alleredelste bewegung/ oder, Kurtzer/ meist theologischer tractat von der liebe/ durch veran-lassung erlittenen verlusts des in der zeitlich-keit am höchstengeliebten vorgestellet durch H. L. Altenburg/ Gedruckt bey Gottfried Richtern, 1689.
6 p.l., 281(i.e. 282), [2]p. front. 13½cm.
Error in paging: 264 repeated; other errors also.
"Vorrede" signed: Hans Löser.

1. Love (Theology) I. Title.

NL 0445856   IU

Löser, Hans, 1910–
... Über das Reaktionsvermögen des Periodontiums ... [n.p.] 1933.
Inaug.-Diss. - Leipzig.
Lebenslauf.
"Literaturverzeichnis": p. 33-34.

NL 0445857   CtY

Löser, Hans Georg, 1916–
Die regelmässigen und zufälligen Fehler bei der Orientie-rung nach Sonnenhöhen mit Feldmessstheodoliten. [Minden, Westf.] 1953.
120 p. illus., map. 21 cm. (Deutsche Geodätische Kommission bei der Bayerischen Akademie der Wissenschaften. Reihe C: Disser-tationen. Veröffentlichung Nr. 10)
Thesis—Technische Hochschule, Hanover.
Vita.
Bibliography: p. 106-120.
1. Surveying. 2. Theodolites.   (Series: Akademie der Wissen-schaften, Munich. Deutsche Geodätische Kommission. Veröffent-lichung. Reihe C: Dissertationen. Nr. 10)
                         Full name: Hermann Hans Georg Löser.

QB301.L6   57-18247

NL 0445858   DLC

Loeser (Herman A.) *Ueber paroxysmale Ta-chycardie. 22 pp. 8°. Berlin, [G. Reimer].
1886.

NL 0445859   DNLM

Löser, Hermann Hans Georg
see
Löser, Hans Georg, 1916–

Löser, J
Führer durch die sociale Frage des Altertums, des Mittelalters und der Neuzeit, bis gegen Ende des neunzehnten Jahrhunderts. Von J. Löser. Mit einer Lichtdrucktafel ... Karlsruhe, O. Nemnich, 1895.
[6], ii, 172 p. front. 24ᶜᵐ.

NL 0445861   ICJ

S
465
L82
Loeser, J
Geschichte der Landwirtschaft, bearb. von J. Loeser. Stuttgart, E. Ulmer, 1890-91.
2 v. in 1. 17 cm. (Des Landmanns Winterabende, 42., 44. Bändchen)

Vol. 2 has title: Geschichte der einzelnen Zweige der Landwirtschaft.

1. Agriculture - Germany - History.
I. Loeser, J   Geschichte der einzelnen Zweige der Landw   irtschaft. II. Title.
III. Title: Geschi   chte der einzelnen Zweige der   Landwirtschaft.

NL 0445862   NIC IU

VOLUME 338

Löser, J.
Geschichte der stadt Baden, von den ältesten zeiten bis auf die gegenwart. Baden-Baden, E. Sommermeyer, 1891.
pp. viii, 571 +. Plates, ports., and other illus.

Baden Baden‖

NL 0445863   MH

Löser, J.
Das kopfrechnen in den deutschen schulen. 2ᵉ vermehrte und verbesserte aufl. Weinheim, F. Ackermann, 1882.
pp. viii, 264. Wdcts. and diagrs.

Arithmetic-Mental‖

NL 0445864   MH

Löser, J.
Landwirthschaftliches rechenbuch nebst anleitung zum feldmessen, nivelliren und berechnen der körper. Für fortbildungs- und landwirthschafts-schulen nach der münz-, maass- und gewichts-ordnung des Deutschen Reiches bearb. von J. Löser ... und H. Zeeb ... Mit 75 in den text gedruckten holzschnitten. Stuttgart, E. Ulmer [1876]
viii, 265, [1] p. illus., tables. 21½ᶜᵐ. (On cover: Bibliothek praktischer lehrbücher für ackerbau-, obst & weinbauschulen, landwirthschaftliche fortbildungsschulen &c. IV. bd.)
1. Agriculture—Accounting. I. Zeeb, Heinrich, joint author.
12-7390
Library of Congress   S567.L82

NL 0445865   DLC

Löser (Joh. Dieterieus). *De hydrope ascite.
13 l. 4°. *Wittebergae, typ. M. Henckelii, [1690?].

NL 0445866   DNLM

Loeser, Johann Albrecht, d. 1939.
Animal behaviour; impulse, intelligence, instinct, by Dr. Johann A. Loeser. Illustrated by Erna Pinner. London, Macmillan and co., limited, 1940.
x, 178 p. incl. illus., pl. 22½ᶜᵐ.
Partly a translation of the author's Die psychologische autonomie des organischen handelns, published 1939. cf. Foreword, by L. J. F. Brimble.
1. Animals, Habits and behavior of. I. Brimble, Lionel John Farnham, 1904-
41-9561 Revised
Library of Congress   QL751.L62
[r41g3]   591.5

OC1W
NL 0445867   DLC CU TU NcD NcRS CtY NcU OCU OU OOxM

Loeser, Johann Albrecht, d. 1939.
... Die psychologische autonomie des organischen handelns, von dr. Johann Albrecht Loeser. Berlin, Gebrüder Borntraeger, 1931.
viii, 146 p. 25½ᶜᵐ. (Abhandlungen zur theoretischen biologie ... hft. 30)
At head of title: ... Die psychologie des emotionalen. [1. teil]
"Literatur": p. [145]-146.
1. Animals, Habits and behavior of. 2. Psychology, Comparative. I. Title.
A C 38-3786
John Crerar library
for Library of Congress   [2]

NL 0445868   ICJ MH CtY

4D-129
Loeser, Johann Albrecht.
El sabotage en la reconstrucción de Francia del Norte, por el doctor J. A. Loeser, Berlin y Arthur Ketzer. Munich, Knorr & Hirth [1923]
46 p.

NL 0445869   DLC-P4

LOESER, JOHANN ALBRECHT, d. 1939.
The sabotage of French reconstruction, by Dr. J. A. Loeser ... Munich: Knorr & Hirth, Inc. [1922] 55 p. illus. 22cm.
Translated by E.Prieth.
806061A. 1. European war, 1914–1918—Reconstruction—France. I. Prieth, E., tr.

NL 0445870   NN DLC-P4 DNW

P636
C92
Loeser, Johann Christoph
Der Evangelisch-Lutherische Glaube, wo er vor zwey hundert Jahren gewesen, wider der papistentäglichen Vorwurff nebst der, itziger Zeit hochstnöthigen Erörterten Bewissens-Frage ... Freyberg, Elias Nicolaus Kuhfuss, 1713.
88, 29 p. 17 cm.
Bound with: Curieuser Geschichts-Calender, des ... Hochleuchteten ... D. Martini Lutheri ... Leipzig, 1717.

NL 0445871   CtHC MoSCS

892
L138un
1774
pt.1
LÖSER, Johann Christoph
Rochlitzer Speiss- und Danck-Opffer. Oder Danck-Predigten nach eingebrachten Feld-Segen, in der Stadt-Kirchen daselbst gehalten, und nebst anderer gepredigten Texte, extendirten, vollkommenen Dispositionibus, dass man an die XII. und mehr Jahre Erndten-Predigten darnach halten kan. Auf Veranlassung herausgegeben durch Johann Christoph Loesern ... Chemnitz,

pt.1
bey Conrad Stoesseln, 1713.
147, [10]p. 17cm.
P.10 mismumbered 01.
With this is bound Lachmann's Unterricht und Trost ... Erster Theil ... 1744.

NL 0445873   MH-AH

P636
C92
Loeser, Johann Christoph
Die wahren, Jesu gefälligen Glaubens-Benossen oder Religions-Verwandten, nach denen Worten Jesu Joh. VIII, 31 ... und zum Anhang des Evangelisch-Lutherischen Glaubens herausgegeben von M. Johann Christoph Lösern ... Freyberg, Elias Nicolaus Kuhfuss, 1714;
48 p. 17 cm.
Bound with: Curieuser Geschichts-Calender, des ... chleuchteten ... D. Martini Lutheri ... Leipzig, 1717.

NL 0445874   CtHC

Loeser, John C
The over-the-counter securities market; what it is and how it operates, by John C. Loeser ... New York, Chicago [etc.] National quotation bureau, incorporated, 1940.
5 p. l., [3]-192 p. 22 cm.
"Notes and references": p. [185]-192.
1. Over-the-counter markets—U. S.
HG4621.L56   332.620973   40—12206
ODW OU OC1FRB PPLas
NL 0445875   DLC FTaSU OkU TU ViU CU NcD OC1 OC1U

HG
4621
L56
1953
Loeser, John C
The over-the-counter securities market; what it is and how it operates. New York, National Quotation Bureau [c1953]
vi, 192 p. 22cm.
"Notes and references": p. [187]-192.
1. Brokers - U.S. 2. Securities - U.S. I. Title.

NL 0445876   CoU OrPS

ar W
747
Loeser, Josef, 1904-
Ein Beitrag zur Frage der Berufsschwielen. Berlin, R. Pfam, 1939.
23 p. illus. 23cm.
Diss.—Berlin.
1. Occupational diseases.

NL 0445877   NIC DNLM

Loeser, Joseph.
Darting rays, and other stories, by Joseph Loeser. Milwaukee, The author, 1924.
4 p. l., 179 p. 19½ᶜᵐ.
I. Title.
Library of Congress   PZ3.L824Da   24-28888

NL 0445878   DLC

Loeser, Karl Ludwig, 1901-
Ueber fremdkoerperschlucker und ihre motive. Inaug. diss. Koenigsberg, 1929.
Bibl.

NL 0445879   ICRL CtY

Loeser, Konrad.
Das beschraenkte akzept. Inaug. diss. Leipzig, 1907
Bibl.

NL 0445880   ICRL

Loeser (Leo). *Beitrag zur Lehre von der Hysterie der Kinder. 37 pp. 8°. Heidelberg, J. Hörning, 1897.

NL 0445881   DNLM ICRL PPC

VOLUME 338

W 1   LOESER, Lewis Henry, 1903–
GR869   Group psychotherapy in private
no. 29   practice; a preliminary report ₁by₁
         Lewis H. Loeser ₁and others₁   New
         York, American Group Therapy
         Association, 1949.
             p. 213–233.   (Group therapy
         brochure, no. 29)
             Reprinted from the American journal
         of psychotherapy, v. 3, 1949.
             1. Group psychotherapy
         Series

NL   0445882   DNLM LU

PT   Löser, Ludwig, 1868–
2623   Herostrat von Ephesus; Tragödie in fünf
082   Aufzügen. Wolfenbüttel, J. Zwissler, 1904.
H4   96p.   19cm.

NL   0445883   WU

Löser, Ludwig, 1868–
   Herostrat von Ephesus. Tragödie in fünf Aufzügen. Wolfenbüttel, Julius Zwissler, 1904.
   96p.

   Microcard edition.

NL   0445884   ICRL

Loeser, Ludwig, 1864–
   Wer spielt auf? Ein Bismarcklustspiel in vier Aufzügen, von
Ludwig Löser.   Wolfenbüttel: Heckners Verlag, 1924.   80 p.
16°.

197190A. 1. Drama, German.   2. Title.
N. Y. P. L.   August 26, 1925

NL   0445885   NN

4BS–154 Loeser, Max, 1909–
             Die Apostelgeschichte, das Buch vom Werden
         der Kirche.   Stuttgart, Quell-Verlag der Evang.
         Gesellschaft [1948]
             95 p.   (Bibelhefte der evang. Jugend)

NL   0445886   DLC-P4

Loeser, Max, 1909–   ed.
   Auf dem Grunde der Apostel und Propheten; Festgabe
für Landesbischof D. Theophil Wurm zum 80. Geburtstag
am 7. Dezember 1948, dargebracht von Emil Brunner ₁et al.₁
Stuttgart, Quell-Verlag der Evang. Gesellschaft, 1948.
   350 p. port. 25 cm.

   1. Lutheran Church—Addresses, essays, lectures. 2. Theology—Addresses, essays, lectures. 3. Wurm, Theophil, 1868–1953. I. Title.
   BX8011.A1L6   57–47488

NL   0445887   DLC InU NcD

Loeser, Nathan, 1840–
   Qualem vim nonnulla venena narcotica in corda rana-
rum excisa exerceant ... Berolini, typis expressit G.
Lange ₁1867₁
   32 p. 19ᵐ.
   Inaug.-diss.—Berlin.
   Vita.

   1. Poisons, Physiological effect of. 2. Heart.
                                              8–5516†
   Library of Congress   ₒP921 A1₁ R

NL   0445888   DLC DNLM PPC

Loeser, Norbert, 1906–
   Anton Bruckner, door W. van Hengel (N. Loeser). Haarlem, Gottmer ₁c1948₁

   285 p. illus., ports. (Componisten-Serie, 8)
Gottmer Muziek pockets, 18

NL   0445889   MH

Loeser, Norbert, 1906–
   Anton Bruckner.   Haarlem, Gottmer [c1949]
   285 p.   illus., ports.
By W. van Hengel.
   1. Bruckner, Anton, 1824–1896.

NL   0445890   CU

ML410
.B88H46   Loeser, Norbert, 1906–
              Anton Bruckner. Haarlem, Gottmer ₁1951₁
          285 p. plates, ports. 23 cm. (Componisten-serie, 8. boek)
          By W. van Hengel, pseud.

              1. Bruckner, Anton, 1824–1896.

          ML410.B88H46   52–27418 ‡

NL   0445891   DLC

GV1787
L6   Loeser, Norbert.
              Het ballet. Haarlem, J. H. Gottmer ₁1953₁
          150 p. illus. 22 cm.

              1. Ballet.
                                              A 54–2217 ‡
          Oregon. Univ. Library
          for Library of Congress   ₁3₁

NL   0445892   OrU DLC NN

Loeser, Norbert.
   Beethoven...   Haarlem ₁etc.₁ Gottmer ₁c1949₁   276 p.
facsims., ports.   23cm. (Componisten-serie. 11)

558895B. 1. Beethoven, Ludwig van,   1770–1827.
N. Y. P. L.   January 29, 1952

NL   0445893   NN

Loeser, Norbert.
   Beethoven. Haarlem, Gottmer ₁1950₁
   276 p. ports., facsims. 23 cm. (Componisten-serie, 11)

   1. Beethoven, Ludwig von, 1770–1827.
   ML410.B4L6   51–33469

NL   0445894   DLC CaBVa

Loeser, Norbert.
   Gustav Mahler. Haarlem, Gottmer ₁1950₁
   209 p. ports. 23 cm. (Componisten-serie, 15. boek)

   1. Mahler, Gustav, 1860–1911.
   ML410.M23L7   53–25055 ‡
   Library of Congress   ₁3₁

NL   0445895   DLC CLU NN

Loeser, Norbert. Haarlem, Gottmer ₁1952₁
   260 p. illus. 23 cm. (Componisten-serie, 22)

   1. Musorgskiĭ, Modest Petrovich, 1839–1881.
                                              A 53–1756
   Oregon. Univ. Libr.
   for Library of Congress   ₁3₁

NL   0445896   OrU CLU

Loeser, Norbert.
   Mozart. Haarlem, Gottmer ₁c1953₁
   288 p. illus. 23 cm. (Componisten-serie, 25)

   1. Mozart, Johann Chrysostom Wolfgang Amadeus, 1756–1791.
   ML410.M9L54   54–36038 ‡

NL   0445897   DLC

Loeser, Norbert.
   Ortega y Gasset en de philosophie van het leven. ₁2., uitge-
breide druk₁ Den Haag, H. P. Leopold, 1949.
   147 p. 20 cm. (Bibliotheek voor weten en denken, no. 23)

   1. Ortega y Gasset, José, 1883–
   B4568.O74L6 1949   51–40055

NL   0445898   DLC

Loeser, Norbert.
   Richard Wagner. Haarlem, Gottmer ₁19—₁
   315 p. illus., ports. 23 cm. (Componisten serie, 3. boek)

   1. Wagner, Richard, 1813–1883.
   ML410.W1L6   927.8   49–43608*

NL   0445899   DLC

ML410
.R8L64   Loeser, Norbert.
              Rossini en zijn Barbier van Sevilla. Utrecht, De Toren-
          trans ₁1952?₁
          78 p. illus. 23 cm. (Kantelenreeks, no. 1)

              1. Rossini, Gioacchino Antonio, 1792–1868. Il barbiere di Siviglia.
          (Series)   A 53–3711
          Oregon. Univ. Library
          for Library of Congress   ₁1₁

NL   0445900   OrU DLC NjP

Loeser, Norbert.
   Verdi. Haarlem, Gottmer ₁1948₁
   300 p. ports. 23 cm. (Componisten-serie, 5)

   1. Verdi, Giuseppe, 1813–1901.
   ML410.V4L56   52–27346

NL   0445901   DLC

VOLUME 338

ML410
.W8L6
Loeser, Norbert.
　　Wolf. Haarlem, Gottmer [1955]
　　212 p. illus. ports. 23 cm. (Componistenserie, 30)

　　　　1. Wolf, Hugo, 1860–1903.

　　　　　　　　　　　　　　　　A 56–2711
　　Oregon. Univ. Libr.
　　for Library of Congress　　　[3]

NL 0445902　　　OrU CLU NIC NN DLC

Loeser, Oscar Edward, 1898–　　joint author.
Knight, Montgomery.
　　... Pressure distribution over a rectangular monoplane wing
model up to 90° angle of attack, by Montgomery Knight and
Oscar Loeser, jr. Washington, U. S. Govt. print. off., 1928.

Loeser, Oscar Edward, 1898–
　　... Pressure distribution tests on PW-9 wing models from
–18° through 90° angle of attack, by Oscar E. Loeser, jr.
Washington, U. S. Govt. print. off., 1929.
　　cover-title, 22 p. illus. diagrs. 29ᵐ. ([U. S.] National advisory
committee for aeronautics. Report no. 296)
　　Bibliography: p. 22.

　　　　1. Aerodynamics. 2. Aeroplanes. I. Title.
　　Library of Congress　　　TL521.A33 no. 296　　　29–26199
　　――――― Copy 2.　　　　TL671.L6

NL 0445904　　　DLC OCU OU OCl MiU ICJ

Löser (Otto Felix) [1877–　　]. *Beitrag zur
Aetiologie des Lupus erythematosus. 46 pp.,
1 l. 8°. Leipzig, B. Georgi. 1904.

NL 0445905　　　DNLM ICRL CtY

Löser, Paul, comp.
　　Vollständige Geschichte des grossen amerikanischen Bürger-
krieges. Nach dem Englischen bearbeitet von Paul Löser. Mit
Portraits und Schlachtenbildern in Stahlstich... New York:
S. Zickel [1865] 2 v. fronts., illus. (incl. maps), plates, ports.,
tables. 20½cm.
　　Paged continuously.
　　Label of C. Seyffarth & sons, B'klyn, N. Y., mounted over original imprint.

　　161309–10B. 1. United States—　　　Hist.—Civil war.
　　N. Y. P. L.　　　　　　　　　　　　　　May 8, 1942

NL 0445906　　　NN PPG PPGi

Löser, Peter.
　　Werthvolles aus d. Nachlass d. jungen Theol.
P. Löser ... 2te. Aufl.　　Berlin, 1853.
　　2 v.　12°.

NL 0445907　　　CtY

DG674　Löser, Rudolf
L64　　　Venedig. 24 Ansichten nach der Natur gezeichnet, gestochen
und hrsg. von J. Poppel und M. Kurz.　München, J. Poppel und
M. Kurz, 1846.
　　　64 p. plates.

　　　　1. Venice (City) - Descr. - Views. I. Title. II. Poppel,
Johann Gabriel Friedrich. III. Kurz, M

NL 0445908　　　CU NIC ICU

Loeser, Rudolf, [1881–　　　Beiträge zur Kenntnis der
Wimperorgane (Wimpertrichter) der Hirudineen. Mit
3 Taf. u. 6 Fig. im Text. Leipzig: W. Engelmann 1909.
67 S. 8° [Taf. werden nicht geliefert.] ¶(Aus: Zeitschr. f.
wiss. Zool. Bd 93, H. 1.)
Heidelberg, Naturw.-math. Diss. v. 2. Juli 1909, Ref. Bütschli
　[Geb. 23. Jan. 81 Homburg v. d. H.; Wohnort: Dillingen a. S.; Staats-
　angeh.: Schwarzburg-Rudolstadt; Vorbildung: Wöhlerschule Frankfurt a. M.
　Reife O. 99; Studium: Heidelberg 9 S.; Rig. 24. Juli 08.]　[U 09. 2053

NL 0445909　　　ICRL CtY PPWI PU MH DNLM

Loeser (Siegfried). *Die in der königlichen Universitäts-Frauenklinik zu Breslau in den
Jahren 1901–1913 nicht nach der Küstner-
Wolkowitsch'schen Operationsmethode behandelten Blasen-Genitalfisteln. 36 pp., 1 l.
8°. Breslau. 1917.

NL 0445910　　　DNLM ICRL

Löser, W
　　Die riene Kritik und ihre Bewegung. Zur
Charakteristik der von Bruno Bauer und seinen
Anhängern in Jüngster Zeit eingeschlagenen
Richtung. Leipzig, G.Brauns, 1845.

NL 0445911　　　MH

Löser, Wilhelm Heinrich, respondent.
　　... De jure qvinqvennalium
　　　see under　Lederer, Michael Friedrich,
praeses.

Loeser laboratory, New York.
　　Parenteral therapy of sulphur, colloidal,
normal; a review of the literature ...
[New York, n. d.]
　　Pamphlet.
　　"Bibliography": p. 12.

NL 0445913　　　CtY

[Loeser laboratory, New York]
　　A question of ethics; university patents;
misuse of the Council on pharmacy and chemistry
and the Journal A. M. A.　[New York? 1934]
　　Pamphlet.

NL 0445914　　　CtY

Loeser Laboratory, New York.
　　A symptomatic treatment of tuberculosis
　　　see under　Boettinger, Rodolfo Alvarez.

Løseth, E[ilert], 1858–
　　Notes de syntaxe française.　Christiania: J. Dybwad, 1910.
18 p.　4°.　(Videnskabs-Selskabet i Christiania. Skrifter. II.
Historisk-filosofisk Klasse. 1910. no. 4.)

　　1. French language.—Grammar.
　　N. Y. P. L.　　　　　　　　　　　　November 20, 1911.

NL 0445916　　　NN CtY NIC MoU

Løseth, Eilert, 1858–
　　Observations sur le Polyeucte de Corneille, par E. Løseth ...
Udg. for Hans A. Benneches fond. Christiania, A commission
chez J. Dybwad, 1899.
　　18 p.　27ᵐ.　(Videnskabsselskabets skrifter. II. Historisk-filosofisk
klasse. 1899, no. 4)

　　　　1. Corneille, Pierre. Polyeucte. I. Hans Andreas Benneches legat,
Christiania.
　　　　　　　　　　　　[Full name: Oluf Eilert Løseth]
　　　　　　　　　　　　　　　　6–30107 Revised
　　Library of Congress　　　AS283.O57 1899 no. 4

NL 0445917　　　DLC CLU NN MoU

Løseth, Eilert, 1858–　　　ed.
Gautier d'Arras, 12th cent.
　　Œuvres de Gautier d'Arras, publiés par E. Løseth ... Paris,
E. Bouillon, 1890.

Løseth, Eilert, 1858–　　　ed.
Robert le Diable.
　　Robert le Diable; roman d'aventures, pub. par E. Løseth.
Paris, Firmin Didot et cⁱᵉ, 1903.

Løseth, Eilert, 1858–
　　Le roman en prose de Tristan, le roman de Palamède, et la
compilation de Rusticien de Pise; analyse critique d'après les
manuscrits de Paris, par E. Løseth ...　Paris, É. Bouillon,
1890.
　　4 p. l., xxvi, 542 p., 1 l. 25ᵐ. (Added t.-p.: Bibliothèque de l'École
des hautes études ... Sciences philologiques et historiques ... 82. fasc.)

　　　　1. Tristan. 2. Palamède, Roman de. 3. Rusticiano da Pisa.
　　　　　　　　　　　　[Full name: Oluf Eilert Løseth]
　　　　　　　　　　　　　　　　4–11017 Revised
　　Library of Congress　　　AS162.B6　fasc. 82
　　――――― Copy 2.　　　　PQ1541.L7

NL 0445920　　　DLC OU TU NcD MiU OCU OCl OClW MB

Løseth (Eilert　) 1858–
　　Le roman en prose de Tristan, le Roman de Palamède et
la compilation de Rusticien de Pise. Analyse critique
d'après les manuscrits de Paris.　Paris: É. Bouillon,
1891. 5 p.l., xxvi; 542 pp. 1l. 8°. (École d. Haut-
Étud.—Sci. Phil. et Hist.　Fasc. 82.)

NL 0445921　　　NN MoU MdBP NjP MH

AS283　Løseth, Eilert, 1858–
.C56　　　Le Tristan et Le Palamède des manuscrits de Rome et de
1924　Florence, par E. Løseth ...　Kristiania, En commission chez
J. Dybwad, 1924.
　　120, [4] p.　27ᵐ.　(Videnskapsselskapets skrifter. II. Hist.-filos. klasse.
1924, no. 3)

　　　　1. Tristan. 2. Palamède, Roman de.

NL 0445922　　　ICU NN TU MoU WaU OCl ICN NIC

Løseth, E[ilert], 1858–
　　Le Tristan et le Palamède des manuscrits français du British
Museum. Étude critique.　Christiania: J. Dybwad, 1905. 38 p.
4°.　(Videnskabs-Selskabet i Christiania. Skrifter. II. Historisk-
filosofisk Klasse. 1905, no. 4.)

　　1. Tristan. 2. Palamedes.
　　N. Y. P. L.　　　　　　　　　　　　November 24, 1911.

NL 0445923　　　NN CaBVaU PBm NjP NcU TU MoU CtY ICU

VOLUME 338

PQ1542 **Løseth, Eilert** *i. e.* Oluf Eilert, 1858–
.L8   Tristanromanens gammelfranske prosahaandskrifter i
Pariser–nationalbibliotheket. Af Eilert Løseth ... Kristiania, A. Cammermeyer, 1888.
[4, 78, [1] p.   21ᶜᵐ.

NL 0445924   ICU MH CU ICN IU

Løseth,   Eilert, 1858–
Une vieille chanson française, par E. Löseth... (In:
Mélanges de philologie offerts à M. Johan Vising.   Göteborg,
1925.   p. [51–]54.   8°.)

230445A.   1. Poetry, French, Old.
N.Y.P.L.   May 20, 1926

NL 0445925   NN

Løseth, Oluf Eilert

see

Løseth, Eilert, 1858–

NL 0445926

Loesevitz, Jean.
... L'organisation corporative du travail national; exposé des idées de m. J.-P.
Mazaroz, par Jean Loesevitz ...   Paris,
A.Ghio, 1883.
84 p.   17ᶜᵐ.   (Études de politique
sociale)
Bibliographical foot-notes.

NL 0445927   MiU-L

Loesevits, Wilhelm,
Ein beitrag zur pathologischen anatomie der amyotrophischen lateralsklerose.
Inaug. diss. Freiburg,1896.

NL 0445928   ICRL DNLM

Loesing, Engelhard, 1906–
Kaufmännisches zurückbehaltungsrecht an eigenen
sachen ... von Engelhard Loesing ... Aurich,
Zuricher zeitung, 1932.
46 p., 1 l. 21ᶜᵐ.

Thesis, Göttingen.
Bibliography: p. [4–7]
1. Commercial law - Germany. 2. Debtor and
creditor - Germany. 3. Liens - Germany.

NL 0445929   NNC ICRL

Loesing, Heinrich, respondent.
... De differentiis iuris Romani et Germanici
in heredis institutione voluntaria
see under Carrach, Johann Tobias,
praeses.

LOESING,Peter,1900–
Untersuchungen über die beziehungen zwischen
körperform und milchleistung an ostfriesischen
rindern,nach korrelationsstatistischer verarbeitung. Halle (Saale),1930.

Inaugural-dissertation - Halle-Wittenberg.
"Lebenslauf",at end.

NL 0445931   MH MiU CtY ICRL

Loeske, Leopold, 1865–
Auswahl von Abbildungen aus Loeske: "Die
Laubmoose Europas". Berlin-Schöneberg, M.
Lande, 1918.

40 l. (chiefly illus.) 29 cm.

Fleischer, Max. Iconographia bryologica
universalis, Ser. 1.
Cover title.

NL 0445932   CaBVaU

Loeske, Leopold, 1865–   *ed.*
Die Laubmoose Europas ... herausgegeben von Leopold
Loeske. I–II.   Berlin-Schöneberg, M. Lande (Hoffmann &
Campe) 1913–1929.

2 v. in 1. illus. 29ᶜᵐ. (v. 2: Repertorium specierum novarum regni vegetabilis. Sonderbeiheft B)
Vol. 2 completed 1914, published 1929; "Nachträge 1915–1929", p. 113–120.
Contents.—1. *Grimmiaceae.*—2. *Funariaceae.*

NL 0445933   ICJ MH MiU NcD MWelC IU TU

Loeske, Leopold, 1865–
... Die laubmoose Europas ... von Leopold Loeske, mit
einem anhang von P. Janzen und einem nachtrage von L.
Loeske ... Berlin-Dahlem, Selbstverlag des herausgebers,
1929.
v. illus. 29ᶜᵐ. (Repertorium specierum novarum regni vegetabilis. Sonderbeiheft B)

1. Mosses.   Agr 30–303
Library, U. S. Dept. of   Agriculture 450R298

NL 0445934   DNAL NNBG NIC TU ICU

Loeske, Leopold, 1865–
Monographie der europäischen grimmiaceen. Von L. Loeske. Mit 2 abbildungen im text. Stuttgart, Schweizerbart,
1930.
ix, 286 p. illus. 31ᶜᵐ. (Added t.-p.: Bibliotheca botanica ... hft. 101)
"Spezielle und grössere gebiete Europas umfassende literatur":
p. 88–89.

1. Grimmiaceae. 2. Mosses—Europe.

Library of Congress   QK539.G7L6   30–22664

NL 0445935   DLC MH NIC NcD OU MiU NcU

Loeske, Leopold, 1865–
Moosflora des Harzes. Hilfsbuch für die bryologische Forschung
im Harze und dessen Umgebung mit Verbreitungsangaben und
Bestimmungstabellen, von Leopold Loeske. Leipzig, Gebrüder
Borntraeger, 1903.
xx, 350 p. 20½ x 12ᶜᵐ.
"Litteratur-Verzeichniss mit Anmerkungen," p. [xi]–xx.

NL 0445936   ICJ NcD

Loeske, Leopold, 1865–
Praktisches Hilfsbuch für Uhrmacher. Anweisungen und Abhandlungen für Werkstatt und Laden sowie für die geschäftliche
und die gewerbliche Praxis des Uhrmachers. Zusammengestellt
und bearbeitet von L. Loeske, ... Mit 22 Abbildungen. Berlin, C. Mariel, 1910.
[2], vi, 199 p. incl. 22 illus., tables. 22ᶜᵐ.

NL 0445937   ICJ NN

Loeske, Leopold, 1865–
Studien zur vergleichenden morphologie und phylogenetischen systematik der laubmoose [by] Leopold Loeske.
Berlin, M. Lande, 1910.
224 p. 21ᶜᵐ.

1. Mosses.

NL 0445938   MiU NBuG ICU TU MH NcD

Loeske, Michael, 1867–

Deutscher uhrmacher-kalender für das jahr
(Grossmanns notizkalender jahrgang
Praktisches geschäfts- und werkstatt-taschenbuch.
Berlin, Deutsche uhrmacher-zeitung

Loeske, Michael, 1867–
Die gesammte Literatur über Uhrmacherei und Zeitmesskunde
alphabetisch und chronologisch geordnet. Mit Stichwortregister
und einem Anhange. Zusammengestellt von M. Loeske. Berlin.
Bautzen, E. Hübner. 1897.
128 p. 14ᶜᵐ.
Advertising matter interspersed.

NL 0445940   ICJ

Loeske, Michael, 1867–   *ed.*
Sievert, Hermann.
Leitfaden für die uhrmacherlehre; handbuch für lehrmeister und lehrbuch für lehrlinge, sowie zur vorbereitung auf
die theoretischen fachprüfungen. Mit einem anhang, enthaltend 210 fragen und antworten, einen kurzen unterricht im
zeichnen ... und eine tafel der natürlichen trigonometrischen
zahlen, von Hermann Sievert. 13., durchgesehene aufl., bearb.
von M. Loeske, mit 138 abbildungen im texte und 5 tafeln.
Berlin, Deutsche verlagswerke Strauss, Vetter & co., 1931.

Loeske, Michael, 1867–
Sander, W.
Uhrenlehre; die wichtigsten mechanischen, physikalischen und technologischen grundsätze für den bau der uhrwerke in elementarer darstellung für fachschulen und zum
selbstunterricht, für konstrukteure und reparateure, von
professor W. Sander ... bearb., ergänzt und hrsg. von
M. Loeske. Mit 152 abbildungen. Leipzig, W. Diebener, 1923.

Lösl, Gotthard, 1909–
... Die Lichtbehandlung in der Zahnheilkunde ...
Günzburg a. Donau, 1936.
Inaug.-Diss. - München.
Lebenslauf.

NL 0445943   CtY

LÖSMENT,Max,1879–
Zur religionsphilosophie Kants. Inaug.-
diss. Königsberg i Pr.1907.

pp.46+.
"Lebenslauf," after p.46. Phil 3481.4

NL 0445944   MH ICRL DLC CtY PU IU

BS2360 **Loesner,Christoph Friedrich,1734–1803.**
.L62   Adami Friderici Kühnii Spicilegivm Christophori Friderici Loesneri Observationvm
ad Novvm Testamentvm e Philone Alexandrino.
Pfortenae,cvm typis E.C.Benekii,1785.
[16,]173 p. 20cm.

1.Bible. N.T.—Criticism,Textual. 2.Philo
Judaeus.

NL 0445945   ICU

VOLUME 338

LOESNER, Christoph Friedrich, *1734-1803*
    Lectionum Philonianarum specimen. [Progr.]
Lipsiae, ex officina Langenheimia, [1758].

    4°. pp.32.

NL 0445946   MH

225.6
L826ơ   Loesner, Christoph Friedrich, 1734-1803.
    Observationes ad Novum Testamentum e Philone
Alexandrino. Leipzig, Adamum Frider. Boehmium,
1777.
    508 p.

    1. Philo Judaeus. 2. N. T.--Crit., interp.,
etc.

NL 0445947   TxDaM-P OCH OO PCC NjNbS NjPT MH-AH CtY

Lösner, Hans.
    Levitation und Flugproblem. Eine naturwissenschaftliche Studie
von Hans Lösner. Gotha, R. Schmidt, 1904.
    18 p. 21ᶜᵐ.

NL 0445948   ICJ ICRL

QD412   Loesner, Hans.
.A7L6   Ueber die nitrophenylarsinsaeure.
    Dresden, 1893.
    42p.
    Inaug. diss. Rostock.

NL 0445949   DLC

FILM   Loess, Henry Bernard.
154   The effect of variation of motivational level
L82e   and changes in motivational level on performance
    in learning. Ann Arbor, Mich., University
Microfilms, 1952.
    [University Microfilms, Ann Arbor, Mich.]
Publication no.4083]
    Microfilm copy of typescript. Positive.
    Collation of the original: v, 51ℓ. diagrs.,
tables.
    Thesis--Iowa State University.

    Abstracted in Dissertation abstracts, v.12
(1952) no.5, p.593.

    1. Learning, Psychology of. 2. Motivation
(Psychology) I. Title.

NL 0445951   IU MiDW

Lösse, Franz, 1909-
    ... Experimentelle Untersuchungen über die
Desinfektionswirkung von Laryngsan und
Anginasin ... Münster (Westf.), 1937.
    Inaug.-Diss. - Münster.
    Lebenslauf.

NL 0445952   CtY

AC   Lösse, Joseph, 1907-
831   Forstwirtschaftliche bodennutzung im
    Sauerlande ... Bonn a. Rh., 1938. 107 p.
    Inaug. Diss. - Bonn, 1938.
    Lebenslauf.

NL 0445953   ICRL IaAS

Lössl, Friedrich: Durch Retention unterer Weisheitszähne verursachte Hyperostosenbildung. [Maschinenschrift.] 45 S. 4° [Lag nicht vor.] — Auszug [Autogr.]: 1 Bl. 8°
Erlangen, Med. Diss. v. 25. Juni 1923   [U 23. 1700

NL 0445954   ICRL

PT2424   LÖSSEL, HEINRICH.
.L635F8   Die freudenbotschaft in liedern und gedichten nach
1861   dem evangelio St. Lucä, von dr. Heinrich Lössel... Potsdam, A. Stein, 1861.
    viii, 376 p. 16½cm.

    1. Religious poetry, German.

NL 0445955   ICU

M787.1   Loesser, Arthur, 1894-
L824c
     California; humoresque (on a tune by
OrP   Paladilhe); for violin and piano. Violin
    part fingered and bowed by Mischa Elman.
New York, C. Fischer ₍1923₎
    score (17p.) and 1 part. 36cm.

    1. Violin and piano music. I. Elman,
Mischa, 1891-   II. Title.

NL 0445956   OrU OrP

M23   Loesser, Arthur, 1894-   ed.
.H4L6
Haydn, Joseph, 1732-1809.
    [Sonatas, piano. Selections]

    Five sonatas for piano. Authentic ed. Sonatas 6, 22, 41,
42 and 48; ed. by Arthur Loesser. New York, Music Press
₍1947₎

Loesser, Arthur, 1894-   *ed.*
    Humor in American song, by Arthur Loesser; arrangements by Alfred Kugel. Illustrated by Samuel M. Adler.
New York, Howell, Soskin ₍1942₎
    315, [2] p. illus. 26 cm.

    1. Folk-songs, American. 2. Ballads, American. 3. Negro songs. 4. Humorous songs. I. Kugel, Alfred, arr. II. Title.

    M1629.L75H8   784.4973   42—50891

           OEac OLak OC1 MB LU ViU CaBVa MtU Or OrU WaE
NL 0445958   DLC NIC OrU PSt NcC OC1CC OU OO OC1JC

Loesser, Arthur, 1894-
    Men, women and pianos; a social history. New York,
Simon and Schuster, 1954.
    xvi, 654 p. 24 cm.
    Bibliography: p. 614-624.

    1. Piano—Hist. I. Title.

    ML650.L64   786.2   54—9801 ‡

    OrSaW
CaBVa CaBViP MtBuM CoU OrAshS Or OrMonO OrStbM
CaBVaU Wa WaE WaPS WaS WaSp WaSpG WaT WaTC WaWW WU
OU OOxM OC1W MiU OrU OrPR OrP OrCS MtU MtBC IdU IdB
TU MiD NN TxU PSt PP NcC NcD PPT PWcS OC1 PBm PU
NL 0445959   DLC MsSM OrU-M IdPI AU NIC PSt NBuT MB

Loesser, Arthur, *1894-*
    Men, women and pianos; a social history. L, Gollancz,
1955
    xvi, 654 p.

NL 0445960   MH CaBVaU

M23   Loesser, Arthur, 1894-   ed.
.S28L6
Scarlatti, Domenico, 1685-1757.
    [Sonatas, harpsichord. Selections]

    Ten sonatas for piano. Authentic ed. Sonatas 46, 49, 131,
203, 204, 212, 289, 380, 405, 416. Ed. by Arthur Loesser.
New York, Music Press ₍1947₎

Loesser, Frank, 1910-*1969.*
    Bloop, bleep. New York, Paramount Music Corp. ₍ᶜ1947₎
    5 p. 30 cm.
    For voice and piano, with added chord symbols.

    1. Music, Popular (Songs, etc.)—U. S.   I. Title.

    M1630.2.L   M 57-183

NL 0445962   DLC

Loesser, Frank, 1910-
    The boys in the backroom
      see under   Hollander, Frederick, 1896-

Music   Loesser, Frank, 1910-
-L0295g   [Guys and dolls. Piano-vocal score]
1953   Feuer and Martin present Guys & dolls, a
    musical fable of Broadway, based on a story and
characters by Damon Runyon. Music and lyrics
by Frank Loesser; book by Jo Swerling and Abe
Burrows. Vocal score. New York, Frank Music
Corp. [1953]
    124 p. 31 cm.

    Publisher's plate no.: 2391.

NL 0445964   RPB OrU LU CLobS

VM   LOESSER, FRANK, *1910-*
1503   The Feuer and Martin production Guys and
L 825g   dolls, based on a story and characters by Damon Runyon. Music and lyrics by Frank Loesser.
    Book by Jo Swerling and Abe Burrows. Vocal
score. London, Edwin H. Morris & Co. ₍c1953₎
    score (124 p.) 28cm.

NL 0445965   ICN

Loesser, Frank, 1910-
    First Class Private Mary Brown. By Frank Loesser. New
York, Famous music corp. ₍c1944₎

    First line: He carries around a heavy old rifle.
    From the Army Special Services revue "About face."

    1. Songs, U. S. I. Song index (2).
N. Y. P. L.   June 14, 1951

NL 0445966   NN

VOLUME 338

784.8 Loesser, Frank, 1910-1969
L82g [Songs. Selections.]

Great songs by Frank Loesser. New York,
Famous Music Corp. [c1955]
36 p. (Famous songwriter series)
Arranged for voice(s) and piano, with
ukelele chords included.
1. Music, Popular (Songs, etc.) - U. S.
2. Musical revues, comedies, etc. -
Excerpts,   Arranged. I. Title.

NL 0445967   LN

LOESSER, FRANK, 1910 -
[GUYS AND DOLLS. LIBRETTO. ENGLISH]
Guys and dolls; a musical fable of Broadway. Based
on a story and characters by Damon Runyon. Music and
lyrics by Frank Loesser; book by Jo Swerling and Abe
Burrows. [New York, 1950] 1 v. (various pagings). 29cm.

Typescript.
Produced at the 46th Street theatre, N.Y., Nov. 24, 1950.

1. Musical comedies--Librettos. Guys and dolls. 2. Drama--Promptbooks
and typescripts. I. Swerling, Joseph, 1897- . Guys and dolls. II. Burrows,
Abe, 1921- . Guys and dolls. III. Runyon, Damon. 1880-1946.
IV. Title.

NL 0445969   NN OC1

782.7 Loesser, Frank, 1910-
L824g [Guys and dolls. Libretto]
Guys and dolls; a musical fable of Broad-
way based on a story and characters by
Damon Runyon. Music and lyrics by Frank
Loesser; book by Jo Swerling and Abe Burrows.
London, Frank Music Co. [c1951]
88 p.

1. Musical revues, comedies, etc. -
Librettos I. Runyon, Damon, 1880-1946
II. Swerling,   Joseph   III. Burrows
Abram S

NL 0445970   MiD RPB

M1503 Loesser, Frank, 1910-
L899G9 [Guys and dolls; acc.arr. piano]
Guys and dolls; a musical fable of Broadway,
based on a story and characters by Damon
Runyon. Book by Jo Swerling and Abe Burrows.
New York, Frank Music Corp. [c1953]
124 p. 28ᵐ.

1. Operettas. I. Runyon, Damon, 1880-1946.
II. Swerling, Jo. III. Burrows, Abram S
IV. Title.

WaT OrU OrP CaBVa
NL 0445971   CSt OC1 LU PP NN MB WaU CLU NcU Wa

Loesser, Frank, 1910-
Hello, my darling, in the Paramount picture
Zaza
    see under   Hollander, Frederick, 1896-

M1500 Loesser, Frank, 1910-   Hi, Yank!
.U6H5 U. S. *Army service forces. Special services division.*

"Hi, Yank!" A soldier shows "blueprint special." Music
and lyrics by Pvt. Frank Loesser, Lt. Alex North, Lt. Jack
Hill and Sgt. Jesse Berkman; sketches by Pvt. Arnold Auerbach, Lt. Bob Eastright, Lt. Jack Hill [and others] ... Costume
and scenery designs by Lt. Robert T. Stevenson and Sgt. Al
Hamilton, drawn by T/4 Edward E. Wolf. Dances by Pvt.
Jose Limon. Cover and other drawings by Sgt. George Baker.
[Washington] Headquarters, Army service forces, Special services division, ASF [1944?]

Loesser, Frank, 1910-
The last thing I want is your pity. New York, E. H.
Morris [°1948]
3 p. 31 cm.
For voice and piano, with added chord symbols.

1. Music, Popular (Songs, etc.)--U. S.   I. Title.

M1630.2.L   M 57-181

NL 0445974   DLC NN

Loesser, Frank, 1910-
Little Joe, the wrangler
    see under   Hollander, Frederick, 1896-

Loesser, Frank, 1910-
Love me as I am
    see under
Alter, Louis, 1902-

Loesser, Frank, 1910-
Music on the shore
    see under   Hollander, Frederick, 1896-

Loesser, Frank, 1910-
Palms of paradise
    see under   Hollander, Frederick, 1896-

LOESSER, FRANK, 1910-
[HANS CHRISTIAN ANDERSEN. SELECTIONS. ARR. FOR PIANO]
Piano selection from Hans Christian Andersen—
and the dancer. [Arr. by Felton Rapley] London,
E. H. Morris; New York, Bedford music corp. [c1952]
11 p. 28cm.

Duration: 6 min.
1. Piano--Arr. 2. Motion pictures. Hans Christian Andersen.
I. Hans Christian Andersen   (Moving picture).

NL 0445979   NN

Loesser, Frank, 1910-
Praise the Lord and pass the ammunition. Words and
music by Frank Loesser. Piano arr. by Geo. N. Terry. New
York, Famous Music Corp. [°1942]
5 p. 31 cm.
For voice and piano, with chord symbols for guitar.

1. War-songs, American.   I. Title.

M1648.L   M 57-392

NL 0445980   DLC OrP IU ScU NN

---

sVM LOESSER, FRANK, 1910-
1649 Rodger Young   New York, B. Miller, inc.
L 82r [c1945]
5 p. 30cm.

Vocal solo with piano accompaniment and
symbols for guitar, ukulele and banjo.

NL 0445981   ICN OrP NN MB

Loesser, Frank, 1910-
[Seventeen. Seventeen; arr.]
Seventeen, in the Paramount picture Seventeen. Words
and music by Frank Loesser. [Piano score by Geo. N. Terry]
New York, Paramount Music Corp. [°1939]
5 p. 31 cm.
For voice and piano, with chord symbols for guitar and diagrs. for
ukulele; acc. originally for orchestra.

1. Moving-picture music—Excerpts—Vocal scores with piano.
I. Title.

M1508   M 56-1874

NL 0445982   DLC

Loesser, Frank, 1910-
Spring will be a little late this year. Words and music by Frank
Loesser.   Hollywood, Saunders publications, c1944.
First line: January and February were never so empty.
Sung by Deanna Durbin in Universal's production Christmas holiday.

NN 1. Spring. I. Song index (2).

NL 0445983   NN

Loesser, Frank, 1910-
Strange enchantment
    see under   Hollander, Frederick, 1896-

Loesser, Frank, 1910-
That sentimental sandwich
    see under   Hollander, Frederick, 1896-

M1630 Loesser, Frank, 1910-   joint composer.
S
Stein, William, 1917-

Wave to me, my lady, by William Stein and Frank Loesser.
New York, Famous Music Corp. [°1945]

Loesser, Frank, 1910-
What do you do in the Infantry. By Frank Loesser.   Hollywood, Saunders publ., c1943.

N.Y.P.L. 1. U. S. army—Infantry. 2. World   war, 1939-1945. I. Song index (1).
April 30, 1947

NL 0445987   NN

Loesser, Frank, 1910-
The white blossoms of Tah-ni
    see under   Hollander, Frederick, 1896-

782.7 Loesser, Frank, 1910-
L824w [Where's Charley? Libretto]
Where's Charley? a musical comedy. Book
by George Abbott. Music and lyrics by
Frank Loesser based on Charley's Aunt by
Brandon Thomas. London, S. French [°1948]
v, 57 p., 4 p. of illus. (French's
acting edition)

1. Musical revues, comedies, etc. -
Librettos I. Abbott, George, 1889-
II. Thomas,   Brandon, 1848-1914.
Charley's Aunt.

NL 0445989   MiD

VOLUME 338

Loesser, Frank, 1910–
Why do they call a private a private? By Frank Loesser and Peter Lind Hayes.   New York, Famous music corp. [c1944]

First line: I know why they call a corporal a corporal.
From the Army special services revue About face.

1. Songs, U. S.   I. Hayes, Peter   Lind.   II. Song index (2).

NL 0445990   NN

Loesser, Frank, 1910–/%?
You've got that look (that leaves me weak)
see under   Hollander, Frederick, 1896–

Loesser, Mrs. Julia (Ehrlich) 1881–   tr.
Naryshkina, Elizaveta (Kurakina)
Under three tsars; the memoirs of the lady-in-waiting, Elizabeth Naryshkin-Kurakin, edited by René Fülöp-Miller; translated from the German by Julia E. Loesser; with fifty illustrations.   New York, E. P. Dutton & co., inc. [*1931]

Lössi, Henri, 1915–
Der sprichwortschatz des Engadins, mit einschluss der sprichwörter des Münstertales sowie der in diesen beiden talschaften gebräuchlichen landwirtschafts- und wetterregeln ... von Henri Lössi ...   Zürich, E. Lang, 1943.

xxiv, 71 p.   21 cm.
Thesis—Zürich.
"Teildruck; die vollständige arbeit erscheint ... 1943 im kommissionsverlag der buchhandlung A. Vogel, Winterthur."
Curriculum vitae.
"Quellen": p. xviii–xxiii.
1. Raeto-Romance language—Dialects—Ladin (Engadine)   I. Title.

PC943.A1L6   47-42988

NL 0445993   DLC NNC ICU IU NN CtY

Lössi, Henri, 1915–
Der sprichwortschatz des Engadins, mit einschluss der sprichwörter des Münstertales sowie der in diesen beiden talschaften gebräuchlichen landwirtschafts- und wetterregeln.   Winterthur, Vogel, 1944.
xxiv, 299 p.

Published in part as thesis, Zürich.
"Bibliographie": p. 295–299.
1. Proverbs, Romansh.   2. Romansh language - Dialects - Engadine   I. Title.

NL 0445994   NNC DCU MH OCU CLU CU PU ICU NjP DCU

Lössl, Franz.
Die volksschulpflicht nach deutschem volksschulrecht, von dr Franz Lössl.   Berlin und München, R. Oldenbourg, 1911.

83, [1] p.   25ᶜᵐ.
"Literatur": 1 p. at end.

1. Education—Germany.   2. School law—Germany.

E 11–1383
Library, U. S. Bur. of   Education LA722.L8

NL 0445995   DHEW CtY ICRL MH-L ICJ

Loessl, Friedrich, *ritter* von, 1817–1907.
Der luftwiderstand im allgemeinen und in seiner besonderen beziehung auf luftschiffahrt.   Ein vortrag gehalten im Vereine zur verbreitung naturwissenschaftlicher kenntnisse in Wien am 10 märz 1886, von Friedrich ritter v. Lössl ... [Mit 2 figuren im texte.]   Wien, Verein zur verbreitung naturwissenschaftlicher kenntnisse, 1886.

45 p.   diagrs.   16½ᶜᵐ.

1. Aerodynamics.   2. Aeronautics.
[Full name: Friedrich Otto Johann Baptist ritter von Loessl]
                                                    31–12591
Library of Congress   TL570.L65A3
                                                    629.13

NL 0445996   DLC ICJ MnU

Loessl, Friedrich, *ritter* von, 1817–1907.
Die luftwiderstands-gesetze, der fall durch die luft und der vogelflug.   Mathematisch-mechanische klärung, auf experimenteller grundlage entwickelt von Friedrich ritter von Loessl ...   Wien, A. Hölder, 1896.

2 p. l., 304 p.   illus., diagrs.   24½ᶜᵐ.

1. Aerodynamics.   2. Flight.
[Full name: Friedrich Otto Johann Baptist ritter von Loessl]
                                                    31–12593
Library of Congress   TL570.L65A35
——— Copy 2.   629.13

NL 0445997   DLC ICJ MiU WU OkU DAS DSI

Loessl, Friedrich, *ritter* von, 1817–1907.
Studie über aërodynamische grundformeln an der hand von experimenten.   Von Friedrich ritter v. Lössl ...   Wien, Verlag des verfassers, druck von R. Spies & co., 1881.

1 p. l., p. [17]–83.   illus., diagrs.   20ᶜᵐ.
From "Sitzungsberichte der Fachgruppe für flugtechnik des Oesterreichischen ingenieur- und architekten-vereines", March–Oct., 1881.

1. Aerodynamics.   I. Oesterreichischer ingenieur- und architektenverein, Vienna.   Fachgruppe für flugtechnik.   Sitzungsberichte.
[Full name: Friedrich Otto Johann Baptist ritter von Loessl]
                                                    31–12592
Library of Congress   TL570.L65A4
                                                    629.13

NL 0445998   DLC

Loessl, Friedrich *ritter* von, 1817–1907.
... Das Zeppelin-luftschiff als neuester versuch zur lenkbarmachung von gasballons.   Von ober-ingenieur v. Loessl.   [Aussee] Selbstverlag des verfassers, druck von R. Spiess & co. in Wien, 1900.

5 p.   33½ x 25½ᶜᵐ.
Caption title.
Dated, at end: Aussee, 11. Juli 1900.
"Sonder-abdruck aus der 'Zeitschrift des Oesterreichischen ingenieur und architekten-vereines' 1900, nr. 35."
1. Air-ships.   I. Title.
[Full name: Friedrich Otto Johann Baptist ritter von Loessl]
                                                    35–4981
Library of Congress   TL658.Z4L57
                                  [2]   629.13325

NL 0445999   DLC

4K   Lössl, Heinrich
6807   Recht auf Unterhalt.   Wien, Manz,
            1902.
                240 p.

NL 0446001   DLC-P4

Lössl, Vinzenz, 1855–
[00937]   Buchführung, Kalkulation und Wechsellehre für Schulen, zur Vorbereitung für die Meisterprüfungen und zum Selbstunterricht.   Von V. Lössl, ..., und J. Moller, ...   Dritte Auflage.   München, R. Oldenbourg, [1912].
viii, 179 p. incl. tables.   22ᶜᵐ.

NL 0446002   ICJ

Lössl, Vinzenz, 1853–
Lesebuch für gewerbliche Fortbildungsschulen und verwandte Anstalten.   Erweiterte Ausgabe.   Herausgegeben von V.Lössl, J.Moller [und] Dr. Zwerger.   8.Aufl.   München, R.Oldenbourg [1910?]

NL 0446003   MH

Loessl, Vinzenz, 1853–   ed.
Lesebuch für höhere Lehranstalten
see under title

Loessner, Anton.
Der Abfall Posens 1918/19 im polnischen Schrifttum.   Danzig, Kommissionsverlag der Danziger Verlags-Gesellschaft, 1933.

45 p.   23 cm.   (Ostland-Schriften, 6)
"Verzeichnis der besprochenen Schriften": p. [3]

1. Posen (Province)—Hist.   2. Poland—Hist.—Wars of 1918–1921.   I. Title.   (Series)
DK401.O72 hft. 6   A C 34–79 rev*
Harvard Univ.   Library
for Library of Congress   [r56cₐ]†

NL 0446005   MH CU ICU NN DLC

Loessner, Anton.
Josef Pilsudski; eine lebensbeschreibung auf grund seiner eigenen schriften, von dr. A. Loessner.   Mit zwei tafeln.   Leipzig, S. Hirzel, 1935.

viii, 202 p.   front.   illus. (maps) port.   25½ᶜᵐ.
"Literaturverzeichnis": p. [201]–202.

1. Pilsudski, Józef, 1867–1935.   2. Poland—Hist.
                                                    36–11614
Library of Congress   DK440.5.P5L6
                                  [2]   [923.5438]   923.1438

NL 0446006   DLC DS ICU CU NN

Loessner, Fritz: Über Reaktionen der unterphosphorigen Säure und Wasserstoffverbindungen der Schwermetalle.   Weida i. Th. 1911: Thomas & Hubert.   91 S. 8°
Leipzig, Phil. Diss. v. 25. Mai 1911, Ref. Beckmann, Hantzsch
[Geb. 2. Mai 81; Wohnort: Leipzig; Staatsangeh.: Sachsen; Vorbildung: Gymn. Schneeberg Reife O. 01; Studium: Leipzig 10 S.; Rig. 16. Mai 11.]   [U 11. 3250

NL 0446007   ICRL CtY OCU MH PU

QD341   Loessner, Linne, 1841–
.L79   Ueber die einwirkung von benzoylchlorid auf rhodankalium in alkoholischer loesung.   Leipzig, 1874.
                29p.
                Inaug. diss. Leipzig.

NL 0446008   DLC

Lössnitzer, Ernst.
Grosses deutsches Kochbuch der feinen und guten bürgerlichen Küche ...   Mit einem Jagdkalender ...   2. ed.   Dresden, W. Baensch, 1906.

ix, 803, (1) p., 6 l.   1 tab., illus.   8°.

NL 0446009   NN

TX353   Lössnitzer, Ernst.
.H17   ... Handbuch der küchenwissenschaft, küchen- und speisenpraxis für fachlehrer, prüfungsmeister und prüflinge der gastgewerblichen fachschulen ...   Gegründet von Ernst Lössnitzer ...   Berlin, K. Kirchner [1941–

VOLUME 338

Loessnitzer, Ernst, compiler.
Lehrbuch der Küchenwissenschaft und Nahrungsmittel-
kunde; für gastwirtsgewerbliche Fachschulen, Koch- und Haus-
haltungsschulen, zum Selbstunterricht für Köche und Kochlehr-
linge sowie Hotel-, Restorations-, Herrschafts- und Privatküchen
bearbeitet von Ernst Lössnitzer... Leipzig: W. Krieg[, 1925].
359 p. front. 8°.

244889A. 1. Cookery. 2. Food.
N. Y. P. L.   July 20, 1926

NL 0446011   NN

Loest, Erich.
Das Jahr der Prüfung; Roman. Halle (Saale) Mitteldeutscher Verlag, 1954.
398 p. 20 cm.

ɪ. Title.

PT2623.O425J3   57-20214 ‡

NL 0446012   DLC NN

Loest, Erich.
Jungen die übrig blieben; roman.
Leipzig, Volk und buch verlag [c1950]
301 p. 22 cm.

NL 0446013   PU

Loest, Erich.
Jungen, die übrigblieben. Halle (Saale),
Mitteldeutscher Verlag, 1954. 342 p. 19cm.

NL 0446014   NN

4PT   **Loest, Erich.**
Ger.   Nacht über dem See und andere Kurzgeschichten.
3542   Leipzig, Volk und Buch Verlag, 1950.
72 p.

NL 0446015   DLC-P4

Loest, Erich
WB   Sportgeschichten. Halle(Saale), Mitteldeutscher
15318   Verlag, 1953.

NL 0446016   CtY

4PT   **Loest, Erich**
Ger.   Die Westmark fällt weiter; Roman.
9538   Halle (Saale) Mitteldeutscher Verlag,
1952.
580 p.

NL 0446017   DLC-P4

Loest, Erich.
Die Westmark fällt weiter; Roman. Halle (Saale),
Mitteldeutscher Verlag, 1953. 580 p. 20cm.

NL 0446018   NN

PT 2361   LOEST, HEINRICH
.Z5 L8   Heinrich Loest über E. T. A. Hoffmann, 15.
August, 1823. Hrsg. von Hans von Müller.
Köln, P. Gehly, 1922.
14 p.

1. Hoffmann, Ernst Theodor Amadeus, 1776-1822.
I. Müller, Hans von, 1875-

NL 0446019   InU CLU

Loest, Heinrich.
Jahrbüchlein deutscher gedichte auf 1815
see under title

Loest, Heinrich.
Sappho; Gesangsscene...
see under   Berger, Ludwig, 1777-1839.

Loest, Heinrich Wilhelm.
Einsiedler-Ansichten und Träume von dem Menschen, dem
Staate, der Politik und der Kirche, hrsg. von Anselm Frie-
dank [pseud.] Hamm, G. A. Wundermann, 1828.
2 v. in 1. 21 cm.

ɪ. Title.

PT2424.L635E4   52-50037

NL 0446022   DLC

Loest, Heinrich Wilhelm.
Patriotische ergiessungen, über öffentliche und privatzu-
stände im preussischen vaterlande. Erstes heft: 1.Die eisenbahnen. 2.Der wucher. 3.Der pauperismus . . . Berlin,
Stuhr, 1844.
64 p. 20 cm.

NL 0446023   MH-BA

Loest, Johannes.
Die Deutsche Genossenschaftskasse; Vorgeschichte, Aufbau and Aufgaben. [1. Aufl.] Neuwied am Rhein, Verlag
der Raiffeisendruckerei [1952]
44 p. 21 cm. (Vorträge und Aufsätze des Instituts für Genossenschaftswesen an der Universität Münster, Heft 4)
"Gesetz über die Deutsche Genossenschaftskasse": p. 37-44.

1. Deutsche Genossenschaftskasse.   ɪ. Germany (Federal Republic, 1949-   ) Laws, statutes, etc. Gesetz über die Deutsche
Genossenschaftskasse.   (Series: Münster. Universität. Institut
für Genossenschaftswesen. Vorträge und Aufsätze, Heft 4)

HD3499.L6   55-30456

NL 0446024   DLC

Loest, Johannes: Das Verpackungsmaterial. [Maschinenschrift.] 136 S.
4°. — Auszug: Breslau 1922: Bresl. Genoss.-Buchdr. 2 Bl. 8°
Breslau, R.- u. staatswiss. Diss. v. 1. Nov. 1922   [U 22. 1150]

NL 0446025   ICRL

Die lösung der judenfrage auf der grundlage des
von den Juden mit Jehova-Gott geschlossen und
beeideten bundes durch die bei anlasse auf
sich herabbeschworene todesstrafe
see under   [Olschowy, Ladislaus Adam N   ]

Die **Lösung** der sozialen Frage vom Standpunkte der Wirklichkeit und Praxis. Von einem praktischen Staatsmanne ...
Bielefeld und Leipzig, Velhagen & Klasing, 1878.
viii, 156 p. 23cm.

NL 0446027   ICJ ICN

Die Lösung des Weltsprache-Problems
see under   Couturat, Louis, 1868-1914.

Lösungen der absolutorial-aufgaben aus der mathematik an den
humanistischen gymnasien Bayerns seit dem jahre 1867. Nebst
einem anhang: Die wichtigsten formeln der mathematik. 2. aufl.
München, E. Pohl, 1894.
pp. (4), 156 +.
I. nachtrag. [München, E. Pohl, 1895.]
pp. 4.

Math.-Problems|Do.-Form.||

NL 0446029   MH

Loet, pseud.
see   Cloetta, Gian Gianett.

Løth, Aksel Mikkelsen-
see
Mikkelsen-Løth, Aksel, 1849-

Løth, J.
David Zeisberger; i tre og tresindstyve Aar Missionær blandt
Indianerne. København: Det Danske Missionsselskab, 1914.
36 p. 8°. (Dansk Missionsselskab Missions-Bibliotheket.
Aargang 1914. Hefte 1.)

1. Zeisberger, David, 1721-1808. 2.   Indians (N. A.).—Missions.
N. Y. P. L.   September 30, 1914.

NL 0446032   NN CtY

Löther, Alois
Die viskosimetrische vorfolgung von
enzymreaktionen. ... 43 p.
Inaug. Diss. - Techn. Hochschule München, [1935]

NL 0446033   ICRL

Löthman (AND[REAS] AD[OLPHUS])
Vita Demosthenis. Part I. *Upsaliæ,* 1813. 2 p.l, 8
pp. 4°.
In: NSK p. v. 1.

NL 0446034   NN

Loetoeng Kasaroeng
see   Lutung Kasarung.

Loets, Bruno, ed.
Holländisch-Deutsch und Deutsch-Holländisch ...
see under title

PT6410   **Claes, Ernest,** 1885-
.C5J44   ... Jugend, übertragen von Bruno Loets. Leipzig, Insel-
verlag, 1943.

Loets, Bruno, tr.

VOLUME 338

PT6460
.W3M34
Loets, Bruno, tr.

Walschap, Gerard, 1898–
... Der mann, der das gute wollte, roman, aus dem flämischen übertragen von Bruno Loets. Leipzig, Insel-verlag, 1938.

PT6442
.P44S64
Loets, Bruno, tr.

Pillecyn, Filip de, 1891–
... Der soldat Johan; roman. Leipzig, G. Altenburg [1942]
2 p. l., 7–206 p., 1 l. 20½ᵐ.

PT2528
.Z5L8
Loets, Bruno.
Theodor Storm, ein rechtes Herz. Sein Leben in Briefen dargestellt. Wiesbaden, Dieterich [1951]
518 p. ports. (Sammlung Dieterich, Bd.103)
Includes bibliography.

1. Storm, Theodor, 1817–1888.

NL 0446040   ICU

Loetsch (Bruno) [1893–]. *Beitrag zur Kenntnis der endogenen Muskelatrophie. [München.] 33 pp. 8°. Berlin, 1919.

NL 0446041   DNLM CtY MiU PPWI

Loetsch, Eduard.
Die veraensserung der namensaktie nach... Inaug. diss. Leipzig, 1908
Bibl.

NL 0446042   ICRL

Lötsch, Ernst Hermann, 1881–
... Zur kenntniss der verdauung von fleisch im magen u. dünndarme des schweines ... Freiberg i. Sa., Druck von H. Köhler, 1908.
54 p., 1 l. fold. tab. 24ᶜᵐ.
Inaug.-diss.—Leipzig.
Lebenslauf.
Bibliographical foot-notes.

1. Digestion. 2. Swine. Anatomy and physiology.

Agr 10–1455

Library, U. S. Dept. of   Agriculture 444L91

NL 0446043   DNAL ICRL DNLM CtY

Loetsch, Franz
Ehe und Geschlechts-Krankheiten (Wann darf man nach geschlechtlicher Ansteckung heiraten?) ... [München,n.d.]
133p. 19cm.

1. Genito-urinary organs - Diseases.

NL 0446044   CtY-M

Loetsch, Franz
"Männer, hütet euch vor Ansteckung." Gemeinverständliche Darstellung der Geschlechtskrankheiten und ihrer Verhütung. 52 pp. 12°. München, F. Stein, 1901.

NL 0446045   DNLM

Loetsch, Franz.
Ueber pathologische elongation der langen... Inaug. diss. Freiburg,1897.
Bibl.

NL 0446046   ICRL DNLM

Loetsch, Fritz.
Report to the government of Indonesia on aspects of forestry in relation to the rayon plant project in South Sumatra
see under Food and Agriculture Organization of the United Nations.

Lötsch, Harald.
Die risikobeschränkungen, von diplom-versicherungsverständigem dr. jur. Harald Lötsch. Hamburg, Friederichsen, de Gruyter & co., 1935.
68 p., 1 l. 23ᶜᵐ. (On cover: Hamburger rechtsstudien ... hft. 27)
"Diese arbeit ist im Versicherungswissenschaftlichen seminar der Hamburgischen universität entstanden und ... wurde als juristische doktor-dissertation von der Rechts- und staatswissenschaftlichen fakultät der Hamburgischen universität angenommen."—Vorwort.
"Schrifttum": p. [65]–68.

1. Insurance law—Germany.   I. Title.

36–6671

NL 0446048   DLC

Loetscher (Alex.) *Ein Beitrag zur Pathologie des Oesophaguscarcinoms. 105 pp. 8°. Zürich, Gebr. Leemann & Co.. 1910.

NL 0446049   DNLM

Lötscher, E

NL 0446050   CtY

Templass
197
L82A4
Loetscher, Frederick William, 1874–
Address on the 200th anniversary of the Adopting act, delivered at the General assembly of the Presbyterian Church in the U.S.A., St.Paul, Minn., May 24, 1929.   Philadelphia, Office of the General Assembly [n.d.]
15 p. 28cm.

Cover title.

NL 0446051   PPT

Loetscher, Frederick William, 1874–
Church history as a science and theological discipline. n.p. [1915]

NL 0446052   NjP

Loetscher, Frederick William, 1874–
Fifty years, the reunion of the old and new school Presbyterian churches 1870–1920, by Frederick William Loetscher ... Pub. on the occasion of the celebration of the fiftieth anniversary of the reunion at the meeting of the one hundred and thirty-second General assembly of the Presbyterian church in the United States of America, Philadelphia, Pennsylvania, May, 1920. Philadelphia, The Presbyterian board of publication and Sabbath school work, 1920.
40 p. 18½ᵐ.
1. Presbyterian church in the U. S. A.—Hist.

20–10547

Library of Congress   BX8935.L6

NL 0446053   DLC OO GDC

Loetscher, Frederick William, *1874–*
Homiletics as a theological discipline. (Biblical and theological studies, by the members of the faculty of Princeton Theological Seminary.   New York, 1912.   8°.   p. 393–422.)

1. Preaching.
N.Y.P.L.   May 15, 1912.

NL 0446054   NN

Loetscher, Frederick William, 1874–   ed.

American society of church history.
Papers of the American society of church history. 2d series ...
New York city, The Red diamond press, 1908–

Templass
197
L8232
Loetscher, Frederick William, 1874–
St. Augustine's conception of the state. [Berne, Ind., American Society of Church History, 1935]
15–42 p. 25cm.

Caption title.
Tear sheets from Church history, Vol. IV., no.1, March, 1935.
Bibliographical footnotes.

NL 0446056   PPT

Loetscher, Frederick William, 1874–
Schwenckfeld's participation in the eucharistic controversy of the sixteenth century ... Philadelphia, MacCalla & company, 1906.
viii, 81 p. 26½ᵐ.
Thesis (PH. D.)—Princeton university.
The following dissertation is substantially a reprint from the Princeton theological review for July and October, 1906. cf. Pref.
Bibliography: p. v–viii.

1. Schwenkfeld, Kaspar von, 1489 or 90–1561.

7–4785

PPeSchw PPT
NL 0446057   DLC PBm NIC PPiPT CU MiU MB NN NjP PU

Film
N2702
Loetscher, Frederick William, 1913–
Ornithology of the Mexican state of Veracruz, with an annotated list of the birds. [Ithaca, N. Y.] 1941.
989 l.

Thesis (Ph.D.)--Cornell University, June 1941.
Microfilm (negative) Ithaca, N. Y., Photo Science, Cornell University, 1969.
1 reel. 35mm.

NL 0446058   NIC

Loetscher, Hans, 1843–1913.
Das Birmenstorfer Bitterwasser. Seine physiologische Wirkung und therapeutische Anwendung ... Zürich, Cotti, 1893.
45 p. illus. 20 cm.

1. Mineral waters—Birmensdorf, Switzerland.

Med 48–1477

U. S. Army Medical Libr.   [W6P3]
for Library of Congress   [1]

NL 0446059   DNAL

VOLUME 338

WBI
L826s
1892
LOETSCHER, Hans, 1843-1913
Handbook to the health resorts of Switzerland; containing full information for the physician, the healthseeker and the traveller as to all the baths, climatic stations, springs and watering places of Switzerland. 4th ed. Zurich, Schröter, 1892.
xxxviii, 311 p. illus.
Translation of his Schweizer Kur-Almanach 1887.
Title

NL 0446060   DNLM

WBI
L826s
LOETSCHER, Hans, 1843-1913
Schweizer Reise- und Kur-Almanach; die Kurorte und Heilquellen der Schweiz. Ein Reisehandbuch für Kurgäste und Sommerfrischler sowie Ratgeber für Ärzte. [1.]– Aufl. Zürich, Schröter [etc.] 1886–
v. illus.
1st-13th eds. have title: Schweizer Kur-Almanach, die Kurorte, Bäder & Heilquellen der Schweiz.

I. Loetscher, Hans, 1843-1913.
Schweizer Kur-Almanach   Title
Title: Schweizer Kur-Almanach

NL 0446062   DNLM NIC MH

Loetscher, Hans, 1843-1913.
Wie erhält man seinen Magen gesund? Eine Hygiene des Magens. 42 pp. 8°. Leipzig & Zürich, T. Schröter, 1890.

NL 0446063   DNLM

Lötscher (J.)   Die Gesundheitspflege im Alter der Schulpflichtigkeit. Zwei Vorträge, gehalten vor der thurgauischen gemeinnützigen Gesellschaft. 1 p. l., 74 pp. 8°. Frauenfeld, J. Hubers, 1874.
by J. Lötscher & J. Christinger.

NL 0446064   DNLM

Lötscher, Konrad.
Der Diener Gottes, Professor Dr. Max Westermaier (1852-1903) ein katholischer Naturforscher. Freiburg, Schweiz, Kanisiuswerk [1948]
168 p. port. 21 cm.
"Quellen": p. 157-166.

1. Westermaier, Maximilien, 1852-1903.   I. Title.

QK31.W4L6   925.8   49-23775*

NL 0446065   DLC

285
L826b
1938
Loetscher, Lefferts Augustine, 1904-
A brief history of the Presbyterians. [Rev. ed.] Philadelphia, Board of Christian Education of the Presbyterian Church in the United States of America, 1945 [c1938]
95p. 19cm.

Bibliography: p. 93-95.

1. Presbyterian Church - History.

NL 0446066   CLSU NjPT OC1 MiD NN MH-AH

Loetscher, Lefferts Augustine, 1904–
The broadening Church; a study of theological issues in the Presbyterian Church since 1869. Philadelphia, University of Pennsylvania Press, 1954.
195 p. 24 cm.
Includes bibliographical references.

1. Presbyterian Church in the U. S. A.—Hist.   I. Title.   II. Title: Theological issues in the Presbyterian Church since 1869.

BX8952.L6   285.173   54—7110

PC1vU
OCU OKentU PU PSt PPWe TxU OOxM PPLT PCC OC1 OO
NL 0446067   DLC MB IdU Or RPB KyLxCB KyU GU PPEB OU

Loetscher, Lefferts Augustine, 1904–   ed.

Schaff-Herzog encyclopedia.
The new Schaff-Herzog encyclopedia of religious knowledge, embracing Biblical, historical, doctrinal, and practical theology, and Biblical, theological, and ecclesiastical biography from the earliest times to the present day; based on the 3d ed. of the Realencyklopädie founded by J. J. Herzog, and edited by Albert Hauck, prepared by more than six hundred scholars and specialists under the supervision of Samuel Macauley Jackson (editor-in-chief) with the assistance of Charles Colebrook Sherman and George William Gilmore (associate editors) and [others] Grand Rapids, Mich., Baker, 1949-50.

Loetscher, Lefferts Augustine, 1904-
Philadelphia Presbyterianism; an historical sketch ... through two centuries and a half with special reference to the erection of the presbytery of Philadelphia on June 14, 1943, by Lefferts A. Loetscher Philadelphia [Presbytery's committee on history] 1943.
17 p., 21½ cm.

NL 0446070   NjPR

Loetscher, Lefferts Augustine, 1904–
... Presbyterianism in Philadelphia since 1870 ... [by] Lefferts Augustine Loetscher. Philadelphia, 1944.
58 p. 23 cm.
Essential portion of thesis (PH. D.)—University of Pennsylvania, 1943. "Consists of selections from chapter III, 'Evangelism', and from chapter IV, 'Interdenominational relations' ... Two microfilms ... of the entire dissertation ... are deposited with the University of Pennsylvania. A part of this essential portion appeared in the Pennsylvania magazine of history and biography, January, 1944, volume lxviii, part I."—Pref. Bibliographical foot-notes.
1. Presbyterian church in Philadelphia. 2. Revivals—Philadelphia. I. Title.

Pennsylvania. Univ. Libr.   A 44–1448
for Library of Congress   BX8049.P5L6
[2]†   285.1748

NL 0446071   PU NIC NcD OC1 OOxM DLC

Loetscher, Lefferts Augustine, 1904–   ed.
Twentieth century encyclopedia of religious knowledge

see under

Schaff-Herzog encyclopedia.

Loetscher, Otto Lütschg-
see Lütschg-Loetscher, Otto.

F113
B45
1941
Lütscher, Paul
... Beitrag zur Liquorpathologie der Heine-Medinschen Krankheit (Meningitisches und Lähmungs-Stadium) ... Bern, 1941.
Inaug.-Diss. - Bern.
"Sonderabdruck aus den 'Helvetica medica acta' 1941, Bd. 8, Hft. 5."

NL 0446074   CtY

833
B549Yℓ
Lötscher, Ulrich.
Jeremias Gotthelf als Politiker. Bern, K.J. Wyss, 1904.
viii, 136p. 23cm.

Inaug.-Diss.—Bern.
Bibliography: p. [vi]-viii.

1. Bitzius, Albert, 1797-1854.

NL 0446075   TxU ICRL NcU

PT
1819
B6Z676
Lötscher, Ulrich.
Jeremias Gotthelf als Politiker. Bern, K.J. Wyss, 1905.
136p. 23cm.

Includes bibliography.

1. Bitzius, Albert, 1797-1854.   I. Title.

NL 0446076   MU

Lötscher, Valentin, 1916–
Der deutsche bauernkrieg in der darstellung und im urteil der zeitgenössischen Schweizer ... von Valentin Lötscher ... Basel, Helbing & Lichtenhahn, 1943.
262 p. 24 cm.
Inaug.-diss.—Basel.
"Die arbeit erscheint gleichzeitig als band 11 der Basler beiträge zur geschichts-wissenschaft ... Verlag von Helbing & Lichtenhahn, Basel." Vita.
"Literatur": p. 256-261.
1. Peasants' war, 1524-1525.   I. Title.
46-17270
Library of Congress   DD183.L6

NL 0446077   DLC NcD OU ICU NNC MoU TU MH

Lötscher, Valentin, 1916–
Der deutsche Bauernkrieg in der Darstellung und im Urteil der zeitgenössischen Schweizer. Basel, Helbing & Lichtenhahn, 1943.
261 p. 24 cm. (Basler Beiträge zur Geschichtswissenschaft, Bd. 11)
Issued also as inaug. diss., Basel.
"Literatur": p. 256-261.

1. Peasant's War, 1524-1525. 2. Public opinion—Switzerland. I. Title.   (Series)
DD183.L6 1943a   943.031   49-29535*

NL 0446078   DLC CtY ICMcC NNUT

Lötscher-von Büren, Simon Leonhard.
Der Gast, Gastgewerbliches Brevier, Erfahrungen und Ratschläge aus der Praxis. Zürich, Amstutz & Herdeg [1940]
84 p. 14 cm.

1. Hotels, taverns, etc. 2. Waiters.

TX931.L6   52-48339

NL 0446079   DLC InLP NIC

Lötschert, Clara, pseud.
see
Brechten, Marga, 1857–

VOLUME 338

Lötschert, Detlef, 1928–
Die völkerrechtliche Stellung des Saarlandes nach 1945.
¡Mainz? 1952?¡
vii, 113 l.   30 cm.
Diss.—Mainz.
Vita.
Bibliography : leaves 104–112.

1. Saarland (1947–   )—For. rel.   I. Title.

JX1549.5.L6   54–43585 rev

NL 0446081   DLC

PR
4588   **Lötschert, Hugo,** *1884–*
L82d   Dickens und Thackeray als humoristen;
eine vergleichende studie ...   Opladen,
Druck von F.A.Arndt, 1912.
15p. 24cm.

1. Dickens, Charles, 1812–1870. 2. Thackeray,
William Makepeace.

NL 0446082   NRU

Lötschert, Hugo, *1884–*
Der Völkerbund im Unterricht; Stoffe und Winke.
Frankfurt a. M., M. Diesterweg, 1929.
67 p.   23 cm.

1. International organization. 2. League of Nations.   I. Title.

JX1944.L6   54–54292 ‡

NL 0446083   DLC IaU

Lötschert, Hugo, 1884–
Die Völkerbund im unterricht; stoffe und
winke ...   2. erw. aufl.   Frankfurt a.M.,
1930.
75 p.   diagr.   23 cm.

NL 0446084   RPB

Lötschert,Hugo,1884–
William Makepeace Thackeray als humorist ...
von Hugo Lötschert ...   Marburg, R.Friedrich's
universitäts-buchdruckerei,inhaber K.Gleiser,
1908.
viii,122 p.,1 l.   22cm.
Inaug.-diss.--Marburg.
Lebenslauf.
"Verzeichnis der benutzten bücher": p.¡vii¡–viii.

1.Thackeray,William Makepeace,1811–1863.

NL 0446085   MiU ICRL CtY NcD MH

W 4
C691   **LÖTSCHERT, Josef,** 1907–
1937   Untersuchungen über die wachstumshem-
mende Wirkung verschiedener **Desinfek-**
tionsmittel auf Diphteriebakterien, in
Abhängigkeit von den drei Diphterie-
bakterien-Typen. Düsseldorf, 1937.
27 p.
Inaug.-Diss.—Cologne.
1. Corynebacterium diphtheriae
2. Disinfection & disinfectants

NL 0446086   DNLM

Lötschert, Wilhelm
La vegetación de El Salvador. 1955.
65–80 p., illus. (Comunicaciones, año 4,
no. 3/4, 1955, Instituto Tropical de
Investigaciones Científicas).

NL 0446087   MH-G

Loetterle, Gerald John, 1907–
The micropaleontology of the Niobrara formation in Kan-
sas, Nebraska, and South Dakota, by Gerald J. Loetterle ...
¡Lincoln, 1937¡
73, ¡4¡ p. illus. (map) xi pl., fold. tab. 25ᶜᵐ. (Nebraska. Geological
survey. Bulletin 12, second series, June, 1937)
Thesis (PH. D.)—Columbia university, 1937.
Vita.
Contributions from the Department of geology, Columbia university,
v. 53, no. 6.
Descriptive letterpress on versos facing the plates.
Bibliography : p. 69–73.
1. Foraminifera, Fossil. 2. Ostracoda, Fossil. 3. Paleontology—Cretaceous. 4. Paleontology—Kansas. 5. Paleontology—Nebraska. 6. Pa-
leontology—South Dakota.   7. Micropaleontology.   I. Title:
Niobrara formation.

Library of Congress   QE734.L8 1937   38–20208
¡a44d1¡   563.12

NL 0446088   DLC MoU CU OU

Loetterle, Gerald John, 1907–
... The micropaleontology of the Niobrara formation in
Kansas, Nebraska and South Dakota, by Gerald J. Loetterle.
¡Lincoln¡ Printed by authority of the state of Nebraska, 1937.
73 p., 2 l. xi pl., fold. tab. 25ᶜᵐ. (Nebraska. Geological survey.
Bulletin 12, 2d ser.)
Descriptive letterpress on versos facing the plates.
Bibliography : p. 69–73.

1. Paleontology — Cretaceous. 2. Foraminifera, Fossil. 3. Ostracoda,
Fossil.   I. Title.
U. S. Geol. survey. Library   (266) N2b ser. 2, no. 12   G S 37–231
————— Copy 2.
for Library of Congress   [QE135.A4 no. 12]
¡3¡

NL 0446089   DI-GS PPAN MtBuM

Lötz, F. J.   *Zur Klinik der Coeliakie (Heub-
ner-Herter'scher   intestinaler   Infantilismus)
[Münster] 29p. 8°. Berl. 1931.

NL 0446090   DNLM

Lötz, Helmut: Die Verwendung von festen und plastischen Wurzel-
füllungsmaterialien. [Maschinenschrift.] 29 S. 4°. — Auszug:
Greifswald 1923: Adler. 1 Bl. 8°
Greifswald, Med. Diss. v. 1. Aug. 1923   [U 23. 4600

NL 0446091   ICRL

LÖTZBEYER, EMMA, 1917–
Studien zur Chemie und Technologie der Trockengemüse. ... [n. p.,
1946] 85 f. illus. 30cm.
Diss. — Johann Wolfgang Goethe-univ.
Bibliography, f. [86–9]

573551B. 1. Drying apparatus—Food. 2. Canning and preserving.

NL 0446092   NN

Lötzbeyer, H.   *Ueber Perioralekzeme. 27p.
23½cm. Berl. 1938.

NL 0446093   DNLM CtY

Lötzbeyer, Philipp, 1881–
Arithmetik, Algebra und Analysis für die Oberstufe
höherer Lehranstalten. Neubearbeitung der 4. Aufl., der
Neubearbeitung 11. durchgesehene Aufl. Dresden, L. Ehlermann, 1937.
x, 161, 99 p. diagrs. (part col.) 23 cm. (Mathematik für höhere
Schulen. Oberstufe, 1)

1. Mathematics.   I. Rohrberg, Albert, 1887–   (Series:
Mathematik für höhere Schulen)

QA37.L8 1937   53–49421

NL 0446094   DLC

Erläuterungen und Beispiele für den Gebrauch der
vierstelligen Tafeln zum praktischen Rechnen.
Berlin, W. de Gruyter [1951] 32 p. (p. 29–32 blank) illus.
25cm.
Cover title.

1. Mathematics--Tables, 1951.   I. Lötzbeyer, Philipp, 1881–
Vierstellige Tafeln zum prak-   tischen Rechnen in Unterricht
und Beruf.

NL 0446095   NN CU

Lötzbeyer, Philipp, 1881–
Geometrie und geometrisches Zeichnen, Einführung in
die Trigonometrie, Aufbau und Aufgaben für die mittleren
Klassen höherer Lehranstalten von Ph. Lötzbeyer und W.
Schmiedeberg. 12. Aufl. Dresden, L. Ehlermann, 1936.
viii, 272 p. diagrs. 23 cm. (Mathematik für höhere Schulen,
Mittelstufe 2)

1. Geometry.   I. Schmiedeberg, Walther, 1880–   (Series)

QA453.L8 1936   54–55815

NL 0446096   DLC

Lötzbeyer, Philipp, 1881–
Geometrie und geometrisches Zeichnen für die Oberstufe
höherer Lehranstalten. 1. Aufbau, bearb. von Ph. Lötzbeyer. 2. Aufgaben, bearb. von Ph. Lötzbeyer und A. Rohrberg. Der Neubearbeitung 11. durchgesehene Aufl. Dresden, L. Ehlermann, 1937.
viii, 208, 111 p. illus., diagrs. (part col.) 23 cm. (Mathematik
für höhere Schulen, Oberstufe 2)
"Neubearbeitung der 4. Auflage des Lehrbuches der Mathematik
für die Oberstufe von Dronke-Lötzbeyer."

1. Geometry.   I. Rohrberg, Albert, 1887–   (Series)

QA453.L82 1937   54–55814

NL 0446097   DLC

Lötzbeyer, Philipp, 1881–
Physikfibel für die Flakartillerie. Berlin, M. Gehlen,
1938.
217 p. illus. 18 cm.

1. Physics.

QC23.L8 1938   530   53–53509 ‡

NL 0446098   DLC

Lötzbeyer, Philipp.
Physikfibel für die Flakartillerie. 3. Aufl. Berlin, W. de
Gruyter, 1944.
167 p. illus., diagrs. 21 cm. (Luftfahrt-Lehrbücherei, Bd. 12)

1. Physics.   (Series)

QC23.L8 1944   530   48–42892*

NL 0446099   DLC

Lötzbeyer, Philipp, *1881–*
Theorie und praxis der tafeln und des
tafelrechnens von ... dr. Ph. Lötzbeyer
... Dresden, L.Ehlermann,1934.
3p.l.,61p. diagrs. 23cm.
Literatur: p.60–61.

NL 0446100   PSt RPB

VOLUME 338

Loetzbeyer, Philipp, 1881–
Ueber die Galois'sche Gruppe des Apollonischen Problems in der Ebene und im Raum. Inaugural-Dissertation . . . Strassburg. = Strassburg i. Els. Gœller. 1903. 33, (1) pp. 8°.

G9536 — Groups. Mathematical term.

NL 0446101   MB CtY MiU NjP RPB MH

QA55   Lötzbeyer, Philipp, 1881–
I57   Vierstellige Tafeln zum Logarithmischen und Zahlenrechnen.   Leipzig, B.G. Teubner (19–?)
iv p.,28 p. of tables. 1 fold.table.

NL 0446102   CU

LÖTZBEYER, PHILIPP, 1881–
Vierstellige Tafeln zum praktischen Rechnen in Unterricht und Beruf, mit Angabe der Genauigkeit in Zahl und Bild. Graphische Rechentafeln. 16. Aufl. Ausg. A. Berlin, W. de Gruyter, 1951. 32 p. illus. 25cm.

Cover title.

1. Mathematics--Tables, 1951.

NL 0446103   NN

LB   Lötze, Curt Adolph, 1864–
14   Joachim Heinrich Campe als Pädagog;
C19L82   ein Beitrag zur Geschichte der Pädagogik im Zeitalter der Aufklärung.   Leipzig-Reudnitz, M. Hoffmann, 1890.
57 p. 23cm.

1. Campe, Joachim Heinrich, 1746-1818.

NL 0446104   NIC ICRL

Loetzen, Eduard Schmidt-
See
Schmidt-Loetzen, Eduard.

Loetzenburg, Arno Schreiber-
see
Schreiber-Loetzenburg, Arno.

Loetzer, C(hristian) E(rnest)
Loetzer's hand-book of practical rules and tables for machinists; complete on lathe screw cutting, turning and boring ... Rules, tables and information necessary for the daily use of practical machinists. By C. E. Loetzer ... (Sayre? Pa., 1892)
55 p. diagrs. 15½cm.
Earlier ed. pub. by Loetzer and G. W. Bynon under the title: Machinists' hand-book of practical rules and shop-kinks.

1. Machinery—Handbooks, manuals, etc.

Library of Congress   TJ1165.L83   6-35665†

NL 0446107   DLC

---

ar V   Loetzer, Christian Ernest.
21035   Hand-book of practical rules and tables for machinists. Rev.and enl. 4th ed. (Sayre, Pa.) 1897.
120 p. illus. 16cm.

Previous ed. published under title: Machinists' hand-book of practical rules and shop-kinks.

I. His Machinists' hand-book of practical rules and shop-   kinks.

NL 0446108   NIC

Loetzer, Christian Ernest.
Loetzer's Hand-book of practical rules and tables for machinists and engineers. Revised and enlarged. Especially written and prepared for mechanics not technically educated. Fifth edition. 120 p. il. T. Sayre, Pa.: C. E. Loetzer, 1900.

NL 0446109   ICJ

Loetzer, Christian Ernest.
Loetzer's hand-book of practical rules and tables for machinists and engineers, including Loetzer's treatise on the slide valve and locomotive valve-setting. 8th ed. 1913, rev. and enl. Philadelphia, Pa., Philadelphia book co. (*1913)
173 p. front. (port.) illus., tables, diagrs. 15½cm. $1.00

1. Machinery—Handbooks, manuals, etc.

Library of Congress   TJ1165.L83 1913   13–10305

NL 0446110   DLC ICJ

Loetzer, Christian Ernest, comp.
Honor roll, soldiers, sailors and nurses from Sayre, Penna., enrolled under the stars and stripes in the world war for liberty ... armistice signed and fighting stopped November 11, 1918; a mark of appreciation to our gallant lads and lassies by the burgess, Town council and citizens of Sayre borough; authorized by Sayre borough council, comp. by C. E. Loetzer. (Sayre, Murrelle printing company) 1919.
50 p. illus. 15cm.
Contains blank pages for "Record."
1. European war, 1914-   —Pennsylvania—Sayre. 2. European war. 1914-   —Registers, lists, etc.
19–17731
Library of Congress   D570.85.P41S3
———— Copy 2.   F159.S271.8

NL 0446111   DLC

Loetzer, C(hristian) E(rnest)
Machinists' hand-book of practical rules and shop-kinks. Containing ... tables, rules and information necessary for the daily use of practical mechanics ... by C. E. Loetzer and G. W. Bynon. (Sayre, Pa., Times printing house, 1891)
42, (2) p. diagrs. 14cm.
Later ed. pub. by Loetzer alone, under the title: Loetzer's handbook of practical rules and tables for machinists.

1. Machinery—Handbooks, manuals, etc. I. Bynon, G. W., joint author.

Library of Congress   TJ1165.L82   6-35664†

NL 0446112   DLC

Loetzer, Christian Ernest.
Loetzer's Treatise on the slide-valve and locomotive valve-setting. A short, comprehensive treatise, clearly and plainly describing the functions of the slide-valve in general and the method of locomotive valve-setting in particular; .... 47 p. il. T. Towanda, Pa.: C. E. Loetzer, 1902.

NL 0446113   ICJ

Lötzsch, Paul
Die bezirks einteilung des deutschen reiches in den verschiedenen verwaltungszweigen. ... Dresden, 1935.   84 p.
Inaug. Diss. - Leipzig, 1935.
Bibliography.

NL 0446114   ICRL

Loeuillard d'Avrigny, A   E   C
see Avrigny, A   E   C
Loeuillard d', b. 1790.

Lœuillard d'Avrigny, Charles Joseph, 1760?–1823
see
Avrigny, Charles Joseph Lœuillard d', 1760?–1823.

---

*FC7   [Loeuillart, Alexis Joseph Marie, fl.1766]
L9297   In mortem serenissimi delphini. Carmen
W766r   lyricum.
v.3   [Parisiis] Typis Barbou, Collegii Sorbonae-Plessaei typographi.[1766]
4p.   24cm.
Caption title; imprint on p.4.
Signed at end: Alexius-Josephus-Maria Loeuillart ...
No.26 in a volume labeled on spine: Receuil[!] sur la mort de monseigneur Louis dauphin. Tom III.

NL 0446117   MH

Rs10   Loeuille, Edmond
Pa950   Mesure de la température de combustion des poudres pendant le tir à la bombe manométrique. [Paris,1950]
Thèse - Paris.

NL 0446118   CtY

Lœuillet (Eugène) [1863–   ]. Des suites de l'ostéomyélite. 1 p. l., 85 pp. 4°. Nancy, 1887, No. 259.

NL 0446119   DNLM

Loeulliet, Bertrand
Specimen des caractères gravés par B. Loeulliet. Paris, Brun, Paul Daubrée (1820?)
cover-title, (56) l. 21cm.

1. Printing - Specimens. 2. Type and type-founding.

NL 0446120   NNC

FILM   Loeus, Robert.
Effigiatio veri Sabbathismi. Londini, Excudebat I.Norton, 1605.
Short-title catalogue no.16692 (carton 893)

1.Sabbath. I.Title.

NL 0446121   MiU

---

x475   L'Oeuvre, Jacques de.
L824a   Les analogies de la langue latine, où tous les mots de cette langue sont distribuez dans un ordre nouveau, & propre à faire comprendre aisément & en peu de temps leur prononciation, leur signification, & leur force; pour servir à la traduction des auteurs classiques, & à la composition. Dressées par l'ordre du roy, pour usage de monseigneur le Dauphin. Par M. de l'Oeuvre.   Paris, Veuve de C. Thiboust et P. Esclassan, 1698.
(56), 573p.   front. 17cm.

NL 0446122   IU

VOLUME 338

QL179
.R5f
L6
Loev, Bernard, 1928–
The active constituents of poison ivy and
related plants; structure and synthesis. New
York City, 1952.
[5] v, 101 [1] ℓ. diagrs. 29 cm.
Thesis (Ph.D.) – Columbia University.
Reproduced from typewritten copy.
Abstracted in Dissertation abstracts, v. 15
(1955) no. 3, p. 327-328.
Vita.
Bibliographical footnotes.
Copy 1: Edwin B.   Matzke library.

NL 0446123   NBBG DNAL NNC

Loev, Bernard, 1928–
The active constituents of poison ivy and related plants;
structure and synthesis. Ann Arbor, University Microfilms
[1955]
([University Microfilms, Ann Arbor, Mich.] Publication no. 10,811)
Microfilm copy of typescript. Positive.
Collation of the original: v, 101 l. diagrs., table.
Thesis—Columbia University.
Abstracted in Dissertation abstracts, v. 15 (1955) no. 3, p. 327-328.
Vita.
Bibliographical footnotes.
1. Poison-ivy. 2. Poison-sumac. 3. Skin—Diseases.   I. Title.
Microfilm AC–1 no. 10,811   Mic A 55-398

Columbia Univ.   Libraries
for Library of Congress   [1]†

NL 0446124   NNC DLC

Löv, Gustav.
Das synchronistische System der
Konigsbucher. [Leipzig, 1900]
p. 161-179.
Excerpt: Zeitschrift fur wissenschaftl.
theologie. v. 43.
Together with: Hilgenfeld, A. Noch einmal
die Essaer. [Leipzig, 1900]

NL 0446125   OCH

Loev, Julie.
Die israelitische Köchin; oder, Neues
vollständiges Kochbuch für Israeliten.
Ein unentbehrliches Handbuch für wirthliche
Frauen und Töchter. Nach vieljähriger
Erfahrung hrsg. von J. Löv. Pressburg:
P. Korn, 1842. 2.ed.
227 (1) p.

NL 0446126   OCH

Löv, Lipót
See
Loew, Leopold, 1811-1875.

Løvdokken, Ole, 1857-1919, ed.
Halling-minne, udg. for Hallinglaget i
Amerika ...
see under title

QK980
.L65
Löve, Áskell, 1916–
Biosystematic remarks on vicariism. Helsing-
foorsiae, 1955.
14 p. 24 cm. (Acta Societatis pro Fauna et
Flora Fennica 72, no.15)
XA   Cover title.
.C76   Bibliography: p.12-14.
v.72:15
1. Plants - Evolution. i.t. ii.t: Vicariism.
iii. s.

NL 0446129   NNBG

QH605
.L655
Löve, Áskell, 1916–
Chromosome numbers of northern plant species
[by] Áskell Löve and Doris Löve. Reykjavík,
Ingólfsprent, 1948.
131 p. 24 cm. (Atvinnudeild Háskólans.
Rit Landbúnaðardeildar, B-flokkur, nr.3)

Bibliography: p.[115]-127.

1. Chromosome numbers. 2. Botany - Scandinavia. i. Löve, Doris, 1918–   ii.s: Rit
Landbúnaðardeildar, B-flokkur, nr.3. iii.t.

NL 0446130   NNBG MH

Löve, Áskell
Cytogenetic studies on Rumex subgenus acetosella
... Lund,1943.
Thesis - Lund.
From Hereditas,XXX.
Title-page with thesis, note laid in.

NL 0446131   CtY OrU CU

QH605
.L6
Löve, Áskell.
The geobotanical significance of polyploidy.
1. Polyploidy and latitude, by Askell Löve and
Doris Löve. [Lisbon, 1949]
p. [273]-352. tables. 23½ cm.

Caption title.
"Separata de: Portugaliae acta biologica.
Series A - R. B. Goldschmidt volumen. -
(1949)"
Bibliography: p. 324-352.

1. Botany.   2. Chromosomes.
3. Phytogeogra-   phy. I. Title.
II. Title: Polyploidy.

NL 0446132   NjR

QK
325
.5
L82
Löve, Áskell.
Íslenzkar jurtir. Med myndum eftir
Dagny Tande Lid. Kaupmannahöfn, E.
Munksgaard [c1945]
291 p. illus. 21 cm.

1. Botany - Iceland. I. Lid, Dagny
Tande. II. Title.

NL 0446133   NIC NcD CoU DGW

Löve, Áskell
Some innovations and nomenclatural suggestions
in the Icelandic flora, 1950.

(In Botaniska notiser, 1950, part 1, p.24-60.
maps)

Bibliography: p.55-60.

NL 0446134   PPAN

B
581.9491
L 9431
LÖVE, ÁSKELL.
Studies on the origin of the Ice-
landic flora. I.Cyto-ecological investi-
gations on Cakile [By] Askell Löve and
Doris Löve. Med yfirliti á íslenzku.
Reykjavík, 1947.
20p. illus. 24cm. (Atvinnud-
eild Háskólans. Rit landbúnaðardeildar,
B-Flokkur, nr.2)

Bibliography: p.[25]-29.

NL 0446135   PU

Löve, Doris
Cytogenetic studies on Dioecious melandrium
... Lund,1944.
Thesis - Lund.
"Reprint from Botaniska notiser 1944".

NL 0446136   CtY

Bot.
lib.
QK1
.M8526
no.50
Löve, Doris.
A plant collection from interior Quebec, by
Doris Löve, James Kucyniak and Gordon John-
ston. [Montreal, Montreal Botanical Garden,
195–]
25-69p. maps. (Memoirs of the Montreal
Botanical Garden, no.50)

"Extrait du Naturaliste canadien, 85: 25-
69. Québec, 1958."

72-12kp
12
1. Botany -   Canada - Quebec (Province)
I. Kucyniak,   James. II. Johnston,
Gordon.

NL 0446137   NcU

Löve, F   Aa   Hansen-
see Hansen-Löve, F   Aa

Loeve, Fritz, 1895 (ca.)-
Wegener, Else, ed.
Alfred Wegeners letzte Grönlandfahrt; die erlebnisse der
Deutschen Grönlandexpedition 1930/1931 geschildert von
seinen reisegefährten und nach tagebüchern des forschers.
Unter mitwirkung von dr. Fritz Loewe hrsg. von Else Wege-
ner. Mit 3 rundbildern, 122 abbildungen in kunst und kup-
fertiefdruck. 11 karten, grundrissen und übersichten; vorwort
von professor dr. Kurt Wegener. 2. auflage. Leipzig. F. A.
Brockhaus, 1932.

Löve, Jón Karlsson
see Karlsson, Jón Löve, 1922-

Loève, Michel Moise, 1907-
Étude asymptotique des sommes de variables
aléatoires liées. Paris, Gauthier-Villars,
1946.

Thèse - Paris.

NL 0446141   MH

QA273
L56
Loève, Michel Moise, 1907-
Notes prepared by a student committee
from a course of lectures on stochastic
processes given at Columbia University,
Spring, 1948. [New York?, 1948?]
22,105 l. diagrs.

1. Probabilities. I. Title: Stochastic
processes.

NL 0446142   CU

QA273
.L6
Loève, Michel Moise, 1907-
On sets of probability laws and their limit elements.
Berkeley, University of California Press, 1950.
53-87 p. 25 cm. (University of California publications in statis-
tics, v. 1, no. 5)
Correction slip inserted.

1. Probabilities. (Series: California. University. University
of California publications in statistics, v. 1, no. 5)

A 50-9460

California. Univ. Libr.
for Library of Congress   [8]

NL 0446143   CU DAU MB ViU TxU DLC

VOLUME 338

QC175
L64
Loève, Michel Moise, 1907-
Probability methods in physics. I: Statistical equilibrium. Seminar by Michel Loève with an appendix by participants. Notes taken by Walter Aron and H.P. Noyes. Berkeley, Statistical Laboratory, Dept. of Mathematics, University of California, 1948-49.
223 *l.* diagrs.

Includes bibliographies.

NL 0446144   CU NcU

519
L823p
Loève, Michel Moise, 1907-
Probability reprints. [New York] Columbia Univ., 1948.
3v. in 1. 28cm.
Bibliographies at end of vols.1 and 2.
Contents.— [1] Fonctions aléatoires à décomposition orthogonale exponentielle.— [2] Sur les fonctions aléatoires stationnaires de second ordre.— [3] Colloque sur l'analyse harmonique; fonctions aléatoires: analyse harmonique au problème ergodique et aux fonctions modulaires.
1. Probabilities.

NL 0446145   IU

Loève, Michel Moise, 1907–
Probability theory: foundations, random sequences. New York, Van Nostrand, 1955.
515 p. 24 cm. (The University series in higher mathematics)

1. Probabilities.   I. Title.

QA273.L63   519   54—9392 ‡

NL 0446146   MB OCl OOxM PPT MiHM NcRS OU OO PBm OrAshS MtBuM MtU
PBL PPD PSC CaBVa CaBVaU WaS OrU OrPR OrCS PSt MH PV
DLC MtBC TxU KEmT ViU TU NN OClW ICJ NcD

*GB8
V6755R
4.26.48
Löve, Paul.
Mitternächtliches Gespräch des Kaiser Joseph mit Kaiser Ferdinand in der Hofburg am 25/26 April 1848. Von Paul Löve.
[Wien,1848]
folder([4]p.) 23x14.5cm.
Printer's imprint on p.[4]: Gedruckt bei Franz Edlem [!] von Schmid.

NL 0446147   MH

*pGB8
V6755R
9.28.48
[Löve, Paul]
Warnungsruf eines Patrioten über Katzenmusiken. [Wien]Gedruckt bei Franz Edlen v.Schmid.[1848]
[2]p. 40.5x25cm.
Caption title; imprint on p.[2]; dated & signed: Wien, am 28. Septbr. 1848. Paul Löve, Redakteur des Stürmers.

NL 0446148   MH

Loeve-Veimars, Adolphe

SEE

Loeve-Veimars, Francois Adolphe, baron, 1801-54.

Loeve-Veimars, Francois Adolphe, baron, 1801-1854.
For works written in collaboration with Auguste Romieu and Louis Émile Vanderburgh see Chamilly, Vicomtesse de, pseud.

PR1179
.F8L8
LOÈVE-VEIMARS, FRANÇOIS ADOLPHE, baron, 1801-1854,ed.
Ballades,légendes et chants populaires de l'Angleterre et de l'Ecosse,par Walter-Scott,Thomas Moore, Campbell et les anciens poètes;pub.et précédés d'une introduction,par A.Loève-Veimars. Paris,A.A.Renouard,1825.
xii,413 p. 21cm.
French prose translations.

NL 0446151   ICU FU NcD CtY OCl OO MH NNC CU

Bf8
74h
Loeve-Veimars, François Adolphe, baron, 1801-1854.
Chronologie universelle; par A.Loève-Veimars. Paris,Raymond,1825.
1p.*l.*,466p. 17½cm.

1. Chronology, Historical.

NL 0446152   CtY

Hfh
L053
Loeve-Veimars, François Adolphe, baron, 1801-1858.
De l'inévitabilité d'une guerre prochaine avec l'Angleterre, présentée comme conséquence de la guerre d'Espagne. Par A. Loève-Veimars. Paris, Plancher, 1823.
66 p. 20ᵐ.
Volume of pamphlets.
1. Gt. Brit. - Foreign relations - Spain.
2. Spain - Foreign relations - Gt. Brit.
3. Spain - History - Ferdinand VII, 1814-1833.

NL 0446153   NNC

LOÈVE-VEIMARS, FRANÇOIS ADOLPHE,baron, 1801-1845.
Histoire des littératures anciennes. Paris, Chez Raymond, éditeur, 1825. 284 p. 17cm.

1. Literature—Hist. and crit., Ancient.

NL 0446154   NN

Hfh
L053
Loeve-Veimars, François Adolphe, baron, 1801-1854.
Le Népenthès. Contes, nouvelles et critiques, par M.Loève-Veimars. Paris,Chez Ladvocat,1833.
2v. 23cm.
Prospectus: Les cent-et-une nouvelles ... Paris,Chez Ladvocat,1833, laid in t.1.
Contents. - t.1. La maréchale de Mailly. Lucrèce. Une soirée chez Madame de Sévigné. Le chat d'Hoffmann. Trop tard. Morceaux imités de Heine: Le Blocksberg et les montagnes du

Hartz. Le tambour Legrand. Les bains de Lucques. - t.2. Contes et notices: Aloysius Block. L'abbé Joie. Henri Estienne. Doña Concha. La nonne de San Iago. Paul Wouvermann. La mort d'un ange. Critiques et portraits: Racine. Corneille. Molière. Beaumarchais. Le régent. La censure. Casimir Delavigne. Victor Hugo. L'ancien et le nouvel opéra.

NL 0446156   CtY

Loeve-Veimars, Francois Adolphe, baron, 1801-1854, tr.
Goethe, Johann Wolfgang von, 1749-1832.
Poésies de Goethe, auteur de Werther; tr. pour la première fois de l'allemand par Mᵐᵉ E. Panckoucke. Paris, C. L. F. Panckoucke, 1825.

[Loève-Veimars, François Adolphe, baron] 1801-1854.
Popular ballads and songs, from tradition manuscripts and scarce editions... iv,92p. Paris, A. A. Renouard, 1825.
Bound with his Ballades, légendes et chants populaires de l'Angleterre et de l'Ecosse. Paris, 1825.

NL 0446158   OCl MH

Loève-Veimars, François Adolphe, *baron*, 1801-1854.
Précis de l'histoire de la littérature française, depuis son origine jusqu'à nos jours; par Loeve Weimar. 3. éd., complétée jusqu'à 1837. Bruxelles, Hauman et cᵉ, 1838.
2 p. l., iv, [5]-400 p. 15ᶜᵐ.

1. French literature—Hist. & crit.
20-7903
Library of Congress   PQ115.L7

NL 0446159   DLC NN

Loeve-Veimars, François Adolphe,baron,1801-1854.
Précis de l'histoire des tribunaux secrets, dans le nord de l'Allemagne. Contenant des recherches sur l'origine des cours wehmiques; sur leur durée,leur influence,l'étendue de leur juridiction et leurs procédures inquisitoriales. Par A.Loève-Veimars. Paris, J.Carez, 1824.
2 p.*l.*,x,306 p.,1 *l.* 14ᶜᵐ.

1.Fehmic courts.

NL 0446160   MiU IEN MH

Loève-Veimars, François Adolphe, *baron*, 1801-1854.
Résumé de l'histoire de la littérature allemande, par A. Loève-Veimars. Paris, L. Janet, 1826.
viii, 476 p. 14½ᵐ.

1. German literature—Hist. & crit.
11-24595
Library of Congress   PT101.L7

NL 0446161   DLC

830.9
L82rIp
Loève-Veimars, François Adolphe, baron, 1801-1854.
Storia della letteratura alemanna di A. Loève-Veimars. Traduzione italiana di Antonio Piazza. Brescia, 1829.
364p.

NL 0446162   IU

LOÈVE-VEIMARS, François Adolphe, baron, 1801-1854.
Tartuffe et le Malade imaginaire. [Paris, 1833.]
pp.(53).
Cut from his "Népenthès," 1833,11.193-255.

NL 0446163   MH

Loeve-Weimars, Adolphe, baron

SEE

Loeve-Veimars, Francois Adolphe, baron, 1801-54.

VOLUME 338

616.834 Lövegren, Elis Alexander, 1873-1937.
L897z   ... Zur kenntnis der poliomyelitis anterior acuta
und subacuta s. chronica. Klinische und pathologisch-anatomische studien ... Berlin, S. Karger,
1905.
   108p. illus., plates(1 col.)
   "Sonder-abdruck a.d. Jahrbuch für kinderheilkunde, bd.LXI."
   At head of title: Aus dem Pathologischen institute ... und der Universitäts-kinderklinik ... in
Helsingfors.
   "Benutzte literatur": p. 103 -108.
   1. Poliomyelitis.

NL 0446165   IU-M DNLM PPC

WC   LOEVEN, André
140   Un angoissant problème: les jeunes
L826a   devant le péril vénérien; étude médicale,
1930   morale et sociologique. Paris,
L'Association des industriels et commer-
çants pour la protection et l'éducation
professionnelle de la jeunesse française,
1930.
   95 p.
   1. Venereal diseases - Popular works

NL 0446166   DNLM

Loeven, Maria (Cunitz) von
    See
Cunitz, Maria, 1610-1664.

Löven, Wilhelm, 1910-
   ... Experimentelle physikalischen Unter-
suchungen der in der konservierenden Zahn-
heilkunde gebräuchlichsten Zahnzemente unter
besonderer Berücksichtigung des neuen Salvit-
Zementes ... Würzburg, 1934.
   Inaug.-Diss. - Würzburg.
   Lebenslauf.
   "Literaturverzeichnis": p. 12.

NL 0446168   CtY DNLM

Loeven, Wilhelmus Antonie, 1925-
   Het complex systeem collageen-mucopolysaccharide in
bindweefsel. With a summary in English. 's-Gravenhage,
Excelsior ,1953,
   125 p. diagrs., tables. 25 cm.
   Proefschrift—Leyden.
   "Stellingen": leaf inserted.
   Bibliography: p. 123-125.

   1. Connective tissues. 2. Collagen. 3. Polysaccharides.

QP551.L84   55–41365

NL 0446169   DLC PU-Sc DNLM

Loevenbein, Adalbert
   Ueber den einfluss m-staendiger hydroxyl-
gruppen in phaenolen bei benzopyronsynthesen
Inaug. diss. Berlin, Techn. Hoch., 1919
   Bibl.

NL 0446170   ICRL

Loevenberg, Edgar,1904-
   Zur frage der cerebralen komponente in der
pathogenese der tetanie.
Inaug. diss. Giessen, 1929.
   Bibl.

NL 0446170-1   ICRL MiU CtY

WBF   LOEVENBRUCK,
L826h   L'hydrothérapie, mise à la portée de
1890   tout le monde; système Kneipp. Paris,
1890.
   107 p.

NL 0446171   DNLM

Loevenburck, Léon, 1902-
   ... Douleurs tardives (syndrome pylorique)
sans hyperchlorhydrie ... Paris, 1927.
   23.5 cm.
   Thèse - Univ. de Paris.
   "Bibliographie": p. 51-56.

NL 0446172   CtY

Loevenbruck, Louis, 1888-
   ... Observations faites sur la trypanosomiase
humaine en Afrique ... Strasbourg, 1935.
   Thèse - Univ. de Strasbourg.
   "Bibliographie": p. [68]

NL 0446173   CtY

[Loevenbruck, Pierre,
   L'Amazone du Nicaragua...by Pierre Demousson
[pseud.] and Jacques Demetz... Paris, Éditions
Jules Tallandier, 1928.
   221 p.   YA6314

   (Bibliothèque des grandes aventures, no. 236.)

NL 0446174   DLC

Loevenbruck, Pierre.
   Les animaux du cirque. Paris, Toison d'or ,1954,
   220 p. illus. 23 cm.

   1. Animals, Training of. 2. Circus.   I. Title.

GV1829.L6   56–56345 ‡

NL 0446175   DLC MoU

Loevenbruck, Pierre.
   Les animaux sauvages dans l'histoire. Préf. de Marcel
Duvau. Paris, Payot, 1955.
   208 p. 23 cm. (Bibliothèque historique)

   1. Animals.   I. Title.

QL50.L58   55–32442 ‡

NL 0446176   DLC CaBVaU ViU NN

LOEVENBRUCK, PIERRE.
   Le blaireau; ses moeurs et sa chasse. Paris, Crépin-
Leblond [c1955] 78 p. illus. 19cm.

   Bibliography, p. [8]

   1. BADGER   2. BADGER HUNTING

NL 0446177   NN

Loevenbruck, Pierre.
   ... Bouches inutiles, quarante mois de captivité en Allemagne; préface de Georges Girard. Paris, J. Tallandier
,*1931,
   3 p. l., ,9,–219 p., 1 l. 19ᶜᵐ.

   1. European war, 1914–1918—Prisoners and prisons, German.
I. Title.

   Library of Congress   D627.G3L6   32–7523
   Copyright A—Foreign   14443
          ,2,   940.47243

NL 0446178   DLC

Loevenbruck, Pierre.
   ... Les cahiers du sergent Walter; lettre-préface du général
Gouraud. Paris, J. Tallandier ,1930,
   255 p. 18ᶜᵐ.
   At head of title: Pierre Loevenbruck et Pierre Hellin.
   On cover: Récits de l'Algérie française.

   1. Algeria—Hist.—1830- —Fiction.   I. Hellin, Pierre, joint
author. II. Title.
   Library of Congress   PQ2623.O3C3 1930   30–32416
   Copyright A—Foreign   7441
          ,2,   843.91

NL 0446179   DLC NN

[Loevenbruck, Pierre,
   Les captifs de la vierge rouge...by Pierre
Demousson [pseud.]... Paris, Éditions Jules
Tallandier, 1926.
   223 p.   YA6163

   (Bibliothèque des grandes aventures, no. 109.)

NL 0446180   DLC

Loevenbruck, Pierre.
   ... Ceux de la réserve, en campagne avec le 269ᵉ d'infanterie;
préface de Désiré Ferry ... Paris, J. Tallandier ,1931,
   3 p. l., ,iii,–vi, ,7,–222 p., 1 l. 19ᶜᵐ.
   "Le récit ... commence avant la mobilisation générale et s'étend jusqu'au 3 octobre 1914."—Préf.

   1. European war, 1914–1918—Personal narratives, French. 2. France—
Army—Infantry—269ᵗʰ regt. I. Title.
   Library of Congress   D640.L63   32–19921
   Copyright A—Foreign   11069
          ,2,   940.481

NL 0446181   DLC

Loevenbruck, Pierre.
   La croisière du "Floréal" ,par, Pierre Demousson ,pseud.,
Paris, Tallandier ,1953,
   127 p. 18 cm. (Le Livre d'aventures, 27)

   I. Title.

PQ2623.O3C7   54–29538 ‡

NL 0446182   DLC

[Loevenbruck, Pierre,
   Les fianos de Manille...by Pierre Demousson
[pseud.]... Paris, Éditions Jules Tallandier,
1927.
   224 p.   YA6176

   (Bibliothèque des grandes aventures, no. 182.)

NL 0446183   DLC

Loevenbruck, Pierre.
   Les garennes et leurs habitants. Photos. de Robert Jac-
quemin. Paris, La Colombe ,1954,
   123 p. illus. 19 cm.

   1. Rabbits. 2. Hares. I. Title.

SK341.R2L6   57–22836 ‡

NL 0446184   DLC NN

Loevenbruck, Pierre, ed.
   Journal de Nicolas Brisset

   see under

   Brisset, Nicolas.

VOLUME 338

[Loevenbruck, Pierre]
La perle de mascate...by Pierre Demousson
[pseud.]... Paris, Éditions Jules Tallandier,
1928.
223 p.   YA 6199

(Bibliothèque des grandes aventures, no. 224.)

NL 0446186   DLC

[Loevenbruck, Pierre]
Les pionniers de Fachoda...by Pierre Demousson
[pseud.]. Paris, Éditions Jules Tallandier,
1927.
223 p.   YA 6118

(Bibliothèque des grandes aventures, no. 146.)

NL 0446187   DLC

Loevenbruck, Pierre.
Pour les yeux d'une blonde... Paris, Éditions
du Livre National, 1928.
64 p.   YA 6034
(Collection hebdomadaire. Le livre de poche.
Nouvelle série, no. 61.)
By Pierre Demousson [pseud.]

NL 0446188   DLC

Loevenbruck, Pierre.
Quand l'amour commande... Paris, Éditions du
Livre National, 1928.
64 p.   YA 6066
(Collection hebdomadaire. Le livre de poche.
Nouvelle série, no. 33.)
By Pierre Demousson [pseud.]

NL 0446189   DLC

[Loevenbruck, Pierre]
Le roi des lacs...by Pierre Demousson [pseud.].
Paris, Éditions Jules Tallandier, 1926.
224 p.   YA 6124

(Bibliothèque des grandes aventures, no. 122.)

NL 0446190   DLC

Loevenbruck, Pierre.
Le secret du lac des Hémiones [par] Pierre Demousson
[pseud.] Paris, J. Tallandier [1954]
128 p. 19 cm. (Le Livre d'aventures, 37)

I. Title.

PQ2623.O3S4   54-39751 ‡

NL 0446191   DLC

[Loevenbruk, Pierre]
La steppe de la faim...by Pierre Demousson
[pseud.]... Paris, Éditions Jules Tallandier,
1928.
224 p.   YA 6142

(Bibliothèque des grandes aventures, no. 206.)

NL 0446192   DLC

Loevenbruck, Pierre.
Le Targui au litham vert; suivi de La felouque aux voiles
d'or [par] Pierre Demousson [pseud.] Paris, Larousse
[*1930]
253 p. 19 cm. (Contes et romans pour tous. [Série pour la
jeunesse (reliure rouge et or) no. 13])

I. Title. II. Title: La felouque aux voiles d'or.

PQ2623.O3T3   843.91   31-30341 rev*

NL 0446193   DLC

Løvendal, Carl Valdemar Danneskjold-
    see   Danneskjold-Løvendal, Carl Valdemar,
    1773-1829.

Løvendal, Emil Adolph, 1839?-1901.
... De danske barkbiller (*Scolytidæ* et *Platypodidæ*) og deres
betydning for skov- og havebruget ... Kjøbenhavn, J. L. Ly-
becker og E. A. Hirschsprung, 1898.
xii, 212 p. illus. v pl. 26cm.
"Citerede afhandlinger og værker": p. [v]-xii.

1. Insects—Denmark. [1. Denmark—Entomology] 2. [Platypodidae]
3. Scolytidae.

U. S. Dept. of agr. Library   427L94   Agr 24-14
for Library of Congress   [a41b1]

NL 0446195   DNAL MH-A MH OrCS

Løvendal, Emil Adolph, 1839?-1901.
Tomicini danici. De danske barkbiller. Af E.
A. Løvendal. [Kjøbenhavn, H. Hagerup, 1889]
84 p. pl. 21½cm. (On cover: Entomologiske med-
delelser, udgivne af Entomologisk forening ved Fr. Meinert.
2.bd., 1.-2.hfte.)
Caption title.
Issued in two parts.
"Vaerker": p.4.

1. Tomicini. 2. Insects—Denmark.

NL 0446196   MiU

Loevenguth, John Christian.
... General science syllabus, by J. C. Loevenguth ...
Yonkers-on-Hudson, N. Y., World book company, 1923.
viii, 63 p. 19½cm. (New-world science series, ed. by J. W. Ritchie)
"References": p. viii.

1. Science—Outlines, syllabi, etc. I. Title.

Library of Congress   Q181.L78   23-16667

NL 0446197   DLC Or ODW MiU OClBE ViU

Loevenhart, Arthur Solomon, 1878-1929.

Bancroft, Wilder Dwight, 1867-
... Medical aspects of gas warfare; prepared under the direc-
tion of Maj. Gen. M. W. Ireland, the surgeon general, by Col.
Wilder D. Bancroft ... Maj. H. C. Bradley ... [and others]
Washington, Govt. print. off., 1926.

Loevenhart, Arthur Solomon, 1878-
On the chemotherapy of neurosyphilis and trypanosomiasis,
by A. S. Loevenhart and W. K. Stratman-Thomas ... [Balti-
more, 1926]
cover-title, p. 69-82. 26cm.
W. K. Stratman-Thomas' thesis (PH. D.)—University of Wisconsin, 1926.
Thesis note stamped on cover.
"Reprinted from the Journal of pharmacology and experimental therapeutics, vol. XXIX, no. 1, October, 1926."
"References": p. 81-82.
1. Nervous system—Syphilis. 2. Trypanosomiasis. 3. Chemotherapy.
4. Tryparsamide. I. Stratman-Thomas, Warren Kidwell, joint author.

Library of Congress   RC201.L57 1926   27-15680
Univ. of Wisconsin Libr.   [2]

NL 0446199   WU ICJ DLC

R   Loevenhart, Arthur Solomon, 1878-1929.
860   A proposed therapeutic institute devoted
+L3   to finding better methods of treating the
sick. Madison [1918?]
17 L. 28 cm.

1. Medical research. I. Title.

NL 0446200   WU

Loevenhart, Arthur Solomon, 1878-   joint author
Young, Albert Gayland.
The relation of the chemical constitution of certain organic arsenical compounds to their action on the optic
tract, by A. G. Young and A. S. Loevenhart ... [Balti-
more, 1924]

Loevenhart, Arthur Solomon, 1878-1929, joint
author.
Schmitz, Henry Lenzen.
A study of two series of procaine derivatives with reference to the relationship between their pharmacological
action and chemical constitution, by H. L. Schmitz and
A. S. Loevenhart ... [Baltimore, 1924]

Loevenich, Ferdinand
Die anstellung und versorgung der kom-
munal-beamten in Preussen. Gesetz vom 30.
Juli 1899 nebst ausführungsbestimmungen
und erläuterungen, sowie den übrigen gesetzlichen bestimmungen über die rechtsverhältnisse der kommmalbeamten. Hrsg.
von F. Loevenich ... Hamm i.W., E.
Griebsch, 1899.
3 p.l., 147, [4] p. 22½cm.

NL 0446203   MH-L

Loevenich, Joseph Carl, 1861-   , editor.
Ernst Moritz Arndt: Gedenkblätter deutscher Dichter zum
50. Todestage: 29 Januar 1910. Gesammelt und herausgegeben von
Joseph Loevenich... Bonn: C. Georgi, 1910. 139 p. front.
(port.) 8°.

474718A. 1. Arndt, Ernst Moritz,   1769-1860. 2. Poetry, German—Col-
N. Y. P. L.   lections.   May 12, 1930

NL 0446204   NN InU

Loevenich, Maria, 1912-
... Die Bedeutung der von Edwards angegebenen
Schleifmaschine zur Erzielung funktionstüchtiger
Artikulation bei der Herstellung totaler Prothesen
... Düsseldorf, 1936.
Inaug.-Diss. - Köln.
Lebenslauf.
"Literatur-Verzeichnis": p. [23]

NL 0446205   CtY

LOEVENICH, Peter.
Über Corneoscleralcysten. Rostock 1911.
35 S.

Rostock, Med. Diss.

NL 0446206   MBCo MiU DNLM ICRL

Loevenoern, Poul de, 1751-1826

SEE

Løvenørn, Poul de, 1751-1826.

VOLUME 338

Løvenørn, Poul Vendelbo, 1686-1740.
　Løvenørn, en historisk fremstilling
　　see under　Giessing, Hans Peter, 1801-
1877.

Løvenskiold, Bartholomæus Herman, 1729-1788.
　Beskrivelse over Bradsbierg amt og Scheens bye med
sine forstæder ved Bartholomæus Herman von Løvenskiold ... Christiania, Paa bogtrykker Bergs forlag, 1784.
　14 p. L, ₍13₎-283, ₍1₎ p., 1 l. 5 fold. tab. 17½ᶜᵐ.

　1. Bratsberg, Norway—Descr. & trav. 2. Skien, Norway—Descr.

　　　　　　　　　　　　　　　　　　　13-2270

Library of Congress　　　　DL576.B8L7

NL 0446209　　DLC CtY

Løvenskiold, Carl Ludvig, 1822-1898.
　Den Løvenskioldske slægtebog. Samlet af Carl Ludvig
Løvenskiold ... Kjøbenhavn, B. Lunos bogtrykkeri, 1882.
　22 p. fold. geneal. tables. 26 x 21ᶜᵐ.
　Interleaved.
　"Trykt som manuscript."

　1. Løvenskiold family.

　　　　　　　　　　　　　　　　　　　16-350

Library of Congress　　　　CS919.L6

NL 0446210　　DLC

Lövenskiold, Herman.
　Einige Studien über die Oxydationsvorgänge ...
München, 1930.
　Inaug.-Diss. - Freiburg i.B.

NL 0446211　　CtY

Løvenskiold, Herman Leopoldus, 1897-
　... Fokstumyren. .Oslo, Gyldendal, 1932.
　120, ₍1₎ p. illus. 26ᶜᵐ.
　"Literaturfortegnelse": p. 120-₍121₎

　1. Birds—Norway. 2. Botany—Norway.　I. Title.
Library of Congress　　QL690.N8L6　　33-7079
Copyright A—Foreign　　19392
　　　　　　　　　　₍2₎　　　　　　598.29481

NL 0446212　　DLC

Løvenskiold, Herman Leopoldus, 1897-
　Håndbok over Norges fugler. Oslo, Gyldendal, 1947-50₁
　ix, 887 p. illus. 24 cm.
　Issued in 5 pts.
　Bibliography: p. ₍871₎-874.

　1. Birds—Norway.　I. Title.

QL690.N8L63　　　　　　　　53-38759

NL 0446213　　DLC CtY IEN

Løvenskiold, Herman Leopoldus, 1897-
　Studies on the avifauna of Spitsbergen. Oslo, I kommisjon hos Brøggers boktr. forlag, 1954.
　181 p. map. 26 cm. (Norsk polarinstitutt. Skrifter. nr. 103)
　At head of title: Det Kongelige Industri-, håndverk- og skipsfarts-
departement.

　1. Birds—Spitsbergen.　(Series: Oslo. Nordisk polarinstitutt.
Skrifter. nr. 103)
　[Q115.N896　nr. 103]　　　　　A 59-1857

Columbia Univ.　　　　　Libraries
for Library of Congress　　　　₍1₎

NL 0446214　　NNC MtU MnU CoU NN DI

M
2
D3518++
v.6
　Løvenskiold, Hermann Severin, 1815-1870.
　　₍Fra Skoven ved Furesø; arr.₎
　　Fra Skoven ved Furesø; idyllisk koncert-
ouverture, op.29. Klaver-udtog for 4 h. af
komponisten. Kjøbenhavn, Samfundet til
udgivelse af dansk musik, 1874.
　　13 p.　33cm. (Samfundet til udgivelse af
dansk musik. ₍Publikation₎ 6)

　　1. Overtures arranged for piano (4 hands)
I. Title.

NL 0446215　　NIC IEN NcU

Lövenskiold, Herman Severin, 1815-1870.
　[SYLPHIDEN. SELECTIONS. ARR. FOR PIANO]
　Ouverture et morceaux choisis de La sylphide,
ballet romantique en deux actes. Musique composée
et arrangée pour le piano. Par H.S. de Lövenskiold.
Copenhague, C.C. Lose et Olsen [ca. 1836] 54 p.

Microfilm (Negative).

1. Ballets (Piano)--Suites, etc.　　2. Piano--Arr.
I. Title: La sylphide.　　　　　II. Title: Sylphiden.

NL 0446216　　NN

Løvenskjold, Herman Severin, 1815-1870.·
　₍Impromptus charactéristiques₎
　　4 ₍i. e. Quatre₎ impromptus charactéristiques, en forme
des scherzos, pour le piano-forte à 4 mains, op. 8, par
Hermann de Lövenskiold. Vienne, chez A. Diabelli ₍1839₎
　　11 p.　32 cm.

　　1. Piano music (4 hands)　　I. Title: Impromptus charactéristiques.
M204.L　　　　　　　　　　72-230024

NL 0446217　　DLC

Løvenskiold, Herman Severin, 1815-1870.
　Sylphiden
　　For editions issued without music, see
under　Bournonville, Auguste, 1805-1879.

Lövenskjöld, Salomon, friherre

see

Löfvenskjöld, Salomon, friherre, 1764-
1850.

Loevenstein, Jan, 1886-1932.
　Capitalism at the cross-roads; a study of the causes of the
world economic crisis and a proposal for its remedy. By Dr.
Jan Loevenstein ... Translated by Vladimír Nosek. Prague,
Orbis publishing co. ₍1932₎
　1 p. l., xi, 151 p. front. (port.) 22ᶜᵐ.

　1. Economic conditions—1918-　2. Panics—1929. 3. Capitalism.
4. Economic policy.　I. Nosek, Vladimir, tr. II. Title. *Translation of Diagnosa a léčení světové krise.*

Library of Congress　　₃C57.L59　　33-9305
　　　　　　　　　　₍2₎　　　　　330.904

NL 0446220　　DLC NSyU DAU OU CtY ScU OCl NN DGW-C

Loevenstein, Jan, 1886-1932
　... Cedulové bankovnictví ve spojených
státech severo-amerických a jeho nejnovější
úprava. Napsal dr. Jan Loevenstein. Praze,
"Sborník věd právních a státních", 1915.
　357 p. tables. 24cm. (Knihovna
sborníku věd právních a státních. B, Řada
státovědecká, čís. 30)
　Bibliography: p. ₍342₎-354.

NL 0446221　　MH-L

Loevenstein, Jan, 1886-1932.
　Diagnosa a léčení světové krise; kapitalismus na rozcestí.
V Praze, Orbis, 1931.
　117 p.　20 cm.　(Časové otázky, sv. 13)

　1. Economic history—1918-1945. 2. Panics—1929. 3. Capitalism.
4. Economic policy.　I. Title.

HC57.L58　　　　　　　　57-56314 †

NL 0446222　　DLC

Loevenstein, Jan, 1886-1932.
　... Grundprobleme der volkswirtschaftlichen
noetik; drei studien über das teleologische
und wirtschaftliche denken. Prag, J. G. Calve,
1932.
　275 p.　23ᶜᵐ.

　1. Economics.

NL 0446223　　NNC

Loevenstein, Jan, 1886-1932
　... O jednotnou konstrukci finanční
vědy. (Poznámky ku Englišově kritice.)
Napsal dr. Jan Loevenstein ... Brno,
Barvič & Novotný, 1929.
　86 p.　24cm. (Sbírka spisů právnických
a národohospodářských, sv.40)

NL 0446224　　MH-L

HB
71
L64
1930
　Loevenstein, Jan, 1886-1932.
　　Sporné otázky teleologické konstrukce; moje
hospodářská konstrukce ve světle odmítavé
kritiky. Praha, A.Wiesner, 1930.
　　36 p.

　　1.Economics--Addresses,essays,lectures.
I.Engliš,Karel,1880-　　II.Title.

NL 0446225　　NSyU

Loevenstein, Jan, 1886-1932.
　... Die weltkrise, der unterverbrauch und der geldwert.
Zu den einwendungen gegen meine theorie der krise. Prag,
Kommissions-verlag der J. G. Calve'schen universitäts buch-
handlung, 1932.
　102 p. 22½ᶜᵐ.
　Two articles, written originally in Bohemian and published in Prague,
in answer to arguments occasioned by his Die weltwirtschaftskrise. cf.
"Vorwort", signed: M. Hejdušek, Th. Uhde.
　CONTENTS.—1. Die weltkrise und der unterbrauch.—2. Die weltwirt-
schaftskrise und der geldwert.
　1. Loevenstein, Jan, 1886-1932. Die weltwirtschaftskrise. 2. Panics,
1929. 3. Consumption (Economics) 4. Gold.　I. Hejdušek, M., ed.
II. Uhde, Theodor, joint ed.
　　　　　　　　　　　　　　　　　　　A C 33-2491

Title from N. Y. Pub.　　Libr. Printed by L. C.

NL 0446226　　NN

LOEVENSTEIN, JAN, 1886-1932.
　Die Weltwirtschaftskrise, ihre Diagnose und Therapie; der
Kapitalismus am Scheidewege, von Dr. Jan Loevenstein...
Brünn: R.M. Rohrer, 1931. iv, 6-83 p. 23cm.

640247A. 1. Crises and panics, 1929-1931.

NL 0446227　　NN IaU OU

Løventhal, Eduard.
　Efter 16 aar i Indien. Et ord til danske
menighed ... København, 1890.
　63 p. 21 cm.

NL 0446228　　CtY

VOLUME 338

MT20 Løventhal, Eduard
L8241   Indien før og nu. Odense, Milo'ske
boghandels forlag, 1895.
363 p. illus., 4 fold. plates. 24 cm.

Includes bibliography.

1. India. 2. India - Religion.   I. Title.

NL 0446229   CtY-D CtY

Løventhal, Eduard.
Til den danske menighed ad folke-
kirken. Mit missionssyn af Edv. Løventhal.
Andet Oplag. Kjøbenhavn, 1871.
72 p. 21 cm.

NL 0446230   CtY

LOEVENTON, L. *Die Behandlung der Kinder-
diarrhöe; nach den Beobachtungen im Zürcher
Kinderspital vom Jahr 1874-1884. 32p. 8°
Zür., 1886.

NL 0446231   DNLM

Løversen, Ragnvald.
Torskens vekst og vandringer på Sørlandet, belyst ved
merkingsforsøk, 1937-1943. Bergen, J. Grieg, 1946.
27 p. maps. 24 cm. (Fiskeridirektoratets skrifter. Serie
Havundersøkelser. Reports on Norwegian fishery and marine investigations, v. 8, no. 6)

1. Codfish. 2. Fishes—Migration.   (Series: Norway. Fiskeridirektoratet. Skrifter. Serie Havundersøkelser, v. 8, no. 6)

QL638.G2L6   49-22049*

NL 0446232   DLC

Løversen, Ragnvald.
Undersøkelser i *Oslofjorden*, 1936-1940. Fiskeyngelens
forekomst i strandregionen. Bergen, J. Grieg, 1946.
34 p. map, diagrs., tables. 24 cm. (Fiskeridirektoratets skrifter.
Serie Havundersøkelser. Reports on Norvegian ₍₁₎ fishery and marine
investigations, v. 8, no. 8)

"Undersøkelsene er utført fra Statens utklekningsanstalt ved fløde-
vigen."

1. Fisheries—Norway.   (Series: Norway. Fiskeridirektoratet.
Skrifter. Serie Havundersøkelser, v. 8, no. 8)

SH280.O7L6   49-4183*

NL 0446233   DLC

Lövestam, Evald
WG   Äktenskapet i Nya Testamentet. Marriage
9914   in the New Testament. Lund [1950]
235 p.

Akademisk avhandling - Lund.
Summary in English.

NL 0446234   CtY DLC-P4 NjPT

De Loevesteinsche gevangenschap
see under   Hasselt, Willem Jan Cornelis van,
1795-1864.

Loevetŝkiĭ, David Abramovich, ed.
Задачи и перспективы госкредита в СССР. Сборник статей
под редакцией Д. А. Лоевецкого. С участпем проф. Л. Н.
Юровского, проф. М. И. Боголепова, проф. Н. Д. Силина
... и др. Москва, Финансовое издательство НКФ СССР,
1927.

Løvgreen, John V., joint author.

Bahnsen, Knud Nyborg Spur, 1900-
9. april. kampene ved Bjergskov og Bredevad, beskrevet af
kaptajn K. Bahnsen og sergent J. V. Løvgreen. København,
Dansk-Nordisk forlag, M. Dall, 1904 ₍i. e. 1940₎

[Loevgren, Albert]
En bok till Rickard Sandler på 60-årsdagen den 29
januari 1944. [Redaktionskommitté: Alb.Lövgren,
Gösta Nygren, Erik Severin. Gävle, Distributör:
Skolforläget, 1944]

236 p. illus.
Imperfect; introd.text lacking? begins with p.9

NL 0446238   MH

Lövgren, Birger, 1885-
Ståndsstridens uppkomst. Ett bidrag till Sveriges
inre politiska historia under drottning Kristina ... Upsala, E. Berlings boktryckeri, 1915.
xii, 148 p. 22½ᶜᵐ.

Akademisk avhandling—Upsala.
"Förteckning över citerade arkivalier": p. ₍vii₎-viii.
"Förteckning över citerade tryckta böcker": p. ₍ix₎-xii.

1. Sweden—Pol. & govt.—1632-1654. 2. Political parties—Sweden.
I. Title.
₍Full name: John Birger Lövgren₎
20-14353

Library of Congress   DL719.2.L7

NL 0446239   DLC CtY

PT9555 Lövgren, Birger, 1885-   ed.
L6   Svensk renässanslitteratur, ett urval till
skolans och allmänhetens tjänst utgivet.
Stockholm, Bonnier ₍1928₎
273 p.

Prose and poetry.

1. Swedish literature - Early modern
(To 1700) I. Title.

NL 0446240   CU MH

Loevgren, Birger, 1885-
Sverges Nyare historia. Stockholm, Hugo Gebers
Forlag, 1926.
252 p.

NL 0446241   PPAmSwM

PT9650 Lövgren, Birger, 1885-   ed
L7.   Ur den svenska upplysningstidens
litteratur, ett urval till skolans och
allmänhetens tjänst. Stockholm, A. Bonnier
₍1929₎
656 p.

"Ur 1700-talets svenska litteratur." -
Förord.
Prose and poetry.

1. Swedish literature - 18th cent.
I. Title.

NL 0446242   CU

Lövgren, Birger, 1885-
Vår kommunala självstyrelse, av Birger Lövgren. Stockholm, A. Bonnier ₍1942₎
192, ₍4₎ p., 1 l. 19ᶜᵐ.

1. Municipal government—Sweden.   I. Title.
₍Full name: John Birger Lövgren₎
46-37164

Library of Congress   JS6258.L6

NL 0446243   DLC NNC

Løvgren, J   F
Filistrene er over deg. Oslo,
Norsk Luthersk Forlag, 1946.

NL 0446244   WaT

Løvgren, J   F
Tre verdener. Oslo, Norsk Luthersk
Forlag, 1946.

NL 0446245   WaT

Løvgren, J   F
Våre lamper slokner. Oslo, Norsk
Luthersk Forlag, 1945.

NL 0446246   WaT

Lövgren, Nils, 1852-
A church history for the use of schools and colleges. With
a series of biographies by August Edman. Tr. by M. Wahlström and C. W. Foss. Rock Island, Ill., Augustana Book
Concern ₍1906₎
viii, 358 p. illus. 20 cm.

1. Church history.   I. Edman, August, 1848-

BR145.L815   6-37865*

NL 0446247   DLC MnHi PPAmSwM

DL706 Lövgren, Nils, 1852-
.L8   Gustaf II Adolf, hans person och betydelse. Några minnesord vid jubelfesten för menige man, af Nils Lövgren ...
2. upplagan. Stockholm, Fosterlands-Stiftelsens förlags-expe-
dition ₍1894₎
₍4₎, 100 p. 19ᶜᵐ.

1. Gustaf II, Adolf, king of Sweden, 1594-1632.

NL 0446248   ICU MiD

911   LOEVGREN, Nils, 1852-
L826ky   Kyrkohistoria till skolornas tjaenst
1894   af Nils Loevgren. Med en serie biografier
af Aug. Edman. Tredje uppl. Stockholm,
Norman, 1894.
viii,314p. illus. 19cm.

NL 0446249   MH-AH

11   Lövgren,   Nils, 1852-
940   Om hela tals delbarhet med hela tal.
Några satser ur den aritmetiska analy-
sen. Stockholm [1915]
30p.

NL 0446250   IU

VOLUME 338

Lövgren, Olle.
... Studien über den intermediären stoffwechsel bei chronischer polyarthritis, von Olle Lövgren. Uppsala, Almqvist & Wiksells, boktryckeri ab, 1945.
150 p. incl. tables, diagrs. 24cm. (*On cover:* Acta medica scandinavica. Supplementum CLXIII)
At head of title: Aus Stockholms Läns centrallasarett, Medizinische abteilung, Stocksund, Schweden.
Translated into German by Dr. med. H. Popper. *cf.* Vorwort.
"Literaturverzeichnis": p. [144]-148.
1. Arthritis deformans. 2. Metabolism. I. Popper, H., tr.
A 47-1475
John Crerar library for library of Congress [4]

NL 0446251 ICJ ViU DNLM PU

BV2470 .S8S75 1954
Lövgren, Oscar, ed.
Svenska missionsförbundet.
Biografiskt album för Svenska missionsförbundet. [Redigeringsarbetet har ... utförts av Oscar Lövgren] 5. uppl. Stockholm, Missionsförbundets förlag [1954]

BV2540 .S8
Lövgren, Oscar, ed.
Svenska missionsförbundet.
Genom Guds nåd; Svenska missionsförbundet under 75 år. [Redaktörer: William Bredberg, Oscar Lövgren] Stockholm, Missionsförbundets förlag [1953]

4PT Swed 440
Lövgren, Oscar
Pennfäktare och predikare; en bok om Carl Boberg. Stockholm, Missionsförbundet förlag [19]
183 p.

NL 0446254 DLC-P4

Lövgren, Oscar.
Så fick vi sånger; en bok om sånger, sångdiktare och kompositörer, av Oscar Lövgren. Stockholm, Missionsförbundets förlag [1949]
269, [1] p. illus. 20 cm.
"Litteratur- och källförteckning": p. 264-266.

NL 0446255 NNUT

VK31 L826 S
Lövgren, Oscar
En sångbok kommer till; några ord om bakgrunden till Sånger och Psalmer och om hur denna sångbok utarbetats. Stockholm, Missionsförbundets förlag [1951]
83p. 20cm.

NL 0446256 NNUT

Lövgren, Oscar.
Stor-Olle; en originell förkunnare. Stockholm, Missionsförbundets förlag [1954]
45 p. illus. 20 cm.
1. Olsson, Nils Olof, 1854-1928. I. Title.
BV3785.O63L6 56-23015 ‡

NL 0446257 DLC CtY-D

Lövgren, Oscar.
Våra psalm- och sångdiktare; en historisk framställning. Stockholm, Svenska Missionsförbundets Förlag [1935-1939]
3 v. illus., ports., facsims. 21 cm.
1. Hymn writers. 2. Hymns, Swedish - History and criticism. I. Title.

NL 0446258 ICLT

ND 623 .R76 L8
LÖVGREN, SVEN, 1921-
Il Rosso Fiorentino a Fontainebleau; une étude préliminaire iconographicue du programme imagier dans la galerie François Ier.
[Uppsala, Almqvist & Wiksell, 1951]
76 p. illus.
Reprinted from Figura.
1. Rosso, Giovanni Battista, 1494-1541. I. Title.

NL 0446259 InU NNC

Loévi, Georges, 1860-
La vinification en Oranie, par Georges Loevi. Montpellier, C. Coulet; Paris, Masson & c^ie^, 1900.
[4], 302 p. 55 illus. 25½cm.

NL 0446260 ICJ

MT260 .L77
Løvig, Harald.
Målet er musikk; midlet er teknikk. [Tvedestrand, Eget forlag [1952]
40 p. port. 20 cm.
1. Violin—Instruction and study. I. Title.
A 53-5389
Oregon. Univ. Libr. for Library of Congress [3]

NL 0446261 OrU DLC

Lövinger, Adolf
see Löwinger, Adolf, 1864-1926.

Loevinger, Jane.
A systematic approach to the construction and evaluation of tests of ability. Washington, American Psychological Assn., 1947.
iii, 49 p. 26 cm. (Psychological monographs, v. 61, no. 4; whole no. 285)
"Essentially the same as a dissertation submitted ... for the degree of doctor of philosophy in the ... University of California, June, 1944."
"References": p. 49.
1. Ability—Testing. I. Title. II. Series.
BF1.P8 vol. 61, no. 4 151.2 47-12284*

NL 0446263 DLC NcU NIC MiU PU TxU IU ViU

Loevinger, Lee, 1913-
Una introducción a la lógica jurídica. Traducción y prólogo por José Puig Brutau. Barcelona, Bosch [1954]
141 p. 18 cm.
Translation of an article published in the Indian law journal, v. 27, no. 4, 1922.
1. Law—Interpretation and construction. I. Title.
62-33213 ‡

NL 0446264 DLC MiU-L MH-L

Loevinger, Lee, 1913-
The law of free enterprise; how to recognize and maintain the American economic system. New York, Funk & Wagnalls Co., in assn. with Modern Industry Magazine [1949]
xi, 431 p. 24 cm. (Modern industry books)
1. Industrial laws and legislation—U. S. 2. Commercial law—U. S. I. Title.
49-7064*

PU-L TxU ICU MB OU NNUN CaBVa OrCS OrU WaS
NL 0446265 DLC OClU CU KMK CoU LU OOxM PPT PP PSt

HB161 S56L64
Lővinger, Miklós
Adam Smith és List Frigyes hatása az erdélyi közgazdasági eszmékre, 1825-1867. Kolozsvár, Társadalomtudományi Intézet, 1947.
88 p.
At head of title: Kolozsvári Bolyai Tudományegyetem.
Reprinted from Társadalomtudomány és politika, 1947; II year, v.1 (III)
Includes bibliographies.
1. Smith, Adam, 1723-1790. 2. List, Friedrich, 1789-1846. 3. Transylvania - Econ. condit. I. Cluj, Transylvania. Universitatea "Bolyai." I. Title.

NL 0446266 CU

Loevinger, Robert, 1916-
Energy transfer from 100 Mev neutrons to ligh nuclei. [Berkeley, Calif., 1948]
v, 93 numb.l. diagrs., tables. 29cm.
Thesis (Ph.D.) - Univ. of California, Feb. 1948.
"References": p.82-83.
1. Neutrons. I. Title.

NL 0446267 CU

Loevinsohn, Emil, 1858-
Ueber den einfluss der verteilung und der masse eine: koerpers...
Inaug. Diss. Berlin, 1883.

NL 0446268 ICRL

Loevinsohn, Hans, 1905-
Der einfluss ultravioletter strahlen auf den erythrozytenspiegel von rana fusca.
Inaug. diss. Berlin, 1930.

NL 0446269 ICRL CtY

Loevinsohn, Hugo, 1879-
Darmverschluss und darmverengerung infolge von perityphlitis.
Inaug. diss. Breslau, 1905 (Jena)

NL 0446270 ICRL CtY

Lövinsohn (Max). *Zur Statistik und operativen Behandlung der Rectumcarcinome. [Heidelberg.] 23 pp. 8°. *Tübingen, H. Laupp,* 1892.

NL 0446271 DNLM

LÖVINSOHN, Walter.
Ueber den medianen und hohen steinschnitt. Königsberg i.Pr., 1894.

NL 0446272 MBCo DNLM

VOLUME 338

Lövinsohn (Werner) [1892-   ]. *Ueber sehr grosse Ovarialtumoren. 22 pp. 8°. Berlin, E. Ebering. 1917.

NL 0446273   DNLM ICRL CtY

Loevinson, Emil, 1860–
Bemerkungen über habituelle Scoliose. 23 pp. 8°. Berlin, F. Schneider & Co., 1893.
Forms 1. Hft. of: Mitth. a. d. Berl. med.-mechan. Inst.

NL 0446274   DNLM

Lövinson (Emil) [1860-   ]. *Ueber die Ehrlich'sche Diazo-Reaction, insbesondere bei der Lungenphthise. 39 pp., 1 l. 12°. Berlin, G. Schade, 1883.

NL 0446275   DNLM

Loevinson, Ermanno
see Loevinson, Hermann, 1863–

Loevinson, Hermann 1863–
Beitraege zur verfassungsgeschichte... Inaug. Diss. Berlin, 1888 (Paderborn)

NL 0446277   ICRL

Loevinson, Hermann, 1863–
Beiträge zur verfassungsgeschichte der westfälischen reichs-stiftsstädte. Paderborn, etc., F. Schöningh, 1889.
pp. 132.

Westphalia.

NL 0446278   MH

Loevinson, Hermann, 1863–
Cristoforo Colombo nella letteratura tedesca. Roma, etc., E. Loescher & co. 1893.
pp. 130 +.

NL 0446279   MH MiU-C NjP

LOEVINSON, Hermann, 1863–
Gli Ebrei di Parma, Piacenza e Guastalla. Reprinted from "La Rassegna Mensile di Israel", vol. 7, 1932, p. 1-10.
1. History-Italy-Parma. 2. History-Italy-Piacenza. 4. History-Italy-Guastalla.

NL 0446280   NNJ

Loevinson, Hermann, 1863–
... Giuseppe Garibaldi e la sua legione nello Stato romano 1848–49 ... Roma, Società editrice Dante Alighieri, 1902–07.
3 v. fold. map, facsim. 19ᶜᵐ. (Biblioteca storica del risorgimento italiano ... pte. 1, ser. III, n. 4-5; pte. 2, ser. IV, n. 6; pte. 3, ser. V, n. 2)
Vol. 2-3 have imprint: Roma, Società editrice Dante Alighieri di Albrighi, Segati & c.

1. Garibaldi, Giuseppe, 1807-1882. 2. Italy—Hist.—1815-1870.

Library of Congress   DG552.A2B6   10-9765

NL 0446281   DLC MH OCl ViU

[LOEVINSON, Hermann, 1863-   , editor.]
Per le nozze di Don Giuseppe dei duchi Caffarelli con Donna Maria dei principi di Lucedio. Roma, [tip. Cuggiani], 1917.

pp. (24)
Caption title: Dolci e rinfreschi del monastero delle Benedettine a Campo Marzio.
Dedication signed: Ermanno Loevinson.

NL 0446282   MH

Loevinson, Hermann, 1863–
Roma israelitica; wanderungen eines Juden durch die kunststätten Roms, von Ermanno Loevinson. Frankfurt a. M., J. Kauffmann, 1927.
4 p. l., 307 p. 16 pl. 18½ᶜᵐ.

1. Rome (City)—Descr. 2. Jews in Rome. 3. Art—Rome.   I. Title.
Library of Congress   DG806.L6   28-31026

NL 0446283   DLC CtY NcD CU OCH PPDrop NN

Loevinson, Hermann, 1863–   ed.
Rome (City)   Archivio di stato.
... Gli ufficiali del periodo napoleonico (1796–1815) nati nello Stato pontificio; elenco compilato su documenti a cura dell'Archivio di stato di Roma. Milano–Roma–Napoli, Società editrice Dante Alighieri di Albrighi, Segati & c., 1914.

LÖVINSON, Käthe, 1901–
Frauenarbeit in bankbetrieben. Inaug.-diss. Wurzburg. Berlin, druck von Thormann & Goetsch, [1925].

pp. 61+.
"Literatur-verzeichnis", pp. [59]-61.
"Lebenslauf", at end.

NL 0446285   MH CtY ICRL

Loevius, Fred,
see
Thaumazo, Frederick, 1870–

Løvland, Helge Andreas, 1890–
Idrettsbok for norske gutter, av Helge Løvland ... og Carl Schiøtz ... Oslo, H. Aschehoug & co. (W. Nygaard) 1925.
3 p. l., 339, [3] p. incl. illus., tables, diagrs. 22½ᶜᵐ.

1. Sports. 2. Physical education and training.   I. Schiøtz, Carl, 1877-   II. Title.
Library of Congress   GV705.L6   26-1080

NL 0446287   DLC

Løvland, Jørgen Gunnarson, 1848–
Menn og minner fra 1905, av statsminister J. Løvlands papirer; utgitt av Torkell J. Løvland.   Oslo: Gyldendal norsk forlag, 1929.   297 p.   front., plates, ports.   8°.
Plates printed on both sides.

478774A. 1. Norway—Hist., 1905. 1890–   . N. Y. P. L.   I. Løvland, Torkell Jørgensson, editor.   May 28, 1930

NL 0446288   NN WaS MnU

Løvland, Lalli, 1906–
... Men en dag går veien videre! Oslo, Gyldendal, 1937.
243 p. 20ᶜᵐ.

I. Title.
Library of Congress   PT8950.L725M4 1937   40-19008
Copyright A—Foreign   38069

NL 0446289   DLC

Løvland, Lalli, 1906–
... Og så fortsetter livet—. Oslo, H. Aschehoug & co., 1933.
190 p. 20ᶜᵐ.
A novel.

I. Title.
Library of Congress   PT8950.L72S05 1933   34-1816
Copyright A—Foreign   22886
[2]   839.8236

NL 0446290   DLC

Løvland, Lalli, 1906–
... Slekten Bonde; roman. Oslo, Gyldendal, 1936.
288 p. 20ᶜᵐ.

I. Title.
Library of Congress   PT8950.L72S86 1936   37-17221
Copyright A—Foreign   34371
        839.8236

NL 0446291   DLC

LØVLIEN, EMIL.
Foredrag på Norges kommunistiske partis 8. landsmøte, 20 mars 1953.   Oslo, Norsk forlag Nydag, 1953.   39 p. (p. 39 advertisement) 19cm.

1. Bolshevism--Norway.

NL 0446292   NN

LØVLIEN, EMIL.
Kommunistene og gjenreisningen.   [Oslo, Norges kommunistiske parti, 1945?]   19 p.   21cm.

1. Bolshevism--Norway. 2. World war, 1939-1945--Post-war problems--Norway. I. Norges kommunistiske parti.

NL 0446293   NN

Løvset, Jørgen, 1896–
Helselære for gravide og mødre.   [2. oppl. Bergen] J. W. Eide [1951, ʼ1950]
111 p.   illus. 20 cm.

1. Pregnancy.   I. Title.
        RG525.L57 1951   51-35913 ‡

NL 0446294   DLC

WQ
150   LØVSET, Jørgen, 1896–
L826h   Helselære for gravide og mødre.
1954   3. utg.   [Bergen] Eide [1954]
        124 p.   illus.
        1. Pregnancy - Hygiene 2. Pregnancy - Popular works

NL 0446295   DNLM

VOLUME 338

Løvset, Jørgen, 1896–
Hvorfor kan kunstig inseminasjon utføres på mennesker. Svar på innvendinger fremsatt av Aksel Sandemose. ₁Bergen₁, J. W. Eide ₁1952₁
29 p. illus. 21 cm.

1. Artificial insemination, Human.   I. Title.

RG134.L59   62–40843 ‡

NL 0446296   DLC

WQ
330
L826k
1935

LØVSET, Jørgen, *1896–*
En klinisk undersøgelse av de habituelle efterbyrdsblødningers etiologi.   Bergen, Eide, 1935.
91 p. illus.
Supplement to Medicinsk revue, nr. 11, 1935.
Summary in English.
1. Hemorrhage, Postpartum   Title: Medicinsk revue.   Supplement

NL 0446297   DNLM MnU

Løvset, Jørgen, 1896–
Problemer omkring kunstig inseminasjon hos mennesket.
Bergen, J. W. Eide ₁1952₁
15 p. 22 cm.

1. Impregnation, Artificial.   I. Title.

RG134.L6   52–41490 ‡

NL 0446298   DLC DNLM

Løvset, Jørgen, 1896–
Somatische konstitutionszüge und ihre beziehungen zur geburt des kindes, von Jørgen Løvset ... Mit 6 textfiguren ... Oslo, I kommisjon hos J. Dybwad, 1940.
4 p. l., 218 p. incl. tables, diagrs. 27ᶜᵐ.
Oslo. Skrifter. I. Mat.-naturv. klasse, 1939, no. 11)
"Trykt for Fridtjof Nansens fond."
"Literaturverzeichnis": p. 206–218.

1. Man—Constitution. 2. Labor (Obstetrics)

AS283.O56 1939,   A 47–3436
no. 11
John Crerar library
for Library of Congress   ₂₁†

NL 0446299   ICJ DNLM DLC

LÖVSTAD, BERGLJOT.
...Bernadotte; skuespil i 5 akter.   Oslo: Steenske boktrykkeri, J. Björnstad a/s, 1933.   78 p. 22½cm.

757653A. 1. Drama, Norwegian. 2. Charles XIV, John, king of Sweden and Norway, 1763–1844—Drama. I.₁ Title,

NL 0446300   NN

₁Løvstad, Theodor Julius₁ 1843–1912.
Glastrompeten. Lidt af hvert til trøst og lusvalelse for markedsgjæster af begge kjøn, udg. af selskabet til udyrenes beskyttelse. Kristiania, Thronsen & co.s bogtrykkeri, 1879.
16 p. 19ᶜᵐ.
In verse.
CONTENTS.—Vejviser for markedsbesøgende.—"Raværgutta" paa Storthinget.—Glastrompeter Hansen.—Repræsentantvise.—Nogle trøstende ord til vore brave Kampegutter.—Hvad man daglig ser paa Youngstorvet.
I. Title.

20–412

Library of Congress   PT8915.L5G6

NL 0446301   DLC

QL
971
L94

Løvtrup, Søren.
Studies on amphibian embryogenesis. Energy sources of amphibian embryogenesis. Utilization of reserve material during amphibian embryogenesis at different temperatures. Changes in the content of peptidases during amphibian embryogenesis at different temperatures. The influence of temperature on amphibian embryogenesis. Copenhagen, 1953.
371–466 p. illus. 23 cm.

"Reprinted from Comp.-rend. Lab, Carlsberg, sér. chim. v. 28, no. 14–17."
Diss.--Copenhagen.

1. Embryology - Amphibians. I. Title.
₁II. Series: Carlsberg laboratoriet, Copenhagen. Comptes-rendus des travaux, v. 28, no. 14–17₁

NL 0446303   NIC IEN

Løvvik, Hilmar.
Rose Dalen; en fortaelling fra Norge. Eau Claire, Wis. ₁192–?₁
45 p. 19cm.

NL 0446304   MnU

Loevy, Arnold, appr. Arzt a. Graudenz: Aus d. II. chir. Abt. d. städt. Rudolf-Virchow-Krankenh. zu Berlin. (Dir. Borchardt). Die Brieger'sche Reaktion und ihr Ausfall bei Carcinomen des Verdauungskanals. Berlin [1913]: Rother. 33 S. 8°
Leipzig, Med. Diss. v. 12. März 1913, Ref. v. Strümpell
[Geb. 2. Dez. 85 Göttingen; Wohnort: Berlin; Staatsangeh.: Preußen; Vorbildung: G. Graudenz Reife 05; Studium: Berlin 10 S.; Coll. 12. März 13; Approb. 5. März 12.]   [U 13. 2349

NL 0446305   ICRL DNLM CtY

Loevy (Eduard). *Ein Beitrag zur Casuistik der Endocarditis ulcerativa. 38 pp., 1 l. 8°. *Dorpat, Schnakenburg, 1876.

NL 0446306   DNLM

Loevy, Erich, Dipl-Ing.: Die Grundlagen zum Schaffen Carl Friedrich Schinkels. Berlin: Der Zirkel 1915. 95 S. 4° (8°)
Dresden TeH., Diss. v. 1915 (26. Aug. 1914), Ref. Gurlitt, Högg
[Geb. 23. Aug. 88 Berlin; Wohnort: Marienburg Wpr.; Staatsangeh.: Preußen; Vorbildung: OR. Marburg Reife 07; Studium: Berlin 4, München 2, Darmstadt 4, Dresden 1 S.; Dipl.: Arch. Darmstadt 19. Dez. 12; Dr.-Prüf. 26. Aug. 14.]   [U 15. 2538

NL 0446307   ICRL NjP

Loevy, Fritz: Die Schadenersatzhaftung für Verschulden beim Abschluss von wirksamen Verträgen, mit bes. Berücks. des Abschlusses durch Dritte. [Maschinenschrift] 74 S. 4°. — Auszug: o. O. (1921). 4 S. 8°
Göttingen, R.- u. staatswiss. Diss. v. 22. April 1921 [1922] [U u. uu

NL 0446308   ICRL

Lövy, H.
Ueber polarität.
Prag, 1831.
8vo.

NL 0446309   NN

WG
23950

Loevy, Hermann, 1872–
Über magnesiumorganische Verbindungen. I. Einwirkung auf Senföle und Isonitrile. II. Verhalten gegen Phosgen. [Berlin] 1904.
60 p.

Inaug.-Diss. - Berlin.

NL 0446310   CtY DLL NN

Loevy, Jacob, 1860–
Libri Kohelet versio arabica quam composuit Ibn-Ghijath... Lugduni-Batavorum, Brill, 1884.
42p.
Inaug. diss.

AC951
.H3
v.44

[Haverford-Bauer pamphlets, v. 44, no. 13]

NL 0446311   ICRL

Loevy (Pincus). *Ueber die Gasansammlung in der Gebärmutter während der Geburt. 35 pp., 2 l. sm. 8°. *Berlin, G. Schade, [1890].

NL 0446312   DNLM

Loevy (Sally). *Beiträge zur Casnistik der Langen-Echinococcen. 25 pp. 8°. *Greifswald, J. Abel, 1885.

NL 0446313   DNLM ICRL MiU

Loevy (Sigismund) [1874–   ]. *Ueber einen Fall von Pylorusstenose nach Oxalsäurevergiftung, nebst Bemerkungen zur Milchsäuregährung im menschlichen Magen. 31 pp. 8°. *Berlin, G. Schade, [1896].

NL 0446314   DNLM

Löw ben Bezaleel
see
Judah Löw ben Bezaleel, *d.* 1609.

Löw von Rožmital und Blatna
see
Lev z Rožmitálu a z Blatné, 1425 (*ca.*)–1485.

Löw, Adolf, 1906–
Die Frankfurter Bundeszentralbehörde von 1833–1842 ... Gelnhausen, 1932.
Inaug.-Diss. - Frankfurt.
Lebenslauf.
Bibliography: p. vii-xx.
Full name: Theodor Adolf Löw.

NL 0446317   CtY

Loew (Adolf Karl Joh.) [1867–   ]. *Beitrag zur Casnistik der Neuritis. 29 pp., 1 l. 8°. *Berlin, O. Francke, [1890].

NL 0446318   DNLM MH

Loew, Adolphus.
Causes of the great natural catastrophes in the U. S. A. Message to his Excellency the President of the United States for the representatives of astronomic science, submitted by Adolphus Loew ... Modern theories, explanations, and computations of the glacial period, of the orbit of the earth, of the orbit of the moon. ₁Reinbach-Basel, 1938₁
₁23₁ p. plates. 29½ᶜᵐ.
Various pagings.
Mimeographed.

1. Catastrophes (Geology) 2. Glacial epoch.   I. Title.

Smithsonian inst. Library   S 38–75
for Library of Congress   ₃₁

NL 0446319   DSI DAS

VOLUME 338

QH
325
L827d
1931

LOEW, Adolphus
The descent question in the light of racial problem [sic] and their solution. The cancer problem in the light of popular healthiness and its solution. [Reinach, Switzerland, 1931]
20 p.
Contents. -pt. 1. Spontaneous generation or creation. - pt. 2. The question of descent.- pt. 3. The cancer problem.

1. Cancer - Popular works 2. Heredity 3. Spontaneous generation

NL 0446321   DNLM

Loew, Adolphus.
Es werde licht! Eiszeit, Erdbahn, Mondbahn, neue Theorien. Basel, 1944.
30 p. plates. 23 cm.
L. C. copy imperfect : plate wanting.

1. Cosmogony.

QB52.L75   523.1   50–50010

NL 0446322   DLC ICU ICRL MH

LÖW, Albert.
Thierschutz im Judenthume; nach Bibel und Talmud. Budapest, Buchdruckerei F. Buschmann, 1890.

24 cm. pp.36,(3).
Label pasted over imprint reads: Brünn, Bernhard Epstein & Co.

NL 0446323   MH NN OCH

Loew, Albert.
Unsere Freunde und unsere Feinde. Vortrag gehalten ... in ... Holleschau ... Budapest: F. Buschmann, 1903.
18 p.

NL 0446324   OCH

Loew, Andreas, 1660-1710.
—— De lue venerea. 42 pp., 1 l. sm. 4°. Jena, stanno Bauhoferiano, [1682].

NL 0446325   DNLM

Löw (Andreas) [1660-1710]. *De morbo Hungarico, 32 pp. sm. 4°. Jenæ, lit. Bauhoferianis, [1682].

NL 0446326   DNLM

W 4
M96
1949

LÖW, Andreas, 1922-
Fixierung und Ribonuklease-Wirkung; Untersuchungen an Blut- und Knochenmarksausstrichen. München, 1949.
19 ℓ. illus.
Inaug-Diss. - Munich.
1. Nucleases

NL 0446327   DNLM

Löw, Anne Marie.
Stiller Glanz; Gedichte [von] Anne-Marie Löw. [Basel, 1951?] 46 p. 19cm.

1.Poetry, Swiss-German.

NL 0446328   NN CtY

Loew (Anton) [1859-84]. Das erste Viertel-Jahrhundert des Rothen Kreuzes in Oesterreich. Denkschrift. 63 pp., 1 tab. 8°. Wien, A. Stiller, 1885.

NL 0446329   DNLM

Loew, Ascher.
Verzeichniss der von dem verstorbenen A. Löw hinterlassenen hebräischen Bücher
see under title

BM695
.P3E6
Hebr

Löw, Benjamin Adolf, 1775-1851.
Emden, Jacob Israel ben Ẓebi, 1697-1776.
דרוש פסח גדול [ותשובה אחדת המציצה העתק תשובת ביומין] זאב וואלף, פאדגאריע, בדפוס ש. ח. דיימשער. תר"ם.
[Podgórze, 1900]

BM523
.8
.L6
Hebr

Löw, Benjamin Adolf, 1775-1851.
שערי תורה. ווין. נעדרוקט ביא אנמאן שמריים. תקפ"א
Wien, 1821-
v. 35 cm.
חלק א. בתוכו יבוארו ארבעה ועשרים כללים דיני הוראת בע"ד
CONTENTS.—[במסו ושחיקה בתוראה וזרושים]

1. Evidence (Jewish law) 2. Sermons, Jewish. 3. Sermons, Hebrew. I. Title. Title transliterated: Sha'are Torah.

New York. Public Libr. for Library of Congress [1]   A 55–6410

NL 0446332   NN CtY MH DLC

Löw, Carl.
Die Chemische Fabrik E. Merck, Darmstadt; ein Rückblick auf die Geschichte der Firma in Wort und Bild, aus Anlass des 125jährigen Bestehens. Darmstadt [Chemische Fabrik E. Merck] 1952.
77 p. illus. 26 cm.

1. Merck (E.) A. G., Darmstadt. I. Title.

HD9654.9.M4L6   58–18702 ‡

NL 0446333   DLC MH-BA

Loew, Carl Anton
see Loew, Karl Anton.

Loew, Carl Benedict Oscar
See
Loew, Oscar, 1844-

Loew, Carl Friedrich Ludwig
see Loew, Ludwig, Freiherr von, 1803-1868.

Loew (Carolus Alexander Reinoldus) [1839-]. *De hysteria acuta. 32 pp. 8°. Berolini, G. Lange, 1863.

NL 0446337   DNLM

Loew, Carolus Fridericus
—— Kurtze doch [gründliche Untersuchung vom Anfang, Fortgang und Ende des durch gantz Europa Anno 1729 im Monath Novemb. und Decemb. grassirenden contagiosen Latharz-Fiebers, vornemlich aber wie solches in Wienn eingerissen, was sich darbey vor verschiedene Umstände zugetragen, woher es gerühret, und wie dieses sicher und vollkommen curiret worden, [etc.] 3 p. l., 28 pp. sm. 4°. [Wien], 1730.

NL 0446338   DNLM

PG6065
L64

Löw, Chaim
Praca laboratoryjna w nauczaniu języka polskiego. Kraków, 1934.
11 p. 23 cm.

"Osobna odbitka z VI. [i.e. szóstego] sprawozdania Żydowskiego Gimnazjum Koedukacyjnego w Krakowie".
Bibliographical footnotes.

1. Polish language - Study and teaching. I. Title(1)

NL 0446339   CtY

Löw, Conrad, tr.
Kurtzer begriff was ... Albrecht, Ertzhertzog zu Oesterreich ... aussgericht hat
see under title

Loew, Conrad, comp. and tr.
Meer oder Seehanen Buch, Darinn Verzeichnet seind, die Wunderbare....Schiffarhten [sic], so recht...sen Meer vnd Seehanen, der Königen von Hispania, Portugal, Engellandt vnd Franckreich, inwendig den letst vergangnen hundert Jahren, gethan... Hierzu seind noch gesetzt zwey seltzame...Stück. Das eine ist, Die Erzehlung der Schiffart, so im Jar 1594. [i. e. 1595] gethan siben Schiff, welche die Vnierte Niderländische

Stånd geschickt gegen Mitternacht... Das ander stück ist. Ein Warhaffter, klarer, eigentlicher Bericht, von der...Reise...ausz Holland, bisz in Jndien gegen Auffgang gethan...1595...1597... Dise Reisen...seind zusamen, ausz andern Spraachen ins Teutsch gebracht, Durch Conrad Löw... Cölln: Getruckt Bey Bertram Buchholtz, 1598. 2 p.l., 110 [i. e. 100] p. 3 maps. 31cm. (f°.)

Sabin 42392. JCB, 1919, I, 364.
Numbers 81–90 omitted in foliation.

Astor 22597. 1. Voyages and travels   —Collections. I. Title.
Card revised June 11, 1943

NL 0446342   NNH RPJCB MnU

Loew, Cornelius Richard.
The development of the idea of estrangement in Hegel's early writings. Ann Arbor, University Microfilms [1952]
[University Microfilms, Ann Arbor, Mich.] Publication no. 3433)
Microfilm copy of typescript. Positive.
Collation of the original : 148 l.
Thesis—Columbia University.
Bibliography : leaves 146-148.

1. Hegel, Georg Wilhelm Friedrich, 1770-1831. 2. Religion—Philosophy. I. Title.

Microfilm AC–1 no. 3433   Mic 54–586

NL 0446343   DLC NNC IU

Loew, Earl R.,   joint author.

Patterson, Thomas Leon, 1884-
Laboratory manual of experimental physiology for students of dentistry, by Thomas L. Patterson ... and Earl R. Loew ... with 29 illustrations ... Detroit, Mich., 1938.

VOLUME 338

Loew, Edgar Allan, 1882–
Direct and alternating currents, theory and machinery, by
E. A. Loew ... 1st ed. New York and London, McGraw-
Hill book company, inc., 1933.
xiii, 656 p. illus., diagrs. 23½ᶜᵐ.

1. Electric currents. 2. Electric machinery.
Library of Congress   TK2000.L6   33–18480
———— Copy 2.
Copyright A 63609   ₍₅₎   621.313

OCU OC1 TU MB WaU
NL 0446345   DLC CaBVa IdU WaS NN CU NcRS ViU OC1W

Loew, Edgar Allan, 1882–
Direct and alternating currents, theory and machinery, by
E. A. Loew ... 2d ed. New York and London, McGraw-Hill
book company, inc., 1938.
xv, 730 p. illus., diagrs. 23½ᶜᵐ.

1. Electric currents. 2. Electric machinery.
Library of Congress   TK2000.L6 1938   38–14560
———— Copy 2.
Copyright A 119639   ₍₅₎   621.313

WaSp OrPR WaSpG
NL 0446346   DLC ViU MB NcD NcRS OC1 OCU OU ICJ WaS

Loew, Edgar Allan, 1882–
Direct and alternating currents, theory and machinery, by
E. A. Loew ... 3d ed. New York and London, McGraw-Hill
book company, inc., 1946.
xvi, 748 p. illus., diagrs. 22ᶜᵐ.

1. Electric currents. 2. Electric machinery.
TK2000.L6 1946   621.313   46–7829

ViU TxU MtBuM Or OrCS OrS WaS WaT
NL 0446347   DLC IdB CaBVa CU OkU PHC TU NcD NcGU

Loew, Edgar Allan, 1882–
Direct and alternating currents: theory and machinery
₍by₎ E. A. Loew assisted by F. R. Bergseth. 4th ed. New
York, McGraw-Hill, 1954.
637 p. illus. 24 cm.

1. Electric currents. 2. Electric machinery.
TK2000.L6 1954   621.313   53–9878 ‡

Or OrCS OrP OC1W OU WaT
PPF PPD MB ViU OC1U OC1 CaBVaU CaBVa IdB MtBC MtBuM
NL 0446348   DLC IaU DSI NBuC NcD TxU PP PU–E1 NN

Loew, Edgar Allan, 1882–
... Electric heating of residences, by Edgar Allan Loew ...
Seattle, Wash., the university, 1921–1923.
2 v. illus., diagrs. 23ᶜᵐ. (Washington. University. Engineering
experiment station. Engineering experiment stations series. Bulletin
nos. 15, 20)
At head of title: Bulletin. University of Washington.

1. Electric heating.
                                          G S 22—412
U. S. Geol. survey. Library   S(284) W28 nos. 15, 20
for Library of Congress   TK4601.L6

MiU DLC MB
NL 0446349   DI–GS OrU WaS MtBuM WaT OU OCU OO OC1

Loew, Edgar Allan, 1882–
Electrical power transmission; principles of design and per-
formance, by E. A. Loew ... 1st ed. New York ₍etc.₎
McGraw-Hill book company, inc., 1928.
xiii, 388 p. diagrs. (part fold.) 23½ᶜᵐ.
Two folded diagrams in pocket.
Bibliography: p. 332.

1. Electric power distribution. 2. Electric lines. i. Title.

Library of Congress   TK3001.L6   28–964

ViU OC1W OU OC1 OC1U ICJ MB PCM
NL 0446350   DLC IdPI CaBVaU CaBVa WaS CU CoU NcD

Loew, Edgar Allan, 1882–
... The production of sodium nitrite from arced nitrogen,
by Edgar Allan Loew ... and Warren Lord Beuschlein ...
Seattle, University of Washington, 1933.
54 p. incl. illus., tables, diagrs. 23ᶜᵐ. (Washington (State) University. Engineering experiment station. Engineering experiment station series. Bulletin no. 73)
Bibliography: p. 54.

1. Nitrogen—Fixation. 2. Sodium nitrite. i. Beuschlein, Warren
Lord, 1895–   joint author.
                                          P O 34–1 †
U. S. Patent office. Libr.
for Library of Congress   TP245.N8L6
                               ₍a45d1₎†   661.4

NL 0446351   DP DLC MtBuM WaT WaS CaBViP OU OCU

TK3231
.W28   Loew, Edgar Allan, 1882–
        Washington (State) University. *Engineering experiment
        station.*
        ... Transmission line design ... by Frederick Kurt Kirsten
        ₍and others₎ ... Seattle, Wash., The University, 1923–29.

Loew, E₍duard₎
Blütenbiologische floristik des mittleren und
nördlichen Europa sowie Grönlands
see   Loew, Ernst, *1843–1908.*

Löw, Eduard
System der universal-philosophie enthaltend
metaphysik, theosophie, kosmosophie und
chronosophie. Berlin, Plahn, 1877.
178 p. diagrs.

Bound with six other pamphlets with binders
title "System of philosophy."

NL 0446354   OC1W

Löw, Eduard.
Theorie des rechnungswesens und systematische anleitung zur buchführung im staats-, kommunal- und pri-
vathaushalte, nebst der geschichte und litteratur des rechnungswesens ... bearbeitet von Eduard Löw ... Berlin,
H. Sauvage, 1860.
viii, 200 p. forms. 21ᶜᵐ.
Bibliography: p. ₍168₎–197.

1. Accounting—Early works to 1900.

NL 0446355   MiU IEN

Löw, Eduard.
Die Vermögens-Wissenschaft, ein neues System der Volkswirth-
schaftlehre nebst Erläuterungen, von Eduard Löw, ... Berlin,
H. Sauvage, 1860.
viii, 79 p. 21ᶜᵐ.

NL 0446356   ICJ

Loew, Eleazar, 1839–1917.
פקודת אלעזר. על סוגיות הש״ס ושו״ת. סאטמאר. בדפוס של מ.
ל. הירש. תרצ״א.   Satu-mare ₍1931₎
196 l. 35 cm.

1. Talmud—Commentaries. 2. Responsa. i. Title.
                               Title transliterated: Pekudat El'azar.

BM504.2.L6   61–57956

NL 0446357   DLC MH

Loew, Elias Avery
see
Lowe, Elias Avery, 1879–

LOEW, Emanuel.
Das heraklitische wirklichkeitsproblem und
seine umdeutung bei Sextus. ₍Progr.₎ Wien,
K.K.Sophiengymnasium,1914.
pp.1–34.

NL 0446359   MH

1843–1908.
Löw, Ernst, Beitrag zur kenntniss einer neuholländischen
schmarotzerpflanze. ₍Wien. 1869.₎ 8°. pp.14. Plate.
"Aus den Verhandlungen der K. K. Zoologisch-botanischen gesellschaft
in Wien," 1868, xviii, 689–702.

NL 0446360   MH–A

Loew, Ernst, *1843–1908.*
Blütenbiologische floristik des mitteleren und nördlichen Europa sowie Grönlands. Systematische zusammenstellung des in den letzten zehn jahren veröffentlichten beobachtungsmaterials. Von dr. E. Loew ... Stuttgart, F. Enke, 1894.
viii, 424 p. 23½ᶜᵐ.
"Litteraturverzeichnis. (1883–1893)": p. ₍4₎–18.

1. Botany — Ecology. 2. Botany — Europe. 3. Botany — Greenland. 4.
Phanerogams.

NL 0446361   MiU MH WaU MnU

Loew, Ernst, *1843–*
Der botanische unterricht an höheren lehranstalten.
Von dr. E. Loew ... Bielefeld und Leipzig, O. Gülker &
cie., 1876.
1 p. l., 119, ₍1₎ p. 23ᶜᵐ.
"Separat-abdruck aus dem Central-organ für die interessen des real-
schulwesens."

1. Botany—Teaching.
                                          E 9–1491
Library, U. S. Bur. of   Education QK51.L82

NL 0446362   DHEW MH

1843–1908
Loew, Ernst, De Casuarinearum caulis foliique evolutione
et structura. Dissertatio inauguralis botanica. Berolini.
1865. 8°. pp. ₍2₎, 54.

NL 0446363   MH–A ICRL

VOLUME 338

QK 15 L82
Loew, Ernst, 1843-1908.
Einführung in die Blütenbiologie auf historischer Grundlage. Berlin, F. Dümmler, 1895.
xii, 432 p. illus. 24 cm.

Bibliographical footnotes.

1. Botany - History. 2. Fertilization of plants. ₁I. Title.₎

NL 0446364   NIC IU OkU DSI MH

Loew, Ernst.
... Gedächtnisrede für Karl Ohrtmann ...
Berlin [1886]
p. 27-34. 26 cm.
Programm. - k. Realschule, Berlin.

NL 0446365   CtY CU

Loew, Ernst, 1843-1908, ed.

Knuth, Paul Erich Otto Wilhelm, 1854-1899.
Handbuch der blütenbiologie; unter zugrundelegung von Hermann Müllers werk: "Die befruchtung der blumen durch insekten" bearb. von d'. Paul Knuth ... Leipzig, W. Engelmann, 1898-1905.

Loew, Ernst, 1843-1908, joint author.

Kirchner, Oskar von, 1851-1925.
Lebensgeschichte der blütenpflanzen Mitteleuropas. Spezielle ökologie der blütenpflanzen Deutschlands, Österreichs und der Schweiz. Von dr. O. von Kirchner ... dr. E. Loew ... ₁und₎ dr. C. Schröter ... Stuttgart, E. Ulmer, 1908-

---

Loew, Ernst, 1843-1908.
Methodisches Uebungsbuch für den Unterricht in der Botanik an höheren Lehranstalten und Seminarien. Erstes-[drittes] Heft. .... Von Dr. E. Loew, ... Bielefeld und Leipzig, O. Gülker & Cie, 1876-1878.
3 vol. in 1. 22cm.
Contents.—1. Heft. Für die Unterstufe. Zweite umgearbeitete Auflage. 1878. vi, 80 p.—2. Heft. Für die Mittelstufe. 1876. vi, 180 p.—3. Heft. Für die Oberstufe. 1876. viii, 120 p.

NL 0446368   ICJ ICRL RPB MWelC

Loew, Ernst, 1843-1908.
Naturbeschreibung. [München, C.H. Beck, 1895]
98 p. 4°. (Handb. d. Erziehungs- und Unterrichtslehre f. höhere Schulen. 4. Bd., No. 13)

NL 0446369   NN ODW

Loew, Ernst, 1843-1908.
Die Prager Produktenbörse. Von Dr. Ernst Loew, ... Wien, Manzsche K. u. k. Hof-Verlags- und Universitäts-Buchhandlung, 1910.
[4], 50, [2] p. incl. tables. 24cm.
"Literatur," p. [2] at end.

NL 0446370   ICJ

Loew, Ernst, 1843-1908
Uber die metamorphose vegetativer sprossanlagen in blüthen bei viscum album, von E. Loew. ₁Leipzig, Breitkopf and Härtel, 1890.₎
4 p. illus.

"Separat-abdruck aus der Botanischen zeitung, 1890."
(Beitrage zur kenntniss des zellkerns und sexualzellen, by E. Zacharias.)

NL 0446371   OU

Löw, Erwin
Überprüfung der ergebnisse mikrobiologischer bodenuntersuchung und beiträge zur erfassung der düngerwirkung bei der aspergillusmethode. ...
Inaug. Diss. - Techn. Hochschule München, [1935]
Literatur-Verzeichnis.

NL 0446372   ICRL

Loew, Eugen, 1880-
Die wette.
Inaug. diss. Marburg, 1907 (Wuerzburg)
Bibl.

NL 0446373   ICRL MH-L

Löwe, Ewald, 1837-1896, ed.
Die Strafprozessordnung und das Gerichtsverfassungsgesetz vom 20. September 1950 ...
see under Germany (Federal Republic, 1949-   ) Laws, statutes, etc.

D
Loew, Fernand.
Les Verrières; la vie rurale d'une communauté du Haut-Jura au Moyen Age. Neuchâtel, La Baconnière ₁1954₎
397 p. map, col. diagr. 24 cm.
Bibliography : p. ₁352₎-382.

1. Les Verrières, Switzerland.

DQ851.L55L6   55-17606

NL 0446375   DLC ICU NNC MdBJ NN MH ViU

949.43 L82v
Loew, Fernand.
La vie rurale d'une communauté du Haut-Jura au moyen âge les Verrières. Neuchatel, Paul Attinger, 1954.
397 p. map. 24 cm.

Thesis - Université de Neuchatel.

1. Les Verrières, Switzerland. I. Title.

NL 0446376   LU IU NN

Löw, Franz, 1829-1889, joint author.

Brauer, Friedrich Moritz, 1832-1904.
Neuroptera austriaca. Die im erzherzogthum Oesterreich bis jetzt aufgefundenen neuropteren nach der analytischen methode zusammengestellt, nebst einer kurzen charakteristik aller europäischen neuropteren-gattungen, von Friedrich Brauer, unter mitarbeitung von Franz Löw ... Wien, C. Gerold's sohn, 1857.

Löw, Franz, 1829-1889, ed.

Wiener entomologische zeitung ... 1.-   jahrg.; 1882-19
Wien, A. Hölder ₁etc.₎ 1882-19

Löw, Erwin
... De eo, qvod ivstvm est principi svccessori circa revocanda avvlsa.
Von veräuserten Domainen-Gütern.
Lipsiae, Ex Officina Langenhemiana, 1747.
52 p. 15½cm.
At head of title: ... Commentatio.

NL 0446379   MH-L

Loew, Friedrich.
Konstantinopel, historisch und statistisch nach den neuesten und besten französischen und englischen quellen. Regensburg, zu haben bei dem verfasser, etc. etc. 1829.
pp. vi, (2), 204.

Constantinople-Hist.∥

NL 0446380   MH

D 385 L6
Löw, Friedrich
Der Westen Europas während der letzten Hälfte des Jahres 1830; oder, Geschichtliche Darstellung der wichtigen Vorgänge zu Paris, Brüssel und in mehreren Gegenden Deutschlands während dieser Zeit. Aus den bewährtesten Quellen zusammengestellt. Bayreuth, 1831.
188p. 18cm.

1. Europe - Hist. - 1815-1848 I. Title II. Title: Geschichtliche Darstellung der wichtigen Vorgänge

NL 0446381   WU

1833-
Löw, Friedrich₎ Sarkom des Schluesselbeines im Anschlusse an eine Verrenkung. Aus d. ersten chir. Abt. d. Augusta-Viktoria-Krankenh. in Berlin-Schöneberg. ⟨Dir.: Kausch.⟩ [In Maschinenschrift.] 22 S. m. 3 Photogr. 4°(2°). — Auszug: Berlin (1921): Blanke. 2 Bl 8°
Berlin, Med. Diss. v. 20. Sept. 1921, Ref. Bier
[Geb. 23. März 83 Wien; Wohnort: Döberitz; Staatsangeh.: Österreich; Vorbildung: Erzherzog-Rainer-G. Wien Reife 02; Studium: Wien 10, Berlin 1 S.; Coll. 19. Sept. 21; Approb. 23. Dez. 07.]   [U 21. 2443]

NL 0446382   ICRL

Löw, Fritz.
Der kleine piepmatz; idee und verse von Fritz Löw, illustriert von Otto Flatter. Wien, Österreichische staatsdruckerei ₁1931₎
₁12₎ p. illus. (part col.) 23 x 28¼cm.
Illustrated cover in colors; illustrated lining-papers.

1. Flatter, Otto, illus. 11. Title.
Library of Congress	PZ36.3.L6	32-18274
Copyright A—Foreign	15428	
	₁2₎	831.91

NL 0446383   DLC

Löw, Fritz.
Wurstelprater; idee und verse von Fritz Löw, illustriert vom atelier "Otto". Wien, Österreichische staatsdruckerei ₁1930₎
₁15₎ p. col. illus. 23½ x 30½cm.
Illustrated cover in colors.

1. Title.
Library of Congress	PZ34.3.L6	31-5347
Copyright A—Foreign	10894	
	₁2₎	831.91

NL 0446384   DLC

VOLUME 338

Löw, Fritz, 1907-
Ueber die spezifität der saccharasen. ...
28 p.
Inaug. Diss. - Berlin, [1933]
Lebenslauf.

NL 0446385   ICRL CtY

Löw, Fritzi, illus.

Grillparzer, Franz, 1791-1872.
Der arme spielmann, novelle von Franz Grillparzer. Mit
12 originallithographien und buchschmuck von Fritzi Löw.
Wien, A. Schroll & co. g. m. b. h. [1920]

Löw, Fritzi, illus.

Brentano, Clemens Maria, 1778-1842.
Drei märchen von Clemens Brentano. Mit 16 originallithographien von Fritzi Löw. Wien, A. Schroll & co., g. m. b. h.
[1914]

PT2434
.M7
1917

Löw, Fritzi, illus.

Mörike, Eduard Friedrich, 1804-1875.
Mozart auf der reise nach Prag, von Eduard Mörike. Mit
14 originallithographien von Fritzi Löw. Wien, A. Schroll
& co. g. m. b. h. [1917]

Löw, Fritzi, illus.

Keller, Gottfried, 1819-1890.
Sieben legenden, von Gottfried Keller. Mit 16 original-
lithographien und buchschmuck von Fritzi Löw. Wien, A.
Schroll & co. g. m. b. h. [1919]

41.2
L82

Loew, Gérard, 1923-
Les filtrats de pénicilline en thérapeutique chirurgicale.   Paris, Foulon, 1950.
80 p.

Thèse - École nationale vétérinaire
d'Alfort.

1. Penicillin in veterinary medicine.

NL 0446390   DNAL

4UA
Aus.
.-3

Löw, Gustav, Edler von.
Die Organisation der Wehrkräfte Oesterreich-
Ungarns, mit Skizzen über die Heeres-
Organisationen Deutschlands, Russlands, Frank-
reichs und Italiens.   Teschen, Buchhandlung für
Militär-Literatur, 1875.
326 p.

NL 0446391   DLC-P4

Löw, Gustav, 1872-   , ed.
Historia och dikt; synkronistisk antologi; utgiven av Gustav
Löw... [Bind] 1: a, b   Stockholm: Björck & Börjesson,
1938-   v. 19½cm.

"En del har förut varit publicerad i en av mig utgiven Allmän historia." — *Förord.*

1. Literature—Collections.
N. Y. P. L.   March 25, 1940

NL 0446392   NN

Loev, Gustav, 1872-
Strängnäs läroverks gårdar; historisk översikt.
[Strängnäs, 1926]

85 p. illus. (Strängnäs Läroverkskollegium. Re-
gium Gustavianum Gymnasium Strengnense, 1626-1926;
minnesskrift, 4)

NL 0446393   MH

Bu63a
908l

Löw, Gustav, 1872-
Sveriges forntid i svensk historieskrivning.
Stockholm, C.E.Fritze[1908-10]
2v. in 1. 22cm.
Bibliography in each vol.

NL 0446394   CtY NIC

Löw, Hans, 1889-
Österreichische Pioniere der Luftfahrt. Wien, Waldheim-
Eberle [1953]
241 p. illus. 23 cm.

1. Air pilots—Austria. 2. Aeronautics—Austria. 3. Aeronautics—
Hist.   I. Title.

                                                    A 55-1008

Mass. Inst. of Tech.   Library
for Library of Congress   [1]

NL 0446395   MCM NN

830.81
L824s

[Loew, Hans M   ] 1924-
Die Sammlung, junge Lyrik aus Österreich.
Wien, Ullstein [c1947]
220p. 19cm.

1. Austrian poetry (German) 2. German poetry--
Austrian authors. I. Title.

NL 0446396   IU MH ICU IEN RPB

PT
3824
.L82

Loew, Hans M , comp. 1914-
Weg und bekennthis; anthologie junger
österreichischer Autoren gesammelt und
eingeleitet von Hans M. Loew. Graz, Stiasny
[1954]
98 p. 19 cm. (Dichtung der Gegenwart.
Band 34)

1. Austrian poetry (German) - Collections.
I. Title.

                NcD WaU
NL 0446397   DCU NIC OCU NNC MH IU ICU NN OO NNU

Löw, Heinrich 1894-
Untersuchungen zur Vorgeschichte der
Gracchischen Bewegung. Darmstadt 1920: Bender. II, 96 S. 8°
Gießen, Phil. Diss. v. 21. Febr. 1921, Ref. Laqueur
[Geb. 10. Nov. 94 Brenbach; Wohnort: Gießen; Staatsangeh.: Hessen; Vor-
bildung: Ludwig-Georgs-G. Darmstadt Reife 13; Studium: Gießen 7 S.; Rig.
29. April 20.]   [U 21. 6505]

NL 0446398   ICRL CtY PU IU MH

Loew, Heinrich, 1896-
Behandlungearten und-erfolge bei sexuellen
abweigkeiten.
Inaug. diss Bonn, [1928?]
Bibl.

NL 0446399   ICRL CtY PU

Löw, Heinrich Hermann
see Löw, Hermann, 1887-

Loew, Hermann, 1807-1879.
Bemerkungen über die Familie der
Asiliden. [Meseritz, F.W.Lorenz,
1851]
22,xviiip. 24cm.

Programm - Realschule zu Meseritz.

NL 0446401   CLSU

Ent.
QL
535.4
L6

Loew, Hermann, 1807-1879.
Beschreibungen europäischer Dipteren.
Halle, H. W. Schmidt, 1869-
v. 21cm. (Systematische Beschreibung
der bekannten europäischen Zweiflügeligen
Insecten, von Johann Willhelm Meigen,
T. 8-

1. Diptera - Europe. I. Meigen,
Johann Wilhelm, 1764-1845. / Systematische Beschreibungen der bekannten
europäischen   Zweiflügeligen
Insecten.

NL 0446402   MU NN PPAN MH-Z

3765
.L837
L8

Loew, Hermann, 1807-1879.
De vita Raymundi Lulli specimen, quod una cum
thesibus quibusdam controversis auctoritate amplissimi philosophorum ordinis pro summis eius ho-
noribus rite obtinendis publice defendet die i.m.
decembris a.MDCCCXXIX Hermannus Loew... Halis
Saxonum, typis expressum Gebaueriis[1830]
29,[1]p. 19ᶜᵐ.

1.Lull, Ramón, 1235-1315.

NL 0446403   ICU ICJ CtY

Loew, Hermann, 1807-1879.
Description of the rye gall-gnat.
(In U. S. Entomological commission. Third report. app. II. p. ⟨6⟩-
⟨8⟩ 23ᶜᵐ. Washington, 1883)
Extracted from "Die neue kornmade ..." 1859.

1. Rye gall-gnat.
                                        Agr 10-300
Library U. S. Dept. of   Agriculture 1En8 vol. 3

NL 0446404   DNAL

Loew, Hermann, 1807-1879.
Diptera Americae Septentrionalis indigena. Descrip-
sit H. Doew. Berolini, typis A. W. Schadii, 1861-72.
2 v. 22ᶜᵐ.
Issued in 10 parts (centuriae)
From Berliner entomologische zeitschrift, 1861-72.

1. Diptera—North America.

Library of Congress   QL535.1.L8   6—32531

NL 0446405   DLC CU MsSM OU IaU

Loew, H[ermann] 1807-1879.
Diptera. Ueber die bisher in Schlesien aufgefundenen
arten der gattung *Chlorops* Macq. Von director Dr. H.
Loew ... Breslau, In commission bei J. U. Kern [1866]
96 p. 22ᶜᵐ.
Separat-abdruck aus der Zeitschrift für entomologie des Vereins für
schlesische insektkunde zu Breslau. 20. jahrgang. 1866.

1. Chlorops. 2. Diptera—Silesia.

Library of Congress   QL537.M6L8   6-22985†

NL 0446406   DLC

VOLUME 338

Loew, H[ermann] 1807–1879.
Diptera. Ueber die schlesischen arten der gattungen *Tachypeza* Meig. (*Tachypeza, Tachista, Dysaletria*) und *Microphorus* Macq. (*Trichina* und *Microphorus*). Von director Dr. H. Loew ... Breslau, In commission bei J. U. Kern [1863]

50 p. 22ᶜᵐ.

Separat-abdruck aus der Zeitschrift für entomologie des Vereins für schlesische insektenkunde zu Breslau. 17. jahrgang. 1863.

1. Tachypeza. 2. Microphorus. 3. Diptera—Silesia.

Library of Congress   QL537.E5L7   6–22982†

NL 0446407   DLC

Loew, Hermann, 1807–1879.
Die dipteren-fauna Südafrika's, bearb. von Dr. Herm. Loew ... ı. abth. ... Aus dem ıı. bande der Abhandlungen des Naturwissenschaftlichen vereins für Sachsen und Thüringen in Halle besonders abgedruckt. Berlin, G. Bosselmann, 1860.

xi, 330 p. ıı pl. 33½ᶜᵐ.

1. Africa. Entomology. 2. Diptera.

Agr 3–344

Library, U. S. Dept. of   Agriculture 428L82D

NL 0446408   DNAL MoU

595.77   Loew, Hermann, 1807–1879.
L82dip   Dipterologische Beiträge.   Posen, 1845.
            66p. 1 plate. 25cm.

Accompanies program (Schulnachrichten von Ostern 1844 bis Ostern 1845)—Friedrich Wilhelm Gymnasium, Posen.

1. Diptera.

NL 0446409   IU CU MH

Loew, Hermann, 1807–1879.
Die europäischen bohrfliegen (*Trypetidae*) Bearb. von H. Loew. Erläutert durch photographische flügel-abbildungen. Wien, Aus der Kais. Kön. Hof- und staatsdruckerei, 1862.

2 p. l., 128 p. xxvı pl. 41ᶜᵐ.

1. Trypetidae. 2. Diptera—Europe.

Library of Congress   QL537.M6L8   6–31351

NL 0446410   DLC IU ICJ

Loew, Hermann, 1807–1879.
Die europäischen bohrfliegen (*Trypetidae*) Bearb. von H. Loew. Erläutert durch photographische flügelabbildungen. Wien, Aus der Kais. Kön. Hof- und staatsdruckerei, 1862.

2 p. L, 128 p. xxvı pl. 42ᶜᵐ.

On cover: Facsimile-ed. Ed. W. Junk, no. 15. Berlin, W. Junk, 1913.

1. Trypetidae. 2. Insects—Europe. [2. Europe—Entomology]

Agr 14–242

Library, U. S. Dept. of   Agriculture 428L82E

NL 0446411   DNAL ICJ CU

QL   Loew, Hermann, 1807–1879
461   Fragmente zur Kenntniss der europäischen
.49   Arten einiger Dipterengattungen.
B5
v.1   (in Linnaea entomologica. Berlin, [etc.],
           1846. v. 1, p. 319–530. plate.)

QL
535.4 ————— Copy 2.
L73

1. Diptera - Europe. 2. Insects - Europe.

NL 0446412   ICF MH-Z

Loew, Hermann, 1807–1879.
Horae anatomicae; Beiträge zur genaueren anatomischen Kenntnis der Evertebraten. Abteilung I: Entomotomien. Posen, J.J. Heine, 1841. 126 p. 6 plates. 20cm.

Issued in 3 parts.
Added title page: Entomotomien, von H. Loew.

NL 0446413   IaAS MH-Z

Loew, Hermann, 1807–1879.
Smithsonian institution.
Instructions for collecting insects.

(*In its* Annual report, 1858. Washington, 1859. 23½ᶜᵐ. p. 158–200. illus.)

Loew, Hermann, 1807–1879.
... Monographs of the *Diptera* of North America. Prepared for the Smithsonian institution ... Washington, Smithsonian institution, 1862–73.

4 v. illus., 15 pl. 23¾ᶜᵐ. (Smithsonian miscellaneous collections. [vol. vı, art. ı–ıı; vol. xı, art. ııı; vol. vııı, art. ı])
Publications 141, 171, 256, and 219.
Part ı: By H. Loew, ed., with additions, by R. Osten Sacken. 1862.
Part ıı: By H. Loew, ed. by R. Osten Sacken. 1864.
Part ııı: By H. Loew. 1873.
Part ıv: By R. Osten Sacken. 1869.
CONTENTS.—pt. ı. *Trypetidæ, Sciomyzidæ, Ephydrinidæ, Cecidomyidæ.*—pt. ıı. *Dolichopodidæ.*—pt. ııı. *Ortalidæ.* Review of North American *Trypetina,* with appendices.—pt. ıv. *Tipulidæ,* pt. ı: *Tipulidæ brevipalpi.*

1. Diptera—North America.   ı. Osten-Sacken, Carl Robert, freiherr von der, 1828–1906. ıı.   Osten-Sacken, Carl Robert, freiherr von der, 1828–1906, ed.   16–5456
Library of Congress   Q11.S7 vol. 6, art. 1–2; vol. 11, art. 3; vol. 8, art. 1
                       Q11.S7 2d set

                       NcU NN DNAL
NL 0446415   DLC MnHi IdU WaS MU NjP DSI ViU NN ICJ

Loew, Hermann, 1807–1879.
Neue beiträge zur kenntniss der dipteren. Vom Prof. Dr. H. Loew ... Berlin, E. S. Mittler & sohn, 1853–61.

8 pts. 23 x 18¼ᶜᵐ.

7. beitrag: Programm—Realschule zu Meseritz.
1.–6., 8. beiträge: Separates, from Programme—Realschule zu Meseritz.

1. Diptera.   ı. Meseritz, Ger. K. Realschule.

6–32530† Additions

Library of Congress   QL534.L8

NL 0446416   DLC MH-Z CU ICJ CLSU

Loew, Hermann, 1807–1879.
... On the *Diptera* or two-winged insects of the amber-fauna (Ueber die diptern-fauna des Bernsteins): a lecture by Director Lœw, at the meeting of the German naturalists in Kœnigsberg in 1861. [New Haven, 1864]

20 p. 24½ᶜᵐ.

Caption title.
"From the Am. jour. of science and arts, vol. xxxvıı, May, 1864."

1. Diptera, Fossil.

CA 17–1964 Unrev'd

Library of Congress   QE832.D6L8

NL 0446417   DLC

Loew, Hermann, 1807–1879.
Ueber den Bernstein und die Bernsteinfauna. Vom Prof. Dr. H. Loew... [Berlin: Mittler & Sohn, 1850.]   44 p.   8°.

1. Amber. 2. Palaeontology,   Zoological.
N. Y. P. L.   August 3, 1928

NL 0446418   NN

Loew, Hermann, 1807–1879.
Ueber den verwandtschaftskreis der *Empis stercorea* Lin., vom director H. Loew ... [Berlin, 1867]

[11]–24 p. 22ᶜᵐ. [With his Ueber *Empis ciliata* Fbr. Berlin, 1867]

Caption title.
From Berliner entomologische zeitschrift, bd. xı, 1867.

1. Empis stercorea.

CA 7–5529 Unrev'd

Library of Congress   QL537.E8L8

NL 0446419   DLC

LOEW, H[ermann] 1807–1879.
Ueber die europäischen raubfliegen [Diptera asilica]. [Berlin],1847–1849.

pp.448.

NL 0446420   MH-Z

Loew, Hermann, 1807–1879. Ueber die europäischen raubfliegen (Diptera asilica)

Becker, Theodor.
Revision der Löw'schen *Diptera asilica* in Linnaea entomologica 1848–49. Von dr. Th. Becker in Liegnitz ... Wien, F. Wagner, 1923.

Loew, Hermann, 1807–1879.
Ueber diejenigen mit *Empis chioptera* Meig. verwandten arten, welche dunkle schwinger haben. Vom director H. Loew ... [Berlin, 1867]

[25]–62 p. 22ᶜᵐ. [With his Ueber *Empis ciliata* Fbr. Berlin, 1867]

Caption title.
From Berliner entomologische zeitschrift, bd. xı, 1867.

1. Empis chioptera.

CA 7–5528 Unrev'd

Library of Congress   QL537.E8L8

NL 0446422   DLC

Loew, Hermann, 1807–1879.
Ueber einige bei Danzig gefangene Dipteren bei denen die flugel verkummert sind oder ganz fehlen. Danzig, 1866.

NL 0446423   NN

Loew, Hermann, 1807–1879.
Ueber *Empis ciliata* Fbr. und über die ihr zunächst verwandten arten, vom director H. Loew ... [Berlin, 1867]

10 p. 22ᶜᵐ.

Caption title.
From Berliner entomologische zeitschrift, bd. xı, 1867.

1. Empis ciliata.

CA 7–5530 Unrev'd

Library of Congress   QL537.E5L8

NL 0446424   DLC

Löw, Hermann, 1887–
Über den Einfluß hochgradiger venöser Stauung auf einen Gehirntuberkel. Leipzig 1911: Hoffmann. 30 S. 8°
Bonn, Med. Diss. v. 10. Juni 1912, Ref. Ribbert
[Geb. 11. Juli 87 Mühlen, Kr. Limburg a. L.; Wohnort: Weilmünster; Staatsangeh.: Preußen; Vorbildung: Gymn. Oberlahnstein Reife O. 06; Studium: Göttingen 3, Marburg 1, Kiel 2, Bonn 4 S.; Coll. 9. Mai 11; Approb. 5. Mai 12.]   [U 12. 439]

NL 0446425   ICRL MH-M DNLM

VOLUME 338

Loew, Hugo: Ein Beitrag zur Therapie der Placenta praevia. Stuttgart 1911: Buchdr. d. Paulinenpflege. 33 S. 8°
Würzburg, Med. Diss. v. 15. Jan. 1912, Ref. Hofmeier
[Geb. 18. Jan. 85 Selters b. Weilburg; Wohnort: Würzburg; Staatsangeh.: Preußen; Vorbildung: Gymn. Montabaur Reife O. 05; Studium: Würzburg 2, Bonn 1, Würzburg 2, München 1, Berlin 1, Freiburg i. B. 1, Würzburg 2 S.; Coll. 18. Jan. 11; Approb. 15. März 12.]   [U 12.4667]

NL 0446426   ICRL DNLM CtY

Loew, Immanuel. 1854-1944.
   Aramäische Fischnamen. Von Immanuel Löw.
(In Orientalische Studien Theodor Nöldeke . . . gewidmet. Vol.
I, pp. 549-570. Giessen. 1906.)
Contents. — Aramäische Fischnamen. — Griechische Lehnwörter. —
Griechische Fremdwörter.

G5630 — Aramæan language. Etym.—Fish. Catalogues.—Greece. Lang. Etym.

NL 0446427   MB

   Loew, Immanuel, 1854–
   Aramäische Lurchnamen. Strassburg, 1909–
1 v. ⸢pt. 1-4⸣

NL 0446428   OCH

   Loew, Immanuel, 1854-1944.
   Aramäische Lurchnamen (Frosch und
Salamander). (In: Florilegium; ou, Recueil de
travaux d'érudition dédiés à Monsieur le marquis
Melchior de Vogüé.   Paris, 1910.   4°.   p. 391-
406)

NL 0446429   NN

Loew, Immanuel.
   Aramäische Lurchnamen.   (Zeitschrift für Assyriologie.
Strassburg, 1912.   8°.   Bd. 26, p. 126-147.)
   Festschrift für Ignaz Goldziher.

1. Aramaic languages.—Lexicog-   raphy. 2. Zoology.
N. Y. P. L.   April 6, 1912.

NL 0446430   NN

Judaica
Fa Jb25
879ℓ   Löw, Immanuel, 1854-1944.
   Aramäische Pflanzennamen ... von Immanuel
Löw.
   Leipzig,W.Engelmann,1879. 1p.ℓ.,48,[2]pp.
23cm.
   Inaug.-Diss. - Leipzig.
   Vita.
   Based on Targumic, Talmudic, and Syriac
sources.
   Published in full with the same title,
Leipzig,Engelmann,1881.

NL 0446431   CtY OCH DLC-P4

   Löw, Immanuel, 1854–
   Aramæische pflanzennamen, von Immanuel Löw. Mit unterstützung der K. Akademie der wissenschaften in Wien. Leipzig, W. Engelmann, 1881.
   4 p. l., 400 p. 24°°.

   1. Aramaic language—Terms and phrases. 2. Syriac language—Terms and phrases. 3. Botany—Nomenclature. 4. Plant names, Popular—Aramaic. 5. Plant names, Popular—Syriac.
   Agr 6-78

U. S. Dept. of agr. Library   4521,95
   for Library of Congress   PJ5257.L6

DLC MH OCH
NL 0446432   DNAL CU NIC NjP KyLoS CtY NNUT DCU-H

PJ3002   Löw, Immanuel, 1854-1944.
.Z5H3   Aramäische Schlangennamen.
            (In Festschrift zu Ehren des Dr. A. Harkavy.
St. Petersburg, 1908. p.⸢27⸣-51)

PJ5205 ————
.L81   Photostat copy (negative) Detached.

            1. Aramaic language—Words—Hist. 2. Serpents.

NL 0446433   ICU

   Loew, Immanuel, 1854–
   Aramäische Schlangennamen.   Szegedin, 1909.   25 p.   8°.
   Title from cover. Repr.: Festschrift zum 70. Geburtstage A. Harkavy's.

1. Aramaic language. 2. Har-   kavy, A.
N. Y. P. L.   October 14, 1911.

NL 0446434   NN

   Loew, Immanuel, 1854-1944
   Beszédei, 1874-1899. Szeged, Traub, 1900

vii, 463 p.

NL 0446435   MH

   Löw, Immanuel, 1854-1944.
   ... Der biblische 'ēzōb, von Immanuel Löw ... Wien, In kommission bei A. Hölder, 1909.
   cover-title, 30 p. pl. 25°°. (Akademie der wissenschaften in Wien. Philosophisch-historische klasse. Sitzungsberichte. 161. bd., 3. abh.)

   1. Hebrew language—Etymology.
   AS142.V31 bd. 161, abh. 3   A 47-1880

Stanford univ. Library
   for Library of Congress   ⸢3⸣†

NL 0446436   CSt OCH MU DLC

   Loew, Immanuel, 1854-1944
   Emlékbeszédek, 1900-1906. [Szeged, Engel Lajos
Könyvnyomdaja, 1907]

65 p.

NL 0446437   MH

   Loew, Immanuel, 1854–
   Festschrift Immanuel Löw zum 80. Geburtstage
   see under title

   Löw, Immanuel, 1854–
   ... Die flora der Juden ... Wien und Leipzig, R. Löwit, 1924-34.
   4 v. in 5. 1 illus. 24°°. (Veröffentlichungen der Alexander Kohut memorial foundation, II-IV, VI)
   Vol. IV has imprint: Wien. Kohut foundation.
   "Abkürzungen": bd. II, p. 532; bd. III, p. 519-522; bd. IV, p. ⸢731⸣-740.
   "Indizes von architekt Moses Löw": bd. IV, p. ⸢503⸣-730.
   CONTENTS.—L., 1. hälfte. *Kryptogamae. Acanthaceae-Compositae.* 1926. 2. hälfte. *Convolvulaceae. Graminaceae.* 1928.—II. *Iridaceae-Papilionaceae.* 1924.—III. *Pedaliaceae-Zygophyllaceae.* 1924.—IV. Zusammenfassung. Nachträge. Berichtigungen. Indizes. Abkürzungen.

   1. Botany—Palestine. ⸢1. Palestine—Botany⸣ 2. Botany—Syria. ⸢2. Syria—Botany⸣ 3. Plant names, Popular. 4. Bible—Natural history. 5. ⸢Hebrew language—Glossaries, vocabularies, etc.⸣ 6. ⸢Aramaic language—Glossaries, vocabularies, etc.⸣ 7. ⸢Yiddish language—Glossaries, vocabularies, etc.⸣   I. Löw, Moses. II. ⸢Title⸣
   Agr 25-349 Revised

Library, U. S. Dept. of   Agriculture 460.17L95
   Library of Congress   QK378.L6
   ⸢r35d2⸣   581.9569

MH MiU NN
NL 0446440   DNAL ICJ OCH MH-A MH-G FTaSU NIC CU

   Löw, Immanuel, 1854-1944.
   Fölszentelő beszéd. Tartotta a Szombathelyi
zsinagóga fölavatása alkalmával 1880 augusztus
hava 30-adikán Löw Immanuel ...   [Szombathely,
1880]
   24 p.   23 cm.
   A sermon.

NL 0446441   CtY

   Loew, Immanuel, 1854–
   Karpas. ⸢Szeged⸣, 1915.
   12 L.

NL 0446442   OCH

   Loew, Immanuel, 1854-1944
   Kétszáz beszéd, 1919-1939. Szeged, Szegedi
Zsidó Hitközség, 1939

   2 v. in 1

NL 0446443   MH

   Loew, Immanuel, 1854–
   Die Meerzwiebel. ⸢Breslau: M. & H.
Marcus, 1911.⸣
   vii p.
   Paged also, p. 47-53.
   Title taken from first page.
   Repr.: Festschrift zu I. Lewy's 70. Geburtstag.

NL 0446444   OCH

   Loew, Immanuel, 1854–
   Meleagros aus Gadara und die Flora
Aramaes. Szegedin: ⸢B. Traub & Co.⸣,
1883.
   22 p.
   Als Ms. gedruckt.
   Reprinted in his: Die Flora der Juden,
v. 4, p. 468-476.

NL 0446445   OCH

   Loew, Immanuel, 1854–
   ...A mi zsinagógánk; jubiláris beszéd.   Szeged, 1928.
   7 p.   8°.

446089A. 1. Szeged—Synagogues.
N. Y. P. L.   December 9, 1929

NL 0446446   NN

   Loew, Immanuel, 1854–
   Mózes Áldása. Prédikáció, tartotta,1893.
Február ... Szeged: Szedi Zsidó Hitközség,
⸢1893⸣.
   20 p.

NL 0446447   OCH

   Loew, Immanuel, 1854–
   Das neue Burgtheater.
   = Wien. Konegen. 1888. 35, (1) pp. 19 cm., in 8s.

K3074 — Vienna. Theatres. Burgtheater.

NL 0446448   MB

VOLUME 338

Loew, Immanuel, 1854–
Perls Ármin. Emlékbeszéd. Mondotta
pécsett 1914 x 27. Szeged: Traub B. és
Társa, 1914.
10 p.

NL 0446449   OCH

Loew, Immanuel, 1854–
Schachtelhalm. Szeged, 1916.
8 L.

Bd. with his: Karpas. ₍Szeged₎, 1915.
12 L.

NL 0446450   OCH

B𝕄
740
L5.85
Löw, Immanuel, 1854–1944.
Száz Beszéd, 1900–1922. Szeged,
Schwarz Jeno Kiadása, 1923.
405 p.   24 cm.
With author's autograph dedication.

1. Sermons, Hungarian--Jewish
authors. I. Title

NL 0446451   OCH MH

Loew, Immanuel, 1854–1944
A szegedi zsidók 1785-től 1885-ig, irták Löw
Immanuel és Kulinyi Zsigmond. Szeged, Kiadja a
Szegedi Zsidó Hitközség, 1885
xxvi, 373 p. ports., map

NL 0446452   MH

Loew, Immanuel, 1854–1944.
Tiz testvérszó; 5688 adar hetediki emlékbeszéd. Mondotta
Löw Immanuel. Szeged, 1928. 15 p. 8°.

430807A.   1. Jews in Hungary—Biog.
N.Y.P.L.   September 26, 1929

NL 0446453   NN

Loew, Jacques, 1908–
Les dockers de Marseille, analyse type d'un complexe.
Pref. de Gustave Thibon. 2. éd., rev. et augm. L'Arbresle
(Rhône) Économie et humanisme ₍1945₎
x, 107 p. maps, diagrs., tables. 23 cm. (Documents économie et
humanisme, 1)

1. Longshoremen—Marseille.   I. Title.
HD8039.L82F86 1945   61-32164

NL 0446454   DLC MH MH-IR NN

LOE W. Jacques, 1908–
Les dockers de Marseille. Analyse type d'un
complexe. Préface de Gustave Thibon. 2. ed. rev.
et augm. L'Arbresle (Rhône). Économie et
humanisme [1945] x. 107 p. illus. 23cm.
(Documents Économie et humanisme, 1)

Film reproduction. Master negative. Original discarded.
Positive in *ZT-42.

NL 0446455   NN

Loew, Jacques, 1908–
En mission prolétarienne. Paris, Économie et humanisme
₍1946–
v. 19 cm. (Spiritualité, 2
CONTENTS.—1. Étapes vers un apostolat intégral.

1. Church and social problems—France. 2. Church and social
problems—Catholic Church. I. Title.

HN39.F8L6   261   48–22308 rev*

NL 0446456   DLC MWAC

Loew, Jacques, 1908–
Mission to the poorest. With an introd. and epilogue by
Maisie Ward. Foreword by Archbishop Cushing. New
York, Sheed and Ward, 1950.
vii, 184 p. 21 cm.
"A translation by Pamela Carswell of ₍v. 1 of₎ En mission prolé-
tarienne, by Père Loew."

1. Church and social problems—France. 2. Church and social problems—Catholic Church. I. Title.

HN39.F8L62   261   50–9864 rev

NL 0446457   DLC OrStbM PV WaSpG MB OKentU

Loew, Jeremiah, 1811–1874.
דברי ירמיהו. פ׳ על הרמב״ם מדע ואהבה ₍זמנים, מזנקאמש.
בדפוס ב. בלייער. תרל״ה-ל״ו.
Munkács, 1875.
2 v. in 1. 34 cm.

1. Moses ben Maimon, 1135–1204. Mishneh Torah—Commentaries.
I. Title.   *Title transliterated:* Divre Yirmiyahu.
BM545.M66L6   A 54–7624
New York. Public Libr.
for Library of Congress   ₍3₎†

NL 0446458   NN MH DLC

Löw, Johann, respondent.
... De praecipuis ad causam feudorvm
efficientem pertinentibus
see under Locamer, Georg David,
1588–1637, praeses.

Loew, Johann Adam, d. 1775.
Sammlung von predigten uber alle sonn und
festtags-Evangelia des ganzen jahres, wie auch
einiger buds-und fasten predigten christlichen
lesern aur erbauung in druck gegeben. Gotha,
Mevius, 1759.
1398 p.

NL 0446460   PPLT

Löw, Johann Franz
see Loew von Erlsfeld, Johann Franz,
ritter, 1648–1725.

A30
L4
1743ℓ
Loew, Johann Gottfried, b. 1708
S.R. Imperii et caesareae maiestatis
ianitorum solemne ministerium et familiare
generosae in Thuringia gentis comitum et L.
baronum de Werthern dominorum ... toparcharum.
Lipsiae, 1743.
Diss. - Leipzig.

NL 0446462   CtY

NA1036
G87.25
C38
L6
1930
Löw, Josef
Kleiner Gurker Domführer. 3., umgearb.
Aufl. ... von P. Josef Löw C.Ss.R.
Klagenfurt, Carinthia d. St. J.-V., 1930
166 p. front., 37 illus., diagrs.,
plans, 16 plates. 19cm.

NL 0446463   MWiCA

Löw (Joseph) [1764–   ]. *Streitsätze aus der
gesammten Medicin. 3 l. sm. 8°. Landshut,
Thomann, 1808.

NL 0446464   DNLM

QY
L826u
1815
LOEW, Joseph, 1764–
Ueber den Urin als diagnostisches und
prognostisches Zeichen in physiologischer
Hinsicht. 2. Aufl. Landshut, Thomann,
1815.
256 p.

NL 0446465   DNLM

Loew, Joseph, 1834–1886.
Allegro brillant für 2 Pianoforte von J. Loew.
Op. 325. Leipzig, Rob. Forberg [1856]
2 pts. f°.

NL 0446466   NN

Löw, Joseph, 1834–1886.
Brillant-Walzer und Tarantella. 2 Stücke für
2 Klaviere zu 4 Händen (2 Spieler), komponirt
von J. Löw. Op. 491. Nos. 1 & 2. Leipzig,
Siegel [18--]
2 pms (4 pts.) f°.

NL 0446467   NN

Löw, Joseph, 1834–1886
8 melodious octave studies for the
pianoforte; rev. and fingered by Hans
Semper. Op. 281. Wood, n.d.

NL 0446468   OrP

Loew, Joseph, 1834–
Evening in spring. Op. 326. [For pianoforte.] New and improved
edition.
Boston. Russell & Co. [188–?] 5 pp. [Salon-Stücke für das
Pianoforte. No. 4.] 35 cm.

L7413 — T.r. — Pianoforte. Music.

NL 0446469   MB

Löw, Joseph, 1834–1886.
Favorite melodies arranged for pianoforte duets
(teacher and pupil) as a supplement to every
pianoforte school...ed. by Hans Semper. v.2.
Boston, Wood music co. n.d.

NL 0446470   OCl

Löw, Joseph, 1834–   , ed.
...Flowers of melody; 40 transcriptions of
favorite songs and opera melodies for the
pianoforte, without octaves...Ed. and fingered by
Wm. Scharfenberg. [2v.] New York, G. Schirmer,
n.d. (Household series of music books, n. 6)
Lacking v. 2.

NL 0446471   OCl

VOLUME 338

Löw, Joseph, 1834-
...Liebchens gruss, op 370. Der rose erwachen op. 376. [16 parts in portfolio.]
Bremen, Fischer, n.d.

Full score lacking.
For contents of portfolio see author card in Musó catalgo, Fine Arts division.

NL 0446472   OC1

---

qM786.3 Löw, Joseph, 1834-
L95n
   New melodious brilliant octave-studies for the pianoforte for both hands alternately, designed to promote flexibility of the wrist for the staccato touch. Op.281. Edited and rev. by I. H. Cornell. Rev. and fingered by Wm. Scharfenberg. New York, G. Schirmer, 1883.
29p. 35cm.

   1. Piano—Studies and exercises.

NL 0446473   IU CaBVa IU MH OC1

---

fM203 Löw, Joseph, 1834-
L64P3
   Paul und Virginie, piano, 4 hands.
   Paul und Virginie; 8 miniatur. Tonbilder für das Pianoforte zu 4 Händen (die Primopartie ohne Octavenspannung und mit Fingersatzbezeichnung). Als rhythnisch melodiös anregende Belgabe zum Unterricht. Op.485. Braunschwe H.Litolff's Verlag n.d., Pl.no.11796.
39p. 30cm. (Collection Litolff)

   Caption titles alternately in French and German.

NL 0446474   IaU

Löw, Joseph, 1834-1886, ed.
   Practischer Lehrgang des vierhändigen Clavierspiels; beliebte Melodien als Supplement zu jeder Clavierschule besonders zu; Köhler's Practischer Lehrgang des Clavierspiels. Braunschweig, Litolff; Boston, Schmidt, n.d.
   2 v. (Collection Litolff, no. 1189, 1190)

NL 0446475   OC1

Löw, Joseph, 1834-1886.
   Reminiscence to Mendelssohn. Nachklänge an Mendelssohn. Allegro by Joseph Löw. Op. 337. C. Für 2 piano. Offenbach a.M., Joh. André [18--]
   2 pts. f°.

NL 0446476   NN

VM LÖW, JOSEPH, 1834-1886.
201   Sechs charakteristische Tonstücke für das
D 85   Pianoforte zu vier Händen. Op.318. Heft II. Bremen, Praeger [18—]
v.2   13p. 34cm.

   Binder's title: Duets, v.2.
   Plate no.: P & M 10019-?
   Contents.—Tirolerlied.—Russische Zigeuner.—Minnelied.

NL 0446477   ICN

M786.494 Löw, Joseph, 1834-1886.
L827s   Serenade, 2 pianos, 4 hands, op.489.
Music   Serenade für zwei Klaviere. Op. 489.
lib.   Leipzig, Rob. Forberg [n.d.] Pl. no. 3221.
   2 parts. 35cm.

   Cover title.

NL 0446478   NcU NN

---

qM786.413 Löw, Joseph, 1834-1886.
L95s
   Spring blossoms. Op.205. Pleasing fantasies upon favorite themes. Arranged without octaves, and carefully fingered for the piano. Cincinnati, J. Church, 1877.
   v. 35cm.

NL 0446479   IU

Loew, Joseph, 1834-1886.
   ...Teacher and pupil; a practical course of four hand piano playing. In two volumes. New York: G. Schirmer, cop. 1893. Publ. pl. nos. 10669-10670. 2 v. in 1. New ed., rev. 4°. (Schirmer's library of musical classics. v. 472-473.)

   1. Piano.—Duets. 2. Title.
N. Y. P. L.   October 23, 1922.

NL 0446480   NN MtBC OrU OrP MH OC1 OO CtW OC1Ur

Löw, Joseph, 1834-1886.
   Wild roses; 12 characteristics pieces in fine notes for piano for four hands. 2 v. in 1. N.Y. Schrimer, 1898. (Schrimer's library of music classics, v.548, 549.)
   Op.4

NL 0446481   OC1

Loew (Josephus). *De dysenteria. 14 pp. 8°.
  *Monachii, typ. Hübschmannianis, 1841.

NL 0446482   DNLM

W Löw, Jürgen, 1919-
4   Das klinische Bild des sporadisch
H46 auftretenden Typhus. Karlsruhe, 1943.
1943   47 p. illus.

   Inaug.-Diss. - Heidelberg.
   Bibliography: p. 46.

NL 0446483   DNLM

WG Loew, Karl, 1876-
27915   "Ueber Kondensationen von Chinaldin und Lepidin mit einigen Aldehyden". Breslau, 1903.
   46 p.

   Inaug.-Diss. - Breslau.

NL 0446484   CtY MH

Loew, Karl, 1889-
   Die Schlacht bei Villmergen im Jahre 1712... von Karl Löw ... Liestal: Buchdruckerei Landschäftler A.-G., 1912. 108 p. maps. 8°.

   Dissertation, Basel.
   Lebens-Abriss.

   1. Switzerland.—History, 1712.
N. Y. P. L.   January 24, 1925.

NL 0446485   NN PU CtY ICRL MiU MH

AC Löw, Karl, 1910-
831   -Die stadt Giessen und ihre umgebung in siedlungsgeographischer entwicklung. ...Giessen, 1937. 140 p.
   Inaug. Diss. - Giessen, 1937.
   Lebenslauf.
   Schrifttumsnachweis.

NL 0446486   ICRL

Loew, Karl Anton.
   Naturgeschichte aller der landwirthschaft schädlichen insecten, mit ausnahme der forstinsecten. Nebst angabe der bewährtesten mittel zu ihrer vertilgung oder verminderung. Für landwirthe und gartenbesitzer, so wie auch zum unterricht in landwirthschaftlichen, polytechnischen und höheren bürgerschulen, von dr. Carl Anton Löw ... 2. aufl. Mannheim, F. Götz, 1846.

   xv, 307 p. 20ᵐᵐ.

   1. Insects, Injurious and beneficial. [1. Entomology, Economic]
                      Agr 28-896
   Library, U. S. Dept. of   Agriculture   423L953

NL 0446487   DNAL IdU

Loew, Karl Benedikt Oscar
   see   Loew, Oscar, 1844-

Löw, Karl Friedrich Ludwig, freiherr von

    see

Löw, Ludwig, freiherr von, 1803-1868.

Löw, Konrad
   see Loew, Conrad.

Loew, Lawrence.
   The how and why of portraiture, by Lawrence Loew. New York, The Galleon publishers [1940]
   93 p. illus. 18ᵐ. (On cover: The how and why series. no. 10)

   1. Photography—Portraits.   ɪ. Title. ɪɪ. Title: Portraiture, The how and why of.

   Library of Congress   TR575.L6   40-6388
   ———— Copy 2.
   Copyright AA 329147   [2]   778

NL 0446491   DLC OC1 WaS OLak

Loew, Lawrence.
   ... Photography by artificial light, by Lawrence Loew. New York, N. Y., Galleon publishers, inc. [1939]
   48 p. incl. illus., tables. 17ᵐ. (Photo amateur series. no. 8)

   1. Photography—Artificial light.   ɪ. Title.
                                 41-1708
   Library of Congress   TR600.L6
   ———— Copy 2.
   Copyright AA 346850   [2]   770

NL 0446492   DLC MB OC1 OC1h OEac

BM45 Löw, Leopold, 1811-1875.
.L6   Gesammelte Schriften; hrsg. von Immanuel Löw. Szegedin, A. Bába, 1889-
   v. 24cm.

   Vols. 4- published by L. Engel.
   Bibliographical footnotes.

   1.Judaism - Collected works. I. Loew, Immanuel, 1854-1944. ed.

NL 0446493   MiDW NN MH OCH OC1 OU CU

Loew, Leopold, 1811-1875.
   Az Aldozatlan Zsidó kultus. Történelmi vázlat ... Szegeden: Z. Burger, 1871.
   24 p.

NL 0446494   OCH

VOLUME 338

DS111 .L73 **Löw, Leopold, 1811-1875.**
Beiträge zur jüdischen alterthumskunde. Von Leopold Löw ... Leipzig, O. Leiner, 1870-
  v. 20cm. [Schriften hrsg. vom Institut zur förderung der israelitischen literatur ... 15. jahr: 1869-1870
Each vol. has also special t.-p.

1. Jews--Antiq. 2. Jews--Hist. I. Title.

NL 0446495 DLC PU MnCS OCH MB NN

BM1 .B4 **Löw, Leopold, 1811-75, ed.**

Ben-Chananja; Monatsschrift für jüdische Theologie.

Szegedin, S. Burger.

Löw, Leopold, 1811-1875.
Die göttliche Offenbarung des 18-ten Februars. Feierlicher Gottesdienst aus Anlass der ... Rettung ... des Kaisers ... Franz Josephs des Ersten gehalten am 26. Februar ... zu Szegedin. Von Leopold Löw ... Szegedin, 1853.
  15 p. 20.5 cm.

NL 0446497 CtY

Löw, Leopold, 1811-1875.
Graphische Requisiten und Erzeugnisse bei den Juden. Von Leopold Löw... Leipzig, O. Leiner, 1870-71. 2 v. in 1. 20cm. (Institut zur Förderung der israelitischen Literatur. Schriften. Jahr 15-16.)

His: Beiträge zur jüdischen Alterthumskunde. Bd. 1.

406233-4. 1. Writing materials— Jews. I. Ser. *Card revised*
N.Y.P.L. *September 12, 1945*

OCH OC1 NNC
NL 0446498 NN MH PPDrop PP CtY IU NNUT CU DCU-H

LÖW, LEOPOLD, 1811-1875.
Graphische Requisiten und Erzeugnisse bei den Juden. Leipzig, O. Leiner, 1870-71. 2 v. 20cm. (Institut zur Förderung der israelitischen Literatur. Schriften. Jahr 15-16)

Film reproduction. Positive.
HIS: Beiträge zur jüdischen Alterthumskunde. Bd. 1.

1. Writing materials--Jews. 2. Writing materials. I. Ser.

NL 0446499 NN

Loew, Leopold, 1811-1875.
Die grosse Synode, ihr Ursprung und ihre Wirkungen. Historischer Versuch über das erste Jahrhundert des Thalmudismus, von Herrn Rabbiner Löw, kritisch beurtheilt von Sigmund Krauss... Pest: F. Pfeifer, 1859. 41 p. incl. tables. 8°.

1. Synagogue, The great. 2. Krauss, Sigmund.
N.Y.P.L. *April 7, 1925*

NL 0446500 NN

Löw, Leopold, 1811-1875.
Die heiligen Lehrer der Vorzeit. Antrittspredigt, am 10-ten Dezember 1850 in der Synagoge zu Szegedin gehalten von Leopold Löw ... Szegedin, 1850.
  24 p. 21 cm.

NL 0446501 CtY

4BM 316 **Löw, Leopold, 1811-1875.**
Jüdische Dogmen. Offenes Sendschreiben an den Herrn Dr. Ignatz Hirschler, Eigenthümer des "Izraelita Közlöny." Pest, L. Aigner, 1871.
  40 p.

NL 0446502 DLC-P4 MH NN OCH

Löw, Leopold, 1811-1875.
Die Lebensalter in der jüdischen Literatur. Von physiologischem, Rechts-, Sitten- u. religionsgeschichtlichem Standpunkte betrachtet. Von Leopold Löw. Szegedin, S. Burger's Wwe. 1875. xvi, 459 p. 22cm. (His: Beiträge zur jüdischen Alterthumskunde. Bd. 2.)

196426A. 1. Age. *Card revised*
N.Y.P.L. *September 12, 1945*

NL 0446503 NN NNU-W CtY ICU MH OCH PP MiDW

Löw, Leopold, 1811-1875.
Löw Lipót végtisztessége
see under title

Löw, Leopold, 1811-1875.
Das neueste Stadium der ungarisch-jüdischen Organisationsfrage. Offenes Sendschreiben an den Herrn Dr. Ignatz Hirschler, Präses der Kongresskommission. Pest, L. Aigner, 1871.
  80 p. 23 cm.

1. Jews in Hungary—Education. I. Title.

LC746.H8L6 53-55694 ‡

NL 0446505 DLC OCH

DH L824p **Löw, Leopold, 1811-1875.**
... Praktische Einleitung in die Heilige Schrift und Geschichte der Schriftauslegung, ein Lehrbuch für die reifere Jugend, ein Handbuch für Gebildeta. Erster Theil. Allgemeine Einleitung und Geschichte der Schriftauslegung. Gross-Kanischa, Druck von J. Markbreiter, 1855.
  2 p. l., ix, [3]-355 p., 1 l. 20 cm.

Title in Hebrew at head of title (romanized): ha-Mafteah.
No more published.

1. Bible - Hermeneutics. 2. Bible. O.T. - Criticism, interpretation, etc. - Hist. 3. Jewish exegesis. I. Title. II. Title: ha-Mafteah.

NL 0446507 CtY-D NjPT

Loew, Leopold, 1811-1875.
Die Theilnahme treuer Unterthanen am Geburtsfeste ihres Fürsten. Rede am Geburtsfeste des Kaisers Ferdinand I. am 19. April 1843 in der Synagoge zu Gross-Kanischa. Warasdin: J. v. Platzer, 1843.
  14 p.

NL 0446508 OCH

Loew, Leopold, 1811-1875.
Zsinagógai beszédek. Szeged, Traub, 1870
  324 p.

NL 0446509 MH

Löw, Leopold, 1811-1875.
Zur neueren geschichte der Juden in Ungarn. Beitrag zur allgemeinen rechts-, religions- und kulturgeschichte. Von Leopold Löw. 2. ausg. Budapest, L. Aigner, 1874.
  xvi, 332, [4] p. 24cm.

1. Jews in Hungary.

22-24625

Library of Congress DS135.H9L6

NL 0446510 DLC MH OU PHC OCH

Loew, Lipót.
Die Maschine als Arbeitsmittel. Wien [1914] 80 S.

Heidelberg, Phil. Diss.

NL 0446511 MH PU CtY ICRL

Löw, Lipot, 1811-1875

see

Loew, Leopold, 1811-1875.

Löw, Loránt
Adalékok a második tervezet birálatához. Irta Dr Löw Loránt ... Budapest, Márkus S., 1913.
  27 p. 23cm.

"Külön lenyomat az 'Ügyvédek lapjá'-ból."

NL 0446513 MH-L

Löw, Loránt
... A bizonyitási teher a polgári törvénykönyv tervezete és a polgári perrendtartás szerint. [Irta, Dr Löw Loránt ... Budapest, Franklin-társulat bizománya, 1915.
  3 p. l., [3]-84 p. 23½cm. (Magyar jogászegyleti értekezések ... Uj folyam. X. köt. 67. füz.)

"Elöadása, a Magyar jogászegylet 1913. februar hó 8-án tartott teljes-ülésén." Bibliography included in "Jegyzetek": p. [78]-84.

NL 0446514 MH-L

Löw, Loránt
Viszonylagos semmisség. Tanulmány a magyar általános polgári törvénykönyv tervezetének jogügyleteiről. Irta Dr. Löw Loránt. Budapest, Politzer-féle könyvkiadó vállalat kiadása, 1905.
  2 p. l., 107, [1] p. 24cm.

Bibliographical footnotes.

NL 0446515 MH-L

Löw, Ludwig, Freiherr von, 1803-1868
De antiquo Germanorum jure marcali specimen primum. Amplissimi Jureconsultorum ordinis jussu pro impetranda facultate legendi in alma literarum Universitate Ruperto-Carolina scripsit Car. Fr. Lud. L.B. de Loew ... Heidelbergae, J.M. Gutmann, 1826.
  1 p. l., 56 p. 19cm.

Bibliographical footnotes.

NL 0446516 MH-L MH-BA MiU

VOLUME 338

Loew, Ludwig, freiherr von, 1803-1868.
Einleitung in das studium der rechtswissenschaft; ein lehrbuch fur akade¡ischen unterricht nebst ¤iner chrestomathis von rechtsquellen.
Zurich, 1835.
178 p.

NL 0446517   PBm

Loew, Ludwig, freiherr von, 1803-1868.
Germanistische rechtsfälle zum gebrauch bei vorlesungen und zum privatstudium, nebst einem repertorium. Heidelberg, 1836.

NL 0446518   MH-L

Löw, Ludwig, *freiherr* von, 1803-1868.
Geschichte der Deutschen reichs- und territorialverfassung, auch zum gebrauche bei academischen vorlesungen. Von d⁴. Ludwig freih. v. Löw ... Heidelberg, Mohr, 1832.
xii, 412 p. 21ᶜᵐ.

1. Holy Roman empire—Constitutional history. 2. Law, Germanic. ι. Title.
¡Full name: Karl Friedrich Ludwig freiherr von Löw¡

35-34363

Library of Congress   JN3249.L6   342.4309

NL 0446519   DLC MiU MH NcD PPL

Löw, Ludwig, freiherr von, 1803-1868.
Ueber die markgenossenschaften ... Heidelberg, Mohr¡ 1828.
276 p.

NL 0446520   MiU

Löw, Ludwig, freiherr von, 1803-1868.
Ueber die Markgenossenschaften, von Dr. K. F. L. Freiherrn von Löw, ... Heidelberg, J. C. B. Mohr, 1829.
viii, 276, [4] p. 20¼ᶜᵐ.
"Literatur," p. 19-23.

NL 0446521   ICJ MH-BA MH

Loew, M   R
see
Loew, Jacques, 1908-

W 4   LOEW, Maria, 1931-
M96   Über einen neuen biologischen
1955   Azetylcholintest, seine Kombination
mit der Papierchromatographie und
seine Eignung zum Nachweis des
Myastheniefaktors im Serum. München,
1955.
50 ℓ. illus.
Inaug.-Diss. - Munich.
1. Acetylcholine 2. Chromatography
3. Serum

NL 0446523   DNLM

Loew, Mayr.
Anleitung zur Erlernung der heiligen hebräischen Sprache ... ¡Regensburg¡:
A. Lang, 1788.
155 (1) p.

NL 0446524   OCH

Löw, Moritz, 1841-1900.
Prussia. *K. Geodätisches institut.*
... Astronomisch-geodätische ortsbestimmungen im Harz. Bestimmung der polhöhen und der geodätischen lage der stationen Blankenburg, Hüttenrode, Hasselfelde und der polhöhe von Nordhausen.   Im jahre 1881, behufs weiterer untersuchung der lothablenkungen angeordnet vom präsidenten des Königlichen geodätischen instituts und des Centralbureaus der Europäischen gradmessung herrn dr. J. J. Baeyer. Ausgeführt von dr. Moritz Löw ...   Berlin, P. Stankiewicz, 1882.

Löw, Moritz, 1841-1900.
Bestimmungen von Azimuten im Harzgebiete
see under   Prussia. Geodätisches Institut.

Löw, Moritz, 1841-1900.
Plantamour, Émile, 1815-1882.
Détermination télégraphique de la différence de longitude entre Genève et Strasbourg, exécutée en 1876, par E. Plantamour et M. Löw. Genève-Bâle-Lyon, H. Georg, 1879.

Löw, Moritz, 1841-1900.
Prussia. *K. Geodätisches institut.*
... Polhöhenbestimmungen aus dem jahre 1886 für zwanzig stationen nahe dem meridian des Brockens vom Harz biz zur dänischen grenze. Gelegentlich ausgeführte polhöhen- und azimutbestimmungen aus den jahren 1878-1884. Berlin, P. Stankiewicz, 1889.

Löw, Moritz, 1841-1900.
Prussia. *K. Geodätisches institut.*
... Polhöhenbestimmungen im Harzgebiet ausgeführt in den jahren 1887 bis 1891. Berlin, P. Stankiewicz, 1894.

Loew, Oscar, 1844-
Die bedeutung der kalk- und magnesiasalze in der landwirtschaft.
Landw. vers. stat. bd. 41, p. 467-475.   Berlin, 1892.

1. Lime. 2. Magnesia.
¡Full name: Carl Benedict Oscar Loew¡
Agr 4-2545 Revised
Library, U. S. Dept. of   Agriculture

NL 0446530   DNAL

Loew, Oscar, 1844-
Bemerkung über die giftwirkung des destillirten wassers.
Landw. jahrb. bd. 20, p. 235.   Berlin, 1891.

1. Distilled water. Poisonous influence on plants.
Agr 4-1372
Library, U. S. Dept. of   Agriculture

NL 0446531   DNAL

Loew, Oscar, 1844-
Das calcium im leben der haustiere, von dr. Oscar Loew .. München, O. Gmelin, 1930.
64 p., 1 l. illus. 22½ᶜᵐ.

1. Calcium ¡in animal nutrition¡
¡Full name: Carl Benedikt Oscar Loew¡
Agr 30-868
Library, U. S. Dept. of   Agriculture 389.7L82

NL 0446532   DNAL ICJ OCU

Loew, Oscar, 1844-
... Catalase, a new enzym of general occurrence, with special reference to the tobacco plant. By Oscar Loew ... Washington, Govt. print. off., 1901.
47 p. incl. tables. 23ᶜᵐ. (U. S. Dept. of agriculture. Report no. 68)

1. Catalase. 2. Tobacco—¡Fermentation¡
¡Full name: Carl Benedikt Oscar Loew¡
Agr 9-1868 Revised
Library, U. S. Dept. of   Agriculture 1Ag84Sp no. 68

NL 0446533   DNAL OCI OO MiU NN

Loew, Oscar, 1844-
Die chemische Craftquelle in lebenden Protoplasma. Theoretisch begründet und experimentell nachgewiesen, von Oscar Loew und Thomas Bokorny in München. (Mit einer colorirten Tafel.) Zugleich zweite Auflage zu: "Die chemische Ursache des Lebens." München, J. A. Finsterlin, 1882.
[2, v]-viii, 100, [1] p. 2 col. pl. 25ᶜᵐ.

NL 0446534   ICJ MH PU PPC PU CSt PPAmP NNC CtY-M

Loew, Oscar, 1844-
Die chemische energie der lebenden zellen, von dr. Oscar Loew ... München, E. Wolff, 1899.
xi, 75 (i. e. 175) p. 25ᶜᵐ.
Pages 172-175 incorrectly numbered 72-75.

1. Cells.
¡Full name: Carl Benedikt Oscar Loew¡
Agr 11-1054
U. S. Dept. of agr. Library   442L82C
for Library of Congress   ¡a39r23f1¡

NL 0446535   DNAL PPC MiU ICJ

Loew, Oscar, 1844-
Die chemische energie der lebenden zellen, von dr. Oscar Loew ... 2. aufl. Stuttgart, F. Grub, 1906.
iv, ¡2¡, 183 p. 24½ᶜᵐ.

1. Cells.
¡Full name: Carl Benedikt Oscar Loew¡
Agr 11-1055 Revised
U. S. Dept. of agr. Library   442L82C
for Library of Congress   ¡r39b2¡

NL 0446536   DNAL ICRL CU ICJ

Loew, Oscar, 1844-
Die chemische ursache des lebens. Theoretisch und experimentell nachgewiesen von Oscar Loew und Thomas Bokorny ... München, In commission bei J. A. Finsterlin, 1881.
1 p. l., ¡2¡, 59 p. col. pl. 24ᶜᵐ.

1. Biology. 2. Protoplasm. 3. Cells. ι. Bokorny, Thomas, 1856-
3-13704
Library of Congress   QH391.L81

NL 0446537   DLC DNLM PPC ICJ

Loew, Oscar, 1844-
...Curing and fermentation of cigar leaf tobacco. By Oscar Loew ... Washington, Govt. print. off., 1899.
34 p. 23ᶜᵐ. (U. S. Dept. of agriculture. Report no. 59)
"Recent foreign literature": p. 34.
1. Tobacco—Curing. 2. Tobacco—Fermentation.
Agr 9-1860
Library, U. S. Dept. of   Agriculture 1Ag84Sp no. 59

NL 0446538   DNAL OCI MiU OO NN MB

VOLUME 338

Loew, Oscar, *1844-*
    Einige bemerkungen zur giftwirkung der salze des magnesiums, strontiums und baryums auf pflanzen.
    Landw. jahrb. bd. 32, p. 509–515.   **Berlin, 1903.**

    1. Poison. Effect on plants.
                                  Agr 4-1878
    Library, U. S. Dept. of   Agriculture

NL 0446539   DNAL

Loew, Oscar, *1844-*
    L'énergie chimique primaire de la matière vivante par M. le dr. Oscar Loew ... avec la collaboration de M. M.-Emm. Pozzi-Escot ... . Paris, J. Rousset, 1904.
    181, [2] p. 19½ᶜᵐ.

NL 0446540   ICJ NjP

Loew, Oscar, *1844-*
    The energy of living protoplasm. By Oscar Loew ... London, K. Paul, Trench, Trübner & co., ltd., 1896.
    iv, 115, [1] p. 19ᶜᵐ.

    1. Protoplasm. I. Title.
                  [Full name: Carl Benedikt Oscar Loew]
    Library of Congress   QH591.L82   2–26625

NL 0446541   DLC CU MBH CtY NIC OO MiU MB

Loew, Oscar *i. e.* **Carl Benedikt Oscar,** *1844-*
    Ist die lehre vom kalkfaktor eine hypothese oder eine bewiesene theorie?
    Landw. jahrb. bd. 46, p. 733–752.   **Berlin, 1914.**

    1. [Liming of soils]
                        Agr 14-1508
    Library, U. S. Dept. of   Agriculture

NL 0446542   DNAL

QP141
929l
    Loew, Oscar, 1844-
    Der Kalkbedarf des Menschen; zur chemischen physiologie des kalks. 5. verb. und ergänzte Aufl., Muchen, Gmelin, 1929.
    73p. tables. 23cm.

    1. Lime - Physiological effect. 2. Nutrition.

NL 0446543   CtY-M NNC OCU IU

Loew, Oscar, *1844-*
    Der kalkbedarf von mensch und tier. Zur chemischen physiologie des kalks bei mensch und tier. Von dr. Oscar Loew ... 2., verm. und verb. aufl. München, O. Gmelin, 1919.
    107 p. illus. 24½ᶜᵐ.

    1. Lime. 2. Nutrition. [1, 2. Lime in animal nutrition]
                  [Full name: Carl Benedict Oscar Loew]
                        Agr 20-741
    Library, U. S. Dept. of   Agriculture 386.2L82

NL 0446544   DNAL DNLM ICJ

Loew, Oscar.
    Der kalkbedarf von Mensch und Tier. Aerztlichen rundschau Otto Gmelin, München. 1924.

NL 0446545   OClW

QU
4
L827k
1924
    LOEW, Oscar, 1844-
    Der Kalkbedarf von Mensch und Tier; zur chemischen Physiologie des Kalks.
    3. neu durchgesehene Aufl. München, Gmelin, 1924.
    95 p. illus.
    Title

NL 0446546   DNLM

Loew, Oscar, 1844-
    Der Kalkbedarf von Mensch und Tier; zur chemischen Physiologie des Kalks, von Dr. Oscar Loew ... Vierte, verbesserte und ergänzte Auflage. München, O. Gmelin, 1927.
    101 p. 23ᶜᵐ.
    Bibliographical foot-notes.

NL 0446547   ICJ

Loew, Oscar, *1844-*
    Kalkdüngung und magnesiadüngung.
    Landw. jahrb. bd. 35, p. 527–540.   **Berlin, 1906.**

    1. Lime. 2. Magnesia.
                         Agr 7-23
    Library, U. S. Dept. of   Agriculture

NL 0446548   DNAL

Loew, Oscar, *1844-*
    Kann das rubidium die physiologische function des kaliums in der pflanzenzelle übernehmen?
    Landw. vers. stat. bd. 21, p. 389–395.   **Berlin, 1878.**

    1. Potassium. 2. Rubidium.
                        Agr 4-2667
    Library, U. S. Dept. of   Agriculture

NL 0446549   DNAL

Loew (Oscar). Kupferoxyd-Ammoniak als Oxydationsmittel. pp. 298–302. 8°. [Leipzig, 1878.]
    Cutting [cover with printed title] *from : J. f. prakt. Chem., Leipz., 1878, xviii.*

NL 0446550   DNLM

Loew, Oscar, 1844-
    Die lehre vom kalkfaktor. Theoretische entwicklung, scheinbare ausnahmen und praktische gesichtspunkte. Von dr. Oscar Loew ... Berlin, P. Parey, 1914.
    31 p. illus. 26ᶜᵐ.
    "Erweiterter sonderabdruck aus: 'Landw. jahrbücher,' bd. xlvi, hft. 5 (1914)"

    1. Lime.
                  [Full name: Carl Benedikt Oscar Loew]
                      Agr 19-795
    Library, U. S. Dept. of   Agriculture 57L952

NL 0446551   DNAL NjR

Loew, Oscar, *1844-*
    Liming of soils from a physiological standpoint.
    (In United States. Department of Agriculture. Bureau of Plant Industry. Bulletin. No. 1, pp. 9–35. Washington, 1901.)

               June 2,   1902
    E4479 — Lime. — Soils. — Physiological chemistry.

NL 0446552   MB

Loew, Oscar, *1844-*
    Ein natürliches System der Gift-Wirkungen von Dr. Oscar Loew, ... München, E. Wolff und H. Lüneburg, 1893.
    viii, 136 p. 23½ᶜᵐ.

NL 0446553   ICJ FMU DNLM OClW KyU MiU IU-M

Loew, Oscar, *1844-*
    ... On the "sick" soils of Porto Rico. By Oscar Loew ... San Juan, P. R., Tip. Boletin mercantil, 1910.
    24 p. 23ᶜᵐ. (Porto Rico agricultural experiment station ... Circular no. 12)

    1. Soils—Porto Rico. 2. Soils, Sick.
                        Agr 11-197
    Library, U. S. Dept. of   Agriculture 1Ex65B no. 12

NL 0446554   DNAL NN

Loew, Oscar, *1844-*
    ... The physiological rôle of mineral nutrients. By Oscar Loew ... Washington, Govt. print. off., 1899.
    60 p. 23ᶜᵐ. (U. S. Dept. of agriculture. Division of vegetable physiology and pathology. Bulletin no. 18)

    1. Mineral nutrients. 2. Plant physiology.
                        Agr 9-234
    Library, U. S. Dept. of   Agriculture

NL 0446555   DNAL NN MB

Loew, Oscar, 1844-
    ... The physiological rôle of mineral nutrients in plants. By Oscar Loew ... Washington, Govt. print. off., 1903.
    70 p. 23ᶜᵐ. (U. S. Bureau of plant industry. Bulletin no. 45)
    At head of title: U. S. Department of agriculture. Bureau of plant industry ...

    1. Plants—Nutrition. [1. Plant nutrition] 2. [Mineral nutrients]
    I. Title.
                  [Full name: Carl Benedikt Oscar Loew]
                      Agr 9-171 Revised
    U. S. Dept. of agr. Library   1P69B no. 45
    for Library of Congress   [QK1.U45 no. 45]

NL 0446556   DNAL MB MH-A MBH

Loew, Oscar, 1844-
    ... Physiological studies of Connecticut leaf tobacco. By Oscar Loew ... Washington, Govt. print. off., 1900.
    57 p. 23ᶜᵐ. (U. S. Dept. of agriculture. Report no. 65)

    1. Tobacco. I. Title.
                  [Full name: Carl Benedikt Oscar Loew]
                      Agr 9-1865 Revised
    Library, U. S. Dept. of   Agriculture 1Ag84Sp no. 65

NL 0446557   DNAL NN

Loew, Oscar, 1844-
    ... The relation of lime and magnesia to plant growth. I. Liming of soils from a physiological standpoint. By Oscar Loew ... II. Experimental study of the relation of lime and magnesia to plant growth. By D. W. May ... Washington, Govt. print. off., 1901.
    53 p. III pl. 26ᶜᵐ. (U. S. Dept. of agriculture. Bureau of plant industry. Bulletin no. 1)
    Reprinted in 1903 with a correction on plate II.

    [1. Soils, Lime in] [2. Liming of soils] [3. Soils, Magnesia in]
    1-3. Soils. 4. Plants—Nutrition. [4. Plant nutrition] I. May, David William, 1868-
                  [Full name: Carl Benedikt Oscar Loew]
                      Agr 9-124 Revised
    Library, U. S. Dept. of   Agriculture 1P69B no. 1

NL 0446558   DNAL OCl OClMN MH-A MBH

VOLUME 338

Loew, Oscar.
—— Report on the geographical distribution of vegetation in the Mohave desert. [Washington. 1876.] 8°. pp. [3].
From "U. S. Geographical and geological explorations and surveys of the territories west of the 100th meridian, G. M. Wheeler in charge."

NL 0446559   MH-A

Loew, Oscar, 1844-
... Report upon mineralogical, agricultural, and chemical conditions observed in portions of Colorado, New Mexico, and Arizona, in 1873. By Oscar Loew ... (*In* U. S. Geographical surveys west of the 100th meridian. Report ... Washington, 1875-89. 30cm. vol. III (1875), p. 569-661. illus., pl. XIII)
CONTENTS.—Agricultural resources, soil, vegetation, cosmical phenomena.—Analyses of mineral springs and minerals.—The eruptive rocks of New Mexico and Arizona.—Mineralogical tables.
Subject entries: 1. Geology—Western states.   2. Mineralogy—Western states.   3. Mineral waters—Western states.
3-26097

Library of Congress, no.   QE74.W6.

NL 0446560   DLC OO OCU ICJ

Loew, Oscar, 1844-
... Soil disinfection in agriculture. By Oscar Loew ... Mayaguez, P. R., Job printer "Bandera americana," 1909.
2 p. l., [3]-12 p. 23cm. (Porto Rico agricultural experiment station. Circular no. 11)
1. Soil disinfection.
Agr 9-2417
Library, U. S. Dept. of   Agriculture 1Ex65C no. 11

NL 0446561   DNAL NN

Loew, Oscar, 1844-
... Some principles in manuring with lime and magnesia, by Oscar Loew ... San Juan, P. R., Press review printing co., 1909.
15 p. 23cm. (Porto Rico agricultural experiment station. Circular no. 10)

1. Lime. 2. Magnesia.
Agr 9-2405
Library, U. S. Dept. of   Agriculture 1Ex65C no. 10

NL 0446562   DNAL NN

Loew, Oscar, 1844-
... Studies on acid soils of Porto Rico. By Oscar Loew ... Washington, Govt. print. off., 1913.
23 p. diagr. 23 cm. (Porto Rico. Agricultural experiment station. Bulletin no. 13)

1. Soils—Puerto Rico. 2. Soil acidity.   I. Title.
Full name: Carl Benedikt Oscar Loew.
S181.E2 no. 13   1Ex65   Agr 13-1864
—— Copy 2.   S593.L85
U. S. Nat'l Agr. Libr.
for Library of Congress   [a63c½]†

NL 0446563   DNAL DLC NN OC1

Loew, Oscar, 1844-
Über abhängigkeit des maximalertrags von einem bestimmten quantitativen verhältnisse zwischen kalk und magnesia im boden. 2 pl.
Landw. jahrb. bd. 31, p. 561-576.   Berlin, 1902.

1. Soils, Lime in. 2. Soils, Magnesia in.
Agr 4-1374
Library, U. S. Dept. of   Agriculture

NL 0446564   DNAL

Loew, Oscar i. e. Carl Benedikt Oscar, 1844-
Über angebliche wiederlegung der lehre vom kalkfaktor.
Landw. jahrb. bd. 39, p. 335-343, 1005-1009; bd 42, p. 181-192.
Berlin, 1910-12.

1. Lime.
Agr 10-1795 Revised
Library, U. S. Dept. of   Agriculture

NL 0446565   DNAL

Loew, Oscar, 1844-
Über das kalkbedürfnis der pflanzen.
Landw. jahrb. bd. 34, p. 131-137.   Berlin, 1905.

1. Lime in plant nutrition.
Agr 5-472
Library, U. S. Dept. of   Agriculture

NL 0446566   DNAL

Loew, Oscar, 1844-   joint author.

Emmerich, Rudolf, 1852-1914.
Über den einfluss der calciumzufuhr auf die fortpflanzung. Von Rudolf Emmerich und Oskar Loew. illus.
Landw. jahrb. bd. 48, p. 313-330.   Berlin, 1915.

QD431 Loew, Oscar, 1844-
.L6   Ueber die einwirkung des cyans auf albumin. Leipzig, 1877.
18p.
Inaug. diss. Leipzig.

NL 0446568   DLC

1844-
Loew (Oscar), Ueber die Quelle der Hippursäure im Harne der Pflanzenfresser. 3 pp. 8°.
[*München, J. A. Finsterlin,* 1879.]
Repr. from: Aerztl. Int-Bl., München, 1879. xx.

NL 0446569   DNLM

Loew, Oscar i. e. Carl Benedict Oscar, 1844-
joint author.
Emmerich, Rudolf.
Ueber die wirkung der kalksalze bei gesunden und kranken. Von dr. Rudolf Emmerich ... und dr. Oscar Loew ... München, Verlag der Aerztlichen rundschau O. Gmelin, 1913.

Loew, Oscar, 1844-
Über mineralsaure böden.
Landw. jahrb. bd. 46, p. 161-164.   Berlin, 1914.

[1. Soil acidity]
Agr 14-1216
Library, U. S. Dept. of   Agriculture

NL 0446571   DNAL

Loew, Oscar, 1844-
Über reizmittel des pflanzenwachstums und deren praktische anwendung. 2 pl.
Landw. jahrb. bd. 32, p. 437-448.   Berlin, 1903.

1. Stimuli in plant growth.
Agr 4-1375
Library, U. S. Dept. of   Agriculture

NL 0446572   DNAL

Loew, Oscar, 1844-
Zur charakterisierung von zuckerarten.
Landw. vers. stat. bd. 41, p. 131-135.   Berlin, 1892.

1. Sugars. Identification.
Agr 4-2558
Library, U. S. Dept. of   Agriculture

NL 0446573   DNAL

QP913 Loew, Oscar, 1844-
.C2L8   Zur chemischen physiologie des kalks bei mensch und
(B)   tier. Von dr. Oscar Loew ... München, O. Gmelin, 1916.
79 p. illus. 23½cm.

1. Lime. 2. Nutrition.

NL 0446574   ICU NjP

LOEW, Otto.
Marpurgi 1908. 90 S.

Marburg, Phil.Diss.   4241.65

NL 0446575   MH NjP CtY ICRL

Loew, Otto, 1903-
Ueber die spaetprognose bei schaedelverletzungen besonders schaedelbasisbruechen. Inaug. diss. Wuerzburg, 1926.
Bibl.

NL 0446576   ICRL DNLM CtY

Löw, Paul Emil Rudolf
see Löw, Rudolf, 1907-

Löw, Per.

VI flätar med peddig-rotting. [Västerås, ICA-förlaget [19

Loew, Pierre.
... Obligations stipulées à cause de mort et droit de succession; étude de droit civil suisse et comparé... Martigny: Imprimerie nouvelle, 1927. 3, 127 p. 8°.

Dissertation, Lausanne, 1927.
Bibliography, p. 3-6.

401725A. 1. Inheritance—Jurisp.—   Switzerland.
N. Y. P. L.   February 25, 1929

NL 0446579   NN

Loew (Pierre) [1875-   ]. *L'atrophie olivoponto-cérébelleuse; type Dejerine-Thomas. 115 pp. 1 l. 8°. Paris. 1903. No. 6.

NL 0446580   DNLM

VOLUME 338

Loew, Ralph W
The church and the amateur adult. Philadelphia, Muhlenberg Press ₁1955₎
108 p. 21 cm.

1. Church work with youth.   I. Title.

BV639.Y7L6   259   55–11780 ‡

NL 0446581   DLC PPT PPLT

Loew, Ralph W
The hinges of destiny. Philadelphia, Muhlenberg Press ₁1955₎
173 p. 20 cm.

1. Lutheran Church—Sermons. 2. Sermons, American.   I. Title.

BX8066.L594H5   252.041   55–7762 ‡

NL 0446582   DLC PPLT

LOEW Richard.
Der code civil,mit den durch die reichs – und landesgesetzgebung geschaffenen abänderungen und zusatzen,fur die Pfalz bearbeitet. Kaiserslautern,1883.

NL 0446583   MH-L

Löw, Robert.
Deutsche bauernstaaten auf russischer steppe, von dr. Robert Löw ... Charlottenburg, Ostlandverlag g. m. b. h., 1916.
64 p. 23ᶜᵐ.

1. Germans in Russia.

24–22721

Library of Congress   DK43.L6

NL 0446584   DLC

Loew, Rodophus.
Quaestiones de graecorum verborum... Inaug. diss. (Basel),1889

NL 0446585   ICRL CU

Löw, Rudolf.
Programmmusik, von Rudolf Löw ... Basel, F. Reinhardt, universitätsbuchdruckerei, 1901.
17 p. 28½ x 21½ᶜᵐ.
Programm—Gymnasium, Basel.

1. Program music.

6–12631

Library of Congress   ML3855.L8

NL 0446586   DLC

Löw, Rudolf, 1878–
Häuser über dem Rhein. Bd. 1–   Zürich ₁etc.₎ Amalthea-Verlag ₁1938₎
v.   20½cm.

CONTENTS.—Bd. 1. Dieter Basilius Deifel.

1. Fiction, Swiss-German.   I. Title. II. Title: Dieter Basilius
Deifel.
N. Y. P. L.   March 27, 1939

NL 0446587   NN

Löw, Rudolf, 1907-
... Über die Speichelsteinkrankheil ... München, 1929.
Inaug.-Diss. -München.
Lebenslauf.
Full name: Low, Paul Emil Rudolf.

NL 0446588   CtY

Löw, S.
see   Löwe S.

Löw, Simon.
Das stottern und dessen beseitigung nach methode dr. Löw; wesen, entstehung, sowie beseitigung von stottern und sprechangst nach eigener methode. Herausgegeben von dr. S. Löw ... Wien, 1932.
95, ₁1₎ p. diagrs. 22½ᶜᵐ.

1. Stammering.   I. Title.

Library of Congress   RC424.L8   33–14561
Copyright A—Foreign   19002
₍2₎   616.87

NL 0446590   DLC

Löw, Theodor.
Gebrechen unseres schulschreibsystems und ihre herkunft mit vorschlägen zur abhilfe, von Theodor Löw. Im anhang Stephan Steinlein wider die vergewaltigung unsrer deutschen schrift. München, K. T. Senger, 1913.
28 p., 1 l., 25 p. incl. front. 27 (i. e. 18) pl. 27½ᶜᵐ.
Plates printed on both sides.
"Literatur": recto of pl. numbered 27.

1. German language—Writing.   I. Steinlein, Stephan.

Library, U. S. Bur. of   Education   E 14–1177

NL 0446591   DHEW

Loew, Theodor Adolf
see   Loew, Adolf, 1906-

Löw, Tibor
... A csödeljárás. Írta: Dʳ. Löv Tibor. Budapest, Lampel R. ₁n.d.₎
72 p. 21½cm. (Magyar kereskedök könyvtára ... III. évfolyam. 9. füz.)

NL 0446593   MH-L

Löw, Tibor, ed. and tr.

FOR OTHER EDITIONS
SEE MAIN ENTRY

Hungary. *Laws, statutes, etc.*
Das ungarische handelsgesetz (Gesetz-artikel XXXVII. vom jahre 1875.) Text-ausgabe in deutscher übersetzung mit anmerkungen und sachregister hrsg. von dʳ Tibor Löw ... 3. aufl. Budapest, K. Grill, 1924.

Law

Löw, Tóbiás, 1844–1880, ed.

Hungary. *Laws, statutes, etc.*
Magyar Büntetötörvénykönyv a büntettekröl és vétségekröl (1878: 5. tcz.) és teljes anyaggyüjteménye. A M. Kir. igazságügyministerium megbizásából szerkesztette dr. Löw Tóbiás ... Budapest, Pesti könyvnyomda-részvény-társaság, 1880.

Löw, Tóbiás, 1844–1880, ed.

JN2069
.B4
1869
Récsi, Emil, 1822–1864.
Magyarország közjoga. Írta Récsi Emil. 2. kiad. bövitve és rendezve dr. Löw Tóbiás által. Buda-Pest, Pfeifer F., 1869.

Löw, Tóbiás, 1844–1880
A polgári házasság. Az elsö jogászgyülés tárgyalásaiból. Löw Tóbiás által. Pest, Aigner L., 1871.
36 p. 22cm.

NL 0446597   MH-L

FILM
833W63
OiYZ
Löw, Walter.
Die Formen der Stanze in Wielands "Idris und Zenide." ₍Wien, 1908₎
iii, 84, xxxvii, 10, 181ℓ.
In manuscript.
Diss.—Vienna.
Bibliography: leaf iii (1st group)
Microfilm (negative) Wien, Universitätsbibliothek, 1970. 1 reel. 35ᵐᵐ.

1. Wieland, Christoph Martin, 1733-1813. Idris und Zenide.

NL 0446598   IU

BS
2280
U7
v.18
Loew, Wilhelm.
Der Glaubensweg des Neuen Bundes; eine Einführung in den Brief an die Hebräer. 2. Aufl. Berlin, Furche Verlag ₍191-?₎
114 p. 23cm. (Die urchristlich Botschaft, 18 Abt.)

1. Bible. N. T. Hebrews—Commentaries.   I. Title. II. Series.

NL 0446599   CBPac

Loew, Wilhelm.
Der Glaubensweg des Neuen Bundes; eine Einführung in den Brief an die Hebräer₎ Berlin, Furche-Verlag ₁Vorwort 1931₎
114 p. 23ᵃ. (Die urchristliche Botschaft. 18)

NL 0446600   NjPT PPWe

Loew, Wilhelm.
... Goethe als religiöser charakter. München, O. Kaiser, 1924.
87 p. 23ᵃᵐ.

1. Goethe, Johann Wolfgang von—Religion and ethics.

NL 0446601   MiU NRU CU MH-AH NNC CSt CtY MWelC

Loew, Wilhelm.
... Das grundproblem der ethik Schleiermachers in seiner beziehung zu Kants ethik. Von Wilhelm Loew ... Berlin, Reuther & Reichard, 1914.
viii, 113 p., 1 l. 24½ᵃᵐ. ("Kantstudien." Ergänzungshefte ... no. 31)
Chapters 1–3 appeared as the author's inaugural dissertation, Marburg.

1. Schleiermacher, Friedrich Ernst Daniel, 1768-1834. 2. Kant, Immanuel, 1724-1804. 3. Ethics.

15–16213

Library of Congress   B2750.K28 no. 31

OC1W OO OrU ICJ NN MB IU
NL 0446602   DLC FTaSU UU NIC ICRL FU NcD CtY OCU OU

LOEW,Wilhelm, lawyer.
Das gebührengesetz samt den zu diesem gesetze erflossenen nechtregs-vorschriften und der einschlagigen judikatur. 20ste auf. Wien,191₎
2 pt.
"Manzsche taschenausgabe der österreichischen gesetze",v.12,pt.1.
By Wilhelm and Ernst Loew

NL 0446603   MH

VOLUME 338

Loew, Wilhelm, *fl. 1885.*
Ueber terephtalaldehyd.
Inaug. Diss. Erlangen, 1885 (Meunchen)

NL 0446604   ICRL DNLM

Löw, Wilhelm, 1900-
Beiträge zur kenntnis der 2,2 - indocyanine und
verwandter farbstoffe
Inaug. Diss. Dresden, 1930.

NL 0446605   ICRL

833
Er67YL   Löw, Wilhelm, 1911-
Paul Ernsts Auffassung vom Amt des Dichters; ein
Beitrag zur Deutung des Grundgefühls seiner theo-
retischen Schriften. Marburg, Wesener Nachf.,
1938.
113p. 22cm.
Inaug.-Diss.—Marburg.
Vita.
Bibliography: p.113.

1. Ernst, Paul, 1866-1933.

NL 0446606   TxU InU NNC CtY MH NIC

Loew, William Noah, *tr., 1847-1922.*
Gems from Petöfi and other Hungarian poets, ⟨trans-
lated⟩ with a memoir of the former, and a review of Hungary's poetical literature. By Wm. N. Loew ... N⟨ew⟩
Y⟨ork⟩ P. O. D'Esterhazy, 1881.
xx, 126 p. 24ᶜᵐ.
An enlarged and revised edition of "Gems from Petöfi" and "Magyar
songs" (New York, 1887) was published under title: Magyar poetry
⟨New York⟩ 1899.

1. English poetry—Translations from Hungarian. 2. Hungarian poetry—
Translations into English. I. Petöfi, Sándor, 1823-1849. II. Title.

Library of Congress   PH3421.E3L6 1881

                                                      18-5700

NL 0446607   DLC NNC NIC OCl MB RPB

Loew, William Noah, *1847-1922.*
Leopold Loew, a biography with a translation of some
of the tributes paid to his memory on the occasion of the
centenary of his birth, celebrated at Szeged, Hungary, June
4, 1911. New York, 1912.
87 p. illus. 24 cm.

1. Löw, Leopold, 1811-1875.

BM755.L584L6   63-56792 ‡

NL 0446608   DLC OCH MdBJ NN CU

Loew, William Noah, *1847-1922*
Louis [Lajos or Ludvik] Kossuth. Eulogy, before
the citizens of Newark, N.J., April 8, 1894.
N.Y., [1894]
10 p.   8°

NL 0446609   MWA CtY

Loew, William Noah, 1847?-1922, tr.
Magyar poetry. Selections from Hungarian poets. Tr. by
William N. Loew... An enl. and rev. ed. of... "Gems from Petöfi,"
1881. "Magyar songs," 1887... ⟨New York⟩ 1899. viii, 6-
349 p. front. 17cm.
"Author-translator's edition."

17337. 1. Poetry, Hungarian—Col-   lections. I. Petöfi, Sandor,
1823-1849. II. Title.   *Card revised*
N. Y. L.   *July 11, 1945*

NL 0446610   NN ICN RPB OCl OO OU MH WaU NIC

Loew, William Noah, *tr.*
Magyar poetry. Selections from Hungarian poets.
Translated by William N. Loew ... An enlarged and revised
edition of the translator's former works: "Gems from
Petöfi," 1881. "Magyar songs," 1887. "Magyar poetry,"
1899 ... New York, Amerikai magyar népszava ⟨1908?⟩
510, xi, ⟨1⟩ p. 17 cm.

1. English poetry—Translations from Hungarian. 2. Hungarian
poetry—Translations into English. I. Petöfi, Sándor, 1823-1849.
II. Title.

PH3441.E3L6 1908   894.511   32—5106

NL 0446611   DLC InU NBuU ViU MB NNC OClW NN

Loew, William Noah, 1847?-1922, tr.
Magyar songs. Selections from Hungarian poets, translated
by Wm. N. Loew...   New York, Samisch & Goldmann, 1887.
248 p.   17cm.
Most of the poems were previously published with title: Gems from Petöfi and
other Hungarian poets.

25598. 1. Poetry, Hungarian—   Collections. I. Petöfi, Sándor, 1823-
1849. II. Title.   *Card revised*
N. Y. L.   *August 8, 1945*

NL 0446612   NN DLC-P4 NBuG ICU RPB NcD

PH3441 Loew, William Noah, 1847-1922, tr.
.E5   Modern magyar lyrics; selected gems from Alex.
L805   Petöfi and other modern Hungarian poets. Buda-
pest, Wodianer F. és Fiai Grafikai Intézet és
Kiadóvállalat, 1926.
107 p.

1. Hungarian poetry—Translations into English.
I. Title.

NL 0446613   ICU CoU MiD NNC ViU DLC-P4 InU

Loew, William Noah, *tr.*

Arany, János, 1817-1882.
... Toldi; Toldi's eve; ballads; selected lyrics. Trans-
lations from the Hungarian of John Arany, by William
N. Loew ... New York, The Co-operative press ⟨1914⟩

Loew, William Noah, *tr., 1847-1922.*

Madách, Imre, 1823-1864.
The tragedy of man; dramatic poem, by Imre Madách.
Tr. from the original Hungarian by William N. Loew ...
New York, The Arcadia press ⟨1908⟩

Löw (Wolfins).   * De nutrimentis animalibus.
41 pp., 1 l. 8°. Vindobona, typ. vid. A. Strauss
et Sommer, [1846].

NL 0446616   DNLM

Löw ab Erlsfeld, Johann Franz
    see Löw von Erlsfeld, Johann Franz, *Ritter,*
1648-1725.

Löw-Beer, Helene.
Heilpädagogische Praxis (Methoden und Material), von Dr.
Helene Löw-Beer und Milan Morgenstern... Vorwort von Dr.
Erich Nassau... 71 Strichzeichnungen von L. Anninger und
M. Rubin. Wien ⟨etc.⟩ Sensen-Verlag ⟨c1936⟩ 174 p. illus.
19½cm.

98340B. 1. Children, Defective—   Education. I. Morgenstern, Milan,
jt. au. II. Title.   *April 21, 1941*
N. Y. L.

NL 0446618   NN

Löw-Beer, Oskar, 1878-
WO   Studien über die Constitution der Oxy-
25053   asokörper. Heidelberg, 1901.
42 p.

Inaug.-Diss. - Heidelberg.

NL 0446619   CtY

Loew-Vogel, H.
Das Himmelreich, von H. Löw-Vogel. ⟨Wien, pref. 1912.⟩
40 p.   8°.
In four acts.

1. Drama, German. 2. Title.
N. Y. P. L.   June 30, 1927

NL 0446620   NN

Loew von Erlsfeld, Johann Franz, ritter, 1648-1725.
Hydriatria nova, das ist, kurtze Beschreibung von dem neu erfundenen Frauenberger
Bad, vor Alters in böhmischer Sprach ins gemein genant: "Smradlawá Woda", auff Teutsch
stinckendes Wasser, dessen Ursprung, und Gelegenheit, Alterthumb, heylsamben Mineralien,
Würckungen, Nutz, und rechter Gebrauch. 7
p. l., 128 pp. 12°. Prag, C. Ferdinandei, 1721.

NL 0446621   DNLM CtY-M

RBS115. Löw von Erlsfeld, Johann Franz, *Ritter,* 1648-172⟨
Nova et vetus aphorismorum...Hippoc-
ratis interpretatio iuxta mentem vete-
rum et recentiorum...explanata...
Francfurt & Leipzig: Impensis Johanni⟨
Ziegeri...1711.

NL 0446622   NNNAM

Loew von Erlsfeld, Johann Franz, *ritter,* 1648-1725.
Partus medicus multo labore à Leone in lucem editus;
seu, Tractatus novissimus de variolis et morbillis ... Cui
accessit apodixis medica de morbis infantum, authore
Joanne Francisco Löw ... Norimbergæ, sumpt. J. Ziegeri
& G. Lehmanni, 1699.
6 p. l., 472, ⟨14⟩ p. 20½ x 16ᶜᵐ.

1. Smallpox. 2. Measles.
                                                      7-29510†
Library of Congress   RC183.L82

NL 0446623   DLC DNLM ICJ

Löw von Erlsfeld, Johann Franz, *Ritter,* 1648-
17th   1725.
cent.   Theatrum medico-juridicum continens varias
easque maxime notabiles tam ad tribunalia ec-
clesiastico-civilia, quam ad medicinam forensem,
pertinentes materias ... Norimbergae, J. F. Rudiger,
1725.
3p. l., 889p. port. 22cm.
                                                      25474
l. Medical jurisprudence.

NL 0446624   CtY-M

RBS26. Löw von Erlsfeld, Johann Franz, *Ritter,* 1648-1725.
Vniversa medicina practica, jvsta vetervm
et recentiorvm mentem efformata et avcta...
Olim in nvcleo compendiose tradita, Ferdinando Carolo Weinhart...
Norimbergae: Apud Joh. Frider. Rvdigervm,
1724..., port. 4 l. 1036 p. 6 l. 21.5 cm.
(4°).

NL 0446625   NNNAM

VOLUME 338

Loew von und zu Steinfurth, Karl Friedrich Ludwig, Freiherr.
See
Loew, Ludwig, Freiherr, 1803–1868.

Loew von und zu Steinfurth, Ludwig,
Freiherr, 1803–1868

see

Löw, Ludwig, freiherr von, 1803–1868.

Loew von und zu Steinfurth, Ludwig, freiherr, 1875–
Das Automobil, sein Bau und sein Betrieb. Praktisches Nachschlagebuch für Automobilisten von Dipl.-Ing. Freiherr v. Löw. Mit 279 Abbildungen. Wiesbaden, C. W. Kreidel, 1909.
xvi, 302 p. 279 diagrs. 20 cm.

NL 0446628   ICJ NN

Löw von und zu Steinfurth, Ludwig, *freiherr*, 1875–
Das automobil, sein bau und sein betrieb, nachschlagebuch für automobilisten, von dipl.-ing. freiherrn v. Löw ... 2. umgearb. aufl., mit 363 abbildungen im text. Wiesbaden, C. W. Kreidel, 1912.
xx, 416 p. illus. 20 cm.   M. 6

1. Automobiles—Handbooks, manuals, etc.

Library of Congress   TL145.L8   12-10297

NL 0446629   DLC N ICJ

D629.2
L953
Loew von und zu Steinfurth, Ludwig, freiherr, 1875–
Das automobil, sein bau und sein betrieb, nachschlagebuch für die praxis, von dipl. Ing. freiherr Löw von und zu Steinfurth ... 4., umgearb. aufl. ... Berlin und Wiesbaden, C. W. Kreidel, 1921.
v, [1], 356 p. illus., tables, diagrs. 19½ cm.
1. Automobiles.

NL 0446630   NNC

Loew von und zu Steinfurth, Ludwig, Freiherr, 1875–
Brennstoffmischungen, Anlassbehälter und moderne Vergaser, ihre Bedeutung für den Automobilbetrieb in dem jetzigen Krieg und in der Zukunft, von Dipl.-Ing. Freiherrn v. Löw ... Wiesbaden: C. W. Kreidel, 1915. vi p., 1 l., 38 p. diagrs. 8°.

1. Automobiles.—Engines: Fuel.   2. Carbureters.
N. Y. P. L.   August 11, 1920.

NL 0446631   NN CtY

Loew von und zu Steinfurth, Ludwig, Freiherr, 1875–
Kleinigkeiten zur Verbesserung des Automobils; ein Leitfaden für Automobilisten und Fabrikanten, von ... Freiherrn v. Löw ... Wiesbaden: C. W. Kreidel, 1914. x, 54 p. illus. 8°.

1. Automobiles.—Construction and   design. 1914.
N. Y. P. L.   October 26, 1915.

NL 0446632   NN

Löw von und zu Steinfurth, Ludwig, freiherr, 1875–
Kraftwagen-Betrieb mit Inlands-Brennstoffen, von ... Freiherrn v. Löw ... Wiesbaden: C. W. Kreidels Verlag, 1916. vii, 71 p. illus. 8°.

1. Engines (Gas and oil).—Fuels.
N. Y. P. L.   May 24, 1916.

NL 0446633   NN

Loew von und zu Steinfurth, Ludwig, Freiherr, 1875–
Neuere Vergaser und Hilfsvorrichtungen für den Kraftwagen-Betrieb mit verschiedenen Brennstoffen; Nachschlagebuch für die Praxis, von Dipl.-Ing. Freiherrn Löw von und zu Steinfurth ... Berlin: C. W. Kreidel, 1920. 94 p. incl. diagrs., tables. 2. enl. ed. 8°.

1. Automobiles.—Engines: Fuel.   2. Carbureters.
N. Y. P. L.   May 3, 1921.

NL 0446634   NN ICJ

Löw von und zu Steinfurth, Ludwig, freiherr, 1875–
Die neuesten Forderungen bei dem Bau und der Ausrüstung von Automobilen. Ein Leitfaden für Automobilisten. Wiesbaden: C. W. Kreidel, 1911. vi p., 1 l., 71 p. illus. 8°.

1. Automobiles.—Construction, etc.
N. Y. P. L.   June 28, 1911.

NL 0446635   NN

[Löw] Lipot végtisztessége. Közzéteszi és kiadja a Szegedi Izr. Hitközség. Szeged: Z. Burger, 1876.
123 p.

NL 0446636   OCH CtY

Löwa, Wilhelm, 1908–
... Ein Beitrag zur sozialen Zahnpflege in den nordischen Ländern und in Deutschland (unter Ausschluss der Schulzahnpflege) ... Quakenbrück, 1934.
Inaug.-Diss. - Kiel.
Lebenslauf.
"Literaturverzeichnis": p. 13.

NL 0446637   CtY

Loewald, Arnold.
Ueber die psychischen Wirkungen des Broms.
(In Kraepelin. Psychologische Arbeiten. Band 1, pp. 489–565. Leipzig, 1895.)

Sept. 18,   1903
F1131 — Bromine. — Psychology. Physiological.

NL 0446638   MB ODW

Loewald (Arnold). *Ueber die psychischen Wirkungen des Broms.* [Heidelberg.] 81 pp. 8°. *Leipzig, W. Engelmann, 1896.*

NL 0446639   DNLM

QD453
.A28
Löwdin, Per Olov, 1916–   ed.
Advances in quantum chemistry. v. 1–   1964–
New York, Academic Press.

Pamphlet
QC
7
Löwdin, Per-Olof.
A quantum mechanical calculation of the cohesive energy, the interior distance, and the elastic constants of some ionic crystals. Stockholm, Almqvist & Wiksell, 1947–48.
2 v. 22cm. (Arkiv för Matematik, Astronomi och Fysik, Bd. 35A, no.9)

Bibliographical foot-notes.

1. Quantum theory.

NL 0446641   NIC

Löwdin, Per Olov, 1916–
A theoretical investigation into some properties of ionic crystals; a quantum mechanical treatment of the cohesive energy, the interionic distance, the elastic constants, and the compression at high pressures, with numerical applications to some alkali halides. Uppsala, Almqvist & Wiksells boktr., 1948.
xi, 128 p. diagrs. 25 cm.
Inaug. diss.—Uppsala.
Extra t. p., with thesis statement, inserted.
Addendum and errata on leaf inserted.
Bibliographical footnotes.
1. Crystallography, Mathematical.

QD911.L7   548.7   50-32479

NL 0446642   DLC CaBVaU PU NCH MH CU DNAL CtY

Loewe ben Bezaleel
see   Judah Loew ben Bezaleel, d. 1609.

DS
135
G3.4L6
Loewe,
Ueber den Entwurf eines Gesetzes betreffend die Verfassung der jüdischen Gemeinden in Preussen. Berlin, Druck von Rudolf Mosse [184–?]
19 p. 22 cm.

1. Jews—Legal status, laws, etc.—Prussia. I. Title

NL 0446644   OCH

Loewe,   Landmesser
see   Loewe, Hans.

Loewe,   teacher at Gymnasium, Strehlen
see   Loewe, Philipp, of *Strehlen.*

Löwe, Adolf
see
Lowe, Adolph, 1893–

Löwe, Adolf Golbeck-
see   Golbeck-Loewe, Adolf, 1865–

Loewe, Adolf Gustav von, 1875–
Konstruktionsberechnungen von kraftfahrzeugen und die organisation des konstruktionsbüros, von dipl.-ing. A. G. von Loewe. Mit 15 figuren im text und 100 berechnungstafeln.   Berlin, M. Krayn, 1915.
x p., 1 l., 264 p. incl. illus., tables, diagrs. (2 double) 24½ cm. (Half-title: Automobiltechnische bibliothek, bd. VIII)

NL 0446649   ICJ NIC MiU NN

VOLUME 338

Loewe, Adolf Gustav von, 1875–
　　Konstruktionsberechnungen von kraftfahrzeugen und die organisation des konstruktionsbüros, von dipl.-ing. A. G. von Loewe. Mit 15 figuren im text und 100 berechnungstafeln. 2. verb. aufl. Berlin, M. Krayn, 1920.
　　　x p., 1 l., 264 p. incl. illus., tables, diagrs. (2 double) 24½ᶜᵐ. (Half-title: Automobiltechnische bibliothek, bd. VIII)

　　1. Automobiles—Design and construction. 2. Automobile industry and trade.

　　Library of Congress   TL240.L6 1920   26–19498

NL 0446650   DLC

LOEWE, Aemilius

　　See LOEWE, Emil.

---

　*
DA40   Löwe, Andreas Friedrich, 1752–
.L57   　Historische und geographische Beschreibung
1777   der zwolf Vereinigten Kolonien von Nord
　　　Amerika. Nebst einer Abschilderung des
　　　gegenwartigen Zustandes von Grossbrittannien.
　　　Bunzlau, Gedruckt und zu finden im Waisenhause ₍Vorrede: 1777₎
　　　½ p. l., 140 p. ; 18cm.
　　　"Vorrede" signed: L.
　　　Based on Friedrich Wilhelm von Taube, Historische und Politische Abschilderung der engländischen Manufacturen ...: Vorrede.
　　　Pages 1–2 torn.
　　　1. gt. Brit.—Pol. & govt. 2.U.S.—Hist.—Colonial period. I. Taube, Friedrich Wilhelm von ₍Historische und   politische Abschilderung der engländischen   Manufacturen ...₎
　　　II. L.

NL 0446652   ViU ICN IU CtY

Loewe, Armin.
　　Der soziologisch bedingte Wandel des Erziehungs- und Bildungsideals; eine pädagogisch historische Skizze. Stuttgart, R. A. Müller ₍1949₎
　　　47 p. 21 cm. (Schriftenreihe der Pädagogischen Arbeitsstelle Heidelberg)

　　1. Educational sociology. I. Title.

　　LC189.L6   56–26515 ‡

NL 0446653   DLC

Loewe, Arno, 1868–
　　Erste Hilfe bei Unfällen und plötzlicher Lebensgefahr. Ein Leitfaden für jedermann. Dresden, C. C. Meinhold & Söhne, 1918.
　　　146p. illus.

NL 0446654   ICRL

Loewe, Arno, 1868–
　　Erste Hilfe bei Unfällen und plötzlicher Lebensgefahr. Ein Leitfaden für jedermann von Sanitätsrat Dr. med. A. Loewe, ... 4.–6. Tausend. Dresden, C. C. Meinhold & Söhne, 1918.
　　　146 p. illus., 4 col. pl. 22ᶜᵐ.

NL 0446655   ICJ

Loewe, Arno, 1868–
　　... Erste hilfe bei verletzungen, von sanitätsrat dr. med. A. Loewe ... New York, N. Y., Workmen's sick and death benefit fund of the United States of America, 1930.
　　　48 p. illus. 19½ᶜᵐ. (Bibliothek für gesundheitspflege und arbeiterschuts ... hft. 2)

　　1. First aid in illness and injury.

　　Library of Congress   RC87.L73   30–8227

NL 0446656   DLC

Loewe, Arno, 1868–
　　... Plötzliche lebensgefahr—was sollen wir tun? Von dr. med. A. Loewe und anderen ärzten ... Brooklyn, N. Y., Workmen's sick and death benefit fund of the United States of America, 1930.
　　　48 p. illus. 19½ᶜᵐ. (Bibliothek für gesundheitspflege und arbeiterschuts ... hft. 3)

　　1. First aid in illness and injury. I. Title.
　　Library of Congress   RC87.L74   30–23211
　　——— Copy 2.
　　Copyright A 26934   ₍3₎   614.8

NL 0446657   DLC

W 6
P3   LOEWE, Arnó, 1868–
　　Verbandtechnik; kurze Anleitung zum Anlegen von Binden-, Tuch- und Schienenverbanden. Dresden, Meinhold, 1940.
　　　56 p. illus.
　　　First published, 1927.
　　　1. Bandages & bandaging

NL 0446658   DNLM

WS
100   LÖWE, Arnold
L827h   Der homöopathische Kinderarzt; ein
1860   Taschenbuch für Mütter. Wien, Seich,
　　　1860.
　　　iv, 156 p.

NL 0446659   DNLM

Loewe, Arthur.
　　... Studien über die spezifischen unterscheidungsmerkmale wilder und domestizierter tiere in der beschaffenheit ihrer extremitätenknochen. Ein beitrag zu den forschungen über die abstammung der haustiere ... Berlin, Buchdr. von C. Wiegler nachf., 1912.
　　　36 p., 1 l. 23ᶜᵐ.
　　　Inaug.-diss.—Bern.
　　　"Literaturverzeichnis": p. ₍35₎–36.

　　1. Domestic animals. Anatomy and physiology. 2. Domestic animals. History.
　　　　　　　　　　　　　Agr 13–117
　　Library, U. S. Dept. of   Agriculture 444L95

NL 0446660   DNAL DNLM PU

Loewe, Bernhard, 1891–
　　Ueber das Verhalten der Oxyde bezw. Hydroxyde des Nickels, Quecksilbers, Kupfers, Silbers, Kadmiums und Kobalts zu Aethylen-Diaminlösungen. (Berlin, Jacobi, 1914)
　　　33 p.   23 cm.
　　　Berlin, Phil. Diss. v. 21 Jan. 1914, Ref. E. Fischer, Beckmann.
　　　[Geb. 22 Juni 91 Friedrichshagen b. Berlin; Wohnort: Berlin; Staatsangeh.: Preussen; Vorbildung: Luisen-G. Berlin Reife 08; Studium: Berlin 10 s.; Rig. 18. Dez. 13.]

NL 0446661   CtY

929.4   Loewe, Busso, 1911–
L82g   　Griechische theophore ortsnamen _ ₍Tübingen₎ Tübinger studentenwerke e.v., 1936.
　　　128p.
　　　Inaug.-diss.--Tübingen.
　　　Lebenslauf.
　　　"Abkürzungen häufig zitierter werke": p.4–6.

　　1. Names, Geographical--Greek. 2. Greece--Mythology and religion.

NL 0446662   IU ICRL ICU CoU PBm MiU CtY

Loewe (Carl). *Ueber Unterschenkelgeschwüre. 38 pp., 1 l. 8°. Bonn, C. Georgi, 1886.

NL 0446663   DNLM

Löwe (Carl). Verzeichniss anatomischer, chirurgischer und geburtshülflicher Instrumente ... so wie der Gegenstände des Bandagen-Magazins von Schindler und Löwe. Mit einem Vorwort von A. Carus. 24 pp. 12°. Leipzig, C. G. Naumann, 1837.

NL 0446664   DNLM

Loewe, Carl, 1796–1869
　　see Loewe, Karl, 1796–1869.

Loewe, Carl, 1846–1907
　　see Loewe, Karl, 1846–1907.

Löwe, Carl Friedrich
　　see
　Löwe, Fritz, 1874–

Loewe, Carl Gustav
　　see Loewe, Gustav, 1852–1883.

Loewe, Christian Ludwig Wilhelm.
　　De partibus, quibus insecta spiritus ducunt. Halae, 1814.
　　　28 p. 8°.
　　　Inaug.-diss.

NL 0446669   MH-Z

Map
G
6014   Loewe, Cornelius.
B7   　Plan-Pharus, Bruxelles. Bruxelles, Pharus Cⁱᵉ, ca. 1930.
　　　col. map 83 x 66 cm.
　　　Scale 1:10,000.

　　1. Brussels--Maps.

NL 0446670   NIC

Loewe, Cornelius C
　　... Aktenmässige Auseinandersetzung und Klarstellung über das sogenannte Scherlsche Sparsystem, seine Geschichte und Aussicht von ... Cornelius C. Loewe. Berlin, Pharus Verlag, 1904.
　　　2 p.l., ₍3₎–63, ₍1₎ p. 24½ᶜᵐ.
　　　At head of title: August Scherl und Dr. Cornelius Loewe. Lotterie und Sparkasse.

NL 0446671   MH-L

LOEWE, Cornelius C.
　　Die form der rechtsgeschäfte im bürgerlichen gesetzbuch. Berlin, 1899.
　　　88 p.
　　　Inaug.-diss. - Rostock.

NL 0446672   MH-L ICRL

VOLUME 338

Loewe, Dietrich E
The application of the Sherman anti-trust law
to labor boycotts. Oral arguments ...
see under title

Loewe, Dietrich E., plaintiff in error.

₁Beck, James Montgomery₁ 1861–
... D. E. Loewe, et al. ₁Martin Fuchs₁ vs. Martin Lawlor, et al ... Motion and application to have the whole
record sent to the Supreme court from the Circuit court
of appeals. ₁n. p., 1907₁

Loewe, Dietrich E., plaintiff in error.

Beck, James Montgomery, 1861–   FOR OTHER EDITIONS
                                      SEE MAIN ENTRY
... Dietrich E. Loewe and Martin Fuchs, plaintiffs in
error, (plaintiffs below), vs. Martin Lawlor et al., defendants in error, (defendants below). Oral arguments
for plaintiffs in error made before the Supreme court,
December 4 and 5, 1907. ⟨Stenographically reported⟩
James M. Beck, Daniel Davenport, counsel for plaintiffs
in error. N₁ew₁ Y₁ork₁ C. G. Burgoyne ₁1907₁

Loewe, Dietrich E., plaintiff in error.

Spelling, Thomas Crisp, 1853–
... Dietrich Loewe et al. ₁Martin Fuchs₁ *vs.* Martin Lawlor
et al. Brief of Thomas Carl Spelling on behalf the American
federation of labor, et al. Washington, D. C., Law reporter
printing co. ₁1907₁

Loewe, Dietrich E., defendant in error.

Lawlor, Martin, *plaintiff in error.*
... Martin Lawlor et al., plaintiffs in error (defendants below) *vs.* D. E. Loewe et al. ₁Martin Fuchs₁ defendants in error
(plaintiffs below) Transcript of record. Error to the Circuit court of the United States for the district of Connecticut
... Printed under the direction of the clerk. ₁New York,
1910₁

Loewe, Dietrich E   *plaintiff in error.*
Transcript of record. Supreme court of the United
States. October term, 1907. No. 389. Dietrich Loewe
et al. ₁Martin Fuchs₁ vs. Martin Lawlor et al. On a cer-
tificate from and writ of certiorari to the United States
Circuit court of appeals for the Second circuit. Certifi-
cate filed July 11, 1907. Certiorari and return filed October 21, 1907. ₁Washington, Judd & Detweiler (inc.),
printers, 1907₁
cover-title, 1 p. l, 42 p. 23½ᶜᵐ.
1. Boycott.   I. Fuchs, Martin, plaintiff in error.   II. Lawlor, Martin,
defendant in error.   III. U. S. Supreme court.   IV. U. S. Circuit court
of appeals (2d circuit)
                                                          13–12405

NL 0446678 DLC

Loewe, Dietrich E   plaintiff in error.
... Transcript of record. Supreme court of the
United States. October term, 1913. No. 900. Martin
Lawlor et al., plaintiffs in error, vs. Dietrich E. Loewe
and Martin Fuchs, partners under the firm name of D. E.
Loewe & co. In error to the United States Circuit court
of appeals for the Second circuit. Filed February 10,
1914 ... [Toledo, O., The Toledo brief & record
company, 1914]
5 v. 24 cm.
D. E. Loewe & company, Danbury hatters, Connecticut
in a suit against Martin Lawlor and other members of
the United hatters of North America.

NL 0446679 CtY

Loewe, Dietrich E
Unanimous decision of the Supreme Court of
the United States in the case of Loewe vs. Lawlor ...
see under U.S. Supreme Court.

LOEWE, Emil.
De Aesculapi figura. Diss. inaug. Argentorati, 1887.
pp. 86.

NL 0446681 MH ICRL

Loewe, Erich, Referendar: Die Verpflichtung des Gläubigers
zur Rückgabe des Schuldscheines. Breslau 1912: Fleischmann. 62 S. 8°
Breslau, Jur. Diss. v. 12. Dez. 1912, Ref. O. Fischer, Schott
[Geb. 23. Sept. 89 Breslau; Wohnort: Breslau; Staatsangeh.: Preußen; Vorbildung: König-Wilhelms-Gymn. Breslau Reife O. 08; Studium: Breslau 2,
Freiburg i. B. 1, München 1, Breslau 2 S.; Rig. 12. Jan. 12.] [U 12. 4929

NL 0446682 ICRL

Loewe, Erna: Zum Gebrauch der Demonstrativa im Italienischen.
[Handschrift.] 243 S. 4°. — Auszug: Bonn 1922: Trapp. 16 S. 8°
Bonn, Phil. Diss. v. 9. März 1923   [U 23. 949

NL 0446683 ICRL

Loewe, Ernst.
Der abnahmeverzug des kaeufers.
Inaug. diss. Leipzig, 1907 (Berlin)
Bibl.

NL 0446684 ICRL

Loewe, Ernst.
Ein neuer Apparat zur Demonstration der Pflanzenatmung. von
Ernst Loewe. Cöln, Gebrüder Brocker, 1903.
12 p. 3 illus. 28ᶜᵐ.
T.-p. illus.
Beilage zum Jahresbericht des Königlichen Friedrich-Wilhelms-Gymnasiums zu Cöln
a. Rh. Nr. 516.

NL 0446685 ICJ CSt

Löwe, Ernst, tr.

Lovén, Sven, 1875–
Über die wurzeln der tainischen kultur ...   Göteborg,
Elanders boktryckeri aktiebolag, 1924–

Loewe, Ernst, 1882–
Beitraege zur metrik Rudyard Kipling's
Inaug. Diss. Marburg, 1905.
Bibl.

NL 0446687 ICRL MH NcD

Löwe, Ernst, 1882–
... Beiträge zur metrik Rudyard Kipling's. Von Ernst
Löwe ... Marburg, N. G. Elwert, 1906.
4 p. l., 103 p. 23ᶜᵐ. (Marburger studien zur englischen philologie.
hft. 10)
Issued first as the author's inaugural dissertation, Marburg, 1905.
"Litteratur": 3d prelim. leaf.

1. Kipling, Rudyard, 1865–   2. English language—Versification.

Library of Congress   PE25.M3 hft. 10   7–32339

NL 0446688   DLC MiU OU OCU OCl ViU NN

Löwe, Ernst, d. 1916.
Das altarbild in der stadtkirche
zu Bad Wildungen. Meister Konrad von
Soest. MCCCCII... 2. aufl. Bad Wildungen,
Pusch, 1928.
30 p. 1 fold. pl.

1. Konrad von Soest, 14th cent.

NL 0446689 NjP

Law   Loewe, Eugen, ed.

Makower, H
... Gesetze, betreffend die privatrechtlichen verhältnisse
der binnenschiffahrt und der flösserei. Nach den materialien
erläutert von H. Makower ... 6. verm. aufl. bearb. von E.
Loewe ... Berlin und Leipzig, W. de Gruyter & co., 1923.

Loewe, Eugen, joint ed.

Germany. *Laws, statutes, etc.*
Handelsgesetzbuch mit kommentar, hrsg. von H. Makower ... unter zugrundelegung der fassung des Handelsgesetzbuchs vom 10. mai 1897 und des Bürgerlichen gesetzbuchs neu bearb. von F. Makower ... 12. (der neuen
bearbeitung erste) aufl. Berlin, J. Guttentag, 1900–04.

Loewe, Eugen.
Der handlungsreisende.
Inaug. Diss. Leipzig, 1904.
Bibl.

NL 0446692 ICRL

WG   Loewe, Eugen, 1857–
22578   Zur Constitution des Dinitro- β -Naphtols.
Berlin, 1892.
34 p.

Inaug.-Diss. - Berlin.

NL 0446693 CtY DNLM CU

Loewe ₁Eugen₁ ₁1860–   ₁. " Ueber das Auf-
treten der rothen Diazoreaction Ehrlich's bei
Krankheiten. 48 pp., 1 l. 8°. Breslau, H.
Proskauer, jr. ₁1888₁.

NL 0446694 DNLM

Loewe, Eugen Johannes
see Loewe, Eugen.

Loewe, Eugen Ludwig, 1903–
Zur frage des suicides.
Inaug. diss. Berlin, 1928
Bibl.

NL 0446696 ICRL CtY

VOLUME 338

Löwe, Ewald Karl August Erdmann, 1837–1896.
Der preussische strafprocess. Mit rücksicht auf die gerichtliche praxis dargestellt von E. Löwe. Breslau, J. U. Kern,
1861.
2 p. l., ₍iii₎–viii, 427 p. 22½ᶜᵐ.

1. Criminal law—Prussia. I. Title.

37–32775

NL 0446697 DLC

Loewe, Ewald Karl August Erdmann,
1837–1896, ed.
Die Seemannsordnung vom 2. Juni 1902
nebst den dazu ergangenen Nebengesetzen
see under Germany. Laws, statutes,
etc.

Löwe, Ewald Karl August Erdmann, 1837–1896, ed.
Germany. *Laws, statutes, etc.*   FOR OTHER EDITIONS
                                              SEE MAIN ENTRY
Die Strafprozessordnung für das Deutsche reich, nebst dem
Gerichtsverfassungsgesetz und den das strafverfahren betref-
fenden bestimmungen der übrigen reichsgesetze. Mit kommen-
tar, von dr. E. Löwe ... 9. aufl., bearb. von A. Hellweg ...
Berlin, J. Guttentag, 1898.

*Löwe, Feodor, 1816–1890.
Korsinsky, Bernhard.
Album des königlich württembergischen Hof-theaters, von
Korsinsky. Mit dem Festspiel zur fünfundzwanzigjährigen
regierungs-feier Seiner Majestät des königs Wilhelm, von
Feodor Löwe ... Nebst einer illustration und sieben bildnis-
sen. Stuttgart, C. F. Etzel, 1843.

HS   Löwe, Feodor, 1816–1890.
431   Aus eigner Werkstatt. Freimaureri-
L82A9   sche Dichtungen. Stuttgart, Konrad
        Wittwer, 1881.
           viii, 193 p. 14cm.

           1. Freemasons—Poetry. I. Title.

NL 0446701 NIC

HS   Löwe, Feodor, 1816–1890.
373   Baustücke; freimaurerische Zeichnungen,
L82   Ansprachen und Aphorismen. Stuttgart, K.
        Wittwer, 1878.
           viii, 344 p. 19cm.

           1. Freemaso   ns—Addresses, essays,
        lectures. I.   Title.

NL 0446702 NIC

HS   Löwe, Feodor, 1816–1890.
431   Den Brüdern. Freimaurerische
L82   Dichtungen. 4. Aufl. Stuttgart,
1901   Konrad Wittwer, 1901.
           vii, 165 p. 16cm.

           1. Freemasons—Poetry. I. Title.

NL 0446703 NIC

854L95 Löwe, Feodor, 1816–1890
L1843   Gedichte ...   Stuttgart, 1843.
        240p.

NL 0446704 IU

Löwe, Feodor, 1816–1890.
Lied im Volkston Die Weinlein
see under Keucken, Friedrich Wilhelm,
1810–1882.

Löwe, Foedor, 1816–1890.
"Wo Freude ihre Kränze flicht. "
see under Kücken, Friedrich Wilhelm,
1810–1882.

HS   Löwe, Feodor, 1816–1890.
373   Zwischen den drei Säulen; freimaurerische
L82   Arbeiten. Stuttgart, K. Wittwer, 1884.
Z9   vii, 342 p. 20cm.

           1. Freemason   s—Addresses, essays,
        lectures. I. Ti   tle.

NL 0446707 NIC

PH648   Löwe, Ferdinand, tr.
.G5   Kreutzwald, Friedrich Reinhold, 1803–1882.
1900   Kalewipoeg. Aus dem Estnischen übertragen von F.
        Löwe. Mit einer Einleitung und mit Anmerkungen hrsg.
        von W. Reiman. Reval, F. Kluge, 1900.

Loewe, Ferdinand, 1845–1922, ed.
Goering, Adolf, 1841–1906.
... Anordnung der bahnhöfe   ... bearb. von
A. Goering † und M. Oder, hrsg. von F. Loewe ... und dr.
H. Zimmermann ... Leipzig, W. Engelmann, 1907–

Loewe, Ferdinand, 1845–1922.
Die Bahnen der Fuhrwerke in den Strassenbögen. Eine ergän-
zende Untersuchung zu dessen "Strassenbaukunde". 21 p. 9 il.
Q. Wiesbaden: C. W. Kreidel, 1901.

NL 0446710 ICJ NcD

Loewe, Ferdinand, 1845–
Die Bekämpfung des Strassen-Staubes. Von F. Loewe.
Eine Ergänzung seines Lehr- und Handbuches "Strassenbau-
kunde". Wiesbaden: C. W. Kreidel, 1910. 2 p.l., 30 p.   8°.

1. Dust.—Prevention.
N. Y. P. L.   January 26, 1911.

NL 0446711 NN

Loewe, Ferdinand, 1845–   ed.
Zimmermann, Hermann, 1845–
... Berechnung, konstruktion, ausführung und unterhaltung des oberbaues. Bearb. von Hermann Zimmermann,
Alfred Blum, Hermann Rosche, hrsg. von F. Loewe ...
und dr. H. Zimmermann ... 2. verm. aufl. Mit drei tafeln, 296 abbildungen im text und ausführlichem namen-
und sachverzeichnis. Leipzig, W. Engelmann, 1906.

Loewe, Ferdinand, 1845–   ed.
Landsberg, Fritz.
... Betriebseinrichtungen, insbesondere für versorgung der lokomotiven mit wasser und brennstoff, bearb.
von dr.-ing. Fritz Landsberg ... hrsg. von dr.-ing. F. Loewe
... und dr.-ing. dr. H. Zimmermann ... mit 289 abbildungen im text. Leipzig, W. Engelmann, 1919.

Löwe, Ferdinand, 1845–
Munich. K. Bayerische technische hochschule.
Darstellungen aus der geschichte der technik der industrie und landwirtschaft in Bayern. Festgabe der Königlichen technischen hochschule in München zur jahrhundertfeier der annahme der königswürde durch kurfürst
Maximilian IV. Joseph von Bayern. München und Berlin, R. Oldenbourg, 1906.

ar X   Loewe, Ferdinand, 1845–   ed.
2787   Der Eisenbahnbau; ausgenommen Vorarbeiten,
        Unterbau und Tunnelbau. Hrsg. von F. Loewe
        und H. Zimmermann.   Leipzig, W. Engelmann,
        1897–
           v. in   illus. 27cm. (Handbuch
        der Ingenieurwissenschaften. 5. Bd.)

           1. Railroads—Construction. I. Zimmermann,
        Hermann, 1845–   II. Title. III.
        Series.

NL 0446715 NIC MiU MB ICJ NN

Loewe, Ferdinand, 1845–   ed.
Gadow, Martin.
... Kraftstellwerke, bearb. von M. Gadow ... hrsg. von
F. Loewe ... und dr.-ing. dr. H. Zimmermann ... mit 143
textfiguren und sachverzeichnis. Leipzig und Berlin,
W. Engelmann, 1913.

Loewe, Ferdinand, 1845–
Der kraftwagen und seine beziehungen zur strasse vom
standpunkte des strasseningenieurs, von F. Loewe ...
Wiesbaden, C. W. Kreidel, 1913.
2 p. l., 31 p. illus. 26ᶜᵐ.
Eine ergänzung seines lehr- und handbuches "Strassenbaukunde".
Bibliographical foot-notes.

1. Automobiles. 2. Roads.
                                              Agr 26–161
Library, U. S. Dept. of   Agriculture 291L822

NL 0446717 DNAL NN

Loewe, Ferdinand, ed., 1845–   FOR OTHER EDITIONS
Abt, Roman, 1850–   SEE MAIN ENTRY
... Lokomotiv-steilbahnen und seilbahnen. Bearb. von
Roman Abt und Siegfried Abt, hrsg. von F. Loewe ... und
dr. H. Zimmermann ... Mit 206 abbildungen im text und
vollständigem sachverzeichnis. Leipzig, W. Engelmann,
1901.

Loewe, Ferdinand, 1845–   ed.
Scheibner, Samuel.
... Mittel zur sicherung des betriebes, bearb. von S.
Scheibner ... hrsg. von F. Loewe ... und dr.-ing. dr. H.
Zimmermann ... mit 1282 textfiguren, sachregister und
9 zum teil lithographierten tafeln ... Leipzig, W. En-
gelmann, 1913.

VOLUME 338

Loewe, Ferdinand, 1845–
Der schienenweg der eisenbahnen. Von **Ferdinand Loewe** ... Mit 142 abbildungen. Wien [etc.] A. Hartleben, 1887.

xi, 380 p. incl. illus., tables, diagrs. 21ᶜᵐ. *(Added t.-p.: Bibliothek des eisenbahnwesens. 8. bd.)*

1. Railroads—Track.

10–967

Library of Congress   TF258.L7

NL   0446720   DLC NjP CU

Loewe, Ferdinand, ed.
Birk, Alfred, 1855–   FOR OTHER EDITIONS SEE MAIN ENTRY
... Schmalspurbahnen. Bearb. von dipl. ingr. Alfred Birk ... hrsg. von F. Loewe ... und dr. H. Zimmermann ... Mit einer tafel, 145 abbildungen im text und vollständigem sachverzeichnis. Leipzig, W. Engelmann, 1902.

LOEWE, Ferdinand, *1845*-
Strassenbaukunde. Wiesbaden, 1895.

1.8°. Illustr.

NL   0446722   MH

TE144
.L78
1906

Loewe, Ferdinand, 1845–*1922.*
Strassenbaukunde. Land- und stadtstrassen. Von Ferdinand Loewe ... 2. völlig umgearb. aufl. mit 155 abbildungen im texte. Wiesbaden, C. W. Kreidel, 1906.

xv, 589 p. incl. illus., diagrs. 25½ᶜᵐ.

1. Roads. 2. Streets.   I. Title.

E S 24—12

U. S. Engineer sch. Libr.
for Library of Congress   [43c1]

NL   0446723   DES DLC CU NN MiU ICJ

Loewe, Ferdinand, 1845–1922.
... Weichen und Kreuzungen. Drehscheiben und Schiebebühnen. Bearbeitet von Ferdinand Loewe, Georg Meyer, herausgegeben von F. Loewe ... und Dr. H. Zimmermann ... Leipzig, W. Engelmann, 1898.

viii, 198 p. diagrs. 26ᶜᵐ.   *(Added t.-p.: Handbuch der Ingenieurwissenschaften ... 5. Bd.: Der Eisenbahnbau ... 3. Abt.)*

2d ed. by E. Borst and others.
"Litteratur" at end of each chapter.

NL   0446724   ICJ MB NN

Loewe, Ferdinand, *1845–1922.*
Zur frage der betriebssicherheit der eisenbahngleise, speciell der wirklichen anstrengung der fahrschienen. Von F. Loewe ... Wiesbaden, C. W. Kreidel, 1883.

26 p. 2 fold. pl. 31ᶜᵐ.

1. Railroads—Rails.

A 15–2281

Title from Bureau of   Railway Economics. Printed by L. C.

NL   0446725   DBRE

Loewe (Franz). *Ueber Addison'sche Nebennieren-Krankheit.* 37 pp. 8°. Halle, W. Plötz, 1887.

NL   0446726   DNLM

Löwe, Franz Ludwig Feodor
see Löwe, Feodor, 1816–1890.

Loewe, Frederick, *1904–*
[Brigadoon. Selections, arr.]
Band selection of the musical play Brigadoon. Arrangement by Erik Leidzén. New York, S. Fox Pub. Co. [1947]

condensed score (12 p.) *and* parts. 31 cm.

Cover title.
"Time of performance : approximately 7 minutes, 45 seconds."

1. Potpourris (Band)—Scores (reduced) and parts. 2. Musical revues, comedies—Excerpts, Arranged.   I. Leidzén, Erik W. G., 1894–   arr.

M1268.L8B7   48–15181*

NL   0446728   DLC

[Loewe, Frederick] 1904–
[Brigadoon. Piano-vocal score. English]
Brigadoon. [194–]

1 v. (various pagings) 35 cm.
Holograph of a musical comedy, in pencil.
Libretto by Alan Jay Lerner.
Published: New York, S. Fox Pub. Co., *1948.

1. Musical revues, comedies, etc.—Vocal scores with piano.
I. Lerner, Alan Jay, 1918–   Brigadoon. II. Title.

ML96.L62   64–37584/M

NL   0446729   DLC

Loewe, Frederick, *1904–*
[Brigadoon. Libretto. English]
Brigadoon; a musical play in two acts by Alan Jay Lerner. New York, Coward-McCann [1947]

xiii, 138 p. front. 20 cm.

"The music ... which is not included ... was composed by **Frederick Loewe.**"

I. Lerner, Alan Jay. Brigadoon.
ML50.L8256B7 1947   782.6   48–1394*

MiDW OEac MH MB IU
NNC MiD TxU IU WaS WaT CaBVa CaBViP IdB OrP Or WaE
NL   0446730   DLC CoU WaU NN MB OCU Mi MiEM NcGU ViU

M
1503
.L818
B7

Loewe, Frederick, 1904–
[Brigadoon. Piano-vocal score. English]
Brigadoon. Music by Frederick Loewe.
Book and lyrics by Alan Jay Lerner. ...
Vocal arrangements ed. by Franz Allers.
New York, Fox [c1948]

196 p. 31 cm.

At head of title: Cheryl Crawford presents a musical play.

1. Musical revues, comedies, etc. - Vocal scores with piano.
I. Lerner, Alan Jay, 1918- [Brigadoon. II. Allers, Franz, ed.
III. Title.

NL   0446731   MiEM NN IEN CSt CoDU PP KU

Loewe, Frederick, 1904–
[Brigadoon. Piano-vocal score. English]
Cheryl Crawford presents a musical play, **Brigadoon**; book and lyrics by Alan Jay Lerner, vocal score ed. by **Franz Allers.** New York, S. Fox Pub. Co., *1948.

191 p. 31 cm.

"A Lowal Corporation publication."

1. Musical revues, comedies, etc.—Vocal scores with piano. I. Lerner, Alan Jay, 1918–   Brigadoon. II. **Allers, Frans,** ed.
M1503.L818B7 1948   48–22797*

NL   0446732   DLC WaT CaBVa WaSp CoU FTaSU OrP

Loewe, Frederick, 1904–
[Paint your wagon. Piano-vocal score. English]
Cheryl Crawford presents James Barton in Paint your wagon, a musical play; book and lyrics by Alan Jay Lerner, vocal score ed. by Franz Allers. [New York, Chappell] c1951.
260 p. 30 cm.

NL   0446733   RPB NN

LOEWE, FREDERICK, 1904-
[BRIGADOON. SELECTIONS]
Choral selection of the musical play Brigadoon.
Book and lyrics by Alan Jay Lerner. Arrangement by Erik Leidzen. New York, S. Fox pub. co. [c1947]
score (24 p.) 27cm.

For mixed voices (SATB) and piano.

Duration: about 7 min., 45 sec.

1. Choral music, Secular (Mixed, 4 pt.)--Keyboard acc. 2. Musical comedies. I. Leidzen, Erik   William Gustaf, 1894-
arr. II. Title: Brigadoon.

NL   0446735   NN

Loewe, Frederick, 1904–
[Gigi. Selections; arr.]
Gigi; selection for orchestra. Arr.: Robert Russell Bennett. [195–]

score (60 l.) 41 cm.

Arranger's ms., in ink.
From the motion-picture score.

1. Potpourris (Orchestra) — Scores. 2. Moving-picture music— Excerpts, Arranged.   I. Bennett, Robert Russell, 1894–   arr.
II. Title.

ML96.B4673 no. 22   68–41078/M

NL   0446736   DLC

Loewe, Frederick, 1904–
[Brigadoon. Selections, arr.]
Orchestra selection of the musical play Brigadoon. Book and lyrics by Alan Jay Lerner. Transcribed by Victor Lamont [pseud.] New York, Fox Pub. Co. [1948]

piano-conductor score (13 p.) *and* parts. 31 cm.

Cover title.
"Time of performance : approximately 7 minutes, 45 seconds."

1. Potpourris (Orchestra)—Scores (reduced) and parts. 2. Musical revues, comedies, etc.—Excerpts, arranged.   I. Malorana, Victor, arr.

M1350.L   48–4206*

NL   0446737   DLC

812
L562p

Loewe, Frederick, 1904–
Paint your wagon; a musical play in two acts. Book and lyrics by Alan Jay Lerner; music by Frederick Loewe. London, Chappell [*1952]
48 p.

Without the music.

NL   0446738   MiD

Loewe, Frederick, 1904–
[Paint your wagon. Piano-vocal score. English]
Paint your wagon, a musical play; book and lyrics by Alan Jay Lerner. Vocal score. Edited by Franz Allers. New York, Chappell [1952]

260 p. 30 cm.

Imprint covered by blank label.

1. Musical revues, comedies, etc.—Vocal scores with piano.
I. Lerner, Alan Jay, 1918–   Paint your wagon.
M1503.L818P3 1952   M 54–1594

Wa IdB IdPI IdU MtU OrCS WaT OrPR WaPS WaS WaSp WaTC
AU CoU OCl OrU FTaSU UU IU CSt WaU NcU CaBVaU CaBVa
NL   0446739   DLC OrStbM OrU-M OrSaW MtBuM WaE Or OrP

VOLUME 338

Loewe, Frederick, 1904–
 ₍Paint your wagon. Libretto. English₎

     Paint your wagon, a musical play in two acts; book and lyrics by Alan Jay Lerner. New York, Coward-McCann ₍1952₎
     140 p. 21 cm.

     1. Musical revues, comedies, etc.—Librettos.   I. Lerner, Alan Jay, 1918–   Paint your wagon.

     ML50.L8256P3 1952   782.8   52—8019 ‡

     WaSpG WaT WaTC WaWW OrPS
     IdPS MtBC MtU OrCS OrP OrPR OrU Wa WaE WaPS WaS
     MH TxU AU OrStbM OrSaW MtBuM CaBViP CaBVaU IdB IdU
NL   0446740   DLC Or NBuU OU NcD PJB NcD PU NN MB NNC

M1503   Loewe, Frederick, 1904–
L418   ₍Brigadoon. Piano-vocal score. English₎
B7   Prince Littler in association with Cheryl Crawford presents a musical play, Brigadoon: book and lyrics by Alan Jay Lerner, music by Frederick Loewe. London, S. Fox ₍c1947₎
     191p. 28cm.

     "A Lowal Corporation Publication."

     1.Musical revues, comedies, etc. - Vocal scores with   piano.

NL   0446741   NcU

Löwe, Friedrich, *1874–*
     see
     Löwe, Fritz, 1874–

LÖWE,Friedrich,1877–
     Die sprache des "Roman de la rose ou de Guillaume de Dole." Inaug.-diss. Göttingen, 1903.

     pp.viii,82+.
     "Lebenslauf," after p.82.

NL   0446743   MH CtY NjP PU

BS   Löwe, Friedrich Anton.
1565   Beiträge zum Verständniss des
L6.4   Propheten Hoseas. (Zugleich als Charakteristik moderner Exegese). Zürich, S. Höhr, 1863.
     40 p.   20 cm.   (Biblische Studien (Zürich), Hft. 1)

     1. Bible. O.T. Hosea--Criticism, interpretation, etc. I. Title II. Series

NL   0446744   OCH ICU

Loewe, *Friedrich Anton*
     Denkwürdigkeiten aus dem leben und wirken des Johann Wilhelm Rautenberg... Hamburg, Rauhen, [1866]
     281p.

AC931   [Haverford-Bauer pamphlets, v. 110, no. 2]
.H3
v.110

NL   0446745   DLC

BT94   LÖWE,FRIEDRICH ANTON.
.L8   Gottes wege in der geschichte seines reichs. Eine anleitung zum verständniss des grossen göttlichen reichsplans und seiner entfaltung durch die jahrhunderte. Von F.A.Löwe... Basel,F.Schneider,1865.
     ₍1₎,iv,₍1₎,259,₍1₎p. 18cm.

     1.Kingdom of God.

NL   0446746   ICU

LÖWE,Friedrich Anton.
     Kritische musterung der traktate deutsch evangelischer gesellschaften. Hamb.,1852.

NL   0446747   MH-AH

---

943   LOEWE, Friedrich Anton
EvK.347   Luther, Schleiermacher und die Mecklen-
L827t   burgische Krisis; ein Wort der Verstaendigung ueber Evangelische Freiheit an alle Freunde derselben. Gotha, Rud. Besser, 1858.
     xvi, 189p. 20.6cm.

NL   0446748   MH-AH CtY

BL   Löwe, Friedrich Anton.
181
L6   Die Zusammenstimmung des Glaubens mit der menschlichen Selbstgewissheit und Wissenschaft... Hamburg, Johann August Meissner, 1842.
     xxiii,328p.   (his Die Offenbarung und die Fragen der Zeit, v.1)
     No more published, cf. BMC, v.140, col.846.
     1. Natural theology. I. Title.

NL   0446749   MoSCS PPDrop

VM   LÖWE, FRIEDRICH AUGUST LEOPOLD, 1767-1816.
1508   ₍Die insel der verführung₎ Ouverture und
L 82i   favorit gesänge aus der oper Die insel der verführung... Im clavier auszuge. Braunschweig. Im musikalischen magazine auf der höhe₍n.d.₎
     38p. 24x32cm.

     German words.
     Plate no.: 219.

NL   0446750   ICN

Loewe (Friedrich Georg Hubert) [1879–].
     ₍Studien über experimentelle Dourine. [Bern.]
     45 pp., 1 l., 1 pl. 8°. Hamburg, M. Baumann. 1910.

NL   0446751   DNLM PU

Loewe, Friedrich ₍Heinrich Wilhelm₎ 1876–
     ... Über neu- und rückbildung im ovarium vom **maifisch.** (*Clupea alosa* Cuv.) ... Bonn, F. Cohen ₍1903?₎
     32 p. 23½ᶜᵐ.

     Inaug.-diss.—Bonn.
     Lebenslauf.
     Sonder-abdruck aus dem Archiv für mikroskopische anatomie und entwicklungsgeschichte, bd. 63. 1903.
     "Literaturverzeichnis": p. 26-31.

     1. Shad. 2. Ovary.

     Library of Congress   QL965.L82

                               6-43435

NL   0446752   DLC DNLM

PT   Löwe, Fritz
2623
.039   Frau Jutta die Päpstin; eine deutsche
F7   Volkssage, Epos in drei Teilen. 2. Aufl. Leipzig, A. Fischer, 1895.
     180p. 19cm.

NL   0446753   TNJ OC1

PT   Löwe, Fritz
2623
.039   Renatus, ein märkisches Reiterlied; Epos
R4   in drei Teilen. Leipzig, A. Fischer, 1894.
     285p. 19cm.

NL   0446754   TNJ

     Löwe, Fritz, 1870–
     Fahrten durch Norwegens Märchenwelt. Berlin, Pontos Verlag ₍c1929₎
     119, ₍1₎ p. illus., map.

     1. Norway - Description and travel. I. Title.

NL   0446755   WaU OrU

     Loewe, Fritz, 1870–
     ...Das Land der hellen Sommernächte; Schwedenfahrt... Berlin: Pontos-Verlag₍, cop. 1929₎. 168 p. map, plates. 8°.

     First edition.
     Plates printed on both sides.

     457551A. 1. Sweden—Descr. and   trav., 1900–
     N.Y.P.L.   March 12, 1930

NL   0446756   NN

4DL   Löwe, Fritz, 1870–
Swed.   Das Land der hellen Sommernächte,
-389   Schwedenfahrt. 2. Aufl. Berlin, Pontos- Verlag [c1929]
     168 p.

NL   0446757   DLC-P4

     Löwe, Fritz, 1870–
     ... Unter der sonne des südens, eine Mittelmeer- und orientfahrt. Berlin, Pons-verlag ₍1930₎
     127 p. plates. 21½ᶜᵐ.

     1. Levant—Descr. & trav.   I. Title.

                                 43-27138
     Library of Congress   DS49.L8

NL   0446758   DLC NN

     Löwe, Fritz, 1874–
     Atlas der analysen-linien der wichtigsten elemente (zweite auflage des "Atlas der letzten linien") von dr. Fritz Löwe ... Dresden und Leipzig, T. Steinkopff, 1936.
     2 p. l., 40 p. xvi pl. on 8 l., tables. 23 cm.
     Pages 38-40, advertising matter.
     "Schrifttum": p. 10.

     1. Spectrum analysis—Tables, etc.   I. Title.

                          ₍Full name: Karl Friedrich Löwe₎
     QC453.L85 1936   535.84   A C 37-1837
     Iowa. State Coll. Libr.   ₍a48c1₎†
     for Library of Congress

NL   0446759   IaAS CU OU DLC

VOLUME 338

Löwe, Fritz, 1874–
Atlas der letzten linien der wichtigsten elemente, von dr. Fritz Löwe ... Dresden und Leipzig, T. Steinkopff, 1928.
2 p. l., 44 p. incl. tables. 16 pl. on 8 l. 23ᶜᵐ.
"Literatur-übersicht": p. 15–18.

1. Spectrum analysis—Tables, etc.   I. Title.
Library of Congress   QC453.L85   29–8074

NL 0446760   DLC OU MiU OO NjP IU NN

Löwe, Fritz, 1874–
Experimental-Untersuchung über electrische Dispersion einiger organischer Säuren, Ester und von zehn Glassorten. Leipzig, Y. A. Barth, 1898.
40 p. 23 cm.
Inaug.-Diss.—Leipzig.
Vita.

1. Dielectrics.
Full name: Karl Friedrich Löwe.
QC585.L79   7–38457 rev*

NL 0446761   DLC CtY

Löwe, Fritz, 1874–
Interferenz-Messgeräte und- Verfahren für technische, chemische und klinische Laboratorien. Berlin, Verlag Technik, 1954.
96 p. illus. 22 cm.
Bibliography: p. 92–95.

1. Interferometer. 2. Interference (Light)   I. Title.
Full name: Karl Friedrich Löwe.
A 55–1032
Illinois. Univ. Library
for Library of Congress   ₍₂₎

NL 0446762   IU ICJ PPF

Löwe, Fri₍₊₂₎, 1874–
Optische Messungen, von Dr. F. Löwe ...
(*In* Chemisch-technische Untersuchungsmethoden. **Achte Auflage. Berlin, 1931. 24ᶜᵐ.** Bd. I, p. ₍807₎–924 incl. illus, tables, diagrs.)
Includes bibliographies.

NL 0446763   ICJ

Löwe, Fritz, *1874–*
Optische messungen des chemikers und des mediziners, von dr. Fritz Löwe ... Dresden und Leipzig, T. Steinkopff, 1925.
xi, 166 p. illus., diagrs. 21½ᶜᵐ. (*Added t.-p.:* Technische fortschrittsberichte; fortschritte der chem. technologie in einzeldarstellungen, hrsg. von prof. dr. B. Rassow ... bd. vi)
Contains bibliographies.

1. ₍Optical analysis₎
Agr 26–1549
Library, U. S. Dept. of   Agriculture 387L95

NL 0446764   DNAL PPF CU CtY NcD OCU MiU NIC DNLM   NjP NN ICJ

Löwe, Fritz, 1874–
Optische messungen des chemikers und des mediziners, von dr. Fritz Löwe ... 2. erweiterte und neubearb. aufl. Mit 58 abbildungen und 4 spektraltafeln. Dresden und Leipzig, T. Steinkopff, 1933.
xii, 205 p. illus., 4 pl., diagrs. 21½ᶜᵐ. ₍Added t.-p.:₎ Technische fortschrittsberichte ... 6)
Contains bibliographies.

1. Optical measurements. 2. Photochemistry.
₍Full name: Karl Friedrich Löwe₎
A C 34–1130
Title from Cornell Univ.   Printed by L. C.

NL 0446765   NIC DNLM NcD OO OU IU NN OrCS

Löwe, Fritz, 1874–
Optische messungen des chemikers und des mediziners, von dr. Fritz Löwe ... 3., erweiterte und neubearb. aufl. Mit 95 abbildungen und 4 spektraltafeln. Dresden und Leipzig, T. Steinkopff, 1939.
xiv, 256 p. incl. illus., tables, diagrs. iv pl. 22ᶜᵐ. (*Added t.-p.:* Technische fortschrittsberichte; fortschritte der chem. technologie in einzeldarstellungen, hrsg. von prof. dr. B. Rassow ... Bd. 6)
Includes bibliographies.

1. Optical measurements. 2. Spectrum analysis. 3. Chemistry, Analytic.
₍Full name: Karl Friedrich Löwe₎
Minnesota. Univ. Libr.   A 40–3638
for Library of Congress   QD95.L75   1939
₍a45c1₎†   544.6

NL 0446766   MnU NcD CU IU DLC

Löwe, Fritz, 1874–
Optische messungen des chemikers und des mediziners, von dr. Fritz Löwe ... 4., neubearb. aufl. Mit 94 abbildungen und 4 spektraltafeln. Dresden und Leipzig, T. Steinkopff, 1943.
xiv, 242 p. incl. illus., tables, diagrs. iv pl. 22½ᶜᵐ. (*Added t.-p.:* Technische fortschrittsberichte; fortschritte der chem. technologie in einzeldarstellungen, hrsg. von prof. dr. B. Rassow ... Bd. 6)
"Published by J. W. Edwards. Lithoprinted by Edwards brothers, inc., Ann Arbor, Michigan, U. S. A., 1945."
"Auswahl aus der fachliteratur": p. 210–232.

1. Optical measurements. 2. Spectrum analysis. 3. Chemistry, Analytic.
₍Full name: Karl Friedrich Löwe₎
Iowa. Univ. Library   A 45–4616 †
for Library of Congress   QD95.L75   1943 a

ICU NcD ViU NNC DLC IU
NL 0446767   IaU PMarhSO OrCS OU CU CtY-M NcU DNLM

Löwe, Fritz, 1874–
Optische Messungen des Chemikers und des Mediziners. 5., neubearb. Aufl. Dresden, T. Steinkopff, 1949.
xvi, 323 p. illus. 22 cm. (Technische Fortschrittsberichte, Bd. 6)
Bibliography: p. ₍282₎–315.

1. Optical measurements. 2. Spectrum analysis. 3. Chemistry, Analytic.   (Series)
Full name: Karl Friedrich Löwe.
QD95.L75   1949   50–36083

NL 0446768   DLC DNLM

Löwe, Fritz, 1874–
Optische Messungen des Chemikers und des Mediziners. 6., neubearb. Aufl. Dresden, T. Steinkopff, 1954.
xx, 364 p. illus. 22 cm. (Technische Fortschrittsberichte, Bd. 6)
Bibliography: p. 310–352.

1. Optical measurements. 2. Spectrochemistry.   I. Title.   (Series)
QD95.L75   1954   65–47007

NL 0446769   DLC DNLM

Löwe, Fritz, 1874–
Refraktometrie, von Dr. F. Löwe ...
(*In* Handbuch der Lebensmittelchemie. Bd. 2, Teil 1, p. 261–297. illus., tables, diagrs. ₍1933₎)

NL 0446770   ICJ

Löwe, Fritz, 1874–
Spektroskopische methoden des mediziners. Von F. Löwe ... (Mit 18 abbildungen.)
(*In* Abderhalden, Emil, ed. Handbuch der biologischen arbeitsmethoden ... Berlin, 1920– 25ᶜᵐ. abt. II, Physikalische methoden. T. 2, 1. hälfte (1928) p. ₍1431₎–1462 incl. illus., tab.)
Bibliographical foot-notes.

1. Spectroscope. 2. Spectrum analysis.
₍Full name: Karl Friedrich Löwe₎
A C 36–3453
Title from Ohio State   Univ.
Library of Congress   [QH324.A3 1920 abt.2, t.2]
₍2₎   (574.072)

NL 0446771   OU

LÖWE, FRITZ, 1874–
Die Untersuchung wichtiger Lebensmittel mit optischen Messinstrumenten; Vortrag, gehalten in der Agfa-Farbenfabrik Wolfen. Berlin, Aufbau-Verlag [Kulturbund zur demokratischen Erneuerung Deutschlands] 1952. 47 p. illus. 20cm. (Vorträge zur Verbreitung wissenschaftlicher Kenntnisse)

1. Food--Analysis. 2. Optics--   Measurements. I. Kulturbund
zur demokratischen Erneuerung   Deutschlands. t. 1952.,

NL 0446772   NN

Löwe, Fritz, 1887–
Das Wesergebirge zwischen Porta- und Süntelgebiet. Mit 5 profiltafeln ... Göttingen, 1912.
1 p. l., 101 p., 1 l. iv fold. tab. 23ᶜᵐ.
Inaug.-diss.—Göttingen.
Lebenslauf.
"Separat-abdruck aus dem Neuen jahrbuch für mineralogie etc. Beil.-bd. xxxvi."
"Verzeichnis der benutzten literatur": p. 94–101.
G S 14–173
Library, U. S. Geol.   survey

NL 0446773   DI-GS CtY NN

Loewe, Fritz, *1895–*
Wegener, Else, *ed.*
Alfred Wegeners letzte Grönlandfahrt: die erlebnisse der deutschen Grönlandexpedition 1930/1931 geschildert von seinen reisegefährten und nach tagebüchern des forschers; unter mitwirkung von dr. Fritz Loewe, herausgegeben von Else Wegener; mit 3 rundbildern, 122 abbildungen in kunst- und kupfertiefdruck, 11 karten, grundrissen und übersichten; vorwort von professor dr. Kurt Wegener. Leipzig, F. A. Brockhaus, 1932.

MB2.1/94
1935b   **Loewe, Fritz,** *1895–*
no.51   Coastal fogs in Australia. By Dr. F. Loewe. Melbourne, H.E. Daw, Govt. Printer, 1944.
19 p. illus., charts, diagrs., tables. 30cm. (Australia. Meteorological branch. Bulletin no. 51)

At head of title: Commonwealth of Australia. Commonwealth Meteorological Bureau.

NL 0446775   DAS

MB2.1/94
A958b   **Loewe,** *Fritz,* *1895–*
no.53   ...Discussion of seven years of aerological observations obtained by means of aeroplanes near Sydney. By Dr. F. Loewe... Melbourne, Govt. printer, 1945.
47p. illus., tables, diagrs. 30½cm. (Australia. Meteorological branch. Bulletin no. 53)

At head of title: Commonwealth of Australia.

Commonwealth meteorological bureau.
"References": p.47.

NL 0446777   DAS

M(055)
A958r   **Loewe,** *Fritz,* *1895–*
ser.10   The distribution of temperatures, pressures,
no.5   humidities and densities between sea level and 40,000 feet in Australia and lower latitudes. ₍Melbourne?₎, 1942.
ii, 11 ℓ. tables. 34cm. (Australia. Meteorological Service. Research reports. Series 10, no. 5)

A.M.S. Circ. no. 29.
Mimeographed.

NL 0446778   DAS

VOLUME 338

Loewe, Fritz, joint ed.
/1895-

Wegener, Else, *ed.*
Greenland journey, the story of Wegener's German expedition to Greenland in 1930–31 as told by members of the expedition and the leader's diary; edited by Else Wegener, with the assistance of Dr. Fritz Loewe. Translated from the 7th German edition by Winifred M. Deans. London and Glasgow, Blackie & son limited ₁1939₎

Löwe, Fritz, 1895–
Variability and periodicity of meteorological elements in the Southern Hemisphere, with particular reference to Australia. ₍Melbourne, 1948₎
49 p. maps, diagrs. 30 cm. (Australia. Bureau of Meteorology. Bulletin, 1948, no. 39)
Includes bibliographies.
CONTENTS.—Some considerations regarding the variability of annual rainfall in Australia, by F. Loewe.—On the nature of variations in Queensland rainfall, by U. Radok.—A contribution to the study of the variability of meteorological elements in the subtropical and temperate latitudes of the Southern Hemisphere, by F. Loewe.
1. Meteorology—Australia.   I. Radok, Uwe.   II. Title. (Series)
QC992.A4 no. 39   50–56884 rev

NL 0446780   DLC

Q213
.C68

Loewe, Fritz P., joint ed.

Coverlid, Dorothea Rebecca, *ed.*
German science texts, edited by Dorothea R. Coverlid, M. A. and Fritz P. Loewe, DR. PHIL. Melbourne and London, Melbourne university press in association with Oxford university press, 1943.

Loewe, Gedaljah, 1831–
Quaestiones de bonorum apud platonem gradibus partes quaedam.
Inaug. Diss. Halle, 1861. (Berlin)

NL 0446782   ICRL

Loewe (Gottlob. Fridericus Sigismundus). *De habitu cutis semiotico pathologico. 1 p. l., 22 pp. 4°. Vitebergae, lit. Tzschiedrichii, ₍1802₎.

NL 0446783   DNLM

Loewe, Günther, 1882–
... Die verpflichtungserklärungen der kommunalbehörden, von G. Loewe ... Berlin-Halensee, Sack & Montanus, 1929.
56 p. 17½cm. (Rechtsfragen der praxis. bd. 22)
Advertisements: p. 55–56.
1. Local government—Prussia.   2. Municipal corporations—Prussia. 3. Municipal finance—Prussia.   I. Title.
                                                 35–15961
Library of Congress   JS5471.P5L55
                              ₍2₎   352.0431

NL 0446784   DLC

Löwe, Günther, 1908–
... Zur Behandlung schwerer Trigeminus-Neuralgien mit Alkoholinjektion in das Ganglion Gasseri ... Griefswald, 1934.
Inaug.-Diss. - Berlin.
Lebenslauf.
"Literaturverzeichnis": p. 69–71.

NL 0446785   CtY

019.02
L825

Loewe, Gustav, 1852–1883.
Bibliotheca Patrum latinorum hispaniensis. 1. bd. Nach den aufzeichnungen Gustav Loewe's; hrsg. und bearb. von Wilhelm von Hartel. Wien, Carl Gerold's sohn, 1887.
542 p.   25cm.
1. Manuscripts, Latin. Catalogs. 2. Manuscripts in Spain. Catalogs. I. Hartel, Wilhelm August, ritter von, 1839–1907, ed. II. Title.

NL 0446786   MnU PLatS ODW

PA6585
.Z9L6
1877

Loewe, Gustav, 1852–1883.
Coniectanea Plautina ad codicem ambrosianum maximam partem spectantia, scripsit Gustavus Loewe. ₍Leipzig? 1877₎
₍155₎–224 p.   23cm.
From: Analecta Plautina, scripserunt Schoell, Goetz, Loewe.
1. Plautus, Titu Maccius. Mss. (Cod. ambrosianus). 2. Codex ambrosianus. I. Title.
Full name: Carl   Gustav Loewe.

NL 0446787   ViU MdBP

Loewe, Gustav, 1852–1883.
Corpvs glossariorvm latinorvm, a Gvstavo Loewe incohatvm, avspiciis Academiae litterarvm saxonicae composvit recensvit edidit Georgivs Goetz ... Lipsiae et Berolini, in aedibvs B. G. Tevbneri, 1888–1923 ₍v. 1, '23₎

---

*Loewe, Gustav, 1852–1883, joint ed.

Ewald, Paul, 1857–1911, *ed.*
Exempla scriptvrae visigoticae XL tabvlis expressa; liberalitate ministerii qvod regni borvssici rebvs ecclesiasticis scholasticis medicinalibvs praeest adivti, edidervnt Pavlvs Ewald et Gvstavvs Loewe. Tabvlas photographicas arte Antonii Selfa Escorialensis maximam partem confectas phototypice descripservnt A. Navmann & Schroeder Lipsienses. Heidelbergae, apvd Gvstavvm Koester, 1883.

Loewe, Gustav, 1852–1883.
Glossae nominum. Edidit Gustavus Loewe. Accedunt eiusdem opuscula glossographica, collecta a Georgio Goetz. Lipsiae: In aedibus B. G. Teubneri, 1884.   xviii, 264 p.   23cm.
Bibliographical footnotes.

889868A. 1. Latin language—
                              ed.
N. Y. P. L.
                        Purchased for J. S. Billings Mem. Coll. Glossaries. I. Goetz, Georg, 1849–
                                            December 14, 1937

CLU
NL 0446790   NN CtY OCU IU CLSU PBm NjR ViU NjP MH IU

Löwe, Gustav, 1852–1883.
In Lucili saturarum fragmenta conjectanea, accedit De militis Plautinae versu 1335 disputatio. (In Commentationes philologae ... Seminarii philologi regii Lipsiensis. 1874. p. ₍237₎–53)

NL 0446791   CU

Loewe, Gustav, 1852–1883.
Prodromvs Corporis glossariorvm latinorvm; qvaestiones de glossariorvm latinorvm fontibvs et vsv, scripsit Gvstavvs Loewe. Lipsiae, in aedibvs B. G. Tevbneri, 1876.
xv, ₍1₎, 450 p.   23ᶜᵐ.
1. Corpvs glossariorvm latinorvm.   2. Latin language—Glossography. I. Title.
                          ₍Full name: Carl Gustav Loewe₎
                                              26–4991
Library of Congress   PA2359.L6

MiU ViU NjP NN IU NjR MH
NL 0446792   DLC CU NIC TxU NcD CtY PBm PU OClW OCU

Loewe, Gustav, 1852–1883.
Quaestionum de glossariorum latinorum fontibus et usu particula commentatio quam ... scripsit Gustavus Löwe. Lipsiae, typis B. G. Teubneri, 1875.
2 p. l, 36 p.   22½ᵐ.
Inaug.-diss.—Leipzig.
Vita.
1. Latin language—Glossaries, vocabularies, etc.
                          ₍Full name: Carl Gustav Loewe₎
                                              46–43159
Library of Congress   PA2359.L63

NL 0446793   DLC CtY PU OO NjP

Loewe, Gustav, 1852–1883, *ed.*

Plautus, Titus Maccius.
T. Macci Plavti Comoediae; recensvit instrvmento critico et prolegomenis avxit Fridericvs Ritschelivs sociis operae adsvmptis Gvstavo Loewe, Georgio Goetz, Friderico Schoell ... Lipsiae, in aedibvs B. G. Tevbneri, 1879–1902.

Loewe, ₍Hans₎.
Anfangsgründe der niederen Geodäsie, mit Berücksichtigung der Formeln der preussischen Vermessungsanweisung (Kasteranweisung VIII u. IX). viii,₍170,30,₎₍2₎ p. il. 25 pl. O. Liebenwerda: R. Reiss, ₍892.

NL 0446795   ICJ NIC

Loewe, ₍Hans₎.
Wassermengen in Kanälen und Drainagen sowie in Rohrleitungen überhaupt, von Loewe, königlicher Landmesser. Teil I–₍II₎. .... Lissa, Selbstverlag, 1905.
viii, 49 p. illus., 6 maps (1 fold.), 1 diagr. 23ᶜᵐ.
5 maps have illustrations on both sides.
"Benutzte Literatur," p. 45.

NL 0446796   ICJ

Loewe, Hans, 1879–
Die Annales Augustani. Eine quellenkritische untersuchung, München, R. Oldenbourg, 1903.
132 p.
München, Phil. Diss.v. 1903.

NL 0446797   PU NjP MH

Loewe, Hans, 1879–
Die entwicklung des schulkampfs in Bayern bis zum vollständigen sieg des neuhumanismus, von dr. Hans Loewe ... Berlin, Weidmann, 1917.
viii, 97, ₍1₎ p. 25½ cm. (Added t.-p.: Monumenta Germaniae paedagogica ... beiheft II)
"Verzeichnis der abgekürzt zitierten schriften": p. vi–viii.
1. Education—Bavaria.
LA720.M8 Suppl., vol. 2   21–8254 rev

NL 0446798   DLC CU NIC MB NN ICJ MH PU OU NcD

DD205 Loewe, Hans, 1879–
.T4L8   Friedrich Thiersch; ein humanistenleben im rahmen der geistesgeschichte seiner zeit, von dr. Hans Loewe ... München und Berlin, R. Oldenbourg, 1925–
v. 23½ᵐ.
"Verzeichnis der abgekürzt zitierten schriften": vol. ₍1₎ p. ₍vii₎–xii.
1. Thiersch, Friedrich Wilhelm von, 1784–1860.

NL 0446799   ICU CU CaBVaU ICarbS TxFTC ICN MH NjP

VOLUME 338

Loewe, Hans, 1879–   ed.
  ₍Bitzius, Albert₎ 1797–1854.
    Jeremias Gotthelf ₍pseud.₎ Grosse deutsche ausgabe; herausgegeben von Hans Löwe ... Naunhof und Leipzig, F. W. Hendel verlag ₍1938–

AC831
M89
1906
Stack

Loewe, Hans, 1879–
  Die Leibesübungen als Erziehungsmittel und ihre Einfügung in den Lehrplan des humanistischen Gymnasiums in Bayern.   München, 1906.
    39 p.
    Programmschrift - Kgl. Wilhelmsgymnasium, München.

    1.Physical education and training - Bavaria.

NL 0446801   CSt

Loewe, Hans, 1879–
  Paul Ehrlich, Schöpfer der Chemotherapie. Stuttgart, Wissenschaftliche Verlagsgesellschaft, 1950.
    255 p. illus. ports. 22 cm. (Grosse Naturforscher, Bd. 8)
    "Chronologische Zusammenstellung der Veröffentlichungen Paul Ehrlichs": p. 287–251. Bibliography: p. 255.

    1. Ehrlich, Paul, 1854–1915.   i. Title.   (Series)

  R512.E4L6   926.1   ₍50–56033

  MtBuM OrSaW OrU-M DNLM
  WaPS WaS WaSp WaSpG WaT WaTC WaWW Or OrStbM IdPI
  NcU CaBVaU IdB IdU MtBC MtU OrCS OrP OrU Wa WaE
NL 0446802   DLC CtY-M PU NcU CU PPC PPT ViU ICJ ICU

Loewe, Hans, 1881–
  Zur Kenntnis der Dimethylamidobenzoylbenzoesäure und ihres Verhaltens gegen salpetrige Säure...von Hans Loewe... Frankfurt a. M.: G. Giesecke, 1914.   46 p. incl. tables.   8°.
    Dissertation, Erlangen, 1913.
    Lebenslauf, last page.
    Bibliographical footnotes.

    1. Acid, Dimethyl-aminobenzophenone-   carboxylic. 2. Acid, Nitrous.
    N.Y.P.L.   November 8, 1926

NL 0446803   NN CtY MH ICRL DNLM

Loewe, Hans, 1888–
  Ueber einen fall von embolie der aorta...
  Inaug. diss. Koenigsberg, 1912.
  Bibl.

NL 0446804   ICRL CtY DNLM

Loewe, Hans, 1899–
  Die elektrochemische oxydation des o-toluolsulfamids su saccharin.
  Inaug. diss.   Basel, 1921

NL 0446805   ICRL MH CtY

Löwe, Hans, 1905–   ed.
  Faust, eine Tragödie von Goethe. 1. u. 2. Teil
  see under   Goethe, Johann Wolfgang von,
  1749–1832. Faust. Parts I and II.

Löwe, Hans, 1905–
  Der Rattenfänger von Helmerode; eine Erzählung aus der Zeit der Kinderkreuzzüge. Mit Zeichnungen von Hanns Georgi. ₍Leipzig₎ Jugendbuchverlag E. Wunderlich ₍1952₎
    107 p. illus. 21 cm.

    i. Title.

    PZ35.L56   52–41049 ‡

NL 0446807   DLC

LÖWE, HANS, 1905–
  Der Rebell von Tauroggen; die Geschichte eines Mannes und einer Konvention. Historische Erzählung.   Leipzig, P. List [c1954]
    65 p.   21cm.

    1. Yorck von Wartenburg, Hans David Ludwig, Graf. 1759–1830 – Fiction. 2. Tauroggen, Convention of, 1812—Fiction. I. Title.

NL 0446808   NN

WA
8305

Löwe, Hans, 1905–
  Sänger und Held; eine Erzählung aus dem Leben Theodor Körners. [Illustrationen von Alfred Will.   Berlin] Verlag der Nation ₍c1953₎

    1. Korner, Theodor, 1791–1813 - Fiction. I. Title(1)

NL 0446809   CtY

LÖWE, HANS, 1905–
  Sänger und Held; eine Erzählung aus dem Leben Theodor Körners. [Berlin] Verlag der Nation [1953]
    53 p. illus. 19cm. (Kleine nationale Bücherei. Bd. 3)

    Film reproduction. Negative.

    1. Körner, Theodor, 1791–1813.

NL 0446810   NN

Löwe, Hans, 1905–
  Soldat seines Volkes; das Leben Ferdinand von Schills. ₍Berlin₎ Verlag der Nation ₍1953₎
    56 p. 19 cm. (Kleine nationale Bücherei, Bd. 1)

    1. Schill, Ferdinand Baptista, 1776–1809.   i. Title.

    DD418.6.S33L6   55–43430

NL 0446811   DLC MH

LÖWE, HANS, 1905–
  Soldat seines Volkes; das Leben Ferdinand von Schills.   [Berlin] Verlag der Nation [1953]   56 p.   19cm. (Kleine nationale Bücherei. Bd. 1)

    Film reproduction. Negative.

    1. Schill, Ferdinand Baptista von, 1776–1809. I. Kleine nationale Bücherei.

NL 0446812   NN

Löwe, Hans-Adolf Goldbeck-
    see Goldbeck-Löwe, Hans-Adolf.

Loewe, Heinrich.
  An exact account on Sir Walter Scott's poem: "The Lady of the lake" ... Neubrandenburg, B. Ahrendt, 1873.
    2 p. l., 24 p. 26ᵐ.
    Inaug.-diss.—Rostock.

    1. Scott, Sir Walter, bart. Lady of the lake.

                                          28–20001

    Library of Congress   PR5308.L6

NL 0446814   DLC CtY NcD NjP

Löwe, Heinrich.
  Das neue Russland und seine sittlichen kräfte, von Heinrich Löwe. Halle an der Saale, M. Niemeyer, 1918.
    2 p. l., 191, ₍1₎ p. 23½ᵐ.

    1. Russia—Soc. condit.   i. Title.

    Library of Congress   DK265.L53   20–22909

NL 0446815   DLC NN NjP

Loewe, Heinrich, philologist, ed.
  Deutsch-englische Phraseologie in systematischer Ordnung nebst einem systematical vocabulary ... unter Mitwirkung von Dr. Bernhard Schmitz. Ed. 9. Berlin, Langenscheidt, n.d.
    198 p.

NL 0446816   OCl

---

ar W
39054

Loewe, Heinrich, philologist, ed.
  Deutsch-englische Phraseologie in systematischer Ordnung, nebst einem systematical vocabulary; unter Mitwirkung von B. Schmitz. 2., gänzlich umgearb. Aufl.   Berlin, Langenscheidt, 1885.
    xv, 180 p. 21cm.

    Ein Seitenstück zur deutsch-französischen Phraseologie von Bernhard Schmitz.

NL 0446817   NIC

Loewe, Heinrich, philologist, ed. and Bernhard Schmitz. 1819–1881.
  Deutsch-englische Phraseologie in systematischer Ordnung nebst einem Systematical vocabulary. 6. Auflage. Berlin. Langensheidt. 1902. xv, 198 pp. 16°.

    Sept. 10,   1902
    —— Germany. Lang. Conv. — Schmitz, Bernhard, jt. auth. 1819–1881.

NL 0446818   MB

Löwe, Heinrich, philologist, ed.
  Deutsch-englische phraseologie in systematischer ordnung, nebst einem... vocabulary; ein seitenstück zur deutsch-französischen phraseologie von Bernhard Schmitz, unter mitwirkung von Bernhard Schmitz; 8. aufl. Berlin, 1908.
    198p.

NL 0446819   OCU

PF
3640
L64

Loewe, Heinrich, philologist, ed.
  Deutsch-englische Phraseologie nebst einem systematischen Wörterverzeichnis, von Dr. Heinrich Loewe; neue, verbesserte Bearbeitung von E. D. ₍Breul. Siebzehnte Auflage. Berlin-Schöneberg, Langenscheidtsche Verlagsbuchhandlung (Prof. G. Langenscheidt) G.m.b.H. ₍c1926₎
    viii, 292 p. 20 cm.

NL 0446820   NcGU CaBVaU

VOLUME 338

Loewe, Heinrich, philologist.
Entwurf eines französischen elementarbuchs nach neueren anschauungen. Mitgeteilt und gewidmet der "Neusprachlichen section" auf der 37. Versammlung deutscher philologen und schulmänner zu Dessau (1.-4. october 1884) von dr. Heinrich Loewe... [Bernberg, A. König, 1884]
2 p.l., [109]-178 p. 25 cm. (In Festschrift zur begrüssing der XXXVII. Versammlung deutscher philologen und schulmänner zu Dessau ... 1884)

1. French language - Textbooks for foreigners - Germans. 2. French language - Grammar.

NL 0446822   CU

Loewe, Heinrich, *philologist.*
La France et les Français. Neues französisches Lesebuch für deutsche Schulen. Unterstufe. Mit Wörterverzeichnissen und vollständigem Wörterbuche. 3. Auflage.
= Dresden. Kühtmann. 1893. viii, 224 pp. [Dr. H. Loewe's Parallelwerk.] 20 cm., in 8s.

L503 — S.r. — France. Lang. Reading-books. German.

NL 0446823   MB

Loewe, Heinrich, *philologist.*
Lexikon der handels-korrespondenz. Deutsch — englisch — französisch. Unter mitwirkung von Harry Alcock und C. Charmillot hrsg. von dr. Heinrich Löwe. 10. aufl. Bonn, Georgi, 1929.
2 p.l., 571 p. 22cm.
Imprint covered by label: Ferd. Dümmlers verlag. Berlin und Bonn.
Parallel text in German, English, and French.
1. Commercial correspondence, German. 2. Commercial correspondence, English. 3. Commercial correspondence, French. 4. Commerce—Terminology. I. Alcock, Harry. II. Charmillot, C.

NL 0446824   ViU

PR
3067
.L83
Loewe, Heinrich, *philologist.*
Shakespeare-studien; 100 stellen weidmännisch erklärt und übersetzt von dr. Heinrich Loewe ... Zerbst, O. Schnee, 1904.
1 p.l., iii, 152 p. 22½cm.
"Wissenschaftliche beilage zu den schulnachrichten des Herzogl. Francisceums zu Zerbst von Ostern 1904."
Separate from Programm.

1. Shakespeare, William—Language—Glossaries, etc. 2. Shakespeare, William—Knowledge—Sports.

NL 0446825   MiU MH NcD PU-F NcU

Loewe, Heinrich, philologist.
Dr. H. Loewe's Unterrichtsbriefe zur schnellen und leichten Erlernung fremder Sprachen nach neuer, natürlicher Methode. Spanisch. Unter mirwirkung von Eduardo H. Echenagucia; hrsg. von Dr. Adolf Kressner. Dritte, vielfach verbesserte Auflage. Berlin, C. Regenhardt, n.d.
vii, 324, 68, 24 p.

NL 0446826   OCl

Loewe, Heinrich, *philologist.*
Dr. H. Loewes Unterrichtsbriefe zur schnellen und leichten erlernung fremder sprachen nach neuer, natürlicher methode. Italienisch. Nach den besten hulfsmitteln bearbeitet von dr. J. A. Scartazzini. Berlin, C. Regenhardt, 1891.
vii, [1], 352, [2], 88, [2], 21, [1] p. 21½cm.

1. Italian language—Grammar. 2. Italian language—Composition and exercises. I. Scartazzini, Giovanni Andrea, 1837-1901, ed.

34-40975
Library of Congress   PC1111.L57
458.243

NL 0446827   DLC NN

Loewe, Heinrich, 1869-1951.
Alter jüdischer Volkshumor aus Talmud und Midrasch. [Reichenberg in Böhmen, 1931]
84 p. 29 cm.

1. Jewish wit and humor.

PN6231.H4L6

52-58190

NL 0446828   DLC MH

DS 149
L8
1903
Loewe, Heinrich, 1869-1951.
Antisemitismus und Zionismus; eine zeitgemasse Betrachtung, von Heinrich Sachse. 2. Aufl. Berlin, H. Schildberger [1903?]
22 p. 23 cm. (Jüdische Aufklarungsschrift, 1)

1. Zionism 2. Antisemitism
II. Series

NL 0446829   OU

Loewe, Heinrich, 1869-1951.
Der Aufbau der Jerusalem-Bibliothek. [Berlin, 1928.]
p. 85-96

Title taken from first page.
Repr.: Soncino-Gesellschaft der Freunde des jüdischen Buches. Soncino-Blätter ...

NL 0446830   OCH

Loewe, Heinrich, 1869-1951.
Berlin, Mark Brandenburg und Altmark. Berlin, Preuss [1919?]

187 p. 59 plates

NL 0446831   MH

Loewe, Heinrich, 1869-
Geschichten von jüdischen Namen, aus dem Volksmunde gesammelt von Heinrich Loewe. Berlin, 1929. 17 p. 25½cm.
"Handpressendruck der Officina Serpentis in einer Auflage von 250 Exemplaren; den Mitgliedern und Freunden der Soncino-Gesellschaft zum Gesellschaftsabend am 17. Februar 1929 überreicht."

1. Names, Jewish. I. Soncino-jüdischen Buches, Berlin.   Gesellschaft der Freunde des
N.Y.P.L.   May 4, 1938

NL 0446832   NN

[Loewe, Heinrich] 1869-
[Ignaz Goldziher. [Berlin, 1929]
[12] p. mounted facsim. 31¼cm.
"Ein wort des gedenkens von Heinrich Loewe."
"Den am 7. adar 5689 zur Jahresversammlung der Soncino-gesellschaft vereinigten freunden des jüdischen buches überreicht von Josef Altmann und buchdruckerei Max Lichtwitz."

1. Goldziher, Ignácz, 1850-1921. 2. Jerusalem. Jewish national and university library. I. Soncino-gesellschaft der freunde des jüdischen buches e. v., Berlin. II. Title.

39-4860
Library of Congress   Z844.J57L8
[2]
924.9

NL 0446833   DLC NN

[Loewe, Heinrich, 1869-1951]
*fGP9
So575
926t
In memoriam Aaron Ember ...
[Berlin, 1926]
[8]p. 28.5cm., in case 30cm.
Signed at end: Heinrich Loewe.
Printer's imprint on p.[4] of wrappers: Druckerei Gutenberg, Berlin N54.
"Dem Andenken des Mitgliedes der Soncino-Gesellschaft Aaron Ember und seiner Frau Regina, geb. Mandelstamm zur zweiten Jahresversammlung der Gesellschaft gewidmet von Frieda und Hermann Stahl 29. kislew   5687."
Original   printed dark green wrappers; in   cloth case.

NL 0446834   MH OCH PPDrop

Loewe, Heinrich, 1869-1951.
Die Juden in der katholischen Legende. Berlin: Jüdischer Verlag, 1912. 3 p.l., (1)10-93 p. 8°.
Part of the work appeared in Monatsschrift für Geschichte und Wissenschaft des Judentums.

1. Jews.—History (Mediaeval). 2.   Jews in folk-lore.
N.Y.P.L.   August 29, 1914.

NL 0446835   NN CtY OCl OCH OClW OCl PPDrop PP

Loewe, Heinrich, 1869-
Die jüdischdeutsche Sprache der Ostjuden; ein Abriss von Heinrich Loewe. Im Auftrage des "Komitees für den Osten." Berlin, 1915. 25 p. 31½cm.
On cover: Als Handschrift gedruckt.
"Litteratur," p. 23-25.

1. Judeo-German language.   SCHIFF COLLECTION.
N.Y.P.L.   I. Komitee für den Osten, Berlin.
    December 10, 1940

NL 0446836   NN MH OCH

Loewe, Heinrich, 1869-
Jüdische Feuersegen, von Heinrich Loewe. [Berlin-Schöneberg: S. Scholem, 1930.] 15 p. mounted illus. (incl. facsim.) 30½cm.
"Dieses Büchlein wurde...in dreihundert Exemplaren hergestellt und den zur Jahresversammlung der Soncino-Gesellschaft versammelten Freunden des jüdischen Buches als Spende überreicht."

705920A. 1. Amulets and talismans,   Jewish. 2. Fires—Prevention and extinction. I. Soncino-Gesellschaft   der Freunde des jüdischen Buches, Berlin.
N.Y.P.L.   April 27, 1934

NL 0446837   NN OCH

Loewe, Heinrich, 1869-
Eine jüdische Nationalbibliothek, von Heinrich Loewe. Berlin, Jüdischer Verlag, 1905.
30 p., 1 l. 24cm.

NL 0446838   ICJ OCH NN

DS135
.G8A256
Loewe, Heinrich, 1869-1951, ed.
Jüdische Rundschau.

Berlin.

Loewe, Heinrich, 1869-
Der jüdische Spieler; eine Gelegenheitsschrift, von Heinrich Loewe. [Berlin-Schöneberg: Druck von S. Scholem, 1930.] 9 p. mounted illus. 30½cm.
No. 155 of 300 copies printed.
"Im Auftrage von Bruno Boas, Martin Brunn, Moritz Hepner und Alfred Peltesohn...hergestellt und...am 30. März 1930 zur Jahresversammlung der Soncino-Gesellschaft...als Spende überreicht."
Bibliography included.

705920A. 1. Games of chance—Jews.   I. Soncino-Gesellschaft der Freunde des jüdischen Buches, Berlin.
N.Y.P.L.   May 2, 1934

NL 0446840   NN OCH

VOLUME 338

Loewe, Heinrich, 1869–
Jüdisches bibliothekswesen im lande Israel, von Heinrich Loewe. Jerusalem, National- u. Universitäts-bibliothek, 5682/1922.

65, [1] p. 23ᶜᵐ.

1. Libraries—Palestine.

Title from Columbia Univ.   Printed by L. C.

A 33–1209

NL 0446841   NNC CtY

Loewe, Heinrich, 1869–   ed.
Lebenserinnerungen [von] A. H. Heymann
see under   Heymann, Aron Hirsch,
1803–1880.

Loewe, Heinrich, 1869–
Der Liberalismus macht selig und der Sonntagsgottesdienst macht liberal. Ein Wort zur Verstandigung an Herrn Gustav Levinstein. Hrsg. von der Berliner Zionistischen Vereinigung. Berlin: H.S. Hermann, 1901–
11 p.

NL 0446843   OCH

Loewe, Heinrich, 1869–1951.
Lieder-buch für jüdische vereine. Nebst einem anhange enthaltend gedichte jüdischen inhalts zum vortragen zusammengestellt von Heinrich Loewe. 1. tausend. Berlin, H. Schildberger, 1894.

99 p. 14 cm. (*Added t.-p.:* Jüdische volksbibliothek, hrsg. von Heinrich Loewe. hft. 1 u. 2)

Contains music.

1. Song-books, Jewish.   I. Title.

M1850.L6L5   22—24209

NL 0446844   DLC

Loewe, Heinrich, 1869–   , ed.
Liederbuch für jüdische Vereine. Im Auftrage der "Zionistischen Vereinigung für Deutschland," herausgegeben von Dr. Heinrich Loewe. Zweite Auflage.   Köln am Rh.: Zionistische Vereinigung für Deutschland, 1898. 128 p. 13½cm. (Jüdische Volksbibliothek.)

Seven songs are also in Hebrew.
Without music, but many tunes indicated by title.

1. Songs, Jewish—Collections.   I. Zionistische Vereinigung für
N. Y. P. L.   Deutschland.
                                                November 8, 1935

NL 0446845   NN

Loewe, Heinrich, 1869–1951.
The life and surprising adventures of Robinson Crusoe
see Defoe, Daniel, 1661?–1731.
Robinson Crusoe. Part I. 1882.

Loewe, Heinrich, 1869–
Proselyten; ein Beitrag zur Geschichte der jüdischen Rasse, von Heinrich Loewe.   Berlin: Soncino-Gesellschaft, 5687 [1926].
30 p. 28½cm.

One of 300 copies printed.

705919A. 1. Proselytes, Jewish.   I. Soncino—Gesellschaft der Freunde
des jüdischen Buches, Berlin.
N. Y. P. L.   July 19, 1934

NL 0446847   NN MH

Loewe, Heinrich, 1869–1951.
Judaica   Reste von altem jüdischen Volkshumor.
Har47   Berlin, Privatdruck, 5682[1922]
922L   100p. 13cm.

1. Jewish wit and humor

NL 0446848   CtY OCH MH

DG861   **LOEWE, HEINRICH,** 1869–
.2   Richard von San Germano und die ältere redaktion
.R5L7   seiner Chronik. 1.t. ...   Magdeburg, 1894.
vi,26,[2]p. 22cm.
Inaug.-diss.--Berlin.
Vita.

1. Ricardus de Sancto Germano, d. 1243. Chronica.

NL 0446849   ICU ICRL NjP CU MdBP PU

Loewe, Heinrich, 1869–1951.
Schelme und narren mit jüdischen kappen, von Heinrich Loewe. Berlin, Welt-verlag, 5680/1920.

63, [1] p. 18½ cm. (*On cover:* Die Weltbücher, eine jüdische schriftenfolge. 8)

1. Jewish wit and humour.   I. Title.

PN6231.J5L6   30—3124

NL 0446850   DLC PPDrop NN

Loewe, Heinrich, 1869–

Berlin. *Universität. Bibliothek.*
Schriften zur einführung in die benutzung der Berliner universität-bibliothek; hrsg. von der verwaltung ...
Berlin, G. Reimer, 1913–

Loewe, Heinrich, 1869–1951.
Die Sprachen der Juden.   Köln, Jüdischer Verlag, 1911.
160 p. 24 cm.

1. Jews—Languages.

DS113.L6   52—57347

NL 0446852   DLC OCl WaU MH NN OCH CtY

[**Loewe, Heinrich**] 1869–
... Zionistenkongress und zionismus eine gefahr? Eine zeitgemässe betrachtung. Von dr. Heinrich Sachse [pseud.] Berlin, H. Schildberger, 1897.

54 p. 23ᶜᵐ. (*At head of title:* Jüdische aufklärungsschrift II)

1. Jews—Restoration.   I. Title.

24—24732

Library of Congress   DS149.L6

NL 0446853   DLC NN MH

LOEWE, HEINRICH, 1869–
Zionistenkongress und Zionismus eine Gefahr?
Eine zeitgemässe Betrachtung, von Dr. Heinrich Sachse [pseud.].   Berlin, H. Schildberger, 1897.
54 p. 24cm. (Juedische Aufklärungsschrift. 2.)

Film reproduction. Positive.

1. Zionism, 1896–1916.

NL 0446854   NN

---

*GC9   [Loewe, Heinrich, 1869–1951]
L8252   ... Zionistenkongress und Zionismus eine
897zb   Gefahr? Eine zeitgemässe Betrachtung. Von
Dr. Heinrich Sachse [pseud.]. Zweite Auflage.
Berlin,1897.Verlag von Hugo Schildberger,NW.,
Flensburgerstrasse 412.Beilage zu No.9 des
"Zion."

54p. 22.5cm. (Jüdische Aufklärungsschrift,
11)

NL 0446855   MH OCH

Loewe, Heinrich, 1869–*1951*.
Zur kunde von den Juden im Kaukasus, aus zwei alten deutschen zeitungen. Von Heinrich Loewe. Charlottenburg [Leipzig, Druck von C. W. Vollrath] 1900.
22 p., 1 l. 16ᶜᵐ.

1. Jews in Caucasus.   44–22433

Library of Congress   DS135.R93C35

NL 0446856   DLC PP NN PPDrop

Löwe, Heinrich der, duke of Saxony, 1129–1195.

SEE

Heinrich der Löwe, duke of Saxony, 1129–1195.

Loewe, Heinrich Georg Fr., tr.
Blut und geld im judentum, dargestellt am jüdischen recht (Schulchan aruch)
see under   [Caro, Joseph] 1488–1575.

BM550   **Loewe, Heinrich Georg Fr.,** tr.
.C335L6
Caro, Joseph, 1488–1575.
Der Schulchan aruch; oder, Die vier jüdischen Gesetzbücher, in 's Deutsche übertragen von Heinr. Georg F. Löwe. Abschrift. [Düsseldorf, 1935?]

Löwe, Heinz, 1913–   ed.
Festgabe Anton Ernstberger
see under   Erlangen. Universität.
Institut für Fränkische Landesforschung.

Me21   **Löwe, Heinz,** 1913–
F80   Die karolingische Reichsgründung und der
v.13   Südosten: Studien zum Werden des Deutschtums
und seiner Auseinandersetzung mit Rom ...
Stuttgart,W.Kohlhammer,1937.
xii,181p. 23½cm. (Forschungen zur Kirchen-
und Geistesgeschichte ... 13.Bd.)
"Literaturverzeichnis": p.[xi]-xii.

1. Germany - Church history - Middle ages.
2. Bavaria - Church history.   I.Ser.

NL 0446861   CtY NjP NjPT GEU

VOLUME 338

DC
65
.E3
Loewe, Heinz, 1913–
Die karolingische Reichsgründung und der Südosten, Studien zum Werden des Deutschtums und seiner Auseinandersetzung mit Rom. Stuttgart, W. Kohlhammer, 1937.
xii, 181 p. (Forschungen zur Kirchen- und Geistesgeschichte. 13. Bd.)
"Diese Arbeit, die von der Philosophischen Fakultät der Universität Berlin als Dissertation angenommen wurde."
Bibliography: p. xi-xii.

Microfilm (negative) Bruxelles, Bibliothèque Royale de Belgique. 1 reel.
On reel with Eiten, Gustav. Das Unterkönigtum im Reiche der Merovinger und Karolinger. Heidelberg, 1907.

1. Carolingians. 2. Germany--Church history. 3. Missions--Germany. I. Title. (Series)

NL 0446863   OkU

AS
182
.M232
1951
no.11
Löwe, Heinz, 1913–
Ein literarischer Widersacher des Bonifatius, Virgil von Salzburg, und die Kosmographie des Aethicus Ister. Mainz, Akademie der Wissenschaften und der Literatur; in Kommission bei F. Steiner, Wiesbaden ₁1952₎
90 p. 25 cm. (Akademie der Wissenschaften und der Literatur, Mainz. Geistes-und Sozialwissenschaftliche Klasse. Abhandlungen, Jahrg. 1951, Nr. 11)
1. Bonifacius, originally Winfried, Saint, Abp. of Mainz, 680-755. 2. Virgil, Saint, Abp. of Salzburg, d. 784? 3. Aethicus Ister. Cosmographia Ethici. 4. Geography, Ancient.

NL 0446864   OkU NIC MB CtY NcU NNC DDO

Löwe, Heinz, 1913–   , ed.
Der Streit um Methodius; Quellen zu den nationalkirchlichen Bestrebungen in Mähren und Pannonien im 9. Jahrhundert.. ₁Köln₎ B. Pick, 1948₎
65 p., 18ᵐ. (Kölner Hefte für den akademischen Unterricht. Historische Reihe. 2)

"Literaturhinweis": p. 63-65.

NL 0446865   NjPT

Loewe, Herbert₎ 1889–   Die nordischen Devongeschiebe Deutschlands. Stuttgart: Schweizerbart 1912. 118 S. 8° ¶ (Aus: Neues Jahrbuch f. Mineral. Beil-Bd 35.)
Königsberg, Phil. Diss. v. 20. Sept. 1912, Ref. Tornquist
₁Geb. 26. Okt. 89 Dresden; Wohnort: Königsberg i. P.; Staatsangeh.: Preußen; Vorbildung: Realgymn. Königsberg Reife O. 09; Studium: Königsberg 6 S.; Rig. 1. März 12.₎   ₁U 12. 6090₎

NL 0446866   ICRL MH-Mu PU

Loewe, Herbert Martin James, 1882–1940.
Cambridge. University. *Trinity college. Library.*
Catalogue of the manuscripts in the Hebrew character collected and bequeathed to Trinity college library by the late William Aldis Wright ... by Herbert Loewe, M. A. Cambridge, At the University press, 1926.

Z6375
.C3
Loewe, Herbert Martin James, 1882–1940, comp.
Cambridge. University. *Girton College. Library.*
Catalogue of the printed books and of the Semitic and Jewish mss. in the Mary Frere Hebrew library at Girton College, Cambridge, by Herbert Loewe. ₁Cambridge, Girton College ₁1916₎₎

Loewe, Herbert ₁Martin James₎ 1882–   joint ed.
Isaac Abravanel; six lectures by Paul Goodman, L. Rabinowitz ... ₁and others₎ with an introductory essay by H. Loewe; edited by J. B. Trend ... and H. Loewe ... Cambridge ₁Eng.₎ The University press, 1937.

Loewe, Herbert ₁Martin James₎ 1882–
Israel Abrahams ₁Philadelphia, 1926.₎
p. 219-234.

Excerpt: American Jewish Year Book. Yrs. 5687.

NL 0446870   OCH

Loewe, Herbert Martin James, 1882-1940.
Israel Abrahams, a biographical sketch. ₁Cambridge?₎ The Arthur Davis memorial trust, 1944.
vi, 159 p. port.

Bibliographical footnotes.

1. Abrahams, Israel, 1858-1925.

NL 0446871   NNC NNJ

BM535
.J8
Loewe, Herbert Martin James, 1882–   ed.
Judaism and Christianity ... London, The Sheldon press; New York, The Macmillan company ₁1937–

LOEWE, Herbert Martin James, 1882-1940.
Judaism and the Presbyterian Church ... Cambridge, 1924. 12p 28cm.

1.History-Great Britain. 2.Judaism and Christianity. 3.Good Will.

NL 0446873   NNJ

Loewe, Herbert Martin James, 1882–   ed. and tr.
Mediæval Hebrew minstrelsy: songs for the Bride queen's feast. Sixteen zemiroth arranged according to the traditional harmonies by Rose L. Henriques, illustrated by Beatrice Hirschfeld and translated into English to fit the Hebrew tunes by Herbert Loewe. With a foreword by the Very Rev. Dr. J. H. Hertz ... London, J. Clarke & co., ltd., 5687—1926.
3 p. l., 134 p. 21 x 17ᶜᵐ.
Head-pieces.
"Selected variant readings" (3 p. at end) autographed from manuscript copy.
"Abbreviations and bibliography": p. 120.
I. Henriques, Mrs. Rose L. II. Hirschfeld, Beatrice, illus. III. Title. IV. Title: Zemiroth.
Library of Congress   M2194.3.H3   29-8321

MB PPDrop
NL 0446874   DLC IU CoU NN NcD NcU CtY PP OCl OCH

Loewe, Herbert Martin James, 1882–
The orthodox position, by Herbert Loewe... Cambridge: W. Heffer & Sons, Ltd., 1915. 23 p. 8°. (Essays on problems in Jewish orthodoxy. ₁no.₎ 1.)

1. Judaism (Orthodox). 2. Title.   3. Series.
N. Y. P. L.   November 29, 1915.

NL 0446875   NN PPDrop OCH

Loewe, Herbert Martin James, 1882–   ed.
Wiener, Harold Marcus, 1875–1929.
Posthumous essays, by Harold M. Wiener ... edited by Herbert Loewe. London, Oxford university press, H. Milford, 1932.

Loewe, Herbert Martin James, 1882–   joint ed. and tr.
Montefiore, Claude Joseph Goldsmid, 1858–1938, *ed. and tr.*
A rabbinic anthology, selected and arranged with comments and introductions by C. G. Montefiore ... and H. Loewe ... London, Macmillan and co., ltd., 1938.

PJ5052
.M6Z8
Loewe, Herbert Martin James, 1882–
Salaman, Nina Ruth (Davis) 1876–1925.
Rahel Morpurgo and contemporary Hebrew poets in Italy, by Nina Salaman; with a foreword by the Very Rev. the chief rabbi, and an afterword by Herbert Loewe ... London, G. Allen & Unwin ltd. ₁1924₎

Loewe, Herbert Martin James, 1882–
"Render unto Caesar"; religious and political loyalty in Palestine, by Herbert Loewe ... Cambridge ₁Eng.₎ The University press, 1940.
xv, 141, ₁1₎ p. pl. 19ᶜᵐ.
"List of abbreviations and editions used": p. 117-118.

1. Jews—Political and social conditions. 2. Jews—Religion. 3. Jesus Christ—Teachings. I. Title.
                                                              A 41-3231
Oberlin college. Library
     for Library of Congress   ₁3₎

OCH OClW NNJ
NL 0446879   OO ScU NjPT MH NcD CtY ICU OO OClTem

Loewe, Herbert Martin James, 1882–
Some mediæval Hebrew poesy, by Herbert Loewe ... With a foreword by Sir Hugh Allen ... and an afterword by H. M. Adler ... London, G. Allen & Unwin, ltd. ₁1927₎
2 p. l., ₁9₎-64 p. 16 cm. (*Half-title:* Arthur Davis memorial lecture 9)
"The minstrels whose work it is proposed to consider wrote semiroth or 'table-songs.' "—p. 15.

1. Hebrew poetry—Hist. & crit. 2. Jews. Liturgy and ritual. Zemirot. 3. Songs, Jewish. I. Title. II. Title: Zemiroth. III. Title: Table-songs.
PJ5023.L6   27—12708

NL 0446880   DLC OrU UU TxU OCH OCl

Loewe, Herbert Martin James, 1882–1940.
... Starrs and Jewish charters preserved in the British museum, with illustrative documents, translations and notes by the late Israel Abrahams ... and the Rev. Canon H. P. Stokes ... with additions by Herbert Loewe ... Cambridge ₁Eng.₎ Printed for the Society at the University press, 1930-32.

Loewe, Hermann.
Disquisito de praepositiones "de" usu apud Livium. Grimma, 1847.

NL 0446882   NjP

LOEWE, Hermann.
Dissertatio de nonnullis figuris,quibus poetae Latini utuntur,in exemplum adhibitis septem primis libris Metamorphoseon.Grimae, typis C.Roessleri,1863.
4°. pp.32.[Progr.]

NL 0446883   MH CU NjP

VOLUME 338

PA
6932
L82+
Loewe, Hermann.
Symbolae ad enarrandum sermonem poetarum Latinorum. Pars altera: De elocutione Vergilii. Grimae, C. Roessler, 1873.
40 p. 27cm.

"Libellus programmati vernali Scholae Regiae Grimensis additus."

1. Vergilius Maro, Publius---Style.

NL 0446884   NIC

Loewe (Hermann), *surgeon.* Das wichtigste Jahr. Zehn Kapitel über Säuglingspflege. 68 pp. 8°.
Leipzig. O. Bonzold Jn. d. l.

NL 0446885   DNLM

QD341
.P6L7
Löwe, Hermann, fl. 1903.
Ueber die einwirkung von thiophenolen auf chlor-nitrobenzole.
Freiburg, 1903.
30p.
Inaug. diss. Freiburg.

NL 0446886   DLC MH PU

Loewe, Hubert i. e. Friedrich Georg Hubert, 1879-
... Studien über experimentale dourine ... Hamburg, Druck von M. Baumann, 1910.
45 p., 1 l. pl. 22½cm.
Inaug.-diss.—Bern.
Lebenslauf.
"Literatur": p. 42-45.

1. Dourine.

           Agr 12-174

Library, U. S. Dept. of   Agriculture   41L953

NL 0446887   DNAL

Loewe, Hugo, ed.
Die Pastoralbriefe des Apostels Paulus in ihrer ursprünglichen Fassung...
Köln, 1929
     see under   Bible. N. T. Pastoral epistles. Greek. 1929.

Loewe, Hugo.
Der Römerbrief des Apostels Paulus...
Köln, C. Roemke, 1927
     see under   Bible. N. T. Romans. Greek. 1927.

Loewe, Hugo, *engineer.*
Elektrotechnischer briefsteller in vier sprachen, deutsch, französisch, englisch, spanisch; unter mitwirkung von spezial-fachleuten bearb. von dipl.-ing. Hugo Loewe. Leipzig, Hachmeister & Thal, 1929.
vii, [1], 287, [1] p. 20cm.

1. Electric engineering—Dictionaries. 2. Commercial correspondence, German. 3. Commercial correspondence, French. 4. Commercial correspondence, English. 5. Commercial correspondence, Spanish. I. Title.

           32-1817

Library of Congress   TK9.L55
        [2]   621.303

NL 0446890   DLC CU

Loewe, Hugo, 1862-
Die stellung des kaisers Ferdinand I. zum Trienter konzil vom oktober 1561 bis zum mai 1562... Bonn, M. Cohen & sohn (Fr. Cohen) 1887.
88 p. 25 cm. [Bonn. Universität. Dissertationen. v. 3, no. 8]
Inaug.-diss. - Bonn.
Lebenslauf.
1. Ferdinand I, emperor of Germany, 1503-1564.

NL 0446891   CU ICRL

Loewe, James H.
    see
Lowe, James H   1852-

LOEWE, Joanne Hornby.
The Divine Comedy in art.

Typewritten. 28 x 22 cm. ff. (2), 30. Plate and other illustr.
Dante Society prize essay - Harvard University 1942.

NL 0446893   MH

Loewe, Joel, 1762-1802.
עמודי הלשון, המיוסדים על אדני ההגיון. ברלין, בדפוס חברת חנוך נערים, תקנ״ד. Berlin, 1794.
viii, 84 columns. 24 cm.

1. Hebrew language—Grammar. I. Title.
Title transliterated: 'Amude ha-lashon.

PJ4566.L56 1794   57-53896

NL 0446894   DLC

Loewe, Joel, 1762-1802.
עמודי הלשון, המיוסדים על אדני ההגיון. 2. פרב. אויפל. פראג, תקס״ב.
[Prag] Gedruckt durch die Gebrüder Stiasny [1802/03]
174 p. 18 cm.

1. Hebrew language—Grammar. I. Title.
Title transliterated: 'Amude ha-lashon.

PJ4566.L56 1802   57-53930

NL 0446895   DLC

BS1222
1824b
Hebr
Loewe, Joel, 1762-1802, tr.
Bible. *O. T. Pentateuch. Hebrew. 1824.*
חמשה חומשי תורה; נעבסט איינער וואָרטמליכען דייטשען איבערזעצצונג פיר אנפאֵנגער פֿאן יואל ברי״ל געטאֵננט לאֵוע. ניע קאָרדעקטע אונד פֿערב. אויוג.
Die fünf Bücher Mosis mit einer wörtlichen deutschen Uibersetzung [sic] von Joel Löwe.
וויען, נעדדוקט ביא א. א. שמיד. Wien, 1824.

NL ......

BM675
.P4A65
1810
Hebr
Loewe, Joel, 1762-1802, tr.
Jews. *Liturgy and ritual. Hagadah. 1810.*
מעלח בית חורין, וחוא סדר הגדה של פסח עם פירושים: מרר״ם אלשיך. נבורות ח. עוללות אפרים ופירוש אברבנאל ודיני פסח. עם תרגום אשכנזי מן יואל ברי״ל ור׳ דוד פריזלענדר. אמשטרדם. בבית ובדפוס אלמנת ובנה מחמנה יעקב פרופס [1810].

BS1472
1788
Hebraic
Sect.
Loewe, Joel, 1762-1802, ed.
Bible. *O. T. Ecclesiastes. Hebrew. 1788.*
מגלת קהלת. מתורגמת אשכנזית מאת דוד פֿרידלֵענדֵר על פי באור משה בן מנחם. ועלי איזה הערות מאת יואל ברי״ל. ברלין, בדפוס חברת חנוך נערים, תקמ״ט.
[Berlin, 1788]

BS1420
.L6
1785
Hebraic
Sect.
Loewe, Joel, 1762-1802.
זמירות ישראל [ספר תהלים עם תרגום אשכנזי מורב משה בן מנחם. ומבואר מאת יואל ברי״ל, pseud.], ברלין. בדפוס חברת חנוך נערים, [Berlin, 1785-91]

Löwe, Johann Friedrich
    see   Löwen, Johann Friedrich, 1727-1771.

Mfd65
V5381
L82
Loewe, Johann Heinrich, 1808-1892.
Johann Emanuel Veith. Eine Biographie ... Mit dem Bildnisse Veith's. Wien, W. Braumüller, 1879.
xx1, 360p. port. 20cm.

1. Veith, Johann Emanuel, 1787-1876.

NL 0446901   CtY NcU ICarbS MH OCH

CT99
.B815L6
Loewe, Johann Heinrich, 1808-1892.
John Bramhall, bischof von Derry und sein verhältniss zu Thomas Hobbes. Von dr. Johann Heinrich Loewe ... Prag, K. böhm. gesellschaft der wissenschaften, 1887.
16 p. 28½cm.

"Abhandlungen der K. böhm. gesellschaft der wissenschaften, VII. folge, 1. band. Phil.-hist.-phil. classe nro. 5."
1. Bramhall, John, 1594-1663.

NL 0446902   DLC

---

f193
L827k
Loewe, Johann Heinrich, 1808-1892.
Der Kampf zwischen dem Realismus und Nominalismus in Mittelalter; sein Ursprung und sein Verlauf. Aus den Abhandlungen der königl. böhmischen Gesellschaft der Wissenschaften Folge 6, Bd. 8. Prag, Kosmack & Neugebauer, 1876.
87p. 30cm.

1. Nominalism. 2. Realism.

NL 0446903   CLSU ICRL NjP OCU

Loewe, Johann Heinrich, 1808-1892.
Lehrbuch der logik ... Wien, W. Braumüller, 1881.
xvii, 283p. tables (1 fold.), diagrs. 23cm.

Original paper covers bound in.

NL 0446904   CLSU MdBP MH

VOLUME 338

Huzt
B
2848
I6

Loewe, Johann Heinrich, 1808–1892.
Die Philosophie Fichte's nach dem Gesammt-
ergebnisse ihrer Entwickelung und in ihrem
Verhältnisse zu Kant und Spinoza. Mit einem
Anhange: Uebr den Gottesbegriff Spinoza's
und dessen Schicksale. Stuttgart, Wilhelm
Nitzschke, 1862.
321p.

1. Fichte, Johann Gottlieb, 1762-1814. 2.
Kant, Immanuel, 1724-1804. 3. Spinoza, Benedictus de,   1632-1677.

IEN NIC MWelC WMM
NL 0446905   FTaSU CU TNJ MH InU CtY OClW NNC CLSU

193
F44Ylo

Loewe, Johann Heinrich, 1808-1892.
Rede zur feier des hundertjährigen
geburtstages J. G. Fichtes gehalten in
der aula der Carl-Ferdinands-Universität
zu Prag am 19. mai 1862. Prag, 1862.
23p.

NL 0446906   IU IEN CtY OCH

Loewe, Johann Heinrich, 1808–1892.
Die speculative idee der freiheit, ihre widersacher, ihre
practische verwertung. Von dr. Johann Heinrich Loewe
... Hrsg. von der Königlich-böhmischen gesellschaft
der wissenschaften. Prag, In commission bei F. Rivnác,
1890.

xvi, 170 p. 1 l. 23½ᶜᵐ.

1. Free will and determinism.

24-21116

Library of Congress   BJ1463.L6

NL 0446907   DLC NIC MdBJ

Loewe, Johann Heinrich, 1808–1892.
Das speculative System Réné Descartes, seine Vorzüge und Mängel.
(In Kaiserliche Akademie der Wissenschaften, Vienna. Philosophisch-historische Classe. Sitzungsberichte. Band 14, pp. 238-
298. Wien. 1854.)

H5678 — Descartes, René. 1596-1650.

NL 0446908   MB ViU

B 1875
L63
1855

Loewe, Johann Heinrich, 1808–1892.
Das speculative System des René
Descartes; seine Vorzüge und Mängel.
Wien, K. k. Hof- und Staatsdruckerei,
1855.
63 p.
1. Descartes, René, 1596-1650. I.
Title.

NL 0446909   CaBVaU

Loewe, Johann Heinrich, 1808–1892.
Ueber den begriff der logik und ihre stellung
zu den anderen philosophischen disciplinen.
Von dr. Johann Heinrich Loewe ... Wien, W.
Braumüller, 1849.
65 p. 19ᶜᵐ.
"Einleitung zu einer ausführlichen darstellung der
logik, welche der verfasser demnächst bekannt zu machen
gedenkt".—Vorbemerkung.

1. Logic.

NL 0446910   MiU CtY CaBVaU NNUT CLSU

Löwe, Johann Jakob, 1628–1703.
[Salzische musenlust. Selections]

... Arien mit ritornellen. Herausgegeben von Albert Rodemann. Hannover, A. Nagel, 1929.
16 p. and 4 pts. 31ᶜᵐ. (Nagels musik-archiv. Nr. 32)
At head of title: ... Johann Jakob Löwe von Eisenach ...
The arias are for solo voice with figured bass realized for piano; the
ritornellos for 2-4 string instruments with figured bass realized for piano.

1. Songs (Medium voice) with orchestra—To 1800—Scores and parts.
I. Rodemann, Albert, ed.

Library of Congress   M2.N25 nr. 32   44-10983

NL 0446911   DLC FTaSU OClW MB NN

Löwe, Johann Jakob, 1628–1703.
[Synfonien, intraden, gagliarden. Selections]

... Zwei suiten für streicher zu 3 oder 5 stimmen und basso
continuo. Herausgegeben von Albert Rodemann. Hannover,
A. Nagel, 1930.
15 p. and 5 pts. 31ᶜᵐ. (Nagels musik-archiv. Nr. 67)
At head of title: ... Johann Jakob Loewe von Eisenach ...
Score (violin 1, violin 2, violin 3 or viola, viola, violoncello or bassoon,
and figured bass realized for piano) and parts.
Numbers 24-28 and 48-51 from his Synfonien, intraden, gagliarden,
arien, balletten, couranten, sarabanden. Bremen, 1658.
1. Suites (Orchestra)—To 1800—Scores and parts. I. Rodemann,
Albert, ed.

Library of Congress   M2.N25 nr. 67   44-36422

NL 0446912   DLC ViU NBC IaU MB

QK 94
.L83
(Rare)

Löwe, Johann Karl Christian, d.1807.
Handbuch der theoretischen und
praktischen Kräuterkunde zum Gebrauch
für Jedermann. Breslau, Bey G.
Löwe, 1787.
409 p.

1. Botany--Classification. I. Title.

NL 0446913   ICU

Kress
Room

Löwe, Johann Karl Christian, d.1807.
J.C.C. Loewe's ... oekonomisch-kameralistische schriften ... Breslau, G.
Löwe, 1788-89.
2 v. tables (part fold.) 20.5 cm.

1. Agriculture - Economic aspects - Germany
I. Title: Oekonomisch-kameralistische
schriften.

NL 0446914   MH-BA

Loewe, Johann Karl Gottfried
see
Loewe, Karl, 1796–1869.

Loewe, Josef, ed.
Befreite Justiz, Rechtsfälle rings um den Nationalsozialismus. Reutlingen, Die Zukunft [Vorwort 1947]
v, 72 p. 21 cm.

1. Justice, Administration of—Germany—Addresses, essays, lectures. 2. Restitution claims (1933-   )—Germany—Cases. I.
Title.

50-15860

NL 0446916   DLC IEdS MH

LOEWE, Josef.
Mietrecht des Deutschen Reiches. Kempten,
München, 1910.

NL 0446917   MH-L

332.5
L42w

Loewe, Josef.
Der wechsel-, scheck- und postscheck-
verkehr; dargestellt unter berücksichtigung der einschlägigen bestimmungen aller
länder ... Stuttgart [1911?]
247p. (Violets-globus-bücherei)

NL 0446918   IU

Loewe, Josef, historian.
Die unmittelbare, wirtschaftliche einwirkung des
kriegs 1870/71 in deutschland.
Inaug. diss. Wuersburg, 1901 (Breslau)
Bibl.

NL 0446919   ICRL

[LOEWE, Jules Marie.]
Episteln an die aristokratie, zu ihrem erbauung von Bonifacius Mild, herzog von Angou-
lême. [pseud.] Wien, Sallmayer & comp., 1848.

pp. 18.

NL 0446920   MH

Loewe, Jules Marie.
Lettres d'Angleterre; études humoristiques, par Jules-
Marie Loewe. Dessins de Bourgerie. Paris, G. Kugel-
mann, 1851.
175, [1] p. incl. front., illus. 23ᶜᵐ.
Title vignette.

Subject entries: England—Soc. life & cust.

3-4206

Library of Congress, no.   DA533.L82.

NL 0446921   DLC MH

834L951
Oz

Löwe, Karl.
Zerstörtes gebiet; ein kriegsgefangenen-drama
in 3 akten ... Bielefeld, Arbeitsgemeinschaft der
vereinigungen ehemal. kriegsgefangener Deutschlands e.v., Gau Ost-Westfalen [c1932]
56p.
"Bühnen ... gegenüber manuskript."

1. European war, 1914–1918--Drama. I. Title.

NL 0446922   IU

Loewe, Karl, 1796–1869.
[Jugendlieder]
Acht Lieder mit Begleitung des Pianoforte, von J. C. G. Loewe.
[n. p., 1810?] 6 l. 35cm.

Autograph manuscript.
For 1 voice with piano acc.
First published in 1891 under title: Acht Jugendlieder.—cf. Loewe, Karl. Werke;
Gesamtausgabe der Balladen, Legenden, Lieder und Gesänge. Bd. 1, p. ix-x, 41-55.
Notice about the manuscript in Max Runze's hand, 1 leaf; and foreword and his-
torical sketch from the first edition, 2 l., inserted.
CONTENTS.—An die Natur.—Die treuen Schwalben.—Das Blumenopfer.—Romanze.
—An die Nachtigall.—Die Jagd.—Heimweh.—Sehnsucht.

1. Autographs—Music—Loewe, K.   2. Autographs—Signatures, etc.—
Runze, M.
N. Y. P. L.   February 9, 1943

NL 0446923   NN

VOLUME 338

Loewe, Karl, 1796–1869.
¿Advents-Motette. Unacc.,
...Advents-Motette. "Mit Ernst, O Menschenkinder." (Bisher
unveröffentlicht!) Leipzig: Rühle & Wendling ¿c1933, Publ.
pl. no. R. & W. 3374.   5 p.   27cm.   (Kirchenchor-Archiv.
No. 32.)

Open score: S.A.T.B. German words.
"Herausgegeben von William Eckardt."

1. Choral music, Sacred—Mixed—   JUILLIARD FOUNDATION FUND.
3. Motets—1600—   I., Eckardt,   4 pt—Unacc. 2. Advent—Motets.
N. Y. P. L.   William, ed.   June 8, 1937

NL 0446924   NN

VM
2002   LÖWE, KARL, 1796–1869.
L 82a   Die apostel von Philippi, vocal-oratorium
          für männerstimmen, gedichtet vom professor Lud-
          wig Giesebrecht, componirt von dr. C.Loewe... 48.
          werk.   Berlin,Wagenführ¿183–?,
          46p.

          Vocal score with trombone accompaniment ad
          lib.
          German words.
          Plate no.: 200.

NL 0446925   ICN MB

M780.3   Löwe, Karl, 1796–1869.
L813a   [Archibald Douglas]
          Archibald Douglas. [op.128] New
          York, G.Schirmer [n.d.]
          19 p. 34 cm.

          For low voice and piano.
          German words by Th. Fontane. English
          version by F. Corder.

          1.Songs (Low voice) with piano. I.Title.

NL 0446926   CLSU

LOEWE, KARL, 1796–1869.
[ARCHIBALD DOUGLAS. ORCH. ACC.]
Archibald Douglas; Ballade von Carl Löwe. Für
Orchester instrumentirt von Hugo Kaun. Leipzig,
C.F. Kahnt [1905?] Pl. no. C.F.K. 4185. score (42 p.) and
17 parts. 34cm.

For baritone and orchestra; acc. originally for piano.
Words by Th. Fontane.

Parts are for stringed instruments only.

1. Ballads, German.   2. Songs, with orchestra,
I. Kaun, Hugo, 1863–1932,   arr.

NL 0446928   NN

M795.22   Löwe, Karl, 1796–1869.
L827   ¿Works, vocal. Selections,
Music   Arien aus ungedruckten Opern und Oratorien.
lib.   Hrsg. und mit einem Vorworte begleitet von
          Max Runze. Klavierauszug von Fritz Schneider
          ... Leipzig, New York, Breitkopf & Härtel
          ¿1892, Pl. no. V.A.1392-1394.
          3 v. 28cm.

          Contents.–v.1. Für Sopran.–v.2. Für Tenor.
          v.3. Für Baryton und Bass.

NL 0446929   NcU NcD

Loewe, Karl, 1796–1869.

Die auferweckung des Lazarus. Ev.Joh.
cap.11, mit begleitung der orgel oder des
pianoforte... Op.132. Clavier-auszug mit
deutschem und englischem text... Magdeburg,
Heinrichshofen ¿188–?,
55 p. 28 cm.

NL 0446930   NjP MB MH

Loewe, Karl, 1796–1869.
¿Loewe-Album, Ausgewählte Balladen für eine Singstimme
mit Pianofortebegleitung, von Carl Loewe... Leipzig: C. F.
Peters ¿187–?, Publ. pl. nos. 7499, 7736. 2 v. in 1. 4°.

German and English words with music for 1 voice with piano acc.
Bd. 2, published by F. Hofmeister, Leipzig.
Bd. 1, has English translations by F. Corder; Bd. 2, by Mrs. John P. Morgan.
On cover: Edition Peters. No. 1106a–b.

1. Songs (German). 2. Corder,   Frederick, 1852–   , translator.
3. Morgan, Geraldine (Woods),   translator.
N. Y. P. L.   April 19, 1922.

NL 0446931   NN MH CtY ViU MiU ICN MB CLSU

Music
M
1620   Loewe,Karl,1796–1869.
.L83   ¿Songs. Selections,
19--   Ausgewählte Balladen für eine Singstimme mit
          Pianofortebegleitung. Kritisch revidirt von Max
          ¿Friedlaender. Original-Ausg. Leipzig, C.F.Peters
          ¿19--?, Pl.nos.8611,8613.
          2 v. port. 28 cm.
          German and English words in v.1; German only
          in v.2.

MB
NL 0446932   MiU ViU FTaSU NN CSt NcU CLSU OO MH IaU

LOEWE, KARL, 1796–1869.
[SONGS. SELECTIONS]
Ausgewählte Balladen für eine Singstimme mit
Pianofortebegleitung von Carl Loewe. Kritisch
revidirt von Max Friedlaender. Originalausg.
Leipzig. C. F. Peters [1900?] Pl. no. 8611. 1 v.
port. 28cm. (Edition Peters. No. 2960a.)

Microfilm.
Bd. 1.

1. Songs, German.

NL 0446933   NN

Loewe, Karl, 1796–1869.
[Sämmtliche Lieder, Gesänge, Romanzen und
Music   Balladen ... Op.9] Ausgewählte Balladen, Lieder
L68   und Romanzen für eine Singstimme mit Begleitung
9a   des Pianoforte von Carl Löwe . . Op.9
          Leipzig,Friedrich Hofmeister 1890.
          Publ nos.   v. 27x34cm.
          Op.9, comprising 54 songs, was originally pub-
          lished in 10 parts, from 1828 to 1839. This
          selection of 32 songs was issued in 10 parts,
          and also in single numbers.

NL 0446934   CtY OrP

Löwe, Karl, 1796–1869.
M1621   ¿Songs. Selections,
L8286r   Ausgewählte Balladen und Gesänge für eine
          mittlere Singstimme. Auf Grund der kritisch
          rev. Gesammtausgabe hrsg. von Dr. Max Runze.
          Leipzig, Breitkopf & Härtel ¿18–?, Pl. no.V.
          A 1819-20.
          2 v. port. 27cm. (Edition Breitkopf, Nr.
          1819-20)

          1. Songs. 2.   Ballads, German. I. Runze,
          Maximilian, 1849–   1931, ed. II. Title:
          Balladen und Ge   sänge.

NL 0446935   CSt OrP

M
784.3   Loewe, Karl, 1796–1869.
L827b   ¿Balladen. Selections,
Sch   Ausgewählte Balladen und Lieder. Für eine
          mittlere Singstimme und Klavierbegleitung.
          Mainz, B. Schott's Söhne ¿n.d., Pl. no. 30465,
          30466.
          score (2v.)   (Edition Schott, 604, 605)

          1. Songs (Medium voice) with piano. I.
          Loewe, Karl, 1796–1869. Legenden. Selections.
          II. Loewe, Karl, 1796–1869. Lieder. Se-
          lections.

NL 0446936   FTaSU

M784.8   Löwe, Karl, 1796–1869.
L827SO   ¿Songs. Selections,
          Ausgewählte Lieder und Balladen für
          eine Singstimme mit Pianofortebegleitung. /
          Neu revidirt von Dr. L. Benda. Braunschweig,
          Henry Litolff, Pl. no. 2241a-d.
          score (4 v. in 2) 28½ cm.

          At head of title:Collection Litolff.
          1. Songs with piano. I. Benda, L
          ed.

NL 0446937   NcD OrU CaBVa CLU NN WaU WaWW CSt

Loewe, Karl, 1796–1869.
          Balladen componirt von Carl Loewe mit Begleitung
Music   des Pianoforte. Ausgewählt aus Opus 1. 2. 3. 8.
L68   20 ... [Op.1] No.3. Erlkönig von Göthe ...
2b   Berlin, Schlesinger'sche Buch- und Musikhandlung
          [1832?] Publ.no.1212. [1],14-19pp. 23½x31½cm.
          Engraved.
          Caption title: Der Erlenkönig.
          The first edition of Op.1, Drei Balladen von
          Göthe, Herder, Uhland, was published in 1824.
          This is a reprint from the plates of the original
          edition with a new title.

NL 0446938   CtY

Loewe, Karl, 1796–1869.
¿Songs. Selections,

Balladen und Lieder für eine Singstimme mit Klavierbegleitung. Ausgewählt und durchgesehen von Hans Joachim Moser. Originalausg. Leipzig, C. F. Peters ¿1940,
Pl nos. 8611, 8613.
2 v. port. 27 cm.

1. Songs with piano. I. Moser, Hans Joachim, 1889–   ed.
Full name: Johann Karl Gottfried Loewe.

M1620.M827M6   48–33082 rev*/M

NL 0446939   DLC CaBVaU KMK UU OU NcU OkU NIC

Loewe, Karl, 1796–1869.
¿Songs. Selections,

Balladen und Lieder für eine Singstimme mit Klavierbegleitung. Ausgewählt und durchgesehen von Hans Joachim Moser. Tiefe Stimme. Leipzig, C. F. Peters ¿1941,
Pl. nos. 1812, 11493.
2 v. port. 27 cm.
For low voice.
1. Songs (Low voice) with piano. I. Moser, Hans Joachim,
1889–   ed.
Full name: Johann Karl Gottfried Loewe.

M1620.L827M63   48–33085 rev*/M

NL 0446940   DLC CoU NRU

M784.3   Löwe, Karl, 1796–1869.
L82b   ¿Songs. Selections,
          Balladen und Lieder für eine Singstimme mit
          Klavierbegleitung; ausgewählt und durchgesehen von
          Hans Joachim Moser. Originalausgabe. Leipzig,
          C. F. Peters ¿1952?, Pl. no.8611-8613, 11,493.
          2v. port. 27cm. (Edition Peters, Nr.2960a-
          2960b)

          German words.

          1. Songs with piano. I. Moser, Hans Joachim,
          1889–   ed.

NL 0446941   IU

LOEWE, KARL, 1796–1869.
[SONGS (RUNZE)]
Ballads and songs for a medium voice, selected from
the critically revised complete edition of Carl Loewe's
songs, and edited by Max Runze. English version by
Mrs. Bertram Shapleigh. Leipzig, Breitkopf & Härtel
[190-] Pl. no. V.A. 1955-1957. 3 v. in 1. 29cm.

1. Songs, German. I. Runze,   Maximilian, 1849–1931, ed.
II. Shapleigh, Mabelle   (Carpenter), tr.

NL 0446942   NN

VOLUME 338

LOEWE, KARL, 1796-1869.
[SONGS(RUNZE)]
Ballads and songs for a medium voice, selected from the critically revised complete edition of Carl Loewe's songs,and edited by Max Runze. English version by Mrs. Bertram Shapleigh.　Leipzig,Breitkopf　Härtel[190-]
Pl. no.V.A.1955-1957.　3 v.　29cm.
Film reproduction. Positive.
1.Songs, German.I.Runze　Maximilian,1849-1931,ed.
II.Shapleigh, Mabelle　　(Carpenter), tr.

NL 0446943　　NN

Loewe, Karl, 1796-1869.
[Der Barmherzige Bruder]
Der Barmherzige Bruder, eine Tondichtung von Loewe. [1830] [4] p.
Microfilm of holograph in the Library of Congress. For piano. TOSCANINI MEMORIAL ARCHIVES.
1. Music - Manuscripts - Facsimiles. (TITLE)

NL 0446944　　NN

M1621
L82B5b
Loewe, Karl, 1796-1869.
[Bilder des Orients]
Bilder des Orients gedichtet von H. Stieglitz für eine Singstimme mit Begleitung des Pianoforte. Op.10. / Leipzig, Breitkopf & Härtel [19-?]　Pl.no. V.A.1397.
37 p. 27   (Volksausgabe Breitkopf & Härtel, Nr.1397).
Contents.- 1. Die Geister der Wüste.- 2. Der verschmachtende Pilger.- 3. Melek in der Wüste.- 4. Die Oasis.- 5. Lied eines Vögleins in der Oasis.- 6. Melek am Quell.- 7. Maisuna am Brunnen.- Ali　im Garten.- Assad mit dem Selam.- Taube　npost.- 11.Gulhinde am Putztische.- 12.A　bendgesang.

NL 0446945　　CSt 00

M784.8
L827BR
Löwe, Karl, 1796-1869.
[Balladen, Op. 68. Blumen Rache]
Der Blumen Rache, op. 68... für eine Singstimme mit Begleitung des Pianoforte. Leipzig, Friedrich Hofmeister,. pl. no. 2967.
27 p. 35 cm.
Cover title.
1. Songs (Medium voice) with piano. I. Title: Der Blumen Rache.

NL 0446946　　NcD

Music
L68
29c
Loewe, Karl, 1796-1869.
... Die Braut von Corinth. Ballade v. Göthe ... [Op.29]
Berlin,A.C.Challier & Co.[1876] Publ.no.2395. 31pp. 27x34cm.
At head of title: Lieder und Balladen für eine Singstimme mit Begleitung des Pianoforte componirt von C.Loewe ...
The original edition was published by Wagenführ in 1830.

NL 0446947　　CtY

Loewe, Karl, 1796-1869.
Commentar zum zweiten Theile des Goethe' schen Faust, von Dr. C. Loewe. Mit 2 Charten; vom alten Griechenland und von der alten Welt, und mit einen genealogisch-mythologischen Tabelle.　Berlin, H.A.W. Logier, 1834.
1 p.l., 109, [1] p.　2 fold. col. maps, fold. table.　18 cm.

NL 0446948　　CtY CU PPG MiU CLSU OCiW NIC IaU

Music
L68
1k
Loewe, Karl, 1796-1869.
... Drei Balladen, Op.1 , ... No.3. Erlkönig... Für tiefe Stimme (t) Bass. Berlin,Verlag und Eigenthum der Schlesinger'schen Buch- und Musikhandlung (Rob.Lienau)[188-]　Publ.no.S.1212(3)A.
7p. 34cm.　(Balladen, Gesänge und Lieder für eine Singstimme mit Begleitung des Pianoforte von Carl Löwe)
Series title.
In caption title: Göthe.
Also paged continuously, 14-19.

NL 0446949　　CtY

Loewe, Karl, 1796-1869.
... Drei Balladen [Op. 43]: No. 1 Der Fischer v. Göthe ... No. 2. Der Räuber v. Uhland ... No. 3.　Das nussbraune Mädchen v. Herder ... Berlin, C.A. Challier & Co. [1876] Publ. nos. 2396-2398.
3 v.　26 x 33 cm.
At head of title: Lieder und Balladen für eine Singstimme mit Begleitung des Pianoforte componirt von C. Loewe ...
Lithographed title-pages.
Composed 1835.
First edition published by Wagenführ, Berlin, 1835.

NL 0446951　　CtY

Music
L68
20
Loewe, Karl, 1796-1869.
Drei Balladen (Das Hochzeitlied, der Zauberlehrling, die wandelnde Glocke.)von Goethe für[!] eine Singstimme mit Begleitung des Pianoforte componirt von C.Loewe. Op.20.
Berlin,in der Schlesinger'schen Buch- und Musikhandlung[1832] Publ.no.1755. 24pp. 27x36cm.
T.-p. lithographed, music printed from plates.

NL 0446952　　CtY

Loewe, Karl, 1796-1869.
[Balladen, op. 1]
Drei Balladen, für eine Singstimme, mit Begleitung des Piano Forte. Berlin, A. M. Schlesinger [1823], Pl. no. 1912.
19 p.　23 x 33 cm.
First ed.
CONTENTS.—Edward (J. G. von Herder).—Der wirthin Töchterlein (J. L. Uhland).—Erlkönig (J. W. von Goethe).
1. Songs (High voice) with piano.

M3.3.L83　op.1　77-204492

NL 0446953　　DLC CtY

M
784.3
L825
MIANI
Loewe, Karl, 1796-1869.
Drei balladen von N. Vogl, für eine Singstimme mit Begleitung des Pianoforte ... von Carl Loewe. Op.56. Dresden, Wilhelm Paul [n.d.] Pub. nos. 208,209,210.
3v. 28x36cm.
Contents.-[no.1] Heinrich der Vogler [no.2] Der Gesang [no.3] Urgrossvaters Gesellschaft.

NL 0446954　　OOxM

Loewe, Karl, 1796-1869.
Die drei Wünsche, komisches Singspiel in 3 Aufzügen .. /gedichtet von Ernst Raupach . . . componirt von C. Loewe.　Vollständiger Clavierauszug.
Bonn. Simrock.　[184-?]　(1), 103 pp.　F°.

April 11,　1902.
E3683 Raupach, Ernst Benjamin Salomon. — Operas,

NL 0446955　　MB

M1621
L82E5
Loewe, Karl, 1796-1869, arr.
[Balladen, op. 1. Edward]
Edward. [For] high [voice] in Eb minor. [Arr. from an old Scottish ballad by A. Geoghegan]　New York, G.Schirmer [19-?]
Pl. no. 21287.
11 p.　30m.
Cover title.
1.Songs (High voice) with piano. I.Title.

NL 0446956　　CSt CLSU

VM
2002
L 82e
LÖWE, KARL, 1796-1869.
Die eherne schlange. Vocal-oratorium für männerstimmen, /gedichtet vom professor Giesebrecht, componirt von dr. C.Loewe. 40. werk. Berlin, Wagenführ [183-?]
22p.
Vocal score, with trombone accompaniment for two numbers.
German words.
Plate no.: 189.

NL 0446957　　ICN MB NcU

M
784.3
L827b
S
Loewe, Karl, 1796-1869.
[Balladen, op. 1. Erlkönig]
Erlkönig (The Erlking) [op. 1, no. 3. Poem by Goethe, English translation by Th. Baker]　New York, G. Schirmer [c1909] Pl. no. 21283.
score (9p.)
Original ke:
1. Songs (High voice) with piano. 2. Goethe, Johann Wolfgang -　ical settings.

NL 0446958　　FTaSU KyU

LOEWE, Karl, 1796-1869.
Die Festzeiten. Geistliches Oratorium in 3 Abtheilungen. [Partitur] Mainz. Schott. [1838?] (6), 192 pp. F°.　**M.225.
Same. [Klavierauszug.] (6), 88 pp. F°.　**M.242.3
"Die Worte sind grösstentheils der Heiligen Schrift entlehnt."

NL 0446959　　MB ICN

Loewe, Karl, 1796-1869.
...Der Fischer (Joh. Wolfg. von Goethe) Op. 43, No. 1.. Instrumentiert von Felix Mottl. Partitur... Berlin: E. Bote & G. Bock[, 1909]. Publ. pl. no. B. & B. 16724. 17 p. 34cm.
Full score. German words.
At head of title: Drei Balladen für eine Singstimme und Klavier, von Karl Loewe. No. 1...Instrumentiert von Felix Mottl.

| 1. Songs, arias, etc., with orchestra—1911, arranger. II. Goethe, Johann Wolfgang von. III. Title. | Full score. L Mottl, Felix, 1856-N. Y. P. L. June 8, 1933 |

NL 0446960　　NN

LÖEWE, KARL, 1796-1869.
Fridericus Rex (W. Alexis [pseud.]). Ballade von Carl Löwe; für vierstimmigen Männerchor a cappella bearb. von Erwin Lendvai.　Mainz, B. Schott's Söhne [c1933]　score (7 p.)　27cm. (Schott's Chor Verlag)
For chorus (TTBB)
First line: Fridericus Rex, König und Herr.

| 1. Choral music, Secular (Men, 4 pt.)—Unacc. I. Lendvai, Erwin, 1882-1949, arr. II. Häring, Wilhelm, 1798-1871. / I Lowe, Karl, 1796- 1869. |

NL 0446962　　NN

VOLUME 338

LÖWE, KARL, 1796-1869.
Fünf oden des Horaz, auf den lateinischen
text mit deutscher uebersetzung von Voss für
männerstimmen componirt... 58. werk. Partitur...
Berlin,H.Wagenführ [18--]
12p. 26x32½cm.

For 4 voices, unaccompanied.
German words.
Plate no.: 209.

NL 0446963   ICN

Löwe, Carl, 1796-1869.
Fundamentalien der Tonkunst für Schulen und
für jeden der Musik lernen will, mit Anmerkungen für obere Klassen, oder in der Musik gelehr-
tere. Berlin, E. H. G. Christiani [1825?]
viii,30p. music., 1 fold. phrm. 21cm.

1. Music. Theory. 2. Music. Instruction and
study. I. Title.

NL 0446964   IEN

Loewe, Karl, 1796-1869.
[Der Gang nach dem Eisenhammer. Ballade von
Schiller mit Beibehaltung von B.A.Weber's melo-
dramatischer Instrumentalmusik, für eine Singstimm
mit Begleitung ... componirt von C.Loewe. Op.17]
[Leipzig,C.F.Peters,1830] Publ.no.2356. 41pp.
27½x34cm.
Music printed from plates.
Imperfect copy. Title taken from copy in Librar
of Congress.

NL 0446965   CtY

Löwe, Karl, 1796-1869.
Gesamtausgabe der Balladen, legenden ...
see his   Werke. Gesamtausgabe der Balladen,
legenden.

Loewe, Karl, 1796-1849.
[Gesang der Geister über den Wassern.
Gedicht von Goethe. Musik von Karl Löwe.
[Fragment]
Manuscript. 2 p. 32 cm.
At end: Johann Karl Gottfried Löwe.
(Apparently not his signature)
The composer's autograph of a fragment from
his op. 88, Gesang der Geister über den
Wassern, for four voices (S.A.T.B.) with
pianoforte accompaniment; the setting, as a
solo for soprano voice, of the second stanza,

beginning: Strömt von der hohen steilen Felswand",
and ending; "wallt or verschleiert les
rauschend".

NL 0446968   CtY

Loewe, Karl, 1796-1869.
Gesang der Geister über den Wassern. Goethe'sche
Ode für vier Solostimmen mit Pianofortebegleitung
componirt von C.Loewe Op.39. Berlin,Eigenthum
von Ad.Mt.Schlesinger,1932. Publ.no.S.2763.
3-14p. 34cm.
Caption title.
Reimpression, 1932, from the plates of the
original edition [1842]
Date of original publication from Espagne -
Verzeichniss sämtlicher Werke Dr. Carl Loewe's.

NL 0446969   CtY

Loewe, Karl, 1796-1869.
Goethe's Paria. Gebet, Legende, Dank für eine
Singstimme/mit Begleitung des Pianoforte componirt
von C.Loewe. 58s. Werk...
Leipzig,Bei Breitkopf & Härtel[1839] Publ.no.
5739. 27pp. 25½x33cm.
Lithographed t.-p. Music printed from plates.
The text is taken from Goethe's Ueber Kunst und
Alterthum, 4.Bd., 3.Hft.

NL 0446970   CtY

Loewe, Karl, 1796-1869.
[Balladen, op. 8. Goldschmieds Tochter]
Goldschmied's Tochter von Uhland. Berlin, Schlesinger,
1826.
13 p. 25 x 33 cm. (*His* Balladen für eine Singstimme mit Be-
gleitung des Pianoforte, ausgewählt aus Opus 1, 2, 8, 8, 20. No. 6)
No. 1 in a vol. with title: [Collection of lieder. v. p., ca. 1820-40]
For voice and piano.
1. Songs (Medium voice) with piano.   I. Title.
Full name: Johann Karl Gottfried Loewe.

M1619.C69 no. 1   M 54-1629 rev

NL 0446971   DLC

Löwe, Karl, 1796-1869.
Goldschmieds Töchterlein, op. 8,
no. 1. [Leipzig, R. Pawliska, n.d.]
Pl. no. R.P.U.B.44.
7p. 34cm. (Grosse musikalische
Universal-Bibliothek)

For deep voice and piano.

NL 0446972   IEN

Loewe, Karl, 1796-1869.
Das Grab zu Ephesus. Aus Op. 75. No. 1. [Lied mit Begleitung
des Pianoforte.]
= Leipzig. Breitkopf & Härtel. [188-?] 7 pp. [Liederkreis:
Sammlung vorzüglicher Lieder und Gesänge für eine Stimme
...] 34 cm.

L5804 — T.r. — Songs. With music.

NL 0446973   MB

Löwe, Karl, 1796-1869.
[Balladen, op.9. Graf Eberhards Weissdorn]
Graf Eberhards Weissdorn: "Graf Eberhard
im Bart, op.9, hft. 4, no.5. Ausgewählte
Balladen, Lieder und Romanzen für eine Sing
stimme mit Begleitund des Pianoforte. Leipzig,
Friedrich Hofmeister, pl. no. 1680.
16-17 p. 27 cm.

Cover title.
1. Songs (Medium Voice) with piano. I. Title
Graf Eberhards Weis   sdorn.

NL 0446974   NcD

LOEWE, KARL, 1796-1869.
Der Graf von Habsburg; Ballade von Fr. v. Schiller
für Gesang und Piano in Musik gesetzt von Carl Loewe,
op. 98. Dresden, B. Friedel [1849?] Pl. no. 363.
19 p. 33cm.

1. Songs, German.

NL 0446975   NN

Loewe, Karl, 1796-1869.
Grand trio pour piano-forte, violon et violoncelle, composé par
C. Loewe... Oeuvre 12... Leipzig: F. Hofmeister [ca. 1832].
Publ. pl. no. 1522. 3 parts in 1 v.   f°.

Piano, violin and violoncello in parts.

1. Trios.—Piano, violin and violon-   cello.
N.Y.P.L.   May 20, 1919.

NL 0446976   NN

Loewe, Karl, 1796-1869.
[Gutenberg. Piano-vocal score. German]
Gutenberg. Oratorium in drei Abtheilungen,
von Ludwig Giesebrecht. Componirt zur Feier
der Inauguration der Bildsaeule Johann
Gutenbergs in Mainz. Op. 55. Mainz, B. Schott
[1837?] Pl. no. 4717.
93 p. 33cm.

NL 0446977   NIC CtY

Loewe, Karl, 1796-1869.
Gutenberg. Oratorium in 3 Abtheilungen von Ludwig Giesebrecht.
Componirt von Carl Loewe. [Partitur.]
Mainz. Schott. [184-?] (11), 125 pp. F°.

April 11,   1902.
E5683 — Giesebrecht, Heinrich Ludwig Theodor. — Oratorios.

NL 0446978   MB

Loewe, Karl, 1796-1869.
[Die Heilung des Blindgebornen]
Die Heilung des Blindgebornen; Vocal-Oratorium nach
Evang.Johannis Cap.9, mit Begleitung von Orgel oder
Pianoforte. Op.131. Berlin, Schlesinger [184-?] Pl.
no.S.4944

Score (43 p.)

NL 0446979   MH

Loewe, Karl, 1796-1869.
Heinrich der Vogler; Ballade. Op.56, Nr.1.
[Mainz, B. Schott's Söhne, n.d.]
5 p.   31 cm. (Edition Schott 01207)

Einzel Ausgabe.
Cover title.
For voice and piano.

NL 0446980   KyU

Loewe, Karl, 1796-1869.
...Die Heinzelmännchen (ein Märchen von A. Kopisch).
Op. 83. [Instrumentiert von Felix Mottl. Partitur... Berlin:
E. Bote & G. Bock [1909]. Publ. pl. no. B. & B. 16726. 38 p.
34cm.

Full score. German words.
At head of title: Drei Balladen für eine Singstimme und Klavier, von Karl
Loewe... No. 2...

1. Songs, arias, etc. with orchestra—   Full score. [. Mottl, Felix,
N.Y.P.L.   1856-1911, arranger. / II. Kopisch,
August, 1799-1853. III. Title.
June 28, 1933

NL 0446981   NN

VOLUME 338

Loewe, Karl, 1796–1869.
[Die Hochzeit der Thetis.]
Die Hochzeit der Thetis. Gedicht von
Schiller ... Op. 120. [1850?] score (33) p.)

Microfilm of holograph in the Library of
Congress. For chorus, soloists, and
orchestra. TOSCANINI MEMORIAL ARCHIVES.

1. Music – Manuscripts – Facsimiles.
(1) [Schiller, Johann Christoph Friedrich
von, 1759–1805.] Die Hochzeit der Thetis.
(TITLE)

NL 0446983   NN

Loewe, Karl, 1796–1869.
[Das hohe Lied Salomonis. Piano-vocal
score. German]
Das Hohelied Salomonis. Unpublished
oratorio. [1855] 136 p.

Microfilm of holograph in the Library of
Congress. Target title. Words by Wilhelm
Telschow. TOSCANINI MEMORIAL ARCHIVES.

1. Music – Manuscripts – Facsimiles.
(1) [Telschow, Wilhelm.] Das hohe Lied
Salomonis. (TITLE)

NL 0446985   NN

Loewe, Karl, 1796–1869.
How deep the slumber. Song [S. or T. Accomp. for pianoforte].
(In Musical Library. Vol. I, p. 20. London, 1854.)

E3682 — T.r. — Songs. With music.   April 11,   1902.

NL 0446986   MB

Loewe, Karl, 1796–1869.
Jephtha's daughter. Song [S. Accomp. for pianoforte].
(In Musical Library. Vol. I, pp. 22–24. London, 1854.)

E3682 — T.r. — Songs. With music.   April 11,   1902.

NL 0446987   MB

LOEWE, KARL, 1796–1869.
[JOHANN HUSS. VOCAL SCORE. GERMAN]
Johann Huss, Oratorium. Gedichtet vom August
Zeune. Op. 82. Klavier Auszug vom Componisten.
Berlin, E. Bote & G. Bock [1842].   Pl. no. B. et B. 585.
122 p.   26x35cm.

1. Oratorios—Vocal scores. I. Zeune, August, 1778–1853. Johann Huss.
II. Title.

NL 0446988   NN MB ICN

LOEWE, Karl, 1796–1869.
Kaiser Karl v. 4 historische Balladen . . . für eine Singstimme [M.-S. b. Bar.] mit Begleitung des Pianoforte. No. 1, 2, 4.
Leipzig. Hofmeister. [185–?] 3 parts in 1 v. L. 8°, obl.
Contents. — 1. Das Wiegenfest zu Gent. 2. Kaiser Karl v. in Wittenberg. 4. Die Leiche zu St. Just.

NL 0446989   MB

Loewe, Karl, 1796–1869.
Kleiner Haushalt. Lyrische Fantasie von Fr. Rückert für eine
Singstimme mit Begleitung des Piano-Forte von Dr. C. Loewe.
Op. 71...   Breslau, C. Cranz [1839?]   Publ.pl.no. 183.   11 p.
25 x 33cm.

For one voice with piano accompaniment.
"No. 1 der lyrisch. Fantasien."
First line: Einen Haushalt klein und fein.

1. Songs, German. I. Rückert,   Friedrich, 1788–1866. II. Song
index (2).   December 22, 1947
N.Y.P.L.

NL 0446990   NN CSt

Loewe, Karl, 1796–1865.
Kleiner Haushalt Lyrische Fantasie von Fr.
Rückert, für eine Singstimme mit Begleitung
des Piano-Forte von Dr. C. Loewe. Op. 71.
Berlin, T. Trautwein, [1866]
7 p.   obl. 4°.

NL 0446991   NN

Loewe, Karl, 1796–1869.
The landlady's little daughter. [Song. Accomp. for pianoforte.]
Boston. Reed. [1842.] 7 pp. [Gems of German song.] F°.

G4007 — T.r. — Songs. With music.

NL 0446992   MB

Loewe, Karl, 1796–1869.
[Legenden, op. 33–34]
Legenden, für eine Singstimme mit Begleitung des Piano-
Forte. Op. 33 und 34. Berlin, Schlesinger, 1860–61.
2 v. 24 x 32 cm.
No. 2 in a vol. with title: [Collection of lieder. v. p., ca., 1820–40]
L. C. set incomplete: v. 2 wanting.
For voice and piano.
CONTENTS. — 1. Heft. Jungfrau Lorenz (F. Kugler) Das heilige
Haus in Loretto (Giesebrecht) Des fremden Kindes heiliger Christ
(Rückert) — 2. Heft. Der grosse Christoph (Kind)
1. Songs (Medium voice) with piano.   I. Title.
    Full name: Johann Karl Gottfried Loewe.

M1619.C69 no. 2   M 54–1630 rev

NL 0446993   DLC

Löwe, Karl, 1796–1869.
Löwe-Album. Ausgewählte Balladen für eine
Singstimme mit Pianofortebegleitung
see his   Ausgewählte Balladen für eine
Singstimme mit Pianofortebegleitung.

LOEWE, KARL, 1796–1869.
[SONGS (REITER)]
Loewe-Album (Balladen, Legenden und andere
Gesänge) für eine Singstimme mit Klavierbegleitung,
von Carl Loewe. Ausgewählt und revidiert von Josef
Reiter. Wien, Universal-Edition [192–?] 1 v. 27cm.
(Universal-Edition 1757)
Bd. 5.
For one voice with piano   accompaniment. German words.
1. Songs, German. I. Reiter,   Josef, 1862–1939, ed.

NL 0446995   NN

M784.31   Loewe, Karl, 1796–1869.
L82sl2   [Songs. Selections]
Loewe-album. 15 ausgewählte Balladen für eine
Singstimme mit Pianoforte-Begleitung.   Leipzig,
G. Heinze [190–?]   Pl. no. G.883 H.
134p.   28cm.

For low voice with piano acc.
German words.

NL 0446996   IU

Loewe, Karl, 1796–1869.
Loewe-album of 20 ballads with English and
German words and a preface, ed. by Albert B.
Bach. Berlin, Schlesinger'sche buch u.
musikhandlung, n.d.
2 v.

NL 0446997   IU

Loewe, Karl, 1796–1869.
Melek am Quell. (Melek at the spring.) Ballad by Carl Loewe.
Transcribed for piano by Ernst Perabo.
Boston. Koppitz, Prüfer & Co. 1871. 7 pp. Decorated title-
page. 35½ cm.
The title is on the cover.

L7917 — T.r. Pianoforte music. — Pianoforte. Music. — Perabo, Johann Ernst,
editor, 1845–

NL 0446998   MB

Loewe, Karl, 1796–1869.
Der Mummelsee... Von C. Loewe. Op. 116, No. 3.
[n.p., n.d.] 61–68 p. Pl. no. S.8853,S.9035
(3) B.u.C. 30cm.

Photostatic reproduction.
Imperfect: t.-p. wanting; title from caption.
For one voice with piano accompaniment.

Words by August Schnezler. First line: Im
Mummelsee, im dunkeln See.

1. Songs, German. I. Schnezler, August, 1809–1853.

NL 0447000   NN

MUSIC   Loewe, Karl, 1796–1869.
M780.3   [Niemand hat's geseh'n]
L827n   Niemand hat's geseh'n [No one saw at all,
op.9, no.4]. New York, G.Schirmer [c1900]
score (7p.) 30cm. (Recital songs)

"Poem by Gruppe."
Words in German and English.
For soprano or tenor, and piano.

1.Songs (High voice) with piano. I.Title.

NL 0447001   CLSU WaT

Loewe, Karl, 1796–1869.
Der Nöck; Ballade. Op.129, Nr.3. [Mainz,
B. Schott's Söhne, n.d.]
13 p.   31 cm.   (Edition Schott 05314)

Einzel Ausgabe.
Cover title.
For voice and piano.

NL 0447002   KyU

Loewe, Karl, 1796–1869.
...Ouverture zu "Die Zerstörung von Jerusalem." Op. 30.
Von Carl Loewe. Partitur. Neu herausgegeben und bearbeitet
von Robert Sondheimer. Berlin: Edition Bernoulli [, cop. 1925].
Publ. pl. no. R. S. 350. 31 p. f°. (Sammlung Sondheimer.
No. 350.)

Full score.

1. Orchestra, Full—Overtures.   I. Sondheimer, Robert,
1881–   editor./ II. Title: Die   Zerstörung von Jerusalem.
N.Y.P.L.   September 22, 1931

NL 0447003   NN ICN MH MB NjP

VOLUME 338

LOEWE, KARL, 1796-1869.

Practisch- theoretische Klavier- und Generalbass-
Schule für Lehrer und Lernende, nach ältern und
neuern Lehrbüchern, u. systemen methodisch
geordnet zugleich für Anfänger und Kinder leicht
fasslich dargestellt, von Carl Loewe. Stettin,
Beim Verfasser, und in Commission bei Logier,
Berlin [1851] 1 v.   34cm.
Th. 1.

1. Piano--Methods. 2. Thorough-bass, 1800-1900. 3. Thorough-bass.

NL 0447005   NN

Loewe, Karl, 1796-1869.
ₜQuatuor spirituel, strings, op. 26, C minorₜ

Quatuor spirituel (Geistliches Quartett) pour deux
violons, viole et violoncelle, oₜp.ₜ 26. Berlin, T. Trautwein
ₜ183-ₜ Pl. no. 398.
parts. 34 cm.

1. String quartets--Parts. I. Title. II. Title: Geistliches Quartett.
Full name: Johann Karl Gottfried Loewe.

M452.L827 op. 26   M 58-250 rev

NL 0447006   DLC

LOEWE, Karl, 1796-1869.
Rückert's Gedichte . . . für eine Singstimme [S. o. T.] mit Begleitungₜ
des piano-forte/componirt von C. Loewe.
= Berlin. Bote & Bock. [185-?] 2 parts in 1 v. L. 8°, obl.
Contents. — 1. Zeislein. — Bescheidung. — O süsse Mutter. — Süsses Begräbniss.
Hinkende Jamben. — Irrlichter. 2. Abendlied. — In der Kirche. — Ich und mein Gevatter.
— Das Pfarrjüngferchen. — Kind und Mädchen. — Die Blume der Ergebung.

Sheet D 562   Oct. 14, 1898

NL 0447007   MB

Loewe, Karl, 1796-1869.
Salvum fac regem. [Motet. Accomp. for organ.]
London. Novello. [184-?] 5 pp. [The Berlin choir. 3.] F°.

April 11,   1902.
F 682 — T.r. — Church music. Anthems, &c.

NL 0447008   MB

M 785.72
1827s   Loewe, Karl, 1796-1869.
Music   ₜSchottische Bilder, clarinet & piano, op. 112.ₜ
lib.   Schottische Bilder, componirt für Clarinette
und Pianoforte oder Violoncello und Piano. Op.
112 ... Berlin, Schlesinger ₜn.d.ₜ Pl no. S.
3612.
score (14p.) and part. 36cm.

Cover title.

NL 0447009   NcU

Loewe, Karl, 1796-1869.
6 Gesänge für fünf und vier Männerstimen. 19tes Werk. 2. Auflage.
Berlin. Wagenführ. [183-?] 34 pp. L. 8°.
Contents. — Jägerlied [T.T.B.B.]. — Die Glückseligkeitsinsel [T.T.B.B.].
— Germania [T.T.B.B.]. — Der Fichtenbaum [T.T.B.B.]. — Mag da
draussen Schnee sich Thürmen [T.T.B.B.]. — Nachtreise [T.T.B.B.B.].

April 11,   1902.
E 3685 — Part songs.

NL 0447010   MB

M
1594   Loewe, Karl, 1796-1869.
L82   ₜGesänge, men's voices. Selections.ₜ
G3+
VI ₜi.e. Sechs, vierstimmige Gesänge für
Männerstimmen, componirt, und der Mainzer
Liedertafel in Hochachtung gewidmet, von C.
Loewe. Mainz, B. Schott's Söhnen ₜ1838ₜ
Pl. no. 5358.
score (15 p.) and 4 parts. 28cm.

1. Choruses, Secular (Men's voices, 4 pts.
Unacc.

NL 0447011   NIC NN MB

Loewe, Karl, 1796-1869.
The secluded. (Die Abgeschiedenen.) Op. 9, vol. 2, no. 3./ Tran-
scribed & fingered [for the pianoforte] by Ernst Perabo.
= Boston. Koppitz, Prüfer & Co. [187-?] 5 pp. 35 cm.
The music is accompanied by the words.

L 7421 — T.r. Pianoforte music. — Pianoforte. Music. — Perabo, Johann Ernst,
ed., 1845-

NL 0447012   MB

Loewe, Karl, 1796-1869.
Selbstbiographie. Für die Öffentlichkeit bearb. von C. H.
Bitter. Mit dem Portrait Loewe's und mehreren Musikbei-
lagen. Berlin, W. Müller, 1870.
xxiii, 458, 31 p. front., music. 21 cm.
"Abtheilung III, Ergänzungen zu Loewe's biographischen Skizzen,
bis zu seinem tode": p. 438-458.
"Verzeichniss sämmtlicher Werke, von Franz Espagne": 31 p., 3d
group.

I. Bitter, Karl Hermann, 1813-1885, ed.

ML410.L8A3   3-25959 rev*

NL 0447013   DLC MiU CtY NN IaU ICU MH

LOEWE, KARL, 1796-1869.
[DIE SIEBEN SCHLÄFER. VOCAL SCORE. ENGLISH]
The 7 sleepers. [1845] 195 p. 35cm.

Manuscript, in ink, copied by J. J. Worrell, Philadelphia, 1845.
Caption title.

1. Manuscripts (Music)--Loewe, K.   I. Title: The seven sleepers.
II. Title: Die sieben schläfer.

NL 0447014   NN MH

A783.3   LOEWE,   KARL,   1796-1869.
L826S   ₜDie sieben schläfer. Op. 46. Vocal scoreₜ
Die sieben schlaefer, oratorium in drei ab-
theilungen, gedichtet vom professor Ludwig
Giesebrecht, componirt... von dr. C. Loewe. Op. 46.
Mainz, Paris ₜetc.ₜ bei B. Schott's söhnen ₜ
4ℓ., 103p. 32cm.

German text.
Publ. plate no. 4201.
Vocal parts, in manuscript, of the sextet "Ab-
endroth erhellt   die gipfel" (at opening of
pt. 3) with German   and English text, in pocket.

NL 0447015   PU

Loewe, Karl, 1796-1869.
Die sieben Schlaefer; Oratorium in drei Abtheilungen, Gedichtet vom Professor Ludwig Giesebrecht, componirt...von Dʳ
C. Loewe. Op. 46. Partitur... Mainz, B. Schott's Söhnen
ₜca. 1836ₜ. Publ. pl. no. 4200. 4 p.l., 142 p. f°.

Binder's title: Oratorio. Seven sleepers. Loewe.
German words accompany score and also precede it.
Full score.

1. Oratorios.—Full score. 2. Giese-   brecht, Ludwig, 1792-1873. 3. Title.
4. Title: Seven sleepers.
N. Y. P. L.   March 3, 1920.

NL 0447016   NN ICN MB NIC CtY

ML   Löwe, Karl, 1796-1869
53   [Die sieben Schläfer. Libretto]
L6   Die sieben Schläfer; Oratorium in drei
S5   Abtheilungen von L. Giesebrecht. Componirt
von C. Löwe. ₜn.p.ₜ 1841.
20p. 22cm.

1. Oratorios - Librettos I. Giesebrecht,
Heinrich Ludwig Theodor, 1792-1873 II.
Title

NL 0447017   WU

ML 53   LÖWE, KARL, 1796-1869.
.L8 S5   Die sieben Schläfer; Oratorium. ₜn. p.ₜ
1844.
15 p.

NL 0447018   InU

Loewe, Karl, 1796-1869.
Das Sühnopfer des neuen Bundes.
Passions-Oratorium nach Worten der heiligen
Schrift gedichtet von Wilhelm Telschow, für
gemischten Chor, Soli, Streichquintett bezw.
Orgelbegleitung. [Hildburghausen: F. W.
Gadow & Sohn, 191-.] 16 p. illus. (Music)
port. 22 1/2 cm.

NL 0447019   NN

Loewe, Karl, 1796-1869.
Das Suehnopfer des neuen Bundes. Passions-Oratorium in 3
Abteilungen nach den Worten der Heiligen Schrift gedichtet von
W. Telschow, komponiert von Carl Loewe. (Aus dem Nachlass
herausgegeben.) Partitur. Hildburghausen: F. W. Gadow &
Sohn, G.m.b.H.ₜ, 1912ₜ, 104 p. 34cm.

Full score (string quintet acc.). German words.

609762A. 1. Oratorios--Full score.   2. Passion music. I. Telschow,
Wilhelm./I. Title.
N. Y. P. L.   October 7, 1932

NL 0447020   NN MH

Loewe, Karl, 1796-1869.
Todtentanz. /Ballad by Carl Loewe. [Op. 44. No. 3.] Transcribed
for piano by Ernst Perabo.
= Boston. Koppitz, Prüfer & Co. 1870. 13 pp. Decorated title-
page. 35½ cm.

L 7917 — T.r. Pianoforte music. — Pianoforte. Music. — Perabo, Johann Ernst,
editor, 1845-

NL 0447021   MB

Löwe, Karl, 1796-1869.
M784.8   [Balladen, op. 123. Trommelständchen]
L827T
Trommelständchen. Balladen, Gesänge
und Lieder , op. 123, no. 2, mit Begleitung
des Pianoforte. Berlin, Schlesinger, pl.
no. S. 4473.
8-11 p. 35 cm.

Cover title.

1. Songs (High voice) with piano. I. Title:
Trommelständchen

NL 0447022   NcD

VOLUME 338

Loewe, Karl, 1796-1869.
...Twelve songs and ballads. In two volumes. The English translations by Dr. Theo. Baker. With a critical note by Richard Aldrich... New York: G. Schirmer, cop. 1903. Publ. pl. no. 16144, 16146. 2 v. in 1. f°. (Schirmer's library of musical classics. v. 717, 719.)

For high voice.
German and English words; music for 1 voice with piano acc.
At head of title: ...Mastersongs by great composers. Carl Loewe.

429974A.　1. Songs, German.　　2. Baker, Theodore, 1851- , translator.
N.Y.P.L.　　　　　　　　　　　　　October 5, 1929

NL 0447023　　NN OrU ViU IU CaBVaU OrSaW IaU OC1

M1619
S69
v.643
Loewe, Karl, 1796-1869.
⌐Gesänge. op.123, no.3. Die Uhr; acc.piano⌐
Die Uhr, für eine Singstimme mit Begleitung. Op. 123. Berlin, Schlesinger ⌐18--?⌐ Pl.no.S. 4474.
p.12-16. 36ᶜᵐ.
No. 2 in a vol. lettered:Songs, v.643.

NL 0447024　　CSt

M784.8
L827V
Löwe, Karl, 1796-1869.
⌐Balladen, op.109. Die verfallene Mühle⌐
Die verfallene Mühle; Ballade von J.N. Vogl für eine Singstimme mit Begleitung des Pianoforte, op. 109. Hanover, Ch. Buchmann, pl. no. 328.
14 p. 34 cm.

1. Songs (Medium voice) with piano. I. Title: Die verfallene Mühle. II. Vogl, Johann Nepomuk, 1802- 1866. Die verfallene Mühle.

NL 0447025　　NcD

Music
L68
25
Loewe, Karl, 1796-1869.
Die Walpurgisnacht, Ballade von Göthe, für Solo und Chorgesang mit Begleitung des Orchesters ... von C Löwe. Partitur. Op.25 ...
Berlin, in der Schlesinger'schen Buch und Musikhandlung[1833] Publ.no.1728. 61pp. 35½cm.
Engraved.

NL 0447026　　CtY

Loewe, Karl, 1796-1869.
...Walpurgisnacht (W. Alexis ⌐pseud.⌐). Op. 2, Nr. 3. Instrumentiert von Felix Mottl. Partitur... Berlin: E. Bote & G. Bock⌐, 1909⌐. Publ. pl. no. B. & B. 16728. 19 p. 34cm.

Full score. German words.
At head of title: Drei Balladen für eine Singstimme und Klavier, von Karl Loewe... No. 3...

1. Songs, arias, etc., with orchestra.　Full score. I. Mottl, Felix, 1856-1911, arranger. II. Haering,　Wilhelm, 1798-1871. III. Title.
N.Y.P.L.　　　　　　　　　　　　　June 28, 1933

NL 0447027　　NN

Loewe, Karl, 1796-1869.
...Weltliche Chöre. In drei Bänden. Zum erstenmal gesammelt und herausgegeben von Dr. Leopold Hirschberg. Bd. 1- ... Hildburghausen: F. W. Gadow & Sohn⌐, pref. 1911-⌐. Publ. pl. no. 22745, 22777　v. in　4°.

Publ. pl. no. on last p. only of each v.
"Carl Loewe: Weltliche Chöre, von Dr. Leopold Hirschberg. Hildburghausen⌐, 1926?⌐" 14 p., bound in.
Contents: Bd. 1. Männerchöre a capella. Bd. 2. Frauenchöre a capella. Gemischte Chöre a capella. Männerchöre mit Begleitung. Gemischte Chöre mit Begleitung.

1. Choruses, Men's voices. 2. Choruses,　Women's voices, 3-part.
3. Choruses, Unaccompanied.　　　4. Choruses, with piano, or organ,
accompaniment. I. Hirschberg,　Leopold, 1867- , editor.
N.Y.P.L.　　　　　　　　　　　　　February 16, 1932

NL 0447028　　NN

LOEWE, KARL, 1796-1869.
[WORKS, VOCAL. SELECTIONS]
Weltliche Chöre. Zum erstenmal gesammelt und hrsg. von Leopold Hirschberg. Hildburghausen, F. W. Gadow [ca. 1911-ca. 1920]. pl. no. 22745, 22777. 3 v. 29cm.

Microfiche (neg.) 11 x 15cm. (NYPL FSN 11, 035)
Bd. 1-2.

CONTENTS. - Bd. 1. Männerchöre a capella. - Bd. 2. Frauenchöre a capella. Gemischte Chöre a capella. Männerchöre mit Begleitung. Gemischte Chöre mit Begleitung.

1. Choral music, Secular--1600- . I. Hirschberg, Leopold, 1867-1929, ed.

NL 0447030　　NN

VM
3
L 82
LÖWE, KARL, 1796-1869.
Carl Loewes werke. Gesamtausgabe der balladen, legenden, lieder und gesänge für eine singstimme, in auftrage der loeweschen familie herausgegeben von dr. Max Runze. Leipzig, Breitkopf & Härtel⌐1898-1904⌐
17v.in 9. 28½cm. (Volkausgabe Breitkopf & Härtel. no.1801-1817)

German words.
Contents.-bd.I. Lieder aus der jugendzeit und kinderlieder.-bd.II. Bisher unveröffentlichte und vergessene lieder, gesänge, romanzen und balladen.-bd.III. Schottische, englische und nordische balladen.-bd.IV. Die deutschen kaiserballaden.-bd.V. Hohenzollern-balladen und -lieder.-bd.VI. Französische, spanische und orientalische balladen.-bd.VII. Die polnischen balladen.-bd.VIII. Geisterballaden und gesichte todesund kirchhofs-bilder.-bd.IX. Sagen, märchen, fabeln, aus thier- und menschenwelt.-bd.X. Romantische balladen aus dem höfischen wie bürgerlichen leben. Bilder aus land und see.-bd.XI-XII. Goethe und Loewe.-bd.XIII-XIV. Legenden.-bd.XV. Lyrische fantasien. Allegorien. Hymnen und gesänge. Hebräische gesänge.-bd.XVI. Das loewesche lied.-bd.XVII. Liederkreise.

NL 0447033　　ICN NIC MU GU NN MH CtY ICU NcU NcD

Microfilm
711
Loewe, Karl, 1796-1869.
[Works, vocal. Selections]
Werke; Gesamtausgabe der Balladen, Legenden, Lieder und Gesänge für eine Singstimme in Aufträge der Loeweschen Familie. Hrsg. von Max Runze. Leipzig, Breitkopf & Härtel [Vorwort, 1899-1904]
Pl. no. V.A. 1801-17.
17 v. port.
Microfilm (negative) of the original in the Library of Congress. Washington, Library of Congress, 1963. 2 reels. 35mm.

Contents.-Reel 1. Bd.1. Lieder aus der Jugendzeit und Kinderlieder. Bd.2. Bisher unveröffentlichte und vergessene Lieder, Gesänge, Romanzen und Balladen. Bd.3. Schottische, englische und nordische Balladen. Bd.4. Die Deutschen Kaiserballaden. Bd.5. Hohenzollern-Balladen und -Lieder (Zugleich neue vervollständigte Ausgabe des Hohenzollern-Albums II) Bd.6. Französische, spanische und orientalische Balladen. Bd.7 Die Polnischen Balladen. Bd.8. Geisterballaden und Gesichte Todes- und Kirchhofs-Bilder. Bd.9. Sagen, Märchen, Fabeln, aus Thier- und Blumenwelt. Bd.10. Romantische Balladen aus den höfischen wie bürgerlichen Leben, Bilder aus Land und See.-Reel 2. Bd.11. Goethe und Loewe. I. Abt.: Lieder und Balladen. Bd.12. Goethe und Loewe. II. Abt.: Gesänge im grossen Stil und Oden, Groselegenden und Grossballaden. Bd.13. Legenden. I. Abt.: Die eigentliche Legendenperiode. Bd.14. Legenden. II. Abt.: Vereinzelte Legenden. Spätere Legendenperioden. Bd.15. Lyrische Fantasien. Allegorien. Hymnen und Gesänge. Hebräische Gesänge. Bd.16. Das Loewesche Lied. Bd.17. Liederkreise.
1. Songs with piano.

NL 0447036　　CoU

M783.3
L825z1
Loewe, Karl, 1796-1869.
⌐Die Zerstörung von Jerusalem. Piano-vocal score. German⌐
Die Zerstörung von Jerusalem, grosses Oratorium in zwei Abtheilungen, von C. Nicolai, componirt von C. Löwe. Op.30. Vollständiger Klavierauszug. Leipzig, F. Hofmeister ⌐1832?⌐ Pl. no. 1665.
148p. 26x35cm.

NL 0447037　　IU MB

VM
2020
L 827z
LÖWE, KARL, 1796-1869.
⌐Die Zerstörung von Jerusalem. German⌐
Die Zerstörung von Jerusalem. Grosses Oratorium in 2 Abtheilungen von G.Nicolai. Op.30. Partitur. Leipzig,F.Hofmeister⌐ca.1832?⌐
4p., score(395p.) 35cm.

In manuscript on p.⌐1⌐: Grosse Aufführung unter Direction Spontinis in Berlin 1832.

NL 0447038　　ICN MB MH

Loewe, Karl, 1796-1869.
Zwist und Sühne. Gedicht von Simrock für eine Singstimme [S. o. T.] mit Begleitung des Piano Forte. Berlin. Bote & Bock. [185-?] 6 pp. L. 8°.

E3682 — T.r. — Songs. With music.
April 11, 1902.

NL 0447039　　MB

---

fH
61
.334
LOEWE, KARL, 1846-1907, ed.
Geschichte des Nord-Ostsee-kanals. Festschrift zu seiner eröffnung am 20., 21. juni 1895. Im amtlichen auftrage und unter benutzung amtlicher quellen herausgegeben von Carl Loewe. Berlin,W.Ernst & sohn,1895.
41,⌐19⌐p. 25 pl.(part fold.) 36½cm.

NL 0447040　　ICN ICJ DN WaU MiD DNW NN

Hda34
1
L82
Löwe, Karl, 1881-
Die Adjektivsuffixe im Dacorumänischen ...
Leipzig,1910.
Pamphlet
Inaug.-Diss. - Leipzig.
Vita.
Literaturverzeichnis.
"Sonderabdruck aus dem XVII.Jahresbericht des Instituts für rumänische Sprache zu Leipzig."

NL 0447041　　CtY ICRL PU MH ICN

Löwe, Karl-Ernst, 1906-
Die Gemeinde als Selbstverwaltungskörper und als Trägerin von ortspolizeilichen Rechten und Pflichten (insbesondere in Preussen) ...
[Syke, 1932]
Inaug.-Diss. - Göttingen.
Lebenslauf.
"Benutztes Schrifttum": p. [51-53]

NL 0447042　　CtY

Löwe, Karl F　　1890-
... Flugzeugortung, von Karl F. Löwe ... Mit 67 abbildungen, 4 tabellen und 2 tafeln. Berlin-Charlottenburg, C. J. E. Volckmann nachf. g. m. b. h., 1934.
87, ⌐1⌐ p. illus., 2 fold. pl. (maps, tables) diagrs. 21ᶜᵐ. (Flugzeugbau und luftfahrt ... hft. 23)

1. Navigation (Aeronautics) I. Title.
34-29934

Library of Congress　　TL586.L6　　629.1325

NL 0447043　　DLC NN

VOLUME 338

Löwe, Karl F 1890–
Flugzeugortung. 3. Aufl. Berlin-Charlottenburg, C. J. E. Volckmann Nachf., 1936.
96 p. illus., maps, diagrs. 21 cm. (Flugzeugbau und Luftfahrt, Heft 23)

1. Navigation (Aeronautics) I. Title. (Series)

TL536.L6 1936   629.1325   50–41078

NL 0447044   DLC

Löwe, Karl F 1890–
Im fluge nach den Azoren; flugerlebnisse und reiseeindrücke, von Karl F. Löwe ... mit 14 abbildungen. Berlin, Union deutsche verlagsgesellschaft ¡1929¡
44 p. illus., map. 25¼ᶜᵐ.

1. Aeronautics — Flights. 2. Lisbon — Descr. 3. Azores — Descr. & trav. I. Title.

31–33947

Library of Congress   TL721.D7L6   [914] 629.13

NL 0447045   DLC NN

Löwe, Karl Friedrich, 1874–
see
Löwe, Fritz, 1874–

Löwe, Karl Richard.
Wie erziehe und belehre ich mein kind bis zum sechsten lebensjahre? Von Karl Richard Löwe ... 2., teilweise neu bearb. aufl. ... Hannover ¡etc.¡ C. Meyer, 1904.
viii, 184 p. 21¼ᶜᵐ.

1. Children—Education. 2. Child study. 3. School age.

E 12—1615

U. S. Off. of educ. Library   LB1117.L9
for Library of Congress   ¡a41b1¡

NL 0447047   DHEW

Loewe, Konrad, 1856–
Festgrüsse an Bernhard Baumeister, von Goethe, Schiller, Lessing, Grillparzer, Otto Ludwig, Scheffel. Dem Jubilar in der Festkneipe beim "Weingartel" vermittelt von Konrad Loewe. ¡Wien, 1902¡ 16 p. 19cm.
Imaginary greetings.

1. Baumeister, Bernhard, 1828–   1917. I. Title.
N. Y. P. L.   September 22, 1948

NL 0447048   NN

Loewe (L.) De diphteritis, hare behandeling en genezing. 16 pp. 12°. *Amsterdam, J. C. auf der Heide.* [s. d.].

NL 0447049   DNLM

Loewe, L.
——— De tering, hare behandling en genezing. 16 pp. 12°. *Amsterdam, J. C. auf der Heide,* [s. d.].

NL 0447050   DNLM

Löwe, Leo, 1877–
Prussia. K. Geologische landesanstalt.
Deutschlands kalibergbau. Festschrift zum x. allgemeinen bergmannstage in Eisenach. Berlin, Verlag and vertrieb der Königlichen geologischen landesanstalt, 1907.

Loewe, Leo, 1877–
Leitfaden für den praktischen Arbeitsschutz im Bergbau. Halle (Saale) C. Marhold, 1950.
107 p. illus. 21 cm.

1. Mining engineering—Safety measures. I. Title.

TN295.L68   51–20733

NL 0447052   DLC

LOEWE, Leo, 1877–
Über sekundäre mineralbildung auf kalisalzlagern. Inaugural-dissertation, Leipzig. Berlin, 1903.
1. 8°.

NL 0447053   MH PU MiU CtY ICRL

LOEWE, Lotte, 1900–
Acetylierungen in der harnsäure-reihe und neue umsetzungen der kaffolide. Inaug.-diss. Breslau, 1927.
pp. 23+.
At head of title: Aus dem chemischen institute der universität Breslau.
"Lebenslauf", p. 23.

NL 0447054   MH-C ICRL CtY

Loewe, Louis, 1809–1888.
An address on the occasion of Sir Moses Montefiore completing his hundredth year. 27th Oct., 1884. In Judith, Lady Montefiore's Theological College, Ramsgate.
London. Wertheimer, Lea & Co. [1884.] 22 pp. 8°.

H⁸₂₂ — Montefiore, Sir Moses Haim, Baronet. 1784–1885.

NL 0447055   MB CtY

[LOEWE, Louis] 1809–1888.
The Damascus Affair. Diary of Dr. Louis Loewe, July–November 1840. Foreword by Rabbi Shemtob Gaguin. Prefatory Note by Herbert Loewe. Introduction by Paul Goodman. Ramsgate, Montefiore Theological College, November 1940. 70, III–VIIIp. (Hebrew) pl. (portr.) 21 cm. (Vol. I, no. 3, of Yehudith, Organ of the Montefiore Theol. College). Foreword in Hebrew.
1. Damascus Affair. 2. Goodman, Paul. 3. Gaguin, Shemtob.

NL 0447056   NNJ

Z6375 Loewe, Louis, 1809–1888.
.L82   A descriptive catalogue of a portion of the library of the late Dr. Louis Loewe ... together with a portrait, a short biography and some rough bibliographical notices. By James H. Loewe. To which is added a reprint of the paper contributed to the Breslauer monatsschrift by Dr. Hartwig Hirschfeld ... describing the manuscripts collected by Dr. Loewe, at present in the possession of his widow. London, Printed in Mayence by the J. Wirth'sche hofbuchdr a.-g., 1895.
68, ¡1¡ p. front. (port. mounted phot.) 29ᶜᵐ.
Errata tipped in.

NL 0447057   ICU NNC OCH CtY NIC

Loewe, Louis, editor, 1809–1888.
Diaries of Sir Moses and Lady Montefiore
see under   Montefiore, Sir Moses Haim, bart., 1784–1885.

Loewe, L¡ouis¡ 1809–1888.
A dictionary of the Circassian language. In two parts: English - Circassian - Turkish, and Circassian - English - Turkish. Containing all the most necessary words for the traveller, the soldier, and the sailor; with the exact pronunciation of each word in the English character. By Dr. L. Loewe ... London, G. Bell, 1854.
9 p., 1 l., 4, clxxvii, ¡1¡ p. 23ᶜᵐ.
Originally printed in the Transactions of the Philological society.

6–21688

MH CSmH
NL 0447059   DLC NjP CtY NN MdBP CU OC1W MiU OC1 NN

Loewe, Louis, 1809–1888, ed. and tr.
Levinsohn, Isaac Baer, 1788–1860.
Éfés dammîm. A series of conversations at Jerusalem between a patriarch of the Greek church and a chief rabbi of the Jews, concerning the malicious charge against the Jews of using Christian blood. By J. B. Levinsohn. Tr. from the Hebrew as a tribute to the memory of the martyrs at Damascus, by Dr. L. Loewe ... London, Longman, Brown, Green and Longmans, 1841.

Loewe, Louis, 1809–1888.
משא אליעזר, והוא משא אשר נשא הרב אליעזר הלוי
לאחיו יושבי וילנא בבה"כ הגדולה ביום ש"ק פ' קדושים
תר"ז. מעתק מפי המדבר בלשון אשכנז על ידי שמואל
יוסף פ‌ין. וילנא, בדפוס י. ר. ראם, תר"ז.
Вильно, 1847.
24 p. 17 cm.

1. Sermons, Jewish.   *Title transliterated:* Masa Eli'eser.

BM740.L584   52–50724

NL 0447061   DLC

LOEWE, Louis, 1809–1888.
Observations on a unique cufic gold coin issued by Al-Aamir Beakheam Allah, Abū Ali Manzour Ben Mustali, tenth Caliph of the Fatimite dynasty. London, D. Nutt, etc., etc., 1849.
pp. (2), 17.
"Read at a meeting of the Numismatic society of London."

NL 0447062   MH

Loewe, Louis, 1809–1888.
The origin of the Egyptian language proved by the analysis of that and the Hebrew, in an introductory essay. London, 1837.
33 p. charts. 21 cm.
Repr.: Asiatic journal.
Author's autograph.

NL 0447063   OCH DCU-H NN

[Loewe, Louis] 1809–1888.
The Sir Moses Montefiore celebrations at Ramsgate. [London, 1883]
24 p. 20 cm.
T.p. wanting; caption-title.
Containing Loewe's address on the occasion of Montefiore's 99th birthday.
(Bound with: Loewe, L. An Address delivered on the occasion of Sir Moses Montefiore ... completing his hundredth year. London, 1884)

NL 0447064   CtY MH

VOLUME 338

Loewe, Louis, 1809-1888.
The Tisza-Eszlar mystery. ₍London, 1883₎.
1 L.

Repr.: Daily Telegraph, 1883.

NL 0447065   OCH

Loewe, Ludwig.
Die ausgaben der deutschen landwirtschaft für industrielle
produktionsmittel. diagrs.
Landw. jahrb. bd. 77, p. 367-423.   Berlin, 1933.
"Literaturverzeichnis": p. 419-420.

1. Agriculture—Economic aspects. 2. Agriculture—Germany. 3. Ag-
ricultural machinery. ₍3. Farm equipment₎   Agr 33-892
Library, U.S. Dept. of   Agriculture 18L23 bd. 77
Library of Congress   [87.L27 bd. 77]

NL 0447066   DNAL

Löwe, Ludwig, 1795-1871.
Aus Ludwig Löwe's Nachlass...   Graz, 1885.   24 p.   illus.
25cm.
"Als Handschrift gedruckt."
Dedicated to Karl Josef Sauer, by his son.

1. Letters, German. 2. Stage—   Austria—Vienna, 19th cent.
1. Sauer, August, 1855-1926, ed.
N.Y.P.L.   October 11, 1948

NL 0447067   NN CLSU

Löwe, Ludwig, 1844-1914.
Beiträge zur Anatomie der Nase und Mundhöhle, von Dr. Ludwig
Löwe, ... Mit 7 Tafeln in Lichtdruck. Ausgeführt von Albert
Frisch in Berlin. Berlin, Denicke's Verlag, 1878.
₍4₎ 21 p. vii pl. 33ᶜᵐ.
Each plate is accompanied by leaf with descriptive letterpress.
Treats of experiments performed on rabbits.

NL 0447068   ICJ PU-D NNC DNLM

QM
505   Löwe, Ludwig, 1844-
L82++   Beiträge zur Anatomie der Nase und
1883   Munhöhle. 2. Aufl.   Leipzig, Denicke,
1883.
iv, 21 p.   illus.   33cm.

1. Nose--Anatomy. 2. Mouth.

NL 0447069   NIC DNLM

Löwe, Ludwig, 1844-
Beiträge zur Anatomie und zur Entwicklungsgeschichte des Nervensystems der Säugethiere und des Menschen, von Dr. Ludwig
Loewe, ... Berlin, Denicke's Verlag, 1880-[1883].
2 vol. in 1.   illus.   40½ᶜᵐ.
Each plate accompanied by leaf with descriptive letter-press.
"Verzeichnis der häufig im Text wiederkehrenden und deshalb nicht jedes Mal angeführten Werke," vol. 1, 1 p. at end.
Contents.— 1. Bd. Die Morphogenesis des centralen Nervensystems.   1880. viii,
₍2₎, 126, ₍2₎ p. xviii pl.—2. Bd. Die Histologie und Histogenese des Nervensystems nebst einem Anhang: Die Schädelwirbeltheorie. Leipzig, 1883. ₍2₎, 50 p.
pl. xix-xxiii.

NL 0447070   ICJ CU MH PPAN DNLM

Loewe, Ludwig, 1844-1914.

Glassberg, Abraham, *ed.*
Die beschneidung in ihrer geschichtlichen, ethnographi-
schen, religiösen und medicinischen bedeutung. Zum ersten
male umfassend dargestellt und unter mitwirkung von prof.
dr. M. Steinschneider, J. Steinschneider, pastor J. Rauchstein
₍and others₎ herausgegeben von A. Glassberg. Berlin, C.
Boas, 1896.

NL 0447072   DNLM

1844-1914.
Löwe (Ludwig). * Die Histologie und Histio-
genese des Fettgewebes. [Wurtzburg.] 35 pp.
8°.   *Leipzig, Metzger u. Wittig,* 1878.
Repr. from: Arch. f. Anat. u. Physiol. Leips., 1878.   C.

NL 0447073   DNLM

WVA
L827k   LÖWE, Ludwig, *1844-1914.*
1884   Die Krankheiten des Ohres und der
Nase. 1. Th. Lehrbuch der Ohrenheilkunde für praktische Aerzte und Studirende
der Medizin.   Berlin, Hampel, 1884.
xi, 307 p.
No more published?

NL 0447073   DNLM

Loewe, Ludwig, 1844-
Morphogensis des centralen nervensystems.
Ber., 1880.

NL 0447074   NjP

Loewe, Ludwig, 1844-1914.
———. Das Ohr in gesunden und kranken Tagen.
2. Aufl.   1 p l., 50 pp. 8°. *Berlin, J. Horrwitz,*
1883.

NL 0447075   DNLM

Loewe, Ludwig, 1844-
———. Das Ohr. Seine Pflege und seine Krankheiten. 64 pp. 8°. *Berlin, H. Steinitz,* 1883.

NL 0447076   DNLM

Löwe, Ludwig, 1844-
Zur Chirurgie der Nase, von Dr. Ludwig Löwe, ... Mit ...
Tafeln und ... Abbildungen im Text. Berlin, O. Coblentz,
1905-1907.
2 vol. in 1.   36½ᶜᵐ.
Paged continuously: vol. 1: ₍4₎, 44 p. 11 illus., xi pl.; vol. 2: ₍4₎, ₍45₎-106 p.
illus. 12-13, pl. xii-xx.

NL 0447077   ICJ DNLM PPC NNC MiU

Löwe (Ludwig) [1844-1914]. Zur Kenntniss des
Bindegewebes, pp. 63-92; 108-170; 33-56, 5 pl.
8°. [*Leipzig,* 1877-9].
Cutting [cover with printed title] *from:* Arch. f. Anat.
u. Physiol. Leipz. 1877; 1878; 1879.

NL 0447078   DNLM

Loewe (Ludwig) & Compagnie, A.G.
Fabrikorganisation, Fabrikbuchführung und
Selbstkostenberechnung der Firma Ludw. Loewe &
Co., ...
see under   Lilienthal, Johann.

Loewe, Ludwig & Compagnie, A. G.
Ludw. Loewe & Co. Actiengesellschaft, Berlin, 1869-1929;
im Jahre 1930 herausgegeben zum sechzigjährigen Jubiläum der
Firma von der Gesellschaft für elektrische Unternehmungen...
₍Berlin, 1930.₎   diagrs., front., illus. (incl. facsims.), ports.   4°.
Half-title: Die Geschichte der Ludw. Loewe & Co.

571999A. 1. Machinery—Companies   —Germany—Berlin.
N.Y.P.L.   May 19, 1932

NL 0447080   NN IaU IU CSt-H MU NNC MH

---

ar X
6747   Loewe, Ludwig & Compagnie, A. G.
Ludw. Loewe & Co. Aktiengesellschaft.
Berlin, 1900.
₍10₎ p. illus. 28cm.

NL 0447081   NIC

---

ar X
6746   Loewe, Ludwig & Compagnie, A. G.
The machine tool works of Ludw. Loewe &
Co. ₍Berlin, 1900?₎
75 p. illus. 23 x 29cm.

NL 0447082   NIC

LOEWE, LUDWIG & COMPAGNIE, A.G.
The Mauser magazine rifle, calibre 7,65-6,5 mm.
(.301 in-.256 in.). Waffenfabrik Mauser, Oberndorf
on the Neckar. Berlin [1891] 19 p. fold.col., plates.
33cm.

1. Rifles.   t. 1891.

NL 0447083   NN

Loewe, M.
A treatise on the phenomena of animal magnetism; in which
the same are systematically explained according to the laws of
nature, by M. Loewe... London: Printed by G. Schulze, for
the author, 1822.   xx, 22-130 p.   22cm.

165849B. 1. Hypnotism.
N.Y.P.L.   June 12, 1942

NL 0447084   NN CtY-M ICJ MiU CtY

Löwe, M   S
see
Lowe, M   S

1887-
Loewe, Manfred, Ueber Gefässangiome und ihre Spontan-
heilung. Bautzen 1913: Müller.   25 S.   8°
Leipzig, Med. Diss. v. 29. Okt. 1913, Ref. Hoffmann
[Geb. 30. Dez. 87 Usch, Pr. Posen; Wohnort: Bautzen; Staatsangeh.: Preußen;
Vorbildung: G. Schneidemühl Reife 08; Studium: Berlin 3, Freiburg 2,
Berlin 2, Leipzig 3 S.; Coll. 29. Okt. 13.]   [U 13.7350

NL 0447086   ICRL DNLM CtY

W 4
M96   LOEWE, Marianne, 1918-
1950   Zur Kasuistik der Impetigo herpetiformis; Bericht über einen Krankheitsfall
bei einer 55-jährigen Frau, jenseits der
Menopause.   München, 1950.
28 ℓ. illus.
Inaug-Diss. - Munich.
1. Impetigo herpetiformis

NL 0447087   DNLM

VOLUME 338

Loewe, Martin
  Vorhang auf! Ein heiteres Vortragsbuch zur Gestaltung bunter Abende. 5.Aufl. Darmstadt, O.Teich[1947?]
  192p. illus.

NL 0447088   OC1

Loewe, Martin, 1881–
  Die juristische Natur der Postanweisung ... von Martin Loewe ... Gleiwitz, Neumann [1906]
  viii, 63 p. 22cm.
  Inaug.-diss. - Breslau.
  "Lebenslauf": p.63.
  "Literaturverzeichnis": p.vi-viii.

NL 0447089   MH-L MH ICRL

Loewe (Mauritius) [1835–   ]. * De paralysi bilaterali nervi facialis casu singulari adjecto. 32 pp. 8°. Berolini, G. Schade, 1860.

NL 0447090   DNLM

Löwe, Max Alfred, 1886–
  ... Blutuntersuchungen bei verdauungskrankheiten des pferdes ... Dresden, Buchdr. O. Franke, 1912.
  69 p., 1 l. 23ᶜᵐ.
  Inaug.-diss.—Leipzig.
  Lebenslauf.
  "Literaturverzeichnis": p. [67]-69.
  1. Blood—[Analysis and] examination. 2. Digestive organs—Diseases. 3. Horse—Diseases.
                                            Agr 14-582
  Library, U. S. Dept. of   Agriculture 41L,955

NL 0447091   DNAL ICRL

Löwe, Maximilian Leopold.
  Grundriss der allgemeinen hodegetik. Als leitfaden bei dem beginn der akademischen studien und bei allgemeinen hodegetisch-methodologisch-encyclopädischen vorträger verfasst von d. Maximilian Leopold Löwe ... Dresden, In der Walther'schen hofbuchhandlung, 1839.
  iv, 84 p. fold. tab. 21½ x 12½ᶜᵐ.
  Includes bibliographies.
  1. Study. Method of. 2. Students—Germany. i. Title: Hodegetik, Grundriss der allgemeinen.
                                            41-33897
  Library of Congress   LB2395.L6

NL 0447092   DLC

Loewe, Maximilian Leopold.
  Historiae criticae grammatices universalis ... lineamenta. Dresdae, [1829]

NL 0447093   NjP PU

Löwe, Maximilian Leopold, ed.

Gesammtverein der deutschen geschichts- und alterthumsvereine.
  Korrespondenzblatt des Gesammtvereins der deutschen geschichts- und alterthumsvereine ...
  Dresden [etc.]

Loewe, Moritz.
  Die Probe- und die Antritts-Predigt des Rabbinats-Candidaten M. Loewe gehalten... am Sabbat vor Pessach ... 5601. Güdtrow, 1841.
  47 p.

NL 0447095   OCH

Löwe, Moritz.
  Prof. M. Löwes aufgaben zum kaufmännischen rechnen, methodisch geordnet und mit ausgeführten beispielen ... neubearbeitet von dr. phil. F. Strothbaum ...   Leipzig, J. Klinkhardt, 1915.
  3 v.   forms.   22 cm.
  Vol. 1, 33d ed.; v. 2, 30th ed.; v. 3, 20th ed.
  1. Arthmetic, Commercial. 2. Accounting - 1901-   I. Strothbaum, Felix,   ed.

NL 0447096   CU

Loewe (Moses). * De remediorum incitantium abusu. 22 pp. 8°. Traj. ad Viadr., e typ. Apitziano, [1804].

NL 0447097   DNLM

Löwe, Otto.
  Anleitung zum gärtnerischen Samenbau. Stuttgart, E. Ulmer, 1929.
  viii, 121 p.   21 cm.
  "Literatur-Nachweis": p. 114.
  1. Seed industry and trade.
  SB117.L6   49-44466*

NL 0447098   DLC

Löwe, Otto.
  Gemüse-, blumen- und obstkulturen unter glas, von Otto Löwe ... Stuttgart, E. Ulmer, 1928.
  viii, 189 p. illus., diagrs. 21ᶜᵐ.
  "Literatur-nachweis": p. 185.
  1. Greenhouses. [1. Greenhouse cultivation]
                                            Agr 29-821
  Library, U. S. Dept. of   Agriculture 90L,953

NL 0447099   DNAL

Loewe, Otto, musician.
  Lieder mit Begleitung des Pianoforte.
  ⹀ *Autograph manuscript.* [184–?] (1), 53 pp. 30 cm.
  L5155 — Songs With music. Colls. — Manuscripts in this Library. Music.

NL 0447100   MB

Loewe, Otto, musician.
  Zwei Terzetten fuer Sopran, Tenor und Bass mit Begleitung des Pianoforte.
  ⹀ *Autograph manuscript.* [1847.] 7 pp. 19 × 23 cm.
  Contents. — Wonne der Wehmuth. — Der Kirchhof.
  L7892 — Part songs. — Manuscripts in this Library. Music.

NL 0447101   MB

Loewe, Otto, of Stettin.
  Ueber den Werth des Kantischen kategorischen Imperativs für die Begründung der Ethik. Stettin, Herrcke & Lebeling, 1878.
  32 p.   25cm.
  Accompanies "Programm"—Vgl. Marienstifts-Gymnasium, Stettin.
  1. Kant, Immanuel, 1724–1804.
  2. Ethics.

NL 0447102   NIC NjP

Löwe, Otto, writer on geometry.
  Ausgewählte capitel aus der darstellenden geometrie zum gebrauch bei constructionsübungen, von dr. Otto Löwe. Hft. 1. Durchdringungen unregelmässiger polyeder ... 2. aufl.   Clausthal, A. Brauns, 1887.
  20 p., 1 l.   diagrs. on ix pl.   26 cm.
  No more published?
  1. Geometry, Descriptive. 2. Polyhedra.

NL 0447103   CU

Löwe, Otto, writer on geometry.
  Ueber die regulären und Poinsot'schen körper und ihre inhaltsbestimmung vermittelst determinanten ... Marburg, Druck von F. W. Kunike, 1875.
  1 p. l., 28 p.   diagrs. on pl.   22ᶜᵐ.
  Inaug.-diss.—Marburg.
  1. Polyhedra. 2. Determinants.
  Library of Congress   QA555.L8   6-2225†

NL 0447104   DLC

Löwe, Otto, writer on lacquering.
  Die PKW-Lackierung in Industrie und Handwerk. Leipzig, Fachbuchverlag, 1952.
  94 p. illus. 23 cm.
  1. Lacquer and lacquering.   i. Title.
  TP939.L6   56-31979 ‡

NL 0447105   DLC MiD

LOEWE, Otto, 1843–
  De Terpandri Lesbii aetate commentatio. Diss.inaug.philol. Halis, [1860].
  pp.(2),60†.
  "Vita",after p.60.   Gt 7.5

NL 0447106   MH ICRL NjP PBm PU

Loewe, Otto, 1878–
  Ueber den einfluss von naehrklystieren auf die peristaltik und secretion im magendarmcanal. Inaug. Diss. Wuersburg, 1903. (Berlin)

NL 0447107   ICRL PU DNLM

Loewe (Paul Christian Samuel) [1862–   ]. * Ueber einen Fall von malignem Nierentumor bei einem Kinde. 29 pp., 1 l. 8°. Berlin, E. Müller, [1894].

NL 0447108   DNLM PPC

VOLUME 338

Loewe, Philipp.
  Erklärung der Fresco-Gemälde am Museum,
Nach Schinkel's Entwürfen bearbeitet. 6te. Aufl.
Berlin.
  16 p.

NL 0447109   CtY

Loewe, Philipp.
  Die Königlichen Museen für Kunst und
Alterthum
    see under   Berlin. K. Museen.

Loewe, Philip.
  Les musées royaux pour l'art et l'antiquité. Guide pour l'ancien   *8069a.6
et le nouveau musée avec de nombreuses explications. 19ᵉ édition entièrement corrigée et augmentée. 1ᵉ édition française.
Berlin. Logier. [186–?] (1), iv, (1), 166 pp. 17½ cm., in 8s.

NL 0447111   MB

Löwe (Philipp)
  Das neue Museum. Eine ausführliche Beschreibung
seiner Kunstwerke und Sehenswürdigkeiten. 4. Aufl.
Berlin: W. Logier, n. d. 5ª pp. 16°.

NL 0447112   NN

Loewe, Philip.
  Das neue Museum. Eine ausführliche Beschreibung seiner Kunst-
werke und Sehenswürdigkeiten. 7. vermehrte und verbesserte
Auflage.
  Berlin. Logier. [185–?] vi, 65, (1) pp. Plan. 16½ cm., in 8s.

NL 0447113   MB CtY

Loewe, Philipp, Dr.
  Die Prostitution aller Zeiten und Völker mit besonderer Berück-
16788 sichtigung von Berlin. Ein Beitrag zu der obschwebenden
Bordellfrage. Von Dr. Philipp Loewe. Berlin, W. Logier,
1852.
  xv, 223, [1] p. 17½ᶜᵐ.
  "Quellen." p. [x].

NL 0447114   ICJ DNLM CtY

LOEWE, Philipp, of Strehlen.
  Lexicalische studien zu Ovid. Strehlen,
[1888].
  4°. pp.16.
  "Beilage zum Progr.d.K.Gym.1888, no.195."

NL 0447115   MH NjP

Loewe, Philipp, of Strehlen.
  Lexicalische studien zu Ovid ...   Strehlen,
T. Erler's buchd. [1888]
  18 p. 28 cm.
  Programm – K. Gymnasium, Strehlen (Beilage,
ost. 1888)

NL 0447116   CU

Loewe, Philipp, of Strehlen.
  Nachträge zum Thesaurus linguae latinae aus
Ovidius. Teil i. Breslau. 1902.
  4°;
  Progr. d. Kgl. Friedrichs-gym. "1902, nr.
194. "

NL 0447117   MH

[LOEWE, Philipp] of Strehlen.
  Die sage von Helgi, dem Hundings-töđter.
[Strehlen,].Erler,1877].
  4°. pp.14.
  Without title-page,caption title.
  Signed:"Loewe."

NL 0447118   NIC MH

PA   Loewe, Philipp, of Strehlen.
6551   Über die Praepositionen a, de, ex
L82   bei Ovid. Strehlen [1889]
  16 p. 25cm.

  "Programm"--K. Gymnasium, Strehlen.

  1. Ovidius Naso, Publius--Language--
Grammar. 2. Latin language--Prepositions.

NL 0447119   NIC CU

LOEWE, Philipp, of Strehlen.
  Über die praepositionen a.de,ex.bei Ovid.
Strehlen,[1889].
  4°. pp.16.
  "Beilage zum Progr.d.K.Gym.1889,nr.197."

NL 0447120   MH NjP

Loewe,Reinhold, 1874-
  Statisches und klinisches zur kenntnis der actio-
nomycose des wurmfortsatzes ...
  Inaug. diss. Greifswald, 1904
  Bibl.

NL 0447121   ICRL DNLM

Loewe, Richard.
  Ueber blasenlachmung...
  Inaug. Diss. Wuersburg, 1885

NL 0447122   ICRL DNLM

PF   Loewe, Richard, 1863-
3580   Deutsches etymologisches Wörterbuch. 2.,
L82   umgearb. und verm. Aufl. Berlin, W. de
1930   Gruyter, 1930.
  186 p. 16cm. (Sammlung Göschen, 64)

  1. German language--Etymology--Dictionar-
ies. I. Title.

NL 0447123   NIC ViU PPT IdU PU OCU NcD OrU NRU MiHM

Loewe, Richard, 1863-
  ... Deutsches wörterbuch, von dr. Richard Loewe. Leipzig, G. J. Göschen, 1910.
  177 p. 15¼ᵐ. (Sammlung Göschen. [64])
  "Literatur": p. [4]

  1. German language—Dictionaries.

  10-14878
  Library of Congress   PF3580.L7

0447124   DLC OkU CU MeB MB

Loewe, Richard, 1863-
  ... Deutsches wörterbuch, von dr. Richard Loewe. Neudruck. Berlin und Leipzig, W. de Gruyter & co., 1919.
  177 p. 16ᵐ. (Sammlung Göschen [64])
  "Literatur": p. [4]

  1. German language—Etymology—Dictionaries.
  43-48367
  Library of Congress   PF3580.L7 1919

NL 0447125   DLC ViU PBm

Loewe, Richard, 1863-
  Die Dialektmischung im Magdeburgischen Gebiete. Norden,
1889. 52 p. map. 23cm.
  Inaug.-Diss. — Leipzig.
  "Die hier vorliegende Arbeit bildet einen Teil der Abhandlung, die unter dem Titel
'Zur sprachlichen Mischung auf Grund des Dialektes im Magdeburgischen' der philo-
sophischen Fakultät der Universität Leipzig als Dissertation eingereicht wurde."
  Vita.

  1. German language—Dialects—   Magdeburg.

NL 0447126   NN ICU NjP MH ICRL NIC

Loewe, Richard, 1863-
  Die ethnische und sprachliche gliederung der Germanen.
Von dr. Richard Loewe. Halle, M. Niemeyer, 1899.
  2 p. l., 59, [1] p. 23½ᵐ. (Gesellschaft für deutsche philologie in
Berlin. Festschrift. no. 16)

  1. Germanic tribes. 2. Germanic languages.
  G-855 Revised
  Library of Congress   DD75.L7

PBm
NL 0447127   DLC CaBVaU CU NIC NcD ViU MiU NjP PU

P597   LOEWE,RICHARD,1863-
.L8   Der freie akzent des indogermanischen. Eine sprach-
(S)   wissenschaftliche untersuchung von Richard Loewe. Berlin und Leipzig,W.de Gruyter & co.,1929.
  viii,83 p. 23cm.

  1.Aryan languages--Accents and accentuation.

  PU PPT ICN ViU OCU IU DCU CtY InU CU
NL 0447128   ICU CaBVaU NcU CSt MiDW NRU ViU MH MiU

Loewe, Richard, 1863-
  Germanic philology, by Dr. Richard Loewe. Translated and
edited by J. D. Jones... London: G. Allen & Co., Ltd., 1913.
  xv, 170 p. 12°.
  Bibliography, p. xi.

  470750A. 1. Germanic languages.   I. Jones, John D., translator.
  N. Y. P. L.   June 30, 1930

  OC1W OC1 NjP CtY
NL 0447129   NN WaU NcD PBm PU NjP MiU MH IEN MiU

Loewe, Richard, 1863-
  Germanische pflanzennamen; etymologische untersuchungen
über hirschbeere, hindebeere, rehbockbeere und ihre verwandten, von Richard Loewe. Heidelberg, C. Winter, 1913.
  xiii, 182, [2] p. 23½ᵐ. (Added t.-p.: Germanische bibliothek, hrsg.
von Wilhelm Streitberg. 2. abt. Untersuchungen und texte. 6. bd.)
  "Abkürzungen für wiederholt zitierte werke": p. xi-xiii.

  1. Germanic languages—Etymology. 2. Plant names, Popular—Germany.
  35-29733
  Library of Congress   QK13.L6
  [2]   580.142

  OU MiU ICN ICU MdBJ MiU NNC PU TU NN IU
NL 0447130   DLC NIC LU NNBG UU OU CU CtY NjP OCU

VOLUME 338

Film
2750
Reel
242
Item
9

Loewe, Richard, 1863–
Germanische Pflanzennamen; etymologische
Untersuchungen über Hirschbeere, Hindebeere,
Rehbockbeere und ihre Verwandten. Heidelberg, C. Winter, 1913.
xiii, 182p. 24cm. (Germanische Bibliothek.
2. Abt. Untersuchungen und Texte. 6. Bd.)
"Abkürzungen für wiederholt zitierte Werke":
p.xi–xiii.
Microfilm. Lexington, Ky., Erasmus Press;
available through General Microfilm Co., Cam-

bridge, Mass. 1 reel (various items) 35mm.
Title on microfilm box label: Literature of
folklore.

1. Germanic languages – Etymology. 2. Plant
names, Popular – Germany. I. Title. II. Series. III. Series: Literature of folklore.
Reel 242.

NL 0447132   TxU

Loewe, Richard, 1863–
... Germanische sprachwissenschaft, von dr. Richard
Loewe. Leipzig, G. J. Göschen, 1905.
148 p. 15½ᶜᵐ. (Sammlung Göschen. ₍238₎)
"Literatur": p. ₍6₎

1. Germanic languages—Grammar, Comparative.
5—26512

Library of Congress   PD91.L8

MiU PP MB
NL 0447133   DLC CU FMU TNJ OKentU OrU IdU NcD OCl

Loewe, Richard, 1863–
... Germanische sprachwissenschaft, von Richard Loewe.
2. aufl. Leipzig, G. J. Göschen, 1911.
151 p. 16ᵐ. (Sammlung Göschen. ₍238₎)
"Literatur": p. ₍5₎

1. Germanic languages—Grammar, Comparative.
34—5117
Library of Congress   PD91.L8 1911
₍2₎   439

OrU CaBVaU
NL 0447134   DLC MoKU WaU MeB OCU OClW MiU PU PSC

PD91
L827g
1922

Loewe, Richard, 1863–
Germanische Sprachwissenschaft. 3. Aufl.
Neudruck. Berlin, W. de Gruyter, 1922–24.
2 v. 16cm. (Sammlung Göschen, 238, 780)

1. Germanic languages – Grammar, Comparative
I. Title.

NcU MH ICU NjP
NL 0447135   GU FMU PPT CtY NIC WU NBuG IU MiU NBC

Loewe, Richard, 1863–
... Germanische sprachwissenschaft, von dr. Richard Loewe
... 4. neubearb. aufl. Berlin ₍etc.₎ W. de Gruyter & co., 1933.
2 v. 16ᵐ. (Sammlung Göschen. ₍238, 780₎)
"Literatur": v. 1, p. 4–5.
CONTENTS.—I. Einleitung und lautlehre.—II. Formenlehre.

1. Germanic languages—Grammar, Comparative.
A 33–1751
Title from Univ. of Minn.   Printed by L. C.

NL 0447136   MnU TxU CU NIC PBm PU NBC

Loewe, Richard 1863–
Der Goldring von Pietroassa. In Indogerm.
Forsch. XXVI. Bd. 1909. p. 203–208.

NL 0447137   NIC

Loewe, Richard, 1863–
Gotisch. Allgemeines und hochdeutsche Mundarten.
(In Ergebnisse und Fortschritte der germanistischen Wissen-
schaft im letzten Vierteljahrhundert . . . Pp. 26–36, 75–88.
Leipzig. 1902.)

F8191 — Gothic language. — Germany. Lang. Dial.

NL 0447138   MB

[Loewe, Richard] 1863–
Mundarten. (Allgemeines und hochdeutsche
mundarten) [Charlottenberg, 1902?]
p. 75–88. 23 cm.
Extracted from: Festschrift der Gesellschaft
für deutsche philologie.
Caption title.
Signed: Richard Loewe.
1. German language– Dialects. I. Title.

NL 0447139   CU

Löwe, Richard, 1863–
Präparationen für den Deutschunterricht. .... Von Richard
Löwe. .... Osterwieck/Harz und Leipzig, A. W. Zickfeldt, 1909–.
Vol. 1–. 22ᵐ.   (Added t.-p.: Bücherschatz des Lehrers, XIV. Band.)

NL 0447140   ICJ

Loewe, Richard, 1863–
Die reste der Germanen am Schwarzen meere. Eine ethno-
logische untersuchung von dr. Richard Loewe. Halle, M. Niemeyer, 1896.
xi, ₍1₎, 269, ₍1₎ p., 1 l. 24ᵐ.

1. Germanic tribes. 2. Goths. 3. Ethnology—Black sea.   I. Title.
2—5682
Library of Congress   GN549.T4L7

MiU ViU PU OrU
NL 0447141   DLC NIC MoU CU TxHR NcU DDO NjP CtY

Löwe, Richard, 1901–
Kosmos und aion; ein beitrag zur heilsgeschichtlichen dia-
lektik des urchristlichen weltverständnisses, von lic. Richard
Löwe ... Gütersloh, C. Bertelsmann, 1935.
x, 161 p. 22¼ᵐ. (Added t.-p.: Neutestamentliche forschungen, hrsg.
von Otto Schmitz. 3. reihe: Beiträge zur sprache und geschichte der
urchristlichen frömmigkeit. 5. hft.)

1. Cosmology. 2. Bible. N. T.—Theology. 3. Bible—Theology—N. T.
I. Title.
36—17175
Library of Congress   BS2545.C6L6
₍2₎   225.8113

NL 0447142   DLC CtY

Pamph.
v.602

LOEWE, Richard, 1901–
Ordnung in der Kirche im Lichte des
Titusbriefes. Guetersloh, Der Rufer,
Evangelischer Verlag [1947]
69p. 17.5cm.

NL 0447143   MH-AH OCH

Loewe, Roland.
It might have been you. London,
Hutchinson ₍1949₎

NL 0447144   CaBVa

Loewe, Rudolf.
Ueber encephalitis myoclonica.
Inaug.diss. Rostock,1926.
Bibl.

NL 0447145   ICRL DNLM

Löwe, S.

Deutsch, David, 1810–1873.
Die orgel in der synagoge, eine erörterung von David
Deutsch ... Breslau ₍etc.₎ W. Jacobsohn & co., 1863.

Löwe, S   M
see
Lowe, M   S

Loewe (Saulus) [1841–]. * De emphysemate
pulmonum. 32 pp. 8°. Berolini, G. Lange, 1863.

NL 0447148   DNLM

Loewe, Siegfried, 1884–
Die quantitativen Probleme der Pharmakologie, von S. Loewe
... Mit 42 Abbildungen im Text.
(In Ergebnisse der Physiologie. München, 1928. 26ᵐ. 27. Bd., p. ₍47₎–187.
diagrs.)
Bibliographical foot-notes.

NL 0447149   ICJ OClW

LOEWE, Siegfried, 1889–
Untersuchungen über den Verlauf der pepti-
schen Verdauung des Kaseins und Serumglobulins.
Strassburg 1908. 46 S.

Strassburg, Med.Diss.

NL 0447150   MBCo DNLM ICRL

Loewe, Siegmund, 1885–
Über die erreichbare Genauigkeit der Widerstandsmessung in
Hochfrequenzkreisen... von Siegmund Loewe... Leipzig: J.
A. Barth, 1913. 60 p. incl. diagrs., tables. 8°.
Dissertation, Jena.
Lebenslauf.

1. Electricity.—Resistance: Measure-   ment. 2. Electricity.—Currents (High
tension), 1913.
N. Y. P. L.   September 8, 1922.

NL 0447151   NN ICRL PU MH

Loewe (Sigismund.) [1801–]. * De paralysi.
29 pp., 1 l. 8°. Berolini, formis Doenchianis, 1824.

NL 0447152   DNLM

VOLUME 338

Loewe, Stephan, 1880–
... Die devonischen korallen von Ellesmereland, mit 7 tafeln ... Kristiania, Printed by A. W. Brøgger, 1913.
23, ₍1₎ p. vɪɪ pl. 27½ᶜᵐ. (Report of the Second Norwegian Arctic expedition in the "Fram" 1898–1902. no. 30)

At the expense of the Fridtjof Nansen fund for the advancement of science.
Published by Videnskabs-selskabet i Kristiania (the Society of arts and sciences of Kristiania)

1. Corals, Fossil. 2. Paleontology—Devonian. 3. Paleontology—Arctic regions.
G S 17–378

Library, U. S. Geological   Survey 502(980) qN8 no. 30

NL 0447153   DI-GS CtY CU

Loewe, Stephan, 1880–
... Die devonischen korallen von Ellesmereland, mit 7 tafeln ... Breslau, Druck von L. Freund, 1914.
iv, ₍3₎–23 p., 1 l. vɪɪ pl. 25½ᶜᵐ.
Inaug.-diss.—Breslau.
Lebenslauf.
At head of title: Aus dem Geologischen institut der Universität Breslau.
"Separat-abdruck aus: Report of the Second Norwegian Arctic expedition in the 'Fram' 1898–1902. no. 30."

1. Corals, Fossil. 2. Paleontology—Devonian. 3. Paleontology—Arctic regions.
G S 16–715

Library, U. S. Geological   Survey

NL 0447154   DI-GS CtY ICRL PU

Loewe, Ulrich.
Schadensersatzansprüche bei Körperverletzungen infolge von Eisenbahnunfällen, nach dem Reichshaftpflichtgesetz vom 7. Juni 1871. Inaugural-Dissertation...vorgelegt von Ulrich Löwe... Greifswald: H. Adler, 1913. 76 p. 8°.
Dissertation, Greifswald.
Bibliography, p. 5–6.

1. Railways.—Accidents: Juris-   prudence, Germany.
N. Y. P. L.   November 4, 1914.

NL 0447155   NN ICRL

Löwe, Ulrich, 1909–
... Über eine seltene Erscheinungsform der eitrigen Osteomyelitis (Osteomyelitis acuta diffusa) ... Freiburg im Breisgau, 1934.
Inaug.-Diss. – Freiburg im Breisgau.
Lebenslauf.
"Literaturverzeichnis": p. 29–30.

NL 0447156   CtY MiU

Loewe, Victor, 1871–1933, joint ed.
Die **behördenorganisation** und die allgemeine staatsverwaltung Preussens im 18. jahrhundert ... Berlin, P. Parey, 1894–19

Loewe, Victor, 1871–
Bibliographie der hannoverschen und braunschweigischen geschichte. Von dr. Victor Loewe ... Posen, J. Jolowicz, 1908.
viii, 450 p. 24½ᶜᵐ.
"Biographien von historikern" (index to collective biography, with dates of birth and death) : p. 9–16.

1. Hanover—Hist.—Bibl. 2. Brunswick—Hist.—Bibl.
8–34121

Library of Congress   Z2244.H3L8

NL 0447158   DLC CtY ICU IaU NN ICJ

LOEWE, Victor, 1871–
Bibliographie der schlesischen geschichte.
Breslau, Priebatsch's buchhandlung, 1927.

1. 3°.
Added title-page: Schlesische bibliographie, 1

NL 0447159   MH NN CtY CU

Loewe, Victor, 1871–1933.
... **Bibliographie** zur deutschen geschichte 1888–1927 ...
(*In* Historische vierteljahrschrift. Freiburg i. B. ₍etc.₎ J. C. B. Mohr, 1889–98; Leipzig, B. G. Teubner; ₍etc., etc.₎ 1898–1931. 23ᶜᵐ. ₍1.₎–33. jahrg.)

Loewe, Victor, 1871–1933, ed.
Bio-bibliographien der Wissenschaften
see under title

Loewe, Victor, 1871–1933.
Bücherkunde der deutschen geschichte. Kritischer wegweiser durch die neuere deutsche historische litteratur. Von dr. Victor Loewe ... Berlin, J. Räde, 1903.
4 p. l., 120 p. 22ᶜᵐ.
"Eine von kurzen erläuterungen begleitete auswahl der wichtigeren arbeiten."
Second edition. The 1st edition, "Kritischer wegweiser durch die neuere deutsche historische litteratur," 1900, appeared under pseud. "F. Förster."

1. Germany—Hist.—Bibl. 2. Bibliography—Best books—German history.

Library of Congress   Z2236.L83   4–16380

NL 0447162   DLC CtY NN PU

Z2236
L83
Stack

Loewe, Victor, 1871–1933.
Bücherkunde der deutschen Geschichte; kritischer Wegweiser durch die neuere deutsche historische Literatur. 2., verm. und verb. Aufl. Berlin, J. Räde, 1905.
viii, 131 p. 21ᶜᵐ.

NL 0447163   CSt PU OCl OClW

Loewe, Victor, 1871–1933.
Bücherkunde der deutschen Geschichte. Kritischer Wegweiser durch die neuere deutsche historische Literatur. 3., vermehrte und verb. Aufl. Altenburg, J. Räde, 1910.
viii, 144 p. 22cm.

First ed. "Kritischer Wegweiser durch die neuere deutsche historische Literatur," 1900, appeared under pseud. "F. Förster."

1. Germany – History – Bibliography. 2. Bibliography – Best books – German history. I. Title.

NL 0447165   FU MdBJ OClW ICN

Loewe, Victor, 1871–
Bücherkunde der deutschen geschichte. Kritischer wegweiser durch die neuere deutsche historische literatur. Von dr. Victor Loewe ... 4. wesentlich umgearb. aufl. Altenburg, J. Räde, 1913.
viii, 154 p. 22½ᶜᵐ.
The 1st edition, "Kritischer wegweiser durch die neuere deutsche historische literatur," appeared 1900 under pseud. "F. Förster."

1. Germany—Hist.—Bibl. 2. Bibliography—Best books—German history.
14–17135

Library of Congress   Z2236.L83 1913

NL 0447166   DLC CoU WU MeB OClW

Loewe, Victor, 1871–
Bücherkunde der deutschen Geschichte; kritischer Wegweiser durch die neuere deutsche historische Literatur, von Dr. Victor Loewe... Leipzig: J. Räde, 1919. viii, 148 p. 5. ed., rev. and enl. 8°.

399165A. 1. Germany—Hist.—Bibl.
N. Y. P. L.   January 29, 1929

NL 0447167   NN NjP

Loewe, Victor, 1871–
Das deutsche archivwesen. Seine geschichte und organization. Von dr. Victor Loewe, staatsarchivar in Breslau. Breslau, Priebatsch, 1921.
3 p. l., 130, ₍2₎ p. 24ᶜᵐ.

1. Archives—Germany. ɪ. Title.
25–12954

Library of Congress   CD1221.L6

NL 0447168   DLC CtY

Loewe, Victor, 1871–1933.
... Deutsche geschichte, von dr. Victor Loewe ... Berlin und Leipzig, W. de Gruyter & co., 1931.
87 p. 22½ᶜᵐ. (Bio-bibliographien der wissenschaften, hrsg. von Victor Loewe. Hft. 1)
"Personal-bibliographie der deutschen geschichtswissenschaft."—Vorwort.

1. Germany—Hist. – Bio-bibl. 2. Bibliography – Bibl. – Germany—Hist.
Library of Congress   Z2236.L8   43–40596
                 ₍3₎   016.943

NL 0447169   DLC CSt IaU IEN OCl OClW MH ICJ NN

Loewe, Victor, 1871–
...Ein Diplomat und Gelehrter, Ezechiel Spanheim (1629–1710). Mit Anhang: Aus dem Briefwechsel zwischen Spanheim und Leibniz. Von Dr. Victor Loewe... Berlin: E. Ebering, 1924. xi, 204 p. 8°. (Historische Studien. Heft 160.)
Bibliography, p. ₍ix₎–ixi.

1. Spanheim, Ezechiël, Freiherr von,   1629–1710. 2. Ser.
N. Y. P. L.   March 3, 1925

NL 0447170   NN ICN NSyU MiU MH OU NIC CtY

Loewe, Victor, 1871–   ed.
Jahresberichte der deutschen geschichte ... jahrg. 1–7; 1918–24. Breslau, Priebatsch, 1920–26.

Loewe, Victor, 1871–1933.
Jahresberichte für deutsche geschichte. 1.–   jahrg.; 1925–   Leipzig, K. F. Koehler, 1927–

Loewe, Victor, 1871–1933.
Kritische bücherkunde der deutschen bildung
see under title

VOLUME 338

[Loewe, Victor] 1871–
Kritischer wegweiser durch die neuere deutsche historische litteratur für studierende und freunde der geschichte. Von F. [Förster [pseud.] Berlin, J. Räde, 1900.
64 p. 17^{cm}.
p. 59–64, advertisements.

1. Germany—Hist.—Bibl. I. Title.
1–18168

Library of Congress   Z2236.L82

NL 0447174   DLC OClW NjP CtY CU NN MB

LOEWE, Victor, 1871–
Oberschlesien und der preussische staat.
Teil I. Breslau, Priebatsch, [1930].

Contents: I. 1740–1815. Mit anhang: Dokumente aus der reformepoche, 1807–1815.

NL 0447175   MH

Loewe, Victor, 1871–1933.
Die Organisation und Verwaltung der wallensteinschen Heere. Freiburg i. B., J. C. B. Mohr, 1895.
viii, 99 p. 23 cm.
Bibliography: p. [vii]–viii.

1. Wallenstein, Albrecht Wenzel Eusebius von, Herzog zu Friedland, 1583–1634. 2. Thirty Years' War, 1618–1648. 3. Armies—Organization. I. Title.
D260.L63   55–47996

NL 0447176   DLC ICRL ICJ MH

DD3
A3
bd. 87

Loewe, Victor, 1871–1933, ed.
Prussia. *Treaties, etc., 1713–1740 (Frederick William I)*
Preussens staatsverträge aus der regierungszeit könig Friedrich Wilhelms I. Hrsg. von dr. Victor Loewe ... Veranlasst und unterstützt durch die K. Archiv-verwaltung. Leipzig, S. Hirzel, 1913.

DD3
.A3
bd. 92

Loewe, Victor, 1871–1933, ed.
Prussia. *Treaties, etc., 1688–1713 (Frederick I)*
Preussens staatsverträge aus der regierungszeit könig Friedrichs I. Hrsg. von dr. Victor Loewe ... Veranlasst und unterstützt durch die Archiv-verwaltung. Leipzig, S. Hirzel] 1923.

Loewe, Victor, 1871–1933.
Die Wallenstein-literatur. Dritte–fünfte ergänzung ... Bibliographische studie, von dr. Victor Loewe.
(In Mittheilungen des Vereines für geschichte der Deutschen in Böhmen. Prag, 1896, 1902, 1911, 22 cm, XXXIV. jahrg., p. 277–315; XL. jahrg., p. 514–538; XLIX. jahrg., p. 29–64)
Caption title.
Titles numbered 1559–2524.
1. Wallenstein, Albrecht Wenzel Eusebius von, herzog zu Friedland, 1583–1634.

NL 0447179   CU

Loewe, W. Erinnerungen an den Gen. Ernst von Pfuel. 30 pp. (Deutsch. rundschau, v. 54, 1888, s. 202.)

NL 0447180   MdBP

Loewe (W.) Die Erkenntniss und Behandlung der Taubheit. 2 p. L, 66 pp., 1 pl. 8°. Pasewalk, C. K. Brunne, 1849.

NL 0447181   DNLM

Loewe, Walter.
Mörkt preludium; dikter. [Stockholm] Rabén & Sjögren [1955]
83 p. 19 cm.

I. Title.

A 55–8581 rev

Minnesota. Univ. Libr.
for Library of Congress   [r56b]

NL 0447182   MnU NN

Loewe, Walther, 1888–
Das Gerichtswesen der Grafschaft Steinfurt ... Münster, 1913.
Inaug.-Diss. – Münster.
Lebenslauf.
Bibliography: p. [5]–6.
1. Courts – Steinfurt.

NL 0447183   CtY MH ICRL PU

Löwe (Walther) [1892–]. *Ueber Dauerresultate der Iridektomie bei primärem Glaukom nach dem Material der Leipziger Universitäts-Augenklinik. 6 pp. 8°. Leipzig, E. Lehmann, 1920.

NL 0447184   DNLM

AC
851

Loewe, Walther, 1912–
Entalkylierungen mit hilfe von aluminiumbromid. ... Bonn, 1936.
Inaug. Diss. – Bonn, 1936.
Lebenslauf.

NL 0447185   ICRL CtY

Loewe, Wolfgang.
Eine kritische Betrachtung der Silvio Gesell'schen "Freiland-Freigeld-Theorie," von Dr. Wolfgang Loewe... Würzburg: K. Triltsch, 1935.   vii, 70 p.   22cm.

Issued also as dissertation, Nuremberg, 1934.
"Literaturverzeichnis," p. iv–vi.

872026A. 1. Gesell, Silvio, 1862–   1930. 2. Money, Paper. 3. Interest.
4. Land—Nationalization.
N.Y.P.L.   March 29, 1937

NL 0447186   NN

LÖWE-CALBE, _____
Die gegenwärtige innere und äussere politische lage Preussens; vortrag. Stenographirt und herausgegeben von H. Roller. Berlin, selbstverlag des herausgebers, [1864]

NL 0447187   MH

Loewe-Lyon, Simone, 1909–
... Les gastrorragies des nourrissons; leur signification au cours des toxi-infections ... Paris, 1937.
Thèse – Univ. de Paris.
"Bibliographie": p. [215]–129.

NL 0447188   CtY

Löwe von Eisenach, Johann Jakob
see
Löwe, Johann Jakob, 1628–1703.

Löwegren, Anders Gunnar Hilding
see Löwegren, Gunnar, 1881–

DL
991
.T85
L8

Löwegren, Georg
A trip to Trollhättan, in a series of letters. Götheborg, Published [and printed] by Geo. Löwegren, 1813.
3 p.l., 44, [4] p. front. (map) 11 x 8½ cm.
Engraved t.-p., with vignette (portrait of Christopher Polhem)
"Description of the map": [4] p. at end.

1. Trollhättan, Sweden—Descr. I. Title.

NL 0447191   MiU

Löwegren, Gunnar, 1881–1958.
Danton; skådespel i fem akter. Malmö, Aktiebolaget Framtidens bokförlag, [1922]

NL 0447192   MH

Löwegren, Gunnar, 1881–
The forest and forest industries of Norrland, by Gunnar Löwegren ... [Stockholm, I. Hæggströms boktryckeri a. b., 1945]
63, [1] p. 23^{cm}.
Map on p. [4] of cover.
"Supplement to Svenska handelsbanken's Index, September, 1945."

1. Forests and forestry—Sweden-Norrland. 2. Wood-using industries—Norrland, Sweden. I. Svenska handelsbanken. Index. Supplement.
II. Title.
[Full name: Anders Gunnar Hilding Löwegren]
46–2928

Library of Congress   SD212.N8L6
[3]   634.909488

NL 0447193   DLC NNC

Löwegren, Gunnar, 1881–
... Franska stämningar; reseskildringar från krigsländerna anno 1915. Malmö, Framtiden [1915]
181, [2] p. 19^{cm}.

1. European war, 1914– —France. I. Title.
[Full name: Anders Gunnar Hilding Löwegren]
21–1890

Library of Congress   D548.L7

NL 0447194   DLC

Löwegren, Gunnar, 1881–
Kampen kring staten; socialpolitiska och ekonomiska essayer, av Gunnar Löwegren. Lund: C. W. K. Gleerups förlag [1929]. 380 p. 8°.

510729A. 1. Economics—Essays   and misc. 2. Sociology—Essays and misc. I. Title.
N.Y.P.L.   January 30, 1931

NL 0447195   NN DS

VOLUME 338

Löwegren, Gunnar, 1881–
Norrlands skogar och skogsindustri. ₍Stockholm, 1945₎
63 p. 24 cm.
"Supplement til Svenska handelsbankens Index, september 1945."

1. Forests and forestry—Sweden—Norrland. 2. Wood-using industries—Norrland. I. Title.
Full name: Anders Gunnar Hilding Löwegren.

SD212.N6L63 54-39232 ‡

NL 0447196 DLC

DC385 Löwegren, Gunnar, 1881–
L827 ..Poincaré och tredje republiken... Stockholm, Bokförlaget Natur och kultur ₍1936₎
251 p. front.(port.) plates. 21½ᶜᵐ.

1.Poincaré, Raymond, pres. France, 1860–1934. 2. France - Politics and government - 1870– 3. France - Foreign relations - 1870–

NL 0447197 CSt-H NN MnU NcD

LÖWEGREN, GUNNAR, 1881–
Studier om Michelangelo, av Gunnar Löwegren. Lund: C.W.K. Gleerup₍, 1932₎. 232 p. front. 20¼cm.

654743A. 1. Buonarroti, Michel Angelo, 1475–1564.

NL 0447198 NN

HC375 Löwegren, Gunnar, 1881–
.C48
Chambre de commerce suédoise en France.
La Suède, aperçu économique et touristique; edité par la Chambre de commerce suédoise en France. ₍Angers, Imprimerie centrale, 193–₎

Löwegren, Gunnar, 1881–
Sveriges sjöfart och skeppsbyggeri genom tiderna. Stockholm, KF:s bokförlag ₍1953₎
124 p. illus., ports. 22 cm.

1. Merchant marine—Sweden—Hist. 2. Shipping—Sweden—Hist. 3. Ship-building—Sweden—Hist. I. Title.
Full name: Anders Gunnar Hilding Löwegren.

VK89.L6 A 54-4922
Minnesota. Univ. Libr.
for Library of Congress ₍1₎†

NL 0447200 MnU DLC WaU NN

Löwegren, Gunnar, 1881–
Swedish iron and steel, a historical survey. English version by Nils G. Sahlin. Stockholm, Svenska handelsbanken, 1948.
122, ₍1₎ p. maps. 24 cm.
"Sources": p. 122–₍123₎

1. Iron industry and trade—Sweden. 2. Steel industry and trade—Sweden. I. Sahlin, Nils Gösta, 1900– tr.
Full name: Anders Gunnar Hilding Löwegren.

TN704.S9L6 669.1 48-4032 *

NL 0447201 PPT ViU CtY NNC ICU LU NNU-W TxU OKentU OO ICJ
DLC NNUN PPAmSwM OrU OCU OkU ViU NN CU

Löwegren, Gunnar, 1881–
Turgot, statsman, ekonom, förkämpe för ett fritt näringsliv. Anne Robert Jacques Turgot, levnadsteckning av Gunnar Löwegren. Skrifter av Turgot, i översättning av Gunnar Löwegren: Äreminne över Gournay, Reflexioner om välståndets tillkomst och utveckling. Stockholm, Natur och kultur ₍1950₎
218 p. port. 22 cm.

1. Turgot, Anne Robert Jacques, baron de l'Aulne, 1727–1781. 2. Vincent de Gournay, Jacques Claude Marie, 1712–1759. 3. Finance, Public—France. I. Turgot, Anne Robert Jacques, baron de l'Aulne, 1727–1781.
Full name: Anders Gunnar Hilding Löwegren.

HB105.T8L6 A 51-2353
New York. Public Libr.
for Library of Congress ₍1₎†

NL 0447202 NN DLC

Löwegren, Gunnar, 1881–
...Vad jag sett och hört i Amerika; gå vi emot en ny civilisation en "skyscraper-civilisation?" Lund: C. W. K. Gleerup₍, 1931₎. 255 p. illus. 20½cm.

603807A. 1. United States— Descr. and trav., 1910–
N. Y. P. L. September 19, 1933

NL 0447203 NN

Löwegren, Gunnar, 1881–1453.
Världsbanken. International Bank for Reconstruction and Development. ₍Stockholm₎ Exportföreningens förlag ₍1953₎
53 p. tables. 20cm. (Internationella ekonomiska fragor. 3)

1. International Bank for Reconstruction and Development. (Series)

NL 0447204 MnU

Löwegren, Gunnar H 1918–
Storbritannien och dollarkrisen. Stockholm, 1949.
82 p. 19 cm. (Världspolitikens dagsfrågor, 1949, nr. 8)

1. Currency question. (Series)

HG255.L6 50-20666

NL 0447205 DLC MH NN

Löwegren, Michaël Kolmodin, 1836–1923.
Om myopi ... Lund, Berlingska boktryckeriet, 1866.
1 p. l., 86 p., 1 l. 28 x 22ᶜᵐ.
Akademisk afhandling—Lund.

1. Myopia.

Library of Congress RE938.L82 7-14331†

NL 0447206 DLC DNLM

WW LÖWEGREN, Michaël Kolmodin, 1836–1923.
L827oe Om ögonsjukdomarne och deras
1891 behandling till tjenst för praktiserande läkare och studerande. Stockholm, Beijer, 1891.
vi, 544 p. illus.

NL 0447207 DNLM

WW LÖWEGREN, Michaël Kolmodin, 1836–1923.
L827oe Om ögonsjukdomarne och deras
1900 behandling till tjenst för praktiserande läkare och studerande. 2. öfversedda uppl. Stockholm, Beijer ₍1900₎
vi, 600 p. illus.

NL 0447208 DNLM

WW LÖWEGREN, Michaël Kolmodin, 1836–1923.
100 Om Øjensygdommene og deres
L826o Behandling, til Brug for praktiserende
1923 Laeger og Studenter. 3. fuldstaendigt omarb. Opl., udg. af F. Ask ₍et al.₎ Red. af A. Dalén og F. Ask. Stockholm, Bonnier ₍1923₎
xxiv, 720 p. illus.
At head of title: Nordisk Laerebog i Ophthalmologi.

Text in Danish or Swedish.
4th ed. edited by F. G. Ask has title: Nordisk lärobok i oftalmiatrik.
I. Ask, Fritz Gustaf, 1876–1934 II. Dalén, Albin, 1866– ed. Title: Nordisk Laerebog i Ophthalmologi

NL 0447210 DNLM MnU

Löwegren, Michaël Kolmodin, 1836–1923.
Om refractionstillstånden hos ögat och bestämmandet af glasögen, af M. K. Löwegren, ... Lund, Trykt på C. W. K. Gleerups förlag, 1870.
[6], 160, [s] p. illus., diagrs. 20⅛ᶜᵐ.

NL 0447211 ICJ ICRL DNLM

Loewegren, Petter, 1783–1871.
En ludensisk borgarsläkt; en skildring av släkten Löwegren
see under Loewegren, Yngve.

Loewegren, Petter, 1783–1871.
Lundensisk vardag för 150 år sedan, ur Petter Löwegrens minnesböcker. Kommentar och personförteckning av Yngve Löwegren. [Lund, Skånska centraltryckeriet, 1951]
103 p. illus. (Det gamla Lund, 1951: Föreningen det gamla Lund. Årsskrift, 33)

NL 0447213 MH

Loewegren, Yngve.
Lundabiskoparnas residens efter reformationen. [Lund, Skånska centraltryckeriet, 1953]
120 p. illus. (Det gamla Lund, 1953; Föreningen det gamla Lund. Årsskrift, 35)

NL 0447214 MH

Loewegren, Yngve.
En lundensisk borgarsläkt; en skildring av släkten Löwegren, byggd på akademie smeden Petter Löwegrens och professor Michael Kolmodin Löwegrens anteckningar. Utarbetad av Yngve Löwegren. [Lund, Skånska centraltryckeriet, 1945]
104 p. illus. (Det gamla Lund, 1945; Föreningen Det gamla Lund. Årsskrift, 27)

NL 0447215 MH

Loewegren, Yngve.
Lundensisk vardag för 150 år sedan
see under Loewegren, Petter, 1783–1871.

VOLUME 338

Löwegren, Yngve.
Naturaliekabinett i Sverige under 1700-talet; ett bidrag till zoologiens historia. ₍Uppsala, Almqvist & Wiksells boktr., i distribution₎ 1952.

407 p. illus., ports., plans. 26 cm. (Lychnos-bibliotek, 13)

Akademisk avhandling—Lund.
Extra t. p., with thesis statement, inserted.
"Samlare och samlingar": p. ₍335₎-370.
Bibliography: p. ₍371₎-397.

1. Natural history museums—Sweden. 2. Zoology—Hist.
I. Title.

QH70.L6   56-34399

NL 0447217   DLC CLSU WU PSt NcU MiD MH NN CtY CU

Löwegren, Yngve.
Våra ryggradsdjur; hur man preparerar dem. Illustrerad fickbok med beskrivning av hur man konserverar och monterar däggdjur, fåglar, kräldjur, groddjur och fiskar. Stockholm, A. Bonnier ₍1946₎

94 p. illus. 18 cm. (Zoologisk teknik, del 1)

1. Taxidermy.   I. Title.   II. Series.
QL63.L7   47-8074*

NL 0447218   DLC

Löwegren, Yngve.
Våra ryggradslösa djur; hur man preparerar dem. Illustrerad fickbok med beskrivning av hur man konserverar och monterar ryggradslösa djur. Stockholm, Bonnier ₍1955₎

73 p. illus. 17 cm. (*His* Zoologisk teknik, del 2)

1. Invertebrates—Collection and preservation.   I. Title.
                                                   A 55-10444
Purdue Univ. Library
for Library of Congress   ₍1₎

NL 0447219   InLP

Loewel, Adelaide L.
Alphabet of life; original epigrams, by Adelaide L. Loewel, interspersed with words of well known philosophers. New York, The author, 1926.

2 p. l., 7-95 p. 17¼ᶜᵐ.

I. Title.

Library of Congress   PN6281.L6   26-9329

NL 0447220   DLC NcD

Lœwel, André.

Flaubert, Gustave, 1821-1880.
Madame Bovary; mœurs de province, par Gustave Flaubert. Paris, Éditions de Cluny ₍1936₎

Lœwel, André.

Flaubert, Gustave, 1821-1880.
Trois contes, par Gustave Flaubert. Paris, Éditions de Cluny ₍1937₎

Loewel, C.
Der Puppenspieler. Weihnachtsspiel in einem Akt. München: V. Höfling ₍1912₎ 8 p. 12°. (Höflings Vereins- u. Dilettanten-Theater. Nr. 57.)

Title from cover.

1. Christmas.—Drama. 2. Title.
N. Y. P. L.   March 14, 1913.

NL 0447223   NN

Loewel, Christian Gottlieb, respondent.
... Theses ivris controversi occasione titvli Pandectarvm L. II. Tit. XIII. de edendo ... see under Krause, Georg Friedrich, 1718-1785, praeses.

SB
953   **Loewel, Ernst Ludwig.**
L82   Die Obstbaumspritzung unter Berücksichtigung der Verbesserung des Gesundheitszustandes des Baumes und der Qualität der Früchte. Stuttgart, E. Ulmer ₍ca. 1935₎
          44 p. illus. 21 cm. (Grundlagen und Fortschritte im Garten- und Weinbau. Heft 4)

          1. Spraying.   2. Fruit - Diseases and
pests. I. Ti   tle. II. Series.

NL 0447225   NIC

Loewel, Ernst Ludwig.
... Die obstbaumspritzung, von dr. E. L. Loewel ... 7. neubearb. aufl. Mit 30 abbildungen. Stuttgart, E. Ulmer, 1945.

63 p. illus. 21 cm. (Grundlagen und fortschritte im garten- und weinbau, herausgeber: professor dr. C. F. Rudloff ... Hft. 4)
"Bücher über schädlinge und schädlingsbekämpfung für den obst züchter": p. 63.

1. Spraying. 2. Fruit—Diseases and pests.   I. Title.
SB953.L815 1945   A F 47-5389
Illinos. Univ. Library
for Library of Congress   ₍2₎†

NL 0447226   IU DNAL DLC NbU

Lœwel (Julius Robert). ⁴ Einiges über penetrirende Lungenschusswunden. 23 pp. 8°. *Leipzig, A. T. Engelhardt,* 1870.

NL 0447227   DNLM

Loewel, Pierre, ₍1890-
... Le canal de Panama; étude historique, politique et financière ... Paris, A. Rousseau, 1913.

156 p., 1 l. 25ᶜᵐ.

Thèse—Univ. de Paris.
"Bibliographie": p. ₍153₎-156.

1. Panama canal.
                                               15-22675
Library of Congress   TC774.L75

NL 0447228   DLC CtY ICJ

Loewel, Pierre, 1890-
... Inventaire 1931. Paris, Valois, 1931.
251 p., 2 l. 20ᶜᵐ. (Bibliothèque syndicaliste, XXII)
"L'édition originale de cet ouvrage comprend: 7 exemplaires sur pur fil Lafuma, de I à VII ... 2,700 exemplaires sur vélin Navarre numérotés de 1 à 2,700 ... No. 01,940."
"Acheve d'imprimer le 4 février 1931 ... par l'imprimerie Floch a Mayenne."

1. France—Pol. & govt.—1914-   2. Europe—Politics—1914-   I. Title. II. Ser.

NL 0447229   ViU NN

Loewel, Pierre, 1890-
... Tableau du Palais ... ₍Paris₎ Gallimard ₍1929₎
2 p. l., ₍7₎-256 p. 19ᶜᵐ. (Les documents bleus. ₍2. sér.₎ Notre temps, no. 13)

1. Paris. Palais de justice. 2. Law—Anecdotes, facetiae, satire, etc. 3. Lawyers—France.   I. Title.
                                               30-7865

NL 0447230   DLC

Loewel, Pierre, 1890-
Tableau du palais. 8 me éd. [Paris, cop., 1929]
12°.

NL 0447231   MH-L

Lœwel, Robert.
... À la recherche de Torquemada; voyage dans les ombres sanglantes de la Péninsule. Paris, Denoël ₍1938₎
3 p. l., ₍9₎-241 p., 1 l. 18¾ᵐ.
Colored illustration on cover.

1. Spain—Descr. & trav. 2. Inquisition. Spain. 3. Portugal—Descr. & trav. 4. National socialism. I. Title.
                                               A 41-2781
New York. Public library
for Library of Congress   ₍2₎

NL 0447232   NN PPRF MH

Lœwel, Robert.
... Condamnés; secrets de prisons. Paris, Éditions des portiques ₍1931₎
2 p. l., ₍7₎-246 p., 3 l. 18¾ᵐ.

1. Prisons—France. 2. Crime and criminals—France.   I. Title. II. Title: Secrets de prisons.
Library of Congress   HV9664.L6   32-9127
Copyright A—Foreign   11283
                           ₍2₎   365.944

NL 0447233   DLC

Loewen, Abram J.
Die Flucht über den Amur
see under Friesen, Abram.

Loewen, Carl Heinz.
Über die diagnose und die therapie der mundschleimhauttuberkulose. Inaugural dissertation, Universität Köln, 1935.

NL 0447235   PPWI CtY

Loewen, Esko, ed.
Mennonite Community sourcebook. Section editors, Ralph Hernley, J.A. Hostetler, Delbert Gratz, Ernest Lehman, Daniel Neufeld, Dwight Weldy, Leland B. Sateren, David Kope, William Ramseyer, Howard Kauffman, Martin Schrag; art ed. Charles Suter; business manager, Wesley Prieb; sponsors, Civilian Public Service Section of the Mennonite Central Committee, Akron, Penna. [1946]

145p. 19 1/2cm.

NL 0447236   ViHarEM

Loewen, Franz Moritz von, respondent.
... De ivre wildfangiatvs serenissimo electori palatino proprio ... see under Hildebrand, Heinrich, 1668-1729, praeses.

VOLUME 338

DS
135
E8L6.3   Loewen, Gotthold Moses, 1859–1921.
    Das Ostjudentum. Ein Abriss seines
    Werdens. Gütersloh, C. Bertelsmann,
    1918.
     23 p.   20 cm.   (Christentum und
    Judentum. Ser. 4, Heft 1)

     1. Jews in Eastern Europe.   I. Title
    II. Series

NL 0447238   OCH

Loewen, Heinrich, 1886–
    ...Einfuehrung in die Chemie, von Dr. Heinrich Loewen...
München: C. W. Kreidel, 1927. 131 p. incl. tables.   diagrs.,
illus. 12°.   (Technische Fachbücher. [Heft] 6.)

   "Aufgaben nebst Lösungen," p. 125–129.

462570A. 1. Chemistry—Textbooks,   1927. 2. Ser.
N. Y. P. L.   March 5, 1930

NL 0447239   NN

Loewen, Heinrich, 1886–
    Einführung in die organische chemie, von dr. H. Loewen ...
1. bis 5. tausend, mit 25 abbildungen. Berlin, J. Springer,
1930.
    vii, 215, [1] p. illus., diagrs. 19ᵐ.   (Added t.-p.: Verständliche wis-
senschaft. 11. bd.)

    1. Chemistry, Organic.
    Library of Congress   QD253.L7   31–17144
    Copyright A—Foreign   11328
                    [2]   547

NL 0447240   DLC CU

             1882–
Loewen, Heinrich, Ueber die Konstitution des Thebenins.
(Berlin 1909: Blanke.)   29 S. 8°
Berlin, Phil. Diss. v. 15. Dez. 1909, Ref. E. Fischer
[Geb. 14. Juni 86 Berlin; Wohnort: Berlin; Staatsangeh.: Preußen; Vorbildung:
Askan. Gymn. Berlin Reife M. 04; Studium: Berlin 10 S.; Rig. 18. Nov. 09.]
                          [U 10. 209

NL 0447241   ICRL CtY PU

Loewen, Jane.
    Millinery, by Jane Loewen ... New York, The Mac-
millan company, 1925.
    viii p., 1 l., 213 p. incl. illus., plates. 21ᵐ.

    1. Millinery.

    Library of Congress   TT655.L6   25–21725

            ViU ICJ MB
NL 0447242   DLC NN Or IdU-SB OrP OCl OClND OClW

Löwen, Johann Christian.

    Wahre Abbildungen und . . . Beschreibung/
der Bischof . Residenz und Gartens, / . . . zu
Eutien/ Mit dem Prospect dieser Stadt, und
umliegenden Gegenden, / Verfertigt und . . .
gezeichnet/ von/ Johann Christian Löwen . . .
gestochen zu Augspurg durch Martin Engelbrecht./

    Engr. t. p., unsigned, n.d., w. German &
French captions (except 2nd engr. w. German
caption only).

    Engr. # 1–8 & 12–14 signed: "J.C. Löwen inv. et
del."(left); engr. # 9, 10 & 11 unsigned; engr. # 15
signed:"J.C. Löwen inv. et del."(left) & "Rolfssen
sculps."(right).

    Contents: engr. pictures & plans of the Eutien
Episcopal Palace & Gardens, designed by Löwen,
engr. by Engelbrecht & (1 engr.) by Rolfssen.
    Binding: paper-covered board w. leather spine
& corners (worn). Size 18" × 23".

NL 0447244   DDO

Löwen, Johann Friedrich, 1727–1771.
    Drama per musica. Das Rätzel ...
    see under   Hertel, Johann Wilhelm,
    1727–1789.

Löwen, Johann Friedrich, 1727–1771.
    ... Johann Friedrich Löwens Geschichte des deutschen thea-
ters (1766) und flugschriften über das Hamburger nationaltheater (1766 und 1767) im neudruck mit einleitung und erläuterungen herausgegeben von Heinrich Stümcke. Berlin, E.
Frensdorff [1905]
    xxxx, 104 p. 21½ᵐ.   (Neudrucke literarhistorischer seltenheiten, hrsg.
von Fedor von Zobeltitz. no. 8)
    CONTENTS.—Geschichte des deutschen theaters.—Auszug aus einem
briefe eines freundes. — Vorläufige nachricht von der auf ostern 1767
vorzunehmenden veränderung des hamburgischen theaters. Hamburg,
1766.—Anrede an die sämtlichen mitglieder des hamburgischen theaters
bey der übernehmung des directorii. Hamburg, 1767.
    1. Theater—Germany—Hist. 2. Theater—Hamburg.   I. Stümcke,
Heinrich, 1872–1923, ed.
                                 40–30673
    Library of Congress   PN2641.L6

    CLSU MH PBm
NL 0447246   DLC CaBVaU IU GU RNJ NcU CU OCU OClW

PT2424   [Löwen, Johann Friedrich] 1727–1771.
L64G6   Götter- und Heldengespräche. / Hamburg,
1758   G. C. Grund und A. H. Holle, 1758.
     127 p.

NL 0447247   CU

Löwen, Johann Friedrich, 1727–1771.
    Poetische Nebenstunden in Hamburg, mit
einer Vorrede des Herrn. Prof. Johann David
Michaelis, von dem Geschmack der Morgen-
Länderischen Dichtkunst.   Leipzig, Bey
Johann Wendler, 1752.
    xlvii, [1], 174, [2] p.   22 cm.
    Title vignette.
    I. Michaelis, Johann David, 1717–1791.
    II. Title.

NL 0447248   MdBJ

     Loewen, Johann Friedrich, 1727–1771.
Zg18   ... Poetische Werke ... Hamburg und
L821   Leipzig, bey Grunds Witwe und Holle, 1760.
760p   2v.   20cm.
    Title vignettes, engraved.

NL 0447249   CtY

              1727–1771.
[Löwen, Johann Friedrich], [Romanzen mit Melodien, und
    einem Schreiben an den Verfasser derselben. / [1. Aufl.]
    Hamburg und Leipzig 1762. 16½ cm.
    G. IV. [205. 10. 15]. Erste sehr seltene Ausgabe. W. o.V.

NL 0447250   CU IU

3469   Löwen, Johann Friedrich, 1727–1771.
.96
.378   Romanzen nebst andern comischen
    gedichten. Neue verb. aufl. Bjel, In
    der Heilmannischen buchhandlung, 1753.
    72 p. 16 ᵐ.

NL 0447251   NjP

PT2424   Löwen, Johann Friedrich, 1727–1771.
L64R6   Romanzen. Neue verb. Aufl. Nebst andern
1771   Comischen Gedichten. Leipzig, Weidmanns
    Erben und Reich, 1771.
    142 p.

NL 0447252   CU MH

Zg18   Löwen, Johann Friedrich, 1727–1771.
L821   Romanzen. Nebst einigen andern Poesien ...
769r   Hamburg und Bremen, Bey J.H.Cramer, 1769.
    112p.   16½cm.

NL 0447253   CtY IU

PT2424   Löwen, Johann Friedrich, 1727–1771.
L6483   Satyrische Versuche. Hamburg, G.C.
1760   Grunds Wittwe und A.H. Holle, 1760.
    184 p.

NL 0447254   CU CLSU

Löwen, Johann Friedrich, 1727–1771.
    ... Schriften. Hamburg, Bock, 1765–66.
    4v. in 2.

    Contents: 1.–2.theil. Poetische schriften. -
3.theil. Die Walpurgis nacht. Marquise. Romanzen, Scherzhafte briefe. - 4.theil. Geschichte
des deutschen theaters. Hermes und Nestan. Das
mistrauen aus zärtlichkeit. Ich habe es beschlossen. Der liebhaber von ohngefähr. Das
räthsel.

NL 0447255   OClW MdBJ NjP CtY IU MH

8339375   [Löwen, Johann, Friedrich] 1727–1771.
Ov   [Zärtliche Lieder und anakreontische Scherze.
    Hamburg, In der Hertelischen Handlung, 1751.
    78p. 19cm.

    Bound with: Schrenkendorf, Gottfried. Versuch
in moralischen Gedichten. Dressden, 1752.

NL 0447256   IU

Loewen, Leo A., respondent.
    ... De abusibus qui in Germania nostra in
collegiis vigent opificum
    see under   Hiller, Christian Heinrich,
    1696–1770, praeses.

Löwen [place]
see Louvain.

Löwenadler, Carl Oscar, respondent.

Fries, Elias Magnus, 1794–1878, *praeses.*
    Botaniskt-antiqvariske excursioner ... [pt.] 1–4. Upsala,
K. Akad. boktryck., 1836.

[Löwenadler, Henrik] 1860–
    Slägterna Kjellman och von Löwenadler
samt deras afkomlingar. [Göteborg,
H. Brusewitz, 1912]

    119 p.   illus. (ports.) col. coat of
arms.   29cm.

    "Trykt i 150 numrerade exemplar ...
No.114."
    1. Kjellman family. 2. Löwenadler
family.

NL 0447260   MnU

VOLUME 338

Löwenbach, Hans, 1905–
... Untersuchungen über Erythrozytenzahl
und Haemoglobinwert bei Wöchnerinnen ...
Hamburg, 1930.
Inaug.-Diss. - Hamburg.
Lebenslauf.
"Literatur": p. 20.

NL 0447261   CtY MiU

₍Löwenbach, Hermann₎
Ein Mädel bei den Rhön-Indianern ₍von₎ Käte Wagner
₍pseud.₎ Buchschmuck von Willy Goertzen. Berlin, F.
Schneider ₍1937₎
63 p. illus. 19 cm.

I. Title.
PZ36.L58   49–36329*

NL 0447262   DLC

Löwenbach, Jan, 1880–
Autorskoprávní abeceda ... ₍Napsal₎
... Jan Löwenbach. Praha, Orbis, 1948.
115, ₍1₎ p. 18½cm. (Československé
právo. Řada II, sv. 4)
Bibliography: p. 109–110.

NL 0447263   MH-L NNC-L CtY-L

Löwenbach, Jan, 1880–
Českoruské vztahy hudební. ₍Vyd. 1.₎ Praha, Hudební
matice Umělecké besedy, 1947.
47 p. illus. 21 cm. (Malá knihovna Tempa, sv. 8)
Bibliographical footnotes.

1. Music—Czechoslovak Republic—Hist. & crit. 2. Music—Russia—
Hist. & crit. I. Title.
ML247.L59   53–20303 rev

NL 0447264   DLC

Löwenbach, Jan, 1880–
Czechoslovak music; the voice of a people. New York,
N. Y., Czechoslovak Information Service ₍1943₎
₍14₎ p. 22 cm.

1. Music, Czech—Hist. & crit. 2. Musicians, Czech. I. Czechoslovak Republic. Informační služba, New York. II. Title.
ML247.L6   780.9437   44–8509 rev*

NL 0447265   DLC FTaSU

Löwenbach, Jan, 1880–
Hudba v Americe. ₍Vyd. 1.₎ Praha, Hudební matice
Umělecké besedy, 1948.
120 p. ports. 21 cm. (Malá knihovna Tempa, sv. 4)

1. Music—U. S.—Hist. & crit. 2. Music, Czech—Hist. & crit.
3. Musicians, Czech. I. Title.
ML200.L6   53–31733 rev

NL 0447266   DLC ICN MB

ML
410
.J4L6   Löwenbach, Jan, 1880–
Jaroslav Ježek. Napsal Jan Lowenbach.
New York, 1942.
21 p. 23 cm.
"Zvláštní otisk ze sborníku 'Jaroslav
Ježek.'"

1. Ježek, Jaroslav, 1906–1942.

NL 0447267   MnHi

Löwenbach, Jan, 1880 –
Novela k zákonu o právu autorském
see under   Czechoslovak republic. Laws,
statutes, etc.

Löwenbach, Jan, 1880–
Právo autorské; zákon za dne 24. listopadu 1926, číslo
218. Sb. z. a nař. s výkladem, judikaturou i prováděcím
nařízením a hlavní normy mezinárodního a zahraničního
práva původského. Sepsal a uspořádal Jan Löwenbach.
Praha, Nákl. Československého kompasu, 1927.
viii, 506 p. 18 cm. (Komentované zákony československé repub-
liky, sv. 22)

1. Copyright—Czechoslovak Republic.   I. Czechoslovak Republic.
Laws, statutes, etc. II. Title.
                                      68–53404

NL 0447269   DLC IU MiU-L

AW
2
G476   Löwenbach, Jan, 1880–
Spuk im Schloss, komische Oper in 6
Bildern (2 Teilen) Text nach einem Motiv
Oscar Wildes von Jan Löwenbach-Budin, über-
setzt von Paul Eisner, Bearbeitung von
Max Brod. Wien-Leipzig, Universal-Edition
.A. G., 1932.
45p. 19½cm.
Micro-opaque.

NL 0447270   CaBVaU

Löwenbach, Josef, tr.

Hába, Alois, 1893–
Von der psychologie der musikalischen gestaltung, gesetz-
mässigkeit der tonbewegung und grundlagen eines neuen
musikstils, von Alois Hába; ins deutsche übertragen von Josef
Löwenbach. Wien, New York, Universal-edition a. g. ₍1925₎

DT
12
.L6   Loewenbach, Lothaire.
Promenade autour de l'Afrique, 1907: Syrie,
Palestine, Egypte, Soudan, Transvaal, Rhodésie,
Le Cap, Sainte-Hélène.   Paris, E. Flammarion,
1908.
446 p. illus. 24 cm.
Author's inscription in manuscript on p. ₍I₎

1. Africa - Descr. & trav. 2. Near East -
Descr. & trav.   I. Title

NL 0447272   WU CLU IEN CU MH MBU

---

ar W
51463   Loewenbach, Lothaire.
Promenade autour du globe; journal de
voyage. Paris, A. Charles, 1903.
308 p. illus. 23cm.

1. Voyages around the world. I. Title.

NL 0447273   NIC MH

LOEWENBACH, LUDWIG.

La bella. Virginia-Valzer.   1893. 8 p. 36cm.

Score: orchestra.
Autograph manuscript, signed.
Expressly composed for and dedicated to Virginia Zucchi who later
presented it to Cia Fornaroli.

1. Waltzes (Orchestra).   2. Zucchi, Virginia.
3. Autographs (Music)--   Loewenbach, L. ₍I. Title.

NL 0447274   NN

₍Loewenbach, Oscar₎
'Business methods you should know. ₍Milwaukee, B.
Loewenbach & sons co., °1914₎
cover-title, ₍31₎ p. incl. mounted forms. 23ᶜᵐ.

1. Office supplies—Catalogs.   I. Title.

Library of Congress   HF5688.L5   14–13477

NL 0447275   DLC

Löwenbach-Budin, Jan
see   Löwenbach, Jan, 1880–

Löwenberg, Adolf, 1869–
Benekes stellung zur Kantschen moralphilosophie ...
Berlin, H. S. Hermann, 1902.
104 p. 23 cm.
Inaug.-dis.—Zürich.
Lebenslauf.
                                      3—13776

NL 0447277   DLC IEN CU-S MH

Löwenberg (Alexander) [1864–]. *Beitrag
zur Behandlung der eitrigen Mittelohr-Entzün-
dung mit Berücksichtigung der Bacteriologie
des Ohreiters. 47 pp., 2 l. 8°. *Königsberg,
M. Liedtke, 1891.

NL 0447278   DNLM

Loewenberg, Alfred, ed.
Allgemeine musikgeschichte
see under   Naumann, Emil, 1827–1888.

Loewenberg, Alfred.
Annals of opera, 1597–1940, compiled from the original
sources by Alfred Loewenberg; with an introduction by Ed-
ward J. Dent. Cambridge ₍Eng.₎ W. Heffer & sons limited
₍1943₎
xxiii, ₍1₎, 879 p. 25¼ᶜᵐ.
"First published January, 1943."
Chronological arrangement.
"Index of operas": p. 756–785. "Index of composers": p. 786–827.
"Index of librettists": p. 828–851.

1. Opera—Dictionaries.   I. Title.
                                      43–7390
Library of Congress   ML102.O6L6
                           ₍3₎   782.03

OrP OrPR WaTC TxU WaS OrU
OOxM CtY MB NcU ViU MB MeB NcD CoU CaBVa CaBVaU KMK
NL 0447280   DLC PBm PP PSt PHC NN ICN OC1 OO OU OCH

Loewenberg, Alfred.
Annals of opera, 1597–1940, compiled from the original
sources; with an introd. by Edward J. Dent. 2d ed., rev.
and corr. ₍by Frank Walker₎ Genève, Societas Bibliographica ₍1955₎
2 v. (xxv p., 1756 columns) 27 cm.
CONTENTS.—v. 1. Text.—v. 2. Indexes.

1. Operas—Dictionaries.   I. Walker, Frank, 1907– ed.
II. Title.
102.O6L3 1955   782.03   A 56—1141
Temple Univ. Library
for Library of Congress   ₍a60f1₎†

AAP KyU MtBuM FMU MH WaTC WaWW WaSpG
WaT MiU MB RPB ICN TU NN DLC OC1W OO OU MoU CoU FTaSU
MtBC IdU IdPI OrU-M OrSaW NBuC OrP OrPR WaE WaPS WaS
ICU NcD FU OrU MsSM MU Or OrStbM CaBVaU IdB Wa OrCS
NL 0447281   PPT LNHT ScU MH NBC TxU IaU IU MoU ViU CU

VOLUME 338

Loewenberg, Alfred.
Early Dutch librettos and plays with music in the British Museum. London, Aslib, 1947.
30 p. 25 cm.
"Reprinted from the Journal of documentation, vol. II, no. 4 (March 1947)"

1. Librettos—Bibl.   I. British Museum.   II. Title.

ML136.L8B85   781.9731   50-15822

NL 0447282   DLC ICN WaS MiD MH MB NN ICU

Loewenberg, Alfred.

Johns Hopkins university. *Library.*
Fifty years of German drama; a bibliography of modern German drama, 1880-1930, based on the Loewenberg collection in the Johns Hopkins university library. Baltimore, The Johns Hopkins press, 1941.

ML1733
.L6P2   Loewenberg, Alfred.
Paisiello's and Rossini's 'Barbiere di Siviglia', by Alfred Loewenberg ... London, 1939₃
₍12₎ p.   25cm.

"Reprinted from 'Music and letters', vol.XX, no.2. April 1939."
"The following records - somewhat enlarged for the purpose of separate publication and furnished with additional details

and references - are extracts from a book by Dr. Loewenberg entitled 'Annals of opera, 1597-1938: compiled from the original sources' ... which is to be published next winter."--p.₍2₎ footnote.

1. Paisiello, Giovanni, 1741-1816. Il barbiere di Siviglia. 2. Rossini, Gioacchino Antonio,   1792-1868. Il barbiere di Sivig-   lia.₄

NL 0447285   DLC

Loewenberg, Alfred.
The theatre of the British Isles, excluding London; a bibliography. London, Printed for the Society for Theatre Research, 1950 (for 1949).
ix, 75 p. 23 cm. (Society for Theatre Research. Annual publication, 1948-49)

1. Theater—Gt. Brit.—Bibl.   (Series)

Z2014.D7L8   016.792   51-34078

CU OU TxU CtY ICN MH ICU WaU MoU PSt
NL 0447286   DLC CLSU CSt CaBVa CaBVaU OrU NcD NIC

Löwenberg, Frau Anne-Marie (Cassirer) 1902-
... Ueber den verlauf der hämorrhagischen Nephritis bei Kindern seit der Einführung der Zuckertage in die Behandlung ...   Berlin [1930]
Inaug.-Diss. - Berlin.
Lebenslauf.
"Literaturverzeichnis": p. [18]

NL 0447287   CtY OU

WVA   LOEWENBERG, Benjamin Benno, 1836-
L829a   Anatomie et physiologie de l'oreille;
1869   la lame spirale du limaçon et l'organe de Corti, d'après des recherches originales. Paris, Martinet, 1869.
74 p. illus.
2d part of the author's thesis, issued in Paris, 1866 under title: La lame spirale du limaçon de l'oreille de l'homme et des mammifères.
I. Loewenberg, Benjamin Benno, 1836-   La lame spirale du limaçon

NL 0447288   DNLM

Loewenberg, Benjamin Benno, 1836-
——— Des champignons parasites de l'oreille humaine. Étiologie, prophylaxie, traitement, applications à la thérapeutique générale. 7 pp. 8°. *Paris, G. Masson,* 1880.

NL 0447289   DNLM

Loewenberg, Benjamin Benno, 1836-
——— Les déviations de la cloison nasale, difficultés qu'elles apportent au cathétérisme de la trompe d'Eustache et nouveau moyen d'y remédier. 32 pp. 8°. *Paris, A. Delahaye & E. Lecrosnier,* 1883.

NL 0447290   DNLM

Löwenberg (Benjamin Benno) [1836-   ].
Étude sur les membranes et les canaux du limaçon. 12 pp. 8°. *Paris, V. Masson & fils,* 1864.

NL 0447291   DNLM

Loewenberg, Benjamin Benno, 1836-
———. Le furoncle de l'oreille et la furonculose. 46 pp. 8°. *Paris, A. Delahaye & E. Lecrosnier,* 1881.

NL 0447292   DNLM

Loewenberg, Benjamin Benno, 1836-
La lame spirale du limaçon de l'oreille de l'homme et des mammifères. Recherches d'anatomie microscopique.   Paris, 1869.
vi, (1), 48 p. + 2 pl. 22.5 cm.

NL 0447293   CtY DNLM

Löwenberg, Benjamin Benno, 1836-
Les tumeurs adénoïdes du pharynx nasal, leur influence sur l'audition, la respiration et la phonation, leur traitement, par Dr B. Lœwenberg. Paris, V. A. Delahaye et cᵉ, 1879.
[4], 75 p. 25ᶜᵐ.

NL 0447294   ICJ MH DNLM CtY

Loewenberg, Benj. W   , 1874-
Aetiologisches zur Hyperaciditas und Hypersecretio ventriculi ...   Berlin [1900]
Inaug.-Diss. - Berlin.
Lebenslauf.

NL 0447295   CtY ICRL DNLM

Loewenberg, Bert James, 1905-
Historical records survey. *Massachusetts.*
Calendar of the letters of Charles Robert Darwin to Asa Gray. With an introduction by Bert James Loewenberg, assistant professor of history, University of South Dakota. Prepared by the Historical records survey, Division of professional and service projects, Work projects administration. Boston, Mass., The Historical records survey, 1939.

Loewenberg, Bert James, 1905-
Darwinism comes to America, 1859-1900.

(In Mississippi Valley historical review. Cedar Rapids, Ia. 26cm. v. 28, no. 3 (1941) p. 339-68)

Bibliographical footnotes.

NL 0447297   NNC

Loewenberg, Bert James, 1905-
Historical scholarship in American culture. Mexico, D. F., Editorial Cultura, 1941.
cover-title, 73-98 p.

"Sobretiro del no. 12 de la Revista de historia de América, agosto de 1941."

1. Historiography.   2. History - Philosophy.
3. U. S. - Civili-   zation.

NL 0447298   NNC MH

Loewenberg, Bert James, 1905-
The history of ideas: 1935-1945 ...   New York ₍1947₎
22 p. 23 cm.
"The substance of this paper was read at the thirty-ninth annual meeting of the Mississippi valley historical association, Bloomington, Indiana, April 18, 1946."
Bibliographical foot-notes.

1. Learning and scholarship—U. S.   I. Title.

AZ508.L6   015.73   47-26345
                                     Brief cataloging

NL 0447299   DLC ICU

E178
.B55   Loewenberg, Bert James, 1905-

Billington, Ray Allen, 1903-
The United States; American democracy in world perspective ₍by₎ Ray Allen Billington ... Bert James Loewenberg ... ₍and₎ Samuel Hugh Brockunier ... New York, Toronto, Rinehart & company, inc. ₍1947₎

Löwenberg, Bruno, 1893-
Häusliche chemische Versuche; eine Anleitung zu eigenen chemischen Versuchen und zur Prüfung von Nahrungsmitteln, mit einer Einführung in die chemische Formelsprache, von Bruno Löwenberg und Gg. Schilling. Neubearb. von K. Kempf und F. Trommsdorff. Hildesheim, F. M. Hörhold ₍1951₎
95 p. illus. 12 cm. (Miniatur-Bibliothek, Nr. N156/57, a-d)

1. Chemistry—Laboratory manuals. 2. Food.   I. Title.

TX149.L56   51-36415 ‡

NL 0447301   DLC

LÖWENBERG, Bruno, 1893-
Über o-phtalimidobenzoylmalonester. Zur kenntnis der a-methylphtalsäure. Inaug.-diss. [Berlin, A. Loewenthal, 1918?]

"Lebenslauf" at end.

NL 0447302   MH-C CtY

WG   Löwenberg, Emanuel, 1869-
22734   Kernsynthesen mit (3,5)=Dibromsalicylsäurechlorid. Bonn a. Rh., 1904.
48 p. illus.

Inaug.-Diss. - Bonn.

NL 0447303   CtY MH PU DNLM

Loewenberg, Ernst, 1896-   ed.
Jakob Loewenberg; Eine Auswahl aus seinen Schriften
      see under   Loewenberg, Jakob, 1856-1929.

Loewenberg, Ernst, 1896-
Jakob Loewenberg; Lebensbild eines deutschen Juden. np, [193-?]

NL 0447305   MH

VOLUME 338

Loewenberg, F.
    Von Strand und Strasse, Gedichte, von F.
Loewenberg
            see   Loewenberg, Jakob, 1856-1929.

Loewenberg, Fritz: Die üble Nachrede in rechtsvergleichender Darstellung mit den deutschen Strafrechtsentwürfen unt. bes. Berücks.
d. Rechtsguts d. Ehre. [Maschinenschrift.] III, 100 S. 4°. —
Auszug: (Marburg 1923: Friedrich). 2 Bl. 8°
Marburg, Jur. Diss. v. 29. Juni 1923   [U 23.8816

NL 0447307   ICRL

Loewenberg, Fritz, 1901-
    Untersuchungen an einer reihe homologer laktone
ueber ihre beeinflussung physikalisch chemischer
vorgaenge mit beruecksichtigung ihrer parhmakolo-
gischen wirksamkeit...
    Inaug. diss., Kiel, 1928.

NL 0447308   ICRL CtY

Loewenberg, Georg.
    Was muss man von der analytischen geometrie wissen? Berlin,
H. Steinitz, [1907].
    pp. 80.

NL 0447309   MH

Loewenberg, Georg, 1861-
    Tabelle der wichtigsten Porzellan-Marken; 116
Abbildungen, mit den nötigen Anmerkungen. [2.Aufl.]
Berlin, Steinitz [1911]

    [4] p. illus.

    1. Pottery - Marks

NL 0447310   MH CU

Loewenberg, Georg, 1861-
    Tabelle der wichtigsten Porzellan-Marken; 116 Abbildungen
(mit den nötigen Anmerkungen), von Dr. Georg Loewenberg...
Berlin: H. Steinitz[,] 1926[]. 2 l.   pl.   12°.

1. Pottery—Marks and monograms.
N. Y. P. L.   July 1, 1927

NL 0447311   NN

WG   Loewenberg, Georg,   1861-
23641   Über aromatische Kohlensäureäther.
          Berlin, 1886.
              39 p.
              Inaug.-Diss. - Berlin.

NL 0447312   CtY

Loewenberg, Gerhard, 1928-
    The effects of governing on the British
Labour Party. [Ithaca, N. Y.] 1955.
    iv, 235 l. 28cm.

    Thesis (Ph. D.)--Cornell Univ., Feb.
1955.

NL 0447313   NIC

LÖWENBERG, HARALD.
    Minnesord över Carl Emil Ekman; utdrag ur minnes-
talet hållet på frimurarlogen s:t Nikolai den 7 maj
1954.   (IN: Gotländskt arkiv. Visby. 24cm. [bd.] 27 (1955) p. 7-13)

    1. Ekman, Carl Emil, 1868-1954

NL 0447314   NN

Löwenberg, Henny, 1909-
    Die Schwerhörigkeit im Kindesalter, ihre Ursachen und
soziale Bedeutung. Duisburg, 1937.

    53 p. fold. tables. 21 cm.

    Inaug.-diss.—Bonn.
    Vita.

    1. Deaf. 2. Children, Abnormal and backward. I. Title.

HV2395.L6   50-43800

NL 0447315   DLC DNLM CtY

LOEWENBERG, I.
    Gedächtnisrede auf Kaiser Friedrich
III. Gehalten in der öffentlichen Trauer-
feier der Henry Jones-Loge des U.O.B.B.
am 24. Juni 1888...Hamburg, 1888. 16p
20cm
    1.B'nai B'rith. 2.History-Germany-
Modern.

NL 0447316   NNJ OCH

LOEWENBERG, Isidor.
    Chlorose und venenthrombose. Königsb.i.Pr.
1894.

NL 0447317   MBCo

Loewenberg, Jacob, 1882-
    Classic and romantic trends in Plato.
[By] J. Loewenberg.   [Cambridge, Mass.,] 1917.
    p. [215]-236.   25 cm.

    Caption title.
    Extract from Harvard theological review, v. 10,
no. 3.
    "An address before the Philosophical union of
the University of California, February 23, 1917."
    1. Plato.

NL 0447318   CU

Loewenberg, Jacob, 1882-
    Dialogues from Delphi. Berkeley, Univ. of California
Press, 1949.
    x, 304 p. 23 cm.

    1. Art—Philosophy. 2. Aesthetics. I. Title.

N70.L475   701   49—6294*

WaE WaPS WaTC WaS WaSpG WaSp WaT WaWW
IdPI FTaSU CaBVaU IdU MtBC MtU OrCS OrPR OrP OrU Wa
OOxM NNC PSt OC1 Or OrStbM OrU-M NBuU PSt KEmT IdB
NL 0447319   DLC MtBuM NBuC AAP PHC MiU MB CU TxU ICU

Loewenberg, Jacob, 1882-
    The fourfold root of truth.
    (In University of California. Publications. Philosophy. Vol. 10,
pp. 207-241. Berkeley, Cal. 1928.)

D1632 — Truth.

NL 0447320   MB

Loewenberg, Jacob, 1882- tr.
Chinard, Gilbert.
    France for the soldier, a few facts for the information
of Americans, by Gilbert Chinard ... tr. by J. Loewenberg ... Berkeley, Military information office of the University of California [1918]

Loewenberg, Jacob, 1882- ed.   FOR OTHER EDITIONS
                                      SEE MAIN ENTRY
Royce, Josiah, 1855-1916.
    Fugitive essays by Josiah Royce; with an introduction by
Dr. J. Loewenberg. Cambridge, Harvard university press,
1920.

LOEWENBERG, Jacob, 1882-
    The genesis of Hegel's dialectical method.
A part pub.,under the title "Die jugendlichen
Denkversuche Hegels," as the introduction (pp.
vii-xxii) to the author's "Hegels Entwürfe zur
Enzyklopädie und Propädeutik," Leipzig,Verlag
Meiner,1912.

    Official copy of the thesis presented for a
doctor's degree at Harvard University.

NL 0447323   MH

Löwenberg, Jacob, 1882- ed.
    Hegels Entwürfe zur Enzyklopädie und Pro-
pädeutik
        see under   Hegel, Georg Wilhelm
Friedrich, 1770-1831.

Loewenberg, Jacob, 1882-
    The idea of the ultimate.
    (In Adams, George Plimpton, and Jacob Loewenberg, editors.
Essays in metaphysics. Pp. 78-111. Berkeley, California. 1924.)

N2105 — Philosophy. — Design, Argument of.

NL 0447325   MB

Loewenberg, Jacob, 1882-
    Is metaphysics descriptive or normative?
    (In University of California. Publications. Philosophy. Vol. 7, pp.
139-180. Berkeley, Cal. 1925.)

D6943 — Philosophy.

NL 0447326   MB

Loewenberg, Jacob, 1882-
    Judgments of fact and of value in relation to
the war; lecture delivered April 1, 1941. n.p.,
1941.

    34 p. 19 cm.
    "Reprinted from the Meaning of the war to the
Americas. Lectures delivered under the auspices
of the committee on international relations on
the Los Angeles campus of the University of
California, 1941."

NL 0447327   MH CU

            Loewenberg, Jacob, ed.
                                1882-
B2745   FOR OTHER EDITIONS
.R8   Royce, Josiah, 1855-1916.   SEE MAIN ENTRY
1919a   Lectures on modern idealism, by Josiah Royce. New
        Haven, Yale university press; [etc., etc.,] 1919.

VOLUME 338

Loewenberg, Jacob, 1882–
The life of Georg Wilhelm Friedrich Hegel. Portrait.
(In German classics of the nineteenth and twentieth centuries.
Vol. 7, pp. 1–15. New York. [1913.])

K5945 — Hegel, Georg Wilhelm Friedrich. 1770–1831.

NL   0447329   MB

Loewenberg, Jacob, 1882–
The metaphysical status of things and ideas.
(In University of California. Publications. Philosophy. Vol.
8, pp. 107–144. Berkeley, Cal. 1926.)

D6946 — Ideas. — Philosophy.

NL   0447330   MB

Loewenberg, Jacob, 1882–
The metaphysics of critical realism.
(In University of California. Publications. Philosophy. Vol.
4, pp. 165–194. Berkeley. 1923.)

M8388 — Realism. In philosophy.

NL   0447331   MB

Loewenberg, Jacob, 1882–
Mysticism and idealism [by] J. Loewenberg.
[Berkeley? 1916?]
cover-title, 22 p.   23 cm.
"Reprint from the University of California
chronicle, vol. xviii, no. 1".
1. Mysticism. 2. Idealism.

NL   0447332   CU

Loewenberg, Jacob, 1882–
The prepositional nature of truth.
(In University of California. Publications. Philosophy. Vol. 11,
pp. 1–32. Berkeley, Cal. 1929.)

D1631 — Truth.

NL   0447333   MB

LOEWENBERG, J[acob,] 1882–
President Wilson's Americanism. [Berkeley,
Calif., 1919].

pp.17.
"Reprint from the University of California
Chronicle, vol.XXI, no.1."

NL   0447334   MH

Loewenberg, Jacob, 1882–
Problematic realism, by J. Loewenberg ...
(In Contemporary American philosophy. New York, 1930. 22½ᵐ. vol. 2,
p. [53–81])
"Principal publications": p. 81.

NL   0447335   ICJ

Loewenberg, Jacob, 1882–
Royce's synoptic vision. Published for the Dept. of Philosophy of the Johns Hopkins University, on the occasion of the centennial of Royce's birth, November 20, 1955. [Baltimore? 1955]
31 p.   23 cm.

1. Royce, Josiah, 1855–1916.   i. Title.

B945.R64L6   921.1   55–12062 ‡

     IdU OrPR OrU WaWW
NL   0447336   DLC ScU OOxM NcD TxU PBL PBm IU OU PLF

Loewenberg, Jacob, ed.
1882–

Hegel, Georg Wilhelm Friedrich, 1770–1831.
... Selections, edited by J. Loewenberg ... New York, Chicago [etc.] C. Scribner's sons [*1929]

Loewenberg, Jacob, 1882–
The spirit of Hegel's philosophy [by] J.
Loewenberg ... [Berkeley, 1916]
23 p.   22 cm.
"Reprint from the University of California
chronicle, vol. XVIII, no. 3."
1. Hegel, Georg Wilhelm Friedrich, 1770–1831.

NL   0447338   CU

Loewenberg, Jakob, 1856–1929.
Aelfrida.   Hamburg, Glogau, 1919.
79 p.   19 cm.

NL   0447339   IEN MH

Loewenberg, Jakob, 1856–
Aus der welt des kindes; ein buch für eltern und erzieher, von dr. J. Loewenberg. Leipzig, R. Voigtländer, 1911.
192 p.   18½ᵐᵐ.

i. Title.

     E 13–1499
Library, U. S. Bur. of   Education

NL   0447340   DHEW OC1

LOEWENBERG, JAKOB, 1856–1929.
Aus jüdischer Seele; Gedichte. 3., verm. Aufl.
Hamburg, M. Glogau, Jr. [19––?]   107 p. 20cm.

1. Jews in poetry. 2. Poetry.   German. I. Title.

NL   0447341   NN OCH

Loewenberg, Jakob, 1856–1929.
Aus jüdischer Seele. Gedichte.   Samburg,
M. Glogau, jr, [1903]
4 p.l., 88 p.   12°.
2. ed.

NL   0447342   NN TNJ

Loewenberg, Jakob, 1856–
Aus zwei quellen, von Jakob Loewenberg. Berlin, E.
Fleischel & co., 1914.
4 p. L, 295, [1] p. 20ᵐᵐ.   M. 4

i. Title.

Library of Congress   PT2424.L65A8 1914   14–10720

NL   0447343   DLC IEN

LOEWENBERG, Jakob, 1856–
Aus zwei quellen. [2te aufl.] Berlin,
E. Fleischel & co., 1919.

NL   0447344   MH

Loewenberg, Jakob, 1856–
Aus zwei Quellen; die Geschichte eines deutschen Juden, von Jakob Loewenberg.   Berlin: E. Fleischel & Co., 1919.   295 p.
[3. ed.]   12°.

90711A. 1. Jews in fiction. 2. Fiction (German). 3. Title.
N. Y. P. L.   July 3, 1923.

NL   0447345   NN OCH

LOEWENBERG, JAKOB, 1856–1929.
Aus zwei Quellen; die Geschichte eines deutschen Juden. [3. Aufl.]   Berlin, E. Fleischel, 1919.   295 p.
20cm.

Film reproduction. Negative.

1. Jews in fiction. 2. Fiction, German. I. Title.

NL   0447346   NN

3469   Loewenberg, Jakob, 1856–1929.
.2
.793   Detlev von Liliencron.   Hamburg,
Gutenberg-verlag (Schultze) 1904.
30 p.   front. (port.)   22 ᶜᵐ

1. Liliencron, Detlev, freiherr von,
1844–1909.

NL   0447347   NjP CtY NjR

Loewenberg, Jakob, 1856–1929, ed.
Deutsche Balladen. Bielefeld, Velhagen &
Klasing, 1926.
viii, 226 p. (Deutsche Schulausgaben, Bd.
197)

NL   0447348   WaU CSt

Loewenberg, Jakob, 1856–
Deutsche Dichter-Abende; eine Sammlung von Vorträgen über neuere deutsche Literatur, von Dr. J. Loewenberg...
Hamburg: E. Schultze, 1904.   198 p.   front. (port.)   22cm.
Contents: Widmung. Inhaltsverzeichnis. Vorwort. Annette von Droste-Hülshoff. Christian Dietrich Grabbe. Nikolaus Lenau. Friedrich Wilhelm Weber. Marie von Ebner-Eschenbach. Detlev von Liliencron. Gustav Frenssen. Gerhart Hauptmanns "Versunkene Glocke" und andere moderne Märchendramen. Moderne Frauenlyrik.

599932A. 1. German literature—   Hist. and crit., 20th cent.
N. Y. P. L.   December 16, 1932.

NL   0447349   NN MiU

Loewenberg, Jakob, 1856–1929.
Deutsche dichter-abende; eine sammlung von vorträgen über neuere deutsche literatur von dr. J.
Loewenberg. Mit einem bildnis Detlevs von Liliencron. 2. aufl.   Hamburg, E. Schultze, 1905.
198 p.   front. (port.)   22cm.
Includes "Literatur".
Contents. – Annette von Droste-Hülshoff (1893). –
Christian Dietrich Grabbe (1901). – Nikolaus
Lenau (1902). – Friedrich Wilhelm Weber (1894). –
Marie von Ebner-Eschenbach (1898). – Detlev von
Liliencron (1904). – Gustav Frenssen (1903). –
Gerhart Hauptmanns "Versunkene Glocke" und
andere moderne mar chendramen (1896).–Moderne
frauenlyrik (1897)

NL   0447350   WU NRU CU

VOLUME 338

Loewenberg, Jakob, 1856–1929.
Der gelbe Fleck. Berlin, Philo Verlag, 1924.
143 p. 20 cm.

1. Jewish question. I. Title.

PT2424.L65G4   49–57968*

NL 0447351   DLC PPDrop NN

833
F889Yℓ Loewenberg, Jakob, 1856–1929.
Gustav Frenssen, von der Sandgräfin bis zum
Jörn Uhl, von J. Loewenberg. Mit einem Bildnis
Gustav Frenssens. Hamburg, M. Glogau, 1903.
38p. port. 23cm.

1. Frenssen, Gustav, 1863–1945.

NL 0447352   TxU NjP MH CtY NcU

Loewenberg, Jakob, 1856–1929.
Jakob Loewenberg; Eine Auswahl aus seinen Schriften, her-
ausgegeben und eingeleitet von Ernst Loewenberg. Berlin:
Schocken Verlag, 1937. 31 p. 19½cm. (On cover: Jüdische
Lesehefte ... Nr. 17.)

Bibliography, p. [3] of cover.

1. German literature—Misc.   2. Jews in fiction. 3. Jews in poetry.
[1] Loewenberg, Ernst, 1896–   , ed.   II. Ser.
N.Y.P.L.   February 27, 1941

NL 0447353   NN NNJ OCH

(LOEWENBERG, Jakob) 1856–
Lieder eines Semiten. Hamburg, A. Goldschmidt, 1892. 32p 18cm
1.Poetry-German. 2.Title. 3.Antisemi-
tism, Refutation of.

NL 0447354   NNJ

PT
2424 Loewenberg, Jakob, 1856–1929.
.L642   Neue Gedichte, von J. Loewenberg. Hamburg,
A6   M. Glogau, 1895.
1895   viii, 116p. 19cm.

NL 0447355   TNJ

Loewenberg, Jakob, 1856–1929.
Rübezahl. Ein Märchenspiel in vier Akten.
[In verse] Hamburg, M. Glogau [1908]
68 p. 12°.
2. ed.

NL 0447356   NN

Loewenberg, Jaakob, 1856–1929.
Stille Helden. Novellen. Hamburg:
E. Schultze, 1906. 2.ed.
223 (1) p.

NL 0447357   OCH

Loewenberg, Jakob, 1856–1929.
Über Otway's und Schiller's Don Carlos ... Von Jacob
Löwenberg. Lippstadt, Druck von A. Staats, 1886.
126 p., 1 l. 21½ᵐ.

Inaug.-diss.—Heidelberg.

1. Otway, Thomas, 1652–1685. Don Carlos, prince of Spain. 2. Schiller, Johann Christoph Friedrich von. Don Carlos, infant von Spanien.
                                                    34–19565

Library of Congress   PR3612.D62L6 1886   822.45

NL 0447358   DLC ICRL CtY NIC MB MiU

Loewenberg, Jakob, 1856–1929, ed.
Vom goldnen überfluss. Eine auswahl
aus neuern deutschen dichtern für schule
und haus im auftrage und unter mitwir-
tung der literarischen kommission der
hamburger lehrer-vereinigung zur pflege
der künstlerischen bildung herausgegeben
von Dr. J. Loewenberg. Leipzig, R.
Voigtländers Verlag, n.d.
272 p.

NL 0447359   WaSpG PLF

831.08
L82v   Loewenberg, Jakob, 1856–1929, comp.
1913   Vom goldnen überfluss. Eine auswahl aus neuern deutschen dichtern
für schule und haus. Im auftrage und
unter mitwirkung der literarischen
Germ. kommission der Hamburger lehrervereinigung zur pflege der künstlerischen
bildung hrsg. von J. Loewenberg...
Leipzig,
320p. D.

NL 0447360   IaU CaBVaU

PT1173 Loewenberg, Jakob, 1856–1929, comp.
.L8   Vom goldnen überfluss. Eine auswahl aus
neuern deutschen dichtern für schule und haus,
im auftrage und unter mitwirkung der Literarischen kommission der "Hamburger lehrervereinigung zur pflege der künstlerischen bildung"
hrsg. von J. Voigtländer. Neue, verm. ausg. ...
Leipzig, R. Voigtländer [1902]
304 p. 18½cm.

1. German poetry--19th cent.

NL 0447361   ICU

831.08
L827V   Loewenberg, Jakob, 1856–1929, ed.
Vom goldnen Uberfluss, eine Auswahl aus neu-
ern deutschen Dichtern für Schule und Haus. Im
auftrage und unter Mitwirkung der Literarischen
Kommission der Hamburger Lehrervereinigung zur
Pflege der künstlerischen Bildung... Neue, verm.
Ausg. 61. – 65. tausend. Leipzig, R. Voigtländ-
er [1906?]
312 p. 19cm
1. German poetry (Selections: Extracts, etc.)
I. Lehrervereinigung zur Pflege der künstlerischen
Bildung in der Schule   Hamburg.

NL 0447362   NcD IU CtY MiD

Loewenberg, Jakob, 1856–   comp.
Vom goldnen überfluss; eine auswahl aus neuern
deutschen dichtern, für schule und haus; im
auftrage und unter mitwirkung der literarischen
kommission der Hamburger lehrervereinigung zur
pflege der künstlerischen bildung, hrsg. von dr.
J. Loewenberg. 191.–195. tausent. Leipzig,
R. Voigtländer, [19-?]
320 p. 19 cm.

NL 0447363   CU

Loewenberg, Jakob, 1856–   , editor.
Vom goldnen Überfluss; eine Auswahl aus neuern deutschen Dichtern für Schule und Haus, im Auftrage und unter
Mitwirkung der Literarischen Kommission der "Hamburger
Lehrervereinigung zur Pflege der künstlerischen Bildung, herausgegeben von Dr. J. Loewenberg... Leipzig: R. Voigtländer [1910] 312 p. new ed. 12°.

465608A. 1. Poetry, German—Col-   lections. 2. Hamburger Lehrervereinigung zur Pflege der künstleri-   schen Bildung. Literarische Kommission. 3. Title.   mission.
N.Y.P.L.   April 15, 1930

NL 0447364   NN MH OC1ND

PT
1155 Loewenberg, Jakob, 1856–1929, ed.
L65   Vom goldnen Überfluss. Eine Auswahl
1912 aus neuern deutschen Dichtern für Schule
und Haus. Leipzig, K. Voigtländer [1912]
320 p. 19cm.
"Vierte Ausgabe."
"Im Auftrage und unter Mitwirkung der Literarischen Kommission der Hamburger lehrervereinigung zur Pflege der künstlerischen Bildung herausgegeben von J. Loewenberg."
1. German poetry (Selections: Extracts, etc.)
I. Lehrervereinigung zur Pflege der künstlerischen Bildung in der Schule, Hamburg. II.
Title.

NL 0447365   CoFS PBL

LOEWENBERG, J[akob], 1856–   editor.
Vom goldnen überfluss; eine auswahl aus
neuern deutschen dichtern für schule und haus.
Im auftrage und unter mitwirkung der literarischen kommission der Hamburger lehrervereinigung. 186.–190.tausend. Leipzig, R. Voigtländer, [1918].

pp.320.

NL 0447366   MH

Loewenberg, Jakob, 1856–1929, ed.
Vom goldnen überfluss, eine auswahl aus neuern deutschen
dichtern für schule und haus. Im auftrage und unter mitwirkung des Literarischen ausschusses der Hamburger
lehrervereinigung zur pflege der künstlerischen bildung herausgegeben von dr. J. Loewenberg. 221.–225. tausend. Leipzig, R.
Voigtländer [1923]
370 p. 18ᵐ.

Sixth edition. First published 1901. cf. Vorwort.

1. German poetry (Selections: Extracts, etc.)   I. Lehrervereinigung
zur pflege der künstlerischen bildung in der schule, Hamburg.
                                                    44–44525

Library of Congress   PT1155.L65 1923

NL 0447367   DLC WaU NBC

830.81 Loewenberg, Jakob, 1856–1929, ed.
L82v7   Vom goldnen überfluss. Eine auswahl
aus neuern deutschen dichtern für schule
und haus. Im auftrage und unter mitwirkung des literarischen ausschusses der
Hamburger lehrervereinigung zur pflege
der künstlerischen bildung ... [7.ausg.]
Leipzig [1927]
375p.

NL 0447368   IU KMK

PT
2424 Loewenberg, Jakob, 1856–1929.
.L642   Von Strand und Strasse, Gedichte, von F.
V66   Loewenberg. Hamburg, M. Glogau, 1905.
vii, 122p. 19cm.

NL 0447369   TNJ

VOLUME 338

Löwenberg, Josephine Chiolich von.

Brillante Variationen über ein ungarisches Thema; für das Pianoforte mit Begleitung des Orchesters. ₍n. p., 18—₎

parts. 37 cm.

1. Variations (Piano with orchestra)—Parts. 2. Folk-songs, Hungarian (Instrumental settings) I. Title.

M1010.L83B7   63–30811/M

NL 0447370   DLC

Loewenberg, J[ulius] 1800-1893.

Afrika. Geschichte der geographischen Entdeckungen in diesem Erdtheile.   Berlin, Vereins-Buchhandlung, 1835.

viii, 267 (1) p. , 1 tab.   16°;

NL 0447371   NN

G509.2
H881Xℓ
Photo-
copy
Löwenberg, Julius, 1800-1893.

Alexander von Humboldt. Bibliographische Uebersicht seiner Werke, Schriften und zerstreuten Abhandlungen. [Leipzig, F.A. Brockhaus, 1872]

p.[476]-552. 22cm.

Photocopy (Positive) of the original in Princeton University.

Detached from v.2, pt.5 of Bruhns, Karl Christian. Alexander von Humboldt. Leipzig, 1872.

NL 0447372   TxU OCIW

Löwenberg, Julius, 1800-1898, ed.

Alexander von Humboldt. Eine Wissenschaftliche Biographie ...

see under   Bruhns, Karl Christian, 1830-1881, ed.

Loewenberg, Julius, 1800-1893, ed.

Alexander von Humboldt's Reisen in Amerika und Asien; eine Darstellung seiner wichtigsten Forschungen

see under   Humboldt, Alexander, Freiherr von, 1769-1859.

Loewenberg, Julius, 1800-1893.

...Die Entdeckungs- und Forschungsreisen in den beiden Polarzonen. Von J. Löwenberg...   Leipzig: G. Freytag, 1886.

152 p.   illus. (maps.)   12°.   (Das Wissen der Gegenwart. Bd. 58.)

1. Arctic expeditions. 2. Antarctic   expeditions. 3. Series.
N.Y.P.L.   May 9, 1922.

NL 0447375   NN CtY MnU ICJ MH CaOTP CU

Löwenberg, Julius, 1800-1893, tr.

Humboldt, Alexander, *freiherr* von, 1769-1859.

... Fragmente einer geologie und klimatologie Asiens. Aus dem französischen mit anmerkungen, einer karte und einer tabelle vermehrt von Julius Loewenberg ... Berlin, J. A. List, 1832.

LD876
L6
t
Löwenberg, Julius, 1800-1893.

Der Fremde in Berlin und Potsdam; neuester und zuverlässigster Wegweiser bei Besuche dieser Hauptstädte und ihrer Umgebungen ... Berlin, E.H.Schroeder, 1841.

iv,130 p. maps. 15cm.

1.Berlin - Descr. 2.Potsdam - Descr. I. Title.

NL 0447377   CSt MH

Löwenberg, Julius, 1800-1893.

Der Fremde in Berlin und Potsdam. Neuester und zuverlässigster Wegweiser beim Besuche dieser Hauptstädte und ihre Umgebungen ... 5., durch verb. Aufl. ...   Berlin, 1845.

14 x 11 cm.

NL 0447378   CtY

G.
80
L82
Löwenberg, Julius, 1800-1893.

Geschichte der Geographie. Mit zwei chronologischen Uebersichtstabellen und neun Erdansichten (in einer Karte).   Berlin, Haude und Spenersche Buchhandlung ,1840.

379 p. fold. tables and map. 21cm.

1. Geography—Hist.

NL 0447379   NIC

Löwenberg, J₍ulius₎ 1800-1893.

Geschichte der geographie von den ältesten zeiten bis auf die gegenwart; von J. Löwenberg.   2. gänzlich umgearb. aufl. Berlin, F. Weidling, 1866.

xii, 475 p. 18¹⁄₂ᵐ.

Subject entries: Geography—Hist.   3–14205

Library of Congress, no.   G80.L82.

NL 0447380   DLC CtY

Löwenberg, J₍ulius₎ 1800-1893.

... Geschichte der geographischen entdeckungsreisen ... Von J. Löwenberg. Mit zahlreichen text-abbildungen, tonbildern, karten, porträts u. s. w. Leipzig und Berlin, O. Spamer, 1881-85.

2 v. fronts., illus. (incl. ports.) maps (partly fold.) 22¹⁄₂ᶜᵐ. (Das neue buch der reisen und entdeckungen. Otto Spamer's Illustrirte bibliothek der länder- u. völkerkunde zur erweiterung der kenntniss der fremde ...)

Each volume has special t-p. added.

CONTENTS.—I. Geschichte der geographischen entdeckungsreisen im alterthum und mittelalter bis zu Magellans erster erdumsegelung.—II. Geschichte der geographischen entdeckungsreisen in der neueren zeit von Magellan bis zum ausgang des achtzehnten jahrhunderts.

1. Voyages and travels. 2. Discoveries (in geography) 3. Explorers.

Library of Congress   G80.L83   6–23954

NL 0447381   DLC ICN CtY

Löwenberg, Julius, 1800-1893.

Geschichte der geographischen Entdeckungsreisen. Von J. Löwenberg. Mit über zweihundert Abbildungen und Kärtchen und sechs grösseren Karten. Wohlfeile Ausgabe. Leipzig, O. Spamer, [1895].

2 vol. in 1. illus., 7 maps (3 fold.), fold. table. 22ᶜᵐ.

NL 0447382   ICJ

1585
.594
Löwenberg, Julius, 1800-1893.

Historischer taschen-atlas des Preussischen staats, bestehend aus 16 historisch-geographischen karten mit erläuterndem texte.. Neue aufl. Berlin, Voss ₍18—₎

91 p. 16 maps,fold.tables. 14 x 21¹⁄₂ cm. .

1.Prussia-Historical geography-Maps.

NL 0447383   NjP

Loewenberg, Julius, 1800-1893.

Historisch-geographischer Atlas zu den allgemeinen Geschichtswerken von C.v.Rotteck, Pölitz und Becker in 40 collorirten Karten. Freiberg, Herder'sche Kunst- und Buchhandlung, 1836

1 v.
Imperfect: lacks 12 maps

NL 0447384   MH

Löwenberg, Julius, 1800-1893.

Historisch-geographischer atlas zu den allgemeinen geschichtswerken von C. v. Rotteck, Politz u Becker, in 4⁰ colorirten karten von Julius Löwenberg. Freiburg im Breisgau, Im verlage der Herder'schen kunst u. buchhandlung, 1839.

34 maps.

NL 0447385   OCl

Löwenberg, Julius, 1800-1893.

Bruhns, Karl Christian, 1830-1881, *ed.*

Life of Alexander von Humboldt. Compiled in commemoration of the centenary of his birth, by J. Löwenberg, Robert Avé-Lallemant, and Alfred Dove. Ed. by Professor Karl Bruhns ... Tr. from the German by Jane and Caroline Lassell ... London, Longmans, Green, and co.; Boston ₍etc.₎, Lee and Shepard, 1873.

Löwenberg, Julius, 1800-1893.

Das Weltbuch Sebastian Francks. Die erste allgemeine geographie in deutscher sprache. Von J.Löwenberg ... Hamburg, Verlagsanstalt und druckerei a.-g. (vormals J.F.Richter) 1893.

37 p. 20¹⁄₂ᶜᵐ. (On cover: Sammlung gemeinverständlicher wissenschaftlicher vorträge,n.f.,8.ser.,hft.177)

1.Franck,Sebastien,1499-1542. Weltbuch.

NL 0447387   MiU NIC MB MH

LOEWENBERG ₍Karl Friedrich Benjamin₎1807-1871.

Beiträge'zur kenntniss der motive der preussischen gesetzgebung; aus amtlichen quellen bearbeitet und mit höhrer genehmigung herausgegeben. Berlin,1843.

2 vol.

NL 0447388   MH-L

Löwenberg, Karl Friedrich Benjamin, 1807-1871.

Ueber den Lieferungs-Vertrag, unter Berücksichtigung des Handels mit geldwerthen Papieren, vom Kammergerichts-Rath Dr. Loewenberg. Berlin, Veit und Comp., 1846.

2 p.l., 90 p. 23¹⁄₂cm.

Bibliographical footnotes.

NL 0447389   MH-L

VOLUME 338

Loewenberg, Mrs. Kate, tr.

Meyerson, Émile, 1859-1933.
... Identity & reality; authorized translation by Kate Loewenberg. London, G. Allen & Unwin ltd.; New York, The Macmillan company ₁1930₎

Loewenberg (Lehmannus) [1824-   ]. * De aaginæ membranaceæ. 31 pp. 8°. *Berolini, C. Schade,* [1846].

NL 0447391   DNLM

Löwenberg (Ludovicus [Liepmannus]) [1817-   ]. * De hypochondria. 27 pp. 2 l. 8°. *Berolini, typ. fratrum Schlesinger,* [1841].

NL 0447392   DNLM

Loewenberg (Mauritius). * De hydrocephalo acuto. 30 pp. 8°. *Halis, typ. Ruffianis,* [1843].

NL 0447393   DNLM

Loewenberg (Max) [1868-   ]. * Ueber einen ungewöhnlichen Fall von chronischer Herdmyelitis. 44 pp., 2 l. 8°. *Berlin, G. Schade.* [1893].

NL 0447394   DNLM

RB1
.B42

Loewenberg, P.
Beiträge zur experimentellen pathologie und physiologie; hrsg. von dr. L. Traube. 1.-2. hft. Berlin, A. Förstner, 1846.

Löwenberg, Paul, joint author.

Rehschuh, Hans.
Die Sozialversicherung im Bundesgebiet und im Land Berlin. Was muss man von der Sozialversicherung im Bundesgebiet und im Land Berlin wissen? Von Hans Rehschuh ₁und₎ Paul Löwenberg. 4. neubearb. und erweiterte Aufl. Frankfurt/M., W. Limpert ₁1954₎

Löwenberg, Paul, 1890-
... Zum Latenzstadium der Masern. Boebachtungen an 76 Fällen von Masern-Hausinfektionen an den Kinderspitälern zu Graz und München. 1893-1912. ... München, 1913.
Inaug.-Diss. - München.
Lebenslauf.
"Literatur": p. [43]

NL 0447397   CtY MiU PPWI DNLM

W 4
B51
1939

Loewenberg, Peter Christian, 1915-
Die Gehirnmetastasen der Melanome.
Charlottenburg, Hoffmann, 1939.
61 p.

Inaug.-Diss. - Berlin.
Bibliography: p. 58-61.

NL 0447398   DNLM

Loewenberg, Samuel Aaron, 1881-
Clinical endocrinology, by Samuel A. Loewenberg ... foreword by Hobart A. Reimann ... with 194 illustrations and 37 charts and tables. Philadelphia, F. A. Davis company, 1937.
xxvii, 825 p. incl. illus., tables, diagr. 24ᶜᵐ.
Bibliography at end of each chapter except the first.

1. Endocrinology.   I. Title.   37-9670

Library of Congress   RC648.L6
Copyright A 106397   ₁3₎   616.4

NL 0447399   DLC ICRL CaBVaU OrU-M DNLM NcD PU

Loewenberg, Samuel Aaron, 1881-
Clinical endocrinology, by Samuel A. Loewenberg ... Foreword by Hobart A. Reimann. 2d rev. ed., with 194 illustrations and 37 charts and tables. Philadelphia, F. A. Davis company, 1941.
xxix, 883 p. incl. illus., tables, diagrs. 25½ᶜᵐ.
Bibliography at end of most of the chapters.

1. Endocrinology.   I. Title.   41-6089

Library of Congress   RC648.L6 1941
                        ₁3₎   616.4

NL 0447400   DLC ICRL TU DNLM ViU OU ICJ PU PPC

Loewenberg, Samuel Aaron, 1881-
Diagnostic methods and interpretations in internal medicine
        see his   Medical and physical diagnosis ...

Loewenberg, Samuel Aaron, 1881-
Medical and physical diagnosis; interpretation of findings. ₁1st₎ ed. Philadelphia, F. A. Davis Co., 1929-
v. illus., plates. 24-27 cm.
Title varies: 1st-4th ed., Diagnostic methods and interpretations in internal medicine.—5th-6th ed., Medical diagnosis and symptomatology.

1. Diagnosis.

RC71.L7   616.075   29-10731 rev*

PPJ
ICJ ICRL DNLM ICU ViU NcU PPC CtY-M PU-UH IaU PCM
NL 0447402   DLC WU-M PU PPHa OrU OrU-M OU OO MiU

Loewenberg, Samuel Aaron, 1881-
Medical diagnosis and symptomatology
        see his   Medical and physical diagnosis ...

Löwenberg, Walter: Ueber die diffuse Ausbreitung von Gliomen in den weichen Häuten des Zentralnervensystems. [Maschinenschrift] 4° [Lag nicht vor.] — Auszug: Berlin (1919): Blanke. 2 Bl. 8°
Berlin, Med. Diss. v. 12. Dez. 1919 [1925]   [U 25. 91

NL 0447404   ICRL

Loewenberg, William.
Hymns and responses from Jastrow's Prayer book, especially adapted... (1894)
                see under   Jews. Liturgy and ritual.

Löwenberg, William Joseph, ed.

Bury, *Eng. (Lancashire)   Parish.*
The registers of the parish church of Bury in the county of Lancaster. Christenings, burials, & weddings ... Transcribed and edited by the Rev. W. J. Löwenberg ... and Henry Brierley ...   Rochdale, Printed for the Lancashire parish register society, 1898-19

Löwenberg (Wolffius) [1806-   ]. * De partu Agrippinæ naturali et artificiali. 32 pp. 8°. *Berolini, typ. Brandesianis & Klewertianis,* [1831]. [P., v. 1647.]

NL 0447407   DNLM

Löwenberger v. Schönholtz, Willi, 1889-
Die kartographische darstellung der wege, strassen, und eisenbahnen, ihre geschichtliche entwicklung und kritische würdigung ... Königsberg i. Pr., Hartungsche buchdruckerei, 1914.
xi, 94 p., 1 l. illus. (incl. plans) diagrs. 22ᶜᵐ.
Inaug.-diss.—Königsberg.
Lebenslauf.
"Literaturnachweis": p. ₁viii₎-xi.

1. Cartography. 2. Cartography—Germany.

Library of Congress   GA203.L6   CA 23-157 Unrev'd

NL 0447408   DLC MH CtY

---

xGV445
.L64

Loewendahl, Evelyn, 1914-
Exercises for the mentally retarded; how to develop physical functions in the growing child. Illustrations by Jackie Stern.   Swarthmore, Pa., A.C. Croft ₁n.d.₎
1 v. (unpaged) illus. 32 cm.

1. Physical education for mentally handicapped children. 2. Mentally handicapped children--Education. I. Title.

NL 0447409   TU

---

f371.7322
L827h

Loewendahl, Evelyn, 1914-
How to develop physical functions in the growing individual. Illus. by Jackie Stern.   New London, Conn., A.C. Croft Publications, c1954.
₁7₎l. illus.

1. Physical education for children.
2. Growth.   I. Title.

NL 0447410   ICarbS NcU OO

RM721
.B62
1949

Loewendahl, Evelyn, 1914-   joint author.

Billig, Harvey E 1907-
Mobilization of the human body; newer concepts in body mechanics ₁by₎ Harvey E. Billig, Jr. and Evelyn Loewendahl. Stanford, Stanford University Press ₁1949₎

Löwendahl, Gösta.
Vapensmedens Viktor Rydberg. ₁Lund₎ C. W. K. Gleerup ₁1954₎
419 p. facsims. 24 cm.
Akademisk avhandling—Lund.
Extra t. p., with thesis statement, inserted.
Bibliography: p. 407-414.

1. Rydberg, Viktor, 1828-1895. Vapensmeden.   I. Title.

PT9788.V33L6   55-30364

NL 0447412   DLC TxU ICU IU MH CtY MiU MnU

VOLUME 338

Löwendorf, Heinz.
Die lustige Filmpalette; ernstes und heiteres Rund um den Film, berichtet von Löf [pseud.] [Hamburg] Star-Filmbildkalender-Verlag [1952] 143 p. illus. ports. 21cm.

1. Moving pictures—Anecdotes,   facetiae, satire, etc.

NL 0447413   NN

AC
831
Löwendorff, Werner, 1901-
Über ein adamantinom des oberkiefers ...
Berlin, n.d.   19 p.
Inaug. Diss. -Berlin, [1927?]
Lebenslauf.
Bibliography.

NL 0447414   ICRL CtY

Löweneck, Max.
Das neue leben und die deutsche schule, von dr. Max Löweneck ... München, J. Kösel & F. Pustet, k.-g. [*1926]
4 p. l., [11]-135, [1] p. incl. facsims. 20cm.
"Literatur" at end of most of the chapters.

1. Education—Germany.   I. Title.
Library of Congress   LA722.L75   27-14628

NL 0447415   DLC

Löweneck, Max.
Peri didaxeon, eine Sammlung von Rezepten in englisher Sprache aus dem 11 - 12.
Jahrundert
    see under   Peri didaxeon.

Löweneck, Sigmund, *1890-*
... Aus den wissenschaftlichen ergebnissen der Merzbacher'schen Tianschan-expedition; beiträge zur kenntnis des paläozoikums im Tianschan, von Sigmund Löweneck. Mit 4 tafeln. Vorgelegt von F. Broili am 9. mai 1931. München, Verlag der Bayerischen akademie der wissenschaften, 1932.
141 p. 4 pl. 29½cm. (Abhandlungen der Bayerischen akademie der wissenschaften. Mathematisch-naturwissenschaftliche abt. n. f., hft. 11)
"Literaturverzeichnis": p. [135]-139.
1. Thian Shan mountains. 2. Scientific expeditions.   I. Merzbacher, Gottfried, d. 1926.   A C 32-214
Title from Princeton   Univ.
Library of Congress   [AS182.M817 n. f., hft. 11]

NL 0447417   NjP NIC OCU OU MB PPAmP

QT
210
L827v
1955
LÖWENECK, Sigmund, 1890-
Vom Menschen und seiner Gesundheit; Mittelstufe und Oberstufe. [5. unveränderte Aufl.] München, Oldenbourg, 1955.
164 p. illus. (Biologisches Unterrichtswerk für höhere Lehranstalten [9]
1. Hygiene - Textbooks 2. Physiology
Title

NL 0447418   DNLM

Löwenell, Johann Wilhelm von.
Forebodings and forbearance; what the Fatherland would do if drawn into an European conflict, by Johann Wilhelm von Löwenell Brandenburg-Hohenzollern ... Detroit, Mich., C. Schwappacher and company, 1915.
4 p. l., [13]-264 p. plates, ports. 20cm. $1.25

1. European war, 1914-   —Miscellanea.   I. Title.
Library of Congress   D640.L75   15-27718

NL 0447419   DLC OKentU MiU OClW NjP

Loewenfeld, Albrecht Hoeffer von
    see   Hoeffer von Loewenfeld, Albrecht.

Loewenfeld, Bernhard Joseph Schleis von
see
Schleis von Loewenfeld, Bernhard Joseph, 1731-1800.

Löwenfeld, Christoph Raphael Schleis von
    see   Schleis von Löwenfeld, Christoph Raphael, 1772-1852.

LOEWENFELD, Erwin.
Bereich und anwendung des art. 78 abs.2 der reichsverfassung. Borna-Leipzig, 1914.
8+68+(2) p.
Inaug.-diss. - Breslau.

NL 0447423   MH-L ICRL

Loewenfeld, Erwin.
Die **beschlagnahme,** liquidation und freigabe deutschen vermögens im auslande ... herausgegeben von den rechtsanwälten dr. W. Loewenfeld, dr. Erwin Loewenfeld, dr. Julius Magnus [und] dr. Ernst Wolff ... Berlin, C. Heymanns verlag, 1924-1930.

Loewenfeld, Erwin.
The Mixed courts in Egypt as part of the system of capitulations after the treaty of Montreux, by Dr. Erwin Loewenfeld ...
(*In* Grotius society, London. Problems of peace and war ... London, 1941. 22cm. Vol. 26, p. 83-123)

1. Egypt. Mixed tribunals. 2. Montreux, Switzerland, Treaty of, 1936.
Library of Congress   JX31.G7 vol. 26   42-25097

NL 0447425   DLC WaU-L

Loewenfeld, Erwin, ed.
Ostrecht; monatsschrift für das recht der osteuropäischen staaten, hrsg. von dr. H. Freund, dr. E. Loewenfeld, dr. U. Rukser ... 1.-3. jahrg.; sept. 1925-märz 1927. Berlin, C. Heymann [1925-27]

Loewenfeld, Erwin.
The protection of private property under the minorities protection treaties. By Erwin Loewenfeld ...
(*In* Grotius society, London. Problems of peace and war. London, 1931. 22cm. v. 16, p. 41-64)
Discussion: p. 63-64.

1. Property. 2. Minorities.   A 81-992
Carnegie endow. int. peace.   Library
for Library of Congress   JX31.G7 vol. 16

NL 0447427   NNCE WaU-L DLC

JX4211
.L55
Loewenfeld, Erwin, joint ed.

Loewenfeld, William, 1851-1931, ed.
Das recht der staatsangehörigkeit der europäischen und der aussereuropäischen staaten ... nach dem tode von justizrat dr. W. Loewenfeld herausgegeben von dr. Georg Crusen ... dr. Erwin Loewenfeld ... prof. dr. Georg Maas ... [und] dr. Adolf Siedler ... Berlin, C. Heymann, 1934-

---

Loewenfeld, Erwin.

Andru, Viktor.
Die rechtlichen grundlagen des ungarisch-rumänischen optantenstreites, dargelegt von dr. Viktor Andru ... [und] dr. Erwin Loewenfeld ... Berlin, C. Heymann, 1930.

Loewenfeld, Erwin.
... Der schutz wohlerworbener rechte von ausländern im völkerrecht und in den friedensverträgen; ein vortrag gehalten im Internationalen anwaltsverband ... von dr. Erwin Loewenfeld ... Berlin, R. L. Prager, 1928.
16 p. 24½cm. (Internationale rechtspraxis ... hft. 12)

1. International law, Private. 2. Property. 3. Eminent domain. I. Title.
    30-10291

NL 0447430   DLC NN MH-L

Loewenfeld, Erwin.
Status of stateless persons, by Dr. Erwin Loewenfeld ...
(*In* Grotius society, London. Problems of peace and war ... London, 1942. 22cm. v. 27, p. 59-112)
Bibliographical foot-notes.

1. Citizenship. [1. Statelessness] 2. [Nationalism and] nationality. I. Title.
Carnegie endow. int. peace.   Library   A 42-4362
for Library of Congress   JX31.G7 vol. 27

NL 0447431   NNCE WaU-L DLC

Loewenfeld, F   , 1881-
Studien über den Giroverkehr ... von F. Loewenfeld ... Würzburg, H. Stürtz, 1906.
vi, 61 p. tables, forms. 22cm.
Inaug.-Diss. - Erlangen.
"Literaturverzeichnis": p. [v]-vi.

NL 0447432   MH-L NIC IEN ICRL MH

Loewenfeld, Günther.
... Die anweisung in gesetz und verkehr, von dr. Günther Loewenfeld. Berlin, J. Springer, 1922.
2 p. l., 46 p. 23½cm. (Beiträge zur kenntnis des rechtslebens ... hft. III)

1. Postal service — Germany — Money-orders. 2. Negotiable instruments—Germany. I. Title.
    38-20861

NL 0447433   DLC

Loewenfeld, Hans [Karl] 1874-
Leonhard Kleber und sein Orgeltabulaturbuch, als beitrag zur geschichte der orgelmusik im beginnenden XVI. jahrhundert ... Berlin, Druck von R. Boll, 1897.
81, [1] p., 1 l. 21cm.
Inaug.-diss.—Berlin.
Vita.
"Der inhalt der Tabulatur": p. 70-81.

1. Kleber, Leonhard, d. 1556. 2. Berlin. Königliche bibliothek. Mss. mus. Z26.
Library of Congress   ML410.K51L7   6-9868

NL 0447434   DLC ICRL ICU MH

Vg8
G2
911L
Loewenfeld, Hans Karl, 1874-
Unser Opernrepertoire; ein Vortrag. Leipzig, E.Rowohlt, 1911.
40p. 20cm.

NL 0447435   CtY CoDB

VOLUME 338

Loewenfeld, Hans Karl, 1874–   ed.

ML50
.M939Z3
1908

Mozart, Johann Chrysostom Wolfgang Amadeus, 1756–1791.
¡Die Zauberflöte. Libretto. German¿

Die Zauberflöte, in der Weimarer Fassung der Goethe-Zeit. Mit einer einleitung von Hans Loewenfeld. Leipzig, W. Drugulin, 1908.

Löwenfeld, Heinrich, 1900–
... Ein Beitrag zur Narkolepsiefrage ... Walldorf (Baden), 1937.
Inaug.-Diss. – Heidelberg.
Lebenslauf.

NL 0447437   CtY

LOEWENFELD, Hermann.
Das erkenntniss des reichsgerichts in sachen des rumanischem retrocessionsvertrages und die preussischen verstaatlichungsvertrage. Berlin, 1881.

29 p.

NL 0447438   MH-L

Löwenfeld, Hermann.
Das recht der actien-gesellschaften. Kritik und reformvorschläge, von Hermann Löwenfeld ... Berlin, J. Guttentag (D. Collin) 1879.
viii, 583 p. 22½ᵐ.

1. Stock companies—Germany. 2. Corporation law—Germany.
ɪ. Title.
42-34247

NL 0447439   DLC

Loewenfeld, J.R. Höffer von
see   Höffer von Löwenfeld, J.R.

Loewenfeld, Kurt

Diepenbroick-Grüter, Hans Dietrich von, *firm, Hamburg.*
Allgemeiner porträt-katalog; verzeichnis einer sammlung von 30000 porträts des sechzehnten bis neunzehnten jahrhunderts in holzschnitt, kupferstich, schabkunst und lithographie, mit biographischen notizen. Hamburg, H. D. v. Diepenbroick-Grüter, 1931.

Loewenfeld, Kurt.
Aus meinem Handschriftenmappen. (Briefe berühmter Astronomen und Physiker.) Mit einem Bildnis von Christian von Wolff aus dem Astronomischen Museum der Treptow-Sternwarte und Facsimiles der Handschriften von Cassini, Wolff u. a. Von Dr. Kurt Loewenfeld, ... Berlin, Verlag der Treptow-Sternwarte, 1907.
[2], 46 p. incl. facsim. front. (port.) 27½ᶜᵐ. (Vorträge und Abhandlungen herausgegeben von der Zeitschrift "Das Weltall". Heft 18.)
"Sonderabdruck aus der Illustrierten Zeitschrift für Astronomie und verwandte Gebiete 'Das Weltall', 7. Jahrgang 1906/07."

NL 0447442   ICJ

Loewenfeld, Kurt.
Contributions to the history of science, period of Priestley-Lavoisier-Dalton, based on autograph documents. Manchester, 1913.
50 p. illus.
From vol. 57, part III of Memoirs and proceedings of the Manchester Literary and Philosophical Society, session 1912–1913.

NL 0447443   MH OCU

Loewenfeld, Kurt, ed.
Englischer Besuch in Hamburg im Jahre 1798; wie zwei grosse englische Dichter nach Hamburg reisten und was sie dort sahen, insbesondere ihre höchst merkwürdigen Gespräche mit Herrn Klopstock, Legationsrath und Verfasser der Messiade. Eingeleitet, übersetzt und mit zahlreichen Anmerkungen versehen von Dr. Kurt Loewenfeld. Hamburg: L. Friederichsen & Co. 1927. 91 p. mounted illus. (incl. facsims.) 22½cm.

"Von diesem Buch wurde eine numerierte Sonderausgabe von 450 Exemplaren... gedruckt und den Teilnehmern an der Jahres-Versammlung der Gesellschaft der Bibliophilen in Hamburg am 24. bis 26. September 1927 überreicht... Dies ist Nr. 316."
"Übersetzung aus der 'Biographia literaria' des Samuel Taylor Coleridge, soweit sie auf Hamburg und Klopstock Bezug hat," p. 17–38.
"Literaturverzeichnis," p. 89–91.

744232A. 1. Klopstock, Friedrich William, 1770–1850. 3. Hamburg—lor, 1772–1834. Biographia literaria. Weimar. III. Title.
N.Y.P.L.
Gottlieb, 1724–1803. 2. Wordsworth, Descr. I. Coleridge, Samuel Taylor—II. Gesellschaft der Bibliophilen.
May 10, 1935

NL 0447445   NN InU

Loewenfeld, Kurt.
Ernst Florens Friedrich Chladni (Skizze von Leben und Werk) von Dr. phil. Kurt Loewenfeld ... Mit 3 Tafeln und 1 Figur im Text.
(*In* Naturwissenschaftlicher Verein, Hamburg. Abhandlungen aus dem Gebiete der Naturwissenschaften. Hamburg, 1929. 28½ᵐ. Bd. xxɪɪ, 3.–4. Heft, p. ¡117¿–144. 1 port., 2 facsims., 1 diagr.)
Individual t.-p. included.
Bibliographical foot-notes.

NL 0447446   ICJ NNC

Loewenfeld, Kurt.
Experimentelle untersuchungen über die capillaritätskonstanten wässriger lösungen von kalium- und natriumsalzen sowie von ammoniak ... Berlin, Adler-druckerei, 1905.
43 p. diagrs. on fold. pl. 21ᶜᵐ.
Inaug.-diss.—Rostock.

1. Capillarity.

Library of Congress   QC183.L82
7-16659

NL 0447447   DLC CtY ICRL

Loewenfeld, Leopold, 1847–1924.
Bewusstsein und psychisches Geschehen; die Phänomene des Unterbewusstseins und ihre Rolle in unserem Geistesleben, von Hofrat Dr. L. Loewenfeld ... Wiesbaden, J. F. Bergmann, 1913.
vi, 94 p. 26ᵐᵐ. (*On verso o, t.-p.:* Grenzfragen des Nerven- und Seelenlebens ... Heft 89)
Bibliographical foot-notes.

NL 0447448   ICJ NjP MiU MB NNC DNLM CtY-M IaU CU

Loewenfeld, Leopold, 1847–1924.
—— Die Erschöpfungszustände des Gehirns.
51 pp. 8°. *München, J. A. Finsterlin,* 1882.

NL 0447449   DNLM

WL
L827e
1881

LÖWENFELD, Leopold, 1847–1924.
Experimentelle und kritische Untersuchungen zur Electrotherapie des Gehirns, insbesonders über die Wirkungen der Galvanisation des Kopfes. München, Finsterlin, 1881.
viii, 146 p.

NL 0447450   DNLM ICJ

Loewenfeld, Leopold, 1847–1924, ed.
Grenzfragen des Nerven- und Seelenlebens
see under title

Loewenfeld, Leopold, 1847–
Homosexualität und Strafgesetz. Nach einem in der kriminalistischen Sektion des akademisch-juristischen Vereins zu München am 17. Dezember 1907 gehaltenen Vortrage.
—— Wiesbaden. Bergmann. 1908. 35, (1) pp. [Grenzfragen des Nerven- und Seelenlebens. Heft 57.] 8°.

H190 — Sexual perversion.

NL 0447452   MB IaU CU NjP ICJ MiU PU-L PU CtY

Loewenfeld, Leopold, 1847–
Hypnose und Kunst. Ein Vortrag.
—— Wiesbaden. Bergmann. 1904. (3), 24 pp. [Grenzfragen des Nerven- und Seelenlebens. Heft 28.] 8°.

H193 — Hypnotism. — Fine arts.

NL 0447453   MB IaU CU DNLM CtY PU MiU ICJ

Loewenfeld, Leopold, 1847–
Der Hypnotismus. Handbuch der Lehre von der Hypnose und der Suggestion mit besonderer Berücksichtigung ihrer Bedeutung für Medicin und Rechtspflege. Von Dr. L. Loewenfeld, ... Wiesbaden, J. F. Bergmann, 1901.
xii, 522 p. 26ᶜᵐ.
"Literatur-Uebersicht," p. 490–503.

NL 0447454   ICJ DNLM NNNAM PPC OCl NjP CU MH

Loewenfeld, Leopold, 1847–1924.
Hypnotismus und Medizin, Grundriss der Lehre von der Hypnose und der Suggestion mit besonderer Berücksichtigung der ärztlichen Praxis. Bergmann. München. 1922.
130 p. 8°.

NL 0447455   OClW-H PPC

Löwenfeld, Leopold, 1847–
Lehrbuch der gesammten psycho-therapie, mit einer einleitenden darstellung der hauptthatsachen der medicinischen psychologie, von dr. L. Löwenfeld ... Wiesbaden, J. F. Bergmann, 1897.
xii, 264 p. illus. 23½ᶜᵐ.

1. Therapeutics, Suggestive. ɪ. Title.
19-11009

Library of Congress   RM921.L8

NL 0447456   DLC CtY-M OClW-H ICJ PPC

VOLUME 338

WM
L827m
1887
 LÖWENFELD, Leopold, 1847-1924.
  Die moderne Behandlung der Nerven-
schwäche (Neurasthenie) der Hysterie und
verwandter Leiden, mit besonderer
Berücksichtigung der Luftcuren, Bäder,
Anstaltsbehandlung und der Mitchell-
Playfair'schen Mastcur.   Wiesbaden,
Bergmann, 1887.
  viii, 117 p.

NL   0447457   DNLM

WM
L827m
1889
 LÖWENFELD, Leopold, 1847-1924.
  Die moderne Behandlung der Nerven-
schwäche (Neurasthenie) der Hysterie und
verwandter Leiden, mit besonderer
Berücksichtigung der Luftcuren, Bäder,
Anstaltsbehandlung, und der Mitchell-
Playfair'schen Mastkur. 2., verm. Aufl.
Wiesbaden, Bergmann, 1889.
  x, 131 p.

NL   0447458   DNLM OC1CC ICJ CtY-M PPC

WM
L827m
1895
 LÖWENFELD, Leopold, 1847-1924.
  Die moderne Behandlung der Nervenschwäche (Neurasthenie) der Hysterie und
verwandter Leiden, mit besonderer
Berücksichtigung der Luftkuren, Bäder,
Gymnastik, der Suggestionsbehandlung und
der Mitchell-Playfair'schen Mastkur.
3., verm. Aufl. Wiesbaden, Bergmann,
1895.
  157 p.

NL   0447459   DNLM OC1W

 Loewenfeld, Leopold, 1847-1924.
  Die moderne behandlung der nervenschwäche (neurasthenie)
der hysterie und verwandter leiden. Mit besonderer berücksichtigung der luftkuren, bäder, gymnastik, der psychischen
behandlung, und der Mitchell-Playfair'schen mastkur. Von
dr. L. Loewenfeld ... 4. umgearb. aufl. Wiesbaden, J. F.
Bergmann, 1904.
  vi p., 1 l., 167, ₁1₎ p. 26ᶜᵐ.

 1. Neurasthenia. 2. Hysteria. 3. Therapeutics, Physiological.
4. Therapeutics, Suggestive. I. Title.

            35-25904

 Library of Congress RC415.L68 1904 616.843

NL   0447460   DLC DNLM PPC

 Loewenfeld, Leopold, 1847-
  Musste er kommen? Der Weltkrieg, seine Ursachen und Folgen im Lichte des Kausalitätsgesetzes, von Hofrat Dr. L. Loewenfeld... Wiesbaden: J. F. Bergmann, 1916. 76 p. 8°.

 1. European war, 1914- .—Causes. 2. European war, 1914- .—Philosophy and the war.
N. Y. P. L.   November 26, 1919.

NL   0447461   NN NjP

 Loewenfeld, Leopold, 1847-
  Die nervösen störungen sexuellen ursprungs. Von dr.
L. Löwenfeld ... Wiesbaden, J. F. Bergmann, 1891.
  xi, 169, ₁1₎ p. 21ᶜᵐ.

 1. Neurasthenia. 2. Hygiene, Sexual.

 Library of Congress RC415.L7   9-5604

NL   0447462   DLC DNLM ICJ

BF412
.L75
 Loewenfeld, Leopold, 1847-1924.
  ... О духовной дѣятельности геніальныхъ людей вообще,
и великихъ художниковъ—въ частности. Д-ра мед. Л. Левенфельда (въ Мюнхенѣ). Переводъ съ нѣмецкаго Э. М.
Зиновьевой, подъ редакціею А. А. Крогіуса ... С.-Петер-
бургъ, Типографія акц. общ. Брокгаузъ-Ефронъ, 1904.
  2 p. l., 122 p. 27ᶜᵐ. (Вопросы психо-неврологіи въ общедоступ-
ныхъ очеркахъ, подъ редакціей Л. Левенфельда ... и Г. Куреллы)
 Bibliographical foot-notes.
 "2-е приложеніе къ журналу Вѣстникъ психологіи, криминальной
антропологіи и гипнотизма за 1904 г."

 1. Genius. 2. Creation (Literary, artistic, etc.) 3. Artists. I. Kro-
gius, Avgust Adol'fovich, 1871- ed. II. Zinov'eva, Ė. M., tr. III.
Вѣстникъ психологіи, криминальной антропологіи и гипнотизма
(*transliterated:* Vйestnik psikhologii, kriminal'noĭ antropologii i gipno-
tizma) Supplement. IV. Title.
        Title transliterated: O dukhovnoĭ dйeĭatel'-
        nosti genial'nykh lйudeĭ.

 Library of Congress BF412.L75   44-36359

NL   0447464   DLC

HQ
739
L713
 Loewenfeld, Leopold, 1847-1924.
  On conjugal happiness. Experiences,
reflections, and advice of a medical man, by
Hofrat Dr. L. Loewenfeld; translated from
the third edition, by Ronald E.S. Krohn.
London, John Bale, sons & Danielsson, ltd.,
1912.
  xvi, 293 p. 23 cm.

  1. Marriage. I. Title. II. Krohn, Ronald
E.S., tr.

NL   0447465   NcGU

HQ728 Loewenfeld, Leopold, 1847-
.L84 On conjugal happiness; experiences, reflections and advice
of a medical man, by Hofrat Dr. L. Loewenfeld ... Tr. from
the 3d ed. by Ronald E. S. Krohn ... London, J. Bale, sons
& Danielsson, ltd., 1913.
  xvi, 293 p. 22¼ᶜᵐ.

 1. Marriage.

NL   0447466   ICU MiU DNLM PPC

616.843 Löwenfeld, Leopold, 1847-1924.
L917p Pathologie und therapie der neurasthenie und
hysterie ... Wiesbaden, J. F. Bergmann, 1893-
94.
  2v.

  Paged continuously.
  "Litteraturübersicht": v.2, p. 705ʸ-724.

  1. Neurasthenia. 2. Hysteria.

NL   0447467   IU-M ICJ MH IaU DNLM

 Loewenfeld, Leopold, 1847-
  Die psychischen Zwangserscheinungen. Auf klinischer Grundlage dargestellt, von Dr. L. Loewenfeld, ... Wiesbaden, J. F.
Bergmann, 1904.
  xi, 568 p. 26ᵐᵐ.

NL   0447468   ICJ ICRL DNLM MiU NNNPsI MH PPC NIC

 Loewenfeld, Leopold, 1847-1924.
  Recent advances in the treatment of chronic
diseases of the spinal cord. Trans. by A. M.
Stalker.
  (Volkmann. Clinical lectures. 3d series
p. 345-393. Lond., 1894)

NL   0447469   MB MdBP

Loewenfeld, Leopold, 1847-
 ——. Semestrale Mittheilungen aus der Privat-
heil- und Pflegeanstalt Maxhrum für Nerven-
kranke, München. Inhalt: Ueber Erschöpfungszustände des Gehirns. 1 p. l., 50 pp. 12°.
München, F. Straub, 1882.

NL   0447470   DNLM

WL
L827n
1899
 LÖWENFELD, Leopold, 1847-1924.
  Sexualleben und Nervenleiden; Die
nervösen Störungen sexuellen Ursprungs.
Nebst einem Anhang über Prophylaxe und
Behandlung der sexuellen Neurasthenie.
2., völlig umgearb. und sehr verm. Aufl.
Wiesbaden, Bergmann, 1899.
  vii, 262 p.
  1st ed. has title: Die nervösen
Störungen sexuellen Ursprungs.

NL   0447471   DNLM CtY-M

 Löwenfeld, Leopold, 1847-1924.
  Sexualleben und nervenleiden. Die nervösen störungen
sexuellen ursprungs. Nebst einem anhang über prophylaxe
und behandlung der sexuellen neurasthenie. Von dr. L. Löwenfeld ... 3. bedeutend verm. aufl. Wiesbaden, J. F. Bergmann, 1903.
  2 p. l., ₁III₎-vi p., 1 l., 326 p. 25ᶜᵐ.

  First and second editions published under title: Die nervösen störungen sexuellen ursprungs.
  "Literatur": p. ₁312₎-319.

 1. Neurasthenia. 2. Hygiene, Sexual. 3. Sex (Psychology) I. Title.

            34-38475

 Library of Congress RC415.L7 1903 616.843

NL   0447472   DLC CtY-M DNLM MiU ICJ

WL
L827n
1906
 LÖWENFELD, Leopold, 1847-1924.
  Sexualleben und Nervenleiden; die
Nervösen Störungen sexuellen Ursprungs.
Nebst einem Anhang über Prophylaxe und
Behandlung der sexuellen Neurasthenie.
4., völlig umgearb. und sehr verm. Aufl.
Wiesbaden, Bergmann, 1906.
  viii, 404 p.

NL   0447473   DNLM NNNPsI ICJ

 Loewenfeld, Leopold, 1847-
  Sexualleben und Nervenleiden. Nebst einem Anhang über Prophylaxe und Behandlung der sexuellen Neurasthenie, von Hofrat
Dr. L. Löwenfeld, ... Fünfte zum Teil umgearbeitete und
sehr vermehrte Auflage. Wiesbaden, J. F. Bergmann, 1914.
  viii, 503, ₁1₎ p. 264ᶜᵐ.
  "Literatur," p. ₁483₎-495.

NL   0447474   ICJ MiU DNLM

RC
415
L7
1922
 Löwenfeld, Leopold, 1847-1924.
  Sexualleben und Nervenleiden. Nebst einem
Anhang über Prophylaxe und Behandlung der
sexuellen Neurasthenie. Von dr. L. Löwenfeld.
6. verm. Aufl. München, J. F. Bergmann, 1922.
  viii, 294 p.
  First and second editions published under
title: Die nervösen Störungen sexuellen Ursprungs.
  "Literatur": p. [282]-289.
  1. Neurasthenia. 2. Hygiene, Sexual. 3. Sex
(Psychology). I. Title.

NL   0447475   NSyU CU

 Löwenfeld, Leopold, 1847-1924.
  Somnambulismus und spiritismus, von L. Loewenfeld ... Wiesbaden, Bergmann, 1900.
  3 p. l., 57, ₁1₎ p. illus. 25.5ᶜᵐ. (Grenzfragen des nerven und seelenlebens ... bd. 1, hft.
1)

  1. Somnambulism. 2. Spiritualism.

   MB ICJ NNNPsan
NL   0447476   NNC CtY-M IaU NNNPsI MiU NjP CtY NN MH

VOLUME 338

Loewenfeld, Leopold, 1847–
—— Somnambulismus und Spiritismus. 2. ed.
2 p. l., 71 pp. 8°. Wiesbaden, J. F. Bergmann. 1907.

NL 0447477   DNLM

Loewenfeld, Leopold, 1847–
Student und alkohol. Vortrag gehalten am 21. februar 1910 von dr. L. Loewenfeld. München, M. Rieger (G. Himmer) 1910.
24 p. 24½ᵐ. (On cover: Schriften des Sozialwissenschaftlichen vereins der Universität München. 1910. hft. 6)
"Literatur betreffs der studentischen trinksitten": p. 24.

1. Liquor problem—Germany. 2. Students—Germany.
15–26922

Library of Congress   HV5128.G3L7

NL 0447478   DLC CtY NN

Löwenfeld, Leopold, 1847–1924.
Studien über ätiologie und pathogenese der spontanen Hirnblutungen. Wiesbaden, J.F. Bergmann, 1886.
viii,166p.(incl.tables,1 double) 3 plates(1 col.,1 double) 25cm.

1.Hemorrhage.

NL 0447479   NcD-MC

Loewenfeld, Leopold, 1847–
Die suggestion in ihrer bedeutung für den weltkrieg, von hofrat dr. L. Loewenfeld ... Wiesbaden, J. F. Bergmann, 1917.
4 p. l., ₍7₎–54 p. 26ᵐ. (Added t.-p.: Grenzfragen des nerven- und seelenlebens ... 101)

1. European war, 1914–1918—Causes. 2. Europe—Politics. 3. Mental suggestion.
30–1854

Library of Congress   D511.L63

NL 0447480   DLC DNLM MiU NjP

₍Loewenfeld, Leopold₎ 1847–1924.
Über das eheliche glück; erfahrungen, reflexionen und ratschläge eines arztes. Wiesbaden, J. F. Bergmann, 1906.
xv, 398 p. 21ᵐ.

1. Marriage.
7–36142

Library of Congress   HQ739.L7 1906

NL 0447481   DLC OClW-H

HQ
L827u   LOEWENFELD, Leopold, 1847–1924.
1909   Über das eheliche Glück; Erfahrungen,
Reflexionen und Ratschläge eines
Arztes. 2. Aufl. Wiesbaden,
Bergmann, 1909.
xv, 398 p.

NL 0447482   DNLM

Loewenfeld, Leopold, 1847–
Über das eheliche glück; erfahrungen, reflexionen und ratschläge eines arztes, von hofrat dr. L. Loewenfeld ... 3. aufl. Wiesbaden, J. F. Bergmann, 1912.
xxi, 410 p. 21ᵐ.   M. 5

1. Marriage.   I. Title.
12–16906

Library of Congress   HQ739.L7

NL 0447483   DLC DNLM ICRL ICJ

Loewenfeld, Leopold, 1847–
Über den National-Charakter der Franzosen und dessen Krankhafte Auswüchse (Die Psychopathia gallica) in ihren Beziehungen zum Weltkrieg.
— Wiesbaden. Bergmann. 1914. (6), 42 pp. [Grenzfragen des Nerven- und Seelenlebens. Heft 100.] 25½ cm., in 8s.

K4811 — S.r.c. — France. Soc. sci. — European War, 1914 — Psychopathia gallica.

NL 0447484   MB DNLM MiU CtY MdBJ NjP ICJ NN CU

Loewenfeld, Leopold, 1847–
Ueber die Behandlung von Gehirn- und Rückenmarkskrankheiten vermittelst des Inductionsstromes, von Dr. L. Löwenfeld ... München, J. A. Finsterlin, 1881.
19 p. 22½ᵐ. bound 24½ᵐ.
Bibliographical foot-notes.

NL 0447485   ICJ

Loewenfeld, Leopold, 1847–
Über die dummheit. Eine umschau im gebiete menschlicher unzulänglichkeit. Von dr. L. Loewenfeld ... Wiesbaden, J. F. Bergmann, 1909.
xv, 339, ₍1₎ p. 22ᵐ.

1. Inefficiency, Intellectual.   I. Title.
9–16151

Library of Congress   BF435.L8

NL 0447486   DLC IU DNLM NjP ICJ ICRL

BF435
.L8   Loewenfeld, Leopold, 1847–1924.
1921
Über die Dummheit. Eine Umschau im Gebiete menschlicher Unzulänglichkeit mit einem Anhange: Die menschliche Intelligenz in Vergangenheit und Zukunft. 2. neubearb. Aufl. München, J. F. Bergmann, 1921.
xvi, 358 p.   21cm.

1. Inefficiency, Intellectual.   I. Title: Die Dummheit.

NL 0447487   ViU DNLM TNJ

Loewenfeld, Leopold, 1847–
Über die geistige Arbeitskraft und ihre Hygiene, von Dr. L. Loewenfeld ... . Wiesbaden, J. F. Bergmann, 1905.
vi, 69, [1] p. 26ᵐ. (In Grenzfragen des Nerven- und Seelenlebens, ... , achtunddreissigstes Heft.)

NL 0447488   ICJ CU IaU DNLM CtY MiU MB

Löwenfeld, Leopold, 1847–1924.
Ueber die geniale geistesthätigkeit mit besonderer berücksichtigung des genie's für bildende kunst, von L. Loewenfeld ... Wiesbaden, Bergmann, 1903.
2 p.l., ₍vii₎–x, 104 p.   25½. (Grenzfragen des nerven- und seelenlebens, bd. 3, hft. 21)

1. Genius.
2. Artists.

CU
NL 0447489   NNC NcU WU-M NIC NNPsI ICJ NN MiU CtY

Loewenfeld, Leopold, 1847–
Ueber die Krankenpflege hysterischer Personen. Von Dr. L. Löwenfeld. Berlin, Fischer's Medicin. Buchhandlung H. Kornfeld, 1896.
16 p. 26ᵐ.

NL 0447490   ICJ

613.9   Loewenfeld, Leopold, 1847–1924.
L827u   Über die sexuelle konstitution und andere sexualprobleme. Von dr. L. Loewenfeld ... Über die sexuelle konstitution. Erotik und sinnlichkeit. Die libido als triebkraft im geistigen leben. Wiesbaden, J. F. Bergmann, 1911.
231p.

Bibliographical foot-notes.

1. Sex.

NL 0447491   IU-M ICRL NSyU CU ICJ DNLM

Loewenfeld, Leopold, 1847–1924.
Ueber Platzangst und verwandte Zustände. München, J.A. Finsterlin, 1882.
43 p., 1 l.   8°.

NL 0447492   DNLM

Löwenfeld, Leopold, 1847–1924.
Untersuchungen zur elektrotherapie des rückenmarkes, von dr. L. Löwenfeld ... München, Finsterlin, 1883.
3 p. l., 74 p.

"Literatur-verzeichniss": p. ₍72₎–74.

1. Spinal cord - Diseases. 2. Electrotherapeutics.

NL 0447493   NNC DNLM DP ICJ

Löwenfeld, Leopold, 1847–1924.
Zur mittelschulreform in Bayern. Bemerkungen vom ärztlichen standpunkte, von dr. Leopold Löwenfeld ... München, T. Ackermann, 1891.
22 p. 23ᵐ.

1. School hygiene—Bavaria.   I. Title.
E 12–1616

Library, U. S. Bur. of   Education LB3409.B2L8

NL 0447494   DHEW

Löwenfeld, Otto: Der Beamtenstreik. [Maschinenschrift.]   v, 67 S.
4°. —Auszug: o. O. (1923). 2 Bl. 8°
Breslau, R.- u. staatswiss. Diss. v. 20. Sept. 1923   [U 23. 1102

NL 0447495   ICRL

Loewenfeld, Philipp.
Pensionskassen und arbeitsvertrag   von Philipp Loewenfeld. München und Berlin, J. Schweitzer (A. Sellier) 1911.
v. 23½ᵐ.
"Literatur": v. 1, p. ₍v₎–vii.

1. Old age pensions. 2. Labor contract.   I. Title.
12–14521

Library of Congress   HD7106.G3L8

NL 0447496   DLC ICRL CtY NcD ICJ

VOLUME 338

Loewenfeld, Philipp.
Das Strafrecht als politische Waffe. Berlin, J. H. W.
Dietz Nachf. [*1933*]
48 p. 22 cm. (Die Sozialistische Rechtsidee, Heft 1)

1. Criminal law—Germany—Addresses, essays, lectures. 2. Criminal procedure—Germany—Addresses, essays, lectures. 3. Justice and politics—Germany.   I. Title.   (Series)

55-50492

NL 0447497   DLC

Löwenfeld, Raphael, 1854–1910, ed.

Z1007
.D48   **Deutsche** Literaturzeitung für Kritik der internationalen
Wissenschaft. 1.– Jahrg.; 2. Okt. 1880–
Berlin, etc., Akademie Verlag, etc.

Löwenfeld, Raphael, 1854–1910.
Gespräche über und mit Tolstoj. Von Raphael Löwenfeld. Berlin, R. Wilhelmi, 1891.
3 p. l., 122 p. front. (port.) 18 cm.

1. Tolstoi, Lev Nikolaevich, graf, 1828–1910.   I. Title.

PG3386.L6   19—8947

NL 0447499   DLC

Loewenfeld, Raphael, 1854–1910.
...Gespraeche über und mit Tolstoj... Leipzig: E. Diederichs, 1901. 170 p. front. (port.) 3. ed., enl. 12°.

1. Tolstoi, Lev Nikolayevich, graf,   1828–1910.   November 17, 1927
N. Y. P. L.

NL 0447500   NN CU InU MH OC1

Löwenfeld, Raphael, 1854–1910, tr.
PG3367
.G5K53   **Tolstoi, Lev Nikolaevich,** *graf,* 1828–1910.
... Der herr und sein knecht; mit vierzehn holzschnitten von
Frans Masereel. Berlin, Transmare [*1930*]

Löwenfeld, Raphael, 1854–1910.
Johann Kochanowski (Joannes Cochanovius) und seine lateinischen dichtungen. Ein beitrag zur literaturgeschichte der Slaven, von Raphael Löwenfeld. Posen, J. Jolowicz, 1877.
viii, 158 p. 21½ᶜᵐ.

1. Kochanowski, Jan, 1530–1584.

33-32488

Library of Congress   PA8540.K6L6   928.9185

NL 0447502   DLC ICU OC1W NN

Loewenfeld, Raphael, 1854–1910.
Johann Kochanowski (Joannes Cochanovius) und seine
lateinischen Dichtungen; ein beitrag zur
Literaturgeschichte der Slaven. Posen, Jolowicz, 1877
viii, 158 p.
Photoreproduction
Film Mas 723
——— Microfilm, negative, of copy in the New York
Public Library

NL 0447503   MH

Löwenfeld, Raphael, 1854–1910.
Leo N. Tolstoj, sein Leben, seine Werke, seine Weltanschauung. Berlin, R. Wilhelmi, 1892–
v. 19 cm.

1. Tolstoi, Leo Nikolaevich, graf, 1828–1910.

PG3385.L6   55-44000

NL 0447504   DLC MB MH MdBP

PG3385   **Löwenfeld, Raphael, 1854–1910.**
L6   Leo N.Tolstoi, sein Leben, seine Werke,
1901   seine Weltanschauung. 2. Aufl. Leipzig,
E.Diederichs, 1901–
v. 19cm.

NL 0447505   CSt OOxM CU MiU

Loewenfeld, Raphael, 1854–1910.
Łukasz Górnicki, jego życie i dzieła; przyczynek
do dziejów humanizmu w Polsce. Warszawa, Nakł.
Redakcyi Wędrowca, 1884
xii, 262,iip.

NL 0447506   MH

Loewenfeld, Raphael, 1854–
Lukasz Gornicki. Sein Leben und seine Werke. Ein Beitrag zur
Geschichte des Humanismus in Polen.
— Breslau. Koebner. 1884. (1), ix, 223 pp. 8°.

F7282 — Górnicki, Łukasz. 1527–1603.

NL 0447507   MB ICN

Löwenfeld, Raphael, 1854–1910, tr.

Mantegazza, Paolo, 1831–1910.
Physiognomik und mimik, von Paolo Mantegazza. Mit
mehr als hundert original-zeichnungen von Hector und Eduard
Ximenes. Vom verfasser genehmigte übersetzung von R.
Löwenfeld ... Leipzig, B. Elischer nachf., 1890.

[**Löwenfeld, Raphael**] 1854–1910.
Schutzjuden oder staatsbürger? Von einem jüdischen
staatsbürger ... 3. aufl. verm. um stimmen der presse
und zuschriften aus dem publikum. Berlin, Schweitzer
& Mohr, 1893.
3 p. l., [3]–27 p. 21¼ᶜᵐ.

1. Jews in Germany. 2. Jews—Political and social conditions.   I. Title.

23-3933

Library of Congress   DS135.G33L6

NL 0447509   DLC OCH

Löwenfeld, Raphael, 1854–1910
Warum die menschen sich betäuben
see under   Tolstoi, Lev Nikolaievich, graf,
1828–1910.

NL 0447511   MH

LÖWENFELD, S[amuel],*1854–*
Elf papstbullen. n.p.,[18–?]
pp.(2).
Without title-page. Caption title.

NL 0447512   MH

Löwenfeld, Samuel, 1854–   ed.

Catholic church. *Pope.*
Epistolae pontificum romanorum ineditae; edidit S. Loewenfeld. Lipsiae, Veit et comp., 1885.

LOEWENFELD, Samuel. 1854–   *2309.
Geschichte des päpstlichen Archivs bis zum Jahre 1817.
(*In* Historisches Taschenbuch. Folge 6, Jahrgang 5, pp. 3
Leipzig, 1886.)

NL 0447514   MB

**Loewenfeld, Samuel, 1854–. Geschicht-
schreiber der deutschen vorzeit. 5 pp. (Deutsch. rundschau. v. 59, 1889, p. 140.)**

NL 0447515   MdBP

Löwenfeld, Samuel, 1854–   ed.
Gesta abbatum fontanellensium
see under   Gesta abbatum fontanellensium.

LÖWENFELD, Samuel,*1854–*
In den Bibliotheken der Normandie; bericht
über eine reise im august 1882. [Hannover,
1884].
sm.8°. pp.(29).
Neues archiv d.Gesellschaft f.ältere deutsch
geschichtskunde,1884,ix.359–387.
The object of the journey was a search for
papal documents and other historical manuscripts.

NL 0447517   MH

Löwenfeld, Samuel, 1854–
Leo von Vercelli ... Posen, Merzbach'sche buchdruckerei, 1877.
3 p. l., 74 p. 22ᶜᵐ.
Inaug.-diss.—Göttingen.
Vita.

1. Leo, von Vercelli, d. 1026.

25-23290

Library of Congress   DD137.9.L4L6

NL 0447518   DLC

VOLUME 338

LOEWENFELD, S[amuel], *1854-*
Päpstliche originalurkunden im Pariser
National archiv, von Formosus bis Coelestin
III. n.p., [18?]

pp. (32).
Half-title only.
Extract from "Neues archiv etc. viii."

NL 0447519   MH

LÖWENFELD, Samuel, *1854-*
Papsturkunden in Italien; ein nachtrag.
Wien, 1880.

1. 8°.

NL 0447520   MH

Loewenfeld, Samuel, 1854-   ed.

Catholic church. *Pope.*
Regesta pontificum romanorum ab condita ecclesia ad annum post Christum natum MCXCVIII, edidit Philippus Jaffé.
Editionem secundam correctam et auctam auspiciis Gulielmi
Wattenbach ... curaverunt S. Loewenfeld, F. Kaltenbrunner,
P. Ewald ... Lipsiae, Veit et comp., 1885-88.

Loewenfeld, Samuel, 1854-
Die wahrheit über der Juden Antheil an
Verbrechen. Auf Grund amtlicher Statistik.
Berlin: Stuhr, 1881.
16 p.

NL 0447522   OCH NcD

LOEWENFELD, Samuel, 1854-   *2309.1
Zur neuesten Geschichte des päpstlichen Archivs.
(*In* Historisches Taschenbuch. Folge 6, Jahrgang 6, p
301. Leipzig, 1887.)

NL 0447523   MB

Loewenfeld, Theodor, 1848-1921, ed.
FOR OTHER EDITIONS
SEE MAIN ENTRY
Germany. *Laws, statutes, etc.*
J. v. Staudingers Kommentar zum Bürgerlichen gesetzbuch
und dem Einführungsgesetze, hrsg. von dr. Theodor Loewenfeld ... dr. Ludwig Kuhlenbeck ... dr. Theodor Engelmann
... dr. Erwin Riezler ... dr. Karl Kober ... [und] dr. Felix
Herzfelder ... 7./8. neubearb. aufl. München und Berlin,
J. Schweitzer, 1912-14.

LÖWENFELD, Theodor, *1848-1921.*
Die selbstständige actio de in rem verso.
München, 1873.

(1)+54+(1) p.
Inaugl-diss.-[München].

NL 0447525   MH-L CtY-L

LOEWENFELD, Theodor, *1848-1921.*
Ueber den dienst-, werk-und auftragsvertrag
nach dem entwurfe des bürgerlichen gesetzbuches
Berlin, 1889.

75 p.
"Sonderabdruck aus heft 10 der Gutachten
aus dem anwaltstande über die erste lesung
des entwurfs eines bürgerlichen gesetzbuchs
für das Deutsche Reich."

NL 0447526   MH-L

LOEWENFELD, Theodor, *1848-1921.*
Zur lehre von den sog. entgeltlichen und unentgeltlichen rechtsgeschäften. München, 1877.

(1)+78 p.
Habilitationsschrift.

NL 0447527   MH-L

Loewenfeld, Victor [Julius].
Die Entschuldungsaktion der ostpreussischen Landschaft.
Borna-Leipzig: R. Noske, 1912.   ix, 81 p., 1 l.   8°.

Dissertation, Erlangen. Bibliography, p. 7-9.

1. Credit (Agricultural), Germany: Prussia.
N. Y. P. L.   December 17, 1912.

NL 0447528   NN NIC ICRL DLC MH CtY MiU

Löwenfeld, Viktor
see Lowenfeld, Viktor.

Löwenfeld, Walther.
Die österreichischen steuern für die praxis erläutert von dr.
Walther Loewenfeld ... 2., erweiterte aufl. Wien, Manz,
1928.

vii, [1], 158 p. 18½ᵐ.

"Die österreichischen steuern ... Nachtrag 1" ([5] p.) laid in.

1. Taxation—Austria—Law.   I. Austria (1918-   ) Laws, statutes, etc.   II. Title.

28-25892

NL 0447530   DLC CSt-H

Loewenfeld, Walther.
Die österreichischen Steuern, für die Praxis erläutert von Dr.
Walther Loewenfeld...3., erw. Aufl.   Wien, Manz, 1931.
vii, 11, p., 1 l., 160 p.   18cm.

"Die österreichischen Steuern...Nachtrag" 11 p., 1 l., inserted.

269340B. 1. Taxation—Jurisp.—   Austria.
N. Y. P. L.   May 8, 1944

NL 0447531   NN

Loewenfeld, Walther.
Die österreichischen steuern, für die praxis erläutert von dr.
Walther Loewenfeld ... 4., erweiterte aufl. Wien, Manz, 1937.
vii, [1], 166 p.   17ᵐ.

"Einlageblatt zu dem buche Die österreichischen steuern": 1 leaf,
laid in.

1. Taxation—Austria—Law.   I. Title.

38-20870

NL 0447532   DLC

Loewenfeld, Wilhelm.
Erlaeuterndes verzeichnis der in der gemaeldesammlung W. L. privatier und realitaetenbesitzer in
Muenchen befindlichen gemaelde alter und zeitgenoessischer meister. [Muenchen, Bruckmann,
1897]

NL 0447533   PPPM

Löwenfeld, Wilhelm.
Katalog von gemälden alter meister, galerie Wilhelm Löwenfeld, Muenchen (nachlass) ... Versteigerung ... den 6. februar
1906 ... Rudolph Lepke's kunst-auctions-haus, Berlin ... mit
25 lichtdrucktafeln illustrirter katalog ... [Berlin, Druck von
A. Seydel & cie., g. m. b. h., 1906]

67, [1], p. xxv. pl. 30½ᵐ.

1. Paintings—Private collections.

Library of Congress   N5265.L6

44-36542

NL 0447534   DLC

Loewenfeld, William, 1851-1931.
Die beschlagnahme, liquidation und freigabe deutschen vermögens im auslande ... herausgegeben von den rechtsanwälten dr. W. Loewenfeld, dr. Erwin Loewenfeld, dr.
Julius Magnus [und] dr. Ernst Wolff ... Berlin, C. Heymanns verlag, 1924-1930.

NL 0447534   DLC

Loewenfeld, William, 1851-
Derecho matrimonial de los estados europeos y sus colonias,
obra escrita con la colaboración de distinguidos magistrados,
profesores y letrados de las diversas naciones, arreglada por
J. Hahn ... Publicada por los doctores Franz Leske ... y
W. Loewenfeld ... Traducida directamente del alemán, con
un prólogo y notas complementarias por d. José María
Planas y Casals ... con la colaboración de los doctores d.
Joaquín Giralt y Verdaguer y d. Dalmacio Iglesias y García
... 2. ed. Barcelona, Tip. El Anuario de la exportación,
1908.

Loewenfeld, William, 1851-   joint author.

Goldmann, Eduard.
Formularbuch für die freiwillige gerichtsbarkeit unter mitwirkung von j.-r. Gerhard, j.-r. dr. Felix Landau ... [u. a.,]
hrsg. von Eduard Goldmann ... dr. Ernst Heinitz ... dr. W.
Loewenfeld ... [und] dr. Walter Zander ... Berlin, C. Heymann, 1928-

Loewenfeld, William, 1851-
Das internationale privatrecht der europäischen und aussereuropäischen staaten ... herausgegeben von justizrat dr. W.
Loewenfeld und dr. Walther v. Simson. 1.-   teil.
Berlin, C. Heymanns verlag, 1929-

Loewenfeld, William, 1851-1931, ed.

Makarov, Aleksandr Nikolaevich.
... Die quellen des internationalen privatrechts, zusammengestellt und systematisch geordnet von A. N. Makarov ...
hrsg. von justizrat dr. W. Loewenfeld und dr. Walther v. Simson ... Berlin, C. Heymann. 1929.

Loewenfeld, William, 1851-1931, ed.
Das recht der staatsangehörigkeit der europäischen und der
aussereuropäischen staaten ... nach dem tode von justizrat dr.
W. Loewenfeld herausgegeben von dr. Georg Crusen ... dr.
Erwin Loewenfeld ... prof. dr. Georg Maas ... [und] dr. Adolf
Siedler ... Berlin, C. Heymann, 1934-

v. 26ᵐ. (*Added t.-p.*: Die Rechtsverfolgung im internationalen
verkehr ... 7. bd.)

CONTENTS.—1. Die europäischen staaten.

1. Citizenship—Europe. 2. Nationalism and nationality.   I. Crusen,
Georg, 1867-   ed. II. Loewenfeld, Erwin, joint ed. III. Maas, Georg,
1863-   joint ed. IV. Siedler, Adolf, joint ed. V. Title.

34-22900 Revised

Library of Congress   JX4211.L55

[r43c2]

323.61

NL 0447540   DLC

VOLUME 338

Loewenfeld, William, 1851-   joint ed.

Die rechtsverfolgung im internationalen verkehr. Darstellung der justizorganisation, des civilprozessrechts, des konkursrechts, der erbschaftsregulierung und der konsulargerichtsbarkeit in den europäischen und aussereuropäischen staaten. Unter mitwirkung von landgerichtsrath R. Altsmann in Berlin, advokat dr. Alves Sá in Lissabon ¡u. a.¡ ... hrsg, von dr. Franz Leske ... und dr. W. Loewenfeld ... Berlin, C. Heymanns verlag, 1895-19

NL 0447542   MH-L

Leowenfeld, William, 1851-1931, ed.
Der zivilprozess in den europäischen Staaten und ihren Kolonien. Berlin, 1930.
4°.
Edited by W. Loewenfeld and Richard Kann.

NL 0447542   MH-L

Loewenfeld, William, 1851-1931, ed.
Der Zivilprozess in den europäischen Staaten und ihren Kolonien. ¡2. Aufl.¡ Hrsg. von W. Loewenfeld, Friedrich Steuber und Richard Kann. Berlin, C. Heymann, 1933.
xxxii, 798 p. (Die Rechtsverfolgung im internationalen Verkehr, 1. Bd.)

"Neue Bearbeitung des Zivilprozessrechts der Bände I-III."

NL 0447543   NNC-L

LOEWENFELD-RUSS, Hans.
Ernährungswirtschaftliche gegenwartsprobleme in Österreich. Wien, Manzsche verlags-und universitätsbuchhandlung, 1919.

NL 0447544   MH

Loewenfeld-Russ, Hans.
Die regelung der volks-ernährung im kriege, von dr. Hans Loewenfeld-Russ ... Wien, Hölder-Pichler-Tempsky a.-g.; New Haven, Yale university press, 1926.
xxvi, 403 p. incl. facsims., diagrs. 25ᶜᵐ. (Added t.-p.: ¡Carnegie endowment for international peace. Division of economics and history¡ Wirtschafts- und sozialgeschichte des weltkrieges ... Österreichische und ungarische serie)
Half-title: Carnegie-stiftung für internationalen frieden. Abteilung für volkswirtschaft und geschichte.
"Literatur und quellen": p. ¡xiii¡-xv.
1. European war, 1914-1918—Food question—Austria.   I. Title.
                                                       26-21752
Library of Congress   HC56.C34 no. 7
————— Copy 2.   HD9015.A8L6

WaTC MtU IdU CaBVaU WaSp WaS
OC1W MiU PU PBm PHC CaBVa OrU DNW OrU NcRS NN MB
NL 0447545   DLC NNUN MU PPAmP ICJ PSC OCU OU OC1

Löwenfelder, Gertraud, 1925-
Die Bühnendekoration am Münchner Hoftheater von den Anfängen der Oper bis zur Gründung des Nationaltheaters, 1651-1778; ein Beitrag zur Münchner Theatergeschichte. ¡München¡ 1955.
11, 148, 25 l. 29 cm.
Typescript (carbon copy)
Inaug.-Diss.—Munich.
Vita.
Bibliography: leaves 19-25 (3rd group)

1. Munich. Nationaltheater. 2. Theater—Munich—Hist.
3. Munich—Theaters.
NA6840.G5M852   58-33332

NL 0447546   DLC

Löwenfels, Gottfried Ferdinand von Buckisch und
     see Buckisch und Löwenfels, Gottfried
Ferdinand von, 1645-1700(ca.)

Löwenfels, M   W.
Gustav Struve's leben, nach authentischen quellen und von ihm selbst mitgetheilten notizen. Basel, Helbig und Scherb, 1848.
pp. 52.

NL 0447548   MH

Loewengard, Heidi Huberta (Freybe)
see
Albrand, Martha.

Loewengard, Joseph M.
Die internationale radiotelegraphie im internationalen recht, von Joseph M. Loewengard. Berlin und Leipzig, Dr. W. Rothschild, 1914.
4 p. l., 62 p. 23½ᶜᵐ. (Added t.-p.: Die rechtseinheit ... hft. xiii)
"Literatur-verzeichnis": verso 3d-4th prelim. leaf.

1. Title.
                                                       16-4632

NL 0447550   DLC CtY-L

Loewengard, M¡ax¡.
Auch einige Worte über das neue Gebetbuch im Hamburger Tempel. Tübingen: L.F. Fues, 1842.
45 p.

Bd. with: Leon, Juda, pseud., ¡i.e. M. Loewengard.¡ Beiträge zur Kritik der Reformbestrebungen in der Synagoge. Stuttgart, 1841.

NL 0447551   OCH

Loewengard, M¡ax¡.
Jehova, nicht Moloch, war der Gott der alten Hebräer. Entgegnung auf ¡F.W.¡ Ghillany's Werk: "die Menschenopfer der alten Hebräer". Berlin: H. Schultze, 1843.
43 (1) p.

NL 0447552   OCH

781.3   Loewengard, Max Julius, 1860-1915.
L825a   ... Aufgaben zur harmonielehre im anschluss an des verfassers lehrbuch der harmonie. Fünfte verbesserte auflage. Berlin, A. Stahl, 1919.
1 p.l., 38p. music. 21½cm.

NL 0447553   ViFreM

MT   Loewengard, Max Julius, 1860-1915.
50   Harmony. Translated from the German
L82   by Helen M. Peacock. Berlin, A. Stahl,
1905   1905.
           108 p. 21cm.

1. Harmony. I. Peacock, Helen M tr.

NL 0447554   NIC IaU OC1 CLU

Loewengard, Max Julius, 1860-1915.
Harmony modernized; a course equally adapted for self-instruction or for a teacher's manual, by Max Loewengard, tr. from the 6th augm. and thoroughly rev. German ed., by Dr. Th. Baker. New York, G. Schirmer; Boston, Boston music co., 1910.
vi, 145 p. 22½ᶜᵐ.

1. Harmony. I. Baker, Theodore, 1851-1934, tr.
                                                  10—16638
Library of Congress   MT50.L825B2

WaPS WaS Or OrStbM WaSp WaWW WaT
MtBuM WaSpG WaTC MtBC MtU OrCS OrP OrPR OrU Wa WaE
NL 0447555   DLC OrSaW OrU-M CaBVaU OrU IdB IdPI IdU

Loewengard, Max Julius, 1860-
... Harmony modernized; a course equally adapted for self-instruction or for a teacher's manual, by Max Loewengard. Translated from the sixth augmented and thoroughly revised German edition by Dr. Th. Baker. New York, Schirmer, 1915.
vi, 145 p. music. 22½ cm.

At head of title: Third edition.

1. Harmony. I. Baker, Theodore, 1851-   tr.

NL 0447556   NNC

Loewengard, Max Julius, 1860-
... Lehrbuch der harmonie. 7. aufl. ... Berlin, A. Stahl, 1909.
vii, ¡1¡, 132 p. 21½ᶜᵐ.

1. Harmony.
                                                  11-12309
Library of Congress   MT50.L827

NL 0447557   DLC

Loewengard, Max Julius, 1860-
Lehrbuch der Harmonie. 9.Aufl. Berlin, A. Stahl, 1914.
vii, 132 p. 22 cm.

NL 0447558   PLatS ViFreM

Loewengard, Max Julius, 1860-1915.
Lehrbuch der harmonie; 14. aufl. Berlin, Stahl, 1930.
vii [1], 132, p. illus. (music) O.

NL 0447559   PP

MT   Loewengard, Max Julius, 1860-1915.
50   Lehrbuch der Harmonie als Leitfaden für
L82   den Unterricht sowie zum Selbststudium.
           Berlin, Raabe & Plothow, 1892.
           vi, 90 p. music. 22cm.

1. Harmony.

NL 0447560   NIC

Loewengard, Max Julius, 1860-
... Lehrbuch der musikalischen Formen. Berlin: M. Staegemann, 1904. 111 p. facsim., illus. (music.) 8°.
Imprint corrected with stamp of A. Stahl, Berlin.

298644A. 1. Musical form.
N. Y. P. L.   June 15, 1927

NL 0447561   NN NcU

VOLUME 338

Leowengard, Max Julius, 1860–
Lehrbuch des Canons und der Fuge.   Berlin,
Verlag Dreililien [Vorwort, 1902]
86 p.   music.   22 cm.

NL 0447562   NcU

Loewengard, Max Julius, 1860-1915.
Lehrbuch des Contrapunkts. Berlin, Dreililien,
1902

100 p.

NL 0447563   MH

Loewengard, Max Julius, 1860–
Lehrbuch des Contrapunkts. 2. veränderte
Aufl. Berlin, Verlag Dreililien, 1907.
101 p. 22 cm.

NL 0447564   PLatS NcU

Loewengard, Max Julius, 1860–
A manual of counterpoint, by Max Loewengard; translated
from the German by Frederick L. Liebing.   Berlin: Verlag
Dreililien, 1908. 99 p.   illus. (music.)   8°.

298647A.   1. Counterpoint. 2. Lie-   bing, Frederick L., translator.
N.Y.P.L.   June 8, 1927

NL 0447565   NN

Loewengard, Max Julius, 1860–
A manual of harmony/by Max Loewengard; compiled and
arranged from the German, by Frederick L. Liebing.   Berlin:
A. Stahl, 1907. vi, 118 p.   illus. (music.)   8°.

298521A.   1. Harmony. 2. Liebing,   Frederick L., translator.
N.Y.P.L.   June 8, 1927

NL 0447566   NN NcU

Loewengard, Max Julius, 1860–
... Praktische anleitung zum generalbassspiel, zum
harmonisieren, transponieren und modulieren ... Hamburg, A. J. Benjamin [*1913]
2 p. l., 68 p. 21½cm.   M. 2.50

1. Thorough-bass.
Library of Congress   MT49.L78   13-15824

NL 0447567   DLC

Loewengard, Max Julius, 1860-1915.
Serenata für Orchester. Partitur.
Frankfurt a/M. [188-?] 15 pp. L. 8°.

April 11,   1902.
E3681 — Serenades. Orchestra.

NL 0447568   MB

Loewengard (Oscar) [1878–   ]. *Ueber
Hygroma colli congenitum. 32 pp. 8°. München, Kastner & Lossen. 1901.*

NL 0447569   DNLM

Loewengard, Paul
La splendeur catholique; du judaisme à
l'Église. [2. éd.] Paris, Perrin, 1910.
298 p. (Librairie académique)

WA
16350

NL 0447570   CtY NjPT

Löwenhalt, Jesaias Rompler von

See

Rompler von Löwenhalt, Jesaias, ca. 1610–
ca. 1660.

Loewenhard (Henri-Stanislaus) [1877–   ].
*Complications génitales de l'appendicite chez
la femme. 96 pp. 8°. Paris, 1904, No. 535.*

NL 0447572   DNLM

Löwenhard, Percy.
Polyglott-Codex; internationaler Wörter-Codex. International words-codex. Hrsg. von Percy Löwenhard und
Welda Löwenhard-Müller. Wien, M. Müller [*1948]
126 p. 21 cm.

1. Language and languages—Glossaries, vocabularies, etc.
I. Löwenhard, Welda (Müller) joint author. II. Title.

P341.L6   51-19949

NL 0447573   DLC NN

Löwenhard, Siegismundus Eduard
see Löwenhardt, Sigismundus Eduard,
1796-1875.

Loewenhard (Stanislas). *Quelques recherches sur l'atrophie musculaire progressive
avec la dégénérescence graisseuse. 64 pp. 4°.
Paris, 1867. No. 212.*

NL 0447575   DNLM PPC

Löwenhard, Welda (Müller) joint author.

Löwenhard, Percy.
Polyglott-Codex; internationaler Wörter-Codex. Inter-
national words-codex. Hrsg. von Percy Löwenhard und
Welda Löwenhard-Müller. Wien, M. Müller [*1948]

P341
.L6

LÖWENHARDT, Eduard.
Ueber Gott, geist und unsterblichkeit. I.
bd. Wolgast, 1875.

I. Ueber Gott in der Jahr. 1875.

NL 0447577   MH

Löwenhardt, Elisabeth, 1893–
... Wirkung der künstlichen Höhensonne
(Quecksilberdampfquarzlampe) auf Blut,
Nieren und Temperatur ... Greifswald, 1919.
76 p. 1 l., incl. tables.
Inaug.-Diss. - Greifswald.
Lebenslauf.

NL 0447578   MiU CtY

Löwenhardt, Emil.
Didaktik und Methodik des Chemie-Unterrichts, von Dr. Emil
Löwenhardt, ... München, C. H. Beck'sche Verlagsbuchhand-
lung, 1920.
[4], 115, [1] p. 24cm.
Bibliographical foot-notes.

NL 0447579   ICJ ICRL

540.7
L82g

Löwenhardt, Emil.
...Grundzüge der chemie für höhere knaben-
und mädchenschulen mit verkürztem chemie-
unterricht... 6. aufl. mit anhang "Chemie und
luftschutz."   Leipzig, B.G. Teubner, 1933–
v. illus. 23cm.

At head of title: Löwenhardt. Chemisches
unterrichtswerk.

1. Chemistry— Study and teaching. I. Title:
Chemie und   luftschutz.

NL 0447580   LU

Löwenhardt, Emil
Lehrbuch der Chemie für höhere Knabenschulen. 6.Aufl.
Leipzig, Teubner, 1928-29

2 v. (His Chemisches Unterrichtswerk)
Vol.2: 4.Aufl. von E.Löwenhardt, O.Prölss, F.Meinecke

NL 0447581   MH

QD33
.L82
(Ed)

Löwenhardt, Emil.
Lehrbuch der chemie für lyzeen und höhere mädchenschulen, von prof. dr. E. Löwenhardt ... 5. aufl. ... Leipzig [etc.] B. G. Teubner, 1925.
v, [1], 150 p. illus., diagrs. 22cm.

1. Chemistry.

NL 0447582   ICU

Löwenhardt, Emil.
Leitfaden für die chemischen Schülerübungen zur
praktischen Einführung in die Chemie. 5.Aufl. Leipzig,
Teubner, 1929

NL 0447583   MH NcU

Löwenhardt, Emil.
Organische Chemie in der Prima der Oberrealschule, von
Oberlehrer Dr. Emil Löwenhardt. [Halle (Saale) Gebauer-
Schwetschke'sche Buchdruckerei, 1896]
18 p. 26cm.

Programm—Oberrealschule, Halle a. S.
Bibliographical foot-notes.

NL 0447584   ICJ

Loewenhardt, Emil Oscar, [1827-1862]
*De pathologia annorum climactericorum. 30
pp. 8°. Halis, typ. Ploetzianis, 1851.*

NL 0447585   DNLM

VOLUME 338

Loewenhardt, Emil Oscar , 1827-69.
——. De tracheotomia contra epilepsiam adhi-
benda. Socio ad respondendum sunto C.
Schweigger. 16 pp. 8°. *Halæ, typ. Plœtzia-
wis,* 1855.
                                      C.

NL 0447586   DNLM

B610.5 ¡LÖWENHARDT, Emil Oscar¿ 1827-1869.
A154   Die zählung der geisteskranken im
v.23   grossherzogthum Mecklenburg-Schwerin im
        jahre 1865... Berlin, A. Hirschwald,
        1866.
          vi, 55, ₁1₂ p. 23cm. (Supplement-
        heft zum XXIII. bande der Allgemeinen
        zeitschrift für psychiatrie)

          Introduction signed: Dr. Löwenhardt.
          1. Insanity in Mecklenburg-Schwerin.
          2. Insanity.   Statistics.

NL 0447587   MnU DNLM

Loewenhardt, Felix, 1862-
Versuche ueber das schicksal und die wirkungsweise
elastischer ligaturen ...
Inaug. diss. Halle, 1884.

NL 0447588   ICRL DNLM

Loewenhardt, Felix, 1892-
Ueber die simulation innerer krankheiten.
Breslau, 1918.
Inaug.-Diss. - Breslau
Lebenslauf.

NL 0447589   ICRL

Loewenhardt, Felix E. R.
   ...Bericht über die Tätigkeit der Wutschutzabteilung am
Hygienischen Institut der Universität Breslau vom 1. April 1918
bis 31. März 1919, erstattet von Dr. med. Felix E. R. Loewenhardt
... Berlin: R. Schoetz, 1921. 14 p. 8°. (Prussia. Medi-
zinal-Abteilung «Ministerium des Innern». Veröffentlichungen
aus dem Gebiete der Medizinalverwaltung. Bd. 14, Heft 4.)

1. Hydrophobia. 2. Series.
N. Y. P. L.   June 29, 1922.

NL 0447590   NN

Löwenhardt, Oskar Aemilius
        see Löwenhardt, Emil Oscar, 1827-1869.

Loewenhardt (Paul) [1862-]. *Ueber
die Aetiologie und Behandlung der nichttrau-
matischen Hydrocele. 29 pp., 1 l. 8°. *Berlin,
M. Goedecke,* 1886.

NL 0447592   DNLM

Löwenhardt, Paul Eduard.
Aphorismen zur geburtshilflichen Chirurgie, von Dr P. E.
Löwenhardt ... . Berlin, A. Hirschwald, 1871.
    vi, [2], 105 p. 24cm.

NL 0447593   ICJ DNLM ICRL

Loewenhardt, Paul Eduard.
De epilepsia.
Inaug. Diss. Halle, 1857.
Bibl.

NL 0447594   ICRL DNLM

UH   LÖWENHARDT, Paul Eduard.
L827o   Die Organisation der Privatbeihilfe
1867   zur Pflege der im Felde verwundeten
        und erkrankten Krieger. Berlin,
        Nicolai, 1867.
          xvi, 219 p.
          "Preisschrift. "

NL 0447595   DNLM

UH   LÖWENHARDT, Paul Eduard.
L827s   Skizze über die Einrichtung des
1865   Sanitätsdienstes im Kriege bei der
        königl. Preuss. Armee. Berlin,
        Hirschwald, 1865.
          iv, 25 p.
          Issued also in the Berliner klinischen
        Wochenschrift, 1865.

NL 0447596   DNLM

Loewenhardt (Reinoldus) [1824-]. *De
medicina efficaci. 47 pp. 8°. *Berolini, typ.
Nietackiana. [1845].

NL 0447597   DNLM

WCB   LÖEWENHARDT, Sigismundus Eduard, ₁1796-1875¿
L827a   Anweisung zur Verhütung der asiati-
1831   schen Cholera, nebst Verhaltungsregeln
        bei deren Ausbruch bis zur Ankunft des
        Arztes. Prenzlau, Ragoczy, 1831.
          32 p.

NL 0447598   DNLM

Loewenhardt, Sigismundus Eduard, 1796-1875.
  Benedict von Spinoza in seinem verhältniss zur philo-
sophie und naturforschung der neueren zeit. Von dr. S. E.
Loewenhardt. Berlin, W. Peiser, 1872.
    ₁2₂, xxv, 419, ₁1₂ p. 23cm.

  1. Spinoza, Benedictus de, 1632-1677.

NL 0447599   ICU MH CLSU NIC CLU CtY NNC OCH

QV   LÖEWENHARDT, Sigismundus Eduard ₁1796-187.¿
L831b   Beobachtungen und Erfahrungen aus
1838   dem Gebiete der praktischen Arznei-
        und Wundarzneikunst. Prenzlau, Vin-
        cent, 1838.
          xv, 425 p. illus.

NL 0447600   DNLM

Loewenhardt[₁] (Sigismundus Eduard.)
[1796-1875]. *De myelophthisi chronica vera
et nothæ. viii, 38 pp., 1 l., 1 pl. 8°. *Berolini,
typ. Hayniana, [1847].

NL 0447601   DNLM PPC

501   Löwenhardt, Sigismundus Eduard, 1796-1875.
L827   Die identität der moral- und natur-
        gesetze. Von dr. S.E.Löwenhardt.
        Leipzig, O.Wignad, 1863.
          xlviii,403,[1]p. 21cm.

          1. Science. Philosophy.   I. Title

NL 0447602   IEN ICJ MH

340.6 Loewenhardt, Siegismundus Eduard, 1796-
L82k   1875.
          Kritische beleuchtung der medicinisch-
Med.   psychischen grundsätze nebst den darauf
        basirten ober-gutachten der Königlichen
        wissenschaftlichen deputation für das
        medicinal-wesen in Preussen. Für ärzte
        und juristen. Ein beitrag zur abschaf-
        fung des sogenannten medicinischen in-
        stanzenzuges bei zweifelhaften seelen-
        zuständen. Berlin, Logier, 1861.
          580p. 0.

NL 0447603   IaU

W   LÖEWENHARDT, Sigismundus Eduard
600   Kritische Beleuchtung der medicinisch-
L827k   psychischen Grundsätze, nebst dem darauf
1867   basirten Ober-Gutachten der Königlichen
        Wissenschaftlichen Deputation für das
        Medicinal-Wesen in Preussen. Für Aerzte
        und Juristen. 2. Ausg. Mit einem Anhange
        über die in praktisch-medicinischer und
        forensischer Hinsicht brauchbarste
        Eintheilung und Untersuchungsmethode
        Seelengestörter. Berlin, Springer, 1867.

          672 p.
          ₁I.¿Prussia. Wissenschaftliche
          Deputation für das Medizinalwesen

NL 0447605   DNLM

W   LÖEWENHARDT, Sigismundus Eduard, 1796-1875.
600   Kritische Untersuchung über zwei
L827kr Streitfragen aus dem Gebiete der gericht-
1858   lichen Psychologie und gerichtlichen
        Medicin für Aerzte und Criminalisten.
        Prenzlau, Vincent, 1858.
          176 p.

NL 0447606   DNLM MH

Loewenhardt, Sigismundus Eduard, 1796-1875.
——. Über die verschiedenen Arten des Schein-
todes der Neugebornen und dessen rationelle Behandlung. ix, 67 pp., 1 pl. 8°. *Prenzlau, F.
W. Kalbersberg,* 1843.

NL 0447607   DNLM

W   LÖEWENHARDT, Sigismundus Eduard, 1796-1875.
600   Untersuchungen im Gebiete der
L827u   gerichtlichen Arznei- Wissenschaft für
1848   Aerzte und Criminalisten. Bd. 1.
        Berlin, Hirschwald, 1848.
          xvi, 400 p.
          No more published?

NL 0447608   DNLM

Löwenhaupt, Friedrich, ed.
  Johann Heinrich Lambert, Leistung und Leben. ₁Mül-
hausen, Els., Braun, 1943₂
    207, ₁3₂ p. illus., ports. 30 cm.
  Extract of Lambert's "Cosmologische Briefe" including reproduc-
tion of original t. p. with imprint Augspurg, Bey Eberhard Kletts
Wittib, 1761 : p. ₁65¿-₁106₂
  Errata slip inserted.
  Bibliography: p. ₁109₂

  1. Lambert, Johann Heinrich, 1728-1777. I. Lambert, Johann
Heinrich, 1728-1777. Cosmologische Briefe über die Einrichtung des
Weltbaues.

Q143.L3L6   58-52014

        MH MiU TxU
NL 0447609   DLC NjP DSI TxU CU-S NNC CaBVaU CU OkU

VOLUME 338

Loewenhaupt, Hans Kurt, 1882–
Ueber postepileptische sprachstoerungen.
Inaug.diss. Freiburg, 1907.
Bibl.

NL 0447610   ICRL DNLM

Löwenhaupt (Richard) [1862–]. *Die
fäulnis- und gährungswidrige Wirkung des
Natrium siliciuim. 34 pp. 8°. Greifswald,
F. W. Kunike, [1899].

NL 0447611   DNLM

Löwenhaupt, V.
Der grosse krieg in zahlen; eine erganzung zu den
rechenbüchern, von V. Löwenhaupt. Mit 2 abbildungen.
Leipzig und Berlin, B. G. Teubner, 1916.
2 p. l., 44 p. 18½ᵐ.

1. European war, 1914–   —Economic aspects.
21–14036

Library of Congress   D635.L7

NL 0447612   DLC

LÖWENHAYN, Henri A   M   J
Recerches [sic] théorétiques et pratiques sur l'établissement des aliénés.
[Ptie. 1. Considérations sur le traitement
des aliénés] St. Pétersbourg [Académie
des sciences] 1833.
x, 144 p. illus.

No more published.

NL 0447613   DNLM

Loewenheim, Arthur.
Lipper, Milton William, 1884–
Investments, by Milton W. Lipper ... New York, Uni-
versal business institute, inc., °1910.

Löwenheim, Bruno.
Ueber einige Derivate des Benzylide-
nacetophenons. Leipzig, Druck von
Metzger & Wittig, 1890.
38 p. 23cm.

NL 0447615   NIC

Löwenheim (Ferdinand). *Chronik der geburtshilflichen Abteilung vom Jahre 1909.
63 pp., 1 l., 1 tab. 8°. München, Kastner &
Callwey, 1911.

NL 0447616   DNLM

Loewenheim, Franz.
Eine neue heilmethode der varicocele.
Inaug. Diss. Erlangen, 1874.

NL 0447617   ICRL DNLM

LÖWENHEIM, H   J   ed.
...Sentenzen, sprüche und lebensregeln aus dem
Talmud und anderen urquellen orientalischer weisheit. Eine reichhaltige sammlung in hebräischer
und deutscher sprache geordnet... Berlin, H.S.
Hermann, 1857.
107p.

Title in Hebrew at head of t.-p.
Text in German and Hebrew on opposite pages.

NL 0447618   ICN

Loewenheim, Julius 1875–
Beitrag zur kenntnis der missbildungen mit
nabelschnurbruch.
Inaug. Diss. Berlin, 1898

NL 0447619   ICRL CtY DNLM

LOEWENHEIM, Kurt.
Der vorsatz des anstifters nach geltendem
rechte. Breslau, 1897.

8+63 p.
Inaug.-diss. - Halle.
Same. Breslau, 1897.
8+61+(2) p.

NL 0447620   MH-L ICRL

Loewenheim, Kurt.
Der vorsatz des anstifters nach geltendem rechte. Von dr.
iur. Kurt Loewenheim. Breslau, Schletter, 1897.
vii, 61 p. 23½ᵐ. (On cover: Strafrechtliche abhandlungen ... hft. 9)
Issued also as inaugural dissertation, Halle, 1897.
"Verzeichnis der benutzten werke": p. iii–vi.

1. Accomplices—Germany. 2. Criminal law—Germany.   I. Title.
34–11321

NL 0447621   DLC MH-L

Löwenheim, Leopold, ed.
FOR OTHER EDITIONS
SEE MAIN ENTRY
Löwenheim, Louis, d. 1894.
... Die wissenschaft Demokrits und ihr einfluss auf die mo-
derne naturwissenschaft. Von dr. Louis Löwenheim, heraus-
gegeben von Leopold Löwenheim. Berlin, L. Simion nf., 1913.

Löwenheim, Louis, d. 1894.
... Die wissenschaft Demokrits und ihr einfluss auf
die moderne naturwissenschaft. Von dr. Louis Löwenheim, hrsg. von Leopold Löwenheim. Berlin, L. Simion
nf., 1913.
cover-title, 48 p. 23½ᵐ.
At head of title: Archiv für philosophie ... Beilage zu heft 4 des
Archivs für geschichte der philosophie, band XXVI.

1. Democritus. 2. Science—Hist.   I. Löwenheim, Leopold, ed.
II. Archiv für geschichte der philosophie. Supplement.
14—14961

Library of Congress   B299.S4L6

NL 0447623   DLC NN

Löwenheim, Louis, d. 1894.
Die wissenschaft Demokrits und ihr einfluss auf die moderne
naturwissenschaft. Von dr. Louis Löwenheim, hrsg. von Leopold Löwenheim. Berlin, L. Simion nf., 1914.
xi, 244 p. 24ᵐ.
Pages 1–48 also published as Beilage zu heft 4 des Archivs für geschichte der philosophie, band XXVI.

1. Democritus. 2. Science—Hist.   I. Löwenheim, Leopold, ed.
27–12432

Library of Congress   B299.S4L62 1914

NL 0447624   DLC OCU MH NN IU

Loewenheim, Moritz, 1878–
Ueber ein sarkom der harnblase ...
Inaug. diss. Waersburg, 1904
Bibl.

NL 0447624-1   ICRL DNLM

QA581 Löwenherz, Arthur, 1890–
.LS   Die Frenet'schen formeln im Rₙ₊₁ ... Königsberg,
Buchdr. O. Kümmel, 1911.
74, (2) p. 21ᵐ.
Inaug.-diss.—Königsberg.
Lebenslauf.
Bibliographical foot-notes.

1. Curves of double curvature.

NL 0447625   ICU ICRL NN MH RPB CtY NjP

Loewenherz, Bruno.
Wirbelstromverluste im ankerkupfer elektrischer maschinen.
Von Bruno Loewenherz und A. H. van der Hoop.
(In Mitteilungen über forschungsarbeiten auf dem gebiete des in-
genieurwesens ... Berlin, 1905. 26½ᵐ. hft. 28, p. 1–42 incl. tables,
diagrs.)
Bibliographical foot-notes.

1. Armatures. 2. Eddy currents (Electric)   I. Hoop, A. H. van der,
joint author.
P O 28–181

Library, U. S. Patent   Office TA3.F782

NL 0447626   DP

LOEWENHERZ Heinrich-Joseph.
Der einfluss der willensmängel (mentalreser-
vation, simulation, irrtum, tauschung, drohung)
auf die wirksamkeit des erbeinsetzungsvertrage
nach gemeinem recht und burgerlichem gesetzbuc.
Rostock, 1900.

10+56 p.
Inaug.-diss. - Rostock.

NL 0447627   MH-L ICRL

Loewenherz, Johanna, 1857–
Prostitution oder Production, Eigentum oder Ehe? Studie zur
Frauenbewegung, von Johanna Loewenherz. Nieuwied, Selbstverlag der Verfasserin, [München, A. Schupp, 1895].
209 (i.e. 210) p. 21ᵐ.

NL 0447628   ICJ

Loewenherz, Joseph, compiler.
A list of German newspapers of the United States and Canada.
Represented by Joseph Loewenherz...New York.   New York,
1895.   22 p.   12°.

1. Newspapers (German-American).   2. Newspapers (German-Cana-
dian).   3. Title.
N. Y. P. L.   August 25, 1916.

NL 0447629   NN

LOEWENHERZ, Leopold, 1847–1892.
Anwendung der torsion von drähten zur
ermittelung kleiner gewichtsgrössen. [Berlin,
1881.]

1. 8°.

NL 0447630   MH

VOLUME 338

Loewenherz, Leopold, 1847–1892, *ed.*
    Bericht über die wissenschaftlichen instrumente auf der Berliner gewerbeausstellung im jahre 1879, bearbeitet von prof. dr. A. Christiani, korvettenkapitän Dittmer, prof. dr. R. Doergens ₍u. a.₎ ... und unter mitwirkung von generallieutenant von Morozowicz ₍u. a.₎ ... herausgegeben von dr. L. Loewenherz ... Mit 292 in den text gedruckten holzschnitten. Berlin, J. Springer, 1880.

    1 p. l., ₍v₎–viii, ₍2₎, 535 p. illus., diagrs. 25ᶜᵐ.

    1. Scientific apparatus and instruments.   i. Christiani, Arthur, 1843–1887. ii. Berlin. Gewerbeausstellung, 1879.

    45–26911

    Library of Congress   Q185.L65

         NjP ICJ
NL 0447631   DLC DAS NIC DSI CtY DN–Ob DP MH MiU

Loewenherz, Leopold, 1847–1892.
    De curvis tangentialibus curvarum algebraicarum ordinis N ... Berolini, typis expresserunt Rosenthal eiusque soc., 1870.

    2 p. l., 22, ₍2₎ p. 20½ᶜᵐ.

    Inaug.-diss.—Berlin.
    Vita.

    1. Curves, Plane.

    4–9799

    Library of Congress   QA565.L8

NL 0447632   DLC NjP PU ICJ

Loewenherz, Leopold, *1847–1892.*
    Ueber Veränderlichkeit von Platin-Gewichtsstücken. Kritische Untersuchungen mit Benutzung von Wägungen der Normal-Eichungs-Kommission. [2].38 p. (*In* GERMANY. KAIS. NORMAL-AICHUNGS-KÖMMISSION. Metronomische Beiträge, no. 2.) Berlin 1875.

NL 0447633   ICJ

Löwenherz, Max, *comp.*
    Rechts-und verwaltungs lexikon für den preussischen landwirt. 1895.

NL 0447634   DNAL

        Loewenherz, Richard, 1867–
WG   Über Derivate des Dimetaditolyls. Berlin,
22579   1892.
        43 p.

        Inaug.-Diss. - Berlin.

NL 0447635   CtY CU DNLM

Loewenherz, Siegmund, 1871–
    Messungen der temperaturdifferenzen bei auf- und absteigenden luftströmen.
    Inaug. diss. Greifswald, 1901

NL 0447636   ICRL DNLM DAS PU

AC   Löwenherz, Walther, 1905–
851   "Bekanntmachungen, plakate und aufrufe" unter
        besonderer berücksichtigung des Bayerischen
        rechtes ... Coburg, 1932.   84 p.
        Inaug. Diss. -Würzburg, 1932.
        Lebenslauf.
        Bibliography.

NL 0447637   ICRL

Löwenhielm, Carl Axel, grefve, 1772–1861.
    ... Min lefvernes beskrifning. Stockholm, L.Hökerbergs bokförlag[1923]
    3p.ℓ.,[9]–150p.incl.front.(mounted port.) 23cm.
    "Dikterade denna sin lefvernesbeskrifning under tiden 20 April 1857–vintern 1860."

NL 0447638   CtY MnU

Löwenhielm, Carl Axel, 1772–1861.
    Om communal-styrelsen och penitentiär-systemet af C. A. Löwenhielm år 1839. Stockholm, P. A. Norstedt & Söner, 1839.

    2 pts. in 1 v. tables. 20cm.

NL 0447639   MH-L

Löwenhielm, Carl Gustaf, greve, 1790–1858.
    Greve Carl Gustaf Löwenhielms minnen... Del 1–
    Stockholm: A. Bonniers förlag₍, 1927– ₎   v. front., illus. (incl. ports.) 8°.

    Preface signed, Natalie Rosensvärd.

    1. Sweden—Social life, 1790– hielm₎, 1842– , translator.   2. Rosensvärd, Natalie (Löwen-
    N. Y. P. L.   December 28, 1927

NL 0447640   NN CtY

Löwenhielm, Fredericus Ad., *respondent.*
    ...Dissertatio politica de moderamine actionum humanarum
        see under   Ihre, Johan, 1707–1780, praeses.

Löwenhielm, Severin, *respondent*

Fant, Erik Mikael, 1754–1817, *praeses.*
    Dissertatio de honore mortuis in patria habito ... Upsaliæ, litteris J. F. Edman ₍1800₎

Löwenhjelm, Harriet Augusta Dorotea, 1887–1918.
    Brev och dikter, med teckningar av författarinnan. Utg. av Elsa Björkman-Goldschmidt. Stockholm, Norstedt ₍1952₎
    190 p. illus.,port. 23 cm.

    i. Björkman-Goldschmidt, Elsa, ed.

    A 53–3952

    Minnesota. Univ. Libr. for Library of Congress   ₍i₎

NL 0447643   MnU WU NN OC1

Löwenhjelm, Harriet Augusta Dorotea, 1887–1918.
    Dikter. Stockholm, P.A. Norstedt & Söner, [1927]
    Port. and other illustr.
    The illustrations are by the author.
    Edited by Christer Mörner.

NL 0447644   MH

PT9875   Löwenhjelm, Harriet Augusta Dorotea, 1887–1918.
.L65A17 Dikter ... 5. väsentligt utökade upplagan.
1941   Stockholm, P. A. Norstedt ₍1941₎
         142, ₍4₎ p. illus.

NL 0447645   ICU

Löwenhjelm, Harriet Augusta Dorotea, 1887–1918.
    Dikter. 7.uppl. Stockholm, Norstedt ₍1946₎
    142p. illus.

    Swedish.

NL 0447646   OC1 NNC

Löwenhjelm, Harriet Augusta Dorotea, 1887–1918.
    Dikter. 8.uppl. Stockholm, P.A. Norstedt & Söners ₍1948₎
    142, ₍4₎p. illus. 22cm.

NL 0447647   KU CU

Loewenich, Walther von, 1903–
    Augustin und das christliche Geschichtsdenken. München, C. Kaiser, 1947.
    46, ₍1₎ p. 19 cm. (Gottes Wort und Geschichte, 6)
    Bibliographical references included in "Anmerkungen" (p. 44–47)

    1. Augustinus, Aurelius, Saint, Bp. of Hippo. 2. History—Philosophy. i. Title.   (Series)

    BR1720.A9L6   A 51–10386
    Catholic Univ. of   America. Library
    for Library of Congress   ₍1₎†

NL 0447648   DCU IaU CtY NN NjPT IU MH DDO DLC

Loewenich, Walther von, 1903–
    Die geschichte der kirche. ₍3. aufl.₎ Witten-Ruhr, Luther-verlag, 1948.
    xv, 476 p. 19 cm.

    "Literatur zur kirchengeschichte": p. ₍xiv₎–xv.

NL 0447649   CtY-D NjPT DCU

Loewenich, Walther von, 1903–
    Die geschichte der kirche von den anfängen bis zur gegenwart ₍von₎ lic. Walther von Loewenich ... Witten, Westdeutscher Lutherverlag, 1938.
    xv, 506 p., 1 l. plates, ports., facsim. 19½ᶜᵐ.
    "Literatur zur kirchengeschichte": p. ₍xiv₎–xv.

    1. Church history.

    39–5948

    Library of Congress   BR145.L82
    ₍2₎   270

NL 0447650   DLC InU

234.2   Loewenich, Walther von, 1903–
L82g   Glaube und erfahrung bei Luther ... ₍Fürstenfeldbruck, Buchdruckerei A. Sighart, 1928₎
        vi, 49p.
        Inaug.-diss.--Erlangen.
        Lebenslauf.
        Part of the complete work, which was pub. in Forschungen zur geschichte und lehre des protestantismus, under title: Luthers theologia crucis.
        Bibliography included in "Abkürzungen" (p. ₍iii₎)
        1. Faith. 2. Knowledge, Theory of (Religion)
        3. Luther, Martin, 1483–1546.

NL 0447651   IU ICRL PU CtY DLC

BR85   Loewenich, Walther von, 1903–
L6
            Humanitas, Christianitas; drei Vorträge. Gütersloh, Bertelsmann ₍1948₎
        129 p. 18 cm.
        Contents.--Menschsein und Christsein bei Augustin.--Gott und Mensch ₍on Luther's De servo arbitrio₎--Jacob Burckhardt und die Kirchengeschichte.

        1. Christianity--Addresses, essays, lectures

NL 0447652   RPB DCU

VOLUME 338

Loewenich, Walther von, 1903–
Das Johannes-verständnis im zweiten jahrhundert, von lic.
W. von Loewenich ... Giessen, A. Töpelmann, 1932.
viii, 168 p. 24½ᶜᵐ. ¡Beihefte zur Zeitschrift für die neutestament-
liche wissenschaft und die kunde der älteren kirche ... beiheft 13¡
"Quellen und literatur": p. 147–155.

1. Bible. N. T. John — Criticism, interpretation, etc. — Hist. 2.
Bible — Criticism, interpretation, etc. — Hist. — N. T. John. 3. Christian
literature, Early — Hist. & crit. 4. Fathers of the church — Hist. & crit.
I. Title.

Library of Congress   BS410.Z7 no. 13   33–6288
                                        ¡3¡   (225.082) 226.5

ICMcC
     NjNbS DDO NIC PPC PBm PHC OCU OCH OO MiU OU PPiPT
NL 0447653   DLC GDC KyLxCB CLSU CSt NIC NcD CBPL

IX   Loewenich, Walther von, 1903–
L825k   Der katholizismus und wir. ¡Erlangen,
          R. Weissmann, 194–¡
          16 p. 21 cm. (Schriftenreihe der Evang.
          studentengemeinde Erlangen, hft. 1)

          "Studentische nachschrift eines vortrags
          vom 23.6.47."

NL 0447654   CtY–D

Loewenich, Walther von, 1903–
Der Katholizismus und Wir ¡studentische
Nachschrift eines Vortrags. München¡ Hrsg.
vom Evangelischen Presseverband für Bayern
[1947?]
23p. 17cm.

1. Catholic church – Relations – Lutheran
church.

NL 0447655   CtY

Loewenich, Walther von, 1903–
Luther als Ausleger der Synoptiker. München, Kaiser,
1954.
303 p. 23 cm. (Forschungen zur Geschichte und Lehre des
Protestantismus, 10. Reihe, Bd. 5)
Bibliographical footnotes.

1. Luther, Martin, 1483–1546. 2. Bible. N. T. Gospels—Criticism,
interpretation, etc.—Hist.   I. Title.   (Series)

                                        A 57–6322
Brown Univ. Library   BR333
for Library of Congress   ¡2¡

MWelC DLC ICMcC CLSU
NL 0447656   RPB IEG CSt InU MH–AH PU ICU NcD OU

Loewenich, Walther von, 1903–
Luther und das johanneische christentum, von lic. Walter
v. Loewenich. München, C. Kaiser, 1935.
93 p. 23 cm. (Added t.-p.: Forschungen zur geschichte und lehre
des protestantismus, hrsg. von Paul Althaus, Karl Barth und Karl
Heim. 7. reihe, bd. IV)
"Quellenangabe": p. ¡6¡

1. Luther, Martin—Theology. 2. Bible. N. T. Johannine literature—Theology. 3. Bible. N. T. Johannine literature—Criticism,
interpretation, etc.—Hist.   I. Title.

BR333.L6   226.5   36–13791 rev

NL 0447657   DLC MH–AH OkU PPLT

Loewenich, Walther von, 1903–
Luthers evangelische Botschaft. ¡München¡ Verlag der
Evang.-Luth. Kirche in Bayern r. d. Rhs., 1946.
56 p. 23 cm. (Kirchlich-theologische Hefte, Heft 1)

1. Luther, Martin, 1483–1546.   I. Series.
BR333.L62   A F 48–1127*
Yale Univ. Library
for Library of Congress   ¡1¡†

NL 0447658   CtY IEG CtY–D NN DLC

BX   Loewenich, Walther von, 1903–
4801   Luthers Theologia crucis. 2. Aufl. unveränderter Abdruck.
F6   München, C. Kaiser, 1933.
ser. 2   236 p. 24cm. (Forschungen zur Geschichte und Lehre des
v. 11   Protestantismus. 2. Reihe, Bd. 11)
1933

1. Luther, Martin, 1483–1546.—Theology. 2. Jesus Christ—
Crucifixion.   I. Title. (Series)

NL 0447659   CBPL CtY

BR333   Loewenich, Walther von, 1903–
L82   Luthers Theologia crucis von Walther v.
          Loewenich. 3. Aufl. unver. Abdruck. München,
          C. Kaiser, 1939.
          236 p. 23 cm. (Forschungen zur Geschichte
          und Lehre des Protestantismus. 2. Reihe, 2)

          Bibliography: p. ¡229¡–234.

          1. Luther, Martin, 1483–1546—Theology.
          I. Title. (Series)

NL 0447660   PPiPT

BR333   Loewenich, Walther von, 1903–
L6   Luthers Theologia crucis. 4. durch-
          gesehene Aufl. mit einem Nachwort und
          Anhang. München, C. Kaiser, 1954.
          248p. 23cm.

          Bibliography: p. ¡229¡–234.

          1. Luther, Martin, 1483–1546. 2.
          Theology, Doctrinal.

     ICU NbFC NjPT CtY–D MWelC
NL 0447661   IaU TxFTC PPPD ICMcC CSt OU PU NcD InU

Loewenich, Walther von, 1903–
Der Mensch im Lichte der Passionsgeschichte; eine biblische Betrachtung. Stuttgart, Calwer ¡1947¡
71 p. 18 cm.

1. Jesus Christ—Passion.   I. Title.
BT430.L575   A F 49–113*
Yale Univ. Library
for Library of Congress   ¡1¡†

NL 0447662   CtY NN DLC

Loewenich, Walther von, 1903–
Menschsein und Christsein bei Augustin. München, C.
Kaiser, 1947.
47 p. 19 cm. (Gottes Wort und Geschichte, 8)

1. Augustinus, Aurelius, Saint, Bp. of Hippo. 2. Christian life.
I. Title.   (Series)
BR65.A9L6   281.4   49–12010*

NL 0447663   DLC IaU CtY–D DCU DDO

Loewenich, Walther von, 1903–
Der moderne Katholizismus; Erscheinung und Probleme.
¡1. Aufl.¡ Witten, Luther-Verlag ¡1955¡
460 p. 21 cm.
Bibliography: p. ¡433¡–442. "Päpstliche und kuriale Verlaut-
barungen": p. ¡459¡–460.

1. Catholic Church—Doctrinal and controversial works—Protestant
authors. 2. Catholic Church—Hist.—Modern period.   I. Title.

                                        A 56–6555
Harvard Univ. Library
for Library of Congress   ¡1¡

NL 0447664   MH IEG DS NcD IaU TxHR CtY–D PPLT MH–AH

Loewenich, Walther von, 1903–
Paulus; sein Leben und Werk. ¡2. Aufl.¡ Witten, Luther-
Verlag ¡1949¡
208 p. illus., port., map. 19 cm.

1. Paul, Saint, apostle. 2. Bible. N. T. Epistles of Paul.
                                        A 51–266
Yale Univ. Library
for Library of Congress   ¡1¡

NL 0447665   CtY ICMcC MH–AH NjPT

Loewenich, Walther von, 1903–
Die Stunde der göttlichen Heimsuchung; zwölf Predigten.
Stuttgart, Calwer Verlag, 1946.
107 p. 22 cm.

1. Lutheran Church—Sermons. 2. Sermons, German.   I. Title.
BX8066.L595S7   A F 48–4904*
Yale Univ. Library
for Library of Congress   ¡1¡†

NL 0447666   CtY NcD DLC NN

Loewenich, Walther von, 1903–
Vom abendmahl Christi, eine historisch-systematische untersuchung zum abendmahlsproblem der gegenwart, von lic.
Walther von Loewenich ... Berlin, Furche-verlag ¡1938¡
116 p. 22½ᶜᵐ. ¡Furche-studien, hrsg. von dr. Hanns Lilje. 18. bd.¡
"Der studie liegt eine vorlesungen ¡1¡ vom wintersemester 1937/38 ¡Er-
langen¡ zugrunde."—Vorwort.

1. Lord's supper—Hist.   I. Title.
                                        41–28734
Library of Congress   BV823.L63
                                        ¡2¡   265.3

NL 0447667   DLC CtY NjPT CBPac

BT   Loewenich, Walther von, 1903–
127   Was heist Offenbarung? Gottes Wort und menschliche Rede
L5   im Alten und Neuen Testament. Berlin, Furche Verlag [1938]
          54 p. 23cm. (Stimmen und Zeugnisse, Heft 103)

          1. Revelation.   I. Title.

NL 0447668   CBPac MoSCS

BR 145   Loewenich, Walther von, 1903–
L55   Der Weg des Evangeliums durch die Welt; Grund-
1949   riss der Kirchengeschichte.. ¡Ausg. B¡ München.
          C. Kaiser, 1949.
          165 p. 23 cm.

          Includes bibliography.

NL 0447669   OU

Löwenigh, Barto von.
Reise nach Spitzbergen.   Aachen und
Leipzig, 1830.
54 p. 17.5 cm.

NL 0447670   CtY

Löwenklau, Johann
     see
Leunclavius, Johannes, 1533?–1593.

VOLUME 338

Loewenkopf, Elias.
A handbook on the taxation of costs as of right in the state of New York, with forms for various bills of costs, by Elias Loewenkopf ... New York, Baker, Voorhis & co., 1916.
1 p. l., v–xxxii, 222 p. 22¾ᶜᵐ. $3.00

1. Costs (Law) 2. Civil procedure—New York (State) 3. Fees—New York
17–170

NL 0447672   DLC

Löwenkreuz, Emmanuela Mattl-,
see   Mattl-Löwenkreuz, Emmanuela von, 1876-

Löwenmark, Joh. Wilh., respondent.
Dissertatio juridica, de probatione ...
see under   Hernbergh, Andreas, praeses.

Loewenmayer, Maiers.
Grab-Rede, gehalten am 24. September 1871 der ...Frau Babetta Löwenmayer von ihrem ...Gatten. Fürth: A. Schröder, 1871.
8 p.

NL 0447675   OCH

Loewenmayer, Maiers.
Grab-Rede, gehalten am 28. Januar 1872 dem Kaufmann Simon Goldschmidt ... Neumarkt: F. Pohl, 1872.
7 p.

NL 0447676   OCH

Loewenmayer, Maiers.
Predigt bei dem ... zu Sulzbürg abgehaltenen Trauergottesdienste für cie ... Königin Karoline von Bayern... Neumarkt: A. Hinderhuber, 1841.
12 p.

NL 0447677   OCH

Loewenmayer, Maiers.
Predigt zum Geburtstage ... des Königs Maximilian II. von Bayern, gehalten am 28. November 1862...zu Regensbrug. Regensburg: J. H. Demmler, 1852.
8 p.

NL 0447678   OCH

BM 744.6   **Löwenmayer, Maier.**
L6   Predigt zur Einweihung der israelitischen Synagoge in Sulzbürg am 15. August 1847, gehalten von Löwenmaier. Neumarkt, A. Hinderhuber [Vorwort 1847]
20 p. 18 cm.
Cover title.
Vorwort signed: M. Löwenmayer.

1. Sermons, Jewish.

NL 0447679   OU

Loewenmeyer (Max) [1863-]. *Beobachtungen über Ernährung mit Hühnereiern in Fällen von Albuminurie. 20 pp., 1 l. roy. 8°. *Berlin, I. Schumacher, 1885.*

NL 0447680   DNLM

Löwenmo, Runo.
Inomhusväxter. Färgplanscher av Ellen Backe. Stockholm, Viking [1955]
198 p. col. plates. 19 cm.

1. Flowers. 2. House plants.
A 56–5259

Purdue Univ. Library
for Library of Congress   [8]

NL 0447681   InLP

Löwenmo, Runo.
Våre stueplanter; med 372 illustrasjoner i farger tegnet av Ellen Backe. [Oslo] Cappelen [1955]
195 p. illus. (part col.) 19 cm.
At head of title: Runo Löwenmo og Maisen Pedersen.

1. House plants. I. Pedersen, Maisen, joint author. II. Title.
A 57–4659

Purdue Univ. Library
for Library of Congress   [8]

NL 0447682   InLP

Löwenørn, Poul de, 1751-1826.
Beretning om en reise, foretaget efter allernaadigst befaling i aarene 1782 og 1783, med fregatten Prøven, for at undersøge de i Dannemark forfærdigede søe-længde uhrer, af Paul de Løwenørn ... Med et tillæg, indeholdende nogle paa søen nyttige observations-methoder. Udg. af det Kongelige danske videnskabers selskab. Kiøbenhavn, Trykt hos A. F. Stein, 1785.
165 p. incl. tables (2 fold.) 2 fold. pl. 25½ x 19½ᶜᵐ.
Folded leaf inserted between pages 84 and 85.
1. Chronometer. 2. Geographical positions—West Indies, Danish. I. K. Danske videnskabernes selskab, Copenhagen.

Library of Congress   QB107.L88   7–34286†

NL 0447683   DLC

Løwenørn, Poul de, 1751-1826.
Beretning om kaartet over en deel af den Iislandske westlige kyst fra Fugle-Skiaerene og Cap-Reikianaes til Stikkelsholm i Breede-Bugten ... med et tillæg indeholdende beskrivel sen over kysten og havnene med deres indesyling; paa den sydlige og ligeledes paa den nord- westlige kyst of Iisland, saavelsom en deel landtoninger of dise kyster. Udgiven fra det Koneglige Søe-kaarte archiv. [Kiöbenhavn, 1788-1822]
26 cm.
Engr. t. -p.

Issued in 4 pts. Each pt. has special t. -p. and separate pagination.

NL 0447685   CtY

GB457   **Løwenørn, Poul de, 1751-1826.**
.3   Beschreibung der Norwegischen Küste, zu den
L6   aus dem Königlichen Seekarten-Archive herausg. sieben Specialkarten dieser Küste, nebst den beigefügten Landvertonungen gehörend ... aus dem Dänischen übers. von P. Clausen. Kopenhagen, E.A.H. Möller, 1816.
88 p. fold.plates.

1. Coasts - Norway

NL 0447686   CU CtY

Løwenørn, Poul de, 1751-1826.
Beskrivelse over den iislandske Kyst og alle Havne fra Fugle-Skiaerene og til Stikkelsholm i Brede-Bugten med Forklaring over deres Indseiling. Kiöbenhavn, 1788-
(4)-72-(2) p.   4°.

NL 0447687   NIC MH

Løwenørn, Poul de, 1751-1826.
Extrait de la relation d'un voyage, fait par ordre de S. M. danoise, pendant l'année 1786, pour la découverte de la côte orientale du Groenland ... par M. de Lowenörn ... traduit, en 1822, par l'auteur ... Paris, De l'Imprimerie royale, 1823.
47 p. front. (fold. map) 21½ᶜᵐ.
Extrait des Annales maritimes et coloniales de 1823.

1. Greenland—Disc. & explor.
A 14–1425

Title from Brown Univ.   Printed by L. C.

NL 0447688   RPB CtY MiU NN

LØWENØRN, Poul de, 1751-1826.
Samlet beskrivelse over den norske kyst, henhørende til de fra det Kongelige Seekaarte-Archiv udgivne trigonometrisk opmaalte, og ved astronomiske observationer verificerede. Udarbeidet af P.de Løwenørn. Kiøbenhavn, E.A.H Møller, [1816].
4°.   Charts.
"Udgivet fra det Kongelige Seekaarte - Archiv, 1816."

NL 0447689   MH

Løwenørn, Poul de, 1751-1826. Über die in der Nähe von Island entstandene vulkanische Insel. *Extr. fr.* Allgemeine geographische Ephemeriden. III. Bd. Weimar, 1799. 8°. pp. 553-562.   IcC18L917

NL 0447690   NIC

Løwenørn, Poul Vendelbo
see   Løwenørn, Poul Vendelbo, 1686-1740.

Löwens, Johann Friedrich
Geschichte des deutschen Theaters (1766) und Flugschriften über das Hamburger Nationaltheater (1766 und 1767) im Neudruck mit Einleitung und Erläuterungen hrsg. von Heinrich Stümcke. Berlin, E. Frensdorff [1905]
104 p. (Neudrucke literarhistorischer Seltenheiten, no.8)
1. Theater - Germany - History. 2. Theater - Hamburg. I. Stümcke, Heinrich, 1872- ed. II. Title.

NL 0447692   InNd KU

Löwens, Johann Friedrich.
Schriften, 1. Teil. Hamburg, M. Bock, 1765.

NL 0447693   CtY

Löwensberg, Hermann von Chiolich
see   Chiolich-Löwensberg, Hermann von.

VOLUME 338

Loewensberg, Isidor, 1882–
Ueber die aetiologie der dupuytren'schen contractur.
Inaug. diss. Wuerzburg, 1906.
Bibl.

NL 0447695 ICRL DNLM

Loewensberg, Paul
Ueber traumatische fernwirkungen.
Inaug. diss. Zurich, 1913
Bibl.

NL 0447696 ICRL DNLM

Löwenschwerdt, Erwin Mayer-
see
Mayer-Löwenschwerdt, Erwin.

Løwenskjold, Herman, baron, 1815–1870
see **Løvenskiold, Herman Severin,**
1815–1870.

Löwensohn (Ezechiel Boris) [1861–].
*Ueber Veratroïdin im Vergleich zu Veratrin. 101 pp., 1 l. 8°. *Dorpat, H. Laakmann,*
1890.

NL 0447699 DNLM CU

Loewensohn, Manne: Erkältung und Nephritis. [Maschinenschrift]
84 S. 4°. — Auszug: Berlin (1922): Ebering. 2 Bl. 8°
Berlin, Med. Diss. v. 4. Nov. 1922 [1923] [U 23. 198

NL 0447700 ICRL

Löwensohn, Meische Wolff, 1877–
Der Kumys und seine Anwendung bei der
Lungentuberkulose ... Berlin, 1901.
Inaug.-Diss. - Berlin.
Lebenslauf.
"Litteratur": p. [32]

NL 0447701 CtY DNLM ICRL

Löwensohn, Moses, 1882–
Die Lehre von der adäquaten Verursachung
in der neueren Rechtsprechung des Reichsgerichts in Zivilsachen ... von Moses Löwensohn. Heidelberg, C. Pfeffer, 1911.

62 p., 1 l. 22cm.

Inaug.-Diss. - Heidelberg.
"Lebenslauf": leaf at end.
"Literaturverzeichnis": p. [61]-62.

NL 0447702 MH-L ICRL

Loewensohn (Salomon) [1814–]. *Quædam
ex dissertatione ampliore de methodi antiphlo-
gistica historia et singulis remediis. 61 pp., 1 l.
8°. *Berolini, typ. Nietackiana,* 1836.

NL 0447703 DNLM PPC

Loewensohn, Theodor, 1866–
Einfall von tic impulsif nach fallschirmabsprung
eines ballonbeobachters, als beitrag zur frage der
kriegsneurosen.
Inaug. diss. Rostock, 1919.

NL 0447704 ICRL CtY

Löwensohn, Viktor: Ueber das Thiochromanom, Thiochromonol, Thio-
chromon und deren Halogenisierungsprodukte. [Maschinenschrift.]
47 S. 4°. — Auszug: Breslau [1924]: Goldstein. 2 Bl. 8°
Breslau, Phil. Diss. v. 28. Juni 1924 [U 24. 1842

NL 0447705 ICRL

LÖWENSOHN, Wulf.
Zur statistik und kasuistik der aussergewöhn-
lich schweren früchte. Inaug.-diss. Basel,
1907.

NL 0447706 MBCo DNLM MiU CtY PU

Loewenson (Erich). *Ein Beitrag zur Kenntnis der spontanen Herzruptur. [München.]
35 pp. 8°. Tilsit, O. v. Mauderode, 1908.

NL 0447707 DNLM

Löwenson, Martin, Zahnarzt: Über die verschiedenen Me-
thoden der Befestigung lockerer Zähne. Aus d. Techn.
Abt. d. Zahnärztl. Inst. d. Univ. Breslau. [In Maschinen-
schrift.] 42 S. m. 25 Abb. 4°(2°). — Auszug: Breslau
1921: Breslauer Genossensch.-Buchdr. 2 Bl. 8°
Breslau, Med. Diss. v. 5. März 1921, Ref. Riegner
[Geb. 11. Aug. 91 Gumbinnen; Wohnort: Breslau; Staatsangeh.: Preußen;
Vorbildung: G. Wohlau bis 09; Studium: Breslau 3, Berlin 1, Breslau 4 S.;
Coll. 16. Febr. 21; Zahnärztl. Approb. 27. Juni 12.] [U 21. 3004

NL 0447708 ICRL

Löwensprung, Erich Lölhöffel von
see
Lölhöffel, Erich von.

Löwenstädt, Hans: Untersuchungen zur Frage des zelligen
Gewebeabbaus und seiner Beziehung zur Eiterung. Aus
d. anatom. Inst. d. Univ. Breslau. [In Maschinenschrift.]
32 S., 4 Fig. 4°(2°). — Auszug: Breslau 1921: Breslauer
Genossensch.-Buchdr. 6 S. 8°
Breslau, Med. Diss. v. 10. Nov. 1921, Ref. Kallius
[Geb. 27. Aug. 95 Breslau; Wohnort: Breslau; Staatsangeh.: Preußen; Vorbildung: Johannes-G. Breslau Reife 15; Studium: Breslau 10 S.; Coll.
31. Juli 20; Approb. 24. Okt. 21.] [U 21. 3005

NL 0447710 ICRL

BM580
.L57
Hebr

Loewenstamm, Abraham ben Aryeh.
קדש הלולים; בו יבאר ויבריח מציאת הנשמה ואיכותה והשארתה.
ענין הנמצל ועניין הבחירה ועבודת ד' והאחרון חיוב איש הישראלי
להאמין ולקיים כל תורת משה שבכתב ושבעל פה. אמשטרדם,
בבית ובדפום דוד בן יעקב פרופם. [Amsterdam, 1818/19]

12, 86 l. 19 cm.

1. Judaism—Works to 1900. 2. Soul. I. Title.
Title transliterated: Kodesh hillulim.

BM580.L57 A 56–2151
New York. Public Libr.
for Library of Congress [8]†

NL 0447711 NN DLC

Loewenstamm, Abraham ben Aryeh.
צרור החיים; תשעה שאלות ותשובות. (א) קל הטיר. בו יבואר
שאסר להתפלל בביה"כ בתלוים בלי ציר הנקרא ארג"ל (ב) ענה
לחש (ג) שפתי ישנים (ד) לשון אש (ה) בישישים הכמה (ו) שפה
נכריה אש (ח) בששישים הכמה (ז) נגינותו ננגן
(ח) כסוי הסאה (ם) קץ הימין. אמשטרדם. ד. פרופם. תק"פ.
[Amsterdam, 1820]

81 l. 21 cm.
1. Jewish Liturgy and ritual. 2. Reform Judaism. 3. Responsa.
I. Title.
Title transliterated: Tseror ha-ḥayyim

A 56–2117

New York. Public Libr. BM 660. L6 1820.
for Library of Congress

NL 0447711–1 NN OU DLC

Loewenstamm, Abraham ben Aryeh.
צרור החיים. כולל תשעה שאלות ותשובות ... הובא שנית
לבית הדפום. אוהעלי. תרכ"ם.
S.-a.-Ujhely, Gedruckt bei M. Weisz, 1868.

71 l. 24 cm.

1. Jews. Liturgy and ritual. 2. Reform Judaism. 3. Responsa.
I. Title. *Title transliterated:* Tseror ha-ḥayim.

BM660.L6 1868 60–56092

NL 0447712 DLC

Loewenstamm, Abraham Levy.
Der Talmudist, wie er ist; oder, Wir sind alle Menschen. Zur
Wegräumung gehegter Vorurtheile gegen die israelitischen Ge-
setze, besonders gegen den Talmud. Der gesammt-verbrüderten
Menschheit gewidmet von Abraham Levy Loewenstamm...
Emden: Gedruckt bei H. Woortman, jr., 1822. xvi, 75 p.
18½cm.

1. Talmud—Crit. *Revised*
N. Y. P. L. May 17, 1934

NL 0447713 NN OCH PPGratz

Loewenstamm, Arthur, 1882–
Hugo Grotius' Stellung zum Judentum. Von Rabbiner Dr.
Arthur Loewenstamm... (Jüdisch-theologisches Seminar, Breslau. Festschrift zum 75-jährigen Bestehen des Jüdisch-theo-
logischen Seminars Fraenckelscher Stiftung. Breslau, 1929.
8°. Bd. 2, p. 295–302.)

1. Groot, Hugo de, 1583–1645. I. Ser.
N. Y. P. L. October 7, 1930

NL 0447714 NN OCH

Löwenstamm, Arthur, 1882–
Lotzes lehre vom ding an sich und ich an sich ... Breslau, Buchdr. H. Fleischmann, 1906.

55, [1] p., 1 l. 22cm.

Inaug.-diss.—Erlangen.
Lebenslauf.
"Literaturangabe": p. [56]

1. Lotze, Hermann i. e. Rudolf Hermann, 1817–1881.

9–15630

Library of Congress B3298.K7L8

NL 0447715 DLC CtY NjP PU NIC NN

Loewenstamm, Artur: Ueber Akrodermatitis chronica atrophicans.
[Maschinenschrift.] 110 S. 4°. — Auszug: Breslau 1924: Preund.
2 Bl. 8°
Breslau, Med. Diss. v. 10. Dez. 1924 [1925] [U 25. 968

NL 0447716 ICRL

VOLUME 338

Loewenstamm, Franz Josef.
Altes Liebeslied . . . Für Männerchor mit Orchester oder Piano-
forte. Op. 11. Partitur mit unterlegtem Clavierauszug.
Leipzig. Leuckart. [187–?] 15 pp. F°.

E3680 — T.r. — Part songs.

NL 0447717   MB

Loewenstamm, Franz Josef, arr.
Herbststurm (Autumn storms) ... für eine
Singstimme mit pianofortebegleitung ...
see under   Grieg, Edvard Hagerup, 1843–1907

Loewenstamm, Franz Josef.
Hüttelein . . . Für vier Männerstimmen. Op. 10.
Leipzig. Leuckart. [187–?] 3 pp. 8°.

E3680 — T.r. — Part songs.   April 11,   1902.

NL 0447719   MB

Loewenstamm, Franz Josef.
Waldrose. [Männerchor.] Op. 16.
Leipzig. Siegel. [1880?] 3 pp. [Vier vierstimmige Männer-
chöre. 2.] L. 8°.

E3680 — T.r. — Part songs.   April 11,   1902.

NL 0447720   MB

Loewenstamm, Fritz, 1872–
Beitrag zur Casuistik der acuten
hämorrhagischen Polioencephalitis
superior ...   Berlin [1895]
Inaug.-Diss. - Berlin.

NL 0447721   CtY DNLM

Loewenstamm, Georg.
De weg zonder einde ... Vertaling: Annie Winkler-Vonk.
Amsterdam, A. Blitz [1946]
262 p. 20 cm.

Translated from a German manuscript without title.

I. Title.

PT2623.O435W43   57-23737 ‡

NL 0447722   DLC

F
2659   **Loewenstamm,** Kurt
J5L619   Vultos judaicos no Brasil; uma contribui-
çao à história dos judeus no Brasil.   Rio
de Janeiro [n. p.] 1949–
v. illus. 19 cm.

Original title: Schicksal und Leistungen
von Juden in Brasilien in Vergangenheit und
Gegenwart.
Contents.– v. 1. Tempo colonial, 1500–1822.
– v.2. Imperio, 1822–1889.

NL 0447723   NBuU OCH OU

Loewenstamm, Marcus
see Loewenstamm, Mordecai ben Aryeh.

Loewenstamm, Mordecai ben Aryeh.
אלון בכות. אשר ספדו כל עדת ישראל ביום הוקם מצבת אבן
על קבר אברהם מיקפין. [Breslau, 1821]
[4] l. 21 cm.

1. Tiktin, Abraham ben Gedaliah, d. 1820.   I. Title.
                    Title transliterated: Alon bakhut.

BM755.T5L6   55–53510

NL 0447725   DLC

Loewenstamm, Mordecai ben Aryeh.
שירי הבחינה. מוסר השכל; ובשיר האחרון יתבארו י״ג העקרים
על דרך הרמבכ״ם. מיוסדת ע״פ מליצת בדרשי בספרו בחינות עולם.
ברעסלויא. נדפס אצל ליב זולצבאך [Breslau, 1832]
125 p. 15 cm.

Vocalized text.

I. Bedersi, Jedaiah ben Abraham, ca. 1270–ca. 1340? Bebinat 'olam.
II. Title.   *Title transliterated:* Shire ha-behinah.

New York. Public Libr.   A 53–7186
for Library of Congress   PJ5052.L6S5

NL 0447726   NN DLC

Löwenstamm, Saul, 1717–1790.
בנין אריאל. אמשטרדם. בדפוס י. פרופס ובדפוס א. פרופס.
[Amsterdam, 1778]
2 v. in 1. 31 cm.
חלק א. חדרי תורה, ובו ביאורים נחמדים על תמשה תומשי—CONTENTS.
תורה וחמש מגילות.—חלק ב. בית חלפוד, ותוא חרושי נ״ת.

1. Bible. O. T. Pentateuch—Commentaries. 2. Talmud—Commentaries.   I. Title.   *Title transliterated:* Binyan Ariel.

BS1225.L6   53–57055

NL 0447727   DLC

Löwenstamm, Saul, 1717–1790.
בנין אריאל. והוא נקרא בשם הדרי תורה. ובו ביאורים נחמדים
על חומשי תורה. יוצא ע״י שמעון נימאן ממארואו. קראקא.
בדפוטו של י. פישער. תרס״ה. Krakau [1904/05]
256+ p. 21 cm.
L. C. copy imperfect: all after p. 256 wanting.

1. Bible. O. T. Pentateuch—Commentaries.   I. Title.
                    Title transliterated: Binyan Ari'el.

BS1225.L6 1904   54–55666

NL 0447728   DLC

Löwenstamm, Saul, 1717–1790.

BM675
.P4A3   **Jews.** *Liturgy and ritual. Hagadah.* 1872.
1872   הגדה של פסח עם פירוש אפוד ב״ד ... מאת הרב ...
במגמך דוד דראבשואיץ ... ונלוה ... עוד פירוש מהבאן
שאול ... אבד״ק אמשטרדם ... העתק ... מספרו ... בנין
אריאל ... ווארשא, בדפוס, י. גאלדמאן, תרל״ב.
Bapmasa, 1872.

Loewenstamm, Willy, 1880–
Ueber Metallsalzverbindungen des Schwefel-
harnstoffs, ein Beitrag zur Kenntnis der
komplexen Verbindungen einwertiger Metalle.
Berlin, A. W. Schade, 1901.
48 p.
Inaug.-Diss. - Berlin, 1901.

NL 0447730   ICRL NN MH-C PU

Löwenstein,   d. 1917.
Niedergang und Aufschwung der deutschen Buchbinderei im
19. Jahrhundert. Von Dr. Löwenstein.   [Halle (Saale), 1920–
22.] 6 l. 32cm.
Caption-title.
An article excerpted from Archiv für Buchbinderei, 1920–22.

679623A. 1. Bookbinding,   German.   January 13, 1934.
N. Y. P. L.

NL 0447731   NN

Löwenstein (A.) Bericht über zweijährige
(1854–5) Wirksamkeit des Instituts für schwedische Heilgymnastik. 25 pp. 8°. *Berlin,*
Gebr. Unger, 1856.

NL 0447732   DNLM

Löwenstein, A.
——. Wirksamkeit und Werth der Heil-Gym-
nastik. 43 pp. 8°. *Berlin, C. Heymann, 1860.*

NL 0447733   DNLM

Loewenstein (Adolf). Humor in der Medicin.
Medicinisch-humoristische Vorträge, Gedichte,
Räthsel, Epigramme, etc. 127 pp. 8°. *Berlin,*
E. Stande, 1872.

NL 0447734   DNLM

Löwenstein, Adolf.
Witz und humor; theorie und praxis.
Stuttgart, Richter & Kappler, 1877.

NL 0447735   MH

Loewenstein (Adolphus). *De funiculo um-*
bilicali partus impedimento. 43 pp. 8°. *Vra-*
tislaviæ, M. Friedlaender, [1833].

NL 0447736   DNLM

WF   **LÖWENSTEIN,** Albert Samuel, 1802–1831
L821d   Die Drüssenkrankheit; oder, Die
1831   Skrofelkrankheit der Kinder und Erwachsenen ...   Berlin, Schlesinger, 1831.
xvi, 96 p.

NL 0447737   DNLM

Löwenstein, Albert Samuel, 1802–1831.
De radice caincæ ejusque in morbis hydropicis
virtute. 36 pp., 1 l. 8°. *Berolini, typ. Feister-*
riæ, 1828.

NL 0447738   DNLM PPC

RG521   **LÖWENSTEIN, ALBERT SAMUEL,** 1802–1831.
.L75   Der theoretische und praktische geburtshelfer; oder,
Vollständiger unterricht der gesammten geburtshülfe
und der krankheiten der schwangern, wöchnerinnen und
neugebornen kinder... Von A.S. Löwenstein... Nebst
einem anhange... Glogau, C. Heymann, 1831.
xxii, 548, [2] p. fold. tab. 19½ cm.
"Literatur": p. [13]–38.

1. Obstetrics.

NL 0447739   ICU

VOLUME 338

WQ
L832t
1836
LÖWENSTEIN, Albert Samuel, 1802-1831
Der theoretische und praktische Geburtshelfer; oder, Vollständiger Unterricht der gesammten Geburtshülfe und der krankheiten der Schwangern, Wöchnerinen und neugebornen Kinder ... 2. verm. und verb. Ausg. Berlin, Heymann, 1836.
xxxii, 567 p.

NL 0447740 DNLM

WQ
L832t
1839
LÖWENSTEIN, Albert Samuel, 1802-1831
Der theoretische und praktische Geburtshelfer; oder, Vollständiger Unterricht der gesammten Geburtshülfe und der krankheiten der Schwangern, Wöchnerinnen und neugebornen Kinder ... 3. verm. und verb. Ausg. Berlin, Heymann, 1839.
xxxii, 564 p.

NL 0447741 DNLM

Loewenstein (Alexander). *Die Leukæmia, mit besonderer Berücksichtigung eines von der Thymusdrüse ausgehenden Falles. 30 pp., 1 l. 8°. *Würzburg, A. Memminger, 1886.

NL 0447742 DNLM ICRL

Law
Löwenstein, Alfred
Die verbrechenskonkurrenz nach dem reichsstrafgesetzbuch mit besonderer berucksichtigung der konkurrenz zwischen munzfalschung einerseits betrug, and urkundenfalschung andererseits.
Stuttgart, gebruder Kroner, 1883.
68 p.

NL 0447743 DLC

Löwenstein (Alfred) [1882–]. *Ein Fall von kongenitaler Kiemengangscyste. 17 pp. 8°. München, C. Wolf & Sohn, 1907.

NL 0447744 DNLM

1887-
Löwenstein, Alfred, Rechtsprakt.: Der Rechtsbegriff als Relationsbegriff. Studien z. Methodol. d. Rechtswissensch. München: Beck 1915. IX, 102 S. 8°
Erlangen, Jur. Diss. v. 2. März 1915, Ref. Binder
[Geb. 11. Juli 87 München; Wohnort: München; Staatsangeh.: Bayern; Vorbildung: Wilhelms-G. München Reife 06; Studium: Grenoble 1, Heidelberg 1, Berlin 2, München 1, Erlangen 5 S.; Rig. 1. März 13.] [U 15. 267

NL 0447745 ICRL CtY NIC

Löwenstein, Alfred, *1887-*
Der rechtsbegriff als relationsbegriff; studien zur methodologie der rechtswissenschaft, von dr. iur. Alfred Löwenstein. München, Beck, 1915.
x, 97 p. 22ᶜᵐ.
"Die vorliegende arbeit bildete im wesentlichen den gegenstand meiner bereits vor zwei jahren fertiggestellten dissertation."—Vorwort.
"Literaturverzeichnis": p. [vii]-x.

ɪ. Title.
20-20385

NL 0447746 DLC CtY-L NIC PU-L

1894-
Löwenstein, Alfred: Ueber einen Fall von Panarteriofibrosis (Kaiserling) der Kranzarterienäste bei Arhythmia perpetua und seine Beziehung zur Typhusinfektion. Aus d. pathol. Inst. zu Königsberg Pr. [In Maschinenschrift.] 22 S. 4°(2°).
— Auszug: Königsberg i. P. 1920: Kümmel. 2 Bl. 8°
Königsberg, Med. Diss. v. 14. Aug. 1920, Ref. Kaiserling
[Geb. 11. Nov. 94 Lessen; Wohnort: Königsberg i. P; Staatsangeh.: Preußen; Vorbildung: Kgl. G. Danzig Reife 13; Studium: Freiburg 1, München 2, Königsberg 2, Rostock 1, Königsberg 3 S.; Coll. 16. Juni 20: Approb. 11. Juni 20.] [U 20. 2628

NL 0447747 ICRL

LÖWENSTEIN, Alois, Erbprinz.
Ist der staat verpflichtet entschädigung zu leisten, wenn seine richter in aus übung der justizhoheit schuldlos einem unschuldigen schaden zugefügt haben? Frankfurt a.M., 1896.
78 p.
Inaug.-diss. - Freiburg i.d. Schweiz.

NL 0447748 MH-L

Loewenstein, Arno.
Genehmigung von ohne vertretungsmacht geschlossenen geschaeften nach buergerlichem gesetzbuche.
Inaug. diss. Leipzig, 1906 (Hamburg)
Bibl.

NL 0447749 ICRL

Löwenstein, Arnold, 1882-
... Allergische augenerkrankungen, von prof. dr. Arnold Löwenstein ... Basel [etc.], Verlag von S. Karger, 1938.
72 p. 25¼ᶜᵐ. (Abhandlungen aus der augenheilkunde und ihren grenzgebieten. Beihefte zur Zeitschrift für augenheilkunde, hrsg. von C. Behr und J. Meller. hft. 26)
"Literatur": p. 71-72.

1. Allergia. 2. Eye—Diseases and defects. ɪ. Title.
A C 38-2596

Iowa. Univ. Library
for Library of Congress [2]

NL 0447750 IaU CtY ICU

Löwenstein, Arnold, *1882-*
[Collected papers chiefly on the eye.]
Reprinted from various medical serials.

NL 0447751 ICJ

RE901
.T8L8
Löwenstein, Arnold, 1882-
Die tuberkulose des auges; ein lehrbuch für den praktiker und den augenarzt, von dr. Arnold Löwenstein... Berlin, Wien, Urban & Schwarzenberg, 1924.
84 p. illus. 25½cm.
"Literatur": p. 76-84.

1. Eye--Tuberculosis.

NL 0447752 ICU MnU CtY DNLM

Löwenstein, Arthur
Depositum irregulare und Darlehn ... von Arthur Löwenstein ... Gummersbach, F. Luyken, 1896.
82 p. 21cm.
Diss. - Erlangen.
"Benutzte Litteratur": p. [5]-8.

NL 0447753 MH-L NIC ICRL

Loewenstein, Arthur.
Geschichte des württembergischen kreditbankwesens und seiner beziehungen zu handel und industrie, von dr. Arthur Loewenstein, mit 6 diagrammen. Tübingen, J. C. B. Mohr (P. Siebeck) 1912.
2 p. l., 244 p. diagrs. 24ᶜᵐ. (Added t.-p.: Archiv für sozialwissenschaft und sozialpolitik ... Ergänzungsheft v)

1. Banks and banking—Württemberg—Hist. 2. Württemberg—Econ. condit.
Library of Congress HG3059.W8L7
12—15173

MiU PU NN
NL 0447754 DLC MB ICRL MH FU CU CtY OU OO OCU

Loewenstein (Augustus) [1813–]. *De mulierum morbis quædam. 36 pp., 2 l. 8°. *Berolini, typ. fratrum Schlesinger, [1838].

NL 0447755 DNLM

QD395
.L82
Loewenstein, Bernhard.
Ueber einige derivate des phenanthrens. Zuerich, 1898.
48p.
Inaug. diss. Zuerich .

NL 0447756 DLC

PT2424
L827A7
Löwenstein, Bernhard, 1821-1889.
Abul-Hassan-Lieder (Nach Jehuda-ben-Halevy) Wien, Perles, 1894.
187 p. 17cm.

NL 0447757 GU NN

Löwenstein, Bernhard, 1821-1889.
Skizze des vortrages ueber die elemente einer universalreligion im judenthum, gehalten von Sr. Ehrwürden Rabbiner B. Löwenstein im Vereine Schomer Israel. Hrsg. von Michael Wolf. Lemberg, Druck von F. Bednarski, 1888.
24 p. front. (port.) 22 cm.

1. Judaism—Works to 1900. ɪ. Wolf, Michael, b. 1807, ed.
BM580.L6
22—25622

NL 0447758 DLC

Loewenstein, Bruno
Ueber dimethylaethylbenzol und dimethyldiaethyl-benzol...
Inaug. Diss. Rostock, 1882

NL 0447759 ICRL

Löwenstein, Carl, *1881-*
Pathologisch-anatomische untersuchungen über zwei Fälle von Akromegalie. Inaugural dissertation...der Rheinischen Friedrich-Wilhelms-universität zu Bonn... Bonn, S. Foppen, 1906.
Cover-title, 2 p. l., [5]-59 p. plate, table (fold.)
"Litteratur": p. 53-58.

NL 0447760 MiDW ICRL DNLM MBCo

Löwenstein, Curt.
Aktenfälle bürgerlicher rechtsstreitigkeiten, mit unterweisenden ausführungen und urteilsbeispielen, von dr. Curt Löwenstein ... Berlin, C. Heymann, 1926.
2 p. l., 154 p. 22ᶜᵐ.

1. Civil law—Germany—Cases. 2. Civil procedure—Germany.
ɪ. Title.
33-7874

NL 0447761 DLC

VOLUME 338

Loewenstein, Curt.
Entwurf einer deutschen verfassung. Von dr. Curt Loewenstein und dr. Fritz Stern. Königsberg i. Pr., W. Telemann ₍1919₎
24 p. 22ᶜᵐ.

1. Germany. Constitution.   I. Stern, Fritz, joint author.
                                                    23–1365
Library of Congress   JN3953.1919.L6

NL 0447762   DLC

Loewenstein, E.
Masonic historical society of the state of New York.
Miscellany of the Masonic historical society of the state of New York. 1902. New York, The Society, 1902.

Löwenstein, Edgar, 1906–
... Beobachtungen über die ambulante Behandlung zuckerkranker Kinder ...   Krefeld, 1933.
Inaug.-Diss. – Münster.
Lebenslauf.

NL 0447764   CtY DNLM

Löwenstein, Edith, 1910–
Autorisiertes kapital. ... Berlin, 1933.
67 p.
Inaug. Diss. – Heidelberg, 1933.
Lebenslauf.
Bibliography.

NL 0447765   ICRL CtY

Löwenstein, Eduard Max, *d.* 1918?
Die bekämpfung des konkubinates in der rechtsentwicklung. Von Eduard Max Löwenstein. Nach dem tode des verfassers hrsg. von prof. dr. Merkel in Greifswald. Breslau, Schletter, 1919.
4 p. l., 119 p. 23½ᶜᵐ. (*Added t.-p.:* Strafrechtliche abhandlungen ... hft. 201₎
"Literatur-verzeichnis": p. ₍107₎–117.

1. Marriage law—Germany.   I. Merkel, Paul, 1872–   ed.
II. Title.
                                                    34–42698
NL 0447766   DLC MH-L

LOEWENSTEIN, Elias.
Über das foramen jugulare spurium und den canalis temporalis am schädel des menschen und einiger affen. Königsberg,i.E.,1895.

NL 0447767   MBCo NjP DNLM CtY

Löwenstein, Else
Ueber subhaloide der homologen des quecksilbers. ... Freiburg i. Br., 1930.   30 p.
Inaug. Diss. Freiburg i. Br., 1930.

NL 0447768   ICRL CtY

Loewenstein, Emil, appr. Arzt: Aus d. Krankenh. d. jüd. Gemeinde zu Berlin. Ein Fall von primärem Carcinom des Ureter. Berlin: Fraenkel 1911. 29 S. 8°
Freiburg i. B., Med. Diss. v. 1911, Ref. Kraske
[Geb. 25. Mai 82 Berlin; Wohnort: Charlottenburg; Staatsangeh.: Preußen; Vorbildung: Gymn. Gartz Reife M. 02; Studium: Berlin 7, Freiburg i. B. 3 S.; Coll. 22. Juli 10; Approb. 16. Aug. 10.]   [U 11.1093]

NL 0447769   ICRL DNLM

Löwenstein, Erich.
Über Hydrate, deren Dampfspannung sich kontinuierlich mit der Zusammensetzung ändert. Göttingen.   Hamburg, L. Voss, 1909.
73, (1) p.   8°.

NL 0447770   NN

LÖWENSTEIN,Erich, assessor.
Ein beitrag zum lotterievertrag. Inaug.-diss.,Rostock. Breslau,M.& H.Marcus,1916.

NL 0447771   MH-L ICRL

Löwenstein, Erich, assessor
Berlin. Industrie- und handelskammer.
Moratorien und andere sonderregelungen des zahlungsverkehrs im auslande. Zusammengestellt von der Handelskammer zu Berlin. 5. vervollständigte aufl. Berlin, Druck von Liebheit & Thiesen, 1916.

Loewenstein, Erich, 1902–
... Fibrogenbestimmungen bei Anämien ... Berlin, 1927.
Inaug.-Diss. – Berlin.
Lebenslauf.
"Literatur" p. 266.
"Sonderdruck aus "Zeitschrift für klinische Medizin", Bd. 105, Hft. 1/2. "

NL 0447773   CtY ICRL

Löwenstein, Ernst.
Ueber die elektrolytische Reduktion aromatischer Mononitrokoerper bei Gegenwart von Vanadinsalzen. München, Leopold-Buchdruckerei, 1910.
84 p.
Inaug.-Diss. – Munich, Tech. Hoch.

NL 0447774   ICRL MH-C PU

WG
22580
Löwenstein, Ernst, 1872–
Ueber die Constitution der Thiocarbizine.
Berlin, 1894.
28 p.
Inaug.-Diss. – Berlin.

NL 0447775   CtY PU DNLM DLC

Loewenstein, Ernst, 1873–   ed.
Handbuch der gesamten tuberkulose-therapie, hrsg. von prof. dr. med. Ernst Loewenstein ... Berlin, Wien, Urban & Schwarzenberg, 1923.

Löwenstein, Ernst, 1878–
Die Krankenversicherung im Entwurfe der österreichischen Regierung von Dr. med. E. Löwenstein, ... Gross-Lichterfelde-Berlin, A. Troschel, 1908.
110800
62 p. 27½ᶜᵐ.

NL 0447777   ICJ IU

Loewenstein, Ernst, 1878–
Reinzüchtung des tuberkelbacillus. Von prof. dr. Ernst Löwenstein ...
(*In* Abderhalden, Emil, ed. Handbuch der biologischen arbeitsmethoden ... Berlin, 1920–   25ᶜᵐ. abt. XII, Leistungen der niederen organismenwelt. t. 1 (1925) p. ₍815₎–836 incl. tab.)
"Literaturverzeichnis": p. 835–836.

1. Bacillus tuberculosis.
                                                    A C 36–4078
Title from Ohio State   Univ.
Library of Congress   [QH324.A3 1920 abt. 12, t. 1]
                            ₍2₎   (574.072)
NL 0447778   OU

Loewenstein, Ernst, 1878–
Toxine und toxoide. Von E. Löwenstein ...
(*In* Abderhalden. Emil. ed. Handbuch der biologischen arbeitsmethoden ... Berlin, 1920–   25ᶜᵐ. abt. XIII, Methoden der experimentellen therapie und der immunitätsforschung. t. 2 (1933) p. ₍1031₎–1140)
"Literatur": p. 1136–1140.

1. Toxins and antitoxins.
                                                    A C 36–3361
Title from Ohio State   Univ.
Library of Congress   [QH324.A3 1920 abt. 13, t. 2]
                            ₍2₎   (574.072)
NL 0447779   OU

QW
125
L827t
1936
LOEWENSTEIN, Ernst, 1878–
Die Tuberkelbazillämie in ihrer Auswirkung auf die Gesamtmedizin, mit einem klinischen Teil von Carl Reitter ₍et al.₎ Leipzig, Deuticke, 1936.
vi, 388 p. illus.
1. Septicemia 2. Tubercle bacillus
I. Reitter, Karl, 1876–

NL 0447780   DNLM

Löwenstein, Ernst, 1878–
Vorlesungen über bakteriologie, immunität, spezifische diagnostik und therapie der tuberkulose für aerzte und tierärzte, von dr. Ernst Löwenstein ... Jena, G. Fischer, 1920.
viii, 476 p. 2 double diagr. 25ᶜᵐ.
Contains bibliographies.

1. Tuberculosis.
                                                    Agr 21–1075
Library, U. S. Dept. of   Agriculture 448L952

NL 0447781   DNAL DNLM PPC OrU-M ICJ

Löwenstein, Ernst, 1878–
Über den Mechanismus der Tuberkulinimmunität, von dr. Löwenstein und dr. Rappoport. Leipzig, J. A. Barth [1904]
p. 485–535. 1 pl. 4°.
n. t.–p.
Repr.: Zeitschrift für Tuberkulose u. Heilstättenwesen. Bd. 5. Hft. 6.
Title from cover.

NL 0447782   NN

1883–
Loewenstein, Ernst/₍Aus d. gynäkol. Klinik d. Univ. Freiburg i. B.₎ Über die operativen Erfolge bei chronischeitrigen Adnexerkrankungen. Hamburg 1909: Berngruber & Henning. 126 S. 8°
Freiburg i. B., Med. Diss. v. 1909, Ref. Krönig
[Geb. 10. Nov. 83 Woldenberg; Wohnort: Pforzheim; Staatsangeh.: Preußen; Vorbildung: Gymn. Stargard i. Pomm. Reife O. 03; Studium: München 2, Berlin 3, Freiburg i. B. 6 S.; Coll. 2. Juli 08.]   [U 09.956]

NL 0447783   ICRL DNLM

VOLUME 338

1896–
Loewenstein, Ernst, Medizinalprakt.: Zur Diagnose multipler primärer Carcinome nebst einem casuistischen Beitrag. Aus d. Pathol. Inst. d. Univ. zu Breslau. [In Maschinenschrift.] 37 S. 4°(2°). — Auszug: Breslau 1921: Gutsmann. 2 Bl. 8°
Breslau, Med. Diss. v. 20. Sept. 1921, Ref. Henke
[Geb. 23. Mai 96 Berlin; Wohnort: Breslau; Staatsangeh.: Preußen; Vorbildung: G. Zehlendorf Reife 14; Studium: Jur. Berlin 1, Med. Berlin 4, Breslau 2, Berlin 2, Breslau 2 S.; Coll. 22. Juli 20; Approb. 17. Aug. 21.]
[U 21. 3006]

NL 0447784   ICRL

Loewenstein, Ernst, 1909–
... Die Behandlung der Metropathia haemorrhagica mit radiumaktiven Substanzen ... Würzburg, 1933.
Inaug.-Diss. - Münster.
Lebenslauf.

NL 0447785   CtY

Löwenstein, Ernst, 1911–
Die Patterson-Probe zum qualitativen Schnellnachweis erhöhten Blutharnstoffs ... Düsseldorf, 1936.
Inaug.-Diss. - Köln.
Lebenslauf.
"Literatur": p. 11.

NL 0447786   CtY

Loewenstein (Eugen). *Ein Fall von ausgebreiteter Ablösung der Pleura pulmonalis von der Lungenoberfläche. 29 pp. 8°. *Würzburg, 1892.

NL 0447787   DNLM

Löwenstein, Eugen.
Die Krankenversicherung im Entwurfe der österreichischen Regierung
see Löwenstein, Ernst, 1878–

Loewenstein, Eugen, 1880–
Ein fall von Brown- sequardscher halberseitenlaesion..
Inaug. diss. Strassburg, 1905 (Stuttgart)
Bibl.

NL 0447789   ICRL DNLM MBCo

158.5   Loewenstein, Eugen, 1880–
L82n   Nervöse leute; gedanken eines laien.
           Leipzig, Wolff, 1914.
           279p. O.

NL 0447790   IaU

Loewenstein, F. E.
see
Loewenstein, Fritz Erwin, 1901–

Löwenstein, Franz
Über periphere bleilähmungen ...
Würzburg, 1934.
           Inaug. Diss. - Basel, 1934.

NL 0447792   MiU

Löwenstein, Friedrich, *prinz* zu, 1860–
Volksvermögen und kriegsentschädigung, von Friedrich prinz zu Löwenstein.   München und Leipzig, Duncker & Humblot, 1918.
44 p. 23½ᶜᵐ.

1. European war, 1914-1918—Finance—Germany.   2. European war, 1914-1918—Economic aspects—Germany.
(Full name: Friedrich Ernst Otto Ludwig, prinz zu Löwenstein-Wertheim-Freudenberg)
25–256

Library of Congress   D635.L75

NL 0447793   DLC

Löwenstein, Friedrich Müller
     see   Müller Löwenstein, Friedrich.

Law
     Loewenstein, Fritz, 1892–
     דע את חקי ארצך.   מורה־הדרך בחוק הארצישראלי, מאת ד״ר פ. לוינשטיין ... ירושלים, ר. מס.
     [Jerusalem, 1942]
     (ספריית מס למדע משלר.   ספר ב)   *(Half-title:* 140 p.   17ᶜᵐ.
     [רשימת ספרים]: p. 139–140.

1. Law—Palestine—Compends.   I. Title.
Title transliterated: Da' eth buke arẓekha.
45–684

NL 0447795   DLC

Loewenstein, Fritz, 1892–
     מורה־דרך בחוק הארצישראלי.   מהדורה ב.   מורחבת מהספר
     "דע את חוקי ארצך."   ירושלים. ר. מס. תש״ח.
     [Jerusalem, 1947]
     144 p.   17 cm.
     Notes (partly bibliographical): p. 139–144.

1. Law—Palestine—Compends.   I. Title.
Title transliterated: Moreh-derekh ba-ḥok ha-artsiyisraeli.
54–55592

NL 0447796   DLC

Loewenstein, Fritz E.
     Die handzeichnungen der japanischen holzschnittmeister, von Fritz E. Loewenstein; mit 2 farbigen und 30 schwarzen tafeln.   Plauen im Vogtland, C. F. Schulz & co., 1922.
     4 p. l., 71 p.   illus, plates (2 col., mounted) 29½ᶜᵐ.   *(Added t.-p.:* Ostasiatische graphik hrsg. von der J. Kurth.   bd. 11)
     The colored plates are accompanied by guard sheets with descriptive letterpress.
     "Literatur und kataloge": p. 70.
     1. Drawings, Japanese.   2. Wood-engravings, Japanese.   I. Title.
     23–17968

Library of Congress   NC1240.L6

OC1SA PP MB NN
NL 0447797   DLC CaBVaU CSt WU CU-S NcD OCU MB NN

Loewenstein, Fritz Erwin, 1901–
     Bernard Shaw through the camera; 238 photos., including many taken by Mr. Shaw, selected and introduced by his bibliographer and remembrancer.   London, B. & H. White Publications, 1948.
     128 p. (p. 17–123 illus., ports.)   24 cm.

1. Shaw, George Bernard, 1856–

PR5366.L6   928.2   49–7272 rev*

INS KMK OrU NNC
RPB NN MiD OC1W OC1JC Or OrU KyLx OCU NcU WaU LU
NL 0447798   DLC WaTC NBuC KEmT PBL PP NIC MH ICU

Shaw
PR   Loewenstein, Fritz Erwin, 1901–
5366   The copyrighting of Shaw's early dramatic
L82C7+   work, containing also a word on the
               vicissitudes of Mrs. Warren's profession.
               London, 1952.
               8 p.   26cm.

           "The Shaw Society.   Bulletin supplement No. 2."

           1. Shaw, George Bernard, 1856–1950.
           2. Copyright—Gt. Brit.

NL 0447799   NIC

Loewenstein, Fritz Erwin, 1901–
     The history of a famous novel, by F. E. Loewenstein.   London, Priv. print., 1946.
     2 p. l., 3–19, [3] p.   2 illus. (incl. facsim.)   22 cm.
     Running title: The history of An unsocial socialist.
     "500 copies."

1. Shaw, George Bernard, 1856–   An unsocial socialist.

Z8814.5.L6   823.91   46–22736 rev

NL 0447800   DLC CaOTP ViW NIC

B   Loewenstein, Fritz Erwin, 1901–
S534lo   The pictorial record of the life of Bernard
           Shaw; over 100 photographs, including several
           taken by Mr. Shaw.   London, H. A. & W. L. Pitkin [1951?]
           23p.   illus., ports.   23cm.

           1. Shaw, George Bernard, 1856-1950--Portraits, caricatures, etc.

NL 0447801   IU MB CU NIC NcU MeB

Loewenstein, Fritz Erwin, 1901–
     The rehearsal copies of Bernard Shaw's plays, a bibliographical study.   London, Reinhardt & Evans, 1950.
     36 p.   25 cm.

1. Shaw, George Bernard, 1856-1950—Bibl.   I. Title.

Z8814.5.L62 1950   012   50–23993

FU CSt NcU FMU
ViU ICU TxU PU IdPI MtU OrU CaBVaU NSyU PSt CaOTP
NL 0447802   DLC PPT NNC OC1W MH NN NcD IaU CtY MB

Loewenstein, Fritz Erwin, 1901–
     What Richard Mansfield thought of "Candida."
     (In Drama [British Drama League] London.
     22 cm.   New series, no. 2 (Autumn 1946) p. 8–10)
     1. Shaw, George Bernard.   Candida.

NL 0447803   NcU

Loewenstein, Georg: (Kritische Betrachtungen und Beiträge zur Statistik der Geschlechtskrankheiten (1910—1921)). [Leipzig: J. A. Barth 1922.] S. 148—197. 8°. — Auszug: Berlin (1922): Ebering. 2 Bl. 8° ¶Aus: Zeitschrift f. Bekämpf. d. Geschlechtskrankh. 90.
Berlin, Med. Diss. v. 27. Juli 1922   [U 22. 391]

NL 0447804   ICRL

1887–
Loewenstein, Georg, Referendar: Kann ein prozessuales Anerkenntnis im Sinne von § 307 ZPO wegen Irrtums im Motiv angefochten oder widerrufen werden? ⟨Ein Beitr. z. Lehre von d. Prozesshandlungen.⟩ Berlin: Blanke 1912. 51 S. 8°
Rostock, Jur. Diss. v. 15. Febr. 1912, Ref. Wachenfeld
[Geb. 8. Febr. 87 Lessen, Kr. Graudenz; Wohnort: Neustadt Wpr.; Staatsangeh.: Preußen; Vorbildung: Gymn. Graudenz Reife O. 08; Studium: Freiburg i. B. 1, München 1, Berlin 2, Königsberg 2 S.; Rig. 11. Dez. 11.]
[U 12. 4109]

NL 0447805   ICRL MH-L

VOLUME 338

Loewenstein, Gustav: Das Verbot des Selbstkontrahierens beim Wechselakzept. [Maschinenschrift.] 51 S. 4°. — Auszug: (Emden 1923: Emder Zeitg). 2 Bl. 8°
Göttingen, R.- u. staatswiss. Diss. v. 24. Nov. 1923   [U 23. 3986

NL 0447806   ICRL

Loewenstein, Gustav: Zur Kenntnis der uraemischen Psychosen. [Maschinenschrift.] 21 S. 4°. — Auszug: Königsberg i. P. 1922: Petzelberger. 2 Bl. 8°
Königsberg, Med. Diss. v. 19. Febr. 1923   [U 23. 7548

NL 0447807   ICRL

1890 -
Löwenstein, Gustav: /Über Reihenentwicklungen, die aus linearen Differentialgleichungen zweiter Ordnung entspringen. Stuttgart 1915: Grüninger. 46 S. 8°
Würzburg, Phil. Diss. v. 18. Febr. 1915, Ref. Rost
[Geb. 27. Nov. 90 Stuttgart; Wohnort: Würzburg; Staatsangeh.: Württemberg; Vorbildung: RG. Stuttgart Reife 09; Studium: Freiburg 1, Berlin 2, Göttingen 3, Würzburg 4 S.; Rig. 6. Nov. 14.]   [U 15. 2399

NL 0447808   ICRL MiU CtY RPB MH IU

Loewenstein, Hans: Die Entwicklung der Hallischen Maschinenindustrie. [Maschinenschrift.] III, 133 S. 4°. — Auszug: Eisleben 1925: Schneider. 2 Bl. 8°
Halle, R.- u. staatswiss. Diss. v. 20. Jan. 1925   [U 25. 3962

NL 0447809   ICRL

Löwenstein, Hans: Das Verhalten der Blutplättchen bei gynäkologischen Blutungen unt. Berücks. d. Calciumtherapie. [Maschinenschrift.] 29 S. 4° [Lag nicht vor] — Auszug: o. O. (1923). 1 Bl. 8°
Leipzig, Med. Diss. v. 26. Nov. 1923 [1924]   [U 24. 6574

NL 0447810   ICRL

Loewenstein, Hans, 1878-
Klinisch-statistische beitraege zur puerperalfieberfrage.
Inaug. Diss. Breslau, 1902 (Berlin)
Bibl.

NL 0447811   ICRL DNLM

Loewenstein, Heinz, 1904
Ueber die einwirkung von primären aromatischen aminen auf furfurol
Inaug. Diss. Berlin, 1931

NL 0447812   ICRL CtY IaAS OU

Loewenstein, Herbert
see his later name
Avenary, Hanoch.

Löwenstein (Hermannus Josephus). *De mentis aberrationibus ex partium sexnalinm conditione abnormi oriundis. 50 pp. 8°. *Bonnæ, typ. Thormannianis,* 1883.

NL 0447814   DNLM

Loewenstein, Howard, 1924-
Gaseous loss of nitrogen from soil. Ann Arbor, University Microfilms [1955]
([University Microfilms, Ann Arbor, Mich.] Publication no. 14,718)
Microfilm copy (positive) of typescript.
Collation of the original: iv, 115 l. illus.
Thesis—University of Wisconsin.
Abstracted in Dissertation abstracts, v. 15 (1955) no. 12, p. 2377-2378.
Vita.
Bibliography: leaves 110-115.
1. Nitrification.   I. Title.
Microfilm AC-1   no. 14,718   Mic 55-1421

Wisconsin. Univ. Libr.
for Library of Congress   [1]†

NL 0447815   WU DLC

Löwenstein, Hubertus, Prinz zu
    see   Löwenstein-Wertheim-Freudenberg, Hubertus, Prinz zu, 1906-

Loewenstein (Ignatius). *De asphyxia.
[Munich.] 16 pp. 8°. *Augusta Vindelicorum,* J. C. Jasper,* 1833.

NL 0447817   DNLM

Löwenstein, Is.
מורה טהורה Menorah tehorah, oder Das reine judenthum als gegenstück des von dr. M. Creizenach, unter dem titel Thariag herausgegebenen ersten theils seines Schulchan aruch. In zwei abtheilungen von J. Löwenstein ... Schaffhausen, Hurter'scho buchh. und beim verfasser, 1835.
xvii p., 1 l., [21]-201 p. 18¼°.
CONTENTS.—1. abth. Das wandeln im lichte des Ewigen, oder Die wahre aufklirung des Israeliten, dargestellt in einer predigt.—2. abth. Beleuchtung des von dr. M. Creizenach herausgegeben "Thariag, oder Inbegriff der mosaischen vorschriften nach talmudischer interpretation."
1. Jews—Religion. 2. Jewish law. 3. Creizenach, Michael, 1789-1842. Thariag. 4. Caro, Joseph, 1488-1575. Shulḥan 'arukh. I. Title.
Title transliterated: Menorah tehorah.
Library of Congress   BM560.L6   31-23601
                          [a 44r43d1]   296

NL 0447818   DLC NN

Loewenstein (Isidorus). *De chlorosi. 30 pp., 1 l. 8°. *Berolini, typ. Schnitzerianis,* [1843].

NL 0447819   DNLM

Loewenstein, J
Eine erzählung aus dem Ghetto zu Rom während der Herrschaft des Tribunen Rienzi
    see in   Auerbach, Bernard.
Die audienz des hohen Rabbi Löw.

[Loewenstein, J]
Zwei Lebensfragen des Vereins selbstündiger Handwerker jüd. Glaubens, [Verein sorgan und Krankenkasse.] n.t.-9.
[Berlin, 191-?]
2 L.
Ti. taken from 1. L.

NL 0447821   OCH

Löwenstein, Jakob, 1869-
Ueber örtliche und metastatische eiterungen des knochenmarkes ... Jurjew (Dorpat), Mattiesen, 1899.
54 p.
Inaug.-Diss. - Dorpat, 1899.
1. Bones - Diseases.

NL 0447822   NNC DNLM

Löwenstein, Jakob, 1879-
Über die Fussgelenksluxation durch Rotation nach aussen in Verbindung mit hoher Fibulafraktur. Giessen, O. Kindt, 1907.
26 p.
Inaug.-Diss. - Giessen, 1908.

NL 0447823   ICRL MH DNLM

Loewenstein, Jakob Julius, b. 1811.
De musices in homines et animalia efficacia ... Berolini, typis Friedlaenderianis [1835]
30 p. 21 x 12°.
Inaug.-diss.—Berlin.
Curriculum vitae.

1. Music, Physical effects of.
                                                    10-9364
Library of Congress   ML3920.L73

NL 0447824   DLC DNLM

Löwenstein (J[akob] S[amuel]) [1804-68]. Beiträge zur Geschichte der medicinischen Facultät au der Hochschule zu Frankfurt a. O. während der Dauer ihres Bestehens von 1506 bis 1811. 28 pp. 8°. [Frankfurt a. O., Trowitzsch & Sohn, 1811. vel subsec.]

NL 0447825   DNLM

Adelmann
R   Loewenstein, Jakob Samuel, 1804-1868.
123   De prosodia medica, sive de recta verbo-
L82   rum in medicina usitatorum pronuntiatione.
        Berolini, Apud A. Hirschwald, 1828.
        44 p. 21cm.

        1. Medicine--Terminology. 2. Latin
    language--Glossaries, vocabularies, etc.
    3. Latin language--Pronunciation.

NL 0447826   NIC NjP DNLM

Loewenstein, Jeanne Marie.
... Les sanctions pénales de la législation du travail (à la veille de la guerre de 1939) ... par Jeanne-Marie Loewenstein ... Epinal, Imprimerie Fricotel, 1941.
xii, 249 p. 23½°.
Thèse—Nancy.
"Bibliographie": p. 237-241.

1. Labor laws and legislation—France. 2. Criminal law—France.
                                                    46-42864
NL 0447827   DLC CtY

Löwenstein, Jeroham Löb
see
Loewenstein, Lipmann Hirsch, *d. ca.* 1850.

Loewenstein, *Prince John.*
Swastika and Yin-Yang, by Prince John Loewenstein. London, The China society, 1942.
28 p. incl. front., illus. 21°. (*Half-title:* China society Occasional papers. New ser., ed. by W. P. Yetts. No. 1)
"A lecture delivered before the society on 16th December, 1941."
Bibliography: p. 26-28.

1. Swastika. 2. Yin Yang symbol.
                                                    42-21364
Library of Congress   BL604.SSL6
                          [3]   291.37

NL 0447829   DLC CtY MH CU

VOLUME 338

Löwenstein (Josef). *Das runde Magen-
geschwür mit besonderer Berücksichtigung
seines Vernarbungsprocesses.* [Freiburg i. B.]
29 pp., 1 l. 8°. *Berlin, G. Schade,* [1894].

NL 0447830   DNLM

Loewenstein (Josef) [1885–]. *Erfahrun-
gen über das Verhalten aromatische Oxykar-
bonsäuren und Oxysulfosäuren sowie ihrer
Ester beim Benzoylieren nach der Schotten-
Baumannschen Methode.* 50 pp., 1 l. 8°.
Königsberg i. Pr., R. Leupold, 1908.

NL 0447831   DNLM ICRL MH PU

Loewenstein, Joseph.
The treatment of impotence, with special reference to
mechanotherapy. Foreword by Eric B. Strauss. [London]
H. Hamilton Medical Books, 1947.
49 p. illus. 19 cm.
"References": p. 47–48.

1. Impotence. 2. Mechanotherapy.
A 49–1599*
Ohio State Univ. Libr.   RC889.L64
for Library of Congress   [1]

NL 0447832   OU OOxM OU DNLM

Loewenstein, Joswph, 1873–
Ueber Erkrankungen der Leber u. Milz
infolge von Unterleibscontusionen ...
Würzburg, 1897.
Inaug.-Diss. - Breslau.

NL 0447833   CtY ICRL DNLM

Loewenstein, Judah Loeb.
see
Loewenstein, Leopold, *1843-1924.*

Löwenstein, Julius.
Die Leder- und Schuhwaren-Industrie auf der Weltausstellung in
Chicago nebst einer Skizze über den Fortschritt dieser Industrien
in America. [*In* AUSTRIA. K. K. CENTRAL-COMMISSION FÜR
DIE WELTAUSSTELLUNG IN CHICAGO 1893. Officieller Bericht,
no. 4. p. 33–45. Wien 1894.]

NL 0447835   ICJ

Löwenstein, Julius
Die stille Gesellschaft nach dem allgemeinen Deutschen Handels-Gesetzbuche
und dem Entwurf eines neuen Handels-
gesetzbuches. Von Dr. Julius Löwenstein ... München, C. Wolf & Sohn,
1896.
44 p. 22cm.
Inaug.-Diss. - Erlangen.
Bibliographical footnotes.

NL 0447836   MH-L ICRL NIC

Löwenstein, Julius, 1857–   ed.
BM506
.B53M65
Mishnah. *Bekorot.*
Maimonides' Commentar zum Tractat Bekhoroth im
arabischen Urtext mit verbesserter hebräischer Uebersetzung
und mit Anmerkungen versehen von Julius Löwenstein.
Berlin, Druck von H. Itzkowski, 1897.

Loewenstein (Julius) [1863–]. *Die Impftuberculose des Praeputiums.* 23 pp., 2 l. 8°.
Königsberg i. Pr., M. Liedtke, 1889.

NL 0447838   DNLM PPC CU

Löwenstein, Julius I
Hegels Staatsidee; ihr Doppelgesicht und ihr Einfluss
im 19. Jahrhundert, von Julius Löwenstein. Berlin, J.
Springer, 1927.
3 p. l., 183, [1] p. 26 cm.
(Added t.-p.: Philosophische Forschungen, hrsg. von Karl Jas-
pers ... 4. hft.)
"Der erste Teil der vorliegenden Arbeit wurde 1925 unter dem
titel 'Das Doppelgesicht der Hegelschen Staatsanschauung' als Dissertation der Philosophischen Fakultät der Heidelberger Universität
eingereicht."—p. [150]
Bibliography included in "Anmerkungen," (p. [150]–183)

1. Hegel, Georg Wilhelm Friedrich, 1770–1831. 2. State, The.
JC233.H45   28–9672

NL 0447839   DLC NcD CtY-L MH

Loewenstein, Käte
Als was sind die verbindlichkeiten, die
der erbe in verwaltung des nachlasses ein-
geht, auzusehen? ... von Käte Loewenstein
... Kulmbach, G. Schuhmann, 1931.
2 p.l., 37 p. 22cm.
Inaug.-diss.- Erlangen.
"Literatur-Verzeichnis": p. 33-36.

NL 0447840   MH-L ICRL

Löwenstein, Karl, 1881–
see   Löwenstein, Carl, 1881–

Loewenstein, Karl, 1891–
B1a16   America's eleventh hour, by Karl Loewenstein
Z9   ... and Lawrence B. Packard ... [Amherst, 1940]
Pamphlet

NL 0447842   CtY

Loewenstein, Karl, 1891–
America's eleventh hour, by Karl Loewenstein... and Lawrence [!], B. Packard ... Easthampton, Mass., The Easthampton news company [1940]
24 p. 23ᵐ.

1. European war, 1939–   —U. S.   I. Packard, Laurence Bradford, 1887–   joint author. II. Title.
Library of Congress   D753.L6   41–9140
[5]   940.5373

NL 0447843   DLC NN IdPI

Loewenstein, Karl, *1891-*
B176j   Autocracy versus democracy in contemporary
A3   Europe ... [Baltimore, 1935]
935t   cover-title, p.571-593,755-784. 25ᵐ
"Reprinted from The American political science
review, vol.XXIX, nos.4 and 5, August and
October, 1935."

NL 0447844   CtY

Loewenstein, Karl, 1891–
The balance between legislative and executive power: a study
in comparative constitutional law [by] Karl Loewenstein.
[Chicago, The University of Chicago press, 1938]
[1], 566–608 p. 24ᵐ.
Caption title.
"Reprinted for private circulation from the University of Chicago law
review. vol. 5, no. 4, June, 1938."

1. Legislative power. 2. Executive power. 3. Separation of powers.
4. Constitutional law. 5. Comparative law.   I. Title.
30–32554

NL 0447845   DLC

Loewenstein, Karl, 1891–
Brazil under Vargas, by Karl Loewenstein ... New York,
The Macmillan company, 1942.
xix, 381 p. front. (map) 21ᵐ.
"First printing."
Bibliographical foot-notes.

1. Brazil—Pol. & govt.—1930–   2. *Vargas, Getulio, pres. Brazil,
1883–   I. Title.
Library of Congress   F2538.L6   42–22052
[35]   981

WaS CoU WaT WaWW NBuU DAU UU PPCCH
NcD NcRS NN CU PLF NSyU IdPI IdU OrCS OrSaW WaE UU
OOxM PBm TxU ViU PPD MiHM OrU OrP Or MH CaBVaU TU
NL 0447846   DLC PP PSC PHC OCl OU OCU OO ODW OClW

Loewenstein, Karl, 1891–
Contrôle législatif de l'extrémisme politique dans les démo-
craties européennes, par Karl Loewenstein ... (traduction française par Albertine Jèze) Paris, Librairie générale de droit &
de jurisprudence, 1939.
136 p., 1 l. 23ᵐ.
"Cette étude a été publiée aux États-Unis en 1938 ... Les directeurs
de la Columbia law review ... ont donné ... l'autorisation de publier une
édition française."—Avant-propos.

1. Representative government and representation. 2. Sedition.
I. Jèze, Albertine, tr. II. Title. III. Title: L'extrémisme politique.
Library of Congress   JC585.L57   40–29625
[3]   351.75

NL 0447847   DLC CaBVaU MH CtY NNC PU

Loewenstein, Karl, 1891–
... Erscheinungsformen der verfassungsänderung; verfas-
sungsrechtsdogmatische untersuchungen zu artikel 76 der
Reichsverfassung, von dr. Karl Loewenstein ... Tübingen,
J. C. B. Mohr, 1931.
xvii, [1], 308 p. 24ᵐ. (Beiträge zum öffentlichen recht der gegenwart.
2)

1. Germany. Constitution—Amendments. I. Title.
A 32–1782 Revised
Wisconsin. Univ. Libr.
for Library of Congress   JN3950.A6L6
[r44b2]†   342.43

NL 0447848   WU ICU CtY-L DLC MH

Loewenstein, Karl, 1891–   FOR OTHER EDITIONS
JF51   SEE MAIN ENTRY
.S5
1944   **Shotwell, James Thomson,** 1874–   ed.
... Governments of continental Europe ... by James T. Shot-
well, R. K. Gooch, Karl Loewenstein ... [and others] [Madison,
Wis.] Pub. for the United States Armed forces institute by the
Macmillan company [1944]

Loewenstein, Karl, *1891*-
Das heutige verfassungsrecht des
britischen weltreichs von.. Karl Loewenstein. Tübingen, J. C. B. Mohr, 1925.
404-497 p.
(Jahrbuch des Öffentlichen Rechts bd. 13.)

NL 0447850   MH

Loewenstein, Karl, 1891–
Hitler's Germany; the Nazi background to war, by Karl
Loewenstein. New York, The Macmillan company, 1939.
xv, 176 p. 19½ᵐ.
"First printing."
Bibliographical foot-notes.

1. Germany—Pol. & govt.—1933–   2. National socialism. I. Title.
30–32513
Library of Congress   DD253.L58
———— Copy 2.
Copyright A 135458   [15]   943.085

Wa WaE CoU OrPR Or AU ScU
OU OCU PBm PU MB ViU PSC MiU PPRETS OrSaW OrCS CaBVa
NL 0447851   DLC WaS PLF NNC NcD OCl OClh OLak OClCC

VOLUME 338

Loewenstein, Karl, 1891–
 Hitler's Germany; the Nazi background to war, by Karl
Loewenstein. New ed. completely rev. New York, The Mac-
millan company, 1940.
  xviii p., 1 l., 230 p. 19½ᵐ.
  Bibliographical foot-notes.

    1. Germany—Pol. & govt.—1933–   2. National socialism.
  I. Title.
     Library of Congress   DD253.L58 1940   40-34526
     ———— Copy 2.
     Copyright   ₍7₎   943.085

   DAU AU NcD OC1 ODW OC1U OLak PPD PP
NL 0447852   DLC WaWW WaSpG DLC MtBC OCH NbU MsU

Loewenstein, Karl, 1891–
 Hitler's Germany, the Nazi background to war,
by ....New ed. completely rev. New York, The
Macmillan company, 1941.
  230 p.
  "New ed...1940. Second printing...1941"

NL 0447853   PSC

  Löwenstein, Karl, 1891–
    Hitler's Germany; the Nazi background to
  war... New ed., completely rev.   New York, The
  Macmillan company, 1944₍c1940₎ xxii p.,1 l.,
  230p. 19½cm.

    Third printing with added preface, dated
  Oct.6, 1943.
    Bibliographical foot-notes.

NL 0447854   MWelC OU NNC MiU

  Loewenstein, Karl
    Law in the third Reich ... [New Haven?1936]
    Pamphlet
    "Reprinted from the Yale law journal, March,
  1936."

NL 0447855   CtY

  Loewenstein, Karl, 1891–
    ... Legislation against subversive activities in
  Argentina ... Cambridge, Mass., Harvard law
  review association, 1943.
    p. 2161-1306. 25.5 cm.
    ["Reprinted from Harvard law review, Vol. LVI,
  No. 8, July, 1943"]

NL 0447856   DPU

  LÖWENSTEIN, Karl, 1891–
  Minderheitsregierung in Grossbritannien,
  verfassungsrechtliche unter suchungen zur
  neuesten entwicklung des britischen Parlamen-
  tarismus. München,1925.

    ₍3₎471 p.

NL 0447857   MH-L

  Loewenstein, Karl, 1891–
    Die Monarchie im modernen Staat. Frankfurt am Main,
  A. Metzner ₍1952₎
    150 p. illus. 21 cm.

    1. Monarchy. I. Title.
     JC381.L62   54-25538 ‡

   IaU MiU ScU CtY
NL 0447858   DLC OrU NBuU   CU MH NN NIC NNC NjP

Loewenstein, Karl, 1891–
 Political reconstruction, by Karl Loewenstein ... New York,
The Macmillan company, 1946.
  xii, 498 p. 22ᶜᵐ.
  "First printing."
  "Footnotes": p. 405–485.

    1. Self-determination, National. 2. Intervention. 3. Political science.
  4. Reconstruction (1939–) I. Title.
                                                          46–900
     Library of Congress *   JX4071.L6
                                  ₍18₎   320.157

   OC1 OCU OC1W PP KEmT NIC
   Or OrP OrSaW Wa WaE WaSp WaS WaSpG WaT OrCS NcD GU
NL 0447859   DLC PSt MiU NBuC NcGU PSC IdB MtU OrU

Loewenstein, Karl, 1891–
JN3971
.A979F6   Forsthoff, Ernst, 1902–
             Die politischen Parteien im Verfassungsrecht; zwei Ab-
           handlungen von Ernst Forsthoff und Karl Loewenstein, und
           ein Bericht von Werner Matz. Tübingen, J. C. B. Mohr
           ₍1950₎

Loewenstein, Karl, 1891–
 South American impressions of a political scientist, by Karl
Loewenstein ... ₍n. p., 1942₎
  cover-title, ₍10₎ p. 23½ᵐ.
  "Reprinted from the Amherst graduates' quarterly, February, 1942."

    1. South America—Politics—20th cent.
     Library of Congress   F2236.L6   42–22188

NL 0447861   DLC

  Loewenstein, Karl, 1891–
    Verfassungsleben in grossbritannien
  1924–1932 von ... Karl Loewenstein. Tübingen, J. C. B. Mohr, 1932.

      195–319p.

    Jahrbuch des Offentlichen Rechts bd. 20.)

NL 0447862   MH

Loewenstein, Karl, 1891–
 Volk und parlament nach der staatstheorie der französischen nationalversammlung von 1789; studien zur dog-
mengeschichte der unmittelbaren volksgesetzgebung, von
dr. Karl Loewenstein. München, Drei masken verlag,
1922.
  xxxviii, ₍1₎, 376, ₍1₎ p., 1 l. 25½ᵐ.
  "Die abhandlung ist die, um einige zusätze erweiterte, dissertation des
verfassers zur erlangung des doktorgrades der Juristischen fakultät der
Universität München."—Vorwort.
  "Bücherverzeichnis": p. xi–₍xiv₎
    1. France—Constitutional history. 2. Representative government and
  representation. 3. France. Assemblée nationale constituante, 1789–1791.
  4. France—Pol. & govt.—Revolution. I. Title.
     Library of Congress   JN2471.L6   24–4085

NL 0447863   DLC CtY-L CtY LU NN

Loewenstein, Karl, 1891–
 Vom Wesen der amerikanischen Verfassung ₍mit Verfas-
sungstext₎ Frankfurt am Main, W. Metzner, 1950.
  75 p. 20 cm. (Kleine Schriften für den Staatsbürger, 8)

    1. U. S.—Pol. & govt. 2. U. S.—Constitutional law—Compends.
  I. U. S. Constitution. (Series)
     JK274.L58   342.73   51–17628

NL 0447864   DLC MiU FU NcD

Loewenstein, Kurt, *doctor of jurisprudence.*
 Die gestaltung der fürsorge für entlassene strafgefangene.
Von dr. jur. Kurt Loewenstein. Breslau, Schletter, 1928.
  xii, 109 p. 24 cm. (Added t.-p.: Strafrechtliche abhandlungen ...
hft. 240)
  "Literaturverzeichnis": p. ₍vii₎–ix.

    1. Rehabilitation of criminals—Germany.
                                           28–23263 rev

NL 0447865   DLC

  Loewenstein, Kurt, 1883–
    Beitrag zur differential- diagnose des kataton-
  ischen und hysterischen stupors.
    Inaug. diss. Leipzig, 1908 (Berlin)
    Bibl.

NL 0447866   ICRL DNLM CtY MH

Löwenstein, Kurt, 1883–
 ... Zur kenntnis der faserung des hinterhaupts- und schläfenlappens (sehstrahlung, unteres längsbündel, Türcksches bün-
del) nebst klinischen bemerkungen über tumoren des rechten
schläfenlappens. Von dr. med. Kurt Löwenstein ... Mit 18
figuren im text.
  (In Zürich. Universität. Hirnanatomisches institut. Arbeiten.
Wiesbaden, 1905–16. 25½ᶜᵐ. Hft. v (1911) p. ₍241₎–351. illus. (part
col.) diagrs.)
    At head of title: Arbeiten aus dem Hirnanatomischen institut der Uni-
  versität Zürich. Direktor prof. v. Monakow.
    "Literaturverzeichnis": p. 349–351.
    1. Nerves, Cranial. 2. Brain. 3. Brain—Tumors.
                                                    A 43–713
     Rochester. Univ. Library
       for Library of Congress   ₍2₎

NL 0447867   NRU CU MiU ICJ

Löwenstein, Kurt, 1885–
 Die Aufgaben der Kinderfreunde. [Referat,
gehalten auf der ersten Reichskonferenz der
Kinderfreunde in Leipzig am 2.Aug.1924. Hrsg.
von der Reichsarbeitsgemeinschaft der Kinderfreunde. Berlin, Dietz, 1924]

    15 p.

NL 0447868   MH

ar W   Löwenstein, Kurt, 1885–
54249   J. M. Guyau's pädagogische Anschauungen
no.4   (Darstellung und Kritik) Hannover, Buchdr.
          E. Schäuffler, 1910.
            ii, 76 p. 23cm.

            Inaug.-Diss.-Erlangen.

            1. Guyau, Jean Marie, 1854–1888.

NL 0447869   NIC NN MH CtY ICRL

Loewenstein, Kurt, 1885–   , ed.
 Land der Jugend; das Buch der Kinder-Rundschau, hrsg. von
Kurt Loewenstein. Berlin, Verlag Jüdische Rundschau, 1936.
  112 p. illus. 20cm.

  "Emek, emek-adamah!" (words and melody), p. 112.

    296378B. 1. Palestine. I. Die   Kinder-Rundschau. II. Title.
  N. Y. P. L.   May 11, 1945

NL 0447870   NN NNJ DLC

Löwenstein, Kurt, 1885–
 Schule und Erziehung. Offenbach-M., Bollwerk-Verlag,
1947.
  32 p. 20 cm. (Schriftenreihe Schule und Erziehung, Heft 1)

    1. Education—Addresses, essays, lectures. I. Title. (Series)
     LB775.L625   A 48-4743*
     Teachers College Library   Columbia Univ.
       for Library of Congress   ₍1₎†

NL 0447871   NNC-T DLC

VOLUME 338

Löwenstein, Kurt Kerlöw-
  see Kerlöw-Löwenstein, Kurt.

Loewenstein (L.) & Loewenstein (H.)
  Fabrik chirurgischer Instrumente, Berlin. Spe-
  cial-Verzeichnis von Instrumenten und Appa-
  raten für Behandlung der Harn- und Sexual-
  organe. 51 pp. roy. 8°. *Berlin*, [n. d.].

NL 0447873   DNLM

Löwenstein, Leo.
  Heroische Gestalten des Jüdischen Stammes
    see under   Reichsbund jüdischer Front-
    soldaten.

LÖWENSTEIN, Leo, 1879-
  Beiträge zur messung von dissociationen bei
  hohen temperaturen. Inaug.-diss. Göttingen,
  1905.

NL 0447875   MH-C

Löwenstein, Leo, 1880-
  Der Schutzballon ...   Celle, 1904.
  Inaug.-Diss. - Marburg.
  Lebenslauf.
  "Literatur-Verzeichnis": p. [49]

NL 0447876   CtY DNLM ICRL

Loewenstein, Leopold, 1843-1924.
  Abbreviaturen.   Berlin, H. Itzkowski,
  1903.
  10 p.
  Title taken from paper-cover.
  Repr.: Festschrift zum 70. Geburtstage
  A. Berliner's.

NL 0447877   OCH

LÖWENSTEIN, Leopold, 1843-1924.
  Beiträge zur Geschichte der Juden in
  Deutschland.   Frankfurt a.M., J.Kauffmann,
  1895-98.

  2 vol. 22 cm.
  "Nachträge und Berichtigungen zu Band I,"
  2 pages at end of vol.II.
  Contents:1.Geschichte der Juden in der
  Kurpfalz.- 11.Nathanael Weil,Oberlandrabbiner
  in Karlsruhe und seine Familie.

NL 0447878   MH OU OCH CtY

Loewenstein, Leopold, 1843-
  David Oppenheim. Breslau: S. Schottlaender,
  1900.
  1 p. L., ii-xxii p.

  Repr.: Gedenkbuch zur Erinnerung an David
  Kaufmann.
  A few mss. notes inserted.

NL 0447879   OCH

LÖWENSTEIN, LEOPOLD, 1843-
  Die Familie Aboab.   Pressburg, Druck von A. Alkalay, 1905.   41 p.   23cm.

  Film reproduction. Positive.
  "Sonderabdruck aus der Monatsschrift für Geschichte und Wissenschaft
  des Judentums."

  1. Aboab family.

NL 0447880   NN

Loewenstein, Leopold, 1843-
  Fest-Predigten ... Adelsheim: R.
  Veith, [1911].
  207 p.

NL 0447881   OCH

Löwenstein, Leopold, 1843-1924.
  Geschichte der Juden am Bodensee und umgebung.   Nach
  gedruckten und ungedruckten quellen dargestellt von dr. L.
  Löwenstein.   Erster theil. [Gailingen] Im selbstverlag des verfassers, 1879.

  viii, 149 p.   20½ᵐ.
  No more published.
  Bibliographical foot-notes.

  1. Jews in Switzerland. 2. Jews in Baden.   I. Title.

                                                    44-36786
  Library of Congress   DS135.S9L6

NL 0447882   DLC NN OU MH OCH

Löwenstein, Leopold, 1843-1924.
  Geschichte der Juden von der babylo-
  nischen Gefangenschaft bis zur Gegenwart,
  für Schule und Haus bearbeitet...   Mainz,
  J. Wirth, 1904.
  viii, 271 p.   22ᶜᵐ.

  "Quellen-Nachweis": p. 253-270.

NL 0447883   NjPT DLC-P4 NN OC1

Löwenstein, [Leopold] 1843-1924.
  Licht- und Schattenseiten aus der Geschichte
  der Juden in Wertheim.   Vortrag gehalten im
  historischen Verein "Alt Wertheim" am
  15 Dezember 1907.   [Wertheim a.M., E.
  Bechstein, 1907]
  20 p.
  Gedruckt als Beilage zum Jahresbericht des
  Vereins 1907.

NL 0447884   OCH NN

Löwenstein, Leopold, 1843-1924.
  מפתח ההסכמות   Index approbationum, bearbeitet von dr.
  Leopold Löwenstein ...   Frankfurt am Main, J. Kauffmann,
  1923.

  xiv p., 1 l., 256 p.   24ᵐ.
  Reproduced from manuscript copy.

  1. Approbations (Hebrew literature) 2. Hebrew literature — Bibl.
  I. Title.   II. Title: Index approbationum.
                    Title transliterated: Mafteaḥ ha-haskamoth.
                                                    45-30266
  Library of Congress   Z7070.L8
                                          [2]

NL 0447885   DLC CtY NN

Löwenstein, Leopold, 1843-1924, supposed
  author.
  Spinoza als Bibelkritiker.
  79 p.   20cm.

  Manuscript in ink, with a few notes in pencil. Notation by Carl Gebhardt on title-page
  attributes the manuscript to Löwenstein and
  the pencilled notes tentatively to Kuno Fischer.
  Some sections in Hebrew.

NL 0447886   NNC

[Loewenstein, Leopold,] 1843-1924.
  Stammbaum [einganum, Oppenheim, Simons].
  [Compiled by L. Loewenstein.] Hrsg. von
  A. Oppenheim. Mannheim, 1908.
  37 (1) p.

NL 0447887   OCH

Löwenstein, Leopold, 1843-1924.
  Zur geschichte der Juden in Fürth, von dr. Leopold Löwenstein ...   Frankfurt a. M., Sänger & Friedberg, 1909-

  v.   geneal. tables.   22½ᵐ.
  Cover-title.
  Reprinted from Jahrbuch der Jüdisch-literarische gesellschaft, vi,
  1908; viii, 1910.
  Bibliographical foot-notes.
  CONTENTS.—1. t. Das rabbinat.—2. t. Rabbinatsbeisitzer und sonstige
  hervorragende persönlichkeiten.

  1. Jews in Fürth.

                                                    43-33461
  Library of Congress   DS135.G4F9G

NL 0447888   DLC MH OU OCH

Loewenstein, Leopold, 1854-
  Ueber den aetiologischen zusammenhang der katamenien
  und ihrer anomalien...
  Inaug.Diss.   Berlin, 1877

NL 0447889   ICRL DNLM

Loewenstein, *Prince* Leopold, 1903-
  Analyze yourself; how to see yourself as you really are, by
  Prince Leopold Loewenstein and William Gerhardi, as
  adapted by Victor Rosen.   [1st ed.] New York, Hawthorn
  Books [1955]
  320 p.   24 cm.

  "Adapted from the work originally published in England as: Meet
  yourself as you really are."

  1. Characters and characteristics.   I. Gerhardi, William Alexander, 1895-   joint author. II. Rosen, Victor, 1900-   III. Title.

  BF831.L55 1955   137.8   55-6442 ‡

NL 0447890   DLC IEG NBuU

Loewenstein, *Prince* Leopold, 1903-
  Meet yourself as you really are, different from others because you combine uniquely features present in everyone.
  About three million detailed individual character studies
  through self-analysis, by Prince Leopold Loewenstein and
  William Gerhardi.   London, Faber and Faber limited [1936]
  336 p.   diagrs. 19½ᵐ.

  "First published in June MCMXXXVI."

  1. Characters and characteristics.   I. Gerhardi, William Alexan-
  der, 1895-   joint author. II. Title.
                                                    36-30346
  Library of Congress   BF831.L55 1936
  —— —— Copy 2.
  Copyright A ad int. 21862   [2]   [159.923] 137

NL 0447891   DLC CtY-M NN

Loewenstein, *Prince* Leopold, 1903-
  Meet yourself as you really are; about three million detailed
  individual character studies through self-analysis, by Prince
  Leopold Loewenstein and William Gerhardi.   Philadelphia,
  London, J. B. Lippincott company [1936]
  336 p.   diagrs. 19½ᵐ.

  1. Characters and characteristics.   I. Gerhardi, William Alexander,
  1895-   joint author. II. Title.
                                                    37-48
  Library of Congress   BF831.L55 1936 a
  —— —— Copy 2.
  Copyright A 101333   [3]   [159.923] 137

NL 0447892   DLC NcRS

VOLUME 338

LOEWENSTEIN, Lipmann Hirsch, d.ca. 1850
Damascia. Die Judenverfolgung
zu Damaskus und ihre Wirkung auf die
Oeffentliche Meinung... Roedelhaim,
Lehrberger & Co., 1840. 2 p.l. xxx
416 p. 18.5 cm.
1.Damascus Affair. 2.Blood
Accusation. 3.Title.
Interleaved,with handwritten
corrections.

NL 0447893   NNJ OCA DLC-P4 CtY MH OCH NN

BM717
L6
1841

Loewenstein, Lippmann Hirsch, comp.
Damascia; die Judenverfolgung zu Damaskus
und ihre Wirkungen auf die öffentliche Meinung, nebst Nachweisungen über den Ursprung
der gegen die Juden wiederholten Beschuldi-
gung, als bedienten sie sich des Menschen-
blutes bei rituellen Zeremonien. Im Laufe
der Ereignisse dargestellt und beleuchtet
von L.H.Loewenstein. 2., verb. Aufl. Frankfurt a. M., 1841.
416 p. 19^{cm}

1.Jews in   Damascus.

NL 0447894   CSt MH PPDrop

BM675
K5L6
Hebraic
Sect.

Loewenstein, Lipmann Hirsch, d. ca. 1850,
ed. and tr.
Jews. *Liturgy and ritual. Kinot.*
קול בוכים. היא מגלת קינות עם פתרון אף תרגום אשכנזי (מאת)
ל. ה. לאוונשטיין. פראנקפורט דמיין. ק. קארונער. תקצ״ח.
(Frankfurt a. M., 1838)

NL 0447895

Loewenstein, Lipmann Hirsch, d. ca. 1850, comp.
Stimmen berühmter Christen über den Damaszener Blut-
prozess. Als Anlage zu der Schrift Damascia. Frankfurt
a. M., Bei'm Herausgeber, 1843.
45 p. 20 cm.
CONTENTS.—Einleitung.—Erklärung des Herrn Schöffen Dr. von
Meyer, Präsidenten des Frankfurter Appellationsgerichts.—Erklärung
des Herrn Prof. Dr. Molitor.—Denkschrift an die Herren Criminaldirektor Dr. Hitzig und Dr. Häring (von L. H. Loewenstein)—Schreiben des Herrn Dr. Häring.—Erklärung der Herren Criminaldirektor
Dr. Hitzig und Dr. Häring.—Schluss.
1. Jews in Damascus. 2. Jews—Persecutions. 3. Blood accusation.
I. Title. II. Title: Damascia.
BM717.L6   24–16590 rev*

NL 0447896   DLC OU OCl OCH CSt

Loewenstein, Lipmann Hirsch, d. ca. 1850.
Ueberzeugungen eines Irsaeliten, gegenüber dem Prose-
lytenthum. Erwiederung auf die Schrift des Herrn Dr. W.
B. Fränkel: Das Bekenntniss des Proselyten. Das Unglück
der Juden und "ihre Emanzipation in Deutschland." Rödelheim, J. Lehrberger, 1842.
170 p. 19 cm.

1. Fränkel, Wolfgang Bernhard, 1795–1851. Das bekenntniss des
proselyten. 2. Judaism. 3. Jews—Converts to Christianity. I. Title.
BV2623.F7L6   25–2751 rev*

NL 0447897   DLC OCH

BS1229
1864a
Hebr

Loewenstein, Lipmann Hirsch, d. ca. 1850, tr.
Bible. *O. T. Pentateuch. Hebrew. 1864.*
חמשה חומשי תורה. גם ההפטרות וחמש מגלות עם תרגום
אשכנזי (את ל. ה. לאוונשטיין. הוצאה ב. רעדלהיים. י.
לעהרבערגער.
(Rödelheim) 1864–

NL 0447898

Loewenstein, Louis Centennial, 1876–
Centrifugal pumps, their design and construction, by Louis
C. Loewenstein ... and Clarence P. Crissey ... 320 illustrations, 8 folding plates. New York, D. Van Nostrand company,
1911.
vii, 435 p. illus., fold. pl., diagrs. (part fold.) 24^{cm}.

1. Pumping machinery.   I. Crissey, Clarence Philip, 1879–   joint
author.   II. Title.
                                 11–17826
Library of Congress   TJ919.L7

OCIW ICJ NN MB
NL 0447899   DLC DN OrP IdU WaS CU ICRL OU OCl MiU

TJ735
.S83
1945

Loewenstein, Louis Centennial, 1876–   tr.
FOR OTHER EDITIONS
SEE MAIN ENTRY
Stodola, Aurel, 1859–
Steam and gas turbines, with a supplement on The prospects
of the thermal prime mover, by Dr. A. Stodola ... Authorized
translation from the sixth German edition by Dr. Louis C.
Loewenstein ... with 1565 illustrations and 7 folding charts.
New York, P. Smith, 1945.

NL 0447900

Loewenstein, Louis Centennial, 1876–   tr.
FOR OTHER EDITIONS
SEE MAIN ENTRY
Stodola, Aurel, 1859–
Steam turbines, with an appendix on gas turbines and the
future of heat engines. by Dr. A. Stodola ... 2d rev. ed. of
the authorized translation from the 2d enl. and rev. German
ed., with mathematical supplement and aid by Dr. Louis C.
Loewenstein ... with 241 cuts and 3 lithograph tables. New
York, D. Van Nostrand company; (etc., etc.) 1906.

NL 0447901

Loewenstein, Louis J.
History of the St. Louis cathedral, of New Orleans.
By Louis J. Loewenstein ... New Orleans, The Times-
Democrat, 1882.
67 p. 22½^{cm}.
Advertisements: p. 1–12, 56–67.

1. New Orleans. St. Louis cathedral.
                                 18–17107
Library of Congress   F379.N5S14

NL 0447902   DLC NN

Löwenstein (Ludwig). *Beitrag zur pathologischen Anatomie der myelogenen epiphysären
Neubildungen. 33 pp. 8°. Würzburg, F. Rörhl,
1889.

NL 0447903   DNLM

Löwenstein, Ludwig
Die beschneidung im lichte der heutigen medicinischen wissenschaft, mit berücksichtigung
ihrer geschichtlichen und unter würdigung ihrer
religiösen bedeutung, von ... Ludwig Löwenstein
... Trier, Stephanus, 1897.
75 p. 23^{cm}.

Bound with Salomon, M. G. Die beschneidung...
1844.
"Sonderabdruck aus dem Archiv für klinische
chirurgie, bd. 54, h. 4."

1. Circumcision.

NL 0447904   NNC CtY OCH

Löwenstein, Ludwig, 1867–
Die Abzahlungsgeschäfte. Eine Zeit-
und Streitfrage ... von Ludwig
Löwenstein. Altona, Der Verfasser,
1891.
23 p. 22½cm.

NL 0447905   MH-L MH

Loewenstein (Magnus Gustavus). *De men-
struatione normali atque parca. 64 pp. 8°. Dorpati Livonorum. typ. J. C. Schuenmanni. 1835.

NL 0447906   DNLM

Loewenstein, Mara, 1891–
Ueber eine neue reihe substituierter chrom-
enyl-rakikale.
Inaug. diss. Berlin, 1930.

NL 0447907   ICRL OU CtY

---

*GC8
L8255
845u

Löwenstein, Martin.
Ueber Juden=Bekehrung und Juden=Emancipation.
in besonderer Beziehung auf Preussen. Von Dr. M.
Löwenstein ... Besonderer Abdruck aus der
"kirchlichen Vierteljahrresschrift." 4. Heft.
Berlin, 1844, im Verlage von G.W.F. Müller.
Breslau,F.E.C.Leuckart.1845.

15p. 23.5cm.

NL 0447908   MH OCH

Loewenstein, Mauja
Untersuchungen ueber die beeinflussung der
leukoocytenzahlen durch digitalis,...
Inaug. diss.   Bern, 1914

NL 0447909   ICRL

Löwenstein (Max). Ueber Gastritis phlegmo-
nosa. 21 pp., 1 l. 4°. Kiel, Schmidt u. Klaunig,
1874.
In: SCHRIFT. d. Univ. zu Kiel, xxi, 1874, vii, med. viii.

NL 0447910   DNLM

Loewenstein, M[ax]
Ueber Juden-Bekehrung und Juden-Emancipation
see   Löwenstein, Martin.

Löwenstein (Max). *Ueber die ulcerierende,
multiloculäre Echinococcengeschwulst. [Erlan-
gen.] 32 pp. 8°. [Berlin, Eyck & Friedlaen-
der], 1889.

NL 0447912   DNLM PPC

PA6241
.A1L6

Löwenstein, Max, Prinz von, ed.
Caesar, C. Julius.
Der gallische Krieg. Ins Deutsche übertragen unter
Berücksichtigung der neuzeitlichen Heeresausdrücke von
Prinz Max zu Löwenstein. Mit 147 Bildern und 16 Karten
und Plänen erläutert von Wilhelm Ament. Bamberg, C. C.
Buchner, 1932.

NL 0447913

RC643
L82

Loewenstein, Max, 1885–
... Zur kenntnis der leukaemie im kindesalter
... vorgelegt von Max Loewenstein ... Berlin,
Blanke (1913)
25 p., 1 l. fold. table. 22½cm.

Inaug.-diss. - Berlin.
At head of title: Aus dem Städtischen kranken-
haus Moabit...
Lebenslauf.

1. Leucemia.

NL 0447914   NNC ICRL CtY DNLM

VOLUME 338

Loewenstein, Morrison, 1915–
The effect of heat on the chemical nature of the materials absorbed on the milk fat globule. 1954.
173 l.
Thesis - Ohio State University.

NL 0447915 OU

Loewenstein, Nathan, joint comp.

Sethness, Charles O *comp.*
Modern, simple and practical formulae, scientific tests, valuable information, etc., pertaining to the manufacture of cordials, bitters, gins, whiskies, brandies, and liquors of all kinds, comp. by C. O. Sethness, Julius Marcus, N. Loewenstein, and ed. by Sethness company ... [Chicago, Sethness company, 1905]

NL 0447917 PP

Löwenstein, Otto.
The nature of individual accident proneness. Geneva, 1934.
(International labour office. Industrial safety survey, v. 10, no. 1. pp. 1–9).

NL 0447917 PP

Loewenstein, Otto, 1841–1896, ed.

Juristisches literaturblatt ... 1.–29. jahrg.; 15. jan. 1889–13. dez. 1918. Berlin, C. Heymann [1889–1918]

Löwenstein, Otto, 1889–
Experimentelle hysterielehre; zugleich ein versuch zur experimentellen grundlegung der begutachtung psychogener unfallfolgen, von dr. Otto Löwenstein ... Mit 243 abbildungen im text. Bonn, F. Cohen, 1923.
ix, 412 p. illus. 26ᶜᵐ.

1. Hysteria. ɪ. Title.
Library of Congress RC403.L6
24–17880

NL 0447919 DLC DNLM ICJ

Löwenstein, Otto, 1889–
... Experimentelle und klinische studien zur physiologie und pathologie der pupillenbewegungen, mit besonderer berücksichtigung der schizophrenie, von dr. O. Löwenstein ... und dr. A. Westphal ... Mit 101 abbildungen im text und auf tafeln. Berlin, S. Karger, 1933.
vi, 181 p. illus., diagrs. (part fold.) 25½ᶜᵐ. (Abhandlungen aus der neurologie, psychiatrie, psychologie und ihren grenzgebieten ... hft. 70)

1. Pupil (Eye) 2. Reflexes. 3. Dementia. ɪ. Westphal, Alexander, 1863– joint author.
A C 33–3775
Title from John Crerar Libr. Printed by L. C.

NL 0447920 ICJ OU MiU PPC

Löwenstein, Otto, 1889–
Der psychische Restitutionseffekt; das Prinzip der psychisch bedingten Wiederherstellung der ermüdeten, der erschöpften und der erkrankten Funktion, von Dr. med. Otto Löwenstein ... Basel, B. Schwabe & Co., 1937.
92 p. incl. front., 1 illus., diagrs. 24ᶜᵐ.
Bibliographical foot-notes.

NL 0447921 ICJ PPC DNLM NNC-M

WW 460 L827s 1935
LÖWENSTEIN, Otto, 1889–
Die Störungen des Lichtreflexes der Pupille bei den luetischen Erkrankungen des Zentralnervensystems; Beiträge zur Frühdiagnostik der Lues nervosa. Basel, Schwabe, 1935.
92 p. illus.
1. Eye - Neurological aspects
2. Neurosyphilis

NL 0447922 DNLM NNC-M

Löwenstein (Otto) [1889–]. *Die Zurechnungsfähigkeit der Halluzinanten nach psychologischen Prinzipien beurteilt. 38 pp., 1 l. 8°. Bonn, A. Fleseler, 1914.

NL 0447923 DNLM MBCo ICRL

Löwenstein, Paul, 1890–
Der Geist der Aufklärungsbewegung in der Musik. Bonn, 1921.
v, 53 p. 21 cm.
Inaug.-Diss.—Bonn.
Vita.
Bibliography : p. [52]–53.

1. Music—Philosophy and aesthetics. 2. Enlightenment. ɪ. Title.
ML3800.L7
55–46371

NL 0447924 DLC CtY NN CU MH

Löwenstein, Paul, June 25, 1890–
Ein eigentümlicher Fall von Poliomyelitis anterior acuta mit abnormen motorischen Reizerscheinungen ... Steinheim, 1914.
Inaug.-Diss. - Würzburg.
Lebenslauf.
"Literatur": p. 21–22.

NL 0447925 CtY DNLM ICRL

Loewenstein, Paul, 1895–
Der deutsche sortimentsbuchhandel. Seine wirtschaftliche entwicklungsgeschichte ... Innsbruck, Wagner'sche universitätsbuchdr., 1921.
174 p., 1 l. tables (2 fold.) 23½ᶜᵐ.
Inaug.-diss.—Zürich.
Vita.
"Literatur-verzeichnis": p. 173–174.

1. Booksellers and bookselling—Germany. ɪ. Title.
Library of Congress Z313.L827
26–17336

NL 0447926 DLC CtY IU ICU NN

Löwenstein (Paula) [1887–]. *Beobachtungen während der Grippeepidemie des Jahres 1918. 54 pp., 2 ch. 8°. Frankfurt a. M., Blazek & Bergmann, 1919.

NL 0447927 DNLM

Loewenstein, Pearl. (Mrs. A. L.)
Woman in Israel. (A realistic allegory for Chanuko) [in one act]. n.t.-p.
[Cincinnati: National Federation of Temple Sisterhoods, 1940.]
7 f. f.

NL 0447928 OCH

LOEWENSTEIN, R. *La conception psychanalytique des troubles de la puissance génitale de l'homme. 64p. 8° Par., 1935.

NL 0447929 DNLM

Löwenstein (Rachül). *Versuche über die Bremer'sche Reaktion des Blutes. 20 pp. 8°. Zürich. J. J. Meier. 1911.

NL 0447930 DNLM NjP

Loewenstein, Richard, Referendar: Das Recht des Theaterbesuches. Borna-Leipzig 1911: Noske. x, 57 S. 8°
Rostock, Jur. Diss. v. 30. Mai 1911, Ref. Hübner
[Geb. 6. Nov. 87 Bocholt; Wohnort: Bocholt; Staatsangeh.: Preußen; Vorbildung: Gymn. Bocholt Reife O. 06; Studium: Heidelberg 1, München 2, Berlin 3, Münster 1 S.; Rig. 25. März 11.]
[U 11. 4052]

NL 0447931 ICRL PU MH-L

Loewenstein, Rodolphe
see Loewenstein, Rudolph Maurice.

Löwenstein, Rudolf.
... Kalkulationsgewinn und bilanzmässige erfolgsrechnung in ihren gegenseitigen beziehungen, von dr. Rudolf Löwenstein ... Leipzig, G. A. Gloeckner, 1922.
viii, 144 p. diagrs. 24ᶜᵐ. (Betriebs- und finanzwirtschaftliche forschungen ... hft. 16)
"Literaturverzeichnis": p. [143]–144.

1. Cost—Accounting. 2. Accounting. ɪ. Title.
Library of Congress HF5686.C8L55
22–20471

NL 0447933 DLC CU NN

PT 2623 .O45 A87
Löwenstein, Rudolf, 1819–1891.
Aus bewegten Zeiten; politische Gedichte. Mit vorwort von Albert Träger. Berlin, F. & P. Lehmann [1890]
viii, 173p. 16cm.

NL 0447934 TNJ

Löwenstein, Rudolf, 1819–1891.
Polytechnische gesellschaft, *Berlin.*
Erinnerungs-blätter an das 25ᵗᵉ stiftungs- und jubelfest der Polytechnischen gesellschaft zu Berlin am 27. februar 1864, enthaltend die gedichte von Rudolf Löwenstein zu den von G. Heil gemalten bildern ... Berlin, Druck von Gebrüder Fickert [1864]

[Loewenstein, Rudolf] 1819–1891.
Friederike von Sesenheim. Wahrheit und Dichtung. Treu nach Wolfgang von Goethe. Eine deutsche Liebesidylle in drei Büchern ... Berlin, A. Hofmann & Co., 1869.
64 p. 18 cm.

NL 0447936 CtY ICU

34299 .594
Löwenstein, Rudolf, 1819–1891.
Kindergarten. Mit zahlreichen Illustrationen von Th. Hosemann, W. Claudius [et al.] Dritte, stark verm. Aufl. Berlin, Hofmann [18–]
124 p. illus. 28 cm.

1. Children's literature, German. ɪ. Title.

NL 0447937 NjP

VOLUME 338

Löwenstein, Rudolf, *1819-1891*
　　Kindergarten;mit zahlreichen illustrationen von Th.Hoselmann,W.Claudius,
Flinzer,Bürkner. Ed.4,rev. illus. Hofmann,n.d.

　　German text.

NL　0447938　　OrP

834L955　Löwenstein, Rudolph, 1819-1891.
Ok　　Kindergarten. Gedichte ... Zeichnungen von Rob.
　　Kretschmer.　Berlin, Verlag der T. Trautwein'schen buch- und musikalienhandlung, 1846.
145p. plates.

　　Added illus. t.-p., engr.

　　I. Kretschmer, Robert, 1818-1872, illus. II.
Title.

NL　0447939　　IU

Löwenstein, Rudolf, 1819-1891.
　　Kindergarten, von Rudolf Löwenstein. Mit zahlreichen Illustrationen von Th. Hosemann, W. Claudius, Flinzer, Bürkner u. A.
5. verbesserte Aufl.　Hamburg: Verlagsanstalt und Druckerei
(vorm. J. F. Richter) ₁1896₁ 128 p. illus. 29cm.

NL　0447940　　NN

Löwenstein, Rudolf, 1819-1891.
　　Kindergarten, von dr. Rudolf Löwenstein. Mit
einem vorwort von ... G. Voigt ... 6. verb. aufl.
Berlin, K.W. Mecklenburg [1907]
　　2 p.l., 128, [4] p.　illus., col. plates.
30 cm.
　　1. Folk-songs, German.

NL　0447941　　CU

Löwenstein, Rudolf, 1819-1891, ed.

Kladderadatsch ... Humoristisch-satirisches wochenblatt.
1.— 　　　jahrg; 7. mai 1848–
₁Berlin. A. Hofmann & comp., 1848-19

Loewenstein, Rudolf, 1903–
　　Der verbrennungsverlauf oberschlesischer
steinkohle auf dem wanderrost eines steilrohr-
kessels mittelerer grösse. ... 1935.
　　Inaug. Diss. - Techn. Hochschule Breslau,1935.
　　Lebenslauf.
　　Literatur.

NL　0447943　　ICRL

Loewenstein, Rudolph Maurice.
　　Christians and Jews, a psychoanalytic study. ₁Translated
from the French by Vera Damman₁ New York, International Universities Press ₁1951₁
　　224 p. 23 cm.
　　Bibliography: p. 203-213.

　　1. Antisemitism.　I. Title.

DS145.L6442　　　296　　　　　　51–9717

WaSpG OrCS GU NNJ MH OkU-M CoDT
ICJ ICU NcU CaBVaU CaBVa WaU DAU MiU CLSU PPFC FMU
NL　0447944　　DLC Or WaS CBPac CBM WaU DNLM NcRS MB

Loewenstein, Rudolph Maurice, *ed.*
　　Drives, affects, behavior, edited by Rudolph M. Loewenstein. Editorial Board: Edward L. Bibring ₁and others₁
New York, International Universities Press ₁1953₁
　　399 p. illus. 24 cm.

　　1. Psychoanalysis.　I. Title.

BF173.L56　　　　131.34082　　　53—11056 ‡

　　　　　IU NIC Wa MiU OO DNLM PPC PRaW MBCo AU KMK ViU
NL　0447945　　DLC OC1W NcRS PPT OU ICJ PBm PPJ PP NN

Loewenstein, Rudolph Maurice.
　　Freud: man and scientist. The Freud anniversary lecture,
delivered May 14, 1951, at the New York Academy of Medicine, in commemoration of the ninety-fifth birthday of Sigmund Freud. ₁New York₁ International Universities Press
₁1951₁
　　20 p. 21 cm.

　　1. Freud, Sigmund, 1856-1939.

BF173.F85L6　　　　　　　58–19002 ‡

NL　0447946　　DLC OrPR OrU DNLM MH MiU NRU NIC

Loewenstein, Rudolph Maurice.
　　Psychanalyse de l'antisémitisme. ₁1. éd.₁ Paris, Presses
universitaires de France, 1952.
　　150 p. 23 cm. (Bibliothèque de psychanalyse et de psychologie
clinique)
　　Bibliography: p. ₁143₁-150.

　　1. Antisemitism.　(Series)

DS145.L6444　　　　　　　　A 54–5779
Harvard Univ. Library
for Library of Congress　　　₁1₁†

NL　0447947　　MH CaBVaU NNJ TxU DLC

Löwenstein, Ruth, 1911–
　　Die soziale lage der verkäuferin im warenhaus, eine sozial-
statistische studie auf grund von untersuchungen in einem
Züricher warenhaus ... von Ruth Löwenstein ... Würzburg,
Buchdruckerei R. Mayr, 1937.
　　3 p. l., ₁v₁-viii, 78 p., 1 l. fold. tab. 21½ᶜᵐ.
　　Inaug.-diss.—Basel.
　　Lebenslauf.
　　"Literaturverzeichnis": p. ₁v₁-viii.

　　1. Woman—Employment—Switzerland. 2. Department stores.
I. Title.

Library of Congress　　　　HD6070.L6
　　　　　　　　　　　　　　₁2₁　　　41–33635
　　　　　　　　　　　　　　　　　331.400494

NL　0447948　　DLC NNC MH CtY

QZA
L827u　LÖWENSTEIN, S
1910　　Über Unfall und Krebskrankheit.
　　Tübingen, Laupp, 1910.
　　iii, 207 p.

NL　0447949　　DNLM ICJ IU-M NNC

Loewenstein (Sally). *Ein histiologischer
Beitrag zur Lehre von Filiroma molluscum.
34 pp., 1 l. 8ᵒ. Würzburg. Becker. 1891.*

NL　0447950　　DNLM

Loewenstein, Sally, 1881–
　　Ueber einen fall von diabetes insipidus.
　　Inaug. diss. Bonn, 1904

NL　0447951　　ICRL DNLM MBCo

Loewenstein, Siegfried.
　　Interposición y fundamentación de la casación en materia
penal. Indicaciones prácticas para la redacción de los escritos
jurídicos penales de casación. Traducción del alemán por
José Manuel Núñez; prólogo del Dr. Ricardo C. Núñez.
Córdoba, Editorial Assandri ₁1953₁
　　147 p. 24 cm.

　　1. Criminal procedure—Germany. 2. Appellate procedure—Germany.　I. Title.

　　　　　　　　　　　　　　　　　　　54–24039 ‡

NL　0447952　　DLC

Loewenstein, Siegfried.
　　Der Prozess Erzberger-Helfferich. Ein Rechts-
gutachten
　　see under title

Loewenstein, Siegfried.
　　Die reichs-amnestie der friedensverträge und revolu-
tionsgesetze des Deutschen Reichs, nebst abdruck der
reichsamnestiegesetze vom 12. november, 3. und 12. dezember 1918 sowie 13. januar 1919; gemeinverständlich
dargestellt von dr. Siegfried Loewenstein ... Berlin,
C. Heymann, 1919.
　　2 p. l., 54 p. 22ᶜᵐ.

　　1. Amnesty—Germany.　I. Germany. Laws, statutes, etc. II. Title.

　　　　　　　　　　　　　　　　　　21–14393

NL　0447954　　DLC DNW

Loewenstein, Siegfried.
　　Die revision in strafsachen; praktische anleitung zur an-
fertigung strafrechtlicher revisionsschriften unter berücksichtigung der neuesten rechtsprechung und gesetzgebung, von dr.
Siegfried Loewenstein ... 3. neubearb. aufl. Berlin, C. Heymann, 1933.
　　vii, ₁1₁, 112 p. 22¼ᶜᵐ.

　　1. Criminal procedure—Germany. 2. Appellate procedure—Germany.
I. Title.

　　　　　　　　　　　　　　　　　　34–42246

NL　0447955　　DLC

Loewenstein (Siegfried) [1865-]. *Zur
Pathologie und Therapie des Genu valgum.
27 pp., 2 l. 12ᵒ. Berlin. G. Schade, 1891.*

NL　0447956　　DNLM

Loewenstein, Siegfried, 1878–
　　Über einen Fall von Cardiospasmus mit
gleichmässiger Erweiterung der Speiseröhre.
Würzburg, A. Boegler, 1903.
　　32 p.
　　Inaug.-Diss. - Leipzig.

NL　0447957　　ICRL CtY DNLM

Löwenstein, Siegmund, 1880–
　　Das Handwahrehandprinzip im deutschen
bürgerlichen Recht ... von Siegmund Löwen-
stein ... Borna-Leipzig, R. Noske, 1907.
　　ix, 95 p., 1 l. 22cm.
　　Inaug.-Diss. - Heidelberg.
　　"Lebenslauf": leaf at end.
　　"Literaturverzeichnis": p.₁vii₁-ix.

NL　0447958　　MH-L ICRL

VOLUME 338

Löwenstein, Sigmund.
Über die mikrocephalische Idiotie und die von Lannelongue vorgeschlagene chirurgische Behandlung derselben. Tübingen, H. Laupp, 1900.
28 p. (Beiträge zur klinischen Chirurgie, Bd. 26, Heft 1)
Inaug.-Diss. - Heidelberg.

NL 0447959   ICRL

Loewenstein, Stefan, 1902-
Die milchviehhaltung im komitat fejer unter besonderer beruecksichtigung ihrer rentabilitaetsverhaeltnisse.
Inaug. diss. Halle, 1926.
Bibl.

NL 0447960   ICRL CtY MiU MH

Löwenstein, Tamara, 1891-
... Ueber Vaginalcysten ...   München, 1917.
Inaug.-Diss. - München.
Lebenslauf.
"Literatur": p. [28]-30.

NL 0447961   CtY DNLM MiU

Löwenstein, Theodor, 1901-
Die bayerische eisenbahnpolitik bis zum eintritt Deutschlands in die weltwirtschaft. 1825 bis 1890 (Teildruck) ... Berlin, 1927.

Frankfurt a.M.
Diss.
1926

NL 0447962   MiU

1886-
Loewenstein, Walter: Der Gegenstand des Grundpfandes. Borna-Leipzig 1912: Noske. XII, 122 S. 8°
Breslau, Jur. Diss. v. 26. Juli 1912, Ref. O. Fischer, H. Meyer
[Geb. 14. Okt. 86 Berlin; Wohnort: Berlin; Staatsangeh.: Preußen; Vorbildung: Kaiser-Wilhelms-Realgymn. Berlin Reife M. 05; Studium: Berlin 4, München 1, Berlin 4 S.; Rig. 12. Juli 12.]   [U 12.598]

NL 0447963   ICRL

Löwenstein, Walter, 1887-
... Zur Frage der Pneumoniebehandlung ...
Borna-Leipzig, 1911.
Inaug.-Diss. - Leipzig.
Lebenslauf.
"Literaturverzeichnis": p. [29]-[30]

NL 0447964   CtY DNLM ICRL

Loewenstein, Walter, 1903-
Die Beteiligung von Arbeitnehmern nach deutschem und ausländischem Recht ...
[Berlin, 1934]
Inaug.-Diss. - Köln.

NL 0447965   CtY

Loewenstein, Walter Bernard, 1926-
Analysis of the vibrations of certain large molecules, including spriopentane, methylenecyclopropane, and cyclopropane. [Columbus, Ohio] 1954.
iii, 179 l. illus.
Thesis - Ohio State University.
Vita.
Bibliography: l. 175-178.
1. Spectrum, Infra-red. 2. Raman effect.
I. Title.

NL 0447966   OU

SCIENCE
Microfilm
QC   Loewenstein, Walter Bernard, 1926-
454   Analysis of the vibrations of certain large
.L6   molecules, including spiropentane, methylenecyclopropane, and cyclopropane. [Columbus, Ohio] 1954.
iii, 179 l. illus.

Microfilm (positive)
Thesis- Ohio State University.
Vita.
Bibliography: l. 175-178.

1. Spectrum, Infra-red. 2. Raman effect.
I. Title.

NL 0447968   OrU OU

Löwenstein, Walther, Referendar: Der Besitz des Finders nach dem Rechte des Bürgerl. Gesetzbuches. Beuel a. Rh. 1910: Weckmann. 63 S. 8°
Würzburg, Jur. Diss. v. 6. Sept. 1910, Ref. Mendelssohn-Bartholdy
[Geb. 24. Okt. 79 Bielefeld; Wohnort: Bonn; Staatsangeh.: Preußen; Vorbildung: Gymn. Bielefeld Reife Juli 00; Rig. 25. Juli 10.]   [U 11.4513]

NL 0447969   ICRL MH-L

Loewenstein, Werner, 1909-
... Über das Vorkommen von Ulcus duodeni und ventriculi im Kindesalter ...   Rietberg i. Westf. [1936]
Inaug.-Diss. - Berlin.
Lebenslauf.
"Literatur": p. 22-23.

NL 0447970   CtY

Löwenstein, Wilhelm, Prinz zu
see Löwenstein-Wertheim-Freudenberg, Wilhelm, Prinz zu, 1817-1887.

Loewenstein, Willi: Über Lösungen von Kalk und Kieselsäure in geschmolzenem Chlorkalzium. (Berlin 1909: G. Schade.) 57 S. 8°
Berlin, Phil. Diss. v. 24. Juli 1909, Ref. Nernst
[Geb. 21. März 82 Berlin; Wohnort: Berlin; Staatsangeh.: Preußen; Vorbildung: Gymn. Elbing Reife O. 02; Studium: Berlin 14 S.; Rig. 24. Juni 09.]   [U 09.227]

NL 0447972   ICRL PU CtY

Löwenstein-Scharffeneck, Hubertus, Graf von
see Löwenstein-Wertheim-Freudenberg, Hubertus, Prinz zu, 1906-

---

4PT   Löwenstein-Wertheim-Freudenberg, Hubertus,
Ger.   Prinz zu, 1906-
3465   Der Adler und das Kreuz.   Heidelberg, F. H. Kerle, 1950 [c1949]
251 p.

NL 0448001   DLC-P4

Löwenstein-Wertheim-Freudenberg, Hubertus, Prinz zu, 1906-
After Hitler's fall; Germany's coming Reich, by Prince Hubertus Loewenstein. Translated by Denis Waldock. London, Faber & Faber, [1934]
xxxvi, 281 p. 20 cm.

1. Germany—Politics and government.   I. Waldock, Denis, tr.   II. Title.   III. Title: Germany's coming Reich.

DD112.L62 1934   943.085   35-1804

MiU
NL 0448002   DLC Or DAU PSC PP OCU OU OO MB NN CtY

Löwenstein-Wertheim-Freudenberg, Hubertus, Prinz zu, 1906-
After Hitler's fall; Germany's coming Reich; tr. by Denis Waldock.   New York, Macmillan, 1935.
xxxvi, 281 p.

NL 0448003   OrU

Löwenstein-Wertheim-Freudenberg, Hubertus, Prinz zu, 1906-
Als Katholik im republikanischen Spanien, von Hubertus, Prinz zu Löwenstein.   Zürich: Verlagsbuchhandlung Staufacher [1938]   77 p. 19cm.

1. Catholic church, Roman—   Spain. 2. Spain—Hist.—Civil war, 1936-1939. I. Title.
N. Y. P. L.   April 29, 1941

NL 0448004   NN

Löwenstein-Wertheim-Freudenberg, Hubertus, Prinz zu, 1906-
A Catholic in republican Spain, by Prince Hubertus Friedrich of Loewenstein. London, V. Gollancz, 1937.
112 p. 19 cm.

1. Spain—History—Civil War, 1936-1939. 2. Church and state in Spain. 3. Catholic Church in Spain.   I. Title.

DP269.L64 1937   946.08   38-4636

NL 0448005   DLC MU NcU KU IaU OC1 PSC CtY NcD TxU

Löwenstein-Wertheim-Freudenberg, Hubertus, Prinz zu, 1906-
The child and the emperor; a legend [by] Prince Hubertus zu Loewenstein. New York, Macmillan, 1945.
70 p. 21 cm.
The 1st vol. of the author's trilogy, the 2d of which is The lance of Longinus, and the 3d: The eagle and the cross.

1. Jesus Christ—Fiction.   I. Title.

BT309.L6   232.993   45-1962

NL 0448006   DLC OrStbM Or NN OOxM OO OEac NNC

Löwenstein-Wertheim-Freudenberg, Hubertus, Prinz zu, 1906-
Conquest of the past, an autobiography [by] Prince Hubertus zu Loewenstein. Boston, Houghton Mifflin, 1938.
325 p. illus., ports. 22 cm.

1. Germany—History—1918-1933. 2. Germany—Politics and government—1918-1933.   I. Title.

DD247.L63A3   923.243   38-27276

OKentU CtY PP PSC PBm Wa OrU OrStbM WaS MtU Or
NL 0448007   DLC OLak ViU NN OC1W OOxM OO PU OC1 MeB

Löwenstein-Wertheim-Freudenberg, Hubertus, Prinz zu, 1906-
Conquest of the past; the autobiography of Prince Hubertus Loewenstein. London, Faber and Faber [1938]
385 p. illus., ports. 23 cm.

1. Germany—History—1918-1933. 2. Germany—Politics and government—1918-1933.   I. Title.

DD247.L63A3 1938a   923.243   38-15622

NL 0448008   DLC

VOLUME 338

Löwenstein-Wertheim-Freudenberg, Hubertus, *Prinz zu,*
1906–
    Deutsche Geschichte; der Weg des Reiches in zwei Jahr-
tausenden. Frankfurt am Main, H. Scheffler ₍1950, *1951₎
    643 p. plates, ports., maps (part col.) facsims. 24 cm.
    Bibliography: p. 594–619.

    1. Germany—History.   I. Title.

    DD89.L58   51-28059

NL 0448009   DLC WaSpG NN PPG PU OU MU

- - - - -

    Löwenstein-Wertheim-Freudenberg, Hubertus,
        Prinz zu, 1906–
DD   Deutsche Geschichte; der Weg des Reiches in zwei Jahr-
89 tausenden. Frankfurt am Main, H. Scheffler
.L83   ₍1954₎ 643 p. plates, ports., maps (part col.) facsims. 24 cm.
1954   Bibliography: p. 594–619.
        "Zweite Auflage, März 1954."

NL 0448010   MiU

- - - - -

Löwenstein-Wertheim-Freundenberg, Hubertus, *Prinz zu,*
1906–
    The eagle and the cross, by Prince Hubertus zu Loewen-
stein. New York, Macmillan, 1947.
    xii, 280 p. 21 cm.
    The 3d vol. of the author's trilogy, the 1st of which is The child
and the emperor, and the 2d: The lance of Longinus.

    1. Rome—History—Tiberius, 14-37—Fiction. 2. Church history—
Primitive and early church—Fiction.   I. Title.

    PZ3.L8243Eag   47-2842

NL 0448011   DLC OrP WaE WaSpG NNC ICU OrStbM

- - - - -

Löwenstein-Wertheim-Freudenberg, Hubertus, *Prinz zu,*
1906–
    The Germans in history, by Prince Hubertus zu Loewen-
stein. New York, Columbia University Press, 1945.
    xii, 584 p. illus. 25 cm.
    "List of works cited": p. ₍513₎–544.

    1. Germany—History. 2. Germany—Politics and government.
3. Europe—History. 4. History—Philosophy.   I. Title.

    DD89.L6   943   A 46-280
    Columbia Univ. Libraries
    for Library of Congress   ₍r70¹²₎† rev

    OrCS OrStbM DLC NcD
    PPT PPD PSt PP PU NcC WaSpG WaWW NcGU OrU Wa MtU OrP
NL 0448012   NNC MB OCU OCl ViU DAU CU InStme OClCC

- - - - -

Löwenstein-Wertheim-Freudenberg, Hubertus, *Prinz zu,*
1906–
    Kleine deutsche Geschichte. Frankfurt am Main, H.
Scheffler ₍1953₎
    166 p. illus. 20 cm.

    1. Germany—History.   I. Title.

    DD89.L63   54-26558 ‡

NL 0448013   DLC TU PSt NN

- - - - -

        Löwenstein-Wertheim-Freudenberg, Hubertus, *Prinz zu,*
        1906–
943   Kleine deutsche Geschichte ₍von₎ Hubertus Prinz
L827K zu Löwenstein. Frankfurt a. M., H. Scheffler
        ₍c1953₎
        172 p. illus., map (on lining papers) 20 cm

NL 0448014   NcD

- - - - -

Löwenstein-Wertheim-Freudenberg, Hubertus, *Prinz zu,*
1906–
    The lance of Longinus, by Prince Hubertus zu Loewen-
stein. New York, Macmillan, 1946.
    166 p. 21 cm.
    The 2d vol. of the author's trilogy, the 1st of which is The child
and the emperor, and the 3d: The eagle and the cross.

    1. Jesus Christ—Fiction.   I. Title.

    PZ3.L8243Lan   46-234

        NN WaSp
NL 0448015   DLC WaS OrP PGladM OCl OCU NcD PPCCH

- - - - -

        Löwenstein-Wertheim-Freudenberg, Hubertus,
4PT   Prinz zu, 1906–
Ger.   Die Lanze des Longinus.   Heidelberg,
557   F. H. Kerle, 1948.
        216 p.

NL 0448016   DLC-P4

- - - - -

Löwenstein-Wertheim-Freudenberg, Hubertus, *Prinz zu,*
1906–
    On borrowed peace ₍by₎ Prince Hubertus zu Loewen-
stein. ₍1st ed.₎ Garden City, N. Y., Doubleday, Doran,
1942.
    xii, 344 p. 22 cm.
    "An American mercury book."

    1. Germany—History—1933-1945. 2. Refugees, Political.
I. Title.

    DD253.L585   943.086   42-25669

        OOxM PPFr FTaSU Or OrP WaS
NL 0448017   DLC DAU NIC PSC NcC NcD OCl OLak OO OU

- - - - -

Löwenstein-Wertheim-Freudenberg, Hubertus, *Prinz zu,*
1906–
    On borrowed peace, by Prince Hubertus Loewenstein.
London, Faber and Faber ₍1943₎
    296 p. port. 21 cm.

    1. Germany—History—1933-1945. 2. Refugees, Political.
I. Title.
    DD253.L585 1943   943.086   43-12130

NL 0448018   DLC

- - - - -

Löwenstein-Wertheim-Freudenberg, Hubertus, *Prinz zu,*
1906–
    On the foundations of peace, by Prince Hubertus Loewen-
stein, April 1941. The university and conservation, by
William J. K. Harkness, December 1940. Gainesville, Uni-
versity of Florida ₍1941?₎
    22 p. 23 cm. (₍Phi Beta Kappa. Florida Beta. University of
Florida₎ ΦBK series, no. 3)
    At head of title: Phi Beta Kappa addresses delivered at the
University of Florida.
    1. World War, 1939-1945—Peace. 2. Wildlife conservation. 3.
Toronto. University. Ontario Fisheries Research Laboratory.   I.
Harkness, William John Knox, 1896-1960. The university and con-
servation.   II. Title.   III. Title: The university and conservation.
(Series)

    AS36.P48 no. 3   940.531   42-50688

NL 0448019   DLC PPT OU ViU

- - - - -

261.873 Löwenstein-Wertheim-Freudenberg, Hubertus,
L825r   Prinz zu, 1906–
        Revolucion mundial cristiana.   Quito, Ecua-
dor, 1942.
        20p. 18cm.

        "Con permiso de la Atlantic Monthly; editori-
al "El Comercio", 1942."

        1. War and religion. 2. World War, 1939-1945
- Religious aspects. I. Title.

NL 0448020   TxU

- - - - -

308   Löwenstein-Wertheim-Freudenberg, Hubertus,
Z   Prinz zu, 1906–
Box 574   ... The republic of science and learning, by
        Hubertus prinz zu Loewenstein-Wertheim-Freuden-
berg ... ₍Ames, Ia.₎ 1940₎
        1 p.l., 8 p. 23½ᶜᵐ. (The Iowa state college
bulletin, vol. XXXVIII, no. 51)

        "Address delivered at the eighteenth annual
Honors day dinner, the Iowa state college, May
22, 1940."

        1. Learning and scholarship.

NL 0448021   NNC

- - - - -

Löwenstein-Wertheim-Freudenberg, Hubertus, *Prinz zu,*
1906–
    Stresemann; das deutsche Schicksal im Spiegel seines
Lebens. Frankfurt am Main, H. Scheffler ₍1952₎
    356 p. illus. 21 cm.

    1. Stresemann, Gustav, 1878-1929.

    DD231.S83L6   923.243   53-16581 ‡

        CaBVaU IEN GU NBuU PU OrU
NL 0448022   DLC NN OCl NIC NcU NjP NcD TU NNC IaU

- - - - -

Löwenstein-Wertheim-Freudenberg, Hubertus, *Prinz zu,*
1906–
    The tragedy of a nation; Germany, 1918-1934, by Prince
Hubertus Loewenstein; with an introd. by Wickham Steed.
London, Faber & Faber ₍1934₎
    viii, 373 p. 20 cm.
    Translation of Die Tragödie eines Volkes.

    1. Germany—Politics and government—1918-1933. 2. Germany—
History—1918-1933. 3. Nationalsozialistische Deutsche Arbeiter-Partei. 4. Political parties—Germany.   I. Title.

    DD240.L5913   34-10399

        WaS
        MWelC OClJC OCX PU NN PPDrop NcU CSt-H OrU Or MtU
NL 0448023   DLC NNC CtY OOxM MiU OCl OCU MdU PPT

- - - - -

    Löwenstein-Wertheim-Freudenberg, Hubertus,
        Prinz zu, 1906–
    The tragedy of a nation; Germany 1918-1934,
    by Prince Hubertus Loewenstein; with an intro-
    duction by Wickham Steed.   New York, The
    Macmillan company, 1934.
        viii, 373 p. 19 cm.

NL 0448024   TNJ OrP Or CSt-H NSyU OO MB WaU

- - - - -

Löwenstein-Wertheim-Freudenberg, Hubertus, *Prinz zu,*
1906–
    Die Tragödie eines Volkes; Deutschland 1918-1934.
Amsterdam, Steenuil-Verlag ₍1934₎
    279 p. 20 cm.

    1. Germany—Politics and government—1918-1933. 2. Germany—
History—1918-1933. 3. Nationalsozialistische Deutsche Arbeiter-
Partei. 4. Political parties—Germany.   I. Title.

    DD240.L59   943.085   44-28404

NL 0448025   DLC NN NcD OCl MH IU MiD

- - - - -

Löwenstein-Wertheim-Freudenberg, Hubertus, *Prinz zu,*
1906–
    Umrisse der Idee des faschistischen Staates und ihre
Verwirklichung, unter Vergleichung mit den wichtigsten
Gebieten des deutschen Staatsrechts. ₍Kirchhain N.-L.₎
1931.
    105 p. 23 cm.
    Thesis—Hamburg.
    "Literaturverzeichnis": p. ₍9₎-11.

    1. Italy—Politics and government—1922-1945. 2. Fascism—Italy.
I. Title.

    JN5455 1931.L6   49-32817

NL 0448026   DLC CtY MiU NN

VOLUME 338

Löwenstein-Wertheim-Freudenberg, Hubertus, *Prinz zu,* 1906–
Von des Deutschen Reiches Erneuerung; eine Rede in Heidelberg. ₍Amorbach₎ Die Amorbacher Buchhandlung, 1949.

15, ₍1₎ p. 21 cm.

Biography of author: p. ₍16₎

1. Germany—Politics and government—1945–   ɪ. Title.

A 52–887

New York. Public Libr.
for Library of Congress   ₍r69b2₎ rev

NL 0448027   NN

Löwenstein-Wertheim-Freudenberg, Wilhelm, **Prinz zu,** 1817–1877.
Ausflug von Lissabon nach Andalusien und in den norden von Marokko im frühjahr 1845, vom prinzen Wilhelm zu Löwenstein. ... Dresden und Leipzig, Arnold, 1846.

vi, 274, ₍2₎ p. front. 20½ᶜᵐ.

1. Spain—Descr. & trav. 2. Morocco—Descr. & trav.

NL 0448028   MiU MH

₍**Loewenstein-Wertheim-Rosenberg, Constantin Joseph,** *erbprinz von*₎ 1802–1838.
Beiträge zur philosophie des rechtes. Heidelberg, A. Osswald, 1836.

xviii, 337 p. 20ᶜᵐ.

Advertisements : p. 334–337.

1. Law—Philosophy. 2. State, The. 3. Political science.   ɪ. Title.

36–29174

NL 0448029   DLC

BR100 **Loewenstein-Wertheim-Rosenberg,** Constantin Joseph,
.L82   erbprinz von, 1802–1838.
Versuch einer systematischen beleuchtung der ersten elemente einer christlichen philosophie. Von Constantin Joseph, erbprinzen zu Löwenstein-Wertheim-Rosenberg. Frankfurt a.M. ₍Andreäische buchhdlg₎ 1840.

xii, 406 p. 22½cm.

1. Christianity—Philosophy.

NL 0448030   ICU

Löwenstein-Wertheim-Rosenberg, Karl,
Erbprinz zu.
Erbverzicht und abfindungsvertrag.
Bielefeld, 1929.

8+68 p.

Inaug.-Diss. - Würzburg.

NL 0448031   MH-L ICRL

Loewenstein zu Loewenstein, Hans Louis
Ferdinand von, 1874–
Technische kulturdenkmale, im auftrag der Agricola-gesellschaft beim Deutschen museum herausgegeben von Conrad Matschoss und Werner Lindner, unter mitarbeit von August Hertwig, Hans v. u. zu Loewenstein, Otto Petersen und Carl Schiffner. München, F. Bruckmann, a. g., 1932.

Löwenstein, gebrüder, *Frankfurt am Main.*
Catalogue of the celebrated collection of works of art and vertu, known as "The Vienna museum," the property of Messrs. Löwenstein, brothers, of Frankfort-on-the-Maine: which will be sold by auction, by Messrs. Christie, Manson & Woods ... on March 12, 1860, and nine following days (Saturdays & Sundays excepted) ... ₍London, Printed by W. Clowes and sons, 1860₎

viii, ₍9₎–90 p. mounted front. (port.) 4 col. pl., mounted photos. (1 col.) 25 cm. ₍Christie, Manson and Woods, ltd., London. Catalogue, Mar. 1860₎

This collection was begun in the sixteenth century by the Emperor Maximilian ɪ, increased by the Emperor Rudolph ɪɪ, and in 1782 was sold to the Chevalier von Schönfeld. cf. p. ₍3₎

1. Art objects—Private collections. 2. Art—Private collections.   ɪ. Title: The Vienna museum.

N8660.C5A3   Mar. 12, etc., 1860   42–51825 rev

NL 0448034   DLC CU

Löwenstern, Detmar, Referendar: Das Vermächtnis des Nießbrauchs an einer Erbschaft. Cassel 1913: Gotthelft.
VII, 67 S. 8°

Marburg. Jur. Diss. v. 20. Aug. 1913, Ref. André
₍Geb. 12. Okt. 90 Arolsen; Wohnort: Kassel; Staatsangeh.: Waldeck; Vorbildung: RG. Erfurt Reife 09; Studium: Freiburg 1, Berlin 3, Marburg 2 S.; Rig. 15. Juli 13.₎   ₍U 13. 1124₎

NL 0448035   ICRL MH-L

DK   **Löwenstern, Eduard von,** 1790–1837
188.6   **Mit Graf Pahlens Reiterei gegen Napoleon,**
.L63   Denkwürdigkeiten. Hrsg. von Georges Wrangell
A24   Berlin, E. S. Mittler, 1910.
338 p. illus. 24 cm.

1. Russia - Hist. - 19th cent. 2. Napoléon I. - Invasion of Russia, 1812. 3. Napoléon I - Campaigns of 1813–1814. I. Title.

NL 0448036   WU MH NIC

Loewenstern, Elard, *baron von,* 1886–
Eine falsche englische rechnung, die fliegerschlacht von Amiens am 8. august 1918, von baron Elard von Loewenstern. Berlin, Bernard & Graefe ₍1938₎

289 p. plates, ports., fold. map (in pocket) 21½ᶜᵐ.

1. Amiens, Battle of, 1918. 2. European war, 1914–1918—Aerial operations.   ɪ. Title.

₍Full name: Adelbert Johann Elard baron von Loewenstern₎

41–26079

Library of Congress   D545.A56L6
₍2₎   940.4353

NL 0448037   DLC TU WU MH

Loewenstern, Elard, *baron von.*
Die fliegersichterkundung im weltkriege, von baron Elard von Loewenstern. Berlin, Bernard & Graefe ₍1937₎

57, ₍1₎ p. incl. illus., fold. pl. 21½ᶜᵐ.

1. European war, 1914–1918—Aerial operations. 2. Military reconnaissance.   ɪ. Title.

39–16178

Library of Congress   D604.L7
₍2₎   940.44943

NL 0448038   DLC

Loewenstern, Elard, *baron von.*
Der frontflieger aus vorkriegs-, kriegs- und nachkriegsfliegertagen; aufzeichnungen auf grund eigener tagebücher, von baron Elard von Loewenstern ... Berlin, Bernard & Graefe, 1937.

273, ₍1₎ p. illus., plates, fold. maps (in pocket) 24½ᶜᵐ. *(Added t.-p.: Deutsche tat im weltkrieg 1914/1918; geschichten der kämpfe deutscher truppen ... bd. 81)*

1. European war, 1914–1918—Personal narratives, German. 2. European war, 1914–1918—Aerial operations.   ɪ. Title.

39–16174

Library of Congress   D604.L72
₍2₎   940.44943

NL 0448039   DLC

Loewenstern, Elard, *Baron* von, 1886–
Luftwaffe über dem Feind. Berlin, W. Limpert ₍1941₎

268 p. plates, map. 21 cm.

1. World War, 1939–1945—Aerial operations, German. 2. Germany. Luftwaffe.   ɪ. Title.

Full name: Adelbert Johann Elard *Baron* von Loewenstern.

D787.L6   940.544943   A F 47–6292*

Illinois. Univ. Library
for Library of Congress   ₍2₎†

NL 0448040   IU OU NcD NN CU GAT MiD DLC

₍**Loewenstern, Elard,** Baron von₎ 1886–
Mobilmachung, Aufmarsch und erster Einsatz der deutschen Luftstreitkräfte im August 1914... Berlin, E. S. Mittler & Sohn, 1939. xi, 120 p. illus. 25cm. (Kriegsgeschichtliche Einzelschriften der Luftwaffe. Bd. 3.)

"Bearbeiter: Oberstleutnant Baron von Loewenstern ₍und₎ Major a. D. Dr. Bertkau. Karten: Oberleutnant a. D. Rummelspacher."

382990B. 1. European war, 1914–1918   —Aerial operations. I. Bertkau,
N. Y. P. L.   jt. au. II. Ser.
April 21, 1947

NL 0448041   NN

Loewenstern, Friedrich Gottlieb, Freiherr von,
respondent.
... Juris communis et Provincialis Marchico-Badensis
see under Harpprecht, Ferdinand Christoph, 1650–1714, praeses.

Spec.   **Löwenstern, Isidor,** 1810–1858 or 9.
Arnold   **Essai de déchiffrement de l'écriture**
PJ 3191   **Assyrienne,** pour servir à l'explication du
L 6   **monument de Khorsabad.** Paris, Franck, 1845.
36 p. 3 fold. plates. 27 cm.
Bibliographical references included in footnotes.

1. Assyro-Babylonian language. 2. Cuneiform writing.

NL 0448043   MoSW PPDrop NcD MH NN NjP PU CtY TxDaM

Löwenstern, Isidor, 1810–1858 *or* 9.
Les États-Unis et la Havane; souvenirs d'un voyageur par m. Isidore Löwenstern ... Paris ₍etc.₎ A. Bertrand ₍etc.₎ 1842.

xii, 372 p. 21ᶜᵐ.

1. U. S.—Descr. & trav. 2. Canada—Descr. & trav. 3. Cuba—Descr. & trav.

1–26859 Revised

Library of Congress   E165.L82

NN KEmT OCIW MsU
NL 0448044   DLC UU ICarbS TxU OOxM CSt PSt OCH CtY

VOLUME 338

MICD
917

Löwenstern, Isidor, 1810-1858?
Les Etats-Unis et la Havane; souvenirs
d'un voyageur ... Paris [etc.] A. Bertrand
[etc.] 1842.
372 p. (Travels in the Old South III, 196)
MICROOPAQUE
#U.S.--Description and travel.
Les Etats-Unis et la Havane.

NL 0448045   MoU

Löwenstern, Isidor, 1810-1858 or 9.
Exposé des éléments constitutifs du système
de la troisième écriture cunéiforme de Persépolis,
par Isidore Löwenstern. Paris, A. Franck, 1847.
101 p. illus. 27 cm.
Bibliographical footnotes.
1. Old Persian inscriptions.

NL 0448046   OU NIC NcD PU MH NN OCl

Löwenstern, Isidor, 1810-1858 or 59.
Journey from the city of Mexico to Mazatlan.
[Royal geographical society, London]
[Papers read before the Royal geographical society.
Central America. London, J. Murray, 1841]

Löwenstern, Isidor, 1810-1858 or 9.
Le Mexique; souvenirs d'un voyageur, par Isidore
Löwenstern ... Paris, A. Bertrand; [etc., etc.] 1843.
viii, 466 p., 1 l. 22cm.

1. Mexico—Descr. & trav. I Title.

Library of Congress   F1213.1.91
2-4793

NL 0448048   DLC OCU GU CU-B NNH NN PU CtY

Löwenstern, Isidor, 1810-1858 or 9.
Le Mexique; souvenirs d'un voyageur, par Isidore
Löwenstern ... Paris, A. Bertrand; [etc., etc.] 1843.
viii, 466 p., 1 l. 22cm.

MICROFILM

NL 0448049   UU

Löwenstern, Isidor, 1810-1858 or 9.
Note sur une table généalogique des rois de
Babylone dans Ker-Porter ... Paris, A.Leleux,
1849.
7 p. fold.facsim. 22cm.
"Extrait de la Revue archéologique, 6e année."
No.3 in [Guizot collection of pamphlets, v.28, (Bind-
er's title: Mélanges historiques. 1849-1854]

1.Cuneiform inscriptions.

NL 0448050   MiU

Löwenstern, Johann Kunckel von

SEE

Kunckel, Johann, von Löwenstern, 1630?-1703.

Löwenstern, M.J.
   see Löwenstern, Isidor, 1810-1858 or 9.

LÖWENSTERN, MATTHAEUS APELLES VON, 1594-1648.

Ich sehe mit Wonne. Weise von M. A. von Löwen-
stern, 1644. Satz von Pierre Jacot. (IN: Sing- und
Spielmusik; Beilage zur Schweizerischen Monatsschrift "Volkslied und
Hausmusik". Zürich. 24cm. Nr. 16, p. [I])
For 2 voices, or for 2 recorders (or other melody instruments), or for
voices and instruments.

1. Instrumental or vocal music.

NL 0448053   NN

Loewenstern, Nikolaus Georg Bernhard von.
... De Ivdaeis eorvmqve diversa conditione
secvndvm ivs romanvm et germanicvm inprimis
qvoqve mecklenbvrgicvm ... Bvetzovii, 1768.
4 p.l., lxxxviii, [8] p. 20.5 cm.
Diss. - Bützow (A. F. Trendelenburg, praeses)

NL 0448054   CtY-L

Löwenstern, Vladimir Ivanovich, *baron fon*
   see
Levenshtern, Vladimir Ivanovich, *baron fon*, 1777-1858.

Löwenstern, Woldemar Hermann, *freiherr von*
   see
Levenshtern, Vladimir Ivanovich, *baron fon*, 1777-1858.

Loewenstimm (Adolphus). *De amputationi-
bus pedis exarticulationibus ejus praeferendis.
46 pp. 8°. Dorpat, typ. vid. J. C. Schünmanni et
C. Mattieseni, 1851.*

NL 0448057   DNLM

4K
7867

Loewenstimm, August
Aberglaube und Strafrecht. Autorisierte Übersetzung aus dem Russischen. Mit einem Vorwort von J.
Kohler. Berlin, J. Räde, 1897.
232 p.

NL 0448058   DLC-P4 NIC OCl OCH CtY CU MH ICU UU TxU

Film
GR
10
L5
reel
245

Löwenstimm, August.
Aberglaube und Strafrecht. Autorisierte
Übersetzung aus dem Russischen. Mit einem
Vorwort von J. Kohler. Berlin, J. Räder,
1897.
xv,232p.
Microfilm (positive. Literature of
folklore, reel 245)

1. Criminal law. 2. Crime and criminals.
3. Superstition. II. Title.

NL 0448059   UU

LOEWENSTIMM, August.
Der fanatismus als quelle der verbrechen.
Berlin,1899.

(2)+44 p.

NL 0448060   MH-L

Loewenstimm, August.
Kriminalistische studien. Von Aug. Loewenstimm ... Berlin, J. Räde, 1901.
viii, 201 p. front. 20cm.
"Litteratur": p. [131]-134.
CONTENTS.—Das bettelgewerbe, mit besonderer berücksichtigung der
russischen verhältnisse.—Fanatismus und verbrechen.

1. Begging. 2. Fanaticism. 3. Poor—Russia. I. Title.

Library of Congress   HV4575.L8
2—19053

NL 0448061   DLC FMU NN ICJ

Löwenstjerna, Hugo, pseud.
   see Almquist, Carl Jonas Love, 1793-1866.

TX941
.R3L6

Löwenström, Bo.
Från klostermässa till tavernans fröjder; notiser från
Ramundeboda kloster och gästgivaregård. Med teckningar
av Hugo Carlsson. [Örebro, Tryckeri-a.-b. Örebro-kuriren,
1955]
123 p. illus. 20 cm.

1. Ramundeboda, Sweden. I. Title.

A 57-6721

Minnesota. Univ. Lit.
for Library of Congress   [8]

NL 0448063   MnU DLC

Löwenthal, ————, landrichter.

Kaufmann, Emil.
Handelsrechtliche rechtsprechung 1900/1901[-
bearb. und zusammengestellt von Emil Kaufmann ... Hannover, Helwing, 1902-

Loewenthal, Abraham, 1868-1928.
Das Buch des "Ewigen Lebens" und seine
Bedeutung in der Literatur des Mittelalters
see under [Gerondi, Jonah] d. 1263.

B759
.A527L79

Loewenthal, Abraham, 1868-1928.
Dominicus Gundisalvi und sein psychologisches
Compendium. Ein Beitrag zur Geschichte der philo-
sophischen Litteratur bei Arabern, Juden und
Christen. Teil I. Von Albert Loewenthal. Ber-
lin [1890]
35 p.
Inaug.--Diss.--Königsberg.
Republished in 1891 as the first part of the
author's Pseudo-Aristoteles über die Seele.
1. Gundissalinus, Dominicus, 12th cent. De
anima. 2. Gershon ben Solomon, 13th cent.
Sha'ar ha-shamayim. 3. Ibn Gabirol Salamon ben
Judah, ca.1021-ca. 1058. ICU

NL 0448066   ICU OCH DNLM NjP OU IU IC CU ICRL

PN6299
.H815

Loewenthal, Abraham, 1869-1928, ed. and tr.

Ḥunayn ibn Isḥāq al-'Ibādī, 809?-873.
Honein ibn Ishāk, Sinnsprüche der philosophen. Nach der
hebräischen uebersetzung Charisi's ins deutsche übertragen
und erläutert, von dr. A. Loewenthal ... Berlin, S. Calvary
& co., 1896.

VOLUME 338

BS1465
.G45
Hebraic
Sect.

Loewenthal, Abraham, 1868-1928, ed.
Perush 'al Mishle

Gerondi, Jonah, d. 1263.
פירוש על משלי. עם מבוא על קורות ימי חיי המחבר והערות
אברהם לאוועגטהאל. הודפס בעזרת החברה "צונץ שטיפטונג"
ווינעצעללשאפט צור פאררערונג דער וויסטענשאפט דעם יודענטומס.
‏(ברלין, מ. פאפפעליויער, תר"ע.‏)

Loewenthal, Abraham, 1868-1928.
Pseudo-Aristoteles über die seele. Eine psychologische
schrift des 11. jahrhunderts und ihre beziehungen zu Salomo
ibn Gabirol. (Avicebron) ... von dr. A. Loewenthal ... Berlin,
Mayer & Müller, 1891.
viii, 181, [1], 12 p. 23ᶜᵐ.
"Gedruckt mit unterstützung der Zunz-stiftung."
The author believes that an Arabic psychological work, no longer
extant, by Avicebron was the original source of Dominicus Gundissalinus'
De anima and of the pseudo-Aristotelian Book of the soul contained in
Gershon's Gate of heaven.
"Excerpte aus Dominicus Gundisalvi's 'De anima' enthaltend die be-
standtteile des psychologischen werkes des Salomo ibn Gabirol": p. [77]-
131.

לקשים מטטר ונפש הפיחוח לארסטו ותמצאים בהעתקה עברית בס' שער השמים לר'
גרשון בן שלמה (12 p. at end)

1. Ibn Gabirol, Solomon ben Judah, ca. 1021-ca. 1058. 2. Soul. I.
Gundissalinus, Dominicus, 12th cent. De anima. II. Gershon ben Solomon, 13th cent. שער השמים (transliterated: Sha'ar ha-shamayim) III.
Title.
40-23397 Revised 2

Library of Congress   B759.A54L6

NL 0448070   DLC NIC CU MH NcU OU OCH NNUT ICU

DS
135
S7L7.6

Loewenthal, Abraham, 1868-1928.
Vor der Vertreibung. Bilder aus den
letzten Tagen der Juden in Spanien.
Berlin, H.Engel [188-?]
54 p.   15 cm.

1. Jews in Spain.   I. Title

NL 0448071   OCH

Loewenthal, Abraham, 1868-1928.
... Die wissenschaftliche Bekämpfung des Antisemitismus in
Deutschland; ein Chanukkah-Vortrag von Rabbiner Dr. Loewen-
thal... Berlin: Philo-Verlag, 1921. 11 p. 12°. (Zeit-
und Streitfragen. Heft 2.)
Cover-title.

1. Jews, Germany.
N.Y.P.L.   May 19, 1923.

NL 0448072   NN

---

ar W
54487
no.3

Löwenthal, Adolf.
Fragen der Anspruchsverjährung.   Berlin,
Druck von W. Pilz, 1916.
viii, 50 p. 23cm.

Inaug.-Diss.---Erlangen.

NL 0448073   NIC ICRL

Loewenthal, Albert
see
Loewenthal, Abraham, 1868-1928.

Loewenthal (Alexander). *De resectionibus
cubiti partialibus atque totalibus. 36 pp. 8°.
Regimonti Pr., Gruber et Longrien, 1866.   C.

NL 0448075   DNLM

Loewenthal, Amelia (Ceide) von
see Ceide, Amelia.

W
4
G32
1945

Löwenthal, Armand
Synthèse de porphyrines par certaines
bactéries (en milieu chimiquement définis)
Genève, Impr. genevoise, 1945.
39 p. (Geneva. Université. Faculté
de médecine. Thèse. [M. D.] no. 1841)

Series

NL 0448077   DNLM

Loewenthal, Artur.
Ueber die Entwicklung und den heutigen Stand
der Lungentuberkulosetherapie m. bes. Berücks.
d. Tuberkulintherapie.   Berlin, Schütz, 1922.
36 p.
Inaug.-Diss. - Bonn, 1922.

NL 0448078   ICRL

Loewenthal (Bernardus). *De neurosibus secundum diversas vitæ ætates. 24 pp. 4°. Herbi-
poli, J. Dorbath, 1824.

NL 0448079   DNLM PPC

Loewenthal, Bernhard.
Erzählungen und Humoresken aus dem
Jüdischen Leben.   Berlin, L. Lamm, 1908.
199 p.

NL 0448080   OCH

Löwenthal, Bernard, 1891-
... Inversio uteri puerperalis acuta ...
Berlin [1920]
37, [3] p.   23 cm.
Inaug.-Diss. - Berlin.
Lebenslauf.

NL 0448081   CtY MiU

Loewenthal, David, 1795?-1868.
אילת השחר; שירים ומליצות, מכתמים ומשלים. וַארשָא,
בדפוס א. לעבענסאהן, תד"ר. W Warszawie, 1843.
116 p. 18 cm.
זאנטאסא איזדניצין רישסקן צעריצסל. p. 111-116.

No more published.

I. Title.   Title transliterated: Ayelet ha-shaḥar

A 52-1005

New York. Public Libr.
for Library of Congress

NL 0448082   NN DLC

Löwenthal, Devora
see
Ginzburg, Devora (Löwenthal)

Loewenthal, Eduard
Beitraege zu erkrankungen der wirbelsaeule.
Inaug. diss. Wuerzburg, 1884.

NL 0448084   ICRL DNLM

4HX
660

Loewenthal, Eduard, 1836-1917.
Der Anarchismus und das Recht der
Schwachen; oder, Die drei Grundubel
unserer Zeit.   2. Aufl.   Berlin, H.
Brieger, 1894.
22 p.

NL 0448085   DLC-P4 ICN ICJ

LOEWENTHAL, Eduard, 1836-
Der bankrott der Darwin-Haeckel'schen ent-
wicklungstheorie und die krönung des monisti-
schen gebaudes.   Berlin, E.Ebering, 1900.

NL 0448086   NN CU

1836-1917.
332. LOEWENTHAL, Eduard. The coins of Tinne-
velly. Madras, 1888, 28 pp. 4 pls. 8°.

NL 0448087   MSaE

Loewenthal, Eduard, 1836-1917.
Die deutschen Einheitsbestrebungen und ihre
Verwirklichung im neunzehnten Jahrhundert.
Berlin, S. Cronbach, 1899.
156 p.

NL 0448088   NjP

Loewenthal, Eduard, 1836-1917.
Fifty cardinal laws relating to the spherical molecular
movements, as a basis for a new and remodeled system
of the sciences of astronomy, dynamics, physics and physiology.   By Dr. Edward Loewenthal ... Tr. by Julius Silversmith, M. A.   Chicago, Cosmopolitan publishing company, 1874.
iv, [5]-38 p. 2 diagr.   22½ᶜᵐ.

I. Silversmith, Julius, tr.
4-26340†

Library of Congress   Q173.L82

NL 0448089   DLC

4CB
74

Loewenthal, Eduard, 1836-1917.
Die Fulguro-Genesis im Gegensatz
zur Evolutionstheorie und die Kultur-
ziele der Menschheit.   Berlin,
E. Ebering, 1902.
31 p.

NL 0448090   DLC-P4

Loewenthal, Eduard, 1836-1917.
Geschichte der friedensbewegung. Nebst anhang: ein welt-
friedens-plebiszit und weltfriedenspreise. Von Eduard Loewenthal ... Berlin, E. Ebering, 1903.
102 p., 2 l. 19½ᶜᵐ.

1. Peace.

Library of Congress   JX1953.L7
4—22319

NL 0448091   DLC ICJ MB

VOLUME 338

LOEWENTHAL,Eduard, *1836-1917*.
Geschichte der friedensbewegung mit berücksichtigung der zweiten haager friedenskonfer-
enz. 2te auf. Berlin,1907.

NL 0448092   MH-L DS

Loewenthal, Eduard, 1836-1917.
Geschichte der Philosophie im Umriss für
Studierende, sowie für jeden Gebildeten. Berlin, Hannemann, 1896.
55 p. 19cm.

Includes a section on Spinoza (p. 33-34)
and other references to him.

NL 0448093   NNC MH NN

Loewenthal, Eduard, 1836-1917.
Geschichte der Philosophie im Umriss für
Studierende, sowie für jeden Gebildeten. 4.
verm. und verb. Aufl. Berlin, M. Hannemann,
1898.
55 p. 19cm.

Includes a section on Spinoza (p. 33-34) and
other references to him.

NL 0448094   NNC MiEM

LOEWENTHAL,Eduard, *1836-1917*.
Grundzüge des inductiven spiritualismus
nebst geschichtlicher einleitung. Berlin,
K.Siegismund,1889.

pp.15.   Phil 7059.889

NL 0448095   MH

Loewenthal (Eduard) *1836-1917*.
Grundzüge zur Reform und Codification des Völkerrechts.
Berlin : Deutscher Flugschriften-Verlag, 1874. 12 pp.
12°.
In : *C. p. v. 1006.

NL 0448096   NN

LOEWENTHAL,Eduard, *1836-1917*,
Grundzuge zur reform und codification des
völkerrechts (in deutscher und franzosischer
sprache). 3te auf. Berlin,1912.

14+(2) p.

NL 0448097   MH-L DS

Loewenthal, Eduard, *1836-1917*.
Mein Lebenswerk auf sozialpolitischem, neu-religiösem, philo-
sophischem und naturwissenschaftlichem Gebiete. Memoiren
von Dr. Eduard Loewenthal. Mit zwei Bildnissen. Berlin, H.
Loewenthal, 1910.
103, [1] p. 2 port. (incl. front.) 24ᶜᵐ.

NL 0448098   ICJ MH NN

Loewenthal, Eduard, 1836-1917.
Die menschliche Unsterblichkeit in naturalistischer
Beleuchtung und Begründung; nebst Anhang; Das
Cogitantentum, die Religion des Wissens und der
Wissenserweiterung, als Religion der Zukunft.
Berlin, H. Loewenthal, 1910.
20 p. 8°.

NL 0448099   NN

LOEWENTHAL,Eduard,*1836-1917*.
Die nächste wissensstufe,oder Der fortschritt vom materialistisochen zum rationellen naturalismus. Leipzig,O.Mutze,1875.

pp.30.   Phil 7059.875

NL 0448100   MH

PQ2338
.L73N32 Loewenthal, **Eduard, 1836-1917.**
Napoleon III, and the commune of Paris ...
Transl by Julius Silversmith.
Chicago Ill.,1880.
73 p.   15 cm.

NL 0448101   DLC

LOEWENTHAL,Eduard, *1837-1917*.
Obligatorische friedensjustiz nicht
schiedsgericht. Berlin,1897.

14 p.

NL 0448102   MH-L

Loewenthal, Eduard, 1836-1917.
Das preussische Völker-Dressur-System und
die europäische Föderativ-Republik der Zukunft ...
Zürich, J. Schröter, 1871.
36 p. 12°.

NL 0448103   NN

Loewenthal, Eduard, 1836-1917.
Die Religion der Religionen. Gedankschrift
zum 25 jährigen Jubiläum der Cogitanten-Allianz.
Grossenhain, Baumert & Ronge, 1890.
19 p.

NL 0448104   OCH

Loewenthal, Eduard, *1836-1917*.
***** Der Staat Bellamy's und seine Nachfolge. Von Dr. Eduard Loewenthal. Dritte Auflage. Berlin. H. Muskalla, 1905.
29 p. 17ᶜᵐ.

NL 0448105   ICJ ICN

B
76
.51   LOEWENTHAL, EDUARD, 1836-1917.
System and history of nature. Together with
an epitome, entitled Fifty cardinal laws, touch-
ing astronomy, dynamics, physics, and physiology,
illustrated... Translated from the seventh German
edition by Julius Silversmith... Chicago,Occident
publishing co.,1882.
140,38p.

Epitome has separate t.-p. and pagination.

NL 0448106   ICN

B3289
.L659 Loewenthal, Eduard, 1836-1917.
1867   System des Naturalismus. Dresden, Selbstver-
lags-Expedition des kritisch-literarischen Instituts, 1867.
54 p.
"Separat-Ausgabe. (Mit zahlreichen Zusätzen zur
Fassung der 5. Auflage des Gesammtwerkes 'System
und Geschichte des Naturalismus' und einem neuen
Anhang.)"

1. Naturalism.

NL 0448107   ICU

Loewenthal, Eduard, *1836-1917*.
System des naturalistischen Transscendentalismus; oder, Die
Lösung der Welträtsel unter Ausschaltung des Uebersinnlich-
keitsprinzips. Dritte, neu bearbeitete Auflage der Schrift: "Die
menschliche Unsterblichkeit in naturalistischer Beleuchtung und
Begründung." Berlin: H. Loewenthal, 1912. 16 p. 8°.

1. Cosmology. 2. Philosophy.—   Essays and misc.
N.Y.P.L.   June 21, 1912.

NL 0448108   NN

Löwenthal, Eduard, *1836-1917*.
System und geschichte des naturalismus. Leipzig,
1863. 16°

NL 0448109   NNUT MH RPB

Loewenthal, Eduard, 1836-1917.
System und Geschichte des Naturalismus.
Leipzig, J.M. Gebhardt, 1868.
2 p.l., 170 p. 12°.
5. ed.
Bd. with: Schmidt, Julian. Herders Ideen.
n.p. [18-?] 12°.

NL 0448110   NN NjNbS

LOEWENTHAL,Eduard, *1836-1917*.
Der welt-statenbund in sicht und die mission
des cogitantentums; ein beitrag zur lösung de
chinesischen problems. Berlin,1900.

8 p.

NL 0448111   MH-L

LOEWENTHAL,Eduard, *1836-1917*.
Zur internationalen friedenspropaganda; flug-
schrift. Berlin,1874.

12 p.

NL 0448112   MH-L

LOEWENTHAL,Else,*1890-*
Zur kenntnis der ueberjodsaure und ihre
alkalisalze. Inaug.-diss. [Berlin,E.Ebering,
1918?]

"Lebenslauf" at end.

NL 0448113   MH-C CtY

Loewenthal, Erich, *1895?-1944, ed.*

Heine, Heinrich, 1797-1856.
Der lyrische nachlass von H. Heine, gesichtet von Erich
Loewenthal; einleitung von Oskar Loerke. Hamburg [etc.]
Hoffmann und Campe [1925]

Loewenthal, Erich, *1895?-1944*
Der Prosa-Nachlass, neu geordnet, gesichtet
und eingeleitet von Erich Loewenthal
see under   Heine, Heinrich, 1797-1856.

VOLUME 338

PT2316
.R2B3
   Loewenthal, Erich, 1895?-1944

   Heine, Heinrich, 1797-1856.
     The rabbi of Bacherach, a fragment; with a selection from
Heine's letters and an epilogue by Erich Loewenthal. ₍Prose
tr. by E. B. Ashton, *pseud.*₎ New York ₍1947₎

   Loewenthal, Erich, 1895?-1944, ed.

   Heine, Heinrich, 1797-1856.
     ... Der rabbi von Bacherach, ein fragment. Mit zeichnungen von Ludwig Schwerin. Berlin, Schocken verlag, 1937.

   Loewenthal, Erich, 1895?-1944
     ... Studien zu Heines "Reisebildern", von Erich Loewenthal.
Berlin und Leipzig, Mayer & Müller, g. m. b. h., 1922.
    4 p. l., 172 p. 23ᶜᵐ. (Palaestra 138 ...)

    "Die folgenden untersuchungen lagen im sommer 1920 der Philosophischen fakultät der Universität Berlin als dissertation vor; jetzt
sind sie etwas knapper gefasst, hie und da auch ergänzt."–Vorwort.

    Contents.– Einleitung. Die vorbilder. Gedankenkreis und inhaltliche tendenzen. Volkslied, märchen und sage in den "Reisebildern".
Die sage von fliegenden Holländer. Heines arbeitsweise.

    1. Heine, Heinrich. Reisebilder.   I. Title.

   Library of Congress   PD25.P3 vol. 138
                                   27-15469

   MiU PU PBm NN ICN ViU
NL 0448118   DLC MU MoU CU NcU PHC CtY OU OCU OCH

   Loewenthal, Erich, 1895?-1944, comp.
     Sturm und Drang; kritische Schriften. Heidelberg, L.
Schneider ₍1949₎
    911 p. 20 cm.

    Selections from Herder, Hamann, Lavater, and others.
    Bibliographical data in "Anmerkungen und Register" (p. 829-904)

    1. Sturm und Drang movement.   I. Herder, Johann Gottfried von,
1744-1803.
    PT317.L6   830.82   50-32599

   MtBuM WaWW OrU OrCS MtU OrSaW OrU-M CaBVaU OrStbM
MH ICU OU PSt PHC WaE Or WaSp WaPS WaSpG WaTC OrPR
TxU OrStbM MiHM ViU IEN CSt NcD NjP CU TU InU NBC
NL 0448119   DLC OKentU OClW KU NcGU OrU CLSU MoSU OO

833S344 Loewenthal, Erich, 1901-
DL82   Johann Georg Schlosser, seine religiösen
Überzeugungen und der Sturm und Drang.
Dortmund, H. Lücker, 1935.
    ₍viii₎, 75p. 21cm.

    Inaug.-Diss.–Berlin.
    Vita.
    Bibliography: p. ₍iv₎-₍viii₎

    1. Schlosser, Johann Georg, 1739-1799.

NL 0448120   IU PU ICRL CtY

CT   Loewenthal, Erich, 1901-
1098   Johann Georg Schlosser: seine religiösen
S42L6 Ueberzeugungen und der Sturm und Drang. [n.p.,
1935]
    82p. 23cm.

    Includes bibliography.

    1. Schlosser, Johann Georg, 1739-1799.

NL 0448121   MU InU

   Loewenthal, Erich, 1905-
     ... Ueber einen Fall von eigenartiger
Zwergwuchsform ... [Berlin, 1933]
    Inaug.-Diss. - Berlin.
    Lebenslauf.
    "Literaturverzeichnis": p. 19-21.

NL 0448122   CtY DNLM

   Loewenthal, Ernst, 1902-
     Der Gerichtseid ... von Ernst Loewenthal ... Frankfurt a.M., Der Verfasser,
1929.
    1 p.l., 100; ₍2₎ p. 20½cm.

    Inaug.-Diss. - Freiburg i.B.
    "Lebenslauf": p. ₍101₎
    "Literaturverzeichnis": p.93-98.

NL 0448123   MH-L CtY ICRL

   Loewenthal, Ernst, 1902-
     Der Gerichtseid. 2. Aufl. Frankfurt a. M., 1930.
    1v, 100 p. 21 cm.

    First ed. pub. as diss., Freiburg.
    "Literaturverzeichnis": p. 93-98.

    1. Oaths–Germany.   I. Title.

                                 49-35478*

NL 0448124   DLC

G103   Löwenthal, Ernst G., ed.
.P45
    Philo-atlas; handbuch für die jüdische auswanderung. Mit
20 mehrfarbigen karten, über 25 tabellen und übersichten,
über 600 stichworten auf 280 textspalten. Berlin, Philo
gmbh., jüdischer buchverlag, 1938.

   Loewenthal, E[rnst] J.
     Die Bedeutung des Deutsch-Französischen
Krieges. Vortrag vor dem Deutschen Club in
Hoboken und in der Turnhalle zu Newark.
New York, Verlag von L.W. Schmidt, 1871.
    15 p. 8°.

NL 0448126   NN MB

3A
2563   LOEWENTHAL, Ernst J
     Robert Blum. Trauerspiel in drei Akten
von Dr. E. J. Loewenthal. New York: In Commission bei G.E.Stechert₍c1886₎
    60p. 20cm.

NL 0448127   ICN MH NN

   Loewenthal, Felix, 1899-
     Der abfindungsvertrag nach §§ 1580 und 1714
B. G.B. und due geldentwertung. (Auszug)
    Inaug. diss. Kiel, 1923

NL 0448128   ICRL

   Löwenthal, Felix Adam, reichsfreiherr von.
     Geschichte des baierisch-landshutischen erbfolge-krieges, nach
dem tode herzog Georg des Reichen zu Baiern Landshut, und Beweis der widerrechtlichen veräusserung der von der reichs-stadt
Nürnberg damals okkupirten pfalz-baierischen stamm- fideikommiss- und lehensherrschaften, und andern güter. München, 1792.
    2 pt. sm. 4°.
    Title of pt. 2: "Beweis," etc.

    Bavaria–Landshut₎

NL 0448129   MH

DD   Löwenthal, Felix **Adam, Reichsfreiherr von**
901
A51L95   Geschichte von dem Ursprung der Stadt Amberg, von dem
Wachsthum derselben unter ihren Beherrschern, den Margrafen
auf dem Nordgaue, dann den Herzogen aus dem Hohenstaufischen
Hause, und endlich der Ausbildung durch die Privilegien,
durch die Gewohnheiten und bürgerliche Verfassung unter den
Herzogen in Baiern, und Pfalzgrafen bey Rhein. In drey Theilen
und dem Urkundenbuche. München, F. G. Hübschmann, 1801.
    xvi, 496, 171 p.

    Urkundenbuch zur Geschichte von dem Ursprung der Stadt
Amberg, 171 p. at end.

    1. Amberg, Ger.   (Palatinate, Upper) - Hist.

NL 0448130   CLU MH

W4   Löwenthal, Francisco
G91   Contribución al estudio de la blenorragia en
1896 general y en particular de la metritis
blenorrágica. Guatemala, Sánchez y de
Guise ₍1896?₎
    30 p.

    Tesis - Guatemala.

NL 0448131   DNLM

   Loewenthal, Friedrich, 1890-
     Hat der in bestehendes Mietverhältnis eintretende Beamte im Falle der
Versetzung das gesetzliche Kündigungsrecht des § 570 BGB.? ... von Friedrich
Loewenthal. Berlin, W. & S. Loewenthal,
1913.
    xii, 144 p., 1 l. 22cm.

    Inaug.-Diss. - Heidelberg.
    "Lebenslauf": leaf at end.
    "Literatur": p.   ₍v₎-x.

NL 0448132   MH-L MH ICRL

   Loewenthal, Fritz, 1886-
     Bibliographisches handbuch zur deutschen philologie, von
Fritz Loewenthal. Halle a. S., M. Niemeyer, 1932.
    xii, 217 p. 23½ᶜᵐ.

    Classified, with index.

    1. Germanic philology–Bibl. 2. German philology–Bibl.   I. Title.
    NNC
    Library of Congress   Z7036.L82   33-11488
                      ₍2₎   016.439

   OClW MB MiHM PSC NNC NcD PSt CoU CSt NIC CU IdPI TxU
NL 0448133   DLC OrU OrCS CtY PPT PU OCU OU MiU ViU

   Loewenthal, Fritz, 1886-
H15.96k Studien zum germanischen Rätsel ... Heidelberg,C.Winter,1914.
    2p.l.,51p.,1l. 22cm.
    Inaug.-Diss. - Königsberg i.Pr.
    Lebenslauf.
    "Die ganze Arbeit, von der hier ... nur die
beiden ersten Kapitel gedruckt sind, wird in den
'Germanistischen Arbeiten' ... in Heidelberg bei
Carl Winter erscheinen".
    "Literatur": verso of 2d p.l.

    1.Riddles,   Germanic.

NL 0448134   CtY RPB IU MH DLC

   Loewenthal, Fritz, 1886-
     Studien zum germanischen Rätsel. Heidelberg, C. Winter, 1914.
    150p. (Germanistische Arbeiten, 1)

    Includes bibliographies.
    Partial contents.–Die Heidreksgátur.–Die Rätsel des Exterbuches.–Das Rätsel bei den mhd. Spruchdichtern von Reinmar v.
Zweter bis Frauenlob, mit Berücksichtigung der Meisterlieder
der Kolm. Hs.

    1. Riddles, Germanic–Hist & crit. 2. Riddles, Anglo-
Saxon–Hist. & crit. 3. German literature–Middle High German–
Hist. & crit. I. Title. II. Series.

   CaBVaU OU NjP NN PSt PU InU TxU CaOTM
NL 0448135   ICarbS ICU NcU MoU CtY NRU TU NBC MH

VOLUME 338

HX276 Löwenthal, Fritz, 1888–
L7   Der neue Geist von Potsdam.   Hamburg,
     Auerdruck, 1948.
     286 p.

     1. Communism - Germany - 1945-
     2. Germany - Hist. - 1945-   (Allied occu-
     pation) 3. Sozialistische Einheitspartei
     Deutschlands. 4. Russia (1923-   U.S.S.R.)
     Narodnyĭ komissariatvnutrennikh del.
     I. Title.

NL 0448136   CU N IU CSt-H MH NjP IEN WU CaBVaU

Löwenthal, Fritz, 1888–
     News from Soviet Germany. Translated by Edward Fitz-
     gerald. London, Gollancz, 1950.
     343 p. 23 cm.

     1. Germany—Hist.—Allied occupation, 1945-   I. Title.
     DD257.L6   943.086   50–2994

NL 0448137   DLC CaBVaU KU CaOTP LU CtY NcU

Löwenthal, Fritz, 1888–
     Den nya andan i Potsdam. ⟨Till svenska av Magnus
     Eriksson⟩ Stockholm, Fahlcrantz & Gumælius ⟨1949⟩
     226 p. 23 cm.

     1. Germany—Hist.—Allied occupation, 1945-   I. Title.
     DD257.L58   50–26456

NL 0448138   DLC

HX276 Löwenthal, Fritz, 1888–
L826   Studien zur Kritik des Marxismus. ⟨Hamburg,
      Auerdruck, 1948?⟩
      41 p. 21ᶜᵐ. (Auer-Schriftenreihe)
      Bibliographical foot-notes.

      1.Communism. 2.   Communism - Anti-com-
      munist litera   ture. I.Title.

NL 0448139   CSt-H

Loewenthal, Fritz ,1889–
     Ein angiofibrom der milz.
     Inaug. diss. Bonn,1912
     Bibl.

NL 0448140   ICRL DNLM CtY MBCo

Loewenthal, Fritz, 1889–
     Der preussische Verfassungsstreit, 1862–1866. Von Dr. Fritz
     Löwenthaı.   München: Duncker & Humblot, 1914.   xi, 342 p.
     8°.

     "Verzeichnis der Quellen," p. ⟨v⟩-xi.
     Bibliographical foot-notes.

     1. Prussia.—History, 1862–66. 2.   Constitutions, Germany: Prussia.—
     History, 1862–66. 3. Title.
     N. Y. P. L.   August 13, 1915.

NL 0448141   NN NNC MH IEN NcD MnU

Loewenthal, Georg: Ein Fall von Koehlerscher Navicularerkrankung.
     [Maschinenschrift.] 17 S. 4°. — Auszug: Breslau 1923: Bresl.
     Genoss.-Buchdr. 2 Bl. 8°.
     Breslau, Med. Diss. v. 10. Dez. 1923 [1924]   [U 24. 1692]

NL 0448142   ICRL

1898-
Loewenthal, Georg, ⟨Kammergerichtsref.: Frauenraub und
     Entführung im Reichs-Straf-Gesetzbuch unter Berücks. d.
     geschichtl. Entwicklung u. d. Entwürfe zu einem neuen
     deutschen Straf-Gesetzbuch. Eine vergleich. Darst. [In
     Maschinenschrift.] 135 S. 4°(2°). — Auszug: Borna-Leipzig
     1920: Noske. 6 S. 8°
     Breslau, R.- u. staatswiss. Diss. v. 10. Febr. 1921, Ref. Heilborn
     [Geb. 22. April 98 Brandenburg a. H.; Wohnort: Brandenburg; Staatsangeh.:
     Preußen; Vorbildung: G. Brandenburg Reife 16; Studium: Berlin 10 S.; Rig.
     22. Juli 20.]   [U 21. 299

NL 0448143   ICRL

Loewenthal, Gerhard, 1904–
     Handeln unter falschem namen.
     Inaug. diss. Goettingen [1927]
     Bibl.

NL 0448144   DLC MiU

Loewenthal, Gustavus C.
     Practical instructions in the art of drawing and en-
     graving on wood ... For schools, students, artisans and
     persons wishing to learn the art without an instructor ...
     By G. C. Loewenthal. With illustrations by the author.
     Philadelphia, G. C. Loewenthal & co., 1878.
     19 p. illus. 21ᶜᵐ.

     1. Wood-engraving—Technique.
                            12–6428
     Library of Congress   NE1225.L8

NL 0448145   DLC

Loewenthal, Hans.
     Illuminazione a fluorescenza e luminescenza. Prontuario
     di voci e notizie coi corrispondenti termini inglesi. 2. ed.,
     interamente rifatta. Torino, A. Viglongo, 1950.
     207 p. illus., plates, diagrs., tables. 20 cm.
     Bibliography : p. ⟨4⟩

     1. Fluorescent lighting. 2. Electric discharge lighting.   I. Title.
                            A 51–5821
     Rochester. Univ. Libr.   TK4386.L6 1950
     for Library of Congress   ⟨2⟩

NL 0448146   NRU

---

91   Loewenthal, Hans.
L82   Nossa horta.   [São Paulo, 1947]
      163 p.   (Biblioteca agronômica
     melhoramentos, no. 6)

      1. Vegetable gardening. Brazil.
     I. Biblioteca agronômica melhoramentos.
     no. 6.

NL 0448147   DNAL

Löwenthal, Hans W   , 1887–
     Die rechtliche Struktur des Pfandrechts
     an Forderungen nach dem Rechte des Bürger-
     lichen Gesetzbuches ... von Hans W. Löwen-
     thal ... Berlin ⟨H. Blanke⟩ 1910.
     64, ⟨2⟩ p. 21cm.

     Inaug.-Diss. - Heidelberg.
     "Lebenslauf": p.⟨65⟩
     "Literaturübersicht": p.⟨7⟩-⟨8⟩

NL 0448148   MH-L ICRL

LÖWENTHAL, HEINRICH.
     Der goldene Galgen; Berichte über Kriminalfälle
     aus dem alten Berlin.   [Berlin] Das Neue Berlin
     [1951]   136, [4] p.   19cm.   (Berlinische Miniaturen. 9)
     Continued by his: Der verschwundene Lord.
     Bibliography, p. [138-140]

     1. Criminology--Germany--Berlin.

NL 0448149   NN

LÖWENTHAL, HEINRICH.
     Köpfe und Käuze; Berliner Kulturbilder.   [Berlin]
     Das Neue Berlin [1951]   96, [20] p. 19cm.   (Berlinische
     Miniaturen. 10)

     Bibliography, p. [113-116]

     1. Berlin--Intellectual life.

NL 0448150   NN CSt MH

LÖWENTHAL, HEINRICH.
     Der verschwundene Lord; Berichte über Kriminalfälle
     aus dem alten Berlin.   [Berlin] Das Neue Leben
     [1952]   101, [3] p.   19cm.   (Berlinische Miniaturen. 14)

     Continues his: Der goldene Galgen.
     Bibliography, p. [103 - 104]

     1. Criminology--Germany--Berlin.

NL 0448151   NN

Löwenthal, Heinrich, of Bern.
     Das bäuerliche erbrecht nach schweizer. Z.G.B.
     und das deutsche reichserbhofrecht. ... Berlin,
     1936.   72 p.
     Inaug. Diss. - Bern, 1936.
     Literaturverzeichnis.

NL 0448152   ICRL

Löwenthal (Heinrich) [1861-   ]. *Ueber
     den Verlauf der vom 1. Januar 1885 bis zum 30.
     Juni 1886 in der königl. Charité beobachteten
     Geburten bei engem Becken. 27 pp., 2 l. 8°.
     Berlin, G. Schade. 1886.

NL 0448153   DNLM

Loewenthal, Helen Rovene.
     What's in a name ? a comedy in three acts,
     by Helen Rovene Loewenthal and Alberta S.
     De Flon.   Minneapolis, Minn., The Northwestern
     press, c1951.
     84 p.   19 cm.
     I. De Flon, Alberta S., jt. au. II. Title.

NL 0448154   RPB NN

LÖWENTHAL, Hermann,1903–
     Zur kenntnis des zeemaneffekts und der
     hyperfeinstruktur im antimonbogenspektrum.
     Inaug.-diss. [Tübingen],1930.

     pp.(17).
     "Lebenslauf",at end.
     pp.[821]-834 of a larger work.
                            Sci.Files.

NL 0448155   MH CtY OU ICRL

Loewenthal (Hermannus) [1836-   ]. *De ar-
     teriarum aneurysmatibus. 31 pp. 8°. Berolini,
     G. Schade. 1860.

NL 0448156   DNLM

VOLUME 338

Loewenthal (Heymannus)[1811-]. *De inflammationum externarum topica curatione. 32 pp. 8°. Berolini, typ. Nietackianis, [1836].*

NL 0448157　　DNLM

Löwenthal (Hugo). Ein Fall von acut entstandener Hemiparese mit hemiathetotischen Bewegungen. 6 pp. 8°. Berlin, J. Sittenfeld, [1889].
Repr. from: Deutsche med. Wchnschr., Leipz. u. Berl., 1889, xv.

NL 0448158　　DNLM

Löwenthal (Hugo). *Ueber die Verwendung der in Jean Wickersheimer'scher Conservirungsflüssigkeit aufbewahrten Präparate zu mikroskopischen Untersuchungen. 30 pp., 1 l. sm. 8°. Berlin, G. Schade, [1880].*

NL 0448159　　DNLM

Loewenthal, Ida, 1903-
... Ein Fall von Endotheliom der Dura mater mit infiltrierendem Wachstum ... München, 1928.
Inaug.-Diss. - München.
Lebenslauf.
"Literatur": p. 28.

NL 0448160　　CtY PPWl DNLM

Löwenthal, Isidor, 1829-1864, tr.
[The New Testament]
　　see under　Bible. N.T. Afghan.1863.

[Loewenthal, Isidor] 1829-1864.
Revolt of the Sepoys. Reprinted from the Princeton review, January, 1858. With additional notes. New York, Printed by E. O. Jenkins, 1858.
31 p. 21ᶜᵐ.

1. India—Hist.—Sepoy rebellion, 1857-1858.　I. Title.
　‡
　　　　　　　　　　　　　　　　　　5—1764
Library of Congress　　DS478.3.L82

NL 0448162　　DLC RPB

Loewenthal, J
Compendium of church History... Madras, 1867.

NL 0448163　　NjNbS

Löwenthal, J.
Ueber die charakteristischen Unterschiede zwischen dem männlichen und weiblichen Geschlechte... Würzburg, Becker, 1841.
16 p.
Inaugural dissertation.

NL 0448164　　PPC DNLM

Löwenthal (Leiwinthal), Jacob. *1884-* Aus d. Frauen-Klinik d. Charité zu Berlin. Geburtsstörungen bei antefixiertem Uteri, speziell bei Interpositio Uteri. Berlin: Ebering (1912). 26 S. 8° ¶(Im Buchh. ebd.)
Berlin, Med. Diss. v. 15. April 1912, Ref. Franz
[Geb. 9. Juli 84 Sekurjany; Wohnort: Berlin; Staatsangeh.: Rußland; Vorbildung: Gymn. Kamenetz-Podolsk Reife M. 04; Studium: Wien 8, Berlin 2 S.; Rig. 15. April 12.]　　　　　　　　[U 12. 121

NL 0448165　　ICRL CtY DNLM

Loewenthal, Jacques.
Über das klima von Rostock unter berücksichtigung der harmonischn analysis ... Schwerin, Druck der Bärensprungschen hofbuchdr., 1906.
3 p. l., 48, [4] p., 1 l. diagrs. 31½ᶜᵐ.
Inaug.-diss.—Rostock.

1. Rostock—Climate.
　　　　　　　　　　　　　　　　　　9–20627
Library of Congress　　QC989.G3R8

NL 0448166　　DLC DAS CtY ICRL

DB 321　Löwenthal, Jakob, 1807-1882.
.L 8　　Geschichte der Stadt Triest.
　　Triest, Österr. Lloyd, 1857-59.
　　2 v.　illus.

　　Contents: 1.T. Triest von der ältesten Zeit bis zum Jahre 1780. 2.T. Von der Regierung des Kaisers Joseph II. bis zum Jahre 1820.

　　1. Trieste--Hist.

NL 0448167　　InU

Löwenthal, Jakob, 1807-1882.
　　　　　Die halbinsel Istrien.　21 pp.
　(*Unsere Zeit*, 1877, v. 2, p. 321.)

NL 0448168　　MdBP

Löwenthal, Jakob, 1807-1882.
Oesterreich's schiffahrt als nachtrag zu E.v.Schwarzer's Land- und seehandel Österreich's u.s.w. ... Triest, J.Papsch [etc.] 1847.
1 p.l., 42 p.incl.tables. fold.tab. 22 cm.

"Aus dem Journal des Österreichischen Lloyd."

NL 0448169　　MH-BA

Loewenthal, Joel Wulf John, 1885–
Die religion der Ostalgonkin ... Berlin, Druck von W. & S. Loewenthal, 1913.
219, [1] p., 1 l. illus. (map) 22ᶜᵐ.
Inaug.-diss.—Leipzig.
"Quellen": p. [7]-13.

1. Algonquian Indians—Religion and mythology.　I. Title.
　　　　　　　　　　　　　　　　　　16–9913
Library of Congress　　E99.A35L8

NL 0448170　　DLC OHi CaBVaU CtY NcD MH

GV1455　Löwenthal, Johann Jacob, 1810-1876, *ed.*
.L8　　The chess congress of 1862. A collection of the games played, and a selection of the problems sent in for competition. Ed. by J. Löwenthal ... To which is prefixed an account of the proceedings and a memoir of the British chess association. By G. W. Medley ... London, H. G. Bohn, 1864.
xcvi, 536 p. front., illus. 18½ᶜᵐ.

1. Chess.

NL 0448171　　ICU MH MiD OCl CtY NN MeWC PU OCU

Löwenthal, Johann Jacob, 1810-1876, *ed.*
　　The Chess Congress of 1862. A collection of the games played, and a selection of the problems sent in for competition. Ed. by J. Löwenthal... To which is prefixed an account of the proceedings and a memoir of the British Chess Association. By G. W. Medley ... London, 1887.
　　536 p. (Bohn's Scientific Lib.)

NL 0448172　　PPL

4GV　Löwenthal, Johann Jacob, 1810-1876.
1335　　The Chess Congress of 1862; a collection of the games played, and a selection of the problems sent in for competition, to which is prefixed an account of the proceedings and a memoir of the British Chess Association by G. W. Medley. London, G. Bell, 1889.
　　xcvi, 536 p.

NL 0448173　　DLC-P4 NNU-W ICN NN

Löwenthal, Johann Jacob, 1810-1876, *ed.*
The Chess player's magazine
　　see under title

Löwenthal, Johann Jacob, 1810–1876, editor.
　　Das Londoner Schachturnier von 1862. Eine Sammlung der bei dieser Gelegenheit gespielten Partien von Anderssen, Paulsen, Steinitz, Owen, Barness, Dubois u. a. nebst den gekrönten Preis-Aufgaben der Turniere von London, Bristol, Birmingham und Manchester. Nach der englischen Ausgabe von J. Löwenthal... Berlin: S. Mode, 1864. iv, 130 p. incl. tables. illus. 18cm.

634167A. 1. Chess—Tournaments,　　　1862-
N. Y. P. L.　　　　　　　　　　　　　September 11, 1933

NL 0448175　　NN CU MH NjP OCl

Löwenthal, Johann Jacob, 1810-1876.
　　　　　　　　　FOR OTHER EDITIONS
　　　　　　　　　SEE MAIN ENTRY
Morphy, Paul Charles, 1837–1884.
　　Morphy's games of chess; being a selection of three hundred of his games, with annotations and a biographical introduction, by Philip W. Sergeant. Philadelphia, David McKay company, 1939.

Löwenthal, Johann Jacob, 1810-1876, *ed.*
Schach-Problem-Turnierbuch; eine Auswahl von 64 der besten für das von der Londoner Zeitschrift "The Era" ausgeschriebene Problemturnier eingesandten Aufgaben, deren Lösungen und den Urtheilen der Preisrichter. Mit einem Vorworte von J. Löwenthal. Leipzig: J. J. Weber, 1857. 127 p. front., illus. 18cm.

　　　　　　　　　　FRANK J. MARSHALL CHESS COLL.
775255A. 1. Chess—Problems, 1857.　　　I. The Era. II. Title.
N. Y. P. L.　　　　　　　　　　　　　December 13, 1935

NL 0448177　　NN MH NjP OCl

VOLUME 338

Löwenthal, Johann Jacob, 1810–1876.
A selection from the problems of the Era
Problem Tournament
see under   The Era (London)

LÖWENTHAL, Johann Nepomuk, reichsfreyherr von.
Geschichte des schultheissenamts und der
stadt Neumarkt. Unter dem vorsitze des Herrn
Nikolaus Thadäus Gönner zur öffentlich
akademischen prüfung vorgelegt. München,
Zängl,1805.

   4°. pp.(10),244. Port.of Ludwig Karl
August churprinz von Pfalz Baiern,plates and
other illus.
   Nikolaus Thadäus   von Gönner,praeses.

NL 0448179   MH

Loewenthal, John, 1885–
      see   Loewenthal, Joel Wulf John, 1885–

Löwenthal, Josef, *freiherr von,* 1873–
   ... Die unsterbliche stadt; eine utopische erzählung aus dem
jahre 2000. Berlin ₍etc.₎ P. Zsolnay, 1936.
   266, ₍1₎ p. 19½ᶜᵐ.

   1. Utopias.   i. Title.
         ₍Full name: Josef Arthur Maximilian freiherr von Löwenthal₎
                                                         37–4004
   Library of Congress   HX811.1936.L6
   Copyright A—Foreign   34576
                            ₍2₎   [321.07] 833.91

NL 0448181   DLC

QD341   Loewenthal, Joseph.
.H9L8   Ueber schwefelhaltige derivate des toluols.
         Berlin, 1869.
            27p.
            Inaug. diss. Freyburg.

NL 0448182   DLC

Loewenthal (Julius) [1854–]. *Ueber
das Auftreten von Diabetes mellitus bei Thieren nach Unterbindung des Ductus choledochus.
31 pp. 8°. *Königsberg, A. Kieuning, 1890.*

NL 0448183   DNLM

Loewenthal (Julius) [1860–]. *Ein Falle
von Impftuberculose der Conjunctiva des Menschen mit Befund von Tuberkelbacillen. 21 pp.,
31. 8°. *Halle a. S., S. Schlesinger, 1887.*

NL 0448184   DNLM

Löwenthal, Julius, 1864–
   Ueber die physiologischen und toxicologischen
eigenschaften der lupinen-alkaloide ...
Königsberg i. Pr., Hartung [1888]
   26, [2] p. 24 cm. [Königsberg. Universität.
Dissertationen. v. 4, no. 13]
      Inaug.-Diss. - Königsberg.
      Vita.

NL 0448185   CU

Löwenthal, Karl, 1892–
   Thymus, von Karl Löwenthal ... (Mit 12 farbigen Abbildungen im Text)

   (*In* Handbuch der inneren Sekretion. Leipzig, 1932. 27½ᶜᵐ. Bd. I,
p. 709–866 incl. col. illus., tables)
   "Literatur": p. 850–866.

NL 0448186   ICJ

1892–
Löwenthal, Karl ₍Feldunterarzt: Zur Physiologie des Cholesterin-
stoffwechsels: Beziehungen zwischen Hoden und Cholesterin-
stoffwechsel. Freiburg i.B. 1915: (Lippert, Naumburg a. d. S.).
8 S. 8° ¶ Aus: Beiträge z. pathol. Anat. Bd 61.
Freiburg i. B., Med. Diss. v. 20. März 1916, Ref. Aschoff
   [Geb. 18. Juli 92 Berlin; Wohnort: Berlin; Staatsangeh.: Preußen; Vorbildung:
Wilhelms-G. Berlin Reife 10; Studium: Berlin 2, Freiburg 1, Berlin 3, Freiburg 1, Berlin 1, Freiburg 1, Berlin 1 S.; Coll. 30. Juli 15; Approb. 1. Aug. 15.]
                                                      [U 16. 875

NL 0448187   ICRL DNLM CtY MiDW-M

Loewenthal, Kurt: Ueber Anzeigepflicht bei Geschlechtskrankheiten.
[Maschinenschrift.] 34 S. 4°. — Auszug: Berlin (1922): Ebering.
2 Bl. 8°
Berlin, Med. Diss. v. 10. Mai 1922   [U 22. 202

NL 0448188   ICRL

Löwenthal (Leo). *Beiträge zur Kenntniss
der physiologischen Wirkungen der Convallaria
majalis.* 32 pp. 8° *Würzburg, Thein,* 1885.

NL 0448189   DNLM ICRL

Loewenthal, Leo, *novelist*
   Achtundvierzig! Tragische Erlebnisse
einer kleinen Stadt. Berlin: M.
Poppelauer, 1910.
   278 p.

NL 0448190   OCH DLC-P4

LÖWENTHAL, Leo, *novelist.*
   Am Freitag Abend. Humoresken aus dem
Jüdischen Familienleben. Printed by Paul
Dünnhaupt, Cothen, 1889. 179p 14.5cm
   1,Belles Lettres-German. 2.Title.
   3.Humoristic Literature.

NL 0448191   NNJ

Loewenthal, Leo, novelist.
   Samuel Reisefertige Memoiren. [A story.]
Berlin, S. Gronbach, 1899.
   173 p.

NL 0448192   OCH

Loewenthal, Leo, *novelist.*
   Wanderstein's Tochter. Roman in zwei
Büchern. Berlin, Cassirer & Danziger,
[1893]
   264 p. 12°.

NL 0448193   NN

Löwenthal, Leo, social scientist
   see Lowenthal, Leo.

Loewenthal, Leonard Joseph Alphonse, *ed.*
   The eczemas; a symposium by ten authors. Edinburgh,
E. & S. Livingstone; ₍Baltimore, Williams & Wilkins₎ 1954.
   vii, 287 p. illus. (part col.) 26 cm.
   Includes bibliographies.

   [RL251]   616.52   54–10353
   Printed for U. S. Q. B. R.
   by Library of Congress   ₍10₎

   DNLM IdPI OrU-M
NL 0448195   OC1W-H OU ICJ ICU NNC PPT-M PPC NcD

Loewenthal, Leopold.
   Frieden auf erden! Von Leopold Loewenthal. Berlin, G. A. Schröder & co., 1923.
   56 p. 20ᶜᵐ.

   1. European war, 1914–1918—Causes.   i. Title.
                                         24–11753
   Library of Congress   D525.L65

NL 0448196   DLC

LOEWENTHAL, Leopold.
   Gotteskindschaft; eine religions-philoso-
phische abhandlung. Von Leopold Loewenthal.
Berlin,G.A.Schröder & Co.,1924.

NL 0448197   MH-AH PPDrop

Loewenthal, Leopold, *writer on glass pictures.*
   Georgian glass pictures and needlework pictures, by L.
Loewenthal. ₍Rushden, Eng., Printed for the Mitre press by
S. L. Hunt, The Printeries, 1934₎
   cover-title, 46, ₍2₎ p. illus. (incl. ports.) 21½ᶜᵐ.

   "The greater portions of this booklet appeared either in 'Apollo' or
in 'The Antique collector.' Other writings of mine upon old English
pictures on glass, being out of print, are incorporated."—Foreword.

   1. Glass painting and staining—England. 2. Embroidery—England.
i. Title. ii. Title: Glass pictures. iii. Title: Needlework pictures.

   Library of Congress   NK5343.L6
                                           37–3320
                            ₍3₎   748

NL 0448198   DLC NN OC1

Löwenthal, Leopold, *writer on glass pictures.*
   Pictures on glass. A monograph, by L. Lowenthal. ₍Lon-
don, 1928.₎ 8 p. illus. (ports.) 12°.
   Cover-title.

   426207A. 1. Painting, Glass.
   N.Y.P.L.   August 26, 1925

NL 0448199   NN

q709.43   Loewenthal, Ludwig.
L825s   Sammlung Ludwig Loewenthal, Berlin: Gemälde,
Art   Skulpturen, Porzellan, Kunstgewerbe ... Ber-
Lib'y   lin, Rudolf Lepke's Kunst-Auctions-Haus, 1931.
            40,[1]p. 38 plates. 30cm.

   1. Art - Catalogs. I. Lepke, Rudolph, firm,
Berlin. II. Title.

NL 0448200   TxU

VOLUME 338

1887-
Löwenthal, Martin, Referendar, Beeskow: Auf welchen Zeitpunkt wirkt die mit zulässiger Einspruchserhebung verknüpfte Restitution zurück? Borna-Leipzig 1910: Noske. VIII, 44 S. 8°
Leipzig, Jur. Diss. v. 28. Nov. 1910
[Geb. 25. Nov. 87 Berlin; Wohnort: Berlin; Staatsangeh.: Preußen; Vorbildung: Gymn. Gr.-Lichterfelde Reife O. 06; Studium: Genf 1, München 2, Berlin 3, Leipzig 1, Berlin 1 S.; Rig. 22. Okt. 10.] [U 11. 2888]

NL 0448201 ICRL

Löwenthal, Martin Leupold von
    see Leupold von Löwenthal, Martin, d. 1624.

3781
S78 **Loewenthal, Martin Moshe.**
L826   Vermilion Dam hydraulic model study of outlet
works stilling basin. [Stanford, Calif.] 1954.
a-b, 49 l. illus.(part fold.) fold.map.
Thesis (Engineer) - Dept. of Civil Engineering, Stanford University.
Bibliography: l. 49.

    1. Hydraulic models. 2. Spillways.

                        Brief

NL 0448203 CSt

Loewenthal, Max.
    Untersuchungen ueber den Nikotingehalt des Tabakrauches. Würzburg, P. Scheiner, 1892.
39 p.
Inaug.-Diss. - Würzburg, 1892.

NL 0448204 ICRL

Loewenthal, Max.
    ... Zur kenntnis experimentell erzeugbarer ödeme ... Breslau, Druck der Breslauer genossenschafts-buchdruckerei, 1909.
37, [1] p., 1 l. pl. 22ᶜᵐ.
Inaug.-diss.—Bern.
"Literatur": p. [38]

    1. Kidneys. Diseases. 2. Edema.

                        Agr 10-1323

    Library, U. S. Dept. of   Agriculture 41L952

NL 0448205 DNAL PU

1894 -
Löwenthal, Max. Ueber die Wirkungen der inneren Sekrete der Schilddrüse und der Keimdrüsen auf den Blutdruck. [In Maschinenschrift.] 38 S. 4°(2°). — Auszug: Berlin [1921]: Ebering. 2 Bl. 8°
Berlin, Med. Diss. v. 8. März 1921, Ref. Goldscheider
[Geb. 29. Jan. 94 Lauenburg, Pomm.; Wohnort: Berlin-Schöneberg; Staatsangeh.: Preußen; Vorbildung: Helmholtz-RG. Schöneberg Reife 13; Studium: Berlin 2, Heidelberg 1, Berlin 7 S.; Coll. 4. März 21; Approb. 13. Aug. 20.] [U 21. 2444]

NL 0448206 ICRL

PT2393
.Z3 **Löwenthal, Max, freiherr von, 1799-1872.**
1906 **Lenau, Nicolaus, 1802-1850.**
    Lenau und die familie Löwenthal; briefe und gespräche, gedichte und entwürfe. Mit bewilligung des †freiherrn Arthur von Löwenthal vollständiger abdruck nach den handschriften. Ausgabe, einleitung und anmerkungen von prof. dr. Eduard Castle. Mit zehn bildnissen und fünf schriftproben ... Leipzig, M. Hesse, 1906.

Löwenthal (Max) [1865-]. *Beiträge zur Diagnostik und Therapie der Magenkrankheiten. 29 pp., 1 l. 8°. *Berlin, L. Schuhmacher, 1892.

NL 0448208 DNLM ICRL

4UA-29 **Loewenthal, Max J.**
    Das jüdische Bekenntnis als Hinderungsgrund bei der Beförderung zum preuszischen Reserveoffizier. Im Auftrage des Verbandes der Deutschen Juden. Berlin, H.S. Hermann, 1911.
134 p.

NL 0448209 DLC-P4

UB415 **Loewenthal, Max J** ed.
G3L42   Jüdische Reserveoffiziere. Im Auftrage
des Verbandes der Deutschen Juden von seinem Generalsekretär. Berlin, 1914.
    152 p. 23cm.
    Excerpts from der Verhandlungen of the Reichstag, 1911-1913.

    1. Germany - Army - Officers. 2. Jews in Germany. 3. Jews as soldiers. I. Germany. Reichst ag. Verhandlungen. II. Verband der Deutschen Juden. III. Title. 11

NL 0448210 CSt-H OCH MH

Loewenthal, Max J.
    Das untersuchungsrecht des internationalen seerechts in krieg und frieden. Von Dr. Max J. Loewenthal. Berlin, E. Ebering, 1905.
185, [1] p., 1 l. 23½ᶜᵐ. (Added t.-p.: Rechts- und staatswissenschaftliche studien, veröffentlicht von Dr. E. Ebering. hft. xxviii)
"Literatur": p. [183]-185.

                        5-37766

NL 0448211 DLC ICJ NN

Loewenthal, Max Sally.
    Life and soul; outlines of a future theoretical physiology and of a critical philosophy, by Max Loewenthal ... With a foreword by Professor J. S. Macdonald ... London, G. Allen & Unwin ltd. [1934]
291, [1] p. illus., plates, diagrs. 22ᶜᵐ.
"References": p. 287-288.

    1. Life (Biology) 2. Soul. I. Title.
                        [Full name: Max Sally Loewenthal]
                                36-3807
    Library of Congress   QH331.L6
                        [5]   577.2

NL 0448212 DLC KEmT NN OClW

Löwenthal, Maximilian.
    Die Caledonier; ein Trauerspiel. Wien, J. B. Wallishausser, 1826.
94 p. 17 cm.
    Bound with Holbein, Franz von. Dilettanten-Bühne für 1826.

NL 0448213 CLSU

Loewenthal, Maximilian von
    see Lowenthal, Maximiliano de.

Loewenthal, Meinhardt.
    Untersuchung zur Frage der C-Hypervitaminose. Basel, 1941.
12 p. diagrs. 23 cm.
Inaug.-Diss.—Basel.
At head of title: Aus der Medizinischen Universitätsklinik Basel. "Sonderabdruck aus der Schweizerischen Medizinischen Wochenschrift, 71. Jahrgang 1941, Nr. 25, Seite 761."

    1. Hypervitaminosis.

    RC632.II9L6   56-55358

NL 0448215 DLC CtY

Loewenthal, Michaela (Skariton)
שנויים במטבוליזם חידקי המעים הנגרמים עקב התפתחותם
בנוכחות המרים כביים בעלי השפעה סלקטיבית. ירושלים, תשי״ב.
[Jerusalem, 1952]
19, [2] l.; 3 l. 33 cm.
Added t. p.: Metabolic changes in intestinal bacteria due to their growth in the presence of chemical compounds having selective properties.
Thesis—Hebrew University, Jerusalem.
Summary in English.
Bibliography: leaves [20]-[21]
    1. Intestines—Bacteriology.
                Title transliterated: Shinuyim be-metabolism haidke ha-me'ayim.

    QR171.L6   56-51893

NL 0448216 DLC

Loewenthal, Moritz.
    Das Ewig-Bestehende im Judenthum. Predigt, gehalten in der Synagoge zu Stockholm am zweiten Tage des Hüttenfestes 5608...
Stockholm: A. Bonnier, 1847.
28 p., 1 L. 8

NL 0448217 OCH

BM
744 **Löwenthal, Moritz.**
L6.49   Rede gehalten am 15. März, bei der gottesdienstlichen Feierlichkeit zur Begrüssung der von Sr. Majestät verliehenen Verfassung, im Tempel der fortschreitenden Israeliten zu Lemberg. Lemberg, J. Schnayder, 1849.
16 p. 20 cm.

    1. Sermons, Jewish--Germany.
    2. Patriotism--Addresses, essays, lectures.

NL 0448218 OCH

Löwenthal, Moriz, ed.
    Ansprachen und Weihrede gehalten bei der Einweihung der Zeremonienhalle und Gedenktafel für David Kaufmann, auf dem israelitischen Friedhofe in Kojetein am 9. November 1902. Pressburg, Druck von A. Alkalay, 1903

NL 0448219 MH OCH

Loewenthal, Moses: Gibt es eine histiogene Retention bei der Gicht? [Maschinenschrift.] 24 S. 4°. — Auszug: Berlin (1921): Ebering. 2 Bl. 8°
Berlin, Med. Diss. v. 29. Nov. 1921 [1922] [U 22. 80]

NL 0448220 ICRL

Loewi, Mrs. Mortimer W
    ...French eighteenth century furniture, oriental rugs...
        see under Fonda, Mrs. Frances (Seymour) Brokaw.

VOLUME 338

LOEWENTHAL, N.
Physiologie des freien willens. Glogau und Leipzig, H.Preusnitz, 1843.

NL 0448222   MH

QL
806
L82++
Loewenthal, Nathan.
Atlas zur vergleichenden Histologie der Wirbeltiere nebst erläuterndem Texte; auf Grund eigener Untersuchungen und Originalpräparate bearb. und gezeichnet. Berlin, S. Karger, 1904.
109 p. illus. 30cm.

1. Histology--Atlases.

NL 0448223   NIC NjP CU DNLM ICJ

Loewenthal, Nathan.
La débâcle de la révolution russe et la paix allemande, par N. Lœwenthal. Lausanne: F. Rouge & Cie., 1918. vi, (1)8–39(1) p. 8°.

1. Russia.—History : Revolution,   1917– . 2. European war, 1914– .
—Peace terms. 3. Title.
N. Y. P. L.   April 29, 1919.

NL 0448224   NN CSt-H

Loewenthal (Nathan). *Des dégénérations secondaires de la mœlle épineère, consécutives aux lésions expérimentales médullaires et corticales. 118 pp., 2 pl., 2 l. 8°. Genève, C. Schuchardt. 1885.

NL 0448225   DNLM

Loewenthal, Nathan.
... Nomenclature histologique, cytologique et embryologique (étendue a toute la série animale) bases d'une classification. (Contribution à l'étude de l'unification de la nomenclature histologique et histogénétique) ... [n. p., 1906?]
At head of title: XV congrès international de médecine. (Lisbonne – Avril 1906) Section I-anatomie. Thème I.

NL 0448226   CtY

QSA
L827q
1901
LOEWENTHAL, Nathan
Questions d'histologie; la cellule et les tissus au point de vue général. Bale, Georg, 1901.
210 p.

NL 0448227   DNLM ICJ ICRL

Loewenthal, Nils Erich, 1905–
Über den gutartigen spontanpneumothorax an hand von drei fällen. 1921.

Inaug.-Diss.- Universität zu Berlin.

NL 0448228   OU CtY

Löwenthal (Oscar). *Untersuchungen über die äussern Geschlechtsverschiedenheiten des gemeinen Schachtwurmes (Idothea entomon Lin.). 21 pp., 3 pl. 8°. St. Petersburg. 1868.

NL 0448229   DNLM

Loewenthal, Reise.
... Komplikation der schwangerschaft mit entzündlichen affektionen des beckenbindegewebes und des beckenbauchfelles ... Strasbourg [1926]

Basel
diss.
1926

NL 0448230   MiU CtY

TP897
.K68
1910
Loewenthal, Richard, joint author.
     FOR OTHER EDITIONS
     SEE MAIN ENTRY
Knecht, Edmund, 1861–1925.
A manual of dyeing: for the use of practical dyers, manufacturers, students, and all interested in the art of dyeing. By Edmund Knecht ... Christopher Rawson ... and Richard Loewenthal ... 2d ed. London, C. Griffin and company, limited, 1910.

1892
Löwenthal, Richard Arzt: Inwieweit wird die Helmholtzsche Hörtheorie durch neuere Anschauungen gestützt? Göttingen 1920: Hubert. 29 S. 8° ¶ Auch b. Vandenhoeck & Ruprecht, Göttingen.
Göttingen, Med. Diss. v. 20. Mai 1920, Ref. Lange
[Geb. 22. Febr. 92 Moringen; Wohnort: Göttingen; Staatsangeh.: Preußen; Vorbildung: G. Bochum Reife 11; Studium: Freiburg 1, Münster 1, Bonn 3, München 10, Göttingen 3 S.; Coll. 26. März 20; Approb. 22. Okt. 19.] [U 20. 2036

NL 0448232   ICRL DNLM CtY MiU

Loewenthal, Richard, 1908–
   see
Löwenthal, Richard, 1908–

Loewenthal, Robert Isber Wilhelm, 1886–
Die rechtliche Bedeutung der Tarifverträge im allgemeinen und der Verbandstarifverträge im besonderen ... von Robert Loewenthal. Berlin, W.& S. Loewenthal [1910]

3 p.l., 127, [1] p. 21½cm.

Inaug.-Diss. - Heidelberg.
"Lebenslauf": p. [128]
"Literaturverzeichnis": p. [122]-127.

NL 0448234   MH-L ICJ ICRL

Löwenthal, Rudolf, 1904 –
Bibliography of Russian literature on China and adjacent countries, 1931–1936. Cambridge, 1949.

iii, 98 l. 28 cm.

At head of title: Russian Research Center, Harvard University.

1. China—Bibl. 2. East—Bibl.

Z3106.L6   016.95   50–2271

CSt-H
NL 0448235   DLC NNC CaBVaU CU OU ViU NN MH NIC ICJ

PN5367
B9L82
Löwenthal, Rudolf, 1904–
The Buddhist periodical press in China, by Rudolf Löwenthal and William W. Y. Liang. Peking, 1938.
Cover title, 48–62 p. fold. map. 24cm.
Authors' names also in Chinese.
"The present survey was prepared by Mr. William W. Y. Liang ... as a thesis under the auspices of the Department of Journalism of Yenching University."
Reprinted from Digest of the Synodal Commission, vol. 11, no. 1, Jan. 1938.
1. Buddha and   Buddhism - China - Period.
2. Press - Chin   a. I. Liang, Yün-i.
II. Title.

NL 0448236   CSt-H

Loewenthal, Rudolf, 1904–
The early Jews in China : a supplementary bibliography. [Peking] Catholic University of Peking [1946]
353–396 p. 26 cm.
At head of title: Folklore studies, published by the Museum of Oriental Ethnology, the Catholic University of Peking. Reprint from vol. v, 1946.
"A supplement to [the author's] 'The Jews in China, an annotated bibliography.'"

1. Jews in China—Bibl.   I. Loewenthal, Rudolf, 1904–   The Jews in China. II. Title.

Z6373.C5L59   016.296   50–20325 rev

NL 0448237   DLC MH CU

LÖWENTHAL, Rudolf, 1904 –
The Extinction of the Krimchaks in World War II. Reprinted from American Slavic and East European Review, vol.10, 1951. April, p.130-136.

1.Antisemitism-Germany-Nazism. 2.East European Jewry. 3.Krimchaks.

NL 0448238   NNJ

PN5367
J4L82
Löwenthal, Rudolf, 1904–
The Jewish press in China. Tientsin, Nankai Institute of Economics [1937]
Cover title, 105–113 p. fold. table. 25cm.
Author's name also in Chinese.
"Reprinted from Nankai social & economic quarterly, vol. X, no. 1, April, 1937."

1. Jews in China - Period. 2. Press - China. 3. Jews - Period. I. Nankai University, Pa li-tai. Nankai   Institute of Economics. II. Title.

NL 0448239   CSt-H

Löwenthal, Rudolf, 1904 –
The Jewish press in China, by Rudolf Löwenthal ... Peking, The Synodal Commission in China, 1940.

cover-title, p. 251–265. fold. tab. 25½cm.

Author's name also in Chinese.
"Reprinted from The religious periodical press in China."

1. Jews in China—Period. 2. Press—China. 3. Jews—Period. I. Title.
Library of Congress   PN5367.J4L6   41–11571
——— Copy 2.   [2]   296.0951

NL 0448240   DLC

Löwenthal, Rudolf, 1904 –
The Jews in China, an annotated bibliography [by] Rudolf Löwenthal ... [Peking?] pref. 1940]

1 p. l., iv, [119]–261 p. 1 illus., facsim. 24cm.

Author's name also in Chinese on t.-p.
The first edition appeared in the Yenching Journal of social studies, Peking, v. 1, no. 2, January, 1939, p. 256–291. cf. Pref.
"Reprinted from the Chinese social & political science review, Peking, [v. 24, no. 2, July–September, 1940."

1. Jews in China—Bibl.   I. Title.   42–18376
Library of Congress   Z6373.C5L6
     [2]   016.2960951

NL 0448241   DLC

Z6373
.C5L59
Loewenthal, Rudolf, 1904–   The Jews in China.

Löwenthal, Rudolf, 1904–
The early Jews in China : a supplementary bibliography. [Peking] Catholic University of Peking [1946]

VOLUME 338

PL 1188 LÖWENTHAL, RUDOLF
.L 82   The nomenclature of Jews in China. Peiping,
Catholic University ₍n.d.₎
97-126 p.

Cover title.
Reprint from Monumenta Serica, Journal of
Oriental Studies of the Catholic University of
Peking, v. 12, 1947.

1. Hebrew language--Transliteration into Chinese.
2. Names--Jewish. 3. Jews--China. I. Title.

NL 0448243   InU OC1

Loewenthal, Rudolf
La presse juive à Shanghai après la guerre du
Pacifique. np [1947]

[185]-191, 429-433 p.
Reprinted from Bulletin de l'Université l'Aurore,
1947

NL 0448244   MH OCH

Loewenthal, Rudolf, 1904-
... The religious periodical press in China, with 7 maps
and 16 charts, by Rudolf Löwenthal ... with the assistance
of Ch'en Hung-shun ... Ku Ting-ch'ang ... ₍and₎ William
W. Y. Liang ... Peking, The Synodal commission in China,
1940.
2 p. l., vi, 294 p. incl. maps (part fold.) tables (part fold.) 25 cm.
and portfolio of 16 fold. charts. 26 cm. (Sinological series, no. 57)
Portfolio has cover-title: Appendix. The religious periodical press
in China.
Revision and enlargement of a series of monographs which appeared as separate articles, 1936-40. cf. Foreword.
1. Journalism--China. 2. Chinese periodicals. 3. Chinese periodi-
cals--Foreign language press. 4. Chinese periodicals--Bibl. 5. Journalism, Religious.   I. Title.

PN5367.R4L6   079.51   41-9344 rev

DCU PU WaU
NL 0448245   DLC OrU NIC IaU ViU OU NN NNC NjP MnU

PN5367 Löwenthal, Rudolf.
O 7L82   The Russian Orthodox press in China.
₍Peiping, 1937₎
8 p. 25cm. (Collectanea commiss. synodal.,
v.10, no. 12, Dec. 1937)
Author's name also in Chinese.

1. Orthodox Eastern Church, Russian, in China
- Period. 2. Press - China. 3. Russian
periodicals.   I. Title.

NL 0448246   CSt-H

Löwenthal, Rudolf, 1904-
Über die versorgung der tagespresse mit
zeitungsdruckpapier unter besonderer
berücksichtigung Deutschlands und der
vereinigten staaten ... Berlin, 1933. 70 p.
Inaug. Diss. -Berlin, 1933.
Lebenslauf.
Bibliography.

NL 0448247   ICRL PU NNC

Loewenthal, Rudolf, 1904-
Western literature on Chinese journalism: a bibliography.
₍Tientsin, China, Nankai Institute of Economics, 1937?₎
iv, 1008-1068 p. 26 cm.
"Reprinted from Nankai social & economic quarterly, vol. IX, no. 4,
January, 1937."

1. Press--China--Bibl. 2. Journalism--China--Bibl. I. Title.

Z6958.C5L75   65-59502

NL 0448248   DLC OrU IaU

Z3001 Löwenthal, Rudolf, 1904-
L827   Works on the Far East and Central Asia pub-
lished in the U.S.S.R., 1937-47. ₍Ithaca,
Cornell Univ. Press, 1949₎
cover-title, p.₍171₎-183. 25ᶜᵐ.
"Reprinted from the Far eastern quarterly, vol.
VIII, February 1949, no.2."
Geographical arrangement.

1. East (Far East) - Bibl. 2. Asia, Central -
Bibl. I. Title

NL 0448249   CSt-H

Loewenthal, Siegbert, 1903-
Die Musikuebende Gesellschaft zu Berlin und die Mitglieder
Joh. Philipp Sack, Fr. Wilh. Riedt und Joh. Gabr. Seyffarth...
Von Siegbert Loewenthal... Laupen bei Bern: Typarsatz und
Offsetdruck der Polygraphischen Gesellschaft, 1928. vii, 97 p.
illus. (music.) 8°.
Dissertation, Basel, 1927.
"Curriculum vitae," p. 97.
Bibliography, p. ₍vi₎-vii.

493721A. 1. Music--Assoc. and org.
Johann Philipp, 1722-1763. 3. Riedt,
4. Seyffarth, Johann Gabriel, 1711-
N.Y.L.
—Germany--Berlin. 2. Sack,
Friedrich Wilhelm, 1712-1784.
1796.
September 8, 1930

NL 0448250   NN NcU NcD ICN CU PBm PU MiU DLC MH

Löwenthal (Siegfried). *Ein Fall von cysti-
scher Erweiterung des Wolff'schen Ganges. 25
pp., 1 pl. 8°. Würzburg, F. Böhrl, 1890.

NL 0448251   DNLM

Loewenthal, Siegfried.
Geschichte der Familie Lessing. Mit biologi-
schen Bemerkungen. Nebst einem Anhang:
Aerztliche Betrachtungen über Lessings letzte
Krankheit und Tod. Leipzig, Degener & co. [1929]
32 p.
At head of title: Veröffentlichungen des
Braunschweiger Genealogischen Abends zum
Goethe-Lessing-Jahr 1929, 1.

NL 0448252   MH PPT CLSU

Loewenthal, Siegfried, *ed.*
Grundriss der radiumtherapie und der biologischen
radiumforschung, unter mitwirkung von F. Gudzent ...
A. Sticker ... E. Schiff ... hrsg. von S. Loewenthal ...
mit 43 abbildungen. Wiesbaden, J. F. Bergmann, 1912.
x, 1 l., 255, ₍1₎ p. illus. 26ᶜᵐ.   mk. 7
"Literaturverzeichnis": p. ₍225₎-251.

1. Radium. 2. Radium--Therapeutic use.
II. Sticker, Anton, 1861- III. Schiff, Eduard, 1849-
I. Gudzent, Friedrich.
12—6256

Library of Congress   RM859.L7

NL 0448253   DLC PPC DNLM OC1W ICJ

Loewenthal, Siegfried, *referendar.*
Das firmenrecht nach dem neuen Handelsgesetzbuche ... von
Siegfried Loewenthal ... Heiligenstadt, Brunn'sche buch-
druckerei, 1899.
4 p. l., 219 p. 22½ᵐ.
Inaug.-diss.--Erlangen.

1. Business names--Germany.

G-2568 Revised

NL 0448254   DLC NIC

Löwenthal (Siegfried) ₍1869- ₎. *Ueber
Rhinolithiasis. ₍Breslau.₎ 28 pp., 1 l. *
Berlin, M. Haase, 1894.

NL 0448255   DNLM

PT2393 Löwenthal, Sophie (von Kleyle) freiin von,
.Z3   1810-1889.
1906   Lenau, Nicolaus, 1802-1850.
Lenau und die familie Löwenthal: briefe und gespräche,
gedichte und entwürfe. Mit bewilligung des †freiherrn Arthur
von Löwenthal vollständiger abdruck nach den handschriften.
Ausgabe, einleitung und anmerkungen von prof. dr. Eduard
Castle. Mit zehn bildnissen und fünf schriftproben ... Leipzig, M. Hesse, 1906.

NL 0448257   InU CU NcD

PT 2424 LÖWENTHAL, SOPHIE (VON KLEYLE) Freiin VON, 1810-
.L65 M5 1889
Mosalliiert; Erzählung aus dem Nachlass.
Hrsg. und eingel. von Eduard Castle. Leipzig,
M. Hesse, 1906.
279 p. port.

NL 0448257   InU CU NcD

Löwenthal, Victor.
Über die säcularfeier des Augustus und das
Carmen saeculare. [Czernowitz? 1901?]
p. [17]-25. 26 cm.
Caption title.
Schulnachrichten, Staatsgymnasium, Czernowitz.

NL 0448258   CU

Löwenthal (Victor). *Ueber Dysmenorrhoe
und Sterilität. 18 pp. 8°. Würzburg, F. Scheiner, 1888.

NL 0448259   DNLM

G1 30.241.9 Löwenthal, Viktor. Die stellung der platäer in Athen
und die dreiundzwanzigste rede des Lysias. Böhm-Leipa.
[1904.] 8°. pp. 21-25. (Progr. d. K. K. Staats-ober-
gym.)

NL 0448260   MH

QR201 Löwenthal, Waldemar, joint author.
.S9S59
Sobernheim, Georg, 1865-
Allgemeines über Spirochäten, von G. Sobernheim und W.
Loewenthal. Jena, G. Fischer ₍1927₎

---

ar W Loewenthal, Waldemar.
53183   Untersuchungen über das Verhalten der
no.1   quergestreiften Muskulatur bei atrophischen
Zuständen. Leipzig, A. Pries, 1898.
43 p. illus. 22cm.

Inaug.-Diss.--Erlangen.

NL 0448262   NIC DNLM ICRL

Loewenthal, Wilhelm.
Die Nutzbarmachung der Ausgaben-Versicherung
durch Rabatt-Spar-Vereine ... Berlin, 1881.
Pamphlet.

NL 0448263   CtY

VOLUME 338

B3413 Loewenthal, Wilhelm, *1850-1894.*
33L3   Die aufgaben der medizin in der schule. Von
prof.dr.Wilhelm Loewenthal... Hamburg, J.F.Rich-
ter, 1888.
    32 p. 21ᶜᵐ. (On cover:Deutsche zeit-und
streit-fragen...heft 33)

    1.Schools-Medical inspection-Germany. 2.School
hygiene.

NL   0448264   ICU MH MB

Loewenthal, Wilhelm, 1850-1894.
    De l'enseignement de l'hy
giène dans les facultés. Conférence d'inauguration faite à Lausanne, le 22 avril 1885. 32 pp.
8°. *Lausanne, B. Benda, 1885.*

NL   0448265   DNLM

RA   Loewenthal, Wilhelm, *1850 1894.*
440   L'enseignement actuel de l'hygiène dans
.L6   les facultés de médecine en Europe. Paris
H. Le Soudier, 1887.
    126 p. illus. 25cm.

    Includes bibliography.

    1. Hygiene - Study and teaching. 2.
Universities and colleges - Curricula. 3.
Education - Europe   - Hist.

NL   0448266   WU DNLM CtY

Loewenthal Wilhelm, 1850-1894.
    Etude comparée sur l'enseignement actuel de
l'hygiène dans les facultés de médecine en Europe. 101 pp. 4°. *Paris, 1887, No. 142.*
——. The same. 136 pp., 1 l. 8°. *Paris, H.
Le Soudier, 1887.*

NL   0448267   DNLM

Loewanthal, Wilhelm, 1850-1894.
    Graf Reckenhorst; ein schauspiel in
funf akten. Leipzig, Friedrich, 1882.
    100 p.

NL   0448268   OClW

Loewenthal, Wilhelm, *1850-1894.*
    Grundzüge einer hygiene des unterrichts. Von dr. Wil-
helm Loewenthal ... Wiesbaden, J. F. Bergmann, 1887.
    viii, 152 p. 23ᶜᵐ.

    1. School hygiene.

                         E 11-1479

Library, U. S. Bur. of   Education LB3405.L7

NL   0448269   DHEW MB

RC530   Loewenthal, Wilhelm, 1850-1894.
872R   Die Lageveränderungen des Uterus; auf Grund
e igener Untersuchungen beurtheilt und dargestell
Heidelberg, Winter, 1872.
    vii, 122p., 1l. 23cm. [Bound with: Reich, E.
Uber Ursachen und Verhütung der Nervosität. 1872]

    1. Uterus - Displacements.

NL   0448270   CtY-M DNLM ICU

RM171   Loewenthal, Wilhelm, 1850-1894.
L82   Ueber die transfusion des blutes. Heidelberg,
1871   Winter, 1871.
    23 p.

    1. Blood - Transfusion.

NL   0448271   NNC-M DNLM ICRL NNC

Loewenthal, Wilhelm, *1877-*
    Anton Tschechow, ein Vortrag gehalten am 16. Februar
1905. Bromberg, Vittler'sche Buchhandlung, R. Fromm i.
Komm., 1906.
    35 p. 25 cm. (Veröffentlichungen der Abteilung für Literatur
der Deutschen Gesellschaft für Kunst und Wissenschaft zu Bromberg, 2)

    1. Chekhov, Anton Pavlovich, 1860-1904. (Series: Deutsche
Gesellschaft für Kunst und Wissenschaft in Bromberg. Abteilung
für Literatur. Veröffentlichungen, 2)

    PG3458.L6   50-47553

NL   0448272   DLC CU

Loewenthal, Wilhelm, *1877-*
    Gogol, sein Werk und seine Persönlichkeit, ein Vortrag
gehalten am 3. Oktober 1910. Lissa i. P., In Kommission
O. Eulitz, 1911.
    26 p. 26 cm. (Veröffentlichungen der Abteilung für Literatur
der Deutschen Gesellschaft für Kunst und Wissenschaft in Bromberg,
4)

    1. Gogol', Nikolaĭ Vasil'evich, 1809-1852. (Series: Deutsche
Gesellschaft für Kunst und Wissenschaft in Bromberg. Abteilung für
Literatur. Veröffentlichungen, 4)

    PG3335.L6   50-47558

NL   0448273   DLC NcD

PG2143 Loewenthal, Wilhelm, *1877-*
.L8   Die russische rechtschreibung. Ein anhang zu
jeder russischen grammatik, von dr.Wilhelm Loewenthal... Leipzig, R.Gerhard, 1910.
    vi, 56 p. 19½ᶜᵐ.

NL   0448274   ICU

Ht20   Loewenthal, Wilhelm, *1877-*
L82   Russisches Lesebuch. Leipzig, H.Haessel,
1913.
    xi, 124p. (His Lehrbuch der russischen
Sprache, T.3)

NL   0448275   CtY

Er13   Loewenthal, Wilhelm, 1877-
L82   Die slavischen Farbenbezeichnungen ... von
Wilhelm Loewenthal ... Leipzig, Druck von A.
Pries, 1901.
    50p., 1l. 23½cm.
    Inaug.-Diss. - Leipzig.
    Vita.

    1.Colors, Words for.   2.Slavic languages -
Semasiology.

NL   0448276   CtY ICRL PU

FG 6117 LOEWENTHAL, WILHELM, *1877-*
.L82   Polnische Texte mit polnisch-deutschem
Wörterverzeichnis. Leipzig, F.A. Brockhaus,
1924.
    91 p.

    1. Polish language--Readers.

NL   0448277   InU

Loewenthal, Wolf Wilhelm
    see   Loewenthal, Wilhelm, 1850-1894.

Löwenthal, Wolfgang
    Das lohngewerbe in wirtschaft und recht...
Berlin, 1932.   79 p.
    Inaug. Diss. Jena, 1932.
    Bibliography.

NL   0448279   ICRL CtY MiU

Löwenthal, Zdenko
    see
Levntal, Zdenko, ed.

Loewenthal-Gelibter, Gitla.
    ... Ueber zentrale schmerzen ... Brüssel,
1931.
Basel
diss.
1931

NL   0448281   MiU CtY

Löwenthal-Kleyle, Sophie, freifrau von
    see   Löwenthal, Sophie (von Kleyle)
Freiin von, 1810-1889.

Loewenton (Alexander) [1864-]. *Experimentelle Untersuchungen über den Einfluss
einiger Abführmittel und der Clysmata auf Secretion und Zusammensetzung der Galle, sowie deren Wirkung bei Galleaabwesenheit im
Darme. 74 pp., 1 l. 8°. *Dorpat, Schnakenburg,
1891.*

NL   0448283   DNLM CU PPC

LOEWENTON, Emanuel.
    Versuche über das gedächtniss im bereiche
des raumsinnes der haut. Inaug.-diss., Jurjew.
Dorpat, H.Laakmann, 1893.

    pp.39+. Plate.   Phil 5545.157

NL   0448284   MH DNLM

Loewenwald, Ludwig, 1876-
    Die Behandlung einer aus irrigem Motiv
hervorgegangenen Erbeinsetzung nach gemeinem Recht ... von Ludwig Loewenwald ...
Greifswald, J. Abel, 1898.
    85 p. 23cm.
    Inaug.-Diss. - Greifswald.
    "Lebenslauf": p. 85.
    "Litteratur": p.[7]-12.

NL   0448285   MH-L ICRL

4K   Loewenwald, Ludwig, *1876-*
Ger.   Lehrbuch der Civilprozessordnung
1334   für das Deutsche Reich. Berlin,
Puttkammer & Mühlbrecht, 1903.
    479 p.

NL   0448286   DLC-P4 MH

VOLUME 338

Loewenwarter, Paul L.
Revenue Act of 1921, relating to income tax on individuals and corporations; war excess profits tax; general administrative provisions; and general provisions; with explanatory digest. Approved by the President...Nov. 23, 1921. ₁New York City? 1921₎, 120 p. incl. tables. nar. 8°.

587354A. 1. Taxation—Jurisp.— U. S., 1921. 2. Income tax—
U. S., 1921.
N. Y. P. L.   June 22, 1932

NL 0448287   NN

Loewenwarter, Viktor, 1887–
Das BGB in der rechtsprechung der gegenwart, von dr. Viktor Loewenwarter ... Berlin, C. Heymann, 1933.
167 p. 22ᶜᵐ.

1. Civil law—Germany. 2. Germany. Laws, statutes, etc. Bürgerliches gesetzbuch. 3. Law reports, digests, etc.—Germany.

₁Full name: Viktor Reginald Loewenwarter₎
34-41668

NL 0448288   DLC NNC

Löwenwarter, Viktor, 1887–
Der bürgerliche wohnsitz im englischen und deutschen recht ... Von Victor Löwenwarter ... Bonn, C. Georgi, 1910.
xii, 90, ₁2₎ p. 22½ᶜᵐ.
Inaug.-diss.—Bonn.
Lebenslauf.
"Literatur": p. ₁viii₎–xii.

1. Domicile—Gt. Brit. 2. Domicile—Germany. I. Title.

₁Full name: Viktor Reginald Löwenwarter₎
34-11178

Library of Congress   JX4241.L6 1910   347.1

NL 0448289   DLC CtY MH-L ICU

Loewenwarter, Viktor, 1887–
Código civil
see under
Chile. Laws, statutes, etc.

Loewenwarter, Viktor, 1887–
Codigo de comercio
see under Chile. Laws, statutes, etc.

Loewenwarter, Viktor, 1887–
Codigo penal...
see under Chile. Laws, statutes, etc.

Loewenwarter, Viktor, 1887–
... Consultorio jurídico; a través de la jurisprudencia moderna de la Corte suprema y de los tribunales superiores sobre cuestiones de derecho civil y comercial. ₁Santiago₎ Prensas de la Universidad de Chile, 1937.
1 p. l., ₁5₎–150 p. 23ᶜᵐ.
At head of title: Dr. Víctor Loewenwarter ...

1. Civil law—Chile—Cases. 2. Commercial law—Chile—Cases. I. Chile. Corte suprema. II. Chile. Courts. III. Title.

₁Full name: Viktor Reginald Loewenwarter₎
42-40912

NL 0448293   DLC DPU NcD

Loewenwarter, Viktor, 1887–
... Cuestionario jurídico, a base de "sesenta casos" auténticos judiciales para el estudio de las tendencias modernas de la ciencia de derecho penal. Santiago de Chile, Imprenta universitaria, 1937.
34 p. 24ᶜᵐ.
At head of title: Dr. Victor Loewenwarter ...

1. Criminal law—Examinations, questions, etc. 2. Criminal law—Chile—Examinations, questions, etc.

₁Full name: Viktor Reginald Loewenwarter₎
44-29207

NL 0448294   DLC DPU

Loewenwarter, Viktor, 1887–
... Derecho civil alemán con las características del derecho mercantil, en comparación con las legislaciones extranjeras, especialmente con la legislación chilena. Código civil alemán ... ₁Santiago₎ Prensas de la Universidad de Chile, 1935–
v. 26½ᶜᵐ.
At head of title: Dr. Victor Loewenwarter ...

1. Civil law—Germany. 2. Commercial law—Germany. 3. Civil law—Chile. 4. Commercial law—Chile. 5. Comparative law. I. Title.

₁Full name: Viktor Reginald Loewenwarter₎
37-7749

Library of Congress   ₁4₎   [347.0943] 349.43

NL 0448295   DLC

Loewenwarter, Viktor, 1887–
... Derecho civil alemán comparado con las características del derecho comercial. 2. ed. refundida. Santiago, Chile, Nascimento, 1943.
735 p. 25ᶜᵐ.
At head of title: Víctor Loewenwarter.
First edition has title: Derecho civil alemán con las características del derecho mercantil, en comparación con las legislaciones extranjeras, especialmente con la legislación chilena ...

1. Civil law—Germany. 2. Civil law—Chile. 3. Comparative law.

₁Full name: Viktor Reginald Loewenwarter₎
44-13562

NL 0448296   DLC TxU CtY DPU

Loewenwarter, Viktor, 1887–
... Instituciones jurídicas chilenas, analizadas sobre la base de "precedentes" para el estudio de las transformaciones del derecho civil e intern. privado. ₁Santiago₎ Prensas de la Universidad de Chile, 1939.
137 p. 23ᶜᵐ.
At head of title: Dr. Víctor Loewenwarter ...

1. Civil law—Chile—Cases. 2. International law, Private—Chile—Cases. I. Title.

₁Full name: Viktor Reginald Loewenwarter₎
43-48548

NL 0448297   DLC CtY-L RPB DPU

Loewenwarter, Viktor, 1887–   ed.

Germany. *Laws, statutes, etc.*
Lehrkommentar zum Bürgerlichen gesetzbuch, von dr. Viktor Loewenwarter ... Berlin, H. Sack, 1924–30.

Loewenwarter, Viktor, 1887–
Wegweiser durch das BGB. unter berücksichtigung anderer reichsgesetze nach dem neuesten stande der rechtslehre und rechtsprechung nebst anhang grundlegender entscheidungen, von dr. Viktor Loewenwarter ... 4. bis 6. völlig neubearb. aufl. Berlin, H. Sack, 1925.
430 p. 23½ᶜᵐ.

1. Germany. Laws, statutes, etc. Bürgerliches gesetzbuch. 2. Civil law—Germany. I. Title.
26-10722

NL 0448299   DLC FU-L CtY-L

Loewenwarter, Viktor, 1887–
Wegweiser durch das BGB unter berücksichtigung anderer reichsgesetze nach dem neuesten stande der rechtslehre und rechtsprechung nebst anhang grundlegender entscheidungen, von dr. Viktor Loewenwarter ... 7. bis 9. stark verb. aufl. Berlin, C. Heymann, 1927.
vii, 407 p. 23ᶜᵐ.

1. Germany. Laws, statutes, etc. Bürgerliches gesetzbuch. 2. Civil law—Germany. 3. Law reports, digests, etc.—Germany. I. Title.
28-24008

NL 0448300   DLC

Loewenwarter, Viktor, 1887–
Wegweiser durch das Bgb unter berücksichtigung anderer reichsgesetze nach dem neuesten stande der rechtslehre und rechtsprechung nebst anhang grundlegender entscheidungen von dr. Viktor Löwenwarter ... 13. bis 15. verb. aufl. Berlin, C. Heymann, 1932.
vii, 454 p. 22½ᶜᵐ.
"Anhang: Entscheidungen und fälle als klausurpraktikum": p. ₁201₎–435.

1. Germany. Laws, statutes, etc. Bürgerliches gesetzbuch. 2. Civil law—Germany. 3. Law reports, digests, etc.—Germany. I. Title.

₁Full name: Viktor Reginald Löwenwarter₎
36-4606

NL 0448301   DLC

---

* **Loewenwarter, Viktor,** 1887–

Amein, Hermann von.
Wegweiser durch Bgb unter berücksichtigung anderer reichsgesetze nach dem neuesten stande der rechtslehre und rechtsprechung nebst anhang grundlegender entscheidungen. 16. und 17. neubearb. und verb. aufl., von Hermann von Amein ... Berlin, C. Heymann, 1935.

Loewenwarter, Viktor, 1887–
Wegweiser durch das BGB unter Berücksichtigung anderer Gesetze nach dem neuesten Stande der Rechtslehre und Rechtsprechung nebst Anhang grundlegender Entscheidungen. 18. neubearb. Aufl. unter Mitwirkung von Heinrich Bohnenberg. Detmold, C. Heymann, 1952.
546 p. 21 cm.
Sixteenth and seventeenth editions, by H. von Amein.

1. Civil law—Germany (Federal Republic, 1949–   ) I. Title.
Full name: Viktor Reginald Loewenwarter.
53-24407

NL 0448303   DLC

Loewer (Æmilius Leopoldus Philippus) [1852–]. * De sputorum dignitate diagnostica. 41 pp., 1 l. 8°. *Berolini, F. G. Nietack,* [1874]. *See also,* Gropius (Martin) & Schmieden. Das zweite Garnison-Lazareth für Berlin, etc. fol. *Berlin,* 1878.

NL 0448304   DNLM

Loewer, Albrecht.
Das wesen des massenverbrechens; eine rechtswissenschaftliche untersuchung. Von Albrecht Loewer ... Freiburg i. Breisgau, J. Bielefeld, 1927.
125 p., 1 l. 22ᶜᵐ.
"Quellennachweis": p. 121–125.

1. Crime and criminals. 2. Crowds. 3. Social psychology. 4. Riots. I. Title.
35-22206

Library of Congress   HV6084.L6   364

NL 0448305   DLC CtY MiU NjP MH-L

VOLUME 338

Hie22 Loewer, Carl, 1871-
16 Patristische Quellenstudien zu Freidanks
Bescheidenheit ... Berlin,G.Schade(O.Francke)
[1900]
49p.,1l. 22½cm.
Vita.

1.Freidank, 13th cent. Bescheidenheit.
2.Fathers of the church, Latin - Hist. & crit.
Full name: Carl Ludwig Eduard Loewer.

NL 0448306   CtY MH

PT 1521
B4 L63 Loewer, Carl, 1871-
Patristische Quellenstudien zu Freidanks
Bescheidenheit. Berlin, G. Schade (Otto
Francke) n.d.
49 p.
Inaug. Diss. - Leipzig.
Photocopy.

1. Freidank, 13th cent. Bescheidenheit.
I. Title.

NL 0448307   CaBVaU NcU ICRL

Loewer, Ernest.
Manuel de cuisine pour hoteliers, restaurateurs et cuisiniers.
Lausanne, F. Rouge, 1950.
362 p. illus. 21 cm.

1. Cookery for institutions, etc.

TX820.L56   641.572   50-55396

NL 0448308   DLC NN InLP

Loewer (Guilelmus Frid.) *De vomitoriis. 32
nn. 8°. Berolini, lit. Petschii, 1828.

NL 0448309   DNLM

Loewer, Karl, 1886- appr. Arzt: Ueber ein Fibromyom des Netzes.
Giessen 1912: Kindt. 31 S. 8°
Gießen, Med. Diss. v. 13. April 1912, Ref. Bostroem
[Geb. 14. Nov. 86 Gießen; Wohnort: Gießen; Staatsangeh.: Hessen; Vorbildung: Gymn. Gießen Reife O. 05; Studium: Gießen 10 S.; Coll. 6. Mai 10; Approb. 10. Mai 11.]   [U 12. 1347]

NL 0448310   ICRL DNLM MBCo

Löwer, Karl, 1899-
Probleme der landwirtschaftlichen Grundsteuer
... Ottweiler-Saar, 1932.
Inaug.-Diss. - Frankfurt am Main.

NL 0448311   CtY

Löwer, Richard.
... Formen und giessen, von fachlehrer Richard Löwer ...
Wittenberg Lutherstadt, A. Ziemsen [1943]
viii, 260, [1] p. incl. illus., tables, diagrs. (1 fold.) 16½". (Deutsche
werkmeister-bücherei, hrsg. von ingenieur Heinz Gramm. Gruppe III A:
Spanlose formung. Bd. 1)
"Benutztes schrifttum": p. [261]

1. Founding.
TS230.L58   A F 47-3122
Engineering societies libr.
for Library of Congress   [2]†

NL 0448312   NNE DLC IU

Löwer, Richard.
Formen und Giessen. 3. Aufl. Leipzig, Fachbuchverlag,
1950.
226 p. illus. 24 cm.

1. Molding (Founding) 2. Pattern-making. I. Title.

TS230.L58 1950   56-30469 ‡

NL 0448313   DLC PPF NN

Löwer, Richard.
... Kostenberechnungen im holzmodellbau, bearbeitet von
Richard Löwer. Wittenberg, A. Ziemsen [1941]
vi, 210 p. illus., diagrs. 16½". (Deutsche werkmeister-bücherei,
hrsg. von ingenieur Heinz Gramm. [Bd. VII, t. 2])

1. Pattern-making.   44-33840
Library of Congress   TS240.L6
[2]   621.72

NL 0448314   DLC

Löwer, Richard.
Kostenberechnungen im Holzmodellbau. 2. Aufl. Wittenberg, A. Ziemsen [1949]
vi, 209 p. illus., diagrs. 17 cm. (Deutsche Werkmeister-Bücherei.
Gruppe 8: Hilfsarbeiten, Bd. 2)

1. Pattern-making. (Series)

TS240.L6 1949   621.72   50-21093

NL 0448315   DLC

Löwer, Richard.
... Manual moderno del modelista mecánico; traducción directa de la edición alemana, por M. Kræmer ... 1. ed. Barcelona, J. Montesó, 1936.
387 p. incl. illus., tables, diagrs. 22½". [Biblioteca moderna de
mecánica]
At head of title: Richard Loewer.
Cover-title: Modelista mecánico.

1. Mechanical models. 2. Machinery—Design. I. Kraemer, M., tr.
44-23164
Library of Congress   TJ248.L58
[2]   600

NL 0448316   DLC DPU

Loewer, Richard.
Der Modellbau; die Modell- und Schablonenformerei, von
Richard Löwer... Berlin: J. Springer, 1931. v, 229 p. incl.
diagrs., tables. illus. 8°.

521973A. 1. Pattern making.
N. Y. P. L.   April 29, 1931

NL 0448317   NN

Löwer, Richard.
Modellschlosserei. [2. Aufl.] Wittenberg, A. Ziemsen
[1949]
vii, 171 p. illus. 17 cm. (Deutsche Werkmeister-Bücherei.
Gruppe 8: Hilfsarbeiten, Bd. 3)
"Benutztes Schrifttum": p. 171.

1. Locks and keys. I. Title. (Series)

TS520.L6 1949   621.883   50-21090

NL 0448318   DLC

Löwer, Richard.
... Modelltischlerei, von Richard Löwer ...
Berlin, J. Springer, 1924
v. illus. 22½". (Werkstattbücher ... hft. 14)

1. Mechanical models.   25-4752
Library of Congress   TJ248.L6

NL 0448319   DLC NN

LÖWER, RICHARD.
Modelltischlerei. Berlin, Springer, 1925-36 [v. 1,
1936] 2 v. in 1. illus. 23cm. (Werkstattbücher für Betriebsbeamte, Vor- und Facharbeiter. Heft 14, 17)

CONTENTS. — T. 1. Allgemeines. Einfachere Modelle. 2. verb.
Aufl. — T. 2. Beispiele von Modellen und Schablonen.

1. Pattern-making. t. 1925.

NL 0448320   NN

Löwer, Richard.
Modelltischlerei. 2., verb. Aufl. Wittenberg, A. Ziemsen
[Vorwort, 1941]
286 p. illus. 17 cm. (Deutsche Werkmeister-Bücherei. Gruppe 8,
Bd. 1)

1. Mechanical models. (Series)

TJ248.L62   50-40259

NL 0448321   DLC

Löwer, Richard.
Modelltischlerei. 3. verb. Aufl. Wittenberg, A. Ziemsen
[1949]
vii, 238 p. illus., diagrs. 17 cm. (Deutsche Werkmeister-Bücherei.
Gruppe 8: Hilfsarbeiten, Bd. 1)

1. Carpentry. 2. Pattern-making. I. Title. (Series)

TH5604.L57 1949   621.72   50-20681
[1]

NL 0448322   DLC

Loewer, Richard, *poet.*
Ouvrez les guillemets; fables express, épitaphes et autres
textes fantaisistes. Suivi de Huit poèmes pour faire sérieux.
[Éd. originale] Neuchâtel, 1954.
47 p. 20 cm.
400 copies printed: "Exemplaire no 246."

I. Title.
A 55-10229
Illinois. Univ. Library
for Library of Congress   [1]

NL 0448323   IU

Löwers, Gerhard, 1911-
... Ergebnisse operativ behandelter Oberarm-
schaftfrakturen an der Leipziger Klinik ...
[Zeulenroda i. Thür.] 1936.
Inaug.-Diss. - Leipzig.
Lebenslauf.

NL 0448324   CtY

VOLUME 338

Löwgren, Erik.
Studies on benign proteinuria, with special reference to the renal lymphatic system. Stockholm, 1955.
52 p. illus. 24 cm. (Acta medica Scandinavica. Supplementum 300)
Bibliography: p. [49]–52.

1. Albuminuria. 2. Urine—Analysis and pathology. (Series)
A 55–8033

Ohio State Univ. Libr.
for Library of Congress [2]

NL 0448325 OU ViU DNLM

LOEWI, ADOLFO.
Exhibition of textile art, from the early Christian times to the XVIII century, giving special representation to the XIII–XIV and XV centuries, collection of Adolfi Loewi of Venice. [held at Arnold Seligmann, Rey & co. gallery, November 1933. New York, 1933] [15] p. (incl. cover) 21cm.

1. Textile fabrics--Collections, Private--Loewi. I. Seligmann (Arnold), Rey & company. New York.

NL 0448326 NN

[Loewi, Babette Hermine (Rosenfeld)]
Deklamatorisches Potpourri, von B. Herwi [pseud.] 2. vermehrte Aufl. Berlin, H. Steinitz [Vorrede 1890]
263p. 18cm.

NL 0448327 IEN

Loewi, Babbette Hermine (Rosenfeld)
Festspiel zur Feier des 50jährigen Bestehens des...Ordens Bnai Briss. (Gleiwitz, Humanitaa-Loge, (1893)
17p 22cm
1.Plays. 2.Festschriften-Institutions-B'nai B'rith. 3.B'nai B'rith.

NL 0448328 NNJ

Loewi, E[
Rede. Bei der feierlichen andacht des 21sten Juni 1815 in der Synagoge zu Inowraclaw gesprochen ... Bromberg, [1815].
15 p.

NL 0448329 OCH

Loewi, Emil.
Untersuchungen über die Blattablösung und verwandte Erscheinungen. Illus. Plates.
(In Kaiserliche Akademie der Wissenschaften, Vienna. Sitzungsberichte. Mathematisch-naturwissenschaftliche Klasse. Band 116, Halbband 2, Abteilung 1, pp. 983–1024. Wien. 1907.)

H 106 — Botany. Physiological. — Leaves.

NL 0448330 MB MH–A

Löwi, Hermann: Aus d. Univ.-Frauenklinik zu Breslau. Über die Komplikation von Schwangerschaft, Geburt und Wochenbett mit Herzfehlern. Breslau 1910: Breslauer Genossensch.-Buchdr. 51 S. 8°
Breslau, Med. Diss. v. 25. Mai 1910, Ref. Küstner
[Geb. 29. Sept. 83 Breslau; Wohnort: Breslau; Staatsangeh.: Österreich; Vorbildung: Elisabeth-Gymn. Breslau Reife O. 02; Studium: Breslau 10 S.; Coll. 2. Mai 10; Approb. 21. Aug. 08.] [U 10. 579]

NL 0448331 ICRL DNLM

Loewi, Isaak.
Antrittsrede ... bei seiner Installation als Rabbiner zu Fuerth, gehalten am 21 März, 1831. Nebst der Rede des Wahlkommissairs Herrn Bürgermeisters v. Baeumen und einer kurzen Erzählung der bei der Einsetzung staltgehabten Feierlichkeiten. Friedberg, 1831.
32 p. 12°.
In *PLL p. v. 1.

NL 0448332 NN

Loewi, Isaak.
Antrittsrede des ... Isaak Loewi, bei seiner Installation als Rabbiner zu Fürth, gehalten am 21. März 1831 ... Fürth: J. Volkhart, 1831.
28 p.

NL 0448333 OCH

Loewi, [Isaak]
Predigt zur gottesdienstlichen Eröffnung der Versammlung der israelitischen Abgeordneten des Rezat-Kreises, gehalten in der Synagoge zu Ansbach ... 1836. Ansbach, C. Brügel, 1836.
27 p. 12°.
In: *PLL p. v. 1.

NL 0448334 NN OCH

Loewi, Isaak
Predigten, gehalten bei der Einweihung der Haupt-Synagoge in Fürth, am 15.und 16.September 1865. Fürth, J.L.Schmid, 1865.
23 p. 21.5 cm.

NL 0448335 MH

Loewi, [Isaak].
Trauer-Rede auf das Ableben ... der Königin Therese, gehalten in der Haupt-Synagoge zu Fürth am 8. November 1854 ... Fürth: J. L. Schmid, [1845].
16 p.

NL 0448336 OCH

LOEWI, Isaak
Trauerrede auf das Ableben...der Koenigin Therese, Gehalten...am 8.November 1854... Fuerth, Bayern, Schmid, (1854). 16 p. 21cm.

1.Sermons-German. 2.Sermons-Funeral. 3.History-Germany-Bavaria-Fuerth.

NL 0448337 NNJ

Loewi, [Isaak].
Trauerpredigt auf das Ableben des Königs Maximilian II. Gehalten ... am 21. März 1864 ... Fürth: J. L. Schmidt, [1864?]. 2d. ed.
12 p.

NL 0448338 OCH

Loewi, Isaak.
I. Was hat die Regierung für Israel, und besonders in Beziehung auf Religion schon gethan? II. Was wird sie nach thun? III. Was kann sie dagegen mit Recht von Israel fordern? ... Vorgetragen in der Synagoge daselbst am 1. Januar 1828. n.p. [1828]
32 p. 12°.
In *PLL p. v. 1.

NL 0448339 NN OCH

Loewi, K
RM725
911ℓ
Orthopädisches Turnen im Hause. Stuttgart, Enke, 1911.
vii. 40p. illus. 21cm.

1. Physical education and training. 2. Physical medicine - Exercise.

NL 0448340 CtY–M

Löwi, Moritz, 1891 -
Grundbegriffe der pädagogik, von dr. phil. Moritz Löwi ... Breslau, M. & H. Marcus, 1934.
viii, 234 p. 22ᵐ.

1. Education. I. Title.
A 34–2976

Title from Yale Univ. Printed by L. C.

NL 0448341 CtY

1891-
Löwi, Moritz, Synthesis und System. Ein Beitrag zur Theorie des Ganzheitsgedankens. [In Maschinenschrift.] 41 S. 4°(2°).— Auszug: Breslau (1921): Hochschulverl. 3 Bl. 8°
Breslau, Phil. Diss. v. 20. Dez. 1921, Ref. Hönigswald
[Geb. 13. Dez. 91 Breslau; Wohnort: Breslau; Staatsangeh.: Deutsch-Böhmen; Vorbildung: G. z. St. Elisabet Breslau Reife 13; Studium: Breslau 16 S.; Rig. 7. Dez. 21.] [U 21.6226]

NL 0448342 ICRL

131
L918U
Löwi, Moritz, 1891-
Über spezifische Sinnesenergien; Psychologie und Physiologie. Breslau, Trewendt & Granier, 1927.
238p.

1. Psychology, Physiological I. Title.

NL 0448343 NBC

Löwi, Moritz, 1891-
Zum problem der ganzheit, synthesis und system, von dr. Moritz Löwi ... Breslau, Trewendt & Granier, 1927.
31 p. 22.5 cm.

NL 0448344 NcD

Loewi, Otto, 1873 -
Festschrift zur Feier des 80. [i. e. achtzigsten] von Otto Loewi
see under title

Loewi, Otto, 1873 -
From the workshop of discoveries. Lawrence, University of Kansas Press, 1953.
62 p. 22 cm. (Porter lectures, ser. 19)

1. Physiology—Addresses, essays, lectures. I. Title.

QP71.L63 612.04 53–7062 ‡

NN ICJ NcU-H ViU OClW-H PPC
NL 0448346 DLC OrU-M CaBVaU DNLM KEmT NcD-MC MB OU

VOLUME 338

Loewi, Otto, 1873–
... Pharmakologie des Wärmehaushalts, von O. Loewi ...
(*In* Ergebnisse der Physiologie. Wiesbaden. 1904. 26ᶜᵐ. 3. Jahrg., 1. Abt., p. ₍332₎–372)
"Literatur": p. ₍332₎–338.

NL 0448347   ICJ

Loewi, Otto, 1873–
Unsere stimmung gegen England und ihre bedeutung für später. Vortrag gehalten am 19. juni 1915 in Graz von Otto Loewi ... Graz und Leipzig, Leuschner & Lubensky, 1915.
29 p. 24ᶜᵐ.

1. Germany—For. rel.—Gt. Brit. 2. Gt. Brit.—For. rel.—Germany. 3. Austria—For. rel.—Gt. Brit. 4. Gt. Brit.—For. rel.—Austria. 1. Title.

Library of Congress   DD228.7.G7L6
                      21—19279

NL 0448348   DLC CtY NN

Loewi, Otto, 1873–
... Untersuchungen über den nucleinstoffwechsel ... Leipzig, F. C. W. Vogel, 1900.
1 p. l., 29 p. 22½ᶜᵐ.
Inaug.-diss.—Marburg.
At head of title: Aus dem Pharmacologischen institut der Universität Marburg.
"Literaturverzeichniss": p. 24–25.

1. Metabolism.
                      11–19938

Library of Congress   QP551.L85

NL 0448349   DLC DNLM CtY

Loewi, Otto, 1873–
*Zur quantitativen Wirkung ⌈von Blausäure, Arsen und Phosphor auf das isolirte Froschherz. [Strasburg.] 14 pp. 8°.
⌊*Inaug. J. B. Hirschfeld.* 1896.

NL 0448350   DNLM

Loewi, Rudolf
Die Post-Anweisung ... von Rudolf Loewi ... Fürth, A. Schröder, 1891.
32 p. 22cm.
Inaug.-Diss. - Erlangen.
"Literaturübersicht": p. ₍31₎–32.

NL 0448351   MH-L ICRL CU

Loewicke, R 1836– ed.
Rätselschatz. Eine Sammlung deutscher poetscher Rätsel, Charaden, Homonyme, Palindrome, Anagramme, Arithmogriphe, Logogriphe, Rösselsprünge und Citaten-Rätsel. Stuttgart, Süddeutsches Verlags-Institut [1888?]
170 p. illus.

NL 0448352   CLU

Loewié, Marie, 1906–
... Über das Verhalten der Retikulozyten im Verlauf der Infektionskrankheiten ... Halle, 1933.
Inaug.-Diss. - Halle-Wittenberg.
Lebenslauf.
"Literatur": p. 30.

NL 0448353   CtY MiU

Loewig, Carl,
     SEE
Loewig, Karl Jacob, 1803–1890.

QD181
.S6L7
Loewig, Friedrich, 1850–
Ueber die einwirkung der kohlensauren alkalien auf thon, feldspath und albit in hoher temperatur. Breslau, 1873.
48p.
Inaug. diss. Breslau.

NL 0448355   DLC

Löwig, Gustav.
Die Freistaaten von Nord-Amerika. Beobachtungen und praktische bemerkungen für auswandernde Deutsche, von Gustav Löwig ... Heidelberg und Leipzig, K. Groos, 1833.
1 p. l., x p., 1 l. 264 p. plan. 18½ x 11ᶜᵐ.
Title vignette.

1. U.S.—Descr. & trav.
                      5—11025

Library of Congress   E165.L825

NL 0448356   DLC CSt OOxM TxU OC MoU MiU OC1W-H NN

Löwig, Gustav.
Die Freistaaten von Nord-Amerika. Beobachtungen und praktische bemerkungen für auswandernde Deutsche, von Gustav Löwig ... Heidelberg und Leipzig, K. Groos, 1833.
1 p. l., x p., 1 l., 264 p. plan. 18½ x 11ᶜᵐ.
Title vignette.
Micro-opaque. (Travels in the Old South. Series III, no.64)

NL 0448357   UU ICRL NNC

Löwig, Karl Jacob, 1803–1890.
Arsenikvergiftung und Mumifikation. Gerichtlichchemische Abhandlung ... Breslau, 1887.
1 p.l., 65, [1] p. 21 cm.

NL 0448358   CtY

QD181
.B7L8
Löwig, Karl Jacob, 1803–1890.
Das brom und seine chemischen verhältnisse von Carl Löwig. Heidelberg, C. F. Winter, 1829.
xvi, 174, ₍1₎ p. 20ᶜᵐ.
Bibliography: p. 7–8.

NL 0448359   ICU MiU

Löwig, Karl Jacob, 1803–1890.
Chemie der organischen verbindungen. 2ᵉ gänzlich umgearbeitete und vermehrte aufl. Zürich, J. Fröbel & comp., etc. etc. 1845–46.
2 vol.

NL 0448360   MH

Löwig, Karl [Jacob] 1803–1890.
Chemie der organischen verbindungen, von Carl Löwig ... 2. gänzlich umgearb. und verm. aufl. Braunschweig, F. Vieweg und sohn, 1846.
2 v. 23½ᶜᵐ.

1. Chemistry, Organic.

Library of Congress   QD251.L78
                      4–35944†

NL 0448361   DLC PPC NNC CU PPF PU OCU

Löwig, Karl [Jacob] 1803–1890.
Grundriss der organischen chemie, von Dr. Carl Löwig ... Braunschweig, F. Vieweg und sohn, 1852.
xxxiv, 474 p. 22½ᶜᵐ.

1. Chemistry, Organic.

Library of Congress   QD251.L81
                      4–35945†

NL 0448362   DLC OkU CU PV PU

540.9
353
L8
Löwig, Karl Jacob, 1803–1890.
Jeremias Benjamin Richter, der entdecker der chemischen proportionen. Eine denkschrift, von Carl Löwig...Breslau, E. Morgenstern, 1874.
2 p.l.,56 p. 30 cm.

NL 0448363   MiU OCU

Löwig, Karl Jacob, 1803–1890.
Principles of organic and physiological chemistry. By Dr. Carl Löwig ... Tr. by Daniel Breed ... Philadelphia, A. Hart, 1853.
xl, ₍33₎–481, ₍1₎ p. 22½ᶜᵐ.

1. Chemistry, Organic.   1. Breed, Daniel, tr.

               QD251.L83
                      7—39331

             OU NN NWM ICJ
NL 0448364   DLC ICRL DNLM PPL PPC PU OC1W-H ODW MWA

Loewig, Karl Jakob, 1803–1890.
Theoretische betrachtungen uber die sauern basischen eigenschaften der nichtmetallischen korper... Zurich, 1835.

NL 0448365   PBm

Löwig, Karl Jacob, 1803–1890.
Ueber bildung und zusammensetzung der organischen verbindungen. Progr. Zurich, Orell Fussli & comp.,1843.
sm.4°.   Chem 478.43

NL 0448366   MH PBm

VOLUME 338

Löwig, Karl Jacob, 1803–1890.
Über die Bestandtheile und Entstehung der Mineralquellen. Eine naturwissenschaftliche Abhandlung. Zürich,
Schulthess, 1837.
xii, 227 p. 20 cm.
Added t.-p.: Die Mineralquellen von Baden im Canton Aargau, in
chemisch-physikalischer Beziehung.

1. Mineral waters—Baden, Switzerland.
Med 48–1647
U. S. Army Medical Libr.   [WB1003.89B134L 1837]
for Library of Congress   [1]

NL 0448367   DNLM

Loewig, Raimund August
Beitraege zur morphologie des auges. n.t.-p.
1858.
137 p.

NL 0448368   PU-Z

Loewig (Raimund August   "Questiones
de oculo physiologica. 29 pp., 1 l., 2 pl. 4°.
Fratislaviæ, R. Nischkowsky, [1857].

NL 0448369   DNLM ICRL

---

40   Loewig, Raimund August.
Ueber das stibaethylium und seine verbindungen.
Eine abhandlung welche hiesiger universitaet
um in ihr dem philosophischen doctorgrad vor-
schriftsmaessig zu erwerben 24 oct. 1854
oeffentliche vertheidigen wird.   Breslau,
R. Nischkowsky [1854]
30 p., 1 l.   8°.   [Chemical pamphlets, v. 9:7]

NL 0448370   DLC

Loewig, Walter.
Der Tribun. Drama in 5 Aufzügen.   Schweidnitz: L. Heege
[1910].   3 p.l., (1)6-91(1) p.   12°

1. Drama (German). 2. Rienzi,   Cola di, in drama. 3. Title.
N. Y. P. L.   March 30, 1911.

NL 0448371   NN

LOEWIG, Walter, 1876–
Über teleologie und mechanismus in der
philosophie Lotzes. Inaug.-diss., Breslau, H.
Fleischmann, 1901.

pp.71+.
"Lebenslauf", after p.71.   Phil 3565.79

NL 0448372   MH CtY NjP PU NIC

Loewin, Johanna.
Das familiäre Vorkommen von Uterusmyomen.
Munich, 1926.
Inaug.-Diss. - Munich.

NL 0448373   PPWI

Löwing, Folke.
I kraftverkens skugga; ett och annat om kraftutbyggnads-
mål. [Stockholm] LTs förlag [1955]
67 p. 19 cm.

1. Water-power electric plants—Sweden.   I. Title.

HD9685.S852L6   57–48791 ‡

NL 0448374   DLC MH-L

Löwing, Folke.
Inträng å kvalificerad allemansrätt. Sthlm [i. e. Stock-
holm] Centraltr. Esselte [1949]
76 p. 21 cm.   (Svenska vattenkraftföreningens publikationer, 408)

1. Eminent domain—Sweden. 2. Commons—Sweden.   I. Title.
(Series: Svenska vattenkraftföreningen. Publikationer, 408)

52–19999

NL 0448375   DLC

Loewing, Herbert.
...Die Organisation des wissenschaftlichen Sozialismus, von
Herbert Löwing.   Berlin: E. Berger & Co., 1921.   15 p.   8°.
(Arbeitsgemeinschaft sozialistischer Nationalökonomen. Schrif-
ten. Nr. 1.)

1. Socialism, Germany. 2. Series.
N. Y. P. L.   April 4, 1923.

NL 0448376   NN

DD248   **Löwing, Herbert.**
.B35   Warum sozialistische Propagenda?
Rare Bk Behne, Adolf Bruno, 1885–1948.
Coll   Das politische Plakat. Hrsg. in amtlichen Auftrage.
Charlottenburg, Verlag "Das Plakat," 1919.

[Löwing, Herbert]
Willst du mein Bruder sein? n.p. [19-]

NL 0448378   MH

Loewinger, Adolf, 1864–1926.
R.Elazar Kalir különös tekintettel nyelvezetére.
Budapest, Neumayer E. könyvnyomda, 1896
30 p.
Bölcseszetdoktori értekezés

NL 0448379   MH

---

ar W   Löwinger, Adolf, 1864–1926.
10739   Der Traum in der jüdischen Literatur.
Leipzig, M. W. Kaufmann, 1908.
35 p.   23cm.

1. Dreams in literature. 2. Jewish
literature—Hist. & crit. I. Title.

NL 0448380   NIC OCH NN

Löwinger, C. G.
Sykes, Frank W.
With Plumer in Matabeleland; an account of the operations
of the Matabeleland relief force during the rebellion of 1896,
by Frank W. Sykes ... assisted by C. G. Löwinger, c. e. and
others; illus. with sketches by F. Vigers Worthington and
from photographs by the author and others. Westminster,
A. Constable & co., 1897.

Löwinger, David Samuel, 1904–
Achikar... Irta Löwinger Sámuel.   Budapest: Neuwald
Illés utódai, 1930.   42 p.   23cm.
Bölcsészetdoktori értekezés — Budapest.
Bibliographical footnotes.

656710A. 1. Aḥikar.
N. Y. P. L.   August 31, 1933

NL 0448382   NN

Löwinger, Dávid Samuel, 1904–
Emlékkönyv néhai Dr. Kohn Sámuel Pesti
förabbi születésének századik évfordulójára
see under title

Löwinger, David Samuel, 1904–
Germánia Prófétája; a nácizmus száz esztendeje.
Budapest, 1947
235 p.

1. National socialism. 2. Germany - Race question

NL 0448384   MH NN

Löwinger, Dávid Sámuel, 1904–   ed.
גנזי קויפמן. יצא לאור בתמיכת יצחק האן ו[אברהם נ. צ.
רות. בעריכת דוד שמואל לוינגר ו]אלכסנדר שייבר. בודפשט.
[1949–
v. illus. 23 cm.
Added t. p.: Genizah publications in memory of Prof. Dr. David
Kaufmann; in collaboration with Stephen Hahn [and] Ernest Roth,
edited by Samuel Löwinger [and] Alexander Scheiber.
"Presented to the xxi[st] International Congress of Orientalists,
Paris 1948."
Articles in Hebrew and German.
"A tentative bibliography of the texts published from the Kauf-
mann Genizah": v. 1, p. [xiii]–xv.
1. Cairo Genizah. 2. Kaufmann, David, 1852–1899.   I. Scheiber,
Sándor, joint ed.
Title transliterated: Ginze Ḳoifman.
Z6605.H4L6   HE 67–958 rev

NL 0448385   DLC OU CSaT MH TNJ-R MWelC

Löwinger, David Samuel, 1904–   ed.
Ignace Goldziher memorial volume, edited by Samuel
Löwinger [and] Joseph Somogyi. Budapest, 1948–58.
2 v. port., facsim., music. 21 cm.
Added t. p.: ספר זכרון לכבוד יצחק יהודה גולדציהר
Vol. 2 edited by S. Löwinger, A. Scheiber and J. Somogyi and pub-
lished in Jerusalem.

1. Goldziher, Ignác, 1850–1921. 2. Semitic philology—Addresses,
essays, lectures.   I. Somogyi, József, 1899–   joint ed.
PJ3002.Z5G6   492.04   53–27024 rev

NcD OCU CSt-H
RPB FTaSU MiU NNUT MWelC NN NNC ICU MiEM IaU OCl PU
NL 0448386   DLC NcD NNJ PPT TxDaM CSt OCH NjMD

Löwinger, Dávid Sámuel, 1904–   ed.
Jewish studies in memory of Michael Guttmann. Buda-
pest, 1946–
v. port. 25 cm.
Added t. p. in Hungarian.
Contributions in Hungarian, English or German.
"List of writings of Prof. Michael Guttmann," by A. Schreiber:
v. 1, p. xxxiii–l.

1. Guttmann, Michael, 1872–1942. 2. Judaism—Addresses, essays,
lectures.   I. Title.
BM40.L6   54–34448 rev

NL 0448387   DLC CtY ICU OU NN

VOLUME 338

Löwinger, David Samuel, 1904– ed.
 Jewish studies in memory of Michael Guttmann.
[Bd.] 1. Budapest, 1946. 1, 418 p. port. 24cm.

 Film reproduction. Positive.
 Added t. p. in Hungarian.
 Bibliographical footnotes.

 1. Guttmann, Michael, 1872-1942. 2. Judaism--Addresses, essays,
lectures. 3. Judaism--Essays.

NL 0448388 NN

Löwinger, David Samuel, 1904– ed.
 Jiddische Handschriften in Breslau, von S. Löwinger und
B. Weinryb. Budapest, 1936.
 11 p. 23 cm.
 "Ein Auszug aus ¡einem¡ Katalog der in der Bibliothek des Jüdisch-
Theologischen Seminars in Breslau vorhandenen Handschriften."

 1. Manuscripts, Yiddish—Catalogs. 2. Manuscripts. Germany—
Catalogs. i. Weinryb, Bernard Dov, 1900– joint author. ii.
Breslau. Jüdisch-Theologisches Seminar. Bibliothek.

Z6605.Y5L6 57–52445

NL 0448389 DLC OCH NNJ

Löwinger, Dávid Sámuel, 1904–
 לתולדות הדקדוק העברי (פתח דברי־סבוא הדקדוק) בודפשם.
¡1939; בדפוס האחים נעויניין, תרצ"ם
 25 p. 23 cm.
 —— Microfilm.
 Negative film in the New York Public Library.

 1. Hebrew language—Grammar. 2. Bozecchi, Benjamin ben
Judah, ca. 1295–ca. 1335. i. Title.
  Title transliterated: Le-toldot ha-dikduk ha-ʻivri.

         A 55–7177 rev
New York. Public Libr.
for Library of Congress ¡r67b2¡

NL 0448390 NN

Löwinger, Dávid Sámuel, 1904– ed.
 Seventy years; a tribute to the seventieth anniversary of
the Jewish Theological Seminary of Hungary (1877-1947)
Budapest, 1948.
 52, 16 p. ports. 24 cm.
 Added t. p.: שבעים שנת, חוברת היובל לבית המדרש לרבנים בבודפשט
בשנת חשבעים לחוסדו (תרל"ח–תש"ח)
 Added t. p. also in Hungarian.

 1. Budapest. Országos Rabbiképző Intézet. i. Title. ii. Title:
Shiv'im shanah.

BM95.B8L6 54–30020 rev

NL 0448391 DLC MH

Löwinger, David Samuel, 1904–
 A zsidó nép szerepe világtörténeti megvilágításban.
Budapest, 1938
 30 p.

NL 0448392 MH

Löwinger, David Samuel, 1904–
 Zecharja könyvének egysége; a második zsidó
honalapítás problémái Zecharja próféciáinak tükrében.
Budapest, 1941. 52 p. 24cm.

 Film reproduction. Positive.
 Bibliographical footnotes.

 1. Bible. O. T. Zechariah--Commentaries.

NL 0448393 NN

4DS Löwinger, Hermann.
Pales. Pressburger Ghettobilder. Mainz,
42 J. Wirth, 1900.
  117 p.

NL 0448394 DLC-P4 OCH

Löwinger, Judah Leb.
ספר שאגת אריה, דברי מוסר שכתבתי ... יודא ארי' בה"נ
מרדכי. וגם תוכו ... דברי אגדה מ(את) צבי הרש חריף העולל.
¡1868; 628 ,האלצוווארטה .זויען. בדפוס י
 24 l. 18 cm.

 1. Ethics, Jewish. i. Heller, Zebi Hirsch, d. 1834. ii. Title:
Sha'agat Aryeh.   *Title romanized:* Sefer Sha'agat Aryeh.

BJ1287.L63S5   74–264850
Library of Congress 71 ¡3¡ HE

NL 0448395 DLC

Loewinger, Rose, 1911–
 Buy low, sell high; how to make money in the stock market, by Lou Ellen ¡pseud.¡ Los Angeles, Savage and Savage
¡1951;
 89 p. 22 cm.

 1. Stocks. 2. Speculation. i. Title.

HG6041.L6 332.64 51–31779 ‡

NL 0448396 DLC CaBVa

Loewinger, Samuel
  see Löwinger, David Samuel, 1904–

Löwinger, Wilhelm
 Spinoza; anlässlich der 250. Wiederkehr
seines Todestages, 21. Februar 1677. ¡1927;
¡117¡-124 p. illus., ports. 25cm.

 From Menorah, 5. Jahrg., Nr. 2, Februar 1927.

 1. Spinoza, Benedictus de, 1632-1677.

NL 0448398 NNC

Loewinski, Henri.
 Die lyrik in den "Miracles de Nostre Dame." Progr. Berlin,
R. Gaertner, 1900.
 4°. pp. 27 +.

Miracles de Nostre   Dame par Personnages¡¡

NL 0448399 MH NjP CtY NIC

Loewinsky, Julius.
 Zur Geschichte des Orthonitrobenzylchlorids.
Berlin, 1895.
 73 p. 8°. [In vol. labeled "Chemical Disserta-
tions. Basel. 1895. v. 1."]
 Inaug.-Diss.

NL 0448400 CtY

Löwinsohn, Berka, 1878–
 *Die Beckenverletzungen
unter der Geburt, ihre Aetiologie, Symptome
und Behandlung. 55 pp. 8°. Freiburg i. Br.,
Hammerschlag & Kahle. 1910

NL 0448401 DNLM ICRL

Loewinsohn, Joseph A.
 Beyond the equator, by Joseph A. Loewinsohn. New York,
Fortuny's ¡*1940¡
 75 p. 19ᵐ.

 i. Title.   40–34746
Library of Congress PZ3.L8245Be

NL 0448402 DLC

Löwinsohn (Julius). *Experimenta de nervi
vagi in respirationem vi et effecta. 43 pp. 8°.
*Dorpati Liv., typ. vid. J. C. Schünmanni & C. Mat-
tiesci.* 1856. [P., v. 1695.]

NL 0448403 DNLM

Loewinson-Lessing, Fedor Iŭl'evich
  see
  Levinson-Lessing, Frants Iŭl'evich, 1861–1939.

Loewinson-Lessing, Frants Iŭl'evich
  see
  Levinson-Lessing, Frants Iŭl'evich, 1861–1939.

Löwinstamm, Roman.
 Masken. Lustspiel in 3 Akten (nach einem
alten französischen Stoff frei bearbeitet) von
R. Löwinstamm. Berlin, R. Bittner, 1869.
 1 p.l., 71 p. 12°.

NL 0448406 NN

Löwinstamm, Roman.
 Die seltsame Wette. Lustspiel in 1 Akt. Nach dem Französischen, von Roman Löwinstamm... Berlin: E. Bloch ¡187–¡
 40 p. 17cm. (Eduard Bloch's Theater-Correspondenz. Nr.
65.)

 1. Drama, German. i. Title.   May 24, 1937
N. Y. P. L.

NL 0448407 NN

SD 500 LÖWIS, ANDREAS VON
.L7 L8 Anleitung zur Forstwirthschaft für Livland,
  von A. von Löwis. Riga, Meinshausen, 1814.
  8+246 p.

  1. Forests and forestry--Livonia. I. tc.

NL 0448408 InU MH-BA

Löwis, Andreas von, tr.

Svinin, Pavel Petrovich, 1788–1839.
 Malerische reise durch Nordamerika von Paul Swinin. Aus
dem russischen übersetzt. Riga, Hartmann, 1816.

VOLUME 338

HF 5715 LÖWIS, ANDREAS VON
.L71 L 8   Tabellarische Uebersicht der Maasse und
Gewichte verschiedener Länder, nebst einer
Vergleichung derselben mit dem rigischen Stoof,
dem rigischen Loof, der revisorischen Loofstelle
und dem rigischen Pfunde. Dorpat, Livl. gemein.
und ökon. Societät, 1829.
120 p. tables.

NL 0448410   InU

Kress   Löwis, Andreas von, 1777-1839.
Room   Tabellarische übersicht der masse und
gewichte verschiedener länder nebst einer
vergleichung derselben mit den früheren
massen und gewichten: dem rigischen stof,
dem rigischen lof, der revisorischen lofstelle
und dem rigischen pfunde ... Dorpat,
E.J.Karow, 1859.
68 p. 23.5 cm.

"Unveränderter abdruck der ausgabe vom
jahre 1829."

1.Weights and measures - Tables, etc.
2.Weights and measures - Livonia.

NL 0448412   MH-BA

Löwis, Andreas von. Ueber die ehemalige verbreitung der
eichen in Liv- und Estland; ein beitrag zur geschichte des
anbaues dieser länder. Dorpat. 1824. sm.8°. pp.275+.

NL 0448413   MH-A

LÖWIS, A[ndreas] von.
Ueber die entstehung,den zweck und den
endlichen untergang der ritterschlösser im
alten Livland. [Riga,etc.,E.Frantzen,1837].

nar.12°. pp.(140). Plate. (Mittheilungen
aus dem gebiete der geschichte Liv- Eh lst-
und Kurland's,i,2.).
Without individual title-page. Caption
title.
Balt 2328.37

NL 0448414   MH

Löwis, Karl von
    see   Löwis of Menar, Karl von.

Löwis of Menar, August Arthur von, 1881-*1930*.
... Die Brünhildsage in Russland, von August von
Löwis of Menar. Leipzig, Mayer & Müller, g. m. b. h.,
1923.
110 p. 24½ᵐ. (Palaestra; untersuchungen und texte aus der deutschen
und englischen philologie. 142)

1. Brunhild. 2. Folk literature—Themes, motives. 3. Fairy tales—Hist.
& crit. 4. Folk litera*u*re—Russia.
                                                                    24—14654
Library of Congress   PD25.P3 no. 142

    ViU
NL 0448416   DLC CoU MoU CU NcD PU PBm MiU OCU NcU

Löwis of Menar, August Arthur von, 1881-1930,
ed.
Das Deutsche buch; monatsschrift für deutsche neuerscheinun-
gen. 1.-11. jahrg.; jan. 1921-nov./dez. 1931. Leipzig,
Deutsche gesellschaft für auslandsbuchhandel e. v. ₁1921-
25₎; Börsenverein der deutschen buchhändler ₁1926-31₎

Löwis of Menar, August Arthur von, 1881-1930.
Finnische und estnische volksmärchen, hrsg. und eingeleitet
von August von Löwis of Menar. Jena, E. Diederichs, 1922.
xv, 301, ₁1₎ p. incl. front. 20ᶜᵐ. (Added t.-p.: Die märchen der weltliteratur. ₍20₎)
"Von frau dr. E. Schmidt sind die finnischen märchen übertragen, von
professor W. Anderson die ungedruckten estnischen und die livischen
stücke."
"Kalevala": p. 152-175. "Kalevipoeg": p. 262-278. "Livische
märchen, aufgezeichnet von stud. O. Loorits": p. 279-292.
"Quellennachweise und anmerkungen": p. 293-298.
1. Fairy tales. 2. Folk-lore, Finnish. 3. Folk-lore, Esthonian. 4.
Folk-lore, Livonian. I. Kalevala. II. Kalevipoeg. III. Loorits, Oskar.
IV. Schmidt, Frau Emmy, tr. v. Anderson, Walter, 1885-   tr.
                                                                    24—6694
Library of Congress   GR200.L6

NL 0448418   DLC NjP PSt CtY MiU CU PPT OCl IU ICU NN

Hk8.79   Löwis of Menar, August Arthur von, 1881-
Der Held im deutschen und russischen Märchen.
Abschnitt I und II ... [Leipzig,Spamersche
Buchdruckerei]1912.
1p.ℓ.,73,[2]p. 23cm.
Inaug.-Diss. - Berlin.
Vita.
"Das Ganze wird in kurzer Zeit im Verlage
von Eugen Diederichs, Jena, erscheinen."
"Literaturverzeichnis": p.70-72.

NL 0448419   CtY MH PU IU ICRL

PN994 Löwis of Menar, August Arthur von, 1881-
.L8   ... Der held im deutschen und russischen märchen. Jena,
E. Diederich, 1912.
₁1₎, 139, ₁1₎ p. 23ᵐ.
At head of title: August von Löwis of Menar.
"Literaturverzeichnis der häufiger benutzten schriften": p. 135-139.

1. Heroes. 2. Fairy tales, German—Hist. & crit. 3. Fairy tales, Russian—
Hist. & crit.

NL 0448420   ICU NcU MiU OCl MH

Löwis of Menar, August von.
... Märchen und sagen, hrsg. von August von Löwis of
Menar, mit leisten und vignetten von R. von Hoerschel-
mann. Berlin-Charlottenburg, Felix Lehmann verlag, g.
m. b. h., 1916.
xviii, 171, ₁1₎ p. 25ᵐᵐ. (Added t.-p.: Ostsee und Ostland ... I. Die
Baltischen Provinzen, bd. 5)
"Verzeichnis der benutzten literatur": 1 page at end.

1. Legends—Baltic Provinces. 2. Fairy tales. I. Title.
                                                                    21—18031
Library of Congress   DK511.B28O8 bd. 5

NL 0448421   DLC MoU OCl PU

Löwis of Menar, August Arthur von, 1881-1930, ed.
and tr.
    Russische Volksmärchen. Übers. und eingel-
eitet von August von Löwis. Jena, E. Diederichs,
1914.
332 p. (Die Märchen der Weltliteratur)

NL 0448422   DLC-P4

Löwis of Menar, August Arthur von, 1881-1930, ed. and tr.
Russische volksmärchen, übersetzt und eingeleitet von
August von Löwis of Menar. 10. bis 19. tausend. Jena,
E. Diederichs, 1921.
2 p. l., ix-xxvi, 332 p., 2 l. front. 19¼ᵐᵐ. (Added t.-p.: Die märchen
der weltliteratur)
"Quellennachweise und anmerkungen": p. 329-331; "Literatur":
p. 331-332.

1. Fairy tales. 2. Tales, Russian. I. Title.
                                                                    35—14961
Library of Congress   PZ34.L7 1921   398.210947

ICN NIC CU-S CU
NL 0448423   DLC TNJ PPT OO MiU MH OCl NIC PBm IU

338.3
L827   Löwis of Menar, August Arthur von,1881-
ed. and tr.
Russische volksmärchen. Übers. und
eingeleitet von August von Löwis of
Menar. Jena,E.Diederichs,1927.
xxii,332p. front. 19cm. (Die
märchen der weltliteratur)

"Literatur":p.351-352.

1.Folk-lore. Russia. I.Title.

NL 0448424   CtY

PN998 ₍Löwis of Menar, August Arthur von₎ 1881-1930, tr.
.R9L82   Russische Volksmärchen. ₍Verb. und erweiterte
Ausg. von Reinhold Olesch. Düsseldorf₎ E.
Diederichs ₍1955₎
340 p. (Die Märchen der Weltliteratur)
Includes bibliography.

1.Fairy tales. 2. Folk-lore—Russia. 3.
Tales, Russian. I. Olesch, Reinhold, 1910-   ed.
II. Title.   Series.

NL 0448425   ICU KMK

DK651   Loewis of Menar, Karl von
R5L7   Die älteste Ordensburg in Livland.   Berlin,
F.Ebhardt & co., 1903.
7p. plan(fold.) 21cm.

1. Riga. Ordensburg. 2. Teutonic knights -
Hist. I. Title.

NL 0448426   IaU NN

Loewis of Menar, Karl von, and F. Bienemann.
Die Burgen der livländischen Schweiz; Segewold, Treyden,
Kremon und Wenden. Zugleich ein Führer durch das Aathal,
von Karl von Loewis of Menar und Dr. F. Bienemann jun...
Riga: A. Stieda, 1895. iv, 64 p. front., illus., plans. 12°.

1. Livonia—Descr. and trav. 2. Biene-   mann, Friedrich, 1860-   , jt. au.
N. Y. P. L.   June 8, 1925

NL 0448427   NN

Loewis of Menar, Karl von.
Burgenlexikon für Alt-Livland... I. Teil. Die hölzernen
Wallburgen der Urzeit. II. Teil. Die Steinburgen des Mittelalters. Anhang. Burgen und Städte als Münzstätten in Alt-Livland.
Zusammengestellt von Karl von Löwis of Menar.. Hrsg. von
der Gesellschaft für Geschichte und Altertumskunde der Ostseeprovinzen in Riga. Riga: Verlag der Aktiengesellschaft Walters
und Rapa, 1922. 129, 55 p. illus. (incl. plans.) 8°.

1. Castles—Russia—Livonia. 2. Ge-   sellschaft für Geschichte und Altertumskunde zu Riga.   September 28, 1925
N. Y. P. L.

NL 0448428   NN CU

4DK   Löwis of Menar, Karl   von
647   Die Düna von der Ogermundung bis
Riga und der Badeort Baldohn; ein
topographisoh-historischer Führer.
Riga, Jonck & Poliewsky, 1910.
124 p.

NL 0448429   DLC-P4

VOLUME 338

GA 935 LÖWIS OF MENAR, KARL VON
.L78 L82   Erläuterungen zu der Karte von Livland
im Mittelalter, entworfen und gezeichnet von
Karl von Löwis of Menar. Reval, F. Kluge,
1895.
29 p. map in pocket.

1. Livonia--Maps.

NL 0448430   InU

Loewis of Menar, Karl von, and F. Bienemann.
Fuehrer durch die livländische Schweiz mit den Burgen Segewold, Treyden, Kremon, die Kreisstädte Wenden u. Wolmar mit
Umgebungen u. dem Aatal von Wolmar bis zum Aa-Düna-Kanal,
von K. v. Löwis of Menar und Dr. F. Bienemann...   Riga:
Jonck & Poliewsky, 1912. 150 p. illus., maps, plan. 3. ed.,
rev. and enl.   12°

1. Livonia--Guidebooks, 1912.   2. Bienemann, Friedrich, 1860-
jt. au.
N. Y. P. L.   June 8, 1925

NL 0448431   NN

Löwis of Menar, Karl von.
...Riga. Kurzer geschichtlicher Führer, von K. von Löwis
... Riga: Jonck & Poliewsky, 1918.   37 p.   front., col'd
plan, 2 pl.   8°.

Plates printed on both sides.

1. Riga--Guidebooks, 1918.
N. Y. P. L.   June 15, 1925

NL 0448432   NN CU

Law
      Löwisch, Günther, 1899-   ed.

Württemberg-Baden. *Laws, statutes, etc.*
Gesetz Nr. 726 über die Beteiligung der Arbeitnehmer an
der Verwaltung und Gestaltung der Betriebe der Privat-
wirtschaft vom 18. August 1948. Für die betriebliche Praxis
erläutert von Günther Löwisch und Franz Müller. Stuttgart, W. Kohlhammer, 1948.

Löwisch, Hans: Städtische Fürsorgearbeit und Sozialistische Kommu-
nalpolitik in der Stadt Weißenfels a./S. während des letzten
Jahrzehnts. Ein Beitr. z. deutsch. Kommunalgesch. in d. Jahren
d. Übergangstendenzen a. d. bürgerl. in die sozialistische Welt.
[Maschinenschrift] 196 S. 4°. — Auszug: Halle a. S. 1922:
Karras & Koennecke. 2 Bl. 8°
Halle, R.- u. staatswiss. Diss. v. 30. Jan. 1923   [U 23.4871

NL 0448434   ICRL

Loewisch, Heinz, 1905-
Was versteht man unter schadensersatz wegen
nichterfuellung in §463 des buergerlichen
gesetzbuchs?
Inaug. diss. Jena, 1930. (Leipzig)
Bibl.

NL 0448435   DLC MH-L ICRL MiU

LOEWISCH. Max.
Die Neugestaltung unseres französischen und englischen Unterrichts.
Eisenach, 1896. 23 pp. [Jahres-Bericht der Grossherzoglichen
Realgymnasiums zu Eisenach.] 4°.

NL 0448436   MB

4LB-55   Löwisch, Max.
Städtische Oberrealschule mit Reformreal-
gymnasium Weissenfels 25 Jahre Schulgeschichte,
1911-1936.   [Weissenfels, 1936]
143 p.

NL 0448437   DLC-P4

Löwisch, Max.
Zur englischen aussprache von 1650-1750 nach frühengli-
schen grammatiken ... von Max Löwisch. Kassel, T. Kay,
1889.
2 p. l., 80 p. 20½^{cm}.
Inaug.-diss.—Jena.

1. English language—Early modern (1500-1700)—Pronunciation.
2. English language—18th cent.—Pronunciation.
Library of Congress   PE1137.L7
                                              11-10730

NL 0448438   DLC NjP NcD CtY OClW MB MH MiU

Löwisch, Walther Max Heinz
see Löwisch, Heinz, 1905-

Loewisohn, Solomon, 1789-1821
Biblische Geographie, enthaltend eine
Beschreibung aller Länder, Meere, Land-
Seen, Flüsse, Bäche, Berge, Hügel, Thäler,
Wälder, Wüsten, Städte und Dörfer, die in
sämmtlichen Büchern des Alten Testaments
vorkommen, wie auch der israelitischen
Stationen, deren in den Büchern Mosis
erwähnt wird. Aus dem Hebräischen. Mit
einer Karte des Schauplatzes der Bibel.
Wien: C. F. Beck, 1821.
241 p.

NL 0448440   OCH

Löwisohn, Solomon, 1789-1821.
ארץ קדומים כולל נלילות ארץ ישראל. ושמות המקומות הנזכא-
ברפיות הנמצאות בכתבי הקדש. מבוארים ע"פ דעת בעלי אסו-
פות. חדשים גם ישנים ובחונים בכור הבקורת החדשה. מאת יעקב
קאפלאן. ווילנא. מ. מן ן,ש. ימל. תקצ"ם. ,Вильно, 1839.
2 v. 19 cm.
Added t. p.: Erez kedumin, das Land des Alterthums; oder,
Alphabetisch geordnete Geographie Palästinas und der Umgegend,
so viel davon in der Heiligen Schrift erwaehnt wird. Jetzt ... bald
erläutert, bald berichtigt, und vorzüglich mit einer grossen Anzahl
vieler neuer Ortsnamen vermehrt, von J. Kaplan.
First ed. published in 1819 under title: ארץ מחקרי
1. Bible. O. T.—Geography. 2. Palestine—Historical geography.
I. Kaplan, Jacob, d. 1841. II. Title.
Title.   *transliterated:* Erets kedumim.
BS630.L62   60-57594

NL 0448441   DLC ICU

Löwisohn, Solomon, 1789-1821.

Jews. *Liturgy and ritual. Kinot.*
סדר הקינות לליל וליום תשעה באב. ועם מגילת איכה מתורגם
ומבואר ע"י אהרן וואלפסזאהן ותרגום אשכנזי ובאור אל הציונים
ע"י שלמה לעוויזאהן. כמנהג פולין. ביהם. מעהרן. שלעזיען,
ליטויא. פריסען ורייסען. ווייע. נעהרוקם ביא אנמאן עדלען פאן
שמיד.   Wien, 1831.

NL 0448443   DLC

Löwisohn, Solomon, 1789-1821.
מחקרי ארץ; ספר מדבר על הארצות וחיים הרים ... אשר
יוכרו בספרי הקדש. נם על תחתוניות אשר חנו בני ישראל במדבר.
Wien, G. Holzinger, Buchdrucker, 1819.
122 l. 19 cm.

1. Bible. O. T.—Geography. 2. Palestine—Historical geography.
I. Title.   *Title transliterated:* Meḥkere erets.
BS630.L6   56-48525

NL 0448443   DLC

Löwisohn, Solomon, 1789-1821.
מחקרי ארץ. לקטיקון ניאוגרפי של כתבי-הקודש. מבוא מאת נ
קרסל. תל-אביב. מחברות לספרות. תש"ת.
,Tel-Aviv, 1944/45;
23, 254 p. 18 cm.

1. Bible. O. T.—Geography. 2. Palestine—Historical geography.
I. Title.
[BS630.L   ]   *Title transliterated:* Meḥkere erets.
                                                A 57-5304
Hebrew Union College.   Library
for Library of Congress   ₍8₎

NL 0448444   OCH ICU CU

Löwisohn, Solomon, 1789-1821.
מחקרי לשון. כולל שיחה בעולם הנשמות ובית האסף. עם
הערות ונוספות הרבה מאת אד"ם הכהן לעבענזאהן ... ווילנא.
ברפוס י. ר. ראם, תר"ם.   ,Wilna, 1849;
xii, 108 p. 18 cm.
Added t. p.: Investigationes linguae, sive duo opera ... Sicha
beolam hanschamoth et Beth haossef; illustrata et aucta a A. B.
Lebensohn, cum multis ₍sic₎ utilibus adnotationibus ab editore Judelo
Behak.

1. Hebrew language—Grammar.
                              Title transliterated: Meḥkere lashon.
PJ4556.L58   1849   57-50059

NL 0448445   DLC

Löwisohn, Solomon, 1789-1821.
מחקרי לשון; הכין לדפום והקרים מבוא. ישראל זמורה. תל-
אביב. מחברות לספרות תש"ז.   ,Tel-Aviv, 1946/47;
9, 105 p. 18 cm.

1. Hebrew language—Grammar.
                              Title transliterated: Meḥkere lashon.
PJ4556.L58   1946   57-50060

NL 0448446   DLC CU

Löwisohn, Solomon, 1789-1821.
מליצת ישרון. ספר כולל למודי המליצה העברית. מבוארים
במשלים רבים מסלוצת ספרי הקודש. ווין. נעדרוקם ביא א.
שמיד.   Wien, 1816.
98 l. 20 cm.

1. Hebrew language—Rhetoric. I. Title.
                              Title transliterated: Melitsat yeshurun.
PJ4740.L6   56-49284

NL 0448447   DLC CtY

Löwisohn, Solomon, 1789-1821.
מליצת ישרון. עם מבוא מאת יעקב פיכמן. תל-אביב. מחברות
לספרות. תש"ד.   ,Tel-Aviv, 1943/44;
184 p. 19 cm.   (ספרית הפואתיקה, א)

1. Hebrew language—Rhetoric. I. Title.
                              Title transliterated: Melitsat yeshurun.
PJ4740.L6   1943   58-54782 ‡

NL 0448448   DLC CU

Löwisohn, Solomon, 1789-1821.
שיחה בעולם הנשמות. בין דוד קמחי ובין יואל ברי"ל; כוללת
שלשה מאמרים בחקירות עיוניות בדקדוק לשון עבר.
Prag, Gedruckt bei F. Sommer, 1811.
38 l. 18 cm.
Later editions published with the author's בית האוסף under the
title מחקרי לשון.

1. Hebrew language—Grammar. I. Title.
                              Title transliterated: Siḥah be-'olam ha-neshamot.
PJ4556.L6   57-50061

NL 0448449   DLC CtY

VOLUME 338

Löwit, Isidor.
... "Schir-hakawod," gottesdienstliche gesänge für israelitische gemeinden nach sephardischem ritus componirt und hrsg. von Isidor Löwit ... [und] Jacob Bauer ... Wien, Verlag der herausgeber [1889]
v. 34 cm.
The title is given also in Hebrew.
The text is in transliterated Hebrew.
Contents. - Theil 1.
I. Jews. Lit. & rit. I. Bauer, Jacob. II. Title. III. Title: Gottesdienstliche gesänge für israelitische gemeinden nach sephardischem ritus.

NL 0448450 MB

Löwit, Moritz, 1851-1918.
[Collected papers on physiology.]
Mostly reprints from various medical and scientific serials.

NL 0448451 ICJ

Loewit, Moritz, 1851-1918.
Infektion und immunität, von dr. M. Loewit ... Nach dem tode des verfassers hrsg. von prof. dr. Gustav Bayer. Mit 33 textfiguren und 2 farbigen tafeln. Berlin, Wien, Urban & Schwarzenberg, 1921.
viii, 550 p. illus., II col. pl. 24½ᶜᵐ.
"Literatur" at end of each chapter.

1. Contagion and contagious diseases. [1. Infection] 2. Immunity. [2. Immunology] 3. Pathology, [General] I. Bayer, Gustav.

Library, U. S. Surgeon-   General's Office   S G 25-42

NL 0448452 DNLM ICRL DNAL ICJ

WH   LOEWIT, Moritz, 1851-1918
L827L   Die Leukämie als Protozoeninfektion;
1900   Untersuchungen zur Ätiologie und
Pathologie. Wiesbaden, Bergmann,
1900.
viii, 280 p. illus.

NL 0448453 DNLM NIC

Löwit, Moritz, 1851-1918.
Studien zur Physiologie und Pathologie des Blutes und der Lymphe. Von Dr. M. Löwit, ... Mit 2 lithographischen Tafeln. Jena, G. Fischer, 1892.
[6], 141, [1] p. incl. tables. II fold. pl. (diagrs.) 26ᶜᵐ.
Bibliographical foot-notes.

NL 0448454 ICJ NNC DNLM MiU CtY-M

Löwit, Moritz, 1851-1918.
...Ueber blutgerinnung und thrombose, von ... M. Löwit. Berlin, Fischer, 1889.
cover-title; 17 p. (Medicinische wander-vorträge, hft. 9, juni 1889)

1. Blood - Coagulation. I. Medicinische wander-vorträge, hft. 9.

NL 0448455 NNC DNLM

QZ   LÖWIT, Moritz, 1851-1918
L827v   Vorlesungen über allgemeine Pathologie.
Jena, Fischer, 1897-
v. illus.
Contents. —1. Heft. Die Lehre vom Fieber.

NL 0448456 DNLM

Loewit, R., firm, booksellers, Vienna.
Altes und neues zur jüdischen Bewegung.
[A catalogue.] Winter 1918/19. Wien,
1919.
67 (1) p.

Ti. taken from paper-cover.

NL 0448457 OCH

016.83   Löwit, R., firm, booksellers, Vienna.
L827v   Ein viertel-Jahrhundert jüdischer Literatur; 1900-1925. Anlässlich des XIV. Zionistenkongresses in Wien. Wien, [1925]
iv, 72p. 22cm.

Cover title.

1. Jewish literature (German) Bibl. 2. German literature. Jewish authors. Bibl. 3. Jews in art. Bibl. 4. Zionism. Bibl. I. Title.

NL 0448458 IEN

Löwith, Karl, 1897-
...Da Hegel a Nietzsche. [Torino] G. Einaudi, 1949. 637 p. 22cm.

580742B. 1. Hegelianism. 2. Philoso-   phy, German. 3. Sociology—Hist.
4. Sociology, Christian. I. Ser.
N. Y. P. L.   July 27, 1951

NL 0448459 NN

Löwith, Karl, 1897-
Heidegger: Denker in dürftiger Zeit. [Frankfurt am Main] S. Fischer, 1953.
109 p. 20 cm. (Schriftenreihe "Ausblicke")

1. Heidegger, Martin, 1889-
A 53—6499

Chicago. Univ. Libr.
for Library of Congress   [54b1]

NcD IaU ICMcC OU KyU
NL 0448460 ICU TxU PPWe IU OCU PU PPG CtY NN NjP

Löwith, Karl, 1897-
Das individuum in der rolle des mitmenschen, von Karl Löwith. München, Drei masken verlag, 1928.
xvi, 180 p. 24½ᶜᵐ.
"Ein beitrag zur anthropologischen grundlegung der ethischen probleme."—p. [V]

1. Individuality. 2. Ethics. I. Title.
36-3158

Library of Congress   BJ1114.L6   171

NL 0448461 DLC WaU CtY NcU NNC

Löwith, Karl, 1897-
... Jacob Burckhardt; der mensch inmitten der geschichte. Luzern, Vita nova verlag, 1936.
2 p. l., 7-380 p., 1 l. 23ᶜᵐ.
"Schriftennachweis": p. 349-350.

1. Burckhardt, Jakob Christoph, 1818-1897.
38-30116

Library of Congress   D15.B8L6
[2]   928.3

NL 0448462 DLC OrPR WaU OU NIC OO CtY ICU

Löwith, Karl, 1897-
Kierkegaard und Nietzsche; oder, Philosophische und theologische überwindung des nihilismus, von Karl Löwith. Frankfurt am Main, V. Klostermann, 1933.
32 p. 1 mounted illus. 24ᶜᵐ.

1. Kierkegaard, Søren Aabye, 1813-1855. 2. Nietzsche, Friedrich Wilhelm, 1844-1900. 3. Nihilism.
35-35738

Library of Congress   B828.3.L6   149.8

NL 0448463 DLC CtY NcD WaU ICU

Löwith, Karl, 1897-
Meaning in history; the theological implications of the philosophy of history. [Chicago] Univ. of Chicago Press [1949]
ix, 257 p. 22 cm.
Bibliographical references included in "Notes" (p. 225-257)

1. History—Philosophy. I. Title.

D16.9.L64   901   49-1624*

WaSpG
Or OrCS OrP OrPR OrSaW OrAshS OrU WaS WaE WaWW
PHC PPWe OOxM PPDrop CaBVa IdU CaBViP CaBVaU MtU
AU KyWAT KyU MU PU PSC PLF CaOTP PBL PSt PPLas PPEB
TxU TU OCU OO OU OKentU NN NNJ FTaSU MH-AH KyLxCB
NL 0448464 DLC PBm NcRS PPT InStme MiU MB ICU ViU

Löwith, Karl, 1897-
... Nietzsches philosophie der ewigen wiederkunft des gleichen. Berlin, Verlag Die Runde, 1935.
183 p. 24½ᶜᵐ.
"Schriftennachweis und anmerkungen": p. [163]-183.

1. Nietzsche, Friedrich Wilhelm, 1844-1900.
35-33944

Library of Congress   B3317.L57
[2]   193.9

NL 0448466 DLC CSt AAP CtY ICU NcD NcU CU MiDW WaU

Löwith, Karl, 1897-
... Von Hegel bis Nietzsche. Zürich, New York, Europa verlag [1941]
588 p. 22ᶜᵐ.
"Schriftennachweis": p. 531-533.

1. Hegel, Georg Wilhelm Friedrich, 1770-1831. 2. Philosophy, Modern. 3. Sociology. 4. Religious thought—19th cent. I. Title.

Library of Congress   B808.L6   41-22509
[5]

Wa WaE WaPS WaS WaSp WaSpG WaT WaTC WaWW MH-AH IdPI
OrU-M MH NcU CaBVaU IdB IdU MtBC MtU OrCS OrPR OrU
NL 0448467 DLC NIC NcD CtY CLU Or OrStbM OrSaW PBm

4BD-148 Löwith, Karl, 1897-
Von Hegel zu Nietzsche; der revolutionäre Bruch im Denken des neuzehnten Jahrhunderts. Marx und Kierkegaard. 2. Aufl. Zürich, Europa-Verlag [c1941]
464 p.

NL 0448468 DLC-P4 NjP IaU MeB

VOLUME 338

B
803
.L83
1949
Löwith, Karl, 1897–
Von Hegel zu Nietzsche; der revolutionäre
Bruch im Denken des neunzehnten Jahrhunderts;
Marx und Kierkegaard. 2.Aufl. Zürich/Wien,
Europa-Verlag [Vorwort 1949]
464 p. 23 cm.
"Schriftennachweis": p.417-419.

1.Hegel,Georg Wilhelm Friedrich,1770-1831.
2.Philosophy,Modern. I.Title.

NL 0448469   MiU CU NRU MH NN

Löwith, Karl, 1897–
Von Hegel zu Nietzsche: der revolutionäre
Bruch im Denken des neunzehnten Jahrhunderts,
Marx und Kierkegaard; 2.Aufl. Stuttgart,
Kohlhammer[1950] 464p. 23cm.

"Schriftennachweis": p.417-419.

1. Hegel, Georg Wilhelm Friedrich, 1770-
1831. 2. Philosophy, Modern. 3. Sociology.
4. Religious thought.19th cent. I. Title.

NL 0448470   MWelC CSt

190.9
L918v
1953
Löwith, Karl, 1897–
Von Hegel zu Nietzsche; der revolutionäre
Bruch im Denken des neunzehnten Jahrhunderts;
Marx und Kierkegaard. 3.Aufl. Stuttgart,
W.Kohlhammer [1953, c1941]
464p. 23cm.

Bibliography: p.417-419.

1.Philosophy, Modern. 2.Hegel, Georg
Wilhelm Friedrich, 1770-1831. 3.Religious
thought - 19th   cent. I.Title.

NL 0448471   CLSU ICMcC NBC MiEM WU ICN

D16
.9
L6415
1953
Löwith. Karl, 1897–
Weltgeschichte und Heilgeschehen; die theologischen
Voraussetzungen der Geschichtsphilosophie. 2. Aufl.
Stuttgart. W. Kohlhammer [1953]
231 p. (Urban-Bücher. 2)

"Der englische Text des von Dr. H. Kesting übersetzten und
vom Verfasser neu durchgesehenen Buches erschien 1949 ... unter
dem Titel 'Meaning in History'

1. History – Philosophy.

NL 0448472   ICU FTaSU TxDaM   OCH NjPT LU IaU CLSU ICN CtY-D
    CU WaSpG MnU MH NN MiU NIC NNC InU PPLT

Löwl, Ferdinand, 1856–1908,
Aus dem Zillerthaler hochgebirge. Gera, E. Amthor, 1878.
pp. iv, (3), 438.
Inserted over imprint: Leipzig, Amthor'sche verlagsbuchhandlung.

Zillerthal, Tyrol[]

NL 0448473   MH

Löwl, Ferdinand, 1856-1908.
Becke, Friedrich Johann Karl, 1855–
... Exkursionen im westlichen und mittleren abschnitt
der Hohen Tauern unter führung von F. Becke und
F. Löwl ... [Wien, 1903?]

Löwl, Ferdinand, 1856–1908.
Die gebirgbildenden felsarten. Eine gesteinskunde für geo-
graphen von prof. dr. Ferdinand Löwl ... Stuttgart, F. Enke,
1893.
159 p. illus., diagrs. 22½ cm.

1. Petrology.

U. S. Geol. survey. Library   G S 6-655
for Library of Congress   [a37b1-]

NL 0448475   DI-GS MB

Löwl, Ferdinand, 1856–
Geologie. Von Dr Ferdinand Löwl ... Leipzig und
Wien, F. Deuticke, 1906.
viii, 332 p. illus., diagrs. 26 cm. (*Added t.-p.*: Die erdkunde. Eine
darstellung ihrer wissensgebiete, ihrer hilfswissenschaften und der methode ihres unterrichtes ... hrsg. von Maximilian Klar ... xi. teil ...)
Bibliographies interspersed.

1. Geology.

Library, U. S. Geol.   survey   G S 6-707

NL 0448476   DI-GS IU NN   ICJ

Löwl, Ferdinand, 1856–
Siedlungsarten in den Hochalpen. Stuttgart, J. Engelhorn,
1888.
pp. 51. (Forschungen zur deutschen landes- und volkskunde,
ii. 6.)

Alps||CB 3: 73|

NL 0448477   MH

GB561
.L8
(G1)
LÖWL, FERDINAND, 1856-1908,
Über thalbildung. Von dr. Ferdinand Löwl...
Prag, H. Dominicus, 1884.
[iii]-vi, 136 p. illus. 23 cm.

1. Valleys.

NL 0448478   ICU IU MH DI-GS

LÖWL, Ferdinand, 1856-1908.
Die ursache der secularen verschiebungen der
strandlini Vortrag. Prag. 1886.

pp.15.

NL 0448479   MH

Löwlein, Hans, 1909–
[Music, violoncello & orchestra, op. 13]

Musik für Violoncell und Orchester. Op. 13. Partitur.
Leipzig, Breitkopf & Härtel [1950]
score (28 p.) 33 cm. (Breitkopf & Härtels Partitur-Bibliothek,
Nr. 4020)
Duration: 9 minutes.

1. Violoncello with orchestra—Scores.

M1016.L85 op. 13   52-27833

NL 0448480   DLC NN

M
1017
L326m13
1951
Löwlein, Hans, 1909–
[Musik, violoncello & orchestra, op.13; arr.]
Musik für Violoncell und Orchester, op.13.
Ausg. für Violoncell und Klavier von Johannes
Schäfer. Leipzig, Breitkopf & Härtel [c1951]
score (14 p.) and part. (Edition Breitkopf,
Nr.5763)

1. Violoncello with orchestra - Solo with
piano. I. Schäfer, Johannes

NL 0448481   CLU

Löwmsohn (Julius). *Experimenta de nervi
vagi in respirationem vi et effecta. 44 pp., 1 pl.
8°. Derpat, typ. vid. J. C. Schünmanni et C. Mat-
tiessni. 1858.

NL 0448482   DNLM

532.5
L82c
Loewner, Charles.
Conservation laws in compressible flu-
id flow and associated mappings. Stan-
ford, Calif., Applied Mathematics and Sta-
tistics Laboratory, Stanford University,
1952.
36 p. 28cm. (U.S. Office of Naval
Research. Technical Report no. 8)
"Prepared under Contract Nonr 225 (11)
(NR-041-086) for Office of Naval Research.
"References": p. 36.

NL 0448483   LU

QA276
.S7
no.2
1954
Loewner, Charles
On some critical points of higher order.
Stanford, Calif., Applied Mathematics and
Statistics Laboratory, Stanford University,
1954.
23, 11 l. 28cm. (Stanford University. Applied
Mathematics and Statistics Laboratory. Technical
note, no. 2)
"This research was supported by the United States
Air Force through the Office of Scientific Research
of the Air Research and Development Command."
Bibliography: leaf [1]-11.
1. Geometry, Analy   tic. 2.Geometry,
Differential. I.   Title: Critical points
of higher order. II.

NL 0448484   ViU

Löwner, Heinrich, 1854–
... Die Herolde in den homerischen Gesängen ...
Eger, 1881.
Programm - K.K. Staats-Ober-Gymnasium
zu Eger.
Pamphlet.

NL 0448485   CtY

Löwner, Heinrich, 1854–
Lexikographische miscellen. n.p., 1895.

NL 0448486   NjP

Löwner, Heinrich, 1854–
Der literarische Charakter des 'Agricola' von
Tacitus ... Eger, 1884.
cover-title, 14 p. 25 cm.
"Aus dem Jahresberichte des K.k. Staats-
Obergymnasium in Eger (Böhmen) v.J. 1884."
"Zur Literatur": p. [2]
1. Tacitus, Cornelius. Agricola.

NL 0448487   CtY OCU CU

VOLUME 338

Løwold, Oluf Andreas, 1830–1899.
Biographiske efterretninger om præster i Høyland med familie og descendenter, indeholdende stamtavle over præstefamilierne Trane, Agricola (Haaland), Schanche, Hagerup, Lund, Ottesen, Wessel-Brown, Dahl, samlet og optegnet af Oluf A. Løwold. Stavanger, Bethania vaisenhus-bogtrykkeri, 1883.

32 p. incl. VIII geneal. tab. 17^{cm}.

1. Clergy—Norway—Høiland. 2. Norway·Biog. 3. Høiland, Norway—Geneal.

19–19658

Library of Congress   CS918.H6L6

NL 0448488   DLC

CS   Løwold, Oluf Andreas, 1830–1899.
918   Biographiske efterretninger om præster i
.H6   Stavanger, fra Reformationen indtil vore dage.
L6   Stavanger, Bethania vaisenhus-bogtr., 1890.
             33 p.   17cm.
Bound with the author's Biographiske efterretninger om præster i Høyland. Stavanger, 1883.

NL 0448489   WU

Løwold, Oluf Andreas, 1830–1899.
Fra Dalene. Gammelt og nyt. Samlet og optegnet af Oluf A. Løwold. Stavanger, Dreyers bogtrykkeri, 1895.

197, (3) p. 18^{cm}.

1. Dalene, Norway.

15–17931

Library of Congress   DL596.D3L7

NL 0448490   DLC

Løwold, Oluf Andreas, 1830–1899.
Fra Jæderen. Gammelt og nyt. Samlet og optegnet af Oluf A. Løwold. Stavanger, Bethania vaisenhus-bogtrykkeri, 1888.

186, (5) p. 18½^{cm}.

CONTENTS.—Natur, kunst og industri.—Oldtidsminder, folkesagn og traditioner.—Presternes biografier.—Stamtavler.

1. Jæderen, Norway. 2. Norway—Geneal.

13–18593

Library of Congress   DL576.J2L7

NL 0448491   DLC

Loew's bridge, a Broadway idyl
            see under [Tucker, Mrs. Mary Eliza
(Perine)] 1838–

Loew's Incorporated
       see
Metro-Goldwyn-Mayer, inc.

Loew's International Films Corporation
       see
Metro-Goldwyn-Mayer International, inc.

Loewus, Frank Abel, 1919–
Studies on the physical and chemical properties of starch. The retrogradation of amylose in the presence and absence of gelatinizing agents and similar compounds. Ann Arbor, University Microfilms (1952)

([University Microfilms, Ann Arbor, Mich.] Publication no. 3414)
Microfilm copy of typescript. Positive.
Collation of the original, as determined from the film: 178 l. illus., diagrs.
Thesis—University of Minnesota.
Abstracted in Dissertation abstracts, v. 12 (1952) no. 3, p. 238.
Biography.
Bibliography: leaves 174–178.
1. Starch.   I. Title.

Microfilm AC–1   no. 3414   Mic 54–143

NL 0448495   DLC

Loewy (A. S.) *De melæna. 2 p. l., 32 pp., 1 l.
8°. Praag. typ. Sommeriana. 1828.

NL 0448496   DNLM

Löwy, Abraham.
Sparta von 479–445 vor Christo ... Rostock, C. Boldt, 1873.

70 p. 21½^{cm}.
Inaug.-dis.—Rostock.

1. Sparta—Hist.

4–35000

Library of Congress   DF227.4.L81

NL 0448497   DLC NjP

Loewy, Adolf.
Gedächtnissrede auf ... den ... Kronprinzen Erzherzog Rudolf, gehalten am 5. Februar 1889...
13 p.

NL 0448498   OCH

Löwy, Adolf, ed. and tr.

Nissim ben Jacob ben Nissim ibn Shahin, 11th cent.
R. Nissim's Orientalischer legendenschatz, enthaltend moralische erzählungen und belehrungen aus Talmud und Midrasch, nach den quellen bedeutend vermehrt und deutsch bearbeitet von Adolf Löwy ... Wien, Im selbstverlage des herausgebers, 1882.

Löwy, Adolf.
Die tugend- und sittenlehre des Talmud. Dargestellt in anziehenden erzählungen, mit besonderer benützung des im 11. jahrhundert vom berühmten gaon rabbenu Nissim ben Jakob verfassten werkes Sefer Massoth, Buch der begebenheiten, von rabbiner Adolf Löwy. Wien, Verlag des verfassers, 1890.

2 p. l., (III)–VIII, 186 p. 21^{cm}.

1. Ethics, Jewish. 2. Talmud—Legends.   I. Nissim ben Jacob ben Nissim ibn Shahin, fl. 1050.

22–20234 Revised

Library of Congress   BJ1281.L6

NL 0448500   DLC NN

Löwy, Adolf, writer on law.
Die stille Gesellschaft in ihrem Verhältnis zu der Gesellschaft des bürgerlichen Rechts ... von Adolf Löwy ... Charlottenburg-Berlin, R. Münch, 1900.

76 p. 22½cm.
Inaug.-Diss. - Göttingen.
Bibliographical footnotes.

NL 0448501   MH-L

Loewy, Adolf, 1862–
[Collected papers chiefly on physiology.]
128896 Mostly extracts or reprints from various scientific and medical serials.

NL 0448502   ICJ

Loewy, Adolf, 1862–
Die berechnung der herzarbeit beim menschen. Von A. Loewy ...

(*In* Abderhalden, Emil, ed. Handbuch der biologischen arbeitsmethoden ... Berlin, 1920–   25^{cm}. abt. v, Methoden zum studium der funktionen der einzelnen organe des tierischen organismus. t. 4, 1 (1923) p. (881)–884)
Bibliographical foot-notes.

1. Heart.   A C 36–3734
Title from Ohio State   Univ.
Library of Congress   (QH324.A3 1920 abt. 5, t. 4, 1)
                              (2)   (574.072)

NL 0448503   OU

Loewy, Adolf, 1862–
Die bestimmung des herzschlagvolumens beim menschen. Von A. Loewy ...

(*In* Abderhalden, Emil, ed. Handbuch der biologischen arbeitsmethoden ... Berlin, 1920–   25^{cm}. abt. v, Methoden zum studium der funktionen der einzelnen organe des tierischen organismus. t. 4, 1 (1923) p. (837)–872. illus., diagr.)
Bibliographical foot-notes.

1. Heart.   A C 36–3732
Title from Ohio State   Univ.
Library of Congress   (QH324.A3 1920 abt. 5, t. 4, 1)
                              (2)   (574.072)

NL 0448504   OU

Loewy, Adolf, 1862–
Darmgase. Von prof. A. Loewy ...

(*In* Abderhalden, Emil, ed. Handbuch der biologischen arbeitsmethoden ... Berlin, 1920–   25^{cm}. abt. IV, Angewandte chemische und physikalische methoden. t. 6, 1. hälfte (1926) p. (397)–410. illus.)
Bibliographical foot-notes.

1. Intestines, Gases in.   A C 36–2671
Title from Ohio State   Univ.
Library of Congress   (QH324.A3 1920 abt. 4, t. 6)
                              (2)   (574.072)

NL 0448505   OU

Loewy, Adolf, 1862–   , and F. Mueller.
Einige Beobachtungen über das elektrische Verhalten der Atmosphäre am Meere. Von A. Löwy und Franz Müller. (Leipzig: S. Hirzel, 1904.) 4 p. Tables. 4°.
Caption-title.
Repr.: Physikalische Zeitschrift, 5. Jahrg.

1. Electricity (Atmospheric).   2. Mueller, Franz, jt. au.
N. Y. P. L.   October 10, 1917.

NL 0448506   NN

Loewy, Adolf, 1862–
Eine Expedition zur Erforschung der physiologischen Wirkungen des Hochgebirges. Von Prof. Dr. A. Loewy... Leipzig: G. Thieme, 1901. 11 p. 8°.
Cover-title.
Repr.: Deutsche medicin. Wochenschrift, 1901. No. 50 & 51.

1. Altitude.—Physiological effect.
N. Y. P. L.   January 12, 1916.

NL 0448507   NN

VOLUME 338

Loewy, Adolf, 1862–
Der heutige stand der physiologie des höhenklimas, von professor dr. A. Loewy ... Mit 13 abbildungen. Berlin, J. Springer, 1926.
60 p., 1 l. diagrs. 26ᶜᵐ.
"Sonderabdruck aus Ergebnisse der hygiene, bd. VIII."
"Literatur": p. 57–60.

1. Altitude, Influence of.   I. Title.
Library of Congress   QP82.L6   27-27519

NL   0448508   DLC

Loewy, Adolf, 1862–   joint author.
Zuntz, Nathan, 1847–1920.
Höhenklima und bergwanderungen in ihrer wirkung auf den menschen; ergebnisse experimenteller forschungen im hochgebirge und laboratorium, von dr. N. Zuntz ... dr. A. Loewy ... dr. Franz Müller ... dr. W. Caspari ... 1. aufl. Berlin ₍etc.₎, Deutsches verlagshaus Bong & co., 1906.

Loewy, Adolf, 1862–
Höhenkrankheit, von Prof. Dr. A. Loewy ...
(*In* Neue deutsche Klinik. Berlin, 1930. 26ᶜᵐ. Bd. 5, p. 141–152)
"Literatur": p. 152.

NL   0448510   ICJ

Loewy, Adolf, 1862–   joint author.
Zuntz, Nathan, 1847–1920, ed.
           FOR OTHER EDITIONS
           SEE MAIN ENTRY
Lehrbuch der physiologie des menschen, unter mitwirkung der herren prof. du Bois-Reymond ... prof. C'ohnheim ... prof. Ellenberger ... ₍u. a.₎, hrsg. von N. Zuntz und A. Loewy ... Mit 289 abbildungen und 3 tafeln. 2. verb. aufl. Leipzig, F. C. W. Vogel, 1913.

Loewy, Adolf, 1862–   joint ed.
Trendelenburg, Wilhelm Ernst Theodor, 1877–   ed.
Lehrbuch der physiologie des menschen; unter mitwirkung der herren R. du Bois-Reymond ... W. Ellenberger ... ₍u. a.₎ hrsg. von W. Trendelenburg ... und A. Loewy ... Mit 280 abbildungen und 2 tafeln. 4. aufl. des Lehrbuches von Zuntz und Loewy. Leipzig, F. C. W. Vogel, 1924.

Loewy, Adolf, 1862–
Neue Untersuchungen über die physiologischen Wirkungen des Höhenklimas, von Prof. Dr. A. Loewy ...
(*In* Ergebnisse der Physiologie. München, 1925. 26ᶜᵐ. 24. Bd., p. ₍216₎–227)
Originally given as a lecture.
"Aus dem Institut für Hochgebirgsphysiologie und Tuberkuloseforschung in Davos."
"Literatur": p. ₍216₎

NL   0448513   ICJ

Loewy, Adolf, 1862–
Neuere Untersuchungen zur Physiologie der Geschlechtsorgane, von A. Loewy ...
(*In* Ergebnisse der Physiologie. Wiesbaden, 1903. 26ᶜᵐ. 2. Jahrg., 1. Abt., p. ₍130₎–158)
"Literatur": p. ₍130₎–131.

NL   0448514   ICJ

Loewy, Adolf, 1862–
... The pathology of high altitude climate, with contributions to the climatology of highland regions and to the constitution of high altitude inhabitants, by A. Loewy ... and E. Wittkower ... London, Oxford university press, H. Milford, 1937.
ix, 212 p. tables (1 fold.) 22½ᶜᵐ. (Oxford medical publications)
"Literature" at end of each chapter except chapters III and V.

1. Altitude, Influence of. 2. Climatology, Medical.   I. Wittkower, Erich, joint author.   II. Title.
                      38–15513
Library of Congress   QP82.L617
          ₍5₎   612.2751

NL   0448515   DLC CU DAS

Loewy, Adolf, 1862–
Physiologie des höhenklimas, von professor dr. A. Loewy ... mit einem beitrag Das hochgebirgsklima von dr. W. Mörikofer ... Berlin, J. Springer, 1932.
xii, 414 p. illus., diagrs. 21ᶜᵐ. (Added t.-p.: Monographien aus dem gesamtgebiet der physiologie der pflanzen und der tiere. Hrsg. von M. Gildemeister ... ₍u. a.₎ 26. bd.)
"Literatur" at end of most chapters.

1. Altitude, Influence of. 2. Climatology. 3. Hygiene. ₍2, 3. Climate and health₎   I. Mörikofer, Walter.
                     Agr 32–853
Library, U. S. Dept. of   Agriculture   447L95

    NN
NL   0448516   DNAL OClW CtY CU MH-GM DLC ICU ICJ MH-M

Loewy, Adolf, 1862–
Stickstoffwechsel des menschen. Von A. Loewy ...
(*In* Abderhalden, Emil, ed. Handbuch der biologischen arbeitsmethoden ... Berlin, 1920–   25ᶜᵐ. abt. IV, Angewandte chemische und physikalische methoden. t. 9 (1925) p. ₍195₎–242 incl. tables)
Bibliographical foot-notes.

1. Nitrogen—Assimilation and excretion.   I. Title.
                     A C 36–2757
Title from Ohio State   Univ.
Library of Congress   ₍QH324.A3 1920 abt. 4, t. 9₎
         ₍2₎   (574.072)

NL   0448517   OU

Loewy (Adolf) [1862–]. *Ueber den Einfluss der Temperatur auf die Filtration von Eiweisslösungen durch tierische Membranen. 31 pp. 8°. Berlin, G. Schade. ₍1885₎.

NL   0448518   DNLM

Loewy, Adolf, 1862–
Über den energieverbrauch bei musikalischer betätigung, von prof. dr. A. Loewy ... und dr. phil. et med. H. Schroetter ... Berlin, J. Springer, 1926.
2 p. l., 63 p. 1 illus., diagrs. 24½ᶜᵐ.
"Aus dem Schweizerischen Institut für hochgebirgsphysiologie und tuberkuloseforschung in Davos."
"Sonderabdruck aus Pflügers archiv für die gesamte physiologie des menschen und der tiere, bd. 211."

1. Music—Physiology.   I. Schroetter, Hermann, ritter von Kristelli, 1870– joint author.
                     28–30803
Library of Congress   ML3822.L7

NL   0448519   DLC

Loewy, Adolf, 1862–
Ueber Haut-und Korpestemperaturen und ihre Beeinflussung durch physikalische Reise.
p. 14–29. fig. 24½ cm.
----- "von A. Loewy und C. Dorno".

NL   0448520   DAS

Loewy, Adolf, 1862–
Über Klimatophysiologie. Mit 13 Abbildungen. Leipzig, G. Thieme, 1931.
77 p. illus. 22 cm.
"Erweiterter Sonderabdruck aus Deutsche medizinische Wochenschrift 1931."
Bibliography: p. 77.

1. Climatology, Medical. 2. Man—Influence of environment.

QP82.L63   51–52469

NL   0448521   DLC NcD MH DAS ICJ

W 1
VE777   LOEWY, Adolf, 1862–
Heft 74   Über künstliche Atmung mit und ohne
1919   Zufuhr von hochprozentigem Sauerstoff;
         Bericht erstattet von A. Loewy und G.
         Meyer. Berlin, Hirschwald, 1919.
           102 p. illus. (Veröffentlichungen aus
         dem Gebiete des Militär-Sanitätswesens,
         Heft 74)
           I. Meyer, George, 1860-1923
         Series

NL   0448522   DNLM

Loewy, Adolf, 1862–
Untersuchungen über die Blutcirculation beim Menschen, von A. Loewy und H.v. Schrötter. Berlin, A. Hirschwald, 1905.
vi,114p.,₄ plates. 27cm.

From Zeit. f. exp. Path. u. Therapie, v.1, 1905.

1.Blood circulation. I.Schrötter, Hermann von.

NL   0448523   NcD-MC

WF
L828u   LOEWY, Adolf, 1862–
1895   Untersuchungen über die Respiration
         und Circulation bei Aenderung des Druckes
         und des Sauerstoffgehaltes der Luft.
         Berlin, Hirschwald, 1895.
           vi, 155 p. illus.

NL   0448524   DNLM ICJ ViU

Loewy, Adolf, 1862–
Der wasserwechsel des menschen. Von A. Loewy ...
(*In* Abderhalden, Emil, ed. Handbuch der biologischen arbeitsmethoden ... Berlin, 1920–   25ᶜᵐ. abt. IV, Angewandte chemische und physikalische methoden. t. 9 (1925) p. ₍243₎–254. illus.)
Bibliographical foot-notes.

1. Water in the body.   I. Title.
                     A C 36–2758
Title from Ohio State   Univ.
Library of Congress   ₍QH324.A3 1920 abt. 4, t. 9₎
         ₍2₎   (574.072)

NL   0448525   OU

Loewy (Adolf) [1862–]. *Ueber die forensische Bedeutung der Uterusruptur. [Breslau.] 41 pp. 8°. Ohlau, M. Neumann, 1888.

NL   0448526   DNLM CU

Lőwy, Adolf, †l.1936
A vízözön Kelet irodalmában. Budapest, 1936
46 p.
Bölcsészdoktori ertekezes - Budapest

1. Deluge

NL   0448527   MH

VOLUME 338

Loewy, Adolph
The Jewish nation's hour of destiny.
Chicago, Ill., Palestine Pub. Co. of
America, c1915.
20 p.

Title taken from paper-cover.

NL 0448528   OCH

Loey, Adolphe van, 1905–
Middelnederlandse spraakkunst. Door A. van Loey.
Groningen, J. B. Wolters, 1948–
2 v. 24 cm.   Ne***
Includes earlier editions of v. 1.
Vol. 1:   uitg. 19 ; v. 2:
uitg. 19
Includes bibliographies.
CONTENTS: 1. Vormleer.—2. Klankleer.

1. Dutch language—Early to 1500—Grammar. I. Title.
PF774.L62   68–86417

NL 0448529   DLC

Löwy (Adolphus). *De diphtheritide. 18 pp.
8°. Buda, typ. Reg. Scient. Univ. Hung., 1835.
[P., v. 1237.]

NL 0448530   DNLM

Löwy, Albert, 1816–1908.
London. Guildhall library.
Catalogue of hebraica and judaica in the library of the
Corporation of the city of London. With a subject index by
the Rev. A. Löwy. London, Printed under the direction of the
Library committee, 1891.

Loewy, Albert, 1816–1908.
A critical examination of the so called Moabite
inscription in the Louvre.
London, 1903
1 v.

NL 0448532   DCU-H

PJ4149   Löwy, Albert, 1816–1908.
.M7L8   A critical examination of the so-called Moabite
inscription in the Louvre. 3d issue, rev. and
amended. London, Printed for private circulation,
1903.
33 p.
Includes text in Hebrew transliteration and in
English translation.

1. Moabite stone.

NL 0448533   CLSU ICU

Div.S. Löwy, Albert, 1816–1908.
492.617   Die Echtheit der Moabitischen Inschrift
L827E   im Louvre. Auf neue geprüft. Wien, A. Holz-
hausen, 1903.
27 p. 25 cm.

1. Moabite stone. I. Title.

NL 0448534   NcD NjP NN OCH

Loewy, Albert, 1816–1906.
...Das Maass unserer Lebenstage... The measure of our
days. A tri-lingual song, dedicated to his friends on the occasion
of his eightieth birthday...by the Rev. Dr. Albert Löwy.   London, 1897.   11 p.   8°.
Hebrew title at head.
Text in Hebrew, German and English.

NL 0448535   NN

Löwy, Albert, 1816–1908.
[Marks, David Woolf] 1811–1909.   FOR OTHER EDITIONS
SEE MAIN ENTRY
Memoir of Sir Francis Henry Goldsmid, bart., Q. C., M. P.
2d ed., rev. and enl. London, K. Paul, Trench & co., 1882.

PJ5059   Löwy, Albert, 1816–1908, ed.
.E1M5
Miscellany of Hebrew literature. London, N. Trübner, 1872–
[77]

Löwy, Albert, 1816–1908.
On a unique specimen of the Lishana shel
Imrani. The Modern Syriac or Targum dialect of
the Jews in Kurdistan and adjacent countries;
with an account of the people by whom it is
spoken. By the Rev. Albert Löwy ...   [London,
1875]
20 p.   22 cm.
Caption-title.
Reprinted from the Transactions of the Society
of Biblical archaeology, V. 4, pt. 1, 1875.
Text in Hebrew characters and transliterated.

NL 0448538   CtY

Löwy, Albert, 1816–1908, tr.
Zunz, Leopold, 1794–1886.
... The sufferings of the Jews during the middle ages, by
Leopold Zunz; tr. from the German by Rev. Dr. A. Löwy;
rev. and ed., with notes, by George Alexander Kohut. New
York, Bloch publishing company, 1907.

Loewy, Alfred, 1873–1935 ed. and tr.
Sturm, Charles, 1803–1855.
Abhandlung über die auflösung der numerischen gleichungen
(1835) von C. Sturm. Aus dem französischen übers. und hrsg.
von Alfred Loewy. Leipzig, W. Engelmann, 1904.

Loewy, Alfred, 1873– ed.
Abel, Niels Henrik, 1802–1829.
Abhandlung über eine besondere klasse algebraisch auflös-
barer gleichungen. Von N. H. Abel (1829) Hrsg. von
Alfred Loewy. Leipzig, W. Engelmann, 1900.

Loewy, Alfred, 1873–1935.
Algebraische Gleichungen (in Pascal,
Ernesto. Repertorium der höheren Mathematik.
2 aufl. 1910. v. 1¹, p. [250]–357)

NL 0448542   RPB

Loewy, Alfred, 1873–1935.
Algebraische Gruppentheorie. (In Pascal,
Ernesto. Repertorium der höheren Mathematik.
2 aufl. 1910. v. 1¹, p. [168]–249)

NL 0448543   RPB

Loewy, Alfred, 1873–1935.
Ein Ansatz von Gauss zur jüdischen
Chronologie [or rather to the Jewish
calendar] aus seinem Nachlass.   Leipzig,
G. B. Teubner, 1917.
p. 304–322.
Title taken from first page.
Repr.: Deutsche Mathematiker-Vereinigung.
Jahresbericht 26. Heft 9/12.

NL 0448544   OCH

Loewy, Alfred, 1873–1935, ed. and tr.
Fourier, Jean Baptiste Joseph, baron, 1768–1830.
Die auflösung der bestimmten gleichungen (Analyse
des équations determinées) Von Jean Baptiste Joseph
baron Fourier ... Paris 1831. Übers. und hrsg. von
Alfred Loewy. Mit 18 figuren im text. Leipzig, W. Engelmann, 1902.

Loewy, Alfred, 1873–1935.
Sehenden zur belehrung, nichtsehen-
den zur erhebung und bewährung; elf biographien, von dr.
Alfred Loewy ... Zürich, Rascher & co. a.-g. [1935]
73 p. 20ᵐᵐ.
CONTENTS.— Einleitung.— Henry Fawcett.—Alexander Rodenbach.—
Nicholas Saunderson.—Leonhard Euler.—Victor Eberhard.—John Mil-
ton.— Gottlieb Planck.— François Huber.— Joseph-Antoine-Ferdinand
Plateau.—Louis Emile Javal.—Georg Friedrich Händel.

1. Blind—Biog.   I. Title.
36–14864
Library of Congress   HV1584.L6
Copyright A—Foreign   29958
[2]   920.9

NL 0448546   DLC NN

Loewy, Alfred, 1873–1935.
Kombinatorik, determinanten und matrices.
(In Pascal, Ernesto. Repertorium der höheren
mathematik. 2 aufl. 1910. v. 1¹, p. [43]–167)

NL 0448547   RPB

Loewy, Alfred, 1873–
Lehrbuch der Algebra, von Dr. Alfred Loewy, ... Erster
Teil. Grundlagen der Arithmetik. Leipzig, Veit & Co., 1915.
vi, 398 p. 214ᵐᵐ.
No more published.

NRU MiDW
NL 0448548   ICJ NcU CtY ODW OC1W MiU OU NjP MH RPB

Loewy, Alfred, 1873–1935.
Mathematik des geld- und zahlungsverkehrs.
Leipzig, Teubner, 1920.
viii, 273 p. tables.

"Literatur": p. 240.

1. Economics, Mathematical. 2. Interest
and usury - Tables. I. Title.

NL 0448549   NNC NIC IU RPB

VOLUME 338

Loewy, Alfred, 1873-1935.
  ... Neue elementare begründung und erweiterung der Galoisschen theorie ... Berlin, Gruyter, 1925-27.
  2 pts. in 1 v. (Sitzungsberichte der Heidelberger akademie der wissenschaften ... Mathematisch-naturwissenschaftliche klasse. Jahrgang 1925, 7. abhandlung (und Jahrgang 1927, 1. abhandlung.)
    1. Galois theory.

NL 0448550   NNC NN

Loewy, Alfred, 1873-1935.
Ueber bilineare Formen mit konjugirt imaginären Variablen.
(In Academia Cæsarea naturæ curiosorum. Nova acta. T. 71, pp. 77-446. Halle, 1898.)

NL 0448551   MB NjP

Loewy, Alfred, 1873-
  ... Ueber bilineare formen mit konjugirt imaginären variablen ... Halle, Druck von E. Karras, 1898.
  70 p. 32½ x 25ᶜᵐ.
  Habilitationsschrift—Freiburg i. B.
  Reprinted from Leop.-Carol. deutsche akademie der naturforscher. Nova acta, v. 71, no. 8.

    1. Forms, Bilinear.
                   1-G-2599
  Library of Congress   QA201.L8

NL 0448552   DLC

---

q512.86 Loewy, Alfred, 1873-1935
L82u   Über die transformationen einer quadratischen form in sich selbst, mit vorzüglicher berücksichtigung der uneigentlichen sowie ihre anwendungen auf linien- und kugelgeometrie. Halle, 1895.
  66p.

  Inaug.--Diss.--München.

NL 0448553   IU NjP MH

Loewy, Alfred, 1873-1935.
Ueber homomorphe Gruppen und die Einwirkung von Adjunktionen auf die Rationalitätsgruppe linearer homogener Differentialgleichungen. (In: Festschrift Heinrich Weber...gewidmet... Leipzig, 1912. 4°. p. 198-227.)

1. Equations (Differential) : Linear.
N. Y. P. L.   September 16, 1912.

NL 0448554   NN

Loewy, Alfred, 1873-1935.
Über lineare homogene Differentialsysteme und ihre Sequenten.
(In Heidelberger Akademie der Wissenschaften. Mathematisch-naturwissenschaftliche Klasse. Sitzungsberichte. Band 4A. Abhandlung 17. Heidelberg. 1913.)

K6641 — Differential expressions.

NL 0448555   MB NN

Loewy, Alfred, 1873-1935.
  ... Versicherungsmathematik; von dr. Alfred Loewy ... Leipzig, G. J. Göschen, 1903.
  145 p. 15½ᶜᵐ. (Sammlung Göschen. [180])
  "Literatur": p. [5]

    1. Insurance, Life—Mathematics.   I. Title.
                             4—6184
  Library of Congress   HG8781.L82

NL 0448556   DLC CoU OU MiU CU ICJ MB

Loewy, Alfred, 1873-1935.
  ... Versicherungs-Mathematik. Von Dr. Alfred Loewy, ... Zweite, umgearbeitete Auflage. Leipzig, G. J. Göschen'sche Verlagshandlung, 1910.
  175 p. incl. table. 16ᶜᵐ. (Sammlung Göschen. [180.])
  "Literatur," p. [2].

NL 0448557   ICJ CU

HG8782 Loewy, Alfred, 1873-1935.
.L81   Versicherungs-mathematik, von dr. Alfred Loewy ... 4. neubearb. und durch hinzunahme der invalidenversicherung erweiterte aufl. Berlin, J. Springer, 1924.
  v, 224 p. incl. tables. 24ᶜᵐ.
  "Literaturübersicht": p. [220]-221.

    1. Insurance—Mathematics.   2. Insurance, Life—Mathematics.

NL 0448558   ICU NjP ICRL NcD NNC IU

Löwy, Alfred, 1876-
  ... Die an der Kgl. chirurg. klinik Breslau in den jahren 1891 bis april 1901 behandelten fälle von hasenscharte ... Breslau, Fleischmann, 1903.
  53, [4] p. tables.

  Inaug.-diss., Breslau.
  Lebenslauf.
  "Literatur": p. [55-56]
    1. Harelip.

NL 0448559   NNC NN MH DNLM

Loewy, Arthur, 1880-
  Die Form der Erbschaftsannahme nach heutigem bürgerlichen Recht ... gegen die ... Opponenten: ... Max Lichtenstein ... Ismar Littmann ... verteidigen wird Arthur Loewy ... Breslau, M. & H. Marcus, 1904.
  3 p.l., 68, [2] p. 22½cm.
  Inaug.-diss. - Breslau.
  "Lebenslauf": p.[69]
  Bibliographical footnotes.

NL 0448560   MH-L ICRL

Löwy, Bella, 1853-   ed.
DS117
.G82   **Graetz, Heinrich Hirsch, 1817-1891.**
1891   History of the Jews. By Professor H. Graetz ... Philadelphia, The Jewish publication society of America, 1891-98.

Löwy, Bella, 1853-   tr.
Errera, Léo Abram, 1858-1905.
  The Russian Jews. Extermination or emancipation? By Leo Errera ... With a prefatory note by Theodore Mommsen. Translated from the French by Bella Löwy ... London, D. Nutt, 1894.

Loewy, Benjamin, 1831-   tr.
  Die colonie Victoria in Australien
    see under   Melbourne. Victorian Exhibition of 1861.

Loewy, Benjamin, 1831-
  A graduated course of natural science, experimental and theoretical for schools and colleges. Part I.-[II] ... By Benjamin Loewy, ... London and New York, Macmillan and Co., 1890-1891.
  2 vol. 17½ᶜᵐ.
  Contents.—pt. 1. First year's course. For elementary schools and the junior classes of colleges and technical schools. 1890. x, 151 p. 18 illus.—pt. 2. Second and third year's course. For the intermediate classes of colleges and technical schools. With sixty diagrams. 1891. viii, 257, [1] p. 60 illus. incl. diagrs.

NL 0448564   ICJ NcD CU MH MiU OCIW

Loewy, Benjamin, ed.
  Handbook of natural philosophy ... Mechanics.
    see under   Lardner, Dionysius, 1793-1859.

Loewy, Benjamin, 1831-   tr.

Weinhold, Adolf Ferdinand, 1841-
  Introduction to experimental physics, theoretical and practical, including directions for constructing physical apparatus and for making experiments, by Adolf F. Weinhold ... Tr. and ed., with the author's sanction, by Benjamin Loewy ... With a preface by G. C. Foster ... London, Longmans, Green, and co., 1875.

Loewy, Benjamin, 1831-
  Questions and examples on elementary experimental physics; sound, light, heat, electricity and magnetism. London, 1888.

NL 0448567   ODW OCIW

Loewy, Benjamin, 1831-
  Questions and examples on elementary experimental physics, sound, light, heat, electricity and magnetism. 2d edition, enlarged.
  — London. Macmillan & Co. 1889. x, (1) 124 pp. 15 cm., in 8s.

M5533 — Physics.

NL 0448568   MB

Loewy, Benno, 1854-1916.
  Report of W.·. Benno Loewy, read at the annual communication of National Lodge, No. 209
    see under   Freemasons. New York (City) National Lodge, No. 209.

Loewy, Benno, 1854-1916 ed.

Vereinigte Staaten zeitung. Hrsg. unter den auspicien der Deutsch-amerikanischen McKinley-Roosevelt liga. no. 1-10; 1. sept.-3. nov. 1900. New York, 1900.

VOLUME 338

Loewy, Bertold: Die Verfärbungen der Zähne. [Maschinenschrift.]
28, v S. 4°. — Auszug: Breslau 1922: Schüler. 2 Bl. 8°
Breslau, Med. Diss. v. 1. Juni 1922   [U 22. 1478]

NL 0448571   ICRL

Löwy, Blanka.
A budai Kis-Svábhegy földtani viszonyai.
Bibl.

NL 0448572   ICRL

Löwy, David.
Rede bei der Gedächtnissfeier für den verewigten Prediger Herrn Isak Noa Mannheimer, am 2. April, (6. Nissan) gehalten im israelit. Bethause zu Mariahilf in Wien, von D. Löwy... Wien: Herzfeld & Bauer, 1865.   16 p.   20cm.

881844A. 1. Mannheimer, Isaac Noah,   1793–1865.   *Revised*
N. Y. P. L.   *May 24, 1937*

NL 0448573   NN

BM550
.C35R6   Löwy, David, tr.
Rodkinson, Michael Levi, 1845–1904.
Der Schulchan aruch und seine beziehungen zu den Juden und nichtjuden von M. L. Rodkinssohn ... Ins deutsche übertragen von D. Löwy ... Wien, D. Löwy [etc.], 1884.

LÖWY, David
Tausend Jahre aus dem Leben des jüdischen Volkes in nachbiblischer Zeit. 1. Bd. Wien, im Selbstverlage des Verfassers, 1888.

18 cm.
Contents:- 1. Das zweite jüdische Staatsleben.
Jud 108.88

NL 0448575   MH OCH

Loewy, David.
Gallerie der verdienstvollsten Juden des XIX. Jahrhunderts zunächst aus Oesterreich-Ungarn. Hrsg. von D. Löwy. Lief. 1–2. Wien, the ed., 1882.
2 c., [bd. in one].
Title taken from paper-cover.

NL 0448576   OCH

Loewy, David.
Lebensbilder und Lebensweisheit den Sabbath-Abschnitten der Thora entnommen. Für Jugendgottesdienst, Religionsunterricht, wie für's Familienhaus. Wien: the auth., 1891.
1 v.

NL 0448577   OCH

Löwy, David
Der talmudjude von Rohling in der schwurgerichtsverhandlung vom 28. oktober 1882. Zur abwehr und verständigung von D. Löwy. Wien, D. Löwy, 1882.

40 p.   20cm.

1. Rohling, August, 1839–1912. Der talmudjude. 2. Jewish question.

24–11178

Library of Congress   DS145.R7L6

NL 0448578   DLC PPDrop OCH

Loewy, David.
Unverfälschte Worte. Von einem Theologen, i.e. D. Löwy. Wien, 1889.
36 p.   [3. ed.]

NL 0448579   OCH

PJ4937
.L6
[Hebr]   Löwy, David, b. 1805.
רש״ן הכמים. מחברת סלים כוללת סלות ומליצות עבריות הדרׁש הנימצאות בתלמוד. אסף וביארן בלשון עבר ותרגמן ללשון אשכנזי, באת, דוד הלוי. פראג. בדפום האחים נאםפליעב האאוו
ואהני, ת״ר״ה-
Prag, 1845-
V. 22 cm.
Added t. p.: Leschon chachamim. Wörterbuch enthaltend hebräische Wörter und Redensarten die sich im Talmud befinden. Gesammelt, hebräisch erläutert und ins Deutsche übersetzt, von David Löwy.
1. Hebrew language, Talmudic—Dictionaries—German.   I. Title.
Title transliterated: Leshon ḥakhamim.

PJ4937.L6   50–47424

NL 0448580   DLC NN

NK4645   [Loewy, Emanuel, 1857–1938.]
f.L6   Altgriechische graphik.   [n.p., 1923?]
9, [1] p.   illus.   32½cm.

Signed: Emanuel Löwy.

1. Vases, Greek.   I. Title.

NL 0448581   OCU

LOEWY, Emanuel, 1857–1938.
Aneddoti giudiziari dipinti in un fregio antico; nota. Roma, 1897.

21 p.

NL 0448582   MH-L

---

f736.5   Löwy, Emanuel, 1857–
L827a   Die anfänge des triumphbogens. Mit 3 Tafeln und 89 Textabbildungen. Wien, A. Schroll, 1928.
40p. illus. 37cm. (Jahrbuch der kunsthistorischen Sammlungen in Wien, n.F., Sonderheft, 11)

Cover title.

1. Arches, Triumphal.   Series: Vienna. Kunsthistorisches Museum. Jahrbuch.

NL 0448583   CLSU DDO NNC PBm OCU NjP OC1W MB

Loewy, Emanuel, 1857–1938.
Conze, Alexander Christian Leopold, 1831–1914, ed.
Die attischen grabreliefs, hrsg. im auftrage der Kaiserlichen akademie der wissenschaften zu Wien von Alexander Conze unter mitwirkung von Adolf Michaelis, Achilleus Postolakkas, Robert von Schneider, Emanuel Loewy, Alfred Brueckner [und Paul Wolters] ... Berlin, W. Spemann, 1893–1922.

Loewy, Emanuel, 1857–1938.
... Der beginn der rotfigurigen vasenmalerei, von weiland Emanuel Löwy ... Mit drei abbildungen im text ... Wien und Leipzig, Hölder-Pichler-Tempsky a. g., 1938.

108, [1] p. diagrs. 23cm. (Akademie der wissenschaften in Wien. Philosophisch-historische klasse. Sitzungsberichte. 217. bd., 2. abh.)

1. Vases, Greek.   A 46–1171
Stanford univ. Library
for Library of Congress   AS142.V31 bd. 217, abh. 2
[3]†   (063.6) 738.38

NL 0448585   CSt MU CU DLC

Loewy, Emanuel, 1857–1938.
Di alcune composizioni di Raffaello, ispirate a monumenti antichi. Roma, Unione coop. edit., 1896.
10 p.

NL 0448586   NjP

Loewy, Emanuel. Enrico Schliemann. 17 pp.
[*Nuov. antol.* 3 s. v. 31, 1891, p. 328.]

NL 0448587   MdBP

Loewy, Emanuel, 1857–1938.
Eranos vindobonensis ... 1893
see under title

Loewy, Emanuel, 1857–1938.
Griechische inschrifttexte.   Prag, 1888.

NL 0448589   NjP

Loewy, Emanuel, 1851–1938, comp.
Griechische Inschrifttexte für akademische Übungen; ausgewählt von Emanuel Löwy. Wien, F. Tempsky, 1888.
iv, 58 p.

Includes bibliographical references.

1. Inscriptions, Greek.

NL 0448590   NNC OCU

Loewy, Emanuel, 1857–
Die griechische plastik, von prof. Emanuel Löwy. Leipzig, Klinkhardt und Biermann, 1911.
2 v. 168 pl. on 84 l. 20½cm.
In case.
Plates printed on both sides.
CONTENTS.—Textband.—Tafelband.

1. Sculpture—Greece—Hist.   I. Title.
                                          13–8424
Library of Congress   NB90.L6

CU OOxM
NL 0448591   DLC CaBVaU NcD CtY NjP PBm PU OO OC1W

NB   Loewy, Emanuel, 1857–
90   Die griechische Plastik. Leipzig, Klinkhardt
L6   und Biermann, 1911–20.
2v. 168pl. on 84l. 21cm.

Plates printed on both sides.
Contents.- [v.1] Textband.- [v.2] Tafelband.
3. Aufl. 1920.

1. Sculpture - Greece - Hist.   I. Title.

NL 0448592   MU

VOLUME 338

NB
90
L68
1916

Löwy, Emanuel.
Die griechische Plastik, von Emanuel
Löwy. 2. aufl. Leipzig, Klinkhardt &
Biermann, 1916.
xiv p. 168 plates.

⟨1. Sculpture, Greek. I. Title.

NL 0448593   WaU DDO OU

Loewy, Emanuel, 1857-*1938*.
Die griechische plastik, von Emanuel Löwy.
4. aufl. Leipzig, Klinkhardt & Biermann, 1924.
2 v. 168 pl. on 84 l. 20½ᶜᵐ.
Plates printed on both sides.
Contents.—Textband.—Tafelband

1. Sculpture—Greece—Hist. I. Title.

NL 0448594   ViU NIC CSt NcGU OCU

Loewy, Emanuel, *1857-1938*.
— (Ed.) Inschriften griechischer bildhauer;
mit facsimiles. Leipzig, 1884. fo.   1991

NL 0448595   MdBP

Loewy, Emanuel, 1857–1938.
Inschriften griechischer bildhauer mit facsimiles herausgegeben von Emanuel Loewy. Gedruckt mit unterstützung der Kaiserlichen akademie der wissenschaften zu Wien. Leipzig, B. G. Teubner, 1885.
xl, 410 p. illus., facsims., fold. tab. 30 x 24ᶜᵐ.
"Bibliographisches register": p. ⟨xxvii⟩–xxxvii.

1. Inscriptions, Greek. 2. Artists, Greek.

CN375.A7L6   6–13551 rev

ViU MiU NcU NIC CSt MdBP CU NcD
NL 0448596   DLC CtY MH MB NjP PPAmP PU PBm OCU ODW

NB90
.M37
Delta

Loewy, Emanuel, 1857–1938. Inschriften
griechischer Bildhauer.

Marcadé, Jean.
Recueil des signatures de sculpteurs grecs. Paris, En
dépôt à la librairie E. de Boccard, 1953–

Loewy, Emanuel, 1857–1938.
Iphigenie in Taurien.
(In Archäologisches institut des Deutschen reichs. Jahrbuch. Berlin ⟨etc.⟩ 1930. 27½ᶜᵐ. 44. bd. (1929) p. ⟨86⟩–108. illus., pl. 1)
Signed: Emanuel Löwy.

1. Iphigenia. 2. Decoration and ornament—Pompeii. 3. Vases, Greek. I. Title.

Hamilton college. Library   A 44–4148
for Library of Congress   DE2.D5 bd. 44
⟨3⟩†   (913.3)

NL 0448598   NCH DLC

Loewy, Emanuel, 1857- *1938*.
Lysipp und seine stellung in der griechischen plastik. Von Emanuel Löwy ... Mit 15 abbildungen. Hamburg, Verlagsanstalt und druckerei a. g. (vormals J. F. Richter) 1891.
35 p. illus., diagrs. 20½ᶜᵐ. (On cover: Sammlung gemeinverständlicher wissenschaftlicher vorträge ... Neue folge. vi. ser., hft. 127)

1. Lysippus, the sculptor.   25-15797

Library of Congress   AC30.S3 n. f., ser. 6, hft. 127
—— Copy 2.   NB98.L6   (082) 733

NL 0448599   DLC NjP NIC CtY PU MH

N5633
L63

Loewy, Emanuel, 1857-1938.
La natura nell' arte greca; una teoria sulla genesi dell'espressione figurata. A cura di Carlo Anti. ⟨Tr. di Clelia Vinciguerra. Padova⟩ "Le Tre Venezie" ⟨1946⟩
xxi, 95 p. 41 plates. (Ligeia. ⟨Contributi alla storia delle civiltà artistiche, collana dir. da Sergio Bettini⟩ 2)

Translation of the author's Die Naturwiedergabe in der älteren griechischen Kunst. Pub. also in English under title: The rendering of nature in early Greek art.

Bibliographical references included in "Note" (p. ⟨65⟩-86)

1. Art, Greek. 2. Nature (Esthetics)
I. Anti, Carlo, 1889-   , ed. II. Vinciguerra, Clelia,   tr.

NL 0448601   CU CSt OU CLU IaU NjP NcD OCU

Loewy, Emanuel, 1857-*1938*.
Die naturwiedergabe in der älteren griechischen kunst. Rom, Loescher & co. 1900.
pp. (2), 60. Illus.

NL 0448602   MH NjP InU PBm CU PU OCU MB NN

N5630
.L65

Loewy, Emanuel, 1857-1938.
Neuattische Kunst.   Leipzig,
E.A. Seemann [1922]
10p. plates. 18cm.
Includes bibliography.

1.Art, Greek.   I.Title.

NL 0448603   NNU CtY PBm MH

Loewy, Emanuel, 1857–1938.
Niobe.
(In Archäologisches institut des Deutschen reichs. Jahrbuch. Berlin ⟨etc.⟩ 1928. 27½ᶜᵐ. bd. XLII (1927) p. ⟨80⟩–136. illus., plates)
Signed: Emanuel Löwy.
CONTENTS.—Marmorgemälde und sarkophage.—Neuattische reliefs.—Vasenbilder.—Statuen.—Urbild und künstler.

1. Niobe. 2. Sculpture, Greek. 3. Vase-painting, Greek.
A 44–4130
Hamilton college. Library
for Library of Congress   DE2.D5 bd. 42
⟨3⟩†   (913.3)

NL 0448604   NCH DLC

Loewy, Emanuel, 1857–1938.
... Polygnot, ein buch von griechischer malerei ... Wien, A. Schroll & co., 1929.
2 v. plates. 27 cm.
In case.
CONTENTS.—Text.—Abbildungen.

1. Polygnotus, 5th cent. B. C. 2. Art, Greek. I. Title.
29—10372

Library of Congress   ND115.P᷂᷂

ViU NN NcD MdBWA NcGU MU GU OU CSt NcU TxU OC1SA
NL 0448605   DLC CaBVaU CtY DDO OC1 OC1MN OCU MiU OO

Loewy, Emanuel, 1857-1938.
The rendering of nature in early Greek art, by Emanuel Loewy; tr. from the German by John Fothergill. London, Duckworth & co., 1907.
xii, 109 p., 1 l. 44 pl. 20½ cm.
"Abbreviations in the notes": p. xi–xii.

1. Art, Greek. I. *Fothergill, John, 1876-   tr.
8—37676

Library of Congress   N5633.L7

NN MB NcD MdBWA OrPR WaS CaBVaU FMU NIC NcU
NL 0448606   DLC OrP CtY OU OO OC1 OC1MN ICJ NjP NN

Loewy, Emanuel, 1857–1938.
Schale der sammlung Faina in Orvieto.
(In Archäologisches institut des Deutschen reichs. Jahrbuch. Berlin, 1889. 27½ᶜᵐ. bd. III (1888) p. 139–144, ⟨370⟩ illus., pl. 4)
Signed: Emanuel Löwy.
Illustrated description by Cecil Smith of the Theseus vase in the British museum mentioned in this article: p. 142–144.

1. Vases—Orvieto. 2. Vases—London. I. Smith, Sir Cecil Harcourt, 1859-
A C 39–271
Hamilton college. Library
for Library of Congress   DE2.D5 bd. 3
⟨a44c1⟩†   (913.3)

NL 0448607   NCH OCU DLC

FINE ARTS
NB
90
L8233

Loewy, Emanuel, 1857-1938.
La scultura greca ⟨di⟩ Emanuele Loewy.
Torino, Società tipográfico-editrice nazionale, 1911.
164 p. plates. 23cm.

1. Sculpture, Greek.

NL 0448608   NNC MWiCA

Loewy, Emanuel, *1857-1938*.
Untersuchungen zur griechischen künstlergeschichte. Wien, C. Gerold's sohn, 1883.
pp. (3), 117. (Abhandlungen des Archäologisch-epigraphischen seminares der Universität Wien, 4.)

Art—Greece‖

NL 0448609   MH NIC ICU OCU OC1W NN

N7450
L6
1930ₐ

Löwy, Emanuel, 1857-1938.
Ursprünge der bildenden Kunst; Vortrag, gehalten in der statutenmässigen Jahressitzung der Akademie der Wissenschaften in Wien am 4. Juni 1930. Wien, Hölder-Pichler-Tempsky, 1930.
21 p. 19 cm.

Cover title.
At head of title: Akademie der Wissenschaften in Wien.
"Sonderabdruck aus dem Almanach für das Jahr 1930."

NL 0448610   OU NNU

LOEWY, Emanuel, *1857-1938*
Venere in bronzo della collezione Tyszkiewicz. Illus. 2 pl.
(Reale accademia dei lincei. Monumenti antichi. Vol. 1. col. 965-968. Milano, 1892.)

NL 0448611   MB

VOLUME 338

Loewy, Emanuel, 1857–*1938.*
Zu den griechischen künstlerinschriften.
(*In* Archäologisches institut des Deutschen reichs. **Jahrbuch.** Berlin, 1888. 27½ᶜᵐ. bd. II (1887) p. 72)
Signed: Emanuel Loewy.

1. Inscriptions, Greek.
A C 39–239
Hamilton college. Library
for Library of Congress [DE2.D5 bd. 2]
₍2₎ (913.3)

NL 0448612 NCH OCU DLC

Loewy, Emanuel, 1857–1938.
Zu den Niobidendenkmälern.
(*In* Archäologisches institut des Deutschen reichs. **Jahrbuch.** Berlin ₍1932₎, 27½ᶜᵐ. bd. 47 (1932) p. ₍47₎–68. illus., pl.)
Signed: Emanuel Löwy.

1. Vases, Greek. 2. Sculpture, Greek. 3. Niobe.
A 44–4173
Hamilton college. Library
for Library of Congress DE2.D5 bd. 47
₍3₎† (913.3)

NL 0448613 NCH DLC

NB165
.A9
.L6
Loewy, Emanuel, 1857–1938.
Zum Augustus von Prima Porta.
₍München, 1927₎
₍203₎–222p. plates. 25cm.
From Mitteilungen des Deutschen Archäologischen Instituts, Römische Abteilung, XLII, 1927.
Bibliographical footnotes.

1. Augustus, emperor of Rome, 63 B.C.–14. A.D. – Portraits. 2. Sculpture, Roman.

NL 0448614 NNU

Lœwy, Emanuel, *1857–1938.*
Zum Harpyienmonument.
(In Mélanges Perrot. Pp. 223–225. Paris, 1903.)

F1575 — Lycia, Asia Minor. Antiq. — Sepulchral monuments.

NL 0448615 MB OO

Löwy, Emanuel, 1857–1938.
Zum Repertorium der späteren Kunst.
(In: Mélanges Nicole. Recueil de mémoires de philologie classique ... Genève, 1905. 8°. p. 653–657. 1 pl.)

NL 0448616 NN

Loewy, Emanuel, 1857–*1938.*
... Zur chronologie der frühgriechischen kunst; die Artemistempel von Ephesos, von Emanuel Löwy ... Mit einer tafel ... Wien und Leipzig, Hölder-Pichler-Tempsky a.-g., 1932.
41, ₍1₎ p. fold. plan. 28½ᶜᵐ. (Akademie der wissenschaften in Wien. Philosophisch-historische klasse. Sitzungsberichte. 213. bd., 4. abhandlung)
"Vorgelegt in der sitzung vom 8. juli 1931."
Bibliographical foot-notes.

1. Ephesus. Temple of Diana. I. Title.
A C 35–2809
Title from Stanford Univ.,
Library of Congress [AS142.V31 bd. 213, abh. 4]

NL 0448617 CSt ICIU MsU MU OU

Loewy, Emanuel, 1857–1938.
... Zur datierung attischer inschriften, von Emanuel Löwy ... Wien und Leipzig, Hölder-Pichler-Tempsky a.g., 1937.
30 p. 23ᶜᵐ. (Akademie der wissenschaften in Wien. Philosophisch-historische klasse. Sitzungsberichte. 216. bd., 4. abh.)

1. Inscriptions, Greek—Athens.
A 46–1169
Stanford univ. Library
for Library of Congress AS142.V31 bd. 216, abh. 4
₍3₎† (063.6) 481.7

NL 0448618 CSt OCIW MsU OU MU NcU ViU DLC IEN

Loewy, Emanuel, 1857–*1938.*
Zwei reliefs der Villa Albani.
(*In* Archäologisches institut des Deutschen reichs. **Jahrbuch.** Berlin, 1888. 27½ᶜᵐ. bd. II (1887) p. 107–111, 195. illus.)
Signed : Emanuel Löwy.
"Berichtigung" : p. 195.

1. Bas-relief. 2. Rome (City) Villa Albani.
A C 39–243
Hamilton college. Library
for Library of Congress [DE2.D5 bd. 2]
₍2₎ (913.3)

NL 0448619 NCH OCU DLC

QD341
.A6L82
Loewy, Emil, 1876–
Zur synthese aromatischer aldehyde.
Heidelberg, 1898.
34p.
Inaug. diss. Heidelberg.

NL 0448620 DLC PPC PU

Löwy, Erich.
... Recherches sur l'absorption des gaz nitreux par le gel d'alumine et par les hydroxydes de calcium et de glucinium ... par Erich Löwy ... Genève, Imprimerie de la Tribune de Genève, 1945.
47 p. 1 illus. 23ᶜᵐ.
Thèse—Geneva.

1. Nitrous oxide. 2. Gases—Absorption and adsorption. 3. Aluminum oxide.
46–7556
Library of Congress QC182.L58
₍2₎ 533.1

NL 0448621 DLC

Loewy, Erna.
Erfahrungen mit der neuen meinickeschen klarungsreaktion (MKR)
Inaugural dissertation, 1929.

NL 0448622 PPWI

Loewy, Erna (Hattendorf) 1890–
... Beitrag zur pathologischen Histologei der unter dem Bilde der Landryschen Paralyse verlaufenden Fälle von Poliomyelitis acuta anterior ... Berlin, 1914.
Inaug.-Diss. - München.
Lebenslauf.

NL 0448623 CtY DNLM MiU PPWI

Loewy, Ernst
Thomas Mann und das deutscne Bürgertum, ₍von₎ Paul Loewy. Wien, Verlag Willy Verkauf, 1947.
22 p. 25cm.

"Sonderabdruck aus der Zeitschrift 'Erbe und Zukunft.'"
"In Heft 3 wurde irrtümlich der Vorname des Autors mit Paul angegeben. Es heisst richtig Ernst Löwy."—Erbe und Zukunft, 1947-/48, Nr. 4, p. 66.

NL 0448624 WU IEN IaU OkU NcD CU NNC NN RPB

PT
2623
045
W4
Loewy, Ernst
Das Weib in der Mitte; Roman in Gesprächen. Ein Spiel in vier Abteilungen ₍von₎ Paul Loewy ₍pseud.₎ Wien, Amalthea-Verlag, 1924.
89p. 23cm.

NL 0448625 WU

Löwy, Ernst, 1870–
Über die Einwirkung der Parawolframate des Natriums, Kaliums und Ammoniums auf die entsprechenden normalen vanadate. Ein Beitrag zur Kenntnis der Doppelsalze der Vanadinsäure und Wolframsäure ... Hamburg, 1893.
45, [1] p. , 1 l. 23.5 cm.
Inaug.-Diss. - Berlin.
Vita.

NL 0448626 CtY DNLM

Loewy, Erwin.
The production of large forgings for airplanes on hydraulic die forging presses ₍presentation to departmental representatives, 20 Feb. 1950. Washington₎ Munitions Board, 1950.
ii, 20 l. illus. 27 cm.
Cover title.

1. Aeroplanes—Parts. 2. Aluminum forgings. 3. Forging machinery. 4. Hydraulic presses. I. Title.
TL671.28.L6 50–61289

NL 0448627 DLC

1889–
Loewy, Erwin. ₍Aus d. psychiatr. u. Nervenkl. d. Charité. Ehem. Dir.: Ziehen.₎ Beitrag zum Verhalten des Kremasterreflexes bei funktionellen und organischen Nervenkrankheiten inkl. Psychosen. Berlin : Karger 1912. 28 S. 8°
¶(Aus: Monatsschrift f. Psychiatrie u. Neurol. Bd 32.)
Berlin, Med. Diss. v. 19. März 1913, Ref. Bonhoeffer
[Geb. 29. Jan. 89 Berlin; Wohnort: Charlottenburg; Staatsangeh.: Preußen; Vorbildung: Wilhelms-Gymn. Berlin Reife M. 06; Studium: Berlin 1, Freiburg i. B. 1, Berlin 5, Würzburg 1, Berlin 2 S.; Coll. 13. Febr. 12; Approb. 13. Febr. 13.] [U 12. 4756]

NL 0448628 ICRL CtY DNLM

Loewy, Eugen, 1869–
Beiträge zur Kenntnis und Würdigung Wilhelm's von Saliceto (XIII. Jahrh.) als Arzt. ... Der Verfasser Eugen Loewy, ... Berlin, Buchdruckerei von G. Schade, [1897].
30, ₍2₎ p. 21½ᶜᵐ.
Inaug.-Diss. — Berlin.
Lebenslauf.

NL 0448629 ICJ ICRL DNLM WU-M

LOEWY, Franz
Beiträge zur Geschichte der Juden in Glatz. Jahresarbeit des Oberprimaners Franz Loewy am Staatl. Kathol. Gymnasium in Glatz 1929/30. 2 p.l. 82 p. 28.5 cm.
Carbon copy of typed original.
1. History—Germany—Glatz.

NL 0448630 NNJ

VOLUME 338

Löwy, Franz.
 Das schöne nackte Weib; vierzehn Reproduk-
tionen nach photographischen Bildern von Franz
Löwy, mit einem Geleitwort von professor Ferdinand Feldegg. Wien-Leipzig, Frisch & Co. [1921]
 11, [1] p. 14 pl. 36 cm.
 In portfolio.
 1. Photographs - Collections. 2. Nudes.
I. Fellner von Feldegg, Ferdinand, ritter, 1855-
4. Anatomy, Artistic.

NL 0448631   CtY

HJ8061   LOEWY,GEORG HERMANN,1878-
.L8   Staatsbankerotte,von bankier Georg Hermann Loewy
         ... Breslau,T.Schatzky,1922.
         83,[1]p. 20cm.
         Bibliography:p.[84]

         1.State bankruptcy.

NL 0448632   ICU NN

Loewy, Georges, 1884-
 ... Les fistules jejuno-coliques par ulcère
perforant après gastro-entérostomie ...
Paris, 1921.
 24 cm.
 Thèse - Univ. de Paris.

NL 0448633   CtY DNLM

W   Löwy, Gisella
4   La curva glicemica nei bambini affetti
P12   da diatesi essudativa. Padova, CEDAM, 1932.
1932   49 p.

          Tesi delle Scuole di perfezionamento,
          R. Università di Padova.

NL 0448634   DNLM

Löwy, Gustav.
 Die Technologie und Terminologie der Müller und Bäcker in
den rabbinischen Quellen... Von Gustav Löwy... Leipzig:
G. Fock, 1898. 51 p. 22½cm.

 Inaugural Dissertation — Bern, 1898.
 Bibliographical footnotes.

1. Baking—Hist. 2. Flour mills—   Hist. 3. Hebrew language, Post-
Biblical.   *Revised*
N. Y. P. L.   *April 4, 1934*

NL 0448635   NN OCH PU PPDrop

Löwy, Heinrich.
 Elektrodynamische erforschung des erdinnern und
luftschiffahrt. Mit einem vorwort von Richard von
Mises.   Wien, Manzsche verlags- und Universitäts-buchhandlung, 1920.
 38 p. diagrs., tables.

NL 0448636   DLC

Löwy, Heinrich.

Popper, Josef, 1838–1921.
 ... Gespräche; mitgeteilt von Margit Ornstein und Heinrich
Löwy; mit einem vorwort von dr. Julius Ofner. Wien und
Leipzig, R. Löwit-verlag [1925]

Löwy, Heinrich, tr.

Laplace, Pierre Simon, *marquis de,* 1749-1827.
 ... Philosophischer versuch über die wahrscheinlichkeit,
hrsg. von R. v. Mises. Leipzig, Akademische verlagsgesellschaft m. b. h., 1932.

W   LOEWY, Heinrich, firm, Berlin
26   [Catalogs of surgical instruments and
qL827   apparatus]
          A file of these publications will be
         found on the shelves under the above call
         number.
          1. Surgical instruments & apparatus -
         Catalogs 2. Trusses - Surgical

NL 0448639   DNLM

Loewy, Heinrich, firm, Berlin.
 Special-Catalog für Bruch-
bänder und Bandagen. 43 pp. 8°. *Berlin, J.
Harrwitz,* [1881].

NL 0448640   DNLM

Loewy, Heinrich, firm, Berlin.
 Special-Catalog für Bruchbänder und Bandagen. Berlin, [1894]
 55[1]p. illus. 22cm.

 4-Page advertisement of Heinrich Loewy
tipped in.

NL 0448641   KU-M

LÖWY,Heinrich,1884–
 Beitrage zur ionentheorie des phosphors.
Inaug.-diss. Göttingen,1908.

NL 0448642   MH-C NN PU

T113   Löwy, Helene
B45   ... Strahlenbiologische Versuche mit den
1940   Puppen der Fruchtfliege Drosophila melano-
          gaster ... Bern,1940.
          Inaug.-Diss. - Bern.

NL 0448643   CtY

1895-
Loewy, Helene. Ueber die Tuberkulinempfindlichkeit bei
 Lupus pernio und den Sarkoiden Boeck-Darier. Aus d.
 Kl. f. Hautkrankh. zu Breslau. [In Maschinenschrift.] 33 S.
 4°(2°). — Auszug: Breslau 1921: Breslauer Genossensch.-
 Buchdr. 2 Bl. 8°
 Breslau, Med. Diss. v. 10. Aug. 1921, Ref. Jadassohn
 [Geb. 29. Sept. 95 Falkenberg, OS.; Wohnort: Breslau; Staatsangeh.: Preußen;
 Vorbildung: RG. Breslau Reife 15; Studium: Breslau 6, München 1, Breslau
 3 S.; Coll. 13. Juli 20; Approb. 6. Aug. 21.]   [U 21. 3007

NL 0448644   ICRL

136.766
L821r Loewy, Herta
        The retarded child; a guide for parents.
       London, Staples Press, 1949.
        52p.

        1. Children, Abnormal and backward.
       I. Title.

NL 0448645   ICarbS IaU

Loewy, Herta.
 The retarded child; a guide for parents and
teachers. [Enl. ed.]   London, Staples Press
[1951]
 160 p. 22cm.

 1. Slow learning children. I. Title.

NL 0448646   AU

Loewy, Herta.
 The retarded child; a guide for parents and teachers. New
York, Philosophical Library [1951]
 160 p. 22 cm.

 1. Children, Abnormal and backward. I. Title.

LC4601.L63   371.922   52–6680 ‡

NIC IU MB NcDur
OrU OrU-M Wa WaSp WaS WaT CU TU IaU NN IEN NNU-W N
NL 0448647   DLC MiU CaBVaU CaBVa TxU Or OrCS OrLgE

LC4601 LOEWY, Herta.
L64   The retarded child; a guide for par-
1953   ents and teachers. London, New York,
          Staples Press [1953]
          160p. 22cm.
          "First published 1949."

          1. Mentally handicapped children -
         Education I. Title

NL 0448648   CtY-M NBuC MB PBL NBC

Loewy, Herta.
 Training the backward child. London, Staples Press
[1955]
 166 p. illus. 22 cm.

 1. Children, Abnormal and backward. I. Title.

LC4601.L65   371.92   56–997 ‡

NL 0448649   DLC CaBViP OrU Wa CU LU TU CaBVa

Löwy, Hugo, 1902–
 Sturz des Tyrannen; Drama in drei Akten, von Hugo
Löwy und Fred A. Angermayer. Wien, Europäischer Verlag, 1954.
 61 p. 22 cm.

 I. Angermayer, Fred Antoine, 1889–   Joint author. II. Title.

PT2623.O44S7   54–30527 ‡

NL 0448650   DLC NN

915.694 Löwy, Hugo, 1902–
L827v   Vom Judenhass zum Judenstaat. Vorwort
          von David Ben Gurion. Wien, Renaissance
          [1948]
          220p. 21cm.

          1. Israel. I. Title.

NL 0448651   IEN MH NN

VOLUME 338

WS
80
L827r
1879
LÖWY, J
Rathgeber in Kinderkrankheiten ...
Wien, Hartleben, 1879.
535 p.   illus.

NL 0448652   DNLM

Loewy (J. P.) *De auri muriatici virtute medica. 1 p. L, 68 pp., 1 l. 8°. Praga, typ. archiepiscopalibus. 1831.*

NL 0448653   DNLM

Löwy, Jacob Ezechiel, 1814–1864.
... בקורת התלמוד על פי ערך א׳ב. כרך הראשון כלל
ערכי את א׳ לבאר יסודות תורה שבעל־פה וקורותיה בכלל
יותר ממאה וחמשים מלות הנוגעות להבנת מסורת אבות. ממי
יעקב יחזקאל הלו ...
Kritisch-talmudisches lexicon, von Jacob Ezechiel Löwy ...
Band I. Wien, Eigenverlag des verfassers, 1863.
1 p. l., II, 494 p. 23ᶜᵐ.
No more published.
1. Talmud—Dictionaries. 2. Hebrew language—Dictionaries—Hebrew. I. Title.
3. Aramaic language—Dictionaries— I. Title.
   Title   transliterated: Biḳoreth ha-Talmud.
                             45–44898
Library of Congress   BM504.L6

NL 0448654   DLC CU

Löwy, Jacob Ezekiel, 1814–1864.
Der Wahrspruch des Judenthums; ein ernstes Wort gesprochen
in einer ernsten Stunde am Azeretfest 5620 in der Synagoge zu
Beuthen O. S., von Jac: Ezechiel Löwy ...   Beuthen O. S.:
Druck von C. Kirsch ₁1860₎ 32 p. 17½cm.

1. Sermons, Jewish, in German.
N. Y. P. L.   December 29, 1939

NL 0448655   NN OCH

LOEWY, James.
Ist die abortivbehandlung der syphilis
möglich? Berl., ₁1892?₎.

NL 0448656   MBCo DNLM

Loewy, James, 1873–
Das loos im system des deutschen wahlrechts.
Inaug. diss. Greifswald,1896.
Bibl.

NL 0448657   ICRL

Löwy, Josef
Judaica Festgabe zur Vermählung seiner Tochter der
Fnel4 Jungfrau Erma mit Herrn Jaques Guthard. Von
865L Jos. Löwy. Gross-Kanizsa,Druck von Ph.Fischel,
1865.
24p. 16ᶜᵐ
Caption-title (p.₍7₎): Zur Kritik der hebr.
Sprache (Aus talmud. Quellen.)

1.Hebrew language. 2.Guthard, Frau Erma
(Löwy). 2.Guthard, Jaques.

NL 0448658   CtY OCH

Löwy, Josef.
Friedens-Opfer. Zur Installation ... Herrn Dr.
Alexander Kohut als Ober-Rabbiner in Fünfkirchen
am Rosch-Haschana 5635 (12. Sept. 1874)... von
Jos. Löwy ...   Gross-Kanizsa, 1847.
11 p.   16.5 cm.

NL 0448659   CtY

Löwy, Josef.
Meine Brüder suche ich! Verscheidene [!] Winke
für den israelitischen Congress vom Jahre 1868, von
Josef Löwy ...   Gross-Kanizsa, 1868.
8 p.   20 cm.

NL 0448660   CtY OCH

Löwy, Josef, *1876–*
87504 .... Die Automobilbeleuchtung, von Ingenieur Josef Löwy,
... Mit 114 Abbildungen. Berlin, R. C. Schmidt & Co., 1913.
130 p. 114 illus. (incl. diagrs.) 17ᶜᵐ. (Autotechnische Bibliothek. Band 48.)

NL 0448661   ICJ NN

Loewy, Josef, 1876–
... Die elektrische Zündung bei Automobilen und Motorfahr-
rädern, von Ingenieur Josef Löwy...   Leipzig: R. C. Schmidt
& Co., 1906. iv, 6–132 p. diagrs., illus., pl. 16°. (Kuester's
autotechnische Bibliothek. Bd. 9.)

418237A. 1. Engines, Gas and   oil—Ignition. 2. Ser.
N. Y. L.   November 6, 1929

NL 0448662   NN ICJ

Löwy, Josef, 1876–
.67294 .... Das Elektromobil und seine Behandlung, von Ingenieur
Josef Löwy, ... Mit 69 Abbildungen im Text. Leipzig,
R. C. Schmidt & Co., 1906.
124 p. illus. 17¼ᶜᵐ. (Küster's Autotechnische Bibliothek, Band 16.)

NL 0448663   ICJ

BM675
.P4L62
1950z
Hebr
Loewy, Joseph, tr.   FOR OTHER EDITIONS
                           SEE MAIN ENTRY
Jews. *Liturgy and ritual. Hagadah. 195–*
הגדה של פסח Service for the first nights of Passover.
With a rev. English translation by Joseph Loewy and
Joseph Guens. With many pictures in colour by G. Doré
and a musical supplement. Tel-Aviv, Sinai ₁195–₎

₍Loewy, Julius,₎ 1851–1905, editor.
Die Costüm-Ausstellung in K. K. oesterreichischen Museum,
1891. ₍Wien: F. Jasper, 1891.₎ 2 p.l., 15 f., 6 diagr., 45 pl.
ob. 4°.

Vorwort signed: J. Löwy.

1. Costume (Austrian). 2. Costume   (Hungarian). 3. Title.
N. Y. P. L.   July 24, 1918.

NL 0448665   NN MWiW-C

Löwy, Julius, 1851–1905.
Figurale compositionen für die malerische
ausschmückung von decken, wanden, zwickeln,
lünetten und kunstgewerblichen objecten
aller art. Lichtdrucke nach gemalden und
Zeichnungen wiener kunstler ...
Wien, Schroll, 1894.
60 pl.

NL 0448666   OCX

Löwy, Julius, 1851–1905.
Die Kaiserliche Gemälde-Galerie in Wien
see under   Vienna. K.K. Kunsthistorisches.
Gemäldegalerie.

NK1530
.V5
folio
Löwy, Julius, 1851–1905
Vienna. Österreichisches Museum für Angewandte Kunst.
Ornamente für Architectur und Kunst-Industrie, nach
den Gypsabgüssen des K. K. Österr. Museums für Kunst
und Industrie, ausgewählt von Albert Ilg, aufgenommen von
J. Löwy. Wien, Lehmann & Wentzel ₁1875–77₎

Löwy, Julius, 1851–1905.
Das Palais Kinsky auf der Freiung in Wien. Erläutern-
der Text von Albert Ilg. Wien, 1894.
15 p. 30 plates. 39 cm.

1. Vienna. Palais Kinsky. I. Ilg, Albert, 1847–1896.

NA7721.V6L6   59–59954

NL 0448669   DLC CtY MB CU MoU INS MH

Löwy, Julius, 1851–1905.
Wiener Galerien; Heliogravuren nach Gemälden
aus den Galerien der Grafen Czernin, Harrach,
Schönborn; mit erläuterndem Texte von O.
Berggruen, C. Bodenstein, Custos E. Chmelarz, Th. von
Frimmel, A. Ilg und F. Wickhoff. Wein, V. A. Heck,
1893.
₍2₎, t. 41 plates

Plates accompanied by guard sheets with
descriptive letterpress.

NL 0448670   MiD

614.23
H236
v.4²
Löwy, Julius, 1855–
Ärztliche sachverständigen-tätigkeit auf dem
gebiete der inneren krankheiten ...

(In Handbuch der ärztlichen sachverständigen-
tätigkeit ... hrsg. von Paul Dittrich. Wien
₍etc.₎ 1906– 4.bd., 1.t.(1931) p. ₍91₎–219)
Caption title.
Includes bibliographies.

1.Jurisprudence, Medical. 2. Evidence, Expert.

NL 0448671   IU-M

Löwy, Julius, 1855–
Die klinik der berufskrankheiten, von dozent dr. Julius
Löwy ... Mit 25 abbildungen im text und 5 farbigen abbildungen auf 2 tafeln. Wien und Breslau, E. Haim &
co., 1924.
xi, 483 p. illus., II col. pl. 25ᶜᵐ.
Contains bibliographies.

1. Occupations—Diseases and hygiene. I. Title.
                                              25–6231
Library of Congress   RC964.L6

NL 0448672   DLC DNLM PPC ICJ

VOLUME 338

Löwy, Julius, 1885-
Werthbestimmung des bismuths & des käuflichen
magisterium bismuthi.
10 p.
Repr. from Archiv. der pharmacie.

NL 0448673   PPF

Loewy, Julius, 1900-
... Die Viscosität des Speichels ...
Rietberg, 1929.
Inaug-Diss. - Hamburg.
Lebenslauf.
"Literaturverzeichnis": p. 22.

NL 0448674   CtY

F983
Löwy, Julius, 1917-
Edith Wharton and her relationship to France
... [Vienna] 1949.
203, [5] l.

Microfilm of typewritten copy.
Diss.--Vienna.
Bibliography: l. [204-208]

NL 0448675   NNC

Loewy, Käthe, 1905-
Die Vermutung ... von Käthe Loewy ...
Bonn, L. Röhrscheid, 1930.
ix, [11]-22, [1] p. 22½cm.

Inaug.-diss. - Bonn.
"Lebenslauf": p. [23]
"Literaturverzeichnis": p. [vii]-ix.

NL 0448676   MH-L ICRL

Loewy, Käthe, 1905-
Die vermutung, von Käthe Loewy ... Bonn und Köln, L.
Röhrscheid, 1931.
ix, 44 p., 1 l. 22½cm. (Added t.-p.: Bonner rechtswissenschaftliche ab-
handlungen. hft. 16)
"Literaturverzeichnis": p. [vii]-ix.

1. Presumptions (Law)—Germany. 2. Evidence (Law)—Germany.
1. Title.
35-25577

NL 0448677   DLC MH-L

Loewy, Karl
WG   Benzolderivate aus Succinylobern-
23689 steinsäureäther. Uster-Zürich, 1887.
53 p.
Inaug.-Diss. - Basel.

NL 0448678   CtY

LÖWY, LEO.
Fern vom Alltag; hundert Aussichten im Schachpanorama,
gesammelt von Leo Löwy; herausgegeben von Bernhard Kagan.
Berlin: B. Kagan[, 1924]. 56 p. illus. 23½cm.

634203A. 1. Chess—Problems, 1924. I. Kagan, Bernhard,
editor.

NL 0448679   NN OC1 MH

Loewy (Léopold). Das Chinolin gegen Inter-
mittens und Intermittens-Neuralgien. 13 pp.
8°. Wien, 1881.
Repr. from: Wien. med. Presse, 1881. xxii.

NL 0448680   DNLM

Löwy, Ludwig: Das Rechtsverhältnis des unehelichen Kindes zur
Mutter. [Maschinenschrift.] IV, 62 S. 4°. — Auszug: Breslau
1922: Bresl. Genoss. Buchdr. 2 Bl. 8°
Breslau, R.- u. staatswiss. Diss. v. 30. Sept. 1922   (U 22. 1139)

NL 0448681   ICRL

Loewy, M. H., comp.
General-register ... 1861-1867.
Das Staatsarchiv. Sammlung der offiziellen aktenstücke zur
aussenpolitik der gegenwart ... 1.-86. bd., juli 1861-1919;
neue folge, bd. 1-   1928-
Leipzig, Akademische verlagsgesellschaft m. b. h.; [etc., etc.]
1861-19

Löwy, Markus.
Geographie sammt separater wandkarte von
Palästina. Ergänzender theil der auf der karte
befindlichen historischen anmerkungen im fragen
und antworten, geeignet zur praktischen hand-
habung des unterrichtes in der Bibel, in den
propheten, etc.; verwendbar an volks-, haupt-,
realschulen und gymnasien, von Markus Löwy. ...
Pressburg, Löwy & Alkalay, 1878.
88 p. plan. 21 cm.

1. Palestine - Historical geography.

NL 0448683   CU

Löwy, Markus.
Historische und geographische beschreibungen Palästina" und aller nachbarländer ... sowie über die seit
einem zeitraume von 14 jahren erst entstandenen (aus
Russland, Rumänien, Bessarabien u. s. w. eingewandert)
colonieen Judäas und Galiläa's, nebst genauer bezeichnung der eisenbahnstationen von Jaffa nach Jerusalem.
Verfasst von Markus Löwy ... Pressburg, Druck von
A. Alkalay, 1894.
18 p. fold. map. 22ᵐᵐ.
All names given in Hebrew and German.
At foot of map: 5. verm. u. verb. aufl.
1. Palestine—Descr. & trav. 2. Agricultural colonies—Palestine.
25-1956

Library of Congress   DS107.L6

NL 0448684   DLC

Loewy, Maurice, 1833-1907.   L520.4 L82
[Astronomical monographs.] Paris, Gauthier-Villars, 1872-1902.
5 vol. in 1. tables, diagrs. 384ᵐᵐ.
Reprinted in part from various scientific serials.
Contents.—Travaux divers de M. Loewy, publiés dans les Annales de l'Observatoire.
1872. Détermination des orbites des comètes. 99 p. Détermination de l'orbite de la
planète Eugénie. 39 p. — Études diverses sur les méthodes d'observation et de réduction des observations méridiennes. 1885. Various pagings.—Loewy, M. & Puiseux, P.
Étude de système optique formé d'une lunette astronomique et d'un double miroir.
Méthode la plus précise pour la mesure des distances en vue de l'étude de l'aberration et
de la réfraction. 1890. cover-title, 23 p.—Same. Théorie du système optique composé d'une lunette astronomique et d'un double miroir plan. Application à la mesure
précise des distances en vue de l'étude de l'aberration et de la réfraction. 1891. cover-
title, 101 p.—Sur la précision des coordonnées des astres obtenues à l'aide des mesures
effectuées sur leurs images photographiées (deuxième et troisième mémoires). 1902.
cover-title, ii, 115, [1] p.

NL 0448685   ICJ

QB595
.P23
Loewy, Maurice, 1833-1907.
Paris. Observatoire.
Atlas photographique de la lune, publié par l'Observatoire
de Paris. Exécuté par M. Loewy [et] P. Puiseux. Paris,
Impr. nationale, 1896-1910.

Löwy, Maurice, 1833-1907.
Bahnbestimmung des ersten Kometen 1857.
Wien, 1859
26 p. 22cm.
Wien, Sitz. Ber., 35, 1859, p. 389-412.

NL 0448687   DN-Ob

Loewy, Maurice, 1833-
Description d'un nouveau systeme d'équatoriaux
et de son installation a l'Observatoire de Paris.
Paris, 1883
12 p. 25cm.
Journ. de Physique, 2, 1883, p. 349-360.

NL 0448688   DN-Ob

Loewy, [Maurice] 1833-
Description d'un nouveau système de télescope; par M.
Loewy. [Paris, Gauthier-Villars, 1884]
38 p., 1 l. illus., diagrs. 25½ᵐᵐ.
Caption title.
"Extrait du Bulletin astronomique, juin-août-septembre 1884."

1. Telescope, Reflecting.

Library of Congress   QB88.L8   6-20657

NL 0448689   DLC MiU

Loewy, Maurice, 1833-1907.
Description sommaire d'un nouveau système
d'équatoriaux et de son installation à l'Observatoire de Paris. [1883]
10 p. tables.
"Extrait des Comptes rendus des séances de
l'Academie des Sciences, t. 96; séance du 19
pars 1883."
Volume of pamphlets.

NL 0448690   NNC DN-Ob

Loewy, Maurice, 1833-1907.
Détermination de la différence des longitudes entre
Paris-Marseille et Alger-Marseille, par M. Loewy ... et
M. Stephan ... Paris, Gauthier-Villars, 1878.
3 p. l., 215 p. 2 fold. pl. 28 x 22½ᵐᵐ.
Extrait du tome premier des Annales de l'Observatoire de Marseille.

1. Longitude. 1. Stephan, Édouard i. e. Jean Marie Édouard, 1837-
8-36125†
Library of Congress   QB229.L7

NL 0448691   DLC

Loewy, Maurice, 1833-1907 & Le Clerc,
Détermination de la difference des longitude entre
Paris et Berlin.
Paris, 1879.
7 p.
Paris, Comptes Rend., 88, 1879, p. 1055-1061.

NL 0448692   DN-Ob

Loewy, Maurice, 1833-1907 & Oppolzer, Th
Détermination de la difference des longitude
entre Paris et Bregenz.
Paris, 1880.
7 p. 28cm.
Paris, Comptes Rendus, 90, 1880, p. 264-269.

NL 0448693   DN-Ob

VOLUME 338

Loewy, Maurice, 1833-1907 & Perigaud
Détermination de la flexion horizontale, de la flexion latérale et de la flexion de l'axe instrumental du cercle méridien de Bischoffsheim à l'aide du nouvel appareil.
Paris, 1881
7 p.   28cm.

Paris, Comptes Rendus, 93, 1831, p. 174-180.

NL 0448694   DN-Ob

Loewy, Maurice , 1833-1907.
Détermination de la latitude d'un lieu par l'observation d'une hauteur de l'etoile polaire.
Par M.M. Loewy....
Paris, Gauthier-Villars...1877.
cover title 11 p. 28cm.

Paris, Annales Bur. Long., 1, 1877, C. 1-C. 11.

NL 0448695   DN-Ob

Loewy, Maurice, 1833-1907.
Détermination des ascensions droites des etoiles de calmination lunaire et de longitude....
Paris, 1877
cover title 94 p.

Paris, Annales Bur. Long., 1, 1877, p. B. 1-B.94.

NL 0448696   DN-Ob MH

Loewy, Maurice, 1833-1907.
Détermination des ascensions droites des étoiles de culminations lunaire et de longitude.
Paris, (1887).
117 p. 28cm.

Paris, Annales, Bur. Long., 4, 1890, (no. 2.)

NL 0448697   DN-Ob MH

Loewy, Maurice, 1833-1907.
Détermination des différences de longitudes entre Paris et Marseille et entre Alger et Marseille, par MM. Loewy et Stephan. ¡Paris, Gauthier-Villars, 1877¿
7 p.

From Comptes rendus of the Academy of Sciences, Paris, 1877.
Volume of pamphlets.

NL 0448698   NNC DN-Ob MH

4GA-25 Loewy, Maurice, 1833-1907.
Détermination des différences de longitude entre Paris-Berlin et Paris-Bonn, par M. Loewy, F. Le Clerc [et] O. de Bernardières.   Paris, Gauthier-Villars, 1882.
336 p.

NL 0448699   DLC-P4

Lœwy, Maurice, 1833-1907.
Détermination télégraphique de la différence de longitude entre Paris et l'Observatoire du Dépôt de la guerre à Alger (colonne Voirol) par MM. Lœwy et Perrier. Paris, Imprimerie nationale, 1877.

1 p. l, 172 p. 10 pl. (4 col.) 27½ x 22ᶜᵐ.
The four colored plates are wanting.
Extrait du tome xi du Mémorial du Dépôt général de la guerre.

1. Longitude.   ɪ. Perrier, François, 1833-1888.

8-36124†

Library of Congress   QB229.L8

NL 0448700   DLC MH

Loewy, Maurice, 1833-1907.
Deux methodes nouvelles pour la determination des ascensions droites des etoiles polaires et de l'inclinaison de l'axe d'un instrument meridien au-dessus de l'equateur.
Paris, 1883.
17 p. 27 cm.

Paris, Comptes Rendus, 96, 1883, p. 1089-1107, 1179-1191.

NL 0448701   DN-Ob

Lœwy, Maurice, 1833-1907.
... Discours prononcé aux funérailles de M. Faye, membre de l'Académie, par M. Lœwy ... le lundi, 7 juillet, 1902. Paris, Typ. de Firmin-Didot et cⁱᵉ, 1902.
cover-title, 7 p. 28½ x 23ᶜᵐ.
At head of title: Institut de France. Académie des sciences.

1. Faye, Hervé Auguste Étienne Albans, 1814-1902.   ɪ. Académie des sciences, Paris. ɪɪ. Title.

20-8979

Library of Congress   QB36.F3L6

NL 0448702   DLC DN-Ob

QB9
.L6
1899 Loewy, Maurice, 1833-1907.
Éphémérides des étoiles de culmination lunaire et de longitude pour 1901₍-1904₎ Paris, Gauthier-Villars, 1899-1902.
4 v. tables. 29cm.
At head of title: Bureau des Longitudes.

1. Stars—Ephemerides. I. France. Bureau des Longitudes. II. Title.

NL 0448703   ViU

Loewy, Maurice; Leveau, & Renan, Henri
Etude de la flexion horizontale de la lunette du cercle meridien Bischoffsheim de l'observatoire de Paris.
Paris, 1887
7 p. 27 cm.

Paris, Comptes Rendus, 104, 1887, p. 154-160.

NL 0448704   DN-Ob

Loewy, Maurice, 1833-1907.
... Étude de la variation de la ligne de visée, faite au grand cercle méridien de l'observatoire de Paris, construit par M. Eichens au moyen d'un nouvel appareil; par M. Loewy. ¡Paris, Gauthier-Villars, 1880¿
7 p. 28 x 22¼ᵐ.
Caption title.
At head of title: Institut de France. Académie des sciences. Extrait des Comptes rendus des séances de l'Académie des sciences. t. xci.

1. Transit circle.

CA 6—2293 Unrev'd
Library of Congress   QB101.L82

NL 0448705   DLC DN-Ob PPAmP

Loewy, Maurice, 1833-1907.
Étude des conditions à realiser dans l'execution des cliches pour obtenir l'homogénéité et le maximum d'exactitude dans la determination des coordonnées des images stellaires. Formules pour evaluer l'influence de l'ensemble des causes d'erreur qui alterent les résultats.
Paris, 1902
7 p. 28cm.

Paris, Comptes Rendus, 134, 1902, p. 381-387.

NL 0448706   DN-Ob

Loewy, Maurice, 1833-1907.
Étude des flexions du grand cercle méridien (flexion en distance polaire, flexion latérale, flexion de l'axe instrumental) et de la forme des tourillons à l'aide de l'appareil imaginé par M. Loewy, par MM. Loewy et Périgaud. Extrait des Annales de l'Observatoire de Paris, Mémoires, tome xvi. Paris, Gauthier-Villars, 1881.
vi, c1-c120 p. diagrs. 30½ x 23½ᶜᵐ.

1. Transit-circle.   ɪ. Périgaud, Ernest Louis Antoine.

CA 9-2113 Unrev'd
Library of Congress   QB101.L84

NL 0448707   DLC DN-Ob

Loewy, Maurice   & Puiseux, P
Etude du systeme optique formé d'une lunette astronomique et d'un double miroir. Méthode la plus precise pour la mesure des distances en vue de l'etude de l'aberration et de la refraction.
Paris, 1890
23 p. 28cm.

Paris, Comptes Rendus, 110, 1890, p. 761-767, 818-825, 1097-1105.

NL 0448708   DN-Ob

Loewy, M₍aurice₎ 1833–
... Études diverses sur les méthodes d'observation et de réduction des observations méridiennes, par M. M. Loewy ... Paris, Gauthier-Villars, 1885.
cover-title, 13, 30, 7 p. 26 x 21½ᶜᵐ.
At head of title: Institut de France. Académie des sciences.
Extraits des Comptes rendus des séances de l'Académie des science t. c et cɪ.
Contents.—I. Méthodes nouvelles pour la détermination des coordonnées absolues des étoiles, sans qu'il soit nécessaire de connaitre les constantes instrumentales.—II. Sur la limite d'exactitude des formules différentielles.—III. Inexactitude commise par l'emploi des formules usuelles dans la réduction des étoiles polaires et dans la détermination de la collimation astronomique.—IV. Méthodes d'observation des polaires à une grande distance du méridien.—V. Sur l'effet des erreurs instrumentales dans la détermination du tour de vis.
1. Astronomy, Spherical   and practical.

6-39821
Library of Congress   QB151.L82

NL 0448709   DLC OCU

Loewy, Maurice   & Puiseux,
Etudes photographiques sur quelques portions de la surface lunaire.
Paris, 1894
6 p. 27cm.

Paris, Comptes Rendus, 119, 1894, p. 876-880.

NL 0448710   DN-Ob

Loewy, Maurice, 1833-1907.
The Institute of France in 1894. By M. Loewy ...
(In Smithsonian institution. Annual report. 1894. Washington, 1896. 23½ᶜᵐ. p. 697-708)
"Translated from Revue scientifique, 4th series, vol. ɪɪ, November 3, 1894."

1. Institut de France, Paris.

8 15-883
Smithsonian inst. Library
for Library of Congress   ¡Q11.S66 1894¿
                                  ¡a37b1¿   (506)

NL 0448711   DSI WaS MdBP DLC DL

VOLUME 338

Loewy, Maurice, 1833-1907.
[Memoires astronomiques. Paris, Gauthier-
Villars, 1872-87]
16 pts. in 1 v. tables, diagrs. 29 cm.
Binder's title.
Contributions from various scientific serials.
1. Astronomy - Addresses, essays, lectures.

NL 0448712   CU

Loewy, Maurice, 1833-1907.
Méthode nouvelle et rapide pour la détermination
des erreurs de division d'un cercle méridien, par
M. Loewy.....
Paris. Gauthier-Villars., 1907.
2 f. 276 p. 31cm.

Paris, Observ. Annales, Mem., 27, 1910, A1-A276.

NL 0448713   DN-Ob

Loewy, [Maurice] 1833-[1907].
... Méthode nouvelle pour la détermination des ascen
sions droites et déclinaisons absolues des étoiles; par
M. Loewy. [Paris, Gauthier-Villars, 1883]
13, [1] p. tables. 27½ x 24½cm.
Caption title.
Extrait des Comptes-rendus des séances de l'Académie des sciences,
t. xcvi.

1. Astronomy, Spherical and practical.   CA 6-2182 Unrev'd

Library of Congress   QB147.L75

NL 0448714   DLC

Loewy, Maurice &Puiseux
Note accompagnant la présentation du quatrième
fascicule de l'Atlas photographique de la lune.
Considérations sur la constitution physique de la
lune.
Paris, 1897
10 p. 27cm.

Paris, Comptes Rendus, 128, 1899, p. 1538-1543;
129, 1899, p. 5-8.

NL 0448715   DN-Ob

Loewy, M[aurice] 1833-
Notice sur la vie et les travaux de M. Oppolzer; par
M. Loewy. [Paris, Gauthier-Villars, 1887]
7 p. 24½cm.
Caption title.
"Extrait du Bulletin astronomique; janvier 1887."

1. Oppolzer, Theodor von, 1841-1886.

Library of Congress   QB36.O62L   6-16245†

NL 0448716   DLC PPAmP

Q311
.L65
v.18,
no.24   Loewy, Maurice, 1833-1907.
Notice sur un nouvel appareil optique, propre
à l'étude de la flexion; par Mm. Loewy et
Tresca. [Paris, Gauthier-Villars, 1882?]
7 p. 33cm. [Lomb miscellaneous pamphlets,
v. 18, no. 24]
Caption title.
"Extrait des Comptes rendus des séances d l'Académie
des Sciences, t. XCV, séance du 4 décembre 1882."
Original paper wrappers.

1. Optics, Physical.   I. Title.

NL 0448717   ViU DN-Ob

Loewy, Maurice, 1833-1907.
Nouvelle méthode pour determiner la flexion des
lunettes.
Paris, 1878.
5 p. 28cm.

Paris, Comptes Rendus, 87, 1878, p. 889-893.

NL 0448718   DN-Ob

Loewy, Maurice, *1833-1907.*   No. 2 in **E.5142.51
Nouvelle méthode pour la détermination des éléments de la ré-
fraction.
— [Paris. Gauthier-Villars. 1886.] 47 pp. [Institut de France.
Académie des sciences.] 27 cm., in 4s.
Reprinted from Comptes rendus des séances de l'Académie des sciences,
vol. 102, which may be found on a separate call-number.
There is no title-page.

D4869 — S.r. Pubs. — Refraction. Atmospheric.

NL 0448719   MB

Loewy, M[aurice] 1833-
... Nouvelles méthodes pour la détermination complète
de la réfraction, par M. M. Loewy ... Paris, Gauthier-
Villars, 1886.
cover-title, 47 p. diagrs. 28 x 22½cm.
At head of title : Institut de France. Académie des sciences.
"Extrait des Comptes rendus des séances de l'Académie des sciences,
t. cii."

1. Refraction, Astronomical.

Library of Congress   QB155.L82   6-32822

NL 0448720   DLC PPAmP NNC MiU

Loewy, Maurice, 1833-1907.
... Nouvelles méthodes pour la détermination de la constante
de l'aberration, par m. M. Loewy ... Paris, Gauthier-Villars,
1887.
1 p. l., 57, [1] p. illus., diagrs. 28 x 22½cm.
At head of title : Institut de France. Académie des sciences.
"Extrait des Comptes rendus hebdomadaires de l'Académie des sciences, tomes civ et cv."

1. Aberration.

Library of Congress   QB163.L82   6-32823

NL 0448721   DLC MB

Loewy, Maurice, 1833-1907.
Nouvelles méthodes pour la détermination de la
position relative de l'équateur instrumental par
rapport à l'équateur réel et des declinaisons
absolues des étoiles et de la latitude absolue.
Paris, 1883.
6 p. 27cm.

Paris, Comptes Rendus, 96, 1883, p. 1329-1334.

NL 0448722   DN-Ob

Loewy, Maurice, 1833-1907.

France. Comité consultatif des observatoires astronomiques de province.
... Rapport sur les observatoires astronomiques de province. Année 1879-19
Paris. Imprimerie nationale, 1880-19

Loewy, Maurice, 1833-1907.
Recent progress accomplished by aid of photography in the
study of the lunar surface. By MM. Loewy and Puiseux.
(*In* Smithsonian institution. Annual report. 1898. Washington,
1899. 23½cm. p. 105-121. 3 pl.)
"Translated from Annuaire du Bureau des longitudes, Paris, 1898."

1. Moon—Surface. 2. Astronomical photography.   I. Puiseux, Pierre
Henri, 1855-1928, joint author.   II. Title.

Smithsonian inst. Library   S 15-982
for Library of Congress   [Q11.S66 1898]

NL 0448724   DSI WaS

Loewy, Maurice, 1833-1907.
Recherches nouvelles sur la determination
absolue des coordonnees equatoriales de etoiles et
de la latitude....
Paris, 1898
22 p. 28cm.

Paris, Comptes Rendus, 125, 1897, p. 1062-1068.
1142-1147; 126, 1898, p. 16-22.

NL 0448725   DN-Ob

QB
145
L82r   Loewy, M[aurice] 1833-
Recherches sur la détermination des
constantes des clichés photographiques
du ciel ... Paris, Gauthier-Villars et
fils, 1893.
viii,39,B21,144p.incl.tables,diagrs. 27½cm.

1. Astronomy, Spherical and practical. 2.
Astronomical photography. 3. Astronomy - Tables,
etc.

NL 0448726   NRU CU

Loewy, Maurice, 1833-1907.
Seance publique annuelle de l'academie des
Sciences du 17 decembre 1894. Discours d'ouverture
de M. le President.
Paris,
17 p. 28cm.

NL 0448727   DN-Ob

Loewy, Maurice &Puiseux,
Sur l'Atlas photographique de la lune publie par
l'Observatoire de Paris. II
Paris, 1897
12 p. 27cm.

Paris, Comptes Rendus, 124, 1897, p. 1055-1061,
1187-1193.

NL 0448728   DN-Ob

Loewy, Maurice &Puiseux,
Sur la constitution physique de la lune et
l'interprétation de divers traits de sa surface,
mis en évidence par la photographie.
Paris, 1895
12 p. 28cm.

Paris, Comptes Rendus, 121, 1895, p. 6-12, 78-85.

NL 0448729   DN-Ob

Loewy, Maurice, 1833-1907.
Sur la construction de la carte du ciel.
Paris, 1893.
12 p. 28 cm.

Paris, Comptes Rendus, 116, 1893, p. 661-666, 705-
711.

NL 0448730   DN-Ob MH

VOLUME 338

Loewy, Maurice, 1833-1907.
Sur la précision des coordonnées des astres
potenues à l'aide des mesures effectuees sur leur
images photographiees. 2e et 3e Memoires.
Paris, 1902.
2 + 115 p. 28cm.

Paris, Com. Carte du Ciel Bull., 3,.

NL 0448731 DN-Ob

Loewy, Maurice, 1833-1907.
Sur la précision des mesures des coordonnées rectilignes des
images stellaires. Mémoires [1]-3. Paris: Gauthier-Villars.
1901-02. 3 parts in 1 v. 4°. (Institut de France. Acad
des sciences.)
Parts 2-3 have title: Sur la précision des coordonnées des astres obtenues à
l'aide des mesures effectuees sur leurs images photographiees.
Repr.: Comité internat. permanent pour l'exécution photographique de la carte
du ciel. Bull. Tome 3.

1. Stars.—Magnitude : Measurement. 2. Stars.—Magnitude (Photo-
metric). 3. Institut de France. Académie des sciences.
N.Y.L. March 4, 1914.

NL 0448732 NN DN-Ob

Loewy, Maurice & Puiseux, P.
Sur la structure et l'histoire de l'écorce
lunaire: observations suggérées par le cinquieme
et le sixieme fasciciele de l'Atlas photographique
de la lune, publie par l'Observatoire de Paris.
Paris, 1902
5 p. 27cm.

Paris, Comptes Rendus, 135, 1902, p. 73-78.

NL 0448733 DN-Ob

Loewy, Maurice, 1833-1907.
Sur le fonctionnement de l'equatorial coudé et
observations de la planete (244) faites par
M. Loewy et Perigaud.)
Paris, 1884
6 (1) p. 27cm.

Paris, Comptes Rendus, 99, 1884, p. 721-726.

NL 0448734 DN-Ob

Loewy, Maurice, 1833-1907.
Sur le grand equatorial coude de l'Observatoire
de Paris.
Paris, 1894.
5 p. 28 cm.

Paris, Comptes Rendus, 118, 1894, p. 1295-1299.

NL 0448735 DN-Ob

Loewy, Maurice & Puiseux
Sur les photographies de la lune obtenues au
grand équatorial coude de l'Observatoire de Paris.
Paris, 1894
7 + 7 p. 27cm.

Paris, Comptes Rendus, 119, 1894, p. 130-135, 254-
259.

NL 0448736 DN-Ob

Loewy, Maurice, 1833-1907.
Tables generales de reduction des observations
meridiennes.
Paris, 1877
39 p. 28cm.

Paris, Ann. Bur. Long., 1, , p. D 1 - D 39.

NL 0448737 DN-Ob

QB151
.L6 Loewy, Maurice, 1833-1907.
1891 Théorie du système optique composé d'une
lunette astronomique et d'un double miroir
plan. Application à la mesure précise des
distances en vue de l'étude de l'aberration
et de la réfraction, par M. Loewy [et] P.
Puiseux. Paris, Gauthier-Villars, 1891.
ii, 101 p. diagrs. 27cm.
"Extrait des Annales de l'Observatoire de Paris,
mémoires, t. XX."
1. Optics. 2. Aberration. 3. Refraction,
Astronomical. I.Puiseux, Pierre Henri,
1855-1928. joint author. II. Title.

NL 0448738 ViU

No. 3 in **E.5142.51
Loewy, Maurice, 1833-1907, and Pierre Henri Puiseux, 1855-
Théories nouvelles de l'équatorial condé et des équatoriaux en
général.
— Paris. Gauthier-Villars. 1888. 52 pp. [Institut de France. Aca-
démie des sciences.] 27 cm., in 4s.
Reprinted from Comptes rendus des séances de l'Académie des sciences,
vol. 106, which may be found on a separate call-number.

D4869 — Jt. auth. — Telescope. Equatorial.

NL 0448739 MB DN-Ob NNC

LOEWY, MAURICE, 1833-1907.
Travaux divers de M. Loewy. Paris, Gauthier-
Villars, 1872. 99, 39 p. 30cm.

"Publie's dans les Annales de l'observatoire. "
CONTENTS.--Détermination des orbites des comètes.--Determination
de l'orbite de la planète Eugénie.

1. Comets--Orbits, 1872. 2. Eugenia (Planetoid).
t.1872.

NL 0448740 NN

Loewy, Maurice, 1833-1907.
Über die Bahn der Eugenia.
Wien, 1858-1860.
2 nos. 24cm.

Wien, Sitz. Ber., 29, 1858, p. 450-458, 38, 1859.
p. 389-412.

NL 0448741 DN-Ob

Loewy, Maurice, 1833-1907.
Über die Bahn der Leda.
Wien, 1857.
9 p. 24cm.

Wien, Sitz. Ber., 24, 1857, p. 173-179.

NL 0448742 DN-Ob

QD401 Loewy, Max.
.L835 Ueber neue derivate des amarins.
Freiburg, 1887.
34p.
Inaug. diss. Freiburg.

NL 0448743 DLC

Löwy, Max, 1875-
... Dementia praecox, intermediäre psychische schicht und
kleinhirn-basalganglien-stirnhirnsysteme, von dr. Max Loewy
... Berlin, S. Karger, 1923.
120 p. 25½ᶜᵐ. (Abhandlungen aus der neurologie, psychiatrie, psychologie und ihren grenzgebieten ... hft. 20)
At head of title: ... Aus der Psychiatrischen und nervenklinik zu
Frankfurt a. M. ... und der Deutschen psychiatrischen universitätsklinik
in Prag.

1. Dementia. 2. Subconsciousness. A C 33-4327

Title from John Crerar Libr. Printed by L. C.

NL 0448744 ICJ CU PPC MiU

Löwy, Max, 1875-
Ueber eine unruheerscheinung: die halluzination
des anrufes mit dem eigenen namen (ohne und mit
beachtungswahn, von Dr. Max Löwy. [n.p.] 1910.
131 p. 23 cm.
Caption title.

NL 0448745 MoSU

RC361 Löwy, Max, 1875-
L827 ... Zur behandlung der psychotraumatiker des
krieges in kriege und nach friedensschluss, vo
oberarzt dr. Max Löwy ... Berlin, S. Karger
[1918]
[46]-58 p. 24ᶜᵐ.
Caption title.
"Sonder-abdruck aus Monatsschrift für psychiatrie und neurologie, bd.XLIII,h.1."
"Auszugsweise vorgetragen in der ärztlichen
tagung der waffenbrüderlichen vereinigung in B
den bei wien (ok tober 1917)"
1.Neuroses,Trau umatic. 2.Psychology,
Pathological. 3. Eur. war, 1914-1918-
Medical and san itary affairs.

NL 0448746 CSt-H

Löwy, Max, 1875-
...Zur kasuistik seltener "dyshumoraler"
(innersekretorischer) störungen. n. p., n. pub.,
n. d.
Cover-title: 37 p.

Sonderabdruck aus der "Prager mediz. wochenschrift bd. xxxvi, no.34-37, 1911.

NL 0448747 MiDW

Löwy (Moritz). *Ueber das syphilitische Fieber
und seine Behandlung mit Jod. 36 pp. 8°. Erlangen, E. T. Jacob, 1874.

NL 0448748 DNLM ICRL

Loewy, Moritz, 1849-
Antwort auf "Religion und Staat", [eine Studie
von B. Schueck.] Temesvár, Brüder Moravetz,
1905.
45, (1) p.

NL 0448749 OCH

B759 Löwy, Moritz, 1849-1908, ed. and tr.
.I 22H4 Ibn Aknin, Joseph, 1160 (ca.)-1226.
Drei abhandlungen, von Josef b. Jehuda, dem schüler
Maimûni's: 1. Ueber den nothwendig-existirenden, 2. Ueber den
modus des hervorgehns der dinge aus ihm, 3. Ueber die
schöpfung der welt. Zum ersten mal herausgegeben, übersetzt
und erläutert von dr. Moritz Löwy. Berlin, In commission bei
B. Baer, 1879.

VOLUME 338

Loewy, Moritz, 1849–
Der Patriarch. Fest-Predigt zur Vorfeier des
Fest's des hundersten Geburtstages Sir M.
Montefiore's am Schemini-Azereth 5645 ₍1884₎.
Hrg. vom Präsidium der Israelitischen
Religionsgemeinde zu Temesvár. Temesvár:
Südungar. Lloyd, ₍1884₎.
25 p.

NL 0448751   OCH CtY

Loewy, Moritz, 1849–
Skizzen zur Geschichte der Juden in
Temesvár bis zum Jahre 1865. Szegedin:
A. Bába, 1890.
85 p.

NL 0448752   OCH MH

Loewy, M₍oritz₎, 1849–1908.
Über das Buch Jona. Exegetisch-kritischer
Versuch. Wien, Ch. D. Lippe [at A. Engel in
Szegedin, 1892]
40 p.

NL 0448753   OCH

BS1225
G54
1930
Hebr

Löwy, Moses, 1760 (ca.)–1834.
Hut ha-meshulash bi-she'arim

Glogau, Asher Lemel, 1705– (ca.)–1789.
הוא הכשולש בשערים: הכולל שלשה ספרים. דרושים כסדר
פרשיות התורה אשר יצאו מפי שלשה דורות. האחד שער אשר.
אשר הברו אשר לעמל הלוי מנלונא. והשני שער הטם. אשר חברו
יהואל מיכל הלוי מנלונא. ושלושי שער הכטן. אשר חברו משה
הלוי מנלונא. ₍הוצא לאור על ידי יהואל שאבטער. מונקאטש.
תרצ"א.   Mukačevo, 1930.

Löwy₍ Moses A.
Worte zur Beherzigung an die Israelitischen
Gemeinde-Vorstände in Ungarn. Pesth, 1841
22 p.

NL 0448755   PPDrop

Loewy, Paul.
Die sekretwege der zirbeldrüse, von cand. med. Paul Loewy
... (Mit 3 abbildungen im texte)
  (*In* Vienna. Universität. Neurologisches institut. Arbeiten. Leipzig und Wien, 1913. 26ᶜᵐ. Bd. xx, p. ₍130₎–144. illus.)
  "Literaturverzeichnis": p. 143–144.

  1. Pineal body.
                                                    A 42–2211
John Crerar library
   for Library of Congress   ₍2₎

NL 0448756   ICJ

Loewy, Paul, pseud.
  see Loewy, Ernst.

Löwy, R.
Druckschwankungen in druckrohrleitungen, von dr. techn.
ing. R. Löwy ... mit 45 abbildungen im text und 7 tafeln.
Wien, J. Springer, 1928.
  v, 162 p., 1 l. vii pl., diagrs. 24ᶜᵐ.
  "Literaturverzeichnis": p. ₍161₎–162.

  1. Hydrostatics. 2. Hydraulic engineering.   i. Title.
                                                    29–4331
Library of Congress   TC174.L6

NL 0448758   DLC

Loewy (Raymond) associates.
... Implementing tomorrow. New York, Raymond Loewy
associates ₍1944₎
  1 v. plates, plans, fold. tables, diagrs. (part fold.) 24½ x 20½ᵐ.
  At head of title: Associated merchandising corporation.

  1. Department stores. 2. Retail trade—U. S.   i. Associated merchandising corporation.   ii. Title.
                                                    45–4075
Library of Congress   HF5461.L6
                             ₍3₎   658.871

NL 0448759   DLC

*NA9127   Loewy (Raymond) Associates.
.S23L8   Proposal for development of the St.
            Paul city plan. New York, 1944.
            9 numb. l. 6 l. illus.   29cm.

            Positive and negative photostats.

NL 0448760   MnHi

Loewy (Raymond) Associates.
Survey report, State of California; California State Fair
study. New York ₍1949₎
  125 p. fold. map, diagrs. 28 cm.

  1. Sacramento, Calif. California State Fair.
  S555.C223L6   630.74   49–45385*

NL 0448761   DLC Or OCl

Loewy, Raymond Fernand, 1893–
The locomotive, by Raymond Loewy. ₍London, The Studio,
ltd.; New York, The Studio publications, inc., 1937₎
  ₍108₎ p. illus. 25½ᵐ. (*Half-title:* The New vision. ₍3₎)
  Mainly illustrations.

  1. Locomotives.
                                        37–13357 Revised
Library of Congress   TJ603.L66
                             ₍r45k2₎   621.132084

NL 0448762   DLC OCl OU OLak MB CU WaS WaSp

Loewy, Raymond Fernand, 1893–
Never leave well enough alone. ₍The personal record of
an industrial designer₎ New York, Simon and Schuster,
1951.
  xii, 377 p. illus., ports. 19 cm.

  i. Title.
  NK839.L6A3   926   51–2096

     NNC CaBVa IdU CaBVaU OrP ViU TU TxU
NL 0448763   DLC OrU Or WaS OKentU AU KyLx MB OCU

Loewy, Richard, 1864–
Die Unmöglichkeit der Leistung bei
zweiseitigen Schuldverhältnissen ...
nebst den angefügten Thesen öffentlich verteidigen wird ... Richard
Loewy ... Opponenten: Herr Rechtsan-
walt Jaffé, Herr Referendar Dr. Meyer,
Herr Referendar Dr. Levin. Berlin,
Dobrzynski & Müllner, 1888.
  29, ₍2₎ p. 20cm.
  Inaug.-Diss. -   Berlin.

  Biography: p. ₍31₎
  "Verzeichnis der Litteratur": p. ₍7₎
  -8.

NL 0448765   MH-L ICRL

Loewy, Richard, 1864–
Die unmöglichkeit der leistung bei zweiseitigen schuldverhältnissen. Eine romanistische abhandlung von dr. Richard
Loewy. Berlin, J. J. Heine, 1888.
  147 p. 21ᶜᵐ.
  "Der verfasser unterwirft ... eine jugendarbeit, auf grund deren er
  den doktorgrad der Berliner universität erlangt hat, dem öffentlichen
  urteil."—Vorwort.

  1. Sales (Roman law) 2. Debtor and creditor (Roman law)
  i. Title.
                                                    37–36801

NL 0448766   DLC CtY-L

QD341   Loewy, Richard, 1870–
A2L8   Zur kenntniss des tetramethoxyldiphtalyls.
          Giessen, 1893.
          15p.
          Inaug. diss. Giessen.

NL 0448767   DLC MH PU

QD445   Loewy, Robert.
.O8L8   Ueber flavon-derivate.
          Wien, 1897.
          40p.
          Inaug. diss. Basel.

NL 0448768   DLC PU

Löwy, Robert.
Über die faseranatomie und physiologie der formatio ver-
micularis cerebelli, von dr. Robert Löwy ... (Mit 6 abbildungen im text)
  (*In* Vienna. Universität. Neurologisches institut. Arbeiten. Leipzig und Wien, 1916. 26ᶜᵐ. Bd. xxi, p. ₍359₎–382. illus.)

  1. ₍Vermiform process₎ 2. Cerebellum.
                                                    A 42–959
John Crerar library
   for Library of Congress   ₍2₎

NL 0448769   ICJ

Löwy, Robert.
... Über störungen von entwicklungskorrelationen am gross-
hirn, von dr. Robert Löwy ... (Mit 14 abbildungen im text)
  (*In* Vienna. Universität. Neurologisches institut. Arbeiten. Leipzig und Wien, 1913. 26ᶜᵐ. Bd. xx, p. ₍175₎–220. illus.)
  At head of title: Aus dem Neurologischen institut und der i. Anatomischen lehrkanzel der Universität in Wien.

  1. Brain—Abnormities and deformities.
                                                    A 42–2214
John Crerar library
   for Library of Congress   ₍2₎

NL 0448770   ICJ

VOLUME 338

Löwy, Robert.
Zur frage der mikrogyrie, ein beitrag zur theorie der windungsbildungen, von dr. Robert Löwy ... (Mit 9 figuren im text)

(*In* Vienna. Universität. Neurologisches institut. Arbeiten. Leipzig und Wien, 1916. 26ᶜᵐ. Bd. XXI, p. 1–40. illus.)

1. Brain—Abnormities and deformities. 2. Brain—[Cortex]

A 42-944

John Crerar library
for Library of Congress   [2]

NL 0448771   ICJ

Löwy, Robert.
Zur frage der superfizellen körnerschichte und markscheidenbildung des kleinhirns; ihre beziehungen zum lokalisationsproblem und zur gehfähigkeit, von Robert Löwy ... (Hierzu 15 textbilder)

(*In* Vienna. Universität. Neurologisches institut. Arbeiten. Leipzig und Wien, 1910. 26ᶜᵐ. Bd. XVIII, p. [253]–293. illus., diagrs.)
"Literaturverzeichnis": p. 292–293.

1. Cerebellum. 2. Brain—Localization of functions.

A 42-2185

John Crerar library
for Library of Congress   [2]

NL 0448772   ICJ

Löwy, Robert.
Zur klinik und pathogenese der nervösen erscheinungen beim fleckfieber, von dr. Robert Löwy ...

(*In* Vienna. Universität. Neurologisches institut. Arbeiten. Leipzig und Wien, 1919. 26ᶜᵐ. Bd. XXII, p. [190]–199. II pl. (1 col.))

1. Typhus fever. 2. Nervous system—Diseases.

A 42-975

John Crerar library
for Library of Congress   [2]

NL 0448773   ICJ

Loewy, Robert, 1870–
... Méthode des greffes péritonéales, par ... Robert Loewy ... Paris, Steinheil, 1901.
48 p. illus., VII plates. 24½cm.

At head of title: Travail du Laboratoire du professeur Lannelongue.
"Bibliographie": p. [45]–48.
Issued also as thesis, Paris, 1901.

1. Skin-grafting.

NL 0448774   NNC DNLM

Loewy, Robert, 1870–
Nouveau procédé de contention des hernies
see also   Berger, Emile, 1855-1926.
Les troubles oculaires [etc.]

TL
574
A4182+   **Loewy, Robert G**
Tables of two-dimensional oscillating airfoil coefficients for rotary wings. Buffalo, N.Y., Cornell Aeronautical Laboratory, inc., 1955.
11,61 l. tables. 28cm. (Cornell Aeronautical Laboratory, inc., Buffalo. Report no 77)

1. Aerodynamics—Tables, etc. 2. Aerofoils. I. Series.

NL 0448776   NIC

---

ar X
819   **Loewy, Robert G**
A two-dimensional approximation to the unsteady aerodynamics of rotary wings. Buffalo, N. Y., Cornell Aeronautical Laboratory, 1955.
v, 48 l. illus. 28cm. (Cornell Aeronautical Laboratory, inc., Buffalo. Report no. 75)

1. Aeroplanes—Wings. 2. Aerodynamics. I. Title. II. Series.

NL 0448777   NIC

Löwy, Salamon
Betűművészet. Budapest, Világosság, 1926.
2 v. illus., plates (part col.) 19cm. (Grafikai művészetek könyvtára, 2-3)

At head of title: Löwy Salamon és Novák László.

1. Printing specimens. I. Novák, László,   jt. au.

NL 0448778   NNC

Löwy, Salamon, and L. Novák.
...Betűművészet.   Budapest: Nyomtatták a világosság könyvnyomda részvénytársaság sajtóin [193–] 143 p. illus., col'd plates. 19cm. (Grafikai művészetek könyvtára. 3.)

792016A. 1. Type—Specimens.   I. Novák, László, jt. au.
N. Y. P. L.   July 2, 1936

NL 0448779   NN

Loewy, Siegfried, 1857–
CS524
L6   Altwiener Familien.   Wien, Steyrermühl, 1925.
100 p. 19ᶜᵐ (Tagblatt-Bibliothek Nr.165/165)
Stack   Cover title.

1. Vienna - Geneal. I. Title.

NL 0448780   CSt

Loewy, Siegfried, 1857–
Aus Wiens grosser Theaterzeit; Monographien und persönliche Erinnerungen von Siegfried Loewy.   Wien: P. Knepler [1921]
viii, 111 p. illus. 23cm.

254594B. 1. Stage—Austria—Vienna.   2. Actors and acting, Austrian.
N. Y. P. L.   December 27, 1943

NL 0448781   NN ICarbS NjP CU OC1W OCU MH

Loewy, Siegfried, 1857–
Das Burgtheater im Wandel der Zeiten; kleine Bausteine zur Geschichte dieser Kunststätte, von Siegfried Loewy. Mit einem Vorwort von Hermann Bahr. Wien: P. Knepler [1926.] 153 p. front., plates, ports. 8°.

Bibliography, last leaf.

280117A. 1. Theatres—Austria—   Vienna.
N. Y. P. L.   January 19, 1927

NL 0448782   NN NjP IEN MH

4PN-393 Loewy, Siegfried, 1857–
Deutsche Theaterkunst von Goethe bis Reinhardt, mit einem Anhang: Das alte Wiener Volkstheater. Wien, P. Knepler [Geleitwort 1922]
215 p.

NL 0448783   DLC-P4 CLSU InU OU CoU WaU IaU NjJStP

PN2616
V5L6   **Loewy, Siegfried, 1857–**
Deutsche Theaterkunst von Goethe bis Reinhardt. Mit einem Anhang: Das alte Wiener Volkstheater. Wien, P. Knepler [1923]
xx, 215 p. ports.

"200 Exemplare ... Nr. 14."

1. Theater - Vienna.

NL 0448784   CU WU ViU MH

Loewy, Siegfried, 1857–
Johann Strauss, der spielmann von der blauen Donau; lebensfragmente, von Siegfried Loewy. Mit 14 tafeln. Wien, Leipzig, Wiener literarische anstalt, aktiengesellschaft, 1924.
191 p., 1 l. plates, ports., facsims. (1 fold.; incl. music) 19½ cm.
"Quellennachweis": 1 leaf at end.

1. Strauss, Johann, 1825-1899.

ML410.S9L6   25—5195

NL 0448785   DLC

Loewy, Siegfried, 1857–
Rund um Johann Strauss; momentbilder aus einem künstlerleben, von Siegfried Loewy. Wien, P. Knepler [1925]
173, [4] p. 4 pl., 2 port. (incl. front.) 2 facsim. (music) 20½ᶜᵐ.
"Gesamtverzeichnis der kompositionen": p. 149–155.
"Quellennachweis": 1 p. at end.

1. Strauss, Johann, 1825-1899.   I. Title.

                                         26-19708
Library of Congress   ML410.L829

NL 0448786   DLC GU PP

1881–
Loewy, Siegfried [Beobachtungen und Untersuchungen an den Kindern der Hilfsschulklassen in Meiningen. Leipzig 1909: Georgi. 67 S. 8°
Leipzig, Med. Diss. v. 3. Febr. 1909, Ref. Flechsig
[Geb. 21. Nov. 81 Berlin; Wohnort: Berlin; Staatsangeh.: Preußen; Vorbildung: Kölln. Gymn. Berlin Reife M. 01; Studium: Berlin 10 S.; Coll. 9. Mai 09; Approb. März 08.]   [U.09. 2824]

NL 0448787   ICRL DNLM CtY

1889–
Loewy, Siegfried, [Referendar, Posen: Die Besitzverhältnisse an gepfändeten im Gewahrsam des Schuldners belassenen beweglichen Sachen. Bromberg 1915: Gruenauer. 38 S. 8°
Breslau, Jur. Diss. v. 17. Juni 1915, Ref. Leonhard, H. Meyer
[Geb. 28. März 89 Exin; Wohnort: Exin; Staatsangeh.: Preußen; Vorbildung: G. Nakel Reife 09; Studium: München 1, Berlin 3, Breslau 2 S.; Prüfg. 8. Nov.12.]   [U 15. 217]

NL 0448788   ICRL

Loewy, Siegmund, Arzt: Die Influenzaform des Paratyphus B. Breslau 1919: Breslauer Genossensch.-Buchdr. 24 S. 8°
Breslau, Med. Diss. v. 26. Mai 1919, Ref. Minkowski
[Geb. 20. Okt. 83 Eintrachthütte, Kr. Beuthen; Wohnort: Breslau; Staatsangeh.: Preußen; Vorbildung: G. Kattowitz Reife 05; Studium: Breslau 10 S.; Coll. 30. Juni 13; Approb. 22. Aug. 11.]   [U 19. 1182]

NL 0448789   ICRL DNLM

Loewy, Theodor.   *3340.3.124
Der Idealismus Berkeley's in den Grundlagen untersucht. 142 pp.
(In Kaiserliche Akademie der Wissenschaften. Vienna. Philosophisch-historische Classe. Sitzungsberichte. Band 124, Abh. 1. Wien. 1891.)

H3891 — Berkeley, George, Bishop of Cloyne. 1684-1753. — Idealism. In philosophy.

NL 0448790   MB NN

VOLUME 338

Loewy, Theodor.
Die vorstellung des dinges auf grund der
erfahrung. Ein entwurf. Leipzig, C. Reissner,
1887.

NL 0448791   MH NjP

Loewy, Walter, 1881–
Die bestrittene verfassungsmässigkeit der arbeiterge-
setze in den Vereinigten Staaten von Nordamerika ...
Heidelberg, C. Winter, 1905.

4 p. l., 88 p., 1 l. 24ᶜᵐ.

Inaug.-diss.—Heidelberg.
Curriculum vitae.

1. Labor laws and legislation—U. S. 2. U. S.—Constitutional law.
                                                                7–10676

Library of Congress   HD7834.L7

NL 0448792   DLC

Loewy, Walter, 1881–
Die bestrittene verfassungsmässigkeit der arbeiterge-
setze in den Vereinigten Staaten von Nordamerika; ein
beispiel der beschränkung der legislativen gewalt durch
das richterliche prüfungsrecht, von Dr. Walter Loewy.
Heidelberg, C. Winter, 1905.

4 p. l., 88 p. 25ᶜᵐ.

Library of Congress   5–24880

NL 0448793   DLC CtY NjP PU-L MH ICJ NN

Loewy, Walter, 1881– tr.
Germany. *Laws, statutes, etc.*
The civil code of the German empire, as enacted on August
18, 1896, with the introductory statute enacted on the same
date. (In effect January 1, 1900) Tr. by Walter Loewy ...
Tr. and published under the auspices of and annotated by a
special committee of the Pennsylvania bar association and the
Law school of the University of Pennsylvania. Boston, The
Boston book co.; ₁etc., etc.₎ 1909.

NL 0448795   CLamB

Sem
915.694   **Löwy, Wilhelm**
L95t   Tvā ār i Israel. Jerusalem, Jerusalem Press
          Service [1950]

175 p. illus.

1. Israel—Descr. & Travel. I. Title.

NL 0448795   CLamB

Loewy, Wilhelm, 1850–   *9314-36127
Finanz- und Steuerverhältnisse der Stadt Wien in den Verwaltungs-
jahren 1861–1884. Nebst einem Anhange . . .
= Wien, 1886. iv, 98 pp. [Mittheilungen des statistischen Departements des Wiener Magistrates.] L. 8°.

April 24.   1901
D⁰620 — Vienna. Fin. — Municipal finance. — Vienna. Statistisches Departement.

NL 0448796   MB

Löwy, Wilhelm, 1850–
... Das unterrichtswesen in Wien   Bearb. von dr
Wilhelm Löwy ... Wien, Hof- und staatsdruckerei, 1890-
91.

2 pt. in 1 v. tables. 25¼ᵐᵐ. (Mittheilungen des Statistischen departements
des Wiener magistrats)

Separatabdruck aus den Österreichischen städtebuche (III.-IV. jahrg.)

CONTENTS.—I. Volks- und specialschulen.—II. Mittel- und hochschulen.

1. Education   Austria   Vienna

I. A689. V61.

NL 0448797   ICU CSt

B205   **Löwy-Cleve, Felix.**
.Z7L6   Die philosophie des Anaxagoras; ver-
         such einer rekonstruktion von dr. Felix
         Löwy-Cleve... Wien, C.Konegen(E.Stülp-
         nagel) 1917.
         5 p.l.,111 p.   23½ cm.

1. Anaxagoras. I. Title.

NL 0448798   OCU MH NjP CU CLSU

Loewy-Hattendorf, Erwin.
...Krieg, Revolution und Unfallneurosen. Von Dr. Erwin
Loewy-Hattendorf... Berlin: R. Schoetz, 1920. 31 p. 8°.
(Prussia. Medizinalabteilungen des Ministeriums des Innern.
Veröffentlichungen aus dem Gebiete der Medizinalverwaltung.
Bd. 11, Heft 4.)

Bibliography, p. ₍29₎–31.

1. Nervous system.—Diseases.   2. European war, 1914- .—
Medical and sanitary affairs.   3. Series.
N. Y. P. L.   August 29, 1921.

NL 0448799   NN

Loewy-Lessényi, Bernhard.
Amnon. Trauerspiel in fünf Aufzügen.
Dresden, E. Pierson [1907]
2 p.l., 108 p. 12°.

NL 0448800   NN

Löwysohn, Gumperz
see Levison, Gumperz, *d.* 1797.

Loey, Adolphe van, 1905–
...Algemeen beschaafd Nederlands in Vlaams-België... Bruxelles, J. Lebègue & cie, 1945. 97 p. 19cm. (Brussels.
Université libre. Institut de sociologie Solvay. Actualités sociales.
nouv. sér. ₍no.₎ 25)

"Bibliographie," p. 95–97.

1. Flemish language. I. Ser.
N. Y. P. L.   May 10, 1950

NL 0448802   NN NcD NIC

Loey, Adolphe van, 1905–
Bijdrage tot de kennis van het zuidwestbrabantsch in de
XIIIᵉ en XIVᵉ eeuw; fonologie, door dr. A. van Loey ... 's-Gra-
venhage, M. Nijhoff, 1937.

3 p. l., ₍IX₎-XXVIII, 251, ₍1₎ p. fold. map. 23¼ᵐᵐ. (Added t.-p.: Nomina geographica flandrica; studiën en monographieën over vlaamsch
plaatsnaamkunde ... Studiën. IV)

Bibliographical foot-notes.

1. Flemish language — Phonetics. 2. Flemish language—Dialects—
Brabant.
                                ₍Full name: Adolphe Clément Henri van Loey₎
                                                               A C 38-2372

Yale univ. Library
   for Library of Congress   ₍2₎

NL 0448803   CtY OC1

Loey, Adolphe van, 1905–
Bijdrage tot de kennis van het Zuidwestbrabantsch
in de 13de en 14de eeuw; fonologie, door A.van Loey.
Tongeren, Druk. G.Michiels-Broeders, 1937.

xxviii, 251 p. map (Werken uitgegeven door de
Koninklijke Commissie voor Toponymie en Dialecto-
logie, Vlaamsche Afdeeling, 1)

NL 0448804   MH NN

PQ1441
.C56D8   **Loey, Adolphe van,** 1905–   ed.
         La chastelaine de Vergi.
         De Borchgrauinne van Vergi; diplomatische uitg. naar
         het Hulthemse handschrift (Koninklijke Bibliotheek te
         Brussel) Bezorgd door A. van Loey. Leiden, E. J. Brill,
         1949.

NL 0448806   DLC ICRL ICU CtY

Loey, Adolphe van, 1905–
Inleiding tot de studie van het Nederlandsch, ten dienste
van het middelbaar en het normaal onderwijs, door A. van
Loey en A. Serayen. Antwerpen, De Sikkel, 1945.

161 p. illus. 25 cm.

Bibliography: p. 151.

1. Dutch language. I. Serayen, Achille G., 1905–   joint author.
                         Full name: Adolphe Clément Henri van Loey.

PF73.L6   439.31   50–57537

NL 0448806   DLC ICRL ICU CtY

4PF   **Loey, Adolphe van,** 1905–
Dutch   Introduction à l'étude du Moyen
18   -Néerlandais. Paris, Aubier, 1951.
        127 p.

(Bibliothèque de philologie germanique,

FTaSU CaBVaU
NcD CU NIC IU CtY TU MB NBuU FU OU IEN GU TxU MU
NL 0448807   DLC-P4 MiU LU ICU MnU RPB InU NNC NN MH

Loey, Adolphe van, 1905–
La langue néerlandaise en pays flamand. Bruxelles, Office
de publicité, 1945.

75 p. 19 cm. (Université libre de Bruxelles. Institut de sociologie
Solvay. Actualités sociales, nouv. sér., 24)

Bibliography: p. ₍73₎–75.

1. Dutch language. (Series: Brussels. Université libre.
Institut de sociologie Solvay. Actualités sociales. Nouv. sér., 24)
                         Full name: Adolphe Clément Henri van Loey.

PF700.L6   439.317   53–16049

NL 0448808   DLC NcD PPT NN ICU CtY ICRL

Loey, Adolphe van, 1905–   ed.

Lodewijk van Velthem, *fl.* 1293-1326.
Lodewijk van Velthem's voortzetting van den Spiegel histo-
riael (1248-1316) opnieuw uitgegeven door Herman vander
Linden en Willem de Vreese ... Brussel, Hayez, drukker der
K. Academie van België, 1906-38.

Loey, Adolphe van, 1905–   ed.
Middelnederlands leerboek. Antwerpen, De Sikkel, 1947.

xvi, 357 p. 25 cm.

"Bibliographie": p. xi-xii.

1. Dutch literature—Early to 1500. I. Title.
                         Full name: Adolphe Clément Henri van Loey.

PT5420.L6   48-27699*

NL 0448810   DLC PU MH ICU OU CaBVaU

VOLUME 338

Loey, Adolphe van, 1905–
Middelnederlandse spraakkunst. Groningen, J. B. Wolters, 1948–
v. 23 cm.
"Bibliographie": v. 1, p. xi–xiii.
Contents.—v. 1. Vormleer.

1. Dutch language—Early to 1500—Grammar. ɪ. Title.
Full name: Adolphe Clément Henri van Loey.

PF774.L6   50–27800

NL 0448811   DLC CaBVaU LU ICU MiU NN NIC MH TxU ICN

Loey, Adolphe van, 1905–
Middelnederlandse spraakkunst. 2., herziene en verm. uitg. Groningen, Wolters, 1955–57.
2 v.
Contents:—1. Vormleer.—2. Klankleer.
ɪ. Dutch language—Middle Dutch—Grammar.

NL 0448812   MH

Loey, Adolphe van, 1905–
... Studie over de nederlandsche plaatsnamen in de gemeenten Elsene en Ukkel, door dr. A. C. H. van Loey ... Leuven, De Vlaamsche drukkerij, N. v., 1931.
372 p. maps (2 fold.) 25°. (Koninklijke vlaamsche academie voor taal- en letterkunde. ₍Uitgaven₎ Reeks vɪ, nr 53)
Folded maps accompanied by transparent guard sheets with outline drawings.
"Door de Koninklijke vlaamsche academie met goud bekroond."
"Lijst der bronnen en geraadpleegde werken": p. ₍9₎–16.
1. Names, Geographical—Belgium—Elsene. 2. Names, Geographical—Belgium—Uccle. 3. Names, Geographical—Dutch.
₍Full name: Adolphe Clément Henri van Loey₎
45–52458

Library of Congress   DH811.E5L6
                           ₍2₎   929.4

NL 0448813   DLC

Loey-Nouri, van, firm, type-founders, Brussels.
Gravure et fonderie typographiques. Maison van Louey-Nouri ... Bruxelles ₍1893?₎   1 v.   illus., plates.   32cm.
Approximately 250 l.

32980B. 1. Type—Specimens.
N. Y. P. L.   April 23, 1940

NL 0448814   NN

Løye, C. V., tr.

HG3836
.D4A7   **Andersen, Poul Nyboe,** 1913–
Danish exchange policy, 1914–1939; a report to the Geneva Research Centre. ₍Tr. from Danish by C. V. Løye₎ Copenhagen, Institute of Economics and History, 1942.

Løye, C V
Høst's Dansk-Engelske og Engelsk-Danske Lommeordbog. Kobenhavn, Andr. Fred. Høst & Sons Forlag, 1930.
xii, 307 p.   24°.

NL 0448816   MH-Z

Løye, C. V.
Høsts dansk-engelske og engelsk-danske Lommeordbog. København, A. F. Høst & sons, 1936.

NL 0448817   MH

Løye, C V
Høst's dansk-engelske og engelsk-danske lommeordbog, revideret og forøget udgave ved C.V. Løye. København, A.F. Høst & søn, 1946.
348 p.   15cm.

1. Danish language. Dictionaries. English. 2. English language. Dictionaries. Danish. I. Title.

NL 0448818   MnU

Løye, C V
Høst's Dansk-Engelske og Engelske-dansk lomme-ordbog; revideret og forøget udgave ved C.V. Løye København, Andr. Fred. Høst, 1947.
348 p.

1. Danish language-Dictionaries-English. 2. English language-Dictionaries-Danish.

NL 0448819   NNC

Løye, C V
Høst's engelsk-danske og dansk-engelske lommeordbog. ₍Revid. og forøget udg.₎ København, A. F. Høst, 1950.
348 p. 15 cm. (Høst's lommeordbøger)

1. English language—Dictionaries—Danish. 2. Danish language—Dictionaries—English. ɪ. Title.

PD3640.L6   54–37646 ‡

NL 0448820   DLC

Løye, O.
Hamlets Grav i Ammelhede ved Randers; en historisk-topografisk Undersøgelse, af cand. pharm. O. Løye... ₍Randers;₎ Propaganda Komiteen for Randers By og Havn, 1933.   15 p. illus., plates.   21cm.   (Serie om Randers. Pjece No. 3.)

747899A. 1. Hamlet. I. Propaganda Komiteen for Randers By og Havn.
N. Y. P. L.   February 18, 1935

NL 0448821   NN

4PT   **Løyning, Ellen.**
Nor.   I gode og vonde dager.   Lutherstiftelsen
129   229 p.

NL 0448822   DLC-P4

Løyning, Paul, 1895–
...Benthoctopus Sibiricus; a supposed new species of cephalopoda from the Siberian Arctic ocean, by Paul Løyning... Bergen: A. S. J. Griegs boktrykkeri, 1930.   11 p.   illus. (charts), 2 pl.   31cm.   (Maud-ekspeditionen, 1918–1925. Scientific results. v. 5, no. 11.)
"Bibliography," p. 10.

1. Cephalopoda—Siberia.   I. Ser.
N. Y. P. L.   January 30, 1940

NL 0448823   NN

Løyning, Paul, 1895–
Fam. Aeolididæ
... Nudibranchfaunaen i Drøbaksundet ... Kristiania, Oslo, I kommission hos J. Dybwad, 1922–25.

Løyning, Paul, 1895–
... Loricata and gastropoda from the Siberian Arctic ocean, by Paul Løyning... Bergen: A. S. J. Griegs boktrykkeri, 1932. 19 p. incl. tables.   illus., 2 pl.   31cm.   (Maudekspeditionen, 1918–1925. Scientific results. v. 5, no. 14.)
"References," p. 19.

1. Loricata (Mollusks)—Siberia.   2. Gasteropoda—Siberia. I. Ser.
N. Y. P. L.   January 26, 1940

NL 0448825   NN

Loeys, Marcel O
Begrotingsevenwicht en conjunctuur; de conjuncturele problematiek van het begrotingsevenwicht. Antwerpen, Standaard-Boekhandel, 1947.
321 p. 26 cm. (Katholieke Universiteit te Leuven. Reeks van de School voor Economische Wetenschappen, nr. 34)
Proefschrift—Université catholique, Louvain.
Pub. also as Economisch-sociale bibliotheek, Monographieën, 25.
"Stellingen": leaf inserted.
"Literatuurlijst": p. ₍307₎–318.
1. Budget. 2. Business cycles.   ɪ. Title.   (Series: Louvain. Université catholique. École des sciences économiques. Collection, no. 34)

HJ2031.L6 1947a   49–28345*

NL 0448826   DLC NN CU NIC ICU

Loeys, Marcel O
Begrotingsevenwicht en conjunctuur; de conjuncturele problematiek van het begrotingsevenwicht. Antwerpen, Standaard-Boekhandel, 1947.
321 p. 26 cm. (Economisch-sociale bibliotheek. Monographieën, 25)
"Literatuurlijst": p. ₍307₎–318.

1. Budget. 2. Business cycles.   ɪ. Title.   (Series)

HJ2031.L6   49–19722*

NL 0448827   DLC OU

PL247   **LÖYTVED, J   H.**
f.K8L8   Konia. Inschriften der seldschukischen bauten, von dr. J. H. Löytved... Berlin ₍J. Springer₎ 1907.
vi, ₍1₎, 108 p. illus. (part col.) 42½cm.
Als manuscript gedruckt.
"Literaturverzeichnis": p. ₍vii₎

1. Inscriptions, Turkish. 2. Konieh. 3. Seljuks.

NL 0448828   ICU CLU NN

Loezius, Emil, ed.
Das Nationale Deutschland ... hrsg. von Emil Loezius. hft. 1–34; 11. nov. 1907–28. juni 1908. Berlin, E. A. Schwetschke und sohn, 1907–08.

Lof, Eric A.
Atmospheric nitrogen fixation, by Eric A. Lof.
(In Smithsonian institution. Annual report, 1923. Washington, 1925. 23½ᶜᵐ. p. 203–222. 4 pl. on 2 l., diagrs.)
"Reprinted ... from the General electric review for March and April, 1923."

1. Nitrogen.

Library of Congress   Q11.S66 1923   25—14610

NL 0448830   DLC WaS OC1 ODW OC1JC OC1MN ICJ

VOLUME 338

Lof, Eric A.
Hydro-electric power stations, by Eric A. Lof and David B. Rushmore. 1st ed. New York, John Wiley & sons, inc.; ₁etc., etc.₎ 1917.
x, 822 p. incl. front., illus., maps, diagrs. forms (1 double) 23½ᶜᵐ.
In another issue of same date, the t.-p., copyright notice and preface have the authors' names in the order: David B. Rushmore and Eric A. Lof.

1. Water-power and electric plants. I. Rushmore, David Barker, 1873– joint author. II. Title.
Library of Congress   TK1081.L7   17—31013

NL 0448831   ICJ NN   DLC CU KMK CaBVaU WaS OU OC1W OC1 OCU

Lof, Eric A., joint author.

Rushmore, David Barker, 1873–
Hydro-electric power stations, by David B. Rushmore and Eric A. Lof. 2d ed., thoroughly rev. and reset. New York, J. Wiley & sons, inc.; ₁etc., etc.₎ 1923.

Lof, Eric A.

General electric company.
... The Mississippi River hydro-electric development at Keokuk, Iowa ... Schenectady, N. Y., General electric company, Power and mining department, ₁1914.

BT198 **LOF, LAURENS JOHAN VAN DER**
.L8   De figuur van Christus in de vrijzinnige Amerikaanse theologie. Arnhem, N. V. Van Loghum Slaterus U. M., 1949.
123 p.

Proefschrift—Amsterdam.

1. Jesus Christ—History of doctrines.
2. Liberalism (Religion). I. Tc.

NL 0448834   InU CtY NNUT IEN MH NjP

Lof-bazuin, ter eeren van de wel ed. groot achtbaare regeering van Amsterdam, strekkende tot een schrik trompet...
          see under ₁Hoefnagel, Nicolaas₎ d. 1783?

Lof der Oost-Indise compagnie, ende de E.ᵉ heeren bewinthebberen van dien. Waer onder anderen aen-ghewesen wort, hoe nootsakelijck het is voor ons vader-land in dese occurrentie van tijden haer versochte octroy niet te weygheren. t'Amsterdam: Gedruckt by H. J. Visscher, anno 1646.   10 l.   18 x 13½cm. (4°.)
Knuttel 5358.   Asher: New-Netherland, 203.
"Relates to the scheme for uniting the East and West India company."— *Sabin 41778.*
Original(?) wrappers of gilt paper stencilled in colors in all-over floral design bound in.

1. Generale Nederlandsche geoc-   troyeerde Oost-Indische compagnie.
2. Generale Nederlandsche geoctroy-   eerde West-Indische compagnie.
N.Y.P.L.   *Revised*
          November 30, 1938

NL 0448836   NN DLC-P4

₁**Lof der reinster vrowen**₎ *13th cent.*
Das rheinische Marienlob; eine deutsche dichtung des 13. jahrhunderts, herausgegeben von Adolf Bach. Leipzig, K. W. Hiersemann, 1934.
lxxv, 231 p. 23 cm. (*Added t.-p.*: Bibliothek des Literarischen vereins in Stuttgart, sitz Tübingen. CCLXXXI)
On cover : 2. jahresgabe für 1933.
"Ich bin de lof der reinster vrowen" the first line of the poem, supplies the anonymous author's own distinctive title for it.
Edited from the only known manuscript: Cod. I 81 of the Provinzialbibliothek, Hanover. First published by W. Grimm under title Marienlieder, in Zs. f. d. alterth., 10. bd. (1856) p. 1–42.

Concerning authorship, various titles in literary history (Marienlieder, Niederrheinisches Marienlob, Niederrheinisches frauenlob, etc.) see the editor's Vorbemerkung, p. xiii–xxi (Name, p. xiv) and Literaturverzeichnis, p. ix–xii.
"Die sprache des dichters und der schreiber" : p. 174–229.

1. Mary, Virgin—Poetry. 2. German language—Dialects—Ripuarian Franconian. I. Hanover. Königliche und Provinzial-bibliothek. Mss. (I 81) II. Bach, Adolf, 1890– ed. III. Title. IV. Title: Marienlob, Das rheinische.

PT1101.L5 vol. 281   (830.82) 831.29   35—1443?

NL 0448838   DLC MB CU MoU WaTC PSt NcD OC1W OU OCU

Lof-dicht des vermaerde, wyt-beroemde, manhaftige zee-heldt Pieter Pietersen Heyn. Generael: der Geoctroyeerde, vereenighde, West-Indische compagnie
          see under ₁Pels, E   ₎

Lof-dicht, Over de heerlijcke Victorie, in het veroveren van de Silver Vlote, in de Baey van Matanca
          see under ₁Wijnandts, Willem₎ fl. 1629.

BT720 **Lof-digt, ter eeren van Mr. Adriaan Beverlant, regts-geleerde, seer konstelik en ciirlik beschréven hebbende de vvaare erf-sonde; tot schrik en afkeer van de schandelike onkuisheit deser EEuwe.** ₁n. p., n. d.₎
B5
          4ł. 18cm.
          54 B.J.
Leaves trimmed and folded.
Bound with Beverland, Adriaan. De stolatae virginitatis jure lucubratio academica. Lugduni in Batavis, 1680. 17cm.

NL 0448841   MWalB

Lof van Arthur van Schendel, 5 maart 1945 ₁1₎ ... ₁s-Gravenhage₎ "De Telg," 1945.
70 p., 1 l. incl. front., illus. (port.) 16½ᶜᵐ. (Het Zwarte lam. ₁2₎)
"De tekst werd geschreven voor den 5den maart 1944, den zeventigsten verjaardag van den schrijver, en onder leiding van Fred Batten en Adriaan Morriën ter perse gebracht bij den terugkeer van Arthur van Schendel in ons land op 1 november 1945."—Colophon.
"500 exemplaren."
"Litteratuur" : p. 45.

CONTENTS.—Batten, Fred. De grote metgezel.—Morriën, Adriaan. De overgave aan de idee.—Weezel, Lies van. Herinnering aan Ede.—Boeschoten, K. van. De sociale achtergrond van "De waterman."—Hans, Bas. Brief aan een vriend.—Bornkamp, Arie. Een anti-climax.—Gelder, G. van. Het fregatschip Johanna Maria.—Dubois, P. H. Een getuigenis.—Barneveld, Bob. De andere werkelijkheid.

1. Schendel, Arthur van, 1874–1946. I. Batten, Fred, ed. II. Morriën, Adriaan, 1912– ed.

          A 47–3195
Harvard univ. Library
for Library of Congress   ₁2₎

NL 0448843   MH CU NN

B
1621
Lo   Het lof vanden oorloghe boven den Spaenschen peys. 'sGraven-Haghe, Aert Mauris, 1621.
          ₁15₎ p. 20cm.

NL 0448844   MnU

Lof-Vysa edur Lovisu-Lilia
          see under Sölvason, Sveinn, 1722–1782.

Lo Faro, Francesco.
Il nuovo Parlamento nello stato fascista; studio giuridico-politico con prefazione di Giuseppe Bottai. Roma: Anonima romana editoriale, 1928. 70 p. 4°. (Rome ₁city₎. Università. Diritto pubblico e legislazione sociale, Istituto di. Studi. ₁no.₎ 5.)

1. Italy—Govt., 1927. 2. Representa-   tion—Italy. 3. Government,
Representative.
N.Y.P.L.   November 21, 1928

NL 0448846   NN CtY NNC

Lo Faso, Ermanno.
Al cuore non si comanda; commedia in tre atti. Milano, Gastaldi ₁1954₎ 55 p. 20cm. (Teatro)

1 Drama, Italian. I. Title.

NL 0448847   NN

4PQ **Lo Faso, Ermanno**
It   Che debbo fare? Dramma in due atti.
659   Milano, Gastaldi ₁1952₎
          38 p.

          (Collana "Teatro")

NL 0448848   DLC-P4 RPB NN

Lo Faso Pietrasanta, Domenico, *duca di Serradifalco*
          see
Serradifalco, Domenico Lo Faso Pietrasanta, *duca di,* 1783–1863.

Lofbazuyn, gevlogten om het hoofd ven den ... samensteller van het nooitvolprezen boek
          see under ₁Wagenaar, Jan₎ 1709–

Lofberg, John Oscar, 1882–1932, ed.

PA1
.C4   **The Classical** journal. Published by the Classical association of the Middle West and South, with the cooperation of the Classical association of New England and the Classical association of the Pacific states. v. 1–
Dec. 1905–
          ₁Menasha, Wis.₎ George Banta publishing company; etc., etc., 1905–

VOLUME 338

Lofberg, John Oscar, 1882-1932.
... Sycophancy in Athens ... by John Oscar Lofberg ... Chicago, Ill., 1917.
xi, 104 p. 24ᵐ.
Thesis (PH. D.)—University of Chicago, 1914.
"Private edition, distributed by the University of Chicago libraries."

1. Justice, Administration of—Athens. 2. Athens—Soc. life & cust. I. Title.
18—2826
Library of Congress   DF277.L7
Univ. of Chicago Libr.   ₍a41d1₎

NL 0448852   ICU DLC MiDW NIC NcU ViU NjP PHC NCH

Lofberg, John Oscar, 1882-1932.
Sycophancy in Athens, by John Oscar Lofberg ... Menasha, Wis., The Collegiate press, Banta publishing company ₍1917?₎
xi, 104 p. 24ᵐᵐ.
Also issued as thesis (PH. D.) University of Chicago, 1914.

1. Justice, Administration of—Athens. 2. Athens—Soc. life & cust. I. Title.
35—32970
Library of Congress   ₍2₎   [347.09385] 349.385

NL 0448853   DLC NcD OO OCU PU

Lofberg, John Oscar, 1882-1932.
...The trial of Socrates ... ₍Cedar Rapids? Iowa?₎ 1928.
p. 601-609.
Caption title.
Reprinted from The Classical journal, Vol. XXIII, May, 1928, No. 8.
Preceded and followed by editorials and book reviews written by him and published in various numbers of the Classical journal.

NL 0448854   OO

Lofberg, Lila.
... Sierra outpost ₍by Lila Lofberg and₎ David Malcolmson. New York, Duell, Sloan and Pearce ₍ᶜ1941₎
vi, 253 p. 1 illus. 22ᵐ.
The first author's name, Lila Lofberg, at head of title.
"First edition."

1. Sierra Nevada mountains. 2. Animals, Habits and behavior of. I. Malcolmson, David, 1899-   joint author. II. Title.
41—18221
Library of Congress   F868.S5L7
₍a45z3₎   917.9482

CU Wa CaBViP
NL 0448855   DLC OrCS CU-B MeB GU OrP Or WaS IdU OClW

Lofberg, Maude (Sparkman).
...Governor Brown and the Confederate administration... by Maude Sparkman.   Chicago. 1914.   v, 48 f.   4°.
Dissertation, Chicago, 1914.
Mimeographed.
Bibliographical footnotes

1. Brown, Joseph Emerson, 1821-1894.   2. Confederate States of America —Hist.
N. Y. P. L.   December 20, 1926

NL 0448856   NN

Lofchie, Stanley H   1925-
The performance of adults under distraction stress: a developmental approach... ₍Worcester, Mass.₎ Clark University ₍1953₎
3 cards. 8 x 13cm.
Microprint copy of typescript.
Collation of the original: vi, 79 l.
Thesis - Clark University.
Bibliography: leaves 72-75.
Vita.
1. Attention.

NL 0448857   MsU OrU OrCS LU

Lofer, Hans.
₍Des Kaisers neue Kleider. Piano-vocal score. German₎
Des Kaisers neue Kleider, komische Oper nach H. Chr. Andersen. ₍Wiesbaden₎ Brucknerverlag Wiesbaden ₍1952₎
140 p. 34 cm.

1. Operas—Vocal scores with piano. I. Title.
M1503.L824K3 1952a   M 54-2150

NL 0448858   DLC

Lofer, Hans.
₍Des Kaisers neue Kleider. Piano-vocal score. German₎
Des Kaisers neue Kleider; komische Oper nach H. Chr. Andersen. Klavierauszug. ₍Wiesbaden₎ Brucknerverlag Wiesbaden ₍ᶜ1952₎
136 p. 33 cm.

1. Operas—Vocal scores with piano. I. Title.
M1503.L824K3 1952   M 54-863

NL 0448859   DLC NcU CU

Loferski, Joseph John.
Infra-red optical properties of tellurium crystals.   [Philadelphia] 1953.
47 numb. l., 28 l.   diagrs.   28 cm.
Thesis (Ph. D.) - University of Pennsylvania, 1953.
Typewritten.
Bibliography: l. 44-45.

NL 0448860   PU PU-Math

Loff, Ottomar.
Den danske kornhandels organisation. København, E. Harck, 1945.
204 p. diagrs. 26 cm. (Foreningen til unge handelsmænds uddannelse. Handelshøjskolen i København. Skriftrække D: Eksportinstituttets skrifter, 4)

1. Grain trade—Denmark.   (Series: Copenhagen. Handelshøjskolen. Skriftrække D, 4)
HD9045.D4L6   49-32831*

NL 0448861   DLC MH

Loff, Ottomar.
Driftsøkonomi ₍af₎ O. Loff og Jens J. Lund. København, G. E. Gad, 1948-50.
2 v. diagrs. 25 cm.
Bibliography: v. 2, p. 265-266.

1. Industry.   I. Lund, Jens J., joint author.
HD21.L6   48-27267 rev*

NL 0448862   DLC

Loff, Ottomar.
Driftsøkonomi ₍af₎ O. Loff og Jens J. Lund. 2. udg. København, G. E. C. Gad, 1953-
v. illus. 24 cm.

1. Industry.   I. Lund, Jens J., joint author.
HD21.L62   58-45209 ‡

NL 0448863   DLC

DT613.9   **Loff de Vasconcellos, L**
V3   A defeza das victimas da guerra de Bissau; o extermínio da Guiné.   Lisboa, Impr. L. da Silva, 1916.
Stack   90 p.   22cm.
Introd. signed: Loff de Vasconcellos.

1.Bissau, Portuguese Guinea - Pol. & govt.
2.Portugal - Colonies - Africa.   I.Title.

NL 0448864   CSt

Loff de Vasconcellos, L
Statistique d'importation et autres indications relatives à l'île de S. Vincent du Cap Vert. Lisboa, L. da Silva, 1899.
19 p. 23cm.

1. São Vicente, Cape Verde Islands - Commerce.   I. Title.

NL 0448865   FU

Loff trompet, uyt-geblasen over den generael, Olivier Cromwell, binnen Londen. Uyt de Luijnsche in 't Nederduytsch ... overgeset.   n. p., 1654.   22l.   4°.

NL 0448866   NN

Loffel, Mannes Mordecai.
... די ערשטע בליטען ₍פּאָעמען און ליעדער₎
New York, Grayzel & co., printers, ᶜ1912.
5 p. l., 9-70 p.   20ᵐ.
Author's name at head of title.
Title transliterated: Di erste bliten (Poemen un lieder)

13-9778
Library of Congress   PJ5165.L7

NL 0448867   DLC MtU OCl

NN5   **Loffeld, Édouard**
L826g   De grondgedachte van missiewerk en missieactie, door Éd. Loffeld. ₍Gemert? ca.1954₎
36 p. 19 cm.

1. Missions - Theory.   2. Catholic Church - Missions.   I. Title.

NL 0448868   CtY-D

Loffelt, Anton Cornelis, 1845-   *4081.69.4
Johannes Warnardus Bilders. Illus.   Portrait.   Plates. (In Rooses. Dutch painters of the Nineteenth Century. Vol. 4, pp. 65-101. London, 1901.)

E4245 — Bilders, Johannes Warnardus.

NL 0448869   MB

VOLUME 338

LOFFELT, Anton Cornelis, 1845–
Jupiter van Vloten en zijn kritiek. 's-Gravenhage, J. Ijkema, 1876.

pp. 48.
Concerning Van Vloten's attacks on Multatuli
(E.D.Dekker).

NL 0448870   MH

Loffelt, Anton Cornelis, 1845–
...Uren met Shakespeare...   Leiden: E. J. Brill, 1889.
vi, 194 p.   8°.

Contents: Hamlet. Shakespeare's Hamlet en Bara's Herstelde Vorst. De liefde
in Romeo en Julia. Mijn indrukken van verschillende Hamlet-vertooners. Bijlagen.

1. Shakespeare, William—Single plays   —Hamlet. 2. Shakespeare, William
—Single plays—Romeo and Juliet.   3. Shakespeare, William, in
Netherlands.
N. Y. P. L.   August 25, 1927

NL 0448871   NN NcU MH

Loffelt, Johannes Michaël Linnenschmidt van
see   Linnenschmidt van Loffelt, Johannes
Michaël.

Loffet, Adolphe
L'Anglais dans l'Allemand, et vice versa,
ou exposé des affinités de ces deux langues
par Adolphe Loffet...
Paris, L. Hachette, 1839.
p. [4]÷122.   21 cm.

NL 0448873   DCU-H PU

LOFFICIAL, LOUIS PROSPER, 1751?-1815.
...Journal d'un conventionnel en Vendée (décembre
1794-juillet 1795) publié par C. Leroux-Cesbron, avec une
préface de H. Baguenier-Desormeaux. Paris, E. Flammarion, 1896.
2 p. l., vi, 206p., 1 l.   front. (port.)   18½cm.

1. France. History. Revolution to 1799. 2. Vendée.   I. Leroux-
Cesbron, Charles, 1861-1931, ed.

NL 0448874   CtW NIC MH LU

Lofficial, Louis Prosper, 1751-1815.
Rapport au nom des Comités de législation et des
domaines réunis, sur l'interprétation de la loi du
9 décembre 1790 ...
see under   France. Convention nationale,
1792-1795. Comité de législation.

Lofficial, Louis Prosper, 1751-1815
Rapport au nom du Comité des domaines sur la demande en
indemnité formée par le citoyen Charles François Main-
bourg, concessionnaire de domaines en l'isle de Corse.
[P, an 2]

32 p.

NL 0448876   MH

French Rev.
DC
141
F87+
v.156
Lofficial, Louis Prosper, 1751-1815.
Rapport fait au nom du Comité de Judica-
ture sur la liquidation des offices munici-
paux acquis par les villes et municipalités.
[Paris, Impr. nat.], 1791]
16 p.   20cm.

Reprinted in Archives Parlementaires, v.
26, p. 715-718.

NL 0448877   NIC

L'Official, Milady Félix de
see
Félix de l'Official, Milady.

Loffing, Aloys: Die soziale und wirtschaftliche Gliederung
der Bevölkerung Erfurts in der zweiten Hälfte des 16. Jahrhunderts. Erfurt 1911: Stenger.   112 S. 8°
Münster, Phil. Diss. v. 24. Juli 1911, Ref. Meister
[Geb. 12. Dez. 84 Streitholz; Wohnort: Münster i. W.; Staatsangeh.: Preußen;
Vorbildung: Gymn. Heiligenstadt Reife M. 05; Studium: Paderborn Priester-
sem. 1, Münster 10 S.; Rig. 2. Dez. 10.]   [U 11. 3972

NL 0448879   ICRL CtY PU MH

Loffing, Willibald, 1899–
... Die Hasenscharten und Gaumenspalten der
chirurgischen Universitätsklinik zu Göttingen
aus den Jahren 1921-1929 ...   Göttingen, 1930.
Inaug.-Diss. - Göttingen.
Lebenslauf.
"Literaturverzeichnis": p. [17]-18.

NL 0448880   CtY

Loffler, Erich J.
Diabetes mellitus; a manual for chiropractors, by Erich J.
Loffler, D. C.   Jacksonville, Fla., The Loffler chiropractic clinic
[°1941]
4 p. l., 182 p.   pl.   18½ x 14½".
"First edition."
Bibliography : p. 102.

1. Diabetes.   I. Title.
                           41-19321
Library of Congress   RC909.L6
                  [2]   616.63

NL 0448881   DLC

GR 158   LOFFLER, PAUL A
.L828   Quelques notes sur le conte populaire hongrois, suivi de 3 contes. Illus. par G. Imbert.
Paris, Librairie orientale & américaine [1952]
54 p.   illus.

1. Folk-lore—Hungarian—Hist. & crit. 2. Folk-
lore—Hungary. I. Tc: Le Conte populaire hongrois. Folk-lore   cd°.

NL 0448882   InU NjR NN OCl MH

Loffler, Paul A
La vie d'Alexandre Petöfi, poète hongrois de l'amour et de
la liberté. Rodez, G. Subervie [1953]
129 p.   illus.   19 cm.

1. Petöfi, Sándor, 1823-1849.

PH3307.L6   55-26246 ‡

NL 0448883   DLC NN MH

QH9
.T6
no. 196
Rare bk.
coll.
Loffman, Axel, respondent.
Thunberg, Karl Peter, 1743-1828, *praeses.*
... Opat[r]um insecti genus ... Upsaliæ, excudebant
Regiæ academiæ typographi [1821]

4K   Loffredo, Antonio.
Ital.   Sull'attuale condizione civile e giuridica dei
997   ciechi in Italia.   Sora, C. Camastro, 1920.
108 p.

NL 0448885   DLC-P4

DP264   Loffredo, Ferdinando, tr.
.F7A55
Franco Bahamonde, Francisco, 1892–
Parole del Caudillo; discorsi, allocuzioni e proclami, mes-
saggi, dichiarazioni alla stampa del generalissimo Franco dal-
l'aprile 1937 al settembre 1939. Traduzione di Ferdinando
Loffredo, con prefazione di Galeazzo Ciano. Firenze, F. Le
Monnier, 1940.

4HQ   Loffredo, Ferdinando
621   Politica della famiglia.   Milano,
V. Bompiani, 1938-XVI.
469 p.

(Libri scelti, 51)

NL 0448887   DLC-P4 NN

1ng   Loffredo, Ferrante,   marchese di Tre-
ZP   vico,   16th cent.
.35   Le antichità di Pozzvolo, et lvoghi
C 2714   convicini, novamente raccolte dall'...Sig.
Ferrante Loffredo, marchese di Treuico...
Napoli.1570.   sq.O.   (with [Castig-
lione, Bonaventura] Gallorvm Insvbrvm
antiqvae sedes.   1541)

Title vignette, initials.

NL 0448888   ICN IU

945.721 Loffredo, Ferrante, marchese di Trivico,
L826a   16th cent.
1573   Le antichita di Pozzvolo et lvoghi
convicini, novamente raccolte.   Napoli, 1573.
22 numb.l.

Title vignette.

NL 0448889   IU

SPEC. COLL.
DG
845
F3
1580
Loffredo, Ferrante, <u>marchese di Trivio</u>, 16th
cent.
Antichita di Pozzvolo, et lvoghi convicini,
novamente raccolte dall' illustrissimo sig.
Ferrante Loffredo marchesa di Treuico, et del
consiglio della guerra di sua maestà. In
Napoli,Appresso Horatio Salvi[ani], & Cesare
Cesari,M. D. LXXXV.
46,[2]p.   15cm.   (Bound with Falco, Benedetto
di. Descrittione dei lvoghi antiqvi di Napoli
... In Napoli,1580)

Signatures: A-C[8].

1. Pozzuoli, Italy - Antiq. I. Title.

NL 0448891   MU

VOLUME 338

Loffredo, Ferrante, *marchese di Trivico, 16th cent.*
Antichita di Pozzvolo, et lvoghi convicini, nvovamente raccolte dall' ... Ferrante Loffredo marchese di Treuico, et del consiglio della guerra di sua maestà. In Napoli, H. Salniani, 1590.

44, (2) p. 16ᶜᵐ.

Title vignette.
With Tarcagnota, G. Del sito, et lodi della citta di Napoli. (1566)

1. Pozzuoli, Italy—Antiq.

NL 0448892 MiU

Loffredo, Ferrante, *marchese di Trivico, 16th cent.*
L'antichità di Pozzvolo, et lvoghi convicini del Sig. Ferrante Loffredo, marchese di Treuico ... Con le descrittioni de bagni d'Agnano, Pozzuolo, e Tripergole, trascritte dal vero antichissimo testo, de lo generosissimo Missere Iohanne Villano, tolte dalle fauci del tempo dal Signor Pompeo Sarnelli. Napoli, A. Bvlifon, 1675.

2 p.l., 38 p. 21½ᶜᵐ. (*With* Summonte, Giovanni A. Historia della citta e regno di Napoli. Napoli, 1640-75. t. 1)
"Trattato de li bagni de Pozzuolo (etc.)": p. 28-38.
1. Pozzuoli, Italy—Antiq. 2. Agnano, Italy. 3. Tripergola, Italy. I. Villani, Giovanni, d. 1348.

4-21217

Library of Congress DG846.3.S95

NL 0448893 DLC MiU

DG846 **Loffredo, Ferrante, marchese di Trivico, 16th**
.3 **cent.**
.S92 L'anticita' di Pozzvolo, e lvoghi convicini,
Rare con le descrizioni de' bagni di Agnano, Pozzuolo,
Bk e Tripergole... de Iohanne Villano... Napoli,
Presso G. Raimondi, 1752.
54 p. (*With* Summonte, Giovanni Antonio,
d. 1602. Historia della citta' e regno di Napoli
... v. 6. Napoli, 1748-50)
1. Pozzuoli-- Antiq.
2. Agnano, Italy. 3. Tripergola,
Italy.

NL 0448894 ICU CtY MB DFo

Loffredo, Ferrante, Marchese di Trevico, 16ᵗʰ No. 1 in *4710.1.9.Part 4
Ferrantis Loffredi ... Antiquitas Puteolorum, cum balneorum Agnani, Puteolorum, et Tripergolarum descriptionibus, per ... Joannem Villarum, ex auctoris vero, & antiquissimo libro desumptis ... per ... Pompeium Sarnellum. Editio novissima ... Sigebertus Havercampus, ex Italicis Latina fecit, praefationes & indices adjecit.
Lugduni Batavorum. Petrus Vander Aa. [MDCCXXIII.] (6) pp. 28 cols. (Graevius, J. G., ed. Thesavrvs antiqvitatvm et historiarvm Italiae ... Neapolis ... Tomus IX, pars 4.] 40 cm., in 4s.

L9927 — S.r.c. — Baths. — Poz zuoli, Italy. Antiq. — Sarnelli, Pompeo, Bishop of Bisceglia, ed. — Villani, Giovanni, ed., about 1280-1342. — Haverkamp, Syvert, tr., 1684-1742.

NL 0448895 MB MnU MdBP

Loffredo, Ferrante, marchese di Trivico, 16ᵗʰ cent.

Summonte, Giovanni Antonio, *d. 1602.*
Historia della citta e regno di Napoli, di Gio: Antonio Svmmonte ... Napoli, A. Bvlifon (etc.) 1640-75.

Loffredo, Rodolfo, 1870–
... Discorso inaugurale per l'anno giudiziario 1933, udienza 14 gennaio 1933, anno XI. Palermo, Arti grafiche G. Fiore & figli, 1933.

90, (25) p. incl. tables. 24ᶜᵐ.

At head of title: Corte d'appello di Palermo ...

1. Justice, Administration of—Italy. 2. Courts—Italy. I. Italy.
Corte d'appello (Palermo)

43-45819

Library of Congress JN5583.L6
(2) [347.9] 349.45079

NL 0448897 DLC

Loffredo, Sigismondo, d. 1539.
Consilia Loffredi. Sigismundi Loffredi...ardua ac resolutissima Consilia: nunc primũ in lucem edita: & aptissimis summa. decorata. Addito insuper amplissimo repertorio, alphabetico ordine... Venetiis (Per Aurelium pincium Jmpressa, Sumptibus Petri de dominicis bibliopole Neap. et sociorum) 1543. 4 pts. in 1 v. illus. 45cm. (f°.)

Pt. (1) comprises t.p. as above, letter of Scipio Capicius to the author and the latter's dedication to the city of Naples, both dated at Naples, March 1, 1536, and index to the Consilia.

Pt. (2) has t.p.: Sigismvndi Loffredi... Jn dubijs compluribus Andree d'Jsernia scriptis. Extricationes: siue Paraphrasis Et Feudales nonnulle questiones. 1539, and colophon dated March 1539.
Pt. (3) has t.p.: Sigismvndi Loffredi...Jn Lege Ivrisconsvltvs. ff. d'. grad. affinita. interpretatio. 1539, and colophon dated March 1539.
Pt. (4) has caption title: Sigismundi Loffredi...in arduis quibusdam causis de iure responsa: siue Cõsilia, and colophon dated 1539.
Illustrations: historiated woodcut title border with printer's mark (on a white ground in pt. 1, on black in pt. 2-3) in lower portion; full-page woodcut (Justice within architectural border) on verso of second t.p. and at end of pt. 3; 2 oblong woodcuts (one signed: PHI). Ornamental initials.
Binding, contemporary, of vellum.

1. Law—Italy—Naples. 2. Law, and ecclesiastical law. 3. Canon and ecclesiastical law. 4. Wood engravings, Italian. I. Andreas de Isernia, d. 1316. i. Andreas. Feudal—Italy—Naples. 3. Canon gravings, Italian. I. Andreas de

NL 0448899 NN

LOFFREDO, Sigismondo, d. 1539.
Consilia. Venetiis, 1563.

f° (18)4126 fol.

NL 0448900 MH-L

DG Loffredo, Sigismondo, d.1539.
403 Consiliia, sive responsa, et paraphrases
C76 feudales, subtilissimaeq. questiones vtiles &
v.358 quotidianae, necnon doctissima commentaria ad
1. iurisconsultus. ff. de gradib. Venetiis,
apvd Ivntas, 1572.
126,16,69 ℓ. (Consilia/statuti collection,
v.358)

1. Roman law. 2. Canon law. 3. Feudal law.
I. Title. II. Series.

NL 0448901 CLU

LOFFREDO, Sigismondo, d. 1539.
In dubiis compluribus Andree de Isernia scriptis, extricationes, siue paraphrasis, et feudales nonnulle questiones,additis summariis & aplissima repertorio. Venetiis, 1563.

f° 71 fol.

NL 0448902 MH-L

LOFFREDO, Sigismondo, d. 1539.
In lege iurisconsultus. ff. de gradi. affini. interpretatio. Venetiis, 1563.

f° 21 fol.

NL 0448903 MH-L

Lofft, Capel, 1751-1824, ed.
Abstract of Mr. Locke's Essay on human understanding ...
see under Locke, John, 1632-1704.

Lofft, Capel, 1751-1824.

Shakespeare, William, 1564-1616.
Aphorisms from Shakespeare: arranged according to the plays, &c. with a preface and notes; numerical references to each subject; and a copious index ... London, Printed for Longman, Hurst, Rees, Orme, and Brown, by Gedge and Barker, Bury, 1812.

[Lofft, Capel, 1751-1824]
*EC75 An argument on the nature of party and
L8263 faction. In which is considered, the duty of
780a a good and peaceable citizen at the present
PHi crisis ...
DFo London: Printed for C.Dilly in the Poultry.
MDCCLXXX.
8°. 2pℓ.,68p. 18cm.
Signed at end: Capel Lofft.

NL 0448906 MH PHi DFo

[Lofft, Capel] 1751-1824, transl.
A brief account of the hospital of St. Elizabeth annexed to the imperial monastery of St. Maximi... see under title

AC901 **Lofft, Capel,** 1751-1824.
.M5 A brief examination of Lord Sheffield's
observations on the commerce of the U.S.
Philadelphia, printed; London, reprinted
by J. Phillips, 1792.
135 p. (Miscellaneous pamphlets, 539:2)

NL 0448908 DLC

Lofft, Capel, 1751-1824.

Burn, John Ilderton.
A digested index to the modern reports of the courts of common law, previous to the commencement of the Term reports: including W. Blackstone, Burrow, Cowper, Douglas, Lofft, L'. Raymond, Salkeld, Strange, Willes, Wilson. By John Ilderton Burn, esq. London, Printed by A. Strahan for J. Butterworth; (etc., etc.) 1804.

P75 [Lofft, Capel] 1751-1824.
L826 Elements of universal law, and particularly of
776g the law of England. Vol.1. Being the first volume
of a translation of a work, intitled Principia
juris universalis. &c. London,Printed by His
Majesty's law printers and sold by W.Owen,1779.
1pℓ.,lxxiv,[1],lxxv-lxxvip.,lℓ.,97,314p. 18cm.
A collection of maxims, etc. cf. p.lviii.
No more published.
Contents. - Preliminary rules. - Abstract of
logic. - Principles of universal law. - Of the
law of nature. - Of the law of nations. - Particular elements of politics. - On laws.

NL 0448910 CtY PU-L

Lofft, Capel, the elder, 1751-1824.
An enquiry into the legality and expediency of increasing the royal navy by subscriptions for building county ships. Being the correspondence on that subject between A. Young & C. Lofft. With a list of the subscribers to the Suffolk man of war. To which are added, Observations on the state of the taxes and resources of the kingdom on the conclusion of the peace. Bury St. Edmund's: Green and Gedge, 1783. 2 p.l., 99 p. 8°.

NL 0448911 NN

VOLUME 338

[Lofft, Capel] 1751–1824.
An essay on the law of libels. With an appendix, containing authorities. To which are subjoined, Remarks on the case in Ireland of attachment; and the letter of the Hon. T. Erskine, Esq. on that subject... London: Printed for C. Dilly, 1785. viii, 64 p. 8°.

Without the Appendix and following items mentioned on the title-page.
Refers at p. 56 to Jackson's Constitutions of the American States.
Autograph presentation copy from the author to James Boswell, Esq., with inscription on the title-page.

1. Libel.—Jurisprudence, Great N. Y. P. L.
Britain. 2. Title. April 7, 1924.

NL 0448912   NN CLL

Y   [LOFFT, CAPEL] 1751–1824.
185   Eudosia: or, A poem on the universe.
.L 82   London, Richardson, 1781.
           247p.

NL 0448913   ICN PPT NNUT MH CtY

Lofft, Capel, 1751–1824, ed. FOR OTHER EDITIONS
                               SEE MAIN ENTRY
Bloomfield, Robert, 1766–1823.
The farmer's boy; a rural poem. Rural tales, &c. &c. By Robert Bloomfield. With the life of the author ... To which are added, The deserted village: The traveller; or, Prospect of society: by Goldsmith. Elegy written in a country churchyard: by Gray. The hermit: by Parnell. The snow-storm: by Dr. Trotter. Wilmington, Del., Printed and sold by James Wilson, Market-street, at the Mirror printing-office and bookstore. 1803.

Lofft, Capel, 1751–1824.
An history of the Corporation and Test acts. With an investigation of their importance to the establishment in church and state. Addressed to the people of England; and particularly to the county of Suffolk. By Capel Lofft. Bury, Printed and sold by J. Rackham, 1790.

1 p. l., 40 p. 21½ᶜᵐ.

1. Corporation act, 1661. 2. Test act, 1673.

28–3105

Library of Congress   BR755.L6

NL 0448915   DLC NNUT CtY

Lofft, Capel, 1751–1824, comp.
Laura: or, An anthology of sonnets, (on the Petrarcan model,) and elegiac quatuorzains: English, Italian, Spanish, Portuguese, French, and German; original and translated; great part never before publisht. With a preface, critical and biographic; notes, and index ... By Capel Lofft. London, printed by R. & A. Taylor for B. and R. Crosby and co., 1813–14.
5 v. front. (port.) 17ᶜᵐ.
Vols. 3 and 4 dated 1813.
The portrait inserted is that which appeared in the monthly mirror, for June, 1802.
Binder's title: Loft's sonnets.
1. Sonnets. I. Title.
12–37059

Library of Congress   PN6110.S6L6
⟨a37b1⟩

NL 0448916   DLC NIC NcU

Lofft, Capel, 1751–1824, ed. FOR OTHER EDITIONS
                               SEE MAIN ENTRY
Gilbert, Sir Geoffrey, 1674–1726.
The law of evidence. By Lord Chief Baron Gilbert. 6th ed. With notes and additional references to contemporary writers, and later cases. By James Sedgwick ... London, W. Clarke and sons [etc.] 1801.

[Lofft, Capel, 1751–1824.]   Br 2827.3.59*
Observations on a late publication, entitled " A dialogue on the actual state of Parliament," and also on " Free Parliaments," *etc.* London, printed for C. Dilly and J. Stockdale, 1783.
pp. iv, 30.
Signed: "Capel Lofft."

Gt. Brit.–Parliament 1714–1820 ‖Title°‖AcS 186968 ·HCL 24–1775

NL 0448918   MH InU

[Lofft, Capel] 1751–1824.
Observations on Mr. Wesley's second Calm address, and incidentally on other writings upon the American question. Together with thoughts on toleration, and on the point how far the conscience of the subject is concerned in a war; remarks on constitution in general, and that of England in particular; on the nature of colonial government, and a recommendation of a plan of peace ... London, Printed for E. and C. Dilly, 1777.
2 p. l., 124 p. 19¼ᶜᵐ.
Signed: Capel Lofft.
1. Wesley, John, 1763–1791. A calm address to the inhabitants of England. 2. U. S.—Pol. & govt.—Revolution. 3. Gt. Brit.—Pol. & govt.—1760–1789. I. Title.
20–12572

Library of Congress   E211.W475

NL 0448919   DLC CtY MiU–C

Div.S.   [Lofft, Capel] 1751–1824.
973.31   Observations on Mr. Wesley's second Calm
W513ZL   address and incidentally on other writings upon
         the American question ... London, Printed for
         E. and C. Dilly, 1777.
            124 p. 20 cm.
            Signed: Capel Lofft.
            Photocopy. New Haven, Conn., Yale University Library, 1971. 65 ℓ.
            1. Wesley, John, 1763–1791. A calm address to the inhabitants of England. 2. U. S. Pol. & govt.   Revolution. 3. Gt. Brit.   Pol. & govt. 1760–1789.
         I. Title.

NL 0448920   NcD

DA470 Lofft, Capel, 1751–1824.
.L82   Observations on Mrs. Macaulay's History of England, (lately published) from the revolution to the resignation of Sir Robert Walpole. In a letter addressed to that lady. By Capel Lofft ... London, Printed for E. and C. Dilly, 1778.
[3], 68 p. 27½ᶜᵐ.

1. Graham, Mrs. Catharine (Sawbridge) Macaulay, 1731–1791. History of England.

NL 0448921   ICU

Mhc9   Lofft, Capel, 1751–1824.
L827   Observations on the first part of Dr.
Ob7   Knowles's testimonies from the writers of
         the first four centuries. In a letter to a
         friend. Bury, Printed by J. Rackham, for J.
         Johnson, 1789.
            viii, 130p. 21cm.
            Relates to part of Knowles, Thomas,
         Primitive Christianity.

NL 0448922   CtY NIC NN MH

Pam.   Lofft, Capel, 1751–1824.
Coll.
16900   On the revival of the cause of reform in
         the representation of the Commons in Parliament. 2nd ed. ... London, Printed by Richard Taylor and Co., 1810.
            37 p. 21½cm.

1. Gt. Brit. Parliament. House of Commons. Reform

NL 0448923   NcD

Lofft, Capel, 1751–1824, ed.
Milton, John, 1608–1674.
Paradise lost. A poem in twelve books. The author John Milton. Printed from the first and second editions collated. The original system of orthography restored; the punctuation corrected and extended. With various readings: and notes; chiefly rythmical. By Capel Lofft ... Bury St. Edmund's, Printed and sold by J. Rackham [etc.] 1792.

Lofft, Capel, 1751–1824, ed.
Bloomfield, Robert, 1766–1823.
The poems of Robert Bloomfield. In two parts ... New-York, J. D. Myers & W. Smith, printers, 1821.

Lofft, Capel, 1751–1824, ed.
The poetical works of Robert Bloomfield...
    see under Bloomfield, Robert, 1766–1823.

PR3541 Lofft, Capel, 1751–1824.
.L6P8   The praises of poetry. A poem. By Capel Lofft ...
1775   London, Printed for W. Owen, 1775.
            [4], 81 p. 18¼ᶜᵐ.

NL 0448927   ICU CtY DLC

[Lofft, Capel] 1751–1824.
Preface [to The law of evidence] containing an explanation of the plan of the present work; with some account of the Lord Chief Baron Gilbert. [n. p., 1788]
xlv p. eng. fronts. (1 port.) 21.5 cm.
Caption title: preface signed C. L.
Was bound with: A letter from a gentleman in Lancashire to his friend in the East Indies ... London, 1792.
Contents. - Preface. - Some additional notices respecting the Chief Baron's residence, &c. - Copy of the will of the Lord Chief Baron Gilbert.

NL 0448928   ViU–L

                              1751–1824.
Lofft, Capel, A Principia cum juris universalis tum
           præcipue anglicani. Ed. 2ᵃ. 2 vol. London.
1779. sm. 12°.   L. S.

NL 0448929   MH PU–L

Lofft, Capel,   1751–1824, ed. and tr.
Proceedings in the National Assembly of France, on the admission of Mr. William Priestley, and the motion for his naturalization
    see under France. Assemblée nationale législative, 1791–1792.

Lofft, Capel, 1751–1824.
Seymour, E H.
Remarks, critical, conjectural, and explanatory, upon the plays of Shakspeare; resulting from a collation of the early copies, with that of Johnson and Steevens, ed. by Isaac Reed, esq., together with some valuable extracts from the mss. of the late Right Honourable John, lord Chedworth. By E. H. Seymour ... London, Printed by J. Wright, for Lackington, Allen & co. [etc.] 1805.

VOLUME 338

W 6   LOFFT, Capel, 1751-1824
P3   Remarks on the letter of Mr. Burke, to a member of
v. 147   the National Assembly; with several papers in addition
no. 13   to the remarks on the reflections of Mr. Burke on the
      Revolution in France ... London, J. Johnson, 1791.
      84 p. 21 cm.

     1. Burke, Edmund, 1729?-1797

NL 0448932   DNLM MH

Lofft, Capel, 1751-1824.
   Remarks on the letter of the Rt. Hon. Edmund Burke, concerning the revolution in France, and on the proceedings in certain societies in London, relative to that event ... By Capel Lofft. London, Printed for J. Johnson. 1790.
   2 p. l., 100 p. 23½ᵐ.

   Caption title: Remarks on the Reflections ...

   1. Burke, Edmund, 1729?-1797. Reflections on the revolution in France. 2. France—Hist.—Revolution—Causes and character.

                                   3—14306
   Library of Congress   DC150.B9L8

NL 0448933   DLC TxU RPJCB IRN PPDrop PHi CSmH NN

Lofft, Capel, 1751-1824.   320.944 F7
   Remarks on the letter of the Rt. Hon. Edmund Burke, concerning the revolution in France, and on the proceedings in certain societies in London, relative to that event. ... . By Capel Lofft. Dublin, Printed by Graisberry and Campbell, for P. Wogan, ... , and J. Rice, 1791.
   [2], 78 p. 21½ᵐ.

NL 0448934   ICJ CtY InU ViU

DC150   Lofft, Capel, 1751-1824.
.B9L8   Remarks on the letter of the Rt. Hon. Edmund
1791   Burke, concerning the Revolution in France,
      and on the proceedings in certain societies in
      London, relative to that event. 2d ed. with
      additions, and Remarks on Mr. Burke's Letter
      to a member of the National Assembly. London,
      J. Johnson, 1791.
      203 p.
      Caption title: Remarks on the Reflection ...

NL 0448935   ICU

Lofft, Capel, 1751-1824,   reporter.
Gt. Brit. *Court of King's bench.*   FOR OTHER EDITIONS
                                  SEE MAIN ENTRY
   Reports of cases adjudged in the Court of King's bench from Easter term 12 Geo. 3. to Michaelmas 14 Geo. 3. (both inclusive.) [1772-1774] With some select cases in the Court of chancery, and of the Common pleas, which are within the same period. To which is added, the case of general warrants, and a collection of maxims. By Capel Lofft ... London, W. Owen. MDCCLXXVI.

Lofft, Capel, 1751-1824, supposed author.

[Heywood, Samuel] 1753-1828.
   The right of Protestant dissenters to a compleat toleration asserted; containing an historical account of the Test laws, and shewing the injustice, inexpediency, and folly of the sacramental test, as now imposed, with respect to Protestant dissenters; with an answer to the objection from the Act of union with Scotland ... By a layman. The 3d ed., cor. London, Printed for J. Johnson [etc.] M,DCC,XC.

[Lofft, Capel] 1751-1824.
   A summary of a treatise by Major Cartwright entitled, The People's Barrier against undue Influence
      see under Cartwright, John, 1740-1824.

Lofft, Capel, 1751-1824, comp.

Jebb, John, 1736-1786.
   Thoughts on the construction and polity of prisons, with hints for their improvement. By John Jebb, M. D. To which is added, an Abstract of felonies created by statute, and other articles relative to the penal system ... London, C. Dilly. 1786.

Lofft, Capel, 1751-1824.
JF514   Three letters on the question of regency.
L6   Addressed to the people of England. Bury,
1788   Printed by J. Rackham, sold by Stockdale, Piccadilly, and Richardson, 1788.
      4 p.ℓ., 64 p. 21ᵐ.

   1. Regency. I. Title.

NL 0448940   CSt CtY MH NN NjP NNC DLC NIC

Lofft, Capel, 1751-1824.

Bloomfield, Robert, 1766-1823.
   Le valet du fermier, poëme champètre; par Robert Bloomfield. Traduit de l'anglais sur la dernière édition. Orné de dix gravures ... Paris, Dentu, an x (1802)

[Lofft, Capel] 1751-1824.
   A view of the several schemes with respect to America; and their comparative merit in promoting the dignity and interest of Great Britain...   London, Printed for W. Owen, 1776.
   2 p.l., 55 p.   21cm. (8°.)

   Sabin 99580.
   Errata slip pasted on verso of t-p.
   First leaf (half-title?) wanting.

53R0654. 1. United States—Hist.—   Revolution—Contemporary opinion.
2. United States—Hist.—Revolution   —Peace negotiations and proposals.
I. Title.

NL 0448942   NN RPJCB MH

                                     322
[Lofft, Capel], 1751-1824.   F3
   A vindication of the short history of the Corporation and Test acts. ... London, Printed for J. Johnson, 1790.
   [2], 38 p. 20ᵐ.
   Published anonymously.

NL 0448943   ICJ

[Lofft, Capel] 1806-1873.
   Self-formation; or, The history of an individual mind; intended as a guide for the intellect through difficulties to success. By a fellow of a college ... London, C. Knight and co., 1837.
   2 v. 19½ᵐ.

   1. Self-culture.   I. Title.

                               8—11313
   Library of Congress   LC31.L7

NL 0448944   DLC MiU

[Lofft, Capel] 1806-1873.
   Self-formation; or, the history of an individual mind: intended as a guide through the intellect through difficulties to success. By a fellow of a college ... 1st American, from the London ed. Boston, W. Crosby and H. P. Nichols, 1846.
   iv, 504 p. 19½ᵐ.

   1. Self-culture.

                              E 10-1817
   Library, U. S. Bur. of   Education LC31.L78

NL 0448945   DHEW NjP FU N NcU PU

J   LOFFT, CAPEL, 1806-1873.
5459   The Whigs, their prospects and policy.
.517   London, E. Wilson, 1835.
      viii, 46p. 22cm.

NL 0448946   ICN

    Thesis
SF   Lofgreen, Glen Pehr, 1919-
35   The protein requirements of growing Holstein
1948   cattle - a comparative study of conventional
L828   allowances and theoretical minimum requirements.
      [Ithaca, N. Y.] 1948.
      135, lviii l. illus. 28 cm.

      Thesis (Ph. D.) - Cornell Univ., Feb. 1948.
Thesis — —— Archival copy.
1948   1. Proteins in animal nutrition. 2. Dairy
L828   cattle - Feeding &   feeds. I. Title.

NL 0448947   NIC

Lofgreen, P   A
   The coming revolution: its principles
      see under title

308t   Lofgren, Edward Joseph, 1914-
L8276   The behavior of a uranium compound in Calutrons. [Berkeley] 1947.
      37 ℓ. illus.

      Thesis (Ph. D. in Physics) - Univ. of California, June 1947.
      Bibliography: ℓ. 33.

      1. Uranium compounds. 2. Calutron.

NL 0448949   CU

Lofgren, Edward Joseph, 1914—

   Operation of the 1/4 scale model Bevatron.
I-   Oak Ridge, Tenn., Technical Information Division, AEC, 1949-
      pts. diagrs. 27ᶜᵐ.
   At head of title: United States Atomic Energy Commission.   AECU-435 (UCRL-398);
AECU-450 (UCRL-412)

   1. Bevatron. I. Title. II. Ser.

NL 0448950   ViU

Lofgren, Kenneth E

   Calculating deflection of curved beams. New York, Cooper Union for the Advancement of Science and Art [1949]
   cover-title, 7 p. illus. 29ᶜᵐ. (Cooper Union bulletin [Cooper Union for the Advancement of Science and Art] Engineering and science series. no. 31)
   "Reprinted from Machine design. November, 1948."

   1. Girders. I. Ser.

NL 0448951   ViU

VOLUME 338

Lofgren, Luiz
     see   Löfgren, Luiz.

W 1
AN452
v. 32
1954
Suppl. 6
    LOFGREN, Lyderik
      Experimental gastric histamine erosions
and ulcers with special reference to the
effect of somatotropic hormone on their
frequency.   Helsinki, Mercatorin
Kirjapaino, 1954.
     20 p.   illus.   (Annales medicinae ex-
perimentalis et biologiae Fenniae, v. 32,
supplementum 6)
     Cover title.
     1. Growth substances   2. Histamine
3. Stomach - Ulcers   Series

NL 0448953   DNLM ViU

Lofgren, Mabel T.
    Elementary school minstrel show, by Mabel T. Lofgren and
Eula M. Baird ... Kansas City, Kan., The Raymond You-
mans publishing co., *1931.
    2 p. L. 2-14 numb. l.   diagrs.   29½ᶜᵐ.
    Mimeographed.

    I. Baird, Eula M., joint author.   II. Title.
                                  CA 36-1930 Unrev'd
    Library of Congress   PN4305.N6L6

NL 0448954   DLC

Lofgren, *Mrs.* May (Nixon)
    Poems, by May Nixon Lofgren ... Revere, Mass., A. R. von
Balsan ₍*1930₎.
    160 p.   port.   22ᶜᵐ.

                                    30-32868
    Library of Congress   PS3523.O33P6 1930

NL 0448955   DLC NcU MB

308t
I8277
    Lofgren, Norman Lowell, 1921-
      The thermodynamics of gaseous, cuprous
chloride monomer and trimer. ₍Berkeley,
1949₎
     15 p.   diagrs., tables.
     Thesis (Ph.D.) - University of California,
Jan. 1949.
     Issued as Atomic Energy Commission AECD-
1854 and MDDC-1834, by Leo Brewer and Norman
L. Lofgren.   Essentially the same as and presented to the Library to replace Lofgren's
thesis, both copies of which were lost.
     Bibliography: p.15.

NL 0448956   CU

Lofgren, Paul V.W.
    The analogous aptitude test in theory and
practice. [Berkeley, Calif., 1947]
    xvii, 287 numb. l.   plates.   29 cm.
    Thesis (Ph.D.) - Univ. of California, June 1947.
    Bibliography: p. 165-192.

NL 0448957   CU

Lofgren, Ruth, 1916-
    The effect of low temperature on the spirochetes of relapsing
fever ... ₍by₎ Ruth Lofgren and Malcolm H. Soule ... ₍n. p.,
1945₎
    3 pts.   illus., tables, diagrs.   25½ᶜᵐ.
    Each part has cover-title; part 3 with special title only.
    Based on thesis (PH. D.)—University of Michigan, 1944.
    Three articles reprinted from the Journal of bacteriology, v. 50, nos. 3,
6, Sept., Dec., 1945.
    "References" at end of each part.
    CONTENTS.—₍pt. 1₎ The viability of four strains of spirochetes stored
at −48 degrees centigrade.—₍pt. 2₎ The structure and motility of *Spirochaeta novyi*.—₍pt. 3₎ The structure of *Spirochaeta novyi* as revealed by
the electron microscope.
    1. Spirochaetae.   2. Re-   lapsing fever.   I. Soule, Malcolm
Herman, 1896-   joint   author.
    QR251.L6   Med 46-112
    Michigan. Univ. Library
    for Library of Congress   ₍4₎†

NL 0448958   MiU DLC

Lofit͡skiĭ, Valeriĭ Nikolaevich.
    Вопросы технологии земляных работ в гидротехниче-
ском строительстве.   Москва, Гос. энерг. изд-во, 1955.
    351 p.   diagrs., tables (1 fold. in pocket)   23 cm.

    1. Earthwork.   2. Hydraulic engineering.   I. Title.
                   Title transliterated: Voprosy tekhnologii zemli͡a-
                   nykh rabot v gidrotekhnicheskom stroitel'stve.

    TC183.L6   56-47013

NL 0448959   DLC

Spec.
F497
.V8L8
    LOFLAND, CHARLES
      A list of all the entries in the Virginia
military district; and also, all the entries in
the United States Military district of 100 acre
lots, located since the first commencement for
locating warrants for military services, to the
present year. By Charles Lofland, chief clerk in
the auditor's office, Ohio.   Columbus, Printed at
the office of the Columbus gazette by P. H. Olmsted,
1821.   32p.

NL 0448960   InU MiU-C OC OClWHi

₍Lofland, John₎ 1798-1849.
    The harp of Delaware; or, The miscellaneous poems of
the Milford bard ... Philadelphia, Atkinson & Alexander, 1828.
    xi, 212 p.   14½ᶜᵐ.

    I. Title.
    Library of Congress   PS2249.L5H3   3-30395

NL 0448961   DLC MB

Lofland, John, 1798-1849.
    The life of John Lofland, "the Milford bard," the earliest and
most distinguished poet of Delaware. With comments and representative selections from his works. By William W. Smithers
... Philadelphia, W. M. Leonard, 1894.
    311 p.   front. (port.)   23½ᶜᵐ.
    "This edition is limited to five hundred copies." This copy not num-
bered.

    I. Smithers, William West, 1864-   ed.   II. Title.
                                      28—9320
    Library of Congress   PS2249.L5Z8

               RPB TU CtY OO KyLx IEN PP
NL 0448962   DLC NIC ICU PPCCH PP PU ViU MH MB MBA

Lofland, John, 1798-1849.
    The poetical and prose writings of John Lofland, M. D., the
Milford bard ... Baltimore, J. Murphy; Pittsburg, G.
Quigley, 1846.
    viii, ₍9₎-332 p.   front. (port.) plates.   19ᶜᵐ.

                               35-35873
    Library of Congress   PS2249.L5 1846   811.39

NL 0448963   DLC ViU MH PHi

Lofland, John, 1798-1849.
    The poetical and prose writings of Dr. John Lofland, the
Milford bard, consisting of sketches in poetry and prose ...
With a portrait of the author and a sketch of his life. Col-
lected and arranged by J. N. M'Jilton, A. M.   Baltimore, J.
Murphy & co.; Wilmington ₍Del.₎ J. T. Heald, 1853.
    x, 30, ₍25₎-587 p.   front. (port.)   23ᶜᵐ.

    I. McJilton, John Nelson, 1805-1875, ed.

                                     28-9321
    Library of Congress   PS2249.L5 1853

NL 0448964   DLC MdU TU NcD ViU CLSU CSmH PP PV

Lofland, John, 1798-1849.
    The poetical and prose writings of Dr. John
Lofland, the Milford bard, consisting of sketches
in poetry and prose... With a portrait of the
author and a sketch of his life. Collected and
arranged by J. N. M'Jilton, A. M.   Baltimore,
J. Murphy; Wilmington ₍Del.₎ J. T. Heald, 1853.
    587 p.   front. (port.)

    Microfilm (positive) Ann Arbor, Mich.,
University Microfilms, 1967. 4th title of 7.
35 mm.   (American fiction series, reel 37.4)
    I. McJilton,   John Nelson, 1805-1875,
ed.

NL 0448965   KEmT CU

Micro
3
    Lofland, John, 1798-1849
      The poetical and prose writings of Dr. John
Lofland, the Milford bard, consisting of sketches
in poetry and prose ... With a portrait of the
author and a sketch of his life.   Collected and
arranged by J. N. M'Jilton.   Baltimore, J.
Murphy & Co.; Wilmington ₍Del., J. T. Heald,
1853 ₍c1852₎
     x, 587p.   front. (port.) 23cm.
     Micro-transparency (negative).   Louisville,
Ky., Lost Cause Press, 1970. 15 cards.
7.5x12.5cm.   (L.   H. Wright. American
fiction, 1851-   1875, no.1573)

NL 0448966   PSt

Hfp
Lo300
    Lofler, Paul
      Au fil de l'heure.   Paris, A. Lemerre, 1928.
     169p.   19cm.
     Poems.

NL 0448967   CtY

    Lofnarljóð. ₍Minningu Kormaks Ögmundarsonar₎
n. p. ₍1884₎
    48 p.   21cm.

    I. Kormákr Ögmundarson, ca. 935-970

NL 0448968   WU

    "Loforð hans hlýtur að standa!" Saga
frá enska hernum. (Akureyri, Prentsmiðja Odds Björnssonar, 1913.) 8°. ff.
(2).   IcH31V513

NL 0448969   NIC MH

Lo Forte (F.) L' ospedale militare di Tempel-
hof. pp. 165-211, 8 pl.   8°.   *Roma*, 1896.
Cutting [cover with printed title] *from:* Rivista di arti-
glieria e genio, Roma, 1896, iv.

NL 0448969-1   DNLM

VOLUME 338

808.8 Lo Forte, Giacomo.
L82a   ... Ad hoc (motti e frasi d'ogni giorno)   Milano
[etc.] R. Sandron [1909]
343p.

1. Terms and phrases.

NL 0448970   IU

---

808 Lo Forte, Giacomo.
L82a2   Ad hoc (motti e frasi d'ogni giorno)
2.ed. riv. ed ampliata.   Milano [1913?]
460p.

NL 0448971   IU

Lo Forte, Giacomo.
Morfologia e biologia delle piante, ad uso dei ginnasi.
Milano, R. Sandron [1912–13]
2 v. illus. (part col.) 24 cm.
Contents.—v. 1. Angiosperme, per la quarta classe.—v. 2. Gimnosperme, crittogame, fitogeografia—specie utili per la quinta classe.

1. Botany.   I. Title.

QK47.L78   58–52174

NL 0448972   DLC

Lo Forte, Giacomo.   580.9 Q201
40478 .... La vita delle piante da Teofrasto a Darwin. .... Milan,
[etc.], R. Sandron, 1902.
viii, 194 p.   12 illus. (ports.) 18½ᶜᵐ.   (On cover: Piccola enciclopedia del secolo
xx. 1.)
At head of title: Giacomo Lo Forte.

NL 0448973   ICJ

Loforte, Guiseppe.
Biografia di Giuseppe barone Rosaroll
see under Ayala, Mariano d', 1809–1877.

Loforte Gonçalves, Manoel
see Gonçalves, Manoel Loforte.

Loforte-Randi, Andrea, 1845–   Ital 8583.12
Giacomo Leopardi e i suoi canti d'amore; saggio critico. 2. ed.
Palermo, A. Reber, 1897.
pp. (4), 90.
"Per il 1. centenario di Giacomo Leopardi."

Leopardi;;

NL 0448976   MH CaBVaU CU CtY

LOFORTE-RANDI, Andrea, 1845–
L'inédit dans Montaigne. [Rome, 1887.]

1.8°. pp. (32).
Revue internationale, 1887, xvi. 40–55, 161–176

NL 0448977   MH

LO FORTE-RANDI, Andrea, 1845–
Michele Cervantes. Milano, Cooperativa Insubria, 1891.

Pamphlet.
Estratto dal Fascicolo 2°. (Febbraio 1891)
del Pensiero Italiano.

NL 0448978   MH

Loforte-Randi, Andrea, 1845–   Lit 358.99
Nelle letterature straniere. 1ª serie. "Universali:" M. de
Montaigne, R. W. Emerson, H. F. Amiel. Palermo, A. Reber,
1899.
pp. 309+.

Montaigne|Emerson |Amiel, Henri Frédéric, 1821–1881

NL 0448979   MH CtY

Loforte-Randi, Andrea, 1845–   Lit 358.99.2
Nelle leterature straniere. 2ª serie. "Sognatori:" M. Cervantes, Ch. Nodier, J. Joubert. Palermo, A. Reber, 1900.
pp. 324 +.

Cervantes|Nodier|Joubert, Joseph||AcS 186971

NL 0448980   MH CtY

Loforte-Randi, Andrea, 1845–   Lit 358.99.3
Nelle letterature straniere. 3ª serie. "Umoristi:" Rabelais e
Folengo, Sterne, de Maistre, Töpffer. Palermo, A. Reber, 1901.
pp. 338 +.

Rabelais|Folengo |Sterne|Maistre|Töpffer||AcS 186972

NL 0448981   MH CtY ODW

Loforte-Randi, Andrea, 1845–   Lit 358.99.3
Nelle letterature straniere. 4ª serie. "Pessimisti": Swift, La
Rochefoucault, Schopenhauer. Palermo, A. Reber, 1902.
pp. 338 +.

Swift|La Rochefoucauld|Schopenhauer||AcS 186973

NL 0448982   MH CtY

Loforte-Randi, Andrea, 1845–   Lit 358.99.4
Nelle letterature straniere. 5ª serie. "Poeti:" W. Shakspeare,
Lord Byron, W. Goethe, P. B. Shelley. Palermo, A. Reber, 1903.
pp. 458 +.

Shakespeare|Byron|Goethe|Shelley||AcS 186974

NL 0448983   MH CtY ODW

Lo Forte Randi, Andrea, 1845–
Nelle letterature straniere, 6ª serie. Voltaire.
Nietzsche. Palermo, A. Reber, 1905.
358 p.   18 cm.
1. Voltaire, François, Marie Arouet de,
1694–1778. 2. Nietzsche, Friedrich Wilhelm,
1884–1900.

NL 0448984   CtY MiDW

Lofquist, Bertil
see Löfquist, Bertil.

Lofoten (The) Islands and their principal product. 30 pp. obl. 16°. Detroit, Parke Davis &
Co., 1897.

NL 0448986   DNLM

Lofquist, Earl.
An index of selected Civil War ballads in the
Harris collection, June 9, 1933.
Typed copy.   29 p.

NL 0448987   RPB

Lofquist, Henry Victor, 1897–
An uncommon commonplace, a collection of sermons and
articles, by Henry V. Lofquist ... [Brookhaven, Miss.] 1942.
140 p. pl. 23ᶜᵐ.

1. Peace. 2. Stewardship, Christian. 3. Sociology, Christian.
I. Title.
Library of Congress   BR115.P4L6   43–4446
[3]   261

NL 0448988   DLC

Film Lofquist, Lloyd Henry
8534   Adapting vocational counseling procedures
to different disability groups.   Ann Arbor,
University Microfilms, 1955.

Microfilm copy (positive) of typescript.
Collation of the original: 417ℓ.
Thesis — University of Minnesota.

1. Disabled — Rehabilitation, etc. 2.
Vocational guidance.

NL 0448989   IaU

Lofsånger och andeliga wisor i nådene ...
see under [Engelke, Fr

GV   Lofstrom, Andrew L
1291   Fullständiga preference- och vira-regler;
.P8L6   utg. af And. L. Lofstrom. Chicago [19--?]
64 p. 12 cm.

1. Cards. 2. Preference (Game) 3. Vira
(Game) I. Titl]

NL 0448991   MnHi

VOLUME 338

PD
5610
.L55
Löfstrom, Andrew L
    Svensk-engelsk och engelsk-svensk fick-ordbok. Chicago, A. L. Löfstroms förlag ₍1901₎.
    2 v. in 1. 14 cm.

    1. Swedish language--Dictionaries--English. 2. English language--Dictionaries--Swedish.

NL   0448992   MnHi

Loft, Abram, 1922–
    Musicians' guild and union: a consideration of the evolution of protective organization among musicians. Ann Arbor, University Microfilms, 1950.
    (₍University Microfilms, Ann Arbor, Mich.₎ Publication no. 1870)
    Microfilm copy of typewritten ms. Positive.
    Collation of the original: v. 408 l.
    Thesis—Columbia University.
    Abstracted in Microfilm abstracts, v. 10 (1950) no. 4, p. 321–322.
    Bibliography : leaves 396–408.
    1. Music as a profession. 2. Gilds—Hist. 3. Trade-unions.
    Microfilm AC-1 no. 1870   Mic A 50–139

    Michigan. Univ. Libr.
    for Library of Congress   ₍1₎†

NL   0448993   MiU CaBVaU MtU NN NNC DLC

TH
5667
L6
Loft, C   **Edward**
    The practical stair-builder, a complete treatise on the art of building stairs and handrails, with a manual of elementary descriptive geometry and practical geometrical constructions. Troy, N.Y., A. J. Bicknell, 1868.
    151 p. illus. 35 cm.

    1. Stair building.

NL   0448994   DSI

Loft, Genivera.
    The Gulf stream and the north Atlantic drift. 1918.

NL   0448995   DAS

Loft, Jacob, 1913–
    ... The printing trades, by Jacob Loft, with a foreword by Henry David. New York, Toronto, Farrar & Rinehart, inc. ₍1944₎
    xiii, 301 p. 21½ᶜᵐ. (Labor in twentieth century America)
    Thesis (PH. D.)—Columbia university.
    Without thesis note.
    Bibliographical references included in "Notes" at end of each chapter except the last. "Selected bibliography": p. 291–292.
    1. Printing as a trade—U. S. 2. Printers—U. S.   I. Title: Twentieth century printing labor.

Library of Congress	Z243.L64	44–6151
—— Copy 2.	Thesis title "Twentieth century printing labor" and thesis note on label mounted on t.-p. Vita on label mounted on p. ₍302₎	₍a44q5₎ 331.7655

    TU NcU MU Or WaS CaBVaU CaBViP
NL   0448996   DLC NNC OrCS OrP OrPR WaTC NcC PBm TxU

Loft, Inc.
    Candy kettle.

    New York, 1917
    v. illus.

    Monthly.

    1. House organs. 2. Title.
    N. Y. P. L.   June 27, 1921.

NL   0448997   NN

Loft handbook
    see under   ₍Lockheed aircraft corporation, Burbank, Calif.₎

Loft manual
    see under   ₍Northrop aircraft, inc., Hawthorne, Calif.₎

LOFTAS, W.
    Bratfischhandel in Grossbritannien. Stuttgart, E. Schweizerbart (Erwin Nägele g.m. b.h.), 1931.

    4°. pp.(3),48. Illustr.
    "Handbuch der seefischerei Nordeuropas, IX, 3a."
    "Aus dem englischen übertragen von W. Schakenbeck."

NL   0449000   MH

TX747
L8
Loftas, W
    The fish frier and his trade, or How to establish and carry on an up-to-date fish frying business; a complete compendium to the arts and appliances of the fried fish trade, together with much other useful information relating thereto, by Chatchip (W. Loftas, ex-President of the National Federation of Fish Caterers) ... London, E. F. Hyde & Sons ₍n.d.₎
    244 p. illus. 22 cm.

    1. Cookery (Fish). 2. Fish trade.   I. Title.

NL   0449001   DI

Loften, Emma Lee.
    Insects beware! Here comes the Jones family, by Emma Lee Loften; illustrations by James A. Martin ... Gainesville, Fla., University of Florida project in applied economics, Florida curriculum laboratory, College of education, 1943.
    1 p. l., 69 p. illus. 23ᶜᵐ.
    Reproduced from type-written copy.
    "Book S-5-2."
    "General statement" : p. ₍2₎ of cover.
    "Books to read": p. 69.
    1. Household pests—Juvenile literature. 2. Insects, Injurious and beneficial—Juvenile literature.   I. Florida. University, Gainesville. Curriculum laboratory.   II. Title.

Library of Congress	PE1127.I 55L6	44–21629
	₍2₎	648.7

NL   0449002   DLC

Loften, Emma Lee.
    School is the place to make things, by Emma Lee Loften; illustrations by Dorothy Hampson ... Gainesville, Fla., University of Florida project in applied economics, Florida curriculum laboratory, College of education, 1944.
    2 p. l., 69 numb. l., 1 l. illus. 27½ x 21½ᶜᵐ.
    Reproduced from type-written copy.
    "Book S-5-3."
    "Publication made possible by a grant from the Alfred P. Sloan foundation, inc."
    "A list of books that proved helpful": leaf 69.
    1. Handicraft.   I. Florida. University, Gainesville. Curriculum laboratory.   II. Title.

Library of Congress	TT160.L6	44–42401
	₍2₎	372.5

NL   0449003   DLC WaS DNAL

Loftfield, Berner, *ed.*
    Norge; det norske folks historie, fra dets bosættelse i Thule eller Norge til det nittende aarhundredes udgang, udarbeidet efter P. A. Munch, O. A. Overland og andre. De tusend hjem, eller en illustreret beskrivelse af hver by og bygd i Norge fra Lindesnæs til Nordkap. Norske mænd og kvinder, biografier og portrætter af fremragende historiske personligheder i ældre og nyere tid. Flere hundrede illustrationer og kolorerede billeder. Udgivet af Berner Loftfield. Minneapolis, Minn., Norge publishing company, 1900.
    xiv p., 1 l., 800 p. front. illus. (incl. ports.) plates (1 double). 24ᶜᵐ.
    1. Norway—Descr. & trav. 2. Norway—Hist. 3. Norway—Biog.
                              Jan. 31, 1901–140

    Library of Congress   DL449.L8 Copyright

NL   0449004   DLC Or NNC

Loftfield, Gabriel, *ed.*
    Deklamatoren. En samling af deklamationsstykker i poesi og prosa, af ældre og nyere forfattere til brug i ungdomsforeninger, afholdsforeninger o. s. v. Samlet og redigeret af Gabriel Loftfield og M. L. Tuve. Minneapolis, Minn., Ungdommens vens forlag ₍1895₎
    xvi, 304 p. 20ᶜᵐ.
    "Korte oplysninger om forfatterne": p. ₍297₎–302.
    1. Readers and speakers—1870–   I. Tuve, Martin L., joint ed.   II. Title.

    Library of Congress   PN4206.L7   13–19289

NL   0449005   DLC

Loftfield, Gabriel E.
    The direct principle in the teaching of modern languages, by Gabriel Loftfield ... ₍Oslo, Printed in Kølbelske bok- og kunsttrykkeri, 1929?₎
    cover-title, 96 p. ports. 24½ᶜᵐ.
    "Reprint, Scandinavian scientific review, vol. III, nos. 3 & 4."
    1. Languages, Modern—₍Study and₎ teaching.   I. Title.
                              E 32–368

    Library, U. S. Office of   Education PB35.L8

NL   0449006   DHEW

Loftfield, Gabriel E.
    ... Norway's contribution to cultural elements in education ₍by₎ Gabriel Loftfield ₍n. p., 1925?₎
    ₍8₎ p. 23½ᶜᵐ.
    Caption title.
    "Reprinted from May, 1925, 'Education'."
    1. Norwegians. 2. Culture. 3. Education.   I. Title.
                              E 32–369

    Library, U. S. Office of   Education CB113.S3L8

NL   0449007   DHEW

Loftfield, Gabriel E.
    ... Secondary education in Norway, by Gabriel E. Loftfield ... Washington, U. S. Govt. print. off., 1930.
    ix, 112 p. 23ᶜᵐ. (U. S. Bureau of education. Bulletin, 1930, no. 17)
    At head of title: United States department of the interior. Ray Lyman Wilbur, secretary. Office of education. William John Cooper, commissioner.
    Bibliography: p. 105–112.
    1. Education—Norway. 2. Education, Secondary. ₍2. Secondary education—Norway₎   I. Title.

U. S. Off. of Educ. Library	L111.A6 1930, no. 17	E 30–340
—— Copy 2.	LA806.L8	
for Library of Congress	L111.A6 1930, no. 17	
—— Copy 2.	LA806.L8	₍a40m1₎

NL   0449008   DHEW WaWW OC1 OCU MiU OU DLC MB

Loftfield, J   **V**   **Gorm,** 1890–
    The behavior of stomata, by J. V. G. Loftfield. Washington, Carnegie institution of Washington, 1921.
    104 p. 16 pl., diagrs. 25½ᶜᵐ. (On verso of t.-p.: Carnegie institution of Washington. Publication no. 314)
    Bibliography : p. 103–104.

    1. Stomata.

    Library of Congress   QK873.L8   22–2162

    OCU MiU OU ViU TU ICJ MB WaSp IdU OrP WaWW
NL   0449009   DLC OrPR OrCS MBH CoU DNLM NcD OO OC1

VOLUME 338

Loftfield, J   V   Gorn, 1890-
The behavior of stomata, by J. V. G. Loftfield. Washington, D. C., 1921.
104ℓ. diagrs. 26cm.

Includes bibliography.
Microfilm. Carnegie Institution of
Washington, 1921.

1. Somata.

NL 0449010   MU

Loftfield, J. V. Gorn, 1890-   joint author.

Taylor, Walter Penn, 1888-
... Damage to range grasses by the Zuni prairie dog.
By Walter P. Taylor ... and J. V. G. Loftfield ... Wash-
ington ₍Govt. print. off.₎ 1924.

Loftfield, Robert Bernard.
[Studies on cantharidine]

Thesis, Ph.D. - Harvard university, 1945.
Typewritten.

NL 0449012   MH

Lofthouse, Charles.

Bahama lullaby. Words by Joe Gilbert. Music by Charles
Lofthouse. New York, Shapiro, Bernstein & co. inc. ₍c1948₎

First line: Sing for me that old Bahama lullaby.

1. Bahama Islands. 2. Lullabies.   I. Gilbert, Joe. II. Song index (2).
N. Y. P. L.   May 26, 1949

NL 0449013   NN

Lofthouse, Charles.

Bahama mama (that goombay tune), by L. Wolfe Gilbert and
Charles Lofthouse. New York, Shapiro, Bernstein & co. ₍c1932₎

First line: You're as graceful as the seagull.
Chorus: Mama, Bahama mama.

1. Goombays. 2. Bahama islands.   Printed for the Music Division
II. Song index (3).   I. Gilbert, L. Wolfe, 1886- .
N. Y. P. L.   March 15, 1948

NL 0449014   NN

Lofthouse, Jessica.

The curious traveller through Lakeland; historic ways
north from Kendal and Cartmel to Keswick and Penrith.
Illus. by the author. London, R. Hale ₍1954₎
190 p. illus. 23 cm.

1. Lake District, Eng.   I. Title.

DA670.L1L76   54-3499 ‡

NL 0449015   DLC PP OCl

Lofthouse, Jessica.

Lancashire landscape; discoveries south of the Ribble.
Illus. by the author. London, R. Hale ₍1951₎
334 p. illus. 22 cm.
Includes bibliography.

1. Lancashire, Eng.—Descr. & trav.   I. Title.

DA670.L2L55   914.272   52-31707 ‡

NL 0449016   DLC CaBViP

Lofthouse, Jessica.
Lancashire-Westmorland highway, with byways and foot-
ways for the curious traveller. Illus. by the author. London, R. Hale ₍1953₎
227 p. illus., maps. 23 cm.

1. Lancashire, Eng.—Descr. & trav. 2. Westmorland, Eng.—Descr.
& trav.   I. Title.

DA670.L2L555   942.72   53-32181

NL 0449017   DLC PP OCl MB

Lofthouse, Jessica.
Lancashire's fair face; discoveries, Ribble to Lune. Illus.
by the author. London, R. Hale ₍1952₎
336 p. illus. 23 cm.

1. Lancashire, Eng.—Descr. & trav.   I. Title.

DA670.L2L553   914.272   52-40693 ‡

NL 0449018   DLC MH PHC OOxM

Lofthouse, Jessica.
Off to the dales, walking by the Aire, Wharfe, Ure and
Swale. Illus. by the author. London, R. Hale ₍1950₎
314 p. illus., maps (on lining papers) 22 cm.

1. Yorkshire, Eng.—Descr. & trav.   I. Title.

DA670.Y6L67   914.274   51-23742

NL 0449019   DLC CaBVa MH NN

Lofthouse, Jessica.
Off to the Lakes; a Lakeland walking year. Illus. by the
author. London, R. Hale ₍1949₎
280 p. illus., map (on lining-paper) 22 cm.

1. Lake District, Eng.   I. Title.

DA670.L1L78   914.28   49-25800*

NL 0449020   DLC

Lofthouse, Jessica.
Three rivers; being an account of many wanderings in the
dales of Ribble, Hodder and Calder, by Jessica Lofthouse ...
London, R. Hale limited, 1946.
301 p. front., illus. (incl. maps) 22ᵐ.
"First published in 1946."

1. Lancashire, Eng.—Descr. & trav. 2. Yorkshire, Eng.—Descr. &
trav.   I. Title.

A 47-1159

Harvard univ. Library
for Library of Congress   ₍3₎

NL 0449021   MH CU

DA670
.L2L6   Lofthouse, Jessica.
Three rivers; being an account of many wander-
ings in the dales of Ribble, Hodder and Calder.
London, R. Hale, 1949.
301 p. front., illus., maps. 22cm.

1. Lancashire, Eng.—Descr. & trav. 2. Yorkshire, Eng.—Descr. & trav.   I. Title.

NL 0449022   MB

Lofthouse, Jessica.
West Pennine Highway; roadside discoveries, Clitheroe
and Craven—to Carlisle. Illus. by the author. London,
Hale ₍1954₎
180 p. illus. 23 cm.

1. Pennine Chain.   I. Title.

DA670.P4L6   55-21747 ‡

NL 0449023   DLC KU NN PP

Lofthouse, Joseph, 1855-
A thousand miles from a post office; or, Twenty years'
life and travel in the Hudson's Bay regions, by the Right
Rev. J. Lofthouse ... With a preface by the Archbishop
of Canterbury ... London, Society for promoting Christian knowledge, 1922.
vii, 183 p. front. (port.) plates, fold. map. 19½ᶜᵐ.

1. Hudson Bay—Descr. & trav. 2. Missions—Canada.   I. Title.

Library of Congress   F1060.L82   23-5218

OCl
NL 0449024   DLC CaBVaU OrHi TxU WaU CtY CU OU NN

Lofthouse, Joseph, 1855-
A thousand miles from a post office, or,
Twenty years' life and travel in the Hudson's
Bay regions. With a preface by the Archbishop
of Canterbury. London, Society for Promoting
Christian Knowledge; New York [etc.] Macmillan,
1922.
vii, 183 p. plates, port., fold. map. 20 cm.
1. Hudson Bay. Descr. and trav. 2. Missions.
Canada. I. Title.

NL 0449025   IEG

Lofthouse, J[oseph] 1855-
A thousand miles from a post office; or, Twenty
years' life and travel in the Hudson's bay region
... with a preface by the Archbishop of Canterbury
... Tor., Macmillan, 1922.
vii, [184] p. front. (port.), 7 pl., fold. map.
D.

NL 0449026   CaBViPA

Lofthouse, Mrs. Kate Lyth (Foster)
Purity and racial health, by K.L.
Lofthouse and W.F. Lofthouse. London,
The Epworth press ₍1920₎
158p. 18½cm. (On cover: Welfare
series. vol.3)

1. Sexual ethics. I. Lofthouse, William
Frederick, 1871- joint author.

NL 0449027   MWelC

Lofthouse, Kate S.
A complete guide to drawn fabric.   8189.03-111
—   London. Sir Isaac Pitman & Sons, Ltd. 1933. 44 pp. Samplers.
20 cm., in 8s.

D5085 — Embroidery.

NL 0449028   MB

746.6   Lofthouse, Kate S.
L827c   A complete guide to drawn
fabric. London, Pitman [1952]
44 [3] p. illus. (part col.)

NL 0449029   MiD

VOLUME 338

Lofthouse, Marion.
"Le pèlerinage de vie humaine" by Guillaume de Deguile-ville. With special reference to the French ms. 2 of the John Rylands library. By Marion Lofthouse, M. A.
(*In* John Rylands library, Manchester. Bulletin. **Manchester, 1935.** 25½ᶜᵐ. v. 19, p. 170–215)

1. Guillaume de Deguilleville, 14th cent. Le pèlerinage de vie hu-maine. ɪ. John Rylands library, Manchester. Mss. (French 2)

Princeton univ. Library   A 37–454
for Library of Congress   [Z921.M18B vol. 19]
                                        (2)   (027.44272)

NL 0449030   NjP OC1

Div.S. Lofthouse, William Frederick, 1871–
291.34   Altar, cross, and community. [1st ed.]
L829A   London, Epworth Press, J. A. Sharp for the
          Fernley Lecture Trust [1921]
          319 p. 20 cm.

          Bibliographical footnotes.

          1. Sacrifice. I. Title.

NL 0449031   NcD MH MWelC CtY

Lofthouse, William Frederick, 1871–
   The Bible, its origin and authority.
By W. F. Lofthouse.   London, Robert
Culley [18--?]
   151 p.   18 cm.
1. Bible. Hist. 2. Bible. Evidences,
authority, etc.

NL 0449032   IEG

Lofthouse, William Frederick, 1871–
   The Bible, its origin and authority, by W. F. Lofthouse
... New York, Eaton and Mains; Cincinnati, Jennings
and Graham [1910?]
   3 p. l., 151, [1] p. 17½ᶜᵐ.

1. Bible—Hist. 2. Bible—Evidences, authority, etc.
                                                      A 11–1843
Title from Enoch Pratt   Free Libr.   Printed by L. C.

NL 0449033   MdBE OO

Lofthouse, William Frederick, 1871– , *ed.*   **177.5 S001**
The Christian use of money. Edited by W. F. Lofthouse, M.A.
for the Wesleyan Methodist Union for Social Service. **London,**
The Epworth Press, [1920].
   180 p. 18½ᶜᵐ.
"Bibliography," p. [174]–178.
Contents.—1. Lofthouse, W. F. The present perplexity.—2. *Same.* The teaching of the Old Testament.—3. Hughes, H. M. The teaching of the New Testament.—4. Richards, F. The attitude of Catholic Christianity.—5. Harrison, A. W. Protestant Christianity.—6. Waterhouse, E. S. The case for ownership.—7. Lewis, F. W. Stewardship.—8. Lofthouse, W. F. The rule of service.—9. Keeble, S. E. The application to individuals.—10. *Same.* The church's use of money.

NL 0449034   ICJ CtY NcD

Lofthouse, William Frederick, 1871–
   Christianity in action, by W. F. Lofthouse ... London, The
Epworth press [1928]
   108 p. 21ᶜᵐ.

1. Christian life. I. Title.
                                                     31–23436
Library of Congress   BV4501.L52
                                        [3]   248

NL 0449035   DLC NcU

Lofthouse, William Frederick, 1871–
   Christianity in the social state, by W. F. Lofthouse, D. D.
London, J. Heritage, The Unicorn press [1936]
   159 p. 19ᶜᵐ. (*On cover:* The Christian challenge series)
"First published, 1936."

1. Sociology, Christian. 2. Social ethics. ɪ. Title.

Library of Congress   BR148.L6   38–15336
                                        [3]   261

NL 0449036   DLC ICU MH–AH

Lofthouse, William Frederick, 1871–
   The disciple whom Jesus loved; lectures on the Fourth
gospel, by W. F. Lofthouse ... London, The Epworth press
(E. C. Barton) [1936]
   187 p. 19ᶜᵐ. (*Half-title:* 'God and life' series)
"First edition, 1936."
"These lectures were delivered at Cambridge in the summer of
1935."—Foreword.

   1. John, Saint. Apostle. 2. Bible. N. T. John—Criticism, interpreta-tion, etc. 3. Bible—Criticism, interpretation, etc.—N. T. John. ɪ. Title.
                                                     36–32923
Library of Congress   BS2615.L54
                                        [2]   226.5

NL 0449037   DLC MH–AH MBrZ

Lofthouse, William Frederick,   1871–
   Ethics and atonement...   London, Methuen,
n.d.   xii,302p.,1 l. front. 23cm.

   "First published in 1906."

NL 0449038   MWelC

BT265   LOFTHOUSE, WILLIAM FREDERICK, 1871–
.L82   Ethics and atonement, by W. F. Lofthouse... London,
Methuen & co. [1906]
          xii,302,[1]p. front. 23cm.

          1.Atonement. 2.Ethics.

NL 0449039   ICU NRCR MH–AH TxDaM ICJ

Lofthouse, William Frederick, 1871–
   Ethics and the family, by W. F. Lofthouse ... **London,**
New York [etc.] Hodder and Stoughton [1912]
   xvi, 403, [1] p. 23ᶜᵐ.

1. Family. ɪ. Title.
                                                     13–15028
Library of Congress   HQ728.L75

          OC1W MH NjP NN
NL 0449040   DLC MSohG IEG ICRL FMU ICMcC LU NcD

Lofthouse, William Frederick, 1871–
   ...Ezekiel. Introduction; Revised version
with notes... Edinburgh [19-]
      see under   Bible. O.T. Ezekiel.
English [19-] Revised.   Also with
date 1907 (New York)

Lofthouse, William Frederick, 1871–
   F. H. Bradley. London, Epworth Press [1949]
   vi, 237 (i. e. 273) p. 19 cm. (Philosopher's library [no. 1])

   1. Bradley, Francis Herbert, 1846–1924. (Series: Philosopher's library (London) [no. 1])

   B1618.B74L57   921.2   50–942

NL 0449042   DLC ICMcC ScU TxU OC1W MH NcD CtY ICU

Lofthouse, William Frederick, 1871–
   The family and the state, by W. F. Lofthouse ... London,
The Epworth press [1944]
   145, [1] p. 22½ᶜᵐ. (The Social service lecture, 1944)
"First published in 1944."
"An expansion of the Beckly lecture delivered during the Methodist
conference in July, 1944."—Pref.

   1. Family. ɪ. Title.
                                                     44–47904
Library of Congress   HQ728.L76
                                                    392

NL 0449043   DLC CoU CU

Lofthouse, William Frederick, 1871–
   The Father and the Son; a study in Johannine thought, by
W. F. Lofthouse ... London, Student Christian movement
press [1934]
   289, [1] p. 22½ᶜᵐ.
"First published, October, 1934."

   1. Bible. N. T. John—Theology. 2. Bible—Theology—N. T. John.
ɪ. Title.
                                                     35–6585
Library of Congress   BS2615.L55
                                        [3]   226.5

NL 0449044   DLC MH–AH MSohG CtY ODW

Lofthouse, *Rev.* **William** Frederick, 1871–   **3499-349**
   The Gospel in human society.
   (*In* Marchant, Sir James, editor. The future of Christianity.
   Pp. 265–285. New York. 1927.)

D5015 — Christian life.

NL 0449045   MB

DX   Lofthouse, William Frederick, 1871–
86   A Hebrew view of evil, by W.F. Lofthouse.
L829   [London] E. Benn, 1928.
          31p. 18cm. (Affirmations; God in the
          modern world. Section IV)

          1. Good and evil - Biblical teaching.
          I. Title.

NL 0449046   ViRUT NjPT MH

Lofthouse, William Frederick, 1871–
   ... Israel after the exile, sixth and fifth centuries, B. C., by
W. F. Lofthouse, D. D. Oxford, The Clarendon press, 1928.
   xiv, [2], 247, 15, [1] p. incl. front., illus. (incl. map, plans, facsims.)
19 cm. (The Clarendon Bible ... Old Testament, vol. ɪᴠ)
   Colored plan on lining-papers.
   Commentary on selected passages from Ezra, Nehemiah, Isaiah,
Jeremiah, Lamentations, Ezekiel, Obadiah, Haggai, Zechariah and
Malachi.
   "The Old Testament chronologically arranged, by Evelyn W. Hip-pisley": 15 p. at end.
   1. Bible. O. T.—Historical books—Commentaries. 2. Bible. O. T.—
Prophets—Commentaries. ɪ. Title.

   BS491.C55 O. T.   vol. ɪᴠ   29—16573

          OO OCH OC1 NN MB MBrZ
NL 0449047   DLC LU AU MH–AH IEG MBtS OWorP CtY NcD

Lofthouse, William Frederick, 1871–
   Israel after the exile; sixth and fifth centuries,
B.C. Oxford, Clarendon Press [1950]

   xiv, 247 p. illus. (Clarendon Bible. Old Testament,
v.4)

NL 0449048   MH

VOLUME 338

Lofthouse, William Frederick, 1871–
Jeremiah and the new covenant, by W. F. Lofthouse ... London, Student Christian movement, 1925.
vii, 222 p. 19½ᶜᵐ.

1. Jeremiah, the prophet.   ɪ. Student Christian movement of Great Britain and Ireland.

36-2413

Library of Congress   BS580.J4L6   221.92

NL 0449049   DLC INS CtY PPFr PHC OO MH ICU IaU

LOFTHOUSE, William Frederick, 1871–
The making of the Old Testament, by William F. Lofthouse... London, C.H.Kelly, [1915]
144 p.   18 cm.   (Manuals for Christian thinkers)
Bibliography: p.141 - 142.

NL 0449050   MH-AH ICMcC

Lofthouse, William Frederick, 1871–
The philosophy of communism. London, Epworth Press [1950]
15 p. 19 cm. (Beckly pamphlets, no. 1)

1. Communism.   ɪ. Title.   (Series)

HX56.L65   335.4   51-23657

NL 0449051   DLC NN

Lofthouse, William Frederick, 1871–
The prophet of reconstruction (Ezekiel) : a patriot's ideal for a new age, by W. F. Lofthouse ... London, J. Clarke [1920]
250 p. 20ᶜᵐ.

1. Bible. O. T. Ezekiel—Criticism, interpretation, etc.   ɪ. Title.

A 22—358

General theol. sem. Libr.
for Library of Congress   [a41c1]

NL 0449052   NNG CtY NcC PPDrop MH CtY-D OCH

Lofthouse, William Frederick, 1871–
The social teaching of the Hebrew law
see in   Keeble, Samuel Edward, 1853–
The social teaching of the bible.

Lofthouse, William Frederick, 1871–
Why do nations fight? by W. F. Lofthouse ...   London: The Epworth press [1939]   24 p.   18½cm.   (Pilot books. no. 3.)

1. War and peace, 1938–
N. Y. P. L.   May 4, 1942

NL 0449054   NN

LOFTHOUSE, William Frederick, 1871–
Wilbert F. Howard; appreciations of the man by W.F. Lofthouse, H.G. Meecham, Edgar T. Selby, T.W. Manson, Ivan Lee Holt, Maurice F. Howard and a brief representative selection from his addresses. London, Epworth [1954]
80p.   front.   19cm.

NL 0449055   MH-AH

TL151
R76

Lofthus, Halvor, ed.

Rütshi, H
Auto-journalen; autotekniske oppslags tabeller for amerikanske og europeiske vogner. Patent: H. Rütshi, Sveits. Norsk redaksjon: Halvor Lofthus. Oslo, Auto-journalen [195–

Lofthus, Johan, 1887–
Eksperimentelle undersøkelser av folkeskolebarns abstraksjonsevne, av Johan Lofthus. Med 10 tekstfigurer, 6 kurver og 2 tabeller ...   Oslo, I kommisjon hos J. Dybwad, 1928.
21, [1] p. incl. tables, diagrs. 27½ᶜᵐ. (Norsk videnskaps-akademi i Oslo. Skrifter. ɪ. Matematisk-naturvidenskapelig klasse, 1928, no. 8)
"Utgitt for Fridtjof Nansens fond."

1. Abstraction. 2. Mental tests.   ɪ. Fridtjof Nansens fond til videnskabens fremme.

Title from John Crerar   Libr. Printed by L. C.   A 30-983

NL 0449057   ICJ CoU

4BF–38 Lofthus, Johan, 1887–
Intelligensmåling.   Oslo, I kommisjon hos H. Aschehoug, 1931.
228 p. and atlas.

NL 0449058   DLC-P4 NN NNC-T MH

Lofthus, Johan, 1887–
Mentalhygiene
Berner, Jørgen Haslef, 1883–
... Helse og hygiene, under redaksjon av dr. Jørgen H. Berner. Oslo, Gyldendal, Norsk forlag, 1938.

Lofthus, Olav
Sange og digte   Larsen, ed.

NL 0449060   NdU NcD

LB3999 Lofti, Mohamed Kadri, 1911–
Changes needed in Egyptian school readers to increase their value as media of instruction. 1948.
253 l.

Typewritten.
Thesis--Univ. of Chicago.

1. Reading (Elementary) 2. Arabic language--Chrestomathies and readers.

NL 0449061   ICU

Loftie, Mrs.
see   Loftie, Martha Jane (Anderson)

Loftie, Arthur Gershom.
Calder abbey: its ruins and history, with plan and illustrations, by Arthur G. Loftie ... In three parts. 2d ed., partly re-written. London [etc.] Bemrose and sons, limited, 1892.
17 cm.
"Some authorities consulted": p. 110.

NL 0449063   CtY

Loftie, Arthur Gershom.
Great Salkeld: its rectors and history. By Arthur Gershom Loftie ... London, Printed by Bemrose & sons, ltd., 1900.
viii, 180 p. front., pl., port., facsim. 17ᶜᵐ.

Subject entries: Salkeld, Great, Eng. (Parish)

2-29011

Library of Congress, no.   DA690.S17L8.

NL 0449064   DLC

TX
855
.L83 Loftie, Martha Jane (Anderson)
The dining-room. By Mrs. Loftie ... London, Macmillan and co., 1878.
xii, 128 p. incl. front., illus.   18½ᶜᵐ.   (Art at home)

1. Dinners and dining.

NL 0449065   MiU KMK MWA TxU CtY MH

PR 4891
.L58 A16
1879 LOFTIE, Mrs. Martha Jane (Anderson)
XLVI social twitters.   London, Macmillan, 1879.
288 p. illus.

Essays reprinted from the Saturday review.

I. Tc.: Forty-six social twitters.   II. Tc.: Social twitters.

NL 0449066   InU MH

LOFTIE, William John, 1839-1911.   4546.158
Alfred and the arts.
(In Bowker, Alfred, editor. Alfred the Great. Pp. 241-257.

NL 0449067   MB DLC

ND-
1380
.L6

B14422 Loftie, William John, 1839-1911.
Animal painting in England; advanced studies after Landseer. Descriptive text by W. J. Loftie, with reproductions of celebrated pictures... Practical hints for drawing and painting animals by Stephen T. Dadd. London, Blackie [1891]
82 p.   illus.   (Vere Foster's water-color series)

Half -title: Landseer and animal painting in England.

#Animal painting and illustration.
#Landseer, Sir Edwin Henry, 1802-1873.
Animal painting in England.
Landseer and animal painting in England.

NL 0449068   MoU

Loftie, William John, 1839–1911.
Authorised guide to the Tower of London. By W. J. Loftie ... London, Printed for H. M. Stationery off., 1886.
152 p. incl. illus., plans. front., pl. (part fold.) 19ᶜᵐ.

1. London. Tower.

3—2563

Library of Congress   DA687.T7L7

NL 0449069   DLC CtY MdBP MB ICJ

VOLUME 338

Loftie, William John, 1839-
Authorised guide to the tower of London.
London, Her Majesty's stationery office, 1887.

NL 0449070   MH

Loftie, William John, 1839-1911.
Authorised guide to the Tower of London. (2d ed.
rev.) By W. J. Loftie ... London, Printed for H. M.
Stationery off., 1888.
152 p. incl. illus., plans. front., plates (1 fold.) 19½ᶜᵐ.

1. London. Tower.

Library of Congress   DA687.T7L72   7—5233

NL 0449071   DLC CU PP MH NN OrP CtY MB OO DNLM NjP

LOFTIE, W₍illiam₎ J₍ohn₎, 1839-
Authorised guide to the Tower of London.
2d ed., revised. With appendix on the armoury
by the Viscount Dillon. London, Harrison and
Sons, 1894.

Plates and plans.

NL 0449072   MH OCl NN

Loftie, William John, 1839-1911.
... Authorized guide to the Tower of London. Rev. ed. By
W. J. Loftie ... with illustrations and plans. And with de-
scription of the armoury by the Viscount Dillon ... London,
H. M. Stationery off., 1897.
158 p. front., illus., plates. 19ᶜᵐ.

1. London. Tower.   I. Dillon, Harold Arthur Lee-Dillon, 17th viscount, 1844-1932, ed.   II. Title.
                                                  G S 34—221
U. S. Geol. survey. Libr.   Geo. F. Kunz collection
for Library of Congress   K590(520) L82
                                [DA687.T7L   ]

NL 0449073   DI-GS CtY IaU TU OU DDO CaBViP

Loftie, W₍illiam₎ J₍ohn₎ 1839-
Authorised guide to the Tower of London. Abridged.
By W. J. Loftie ... London, Printed for H. M. Stationery
off. ₍by Harrison and sons₎ 1886.
30 p. incl. front., plan. 19ᶜᵐ.
Title vignette.

Subject entries: London. Tower.
                                          2-22948
Library of Congress, no.   DA687.T7L8.

NL 0449074   DLC

Loftie, Rev. W₍illiam₎ J₍ohn₎ 1839-1911.
Authorized guide to the Tower of London. Revised edition,
with...a description of the armoury, by the viscount Dillon.
London: Harrison & Sons, 1903.   37 p., 12 pl.   illus.   12°.

1. Tower of London. 2. Dillon (17.   viscount), Harold Arthur Lee
Dillon.
N. Y. P. L.   January 16, 1911

NL 0449075   NN MB

Loftie, W₍illiam₎ J₍ohn₎ 1839-1911.
Authorised guide to the Tower of London, with...a description of the armoury, by the Viscount Dillon.   London: Harrison
and Sons, 1904.   37 p., 12 pl.   rev. ed.   12°.

1. Tower of London. 2. Dillon,   (17. viscount), Harold Arthur
Dillon-Lee.
N. Y. P. L.   April 23, 1913.

NL 0449076   NN

Pam.   Loftie, William John, 1839-1911.
Coll.   Authorised guide to the Tower of London.
36794   Rev. ed. With ... a description of the
        armoury, by the Viscount Dillon. London,
        Printed for H. M. Stationery Off., by Harrison
        and sons, 1905.
            37 p. plans., 12 plates. 20 cm.

            First published 1904.
            1. London. Tower. Description. Guide-books
        I. Dillon, Harold Arthur Lee-Dillon, 17th
        viscount, 1844-   1932.

NL 0449077   NcD

Loftie, Rev. W₍illiam₎ J₍ohn₎, 1839-1911.
Authorised guide to the Tower of London.   Revised edition.
With twelve views and two plans, and a description of the armoury
by the Viscount Dillon.   London: Harrison and Sons, 1904, repr.
1907.   37 p., 12 pl.   12°.

1. Tower of London. 2. Dillon (17.   viscount), Harold Arthur Lee
Dillon.
N. Y. P. L.   June 7, 1913.

NL 0449078   NN CtY

Loftie, William John, 1839-
... Authorised guide to the Tower of London.   By W. J.
Loftie ...   Rev. ed.   With ... a description of the armoury,
by the Viscount Dillon ...   London, Printed for H. M.
Stationery off., by Harrison and sons, 1908.
38 p. incl. 2 plans. XII pl. 19½ᶜᵐ.

1. London. Tower.   I. Dillon, Harold Arthur Lee-Dillon, 17th viscount, 1844-
                                                  9-12406
Library of Congress   DA687.T7L83

NL 0449079   DLC MiU

Loftie, William John, 1839-
Authorised guide to the Tower of London, by W. J.
Loftie ...   Rev. ed. with twelve views and two plans and a
description of the armoury, by the Viscount Dillon ...
London, Printed for H. M. Stationery off., by Darling &
son ltd., 1909.
37, ₍1₎ p. illus. (plans) XII pl. on 6 l. 19ᶜᵐ.
Plates printed on both sides.

1. London. Tower.   I. Dillon, Harold Arthur Lee-Dillon, 17th viscount, 1844-
                                                  11-11960
Library of Congress   DA687.T7L835

NL 0449080   DLC N NN

Loftie, William John, 1839-1911.
... Authorised guide to the Tower of London.   By W. J.
Loftie ...   Rev. ed.   With twelve views and two plans, and
a description of the armoury, by the Viscount Dillon ...
London, Printed for H. M. Stationery off., by Darling &
son, ltd., 1910.
37, ₍1₎ p. illus. (plans) XII pl. on 6 l. 19ᶜᵐ.
Plates printed on both sides.

1. London. Tower.   I. Dillon, Harold Arthur Lee-Dillon, 17th viscount, 1844-
                                                  11-11959
Library of Congress   DA687.T7L84

NL 0449081   DLC

Loftie, William John, 1839-1911.
... Authorised guide to the Tower of London. By the
late Rev. W. J. Loftie ... Rev. ed. With twelve views
and two plans, and a description of the armoury, by the
Viscount Dillon ... London, Printed for H. M. Stationery
off., by Darling & son, ltd., 1912.
39, ₍1₎ p. incl. plans. XII pl. on 6 l. 19½ᶜᵐ.

1. London. Tower.   I. Dillon, Harold Arthur Lee-Dillon, 17th viscount, 1844-
                                                  12-30742
Library of Congress   DA687.T7L7 1912

NL 0449082   DLC

Loftie, William John, 1839-1911.
... Authorised guide to the tower of London.   By the late
Rev. W. J. Loftie ...   Rev. ed.   With twelve views
and two plans, and a description of the armoury, by the
Viscount Dillon ...   London, Printed for H. M. Stationery off., by Darling & son, ltd., 1913.
39, ₍1₎ p. incl. plans. XII pl. on 6 l. 19½ᶜᵐ.

1. London. Tower.   I. Dillon, Harold Arthur Lee-Dillon, 17th viscount, 1844-
                                                  13-23950
Library of Congress   DA687.T7L7 1913

NL 0449083   DLC CaBViP OrU CtY

Loftie, William John, 1839-1911.
... Authorised guide to the Tower of London.   By the late
Rev. W. J. Loftie ...   Rev. ed.   With twelve views and two
plans, and a description of the armoury, by the Viscount Dillon ...   Rev. by Charles Ffoulkes ...   London, H. M. Stationery office, Darling & son, ltd. ₍printers₎ 1914.
40 p. incl. plans. XII pl. on 6 l. 19ᶜᵐ.

1. London. Tower.   I. Dillon, Harold Arthur Lee-Dillon, 17th viscount, 1844-1932, ed.   II. Ffoulkes, Charles John, 1868-   ed.   III. Title.
                                                  39-15340
Library of Congress   DA687.T7L7 1914
                             ₍2₎   914.212

NL 0449084   DLC

Loftie, William John, 1839-1911.
... Authorised guide to the Tower of London.   By the
late Rev. W. J. Loftie ...   Rev. ed., with twelve views and
two plans, and a description of the armoury, by the Viscount Dillon ...   Rev. by Charles Ffoulkes ...   London,
H. M. Stationery off., Darling & son, ltd. ₍printers₎ 1916.
32 p. incl. plans. XII pl. on 6 l. 20½ᶜᵐ.

1. London. Tower.   I. Dillon, Harold Arthur Lee-Dillon, 17th viscount, 1844-   ed.   II. Ffoulkes, Charles John, 1868-   ed.   III. Title.
                                                  18-23922
Library of Congress   DA687.T7L7 1916

NL 0449085   DLC

LOFTIE, William John, 1839-
Authorised guide to the tower of London.
Revised ed. With views and plans and a descrip-
tion of the armoury, by the Viscount Dillon.
Revised by Charles Ffoulkes. London, Darling &
Son, 1919.

18 cm. pp. 32. 12 plates and plans.
At head of title: Under revision.
Plates printed on both sides.

NL 0449086   MH WaT

Loftie, William John, 1839-1911.
Authorised guide to the Tower of London. Rev.
ed. With a description of the armoury by the
Viscount Dillon. Revised by Charles Ffoulkes.
London, H. M's S.O., 1920.

NL 0449087   MH

VOLUME 338

DA687
T7L7
1921
Loftie, William John, 1839-1911.
Authorised guide to the Tower of London,
by W.J. Loftie. Rev. ed. by the Viscount
Dillon. Rev. by Charles Ffoulkes. London,
Printed by Barclay & Fry and sold at the
Tower, 1921.
32 p. plans, plates. 19cm.

1. London. Tower. I. Dillon, Harold
Arthur Lee-Dillon, 17th viscount, 1844-
ed. II. Ffoulkes, Charles John, 1868-
ed. III. Title.

NL 0449088   CoU

Q 41
[Loftie, William John, 1839-1911]
Authorised guide to the Tower of London.
London, Printed by Barclay & Fry, 1924.

32 p. illus.

NL 0449089   MH NBuG KU

[Loftie, William John] 1839-1911.
... Authorised guide to the Tower of London.
London, Sold at the Tower, 1927.
32 p. illus. (incl. plan.) 18 cm.

NL 0449090   CtY

[Loftie, William John] 1839-1911.
... Authorised guide to the Tower of London. London,
Sold at the Tower, 1929.
32 p. illus., fold. plan. 18ᶜᵐ.

1. London. Tower. I. Title.

Library of Congress   DA687.T7L7 1929   31-5085
                             [2]   914.212

NL 0449091   DLC

[Loftie, William John] 1839-1911.
... Authorised guide to the Tower of London ... London
[H. M. Stationery off.], Eyre and Spottiswoode, limited, print-
ers, 1932.
iv, 32, v-viii p. illus., fold. plan. 19ᶜᵐ.
At head of title: Under revision.
Contains advertising matter.

1. London. Tower. I. Title.

Library of Congress   DA687.T7L7 1932   33-17612
                             [2]   914.212

NL 0449092   DLC

[Loftie, William John] 1839-1911.
Authorised guide to the Tower of London ...
London, H. M. Stationery office, 1937.
iv, 31, [1] p. illus., fold. plan. 20 cm.
On cover: Revised 1937.
Contains advertising matter.

NL 0449093   CU

DA687.W5
L8
Loftie, William John, 1839-1911.
A brief account of Westminster Abbey
abridged from the larger work. With
illustrations by Herbert Railton. London,
Seele and co., limited, 1894.

3p.ℓ.,150p. illus. 20cm.

1. Westminster Abbey.

NL 0449094   NBuG RPD

[Loftie, William John] 1839-1911.
Catalogue of the prints and etchings of Hans Sebald
Beham, painter, of Nuremberg, citizen of Frankfort,
1500-1550. London, Mrs. Noseda, 1877.
xii, 91, [1] p. illus. 15 x 13ᶜᵐ.
"The impression is limited to one hundred copies, of which this is no.
46."
Biographical introduction signed: W. J. Loftie.

1. Beham, Hans Sebald, 1500-1550. 2. Engravings—Catalogs.
                                                      14-8365
Library of Congress   NE654.B4L6

NL 0449095   DLC CSmH PP

Loftie, William John, 1839-1911.
The cathedral churches of England and Wales, their history,
architecture and monuments. By W. J. Loftie ... London,
E. Stanford, 1892.
viii, 263, [1] p. 29 plans (part fold.) 17ᶜᵐ.

1. Cathedrals—England. 2. Cathedrals—Wales.
                                                      11—7123
Library of Congress   NA5461.L6

NL 0449096   DLC CaBViP OrP FMU CU MB MH NN

Loftie, William John, 1839-1911.
A century of Bibles; or, The authorised version from
1611 to 1711; to which is added William Kilburne's tract
on Dangerous errors in the late printed Bibles, 1659;
with lists of Bibles in the British museum, Bodleian,
Stuttgart and other libraries; comp. by the Reverend
W. J. Loftie ... London, B. M. Pickering, 1872.
vi, [2], 249, [2] p. illus. 21½ᶜᵐ.
Title vignette.

1. Bible—Bibl.   I. Kilburne, William. Dangerous errors in several
late printed Bibles. II. Title.
                                                      1-144'2
Library of Congress   Z7771.E5L8

NL 0449097   DLC NIC CU-A MeB CtY MBrZ ICU NN MB

Loftie, William John, 1839-1911.
The colour of London, historic, personal, & local, by W. J.
Loftie, F. S. A. Illustrated by Yoshio Markino. With an intro-
duction by M. H. Spielmann, F. S. A. and an essay by the artist.
London, Chatto & Windus, 1907.
xii, 236 p. 60 pl. (48 col., incl. front.) 24ᶜᵐ.

1. London—Descr.   I. Markino, Yoshio, 1874-   illus. II. Spielmann, Marion Harry, 1858-   III. Title.
                                                      8—4480
Library of Congress   DA684.L7

NL 0449098   DLC ICN AAP MoU OKentU GU IU PPL

Loftie, William John, 1839-1911.
The colour of London, historic, personal & local. Illustrated by Yoshio Markino. With an introd. by M. H. Spielmann and an essay by the artist. Philadelphia, G. W.
Jacobs [1907]
xiii, 236 p. illus. (part col.) 24 cm.

1. London—Descr.   I. Title.

DA684.L7 1907   58—53801

NL 0449099   DLC OC1 CLSU CaBVaU IdU ViU MB

Loftie, W[illiam] J[ohn] 1839-1911.
The colour of London: historic, personal,
& local. Illustrated by Yoshio Markino.
With an introduction by M.H. Spielmann, and
an essay by the artist. Philadelphia, G. W.
Jacobs & Co. [1908]
xlii, 236 p. 60 pl. 8°.

NL 0449100   NN

Loftie, William John, 1839-1911.
The colour of London, historic, personal, & local, by W. J.
Loftie, F. S. A. Illustrated by Yoshio Markino. With an intro-
duction by M. H. Spielmann, F. S. A. and an essay by the artist.
Toronto, Musson Book Co., 1910.
xii, 236 p. 60 pl. (48 col., incl. front.) 24ᶜᵐ.

NL 0449101   CaOTU

Loftie, W[illiam] J[ohn] 1839-1911.   914.21
The colour of London; historic; personal & local, illustrated
by Yoshio Markino, with an introduction by M. H. Spielmann and
an essay by the artist. Philadelphia: George W. Jacobs & Co.
[1911]   xlii, 236 p., 60 col'd pl. 8°.

1. London. 2. Markino, Yoshio,   CENTRAL CIRCULATION.
N. Y. P. L.   illus. 3. Title.
                                     June 28, 1911.

NL 0449102   NN

LOFTIE, William John, 1839-1911.
The colour of London; historic, personal &
local. Illustrated by Yoshio Markino. With an
introduction by M.H.Spielmann, and an essay by
the artist. London, Chatto & Windus, 1914.

24 cm. Colored plates.

NL 0449103   MH TU PP OLak NcD NNC

Loftie, W[illiam] J[ohn] 1839-
The coronation book of Edward VII., king of all the
Britains and emperor of India. By W. J. Loftie ... London, Paris, New York & Melbourne, Cassell & company,
ltd. [1902]
1 p. l., iv, [3]-188 p. illus. (partly in gold and colors) 24 col. pl. (incl.
front., port.) 29ᶜᵐ.
Title in red, gold and black within gold ornamental border.

Subject entries: Coronations—Gt. Brit.
                                                      3-22?1
Library of Congress, no.   DA112.L8.

NL 0449104   DLC TxU PPL OC1 MB

Loftie, William John, 1839-1911, comp.
English lake scenery from original drawings by T. L.
Rowbotham ... with archæological, historical, poetical, and
descriptive notes compiled by the Rev. W. J. Loftie ...
New York, Scribner, Welford, & Armstrong; London, M.
Ward & co., 1875.
114 p. incl. col. front., illus., 5 col. pl. 23 cm.

1. Lake district, Eng.

DA670.L1L8   3—3490

NL 0449105   DLC NN

Loftie, William John, 1839-
An essay of scarabs, by W. J. Loftie ... together with
the catalogue of a private collection of ancient Egyptian
amulets of various kinds bearing the names of kings.
London, Field & Tuer [etc.]; New York, Scribner & Wal-
ford [1884]
xxxii, 62 p. illus. 19½ᶜᵐ.
"Only one hundred and twenty-five copies printed, of which this is no.
50."

1. Scarabs.
                                                      10-30232
Library of Congress   NK5561.L6

NL 0449106   DLC NIC OC1 ViU NN

VOLUME 338

Wordsworth
DA
670
L1
L829

Loftie, William John, 1839-1911.
Gems of home scenery. Views in the English Lake District, from original drawings by T. L. Rowbotham ... With descriptive notes. 2d ed. London, M. Ward, 1875
114 p. illus. 23cm.

Healey 2053.
Lacks front.

1. Lake District, Eng.--Description and travel--Views. I. Title.

NL 0449107   NIC

Loftie, William John, 1839-1911.
A history of London. By W. J. Loftie ... with maps and illustrations ... London, E. Stanford, 1883.
2 v. fold. fronts., plates (partly fold.) maps (partly fold.) plans (partly fold.) 21ᶜᵐ.

1. London--Hist.

3-7115

Library of Congress   DA677.L82

     PU MiU OC1W ViU
NL 0449108   DLC CaBViP MtU OrU OrP CtY PU-F PPL NjP

Loftie, William John, 1839-1911.
A history of London. By W. J. Loftie... Second edition, revised and enlarged. London: E. Stanford, 1884. 2 v. front., maps, plans, pl. 21cm.

Appendices contain lists of mayors and sheriffs of London from 1189 to 1883, the members of Parliament for the city of London, 1284-1880, members for Westminster City, Southwark, and Middlesex, parishes in London, etc.

Astor 11712-13. 1. London--Hist.   2. London--Registers. 3. Representation--Gt. Br.--Eng.--London.   Revised
N.Y.P.L.   March 29, 1937

     PU MdBP MH
NL 0449109   NN PU OC1 ICJ OrU MdBP CaBVaU CtY PP

[Loftie, William John] 1839-1911, ed.
Illustrated guide of the Orient line of steamers between England and Australia. Issued on behalf of the Orient steam navigation company ... and the Pacific steam navigation company, by the managers of the line, F. Green & co.,--Anderson, Anderson & co. ... London, Maclure & Macdonald [1883]

7 p. l., 120 p. plates (part col.) maps, charts, plans. 28¼ x 38ᶜᵐ.

Preface signed: W. J. Loftie.
Cover-title: Orient line guide. Chapters for travellers by sea & by land.
1. Voyages and travels--Guide-books. 2. Ocean travel. I. Title.

Library of Congress   G153.L73

2--20555

NL 0449110   DLC

Loftie, W[illiam] J[ohn] 1839-1911.
In and out of London: or, The half-holidays of a town clerk. By W. J. Loftie ... London, Society for promoting Christian knowledge; New York, Pott, Young, & co. [1875]

251, [1] p. front., illus., pl., port. 18ᶜᵐ.

"Published under the direction of the Committee of general literature and education, appointed by the Society for promoting Christian knowledge."
Originally published, in part, in the Guardian, Long ago, etc.
CONTENTS.--London geography.--London four centuries ago.--London a century ago.--Pepys and St. Olave's.--Great St. Helen's.--Dr. Fuller and the Savoy.--Northumberland house.--Holland house and Lady Sarah.--Fulham.--Knole.--Ingatestone.--Berkhamsted.--On the Surrey hills.--St. Albans.

Subject entries: London   --Antiq.

2--22082

Library of Congress, no.   DA677.L83.

NL 0449111   DLC AAP

Loftie, William John, *1839-1911.*
In and out of London: or, the half holidays of a town clerk. By W. J. Loftie. 4th thousand, revised and corrected.
= London. Society for Promoting Christian Knowledge. [1879?] 251, (1) pp. Illus. Portrait. Plates. Coats of arms. 17 cm., in 8s.

2499.193

D439 — T.r. — London. Hist. — London. Descr.

NL 0449112   MB

Loftie, William John, 1839-1911.
Inigo Jones and Wren; or, The rise and decline of modern architecture in England. xvi,284 p. il. 45 pl. paged in. sq.Q. London: Rivington. Percival & Co., 1893.

L724.142 L82

NL 0449113   ICJ CtY CaBViP MH MB ICN PBa ViU PPAN

Loftie, William John, 1839-
Inigo Jones and Wren; or, The rise and decline of modern architecture in England, by W. J. Loftie. New York, Macmillan and co., 1893.
xvi, 284 p. incl. front., 49 pl. 26ᶜᵐ.

1. Jones, Inigo, 1573-1652. 2. Wren, Sir Christopher, 1632-1723. 3. Architecture--England--Hist.

11-8045

Library of Congress   NA997.J7L8

     MiU PP PU PPL PPD CtY NjP CCSC IaU N
NL 0449114   DLC WaS CaBVa FU N NBuU NN OC1W ViU OC1

Loftie, William John, 1839-1911.
The Inns of court and chancery, by W. J. Loftie ... With many illustrations by Herbert Railton. London, Seeley and co., limited, 1893.
viii, 88 p., 1 l. front., illus., pl. 35¼ᶜᵐ.

1. Inns of court. 2. Inns of chancery.

Library of Congress   DA687.I 5L8

3-12115

NL 0449115   DLC WaU-L CSt-L GU MdBP PPL ViU OC1 MH

Loftie, William John, 1839-1911.
The Inns of court and chancery. With many illustrations by Herbert Railton. New York, Macmillan, 1893.
viii, 88 p. illus., plates. 35cm.

1. Inns of court. 2. Inns of chancery.

NL 0449116   ViU NN WaSp

Loftie, William John, 1839-1911.
The Inns of court and chancery, by W. J. Loftie ... With many illustrations by Herbert Railton. New ed. London, Seeley and co. limited; New York, Macmillan & co., 1895.
xi, 302 p. incl. front., illus., plates. 19¼ᶜᵐ.

1. Inns of court, London. 2. Inns of chancery, London.

35-81824

     OKentU PPFr MiU OC1 MH
NL 0449117   DLC CaBVaU GU-L OrP ICU NjP PSt NcD PU-L

DA687
.I 5L8
1908

Loftie, William John, 1839-1911.
The Inns of court and chancery. With many illus. by Herbert Railton. New ed. London, Seeley, 1908.
xi, 302 p. illus. 18cm.

1. Inns of court, London. 2. Inns of chancery, London.

NL 0449118   MB

GROSVENOR
LIBRARY
DA685
K4L6

Loftie, William John, 1839-
Kensington, picturesque & historical, by W. J. Loftie. With upwards of three hundred illustrations (some in colours) by William Luker, jun. from drawings taken on the spot. Engraved by Chs. Guillaume et cie, Paris. London, Field and Tuer [etc.] New York, Scribner & Welford, 1888.

xix, 287p. col. front., illus., col. plates, maps, double plan. 26½cm.

NL 0449119   InU NBuG

Loftie, William John, 1839-1911.
Kensington, picturesque & historical, by W. J. Loftie ... With upwards of three hundred illustrations (some in colours) by William Luker, jun. From drawings taken on the spot. Engraved by Chs. Guillaume et cie, Paris. London, Field and Tuer, Simpkin, Marshall & co. [etc.]; New York, Scribner & Welford, 1888.
xix, 287, lxiv p. incl. illus., geneal. tables. col. front., col. plates, maps. 26ᶜᵐ.

1. Kensington, Eng.--Descr. 2. Kensington, Eng.--Hist.

     MH CtY CSmH OC1 PPT MdBP NBu
NL 0449120   ViU CLSU IU MiU PPFr PP PHC MdBP ICU

Loftie, William John, 1839-1911.
Kensington palace, by W. J. Loftie ... London, Farmer & sons, 1898.
71 p. incl. front., illus., plates. 21.5 x 16.5 cm.

NL 0449121   CtY

Loftie, William John, *1839-1911.*
Kensington Palace and Gardens. By W. J. Loftie.
= London. Farmer. 1900. 80 pp. Illus. Portrait. Plates. 21 cm., in 8s.

2496.33

D300 — Kensington Palace, London.

NL 0449122   MB CSmH

[Loftie, William John] 1839-1911.
The Latin year; a collection of hymns for the seasons of the church selected from mediaeval and modern authors. London, n.d.
4 v. illus. 27 cm.
Preface signed: W.J. Loftie, Robert Bateman.

NL 0449123   RPB

VS36
L327l

Loftie, William John, 1839-1911, comp.
The Latin year; with illustrations by Robert Bateman. London, B.M. Pickering, 1873.
343 p. illus. 20 cm.

"A collection of hymns for the seasons of the church selected from mediaeval and modern authors."
Contents.- pt. 1. Lent and Easter.- pt. 2. Ascension and Whitsuntide.- pt. 3. Trinity.- pt. 4. Advent and Christmas.

     NNUT ICN
NL 0449124   CtY-D CLU NjP CSmH CU NN MB NRCR MiU

VOLUME 338

Loftie, William John, 1839–1911, comp.
The Latin year; compiled by ... W. J. Loftie.
With illustrations by Robert Bateman.   London,
Marcus Ward & co. ... [etc., etc.] 1877.
4 p.l., 343, [1] p.   illus.   26 cm.

NL 0449125   NNUT

Loftie, William John, 1839–1911.
Lessons in the art of illuminating; a series of
examples selected from works in the British
museum, Lambeth palace library and the South
Kensington museum, with practical instructions
and a sketch of the history of the art.   London,
Blackie, n.d.
illus.

NL 0449126   RPD

Wing
ZB
26
.518   LOFTIE, WILLIAM JOHN, 1839–1911.
Lessons in the art of illuminating; a series
of examples selected from works in the British
Museum, Lambeth Palace Library, and the South
Kensington Museum. With practical instructions,
and a sketch of the history of the art.   London, Blackie & Son [1880]
xviii, 34p. illus.(part col.) 26cm. (Vere
Foster's water-color series)

NL 0449127   ICN

Spec.
ND 3310 Loftie, William John, 1839–1911.
L 6   Lessons in the art of illuminating; a
series of examples selected from works in the
British Museum, Lambeth Palace library, and
the South Kensington Museum. With practical
instructions, and a sketch of the history of
the art.   London, Blackie [1885]
xviii, 34 p. illus., col. facsims. (incl.
front.) 26 cm. (Vere Foster's Water-colour
series)
Mendle collection.

NL 0449128   MoSW ODW IU LU CtY

AC-L
W357L   Loftie, William John, 1839–1911.
L828l   ... Lessons in the art of illuminating; a
series of examples selected from works in the
British Museum, Lambeth Palace Library, and the
South Kensington Museum. With practical instructions, and a sketch of the history of the
art, by W.J. Loftie ...   London, Glasgow [etc.]
Blackie & son, limited [1895]
xviii, 34p. incl. illus., plates (col., facsim.
mounted) 26cm. (Vere Foster's water-colour
series)

Illustrated t.-p.; initials; tail-pieces.
Publisher's advertisements ([4]p.) bound in
at end.
With autograph of P.A. Robson.
Bookplate of Evelyn Waugh.

1. Title. II. Series. A.F.: Robson,
P   A

NL 0449130   TxU CU

Loftie, William John, 1839–1911.
Lang, Andrew, 1844–1912.   **FOR OTHER EDITIONS
SEE MAIN ENTRY**
The library. By Andrew Lang. With a chapter on modern
English illustrated books, by Austin Dobson. London, Mac-
millan & co., 1881.

Case
0   [LOFTIE, WILLIAM JOHN] 1839–1911.
2   List of a collection of Bibles, chiefly of
.52 the authorized version.   [London, Wyman & sons]
1872.
31p.

Inserted: ms. letter of W.J. Loftie.
Title vignette contains the initials, W.I.L.
"50 copies printed; 25 destroyed [signed]
W.J.L."—pencilled note on half-title.

NL 0449132   ICN

LOFTIE, W[illiam] J[ohn], 1839–1911.
London.   London, Longmans, Green, and co., 1887

Plans.
At head of title:- Historic towns.

NL 0449133   MH NjP MdBP MH CtY PPFr I OC1 MtU ViU

Loftie, William John, 1839–1911.
... London, by W. J. Loftie ... 2d ed. London and
New York, Longmans, Green, and co., 1889.
viii, 223 p. 3 plans (incl. fold. front.) 19ᶜᵐ. (Historic towns)

1. London—Hist.   I. Title.
17–11493
Library of Congress   DA678.L82 1889

NL 0449134   DLC OKentU FU OrP PPA PPL PPD NN ICJ

Loftie, William John, 1839–1911.
... London, by W. J. Loftie ... 3d impression. London
and New York, Longmans, Green, and co., 1892.
x, 223 p. 3 plans (incl. fold. front.) 19ᵐ. (Half-title: Historic
towns)
Series title also at head of t.-p.

1. London—Hist.   I. Title.
1–4147
Library of Congress   DA678.L82

NL 0449135   DLC OKentU PPPM OU OCU

Loftie, William John, 1839–1911.
London.   1906.

NL 0449136   OrPR

Loftie, William John, 1839–1911.
London afternoons; chapters on the social life, architecture, and records of the great city and its neighbourhood, by W. J. Loftie ... London, New York [etc.] Cassell
and company, limited, 1901.
xii, 292 p. front., pl. 21ᶜᵐ.

1. London—Hist. 2. London—Soc. life & cust.   I. Title.
2–12219
Library of Congress   DA678.L80

NL 0449137   DLC WaS CLSU WaU IaU PPA PPL

DA678
L80   Loftie, William John, 1839–1911
London afternoons; chapters on the social
life, architecture, and records of the great
city and its neighbourhood, by W. J. Loftie.
London, Cassell, New York, Brentanos, 1902.
xii, 292 p. illus. 22 cm.

1. London - History. 2. London - Soc. life
and cust. I. Title.

NL 0449138   MeB TxU NN

Loftie, William John, 1839–1911.
London city; its history—streets—traffic—buildings—
people, by W. J. Loftie ... illustrated by W. Luker, jr.,
from original drawings. London, The Leadenhall press
[etc.]; New York, Scribner & Welford, 1891.
xvi, 377 p. incl. front., illus., pl. 29ᶜᵐ.
"List of subscribers": p. [295]–377.

1. London.

Library of Congress   DA678.L81
3—11949

MdBP NcD OC1 WaU OC1W CSmH MB
NL 0449139   DLC WaS ICN CaBVaU WaSpG AAP TxU MU Vi

Loftie, William John, 1839–
Memorials of the Savoy; the palace: the hospital: the
chapel. By the Rev. William John Loftie ... With an
appendix of original documents contributed by Charles
Trice Martin ... and a preface by the Rev. Henry White
... London, Macmillan and co., 1878.
ix, 267 p. front., plan. 18½ᶜᵐ.

Subject entries: London. The Savoy.

Library of Congress, no.   DA687.S2L8.
3–11637

NL 0449140   DLC CtY MdBP FMU OC1 NN MH

Loftie, William John, 1839–
Notes on the worship of Chonsu.
[London, 1882]
[399]–401 p.

Caption title.

NL 0449141   OC1

Loftie, W[illiam] J[ohn], 1839–1911, editor.
Orient line guide, chapters for travellers by sea and by land, illustrated. 3d ed. re-written. Edited for the managers of the line by
W. J. Loftie. London, Sampson Low, Marston, Searle, & Rivington, etc. 1888.
sm. 4°. pp. vii, (1), [viii]–xxxvii, (2), 439. Maps and plates.
pp. 361–439, advertising matter. Half title within illustrative border by
Kate Greenaway.

NL 0449142   MH NN MiD

Loftie, W[illiam] J[ohn], 1839–1911.
Orient line guide ... 3d ed. ...
Lond. Sampson, 1889.
360p. plates, maps, diagrs. sq.O.

NL 0449143   CaBViP

Loftie, William John, 1839–1911, ed.
Orient line guide, chapters for travellers by sea and by land,
illustrated. The 4th ed., rev., with maps and plans. Ed. for
the managers of the line by W. J. Loftie ... London, S. Low,
Marston, Searle, & Rivington, limited [etc.] 1890.
xliii, 439 p. illus., plates (part col.) maps, plans, charts. 21 x 17½ᵐ.
Advertising matter: p. i–ix, 361–439.
Added t.-p., illustrated by Kate Greenaway.
Managers: F. Green & co., and Anderson, Anderson, & co.
"List of standard books on Australia, Egypt, and Italy": p. [xxx]–
xxxii.
1. Voyages and travels—Guide-books. 2. Ocean travel.   I. Title.
4–2698
Library of Congress   G153.L74

NL 0449144   DLC ViU MH MB

Loftie, William John, 1839–1911, editor.
...Orient line guide; chapters for travellers by sea and by
land. Edited for the managers of the line, by W. J. Loftie...
London: S. Low, Marston & Co., Ltd. [1901] xix–xlviii, 407 p.
incl. tables. charts, illus., maps, plates (part col'd). 21½cm.

At head of title: Sixth edition.
Advertising matter, p. v–xvi, 319–407.
"List of books," p. xxxv–xxxvi.

705237A. 1. Voyages and travels,   1900– . 2. Australia—Descr. and
trav., 1900– . I. Orient Steam   Navigation Company, Ltd.
N. Y. P. L.   September 19, 1934

NL 0449145   NN

VOLUME 338

G153
L64
1901
Loftie, William John, 1839-1911, ed.
Orient-Pacific line guide. Chapters for
travellers by sea and by land. Ed. for the
managers of the line. 6th ed. London,
S. Low, Marston [1901]
xlviii,407 p. illus.,plates(part col.)
maps(part col.) charts,plans,tables.

Advertising matter interspersed.
Earlier eds. have title: Orient line guide.
"List of books": p.xxxv-xxxvi.

NL 0449146   CU NIC

LOFTIE, WILLIAM JOHN, 1839-1911.
Picturesque Scottish scenery from original drawings by
T.L.Rowbotham...with archaeological, historical, poetical,
and descriptive notes, compiled by the Rev. W.J.Loftie...
London: M.Ward & Co.[, etc.], 1875. 114 p. incl. mounted
col'd. front., mounted col'd pl. 23cm.

720341A. 1. Scotland—Descr. and trav., 1800-1900. 2. Scotland—Views. I. Rowbotham, Thomas Charles Leeson, 1823-
1875.

NL 0449147   NN ArLsJ IU

Loftie, William John, 1839-1911.
A plea for art in the house, with special reference to
the economy of collecting works of art, and the importance of taste in education and morals. By W. J. Loftie
... Philadelphia, Porter & Coates [1876]
x p., 1 l., 100 p. incl. front., illus. 2 pl. 19½ᶜᵐ. (Lettered on cover:
Art at home series. (v. 1))

1. House decoration. 2. Furniture. 3. Collectors and collecting.
I. Title.

Library of Congress   NK2115.L8 1876
                                            15—7647

OCl MB
NL 0449148   DLC DSI T ViU MnHi MH PSt MiGr PLF OO

Loftie, William John, 1839-1911.
Plea for Art in the House, with special ref. to
the economy of collecting works of art, and the
importance of taste ...   Philadelphia [1877]
19.5 cm.

NL 0449149   CtY MB MH

Loftie, William John, 1839-
A plea for art in the house, with special reference to
the economy of collecting works of art, and the importance of taste in education and morals. By W. J. Loftie
... 2d ed. London, Macmillan and co., 1877.
x p., 1 l., 100 p. incl. front., illus. 18½ᶜᵐ. (On cover: Art at home series.
(v. 1))
Title vignette.

1. House decoration. 2. Furniture.   I. Title.

Library of Congress   NK2115.L8
                                            12—3941

NL 0449150   DLC MWA

Loftie, William John, 1839-1911.
A plea for art in the house, with special reference to
the economy of collecting works of art, and the importance of taste in education and morals. By W. J. Loftie
... 3d ed. London, Macmillan and co., 1877.
x p., 1 l., 100 p. incl. front. illus. 18 cm. (Art at home
series)
On spine: Art at home, vol. 1.
Title vignette.
Bound with: Hullah, John. Music in the
house. [3d ed.] London, 1877.
Bookplate of Evelyn Waugh.

NL 0449151   TxU

LOFTIE, W[illiam] J[ohn] 1839-1911.
A plea for art in the house, with special reference to the economy of collecting works of
art, etc. 4th ed. London, Macmillan and Co.,
1878.

Front.and illustr.
On cover:-Art at home [Series].   FA 1063.8.4

NL 0449152   MH NN

Loftie, William John, 1839-
Lang, Andrew, 1844-1912, ed.
Poets' country, ed. by Andrew Lang. Contributors: Prof.
J. Churton Collins, E. Hartley Coleridge, W. J. Loftie, f. s. a.,
Michael Macmillan, Andrew Lang. With fifty illustrations
in colour by Francis S. Walker. London and Edinburgh,
T. C. & E. C. Jack, 1907.

Loftie, William John, 1839-1911, ed.
[Lewis, Jenkin]
Queen Anne's son. The memoirs of William Henry,
duke of Gloucester, reprinted from a tract published in
1789, and edited, with notes, by W. J. Loftie ... London, E. Stanford, 1881.

914.21
L829R
Loftie, William John, 1839-1911.
Rambles in and near London; or, London
afternoons. London, New York, Cassell, 1903.
xii, 292 p. illus. 22 cm.
Originally published 1901 under title:
London afternoons.

1. London. Hist. 2. London. Soc. life &
cust. I. Title. II. Title: London afternoons.

NL 0449155   NcD MB OCl OO MB NIC N MoU

DA678
L84
Loftie, William John, 1839-1911
Rambles in and near London; or, London
afternoons, by W. J. Loftie. London,
Cassell; New York, Brentano's, 1903.
xii, 292 p. illus. 22 cm.

Originally published under the title,
London afternoons.

1. London - Hist. 2. London - Soc. life
& cust. I. Title. II. Title: London
afternoons.

NL 0449156   MeB

Loftie, William John, 1839-1911.
...Reynolds and children's portraiture
in England... Practical hints for figure
painting in water colours, by E.J.Floris.
London, Blackie, n.d.
84p.

NL 0449157   MeWC

Loftie, W[illiam] J[ohn], 1839-1911.   Afr 3978.79.5
A ride in Egypt from Sioot to Luxor in 1879: with notes on the
present state and ancient history of the Nile valley. London, Macmillan and Co. 1879.
pp. xix, 399 +. Front and other illus.

Egypt-Descr. 1840-1889.

NL 0449158   MH PPiU NN PU PSC OClW PPL NcD

Loftie, William John, 1839-1911.
A ride in Egypt, from Sioot to Luxor in 1879: with
notes on the present state and ancient history of the
Nile Valley, and some account of the various ways of
making the voyage out and home. By W. J. Loftie ...
London and New York, Macmillan and co., 1886.
xix, 399, [1] p. incl. front., illus. 19ᶜᵐ.

1. Egypt—Descr. & trav. 2. Nile Valley—Hist.   I. Title.
                                                            24—5015
Library of Congress   DT54.L8

NL 0449159   DLC NSyU NBB

DA679
L8
[Loftie, William John] 1839-1911.
Round about London; historical, archaeological, architectural
and picturesque notes suitable for the tourist within a circle of
twelve miles; to which is added specimens of short walking
excursions'... by a fellow of the Society of Antiquaries.   London, E. Stanford, 1877.
148 p. fold. map.

1. London. Eng. (City) - Descr. - Guide-books. I. Title.

NL 0449160   CU

[Loftie, William John] 1839-1911.
ROUND about London. Historica,archaeological
architectural,and picturesque notes suitable
for the tourist,within a circle of twelve
miles. To which are added specimens of short
walking excursions and visits to Hatfield,Knole
St.Albans and Windsor. By a fellow of the
society of antiquaries. 2d ed. L.,1877.

Map.

NL 0449161   MH

Loftie, William John, 1839-1911. Br 3636.78
ROUND about London. Historical,archaeological
architectural,and picturesque notes suitable
for the tourist,within a circle of twelve miles.
To which are added specimens of short walking
excursions and visits to Hatfield,Knole,St.Aban
and Windsor. By a fellow of the Society of
Antiquaries. 3d ed. London,E.Stanford,1878.

17 cm. Map,(folded).

NL 0449162   MH

Loftie, William John, 1839-1911.
Round about London. Historical, archaeological, architectural,
and picturesque notes suitable for the tourist, within a circle of
twelve miles. To which are added specimens of short walking
excursions and visits to Hatfield, Knole, St. Albans, and Windsor.
By a fellow of the Society of antiquaries... 4. ed.   London, E.
Stanford, 1878. 148 p.   map. 17cm.

Cover-title: Tourists' guide round about London.

318615B. 1. London—Guidebooks,   1878. I. A fellow of the Society
of antiquaries. II. Title: Tourists'   guide round about London.
N. Y. P. L.   May 23, 1946

NL 0449163   NN

Loftie, William J[ohn], 1839-1911.   Br 4738.80.5
Round about London; historical, archæological, architectural,
and picturesque notes suitable for the tourist, within a circle of
twelve miles. 4th ed. London, E. Stanford, 1880.
pp. (4), 148. Map.
Cover: Tourists' guide round about London.

London-Environs.

NL 0449164   MH IEN CtY DN

VOLUME 338

Loftie, William John, 1839–1911.
Round about London. Historical, archæological, architectural, and picturesque notes suitable for the tourist, within a circle of twelve miles. To which are added specimens of short walking excursions and visits to Hatfield, Knole, St. Albans, and Windsor. By W. J. Loftie... With a map and copious index... London: E. Stanford, 1887.   148 p.   front. (plan.)   5. ed.   16°.

270554A.   1. England—Guidebooks,   1887. 2. Title.
N. Y. P. L.   April 13, 1927

NL 0449165   NN

Za877f

Loftie, William John, 1839–1911.
Round about London. Historical, archæological, architectural, and picturesque notes suitable for the tourist, within a circle of twelve miles. To which are added, Specimens of short walking excursions and visits to Hatfield, Knole, St.Albans, and Windsor ... With a map and copious index. 6th ed., revised and partly re-written.   London,E.Stanford,1893.
3p.ℓ.,153p. front.(fold.map) 16½cm.
Half-title: Tourist's guide round about London.

NL 0449166   CtY MB CU

Loftie, William John, 1839–1911.
Tourist's guide through London, Lond., 1881.
16782

NL 0449167   DN-Ob NjP

LOFTIE, WILLIAM JOHN, 1839–1911.
Views in North Wales, from original drawings by T.L.Rowbotham...with archaeological, historical, poetical, and descriptive notes, compiled by the Rev. W.J.Loftie...   London, Marcus Ward & co.; Belfast, Royal Ulster works, 1875.
116 p.incl.front.,illus.,5 col.pl. 23cm.

754839A. 1. Wales—Descr. and trav., 1800–!900.

NL 0449168   NN MB

---

*A085
M4977
Zz875ℓ3

... Views in North Wales from original drawings by T. L. Rowbotham ... With descriptive notes compiled by the Rev. W. J. Loftie ... Second edition.
London:Marcus Ward & co.,67 & 68, Chandos street,Covent Garden and Royal Ulster works, Belfast,1875.
116p.incl.mounted col.front.,illus.,5 mounted col.pl. 23cm. (Gems of home scenery).
Publisher's device on t.-p.
From the family   library of Herman Melville.

NL 0449169   MH

Loftie, William John, 1839–1911.
Views in North Wales, from original drawings by T. L. Rowbotham ... with archæological, historical, poetical, and descriptive notes, compiled by the Rev. W. J. Loftie ... New York, Scribner, Welford, & Armstrong; London, M. Ward & co., 1875.
116 p. incl. col. front., illus., 5 col. pl. 23ᶜᵐ.

1. Wales, North—Descr. & trav. I. Rowbotham, Thomas Charles Leeson, 1823–1875, illus.

Library of Congress   DA730.L82
                                          3—16728

NL 0449170   DLC I OCU OC1W

Loftie, William John, 1839–1911.
Views in Wicklow and Killarney from original drawings by T. L. Rowbotham ... with archæological, historical, poetical, and descriptive notes, compiled by the Rev. W. J. Loftie ... New York, Scribner, Welford & Armstrong; London, M. Ward & co., 1875.
83 p.   illus. 6 col. pl. (incl. front.) 23ᶜᵐ.
Line borders; head and tail pieces.

1. Killarney, Lakes of. 2. Wicklow, Ire. (County)—Descr. & trav.
I. Rowbotham, Thomas Charles Leeson, 1823–1875, illus.

Library of Congress   DA990.K45L8   4—5489

NL 0449171   DLC

---

*DA687
.W5L8
Folio

Loftie, William John, 1839–1911.
Westminster abbey, by W. J. Loftie ... With many illustrations, chiefly by Herbert Railton. London, Seeley and co. limited, 1890.
viii, 104 p., 1 l. front., illus., plates. 35 1/2 x 26 1/2ᶜᵐ.

1. Westminster abbey.

NL 0449172   MB MWe1C WaSp MdBP NN OO MH

---

q942.1
L827w
1890

Loftie, William John, 1839–1911.
Westminster Abbey. With many illus., chiefly by Herbert Railton. London, Seeley; New York, Macmillan, 1890.
viii, 104p. illus.,plates. 36cm.

1. Westminster Abbey.

NL 0449173   TxU NcD PPT CaBVaU

DA687
W5L8

Loftie, William John, 1839–1911.
Westminster Abbey. With many illustrations, chiefly by Herbert Railton. New ed., rev. London, Seeley, 1891.
xii, 319 p. illus., pl. 22cm.

1. Westminster Abbey.

NL 0449174   CoU OrU

Loftie, William John, 1839–
Westminster abbey, by W. J. Loftie ... With many illustrations, chiefly by Herbert Railton. New ed., rev. London, Seeley and co., limited; New York, Macmillan & co., 1891.
xii, 319, ⟨1⟩ p. incl. front., illus., pl. 21½ᶜᵐ.

1. Westminster abbey.
                                          3–11529
Library of Congress   DA687.W5L8

ViU MiU OC1 NjR MH MB
NL 0449175   DLC OrU OKentU PP NjP TxU PPL PP PPD PU

DA687
.W5L8
1914

Loftie, William John, 1839–1911.
Westminster abbey, by W. J. Loftie. With many illustrations by Herbert Railton. New ed. London, Seeley New York, Macmillan 1914.
xii, 319 p. illus. 22 cm.

NL 0449176   OCU

Loftie, William John, 1839–1911.
Westminster abbey, by W. J. Loftie ... With many illustrations by Herbert Railton. New ed. Philadelphia, J. B. Lippincott company; London, Seeley, Service & co., ltd., 1914.
xii, 319 p. incl. illus., plates. col. front. 20¼ᶜᵐ.

1. Westminster abbey.

                                          A 13–2304
Title from A.L.A. Booklist.   Printed by L. C.

NL 0449177   NN MB OO OC1W WaS

Loftie, William John, 1839–1911.
Whitehall; historical and architectural notes, by W. J. Loftie ... London, Seeley and co.; New York, Macmillan and co., 1895.
80 p. incl. illus., double pl. front. (port.) plates. 27ᶜᵐ. (On cover: The Portfolio: monographs on artistic subjects ... no. 16)

1. Whitehall, London.
                                          40–87696
Library of Congress   DA687.W65L7

MiU OC1 OO ICU OrP WU MdBP
NL 0449178   DLC PP PPD PBm CtY NN MB CU PPAFA NcD

Loftie, W⟨illiam⟩ J⟨ohn⟩, 1839–1911.   Br 5245.112F
Windsor; a description of the castle, park, town and neighbourhood. London, Seeley & Co. 1886.
f°. pp. viii, 91. Plates, and other illus.

Windsor, Eng.‖AcS 18698c

NL 0449179   MH MdBP NN CSmH

G
45975
.5

LOFTIE, WILLIAM JOHN, 1839–1911.
...Windsor castle; with a description of the park, town, and neighbourhood...   London,Seeley & co.,1887.
297p.

At head of title: Jubilee edition.

NL 0449180   ICN CU MH OC1 CtY I1B OrP ViLxW

914.229
L829

Loftie, William John, 1839–1911.
Windsor Castle, with a description of the park, town and neighborhood. 3d ed., rev. London, Seeley, 1891.
xi, 297 p. illus. 19 cm.

1. Windsor Castle.

NL 0449181   N OrU

Loftie, William John, 1839–1911, ed.
Torkington, Sir Richard, fl. 1517.
... Ye oldest diarie of Englysshe travell: being the hitherto unpublished narrative of the pilgrimage of Sir Richard Torkington to Jerusalem in 1517. Edited by W. J. Loftie ... London, Field & Tuer ⟨etc., 1884⟩

VOLUME 338

Loftin, Fred Thurston, 1865–
The Indianapolis centennial guide book, showing location of places of interest, organizations, roster of officials, floor arrangement of public buildings, facts about Indianapolis, car lines, etc. ... Copyright ... by Fred T. Loftin. Indianapolis ₍Enquirer printing and publishing co.₎ 1920.
cover-title, 24 p. illus. (incl. plans) 21½ᶜᵐ.

1. Indianapolis—Descr.—Guide-books.

Library of Congress   F534.I 3L79
                                                        20–10626

NL 0449183   DLC

₍**Loftin, Fred Thurston**₎ 1865–   *comp.*
... Where's what and who's who in Indianapolis: guide to "The pivot city," showing at a glance location of places of interest, floor arrangements of public buildings, roster of officials, important industries, transportation, organizations, etc. ... ₍Indianapolis, U. S. Realty co.₎ 1913.
cover-title, 24 p. illus. (incl. plans) 21½ᶜᵐ. $0.10

1. Indianapolis—Descr.—Guide-books.   ɪ. Title.

Library of Congress   F534.I 3L8
                                                        13–21829

NL 0449184   DLC

Loftin, James Carr
The activity coefficients of lead chloride in aqueous solutions of mannitol: an investigation of the ion-size parameter.   Chapel Hill, 1937.   35p. illus. tables, diagrs. Q.

Thesis (Ph.D.) – University of North Carolina, 1937.
Carbon copy of typewritten manuscript.
Bibliography: p.35.

NL 0449185   NcU

₍**Loftin, James O.,** and **L. W. Fox.**₎
...Instrucción vocacional en la escuela secundaria inferior...
₍Wáshington, D. C.₎ La Unión panamericana, 1925. ii, 13 p. illus. 8°. (Pan American Union. Educación. no. 9.)
"Por J. O. Loftin...y L. W. Fox," p. 1.

1. Education, Industrial and technical   —U. S.—Tex.—San Antonio.
2. Fox, Louis William, jt. au. 3. Ser.
N.Y.F.L.   February 27, 1928

NL 0449186   NN

---

q707
L827a **Loftin, Joe D**
Art   Art in the elementary schools.   **Gladewater,**
Lib'y   Texas ₍n.d.₎
             111ℓ. 31cm.

Bibliography: ℓ.111.

1. Art – Study and teaching. I. Title.

NL 0449187   TxU

Loftin, Laurence K
The effects of variations in Reynolds number between 3.0 x 10⁶ and 25.0 x 10⁶ upon the aerodynamic characteristics of a number of NACA 6-series airfoil sections, by Laurence K. Loftin, Jr. and William J. Bursnall. Washington, U. S. Govt. Print. Off., 1950.
ii, 20 p. diagrs. 30 cm. ₍U. S.₎ National Advisory Committee for Aeronautics. Report 964)
Cover title.
"References": p. 19.
1. Aerofoils. 2. Reynolds number.   ɪ. Bursnall, William J., joint author.   (Series)
TL521.A33 no. 964   629.134323   50–61632
———— Copy 2.   TL574.A4L57

NL 0449188   DLC

Loftin, Laurence K
Theoretical and experimental data for a number of NACA 6A-series airfoil sections. Washington, U. S. Govt. Print. Off., 1948 ₍i. e. 1950₎
ii, 21 p. diagrs. 30 cm. ₍U. S.₎ National Advisory Committee for Aeronautics. Report no. 903)
Cover title.
"References": p. 21.

1. Aerofoils.   (Series)
TL521.A33 no. 903   629.134323   50–60211
———— Copy 2.   TL574.A4L575

NL 0449189   DLC

Loftin, Marion Theo.
The Japanese in Brazil; a study in immigration and acculturation. Ann Arbor, University Microfilms ₍1952₎
(₍University Microfilms, Ann Arbor, Mich.₎ Publication no. 3974)
Microfilm copy of typescript. Positive.
Collation of the original: 348 ℓ. plates, maps, tables.
Thesis–Vanderbilt University.
Abstracted in Dissertation abstracts, v. 12 (1952) no. 5, p. 759.
Bibliography: leaves 330–336.
1. Japanese in Brazil. 2. Emigration and immigration.
Microfilm AC–1 no. 3974   Mic A 54–1094

Joint University   Libraries, Nashville
for Library of Congress   ₍1₎†

NL 0449190   TNJ LNHT InU GU WU FU NN DLC

Loftin, Marion Theo.
The use of health services

see under

Mississippi. Agricultural Experiment Station, State College.

Law   **Loftin, Scott Marion,** 1878–

₍**Lee, Edward Thomas**₎ 1860?–1943.
A letter to our president ... Hon. Scott Marion Loftin, president, American bar association ... ₍Chicago? 1934₎

NL 0449193   DLC WaS

Loftin, Ulphian Carl, 1890–1946.
Living with the boll weevil for fifty years, by U. C. Loftin ...
(*In* Smithsonian institution. Annual report, 1945. Washington, 1946. 23½ᶜᵐ. p. 273–291. illus. (map) 10 pl. on 5 ℓ., diagr.)

1. Boll-weevil.
Q11.S66 1945   47–1861

NL 0449193   DLC WaS

Loftin, Ulphian Carl, 1890–   *joint author.*

Marsh, Charles Dwight, 1855–
... Oak-leaf poisoning of domestic animals. By C. Dwight Marsh ... A. B. Clawson ... and Hadleigh Marsh ... Washington, Govt. print. off., 1919.

NL —

Loftin, Ulphian Carl, 1890–
... Report on investigations of the pink bollworm of cotton in Mexico. By U. C. Loftin ... K. B. McKinney ... and W. K. Hanson ... Washington, Govt. print. off., 1921.
cover-title, 64 p. incl. illus., diagrs. v pl. on 4 ℓ. 23ᶜᵐ. (U. S. Dept. of agriculture. Bulletin no. 918. Professional paper)
Contribution from the Bureau of entomology in collaboration with the Federal horticultural board.
"Literature cited": p. 57.
1. ₍Pink boll-worm₎ ɪ. Hanson, Wrathall King, 1894–   joint author.
ɪɪ. McKinney, Kenneth Barbee, 1890–   joint author.
₍DLC (Dock List)₎   Agr 21–532
Library, U. S. Dept. of   Agriculture 1Ag84B no. 918

NL 0449195   DNAL WaWW DLC

Loftin, Ulphian Carl, 1890–   *joint author.*
Holloway, Thomas Edmunds, 1886–   FOR OTHER EDITIONS SEE MAIN ENTRY
... The sugar-cane moth borer ₍*Diatraea saccharalis* Fabricius₎ in the United States. By T. E. Holloway ... W. E. Haley ... and U. C. Loftin ... With technical description by Carl Heinrich ... Washington, U. S. Govt. print. off., 1928.

Lofting, Hilary Joseph Francis.
"Bail up!" Ned Kelly, bushranger, by Hilary Lofting. Sydney, New century press pty. ltd., 1939.
3 p. l., 9–282 p. 18½ᶜᵐ.

1. Kelly, Edward, 1854–1880. 2. Kelly, Edward, 1854–1880—Fiction.
ɪ. Title.   43–14884
Library of Congress   PZ3.L8248Bai

NL 0449197   DLC CaBVaU

Lofting, Hugh, 1886–1947.
Cesty Doktora Malodelala; illustroval autor; prelozila Zofie Pohorecka.

Voyages of Doctor Dolittle.

NL 0449198   OC1

Lofting, Hugh, 1886–1947
Cirkus Doktora Dolittla. Preveo Zlatko Gorjan Zagreb, Ognjen Prica, 1952.
332p. illus.

Croatian.

NL 0449199   OC1

Lofting, Hugh, 1886–
Daktaras Dolitlis ir jo gyvuliai; verte Pr. Masiotas.

NL 0449200   OC1

Lofting, Hugh, 1886–
...Daktaro Dolitlio plaukiojanti sala; verte Pr. Masiotas.

Lithuanian.

NL 0449201   OC1

Lofting, Hugh, 1886–1947.
Doctor Dolittle and the green canary; written and illustrated by Hugh Lofting. Philadelphia, Lippincott ₍1950₎
xi, 276 p. illus. 21 cm.

ɪ. Title.
                            Full name: Hugh John Lofting.
PZ7.L827Dm   50–14875

MsSM NcGU
NL 0449202   DLC MB ICarbS KU OrU Or OrP WaS WaSp

Lofting, Hugh, 1886–1947
Doctor Dolittle and the green canary. Written and illustrated by H. Lofting. L, Cape ₍1951₎
286 p. illus.

NL 0449203   MH

VOLUME 338

Lofting, Hugh, 1886–1947.
Doctor Dolittle and the secret lake. Illus. by the author. [1st ed.] Philadelphia, J. B. Lippincott Co. [1948]
xii, 366 p. illus. 21 cm.

"A Stokes book."
"Some of the text and drawings ... appeared serially in the New York Herald Tribune."

i. Title.

Full name: Hugh John Lofting.

PZ10.3.L85Dat   48–8401*

NL 0449204   DLC ScU PPT PP MB Or OrP WaS WaSp

Lofting, Hugh, 1886–1949.
Doctor Dolittle in the moon, told and illustrated by Hugh Lofting. [New York] Frederick A. Stokes co. [1928]
x p., 1 l., 307 p. incl. plates. col. front. 21 cm.
Illustrated t.-p. and lining-papers in colors.

i. Title.

Full name: Hugh John Lofting.

PZ10.3.L85Db   28–22386

NL 0449205   DLC MB OKentU Or OrP WaSp WaS CaBVaU

P
L82dm

Lofting, Hugh, 1886–
Doctor Dolittle in the moon, told and illustrated by Hugh Lofting. Philadelphia, J. B. Lippincott Company =1928=
307 p. illus.

NL 0449206   WaU

Lofting, Hugh, 1886–
Doctor Dolittle's birthday book, by Hugh Lofting. New York, Frederick A. Stokes co. [1935]
ix, [216] p. illus. 16½ cm.
Illustrated t.-p. in colors.

1. Birthday books.   i. Title.
                                                      36–619
Library of Congress   PS3523.O335D6 1935
———— Copy 2.
Copyright A 90117   [3]   813.5

NL 0449207   DLC

Lofting, Hugh, 1886–1947.
Doctor Dolittle's caravan, written and illustrated by Hugh Lofting. New York, Fredᵏ A. Stokes co. [1926]
ix p., 1 l., 342 p. col. front., illus. 21½ cm.

i. Title

PZ10.3.L85Dc   26–18089

NL 0449208   DLC MB CoU OKentU Or OrP WaS IdB NN

Lofting, Hugh, 1886–1947.
Doctor Dolittle's caravan. [c1954]

NL 0449209   CaBVaU

Lofting, Hugh, 1886–1947.
Doctor Dolittle's circus, told and illustrated by Hugh Lofting. New York, Fredᵏ A. Stokes co. [1924]
x p., 1 l., 379 p. col. front. illus. 21 cm.

i. Title.

Library of Congress   PZ10.3.L85Do   24–24604

NL 0449210   DLC CoU MoU OrP WaS Or MB NN

Lofting, Hugh, 1886–1947.
Doctor Dolittle's circus. Told and illustrated by Hugh Lofting. Philadelphia, Lippincott [c1952]
x, 379 p. illus. 22 cm.

i. Title.

PZ7.L827Dnf   65–6818

NL 0449211   DLC MB CaBVaU

Lofting, Hugh, 1886–
Doctor Dolittle's garden, told & pictured by Hugh Lofting. New York, Frederick A. Stokes co. [c1927]
viii, 327 p. col. front., illus. 21 cm.

i. Title.

Library of Congress   PZ10.3.L85Doc   27–22200

NL 0449212   DLC IEdS OrP Or WaS WaSp CaBVaU MB NN

Lofting, Hugh, 1886–1947.
Doctor Dolittle's garden. Told & pictured by Hugh Lofting. Philadelphia, Lippincott [1955? c1927]
viii, 327 p. illus. 22 cm.

i. Title.

PZ10.3.L85Doc 3   66–34862

NL 0449213   DLC NvU

Lofting, Hugh, 1886–
Doctor Dolittle's post office, written and illustrated by Hugh Lofting. New York, F. A. Stokes co. [c1923]
x p., 1 l., 359 p. col. front., illus. 21 cm.

i. Title.

Library of Congress   PZ7.L827Do   23–12962

MB NN
NL 0449214   DLC MB ViU OrU Or OrP WaS OrLgE WaSp

Lofting, Hugh, 1886–1947.
Doctor Dolittle's Puddleby adventures, written & illustrated by Hugh Lofting. [1st ed.] Philadelphia, Lippincott [1952]
241 p. illus. 21 cm.

i. Title.

Full name: Hugh John Lofting.

PZ10.3.L85Dog   52–7457 ‡

WaSp
NL 0449215   DLC GU ScU OCl KU OO NcU Or OrP WaS

Lofting, Hugh, 1886–1947.
Doctor Dolittle's Puddleby adventures. Written and illustrated by Hugh Lofting. [London] J. Cape [1953] 254 p. illus. 21cm.

1. Animals—Legends and stories.   i. Title.

NL 0449216   NN

Lofting, Hugh, 1886–
Doctor Dolittle's return, by Hugh Lofting; illustrated by the author. New York, Fredᵏ A. Stokes cᵒ, 1933.
viii, 2 l., 273 p. incl. 1 illus., plates. col. front. 21 cm.
Illustrated t.-p. and lining-papers.

i. Title.

Library of Congress   PZ7.L827Doc   33–30721

NL 0449217   DLC OrMonO Or OrP WaS WaSp NN ViU MoU

Lofting, Hugh, 1886–
Doctor Dolittle's zoo, written & illustrated by Hugh Lofting. [New York] Fredᵏ A. Stokes co. [c1925]
xi p., 1 l., 338 p. incl. illus., plates. col. front. 21 cm.

i. Title.

Library of Congress   PZ10.3.L85Dol   25–20167

WaSp MB NN
NL 0449218   DLC CoU OrU OKentU OrP WaS Or CaBVaU

Lofting, Hugh, 1886–1947.
Doctor Dolittle's zoo. Written & illustrated by Hugh Lofting. [Philadelphia, Lippincott [1953? c1925]
xi, 338 p. illus. 21 cm.
"Nineteenth printing."

i. Title.

PZ10.3.L85Dol 2   66–40945

NL 0449219   DLC OKentU

PZ66
.3
.C52

Lofting, Hugh, 1886–1947.
Chukovskiĭ, Korneĭ Ivanovich, 1882–
    Доктор Айболит. Рисунки В. Конашевича. [По мотивам Гью Лофтинга] Москва, Гос. изд-во детской лит-ры, 1954.

Lofting, Hugh, 1886–
    Doktor Dolittle auf dem Mond, von Hugh Lofting. Illustriert vom Autor. Berlin [etc.] Williams u. Co Verlag G.m.b.H. [1933]
200 p. illus. 22½cm.

"Berechtigte Übertragung von E. L. Schiffer."

89036B. 1. Juvenile literature—
Fiction. I. Schiffer, Edith Lotte1891–   Fiction, American. 2. Astronomy—
N. Y. P. L.   .tr. II. Title.   January 27, 1941

NL 0449221   NN

PS
3523
O35
M6
G4

Lofting, Hugh, 1886–
    .. Doktor Dolittle auf dem Mond [Berrchtige Übertragung von E. L. Schiffer, neubearb.] Zurich, Atrium [c1954]
149 p. illus. 23cm.

Translation of Doctor Dolittle in the moon.

NL 0449222   C

VOLUME 338

Lofting, Hugh, 1886–
...Doktor Dolittle es az allatok;
Reiter Laszlo rajzaival. ₍Budapest₎
Kaldor konyvkiadovallalat ₍c1933₎
141 p. illus.

The story of Doctor Dolittle.
Hungarian.

NL 0449223   OC1

Lofting, Hugh, 1886–1947
Doktor Dolittle i jego zwierzeta.
Przeklad Wandy Kragen. Warszawa,
Ksiazka, 1946.
108p. illus.

Polish.

NL 0449224   OC1

Lofting, Hugh, 1886–
Doktor Dolittle und seine tiere, von Hugh Lofting, illustriert vom autor; mit einer einleitung von Oskar Loerke. Berlin, Williams & co.   1928.
170 p. illus. 23 cm.
"Titel des originals: The story of Dr. Dolittle."
"Berechtigte übertragung aus dem englischen von E. L. Schiffer."

NL 0449225   MiU

PS
3523
O35
S86
G4
Lofting, Hugh, 1886–
Doktor Dolittle und seine Tiere. Illustriert vom Autor. ₍Berechtigte Übertragung von E. L. Schiffer, neubearb.₎ Zürich, Atrium ₍c1929₎
138 p. illus. 23cm.

Translation of The Story of Dr. Dolittle.

NL 0449226   C

LOFTING, Hugh, 1886–
Doktor Dolittle und seine tiere.
Berlin-Grünewald. Williams. c1930.
170p. illus.

NL 0449227   WaS

Lofting, Hugh, 1886–
Doktor Dolittle und seine tiere, von Hugh Lofting, illustriert vom autor; mit einer einleitung von Oskar Loerke. Berlin, Williams & co. ₍1946?₎
159 p. illus. 23 cm.
"Titel des originals: The story of Dr. Dolittle."
"Berechtigte übertragung aus dem englischen von E. L. Schiffer."

I. Schiffer, Edith Lotte, 1891–   tr.

PZ33.L55   A F 47–5361
Brown univ. Library
for Library of Congress   ₍2₎†

NL 0449228   RPB DLC MnU

Lofting, Hugh, 1886–1947
Doktor Dolittles geheimnisvoller See. ₍Übersetzung von Ursula Lehrburger₎ Zürich, Atrium ₍1952₎
270p. illus.

OC1

Lofting, Hugh, 1886–1947
Doktor Dolittles grösste Reise. ₍Übertragung von E. L. Schiffer, neubearbeitet₎ Zürich, Atrium ₍1953₎
207p. illus.

NL 0449230   OC1

Lofting, Hugh, 1886–
Doktor Dolittles Postamt.   Berlin: Williams und Co., 1930.
300 p. illus. 23cm.
"Berechtigte Übertragung von E. L. Schiffer."

251711B.   1. No subject.   I. Schiffer,   Edith Lotte, 1891–   tr.   II. Title.
N.Y.P.L.   December 17, 1943

NL 0449231   NN

Lofting, Hugh, 1886–1947
Doktor Dolittles Postamt. ₍Berechtigte Übertragung aus dem Englischen von E. L. Schiffer₎ Berlin, Williams ₍195–₎
220. illus.

NL 0449232   OC1

JF3
L82dr
Lofting, Hugh, 1886–1947.
Doktor Dolittles Rückkehr, von Hugh Lofting, illustriert vom autor. Berlin, Williams & co. ₍c1934₎
179 p. illus. 23 cm.

NL 0449233   NcGU

Lofting, Hugh, 1886–
Doktor Dolittles schwimmende Insel. Illustriert vom Autor. Von Hugh Lofting. Berlin: Williams & Co. Verlag, G.m.b.H. ₍c1928₎ 281 p. illus. 22½cm. ₍His: Dr. Dolittle Bücher. Bd. 2₎
"8.–12. Auflage."
"Berechtigte Übertragung von E. L. Schiffer."

94095B.   1. Juvenile literature—Fic-   tion, American.   I. Schiffer, Edith
Lotte, 1891–   , tr.   II. Title.
N.Y.P.L.   January 27, 1941

NL 0449234   NN

Lofting, Hugh, 1886–1947.
Doktor Dolittles Schwimmende Insel, von Hugh Lofting, illustriert vom autor. [Berlin] Williams [c1930]
281 p. illus. 23 cm.

NL 0449235   NcGU OrP

Lofting, Hugh, 1886–1947
Doktor Dolittles schwimmende Insel. ₍Berechtigte Übertragung aus dem Englischen von E.L. Schiffer₎ Zürich, Atrium ₍195–₎

NL 0449236   OC1

Lofting, Hugh, 1886–
Doktor Dolittles Tier Oper, von Hugh Lofting. Illustriert vom Autor. Berlin-Grunewald: Williams & Co. Verlag G.m.b.H. ₍c1928₎ 288 p. illus. 22½cm.
"Berechtigte Übertragung von E. L. Schiffer."

102682B.   1. Juvenile literature—   Fiction, American.   2. Animals
—Legends and stories.   I. Schiffer,   Edith Lotte, 1891–   , tr.   II. Title.
N.Y.P.L.   June 26, 1941

NL 0449237   NN NcGU

Lofting, Hugh, 1886–1947
Doktor Dolittles Tieroper. 2. Aufl. Übertragung von E. L. Schiffer, neubearb. Wien, Ueberreuter ₍1953₎
255p. illus.

NL 0449238   OC1

JF3
L82dzi
Lofting, Hugh, 1886–1947.
Doktor Dolittles Zirkus; text und illustrationen von Hugh Lofting. Berlin, Williams ₍c1930₎
324 p. illus. 23 cm.

NL 0449239   NcGU WaS

PS
3523
O35
C5
G4
Lofting, Hugh, 1886–
Doktor Dolittles Zirkus ₍Umschlagzeichnung von A. Reibstein-Albrecht. Berechtigte Übertragung aus dem Englischen von E. L. Schiffer₎ Zürich, Atrium ₍1952₎
232 p. illus. 22cm.

Translation of Dr. Dolittle's circus.

NL 0449240   C OC1

Lofting, Hugh, 1886–
Doktor Dolittles Zoo; Text und Illustrationen von Hugh Lofting. Berlin: Williams & co. ₍1931₎ 283 p. illus. 23cm.

253814B.   1. Animals—Legends and   stories.
N.Y.P.L.   December 30, 1943

NL 0449241   NN

Lofting, Hugh, 1886–1947
Doktor Dolittles Zoo. ₍Übertragung von E.L. Schiffer, neubearbeitet₎ Zürich, Atrium ₍1952₎
197p. illus.

NL 0449242   OC1

J839.8
L82d
Lofting, Hugh, 1886–1947.
Doktor Dyregod. Gjenfortalt og illustrert av Thorbjørn Egner. Oslo, Aschehoug, 1954.
88 ₍1₎ p. illus. (incl. music)

"Oversatt etter ...'Doctor Doolittle'."

NL 0449243   MiD

PZ90
.Y5
C564
Hebr
Lofting, Hugh, 1886–1947.
Der Doktor Oystutvey
Chukovskii, Kornei Ivanovich, 1882–
דער דאקטער אייםמומווי. לויט ניו לאםמינונג
נוםיאנסקי. קינעו. מעלוכע־פארלאג פאר די נאציאנאלע מינדער־
היימן אין אוסםר. ₍Kiev₎ 1937.

PZ
7
L827Gu
1933
Lofting, Hugh, 1886–1946.
Göb-Göb's Buch, von Hugh Lofting. ₍Berechtigte Übertragung aus dem Englischen von Steffi Anton₎ Illustriert vom Autor. Berlin, Verlegt im Williams u.Co. Verlag ₍1933₎
137 p. illus. 22 cm.

Translation of Gub-Gub's book; an encyclopedia of food.

NL 0449245   NcGU

VOLUME 338

Lofting, Hugh, 1886–
Gub Gub's book; an encyclopedia of food ... by Hugh Lofting. ₍New York₎ Frederick A. Stokes co. ₍ᶜ1932₎
6 p. l., 3–185 p. incl. plates. col. front., col. pl. 19½ᵐ.
Map on lining-papers.

ı. Title.

Library of Congress   PZ7.L827Gu   32–29908

NL 0449246   DLC Or MB ViU

PS3523
.O 336S72 Lofting, Hugh, 1886–1947.
1931   L'histoire du docteur Dolittle; sa
vie singulière dans son pays et ses
étonnantes aventures dans les pays
étrangers. Illustrée par l'auteur.
Traduite par Sarah J. Silberstein et
Claire Brugell. Paris, A. Michel ₍1931₎
250 p. illus. 23cm.

ı. Title.
Full name: Hugh John Lofting.

NL 0449247   MB

Lofting, Hugh, 1886–
La mésaventure de Madame Popotte; d'après "The story of Mrs. Tubbs", racontée et illustrée par Hugh Lofting, adaptation par Sarah J. Silberstein et Claire Brugell. New York, Frederick A. Stokes company, 1930.
77, ₍3₎ p., 1 l. incl. front., plates. 14 x 18¼ᵐ.

ı. Silberstein, Sarah J., tr. ıı. Brugell, Claire, joint tr. ııı. Title.

Library of Congress   PZ26.3.L6   30–30202
——— Copy 2.
Copyright A 27885   ₍3₎   813.5

NL 0449248   DLC OC1

Lofting, Hugh, 1886–
Noisy Nora, pictured, told, and printed by Hugh Lofting. New York, F. A. Stokes co. ₍ᶜ1929₎
₍53₎ p. incl. front., illus. (part col.) pl. 16ᵐ.

ı. Title.

Library of Congress   PZ7.L827No   29–13473

            NN
NL 0449249   DLC OrMonO OrP WaS OrLgE OC1 OO OCU MB

Lofting, Hugh, 1886–1947
Podróże Doktora Dolittle. Przekład Janiny Mortkowiczowej. Warszawa, Książka, 1946.
275p.

Polish.

NL 0449250   OC1

Lofting, Hugh, 1886–
Porridge poetry, cooked, ornamented and served up by Hugh Lofting. New York, F. A. Stokes co. ₍ᶜ1924₎
94,₍1₎ p. incl. illus. (part col.) plates (part col.) 13¼ x 18¼ᵐ.

ı. Title.

Library of Congress   PZ8.3.L827Po   24–28245

NL 0449251   DLC WaSp CoU OC1 OLak

Lofting, Hugh, 1886–
Porridge poetry; cooked, ornamented and served up, by Hugh Lofting. London: J. Cape, Ltd.₍,₎ 1925.₎ 101 p. incl. col'd plates. illus. obl. 24°.

Illustrated t.-p.

234126A.   1. Juvenile literature—   Poetry, American. 2. Title.
N.Y.P.L.   May 3, 1926

NL 0449252   NN

Lofting, Hugh , 1886–
Příběh Doktora Malodělala, jenž jest kronikou jeho neobyčejného života doma a překvapujících dobrodružství v cizích zemích...illustruje spisovatel; přeložila Žofie Pohorecká.

Story of Doctor Dolittle.

NL 0449253   OC1

Lofting, Hugh, 1886–
The story of Doctor Dolittle, being the history of his peculiar life at home and astonishing adventures in foreign parts. Never before printed. Told by Hugh Lofting, illustrated by the author. New York, Frederick A. Stokes company, 1920.
6 p. l., 180 p. col. front., illus., plates. 21ᵐ. $2.25

ı. Title.

Library of Congress   PZ7.L827St   20—18925

            OrPS
            OC1 OO ODW OU NN MH OrCS OrMonO OrLgE OrAshS WaSp
NL 0449254   DLC MB ViU MoU IEN MiU OrP Or WaS OrU

PZ7
L827S8   Lofting, Hugh, 1886–1947.
1923x1   The story of Doctor Dolittle; being the history of his peculiar life at home and astonishing adventures in foreign parts. Never before printed. Told by Hugh Lofting, illustrated by the author. With an introd. to the tenth printing by Hugh Walpole. New York, F.A.Stokes, 1920 ₍reprinted 1923₎
xvi p.,1 l.,180 p. illus.(part col.) 21ᵐ
"Fifteenth printing, Nov.30, 1923."
Orange cloth.

NL 0449255   CSt

PZ7
.L827St8   Lofting, Hugh, 1866–1947.
            The story of Doctor Dolittle, being the history of his peculiar life at home and astonishing adventures in foreign parts. Never before printed. Illus. by the author. London, J. Cape ₍1924₎
            223p. illus. 21cm.

NL 0449256   FMU

PZ7
.L827St   Lofting, Hugh, 1886–1947.
1924
            The story of Doctor Doolittle, being the history of his peculiar life at home and astonishing adventures in foreign parts. Never before printed. With an introduction to the tenth printing by Hugh Walpole. New York, F. A. Stokes, 1920 ₍i. e. 1924₎
            xii, 180 p. illus. 20cm.

NL 0449257   ViU

962
L829   Lofting, Hugh, 1886–
st   The story of Doctor Dolittle, being the history of his
1920   peculiar life at home and astonishing adventures in for-
Educ.-   eign parts. Never before printed. Told by Hugh Loft-
Psych.   ing, illustrated by the author. New York, Frederick A.
Library   Stokes company, 1920 ₍i.e.1930₎
            6 p. l., 180 p. col. front., illus., plates. 21ᵐ.

NL 0449258   CU

PZ7
.L827St Lofting, Hugh, 1886–1947.
1932a
            The story of Doctor Dolittle, being the history of his peculiar life at home and astonishing adventures in foreign parts. Never before printed. Illustrated by the author. London, J. Cape ₍1932₎
            223 p. illus. 21cm.

NL 0449259   ViU

Lofting, Hugh, 1886–
The story of Doctor Dolittle, being the history of his peculiar life at home and astonishing adventures in foreign parts. Never before printed. Told by Hugh Lofting, illustrated by the author. With an introduction to the tenth printing by Hugh Walpole. New York, Frederick A. Stokes company ₍1938₎
xii p., 3 l., 180 p. incl. front., illus., pl. 19ᵐ.
"Thirty-second printing, August, 1939."

ı. Title.
                                                  40–4714

Library of Congress   PZ7.L827St 8

NL 0449260   DLC

PZ
7   Lofting, Hugh, 1886–1947.
L827   The story of Doctor Dolittle, being the
S8   history of his peculiar life at home and as-
1948   tonishing adventures in foreign parts, never
            before printed. Illustrated by the author.
            With an introduction to the 10th printing by
            Sir Hugh Walpole. Philadelphia, Lippincott
            ₍ᶜ1948₎
            xvi, 172 p. illus. 20 cm.

            I. Title. II. Title: Doctor Dolittle.

            OU WaU MB
NL 0449261   Vi NcD MsSM IU ViU CaBVaU ScU GU MoU

Lofting, Hugh, 1886–
... The story of Mrˢ Tubbs. New York, Fredˣ A. Stokes co. ₍ᶜ1923₎
91, ₍3₎ p. incl. front., plates (part col.) 14ᵐ.
At head of title: Told and illustrated by Hugh Lofting.
Printed on one side of leaf only.

ı. Title.

Library of Congress   PZ10.3.L85St   23—13420

            RP MiU CoU OO OC1 OU MB
NL 0449262   DLC OrAshS OrLgE CaBVaU OrCS Or WaS

Lofting, Hugh, 1886–
Chukovskiĭ, Korneĭ Ivanovich, 1882–
₍Москва₎ 1937. "דאָקטאָר מאַסקוס, פאַרלאַג "עמעס. מעלעפאַנ

Lofting, Hugh, 1886–
Tohori Tuulisen tarina; ₍Suomentanut T.T.Kaila. 1929₎

NL 0449264   OC1

VOLUME 338

Lofting, Hugh, 1886–
Tommy, Tilly and Mrs. Tubbs; story and pictures by **Hugh** Lofting. New York, F. A. Stokes co. [*1936]
3 p. l., 119, [2] p. incl. plates. col. front. 14 x 18½ᶜᵐ.
Printed on one side of leaf only.

I. Title.   36-34682

Library of Congress   PZ7.L827To

NL 0449265   DLC Or

Lofting, Hugh, 1886–
Tommy, Tilly and Mrs. Tubbs; story and pictures by **Hugh** Lofting. New York, F. A. Stokes co. [*1937]
4 p. l., 78, [3] p. incl. col. front., illus., plates (part col.) 13½ x 19½ᶜᵐ.
Illustrated lining-papers.
"Revised edition—numerous new illustrations."

I. Title.   37-32420

Library of Congress   PZ7.L827To 2

NL 0449266   DLC Or OClW

Lofting, Hugh, 1886–
The twilight of magic, by Hugh Lofting; illustrations by Lois Lenski. New York, Frederick A. Stokes co., 1930.
vi p., 1 l., 303 p. col. front., illus. 21ᶜᵐ.
Illustrated lining-papers in colors.

I. Title.   30-29904

Library of Congress   PZ7.L827Tw

NL 0449267   DLC NcD NN MH OrU OCl

Lofting, Hugh, 1886–
Victory for the slain, by Hugh Lofting. London, J. Cape [1942]
40 p. 20ᶜᵐ.
A poem.
"First published 1942."

I. Title.   42-51986

Library of Congress   PS3523.O335V5
[2]   811.5

NL 0449268   DLC

Lofting, Hugh, 1886–1947.
The voyages of Doctor Dolittle, by Hugh Lofting, illustrated by the author. New York, Fredᵏ A. Stokes co., 1922.
ix p., 2 l., 364 p. col. front., illus., col. pl. 21 cm.
Frontispiece accompanied by transparent guard sheet with descriptive letterpress.
Illustrated lining-papers in colors.

I. Title.   *Full name:* Hugh John Lofting.
PZ7.L827Vo   22-20686

OCl OO NN MB NcGU PSt DNLM WaS MBuT NBuT
NL 0449269   DLC MsSM OrLgE Or OrP OrCS MiU OLak

PZ7   **Lofting, Hugh,** 1886–1947.
.L827Vo2   The voyages of Doctor Dolittle. Illus. by the author. London, J. Cape [1923]
320p. illus. 21cm.

NL 0449270   FMU

Lofting, Hugh, 1886–1947.
The voyages of Doctor Dolittle. Illustrated by the author. Philadelphia, Lippincott [*1950]
ix, 364 p. illus. 21 cm.

I. Title.

PZ7.L827Vo 5   64-2997

CaBVaU NcD NRU MiU
NL 0449271   DLC MU OU GU CLSU KU MB IU OrCS OrU

Lofting, Lynne.
Squawky and Bawky, by Lynne *Lofting, illustrated by* Waldo Peirce. New York, C. Scribner's sons; London, C. Scribner's sons, ltd., *1939.
[16] p. col. illus. 32ᶜᵐ.
Illustrated t.-p. in colors.

1. Penguins.   I. Peirce, Waldo, 1884–   illus.   II. Title.

Library of Congress   PZ10.3.L852Sq   39-30829

NL 0449272   DLC WaSp

Loftis, J.   D.
Head-end power for streamlined passenger trains; an address by J. D. Loftis, General supt. Motive Power, Atlantic Coast Line Railroad Co., before the Raleigh section of American Society of Mechanical Engineers. Wilmington, N. C., Cape Fear Club, 1946.
22 p. illus. (4 plans. part fold.) 28cm.

NL 0449273   NcRS

Loftis, John Clyde, 1919–
Steele at Drury Lane. Berkeley, University of **California** Press, 1952.
260 p. 23 cm.
Thesis—Princeton University.
Bibliographical footnotes.

1. Steele, Sir Richard, 1672–1729.   2. London.   Drury Lane Theatre.
I. Title.
PR3706.L6   792   A 52—5209
Princeton Univ. Libr.
for Library of Congress   [53r52c2]†

WaTC OrSaW OrU WaWW NjP
TxU NN MH CU DLC IdPI DAU GAT CaBVaU WaS MtBC OrCS
NL 0449274   DLC MoSMed MB FTaSU NcGU NBuC PLF PBm

Loftis, John Clyde, 1919–
Steele at Drury Lane. Berkeley, University of California Press, 1952.
260 p. 23 cm.
Bibliographical footnotes.

1. Steele, Sir Richard, 1672–1729.   2. London.   Drury Lane Theatre.
I. Title.
PR3706.L6   792   52—7954

NL 0449275   DLC NRCR NjNbS TU ViU MiU

Loftis, Zenas Sanford, 1881–1909.
A message from Batang; the diary of Z. S. Loftis, M. D., missionary to Tibetans. New York, Chicago [etc.] Fleming H. Revell company [*1911]
160 p. front., plates, port. group. 20ᶜᵐ. $0.75

I. Title.

Library of Congress   12-496

NL 0449276   DLC WaE

Loftis bros. & co., *Chicago.*
Historic diamonds. Chicago, Loftis bros. & co. [*1917]
cover-title, 48 p. illus. 16ᶜᵐ.
Includes advertising matter.

1. Diamonds.   2. Jewelry—Catalogs.

G S 34-929
Libr., U. S. Geol. Surv.,   Geo. F. Kunz Collection   K481 L82h

NL 0449277   DI-GS MH

LOFTIS BROS. & COMPANY, *Chicago.*
Historic diamonds. Chicago, Loftis Bros. & Co. cop. 1925.
16°. pp. 32. Illustr.

NL 0449278   MH

Loftman, Karl.
Kritisk undersoekning af den masoretiska texten till profeten Hoseas bok.
Inaug. diss. Upsala, 1894.

NL 0449279   ICRL PPAmP CtY

Loftman, Karl.
Ofwersättning och kommentar till profeten Hoseas bok ...
see under   Bible. O.T. Hosea.
Swedish. 1896. Loftman.

LOFTNESS, Sonya
Norwegian delicacies for your coffee table; a collection of Norse recipes. [Pasadena Calif House of printing c1943] 18p
Benefit.of...Royal Norwegian flyers

NL 0449281   WaT

Lofton, Blanche De Good, 1885–
Mazama & Wecoma. Portland, Or., Binfords & Mort [1952]
92 p. 23 cm.
Poems.

I. Title.

PS3523.O337M3   811.5   53—15205 ‡

NL 0449282   DLC Or OrP OrU Wa NN

BV   **Lofton, George Augustus,** 1839–1914.
811   The baptismal remission theory. Nashville,
L6   Tenn., Southern Baptist Convention, [1913]
78p. 16cm.

1. Baptism.   I. Title.

NL 0449283   NRCR

VOLUME 338

Lofton, George Augustus, 1839-1914.
The Baptist trophy : a centennial poem on religious liberty. By Rev. G. A. Lofton ... Memphis, Southern Baptist publication society, 1876.
100 p. 21½ᶜᵐ.

1. Baptists. 2. Religious liberty. I. Title.

Library of Congress   PS2249.L55   28-9345

NL 0449284   DLC NcD TU

Lofton, George Augustus, 1839-1914.
The bar room, as a business and social resort, by G. A. Lofton, D. D., delivered at Talladega, Alabama, Sunday, October 23, 1887. Talladega, Ala., Our mountain home, 1887.
19 p. illus. (port.) 21ᶜᵐ.

1. Hotels, taverns, etc. 2. Temperance—Addresses, essays, lectures. I. Title.
Library of Congress   HV5261.L6   43-21823

NL 0449285   DLC

B
204
L82   Lofton, George Augustus, 1839-1914.
Bible thoughts and themes for young men and women. St. Louis, C. R. Barns, 1880.
456p. front. (port.) 20cm.

NL 0449286   NcWsW

Lofton, George Augustus, 1839-1914.
Character sketches; or, The blackboard mirror. A series of illustrated discussions, depicting those peculiarities of character which contribute to the ridicule and failure, or to the dignity and success of mankind ... By George A. Lofton ... Nashville, Tenn., Southwestern publishing house ₍*1890₎
454 p. incl. plates. front. (port.) 25½ᶜᵐ.

1. Character. 2. Conduct of life.
                                                12—36278
Library of Congress   BJ1521.L74

NL 0449287   DLC NcU FU AAP TU ICU NcD ODW

*
BJ1531
.L6   Lofton, George Augustus, 1839-1914.
1898
Character sketches; or, The blackboard mirror. A series of illustrated discussions, depicting those peculiarities of character which contribute to the ridicule and failure, or to the dignity and success of mankind. Nashville, Tenn., Southwestern Pub. House ₍1898₎
454 p. plates, port. 26cm.
1. Character. 2. Conduct of life.

NL 0449288   ViU

Hum
BJ
1521
L74   Lofton, George Augustus, 1839-1914.
Character sketches; or, The blackboard mirror. A series of illustrated discussions, depicting those peculiarities of character which contribute to the ridicule and failure, or to the dignity and success of mankind ... Engravings from the original blackboard drawings. Nashville, Tenn., The Southwestern Co. ₍c1908₎
448p. illus.

1. Character.   2. Conduct of life.

NL 0449289   FTaSU

Lofton, George Augustus, 1839-1914.
Defense of the Jessey records and Kiffin manuscript, with a review of Dr. Jno. T. Christian's work, entitled : "Baptist history vindicated." By Geo. A. Lofton ... Appendix to English Baptist reformation from 1609 to 1641 A. D. Nashville, Tenn., Press of Marshall & Bruce co., 1899.
v, ₍1₎, 7-138 p. 22½ᶜᵐ.

1. Christian, John Tyler, 1854-   Baptist history vindicated. 2. Baptists—Hist. 3. Baptists—England.   I. Title.
                                                4-3361
Library of Congress   BX6231.C52L6

NL 0449290   DLC

Lofton, George Augustus, 1839-1914.
English Baptist reformation. (From 1609 to 1641 A. D.) By Geo. A. Lofton ... Louisville, Ky., C. T. Dearing, 1899.
viii, ₍9₎-280 p. 19ᶜᵐ.

1. Baptists—Hist.   I. Title.
                                                99-1448 Revised
Library of Congress   BX6276.L7

NL 0449291   DLC MH-AH WaTC NcWsW TxU PPEB IObNB

Lofton, George Augustus, 1839-1914.
Habitual drinking and its remedy. By Rev. George A. Lofton ... Memphis, Tenn., Southern Baptist publication society, 1874.
xii, ₍9₎-99 p. 15 x 11½ᶜᵐ.

1. Temperance.
                                                10—12938
Library of Congress   HV5296.L8

NL 0449292   DLC NcD TU

Lofton, George Augustus, 1839-1914.
Harp of life, its harmonies and discords, by Geo. A. Lofton ... Nashville, Tenn., J. R. Florida & company ₍1896₎
463 p. incl. front. (port.) plates. 24ᶜᵐ.

1. Character. 2. Conduct of life.
                                                99-5521
Library of Congress   BJ1521.L743

NL 0449293   DLC FMU NcU

Lofton, George Augustus, 1839-1914.
John the Baptist (in verse) by Geo. A. Lofton ... Nashville, Tenn., Sunday school board, Southern Baptist convention, 1905.
56 p. 19ᶜᵐ.

1. John, the Baptist—Poetry.
                                                12—36295
Library of Congress   PS2249.L55J6

NL 0449294   DLC NcWsW

Lofton, George Augustus, 1839-1914.
The masterwheel; or, The power of love; being a discussion of that passion by which God transmits the moving force of His being to the universe, through whose highest development man becomes like unto Deity, and without which he would cease to be in his Maker's image, by George A. Lofton ... with illustrations by the author. Nashville, Tenn., Macon, Ga. ₍etc.₎ The Southwestern company ₍*1906₎
477 p. incl. front. (port.) plates. 25½ᶜᵐ.

1. Title.
                                                7—21433
Library of Congress   BJ4521.L746

NL 0449295   DLC NcD TxU

C
8989
.515   LOFTON, GEORGE AUGUSTUS, 1839-1914.
Mighty to save; (a discourse in verse), and other poems... Chattanooga, Tenn., Times printing co., 1884.
48p.

NL 0449296   ICN GU

BX6276 Lofton, George Augustus, 1839-1914.
.W6L8   A review of the question. By George Augustus Lofton ... Being a review of Dr. William H. Whitsitt's "Question in Baptist history," including the reviews of Albert H. Newman ... ₍and₎ Henry C. Vedder ... Nashville, Tenn., Pub. for the author by University press co., 1897.
234 p. 20½ᶜᵐ.

1. Whitsitt, William Heth, 1841-1911. A question in Baptist history. 2. Baptists—Hist. 3. Baptism.

NL 0449297   ICU TNJ-R NRCR

Lofton, George Augustus, 1839-1914.
So: or, The gospel in a monosyllable. Chicago, New York ₍etc.₎ F. H. Revell co., 1900.
229, ₍1₎ p. 12ᶜᵐ.

Library of Congress   Copyright   Sept. 27, 1900-60

NL 0449298   DLC NRAB

Lofton, George Augustus, 1839-1914.
Why the Baptist name. A discussion between Dr. George A. Lofton (Baptist) and F. W. Smith (Christian) Nashville, Tenn., McQuiddy printing company, 1912.
345 p. 2 port. (incl. front.) 19½ᶜᵐ. $1.00

1. Smith, F. W., joint author.
                                                13-2471
Library of Congress

NL 0449299   DLC NcWsW CCovB

Lofton, George Augustus, 1839-
The wreck restored ... Nashville, Tennessee, 1914.
31 p.   17 cm.

NL 0449300   RPB

Lofton, Roscoe Elwood, 1879-
... A measure of the color characteristics of white papers, by R. E. Lofton, associate physicist, Bureau of standards. November 17, 1923 ... Washington, Govt. print. off., 1923.
1 p. L., p. 667-676 incl. 1 illus., tab., diagrs. 25½ᶜᵐ. (₍U. S.₎ Bureau of standards. Technologic papers, no. 244)
Running title: Color characteristics of white paper.

1. Paper—Testing.   I. Title. II. Title: Color characteristics of white paper.
Library of Congress   T1.U4 no. 244   23-27481
———— Copy 2.   TS1109.L79

NL 0449301   DLC WaWW OrU OrCS OC1 MiU OO OU MB

Lofton, Roscoe Elwood, 1879-
... Method for differentiating and estimating unbleached sulphite and sulphate pulps in paper, by R. E. Lofton, associate physicist, M. F. Merritt, laboratory assistant, Bureau of standards. April 4, 1921 ... Washington, Govt. print. off., 1921.
18 p. incl. tables. 28ᶜᵐ. (₍U. S.₎ Bureau of standards. Technologic papers, no. 189)
Running title: Differentiating unbleached sulphite and sulphate pulps.

1. Paper making and trade. 2. Wood-pulp. I. Merritt, Mrs. Muriel Fleming, 1899-   joint author. II. Title. III. Title: Differentiating unbleached sulphite and sulphate pulps.
Library of Congress   T1.U4 no. 189   21-26365
———— Copy 2.   TS1175.L6

NL 0449302   DLC WaWW MH OU MiU OO OC1 MB

VOLUME 338

Lofton, Roscoe Elwood, 1879–
... Photomicrography of paper fibers, by R. E. Lofton, associate physicist, Bureau of standards. August 2, 1922 ... Washington, Govt. print. off., 1922.

1 p. l., p. 629–650. illus. 26¼ᶜᵐ. (₍U. S.₎ Bureau of standards. Technologic papers, no. 217)

Bibliography: p. 649–650.

1. Paper. 2. Fibers. 3. Photomicrography.   ɪ. Title: Paper fibers, Photomicrography of.

Library of Congress   T1.U4   no. 217   22–26829
—— Copy 2.   TS1109.L8

NL   0449303   DLC WaWW OrCS OrU MiU OCl OO OU MB

Lofton, Roscoe Elwood, 1879–
... Study of the windows of window envelopes for the purpose of developing standard specifications, by R. E. Lofton, associate physicist, Bureau of standards. June 6, 1927 ... Washington, U. S. Govt. print. off., 1927.

1 p. l., p. 385–399 incl. tables. 26ᶜᵐ. (₍U. S.₎ Bureau of standards. Technologic papers, no. 343)

At head of title: Department of commerce. Bureau of standards. George K. Burgess, director ...

1. Envelopes (Stationery) 2. Paper—Testing.   ɪ. Title.

Library of Congress   T1.U4   no. 343   27–26788
—— Copy 2.   TS1233.L85

NL   0449304   DLC WaWW OrCS OrU MiU OO OCl OU ICJ

Lofton, William M., Jr.   Chapel Hill, 1926.
Combustible and non-combustible lubricating oils.

NL   0449305   NcU

Lofton, William M., Jr.   Chapel Hill, 1928.
Emulsification of tars and asphalts.

NL   0449306   NcU

Lofts, Norah (Robinson) 1904–
Araminta, den sejrende dyd; paa dansk ved Tove Castenskiold. ₍Odense₎ Skandinavisk bogforlag ₍1947₎

250 p. 23 cm.

"Originalens titel: To see a fine lady."

ɪ. Title.   *Full name:* Norah Ethel (Robinson) Lofts.

PR6023.O35T62   50–23873

NL   0449307   DLC

Lofts, Norah (Robinson) 1904–
Araminta, Roman. ₍Berechtigte Übertragung aus dem Englischen, besorgt von Ursula von Wiese₎ Rüschlikon-Zch., A. Müller ₍194–₎

279 p. 22 cm.

Translation of To see a fine lady.

ɪ. Title.   *Full name:* Norah Ethel (Robinson) Lofts.

PR6023.O35T65   50–28914

NL   0449308   DLC

Lofts, Norah (Robinson) 1904–
Bless this house. ₍1st ed.₎ Garden City, N. Y., Doubleday, 1954.

285 p. 22 cm.

ɪ. Title.

         Full name: Norah Ethel (Robinson) Lofts.

PZ3.L825Bj   54–5363 ‡

      MtBC IdB CaBVaU CoU OU MB OrCS OrMonO OrP OrU WaE Or
      TU TxU NcD OClW OU OCU PWcS PBa OCl OO NcU IdU WaS
NL   0449309   DLC WaT NcGU KyLx OClUr PJB PPL PP ViU

Lofts, Norah (Robinson) 1904–
Bless this house. London, M. Joseph ₍1954₎

365 p. 20 cm.

ɪ. Title.

PZ3.L825Bj 2   54–1206 ‡

NL   0449310   DLC CaBVaU PU OO

Lofts, Norah (Robinson) 1904–
Blossom like the rose, by Norah Lofts. New York, A. A. Knopf, 1939.

6 p. l., 3–363, ₍1₎ p. 20ᶜᵐ.

"Decorations by John Alan Maxwell."
"First American edition."

ɪ. Title.   39–23752 Revised

Library of Congress   PZ3.L825Bl

NL   0449311   DLC CaBVa Or OrP WaS LU IU OOxM OO OCl

4PR-147   Lofts, Norah (Robinson) 1904–
Bohémienne, tr. de l'anglais par Edmée Montandon. [Lausanne] Marguerat [1946]

252 p. (Collection "La Caravelle")

NL   0449312   DLC-P4

Lofts, Norah (Robinson) 1904–
The brittle glass, by Norah Lofts ... New York, A. A. Knopf, 1943.

4 p. l., 3–258 p., 2 l. 20ᶜᵐ.

"First American edition."

ɪ. Title.   43–51

Library of Congress   PZ3.L825Br

NL   0449313   DLC CaBVa Or OrP WaS

Lofts, Norah (Robinson) 1904–
The brittle glass. London, Joseph ₍1953₎

189 p. (Mermaid books)

NL   0449314   NNC

Lofts, Norah (Robinson) 1904–
A calf for Venus. ₍1st ed.₎ Garden City, N. Y., Doubleday, 1949.

253 p. 22 cm.

ɪ. Title.

         Full name: Norah Ethel (Robinson) Lofts.

PZ3.L825Cal   49–7634*

      ViU PP OClU OEac OrP Or WaE WaS WaSp WaT IdPI
NL   0449315   DLC CaBVaU CaBVa FTaSU CoU MoU PPA PPL

Lofts, Norah (Robinson) 1904–
Când înflorește pustiul, roman tradus de Ada Petrescu. ₍București₎ Pro-Pace ₍1945–₎

v. 19 cm.

Translation of Blossom like the rose.

ɪ. Title.

         Full name: Norah Ethel (Robinson) Lofts.

PR6023.O35B57   53–37992

NL   0449316   DLC

Lofts, Norah (Robinson) 1904–
Colin Lowrie, by Norah Lofts. New York, A. A. Knopf, 1939.

5 p. l., 3–393, ₍1₎ p. 20¼ᶜᵐ.

Illustrated t.-p.

ɪ. Title.   38–29023 Revised

Library of Congress   PZ3.L825Co

NL   0449317   DLC OrMonO WaE NBuU CoU OU PBm ViU OCl

₍Lofts, *Mrs.* Norah (Robinson)₎ 1904–
Dead march in three keys, a murder story, by Peter Curtis ₍pseud.₎ London, P. Davies ₍1940₎

3 p. l., 3–266 p. 19ᶜᵐ.

"First published 1940."

ɪ. Title.   40–34422

Library of Congress   PZ3.L825De

NL   0449318   DLC

Lofts, Norah (Robinson) 1904–
Dead march in three keys, a murder story. Harmondsworth, Middlesex ₍Eng.₎ Penguin books ₍1949₎

175 p. 18 ᶜᵐ. (Penguin books. 629)
By Peter Curtis, pseud.

NL   0449319   NjP

Lofts, Norah (Robinson) 1904–
Eleanor the queen; the story of the most famous woman of the Middle Ages. ₍1st ed.₎ Garden City, N. Y., Doubleday, 1955.

249 p. 22 cm. (Cavalcade books)

1. Eleanor of Aquitaine, consort of Henry II, 1122?–1204—Fiction.
ɪ. Title.   *Full name:* Norah Ethel (Robinson) Lofts.

PZ3.L825El   55–5509 ‡

      PP TxU OOxM OrMonO OrP WaE WaS WaT
NL   0449320   DLC CaBVa Or WU CoU MB FMU NcD ScU OCl

Lofts, Norah (Robinson) 1904–
Esther. New York, Macmillan, 1950.

163 p. 21 cm.

1. Esther, Queen of Persia—Fiction.
         Full name: Nora Ethel (Robinson) Lofts.

BS580.E8L57   823.91   50–10143

NL   0449321   DLC Or WaS WaT WaE PPDrop TU

VOLUME 338

823
L827e
1951
LOFTS, NORAH (ROBINSON) 1904-
Esther. London, Joseph [1951]
163p. 21cm.

"First published by Michael Joseph ...
1951."

1. Esther, Queen of Persia - Fiction.

NL 0449322   TxU

4PR
5037
Lofts, Norah (Robinson) 1904-
Ferne, silberne Insel, Roman, [Berechtigte
Übertragung von Gertrud Müller] Zürich,
Schweizer Druck- und Verlagshaus [1949 or 50]
440 p.

NL 0449323   DLC-P4

Lofts, Norah (Robinson) 1904-
... Frau im spiegel, roman. Zürich, A. Müller [1943]
276 p. 21 cm.
At head of title: Norah Lofts.
"Berechtigte uebersetzung aus dem amerikanischen, besorgt von
Ursula von Wiese. Titel des originals: 'The brittle glass.'"
"Erstes bis viertes tausend."

I. Wiese und Kaiserswaldau, Ursula Renate von, 1905-   tr.
II. Title.

PR6023.O35B74   47-42463

NL 0449324   DLC

---

*
AC8
.A6
no.J-288
1943
Lofts, Norah (Robinson) 1904-
The golden fleece. New York, Editions
for the Armed Services, ᶜ1943.
319 p. 10 x 14cm. (Armed Services ed.
J-288)

NL 0449325   ViU

Lofts, Norah (Robinson) 1904-
The Golden Fleece, by Norah Lofts. New York, A. A.
Knopf, 1944.
3 p. l., 3-249, [1] p. 20½ᵐ.
"First American edition."

I. Title.
                                      43-18854
Library of Congress   PZ3.L825Go 2

       OC1
NL 0449326   DLC IU MB Or OrP WaS WaT PHC OLak OO

Lofts, Norah (Robinson) 1904-
Here was a man; a romantic history of Sir Walter Raleigh,
his voyages, his discoveries & his queen, by Norah Lofts. London, Methuen and company, limited [1936]
vi, 282 p. 19ᵐ.

1. Raleigh, Sir Walter, 1552?-1618—Fiction. 2. Gt. Brit.—Hist.—
Elizabeth, 1558-1603—Fiction. I. Title.

                                      36-15576 Revised
Library of Congress   PZ3.L825He

NL 0449327   DLC CaBVa OC1h OU OC1

Lofts, Norah (Robinson) 1904-
Here was a man; a romantic history of Sir Walter
Raleigh, his voyages, his discoveries, and his queen, by
Norah Lofts. New York, A. A. Knopf, 1936.
5 p. l., 3-304 p. 20 cm.
Illustrated t.-p.
"First American edition."

1. Raleigh, Sir Walter, 1552?-1618—Fiction. I. Title.
                              [Full name: Norah Ethel (Robinson) Lofts]

PZ3.L825He 2   36-25287 rev

NL 0449328   DLC WaS Or NN

Lofts Norah (Robinson) 1904-
Here was a man; a romantic history of Sir
Walter Raleigh, his voyages, his discoveries,
and his queen. Sydney, etc., Invincible press
[1947?]

253 p. 22 cm.

NL 0449329   MH

Lofts, Norah (Robinson) 1904-
Hester Roon, a novel by Norah Lofts. London, P. Davies
[1940]
4 p. l., 11-396, [1] p. 19 cm.
"First published 1940."

I. Title.
                              [Full name: Norah Ethel (Robinson) Lofts]

PZ3.L825Hes   40-13552 rev

NL 0449330   DLC OEac OC1 OU NNC LU

Lofts, Norah (Robinson) 1904-
Hester Roon, by Norah Lofts. New York, A. A. Knopf,
1940.
4 p. l., 3-457, [1] p. 20½ᵐ.
Illustrated t.-p.

I. Title.
                                      40-30576 Revised
Library of Congress   PZ3.L825Hes 2

NL 0449331   DLC WaS WaE IdB ViU

4PR-155 Lofts, Norah (Robinson) 1904-
Hester Roon. Traduit de l'anglais par
Madeleine Santschi. [Lausanne] Marguerat [1945]
366 p. (Collection "La Caravelle" 18)

NL 0449332   DLC-P4

Lofts, Norah (Robinson) 1904-
... Hester Roon, roman. 2. aufl.
Zürich, A. Muller, n.d.

360 p.

Title of American edition: Hester
Roon.
Translated by Rudolf Hochgland.

NL 0449333   OC1

Lofts, Norah (Robinson) 1904-
... Hester Roon, roman. 4. aufl. Zürich, A. Muller [1944]
360 p. 21½ cm.
At head of title: Norah Lofts.
"Berechtigte übertragung aus dem amerikanischen, besorgt von dr.
Rudolf Hochglend."

I. Hochglend, Rudolf, tr. II. Title.

PR6023.O35H44   47-25173

NL 0449334   DLC

Lofts, Norah (Robinson) 1904-
... Hölle der barmherzigkeit, roman. Zürich, A. Müller
[1944]
264 p. 21ᵐ.
At head of title: Norah Lofts.
"Berechtigte uebersetzung aus dem amerikanischen, besorgt von Ur-
sula von Wiese. Titel des originals: 'White hell of pity'."
"Erstes bis viertes tausend."

I. Wiese und Kaiserswaldau, Ursula Renate von, 1905-   tr.
II. Title.

PR6023.O35W54   47-23558

NL 0449335   DLC

Lofts, Norah (Robinson) 1904-
I met a gypsy, by Norah Lofts. London, Methuen & co.,
ltd. 1935.
v, 249, [1] p. 19½ cm.

I. Title.
                              [Full name: Norah Ethel (Robinson) Lofts]

PZ3.L825 I   35-15041 rev

NL 0449336   DLC OrCS WaE

Lofts, Norah (Robinson) 1904-
I met a gypsy, by Norah Lofts. New York, A. A. Knopf,
1935.
3 p. l., 3-272, [3] p. illus. 21ᵐ.
"First American edition."
CONTENTS.—Bride of Christ.—The slave.—Iconoclasts.—Arctic inter-
lude.—The Frenchman.—Wild flower transplanted.—Indian dust-heap.—
Free beer.—No love.—Chinese finale.

I. Title.
                                      35-38584 Revised
Library of Congress   PZ3.L825 I 2

NL 0449337   DLC

828
L8281m
Lofts, Norah (Robinson) 1904-
I met a gypsy, by Norah Lofts. New York,
Grosset & Dunlap [c1935]
3 p. l., 3-272, [3] p. illus. 21ᵐ.

CONTENTS.—Bride of Christ.—The slave.—Iconoclasts.—Arctic interlude.—The Frenchman.—Wild flower transplanted.—Indian dust-heap.—
Free beer.—No love.—Chinese finale.

NL 0449338   MiU MH

PR6023
.O32
1936
Lofts, Norah.
I met a gypsy, by Norah Lofts. New York, A. A. Knopf,
1936.
3 p. l., 3-272, [3] p. illus. 21ᵐ.

CONTENTS.—Bride of Christ.—The slave.—Iconoclasts.—Arctic interlude.—The Frenchman.—Wild flower transplanted.—Indian dust-heap.—
Free beer.—No love.—Chinese finale.

NL 0449339   ViU OC1 OC1W OU OO NN NcD

VOLUME 338

Lofts, Norah (Robinson) 1904–
... Jassy. London, M. Joseph ltd. ₁1944₎
222, ₁1₎ p. 19ᶜᵐ.
At head of title : Norah Lofts.
"First published 1944."

ɪ. Title.

Library of Congress   PZ3.L825Jas

NL 0449340   DLC IEN OEac

Lofts, Norah (Robinson) 1904–
... Jassy. New York, A. A. Knopf, 1945.
4 p. l., 276, ₂2₎ p. 19ᶜᵐ.
At head of title : Norah Lofts.
"First American edition."

ɪ. Title.

Library of Congress °   PZ3.L825Jas 2

45–5092

WaT WaE
NcGU TxU OO OC1 OU CaBVa Or OrP OrU WaS OrSaW WaTC
NL 0449341   DLC NcU NcD MoU LU CU–I MB KEmT ViU

Lofts, Norah (Robinson) 1904–
Jassy. London, M. Joseph ₁1949₎
222 p.

NL 0449342   NNC

Lofts, Norah (Robinson) 1904–
Jassy, Roman. ₁Berechtigte Uebertragung besorgt von Ursula von Wiese₎ Rüschlikon-Zch., A. Müller ₁1945 ?₎
331 p. 22 cm.

ɪ. Title.

PR6023.O35J34

49–25671*

NL 0449343   DLC

Lofts, Norah (Robinson) 1904–
Jassy, roman ; version française de Marianne Gagnebin. Genève, Jeheber ₁1948₎
294 p. 19 cm.

ɪ. Gagnebin, Marianne (Maurer) 1881–   tr. ɪɪ. Title.
Full name : Norah Ethel (Robinson) Lofts.
PR6023.O35J3.

48–21974*

NL 0449344   DLC

Lofts, Norah (Robinson) 1904–
The lute player. ₁1st ed.₎ Garden City, N. Y., Doubleday, 1951.
465 p. 22 cm.

1. Blondel de Nesle, 12th cent.—Fiction. 2. Richard ɪ, King of England, 1157–1199—Fiction. ɪ. Title.
Full name : Norah Ethel (Robinson) Lofts.
PZ3.L825Lu

51–13985 ‡

OrCS
FTaSU CaBVa IdB Or ViU IdPI OrP WaE WaS WaT WaSp
NL 0449345   DLC TxU MsU KyU GU KyBB KyLxCB KyLx

Lofts, Norah (Robinson) 1904–
... Michael and all angels. London, M. Joseph ltd. ₁1943₎
224 p. 19ᶜᵐ.
At head of title : Norah Lofts.
"First published in 1943."

ɪ. Title.

43–16005

Library of Congress   PZ3.L825Mi

NL 0449346   DLC

Lofts, Norah (Robinson) 1904–
... Die nacht der entscheidung, roman. Rüschlikon-Zch., A. Müller ₁1945₎
285 p. 21ᶜᵐ.
At head of title : Norah Lofts.
"Berichtigte uebersetzung aus dem englischen, besorgt von Renate Hertenstein. Titel des englischen originals: 'Michael and all angels.' Titel der amerikanischen ausgabe : 'The Golden Fleece'."
"Erstes bis viertes tausend."

ɪ. Hertenstein, Renate, tr. ɪɪ. Title.

PR6023.O35M54

47–24582

NL 0449347   DLC

Lofts, Norah (Robinson) 1904–
Out of this nettle, by Norah Lofts ... London, V. Gollancz, ltd., 1938.
445 p. 20¼ cm.
American edition has title : Colin Lowrie.

ɪ. Title.
₁Full name : Norah Ethel (Robinson) Lofts₎
PZ3.L825Ou

38–29160 rev

NL 0449348   DLC

Lofts, Norah (Robinson), 1904–
...La piste. Traduit de l'anglais par Madeleine Santschi. ₁Lausanne₎ Marguerat ₁1943₎   352 p.   19cm. (Collection "La caravelle.")

Original title : The road to revelation.

440896B. ɪ. Santschi, Madeleine, tr.   ɪɪ. Title.
N. Y. P. L.   May 26, 1948

NL 0449349   NN DLC

PR6023
.O 35S58
1950   Lofts, Nora (Robinson), 1904–
Plantageägarens hustru ₁till svenska av Ingrid Rääf₎ Stockholm, Natur och Kultur ₁1950₎
473 p.   24 cm.
Swedish translation of The silver nutmeg.

ɪ. Rääf, Ingrid, tr. ɪɪ. Title.

NL 0449350   MB

823
L827q   Lofts, Norah (Robinson) 1904–
Queen in waiting. London, M. Joseph ₁1955₎
272p. illus.

"First published by Michael Joseph ... 1955."

1. Eleanor of Aquitaine, consort of Henry II, 1122?–1204--Fiction. ɪ. Title.

NL 0449351   TxFTC

Lofts, Norah (Robinson) 1904–
Requiem for idols, by Norah Lofts. London, Methuen and co., limited ₁1938₎
v p., 1 l., 199, ₁1₎ p. 19 cm.
"First published in 1938."

ɪ. Title.
₁Full name : Norah Ethel (Robinson) Lofts₎
PZ3.L825Re

38–14588 rev

NL 0449352   DLC WaE

Lofts, Norah (Robinson) 1904–
... Requiem for idols. New York, A. A. Knopf, 1938.
5 p. l., ₃3₎–213, ₁1₎ p. 20ᶜᵐ.
Title on two leaves.

∴ Title.

38–16224 Revised

Library of Congress   PZ3.L825Re 2

NL 0449353   DLC OrP WaS WaSp

Lofts, *Mrs.* Norah (Robinson) 1904–
The road to revelation, a novel by Norah Lofts. London, P. Davies ₁1941₎
5 p. l., ₃3₎–312 p. 19ᶜᵐ.
"First published 1941."

ɪ. Title.

41–23173

Library of Congress   PZ3.L825Ro

NL 0449354   DLC CaBVaU CaBVa

Lofts, Norah (Robinson) 1904–
La signorina Kingaby ; versione di Susanna Comi. Milano, A. Martello ₁1946₎
261 p. 22 cm. (I Grandi romanzi Martello ₁7₎)
Translation of The brittle glass.

ɪ. Title.
Full name : Norah Ethel (Robinson) Lofts.
PR6023.O35B75

50–27247

NL 0449355   DLC

Lofts, Norah (Robinson) 1904–
Silver nutmeg. ₁1st Amer. ed.₎ Garden City, N. Y., Doubleday, 1947.
₁5₎ l., 3–368 p. 23 cm.

ɪ. Title.
Full name : Norah Ethel (Robinson) Lofts.
PZ3.L825Si

47–31097*

OrCS IdPI OrP OrU–M WaE WaT WaSp WaS
NL 0449356   DLC NcGU MB OOxM CaBVa IdB Or ViU MH

Lofts, Norah (Robinson) 1904–
Silver nutmeg. Garden City, N. Y., Sun Dial Press [c1947]
[5] l., 3–368 p. 23 cm.

NL 0449357   NcGU

VOLUME 338

Lofts, Norah (Robinson) 1904–
Silver nutmeg. London, M. Joseph [1947]
367 p. 21 cm.

ɪ. Title.

PZ3.L825Si 2   47–6643*

NL 0449358   DLC CtY

Lofts, Norah (Robinson) 1904–
Silver nutmeg.   Garden City, N. Y.,
Doubleday, 1948 [c1947]
[5] l. 3–368 p. 21 cm.

NL 0449359   LU

Lofts, Norah (Robinson) 1904–
... To see a fine lady. London, M. Joseph ltd. [1946]
221, [1] p. 19ᵐ.
At head of title: Norah Lofts.
"First published 1946."

ɪ. Title.

Library of Congress   PZ3.L825To   46–16157

NL 0449360   DLC

Lofts, Norah (Robinson) 1904–
... To see a fine lady. New York, A. A. Knopf, 1946.
3 p. l., 3–247, [1] p., 1 l. 19 cm.
At head of title: Norah Lofts.
"First American edition."

ɪ. Title.

Full name: Norah Ethel (Robinson) Lofts.

PZ3.L825To 2   46–5944

NL 0449361   DLC CaBVa Or WaE WaS WaT MH IaU ViU

Lofts, Norah (Robinson) 1904–
... Weg der enthüllung, roman. Zürich, A. Müller [1942]
317, [1] p. 21½ᵐ.
At head of title: Norah Lofts.
"Berechtigte uebersetzung aus dem amerikanischen, besorgt von Ursula von Wiese. Titel der amerikanischen ausgabe: 'The road to revelation'."
"Erstes bis drittes tausend."

ɪ. Wiese und Kaiserswaldau, Ursula Renate von, 1905–   tr. ɪɪ. Title.

PR6023.O35R64   47–39499

NL 0449362   DLC

Lofts, Norah (Robinson) 1904–
... Wenn die wildnis blüht, roman.
3. Aufl.   Zürich, A. Muller verlag [c1940]
336 p.
Title of American original: Blossom like the roses.
Transl.. into German by Heinz Zurcher.

NL 0449363   OCl

Lofts, Norah (Robinson) 1904–
... Wenn die wildnis blüht, roman. 4. aufl. Zürich, A. Müller [°1940]
336 p. 21½ cm.
At head of title: Norah Lofts.
"Berechtigte übertragung, besorgt auf grund der amerikanischen ausgabe von dr. H. Zürcher. Titel der amerikanischen ausgabe: 'Blossom like the rose'."
"9. und 10. tausend."

ɪ. Zürcher, Heinz, tr. ɪɪ. Title.

PR6023.O35B54   47–39655

NL 0449364   DLC

Lofts, Norah (Robinson) 1904–
White hell of pity, by Norah Lofts. New York, A. A. Knopf, 1937.
3 p. l., 273 p. 19 cm.
"First American edition."

ɪ. Title.
[Full name: Norah Ethel (Robinson) Lofts]

PZ3.L825Wh   37–28782 rev

NL 0449365   DLC WaTC WaS OLak OClh IU NN

PR6023
O3
I25

Lofts, Norah (Robinson) 1904–
... Wildes Blut; roman in zehn geschichten ... Zürich, Albert Müller [1942?]
226 p., 1 l. 21 cm

"Erstes bis drittes tausend."
"Berechtigte übersetzung aus dem amerikanischen, besorgt von Ursula von Wiese."
Translation of I met a gypsy

NL 0449366   RPB

Lofts, Norah (Robinson) 1904–
... Wildes blut, roman in zehn geschichten. 2. aufl. Zürich, A. Müller [1944]
226 p. 21 cm.
At head of title: Norah Lofts.
"Berechtigte übersetzung aus dem amerikanischen, besorgt von Ursula von Wiese. Titel des amerikanischen originals: 'I met a gypsy'."
"Viertes bis sechstes tausend."

ɪ. Wiese und Kaiserswaldau, Ursula Renate von, 1905–   tr. ɪɪ. Title.

PR6023.O35 I24   47–29053

NL 0449367   DLC

Lofts, Norah (Robinson) 1904–
Winter harvest, a novel. Introd. by Stewart H. Holbrook. Garden City, N. Y., Doubleday, 1955.
347 p. 22 cm.

1. Donner Party—Fiction.   ɪ. Title.
Full name: Norah Ethel (Robinson) Lofts.

PZ3.L825Wi   55–10512 ‡

PWcS OOxM FU
NL 0449368   DLC KEmT NN NcD PPL PP TxU CU OCU OCl

Lofts, Norah (Robinson) 1904–
Women in the Old Testament; twenty psychological portraits. London, Low [1949]
xi, 196 p. 22 cm.

1. Women in the Bible.   ɪ. Title.
Full name: Norah Ethel (Robinson) Lofts.

BS575.L58 1949a   221.92   50–3393

WaT NcU
NL 0449369   DLC CaBVa Or OrCS OrP Wa WaE WaSp WaS

Lofts, Norah (Robinson) 1904–
Women in the Old Testament; twenty psychological portraits. New York, Macmillan, 1949.
xi, 178 p. 21 cm.

1. Women in the Bible.   ɪ. Title.
Full name: Norah Ethel (Robinson) Lofts.

BS575.L58   221.92   49–11604*

MB OO OEac OClTem OClW ViU PP PPA
NL 0449370   DLC KyLxCB KyLx KyU NcGU OClW PPDrop

Lofts, Norah (Robinson) 1904–
De zilveren notemuskaat. Uit het engels vertaald door S.Franke. Amsterdam, Arbeiderspers, 1950.   464p.

NL 0449371   CaBVa

Loftsson, J
Draumaráðningar
see under title

Loftunga, Þorarinn
see   Thorarinn Loftunga, 11th cent.

Loftus, Alfred John.
The kingdom of Siam: its progress and prospects. By Captain A. J. Loftus ... (Phra Nidesa Jalahdi, ᴋ. ᴄ. ᴄ. ꜱ.) ... Huntingdon [Eng.], The "Hunts county news" co., limited, 1891.
cover-title, [5]–43, [1], 6 p. 24½ᵐ.
"Siam as a market for the British trader" (a paper written by the author with a view to its being read before the Birmingham Chamber of commerce) : 6 p. at end.

1. Siam—Pol. & govt. 2. Siam—Comm.—Gt. Brit. 3. Gt. Brit.—Comm.—Siam.

Library of Congress   DS582.L6   45–28128

NL 0449374   DLC

4TC
76

Loftus, Alfred John
Notes of a journey across the Isthmus of Kra, made with the French Government Survey Expedition, January–April, 1883... Appendix containing reprint of report to the Indian government by Fraser and Forlong, in 1863. Singapore: Printed at the "Straits Times" Press, by A. Frois, 1883.
30 p. [Captains]

NL 0449375   DLC-P4 WU

Wason
DS588
K8 L82

Loftus, Alfred John.
Notes of a journey across the Isthmus of Krà, made with the French government survey expedition, January–April, 1883. With explanatory map and sections, and appendix containing reprint of report to the Indian government, by Captains Fraser and Forlong, 1863. Singapore and Straits Printing Office, 1883.
55 p. 2 fold. maps. 21cm.

NL 0449376   NIC CtY MH ICN

Loftus, Alfred John.
On constructing sea anchors and jury rudders.. Hongkong, 1870.
53p.

YA 21297

NL 0449377   DLC

VOLUME 338

Loftus, *Lord* **Augustus William Frederick Spencer,** 1817–1904.
The diplomatic reminiscences of Lord Augustus Loftus ... 1837–1862. London [etc.] Cassell & company, limited, 1892.
2 v. front. (port.) 23ᶜᵐ.

1. Europe—Politics—1815–1871.

8–20427

Library of Congress   DA46.L7

PU MiU OCl OClW MH NcD
NL 0449378   DLC TxU MeB OrU WaSpG OrP PU CtY MdBP

Loftus, *Lord* **Augustus William Frederick Spencer,** 1817–1904.
The diplomatic reminiscences of Lord Augustus Loftus ... 1837–1862. London [etc.] Cassell & company, limited, 1892.
2 v. front. (port.) 23 cm.
Ultra microfiche. Dayton, Ohio, National Cash Register, 1970. 1st title of 4. 10.5 x 14.8 cm. (PCMI library collection, 224-1)

NL 0449379   KEmT

Loftus, *Lord* **Augustus William Frederick Spencer,** 1817–1904.
The diplomatic reminiscences of Lord Augustus Loftus ... 1862–1879. 2d series. London [etc.] Cassell and company, limited, 1894.
2 v. 23ᶜᵐ.

1. Europe—Politics—1848–1871. 2. Europe—Politics—1871–

Library of Congress   DA46.L72

8–20426

MiU NN NjP
NL 0449380   DLC MeB TxU NcD CtY PU PPL PPFr DN OClW

Loftus, Charles, 1796–1883.
My life. From 1815 to 1849. By Charles Loftus. London, Hurst and Blackett, 1877.
2 v. 18½ᶜᵐ.

1. Gt. Brit.—Hist.—19th cent.   i. Title.

22–13870

Library of Congress   DA536.L8A3

NL 0449381   DLC MdBP DN ODW CtY CLU ICU NcD NN

Loftus, Charles, 1796–1883.
My youth by sea and land from 1809 to 1816. By Charles Loftus ... London, Hurst and Blackett, 1876.
2 v. 18½ᶜᵐ.

1. Gt. Brit.—Hist.—1800–1837.   i. Title.

22–13871

Library of Congress   DA536.L8A2

NL 0449382   DLC MdBP NcU NcD DN CtY NN

Loftus, Cissie, 1876–
First verses, by Cissie Loftus. [New York, The Lotus Press, 1895]
30 p. 15cm.

Author's inscription and signature on t.-p.
"Of this booklet one hundred copies have been printed, of which this is number 93."

NL 0449383   NNC

---

*fEC85
St487
Gzl

Loftus, Cissie, 1876–
... Shadow song. (Words by Robert Louis Stevenson) ...
M.Witmark & sons, New York, London, Chicago. Toronto, The Canadian-American music co., limited. [1900]
cover-title, 3–5p.   36cm., in case 37cm.
Plate number: 3567–3.
A poem from A child's garden of verses.
Original printed white wrappers; in cloth case with other settings of Stevenson poems.

NL 0449384   MH

---

*fEC85
St487
Gzl

Loftus, Cissie, 1876–
... Where the boats go. (Words by Robert Louis Stevenson) ...
M.Witmark & sons, New York, London, Chicago. Toronto, The Canadian-American music co., limited. [1900]
cover-title, 3–5p.   35cm., in case 37cm.
Plate number: 3675–3.
A poem from A child's garden of verses.
Original printed white wrappers; in cloth case with other settings of Stevenson poems.

NL 0449385   MH

HE1035
.B4

Loftus, Donald L., 1921–   joint author.

Berge, Stanley.
Diesel motor trains, an economic evaluation, by Stanley Berge and Donald L. Loftus. Chicago, Northwestern Univ., School of Commerce [1949]

Loftus, Dudley, 1619–1695.
The case of Ware and Sherley as it was set forth in matter of fact and argued in several points of law in the consistory of Dublin, in Michaelmas term 1668. Dublin, B. Tooke, 1669.
Microfilm copy made by the Oxford University Press. Negative. Collation of the original: 2 pts. (93 p.)

1. Ware, Mary, plaintiff in law suit. 2. Shirley, James, defendant in law suit.

Microfilm 1668 Law   Mic 55–3096

NL 0449387   DLC ICN MH

Case
K
76
.221

LOFTUS, DUDLEY, 1619–1695.
Διγαμίας αδικία: or, The first marriage of Katherine Fitzgerald, (now Lady Decies) contracted in facie ecclesiæ with John Power, now Lord of Decies, asserted, by Dudley Loftus... London, 1677.
[6], 26p.

NL 0449388   ICN

---

*EC65
L8278
642a

[Loftus, Edward, fl. 1642]
Approved, good, and happy newes from Ireland: relating how the castle of Artaine was taken from the rebels, two of their captaines kild, and one taken prisoners by the protestants. With the arrivall of 2000 foot, and 300 horse from England. Also a great skirmish betweene the Protestants and the rebels at a place neere Feleston, wherein the English obtained great renowne and victory. Whereunto is added, a true relation of the great overthrow which the English gave the   rebels before Drogheda

sent in a letter bearing date the 27 of February. to Sir Robert King knight at Cecill house in the Strand ...
London, Printed for Iohn Wright, 1641[1642].
[8]p. 18.5cm.
Woodcut illus. on t.-p.
"A letter sent from Drogheda, to Sir Robert King, dated Febr.   27." is signed: Ed. Loftus ...

NL 0449390   MH DFo

Y942.062
L827

[LOFTUS, Edward] fl. 1642.
Ioyfull nevves from Ireland, or, A trve relation of the great overthrow which the English gave the rebels before Droheda, sent in a letter bearing date the 27 of February, to Sir Robert King ... London, Printed for Iohn Franke, 1642.
1 p.l., 4 p. 17cm.
Signed: Ed. Loftus.
1. Gt. Brit.   History. 1642. 2. Ireland. History.   1641.
3. News-letters,   English.

NL 0449391   MnU CtY

Loftus, Edward, fl. 1642.
Joyfull news from Ireland
see also   Bristol, George Digby, 2d earl of, 1612–1677.
Two letters of note.

Loftus, Elisabeth Marie Thérèse.
Reflets étranges, by Elisabeth Marie Thérèse Loftus ... illustrated by Henry Meloy. New York, Cincinnati [etc.] American book company [1934]
ix, 203 p. incl. front., illus. 19½ᶜᵐ.
Adapted and published for school use. cf. Acknowledgments.
CONTENTS.—La demoiselle au chat d'or, d'après M. Prévost.—Apparition, d'après G. de Maupassant.—La nuit des morts, d'après A. Le Braz.—Les trois femmes, d'après A. Le Braz.—L'horloge arrêtée, by A. Le Braz.—Le savatier et le financier, by La Fontaine.—Un cas de hantise, d'après Camille Flammarion.—La chanson qui vente, by A. Le Braz.
1. Short stories, French. 2. French language—Chrestomathies and readers. i. Title.

Library of Congress   PQ1275.L6   34–23454
———— Copy 2.
Copyright A 74443   [2]   [448.6] 840.822

NL 0449393   DLC OrCS IdPI NN ODW

Loftus, Ernest Achey, 1884–   ed.
Baker and Lake Albert
see under
Baker, Sir Samuel White, 1821–1893.

Loftus, Ernest Achey, 1884–
Education and the citizen, by Colonel E. A. Loftus ... London, G. Routledge and sons, ltd., 1935.
viii, 201 p. 19½ᶜᵐ. (Half-title: The New-world series, ed. by Hubert Williams)

1. Education—Gt. Brit. i. Title.

Library of Congress   LB775.L65   35–29652
[5]   370.942

NL 0449395   DLC NcD ICU

Loftus, Ernest Achey, 1884–
Elton and the East African Coast slave-trade
see under Elton, James Frederick.

Loftus, Ernest Achey, 1884–   ed.
Gregory
see under
Gregory, John Walter, 1864–1932.

VOLUME 338

LOFTUS, ERNEST ACHEY, 1884–
A history of Barking abbey, by E.A. Loftus and H.F. Chettle. [Barking, Essex, Wilson & Whitworth, 1954?] 84 p. illus. 22cm.

"Part I of this work is a contraction of a thesis," by E.A. Loftus. Bibliographical footnotes.

1. Barking abbey. I. Chettle, Henry, Francis.

NL 0449398   NN

Loftus, Ernest Achey, 1884–
A history of the descendants of Maximilian Cole of Oxford, who flourished in the 17th century. London, Adlard, 1938.

iv, 48 p. fold. geneal. table (in pocket) 29 cm.

1. Cole family.

CS439.C69 1938   56–54711

NL 0449399   DLC NcD

Loftus, Ernest Achey, 1884–   ed.
Johnston on Kilimanjaro

see under

Johnston, Sir Harry Hamilton, 1858–1927.

Loftus, Ernest Achey, 1884–   ed.
Speke and the Nile source

see under

Speke, John Hanning, 1827–1864.

Loftus, Ernest Achey, 1884–
A visual history of Africa.   London, Evans bros. [1954]   48 p.   illus., maps.   25cm.

1. Africa—Hist.—Outlines, syllabi, etc.

NL 0449402   NN IEN

Loftus, Helen.
Automation in the library; an annotated bibliography. [n. p., 1955]

13 p. 22 cm.

Cover title.
"Prepared in connection with a program [sponsored by the Business Division] entitled 'Automation in the library—fact or fantasy' presented at the Special Libraries Association Convention held in Detroit, June 13–17, 1955."

1. Automation—Bibl. 2. Libraries—Mechanical aids—Bibl. I. Title.

                                               A 56–5871
Columbia Univ.   Libraries
for Library of Congress   [1]

NL 0449403   NNC IaU MiU

Loftus, J   P
Chronicle of activities, 1941–1955

see under

U.S. Dept. of Agriculture. Organization and Methods Conference.

SF285
.D8   Loftus, James, ed.
Dunstan, Nelson.
The thoroughbred in New Jersey; his days and deeds, by Nelson Dunstan. Edited by James Loftus. Camden, N. J., Garden state racing association inc., °1944.

Loftus, John.
Troubled river.   New York, Shapiro, Bernstein & co. [c1954]

First line: I dreamed that I stood.
Chorus: Well, roll along troubled river.
Portrait of Matthews brothers quartet on t.-p.
1. Songs, Popular—1890–   2. Rivers. 3. Matthews brothers quartet—Port.

NL 0449406   NN

Loftus, John Alphonsus, 1911–
Investment management; an analysis of the experiences of American management investment trusts, by John A. Loftus ... Baltimore, The Johns Hopkins press, 1941.

136 p., 1 l. incl. tables. 25ᶜᵐ.

Thesis (PH. D.)—Johns Hopkins university, 1940.
"Reprinted from Studies in historical and political science, series LIX, no. 1."
Vita.

1. Investment trusts. 2. Investments—U. S.   I. Title.

                                               A 41–4289
Johns Hopkins univ. Libr.
for Library of Congress   HG4497.L6 1941 a
                                [2]   332.140973

NL 0449407   MdBJ PPT DLC

Loftus, John Alphonsus, 1911–
... Investment management; an analysis of the experiences of American management investment trusts, by John A. Loftus ... Baltimore, The Johns Hopkins press, 1941.

136 p. incl. tables. 24½ᶜᵐ.   (The Johns Hopkins university studies in historical and political science, ser. LIX, no. 1)

Issued also as thesis (PH. D.) Johns Hopkins university.

1. Investment trusts. 2. Investments—U. S.   I. Title.

                                               41–20178
Library of Congress   H31.J6 ser. 59, no. 1
——— Copy 2.   HG4497.L6
                                [20]   (308.2) 332.140973

                OU MH ViU OCU OO PU-L WaTC WaS Or
NL 0449408   DLC PSt CoU GU-L NBuU GU PPT PSC OOxM

Loftus, John James, 1882–   joint author.
Sallen, Benjamin.
At home and school ... [by] Benjamin Sallen ... John J. Loftus ... Myron R. Goldin ... [and] Helen Hay Heyl ... Illustrators: Miriam Story Hurford, A. F. Hurford. Chicago, New York [etc.] Lyons and Carnahan, °1942.

Loftus, John James, 1882–   joint author.
Gordon, Dorothy, 1895–
Come to France [by] Dorothy Gordon ... and John J. Loftus ... illustrated by Veronica Reed. New York, Cincinnati [etc.] American book company [°1939]

Loftus, John James, 1882–   joint author.
Sallen, Benjamin.
Happy children ... [by] Benjamin Sallen ... John J. Loftus ... Myron R. Goldin ... [and] Helen Hay Heyl ... Illustrators: Miriam Story Hurford, A. F. Hurford. Chicago, New York [etc.] Lyons and Carnahan, °1943.

PE1127
.D9S3   Loftus, John James, 1882–   joint author.
Sallen, Benjamin.
Homes for all ... [by] Benjamin Sallen ... John J. Loftus ... Myron R. Goldin ... [and] Helen Hay Heyl ... Illustrators: Martha E. Miller, Vera S. Norman [and] Mildred L. Hetherington. Chicago, Dallas [etc.] Lyons and Carnahan, °1945.

Loftus, John J., 1882–   joint author.
Gordon, Dorothy, 1895–
Knowing the Netherlands [by] Dorothy Gordon ... and John J. Loftus ... illustrated by Veronica Reed. New York, Cincinnati [etc.] American book company [°1940]

QA106
.G72   Loftus, John James, 1882–   joint author.
Graham, Frederick Burton.
Modern-city arithmetic, third[–eighth] year ... by Frederick B. Graham ... and John J. Loftus ... Yonkers-on-Hudson, N. Y., World book company, 1929–[30]

Loftus, John James, 1882–
A program for the desirable use of leisure time as a cardinal objective of the public elementary schools.

(*In* National education association of the United States. Addresses and proceedings, 1928. p. 390–394)

1. Leisure.

                                               E 31–127 Revised
U. S. Off. of educ. Library   L13.N212 1928
for Library of Congress   [r43c2]

NL 0449415   DHEW

Loftus, John James, 1882–
The story of how a great school system developed a new educational program ... Chicago, F. E. Compton [1948]

24 p. illus., port. 18 cm.

1. New York (City) Board of Education. Division of Elementary Schools. 2. Education—New York (City)—Curricula.

LB1563.N62L6   372.9747   48–9907*

NL 0449416   DLC

PE1119
.S232   Loftus, John James, 1882–   joint author.
Sallen, Benjamin.
Teachers manual, Child experience readers [by] Benjamin Sallen ... John J. Loftus ... Myron R. Goldin ... [and] Helen Hay Heyl ... Chicago, New York [etc.] Lyons and Carnahan, °1944.

PE1119
.S23   Loftus, John James, 1882–   joint author.
Sallen, Benjamin.
Visits with friends ... [by] Benjamin Sallen ... John J. Loftus ... Myron R. Goldin ... [and] Helen Hay Heyl ... Illustrators: Martha E. Miller, Vera S. Norman. Chicago, New York [etc.] Lyons and Carnahan, °1944.

VOLUME 338

Loftus, John Thomas.
The constables' manual containing a summary of the law relating to the duties of constables, being a revision of Jones' Constables' manual. Rev. and re-written by John Thomas Loftus ... and John Alexander Milne ...   Toronto, Canada, The Carswell company, limited, 1906.
xii, 242 p.   16.5 cm.

NL 0449419   CU CaBViP

Loftus, John Thomas.
The constables' manual, containing a summary of the law relating to the duties of constables, being a re-vision of Jones' Constables' manual. Rev. and re-written by John Thomas Loftus ... and John Alexander Milne ... 4. ed. rev. by George Patterson ... Toronto, Can., Carswell co., 1916.
xiv, 248 p.   15½cm.

NL 0449420   MH-L CaNSWA

280
L822
Loftus, Joseph E
The impact of atomic energy on economic studies. [Washington, 1949?]
8 l.

1. Atomic energy. Economic aspects.
I. Isard, Walter,   joint author.

NL 0449421   DNAL

Loftus, Justa.
Pot pourri of/van verse ⌈by⌉ Justa Loftus. ⌈Cape Town, Galvin & Sales ltd., 1943?⌉
cover-title, 56 p.   18½ᶜᵐ.
Poems in English and Afrikaans.

I. Title.

New York. Public library   A 45-1537
for Library of Congress   PR6023.O36P6
⌈2⌉†   821.91

NL 0449422   NN DLC

Loftus, Murrough.
A sword unearthed, by Murrough Loftus. Oxford, Printed at the Shakespeare head press and sold by B. Blackwell, 1934.
4 p.l., 30 p.   19 cm.
"Several of these poems have been published in the 'New English Weekly' ".

NL 0449423   CtY

Loftus, P   C.
A main cause of unemployment: an indictment of foreign investment, by P. C. Loftus; with an appendix on agriculture and export trade. 2d ed. (enl. and rev.) London, Sir I. Pitman & sons, ltd., 1932.
viii, 87, ⌈1⌉ p. 19ᶜᵐ.

1. Investments. 2. Debts, Public. 3. Economic policy. 4. Gt. Brit.— Economic policy. I. Title.

Library of Congress   HG4538.L6 1932
                              33-11808
⌈5⌉   332

NL 0449424   DLC NN OCl

Loftus, P   J
National income of Palestine, 1944. Pales-tine, Government printer, 1946.
48 p. tables.

1. Palestine - Economic conditions. 2. Income - Palestine.

NL 0449425   NNC CU NNZI

Loftus, Peter F., firm, consulting engineer, Pittsburgh.
A study of the engineering and economic status of the municipal electric utility for the Board of public utilities, Jamestown, New York... Peter F. Loftus, consulting engineers, Pittsburgh, Pa. ⌈Pittsburgh, 1935⌉ 2 v. illus. 29cm.

Ten reports, each with special t.-p.
Prepared at the request of the Public utilities board.

421065–66B. 1. Electric power plant   —U.S.—N. Y.—Jamestown.
I. Jamestown, N. Y. Public utilities   board.
N. Y. P. L.   December 22, 1947

NL 0449426   NN

Loftus, Pierse Creagh.
... Agriculture and finance, by P. C. Loftus ... ⌈London, 1942⌉
18, ⌈2⌉ p. 21½ᶜᵐ.
At head of title: Economic reform club and institute ... London.
"The first two articles appeared in the 'East Anglian daily times' early in 1939. The last appeared in the 'Dairy farmer' of May, 1941."

1. Agriculture—Economic aspects—Gt. Brit. 2. Gt. Brit.—Comm. I. Economic reform club and institute, London. II. Title.
                                          43-13552
Library of Congress   HD1927.1942.L6
⌈2⌉   338.1

NL 0449427   DLC CtY NN

Loftus, Pierse Creagh.
The Conservative party and the future; a programme for Tory democracy, by Pierse Loftus. London, S. Swift and co. ltd. ⌈1912⌉
124 p. 18½ᶜᵐ.

1. Conservative party (Gt. Brit.) 2. Gt. Brit.—Pol. & govt.—1910-1936.
Library of Congress   JN1129.C7L6
                              43-46047
⌈2⌉   329.942

NL 0449428   DLC

Loftus, Pierse Creagh.
The creed of a Tory, by Pierse Loftus. London, P. Allan & co., ltd. ⌈1926⌉
2 p. l., 7-318 p. 22½ᶜᵐ.

1. Gt. Brit.—Pol. & govt.—1910-1936. 2. Conservative party (Gt. Brit.) I. Title.
Library of Congress   DA566.7.L6
                              27-1028 Revised

NL 0449429   DLC CtY NN OU

Loftus, Pierse Creagh.
A main cause of unemployment; an indictment of foreign investment, by P. C. Loftus; with an appendix on agriculture and export trade. 2d ed. (enl. and rev.) London, Sir I. Pit-man & sons, ltd., 1932.
viii, 87, ⌈1⌉ p. 19ᶜᵐ.

1. Investments. 2. Debts, Public. 3. Economic policy. 4. Gt. Brit.— Economic policy. I. Title.
                                  33-11808 Revised
Library of Congress   HG4538.L6 1932
⌈r43f2⌉   332

NL 0449430   DLC NIC FU CtY

Loftus, Pierse Creagh.
...Money and national reconstruction, by P. C. Loftus... ⌈London, 1941⌉ 15 p. 21cm.

At head of title: Economic reform club and institute.

1. Money—Gt. Br., 1925-   2. World war, 1939-   —Reconstruction, Economic—Gt. Br.   construction, Economic reform club,
N. Y. P. L.   I. Economic reform club, London.
                                       January 9, 1943

NL 0449431   NN

HD1927   Loftus, Pierse Creagh.
.1940
.N6   **Northbourne, Walter Ernest Christopher James,** baron, 1896-
"Where is the food to come from?" By the Rt. Hon. Lord Northbourne. "Parliament and agriculture," by P. C. Loftus, M. P. "The land and demobilisation," by the Rt. Hon. Viscount Lymington. Three addresses on food production in relation to economic reform, delivered at the Economic reform club and institute ... London ⌈Economic reform club and institute, 1940?⌉

NL 0449433   MiU

DG311   LOFTUS, SMYTH, b. 1707?
.G467D3   A reply to the reasonings of Mr.Gibbons, in his History of the decline and fall of the Roman em-pire,which seem to affect the truth of Christianity; but have not been noticed in the answer which Dr. Watson hath given to that book. By Smyth Loftus... Dublin,1777.
87 p. 21cm. ⌈With Davis,H.E. An examination of the fifteenth and sixteenth chapters of Mr.Gibbon's History. London,1778⌉
1.Gibbon,Edward,   1737-1794. History of the decline and fall of   the Roman empire.

NL 0449434   ICU MH

Rare
DG
311   Loftus, Smyth, b. 1707?
G44L82   A reply to the reasonings of Mr. Gibbon, in his History of the decline and fall of
1778   the Roman Empire, which seem to affect the truth of Christianity, but have not been noticed in the answer which Dr. Watson hath given to that book. Dublin, Printed Lon-don, reprinted for J. Williams and J. Bew, 1778.
236 p. 16cm.

NL 0449435   NIC NN

Loftus, William Kennett.
Travels and researches in Chaldæa and Susiana; with an account of excavations at Warka, the "Erech" of Nim-rod, and Shúsh, "Shushan the palace" of Esther, in 1849-52 ... By William Kennett Loftus ... London, J. Nisbet and co., 1857.
xvi, 436 p. front., illus., plates, 3 fold. maps. 22½ᶜᵐ.

1. Babylonia—Antiq. 2. Khuzistan—Antiq.

Library of Congress   DS70.L82
                              5-11557

PPL PU PP NBB PHC NN MH MB NjP
NL 0449436   DLC OrU MdBP CPFT InU MdBP IEG CU CtY

VOLUME 338

DS70
.L82t
1857
Loftus, William Kennett,
Travels and researches in Chaldæa and Susiana; with an account of excavations at Warka, the "Erech" of Nimrod, and Shush, "Shushan The Palace" of Esther, in 1849-52, under the orders of W.F. Williams of Kars, and also of the Assyrian Excavation Fund in 1853-4. New York, Robert Carter, 1857.
xvi, 436p. front., illus., 3 fold maps. 23cm.

1. Babylonia--Antiq. 2. Khuzistan--Antiq. I. Title.

OO OCl OClW PPT CtY
NL 0449437   IEG NjP NjR MeB DCU-H ViU MWA MB NjNbS

TP
570
L6
1858
Loftus, William Robert.
The brewer: a familiar treatise on the art of brewing, with special directions for the manufacture of pale ale & bitter beer, and the use of sugar by brewers. New ed. London ₁1858?₎
176, 23 p. illus.

√1. Brewing. √2. Ale. √3. Beer. √I. Title.

NL 0449438   CU-A

LOFTUS, WILLIAM ROBERT.
The maltster: a compendious treatise on the art of malting in all its branches. Including a description of the various systems now practised; the construction of malthouses; an account of the excise regulations. And an abstract of the whole of the malt laws. New and revised edition. By W.R. Loftus. London: W.R.Loftus[, 1877]. 186 p. 18½cm.

724567A. 1. Malt—Manufacture.

N. Y. P. L.   November 1, 1934

NL 0449439   NN

LOFTUS, William Robert.
The tobacconist. a practical guide to the retail tobacco trade in all its branches. London, W.R.Loftus, etc.,1881.

pp.56. Illustr.

NL 0449440   MH

Loftus-Hills, G
see Hills, G   Loftus.

Loftus-Price, Henry James, 1896–
The mystery of the Silver dart, by Captain Harry J. Loftus-Price; illustrated by Raymond C. Wardel. New York, The Mohawk press, 1931.
3 p. l., 221 p. incl. plates. col. front. 19½ᶜᵐ.

I. Title.
Library of Congress   PZ7.L8275My
                                           31–14062

NL 0449442   DLC

Loftvarnir. Leiðbeiningar fyrir almenning. Reykjavík, Loftvarnanefndin, 1940.
8°.   IcC55P215

NL 0449443   NIC

Adventures and misadventures; or, An undergraduate's experiences in Canada…a simple narrative told in XXXIX episodes …by "Lofty."   London: J. Bale, Sons & Danielsson, Ltd., 1922.
viii, 219 p.   front. (port.), illus.   12°.

53283A. 1. Canada.—Description and   travel, 1910–   2. Wit and humor
(English). 3. Title.
N. Y. P. L.   September 5, 1922.

NL 0449444   NN CaBViPA CaBVaU

Lofty, Henry W., comp.

Barbados.
Report on the census of Barbados, 1911–1921. Henry W. Lofty, compiler. ₁Bridgetown₎ Advocate co., ltd., printers to the government of Barbados ₁1921?₎

The LOFTY and the lowly: a sermon by a presbyter of New Jersey. New York, 1845.

Sermon (box)

NL 0449446   MH

FILM
The Lofty bishop, the lazy Brovvnist, and the loyall avthor. ₍n.p.₎ 1640.
Broadside.
Ballad.
Short-title catalogue no.3090 ₍carton 1090₎

NL 0449447   MiU MH

Lofvall, Mme. J   H
see Löfvall, Mme. J   H

Amst. 1773
Lofzangen in gestelyke liederen...

NL 0449449   NjNbS

De lofzangen Israels, waaronder de Heere woont
see under Groenewegen, Jacob, 1710-1755, ed.

Log, Abel, pseud.
see
Greatrex, Charles Butler.

Log.

₍Bangalore City, India₎
v. illus., ports. 29 cm.
Compiler: D. F. Karaka.

1. Almanacs, English—India.   I. Karaka, D. F., comp.

AY1057.E53L6   51–23831 ‡

NL 0449452   DLC

The log (Bristol, Conn. etc.)
see   The log of America's maritime industries.

The Log   published by the senior class of Central high school. Columbus, Ind.
v. illus., plates (part col.) ports. 27½ᶜᵐ.

1. Columbus, Ind. Central high school.

Library of Congress   LD7501.C745
                                          24–10020

NL 0449454   DLC

Oversize
BV4070 The log. Dallas, Perkins School of Theology,
.P315
v. illus. 28cm. monthly.

1. Theological seminaries, Methodist—Period. 2. Methodist Church in the U.S.—Education. I. Perkins School of Theology.

NL 0449455   IEG

The Log ... v. 1–
Feb. 26, 1934–
Galveston, Tex. ₁1934–
v. illus. 28ᶜᵐ. weekly.
Reproduced from type-written copy.
Published by the Galveston division, Texas Transient bureau.

1. Unemployed—Texas. 2. Public welfare—Texas. 3. Migrant labor—Texas. I. Texas. Transient bureau.
                                           42–32322
Library of Congress   HV4506.T4L6
                            ₍a44c1₎   361.609764

NL 0449456   DLC CU

The Log.

₍Hamilton, Ohio, Champion Paper and Fibre Co.₎
v. in   illus., ports. 31 cm. monthly.
Began publication in May 1914.
Title varies: The Log of Champion activities.
Pub. by "The Champion Family," 19

I. Champion Paper and Fibre Company.

HD9829.C5A55   676.065   49–38171*

NL 0449457   DLC NcU

The Log ... published by class of ...   Kearney high school. Kearney, Nebr. ₍¹19
v. illus., plates, ports. 27½ᶜᵐ.

I. Kearney, Neb. High school.
                                        CA 28–397 Unrev'd
Library of Congress   LD7501.K2695

NL 0449458   DLC

The Log.

₍New York, 19
v. illus. 23ᶜᵐ.
Organ of the Circumnavigators' club.
Editor: 19   J. H. Birch, jr.

1. Travel—Period.   I. Circumnavigators' club, New York. II. Birch, James H., jr., ed.
                                        CA 16–760 Unrev'd
Library of Congress   G149.L7

NL 0449459   DLC

VOLUME 338

The Log.   Vancouver,B.C.,etc.,1906-

Irregular.
Numbered irregularly. Vol.17
omitted in numbering.
Not published Christmas 1956.
Official publication of the Columbia
coast mission (Anglican church of Canada)
Title varies: Mar.1906-Mar./Apr.1940,
The Log of the Columbia.

NL 0449460   CaBVa

The Log of ₍Worcester, Mass., 18
v. illus., port. 24½ᶜᵐ.
1888, éd. de luxe, no. 311.
Pub. by the Senior class of the Worcester polytechnic institute.

ɪ. Worcester polytechnic institute, Worcester, Mass.

CA 11-2486 Unrev'd
Library of Congress   T171.W965

NL 0449461   DLC

The Log; the official organ of the British air line pilots
association. v. 1-
Aug. 1937-   ₍Croydon, The British air
line pilots association, 1937-
v. illus., ports. 21½ᶜᵐ. monthly.

1. Aeronautics—Period. 2. Aeronautics—Gt. Brit.   ɪ. British air
line pilots association.

42-41366
Library of Congress   TL501.B7
₍2₎   629.1305

NL 0449462   DLC NN

Log book
Filed as one word: i.e.,   Logbook.

Log cabin.   no. 1-
E 390* Mar. 21-   1840.
A1 L6 Dayton, Ohio.
nos. 44 x 30 cm. biweekly.

Campaign paper.

1. Campaign literature, 1840 - Whig.

NL 0449464   OU

The Log cabin. v. 1 (no. 1-28) May 2-Nov. 9, 1840; new ser.,
v. 1 (no. 1-51) Dec. 5, 1840-Nov. 20, 1841. New-York ₍etc.₎
1840-41.

2 v. in 1. illus. 52½ᶜᵐ. weekly.

Includes music.
Horace Greeley, editor.
"Published simultaneously in New-York and Albany" by H. Greeley
& co., May-Nov. 1840; in New York, by H. Greeley, Dec. 1840-Nov. 1841.
Includes extra number 1, July 4, 1840, and extra number 1-2, Aug.
29, 1840.
No numbers issued, Nov. 10-Dec. 4, 1840.

In L. C. set the New-York weekly tribune by Greeley & McElrath,
v. 1, no. 1 (Sept. 18, 1841) replaces new ser., v. 1, no. 42. A manuscript note on the fly-leaf states it was issued to subscribers in place
of the Log cabin.
Ceased publication with new ser. v. 1, no. 51, in which there is a
statement that the next week's issue of the New-York weekly tribune
will be sent to subscribers to complete the volume.

1. Campaign literature, 1840—Whig. 2. U. S.—Pol. & govt.—Period.
3. U. S.—Pol. & govt.—1837-1841 4. Campaign songs, 1840—Whig.
ɪ. Greeley, Horace, 1811-1872, ed.

34-8758
Library of Congress   E390.L85
——— 2d set.

NL 0449466   DLC NIC MB PHi ICU

---

* The log cabin; a favorite patriotic ballad,
M₁ as sung at the Tippecanoe Associations, with
.A13N great applause. Partly written and arr.
.L654 for the piano forte, by a member of the
1840 Fifth Ward Club. ₍New York, Thomas Birch₎
°1840.
3 p. 35cm.
Caption title.

1. Harrison, William Henry, Pres. U. S., 1773-
1841—Music. 2. Campaign songs, 1840—Whig. I.
A Member of the Fifth Ward Club.

NL 0449467   ViU

The log cabin & hard cider melodies
see under Adams, Charles, pub.

'Log cabin anecdotes.' Illustrated incidents
in the life of Gen. William Henry Harrison.
New York, Published by J. P. Giffing, at the office
of the Harrison almanac, J. F. Trow, printer, 1840.
broadside. illus. 64 x 49½ᶜᵐ.
Title and text in red and black.

1. Harrison, William Henry, pres. U. S., 1773-1841.
2. Campaign literature, 1840—Whig. 3. U.S.—Pol. &
govt.—1837-1841

NL 0449469   ViU

42846 Log Cabin Chess Club.
.594   Championship tournament, class A, 1951,
and the story of the famous Log Cabin Travelling Chess Team. Ed. and annotated by A.N.
Towsen. New York, Gamecraft Company ₍1952₎
67 p. illus. 23 cm.

1.Chess - Tournaments. I.Towsen, A
N

NL 0449470   NjP OC1

Log Cabin Club, Marysville, Wash.
Log Cabin kitchen secrets. ₍Kansas City. Mo.,
Bev-Ron publishing Company, c1951₎
46 p.

NL 0449471   Wa

The log-cabin lady; an anonymous autobiography ... Boston, Little, Brown, and company, 1922.
xvi p., 2 l., 3-107, ₍1₎ p. front., plates. 20ᶜᵐ.

Library of Congress   CT275.Z9L6
22—24814

OC1W OC1 OU NN MB CaBVa CaBVaU IdU OrP Wa
NL 0449472   DLC WaS MtU OrU OrCS IdB Or KyLx ViU

The log-cabin lady; an anonymous autobiography...
Boston, Little, Brown, and company, 1924.

xvi p., 2 l., 3-107, ₍1₎ p. front., plates.
20 cm.

NL 0449473   ViU NcD

The Log-Cabin Lady; an anonymous autobiography...
Boston, Little, Brown, & Co., 1928.
107p. illus.

NL 0449474   ICRL TU

The log-cabin lady; an anonymous autobiography ...
Boston, Little, Brown, and company, 1931.
xvi p., 2 l., 3-107, [1] p. front., plates.
20 cm.

NL 0449475   WaSp

CT   The log-cabin lady; an anonymous autobiography.
275 Boston, Little, Brown, and company, 1937
Z9   ₍°1922₎
L6   x p.,2l.,3-107,₍1₎p. front.,plates.
1937

NL 0449476   UU

The log-cabin lady; an anonymous
autobiography ... Boston,Little,Brown
and company,1940.
1x,₍1₎p.,2l.,3-107,₍1₎p. front.,plates.
20cm.

NL 0449477   PSt

The Log cabin minstrel: or Tippecanoe songster:
containing a selection of songs, original
and selected, many of them written expressly for this work. Compiled, published
and arranged, by a member of the Roxbury
Democratic Whig Association, and respectfully dedicated to the Log Cabin boys of
the United States. Roxbury ₍Mass.₎:
Patriot and Democrat Office, 1840.
60p. 19cm.

NL 0449478   NBu MH MB ViU OC1WHi RPB

The log cabin; or, The world before you
see under ₍Lee, Mrs. Hannah Farnham
(Sawyer)₎ 1780-1865.

Log cabin patriot. v. 1 (no. 1-12); Aug. 7-Nov. 17, 1840.
East Bridgewater, Mass., 1840.
₍48₎ p. illus. 38½ᶜᵐ.

Two numbers were issued in August; 3 in September; 5 in October; 2 in
November.
Caption title.
Includes music.
No more published.

1. Campaign literature, 1840—Whig. 2. Campaign songs, 1840—Whig.

Library of Congress   E390.L7
26—23325

NL 0449480   DLC

The Log cabin song-book. A collection of popular and
patriotic songs, respectfully dedicated to the friends of
Harrison and Tyler ... New-York, Log cabin office, 1840.
72 p. incl. 2 pl. front. (port.) 18½ᶜᵐ.

Title vignette.
"Perhaps by Samuel D. Taylor."—Sabin, Bibl. amer.

ɪ. Campaign songs, 1840—Whig.   ɪ. Taylor, Samuel D., supposed
comp.

17—1090
Library of Congress   E390.L8

NL 0449481   DLC NBu MiEM Vi MiU-C OC1WHi NjP MB OU

VOLUME 338

The Log cabin song book: a compendious selection
of the most popular Tippecanoe melodies.
Springfield, O., J. R. Crain, 1840.
96 p. illus. 12 cm.
Illustrated t.-p.

NL 0449482 RPB

The Log cabin songster, being a collection of the
most popular Tippecanoe songs. Respectfully
dedicated to the friends of Harrison & democracy.
Steubenville [Ohio] Printed by J & R.C. Wilson,
1840.
64 p. 12 cm.
Cover-title: Whig songs, 1840.

NL 0449483 RPB

LOG chips. v. 3-date; July 1952-date.
Washington, D.C., J. Lyman. v. 28cm.

Bimonthly, July 1952-Jan. 1953; quarterly, April 1953-date. Sept.
1952-date have subtitle: the periodical publication of recent maritime
history.

1. Shipping--Per. and soc. publ.--U.S.

NL 0449484 NN

LOG chips. v. 3-4, no. 8; July, 1952-Sept./Dec. 1959
Washington, J. Lyman. v. 28cm.

Film reproduction. Negative.
Irregular.
"The periodical publication of recent maritime history."
Ceased publication with v. 4, no. 8, Sept./Dec. 1959?

1. Shipping--Per. and soc. publ.--U.S.

NL 0449485 NN

Log City days; two narratives on the settlement of Galesburg,
Illinois. The diary of Jerusha Loomis Farnham. Sketch
of Log City, by Samuel Holyoke; introduction by Earnest
Elmo Calkins. Galesburg, Knox college centenary publications, 1937.
79, [1] p. fold. pl., port. group. 21ᶜᵐ.

1. Galesburg, Ill.--Hist. I. *Farnham, Mrs. Jerusha (Loomis)
1807?-1872. II. *Holyoke, Samuel. III. Calkins, Earnest Elmo, 1868-

Library of Congress F549.G15L6 37-33663
——— Copy 2.
Copyright A 111043 [3] 977.349

NL 0449486 DLC WHi OKentU ICU

Log college committee.

Celebration of the two hundredth anniversary of the founding of the log college by William Tennent, October 2-5,
1927. [Philadelphia, 1927]
[8] p. illus.

1. Neshaminy, Pa. Log college.

NL 0449487 NjP

The log log trig slide rule
see under Keuffel & Esser co.

The log of a cabin boy
see under [Eldy, Elford]

The Log of America's maritime industries. v. 1-51,
no. 3; 1923-Mar. 1956. Los Angeles, M. Freeman.
1923-1956.
51 v. in
Crerar has v. 44-v. 51, no. 3; 1949-Mar. 1956.
Official organ of the Society of Marine Port
Engineers, N.Y.; The Society of Port Engineers,
San Francisco, Los Angeles; Columbia River Area,
Puget Sound; the Port Stewards' Association of the
Pacific Coast.
Absorbed Pacific Marine review. Merged Marine

engineering and shipping review to form Marine
engineering and the Log, Apr. 1956.
I. Society of Marine Port Engineers, N.Y.
II. Society of Port Engineers, San Francisco.
III. Society of Port Engineers, Los Angeles.
IV. Society of Port Engineers, Columbia River Area.
V. Society of Port Engineers of Puget Sound.
VI. Port Stewards' Association of the Pacific
Coast. 387.051 656.051

NL 0449491 ICJ ICRL NN CU

(The) Log of America's maritime industries.

Shipbuilding activity in Portland, Ore.
until recently a peaceful industrial
center, this Northwest city now humming
with shipyard work and is breaking construction records. illus. Author, 1942.

Excerpt from The Log, June 1942, vol. 37,
p. 31-37.

NL 0449492 OrP

The log of an aeromarine; a modern adventure in
path-finding
see under [Aeromarine plane and motor
company]

The Log of Champion activities
see The Log (Hamilton, Ohio)

The log of my leisure hours. By an old sailor ... London,
S. Low, son, and Marston, 1868.
3 v. 19½ᶜᵐ.

1. An old sailor.
41-40514
Library of Congress PZ3.L826

NL 0449495 DLC

825
L828
1872
The log of my leisure hours. By an
old sailor. 2d ed. London, 1872.
309p. front.

NL 0449496 IU

The Log of Mystic seaport. v. 1-
Oct. 1948-
Mystic, Conn.
v. in illus., ports. 23 cm. quarterly.
Published by the Marine Historical Association.

1. Mystic Seaport, Mystic, Conn. I. Marine Historical Association, Mystic, Conn.
F104.M99L6 974.65 58-37267

NL 0449497 DLC NN N NB PHi CtNlC WHi NlC CaBVaU

Log of Pennsylvania highways. Pittsburgh, Pa., The Duff-
man company [°1936]
4 p. l., 145, [7] p. fold. map. 12½ᶜᵐ.
Blank ruled pages for "Memoranda" ([7] at end)
Pocket on inside of front cover.

1. Roads--Pennsylvania. 2. Automobiles--Road guides.
Library of Congress GV1024.L54 36-29863
——— Copy 2.
Copyright A 98844 [2] 629.28109748

NL 0449498 DLC

Log of President Truman's vacation cruise in the Chesapeake
and Delaware bays, 20-29 August 1948. [Washington? 1948]
viii, 41 p. illus., group ports. 27cm.

1. Truman, Harry S., 33d pres. U.S.

NL 0449499 NN

Log of the Anemone, June 11 to August 29, 1906.
Colorado Springs, Colo. [The Prompt Printery]
1907.
(4), 76 p. plates.

NL 0449500 MH

The log of the Bon Homme Richard
see under Bon Homme Richard (Ship)

... The log of the brig Hope, called The Hope's
track among the Sandwich islands
see [Ingraham, Joseph] fl. 1762-1800.

The log of the Brig Nymph from Shields to Leith Roads
see under Nymph (Brig)

The log of the Columbia
see The log (Vancouver)

Log of the Jamestown, out and home, 1847.
Boston, J.F. Cotter, Printers, 1884
see under [Forbes, Robert Bennet] 1804-
1889.

VOLUME 338

Log of the LST 530; ed. by Anthony Drexel Duke... New York, Privately printed by the P. Andrews pub. co. ₁1946?₁ 1 v. illus. 24 x 31cm.

1. Landing craft, U. S.—LST 530. I. Duke, Anthony Drexel, ed.
N. Y. P. L. February 5, 1952

NL 0449506 NN

The Log of the lab; items of current research.

Madison, Wis., 19 20cm.
Irregular.
Caption-title.
Issued by the Forest Products Laboratory of the United States Forest Service.
Ceased publication with the issue for Feb., 1932.

1. Forest products—U. S. I. United States. Forest Service. Forest
Products Laboratory, Madison, Wis.
N. Y. P. L. June 21, 1934

NL 0449507 NN

The log of the Mighty "A," 1943-1945 — being the story, in words and pictures, of the wanderings of the USS General A. E. Anderson in obedience to her orders and the dictates of global war; of her search for area ribbons; and of the adventures and misadventures of a typical sailor in the ship's crew, herein to be known as "Andy." ₁n. p., 1945?₁ 1 v. illus., ports. 31cm.

436506B. 1. World war, 1939-1945 —Transportation—Indiv. ships—
General A. E. Anderson.
N. Y. P. L. December 27, 1949

NL 0449508 NN

SPECIAL COLLECTIONS
B825L828
S7
1886 The log of the "Old un," from Liverpool to San Francisco. ₁Exeter₁ Printed for private circulation ₁by M. S. Eland, printer, 1886₁ 30 p. 19 cm.

Attributed by bookseller to William Sim.

I. Sim, William

NL 0449509 NNC

The log of the Oregon; a sailor's story of the voyage from San Francisco to Santiago in 1898
see under [Cross, R]

The log of the Shanghai pilot service, 1831-1932
see under [Philip, George]

The log of the "Thomas"
see under Gleason, Ronald P ed.

A log of the trip around the world on the U.S.A.T. President Grant
see under [Lynas, John C]

Log of the U. S. S. General Leroy Eltinge, AP 154. ₁Seattle, Sterling engraving co., 1946?₁ 1 v. illus., ports. 28cm.

513085B. 1. World war, 1939-1945 J. S. BILLINGS MEM. COLL.
Leroy Eltinge. —Transports—Indiv. ships—General
N. Y. P. L. January 25, 1950

NL 0449514 NN

Log of the voyage of the Atlantic fleet, December 16, 1907-February 22, 1909. Washington, D. C., The Navy publishing co., ᵗ1909.
1 p. l., 47 p. 18ᶜᵐ. $0.25

1. U. S.—Navy—Cruise, 1907-1909. I. The Navy publishing co.,
Washington, D. C.
Library of Congress VA58.L7 9-25212

NL 0449515 DLC

Log of yacht Seadrift ...
see under [Coxe, Lola De]

The log, S. S. "Finland." ₁Boston, Mass., Printed by Nathan Sawyer & son, inc.₁ 1915.
₁50₁ p. illus., plates. 26ᶜᵐ. $1.00
Log committee: A. Guiterman, C. Hackett, and others.
"Log" of a voyage of the Finland from New York to San Francisco via the Panama canal, in the summer of 1915. Most of the passengers were Harvard men, their relatives and friends.
Interleaved.

1. Finland (Steamship) 2. Harvard university. I. Guiterman, Arthur,
1871– II. Hackett, Chauncey.
Library of Congress LD2185.A15 1915 16-2202

NL 0449517 DLC ICRL ViU

Log scaling, by R. W. McIntyre, Bernard Brereton, Emanuel Fritz, Clyde E. Knouf ₁and₁ E. I. Karr. Portland, Or., San Francisco, Calif., The Timberman, 1936.
3 p. l. ₁9₁-157 p. illus., diagrs. 21 x 10½ᶜᵐ.

1. Forests and forestry—Mensuration. I. McIntyre, R. W. II.
Brereton, Bernard John Stephen, 1868– III. Fritz, Emanuel,
1886– IV. Knouf, Clyde E. V. Karr, E. I., d. 1927.
36-35960
Library of Congress SD555.L6
—— Copy 2.
Copyright A 100622 ₁5₁ 634.9826

NL 0449518 DLC Or WaS OrCS CaBVa NcRS ICJ

The Log: USNR mobile power, 43rd construction battalion 1942-1946
see U.S. Navy. 43d Construction Battalion.
The Log, 1942-1946.

DS Loga, Aharon.
126.97 Jerusalemer Kriegstage; ernste und
L6 heitere Erlebnisse eines Mischmar Haam-
Mannes und Chim-Soldaten. Jerusalem,
1949.
130 p. 21 cm. (Edition Dr. Peter
Freund, no. 40.)

1. Israel-Arab War, 1948-1949--
Personal narratives. I. Title

NL 0449520 OCH IEN

Loga, Valerian von, 1861- *8065.201.27.Heft 3
Antonis Mor als Hofmaler Karls V. und Philipps II.
Wien. Tempsky. 1908. 91-123 pp. Portraits. [Kaiserlich-
koenigliches kunsthistorisches Hof-Museum. Jahrbuch ... Band
27, Heft 3.] 33 cm., in 8s.

H5610 — Mor, Antonis. Fl. 16th centu._. —Charles V., of Germany, I., of Spain.
1500-1558. — Philip II., of Spain. 1527-1598. — S.r.c.

NL 0449521 MB NN

Loga, Valerian von, 1861-
...Beiträge zum holzschnittwerk Michel Wolgemuts.
₁Berlin? Reichsfruckerei,₁ 1895.
17 p.

NL 0449522 PP

Loga, Valerian von, 1861-
Caprichos von Goya...
see under Goya y Lucientes, Francisco
José de, 1746-1828.

NE2115 Loga, Valerian von, 1861-1918.
.G7L78 Francisco de Goya. Berlin, G. Grote, 1903.
248 p. plates, port., facsim.
"Verzeichnis der Werke Goyas": p. ₁177₁-239;
"Verzeichnis der wichtigsten Literatur über
Goya": p. ₁240₁-241.

1. Goya y Lucientes, Francisco José de, 1746-
1828.

NL 0449524 ICU CU GU WaU PP PPPM MdBP OClMA NN

Art Loga, Valerian von, 1861-
Library Francisco de Goya. 2. verm. Aufl. Berlin,
J18 G. Grote, 1921.
G69 247 p. 96 plates, port., facsim. 27 cm.
+910Lab

1. Goya y Lucientes, Francisco José de,
1746-1828.

NL 0449525 CtY OU NcU MnU MH PSC MWiCA CSt

Loga, Valerian von, 1861-1918.
... Francisco de Goya, von Valerian von Loga; mit einem
titelblatt & 71 tafeln. Leipzig, Klinkhardt & Biermann ₁1910₁
2 p. l., 52 p. 72 pl. (incl. front., ports.) 30ᶜᵐ. (Half-title: Meister der
graphik, bd. IV)
Series title also at head of t.-p.

1. Goya y Lucientes, Francisco José de, 1746-1828.
11-28715
Library of Congress NE2115.G6L6

NL 0449526 DLC OClMA NN MB OCl MiU PP

Loga, Valerian von, 1861-1918.
... Francisco de Goya, von Valerian von Loga; mit einem
titelbild & 71 tafeln. 2. aufl. Leipzig, Klinkhardt & Biermann ₁1923₁
2 p. l., 41 p. front. (port.) 71 pl. 32ᶜᵐ. (Meister der graphik ..
bd. IV)

1. Goya y Lucientes, Francisco José de, 1746-1828.
20-12908
Library of Congress NE2115.G6L6 1923

NL 0449527 DLC CtY MoU NBC WaU PSC OU PHC PBm

VOLUME 338

Loga, Valerian von, 1861-

Goya y Lucientes, Francisco José de, 1746-1828.
Goya's seltene radierungen und lithographien; 44 getreue nachbildungen in kupfer- und lichtdruck der Reichsdruckerei, hrsg. von Valerian von Loga. Berlin, G. Grote, 1907.

Loga, Valerian von, 1861- 1918.
...Hat Velazquez radiert? Von Valerian von Loga. ₍Berlin: Reichsdruckerei, 1908.₎ 4 p. ports. f°.

Caption-title.
Repr.: Königlich Preussische Kunstsammlungen, Jahrb. Heft 3, 1908.
Bibliographical footnotes.

1. Velazquez, Diego Rodriguez de Silva y, 1599-1660.
N.Y.P.L.   November 30, 1926

NL 0449529   NN

Loga, Valerian von, 1861-

Hessus, Helius Eobanus, 1488-1540.
... Helivs Eobanvs Hessvs Noriberga illvstrata und andere städtegedichte. Hrsg. von Joseph Neff. Mit illustrationen des 16. jahrhunderts und kunsthistorischen erläuterungen von Valer von Loga. Berlin, Weidmann. 1896.

Loga, Valerian von, 1861, ed.
Jahrbuch der preuszischen kunstsammlungen. 1.- bd.; 1880-19
Berlin, Weidmann ₍etc.₎, 1880-19

1861-1918.

Loga, Valer von, ₍^Ein jugendbildnis der Maria von Ungarn. 2 pp. 1 pl. (Koenigl. Preussisch. kunstsamml. Jahrb. v. 10, 1889, p. 200.)—

NL 0449532   MdBP

Loga, Valerian von, 1861-
Königliche Museen zu Berlin. Ordnung und Katalogisierung eines Kupferstich-Kabinetts
see his Ordnung und Katalogisierung eines Kupferstich-Kabinetts.

Loga, Valerian von, 1861-
Die malerei in Spanien vom XIV. bis XVIII. jahrhundert, von Valerian von Loga. Aus seinem nachlass herausgegeben. Mit 212 abbildungen. Berlin, G. Grote, 1923.

vii, ₍1₎, 439, ₍1₎ p. illus. (incl. ports.) 28¹ᶜᵐ.
"Vorwort" signed: Oskar Fischel. Ernst Kühnel.

1. Painting—Spain.   I. Fischel, Oskar, 1870-   II. Kühnel, Ernst.
Library of Congress   ND804.L6   24-20727

PBm NN MB
NL 0449534   DLC OU TNJ CSt WU CtY GU OCl NcU PPPM

Loga, Valerian von, ₍1861-   *8065.201.28, Heft 4
Las meninas. Ein Beitrag zur Ikonographie des Hauses Habsburg. Portraits.
(In Zimmermann, H. Zur Ikonographie des Hauses Habsburg. [Theil] 2, pp. 171-199. Wien. 1909.)
Concerning, principally, the portraits of the Infanta Margarita Teresa.

H5615 — T.r. — Hapsburg, House of.   Margaret Theresa, of Spain, Empress of Germany. 1651-1673.

NL 0449535   MB

Loga, Valerian von, 1861–
... Ordnung und katalogisierung eines kupferstich-kabinetts, erfahrungen und vorschläge, von V. v. Loga. Berlin, G. Reimer, 1910.

54 p., 1 l. 3 fold. tab. 20½ᶜᵐ.
At head of title: Königliche museen zu Berlin.
"Literatur-verzeichnis" : p. ₍53₎–54.

1. Cataloging — Engravings. 2. Classification—Engravings. 3. Engravings—Collectors and collecting. I. Berlin. K. Museen. II. Title.

32–4830

Library of Congress   NE60.L6   769

NL 0449536   DLC NN MH PPPM

Loga, Valerian von, 1861-1918.   *8083.74
Die spanische Plastik vom XV. bis XVIII. Jahrhundert.
(In Knapp, F. Die italienische Plastik. Pp. 121-144. Berlin. [1910.])

H5986 — Spain. Fine arts. Sculp.

NL 0449537   MB MH NN OO

Loga, Valerian von, 1861-1918.
... Spanische plastik vom fünfzehnten bis achtzehnten jahrhundert. München, Hyperion verlag ₍1923₎

31, ₍1₎ p., 1 l. 32 pl. 29ᶜᵐ.
"1.-4. tausend."
"Neue ausgabe des erstmalig in der von Ludwig Justi herausgegebenen 'Geschichte der kunst' erschienenen werkes, druck: A. Wohlfeld, Magdeburg."

1. Sculpture—Spain.
29-15614

Library of Congress   NB804.L6 1923

NL 0449538   DLC CU CtY CSt NcD PBm PP

Loga, Valerian von, 1861-
Die Staedteansichten in Hartman Schedels Weltchronik.   Leipzig, 1888.
Inaug.-Diss. - Berlin.

NL 0449539   ICRL

Loga, Valerian von, 1861-1918.
... Tauromachie
see under Goya y Lucientes, Francisco José de, 1746-1828.

Loga, Valerian von, 1861-1918, ed.

Gensel, Walther, 1870-1910.
Velazquez; des meisters gemälde in 256 abbildungen, mit einer biographischen einleitung von Walter Gensel. 3. aufl., hrsg. von Valerian von Loga. Stuttgart und Berlin, Deutsche verlags-anstalt ₍1914₎

Loga del nino Dios representacion s⌃cenica de los Manques en Nomotiva. Santa Catarina, n.p., 1874.
10 p.

NL 0449542   PU-Mu

Logachev, Aleksandr Andreevich.

TN269   Russia (1923–   U. S. S. R.) Glavnoe geofizicheskoe
.R816   upravlenie.
Инструкция по аэромагнитной съемке. ₍Составлена А. А. Логачевым₎ Утверждена 30 июня 1952 г. Москва, Гос. изд-во геол. лит-ры, 1952.

Logachev, Aleksandr Andreevich.
Курс магниторазведки. Допущено в качестве учебника для вузов по специальности "Геофизические методы разведки полезных ископаемых." Москва, Гос. изд-во геол. лит-ры, 1951.

305 p. charts, diagrs. 23 cm.
Bibliography: p. 302–303₎

1. Prospecting—Geophysical methods. 2. Magnetometer. I. Title.
Title transliterated: Kurs magnitorazvedki.
TN269.L6   55-41099

NL 0449544   DLC

Logachev, Aleksandr Andreevich.
Курс магниторазведки. Допущено в качестве учебника для геолого-разведочных техникумов. Москва, Гос. научно-техн. изд-во лит-ры по геологии и охране недр, 1955.

301 p. illus. 23 cm.
Third ed. published in 1968 under title: Магниторазведка.
Bibliography: p. ₍297₎

1. Prospecting—Geophysical methods. 2. Magnetism, Terrestrial. I. Title.
Title transliterated: Kurs magnitorazvedki.
TN269.L6 1955   56-35178

NL 0449545   DLC CaBVaU

Logachev, Aleksandr Andreevich.
Методическое руководство по аэромагнитной съемке. Москва, Гос. научно-техн. изд-во лит-ры по геологии и охране недр, 1955.

145 p. diagrs. 23 cm.
At head of title: Всесоюзный научно-исследовательский геологический институт Министерства геологии и охраны недр.
Bibliography: p. 143–₍144₎

1. Prospecting—Geophysical methods. 2. Magnetism, Terrestrial. I. Title.
Title transliterated: Metodicheskoe rukovodstvo po aéromagnitnoĭ s"emke.
TN269.L63   56-21866

NL 0449546   DLC

Logadēs, Nikolaos, 1779-1835.
Ἀληθοφωνήσεις μητρικαὶ πρὸς ψευδοφωνήσεις ἀντιμητρικάς. Ἐν Βενετία, Ἐκ τῆς Ἑλληνικῆς Τυπ. Φραγκίσκου Ἀνδρεόλα, 1833.

70 p.

NL 0449547   MH OCU RPB

BX320   ₍Parallēlon philosophias
.L6   **Logadēs, Nikolaos, 1779-1835.**
Παράλληλον φιλοσοφίας καὶ χριστιανισμοῦ, ἀθεϊσμοῦ καὶ δεισιδαιμονίας. Ἤτοι, Ἐγκώμιον τοῦ ἀληθινοῦ φιλοσόφου, μακαρισμὸς τοῦ ὀρθοδόξου χριστιανοῦ· ψόγος τοῦ ἀθέου, ταλανισμὸς τοῦ δεισιδαίμονος· ᾧ προσετέθη καὶ τις Ἐπιστολὴ ἀνέκδοτος ... τοῦ ... Εὐγενίου· καὶ τι Σκολιὸν, εἴτουν Ὠδάριον ἠθικὸν Ν. τοῦ Λογάδου· ἅπερ συνεξεδόθησαν ... ὑπὸ τοῦ αὐτοῦ Λογάδου ... Ἐν τῷ τοῦ Πατριαρχείου τῆς Κωνσταντινουπόλεως τυπογραφείῳ παρὰ Παναγιώτῃ Δημη-

Continued in next column

VOLUME 338

Continued from preceding column

τρίου τῷ ἐξ ᾽Αργυροκάστρου, ἐν ἔτει 1830.
ιε´, 113 p.   19½cm.
End pieces.
After the first paging, the odd numbered pages are on the verso and even on
the recto.
Published at the expense of Eustathi-
os Katakouzenos.
   1.Orthodox Eastern church—Doctr. and
contr. works. 2.Atheism. I.Title: Paral-
lelon philoso-   phias kai christianis-
mou.

NL 0449549   OCU MH

BX320 Logadēs, Nikolaos, 1779–1835.
.L6   Παράλληλον φιλοσοφίας καὶ χριστιανι-
1869   σμοῦ, ἀθεϊσμοῦ καὶ φιλοσοφίας. Ήτοι
         Έγκώμιον τοῦ ἀληθινοῦ φιλοσόφου, μακα-
         ρισμὸς τοῦ ὀρθοδόξου χριστιανοῦ, ψόγος
         τοῦ ἀθέου, ταλανισμὸς τοῦ δεισιδαίμονος.
         Ὁ προσετέθη καί τις Ἐπιστολή ἀνέκδοτος
         ... τοῦ ... Εὐγενίου· καί τι Σχολίον, εἴ-
         τουν Ὑπόμνημα ἠθικὸν Ν. τοῦ Λογάδου, ἅπερ
         συνεξεδόθησαν ... ὑπὸ τοῦ αὐτοῦ Ν.Λογάδου
         ... Ἔκδοσις δευτέρα. Ἐν ᾽Ερμουπόλει,
         ἐκ τοῦ τυπογραφείου τῆς "Πατρίδος", 1869.

         κ´, 139 p.   19½cm.
         "᾽Αγγελία" signed. Ὁ ἐκδότης Δανιήλ
         Λίβανος ...
         First edition, Constantinople, 1830.
         List of subscribers: p. [133,]–139.
         1.Orthodox Eastern church—Doctrinal
         and controversial works. 2.Atheism. I.Li-
         banos, Daniēl, ed. II.Title: Parallēlon
         philosophias kai christianismos.

NL 0449551   OCU

D569   Logaj, Josef.
.A2   Československé legie v Italii, 1915–1918.
L58   V Praze [Grafie] 1920.
         109p. (Československé Expedice, sv. 4)

         1. Československý dobrovolnický sbor v
         Italii. 2. European War, 1914–1918 -
         Bohemia. 3. European War, 1914–1918 - Italy.
         I. Title.

NL 0449552   NcU ICU CoU

Logaj, Josef.
   Československé legie v Italii, 1915–1918. 2. opravené a
rozšířené vyd. V Praze, Nákl. "Památníku odboje," 1922.
   147 p. 25 cm. (Knihovna "Památníku odboje," čís. 19)

   1. Československý dobrovolnický sbor v Italii. 2. European War,
1914–1918—Bohemia. 3. European War, 1914–1918—Italy.   I.
Title.

D569.A2L58 1922   63–56909

NL 0449553   DLC MH CSt-H InU NN

D569   Logaj, Josef
A2   Oběti. [Památce Československých legionářů
L64   v Italii popravených Rakousko-Uherskem]
         Praha [Melantrich] 1921.
         58 p. 32 p. of illus. 17 cm.

         1. Československý Dobrovolnický Sbor v
         Italii. 2. European War, 1914–1918 - Bohemia.
         3. European War, 1914–1918 - Italy. I. Title[

NL 0449554   CtY

Logal, Nelson William, 1910–
   A history of St. Joseph's Old Cathedral, 50 Franklin
Street, Buffalo, New York [1847–1947] [Buffalo] Printed
by Turner & Porter, °1947.
   144 p. illus., ports. 19 cm.

   1. Buffalo. St. Joseph's Old Cathedral.

BX4603.B852S3   282.747   48–15026*

NL 0449555   DLC NN NBuC

Logan, pseud.
   see
Thorpe, Thomas Bangs, 1815–1878, supposed author.

FOR OTHER EDITIONS
SEE MAIN ENTRY

Logan, ------ tr.

   Der freischutz, or, The seventh bullet: an opera, in
three acts, by Carl Maria von Weber. Printed from the
acting copy, with remarks, biographical and critical, by
D.—G. ... As performed at the Theatres Royal ... London, Davidson [n. d.]

Logan, Abram L., & Co.
   Logan's post office, census, express, telegraph
ands railroad directory ...
      see under Logan publishing co., St. Louis, comp

Logan, Abram L., & co.
   Logan's railway business directory from Saint Louis
to Galveston ... via the Missouri Pacific railroad (to Se-
dalia), Missouri, Kansas & Texas r. w., Houston &
Texas central r. w., Galveston, Houston & Henderson r. w.
Containing a complete list of ... all persons doing business in each of the cities, towns and stations on these railroads, together with a brief historical sketch of each; also,
a new post office directory of the southwestern states ...
St. Louis, Mo., A. L. Logan & co. [1873?]
   1 p. l., vi–xv, 200 p. 22½cm.
   1. Southwest, Old—Direct. 2. Missouri Pacific railway company. 3.
Missouri, Kansas & Texas railway company. 4. Houston & Texas central railway company.   5. Galveston, Houston & Henderson
railway company.

Library of Congress   F396.A18 1873   10–31598

NL 0449559   DLC

Logan, Adam D
   Far awa. [New York?] Adam D. Logan, °1864.
   3 p. 36 cm.
   Caption title.
   For voice and piano.

   1. Songs (Medium voice) with piano.   I. Title.
   M1621.L   52–57863

NL 0449560   DLC

Logan, Adam D
   Freedom's jubilee! [New York?] °1865.
   close score ([1] l.) 36 cm.
   Caption title.
   For chorus (SATB)

   1. War-songs, American. 2. U. S.—Hist.—Civil War—Songs and
music.   I. Title.
   M1640.L   52–51200

NL 0449561   DLC

Logan, Adam D
   Freedom's rally. [New York?] °1865.
   close score ([1] l.) 36 cm.
   Caption title.
   For chorus (SATB)

   1. War-songs, American. 2. U. S.—Hist.—Civil War—Songs and
music.   I. Title.
   M1640.L   52–51183

NL 0449562   DLC

Logan, Adam David, d. 1869.
   The silent tongue, by Adam D. Logan ... New York, 1865.
   vi, [5]–35 p. 21cm.

   1. Cryptography.   I. Title.

Library of Congress   Z104.L8   44–34839

NL 0449563   DLC

Logan, Agnes, pseud.
   see
Adams, Agnes Louise Logan, 1891–

QD251   Logan, Albert V., joint author.
.M22
      Marvell, Elliot Nelson, 1922–
         Chemical properties of organic compounds, an introduc-
         tion [by] Elliot N. Marvell [and] Albert V. Logan. New
         York, Wiley [1955]

Logan, Alexander.
   A first book of school gardening, by Alexander Logan
... London, Macmillan and co., limited, 1915.
   vi p., 1 l., 151 p. illus. 18cm. (Half-title: First books of science)

   1. School gardens.

                                                Agr 16–543

Library, U. S. Dept. of   Agriculture 90L823F

NL 0449566   DNAL

Logan, Alexander.
   Principles and practice of school gardening, by Alexander Logan ... With 102 illustrations and coloured frontispiece. London, Macmillan and co., limited, 1913.
   xv, 313 p. col. front., illus., diagrs. 19cm.

   1. School gardens.

                                                E 13–1827

Library, U. S. Bur. of   Education LB3503.L82

NL 0449567   DHEW ICJ

Logan, Alexander.
   ... The school garden, its making, management, and
educational value, being notes on the methods followed
at the college demonstration garden, Huntly. By Alex.
Logan ... Aberdeen, Printed at the Rosemount press
[1911]
   47 p. illus., v pl., fold. plan. 22cm.
   At head of title: North of Scotland college of agriculture.
   Issued with approval of Scotch education department.

   1. School gardens.   I. Aberdeen and North of Scotland college of
agriculture.

                                                Agr 13–215

Library, U. S. Dept. of   Agriculture 90L823

NL 0449568   DNAL ICJ

VOLUME 338

PR 4891 .L5 A9
Logan, Alexander, 1826-1886?
Auld reekie musings; being poems and lyrics, with a glossary. Edinburgh, Printed by Reid & Reynolds, 1864.
130 p. 17 cm.

NL 0449569   WU

Logan, Alexander: (1826-1886?)
Lays o'hame an' country: Being poems, songs, and ballads. 12mo. Edinburgh 1883.
821.3-L831L

NL 0449570   NBuG

DS 418 L58
Logan, Alexander Cochrane.
Old chipped stones of India; founded on the collection in the Calcutta Museum, by A. C. Logan. Calcutta, Thacker, Spink, 1906.
85 p. illus. 23cm.
Bibliographical footnotes.

1. Stone implements 2. India - Antiq. I. Title

NL 0449571   WU MiD NSyU

PR 4331 L639 1871
Logan, Alexander Stuart.
On Robert Burns; an address. Judas the betrayer, his ending; a poetical fragment. Edinburgh, Edmonston and Douglas, 1871.
vi, 88 p. 19 cm.
Cover and spine title: Literary relics of A. S. Logan.
1. Burns, Robert, 1759-1796. I. Title.   II. Title: Judas the be-   trayer.

NL 0449572   CaBVaU

Logan, Algernon Sydney, 1849-1925.   *2404.112
[Works.] Collected edition. With biographical sketch of the author by his son, Robert Restalrig Logan.
= Philadelphia. National Publishing Co. 1934. 7 v. Portraits. Plates. Music. 21 cm.
Contents. — [1, 2.] Vistas from the stream. Comments upon men and events and opinions upon life and art jotted down in note books from 1881 to 1925. [Diary.] Vol. 1. 2. [3.] Not on the chart. A novel. [4.] Jesus in modern life. [5.] A feather from world's wing. — Messalina. — Vestigia. [Verse.] [6.] The mirror of a mind. — The image of air. — Saul. — The last crusade. [Verse.] [7.] Amy Warren. A tale of the [Delaware] Bay shore.

D5607 — Logan, Robert Restalrig, ed. — Diaries.

NL 0449573   CtY PSt RPB OO MB

Logan, Algernon Sydney, 1849-1925.
Amy Warren; a tale of the Bay shore, by Algernon Sydney Logan ... New York, G. W. Dillingham co., 1900.
3 p. l., [9]-370 p. 19cm.

I. Title.
                                        0-2024 Revised
Library of Congress   PZ3.L828A

NL 0449574   DLC

Logan, Algernon Sydney, 1849-1925.
Amy Warren; a tale of the Bay shore, by Algernon Sydney Logan. Collected ed. Philadelphia, National publishing company, 1934.
3 p. l., 9-382 p. 22cm.

I. Title.

Library of Congress   PZ3.L828.A 5   34-24492

NL 0449575   DLC OrU ViU OO OCU MiU OClJC NN ICN IJ

Logan, Algernon Sydney, 1849-1925.
Amy Warren; a tale of the Bay shore, by Algernon Sydney Logan. Collected ed. Philadelphia, National publishing company, 1934 [°1900]
3 p. l., 9-382 p. 22cm.

NL 0449576   NIC

FILM 4274 PR v.3 reel L24
Logan, Algernon Sydney, 1849-1925.
Amy Warren: a tale of the Bay Shore ... New York, G. W. Dillingham, 1900.
370 p. (Wright American fiction, v.III, 1876-1900, no.3383, Research Publications, Inc. Microfilm, Reel L-24)

NL 0449577   CU

Logan, Algernon Sydney, 1849-1925.
A feather from the world's wing. A modern romance. By Algernon Sydney Logan ... Philadelphia, J. B. Lippincott company, 1885.
124 p. 18½cm.
In verse.

I. Title.

Library of Congress   PS2249.L6F4   28-0346

NL 0449578   DLC WaSp OrU NIC NcD NN NBuG

Logan, Algernon Sydney, 1849-1925.
A feather from the world's wing, Messalina, Vestigia, by Algernon Sydney Logan. Collected ed. Philadelphia, National publishing company, 1934.
2 p. l., 7-302 p. 22cm.

I. Title. II. Title: Messalina. III. Title: Vestigia.

Library of Congress   PS2249.L6F4 1934   34-24097
                           [5]   811.49

NL 0449579   DLC OO OC1W ViU OCU ODW MiU ICU ICN NN

Logan, Algernon Sydney, 1849-
The image of air, and other poems. By Algernon Sydney Logan ... Philadelphia, J. B. Lippincott & co., 1878.
45 p. 19cm.

I. Title.

Library of Congress   PS2249.L6I6   28-0347

NL 0449580   DLC NN

Logan, Algernon Sydney, 1849-1925.
Jesus in modern life. By Algernon Sydney Logan ... Philadelphia. J. B. Lippincott company, 1888.
299 p. 19½cm.

1. Jesus Christ. I. Title.

Library of Congress   BT301.L55   28—9350
                           [a35c2]   232.9

NL 0449581   DLC NjNbS NNUT

Logan, Algernon Sydney, 1849-1925.
Jesus in modern life, by Algernon Sydney Logan ... Collected ed. Philadelphia, National publishing company, 1934.
253 p. 22½cm.

1. Jesus Christ—Biog. I. Title.

Library of Congress   BT301.L55 1934   34-24118
                                                  232.9

IU ICN NN
NL 0449582   DLC WaSp OrU KEmT MiU OCl ViU OO ODW OU

---

76 L831 1873 Nawis Collection
[Logan, Algernon Sydney] 1849-1925
The last crusade: a satire ... New York, 1873.
1 p. l., [5]-63p. 19cm.
Covers bound in at back of book.
Author's autographed presentation copy

NL 0449583   RPB

Logan, Algernon Sydney, 1849-
Messalina: a tragedy in five acts. By Algernon Sydney Logan ... Philadelphia, J. B. Lippincott company, 1890.
147 p. 18½cm.
In verse.

1. Messallina, Valeria—Drama. I. Title.

Library of Congress   PS2249.L6M4   28-9848

NL 0449584   DLC MB InU MH NN

Logan, Algernon Sydney, 1849-1925.
The mirror of a mind; a poem, by Algernon Sydney Logan ... New York, Published for the author by G. P. Putnam's sons, 1875.
116 p. 17½cm.

I. Title.

Library of Congress   PS2249.L6M5   28-9849
Copyright 1875: 5543   [a34b1]

NL 0449585   DLC FMU NBuG MH NN

Logan, Algernon Sydney, 1849-1925.
The mirror of a mind, The image of air, Saul, The last crusade, by Algernon Sydney Logan. Collected ed. Philadelphia, National publishing company, 1934.
2 p. l., [7]-188 p. 22cm.
Poems.

I. Title. II. Title: The image of air. III. Title: Saul. IV. Title: The last crusade.

Library of Congress   PS2249.L6M5 1934   34-24098
                           [5]   811.49

IU NN ICN
NL 0449586   DLC WaSp OrU OC1W OC1 ViU OO ODW MiU

Logan, Algernon Sydney, 1849-1925.
Not on the chart; a novel of to-day, by Algernon Sydney Logan ... with illustrations by Gordon H. Grant. New York, G. W. Dillingham co., 1899.
277 p. incl. front. plates. 20cm.

I. Title.

Library of Congress   PZ3.L828N   99-717 Revised

NL 0449587   DLC ViU CU

VOLUME 338

Logan, Algernon Sydney, 1849–1925.
Not on the chart; a novel, by Algernon Sydney Logan. Collected ed. Philadelphia, National publishing company, 1934.
1 p. l., 5–255 p. 22ᶜᵐ.

I. Title.

Library of Congress　　　　PZ3.L828N 5　　　　34-24491

OC1W ViU
NL 0449588　　DLC WaSp OrU NIC NN ICN ODW MiU OCU

Logan, Algernon Sydney, 1849–1925.
Saul: a dramatic poem. By Algernon Sydney Logan ... Philadelphia, J. B. Lippincott & co., 1883.
80 p. 18½ᶜᵐ.

1. Saul, king of Israel—Drama.　I. Title.

Library of Congress　　　　PS2249.L6S3　　　　28-9851

NL 0449589　　DLC MiU NN MH

Logan, Algernon Sydney, 1849–1925.
Vestigia; collected poems, by Algernon Sydney Logan ... New York, Moffat, Yard and company, 1913.
3 p. l., 3–116 p. 19¾ᶜᵐ.　　$1.00

I. Title.

Library of Congress　　　　PS3523.O345V4 1913　　　13-24130

NL 0449590　　DLC CLSU TxU

Logan, Algernon Sydney, 1849–1925.
Vistas from the stream, by Algernon Sydney Logan; comments upon men and events and opinions upon life and art jotted down in note books from 1881 to 1925 ... Collected ed. Philadelphia, National publishing company, 1934.
2 v. front., plates (incl. music) ports. 22ᶜᵐ.

Vol. I includes Biographical sketch of the author by his son, Robert Restalrig Logan.

I. Logan, Robert Restalrig, 1874–　ed.　II. Title.

Library of Congress　　　　PS2249.L6V5 1934　　34-20886
—— Copy 2.
Copyright A 73378　　　　[5-3]　　　　928.1

MiU OC1W OCU OCl ICN IU
NL 0449591　　DLC WaSp OrU WHi KEmT NIC AU TU ViU

[Logan, Allen, fl. 1730.
The necessity of zeal for truth; and of restraining error by the exercise of church-discipline:/with an answer to several objections. [n. p.] Printed in the year MDCCXXX. [1730]
61 p. 17½cm.
Attributed to Allen Logan, minister of Torrieburn by Hallkett & Laing. Mss. note on bottom of t.-p. attributes it to "Reverend Mr. Daniell Hunter."
1. Church of Scotland - Discipline. I. Title.

NL 0449592　　ViW

F128
.67
.F4S7

Stein, Fred.
5th ave.; 100 photographs by Fred Stein, picture text by Andy Logan ... [New York] Pantheon [1947]

Logan, Andy.

Logan, Ann Stuart.
U. S. *Council of national defense. Committee on women's defense work. Illinois division.*
Citizens' almanac, issued by Americanization department, Woman's committee, Council of national defense, Illinois division. Caroline Hedger, M. D., chairman, by Ann Stuart Logan. Chicago, Ill., 1919.

Logan, Anna.
Answering gods, poems by Anna Logan; Dioses que responden, version Castellana de Mario Puga. Mexico, Ediciones Sol, 1951.
291p. 25cm.

English and Spanish on opposite pages.

I. Puga, Mario A　tr.　II. Title.
III. Title: Dioses que responden.

NL 0449595　　NcU

026.21　**Logan, Anna E**
L831s　　A list of stories for the elementary grades.　Oxford, O., 1908.
20p.　(Miami university. Miami bulletin, ser.7, no.4. Ohio—State normal college. Teachers' bulletin, no.8)

NL 0449596　　IU

Logan, Anne E.
Reports on practical experiments in everyday school-rooms in revision of programs.

(*In* National education association of the United States. **Addresses and proceedings,** 1919. p. 186–189)

1. Education of children—Curricula.　[1. Course of study—Elementary schools]

Library, U. S. Bur. of　　　　Education　　　　E 20-99

NL 0449596-1　　DHEW

S
818
L828c　　**Logan, Annie Kuykendall.**
Christmas in the home of a Texas pioneer. [n.p., c1950]
[16]p. illus.

NL 0449597　　TxFTC

Logan, Mrs. Annie Robertson (Macfarlane)
An account of the explorations and discoveries of Samuel de Champlain, and of the founding of Quebec, by Mrs. J. E. Logan... Montreal, Montreal news co., [1908]
50 p. illus.

"For Quebec battlefields fund".

NL 0449598　　MiD-B IdU

Logan, Arnold R　　1909-
Blood of adventure. New York, Vantage Press [1951]
190 p. 23 cm.

I. Title.

PZ4.L83Bl　　　　51-14568 †

NL 0449599　　DLC

1926　**Logan, Arnold R**　　1909-
L03402s　　Sir Brock's curse [and other ballads] Dallas, Story Book Press [c1951]
36 p. 20 cm.

NL 0449600　　RPB

Logan, Arthur L
Remembering made easy. New York, Arco Pub. Co. [1955]
94 p. illus. 21 cm.

1. Mnemonics.　I. Title.

BF385.L68　　　　154.1　　　　55-6608 †

NcD PP NcD NN WaSp
NL 0449601　　DLC CaBVa Wa WaS KMK MoU FU-HC ViU MB

T252
L828e　　**Logan, B**　F
Eleven selected sermons.　[n.p., 19--]
1p.l.,48p. port. 20cm.

Cover title.
Stamped on cover: Rev. B.F. Logan, Austin, Texas.

NL 0449602　　TxU

Tx
232
L828f　　**Logan, B**　F
Fruit from an old tree.　Austin, Tex. [n.d.]
16p. 22cm.

Cover title.

1. Jesus Christ.　2. God.　I. Title.

NL 0449603　　TxU

Logan, Belle V.
Her shattered idol, by Belle V. Logan. Chicago, Morrill, Higgins & co. [1893]
250 p. incl. front. 20ᶜᵐ. (*On cover:* The Midland series. v. 1, no. 38)

I. Title.

Library of Congress　　　　PZ3.L8284H　　　　7-14800

NL 0449604　　DLC

FILM
4274
PR
V. 3
Reel
L25　　**Logan, Belle V.**
Her shattered idol, by Belle V. Logan. Chicago, Morrill, Higgins & co. c. 1892.
250 p. incl. front.　20 cm. (Wright American fiction, v.III, 1876–1900, no. 3385, Research Publications, Inc., Microfilm, Reel L–25) (On cover: The Midland series. v.1, no. 38)

NL 0449605　　CU

Logan, Black Jack
see
Logan, John Alexander, 1826–1886.

VOLUME 338

✳
976.92
L826

Logan, Boone.
Letters to the Sentinel-Democrat (Mt.
Sterling, Ky.) pertaining to the Rowan
county feud and other matters.   [More-
head? Ky., 1885?]
29 p.   21 cm.

Cover title.

NL 0449607   KyU KyHi

1926
L0346u

Harris
Coll. 1935

Logan, Caroline E
The United States history in rhyme.
[York, Pa., Gazette Print Shop, c1934]
27 p.   17 cm.

Author's autographed presentation copy.

1. U.S.—Hist.—Poetry. I. Title.

NL 0449608   RPB

Logan, Carolynne (Chitwood) 1902-
One of these seven, a Justus Drum mystery, by Carolynne
and Malcolm Logan. New York, Mystery house, 1946.
272 p. 19½ᵐ.

I. Logan, Malcolm, joint author. II. Title.
46-6100
Library of Congress   PZ3.L82843On

NL 0449609   DLC NN

Logan, Carolynne (Chitwood) 1902-
One of these seven. Abridged ed. ... By Carolynne and
Malcolm Logan. [New York, 1947]
127 p. 17ᵐ. (On cover: Handi-book mysteries. [No. 59])

I. Logan, Malcolm Roderick, 1901-   joint author. II. Title.
PZ3.L82843On 2   47-23057
                                 Brief cataloging

NL 0449610   DLC

Logan, Carrie Elizabeth.
The psychology of Schopenhauer in its relation to his
system of metaphysics. By Carrie Elizabeth Logan, PH. D.
... [Brooklyn? N. Y., 1903]
103 p. 23ᵐ.
Thesis—New York university.
3-30974

NL 0449611   DLC NjP

Logan, Celia
see
Connelly, Mrs. Celia (Logan) 1837-1904.

TS2158
.F4

Logan, Charles Alden, joint author.

Fenton, Frederick Charles, 1891-
... Farm grinding of grain and forage, by F. C. Fenton and
C. A. Logan ... Manhattan, Kan., The College [1931]

Logan, Charles Alden.
Farm lighting systems. Manhattan, Kan., The College,
1932.
58 p. illus. 23 cm. ([Kansas. State College of Agriculture and
Applied Science, Manhattan] Engineering Experiment Station. Bul-
letin no. 80)
Kansas State College bulletin, v. 16, no. 7.
Bibliography: p. 57.

1. Lighting. 2. Electric lighting. I. Title. (Series)
TH7725.L6   A 32-2882 rev*
Kansas. State Coll.   Library
for Library of Congress   [r58c2]†

NL 0449614   KEmT DLC Or

Logan, Charles Alexander, 1874-   tr.

Kagawa, Toyohiko, 1888-
... Meditations on the Holy Spirit [by] Toyohiko Kagawa,
translated by Charles A. Logan. Nashville, Cokesbury press
[1939]

Logan, Clarence August, 1887-   joint author.

Bradley, Walter Wadsworth, 1878-
... Manganese and chromium in California, by Walter W.
Bradley, Emile Huguenin, C. A. Logan, W. Burling Tucker
and Clarence A. Waring. Sacramento, California state printing office, 1918.

TN24
.C2A3
no. 138

Logan, Clarence August, 1887-

Ricketts, Alfred Herbert, 1849-1938.
... Manner of locating and holding mineral claims in Cali-
fornia (with forms) by A. H. Ricketts, with revisions by C. A.
Logan ... San Francisco, 1946.

Logan, Clarence August, 1887-   joint
author.

Bradley, Walter Wadsworth, 1878-
... Mines and mineral resources of the counties of Monterey,
San Benito, San Luis Obispo, Santa Barbara, Ventura. By
Walter W. Bradley, Emile Huguenin, C. A. Logan [and]
Clarence A. Waring, field assistants. [Sacramento] California
state printing office, 1917.

Map
G
4362
M6
1934

Logan, Clarence August, 1887-
Mother Lode gold belt [of California]
showing mining claims and areal geology.
[Sacramento] 1934.
5 col. maps. Size varies.

Scales vary.
Shows extent of Mother Lode in Amador
Calaveras, El Dorado, Mariposa, and
Tuolumne Counties.

NL 0449619   NIC

Logan, Clarence August, 1887-
... Mother Lode gold belt of California, by Clarence A.
Logan. Sacramento, California state printing office, 1935.
240 p. incl. illus., tables, diagrs.   x pl. (incl. maps (6 in pocket)
diagrs.) fold. tab. 23½ᵐ. (California. Dept. of natural resources. Division of mines. Bulletin no. 108)
Bibliography: p. 214-219.

1. Gold mines and mining—California.   I. Title.
                                         G S 35-94
Library, U. S. Geological   Survey (276) C4b no. 108
——— ——— Copy 2.
Library of Congress   [TN24.C2A3 no. 108]

NL 0449620   MoU OCl OCU MiU OU
DLC CaBVaU MtBuM WaS WaT OrP IdU UU

Logan, Clarence August, 1887-
... Platinum and allied metals in California, by C. A. Logan.
Sacramento, California state printing office, 1919.
v p., 1 l., [9]-120 p. illus., 3 fold. charts. 23ᵐ. (California. State
mining bureau. Bulletin no. 85)

1. Platinum.   I. Title.
                                              G S 20—220
U. S. Geol. survey. Library   (276) C4b no. 85
for Library of Congress   TN24.C2A3 no. 85

NL 0449621   DI-GS MtBuM WaS UU DLC ICJ NN

Logan, Clement.
A history of the pilchard industry off the west
coast of Vancouver Island, British Columbia.
Vancouver, B. C., 1935.
7 p.
Typewritten.
Paper submitted in History 11, Canadian history,
Summer school, University of British Columbia,
1935.
1. Fisheries - British Columbia. 2. Pilchard
fisheries.

NL 0449622   CaBVa

---

q371.26
L8211

Logan, Conrad Travis, 1890-
Logan and Parks's literary background
tests.   Boston [c1930]
32 pieces.

Literary background test.- Re-test of
literary background.- Keys.

NL 0449623   IU

Logan, Conrad Travis, 1890-
Native drama.

Extract from Virginia teacher,   Mar.1923.

NL 0449624   NcU

Logan, Conrad Travis, 1890-
Practice leaves in English fundamentals
(form A) for rapid drills and tests, by...
E.P. Cleveland, and M.V.Hoffman... State
teachers college, Harrisonburg, Virginia. Bost.
N.Y.,[etc.] D.C Heath and co. c1925.
[64] p.

NL 0449625   ViU NcD

Logan, Conrad Travis, 1890-
Practice leaves in junior English (form J),
... and K.M.Anthony ...State teachers college.
Harrisonburg,Virginia. Boston, N.Y.[etc.]
Heath [c1928.
[76]p.

NL 0449626   ViU

Logan, Conrad Travis, 1890-   comp.
Study tests for literary understanding, by
Conrad T. Logan and Carrie Belle Parks.
Preliminary section: literary background tests.
Boston, New York, [etc.] D. C. Heath and company
[c1930]
cover-title, [60] p.   26 cm.
1. English literature-examinations, questions,
etc. 2. Mental tests. I. Parks, Carrie Belle, joint
comp. II. Title. III. Title: Literary background
tests.

NL 0449627   CU

VOLUME 338

Logan, Cornelius Ambrose, 1836–
An Address / delivered by / Grand Rep. C. A. Logan / before the Odd-fellows, / in / Re-union, / Leavenworth City, / November 26th, 1863. / [rule] / Leavenworth: / Printed at the Evening Bulletin Book and Job Office. / [rule] / 1863.
16 p. 14.5 x 21.5 cm. Printed paper wrappers.

NL 0449628   KHi

Logan, Cornelius Ambrose, 1836–1899.
An essay on the remote and proximate causes of miasmatic fever. By C. A. Logan ... Leavenworth, Printed at the Daily conservative book and job office, 1861.
19 p. 23 ᵐ.
"Read before the Leavenworth medical and surgical association ... February 7, 1861."

1. Malarial fever.

Library of Congress   RC156.L83   7–30271†

NL 0449629   DLC

Logan, Cornelius Ambrose, 1836–1899.
García Calderón, Francisco, 1834–1905.
Mediacion de los Estados Unidos de Norte América en la guerra del Pacífico, el Señor doctor Don Cornelius A. Logan y el Dr. D. Francisco Garcia Calderon. Buenos Aires, Impr. y libreria de Mayo, 1884.

Logan, Cornelius Ambrose, 1836–1899.
Physics of the infectious diseases. Comprehending a discussion of certain physical phenomena in connection with the acute infectious diseases. By C. A. Logan ... Chicago, Jansen, McClurg and company, 1878.
2 p. l., [3]–212 p. front. (map) 19⅔ᵐ.
CONTENTS.—Introductory remarks.—Physical aspects of the Pacific coast of South America.—Medical aspects of the Pacific coast of South America.—The physics of specific causation.—Therapeutics of the infectious diseases.—The question of energy as related to general disorders.

1. Contagion and contagious diseases. 2. South America—Sanit. affairs.

Library of Congress   RC112.L83   7–30899 Revised

NL 0449631   DLC ICRL DNLM PU PP Nh ICJ NN

Logan, Cornelius Ambrose, 1836–1899.
Kansas. *Geological survey.*
Preliminary report of the Geological survey of Kansas. By G. C. Swallow, state geologist. Lawrence, Kans., J. Speer, printer to the state, 1866.

WZ   Logan, Cornelius Ambrose, 1836–
270   Report on the sanitary relations of the State of
L836r   Kansas. Lawrence [Kan.] J. Speer, 1866.
1866   50 p.
         I. Title

NL 0449633   DNLM KHi

Logan, Cornelius Ambrose, 1836–1899.
Logan, John Alexander, 1826–1886.
The volunteer soldier of America. By John A. Logan. With Memoir of the author and Military reminiscences from General Logan's private journal. Chicago and New York, R. S. Peale & company, 1887.

LOGAN, CORNELIUS AMBROSIUS, 1806–1853.
Chloroform, or, One hundred years hence: a local burletta in 1 act. [n. p., 18–] 58 p. 32cm.

In ms.
Property list included.
Produced at Burton's theatre, New York, May, 1849.

l. Drama, American. I. Title.   II. Title: One hundred years hence.

NL 0449635   NN

Amer. Lit.
810   [Logan, Cornelius Ambrosius] 1806–1853.
B9591   Vermont wool dealer; a farce in one
tV   act. Clyde, Ohio, A.D. Ames [n.d.]
             17p. 19cm. (On cover: Ames' series of
             standard and minor drama, no.213)

             Performed Cincinnati 1844.

NL 0449636   CLSU

[Logan, Cornelius Ambrosius] 1806–1853.
... Vermont wool-dealer: a farce in one act [Anon] New York, n. d.
18 p.   nar. D. (The minor drama, the acting ed. no. 173)

NL 0449637   RPB NcU PPL

PS2249 [Logan, Cornelius Ambrosius] 1806–1853.
.L64V6 ... Vermont wool-dealer. A farce, in one act ... As per-
18--   formed at the principal English and American theaters.
         New York, S. French [18–]
         18 p. 19ᵐᵐ. (The minor drama. The acting edition. No. CLXXIII)

NL 0449638   ICU NN IRU MiU MH MiD CtY

Logan, Cornelius Ambrosius, 1806–1853.
... Vermont wool-dealer; a farce, in one act. New York, Samuel French & son, London, Samuel French, [1844?]
18 p.

NL 0449639   OC1

[Logan, Cornelius Ambrosius] 1806–1853.
VERMONT wool-dealer; a farce, in one act. New York, [185–].
pp.18.
(Minor drama, vol. XXII, no.173.)
11434.25

NL 0449640   MH NNC

Lilly
PS 2249 [LOGAN, CORNELIUS AMBROSIUS, 1806–1853
.L 97 V4 ... Vermont wool-dealer. A farce, in one
          act ... As performed at the principal English
          and American theatres. New York, S. French
          [1854]
          18 p. 19 cm. (French's Minor drama,
          no. 173)

          In yellow printed paper wrappers; series
          advts. to no. 320.

NL 0449641   InU

[Logan, Cornelius Ambrosius] 1806–1853.
... Vermont wool-dealer, a farce, in one act [by Cornelius Ambrosius Logan] To which are added a description of the costume, cast of the characters ... and the whole of the stage business ... New York, S. French [1859?]
18 p. 19 cm. (The minor drama. The acting ed. no. CLXXIII)
Original covers wanting.

NL 0449642   RPB

812   [Logan, Cornelius Ambrosius] 1806–1853.
V592   Vermont wool dealer. A farce, in one act.
          With the stage business, cast of characters ...
          Clyde, O., A. D. Ames [188–?]
          17p. (On cover: Ames' series of standard and
          minor drama. no.213)

NL 0449643   IU

[Logan, Cornelius Ambrosius] 1806–1853.
VERMONT wool dealer; a farce in one act.
New ed. revised and improved. Boston, W.H.
Baker & co., [cop.1889.]
pp.19.
Date taken from cover.   DAL 4340.48

NL 0449644   MH

812.08   [Logan, Cornelius Ambrosius] 1806–1853.
F876   ...Vermont wool-dealer; a farce, in
v.22   one act... New York, French [1890?]
no.5   18p. D. (The Minor drama. The
          acting edition, no.173)
          Lettered on cover: French's minor
          drama, v.22 [no.5]

NL 0449645   IaU

PS
2249   Logan, Cornelius Ambrosius, 1806–1853.
.L62   Yankee land. A comedy, in two acts. By C.A.
Y2   Logan, esq. ... With original casts, costumes,
18--   and the whole of the stage business, correct-
          ly marked and arranged, by Mr. J. B. Wright ...
          of the Boston theatre. New York, S. French &
          son; London, S. French [18--]
          31 p. 19ᶜᵐ. (On cover: French's minor drama.
          The acting edition. no. CCII)
          Cast of characters of earliest representation
          dated 1834.

NL 0449646   MiU MdBP RPB MB

Logan, Cornelius Ambrosius, 1806–1853.
Yankee Land. A comedy, in two acts. With original cast, costumes, and the whole of the stage business, marked and arranged, by J. B. Wright.
New York. French. [185–?] 31 pp. [French's Minor drama. No. 202.] 16°.
Two copies.

F7578 — T.r. — S.r.

NL 0449647   MB MH

Logan, Cornelius Ambrosius, 1806–1853.
Yankee land. A comedy, in two acts. By C. A. Logan ... Boston, W. V. Spencer [1856?]
31 p. 18ᶜᵐ. (Spencer's Boston theatre. [v. 9] no. 70)

A 10–249

Title from Univ. of Mich.   Printed by L. C.

NL 0449648   MiU

VOLUME 338

Logan, Daniel, *1852 - 1925.*
All about Hawaii, by Daniel Logan ... Boston, Mass., Press of Chapple publishing company, 1921.
3 p. l., 56 p. illus., 2 pl. (1 fold.) 23½ᶜᵐ.

1. Hawaiian Islands—Descr. & trav.
Library of Congress   DU623.L57   21-14125

NL 0449649   DLC NN

LOGAN, Daniel.
Education in the Hawaiian islands.

North American review, 1897, pp. 20-25.

NL 0449650   MH

Logan, Daniel.

Hawaiian Islands. *Dept. of foreign affairs.*
A handbook of information issued by the Department of foreign affairs, Honolulu, 1899. ₍San Francisco, Sunset press, 1899₎

Logan, Daniel.
Hawaii; its people, climate and resources, written by Daniel Logan. Honolulu, Pioneer advertising company ₍1903₎
117 p. illus. (incl. map) 20½ᶜᵐ.

1. Hawaiian Islands—Descr. & trav.
Library of Congress   DU622.L83   3-14559

NL 0449652   DLC CU OrU NjP OO MWA MiU NN ICJ MB

Logan, Daniel, 1852-1925, ed.

The Hawaiian forester and agriculturist; issued under the direction of the Board of commissioners of agriculture and forestry ... v. 1– Jan. 1904– Honolulu, Hawaiian gazette co., ltd. ₍etc.₎ 1904–

Logan, Daniel, *ed.*
A history of the Hawaiian Islands, their resources and people; ed. by Daniel Logan ... New York, Chicago, The Lewis publishing company, 1907.
viii, 259 p. double front., plates, ports. 27ᶜᵐ.

1. Hawaiian Islands—Hist.
                                       7-10614
Library of Congress   DU625.L8   (Copyright A 169802)

NL 0449654   DLC

Logan, David.
An introductory address, delivered ... February 2, 1823, in the Unitarian Chapel of Dundee; to which is added, a summary statement of the principles and defence of the dissent of the Unitarians in that town.   Dundee, J. Chalmers, 1823.
31 p.   8°.
In: * C. p. v. 1232.

NL 0449655   NN MH

Logan, Daniel.
Hawaiian Volcanoes. By Daniel Logan.
[Honolulu? n. p. , 1903]
cover-title, 24 p. illus. ob. 12 mo. Bound in red cloth.
The Macdonald Collection.

NL 0449656   CSmH

₍Logan, David,₎ 1799–1849.
Observations on the peculiar and surpassing excellence of the constitution of the Church of Scotland; as illustrated in the late disruption, and present continued struggle.   Edinburgh: M. M'Phail, 1844.   15 p.   8°.

474685A. 1. Church of Scotland—   Govt. and discipline. ₍1. Title.
N. Y. P. L.   November 26, 1930

NL 0449657   NN

Logan, David.
Report on the improvements of the river Clyde and harbour of Glasgow, ordered by the parliamentary trustees, with tables of soundings and borings, by David Logan ... Glasgow, Printed by Bell & Bain, 1835.
22 p. fold. pl., fold. plan, 2 tab. 28½ x 22½ᶜᵐ.

1. Glasgow—Harbor. 2. Clyde River. I. Glasgow. Clyde trustees.

Library of Congress   TC464.C6L7   6-14864†

NL 0449658   DLC MdBJ

Logan, David, *d. Kentucky*
To the Public.   [Kentucky printing, 1818]
94 + p.   13. 5 x 22 cm.
Name and day at bottom of p. 63: David Logan, September 1st, 1818. The incomplete ICU copy contains no indication of the place of printing, but the text is concerned exclusively with affairs in Kentucky.

NL 0449659   ICU

Logan, David Dale, *joint author.*

Glaister, John, 1856–
Gas poisoning in mining and other industries. By John Glaister ... and David Dale Logan ... With plans, coloured plates and thirty-six other illustrations. New York, W. Wood and company, 1914.

Logan, David Dale.
... Mine rescue work on the western front. ₍By₎ Lieut.-Colonel D. Dale Logan, D. S. O. ... London, H. M. Stationery off. ₍Harrison and sons, printers₎ 1920.
79 p. incl. illus., forms. plates. 24½ᶜᵐ.
Some plates printed on both sides.

1. Mine rescue work. 2. Mines, Military. 3. Gases, Asphyxiating and poisonous.
Library of Congress   TN297.L6   21-3083

NL 0449661   DLC ICJ

WR   LOGAN, David Duncan
L831o   On certain obstinate diseases of the
1864   skin. London, Churchill, 1864.
             67 p.

NL 0449662   DNLM OC1W-H

Logan, David Matthew, 1894–
The structure of Oklahoma government, by David M. Logan ... Oklahoma City, Harlow publishing co., 1931.
xiii, ₍1₎ p., 1 l., 219 p. front., illus. (incl. maps) 23½ᶜᵐ.

1. Oklahoma—Pol. & govt. I. Title.
Library of Congress   JK7125.1931.L6   31-6885
——— Copy 2.
Copyright A 33738   ₍3₎   342.766

NL 0449663   DLC

Logan, Dawn
     see Logan, Rhea Dawn, 1898–

Logan, Mrs. Deborah (Norris) 1761-1839, ed.

Penn, William, 1644-1718.
Correspondence between William Penn and James Logan, secretary of the province of Pennsylvania, and others. 1700-1750. From the original letters in possession of the Logan family. With notes by the late Mrs. Deborah Logan. Ed. with additional notes by Edward Armstrong ... vol. I–II. Philadelphia, The Historical society of Pennsylvania, 1870–72.

Logan, *Mrs.* Deborah (Norris) 1761–1839.
Memoir of Dr. George Logan of Stenton, by his widow Deborah Norris Logan, with selections from his correspondence; ed. by their great-granddaughter, Frances A. Logan; with an introduction by Charles J. Stillé. Illustrations from photographs by C. S. Bradford. Philadelphia, The Historical society of Pennsylvania, 1899.
207 p. 3 pl., 2 port. (incl. front.) facsim. 26½ᶜᵐ.

1. Logan, George, 1753–1821. I. Logan, Frances Armatt, ed.
                                               99-3378 Revised
Library of Congress   E302.6.L8L8

MB
PP PPL NN Nh ViU PHC PU MnU PHi PSC OC1WHi PBm ICJ
NL 0449666   DLC MiU TU CSt NIC MdBP DNLM NjP MWA

Logan, Deborah (Norris), 1761–1839.
The Norris house. By Deborah Logan.   Philadelphia: Printed on the Fair-Hill Press, 1867.   1 p.l., 12 p.   8°.

106740A. 1. Historic houses, U. S.:   J. S. BILLINGS MEM. COLL.
N. Y. P. L.   Pa.: Philadelphia.   November 7, 1923.

NL 0449667   NN PSt

Logan, Douglas William, 1910–   joint author.
A report on the University of Hong Kong

see under

Jennings, Sir William Ivor, 1903–

C   Logan, Douglas William, *1910–*
L84uEl   The University of London, an introduction.
             With a foreword by Her Majesty Queen Elizabeth, the Queen Mother.   London, University of London ₍1955₎
             43p. fold. maps. 22cm.

1. London. University.

NL 0449669   IU

VOLUME 338

Logan, Dwight.
    Pete, the great magician. New York, C. Scribner's Sons,
ᵗ1948.
    ₍56₎ p. col. illus. 15 x 20 cm.
    Cover title: Pete the great.

    ɪ. Title.

    PZ10.3.L853Pe   48–6239*

NL 0449670   DLC

Logan, E. A.
    see Logan, Eugene Adolphus, 1872–

Logan, Edgar, joint ed.   FOR OTHER EDITIONS
                                  SEE MAIN ENTRY
Gerard, James Watson, 1822–1900.
    A digested treatise and compendium of law applicable
to titles to real estate in the state of New York. By
James W. Gerard ... 3d ed.—rev. and enl. giving all the
code and statute changes to date. With notes of decisions. By Edward B. Hill and Edgar Logan ... New
York, Baker, Voorhis & co., 1889.

Logan, Edgar, ed.
    The Real property law of the state of New York, being
chapter XLVI of the General laws (to take effect October 1,
1896) with full notes referring to the Revised statutes and
other laws from which the act is derived, and citations of
cases applicable thereunder, by Edgar Logan ... New York,
Baker, Voorhis and company, 1896.

    2 p. l., 140 p. 24ᶜᵐ.

    1. Real property—New York (State)   ɪ. New York (State) Laws,
statutes, etc.
                                              33–13245

NL 0449673   DLC NBuU-L NcD NN MB OU

Logan, Edgar, ed.
    The real property law of the state of New York being chapter
XLVI of the General laws (to take effect October 1, 1896). With
full notes referring to the revised statutes and other laws from
which the act is derived, and citations of cases applicable thereunder. By Edgar Logan... New York: Baker, Voorhis and
Co., 1900.   140 (really 148) p.   8°.

12935A. 1. Property (Real).—Ju-   risprudence, U. S.: New York,
1896. 2. Logan, Edgar, editor.   N. Y. City.
N. Y. P. L.   July 5, 19??.

NL 0449674   NN

Logan, Edward Bates, ed.
    The American political scene, by A. N. Holcombe, Edward
B. Logan, J. T. Salter ... ₍and others₎ Edited by Edward B.
Logan. New York and London, Harper & brothers, 1936.
    viii p., 1 l., 264 p. illus. (maps) 20½ᶜᵐ.
    "First edition."
    Contents.—Present-day characteristics of American political parties,
by A. N. Holcombe.—Party organization in the United States, by E. B.
Logan.—The politician and the voter, by J. T. Salter.—Presidential campaigns, by H. R. Bruce.—The use of money in elections, by J. K. Pol-
lock.—Pressure groups and propaganda, by H. L. Childs.
    1. Political parties—U. S. 2. U. S.—Pol. & govt. 3. Elections—U. S.
ɪ. Holcombe, Arthur Norman, 1884–   ɪɪ. Salter, John Thomas. ɪɪɪ.
Title.
                                                    36–23504
    Library of Congress   JK1726.L6
    ——— Copy 2.
    Copyright A 98471   ₍5–5₎   329

        WHi TU NcD NcRS OOxM OU ODW OCl OO ViU MB
NL 0449675   DLC NN KEmT NIC OrU WaTC OrP OrPR WaWW

Logan, Edward Bates, *ed.*
    The American political scene. Rev. ed., by A. N. Holcombe.
Edward B. Logan, J. T. Salter ... ₍and others₎ Edited by
Edward B. Logan. New York and London, Harper & broth-
ers ₍ᵗ1938₎

    viii p., 1 l., 311 p. illus. (maps) 21ᶜᵐ.

    Contents.—Present-day characteristics of American political parties,
by A. N. Holcombe.—Party organization in the United States, by E. B.
Logan.—The politician and the voter, by J. T. Salter.—Presidential campaigns, by H. R. Bruce.—The use of money in elections, by J. K. Pol-
lock.—Pressure groups and propaganda, by H. L. Childs.—Nominations,
by Louise Overacker.—Appendix ɪ. The changing outlook for a realign-
ment of parties, by A. N. Holcombe.—Appendix ɪɪ. The platforms of
the two major parties.

    1. Political parties—U. S. 2. U. S.—Pol. & govt. 3. Elections—U. S.
ɪ. Holcombe, Arthur Norman, 1884–   ɪɪ. Salter, John Thomas. ɪɪɪ.
Title.
                                                    38–31039
    Library of Congress   JK1726.L6 1938
    ——— Copy 2.
    Copyright A 120952   ₍5₎   329

              PSC OCU OCIW NN
NL 0449677   DLC IU WU IdU PPLas MiU ViU PPD PU PPT

Logan, Edward Bates.
    Lobbying, by Edward B. Logan ... ₍Philadelphia, Amer-
ican academy of political and social science, 1929₎
    v, 91 p. 24ᶜᵐ. (Supplement to vol. cxliv of the Annals of the Ameri-
can academy of political and social science ... July, 1929)
    On cover: Publication no. 2305.

    1. Lobbying.
                                                    29–17421
    Library of Congress   H1.A4 vol. cxliv Suppl.
    ——— Copy 2.   JK1118.L6

              OCU ODW MiU ICJ MH NN MB NcD OrPS OrP OrSaW CaBVaU
NL 0449678   DLC OrP Or DNLM CU PU-L PHC PPT OO OCl

Logan, Edward Bates.
    Supervision of the conduct of elections and returns, with
special reference to Pennsylvania ... by Edward Bates Logan.
₍Lancaster, Pa.₎ Lancaster press, inc., 1927.
    v, 156 p. illus., diagr. 23ᶜᵐ.
    Thesis (ph. d.)—University of Pennsylvania, 1927.
    Bibliography: p. 154–156.

    1. Elections—U. S. 2. Elections—Pennsylvania.   ɪ. Title.
                                                    28–9134
    Library of Congress   JK1976.L6 1927
    Univ. of Pennsylvania   Libr.

NL 0449679   PU IdU WaS NIC NcD MiU OU OO OCl.MB DLC

Logan, Edward Bates.
    Supervision of the conduct of elections and returns, with
special reference to Pennsylvania, by Edward Bates Logan ...
₍Lancaster, Pa.₎ Lancaster press, inc.₎ 1927.
    v, 156 p. illus., diagr. 23ᶜᵐ.
    Issued also as thesis (ph. d.) University of Pennsylvania.
    Bibliography: p. 154–156.

    1. Elections—U. S. 2. Elections—Pennsylvania.   ɪ. Title.
                                                    39–33176
    Library of Congress   JK1976.L6 1927 a
                                 ₍2₎   324.240973

NL 0449680   DLC MH-L

Logan, Edward Bates.
    Taxation of real property in Pennsylvania, by Edward B.
Logan ... ₍Philadelphia, University of Pennsylvania₎ 1934.
    6 p. l., 86 p., 1 l., 134 p. tables. 28ᶜᵐ.
    Mimeographed.

    1. Taxation—Pennsylvania. 2. Real property—Pennsylvania. 3. Real
property—Valuation.
                                                    A 40–8807
    Penn. state college. Libr.
    for Library of Congress   ₍2₎

NL 0449681   PSt NN ICU IU ICJ Or

Logan, Edward Lawrence, 1875–
    Massachusetts. *Memorial commission for Massachusetts
    dead of world war in foreign countries.*
    ... Supplementary report of the Special commission ap-
pointed to identify the graves of the men and women of
Massachusetts who gave their lives for their country in
France and in other foreign countries during the world
war; and "to inquire into the wisdom of construction by
the commonwealth, in France or elsewhere, of a monument or other suitable memorial, in commemoration of
Massachusetts citizens whose lives were so given" ...
₍Boston? 1921₎

Rare Book   ₍Logan, Eliza₎
₍room₎   `Restalrig; or, The forfeiture. By the
In   author of St. Johnstoun, or John Earl of
L828   Gowrie. In two volumes ... Edinburgh:
829R   Maclachlan & Stewart, ₍Edinburgh₎ and
              Simpkin & Marshall, London, 1829.
              2v. 19cm.

NL 0449683   CtY CLU

PR4935   ₍Logan, Eliza₎
.L78R4   Restalrig; or, The forfeiture, by the author of
1829   St. Johnstoun, or John, earl of Gowrie. 2d ed.
          Edinburgh, Maclachlan & Stewart, 1829.
          2 v.

NL 0449684   ICU MH

PR4935   ₍Logan,   ... Eliza₎
.L78S4 / St. Johnstoun; or, John, earl of Gowrie ...   Edinburgh,
1823   Printed for Maclachlan and Stewart; ₍etc., etc.₎ 1823.
          3 v. 17½ᶜᵐ.
          Prefatory notice signed: Peregrine Rover ₍pseud.₎

          1. Gowrie conspiracy, 1600—Fiction. 2. Gowrie, John Ruthven, 3d earl of,
          1578?–1600—Fiction.

NL 0449685   ICU IEN GEU MH IU ICN NcU NjP LU CtY

Logan, Eliza.
    St. Johnstoun; or, John, Earl of Gowrie ...
Edinburgh: Printed for Maclachlan and Stewart;
London, Baldwin, Craddock, and Joy, 1823.
    3 vols. 19.5 cm.
    Deckle edge.
    Inscription on front fly leaf "M. Robertson,
12 North William St., Perth, 1891."
    1. Gowrie conspiracy, 1600 - Fiction. I. Title.

NL 0449686   ScU

₍Logan, Eliza₎
    St. Johnstoun; or, John, earl of Gowrie. A Scottish ro-
mance of the 16th century ... ₍etc., etc.₎ 2d ed. Edinburgh, Maclachlan
and Stewart; ₍etc., etc.₎ 1839.
    3 v. 18ᶜᵐ.

    1. Gowrie conspiracy, 1600—Fiction.   ɪ. Title.
                                                    42–18955
    Library of Congress   PZ3.L8285Sa1 2

NL 0449687   DLC ScU InU

Logan, Miss Eliza.
    Memoir of Miss Eliza Logan
    see under title

VOLUME 338

Logan, *Mrs.* Elizabeth.
My book of memories, by Elizabeth Logan. ₍Elkton, Md.,
Printed by Cecil Whig printing office, 1939₎
cover-title, ₍52₎ p. 24ᶜᵐ.
Poems.

ɪ. Title.
39–16243

Library of Congress PS3523.O342M9 1939
────── Copy 2.
Copyright A 128314 ₍2₎ 811.5

NL 0449689 DLC

M1746
.K7E4
Logan, Ella, 1913–
Kramer, Alexander Milton, 1893– *arr.*
Ella Logan in a wee bit o' Scotch song, compiled and ar-
ranged by Alex M. Kramer ... New York, Leeds music corpo-
ration, ᶜ1944.

355.07
L831
Logan, Emilie Louise.
"West Point–the Gibraltar of the
Hudson." West Point, N. Y., West Point
Hotel, ᶜ1918.
32 p. illus., ports., maps.
16 x 24 cm.

1. U.S. Military Academy, West Point.

NL 0449691 N

LOGAN, ERIC.
The recoil; a thriller, by Eric Logan. (In: Box, S.,
comp. One–act plays for players. London [1935] 19cm.
p. [165]–186.)

784984A. 1. Drama, English. I. Title.

NL 0449692 NN

Logan, Eugene, 1884–
... Columbia basin project. Idaho allocation
data ... [by] Eugene Logan ... [and] Glenn L.
Parker ... n. p., 1927.
v. p. tables, diagrs.
Supplementary material including blue print
diagrams and tables attached.
At head of title: Copy.
1. Irrigation - Idaho. 2. Water-power - Idaho.
3. Columbia basin irrigation project. 4. Flood
control. I. Parker, Glenn Lane, 1884–
II. Title: Idaho allocation data. III. PNC cd.

NL 0449693 WaPS

Logan, Eugene, 1884–
Preliminary report, Columbia basin project;
water power analyses, Albany Falls power project.
[n. p.] 1926.
31 l. tables, diagrs.
Cover-title.
Typewritten.
Some tables and diagrs. on blue prints.
1. Water power - Northwest, Pacific. 2. Albany
Falls - Power utilization. 3. Irrigation - Northwest,
Pacific. 4. Columbia basin irrigation project.
I. Parker, Glenn Lane, 1884– II. U. S.
Geological survey. Water resources branch.

III. Title. IV. Water power analyses, Albany Falls
power project. V. PNC sh. cd.

NL 0449695 WaPS

Logan, Eugene, 1884–
Preliminary report, Columbia Basin project.
Water power analyses. Power possibilities of
Priest River, Idaho [by] Eugene Logan ... [and]
Glenn L. Parker ... n. p., 1926.
21 l.
Cover-title.
Blueprints attached.
Typewritten c. c.
1. Water power - Idaho. 2. Priest river, Idaho -
Power utilization. 3. Irrigation - Idaho.
4. Columbia basin irrigation project. I. Water power
analyses.

II. Power possibilites of Priest river, Idaho.
III. Parker, Glenn Lane, 1884– IV. PNC sh. cd.

NL 0449698 WaPS

Logan, Eugene Adolphus, 1872–
Missouri farm census by counties. By E. A. Logan and
Jewell Mayes ... Jefferson City. Mo., 1926.
16 p. fold. tab. 23ᶜᵐ. (Missouri. State board of agriculture.
Monthly bulletin. April. May. June. 1926. v. 24, no. 2)

1. Agriculture—Missouri—Statistics. ₍1. Missouri—Agriculture—Sta-
tistics₎ ɪ. Mayes, Jewell, 1873– joint author. ɪɪ. Title.
Agr 26–1723
Library, U. S. Dept. of Agriculture 2M69B vol. 24, no. 2

NL 0449699 DNAL

Logan, Eugenia, *sister.*
A concordance to the poetry of Samuel Taylor Coleridge,
edited by Sister Eugenia Logan ... Saint Mary-of-the-
Woods, Ind. ₍Priv. print.₎ 1940.
xvi, 901 p. 27 cm.
"Limited edition of 525 copies."

1. Coleridge, Samuel Taylor, 1772–1834—Concordances.

PR4482.L6 821.72 40–5958

CaBVaU NcD OO OCl OCU OU ViU MsU ScU MeB
NL 0449700 DLC MtU CLSU UU IdU NNiaU WaS OrU TU

Logan, Mrs. F.A.
Poems. Sacramento, Cal., 1883.
47 [1] p. 17 cm.

NL 0449701 RPB

Logan, F M.
Model farm buildings, by F. M. Logan ... Victoria,
Printed by R. Wolfenden, printer to the King's most
excellent Majesty, 1906.
30 p. plates (2 fold.) 21½ᶜᵐ. (British Columbia. Dept. of agriculture.
Bulletin no. 18)

1. Farm buildings.
Agr 12–1901
Library, U. S. Dept. of Agriculture 7B77 no. 18

NL 0449702 DNAL CaBVaU

Logan, Ford, *pseud.*
see
Newton, Dwight Bennett, 1916–

Logan, Frances.
The Old Sweet, biography of a spring, by Frances Logan.
Roanoke, Va. ₍Lithographed by Hammond's printing & litho.
works₎ 1940.
3 p. l., 42 (i. e. 44) p. incl. front. (map) illus. 26ᶜᵐ.
Cover-title: Old Sweet Springs, West Virginia.
"Sources consulted": p. 41.

1. Sweetsprings, W. Va.—Hist. ɪ. Title.
42–9286
Library of Congress F249.S9L6
₍2₎ 975.478

NL 0449704 DLC TxU NcD ViU

Logan, Frances Armatt, ed.

Logan, *Mrs.* Deborah (Norris) 1761–1839.
Memoir of Dr. George Logan of Stenton, by his widow
Deborah Norris Logan, with selections from his correspondence; ed. by their great-granddaughter, Frances A. Logan;
with an introduction by Charles J. Stillé. Illustrations from
photographs by C. S. Bradford. Philadelphia, The Historical
society of Pennsylvania, 1899.

Logan, Frances (Dee)
The heart of a woman. Dallas, Wilkinson Pub. Co. ₍1953₎
79 p. 23 cm.
Poems.

ɪ. Title.
PS3523.O3425H4 811.5 54–15647 ‡

NL 0449706 DLC

Logan, Francis Donald.
The community capable of inducing custom: an
historical synopsis and commentary, by ...
Francis Donald Logan ... Brighton, Mass., 1954.
vii, 95 l. 29.5 cm. (Series: St. John's
Seminary. Canon law series)
1. Customary law (Canon law) I. Title.

NL 0449707 MBtJ

Logan, Frank A
Behavior theory and social science, by Frank A. Logan
₍and others₎ New Haven, Published for the Institute of
Human Relations by Yale University Press, 1955.
x, 188 p. diagrs. 24 cm.
"Preparation of this volume was a terminal-year project of the
authors' three years of close association while Ford fellows in behavior science at the Institute of Human Relations of Yale University."
Bibliography: p. 175–185.

1. Psychology. 2. Social sciences. ɪ. Title. 55–8705
H61.L63 301.15

PWcS PSt OClW PSC OCU OO
IdPI MH-BA MtBC MtU AAP Or KEmT OrCS OrPR PPT NN
PPPH-I MiU OOxM OCl OU CaOTP CaBVa CaBVaU KyMurT
NL 0449709 DLC WaTC ViU OrU PBL TU NcD PP MB TxU

LOGAN, FRANK GRANGER.
Famous paintings by Corot, Daubigny, Rousseau...
and other artists, and one of America's most famous
paintings, Tintoretto's "Baptism of Clorinda"...
Furnishings and art collection removed from 1150
Lakeshore drive, Chicago, the Frank G. Logan collection... sale, February 1...2 and 3... Kende galleries
at Gimbel brothers. New York, 1945. 201 p. illus.
27cm.
Gift of Mr. & Mrs. R. Stora
1. Art— Collections, Private— Logan. I. Kende galleries, inc.,
New York.

NL 0449710 NN

VOLUME 338

Logan, Frank Granger, 1851–
The Logan emancipation cabinet of letters and relics of John Brown and Abraham Lincoln. Being an article prepared specially for The Chicago Tribune. Chicago [Chicago Tribune] 1892.
40 p. incl. illus. (ports) 8 vo. In 3/4 green morocco and marbled boards; with orig. lt. blue paper covers bound in.
The Judd Stewart collection, May 1922.

NL 0449711 CSmH

Logan, Frederic Knight, 1871–1928.
Blue rose. Lyric by J. R. Shannon. Music by Frederic Knight Logan. Chicago, Forster music pub. inc. [c1917]
First line: A bluebird, one day, in a garden fair.

1. Roses. I. Shannon, James   Printed for the Music Division
Royce, 1881–1946. II. Song index (2).
N. Y. P. L.   December 5, 1949.

NL 0449712 NN

Logan, Frederic Knight, 1871–1928.
But why; song. Boston, Ditson [c1909]
3 p. 35.5 cm. (His Songs of cupid. no. 4)

NL 0449713 OrU

*M
1
.M5
no.262
Logan, Frederic Knight, 1871–1928.
Dear little heart. Poem by Victor Fuller; music by Frederic Knight Logan. [Minneapolis] P. A. Schmitt, 1910.
5 p. 35 cm.

"Song."

1. Music—Minnesota. I. Fuller, Victor. II. Schmitt, Paul A., pub. III. Title.

NL 0449714 MnHi

Logan, Frederick Knight, 1871–1928.
Four Castilian sketches, suite espagnole for piano. Op. 94. Foster, c1921.
Contents: 1. At twilight. 2. Plaza dance. 3. 'Neath a balcony. 4. La fiesta.

NL 0449715 OrP

M784
L835
Logan, Frederic Knight, 1871–1928.
In a Brahmin garden, a song cycle. Chicago, Knight-Logan Co. [c1907]
24 p.

Contents. – Lo! Tis the hour. – Fair Radha. – Ganges boat song. – Krishna's lament.

NL 0449716 OrP

Logan, Frederic Knight, 1871–1928.
In a brahmin garden. A song cycle... [By] Frederic Knight Logan... Chicago, Ill.: The Knight-Logan Co. [cop. 1908.]
24 p. f°.
t.-p. illustrated.
With autograph of composer.
Verses by Virginia K. Logan.
Words and music.
Contents: 1. Lo! 'tis the hour. 2. Fair Radha. 3. Ganges boat song. 4. Krishna's lament.

1. Songs (American). 2. Logan,   Virginia K. 3. Title.
N. Y. P. L.   June 23, 1919.

NL 0449717 NN

*M1621.4
L74I6
Logan, Frederic Knight, 1871–1928.
In a Brahmin garden. A song cycle. New York, Luckhardt & Belder, c1908.

24p. 31cm.

Text by Virginia K. Logan.

I. Title.
II. Logan, Virginia Knight, 1850–1940.
1. Song cycles.

NL 0449718 NBuG

Logan, Frederic Knight, 1871–1928, arr.
Missouri waltz...
see under Eppel, John Valentine.

Q786.4
L82o
Logan, Frederic Knight, 1871–1928.
Over the hills (a pastoral reverie) Op.107. Chicago, Forster music publisher, inc., n.d.
5p.

NL 0449720 IU

LOGAN, FREDERIC KNIGHT. 1871–1928.
Over the hills. [Op.107] Poem by Virginia K. Logan. Music by Frederic Knight Logan. Chicago. Forster music publisher [c1924]
Song with piano accompaniment.
First line: O blissful memory!
1. Songs. U.S. 2. Songs. Secular—1870- . 3. Memories. I. Logan, Virginia K.

NL 0449721 NN IU

M787.1
L828p
Logan, Frederic Knight, 1871–1928.
Pale Moon; Indian love song. Free transcription for violin and piano by Fritz Kreisler. Chicago, Forster Music Publisher, 1920.
score (6p.) and 1 part. 36cm.

1. Violin and piano music. I. Kreisler, Fritz, 1875- arr. II. Title.

NL 0449722 OrU

Logan, Frederic Knight, 1871–1928.
Song miniatures... [By] Frederic Knight Logan. New York: G. Ricordi & C°. [cop. 1906.] 13 p. illus. (facsim.) f°.
With autograph of composer.
Words and music.
Contents: 1. Were I a bird. 2. Phyllis. 3. Lift thine eyes.

1. Songs (American). 2. Title.
N. Y. P. L.   June 23, 1919.

NL 0449723 NN

Logan, Frederic Knight, 1871–1928
Songs of Cupid... [By] Frederic Knight Logan. [n. p., cop. 1909.] (1)4–31 p. f°.
t.-p. illustrated.
With autograph of composer.
Verses by Virginia K. Logan.
Words and music.
Contents: 1. Love's springtime. 2. My heart's desire. 3. Ecstasy. 4. But why? 5. Sylvia. 6. Thy magic song. 7. Oh! vision fair.

1. Songs (American). 2. Logan, Vir-   ginia K. 3. Title.
N. Y. P. L.   June 28, 1919.

NL 0449724 NN OrU

Logan, Frederic Knight, 1871–1928.
Songs of Cupid. [Poems by Virginia K. Logan. Music [by] Frederic Knight Logan. Boston, 1919.
31 p. 31 cm.
Illus. t. p.

NL 0449725 RPB

Logan, Frederic. Knight, 1871–1928.
Wishing that dreams would come true. Song. Words by Virginia Knight Logan. Music by Frederic Knight Logan. Chicago, Forster music publisher inc. [c1918]
First line: Daylight was closing.
Chorus: Dreams, dreams, beautiful dreams.

1. Dreams. I. Logan, Virginia   Printed for the Music Division
index (3).   Knight, 1850–1940. II. Song
N. Y. P. L.   November 13, 1950.

NL 0449726 NN

Logan, Frederick.
Sanderson, Edgar, d. 1907.
Six thousand years of history, by Edgar Sanderson ... J. P. Lamberton ... John McGovern ... and the following eminent American editors and writers: Joseph M. Rogers, A. M.; Laurence E. Greene; M. A. Lane; G. Seneca Jones, A. M.; Frederick Logan; William Matthews Handy; introduction by Marshall S. Snow ... New York, Chicago [etc.] E. R. Du Mont, 1899.

Logan, Frederick
Sanderson, Edgar, d. 1907.
The world's history and its makers, by Edgar Sanderson ... J. P. Lamberton ... John McGovern ... and the following eminent American editors and writers: Joseph M. Rogers, A. M.; Laurence E. Greene; M. A. Lane; G. Seneca Jones, A. M.; Frederick Logan; William Matthews Handy. Introduction by Marshall S. Snow ... [Éd. de luxe, Chicago, Philadelphia, etc.] Universal history publishing company, 1900.

Logan, Frederick M
Growth of art in American schools. New York, Harper [*1955]
310 p. illus. 25 cm. (Harper's exploration series in education)

1. Art—Study and teaching—U. S. I. Title.

N105.L6   707   54–11013 ‡

OrCS MsSM OrLgE OrMonO OrPR OrPS
OCU OC1MA ViU IdU CaBVaU CaBVa MtU Or MsU OrAshS
OrU WaTC WaSp PPPL OC1 OOxM NcD TxU OC1SA TU PU-Penn
NL 0449729 DLC NcU OO MiU PIm OO PP OrSaW WaT WaS

Logan, Frenise Avedis
The Negro in North Carolina, 1876–1894.
v, 383, 6 l. tables.
Thesis. – Ph. D. degree. – Western Reserve University. – Department of History. – September 10 1953.

NL 0449730 OC1W

Logan, G. F.
The last great battle; or, War among the nations until the year 2000. Britons, prepare! Glasgow, G. Gallie, 1869. 32 p. 21cm.

1. Prophecies, Biblical—Interpreta-   tion. 2. War and peace, 1815–1898.

NL 0449731 NN

VOLUME 338

612.7 Logan, Gene Adams, 1922-
L828c Comparative gains in strength resulting from eccentric and concentric muscular contraction. Urbana [1952]
46 l. diagrs., tables. 28cm.

Thesis--University of Illinois.
Typewritten (carbon copy)
Bibliography: leaves 44-46.
---- ---- Thesis copy.

1. Muscles.

NL 0449732 IU

Logan, Gene Adams, 1922-
Techniques of athletic training [by] Gene A. Logan and Roland F. Logan. Forword [sic] by Herman J. Bearzy; illustrated by Gene A. Logan. Los Angeles, Franklin-Adams Press, 1952.
138 p. illus. 28 cm.

1. Physical education and training. I. Title.

GV711.L6 371.732 52—64776 ‡

NL 0449733 DLC OrMonO CaBVaU NcU OCl TU TxU

Logan, Georg Adam, fl. 1691, respondent.
Disputatio medica de anima, causa morborum proxima ...
see under Jacobi, Ludwig Friedrich, fl. 1679-1714, praeses.

[Logan, George,] 1678–1755.
A continuation of the Modest and humble inquiry concerning the right and power of electing and calling ministers to vacant churches... By a minister of the Church of Scotland. Edinburgh: Printed by G. Hamilton, 1733. 170 p. 8°.

A reply to "The defection of the Church of Scotland from her Reformation-principles considered," by Sir Thomas Gordon, "An inquiry into the method of settling parishes," by Sir Thomas Gordon and Halbert Monro, and "Populi suffragia," by James Hill.

1. Church of Scotland—Clergy. 2. Gordon, Sir Thomas, 1684–1766: The defection of the Church of Scotland from her Reformation-principles considered. 3. Gordon, Sir Thomas, 1684–1766, and H. Monro: An inquiry into the method of settling parishes. 4. Hill, James, of Kilpatrick: Populi suffragia. I. Title.
N. Y. P. L. Revised August 29, 1932

NL 0449736 NN RP

Logan, George, 1678-1755.
A discourse on John XXI, 15, 16, 17, 18, 19. In the High Church of Edinburgh, May 4th, 1729, before His Majesty's Commissioner to the General Assembly. By Mr. George Logan ... Edinburgh, Printed by Mrs. Tho. and Wal. Ruddimans, and sold by David Randie, 1729.
1 p. l., 24 p. 19 cm.

No. [8] in a volume with binder's title: Miscellaneous sermons.

NL 0449737 NSchU

SPECIAL COLLECTIONS
B342.41
L821

Logan, George, 1678-1755.
The doctrine of the jure-divino-ship of hereditary indefeasible monarchy enquired into and exploded, in a letter to Mr. Thomas Ruddiman ... from Mr. George Logan ... Edinburgh: Printed by Thomas Lumisden and company, 1749.
114 p. 18cm.

Volume of pamphlets.

NL 0449738 NNC PPL

JN1239 [Logan, George] 1678-1755.
.L81 The finishing stroke: or, Mr. Ruddiman self-condemned;
1748 being a reply to Mr. Ruddiman's answer to (only) Mr. Logan's First treatise on government ... Edinburgh, Printed by R. Fleming, 1748.
2 v. 18cm.
Sub-title of vol. 2 varies slightly.

1. Ruddiman, Thomas, 1674-1757. 2. Scotland—Kings and rulers—Succession.

NL 0449739 ICU

Logan, George, 1678-1755.
The humble and modest inquiry concerning the right and power of electing and calling ministers to vacant churches, finished. Edinburgh, 1733.

NL 0449740 RP

[LOGAN, George] 1678-1755.
The lawfulness and necessity of ministers their reading the act of Parliament, etc. Edinburgh, 1737.

Imperfect: wanting after p.48. 19458.44

NL 0449741 MH

Logan, George, 1678-1755.
A letter to the Reverend Mr. G. Logan, A. M., one of the ministers of Edinburgh ...
see under title

[LOGAN, GEORGE,] 1678-1755.
A modest and humble inquiry concerning the right and power of electing and calling ministers to vacant churches... By a minister of the Church of Scotland. Edinburgh: Printed by G. Hamilton, 1732. 127 p. 8°.

Includes many comments on "Jus populi divinum," by John Currie.

1. Church of Scotland--Clergy. 2. Currie, John, 1679?-1765: Jus populi divinum. I. Title.
Revised.

NL 0449743 NN

[Logan, George,] 1678–1755.
The publick testimony of about 1600 Christian people against the overture of the Assembly 1731, made more publick, and set in its due light. Being a full confutation of their arguments, adduced for the divine right of popular elections... By the author of the Modest and humble inquiry. Edinburgh: Printed for G. Hamilton, 1733. 74 p. 8°.

A reply to "The defection of the Church of Scotland from her Reformation-principles considered," by Sir Thomas Gordon, and "Publick testimony; being the representation and petition of a considerable number of Christian people..."

1. Church of Scotland—Clergy. 2. Gordon, Sir Thomas, 1684–1766: The defection of the Church of Scotland from her Reformation principles considered. I. Title.
N. Y. P. L. Revised September 6, 1932

NL 0449745 NN MB

B342.41
L821

Logan, George, 1678-1755.
A second letter from Mr. George Logan ... to Mr. Thomas Ruddiman ... vindicating the celebrated Mr. Alexander Henderson ... from the vile aspersions cast upon him by Messieurs Sage and Ruddiman ... with an appendix containing the letters past betwixt the King's Majesty and ... Mr. Henderson ... Edinburgh: Printed by Thomas Lumisden and company, 1749.
110, 63 p. 18cm.

Volume of pamphlets.

NL 0449746 NNC

Logan, George, 1678–1755.
A second treatise on government; shewing that the right to the crown of Scotland was not hereditary, in the sense of Jacobites; against the Earl of Cromarty, Sir George Mackenzie the King's advocate, Mr. John Sage stiled the Cyprianick doctor, and the learned antiquarian, Mr. Thomas Ruddiman. By George Logan ... Edinburgh, 1747.
8 p. l., 160 p. 17½cm.

1. Scotland—Kings and rulers—Succession.

9-34386†

Library of Congress JN1239 1747

NL 0449747 DLC CaBVaU MoU NNC

Micro-opaque
JN
1239
1747

Logan, George, 1678-1755.
A second treatise on government; shewing that the right to the crown of Scotland was not hereditary, in the sense of Jacobites; against the Earl of Cromarty, Sir George Mackenzie the King's advocate, Mr. John Sage stiled the Cyprianick doctor, and the learned antiquarian, Mr. Thomas Ruddiman. By George Logan. Edinburgh, 1747.
160 p. 18 cm.
Micro-opaque. Louisville, Ky., Lost Cause Press, 1964. 3 cards. 8x13 cm.

1. Scotland--Kings and rulers--Succession.

NL 0449748 OKentU MsU FU ICRL

Logan, George, 1678–1755.
A treatise on government; shewing, that the right of the kings of Scotland to the crown was not strictly and absolutely hereditary. Against the Earl of Cromarty, Sir George Mackenzie ... Mr. John Sage ... and ... Mr. Thomas Ruddiman. By George Logan ... Edinburgh, 1746.
xxxii, 182, [4] p. 18 cm.

1. Scotland—Kings and rulers—Succession.

JN1239 1746 9—34396

NL 0449749 DLC NjP CaBVaU CtY

Logan, George, 1751–1793.
Dissertatio inauguralis, de morbis infantium arcendis et curandis. Quam ... ex auctoritate ... Gulielmi Robertson ... Academiæ edinburgenæ præfecti ... pro gradu doctoratus ... eruditorum examini subjicit Georgius Logan, Carolinensis ... Prid. id. junii [1773], ... Edinburgi, apud Balfour et Smellie, academiae typographos, M,DCC,LXXIII.
3 p. l., 44 p. 19½cm.

1. Children—Diseases.

34-40050

Library of Congress RJ44.L6 1773

NL 0449750 DLC NcD-MC DNLM PHi PPL PPPH

Logan, George, 1753–1821.
Works by this author printed in America before 1801 are available in this library in the Readex Microprint edition of Early American Imprints published by the American Antiquarian Society.
This collection is arranged according to the numbers in Charles Evans' American Bibliography.

NL 0449751 DLC

S523
.L65
Toner
Coll.

Logan, George, 1753-1821.
An address on the errors of husbandry, in the United States. Delivered before the Philadelphia society for promoting agriculture, at their annual meeting, January 14, 1818. By George Logan ... Philadelphia: Printed by Lydia R. Bailey, 1818.
11 p. 21½cm.

1. Agriculture--Addresses, essays, lectures.

NL 0449752 DLC NNC

VOLUME 338

Logan, George, 1753–1821.
   An address on the natural and social order of the world, as intended to produce universal good; delivered before the Tammany society, at their anniversary, on the 12th of May, 1798 ... By George Logan. Philadelphia: Printed by Benjamin Franklin Bache. [1798]
   12 p. 23ᶜᵐ.

   1. Social conditions—Addresses, essays, lectures. 2. U. S.—Commercial policy.
                                                          8–34471
      Library of Congress   HN61.L8
      ——— Copy 2. 23½ᶜᵐ.   [43g1]

NL 0449753   DLC PPiPT MiU-C MiU NN CU MB N NjP

S643   Logan, George, 1753–1821.
.L8   Agricultural experiments, on gypsum, or plaister of Paris: with some observations, on the fertilizing quality, and natural history of that fossil. By George Logan... Philadelphia, Printed by F. and R. Bailey, 1797.
       18 p. 19cm.

       1. Gypsum. 2. Fertilizers and manures.

NL 0449754   ICU ViU

[Logan, George] 1753–1821.
   [Five letters addressed to the yeomanry of the U.S. ... Philadelphia, Eleazer Oswald, 1789.
   28 p.

NL 0449755   PPL

[Logan, George] 1753–1821.
   Five letters, addressed to the yeomanry of the United States: containing some observations on the dangerous scheme of Governor Duer and Mr. Secretary Hamilton, to establish national manufactories. By a farmer. Philadelphia: Printed by Eleazer Oswald, No. 156, Marketstreet, between Fourth and Fifth-streets. 1792.
   28 p. 22ᶜᵐ.
   The authorship of this pamphlet and of "Letters addressed to the yeomanry of the United States ... by a farmer", Philadelphia, 1791, and the

   similar "Letters ... by an American farmer", Philadelphia, 1793, is attributed to George Logan on the authority of Citizen Adet, who had a copy of the Letters, 1793, with ms. dedication "from his friend, the author", whom Adet identified as "Dr. Laughan" [i. e. George Logan] cf. Rich, Suppl. to the Biblioth. amer. nova, pt. 1 [1841] 1793, no. 26; also Ford, P. L., Biblioth. Hamiltoniana, 1886, nos. 47, 50, 52.

   1. Free trade and protection—Free trade. 2. U. S.—Pol. & govt.—Constitutional period, 1789–1809. I. Title.
                                                          6–118 Revised
      Library of Congress   HF1754.L6
      ——— Copy 2.   [Political pamphlets, v. 96, no. 7]
                                 JA36.P8 vol. 96

         MB MWA MiU-C
NL 0449757   DLC CaBVaU PPAmP RPJCB PPL MH MBAt NN

Logan, George, 1753–1821.
   Fourteen agricultural experiments, to ascertain the best rotation of crops: addressed to the "Philadelphia agricultural society." By George Logan, M. D. Philadelphia, Printed by Francis and Robert Bailey, at Yorick's-head, nᵒ 116 High-street, 1797.
   2 p. l., [3]–41 p. 20¼ᶜᵐ.

   1. Rotation of crops.

      Library of Congress   S603.L83   12–12312

NL 0449758   DLC MiU-C NN PPL MBAt MdBP

Logan, George, 1753–1821.
   A letter to the citizens of Pennsylvania, on the necessity of promoting agriculture, manufactures, and the useful arts. By George Logan, M. D. Lancaster, Printed by W. & R. Dickson, 1800.
   28 p. 21ᶜᵐ.
   Contains the constitution of the Lancaster County society, for promoting of agriculture, manufactures, and the useful arts.

   1. Pennsylvania—Econ. condit. I. Lancaster County society for promoting of agriculture, manufactures and the useful arts.

      Library of Congress   HC107.P4L8   7–8883†

NL 0449759   DLC MWA PU NN

Logan, George, 1753–1821.
   A letter to the citizens of Pennsylvania, on the necessity of promoting agriculture, manufactures, and the useful arts. By George Logan, M. D. 2d ed. Philadelphia, Printed by Patterson & Cochran, 1800.
   30 p. 19ᶜᵐ.
   Contains the constitution of the Lancaster County society for promoting of agriculture, manufactures, and the useful arts.

   1. Pennsylvania—Econ. condit. I. Lancaster County society for promoting of agriculture, manufactures, and the useful arts.
                                                          7–10847
      Library of Congress   HC107.P4L8
      ——— Copy 2. 22ᶜᵐ.
      ——— Copy 3. 21ᶜᵐ.   [Miscellaneous pamphlets, v. 962, no. 8]
                                 AC901.M5 vol. 962

         DNAL ICJ ICU
NL 0449760   DLC MH NjP PU NcU RPJCB PPL PHC PHi PSt

M-film   Logan, George, 1753–1821.
330   A letter to the citizens of Pennsylvania, on
Am3   the necessity of promoting agriculture, manufac-
404-8   tures, and the useful arts. 2d ed. Philadel-
          phia, Printed by Patterson & Cochran, 1800.
          30 p.

          Microfilm (positive) Ann Arbor, Mich.,
       University Microfilms, 1969. 8th title of 15.
       35 mm. (American culture series, reel 404.8)

       1. Pennsylvania - Economic conditions.

NL 0449761   KEmT PSt

[Logan, George] 1753–1821.
   Letters, addressed to the yeomanry of the United States: shewing the necessity of confining the public revenue to a fixed proportion of the net produce of the land; and the bad policy and injustice of every species of indirect taxation and commercial regulations. By a farmer. Philadelphia: Printed by Eleazer Oswald, in Marketstreet, No. 156, between Fourth and Fifth-streets. 1791.
   47 p. 23ᶜᵐ.
   [Political pamphlets, v. 96, no. 6]

   The authorship of this pamphlet and of "Five letters addressed to the yeomanry of the United States ... by a farmer, Philadelphia, 1792", and the similar "Letters ... by an American farmer", Philadelphia, 1793, is attributed to George Logan on the authority of Citizen Adet who had a copy of the Letters, 1793, with ms. dedication "from his friend, the author", whom Adet identified as "Dr. Laughan" [i. e. George Logan] cf. Rich, Suppl. to the Biblioth. amer. nova, pt. 1 [1841] 1793, no. 26; also Ford, P. L., Biblioth. Hamiltoniana, 1886, nos. 47, 50, 52.

   1. Taxation—U. S. 2. U. S.—Pol. & govt.—Constitutional period, 1789–1809. 3. U. S.—Econ. condit. I. Title.
                                                          26–23727
      Library of Congress   JA36.P8

         NNC MiU-C MH CSt PHi PPAmP RPJCB MH ViU PU NN
NL 0449763   DLC ICU ViU RPJCB MWA PP VtU PPAmP PHi

[Logan, George] 1753–1821.
   Letters addressed to the yeomanry of the United States, containing some observations on funding and bank systems. By an American farmer. Philadelphia, 1793.
   24 p. 22ᶜᵐ.
   The authorship of this pamphlet and of "Letters addressed to the yeomanry of the United States ... by a farmer", Philadelphia, 1791, and the similar "Five letters addressed to the yeomanry of the United States ... by a farmer, Philadelphia, 1792", is attributed to George Logan on the authority of Citizen Adet who had a copy of the Letters, 1793, with ms. dedication "from his friend, the author", whom Adet identified as "Dr. Laughan" [i. e. George Logan] cf. Rich, Suppl. to the Biblioth. amer. nova, pt. 1 [1841] 1793, no. 26; also P. L. Ford, Biblioth. Hamiltonians, 1886, no. 47, 50, 52.
   1. Finance—U. S. I. Title.

      Library of Congress   HJ8106.L8   7–9037 Revised

NL 0449764   DLC ViW MH-BA MH NN PHi NHi CtY

Micro   [Logan, George] 1753–1821.
3   Letters, addressed to the yeomanry of the United States: shewing the necessity of confining the public revenue to a fixed proportion of the net produce of the land; and the bad policy and injustice of every species of indirect taxation and commercial regulations. [1st ed.] By a farmer. Philadelphia: Printed by Eleazer Oswald, 1791.
       2 sheets. 7.5x12.5cm. (The Library of Thomas Jefferson)
       Wrongly attributed to Hamilton and Crevecoeur. The attribution to Logan on the title page is in Jefferson's hand.
       Evans 23507. Sabin 39213. Sowerby 3156.
       Micro-transparency (positive). Washington, Microcard Editions, 1973.
       Collation of the   original: 47p.
       1. Taxation -   U.S.

NL 0449765   PSt

Logan, George, 1753–1821.
   Tentamen medicum inaugurale, de venenis. Quod ... ex auctoritate ... d. Gulielmi Robertson ... Academiæ edinburgenæ præfecti ... pro gradu doctoratus ... eruditorum examini subjicit Georgius Logan, Pennsylvaniensis ... Ad diem 24. junii [1779] ... Edinburgi, apud Balfour et Smellie, academiæ typographos, M,DCC,LXXIX.
   26 p. 21ᶜᵐ.

   1. Poisons.

      Library of Congress   RA1201.L6 1779   37–35595

NL 0449766   DLC DNLM PHi PU-M

R154   Logan, George, 1778–1861.
.H265L6   A biographical sketch of Tucker Harris, M. D.,
Toner   delivered on the first of September, 1821, at the
Coll.   request of the Medical society of Charleston, South-
        Carolina. By Geo. Logan ... Charleston, W. C.
        Young, printer, 1821.
        15 p. 21 cm.
        1. Harris, Tucker, 1747–1821.

NL 0449767   DLC MWA

Toner   Logan, George, 1778–1861.
           Observations on the hepatic state of fever. By George Logan, of Charleston, South Carolina ... Philadelphia: Printed for the author, by W. F. M'Laughlin, no. 34, Carter's alley. 1802.
        34 p. 20ᶜᵐ.
        Thesis (M. D.)—University of Pennsylvania, 1802.

        1. Liver—Diseases.

           Library of Congress   RC853.L63 1802   33–14479
                                       [2]   616.36

NL 0449768   DLC DNLM NNNAM PU

Toner   Logan, George, 1778–1861.
           Practical observations on diseases of children, comprehending a description of complaints & disorders, incident to the early stages of life, and method of treatment. By George Logan ... Charleston [S. C.] Printed by A. E. Miller, 1825.
        218 p. 18½ᶜᵐ.
        With this is bound: The maternal physician; a treatise on the nurture and management of infants ... By an American matron ... New-York, 1811.

        1. Children—Diseases.
                                                          34–38257
           Library of Congress   RJ45.L6

NL 0449769   DLC NcU DNLM

Logan (George) [1824–   ]
   Hahnemannian homœopathy; being papers read before the Canadian Institute of Homœopathy. 20 pp. 8ᵒ. Ottawa, C. W. Mitchell, 1891.
   By George Logan and C. T. Campbell.

NL 0449770   DNLM MiU

VOLUME 338

Logan, George, 1852–
Histories of the North Montana Mission,
Kalispell Mission and Montana Deaconess
Hospital with some biographical and autobiographical sketches. ₍n. p., 19--?₎
158 p. illus. ports. (incl. front.) 23 cm.
Cover-title: North Montana missions, Methodist Episcopal Church.

1. Methodist Church in Montana.

NL 0449771   IEG CtY WaS CaBViPA MtBC MtU WaSp MtHi

BV4015
.L8   Logan, George, 1852–
Sagebrush philosophy on the problems of
Tenderfoot. Helena, Mont., 1915.
41 p. illus. 20 cm.

1. Pastoral theology--Anecdotes, facetiae,
satire, etc. I. Title

NL 0449772   IEG MtHi

Z
321.4   Logan, George, 1913–
L828w   What is democracy? A paper submitted for
Thesis   education 135 ... January 21, 1936. ₍Pullman,
Washington₎ 1936.
34 l.

Honors thesis - State college of Washington.
Typewritten.
Bibliography: l.34.

NL 0449773   WaPS

Logan, George Bryan, 1886–
Aeronautical law review--1936.
[by] George B. Logan. [Chicago? Ill, 1936]
cover-title, 16 p.
"Preprinted from the Journal of air law
(October, 1936)"

NL 0449774   OO

Logan, George Bryan, 1886–
Aircraft law--made plain, by George B. Logan ... St.
Louis, 1928.
155 p. 23½ᶜᵐ.
"Written especially for those interested in aviation, as prospective
craft owners, operators, investors and students."
"Table of cases cited": p. 153-155.
Bibliography: p. 150-152.

1. Aeronautics--U. S.--Laws and regulations. 2. Aeronautics, Commercial--U. S. 3. Law--U. S. I. Title.
Library of Congress   HE9925.U6L6
29-9113

NcRS OC1 ICJ MH-BA ViU-L
NL 0449775   DLC WaSp WaS WaU-L CaBVa OU DAL DN MB

Logan, George Bryan, 1892-1927.
Liberty in the modern world, by George Bryan Logan, jr.
... Chapel Hill, The University of North Carolina press,
1928.
xi p., 2 l., ₍3₎-142 p. 21½ᶜᵐ.

1. Liberty. I. Title.
Library of Congress   JC585.L6
29-9

OC1 CU-AL ViU OCU MiU ICJ NcU NcRS
NL 0449776   DLC OrP OrPR WaTC PSt OKentU CBPac NcD

Logan, George Bryan, 1892/1927.
The reconstruction of humanism.

(In Journal of social forces.   Mar.1924.
v.2, no.3.)

NL 0449777   NcU

Logan, George Bryan, 1892-1927.
Uses of liberty.

(In Journal of social forces.   Sept.1924.
v.2, no.5.)

NL 0449778   NcU

Logan, George F
Public letters by a private citizen : our nation is having a
difficult time because certain very simple truths are being
overlooked. New York, William-Frederick Press, 1948.
29 p. 22 cm.

1. Communism. 2. Democracy. I. Title.
HX87.L56   335.4   48-11759*

NL 0449779   DLC NcD

Logan, George William, Engagement between
the Federal gunboats and Fort Beauregard, 10, 11 May,
1862. 4 pp. (Southern Hist. Soc. Papers, v. 11, 1883,
p. 497.)

NL 0449780   MdBP

Logan, George William, 1804-1876.
A record of the Logan family of Charleston, South Carolina,
Sacramento, Record Book and Job Printing Office, 1874.
F860   43 p. 23cm.   [Pamphlets on California biography, v. 5,
C2   no. 1]
v. 5:1
x

NL 0449781   CU-B NcD

Logan, George William, 1804-1876.
A record of the Logan family of Charleston, South Carolina,
by George William Logan, Richmond, Virginia, 1874. New
edition with preface, biographical additions and tables, by
Lily Logan Morrill. Cincinnati, O., 1923.
70 p. 22ᶜᵐ.
With reproduction of t.-p. of original edition, Sacramento, 1874.

1. Logan family. I. Morrill, Mrs. Lily (Logan) 1877–
31-18490
Library of Congress   CS71.L82 1923

NL 0449782   DLC NcD

E
7   LOGAN, GEORGE WILLIAM, 1804-1876.
.L 8249   A record of the Logan family of Charleston,
South Carolina. New edition with preface,
biographical additions and tables by Lily Logan
Morrill.   Chicinnati, O., 1923.
70p. 22cm.

NL 0449783   ICN

Logan, George Wood, 1868-1915.
FOR OTHER EDITIONS
SEE MAIN ENTRY
Bowditch, Nathaniel, 1773-1838.
... American practical navigator, an epitome of navigation
and nautical astronomy. Originally by Nathaniel Bowditch,
LL. D. Published by the United States Hydrographic office under
the authority of the secretary of the navy ... Washington, U. S. Govt. print. off., 1934.

Logan, George Wood, 1868-1915.
Elements of hydrographic surveying, by George Wood
Logan ... Annapolis, Md., The United States Naval institute, 1908.
176 p. illus., fold. pl., diagrs. (1 fold.) 20ᶜᵐ.

1. Hydrographic surveying. I. U. S. Naval institute, Annapolis.
Library of Congress   VK591.L83   8–3948

NL 0449785   DLC DN ICJ

Logan, George Wood, 1868-1915.
Elements of hydrographic surveying.
— Annapolis, Md. The United States Naval Institute. 1911. 176
pp. Illus. Plate. Diagrams. Tables. 19 cm., in 8s.

L2537 — Marine surveying. — Hydrography.

NL 0449786   MB WaS ICJ ViU OC1 DN-Ob NN

Logan, George Wood, 1868-1915.
U. S. Hydrographic office.
... Tables showing the local mean time of the sun's
visible rising and setting for each degree of latitude between 60° north and 60° south, and for each degree of the
sun's declination. Computed by Ensign George Wood
Logan ... Washington, Gov't print. off., 1899.

Logan (Georgius). *De venenis. 26 pp. 8°.
Edinburgi, Balfour et Smellie, 1779.

NL 0449788   DNLM PPC NNNAM

Logan (Georgius Carolina). *De morbis infantium arcendis et curandis. 1 p. l., 44 pp. 8°.
Edinburgi, Balfour et Smellie, 1773.

NL 0449789   DNLM

Logan, Gertrude Moore.
The rambler. Cedar Rapids, Torch Press ₍1947₎
71 p. 21 cm.
"A Bookfellow book."
Verse.

I. Title.
PS3523.O343R3   811.5   48-19723*

NL 0449790   DLC NcD

Logan, Grace Virginia.
Life's puckering strings, by Grace Virginia Logan. Los
Angeles, Calif., Wetzel publishing co., inc., 1931.
3 p. l., 9-345 p. 19½ᶜᵐ.

I. Title.
Library of Congress   PZ3.L8286Li   33-16999

NL 0449791   DLC

VOLUME 338

Logan, Greba T,
German lore; [a scrapbook of pictures extracted from the National geographic magazine and other sources] [Portland, Ore. , 1935]
Cover title, unpaged, mounted illus. maps, 28 cm.
"The material in this notebook represents and attempt to gather together information which will assist in explaining the different types of folk-costumes and dances in Germany".

NL 0449792   OrU

Logan, Gulielmus
see Logan, William, 1747-1772.

Logan, Guy B   H.
The classic races of the turf, by Guy B. H. Logan ... with a foreword by Sir George Thursby ... With twenty-four half-tone illustrations. London, S. Paul & co. ltd. [1931]
3 p. l., 9-288 p. front. (port.) plates. 24cm.

1. Horse-racing—Gt. Brit.   I. Title.

Library of Congress   SF335.G7L6   31-30487
                                    [3]   798.40942

NL 0449794   DLC NN

Logan, Guy B. H.
Dramas of the Dock; true stories of crime.
London, 1928.
286 p.   Pls.

NL 0449795   MH-L

Logan, Guy B   H.
Dramas of the dock; true stories of crime, by Guy. B. H. Logan ... London, S. Paul & co. (1928) ltd. [1930]
xv p., 1 l., 19-286 p. incl. front. plates, ports. 24cm.
CONTENTS.—Introduction.—No. 4, Euston square.—The double murder at Chelsea.—James Blomfield Rush.—The Northampton tragedy.—Murder and mutilation.—A Manchester mystery.—The Norwich horror.—The accuser accused.—Was Robert Emond mad?—The case of Richard Gould.—The old toll-gate murders.—Drama of the Ash flats.—Some "attractive" murderers.
1. Trials—Gt. Brit. 2. Trials (Murder) 3. Crime and criminals—Gt. Brit. I. Title.

32-4522

NL 0449796   DLC WaU-L CU NN

Logan, Guy B   H.
Great murder mysteries, by Guy B. H. Logan ... London, S. Paul & co., ltd. [1931]
288 p. front., plates, ports., facsim. 24cm.
CONTENTS.—The murder of Mrs. Wallace.—The church steeple murders.—A Camden town mystery.—James Canham Read.—Herbert John Bennett.—California's worst crime.—The clue of the cigarette holder.—German and French vampires.—A cosmopolitan criminal.—The case of Edward Keller.—"More deadly than the male."—The murder in the tunnel.—The "man of mystery".—A bigamist murderer.—Memorial stones to murder.
1. Trials (Murder) 2. Crime and criminals.   I. Title.

32-17775

NL 0449797   DLC WaU-L MH-L CU NN

Logan, Guy B   H.
Guilty or not guilty? Stories of celebrated crimes, by Guy B. H. Logan ... London, S. Paul & co., ltd., 1928.
288 p. front., plates, ports. 22½cm.
CONTENTS.—The story of Mary Ashford.—The case of Harriet Candler.—New light on an old mystery.—Edmund Pook and Jane Clousen.—The murder in a third-class carriage.—The mysterious murder at Gorse hall.—The case of Willie Starchfield.—Who killed Mrs. Reville?—The great Glasgow mystery.—The "Bill o' Jack's" murders.—The strange case of the German baker.—Mysterious murders of women.—A study of Browne and Kennedy.—Voirbo, Mullins, and Maynard.

1. Trials—Gt. Brit. 2. Trials (Murder) 3. Crime and criminals—Gt. Brit.   I. Title.

30-23340

NL 0449798   DLC CtY CU NN

Logan, Guy B   H
Guilty or not guilty? Stories of celebrated crimes, by Guy B. H. Logan. [London] Duffield, 1929.
288 p. front., plates, ports. 22cm.

CONTENTS.- The story of Mary Ashford.- The case of Harriet Candler.- New light on an old mystery.- Edmund Pook and Jane Clousen.- The murder in third-class carriage.- The mysterious murder at Gorse Hall.- The case of Willie

Starchfield.- Who killed Mrs. Reville?- The great Glasgow mystery.- The "Bill O'Jack's" murders.- The strange case of the German baker.- Mysterious murders of women.- A study of Browne and Kennedy.- Voirbo, Mullins and Maynard.

1. Trials - Gt. Brit. 2. Trials (Murder) - Gt. Brit. 3. Crime and criminals - Gt. Brit. I. Title.

NL 0449800   GU-L NN LU MH-L CLSU

Logan, Guy B. H.
Masters of crime; studies of multiple murders, by Guy B. H. Logan... London: S. Paul & Co., Ltd., 1928. 288 p. facsim., front., plates, port. 8°. (The library of crime.)

388612A. 1. Murder. 2. Title.
N. Y. P. L.   January 4, 1929

NL 0449801   NN CU CLSU NBuG NCH InU WaU-L

364.1 Logan, Guy B   H.
L831r   Rope, knife and chair; studies of English, French and American crimes. New York, Duffield [19--]
280p. illus.,ports. 24cm.

1.Crime and criminals. 2.Murder. I.Title.

NL 0449802   CLSU MH-L

LOGAN,Guy B.   H.
Rope,knife and chair;studies of English, French and American crimes. London,Stanley Paul & Co.,Ltd.,1928.

Ports.and plates.
Paper jacket: Murder mysteries of Europe and America.

NL 0449803   MH

Logan, Guy B   H.
Rope, knife and chair; studies of English, French and American crimes, by Guy B. H. Logan ... Duffield and company [1930?]

NL 0449804   OC1

Logan, Guy B   H.
Rope, knife and chair; studies of English, French and American crimes, by Guy B. H. Logan ... London, S. Paul & co., ltd. [1930]
280 p. front., plates, ports. 23½cm.

1. Crime and criminals. 2. Murder.   I. Title.

Library of Congress   HV6513.L6   30-30053
                                    [3]   364

NL 0449805   DLC NN

HV   Logan, Guy B   H
6021   Rope, knife and chair; studies of Eng-
G6   lish, French and American crimes. [London]
1933   Rich & Cowan [1933?]
127 p.
Bound with Goodwin, John Cuthbert. Side-lights on criminal matters. [London, 1933?]

1. Crime and criminals. 2. Murder. I. Title.
409/11je69bh

NL 0449806   CaBVaU

Logan, Guy B   H.
Verdict and sentence; famous crimes recalled by Guy B. H. Logan, with foreword by Sir Basil Thomson, K. C. B. London, Eldon press limited [1935]
3 p. l., ix-x, 11-280 p. 19cm.
CONTENTS.—19th century crimes: Mr. and Mrs. Manning. The first train murder. A Leicester horror. Chatham and Cudham crimes. Tragedy of John Thurtell. Case of the Dundee cake. The Fall River mystery.—20th century crimes: The Leyton-Camberwell murders. A case of matricide. The corpse in the chicken run. The Evangelista massacre. Strange American crimes. A prince of rogues. On the scaffold.
1. Crime and criminals—Gt. Brit. 2. Trials (Murder)—Gt. Brit. 3. Crime and criminals—U. S. 4. Trials (Murder)—U. S.   I. Title.

36-14793

Library of Congress   [3]   364

NL 0449807   DLC WaU-L NN CtY-L

Logan, Guy B   H.
Wilful murder; studies of notable crimes, by Guy Logan ... London, Eldon press limited [1935]
3 p. l., 9-280 p. 19cm.
CONTENTS.—The "man with a scar".—Was Steinie Morrison guilty?—Murder by poison.—The case of the Swiss valet.—Kate Webster and Mrs. Thomas.—Murder or accident—which?—New light on Charles Peace.—Murder without motive.—Double murder in Varden street.—Mystery of the Herbert Fuller.—Chicago's "murder castle".—The "magnificent darling".—The "affaire Eyraud".—Curious clues to murder.—Crime puzzles unsolved.
1. Trials (Murder) 2. Crime and criminals.   I. Title.

36-6986

343

NL 0449808   DLC WaU-L CtY

Logan, H. A. , 1889-
see Logan, Harold Amos, 1889-

Logan, Haldor.
When love was born; an allegory, by Haldor Logan. [New York? cop. 1925.] 22 l. 4°.

409494A. 1. Allegories, American.   2. Title.
N. Y. P. L.   May 9, 1929

NL 0449809   NN

VOLUME 338

TD1952
L828

Logan, Hall Hamilton, 1905–
Some problems in the installation of a merit system in Texas state government. Austin, Tex., 1952.
229,[2]ℓ. tables. 29cm.
Thesis (Ph.D.) – University of Texas, 1952.
Vita.
Bibliography: ℓ.[218]-229.

1. Civil service - Texas. I. Title: A merit system in Texas state government.

NL 0449810 TxU

Logan, Hance James, 1869–

Canada. *Parliament. House of commons. Select standing committee on privileges and elections.*
... Enquiry into loss of papers relating to the Stanstead by-election, 1908. Minutes of proceedings and evidence. Ottawa, Printed by S. E. Dawson, 1908.

Logan, Hannah
see Smith, Mrs. Hannah (Logan) 1777-1846.

F866
.H45

Logan, Harlan, *joint author.*

Hepburn, Andrew.
California; a complete guide, by Andrew Hepburn and Harlan Logan. New York, Simon and Schuster, ᶜ1950.

F309
.3
.H4
1949

Logan, Harlan, *joint author.*

Hepburn, Andrew.
Florida; a complete guide to the State of Florida, telling you what to see, where to go, how to get there, what to do, how much to pay. By Andrew Hepburn and Harlan Logan with the assistance of the American Express Travel Service. [New York, Simon and Schuster, 1949]

Logan, Harlan, *ed.*
How much do you know about glass? Designed by Barbara Ellwood. New York, Dodd, Mead [1951]
191 p. illus. 28 cm.
Bibliography: p. 178-183.

1. Glass. I. Title.

TP857.L55   666.1   51-11297

MtBC WaS Or OrCS WaSp WaT OrP OrU CaBVa
MH ICU ICJ ViU TxU NCorniC OC1W NN MtU WaWW IdU WaE
NL 0449814   DLC CaBViP NBuU CoU CU NNC MB NcU TU

F2
.3
.H4
1951

Logan, Harlan, *joint author.*

Hepburn, Andrew.
New England, a complete guide, by Andrew Hepburn and Harlan Logan. New York, Simon and Schuster, ᶜ1951.

Logan, Harlan, ed.

Scribner's magazine ... v. 1-104, v. 105, no. 1-5; Jan. 1887-May 1939. New York, C. Scribner's sons; [etc., etc., 1887-1939]

Logan, Harold Amos, 1889–
Canada's control of labour relations [by] H. A. Logan. [Toronto, Pub. jointly by the Canadian association for adult education and the Canadian institute of international affairs] 1941.
cover-title, 29 p. 20½ᵐᵐ. (Behind the headlines, v. 2, no. 2)
Page 29 is third page of cover.
Bibliographical foot-notes.

1. Labor laws and legislation—Canada. I. Canadian association for adult education. II. Canadian institute of international affairs. III. Title.

Library of Congress   F1034.B4 vol. 2, no. 2   43-4564
                                                              [3]   (971.0082) 331

NL 0449817   DLC CaBViP ICN OU

HD10000
.L84

Logan, Harold Amos, 1889–
...A history of trade union organization in Canada... By Harold Amos Logan. Chicago 1925.
1 l.,xxii,525,3,13 numb.l. 29ᵐᵐ.
Typewritten.
Thesis(Ph.D.)–University of Chicago,1925.
Bibliography:4th group of paging.
"Abstract":13 l.at end.

1.Trade unions-Canada.

NL 0449818   ICU

Logan, Harold Amos, 1889–
The history of trade-union organization in Canada, by Harold A. Logan ... Chicago, Ill., The University of Chicago press [1928]
xiii, 427 p. 21½ᵐᵐ. (Half-title: Materials for the study of business)
Bibliography: p. 413-414.

1. Trade-unions—Canada.

Library of Congress   HD6524.L6   28-30667

OCU OO OU ICJ CaBVaU CaBVa
NL 0449819   DLC OrPR OrCS OrU CU NcD NcRS MiU OC1

Logan, Harold Amos, 1889–

Innis, Harold Adams, 1894–   *ed.*
Labor in Canadian-American relations: The history of labor interaction, by Norman J. Ware; Labor costs and labor standards, by H. A. Logan, edited by H. A. Innis. Toronto, The Ryerson press; New Haven, Yale university press; [etc., etc.] for the Carnegie endowment for international peace, Division of economics and history, 1937.

Logan, Harold Amos, 1889–
A social approach to economics [by] Harold A. Logan ... [and] Mark K. Inman ... Toronto, Can., The University of Toronto press, 1939.
xvi, 659 p. diagrs. 23½ᵐᵐ.
Bibliography: p. 641-646.

1. Economics. 2. Canada—Econ. condit.—1918– 3. Economic conditions—1918– I. Inman, Mark Keith, joint author. II. Title.

Library of Congress   HB171.5.L74   40-10317
                                                   [a44i1]   330.1

ViU MiHM OU OCU PPT TU
NL 0449821   DLC CaBVa MtU OrU CoU CU NcD PPD ICJ

Logan, Harold Amos, 1889–
A social approach to economics [by] Harold A. Logan [and] Mark K. Inman. 2d ed., rev. and enl. Toronto, University of Toronto Press, 1949 [ᶜ1948]
xix, 757 p. illus. 24 cm.
Bibliography: p. 729-735.

1. Economics. 2. Canada — Econ. condit. — 1918– 3. Econ. condit.—1918– I. Inman, Mark Keith, joint author. II. Title.

[HB171.5.L]   330.1   A 50-5794
New York. Public Libr.
for Library of Congress   [1]

NL 0449822   NN CaBVaU CaBVa CU MH

Logan, Harold Amos, 1889–
Trade unions in Canada, their development and functioning. Toronto, Macmillan Co. of Canada, 1948.
xvii, 639 p. diagrs. 24 cm.
"Bibliography of books on Canada": p. 623.

1. Trade-unions—Canada. I. Title.

HD6524.L65   331.880971   48-3282*

CaBVa OrCS WaS MtBC
TxU ICU OC1U OU OC1W PPLas ScU PSt MiU CaNSWA CaBViP
NL 0449823   DLC CaBVaU CU MiU PPD PPT NcU ViU CtY

SB321
.C813

Logan, Harry Britton, 1910–   joint author.

Cosper, Lloyd Claggett.
How to grow vegetables; the complete garden guide to planning, growing, preserving, and storing vegetables, fruits, and berries, by Lloyd C. Cosper and Harry B. Logan. Photos. and drawings by Lynette Arouni. New York, Duell, Sloan and Pearce [1951]

Logan, Harry Britton, 1910–
Orchids are easy to grow, by Harry B. Logan and Lloyd C. Cosper; drawings by Lynette Arouni. Chicago, Ziff-Davis Pub. Co. [1949]
viii, 312 p. illus. (part col.) 24 cm.
"Orchid bibliography": p. 299-307.

1. Orchids. I. Cosper, Lloyd Claggett, joint author.

SB409.L6   635.93415   49-3867*

PP NcSal MB OOxM Or OrCS OrP Wa WaS WaT
NL 0449825   DLC CaBVaU CaBViP MH-A CU-A NNBG CU CoU

SB
409
L6
1949

Logan, Harry Britton, 1910–
Orchids are easy to grow, by Harry B. Logan and Lloyd C. Cosper. Drawings by Lynette Arouni. Englewood Cliffs [N.J.] Prentice-Hall [1949]
312 p. illus.

"Fifth printing, September 1955"
"Orchid bibliography": p. 299-307

NL 0449826   KMK

Logan, Harry Britton, 1910–
Science in the garden [by] H. Britton Logan and Jean-Marie Putnam, in consultation with Lloyd C. Cosper; foreword by Dr. F. W. Kent. New York, Duell, Sloan and Pearce, ᶜ1941]
xiv, 255 p. illus. 22ᵐᵐ.
"First edition."

1. Gardening. I. Putnam, Mrs. Jean Marie (Consigny) 1911– joint author. II. Cosper, Lloyd Claggett. III. Title.

Library of Congress   SB453.L75   41-51781
                                                 [12]   635.91

NcRS PPT PPGi OEac OC1 OU PPD PP
NL 0449827   DLC DAU OrU MBH KEmT OrP WaSp Wa Or WaS

Logan, Henry, 1784-1866.
The preamble and resolution offered by Mr. Logan, as a substitute for the report and resolution of the Committee on roads, bridges and inland navigation on granting the Baltimore and Susquehanna railroad company the privilege of extending their rail road into the state of Pennsylvania. Read in the Senate, January 24, 1829. Harrisburg: Printed at the office of the reporter, 1829.
12 p. 18½cm.

PARSONS COLLECTION.
N.Y.P.L.

873168A. 1. Baltimore and Susque-   hanna railroad. I. Title.
                                                     May 20, 1938

NL 0449828   NN DBRE DLC

VOLUME 338

J
5854
.516
LOGAN, Henry. 1784-1866.
Reply to the address of the Native American convention, assembled at Harrisburg, Pa. February, 1845. In a series of letters, by Logan. Philadelphia, W.J.Cunningham, 1845.
34p. 15cm.

NL 0449829   ICN

Logan, Henry C.
... The hygienic curative treatment; a rational and advanced method for curing, without the aid of drugs, nauseous medicines or electric belts ... By Henry C. Logan. Philadelphia, Pa., The author, 1888.
20 p. 14½ᵐ.

1. Hygiene.

Library of Congress   RA776.L84
8-4210†

NL 0449830   DLC

Logan, Herbert H.
Arizona and some of her friends; the toasts and responses at a complimentary dinner given by Walter S. Logan, at the Marine and field club, N. Y., Tuesday July 28th, 1891, to Hon. John N. Irwin, governor of Arizona, and Herbert H. Logan of Phœnix, Arizona. [New York? 1891]

Logan, Herschel C   1901–
Buckskin and satin; the life of Texas Jack (J. B. Omohundro) buckskin clad scout, Indian fighter, plainsman, cowboy, hunter, guide, and actor, and his wife, Mlle. Morlacchi, premiere danseuse in satin slippers. With a foreword by Paul I. Wellman. [1st ed.] Harrisburg, Pa., Stackpole Co. [1954]
218 p. illus. 23 cm.
Includes bibliography.

1. Omohundro, John Burwell, 1846–1880. 2. Morlacchi, Giuseppina, 1846–1886. I. Title.

F594.O5L6   923.973   54-11498 ‡

WaS KEmT PSt GU Or OrU FTaSU NcU
NL 0449832   DLC NmU MH OrU UU PU MB TxU NN NcD PP

Logan, Herschel C   1901–
Cartridges, a pictorial digest of small arms ammunition. Huntington, W. Va., Standard Publications, 1948.
199 p. illus. 28 cm.
A companion book to the author's Hand cannon to automatic.

1. Cartridges.

UF740.L6   623.4553   49-1611*

NL 0449833   DLC CaBVa WHi OrP WaS ViU

UF740
.L6
1954
Logan, Herschel C   1901–
Cartridges, a pictorial digest of small arms ammunition. Huntington, W. Va., Standard Publications [1954, c1948]
204 p. illus. 28cm.
A companion book to the author's Hand cannon to automatic.

1. Cartridges.

NL 0449834   MB

Logan, Herschel C   1901–
Hand cannon to automatic; a pictorial *Parade of hand arms*, by Herschel C. Logan ... Huntington, W. Va., Standard publications, incorporated, 1944.
[202] p. incl. front., illus. 20½ x 27ᵐ.

1. Firearms—Hist. 2. Firearms—Pictorial works.   I. Title.
45–751

Library of Congress *   TS535.L6
[3]   688

NL 0449835   DLC Wa OrP Or CU-B MB OCl

Logan, Herschel C   1901–
Other days, in pictures and verse; twelve original woodcuts by Herschel C. Logan, prose poems written especially for this book by Everett Scrogin, decorations by C. A. Seward. Kansas City, Mo., Burton publishing co. [*1928]
[34] p. illus., plates. 32ᵐ.

1. Wood-engravings, American.   I. Scrogin, Everett.   II. Seward, C. A., 1884–   III. Title.

Library of Congress   NE1215.L6A4
29–23064

NL 0449836   DLC WaS

WB
905
L831L
1942
LOGAN, Hugh Benedict, 1880-1943.
Logan basic technique; abundant proof of the ultimate in health restoration methods. [St. Louis, c1942]
1 v. (unpaged) illus., port.
1. Chiropractic

NL 0449837   DNLM

Logan, Hugh Benedict, 1880–1943.
Textbook of Logan basic methods, from the original manuscript. Edited by Vinton F. Logan and Fern M. Murray. [St. Louis] 1950.
xx, 257 p. illus., port. 24 cm.

1. Chiropractic.

RM730.L66   615.82   50-14344

NL 0449838   DLC DNLM

Logan, Hugh David, joint author.

Olmsted, James Montrose Duncan, 1886–
...The effect of insulin on the central nervous system and its relation to the pituitary body, by J. M. D. Olmsted and H. D. Logan ... [Toronto] The University library: pub. by the librarian, 1923.

Logan, Hugh Lynn.
Effect of artificial aging on tensile properties and resistance to corrosion of 24S–T aluminum alloy, by Hugh L. Logan, Harold Hessing, and Harold E. Francis.
[R P 1788, in U. S. National Bureau of Standards. Journal of research. Washington, U. S. Govt. Print. Off., 1947. 26 cm. May 1947, v. 38, no. 5, p. 465–489. illus.]
Caption title.
"References": p. 489.
1. Aluminum alloys—Testing. 2. Strength of materials. 3. Corrosion and anti-corrosives. I. Hessing, Harold, joint author. II. Francis, Harold E., joint author. (Series: U. S. National Bureau of Standards. Journal of research, v. 38, no. 5, R P 1788)
QC1.U52   vol. 38, no. 5   620.18
————Copy 2.   T1.U42   vol. 38, no. 5
47-46719*

NL 0449840   DLC OU

Logan, Hugh Lynn.
... Effect of the quenching rate on susceptibility to intercrystalline corrosion of heat-treated 24S aluminum alloy sheet, by Hugh L. Logan ...
[R P 1378, in U. S. National bureau of standards. Journal of research of the National bureau of standards. Washington, U. S. Govt. print. off., 1941. 23½ᵐ. April, 1941, v. 26, no. 4, p. 321–329 incl. tables, diagr. plates]
"A preliminary report was presented before the American physical society, April 29, 1939. Phys. rev. 55, 1139 (1939)."—p. 322.
1. Corrosion and anti-corrosives. 2. Aluminum alloys.
41–50370 Revised

Library of Congress   QC1.U52   vol. 26, no. 4
————Copy 2.   T1.U42   vol. 26, no. 4
[r43†3]   (506.173)   620.18

NL 0449841   DLC OU

Logan, Hugh Lynn.
... Electrode potential measurements as a means of studying the corrosion characteristics of wrought aluminum alloys of the duralumin type, by Hugh L. Logan ...
[R P 1328, in U. S. National bureau of standards. Journal of research of the National bureau of standards. Washington, U. S. Govt. print. off., 1940. 23½ᵐ. September, 1940, v. 25, no. 3, p. 315–335 incl. illus., tables. plates]
1. Corrosion and anti-corrosives. 2. Aluminum alloys. 3. Potentiometer.   I. Title.
40–29185 Revised

Library of Congress   QC1.U52   vol. 25, no. 3
————Copy 2.   T1.U42   vol. 25, no. 3
[r43c3]   (506.173)   620.18

NL 0449842   DLC WaWW OU

DO22.7
L828
Logan, Hugh Lynn.
Light for living, by H. L. Logan. [1946]
29 p. illus., diagrs.
"A paper presented at the annual convention of the Illuminating engineering society, Quebec ... September 18–20, 1946."

1. Lighting. I. Title.

NL 0449843   NNC NBuC

Logan, Hugh Lynn.
Modeling with light.
14 p. illus., plans.
"A paper presented before the Thirty-fourth Annual Convention, of the Illuminating Engineering Society, Spring Lake, New Jersey, September 9–12, 1940."

NL 0449844   DDO OClMA MiDA

Logan, Indiana Washington (Peddicord) 1835–
Kelion Franklin Peddicord of Quirk's scouts, Morgan's Kentucky cavalry, C. S. A.; biographical and autobiographical, together with a general biographical outline of the Peddicord family, by Mrs. India W. P. Logan. New York and Washington, The Neale publishing company, 1908.
170 p. 4 port. (incl. front.) 21ᵐ.

1. Peddicord, Kelion Franklin, 1833–1905. 2. U. S.—Hist.—Civil war—Personal narratives—Confederate side. 3. Morgan's raid, 1863.
8–19229

Library of Congress   E605.P37

NNC KyBgW
NL 0449845   DLC KyHi MsU NcD CLU ICU KyU TxU NN WHi

Micro
3
Logan, Indiana Washington (Peddicord) 1835–
Kelion Franklin Peddicord of Quirk's scouts, Morgan's Kentucky cavalry, C.S.A; biographical and autobiographical, together with a general biographical outline of the Peddicord family, by Mrs. India W.P. Logan. New York and Washington, The Neale publishing company, 1908.
170p. 4 port. (incl. front.) 21cm.
Micro-opaque. Louisville, Ky., Lost Cause Press, 1958. 5 cards. 7.5x12.5cm. (Travels in the Confederate states)
1. Peddicord, Kelion Franklin, 1823–1905.

NL 0449846   PSt MH AU OU OOxM UU

VOLUME 338

Logan, Innes.
   The enterprise of faith; a handbook for first
communion.   Edinburgh, The church of Scotland
Youth Com., 1955.
   79 p.   19 cm.
   1. First communion - instruction and study.
2. Church of Scotland - Catechisms and creeds.
I. Title.

NL 0449847   MH-AH

Logan, Innes.
   On the King's service; inward glimpses of men at arms, by
the Rev. Innes Logan...   London: Hodder & Stoughton, 1917.
xi, 141 p.   12°.

1. European war, 1914- .—Personal   narratives (Scottish). 2. Title.
N. Y. P. L.   August 22, 1917.

NL 0449848   NN MH

Logan, Innes.
   War and peace; a study in citizenship, by Innes Logan...
Cambridge: Bowes & Bowes, 1925.   24 p.   8°.

Printed in Great Britain.

1. War and peace.
N. Y. P. L.   October 15, 1925

NL 0449849   NN

Logan, Mrs. J.A., 1838-1923.
      see Logan, Mary Simmerson (Cunningham)
1838-1923.

Spec.
PS 2109 Logan, J   B
J 2   Alice M'Donald; or, The heroine of
A 8   principle. Being a succinct account of her
1871   parentage, family, birth, education, conversion
       to Christ, union with the Cumberland Presby-
       terian Church, and subsequent life to the
       present day. A tale of the nineteenth century.
       [2d ed.] St. Louis, Southwestern Book and
       Pub. Co., 1871.
          294 p. 18 cm.
          Sequel: Chronicles of Sylvanton.

       By James the Less [pseud]
       Arthur C. Hoskins collection of Saint
       Louisiana and Missouriana.

NL 0449852   MoSW

PZ3
.LS29A4 Logan, J   B
         Alice M'Donald; or, The heroine of principle,
      being a succinct account of her parentage,
      family, birth, education, conversion to Christ,
      union with the Cumberland Presbyterian church,
      and subsequent life to the present day.   St.
      Louis, Cumberland Presbyterian Printing House,
      1873.
          294 p. front. 18cm.

          1. Cumberland Presbyterian Church--Fiction.
      I. Title.

NL 0449853   T NcD

PZ3
.LS29A3 Logan, J   B
         Alice M'Donald; or, The heroine of principle,
      being a succinct account of her parentage,
      family, birth, education, conversion to Christ,
      union with the Cumberland Presbyterian Church,
      and subsequent life to the present day. A tale
      of the nineteenth century. By James the Less
      [pseud.]   St. Louis, Cumberland Presbyterian
      Print. House, 1873.
          294 p. front.(port.) 18 cm.

          "Third edition."

NL 0449854   T

Logan, J   B.
   Alice McDonald; or, The heroine of principle; a story of the
early Cumberland Presbyterian church.   Rev. ed., by James
the Less (J. B. Logan, D. D.)   Nashville, Tenn., C. P. publishing house, 1900.
   8 p. l., 5-243 p. front. (port.) 20½ᵐ.

   1. Cumberland Presbyterian church—Fiction.   I. Title.

                                              1-29526 Revised
   Library of Congress   PZ3.LS29A4

NL 0449855   DLC KyBgW

PZ3
.LS29A4 Logan, J   B
1901   Alice McDonald; or, The heroine of princi-
       ple; The story of the early Cumberland
       Presbyterian Church. 2d rev. ed. By James
       the Less (J.B. Logan) Nashville, C.P.
       Publishing House, 1901.
          243 p. front.(port.) 20 cm.

          1. Cumberland Presbyterian Church--Fic-
       tion. I. Title.

NL 0449856   T MH-AH

PZ3
.LS29C29 Logan, J   B
         Carrie Holmes. By Rev. J.B. Logan ...
      Nashville, Cumberland Presbyterian Board of
      Publication, 1873.
          153 p. 16 cm.

          1. Cumberland Presbyterian Church--Fic-
      tion. I. Title.

NL 0449857   T

Spec.
PS 2109 [Logan, J   B   ]
J 2   Chronicles of Sylvanton; a sequel to
C 4   Alice McDonald. By the author of "Alice
1873   McDonald." Saint Louis, Southwestern Book and
       Pub. Co., 1873.
          356 p. 18 cm.

       Arthur C. Hoskins collection of Saint
       Louisiana and Missouriana.

       I. Alice McDonald, Author of. II. Title.

NL 0449858   MoSW T

Logan, J   B.
   History of the Cumberland Presbyterian
church in Illinois, containing sketches of the
first ministers, churches, presbyteries and
synods; also a history of missions, publication and education. By J.B. Logan ... Alton,
Ill., Perrin & Smith, 1878.
   vii[8]-217p. 22½ cm.

NL 0449859   MoU NjPT WHi

Rare   Logan, J   B
Book   Is the system of American slavery sanctioned
Room   by the Holy Scriptures? Alton, Ill.,
E   R. B. Crossman, printer, 1864.
449   68 p. 18 cm.
L83
          In slip-case. 24 cm.

          1. Slavery in the U. S.—Controversial
       literature. 2. Slavery and the church—
       Presbyterian Church. I. Title.   mcm

NL 0449860   IEdS

Logan, J   B
   A plain and scriptural guide to the
honest inquirer after truth, in reference to the doctrine of baptism, as
taught in the Holy Scriptures. By Rev.
J.B. Logan. Seventh edition. Alton,
Ill., S.V. Crossman, book and job
printer, 1867.
   94 p. 19 cm.

NL 0449861   IHi

Logan, J.D..
      see Logan, John Daniel, 1869-1929.

Logan, Mrs. J.E.
      see Logan, Annie Robertson (Macfarlane)

Logan, J. F.
      see Logan, John Fremont.

D619   Logan, J   Francis.
.3   ... Spy proof America! or, the "V.S.S", by
L6   J. Francis Logan ... [Buffalo, N.Y.] c1917.
          39 p. 19.5 cm.

NL 0449865   DLC

Logan, J   G.
   The effect of isotopic substitution on the
vibrational wave functions and the dissociation
probability of diatomic and linear triatomic
molecules; a dissertation submitted in partial
fulfillment of the requirements for the degree of
Doctor of Philosophy. Buffalo, 1955.
   163 numb. l. 29 cm. (Buffalo. University.
Doctors' theses)

NL 0449866   NBuG

Logan, Mrs. J.H.
      see Logan, Mary E.

WY   LOGAN, Mrs. J   M
157   Questions and answers on "Obstetrics
D346oa for nurses" (Joseph B. De Lee) Shanghai,
1943   Kwang Hsüeh Pub. House, 1943.
          [37] p.
          Added title-page and text in Chinese.
          1. Chinese language - Texts
       2. Nursing - Obstetrical I. De Lee,
       Joseph Bolivar, 1869-1942. Obstetrics
       for nurses

NL 0449868   DNLM

VOLUME 338

Logan, J. Moffat
    see Logan, James Moffat.

Logan, Jacobus, 1674–1751.
    see Logan, James, 1674–1751.

Logan, James, Advocate, of Edinburgh.
    Compendium of the laws of England, Scotland and Ancient Rome, on marriage. Edinburgh, 1839.

NL 0449871   PU-L

Logan, James, *advocate, of Edinburgh.*
    Notes of a journey through Canada, the United States of America, and the West Indies ... Edinburgh [etc.] Fraser and co., 1838.
    xii, 259 p. front. (fold. map) 20½ᶜᵐ.

    1. U. S.—Descr. & trav. 2. Canada—Descr. & trav. 3. West Indies—Descr. & trav.

    Library of Congress   E165.L83   1–26860

    MiU OC1 NN MB NcD CaOTU
NL 0449872   DLC CaBVaU IGK DNLM Ct CtY TxU PSC PPL

Logan, James, *advocate, of Edinburgh.*
    Notes of a journey through Canada, the United States of America, and the West Indies. Edinburgh, Fraser, 1838.
    (American culture series, 104:3)
    Microfilm copy (positive) made in 1960 by University Microfilms, Ann Arbor, Mich.
    Collation of the original: xii, 259 p. fold. map.

    1. U. S.—Descr. & trav.—1783–1848. 2. Canada—Descr. & trav. 3. West Indies—Descr. & trav.

    Microfilm 01291 reel 104, no. 3 E   Mic 60–7507

NL 0449873   DLC MiU KEmT FTaSU ICRL

Micro-   Logan, James, advocate, of Edinburgh.
card   Notes of a journey through Canada, the United
95   States of America, and the West Indies ...
v.3   Edinburgh, Fraser, 1838.
no.197   xii, 259p. fold. map. 21cm.
             Micro-opaque. Louisville, Ky., Lost Cause
         Press, 1961. 4 cards. 8 x 13cm. (Travels in
         the old South, 3, 197)
             1. U.S. - Descr. & trav. - 1783–1848.
         2. Canada - Descr. & trav. 3. West Indies -
         Descr. & trav. I. Title. II. Series: Travels
         in the old South.   3. 197.

NL 0449874   TxU OOxM CSt MsU MoU

Logan, James, 1674–1751.
    Works by this author printed in America before 1801 are available in this library in the Readex Microprint edition of Early American Imprints published by the American Antiquarian Society. This collection is arranged according to the numbers in Charles Evans' American Bibliography.

NL 0449875   DLC

Logan, James, 1674–1751.
    Account of the Titles of James Logans Lands as kept by himself, 1730 (Ms.)
    22 p.

NL 0449876   PPL

[Logan, James] 1674–1751.
    The antidote. In some remarks on a paper of David Lloyd's, called A vindication of the legislative power. Submitted to the representatives of all the freemen of Pennsylvania. [Philadelphia, A. Bradford, 1725]
    8 p. 33ᶜᵐ.
    Caption title.
    Signed: J. Logan; dated: 25. Sept. 1725.
    This issue has on p. 8 list of errata (3 lines) but not the "Advertisement" found in another issue of same date.

    1. Lloyd, David, 1656–1731. A vindication of the legislative power.
    2. Pennsylvania—Pol. & govt.—Colonial period. I. Title.

    Library of Congress   F152.L815   14–14061

NL 0449877   DLC PPAmP PPL RPJCB PHi

[Logan, James] 1674–1751.
    The antidote. In some remarks on a paper of David Lloyd's, called A vindication of the legislative power. Submitted to the representatives of all the freemen of Pennsylvania. [2d ed. Philadelphia, A. Bradford, 1725]
    8 p. 32½ᶜᵐ.
    Caption title.
    Signed: J. Logan.

    1. Lloyd, David, 1656–1731. A vindication of the legislative power.
    2. Pennsylvania—Pol. & govt.—Colonial period.

    Library of Congress   F152.L81   5–4102

NL 0449878   DLC CSmH NN PHi MiU-C

[Logan, James] 1674–1751.
    The antidote. In some remarks on a paper of David Lloyd's, called A vindication of the legislative power. Submitted to the representatives of all the freeman of Pennsylvania. [2d ed. Philadelphia: Printed by Andrew Bradford. 1725]
    Microcard edition.
    Caption title.
    Signed: J. Logan.
    Evans 2651.
    1. Lloyd, David,   1656–1731. A vindication of the legisla-   tive power. 2. Pa.—Pol.
    & govt.—Colonial per   iod. I.Title.

NL 0449879   ViU

Logan, James, 1674–1751, ed. and tr.
                                        FOR OTHER EDITIONS
                                        SEE MAIN ENTRY
Cicero, Marcus Tullius.
    M. T. Cicero's [Cato major, or Discourse on old age. Addressed to Titus Pomponius Atticus. With explanatory notes. By Benj. Franklin, LL. D. London: Printed for Fielding and Walker, MDCCLXXVIII.

Logan, James, 1674–1751, ed. and tr.
Cicero, Marcus Tullius.
    Cato major; or, A treatise on old age, by M. Tullius Cicero. With explanatory notes from the Roman history. By the Honourable James Logan, esq; ... 4th ed. Philadelphia, Printed. Glasgow, Reprinted by R. Urie. M.DCC.LVIII.

Logan, James, 1674–1751.
    The charge delivered from the Bench to the Grand Inquest at a court of Oyer and Terminer ...
        see under Pennsylvania (Colony) Court of Oyer and Terminer (Philadelphia Co.)

                                        FOR OTHER EDITIONS
                                        SEE MAIN ENTRY
Logan, James, 1674–1751.
Pennsylvania (*Colony*) *Court of quarter sessions of the peace* (*Philadelphia Co.*)
    The Charge Delivered from the Bench to the Grand-Jury, At the Court of Quarter Sessions, held for the County of Philadelphia, the second day of September 1723. Published at the Desire of the said Grand-Jury. Together with Their Address. Philadelphia, Printed and Sold by Andrew Bradford, at the Sign of the Bible, in the Second Street, 1723.

Logan, James, 1674–1751.
    Penn, William, 1644–1718.
    Correspondence between William Penn and James Logan, secretary of the province of Pennsylvania, and others. 1700–1750. From the original letters in possession of the Logan family. With notes by the late Mrs. Deborah Logan. Ed. with additional notes by Edward Armstrong ... vol. I–II. Philadelphia, The Historical society of Pennsylvania, 1870–72.

Logan, James, 1674–1751.
    The correspondence of James Logan and Thomas Story, 1724–1741, edited by Norman Penney ... Philadelphia, Pa., Friends' historical association [1927]
    2 p. l., 100 p. 23½ᶜᵐ.

    I. Story, Thomas, 1662–1742. II. Penney, Norman, 1858–   ed.
    III. Title.
    Library of Congress   BX7795.L6A3   27–3829

                PHC
NL 0449885   DLC WaS MWA NcD PCC PPAmP PU OC1W MH

QK138   Logan, James, 1674–1751.
.G7   De plantarum generatione experimenta et
v.1   meletemata. [Philadelphia, 1737]
            13 p. 20 cm.

            Caption title.
            Bound with Gronovius, Joannes Fredericus.
        Flora Virginica ... Lugduni Batavorum, 1739–43.

            1. Fertilization of plants. i.t.

NL 0449886   NNBG

Logan, James. 1674–1751. Defensive war, or Pennsylvania politics in 1741. (Pa. Mag. Hist. v. 6, 1882, p. 402.)

NL 0449887   MdBP

421   Logan, James, 1674–1751
1741ℓ   Demonstrationes de radiorum lucis in superficies sphaericas, remotius ab axe incidentium a primario foco aberrationibus ... Lugduni Batavorum, Apud C. Haak, 1741.
            1p. ℓ., 29p. fold. diagrs. 19cm.

            1. Refraction

NL 0449888   CtY PPL RPJCB

[Logan, James] 1674–1751.
725   A dialogue shewing, what's therein to be
L8   found. A motto being modish, for want of good
        Latin, are put English quotations ... [Philadelphia]Printed in the year MDCCXXV.
            40p., 1ℓ. 15½cm.
            Signatures: [A]-E⁴,1ℓ., unsigned?
            Printed by S. Keimer. - cf. Evans, v.1,p.349
            An answer to Francis Rawle's Ways and means
        for the inhabitants of Delaware to become rich
        ...
            Leaf of errata at end wanting.

NL 0449889   CtY

[Logan, James,] 1674–1751.
    A dialogue shewing, what's therein to be found... [Philadelphia,] Printed in the year 1725. [Photostat reproduction, 1925.]
    40 p. 4°.
    Reproduced in photostat from the original in the Henry E. Huntington Library, 1925.
    Hildeburn 252.
    A discussion of Francis Rawle's pamphlet, Way and means.
    p. 8 wrongly numbered 12.

    367469A. 1. Rawle, Francis,   1660?–1727: Ways and means.
    2. Title.
    N. Y. P. L.   July 30, 1928

NL 0449890   NN MH-BA PHi

VOLUME 338

Logan, James, 1674–1751.
Experimenta et meletemata de plantarum generatione.
Autore Jacobo Logan ... Experiments and considerations on
the generation of plants. By James Logan ... Translated
from the original Latin. London: Printed for C. Davis, 1747.

1 p. l., iii, [2], 2–39 p. 20⁰ᵐ.

"The translator's advertisement" signed: J. F.
Latin and English on opposite pages.

1. Fertilization of plants.   I. Fothergill, John, 1712–1780, tr.   II.
Title.   III. Title: Experiments and considerations on the generation of
plants.

31–8227

Library of Congress   QK827.L75   581.166

PHi PHC
NL   0449891   DLC RPJCB NNBG WU MWA MB DNLM CtY PPL

M-film
540   Logan, James, 1674–1751.
Am3   Experimenta et meletemata de plantarum
348-2   generatione. Autore Jacobo Logan. Experiments
         and considerations on the generation of plants.
         By James Logan, translated from the original
         Latin.   London, Printed for C. Davis, 1747.
         iii, 39 p.

         "The translator's advertisement" signed:
         J. F.
         Latin and English on opposite pages.

         Microfilm (positive) Ann Arbor, Mich.,
         University Microfilms, 1967. 2d title of 5.
         35 mm. (American culture series, reel 348.2)

         1. Fertilization of plants. I. Fothergill,
         John, 1712–1780, tr. II. Title. III. Title:
         Experiments and considerations on the generation
         of plants.

NL   0449893   KEmT PSt

Logan, James, 1674–1751.
Experimenta et meletemata de plantarum generatione
nec non canonum pro inveniendis refractionum, tum simplicium, tum in lentibus duplicium focis demonstrationes
geometricae. Auctore Jacobo Logan ... Lugduni Batavorum, apud C. Haak, 1739.

32 p. 2 fold. diagr. 20½ᶜᵐ.

1. Plant reproduction.

Agr 13–1392

Library, U. S. Dept. of   Agriculture 452.2L83

NL   0449894   DNAL RPJCB MB NNBG PPL PPC

LOGAN, James, 1674.1751.

Experimenta et meletemata de plantarum
generatione nec non inveniendis refractionum, tum simplicium, tum in lentibus
duplicium focis demonstrationes geometricae.
Lugduni Batavorum, apud Cornelium Haak,
1739.
13 p.
Bound with Hermann, Paul. Musaeum
zeylanicum and Magnol, Pierre. Hortus regius
monspeliensis.

R QK41.L6

Title translated: Experiments with
plants.
(40) 1. Botany.   Pre-Linnean works.
I. Hermann, Paul.   Musaeum zeylanicum.
II. Magnol, Pierre.   Hortus regius
monspeliensis.   III. Title.

NL   0449896   DNAL

FILM   Logan, James, 1674–1751.
B   Letter book, 1717–31.
L831L1L   683p.

          In Historical Society of Pennsylvania collec-
          tions.
          Statesman and scholar. Letter book dealing
          chiefly with his business transactions.
          Microfilm (negative) of MSS. Philadelphia,
          Pennsylvania Historical Society, 1949. 2
          reels. 35mm.

NL   0449897   IU

Logan, James, 1674–1751.
A Letter from James Logan to The Society of
Friends on the Subject of Their Opposition in the
Legislature to all Measures for the Defence of The
Colony.   September 22, 1741.
(16) p.
Manuscript.

NL   0449898   PPL

Logan, James, 1674-1751.
Letter of Sept. 22, 1741 to the yearly
meeting. Philadelphia, B. Franklin, 174
N.t.p.   Pp. 4.

NL   0449899   PPL

Logan, James, 1674-1751.
Letters on Indian and colonial affairs from James
Logan to Geo. Clarke, Gov. of N.Y., W. Gooch, Gov.
of Vir., Thomas, Gov. of Penna. Copied by Francis
Fisher...Being the 4th. vol. of the MSS Logan papers.
274 p.

NL   0449900   PPAmP

Logan, James, 1674–1751.
Manuscript Letter to Rev. R. Peters of April 21,
1736, relating to his Charge to the Grand Inquest.
(2) p.

NL   0449901   PPL

Logan, James, 1674–1751.
Memoirs of James Logan; a distinguished
scholar and Christian legislator; founder of
the Loganian library at Philadelphia; secretary of the province of Pennsylvania ...
including several of his letters and those
of his correspondents, many of which are now
first printed from the original MSS. collated
and arranged for the purpose; by Wilson
Armistead. London, C. Gilpin, 1851.
192 p. port.

NL   0449902   NNC NcD

FILM   Logan, James, 1674–1751.
B   Miscellaneous letters, 1716–42.
L831L1   446p. (Logan papers, v.4)

          In Historical Society of Pennsylvania collec-
          tions.
          Statesman and scholar. Letters relating to
          family, business, and land matters.
          Microfilm (negative) of MSS. Philadelphia,
          Pennsylvania Historical Society, 1949. 2 reels.
          35mm.

NL   0449903   IU

[Logan, James] 1674–1751.
A more just vindication of the Honourable Sir William
Keith, bart., against the unparalleled abuses put upon
him, in a scandalous libel call'd, A just and plain vindi-
cation of Sir William Keith, &c. [Philadelphia, A. Brad-
ford, 1726]
4 p. 33ᶜᵐ.
Caption title.
Signed: Philo-Keithius.
An attack on Keith and his acts as governor of Pennsylvania.
1. Keith, Sir William, bart., 1680–1749. A just and plain vindication of
Sir William Keith. 2. Pennsylvania — Pol. & govt. — Colonial period.
I. Philo-Keithius, pseud.

Library of Congress   F152.L82   4–36345

NL   0449904   DLC PPL RPJCB PPAmP PHi NN

[Logan, James] 1674–1751.
A more just vindication of the Honourable
Sir William Keith, bart., against the unparalleled abuses put upon him, in a scandalous libel call'd, A just and plain vindication of Sir William Keith, &c. [Philadel-
phia, A. Bradford, 1726]

Microcard edition.
Caption title.
Signed: Philo-Keithius.
An attack on Keith and his acts as gov-
ernor of Pennsylvania   nia.
Evans 2759.
1. Keith, Sir Willi   am bart. 1680–1749. A just
and plain vindication   of Sir William Keith. 2. Pa.—
Pol. & govt.—Colonial period. I. Philo-Keithius,
pseud. II. Title.

NL   0449905   ViU

F152   [Logan, James] 1674–1751
.L822   Pamphlet relating to a controversy between
            Sir Wm. Keith of Penn. & James Logan...
            Phil.? 172-   ?]
            32 cm.

NL   0449906   DLC

BV
806   Logan, James, 1674-1751.
H65   Pastoral advice.   Philadelphia,
           Baptist General Tract Society [18—]
           12 p.   18 cm.   (Baptist General
           Tract Society.   Tract, no.109)
           Bound with The Holy Bible on baptism.
           [n. p., 185–]
           1. Pastoral theology – Baptists.
           I. American Baptist Publication
           Society. II. Title.

NL   0449907   NRCR NRAB

Logan, James, 1674-1751.
Some account of the reception of William Penn
when he arrived in Penna. anno 1700; being a
part of a letter from James Logan to Wm Penn, junr.
Sept.25, 1700.
6 p.

NL   0449908   PPAmP

Logan, James, 1674–1751.
To Robert Jordan, And Others The Friends Of The
Yearly Meeting For Business, Now Conven'd In
Philadelphia. (Signed. J. L.) (Philadelphia,
Printed by B. Franklin, 1741)
4 p. Sm. fol.
Thirty copies privately printed, only two of which
are known to be extant.   Reprinted in the Pennsylvania
Magazine of History and Biography. Vol. VI.

NL   0449909   ICMcC PPL PHi

VOLUME 338

Logan, James, 1794?–1872.   **FOR OTHER EDITIONS SEE MAIN ENTRY**
An account of the manners...of the ancient Caledonians.
Mackenzie, John, 1806–1848.
  Sar-obair nam bard gaelach: or, The beauties of Gaelic poetry, and lives of the Highland bards; with historical and critical notes, and a comprehensive glossary of provincial words. By John Mackenzie ... With an historical introduction containing an account of the manners, habits, etc., of the ancient Caledonians. By James Logan ... New ed. Edinburgh, N. Macleod, 1904.

Logan, James, 1794?–1872.

Aberdeen, Scot. St. Nicholas church.
  Cartularium ecclesiae Sancti Nicholai aberdonensis, recognovit Jacobus Cooper ... Impressum Aberdoniae, Soc. nov. Spald. impensis, 1888–92.

Logan, James, 1794?–1872.
  The clans of the Scottish Highlands, illustrated by appropriate figures, displaying their dress, tartans, arms, armorial insignia, and social occupations, from original sketches, by R. R. M'Ian, esq. With accompanying description and historical memoranda of character, mode of life, &c., &c., by James Logan ... London, Ackermann and co., 1845–47.
  2 v. col. fronts., col. plates. 38½ᶜᵐ.
  1. Clans and clan system. 2. Tartans. 3. Costume—Highlands of Scotland. i. McIan, Robert Ronald, d. 1856, illus.

                   12–36289

  Library of Congress   DA880.H7 L7

       MdBP NjP CtY PPL PHi OC1 PU
NL 0449912   DLC CaBVaU CaBVa NBu WaE OrP WaSp MeB

Logan, James, 1794?–1872.
  The clans of the Scottish Highlands, illustrated by appropriate figures, displaying their dress, tartans, arms, armorial insignia and social occupations, from original sketches, by Robert Ronald McIan.
  London. Willis & Sotheran. 1857. 2 v. Colored plates. 36 cm.

N1345 — Highlands of Scotland. Costume. — MacIan [McIan], Robert Ronald, illus. — Scotland. Costume. — Clans of Scotland. — Costume.

NL 0449913   MB OC1WHi NN

Logan, James, 1794?–1872.
  The clans of the Scottish highlands, illustrated by their dress, arms, armorial insignia, etc., with descriptions. London, 1859.
  2 v. fol.

NL 0449914   NN

Logan, James, 1794–1872.
  Gaelic gatherings
    see under McIan, Robert Ronald, d. 1856.

Logan, James, 1794?–1872.
  Logan's collections, edited by James Cruickshank. Aberdeen, The Third Spalding club, 1941.
  xliii, 178 (i. e. 180) p., 1 l. incl. illus., plates, plan (1 double) col. front., col. plates, coats of arms (part col.) 26ᶜᵐ.
  Errata slip inserted.
  CONTENTS.—James Logan: his life and work, by James Cruickshank.—Collectanea ecclesiastica in provincia abredonensi, by James Logan.—Ecclesiastical antiquities of Aberdeenshire, by James Logan.—Drawings from Descriptio cathedralis abredonensis, by James Logan.—Description of St. Machar's cathedral, by William Kelly.—Three fifteenth century effigies of canons in Aberdeen cathedral, by F. C. Eeles.
  1. Aberdeenshire, Scot.—Antiq. 2. Churches—Scotland—Aberdeenshire. i. Cruickshank, James, ed. ii. Third Spalding club, Aberdeen.

                45–43191

  Library of Congress   DA880.A1L6
          (2)   941.25

NL 0449916   DLC TU CtY NNC MH ICU NN OC1 PU

Logan, James, 1794?–1872.
  M'Ian's costumes of the clans of Scotland; seventy-four coloured illustrations, with descriptive letterpress by James Logan. The original work in two large quarto volumes is given here complete and unaltered further than being reduced in size, properly paged, and indexed for easy reference, with suitable tail-piece illustrations. Glasgow, D. Bryce and son; New York, Frederick A. Stokes company, 1899.
  343, [1] p. 74 col. pl. (incl. front.) 20 cm.
  Tail-pieces.

  With reproduction of t-p. of original edition: The clans of the Scottish Highlands, illustrated by appropriate figures ... from original sketches, by R. R. M'Ian, esq. With accompanying description ... by James Logan ... London, 1845–[47]

  1. Clans and clan system. 2. Tartans. 3. Costume—Highlands of Scotland. i. McIan, Robert Ronald, d. 1856, illus.

               A 29–394

James Jerome Hill Ref.   Library DA888.H76L7 1899
for Library of Congress   [a55d½]

       NN MB MH ScU
NL 0449918   MnSJ WaE CaBVaU OrCS OrU LU NBuU OC1WHi

Logan, James, 1794?–1872.
  McIan's costumes of the clans of Scotland; ... The original work in two large quarto volumes is given here complete and unaltered further than being reduced in size, properly paged and indexed for easy reference ... Glasgow, Bryce, 1909.
  344 p.
  First publ. in 1845 with title: The Clans of the Scottish highlands.

NL 0449919   OC1

Logan, James, 1794?–1872.
  McIan's Highlanders at home; or, Gaelic gatherings... Twenty-four coloured illustrations, with descriptive letterpress by James Logan... Glasgow: D. Bryce and Son, 1900. 268 p. col'd front., illus., col'd plates. 12°.
  With reproduction of original t-p.: Gaelic gatherings; or, The Highlanders at home, on the heath, the river, and the loch... London, 1848.

407207A. 1. Scotland—Highlands—   Social life. 2. McIan, Robert
N. Y. P. L.   Ronald, 1805–1856.   May 15, 1929

NL 0449920   NN NJQ MB MH OC1 ICN OC1W

Logan, James, 1794?–1872.
  The Scottish Gaël; or, Celtic manners, as preserved among the Highlanders: being an historical and descriptive account of the inhabitants, antiquities, and national peculiarities of Scotland; more particularly of the northern, or Gaëlic parts of the country, where the singular habits of the aboriginal Celts are most tenaciously retained. By James Logan ... London, Smith, Elder, and co., 1831.
  2 v. col. fronts, illus, plates (part col.; incl. music) col. coat of arms. 21½ᶜᵐ.
  "Table of clan tartans": v. 2, p. [401]–408.
  1. Celts. 2. Highlands of Scotland—Soc. life & cust. i. Title.

             17–7143

  Library of Congress   A772.L7

       OCU OC1WHi MH MB NN
NL 0449921   DLC IU WaS NBuC CU IaU CtY MdBP PPL PHi

RA914.1
LB3.2   Logan, James, 1794?–1872.
  The Scottish Gaël; or, Celtic manners, as preserved among the Highlanders; being an historical and descriptive account of the inhabitants, antiquities, and national peculiarities of Scotland ... By James Logan ... First American edition. Boston: Marsh, Capen & Lyon [etc.], Hubbard & Edmands, Cincinnati, 1833.
  432,8,433–520p.illus.coat of arms.music. 6plates.23cm.

  Frontispiece (plate) lacking.
  Pp. 323–334 misbound.

  1. Celts. 2. Highlands of Scotland—Soc. life & cust. I. Title.

NL 0449923   OC KyLx NjP PU MB CtY MH PPAN PPA

914.11
L836   Logan, James, 1794?–1872.
1843   The Scottish Gaël; or, Celtic manners, as preserved among the Highlanders, being an historical and descriptive account of the inhabitants, antiquities, and national peculiarities of Scotland; more particularly of the northern, or Gaëlic parts of the country, where the singular habits of the aboriginal Celts are most tenaciously retained. By James Logan ... 1st American ed. Hartford, S. Andrus and son, 1843.
  520p. front., illus.,7 plates (1 col.) 23cm.
  8p. of music   inserted.
  Bibliographi-   cal foot-notes.

NL 0449924   TxU DLC NjP MB DNLM I OC1WHi CU OrU

DA
880   Logan, James, 1794?–1872.
.H6L8   The Scotish Gaël; or, Celtic
1845   manners, as preserved among the Highlanders, being an historical and descriptive account of the inhabitants, antiquities; and national peculiarities of Scotland; more particularly of the northern, or Gaëlic parts of the country, where the singular habits of the aboriginal Celts are most tenaciously retained. By James Logan. 1st American ed. Hartford, S. Andrus and son, 1845.
  520 p. illus. 24 cm.
  1. Celts. 2. Highlands of Scotland --Soc. life & cust. I. Title.

NL 0449925   OKentU CSmH MiU OC1 PP NcU ScU MB

DA
880   Logan, James, 1794?–1872.
H6L83   The Scotish Gaël; or, Celtic manners,
1846   as preserved among the Highlanders, being an historical and descriptive account of the inhabitants, antiquities, and national peculiarities of Scotland; more particularly of the northern, or Gaëlic parts of the country, 5th American ed. Hartford, S. Andrus, 1846.
  520 p. illus. 24cm.

NL 0449926   NIC NjR OC1W

Logan, James, 1794?–1872.
  The Scottish Goel, etc. Hartford, Ct., 1847.

NL 0449927   RP

Logan, James, 1794?–1872.
  The Scotish Gaël; or, Celtic manners, as preserved among the Highlanders, being an historical and descriptive account of the inhabitants, antiquities, and national peculiarities of Scotland; more particularly of the northern, or Gaëlic parts of the country, where the singular habits of the aboriginal Celts are most tenaciously retained. By James Logan ... 5th American ed. Hartford, S. Andrus and son, 1849.
  520 p. front., illus., 7 pl., plans. 23½ᶜᵐ.

NL 0449928   ViU MWA

Logan, James, 1794?–1872.
  The Scotish Gaël; or, Celtic manners, as preserved among the Highlanders, being an historical and descriptive account of the inhabitants, antiquities, and national peculiarities of Scotland; more particularly of the northern, or Gaëlic parts of the country, where the singular habits of the aboriginal Celts are most tenaciously retained. By James Logan ... 5th American ed. Hartford, S. Andrus and son, 1850.
  520 p. front., illus., 7 pl., plans. 23½ᶜᵐ.

  1. Celts. 2. Highlands of Scotland—Soc. life & cust. i. Title.
             2–30270

  Library of Congress   DA880.H6L8 1850

       NjNbS
NL 0449929   DLC CaBVa IEN IU KyU NcU PU MB OC1JC

VOLUME 338

Logan, James, 1794?-1872.
The Scotish Gaël; or, Celtic manners, as preserved among the Highlanders, being an historical and descriptive account of the inhabitants, antiquities, and national peculiarities of Scotland; more particularly of the northern, or Gaëlic parts of the country, where the singular habits of the aboriginal Celts are most tenaciously retained. By James Logan ... 5th American ed. Hartford, S. Andrus and son, 1851.
440 p., 8 p. (music), 441-520 p. front., illus., plates (1 col.) 23½ᶜᵐ.
"Table of clan tartans": p. ⟨501⟩-507.
1. Celts. 2. Highlands of Scotland—Soc. life & cust. I. Title.
35-32068
Library of Congress   DA880.H6L8 1851

NL 0449930   DLC CaBViP PV

914.11
L828s
1853
Logan, James, 1794?-1872.
The Scotish Gaël; or, Celtic manners, as preserved among the Highlanders, being an historical and descriptive account of the inhabitants, antiquities, and national peculiarities of Scotland; more particularly of the northern, or Gaëlic parts of the country, where the singular habits of the aboriginal Celts are most tenaciously retained. By James Logan ... 5th American ed. Hartford, S. Andrus and son, 1853.
520p. front.,illus.,3 plates (1 col.) 24cm.
8p. of music   inserted.
Bibliographi-   cal foot-notes.

NL 0449931   TxU DLC PP

Logan, James, 1794?-1872.
The Scottish Gaël; or, Celtic manners, as preserved among the Highlanders, being an historical and descriptive account of the inhabitants, antiquities, and national peculiarities of Scotland; more particularly of the northern, or Gaëlic parts of the country, where the singular habits of the aboriginal Celts are most tenaciously retained. By the late James Logan ... Ed., with memoir and notes, by the Rev. Alex. Stewart ... Inverness, H. Mackenzie; ⟨etc., etc.⟩, 1876⟨?⟩
2 v. col. fronts, illus., plates (part col.) coat of arms. 22ᶜᵐ.
"Table of clan tartans": v. 2, p. ⟨417⟩-424.
Contains music.
1. Celts. 2. Highlands of   Scotland—Soc. life & cust.   I. Stewart, Alexander, ed.
15-23694
Library of Congress   DA880.H6L8 1876

MH NN MB
NL 0449932   DLC ILfC CaBVa OO CaBVaU MiEM ViU OC1

Logan, James, 1852-
Changing industrial conditions; commencement address at the Worcester polytechnic institute, June 11, 1908, by James Logan, mayor of Worcester. ⟨Worcester? Mass., 1908⟩
cover-title, 24 p. 22ᶜᵐ.
Reprinted from the Journal of the Worcester polytechnic institute, vol. XI, no. 5, July, 1908.
1. U. S.—Indus.—Addresses, essays, lectures.   I. Worcester polytechnic institute, Worcester, Mass. II. Title.
16-3837
Library of Congress   HC106.L75

NL 0449933   DLC

LOGAN, James, 1852-
"A closer commercial relationship with Latin America". [Address] delivered before the 13th Annual convention of the National Machine Tool Builders' Association, New York, Oct.23,1914. [New York,1914.]

NL 0449934   MH

Logan, James, 1852-

... The Red envelope. no. 1-24; July 1915-July 1925. Hartford, Conn., Press of Plimpton manufacturing co. ⟨1915-25⟩

LOGAN, James, 1852-
The steading power and influence of consolidation. n.p.,n.d.

NL 0449936   MH

Logan, James, 1880-
Arithmetical wrinkles, containing notes on the various rules; solutions of knotty problems; hints on methods of working; mensuration rules, tables, etc. By J. Logan, ... London, S. Sonnenschein & Co., ltd., 1905.
[8], 84 p. diagrs. 18ᶜᵐ.

NL 0449937   ICJ

Logan, James, 1880-
Diary of a dominie; being the log-book of Mr. George Gerund, as re-written by J. Logan... London: C. Stacey, Ltd., 1927.
159 p. 12°.

362511A.   1. Ireland—Social life,   20th century. 2. Title.
N.Y.P.L.   June 27, 1928

NL 0449938   NN CaBVaU MH

LOGAN, JAMES, 1880-
Four one-act comedies: Dacency; Mary's man; Village statesmen; One never knows, by James Logan... Belfast: The Quota Press, 1931. 94 p. 12°.

632262A. 1. Drama, Irish. I. Title: Dacency. II. Title: Mary's man. III. Title: Village statesmen. IV. Title: One never knows.

NL 0449939   NN IaU

823.8
L831m
Logan, James, 1880-
The McCluskey twins. London, H. J. Drane [19--]
112p. 19cm.

NL 0449940   IEN

Logan, James, 1880-
Talks to boys; or, Men in the making, by James Logan ... London, R. Scott, 1915.
viii, 147 p. 19½ᶜᵐ.

1. Boys. 2. Conduct of life.   I. Title. II. Title: Men in the making.
E 16-468
Library, U. S. Bur. of   Education BJ1641.L82

NL 0449941   DHEW

914.16
L828u
Logan, James, 1880-
Ulster in the x-rays; a short review of the real Ulster, its people, pursuits, principles, poetry, dialect and humour. With an introduction by Ernest Hamilton. London, A. H. Stockwell ⟨1923⟩.
188 p. tables.

NL 0449942   WaU CtY MH NN

Logan, James, 1880-
Ulster in the X-rays; a short review of the real Ulster, its people, pursuits, principles, poetry, dialect and humour, by James Logan ... With an introduction by Lord Ernest Hamilton... [2. ed] ... London, A. H. Stockwell [1923]
188 p. front. (port.) 19 cm.

NL 0449943   CSt-H MB

821.91
L831v
Logan, James, 1880-
Verses: grave and gladsome; with a foreword by Sir John Ross. London, A. H. Stockwell [1925]
84 p. 19cm.

Author's autograph presentation copy.

NL 0449944   FU

Logan, James A.
... United States, complainant, vs. the Joint traffic association et al. Brief on behalf of the Pennsylvania railroad company ⟨et al.⟩ ... James A. Logan, John G. Johnson, of counsel. Phila⟨delphia⟩ Allen, Lane & Scott, prs. ⟨1898⟩
cover-title, 17 p. 23½ᶜᵐ.
No. 341 in the U. S. Supreme court, October term, 1897.
1. Railroad law—U. S.—Cases. 2. Railroads—U. S.—Rates. 3. Trusts, Industrial—Law. I. Johnson, John G. II. Pennsylvania railroad company, appellee. III. Joint traffic association, appellee. IV. United States, appellant.
13-12428

NL 0449945   DLC

Logan, James Addison, 1879-   comp.
Aeronautical notes: a collection of photographs. Submitted by Major James A. Logan, jr., Q.M.C., Military observer with the French army.
Photographs mounted on sheets 31 x 21½cm.

NL 0449946   DNW

Logan, James Addison, 1879-
Asphyxiating gas. Translated from Journal de Geneve 13, July 1915. Typewritten manuscript 1915.
5 p. 33 cm.
Article dealing with the difference of the French and German asphyxiating gases.

NL 0449947   DNW

Logan, James Addison, 1879-   comp.
Collection of photographs showing certain phases of the operation of the sanitary service in the French army during the European war.
Photographs mounted on sheets in binder 34½ x 23 cm., and accompanied by typewritten descriptive data.

NL 0449948   DNW

Logan, James Addison, 1879-
Collection of photographs showing some of the different types of guns used in anti-aircraft work and some of the improvised mountings. Submitted by Major James A. Logan, military observer, with the French army. Typewritten manuscript, 1916.
19 photos. mounted on sheets 31 x 21 cm. with descriptive letterpress.

NL 0449949   DNW

VOLUME 338

Logan, James Addison, 1879-   comp.
Collection of photographs showing some of
the different types of transportation employed
in the French army. Submitted by Major James
A. Logan, jr. Military observer with the French
army.
Photographs mounted on sheets 31 x 21.5 cm.

NL 0449950   DNW

Logan, James Addison, 1879-
In the matter of the arbitration of
certain questions under the Luxembourg
protocol of December 25, 1918. The ar-
bitrator's decisions upon questions in
dispute and submitted by the French and
German governments for arbitration. James
A. Logan, jr., arbitrator. Paris, Printed by
H. Clarke, 1922.
cover-title, 111p. 23cm.
Library, U.S. Dept. of State.
JX688.G3 1921 .A5

NL 0449951   DS CSt-H MH

CS71   Logan, James Allen.
.L82
1942 a   Mills, Harry Willard, 1898-
... Logan family; some items of family history and family
papers concerning a number of early settlers of Maryland
named Logan. Compiled by Harry Willard Mills ... and
associate compilers: Rev. James Allen Logan ... and others.
Washington, D. C., Mills' Lettergram, 1942.

Logan, James Douglas, 1857-
... Report of the Select committee on foreign
railway competition
see under Cape of Good Hope. Parliament.
Legislative council. Select committee on foreign
railway competition.

Logan, James Douglas, 1857-
... Report of the Select committee on the
Railway sick fund board.
see under Cape of Good Hope. Parliament.
Legislative council. Select committee on Railway
sick fund board.

Logan, James Douglas, 1857-

Cape of Good Hope. *Parliament. Legislative council.
Select committee on water-boring and diamond drills.*
... Report of the Select committee on water-boring and
diamond drills. (In continuation of C. 1.—1903) Printed
by order of the Legislative council. May, 1904. Cape
Town, Cape times limited, 1904.

Logan, James H   comp.
Raindrop; a collection of entertaining stories for
young people. 1910.

NL 0449956   OrP

Logan, James Moffat.
Christian science expounded and exposed ₍by₎ J. Moffat
Logan. London, The Kingsgate press ₍1923₎
4 p. l., 7-249 p. 20ᵐ.

1. Christian science.

Library of Congress   BX6955.L75   25-7966

NL 0449957   DLC NN

Logan, James Moffat.
Did Jesus claim to be God? Two sermons, by Rev. J. Moffat
Logan.   London: A. H. Stockwell ₍190-?₎ 32 p. illus.
(port.)   18½cm.

1. Jesus Christ—Divinity.
N.Y.P.L.   August 25, 1942

NL 0449958   NN

HD31   Logan, James P., joint author.
.N482
Newman, William Herman, 1909-
Management of expanding enterprises; report of round
table discussions by leading business and professional men,
by William H. Newman and James P. Logan. ₍Sponsored
by the Columbia University Graduate School of Business₎
New York, Columbia University Press, 1955.

Logan, James Richardson, d. 1869.
Raffles museum and library, *Singapore.*
Catalogue of the Logan philological library, forming a trust
portion of the Raffles library. Singapore, Printed at the
"Straits Times" press, by A. Frois. 1880.

Logan, James Richardson, d. 1869.
The ethnology of the India archipelago
embracing enquiries into the contental relations
of the Indo-Pacific islanders. [Singapore, 1850]
252-347 p.
caption-title.

NL 0449961   OCl

LOGAN, James Richardson, d. 1869.
Ethnology of the Indo-Pacific islands; lan-
guage. 3 pt. in 1 vol. Singapore, printed by
G. M. Frederick, 1851-52.
Journal of the Indian archipelago of eastern
Asia, 1851, vol. V, pp. 211-243, 549-585; 1852,
vol. VI, pp. 653-688.

NL 0449962   MH MiU

Logan, James Richardson, d. 1869, ed.
The Journal of the Indian archipelago and eastern Asia.
v. 1-   ₍1847₎
Singapore, Printed at the Mission press ₍etc.₎ 1847-

Wason   Logan, James Richardson, d. 1869.
AS522   The rocks of Pulo Ubin. ₍Batavia,
B29+   Lange, 1849₎
v.22   43 p. 27cm. (Verhandelingen van het
pt.9   Bataviaasch Genootschap van Kunsten en
Wetenschappen, deel 22 ₍9. stuk₎)

NL 0449964   NIC

Logan, James Venable, 1901-
... The poetry and aesthetics of Erasmus Darwin, by James
Venable Logan. Princeton, Princeton university press, 1936.
4 p. l., 162 p., 1 l. 23ᵐ. (₍Princeton university₎ Princeton studies
in English, ed. by G. H. Gerould. 15)
"Originally presented as a dissertation to the faculty of Princeton
university in candidacy for the degree of doctor of philosophy. It was
accepted ... in June, 1932. It has since been revised, and much has
been added."—Prefatory note.
"Bibliography of the major works": p. ₍149₎-151; "The occasional
poetry": p. ₍152₎-154; "General bibliography": p. ₍155₎-159.
1. Darwin, Erasmus, 1731-1802. I. Title.
36-19815
Library of Congress   PR3396.L6 1936
————— Copy 2.
Copyright A 97791   ₍5₎   821.69

CaBVaU WaWW
NL 0449965   DLC MoU OCl MiU OU OCU ViU OrCS OrU

Logan, James Venable, 1901-
Wordsworthian criticism, a guide and bibliography.
Columbus, Ohio State Univ., 1947.
xii, 304 p. 24 cm. (Graduate School monographs. Contributions
in languages and literature, no. 12. English series, 4)
1. Wordsworth, William, 1770-1850. 2. Wordsworth, William,
1770-1850—Bibl. 3. Criticism—Hist. I. Title. (Series: Ohio.
State University, Columbus. Graduate School studies. Series: Ohio.
State University, Columbus. Contributions in languages and litera-
ture, no. 12. Series: Ohio. State University, Columbus. Contributions in languages and literature. English series, 4)
PR5888.L6   821.71   48-394*
OrU CaBVaU
NL 0449966   DLC NIC NN OClU PSt ODW OrU ViU TxU ICU

Logan, James W., joint comp.
Nichols, Egbert Ray, 1884-   comp.
... Arbitration and the National labor relations board, com-
piled by Egbert Ray Nichols and James W. Logan ... New
York, The H. W. Wilson company, 1937.

Logan, Jean Wilson, 1875-1935.
Teacher training in Detroit, by Jean W. Logan.
₍Detroit?₎ 1921.
2 p.l., 47 numb.l. incl. mounted diagr. 29ᶜᵐ.
Mimeographed.
"Bibliography and other sources of information": numb.
leaves 2-3.
1. Wayne university, Detroit. College of education—
Hist. 2. Teachers, Training of—Detroit.
LB1891.D61L8

NL 0449968   MiU

Logan, Jean Zacharie
see Logan, Johann Zacharias.

TL789   Logan, Jeffrey, ed.
.C66
The Complete book of outer space. ₍Editor: Jeffrey Logan₎
New York₎ Gnome Press ₍1953₎

Logan, Jessie E   ed.
Goodly company, a book of quotations and proverbs for
character development, by Jessie E. Logan ... with introductions by Carrie E. Scott ... and Clara W. Nieman ... Chicago, Beckley-Cardy company ₍1930₎
221 p. front. 19ᵐ.
1. Quotations. 2. Character. I. Title.
Library of Congress   PN6081.L6   31-513
————— Copy 2.
Copyright A 32452   ₍3₎   808.8

OrP Wa CaBVa OrMonO
NL 0449971   DLC NcGU OClh OCl MB WaS Or WaSp IdB

Logan, Joannes Murdoch
see
Logan, John Murdoch.

VOLUME 338

Logan, Johann Zacharias, tr.
Shelekhov, Grigorii *Ivanovich* 1748-1795.
Grigori Schelechof russischen kaufmanns erste und zweyte reise von Ochotsk in Siberien durch den östlichen ocean nach den küsten von Amerika in den jahren 1783. bis 1789. Nebst umständlicher beschreibung der von ihm neuentdeckten inseln Küktak, Afagnak und mehrerer andrer, zu welchen selbst der berühmte Cap. Cook nicht gekommen und die sich der russischen herrschaft unterworfen haben. Aus dem russischen übersetzt. von J. Z. Logan. St. Petersburg, J. Z. Logan, 1793.

NL 0449974   DLC-P4

4Z
1247
Logan, Johann Zacharias.
Livres françois, anglois, jtaliens, etc. Chez Jean Zacharie Logan, libraire... St. Petersbourg, 1786.
90 p.

Part of title covered by label: "Chr. Pornow, librairie of pres du Pontbleu, no. 354."

NL 0449974   DLC-P4

Logan, John
... John Logan versus William Wallace Young, and others *n.p., 1846?*
cover-title, 16 p. 22½cm.

At head of title: In Chancery.

NL 0449975   MH-L

Logan, Capt. John
Analogia honorum: or, A treatise of honour and nobility, according to the laws and customes of England. Collected out of the most authentick authors, both ancient and modern. In two parts. The first containing honour military, and relateth to war. The second, honour civil, and relateth to court and city. Illustrated with variety of sculptures sutable to the several subjects. London, Printed by T. Roycroft, 1677.
181, (8) p. plates, ports. 35½cm. *With* Guillim, John. A display of heraldry. 5th ed. London, 1679.

"The book is illustrated with a portrait of the King, and portraits of a peer of each degree in their robes, engraved by Edw. Le Davis, A. Bloteling, R. White, &c.; the arms of the nobility, and of a select number of knights, esquires, and gentry." *cf.* Moule's Bibliotheca heraldica.
Wood attributes the authorship of this treatise to Richard Blome. *cf.* Dict. nat. biog.

1. Heraldry. 2. England—Nobility. I. Blome, Richard, d. 1705, supposed author.
10-15847

Library of Congress   CR19.C8

NL 0449977   DLC CtY

Logan, Capt. John. Analogia honorum: or, a treatise of honour and nobility, according to the laws and customs of England. London, 1724. fo. (*With* Guillim, J., Display of heraldry.)

NL 0449978   MdBP MH OC1

FOR OTHER EDITIONS
SEE MAIN ENTRY

Logan, Capt. John.

Guillim, John, 1565-1621.
A display of heraldry. By John Guillim ... The 6th ed. Improv'd with large additions of many hundred coats of arms, under their respective bearings, with good authorities from the Ashmolean library, Sir George Mackenzie, &c. With his tract of precedency, containing all his rules, observations, arguments, and chief instances. To which is added, A treatise of honour military and civil, according to the laws and customs of England. By Capt. John Logan. Illustrated with the arms, crests, supporters, and motto's of the royal family, and nobility: the arms of the sees of the English bishops, and several of the gentry... London, Printed by T. W. for R. and J. Bonwicke and R. Wilkin, and J. Walthoe and T. Ward, 1724.

Logan, John, minister of Alloa.
A sermon preached before His Grace James duke of Queensberry, Her Majesties High Commissioner, and the honourable Estates of Parliament, in the New church of Edinburgh, upon the 27 of October 1706 ... Edinburgh, Printed by the heirs and successors of Andrew Anderson, 1706.
14 p. 20x16cm.

Book-plate of Robert A. S. Macfie.

NL 0449980   CLU-C

Logan, John, *of Georgetown, D. C.?*
The western woodpecker, being the journal of a journey performed in the months of February, March and April, 1818. From Georgetown, in the District of Columbia, to the Miami, in the state of Ohio, and back again. Georgetown, D. C., For the author, 1818.
38 pp. 12°.

Subject entries: 1. Maryland—Descr. & trav. 2. Ohio—Descr. & trav.
2-6385

Library of Congress, no.   F516.L83.
———— Copy 2. [Miscellaneous pamphlets, v. 569, no. 16]
———— Copy 3. [Miscellaneous pamphlets, v. 875, no. 9]

NL 0449981   DLC

Logan, John, 1748-1788.
The Christian's victory over death.
(In Fish, Henry Clay. History and repository of pulpit eloquence. v. 2, p. 294-301)

NL 0450001   RPB

Logan, John, 1748-1788.
Elements of the philosophy of history. Pt. 1
Edinburgh, 1781

NL 0450002   PPL NNC

Logan, John, 1748-1788, supposed author.

Philpot, Charles
An introduction to the literary history of the fourteenth and fifteenth centuries. London, Printed for T. Cadell jr. and W. Davies, 1798.

821
L8279
C1
Logan, John, 1748-1788.
Poems. London, Printed for T. Cadell, 1781.
vii, 118p. 21cm.

CU-A NNUT InU CaBVaU TxUNcD CtY
NL 0450004   TxU NcD ICU ScU CSmH ICN MiU OU IU NjP

Logan, John, 1748-1788.
Poems. 2d ed. London, Printed for T. Cadell, 1782.

NL 0450005   MH

Logan, John, 1748-1788.
The poems of John Logan ...
(In Chalmers, Alexander, ed. The works of the English poets ... London, 1810. 24cm. v. 18, p. (471-72)
12-3696
Library of Congress   PR1173.C5 vol. 18

NL 0450006   DLC WaS

Logan, John, 1748-1788.
Poems, by the Rev. John Logan ... With a life of the author ... Philadelphia: Published by Edward Earle. William Fry, printer. 1814.
2 p. l., 139 p. 14½cm.

Library of Congress   PR3541.L7 1814   31-25884
821.69

NL 0450007   NNUT WaS DLC

821
L828p
1805
Logan, John, 1748-1788.
Poems; and Runnamede, a tragedy. New ed. with a life of the author. Edinburgh, Printed for Bell & Bradfute, 1805.
xxxiv, 189p. port. 16cm.

NL 0450008   IU WU ICN ViW OU

Logan, John, 1748-1788.
Poems; and Runnamede, a tragedy. By the Rev. John Logan... A new edition with a life of the author.
Edinburgh, Printed for Gavin Cunningham, 1807.
xxx, 194 p. front. (port.) 10.5cm.

NL 0450009   NNUT

Rare Book
Collection
PR3541
.L7
P6
1812
Logan, John, 1748-1788.
Poems, and Runnamede, a tragedy. By the Rev. John Logan, F.R.S. Edin., one of the ministers of Leith. With the life of the author. *quot.* Edinburgh, Printed for Bell & Bradfute, William Blackwood, John Anderson & co., Edinburgh; and John Murray, London, 1812.
xxxii, 206 p. 17 cm.
Runnamede, p.93-206, has special t.-p.

I. Title: Runnamede, a tragedy.

NL 0450010   NcU InU OC1 MH

LOGAN, John, 1748-1788.
Poems; and Runnamede, a Tragedy With a Life of the Author. L. 1825.
64°. (University ed.)
"Life", pp. v-xvi.   8.105

NL 0450011   MH

Logan, John, 1748-1788.
Poems; and Runnamede, a tragedy. With a life of the author. London, Jones & Co., 184?.
viii, 27 p. nar. 12°. (In: Cabinet edition of the British poets. London, 1847. nar. 12°, v. 3)

NL 0450012   NN

Logan, John, 1748-1788.

Scott, John, 1730-1783.
The poems of Scott, and Logan. Chiswick, Press of C. Whittingham *1822*

VOLUME 338

●PR1171
.A5　Logan, John, 1748-1788.
v.11　　The poetical works of John Logan ... To
　　　　which is prefixed, the life of the author ...
　　　　Edinburgh, Printed by Mundell and son, 1795.
　　　　(In Anderson, Robert, ed. A complete edition
　　　　of the poets of Great Britain. London [1792-95]
　　　　24cm. v.11, p. [1025]-1049)
　　　　Printed in double columns.

NL 0450014　　MB NN MdBP OU

Logan, John, 1748-1788.
　　...Poetical works...collated with the best
editions by Thomas Park... Lond., J. Sharpe,
1807.
　　65 p. 1 pl.

　　Bound with The poetical works of Thomas Parnell,
and The poetical works of Tobias Smollett.

NL 0450015　　MiD MH

Logan, John, 1748-1788.
　　The poetical works of John Logan. Collated with the
best editions: by Thomas Park ... London, Suttaby,
Evance, and Fox, 1813.
　　iv, [5]-64 p. front. 13½cm. (In The works of the British poets, collated
by T. Park. v. 33. 1828)

　　　　　　　　　　　　　　　　　　　　　　　12-2327

　　　Library of Congress　　PR1173.B62

NL 0450016　　DLC

DS　[Logan, John] 1748-1788.
473.5　　A review of the principal charges against
A1　Warren Hastings, esquire, late governor general
　　of Bengal. London, Printed for J. Stockdale,
　　and J. Murray, 1788.
　　111 p. 20½cm.
　　Fourth in a collection of six pamphlets bound
together with binder's title: Warren Hastings.

　　1. Hastings, Warren, 1732-1818. 2. India -
Hist. - British occupation, 1765- 　　3. India -
Pol. & govt. - 1765- 　　I. Title.

NL 　　CLU DLC ICN MH NNC MdBP MnU CtY MH-BA
0450017

[Logan, John] 1748-1788.
　　Runnamede, a tragedy ... London, T. Cadell; [etc., etc.]
1783.
　　v, [1] p., 1 l., 101 p. 21½cm.
　　[Longe, F. Collection of plays. v. 92, no. 5]

　　1. Gt. Brit.—Hist.—John, 1199-1216—Drama. 　I. Title.
　　　　　　　　　　　　　　　　　　　　　　25-16622
　　Library of Congress　　PR1241.L6 vol. 92

NL 0450018　　DLC CSmH ICU CtY IU NcD MH

Logan, John, 1748-1788.
　　Runnamede. London, 1783.
　　(In Three centuries of drama: English,
1751-1800)

　　Microprint.

　　1. Gt. Brit.—Hist.—John, 1199-1216—
Drama. I. Title.

NL 0450019　　MoU

Wm　[LOGAN, JOHN] 1748-1788.
L828　　Runnamede, a tragedy ...
783rb　　London:Printed for G.Robinson,Nº 25,Pater-
　　Noster-Row;And W.Creech,Edinburgh.1784.
　　v.[1]p.,1ℓ.,101p. 21cm.

NL 0450020　　TxU MiU

Logan, John, 1748-1788.
　　[Select poems of] John Logan.
　　(In The works of the British poets ... Philadelphia, 1819-23. 15^{cm}.
　　v. 37, p. [241]-252)

　　　　　　　　　　　　　　　　　　　　　11-29532
　　　Library of Congress　　PR1173.B64

NL 0450021　　DLC DGU ViU

BX　Logan, John, 1748-1788.
9178　　Sermons. Edinburgh, Bell & Bradfute, 1790.
.L7S4　　427 p.

NL 0450022　　MoU

Logan, John, 1748-1788.
　　Sermons. 3d. ed.　Edinb., 1793.
　　2 v.　8°.

NL 0450023　　CtY

Logan, John, 1748-1788.
　　Sermons. 4th edition. Vol. 2.
　　Edinburgh. Bell & Bradfute. 1800. viii, 427 pp. 8°.　5456.58

F4396

NL 0450024　　MB

Logan, John, 1748-1788.
　　Sermons, by the late Reverend John Logan ...
one of the ministers of Leith. 1st Amer., from
the 4th Eng. ed. Boston, Printed for Caleb
Bingham, No.44, Cornhill; David Carlyle, Printer,
Cambridge Street, 1804.
　　499p. 22cm.

NL 0450025　　ScU MB OClWHi ODW NjR MH CtY N RPN NRCR

B X　Logan, John, 1748-1788.
9178　　Sermons, by the late Rev. John Logan...including
.L82　　a complete detail of the service of a communion
　　Sunday, according to the usage of the Church of
　　Scotland...5th ed. To which is prefixed, a life of
　　the author... Edinburgh, Printed for Bell & Brad-
　　fute; and sold by Longman [etc.] London, 1807.
　　2 v.　22cm.

NL 0450026　　DNC

Logan, John, 1748-1788.
　　Sermons, by the late Rev. John Logan ... one of the ministers
of Leith. Including a complete detail of the service of a communion Sunday, according to the usage of the Church of Scotland ... The 6th ed. To which is now prefixed, a life of the
author ... Edinburgh, Bell & Bradfute; [etc., etc.] 1819.
　　2 v. 21½cm.

　　1. Church of Scotland—Sermons. 2. Sermons, English—Scotland.
　　　　　　　　　　　　　　　　　　　　　45-25373
　　Library of Congress　　BX9178.L7S38　1819

NL 0450027　　DLC CLamB

Logan, John, 1748-1788.
　　Sermons and expository lectures. By the late Rev.
John Logan ... with an introduction, by Rev. D. D. Whedon, D. D., ed. by "The Minister's library association."
6th ed. New York, D. Appleton and company, 1855.
　　188 p. 24^{cm}.

　　1. Whedon, Daniel Denison, 1808-1885. II. Minister's library association, ed.
　　　　　　　　　　　　　　　　　　　　　18-4912
　　Library of Congress　　BX9178.L7S4

NL 0450028　　DLC MiU

Logan, John, 1748-1788.
　　Sermons, by ... John Logan ... including a
complete detail of the service of a communion
Sunday, according to the usage of the Church of
Scotland ... A new ed. To which is prefixed,
A memoir of the life and writings of the author.
... v. 1　Edinburg, Printed for Macredie,
Skelley and co., [etc., etc.] 1822-
　　1 v.　front. (port.)　22 cm.
　　1. Sermons, English. 2. Lord's supper.

NL 0450029　　CU

Logan, John, 1748-1788.
　　Sermons, including a complete detail of the
service of a communion sabbath, according to
the usage of the Church of Scotland. With a
life of the author. New ed. Edinburgh, T.
Nelson, 1839.
　　Port.

NL 0450030　　MH

WV17　Logan, John, 1748-1788.
L83　　Sermons, lectures, and communion service
S　　according to the usage of the Church of
　　Scotland; by the Rev. John Logan ... To which
　　is prefixed, a short account of the life of
　　the author ... A correct edition. Edinburgh:
　　Printed for A.Wallace & co.[etc.,etc.]1814.
　　xiii,11,[9]-386p. 22cm.

NL 0450031　　NNUT MWA

Logan, John, 1923-
　　Cycle for Mother Cabrini; [poems]　New York, Grove
Press [1955]
　　51 p.　21 cm.　(An Evergreen book of poetry, E-19)

　　I. Title.

　　PS3523.O344C9　　　　811.5　　　　55-8628 ‡

NL 　　PIm ViU PP PV InU TxU
0450032　　DLC FMU CU OrU LU NN OCl ICU MB MiU

Logan, John A.
　　Echoes from the hills of the Mammoth cave
country. Bowling Green, Ky., Porter-Coombs
printing co., 1930.

NL 0450033　　KyBgW

HD　Logan, John A
9015　　Food distribution in Europe. [Washington,
A3L6　　D.C., National Association of Food Chains,
　　1950]
　　19p. 23cm.

　　√1.Food supply - Europe. √I.Title. √LC

NL 0450034　　CLSU

VOLUME 338

LOGAN, John Alexander.
Activated-sludge studies -- purification at high rates.

Typewritten.   28 x 21 cm.   Charts,diagrs.and other illustr.
Thesis,S.D.- Harvard University,1942.

NL 0450035   MH

Logan, John Alexander, M.E.
Practical mining in South Africa. For the use of mine managers, mining engineers ... and all those interested in mining operations generally. By John Alexander Logan ... Durban, J. Jones, 1908.
6 p. l., 252 p. front. (port.) 22ᶜᵐ.

1. Mining engineering.

9–16227

Library of Congress   TN145.L75

NL 0450036   DLC ICJ

Logan, *Mrs.* John Alexander
see
Logan, Mary Simmerson (Cunningham) 1838–1923.

Logan, John Alexander, 1826-1886.
The admission of Dakota. Speeches...
February 3, and February 5, 1886.
Wash., 1886

YA5000   (Congressional speeches,by author)
J 17

NL 0450038   DLC

LOGAN, John Alexander, 1826-1886.
Argument before the Senate on the impeachment of Andrew Johnson, President of the United States. Washington, 1868.
pp. 55.   US 6317.1.5

NL 0450039   MH PPL OClWHi ICN NN

Logan, John Alexander, 1826-1886.
Belligerency of Cuba. Speech of Hon. John A. Logan, of Illinois, in the House of representatives, February 14, 1870. ₍Washington: Printed at the Congressional globe office, 1870?₎
8 p. 22½ᶜᵐ.
Caption title.   DLC YA 5000.J17
With his Remarks ... upon Gov. Bissell's inaugural. Springfield. 1857.

1. Cuba—For. rel.—U.S. 2. U.S.—For. rel.—Cuba.
3. Cuba—Hist.—Insurrection, 1868–1878. I. Title.

NL 0450040   ViU DLC MnHi

Logan, John Alexander, 1826-1886.
Champion Blaine and Logan songster
see under title

Logan, John A₍lexander₎ 1826–1886.
The Chicago fire. Speech of Hon. John A. Logan, of Illinois, in the Senate of the United States, January 16, 1872. ₍Washington, Congressional globe office₎ 1872.
7 p. 24ᶜᵐ.
Caption title.

1. Chicago—Fire. 1871.

4-33422†

Library of Congress   F548.42.L83

NL 0450042   DLC ViU

Logan, John Alexander, 1826-1886.
A claim of the state of Illinois, with other western and southern states, based upon the five per cent clause of the act of admission into the union, for land entered by the location of military land warrants within their limits. Washington, 1878.
30p.

YA 8756

NL 0450043   DLC MnHi

Logan, John Alexander, 1826-1886.
The collection of the revenue. Correspondence of Hon. John A. Logan, and the advisory board of the Civil service. ₍Washington? 1872₎
4 p. 23ᶜᵐ.

1. Revenue—U. S.   I. U. S. Civil service commission, 1871–1875.

CA 11–546 Unrev'd

Library of Congress   HJ5021.L7

NL 0450044   DLC

LOGAN, John Alexander, 1826-1886.
The Currency- Specie Payments-Speech, in the Senate, Jan.19,1874. Wash. 1874.
f. (1), pp. 30.   Econ 4618.74.
                        Tr. 1181.(7).

NL 0450045   MH MnHi

LOGAN, John Alexander, 1826-1886.
The Democratic party, Did it abolish slavery and put down the Rebellion? Over-whelming reply of John A. Logan to Ex-Senator Lyman Trumbull. n.p., ₍1880₎.
pp. 16
Without title-page. Caption title.

NL 0450046   MH

Logan, John Alexander, 1826-1886.
Election of Senator Caldwell. Speech of Hon. John A. Logan, of Illinois, delivered in the Senate of the United States, March 12 and 13, 1873. Washington: Printed at the Congressional globe office, 1873.
32 p. 22½ᶜᵐ.
With his Remarks ... upon Gov. Bissell's inaugural. Springfield. 1857.

1 Caldwell, Alexander, 1830–1917. 2. U.S.—Pol. & govt.—1869–1877.

NL 0450047   ViU

Logan, John Alexander, 1826-1886.
Eulogy...on Senator Chandler...Jan. 28, 1880.
Wash., 1880.

YA5000   (Congressional speeches,by author)
J 17

NL 0450048   DLC

Logan, John Alexander, 1826–1886.
Finance—currency. Speech of Hon. John A. Logan, of Illinois, in the United States Senate, March 17, 1874, in reply to Senator Schurz. Washington. Govt. print. off., 1874.
50 p. incl. tables. 21½ᶜᵐ.

1. Currency question—U. S.—Speeches in Congress. 2. Schurz, Carl, 1829–1906.

Library of Congress   HG525.S4

6—19223

NL 0450049   DLC MnHi

E473
.772
.L82
.L83
Logan, John Alexander, 1826–1886.
Fitz-John Porter. Speech of John A. Logan, of Illinois, in the Senate of the United States, Friday, December 29, 1882, and Tuesday and Wednesday, January 2 and 3, 1883, on the bill (S. 1844) for the relief of Fitz-John Porter. Washington, 1883.
182 p. port., map. 24cm.
1. Porter, Fitz-John, 1822–1901. 2. Bull Run, 2d battle, 1862.

NL 0450050   ViU DNW OOxM DAU MiD CSmH MH I

Logan, John Alexander, 1826-1886.
Fitz-John Porter. Speech of Hon. John A. Logan, of Illinois, in the Senate of the United States, Thursday, March 13, 1884. Washington ₍Govt. print. off.₎ 1884.
112 p. 23½ᶜᵐ.

1. Porter, Fitz-John, 1822–1901.

12–30015

Library of Congress   E473.772.L83

NL 0450051   DLC MiU OO Nh MnHi

E
179
U11
v.5
no.23
Logan, John Alexander, 1826–1886.
Fitz-John Porter. Speech of Hon. John A. Logan, of Illinois, in the Senate of the United States, Friday, June 25, 1886. Washington, 1886.
48 p. 24cm.

1. Porter, Fitz-John, 1822–1901.

NL 0450052   NIC CSmH

1886
Logan, John Alexander, 1826-1886.
Gen. Logans story of Gen. U. S. Grant.
Washington, Republican, 1885.
12 p. 12°. [National Republican, Oct. 8, 1885]

NL 0450053   DLC

VOLUME 338

Logan, John Alexander, 1826–1886.
The great conspiracy: its origin and history. By John A. Logan. New York, A. R. Hart & co., 1886.
xxviii p., 1 l., 810 p. front., port., maps (part fold.) 23ᶜᵐ.

1. U. S.—Pol. & govt.—Civil war. 2. Slavery in the U. S.   I. Title.

Library of Congress   E459.L83
                                                    2—8027

MtU WaT WaS Or WaSpG I Nh MB MWA PHi NjP
ICRL MeB KMK GU NcD PP PU OrSaW PU–L Wa KU–M DI
OCl OU MiU OCU DNW NBuC NBuHi GAU KyBgW NIC ViN
NL 0450054   DLC CaBVaU DSI NjN PHC ODW OO ViU PPL

E458 Logan, John Alexander, 1826–1886.
.4   ...Great speech of Major Gen. John A. Logan,
.L8   delivered at Carbondale, Ill., Oct. 1, 1864. ₍Chi-
Lincoln   cago?1864?₎
            8 p. 21cm.
            At head of caption title: Chicago Tribune cam-
        paign document, no. 3.

            1. U.S.—Hist.—Civil war—Addresses, sermons, etc.

NL 0450055   ICU

YA   Logan, John Alexander, 1826–1886.
20407   The great speech ... June 30, 1866.   n. p., 1886?
            16 p.

NL 0450056   DLC

E   Logan, John Alexander, 1826–1886.
464   Great Union speech by Major Gen. John A.
C585   Logan, delivered in Chicago, Monday evening,
v.76   August 10th, 1863. Chicago, Tribune Book and
no.10   Job Printing Office, 1863.
            12 p. 25cm.

            1. U. S.—   Pol. & govt.—Civil War—
            Addresses, ess   ays, lectures.

NL 0450057   NIC

Logan, John Alexander, 1826–1886.
Great Union speech, by Major Gen. John A. Logan, delivered in Chicago ... August 10th, 1863. Chicago. Tribune Printing Office. 1863. 16 pp. 22.5 cm.

D7135 — United States. Hist. Civil War. Disc. of prin.

NL 0450058   MB IHi CtY NN NBuC

J   LOGAN, JOHN ALEXANDER, 1826–1886.
5835   Impeachment of the president; speech...
.44   in the House...February 22, 1868. Washing-
no.27   ton, F. & J. Rives & G.A. Bailey, 1868.
            8p. 25cm.

NL 0450059   ICN

Logan, John Alexander, 1826–1886.
In answer to the letter of General W. T. Sherman. Speech of Hon. John A. Logan, of Illinois, delivered in the House of representatives, March 29, 1870. Washington: F. & J. Rives & Geo. A. Bailey, reporters and printers of the debates of Congress, 1870.
14 p.
Caption title: Reduction of the army.
With his Remarks ... upon Gov. Bissell's inaugural. Springfield, 1857.
1. U. S.—Army. I. Sherman, William Tecumseh, 1820–1891. II. Title. III. Title: Reduction of the army.

NL 0450060   ViU

Logan, John Alexander, 1826–1886.
Independence of Cuba. Speech of Hon. John A. Logan, of Illinois, delivered in the House of representatives, June 15, 1870. Washington: F. & J. Rives & Geo. A. Bailey, reporters and printers of the debates of Congress, 1870.
8 p. 22½cm.
With his Remarks ... upon Gov. Bissell's inaugural. Springfield, 1857.   YA 5000 J17
1. Cuba—Hist.—Insurrection, 1868–1878. 2. U.S.—For. rel.—Cuba. 3. Cuba—For. rel.—U. S. I. Title.

NL 0450061   ViU DLC OC1WHi MB MnHi

Logan, John Alexander, 1826–1886.
Internal-revenue educational fund. Speech of Hon. John A. Logan, of Illinois, delivered in the Senate of the United States, Thursday, March 16, 1882. Washington, 1882.
22 p. 20½ᵐ.

1. Education—U. S.—Finance. 2. Education and state. 3. ₍Grants to schools—U. S.₎ I. Title.
                                                    E 15—1446

U. S. Off. of educ. Library   LC80.L8
for Library of Congress   ₍a41b1₎

NL 0450062   DHEW

LOGAN, John Alexander, 1826–1886.
The issues of the day. Address delivered at Marion, Ill., Monday, Oct. 4, 1886. [Chicago, Brown, Pettibone & Co., Printers, 1886].

pp. 24.
Without title-page. Caption title.

NL 0450063   MH

Logan, John Alexander, 1826–1886.
J.C. Abbott's claim to a seat in the Senate from North Carolina. Speech of ...John A. Logan, of Illinois, in the Senate of the United States, April 11, 1872. Washington, F. & J. Rives & Geo.A. Bailey, reporters and printers of the debates of Congress, 1872.
Cover-title, 23 p. 24cm.

NL 0450064   IHi DLC ViU

LOGAN, John A[lexander], 1826–1886.
Letter of Gen. John A. Logan, accepting the nomination for vice-president. Boston, Republican State Committee, 1884.

pp. 15.

NL 0450065   MH NN

Logan, John Alexander, 1826–1886.
Letters of Mrs. John A. Logan (Oct. 6, 1921) and Gen. John A. Logan (June 5, 1884) to C. B. Watson
    see under Logan, Mary Simmerson (Cunningham) 1838–1923.

Logan, John Alexander, 1826–1886.
Letters to Judge David Davis and Mrs. Davis ...
    see under title [supplement]

Logan, John Alexander, 1826–1886.
Memorial addresses on the life and Character of John Alexander Logan ...
    see under U. S. 49th Cong., 2d sess., 1886–1887. Senate.

E   Logan, John Alexander, 1826–1886.
464   Oration at the tomb of General U. S. Grant,
R29   Riverside Park, N. Y. May 31st, 1886. Wash-
v.15   ington, Gibson Brothers, printers, 1886.
no.10   15 p. 25cm.   YA 19067   4

            1. Grant, Uly   sses Simpson, Pres. U. S.,
            1822–1885.

DLC
NL 0450069   NIC I CU MiD OO OC1WHi Nh ICN WyU

Logan, John Alexander, 1826–1886.
... Oration of General John A. Logan ... delivered upon the occasion of the decoration of Union soldiers' graves at the National cemetery, Arlington, Va., on Memorial day, May 30, 1870. Washington, Office of the Grand army journal, 1870.
cover-title, 12 p. 22½ᵐ.

1. Memorial day addresses.
                                                    18–2393

Library of Congress   E642.L83

NL 0450070   DLC ViU OC1WHi

Logan, John Alexander, 1826–1886.
Principles of the Democratic party. Speech of General John A. Logan of Illinois, delivered in the House of representatives, July 16, 1868. Washington, D. C., Union Republican congressional committee ₍1868₎
8 p. 23½ᵐ.
Caption title.

1. Campaign literature, 1868—Republican. 2. Democratic party.
                                                    11–32555

Library of Congress   E666.L83

NL 0450071   DLC DHU NIC ViU OC1WHi

Logan, John Alexander, 1826–1886.
Principles of the Democratic party. Speech of Gen. John A. Logan of Illinois, in the House of representatives, July 16, 1868. Fourth edition: one hundredth thousand. Washington: Published by the United press association, 1868.
cover-title, 8 p. 22½cm.
With his Remarks .. upon Gov. Bissell's inaugural. Springfield, 1857.
1. Democratic party. 2. Campaign literature, 1868—Republican.

NL 0450072   ViU

Logan, John Alexander, 1826–1886.
Reconstruction. Speech of Hon. John A. Logan, of Ill., in the House of Representatives, July 12, 1867 on the supplementary reconstruction bill, and in reply to Mr. Robinson, of New York. [Washington, Chronicle print] n. d.
16 p.

NL 0450073   OC1WHi

Logan, John Alexander, 1826–1886.
Reconstruction. Speech of Hon. J. A. Logan, of Illinois, in the House of representatives, July 11, 1867, on the supplementary reconstruction bill, and in reply to Hon. William E. Robinson, of New York ... ₍Washington, Printed at the Great republic office, 1867₎
7 p. 24ᵐ.
Caption title.
Published by the Union Republican congressional committee, Washington, D. C.

1. Reconstruction—Speeches in Congress. I. Republican congressional committee.
                                                    11–34237

Library of Congress   E668.L83

NL 0450074   DLC ViU MnHi CSmH

VOLUME 338

Logan, John Alexander, 1826–1886.
Rede des general John A. Logan, von Illinois, gehalten im Repräsentantenhause am 16. juli 1868. Die prinzipien der Demokratischen partei. ₍Washington? 1868?₎

8 p. 22½ᶜᵐ.
Caption title.

1. Democratic party. 2. Campaign literature, 1868—Republican.

12-9023

Library of Congress E670.L83

NL 0450075 DLC

Logan, John Alexander, 1826–1886.
... Rede des general-majors John A. Logan, bei seiner rückkehr nach Illinois nach der einnahme von Vicksburg ... Cincinnati, O., Gedruckt in der office der "Cincinnati union," 1863.

32 p. 22½ᶜᵐ. (Loyale bekanntmachungen der National Union's association von Ohio. no. IV)
Berichtet von "Mack" vom "Cincinnati commercial."

1. U. S.—Hist.—Civil war—Addresses, sermons, etc.

11-27442

Library of Congress E458.3.L851

NL 0450076 DLC OC1WHi

LOGAN, John Alexander, 1826–1886.
Reduction of the army. Speech in the House of Representatives, March 10, 1870. ₍Washington, 1870.₎

pp. 15.
Without title-page. Caption title.

NL 0450077 MH MnHi OC1WHi ViU

ar W
32094   Logan, John Alexander, 1826–1886.
v.6   Relations between the Senate and executive departments. Speech in the Senate of the United States, Friday, March 26, 1886. Washington, 1886.

11 p. 23cm.

No. 10 in a vol. lettered: Political science pamphlets, 6.
1. U. S.—Executive departments.
2. U. S. Congress. Senate.

NL 0450078 NIC MnHi MH OC1WHi

Logan, John Alexander, 1826–1886.
Remarks of John A. Logan, of Franklin county, in the House of representatives of Illinois, January 12–13th, 1857, upon Gov. Bissell's inaugural. Springfield [Ill.] Lamphier & Walker, printers, 1857.

20 p. 21 1|2 cm.

1. Illinois. Governor, 1857–1860 (William H. Bissell)

NL 0450079 CSmH NcU

Logan, John Alexander, 1826–1886.
Remarks of John A. Logan, of Franklin county, in the House of representatives of Illinois, January 12–13th, 1857, upon Gov. Bissell's inaugural. Springfield: Lanphier & Walker, printers, 1857.
29 p. 22½ᶜᵐ
With this are bound: Relief of the suffering poor of the South. Washington, 1867; and his Reconstruction. ₍Washington, 1867;₎ Remarks ... on favoritism in the sale of government bonds. Washington, 1868; Impeachment of the president. Washington, 1868; Argument ... on the impeach-

Continued in next column

Continued from preceding column

ment of Andrew Johnson. Washington, 1868; Speech ... in answer to Mr. Van Wyck's defense of the Printing bureau of the Treasury department. ₍n.p., 1868?₎; Principles of the Democratic party. Washington, 1868; Speech ... against bond subsidies to eastern division Pacific railroad. ₍Washington,186–?₎; Tenure of office. Washington, 1869; Removal of the capital. Washington, 1870; Belligerency of Cuba. ₍Washington, 1870?₎; Reduction of the army. ₍Washington, 1870?₎; In answer to the letter of General W.T.Sherman. Washington, 1870; oration ... on Memorial day. Washington, 1870; Independence of Cuba. Washington, 1870; The Chicago fire. ₍Washington, 1872?₎; J.C.Abbott's claim to a seat in the .... Senate from North

Carolina. Washington, 1872; Speech ... in reply to Senator Sumner's attack on the administration of President Grant. ₍Washington, 1872?₎ and Election of Senator Caldwell. Washington, 1873.

1. Bissell, William Henry, 1811–1860. 2. Illinois—Pol. & govt.—1775–1865. 3. Illinois·Governor, 1811–1860 (William Henry Bissell)

NL 0450082 ViU

Logan, John Alexander, 1826–1886.
Remarks of Hon. John A. Logan, of Illinois, on favoritism in the sale of government bonds; delivered in the House of representatives, February 20, 1868. Washington, Published by the United press association, 1868.
8 p. 22½cm.
With his Remarks ... upon Gov. Bissell's inaugural. Springfield, 1857.

1. Bonds—U.S. 2 U.S.—Pol. & govt.—1865–1869. I. Title: Favoritism in the sale of government bonds.

NL 0450083 ViU DHU DLC

YA5000
J 17   Logan, John Alexander, 1826–1886.
Removal of the Capital. Speech delivered in the House of representatives Jan. 22, 1870. Washington, 1870.
16 p. (Congressional speeches, by author)

NL 0450084 DLC

Logan, John Alexander, 1826–1886.
Removal of the capital. Speech of Hon. John A. Logan, of Illinois, delivered in the House of representatives, January 22, 1870. Washington: F. & J. Rives & Geo. A. Bailey, reporters and printers of the debates of Congress, 1870.
16 p. 22½cm.
With his Remarks ... upon Gov. Bissell's inaugural. Springfield, 1857.

1. U.S.—Capital. 2. Washington, D.C.—Hist. I. Title.

NL 0450085 ViU MnHi MH

Logan, John Alexander, 1826–1886.
Self-government in Louisiana. Speech of Hon. John A. Logan, of Illinois, in the Senate of the United States, January 13 and 14, 1875. Washington, Govt. print. off., 1875.
48 p. 21½ᶜᵐ.

1. Reconstruction—Louisiana. I. Title.

18-8830

Library of Congress F375.L83

NL 0450086 DLC LU PHi PU MnHi

Logan, John Alexander, 1826–1886.
...Speech...Washington,1883.

NL 0450087 DSI

Logan, John Alexander, 1826–1886.
Speech ... against bond subsidies to Eastern division, Pacific railroad. [n.p., Powell & O'Brien,printers,1869?]
8p. 21cm.
Caption title.

NL 0450088 CtY IHi ViU

AC901
.M5   Logan, John Alexander, 1826–1886.
Speech ... delivered at Salem, Ill., July 4, 1886.
11 p. (Miscellaneous pamphlets, 484:4)

NL 0450089 DLC

Logan, John Alexander, 1826–1886.
Speech in Senate of U. S., April 11, 1872. [North Carolina senatorship] Wash., 1872.
8°

NL 0450090 MnHi

Logan, John Alexander, 1826–1886.
Speech of Hon. John A. Logan, of Illinois, in the House of representatives, March 11 and 12, 1868, in answer to Mr. Van Wyck's defense of the Printing bureau of the Treasury department. ₍n.p., 1868?₎
8 p. 22½cm.
Caption title.
With his Remarks ... upon Gov. Bissell's inaugural. Springfield, 1857.
1. Currency question—U.S.—Speeches in Congress. 2. U.S.—Pol. & govt.—1865–1869. I. Van Wyck, Charles Henry, 1824–1895.

NL 0450091 ViU

J
5835   LOGAN, JOHN ALEXANDER, 1826–1886.
.023   Speech of Hon. John A.Logan, of Illinois, in the Senate of the United States, April 15, 1879. [Washington,1879] YA5000
16p.   J17

Binder's title: American politics, 1866-1909.
Caption title.

NL 0450092 ICN CSmH OFH DLC

J
5835   LOGAN, JOHN ALEXANDER, 1826–1886.
.023   Speech of Hon. John A.Logan, of Illinois, in the Senate of the United States, June 3, 1872; in reply to Senator Sumner's attack on the administration of President Grant. [Washington,Congressional globe office,1872]
16p.

Binder's title: American politics, 1866-1909.
Caption title.

NL 0450093 ICN DLC MH ViU

SPECIAL COLLECTIONS
B973.7
L828
Logan, John Alexander, 1826–1886.
Speech of Hon. John A. Logan, of Illinois, on the state of the union, delivered in the House of representatives of the United States, February 5, 1861. Washington, Printed by L. Towers, 1861.
16 p. 25cm.

1. U. S. - Pol. & govt. - Civil war.

NL 0450094 NNC ViU MH DI GEU

VOLUME 338

Logan, John Alexander, 1826–1886.
... Speech of Major-General John A. Logan on return to Illinois, after capture of Vicksburg. Reported by "Mack", of the Cincinnati commercial. Cincinnati, C. Clark, printer, 1863.
iv, ₍5₎-32 p. 22½ᵐ. (National union association of Ohio. Loyal publications. no. 4)

1. U. S.—Hist.—Civil war—Addresses, sermons, etc.

Library of Congress   E458.3.L85   2—18875

NL 0450095   DLC NIC DNW IU MB MiU-C

YA5000   Logan, John Alexander, 1826–1886.
J 17   Speech ... on the election of speaker and in reply to Mr. Kellog of Ill. in the House of representatives Dec. 9, 1859.   Washington, 1859.
16 p.   (Congressional speeches, by author)

NL 0450096   DLC

AC901   Logan, John Alexander, 1826–1886.
P75   Tenure of office. Speech of Hon. John A.
v.12   Logan, of Illinois, delivered in the House of
no.8   Representatives, January 8, 1869. Washington, F. & J. Rives & G.A. Bailey, 1869.
16 p. 22 cm.

NL 0450097   ICHi ViU NBu MH MnHi

Logan, John Alexander, 1826–1886.
Vindication of the President. Extract from the speech of Hon. John A. Logan, delivered in the Senate of the United States, June 3, 1872, in reply to Senator Sumner's attack on President Grant's administration. ₍Washington?₎ 1872₎
8 p. 24ᵐ.
Caption title.

1. Sumner, Charles, 1811–1874. 2. Grant, Ulysses Simpson, pres. U. S., 1822–1885. 3. U. S.—Pol. & govt.—1869–1877.

Library of Congress   E671.L83   12–10067

NL 0450098   DLC OFH OClWHi DN OO

Logan, John Alexander, 1826–1886.
The volunteer soldier of America. By John A. Logan. With Memoir of the author and Military reminiscences from General Logan's private journal. Chicago and New York, R. S. Peale & company, 1887.
xxiii, 25-706 p. col. front., plates, ports. 24½ cm.
Memoir by C. A. Logan.

1. U. S. Army—Hist. 2. U. S. Navy—Hist. 3. U. S.—Hist.—Civil war—Personal narratives. i. Logan, Cornelius Ambrose, 1836–1899. ii. Title.

UA42.L8   15—10003

OrStbM MtHi OrSaW OrU-M
OrU Wa WaE WaPS WaS WaSp WaSpG WaT WaTC WaWW IdPI
AAP CoU NIC CaBVaU IdB IdU MtBC MtU OrCS OrP OrPR
PU NjN NjP MdBP FTaSU MWA MtBuM OKentU KU-M DSI
NL 0450099   DLC Ok PHi OCl OO OU ViU OClW DNW PPL

Logan, John Alexander, 1865–1899.
In joyful Russia, by John A. Logan, jr. ... New York, D. Appleton and company, 1897.
x, 275 p. col. front., plates (part col.) ports. (part col.) 20ᵐ.

1. Nicholas ii, emperor of Russia, 1868–1918—Coronation. 2. Russia—Descr. & trav. i. Title.

Library of Congress   DK26.L83   4—4161

NL 0450101   DLC MtBC Wa DN IU NN MB

Logan, John Alexander, 1865–1899.
In joyful Russia, by John A. Logan ... 2d. ed.
New York, D. Appleton and company, 1899.
x, 275 p. col. front., plates (part col.) ports. (part col.) 21 cm.

1. Russia - Descr. & trav. 2, 2a, Nicholas II, emperor of Russia, 1868–1918.

NL 0450102   CU

RA640   Logan, John Alexander, 1908-
.E5   Ente regionale per la lotta anti-anofelica in Sardegna.
The Sardinian project: an experiment in the eradication of an indigenous malarious vector, by John A. Logan ₍superintendent₎ with the collaboration of Thomas H. G. Aitken ₍and others₎ Baltimore, Johns Hopkins Press, 1953.

LOGAN, John Daniel, 1869-1929.
The absolute as ethical postulate. n.p., 1899.

NL 0450104   MH

PN   Logan, John Daniel, 1869-1929
99   Aesthetic criticism in Canada: its aims,
.C52   methods and status. Being a short propae-
L6   deutic to the appreciation of the fine arts
and the writing of criticism, on literature, painting and dramatic and musical performances. Toronto, McClelland, Goodchild & Stewart ₍c1917₎
29 p. 23 cm.

1. Criticism - Canada. 2. Aesthetics. I. Title.

NL 0450105   WU OClW MH MiD RPB OO NN CtY CU

Logan, John Daniel, 1869-1929.
American prose style. n. p., n. p., n. d.
c. p. O. (In, Collected monographs. V. 290)

NL 0450106   NcD

LOGAN, John Daniel, 1869-
The Aristotelian concept of $\phi \upsilon \sigma \iota \varsigma$. Philos. Rev., 1897.

6: 18-42, 386-400. The second paper is entitled "The Aristotelian teleology."
Official copy of a thesis presented for the doctor's degree at Harvard University.

NL 0450107   MH

LOGAN, J₍ohn₎ D₍aniel₎, 1869-
Canada's champion regimental band; a critical study of the musicianship of the band of the 85th Overseas Battalion, C.E.F., Nova Scotia Highlanders. An essay in the appreciation of martial and of concert music. [Pictou, N.S., Advocate printing & publishing co., limited, cop.1916.]

Port. and plate.   H 322.4285.30

NL 0450108   MH

LOGAN, J₍ohn₎ D₍aniel₎, 1869-
Confessio amantis; an epistle in verse to welcome Rt. Rev. Monsignor William Foley, on the occasion of his home-coming, from California, June, 1926. Halifax, 1926.

f°. pp. (1), iii+. Port.
Privately printed.
"Transitus in pacem" - 1 leaf prefixed.
"A life large and sweet", 4 pp. appended.
"100 copies printed, of which 50 copies were numbered and signed by the author. No. 29."

NL 0450109   MH

Logan, John Daniel, 1869-
Dalhousie University and Canadian literature; being the history of an attempt to have Canadian literature included in the curriculum of Dalhousie University. With a criticism and a justification, as a further attempt, embodied in a letter addressed to Mr. John S. Roper, A.B., LL.B., M.C., President of the Alumni Association of Dalhousie University. By J. D. Logan... Halifax, N. S.: Privately printed, 1922. 24 p. 4°.
Cover-title.

1. Canadian literature—Study and   teaching. 2. Dalhousie University.
                                        October 26, 1926

NL 0450110   NN MH CaBVaU

Logan, John Daniel, 1869-
Democracy, education, and the new dispensation, a constructive essay in social theory with an epistolary introduction addressed to the Honorable William Stevens Fielding ... and Robert Alexander Falconer ... by J. D. Logan ... Toronto, W. Briggs, 1908.
20 p. 26ᵐ.

1. Democracy. 2. Education.

NL 0450111   ICU ICN

Logan, John Daniel, 1869-1929.
An epistle in verse, to Bliss Carman in Vagabondia.
(In- To Bliss Carman on the anniversary of his nativity, Toronto, Canada. 1913. 21 cm. p. [11-17])

NL 0450112   RPB

LOGAN, J₍ohn₎ D₍aniel₎, 1869-
The high moral status of our field army. Toronto, 1918.

pp. (6).
The Canadian magazine, Vol. LI, no. 2, June, 1918.

NL 0450113   MH

Logan, John Daniel, 1869-1929.
Highways of Canadian literature; a synoptic introduction to the literary history of Canada (English) from 1760 to 1924, by J. D. Logan ... and Donald G. French ... Toronto, McClelland & Stewart ₍c1924₎
2 p. l., 3-418 p. 22½ᵐ.

1. Canadian literature—Hist. & crit. i. French, Donald Graham, 1873- joint author. ii. Title.

Library of Congress   PR9112.L6   25—15157

                        MiU
NL 0450114   DLC MtU CaBVaU CaBVa NcU TxU ViU NcD OO

VOLUME 338

PS
8063
L6
1928

Logan, John Daniel, 1869-1929
Highways of Canadian literature; a synoptic introduction to the literary history of Canada (English) from 1760 to 1924, by J.D. Logan and Donald G. French. ₂2d ed.₎ Toronto, McClelland & Stewart ₍1928₎
418 p.

1. Canadian literature - Hist. & crit. I. French, Donald Graham, 1873-1945 (jt. author) II. Title CaOTU

NL 0450115   CaOTU ICN OC1 MB

LOGAN, John Daniel, 1869-
The inn at the end of the world: Prelude and Victors' chant to "Songs of the Happy Highway". With An essay on G.K.Chesterton's Apostolate of laughter,etc. Cover design by D.John MacGillivray. Halifax,Canada,T.C.Allen & Co., 1923.

pp. 27.
With author's autograph.
"From the MS. of the author's unpublished 'Songs of the happy   highway'"-Verso of cover.   Can 9783.1.60

NL 0450116   MH CaBVaU RPB NN

Logan, John Daniel, 1869-1929.
Insulters of death and other poems of the great departure. With a prose preachment entitled "The fatal paradox and sin of sorrow for the dead."   Halifax, N. S., L. C. Davidson 1916.   37 p. 24cm.

.1. Death—Poetry. I. Title.

NL 0450117   RPB MH CaOTU NN

Logan, John Daniel, 1869-
A literary chameleon; a new estimate of Mr. H. L. Mencken, by J. D. Logan ... with a foreword by J. L. O'Sullivan ... Milwaukee, Privately printed. 1926.
22 p. incl. front. (port.) 23ᶜᵐ.

1. Mencken, Henry Louis, 1880-   I. Title.
27-6279
Library of Congress   PS3525.E43Z6

NL 0450118   DLC IEN NN

819.1
L828ℓ   Logan, John Daniel, 1869-1929.
The little blue ghost; an Easter madrigal, with The lost love letters of Florian the Apostate ... Illustrated by J.H. Jefferson.   Halifax, T.C. Allen, 1922.
23p. illus. 19cm.

Poems and prose.

I. Title. II. Title: The lost love letters of Florian the Apostate.

NL 0450119   TxU CaBVaU RPB

Logan, John Daniel, 1869-1929
76-01
BA8712ℓ Love's pilgrim; a new vision of love among the ruins, being the pathetic story of an obscure and forlorn emigrant poet, and of the strange recovery of the most poignantly beautiful love lyric in Canadian poetry. First recounted by John Daniel Logan.   Halifax, T. C. Allen & Co., 1921.
22 p. 19 cm.

Includes two poems, Love's pilgrim, and The stained garment,   by John Killick Bathurst.

NL 0450120   RPB NN TxU CaBVaU MH

Logan, John Daniel, 1869-1929
The making of the new Ireland. An essay in social psychology chiefly about the relation between the cultural studies conducted by the Gaelic league and the social and industrial renascence in Ireland, with a critical account of the contributions by the Irish Gaels to creative literature.
= Toronto. The Gaelic League. 1909. 20 pp. 26 cm.

H1543 — Gaelic League. Publications. — Ireland. Soc. sci. — Sociology.

NL 0450121   MB MH

Logan, John Daniel, 1869-
Marjorie Pickthall, her poetic genius and art; an appreciation and an analysis of aesthetic paradox. By J. D. Logan ... Halifax, Canada, T. C. Allen & co., 1922.
44 p. front., ports. facsim. 23½ᶜᵐ.
Five hundred copies of this pamphlet were printed, after which the type was distributed.
Bibliography: p. 34-35.
Presentation copy to Lorne Pierce, with author's inscription on fly-leaf.
Lorne Pierce collection.

1. Pickthall, Marjorie Lowry Christie, 1883-1922. 2. Canadian poetry—Hist. & crit.

Queen's Univ. Library.   1925-16

NL 0450122   CaOKQ CaBVa NcU NcD TxU RPB NN MH

LOGAN, John Daniel, 1869-
Mater coronata; an ode,with lyrical interlude Halifax, Canada, published by the Alumni Association, [Dalhousie University], 1924.

1.8°. pp. (16).
"500 copies. No. 14."
With author's autograph.
Cover serves as title-page.

NL 0450123   MH

Logan, John Daniel, 1869-1929.

The new apocalypse, and other poems of days and deeds in France, with an essay in paradox, entitled "The new atonement of the living dead." By John Daniel Logan ... cover design and ornaments by P.E. Covey ... Halifax, N.S., T.C. Allen & co., 1919.

xvi p., 1 l., 3-39 p. front. (port.) facsim. 23.5cm.

"First one hundred copies are numbered and autographed by the author. This is copy no. 70."

NL 0450124   CaBVaU MH MB CaOTP CaOTU

Logan, John Daniel, 1869-1929.
The postulates of a psychology of prose style; an essay read before the Western philosophical association, at Lincoln, Neb., Jan. 2, 1901.
8 p.
Reprinted from "Education", Boston, Mass., Dec., 1901.
Bound 8th in vol. 4. of the pamphlets bound together with binder's title "Studies in psychology."

NL 0450125   OC1W

Logan, John Daniel, 1869-
Preludes; sonnets and other verses. With an epistle in criticism and an essay entitled " The rhythmical dummy; a recipe for verse-makers." Toronto, W. Briggs, 1906.
pp. 68.

MB
NL 0450126   MH CaBVaU CaOTU NN MWelC TxU NcD CtY

LOGAN, John Daniel, 1869-1929
Psychology and the argument from design.
[Boston], 1898.

NL 0450127   MH

Logan, John Daniel, 1869-1929
Quantitative punctuation. A new practical method based on the evolution of the literary sentence in modern English prose. A manual for teachers and students . . .
— Toronto. Briggs. 1907. 44, (1) pp. 12°.

G5907 — Punctuation.

NL 0450128   MB N MiU MH NNC

Logan, John Daniel, 1869-
Gd7.05   The religious function of comedy; a phase of the problem of evil, treated from the point of view of Aristotle's Poetics and Metaphysics and of spiritual monism ... by J.D.Logan ... Toronto,W.Briggs,1907.
18p. 27cm.
"An essay based on a lecture delivered before the Philosophical society of the University of Toronto,1907.

1.Greek drama.   2.Aristoteles. Crit.

NL 0450129   CtY MH MB

[Logan, John Daniel] 1869-1929.
A rosary of renunciation; six sestets, with a little prose homily on mystical union with the idea beauty. Halifax, Can., Priv. print., 1925.
[9] p. 22 cm.
"Only twenty-five copies of this booklet, each numbered and autographed by the author, were printed. This is number 8." With a presentation note to John W. Garvin.

NL 0450130   RPB

Logan, John Daniel, 1869-1929.
Scott and Haliburton; an essay in the psychology of creative satiric humor; occasioned by the celebration of the 150th anniversary of the birth of Sir Walter Scott, by J.D. Logan.   Halifax, T.C. Allen & co., 1921.
22 p.   24 cm.
One copy author's personal copy; one author's final press proofs; another, author's manuscript.

NL 0450132   CaNSWA MH CaNBaU

Logan, John Daniel, 1869-1929
1901
-L8316ai The singing silence; an elegy in memory of the late Monsignor William Foley, P. D., D.D., Rector of St. Mary's Cathedral, Halifax, Nova Scotia. [Milwaukee, Wis.] Marquette University Press, Priv. print., 1927.
6 p., 2 l. front. (port.) 29 cm.
"Fifty-eight copies of this booklet, numbered and autographed by the author, were printed. This is no. 16."   With inscription to Melvin O. Hammond.

NL 0450133   RPB MH

Tr.R. Logan, John Daniel, 1869-1929.

Songs of the makers of Canada, and other homeland lyrics; with an introductory essay on The genius and distinction of Canadian poetry. Foreword by John Boyd, cover design and ornaments by Walter R. Duff. Toronto, W. Briggs, 1911.
64 p. 20 cm.

Author's autograph inscribed presentation copy to Lionel Stevenson.

NL 0450134   NcD CaBVaU TxU NBuC MB MH NN RPB N

VOLUME 338

Logan, John Daniel, *1869-1929*
The structural principles of style applied. A manual of English prose composition. Vermillion, S. D., Willey & Danforth, 1900.

ix, 188 p. 16°.

Feb. 14, 1901-134

NL 0450135   DLC MH

Logan, John Daniel, 1869-   ed.

Haliburton, Thomas Chandler, 1796-1865.
Thomas Chandler Haliburton, by John Daniel Logan. Toronto, The Ryerson press [1923?]

Logan, John Daniel, 1869-1929.
Twilight litanies, and other poems from the ivory tower, in two books: I. — Twilight litanies. II. — Stopped flutes and undertones. With an essay, entitled: "Christ as poet." By John Daniel Logan... Foreword by Rev. Dr. William Foley; cover design and frontispiece by P. E. Covey... Halifax, N. S., 1920.
xiii, 92 p. front. 20cm.

285808B. 1. No subject. I. Title.

January 31, 1945

NL 0450137   NN CaBVa CaBVaU OU MH RPB TxU

Logan, John Daniel, 1869-1929
1901
L8316tp   Two poems: I. The Lady of the Lambs. II.
The inn at the end of the world. Halifax, Priv. print., 1922.
cover-title, [3] p. 16 cm.

Author's mss. note: This booklet was suppressed after it was discovered that the printing make-up man had dropped one of the stanzas in "The inn at the end of the world." The stanza is here inserted ...

NL 0450138   RPB

Logan, John Daniel, *1869-1929*
When I write an advertisement. A practical vest-pocket manual for ad-writers.
= Toronto. Briggs. 1907. 20 pp. Sm. 8°.
Bibliography, p. 20.

G6789 — Advertising. — T.r.

NL 0450139   MB

WU
500
L831d   LOGAN, John Douglas
1926   Dental prosthetics. Edinburgh, Livingstone, 1926.
218 p. illus. (Outlines of dental science, v. 4)
1. Teeth - Prosthetic

NL 0450140   DNLM ICRL NNC MiD

Logan, John Douglas.
... Dental prosthetics, by J. Douglas Logan ... and W. Russell Logan ... Second edition. Edinburgh, E. & S. Livingstone, 1934.
xii, 211, [1] p. illus. 19½cm. (Half-title: Outlines of dental science. vol. IV)
Series title also at head of t.-p.

1. Teeth, Artificial. I. Logan, William Russell, joint author. II. Title.
S G 36-50
Library, U. S. Surgeon-   General's Office
[RK656]

NL 0450141   DI-GS DNLM PPiU-D

Logan, John Douglas.
Dental prosthetics. Edinburgh, Livingston, 1946.
219 p. il. 20 cm. (Outlines of dental science)

NL 0450142   PU-D

[Logan, John Edward] d. 1915.
A cry from the Saskatchewan
see under title

819.1
L8285
C1   Logan, John Edward, d. 1915.
Verses. Montreal, Pen and Pencil Club, 1916.
viii, 129p. illus. 23cm.

Copyright date on verso of t.p. changed in ms. from 1916 to 1917.

NL 0450143   TxU CaBVaU RPB NN PBa NBuG MnU CU

SPECIAL
COLL.
CA
L828   Logan, John F., comp.
[Scrapbook of Portland theater photographs and clippings] 1894-1895.
1v.

1. Oregon. Theater.

NL 0450144   OrU

Logan, John Fremont.
...The protein matter of bile, by J. F. Logan... [Baltimore: Waverly Press,] 1924. p. 17–32. 8°. (McGill Univ., Montreal. McGill Univ. publ. ser. 3 [chemistry].)

Cover-title.
Repr.: The Jour. of biological chemistry. v. 58, no. 1.
Bibliography, p. 31–32.

1. Bile. 2. Ser.

April 25, 1925

NL 0450145   NN DLC

Logan, John Henry.
A history of the Upper country of South Carolina from earliest periods to war of Independence. n. d.

NL 0450146   AU

Logan, John Henry.
A history of the upper country of South Carolina, from the earliest periods to the close of the war of independence. By John H. Logan, A. M. Vol. I. Charleston, S. G. Courtenay & co.; Columbia, P. B. Glass, 1859.
xi, 521 p. 19cm.
Page [vii] incorrectly numbered viii.
Running title: History of upper Carolina, ancient territory of the Cherokees.
Volume 1 extends only to 1758. A part of the manuscript for v. 2 published in Historical collections of Joseph Habersham chapter, D. A. R. v. 3, 1910.
No more published.
1. South Carolina—Hist.—Colonial period. 2. Cherokee Indians.
1–10804
Library of Congress   F272.L83

ViU MH ICJ DI-GS NcU NcA-S IEN NcGU GA
NL 0450147   DLC MWA ScU OCU IC NcA NcD TU MdBP NcU

Logan, John Henry.
Upper country of South Carolina: notes collected preparatory to writing volume 2 of the History; copied in April, 1906, from the original [manuscript] in the Library of the Wisconsin Historical Society. Typewritten. Map case.

NL 0450148   ScU

Logan, John Hubbard, 1876–

National education association of the United States. *Dept. of superintendence.*
Achievements of American education.
(In National education association of the United States. Addresses and proceedings, 1930. p. 664–694)

Logan, John Hubbard, 1876–
The state and the rural school.
(In National education association of the United States. Addresses and proceedings, 1926. p. 583–588)

1. Rural schools—U. S. I. Title.
E 27–382
Library, U. S. Bur. of   Education

NL 0450150   DHEW

Logan, John Hubbard, 1876–
Working with industries and business houses—abstract [by] John H. Logan.
(In National education association of the United States. Addresses and proceedings, 1931. p. 768–769)

1. Technical education. [1. Co-operative system of industrial education] I. Title.
E 33–623
Library, U. S. Office of   Education L13.N212 1931
Library of Congress   [L13.N4 1931]

NL 0450151   DHEW

Logan, John Murdoch.
Dissertatio medica inauguralis, de morbo venereo. Quam ... ex auctoritate ... d. Gulielmi Robertson ... Academiæ edinburgenæ præfecti ... pro gradu doctoratus ... eruditorum examini subjicit Joannes Murdoch Logan, A. M. Civis Bostoniensis Americanus. Ad diem 24. junii [1784] ... Edinburgi, apud Balfour et Smellie, academiæ typographos, M,DCC,LXXXIV.
2 p. l., 50 p. 21cm.

1. Venereal diseases.
36–36684
Library of Congress   RC201.L58

NL 0450152   DLC PPC DNLM

LOGAN, JOHN O
Calcium hypochlorite in water purification. 60 E 42d St., N.Y., Mathieson alkali works [1940].
p.1517-27.

By John O. Logan and W. L. Savell

NL 0450153   Or

Logan, John Randolph, 1811-1884.
Circular letter on "The terms of communion", republished and dedicated to the Broad River Baptist association. Charlotte, N. C., 1850.

NL 0450154   NcWsW

Logan, John Randolph, 1811-1884.
Sketches, historical and biographical, of the Broad River and King's Mountain Baptist Associations, from 1800 to 1882. By Deacon John R. Logan. Together with an introductory sketch of the author, by R. L. Ryburn, Esq. Shelby, N. C.: Babington, Roberts & Co., 1887. xx, 605 p. 8°.

1. Baptist Church, U. S.: North Carolina, 1800-82. 2. Baptist Church, U. S.: South Carolina, 1800-82. 3. Broad River Baptist Association. 4. King's Mountain Baptist Association. 5. Ryburn, R. L.

September 28, 1915.

NL 0450155   NN Nc NcD TxU PHi T NcWsW DLC MH ICN NcU

VOLUME 338

Logan, John Vincent Raymond.
Poliomyelitis and the use of hydrogymnastics as a remedial measure... ₍Philadelphia, Pa.₎ 1936.
149 p.

NL 0450156   PPT

Logan, John W
Pigeon racer's handbook; practical suggestions for successful pigeon racing. London, Racing Pigeon Pub. Co. ₍1923?₎
100 p. ₍p. 95-100 advertisements₎ illus., port., maps (1 fold.) 19 cm.

1. Homing pigeons.   I. Title.

SF469.L6   49-43186*

NL 0450157   DLC

Logan, Joseph Payne, 1821-1891.
Address introductory to the fifth course of lectures in the Atlanta Medical College. 30 pp. 8°. *Atlanta, J. L. Miller & Co., 1859.*

NL 0450158   DNLM

Logan, Joseph Payne, 1821-1891.

Georgia. *Board of health.*
Georgia state Board of health. Report of the Special committee upon the most effectual means of preventing smallpox in the state of Georgia. Presented to the annual meeting of the board, held in the city of Atlanta, October 12th, 1875. From the Atlanta medical and surgical journal, December, 1875. Atlanta, Ga., Dunlop & Dickson, printers, 1875.

Logan, Josephine (Hancock)
The collected poems of Josephine Hancock Logan. Chicago, A. Kroch and son, 1942.
9 p. l., 226 p., 1 l. col. front. (port.) 23 cm.

PS3523.O345 1942   811.5   42-4762

NL 0450160   DLC CBSK

Logan, *Mrs.* Josephine (Hancock)
Heights and depths, poems by Josephine Hancock Logan. Chicago, A. Kroch, 1935.
93 p. 23ᶜᵐ.

I. Title.   35-4697
Library of Congress   PS3523.O345H4 1935
Copyright A 81120   811.5

NL 0450161   DLC IEN

Logan, *Mrs.* Josephine (Hancock)
Lights and shadows, poems by Josephine Hancock Logan. Chicago, A. Kroch, 1932.
101 p. front. (col. port.) 23ᶜᵐ.

I. Title.
Library of Congress   PS3523.O345L5 1932   32-28950
——— Copy 2.
Copyright A 56226   811.5

NL 0450162   DLC WU NN OU IU

Logan, *Mrs.* Josephine (Hancock)
Sanity in art, by Josephine Hancock Logan. Chicago, A. Kroch, 1937.
xv, 127 p. incl. plates. 27ᶜᵐ.

"Mrs. Logan's book ... calls our attention to the havoc primitive, cubist, futurist or modern whatnots have wrought."—Pref., by Gutzon Borglum.
"First edition."
"Press comments": p. 23-33; "Excerpts from letters": p. 34-75.

1. Art—Hist.—20th cent. 2. Art, American. 3. Art criticism.
I. Title.   37-4292
Library of Congress   N6490.L6
Copyright A 103873   709.04

NL 0450163   DLC WaS MtU DSI MdBWA OCl OO

ML50
.R7517F3
1955
Logan, Joshua. Fanny.

Rome, Harold Jacob, 1908–
₍Fanny. Libretto. English₎

Fanny; a musical play, by S. N. Behrman and Joshua Logan. Based on the trilogy of Marcel Pagnol. Music and lyrics by Harold Rome. New York, Random House ₍1955₎

PS3515
.E263M5
Logan, Joshua, joint author.

Heggen, Thomas, 1919–
Mister Roberts, a play by Thomas Heggen & Joshua Logan, with a foreword by John Mason Brown. New York, Random House ₍1948₎

ML50
.R6787
1949a
Logan, Joshua. South Pacific.

Rodgers, Richard, 1902–
₍South Pacific. Libretto. English₎

South Pacific; a musical play, music by Richard Rodgers; lyrics by Oscar Hammerstein, 2nd, and Joshua Logan; adapted from James A. Michener's Pulitzer prize-winning Tales of the South Pacific. New York, Random House ₍1949₎

M1508
.R684S6
1949
Logan, Joshua. South Pacific.

Rodgers, Richard, 1902–
₍South Pacific. Piano-vocal score. English₎

South Pacific; a musical play, music by Richard Rodgers, lyrics by Oscar Hammerstein 2nd. Book by Oscar Hammerstein 2nd and Joshua Logan, adapted from James A. Michener's Tales of the South Pacific. Vocal score edited by Albert Sirmay. ₍New York, Williamson Music, 1949₎

Logan, Joshua.
The wisteria trees, an American play based on Anton Chekhov's The cherry orchard. New York, Random House ₍1950₎
112 p. illus. 21 cm.

I. Chekhov, Anton Pavlovich, 1860-1904. Vishnevyi sad. II. Title.
Full name: Joshua Lockwood Logan.
PS3523.O346W5 1950   812.5   50-8392

PSt NcGU NcU ICU TU MB OClW TxU
WaS MsU MtU Or OrP WaSp WaT OrPS CaBVa CaBVaU PPL PP
NL 0450168   DLC IdPI NcD NIC CaOTP ViU CoU Wa WaE

Logan, Josiah. Voyage of, to Pechora, and his wintering there, 1611. 7 pp. ₍Purchas, S., *His pilgrimes,* v. 3, p. 541.₎

NL 0450169   MdBP

Logan, June Ruby, 1928–
Central pathways subserving weight discrimination in monkey. Ann Arbor, University Microfilms ₍1954₎
(₍University Microfilms, Ann Arbor, Mich.₎ Publication 8099)
Microfilm copy of typescript. Positive.
Collation of the original: ix, 173 l. illus. (part mounted)
Thesis—University of Washington.
Abstracted in Dissertation abstracts, v. 14 (1954) no. 5, p. 859-860.
Vita.
Bibliography: leaves ₍164₎-173.

1. Nervous system.   I. Title.
Microfilm AC-1 no. 8099   Mic A 54-1263

Washington. Univ.,   Seattle. Library
for Library of Congress   ₍1.†
NL 0450170   WaS DLC

Logan, K. H.
see Logan, Kirk Harold, 1879–

Logan, K   T.
An integrating light meter for ecological research. [Ottawa, Minister of Northern Affairs and National Resources] 1955.
4 p.   illus.   24.5 cm.   (Canada. Forestry Branch. Forest Research Division. Technical note, no. 13)

NL 0450172   NcD

Logan, *Mrs.* Kate Virginia (Cox) 1840–1915.
My Confederate girlhood; the memoirs of Kate Virginia Cox Logan, edited by her daughter, Lily Logan Morrill. Richmond, Garrett & Massie, incorporated, 1932.
xv p., 1 l. 150 p. plates, ports. 24ᶜᵐ.

Illustration on t.-p.
Written in 1890. *cf.* Introd.
"List of war records, cyclopedia, the newspaper and other sketches of life of General T. M. Logan": p. 146-147.

I. Morrill, Mrs. Lily (Logan) 1877–   ed. II. Title.
Library of Congress   F213.L74   32-11352
Copyright A 50965   [920.7] 973.784

ViU OCU OCl
NL 0450173   DLC WaS Or MB DSI CU TU NcD NcGU OU

Logan, Kathrine Ross, 1868–
The call of the upper road, by Katherine R. Logan. New York, George H. Doran company ₍ᶜ1924₎
xi, ₍2₎, 15-159 p. front. 20ᶜᵐ. (*Half-title:* The Upper road series, bk. 1)

1. Conduct of life. 2. Christian life.   I. Title.
24-9140 Revised
Library of Congress   BJ1581.L56

NL 0450174   DLC NjPT MiU

Logan, Kathrine Ross, 1868–
The call of the stars ₍by₎ Kathrine R. Logan ... Los Angeles, Calif., Wetzel publishing co., inc., 1930.
164 p.   illus., fold. pl.   20½ᶜᵐ.

The folded plate is mounted on lining-paper.
"The twelve signs of the zodiac ₍with₎ original interpretations"—p. 15.
"Sources": p. ₍6₎

1. Constellations.   I. Title.
30-24960 Revised
Library of Congress   QB802.L6
Copyright A 27389   ₍ᵣ40d2₎   133.5

NL 0450175   DLC

Logan, Kathrine Ross, 1868–
There's something better on the way, by Kathrine R. Logan ... New York ₍etc.₎, Fleming H. Revell company ₍ᶜ1938₎
91 p. 19½ᶜᵐ.

1. Future life.   I. Title.
Library of Congress   BT904.L6   38-15331
Copyright A 117813   237

NL 0450176   DLC

VOLUME 338

Logan, Kathrine Ross, 1868-
The upper road of vision, by Kathrine R. Logan ...
New York, George H. Doran company [1925]
xii p., 1 l., [13]-200 p. front. 19½ᶜᵐ. (*Half-title:* The upper road series, bk. 2)
Bibliography: p. ix-xii.

1. Conduct of life. 2. Christian life. I. Title.
Library of Congress BJ1581.L563 25-22000

NL 0450177 DLC NcD

Logan, Kathrine Ross, 1868-
Your thoughts and you, by Kathrine R. Logan ... New York, George H. Doran company [1927]
xii p., 2 l., 17-188 p. 19½ᶜᵐ.
Blank pages for "Preserving the best" (178-188)

1. Spiritual life. I. Title.
Library of Congress BJ1581.L565 27-11000

NL 0450178 DLC

Logan, Kirk Harold, 1879-
... Bureau of standards soil-corrosion studies. I. Soils, materials, and results of early observations, by K. H. Logan, electrical engineer, S. P. Ewing, junior physicist, C. D. Yeomans, junior scientific aid, Bureau of standards. April 28, 1928. Washington, U. S. Govt. print. off., 1928.
1 p. l., p. 447-554 incl. tables, diagrs. plates. 29ᶜᵐ. ([U. S.] Bureau of standards. Technologic papers, no. 368)
At head of title: Dept. of commerce. Bureau of standards. George K. Burgess, director ...
Running title: Soil-corrosion studies.
"Bibliography on soil publications": p. 552-553.
1. Corrosion and anti-corrosives. 2. Soils. I. Ewing, Scott Preston, 1898- joint author. II. Yeomans, Clyde Dawson, 1906- joint author. III. Title. IV. Title: Soil-corrosion studies.
28-26426 Revised
Library of Congress T1.U4 no. 368
TA467.L74
[r41b2] (608.2) 620.1122

NL 0450179 DLC MB

Logan, Kirk Harold, joint author
McCollum, Burton.
... Earth resistance and its relation to electrolysis of underground structures, by Burton McCollum, electrical engineer, and K. H. Logan, assistant physicist, Bureau of standards. <Issued December 20, 1915> Washington, Govt. print. off., 1915.

Logan, Kirk Harold, joint author.
McCollum, Burton, 1880-
... Electrolysis testing, by Burton McCollum, consulting electrical engineer [and] K. H. Logan, electrical engineer, Bureau of standards. September 28, 1927 ... Washington, U. S. Govt. print. off., 1927.

Logan, Kirk Harold, 1879-
McCollum, Burton.
... Electrolytic corrosion of iron in soils, by Burton McCollum, associate physicist, and K. H. Logan, assistant physicist, Bureau of standards. <June 12, 1913> Washington, Govt. print. off., 1913.

Logan, Kirk Harold, 1879-
... Engineering significance of National bureau of standards soil-corrosion data, by Kirk H. Logan ...
(R P 1171, *in* U. S. National bureau of standards. Journal of research of the National bureau of standards. Washington, U. S. Govt. print. off., 1939. 23½ᶜᵐ. January, 1939, v. 22, no. 1, p. 109-125 incl. tables, diagrs.)
Running title: Significance of soil-corrosion data.
"References": p. 125.
1. Corrosion and anti-corrosives. 2. Soils. I. Title. II. Title: Significance of soil-corrosion data. III. Title: Soil-corrosion data.
39-26214
Library of Congress QC1.U52 vol. 22, no. 1
T1.U42 vol. 22, no. 1
(506.173) 620.1122

NL 0450183 DLC OU

Logan, Kirk Harold, 1879- joint author
McCollum, Burton.
... Leakage of currents from electric railways, by Burton M'Collum, electrical engineer, and K. H. Logan, assistant physicist, Bureau of standards. Issued March 14, 1916. Washington, Govt. print. off., 1916.

Logan, Kirk Harold, joint author.
McCollum, Burton.
... Practical application of the earth-current meter, by Burton McCollum, consulting electrical engineer [and] K. H. Logan, electrical engineer, Bureau of standards. August 18, 1927 ... Washington, U. S. Govt. print. off., 1927.

Logan, Kirk Harold, 1879-
... Soil-corrosion studies. Nonferrous metals and alloys, metallic coatings and specially prepared ferrous pipes removed in 1930, by K. H. Logan ...
(R P 359, *in* U. S. Bureau of standards. Bureau of standards journal of research. Washington, U. S. Govt. print. off., 1931. 23½ᶜᵐ. September, 1931, v. 7, no. 3, p. 585-605 incl. tables. pl.)
Running title: Effects of soils on nonferrous metals.
1. Corrosion and anti-corrosives. 2. Soils. I. Title. II. Title: Effects of soils on nonferrous metals.
31-28195
Library of Congress QC1.U52 vol. 7, no. 3
T1.U42 vol. 7, no. 3
(506) 620.1122

NL 0450186 DLC

Logan, Kirk Harold, 1879-
... Soil-corrosion studies, 1927-28, by K. H. Logan ...
(R P 95, *in* U. S. Bureau of standards. Bureau of standards journal of research. Washington, U. S. Govt. print. off., 1929. 23½ᶜᵐ. August, 1929, v. 3, no. 2, p. 275-302 incl. tables, diagr.)
QC1.U52 vol. 3, no. 2
T1.U42 vol. 3, no. 2
—— [Washington, U. S. Govt. print. off., 1929]
cover-title, p. 275-302 incl. tables, diagr. 23½ᶜᵐ. ([U. S.] Bureau of standards. Research paper no. 95. Reprint from Bureau of standards Journal of research, v. 3, August, 1929)
1. Corrosion and anti-corrosives. 2. Soils. I. Title.
29-26777
Library of Congress TA462.L6

NL 0450187 DLC MiU OU OC1

Logan, Kirk Harold, 1879-
... Soil-corrosion studies, 1930. Rates of corrosion and pitting of bare ferrous specimens, by K. H. Logan and V. A. Grodsky ...
(R P 329, *in* U. S. Bureau of standards. Bureau of standards journal of research. Washington, U. S. Govt. print. off., 1931. 23½ᶜᵐ. July, 1931, v. 7, no. 1, 35 p. incl. tables, diagrs.)
1. Corrosion and anti-corrosives. 2. Soils. I. Grodsky, V. A., joint author. II. Title.
31-27164
Library of Congress QC1.U52 vol. 7, no. 1
T1.U42 vol. 7, no. 1
(506) 620.1122

NL 0450188 DLC MiU OC1 OU

Logan, Kirk Harold, 1879-
... Soil-corrosion studies, 1932. Rates of loss of weight and pitting of ferrous and non-ferrous specimens and metallic protective coatings, by K. H. Logan and R. H. Taylor ...
(R P 638, *in* U. S. Bureau of standards. Bureau of standards journal of research. Washington, U. S. Govt. print. off., 1934. 23½ᶜᵐ. January, 1934, v. 12, no. 1, p. 119-145 incl. tables, diagrs.)
"Appendix 1. Errata in earlier publications": p. 145.
1. Corrosion and anti-corrosives. I. Taylor, Rolla Holmes, 1904- joint author. II. Title. III. Title: Rates of loss of weight and pitting of ferrous and non-ferrous specimens ...
34-26019
Library of Congress QC1.U52 vol. 12, no. 1
T1.U42 vol. 12, no. 1
(506.1) 620.18

NL 0450189 DLC OU OC1 MiU

Logan, Kirk Harold, 1879-
... Soil-corrosion studies, 1934. Bituminous coatings for underground service, by Kirk H. Logan ...
(R P 1058, *in* U. S. National bureau of standards. Journal of research of the National bureau of standards. Washington, U. S. Govt. print. off., 1937. 23½ᶜᵐ. December, 1937, v. 19, no. 6, p. 695-740 incl. tables, diagrs. plates)
1. Corrosion and anti-corrosives. 2. Soils. I. Title. II. Title: Bituminous coatings for underground service.
37-29077
Library of Congress QC1.U52 vol. 19, no. 6
T1.U42 vol. 19, no. 6
(506.173) 620.1122

NL 0450190 DLC

Logan, Kirk Harold, 1879-
... Soil-corrosion studies, 1934. Field tests of nonbituminous coatings for underground use, by Kirk H. Logan and Scott P. Ewing ...
(R P 962, *in* U. S. Bureau of standards. Journal of research of the National bureau of standards. Washington, U. S. Govt. print. off., 1937. 23½ᶜᵐ. March, 1937, v. 18, no. 3, p. 361-388 incl. tables, diagrs. plates)
1. Corrosion and anti-corrosives. I. Ewing, Scott Preston, 1898- joint author. II. Title. III. Title: Field tests of nonbituminous coatings for underground use.
37-26310
Library of Congress QC1.U52 vol. 18, no. 3
—— Copy 2. T1.U42 vol. 18, no. 3
(506.173) 620.1122

NL 0450191 DLC

Logan, Kirk Harold, 1879-
... Soil-corrosion studies, 1934. Rates of loss of weight and penetration of nonferrous materials, by Kirk H. Logan ...
(R P 945, *in* U. S. Bureau of standards. Journal of research of the National bureau of standards. Washington, U. S. Govt. print. off., 1936. 23½ cm. November, 1936, v. 17, no. 5, p. 781-804 incl. tables, diagrs. plates)
1. Soil corrosion. I. Title. II. Title: Rates of loss of weight and penetration of nonferrous materials.
QC1.U52 vol. 17, no. 5 620.18 36-26924
T1.U42 vol. 17, no. 5

NL 0450192 DLC

Logan, Kirk Harold, 1879-
... Soil-corrosion studies, 1934. Rates of loss of weight and pitting of ferrous specimens, by K. H. Logan ...
(R P 883, *in* U. S. Bureau of standards. Journal of research of the National bureau of standards. Washington, U. S. Govt. print. off., 1936. 23½ᶜᵐ. May, 1936, v. 16, no. 5, p. 431-466 incl. tables, diagrs.)
1. Corrosion and anti-corrosives. I. Title. II. Title: Rates of loss of weight and pitting of ferrous specimens.
36-26407
Library of Congress QC1.U52 vol. 16, no. 5
T1.U42 vol. 16, no. 5
(506.173) 620.17

NL 0450193 DLC OU

Logan, Kirk Harold, 1879-
... Soil-corrosion studies, 1937. Corrosion-resistant materials and special tests [by] Kirk H. Logan ...
(R P 1250, *in* U. S. National bureau of standards. Journal of research of the National bureau of standards. Washington, U. S. Govt. print. off., 1939. 23½ᶜᵐ. October, 1939, v. 23, no. 4, p. 515-542 incl. tables, diagrs. plates)
"References": p. 541-542.
1. Corrosion and anti-corrosives. 2. Soils. I. Title.
39-29206
Library of Congress QC1.U52 vol. 23, no. 4
T1.U42 vol. 23, no. 4
(506.173) 620.1122

NL 0450194 DLC OU

VOLUME 338

Logan, Kirk Harold, 1879–
... Soil-corrosion studies, 1939. Coatings for the protection of metals underground, by Kirk H. Logan ...

(R P 1446, *in* U. S. National bureau of standards. Journal of research of the National bureau of standards. Washington, U. S. Govt. print. off., 1942. 23½ᶜᵐ. January, 1942, v. 28, no. 1, p. 57–71 incl. tables)

1. Corrosion and anti-corrosives.   I. Title.

                                      42–37688
Library of Congress   QC1.U52 vol. 28, no. 1
                      T1.U42 vol. 28, no. 1
     ₃₁   (506.173)   620.1122

NL 0450195   DLC WaWW OU

Logan, Kirk Harold, 1879–
... Soil-corrosion studies, 1939: ferrous and non-ferrous corrosion-resistant materials, by Kirk H. Logan ...

(R P 1460, *in* U. S. National bureau of standards. Journal of research of the National bureau of standards. Washington, U. S. Govt. print. off., 1942. 23½ᶜᵐ. March, 1942, v. 28, no. 3, p. 379–400 incl. tables, diagrs.)

1. Corrosion and anti-corrosives.

                                        42–37916
Library of Congress   QC1.U52 vol. 28, no. 3
                      T1.U42 vol. 28, no. 3
                          (506.173)   620.18

NL 0450196   DLC WaWW OU

Logan, Kirk Harold, 1879–
... Soil-corrosion studies, 1941: ferrous and nonferrous corrosion-resistant materials and nonbituminous coatings, by Kirk H. Logan and Melvin Romanoff ...

(R P 1602, *in* U. S. National bureau of standards. Journal of research of the National bureau of standards. Washington, U. S. Govt. print. off., 1944. 23½ᶜᵐ. September, 1944, v. 33, no. 3, p. 145–198 incl. tables, diagrs. plates)

"References": p. 197–198.

1. Corrosion and anti-corrosives.   I. Romanoff, Melvin, joint author.   II. Title.
                                        44–41670
Library of Congress   QC1.U52 vol. 33, no. 3
—— ——2d set.   T1.U42 vol. 33, no. 3
                          (506.173)   624.1122

NL 0450197   DLC

Logan, Kirk Harold, joint author
McCollum, Burton.
... Special studies in electrolysis mitigation. IV. A preliminary report on electrolysis mitigation in Elyria, Ohio, with recommendations for mitigation, by Burton McCollum, electrical engineer, and K. H. Logan, assistant physicist, Bureau of standards. Issued January 22, 1916. Washington, Govt. print. off., 1916.

Logan, Kirk Harold, joint author
Rosa, Edward Bennett, 1861–
... Special studies in electrolysis mitigation, no. 2. Electrolysis from electric railway currents and its prevention—an experimental test on a system of insulated negative feeders in St. Louis, by E. B. Rosa, chief physicist, Burton McCollum, associate physicist, and K. H. Logan, assistant physicist, Bureau of standards ⟨December 27, 1913⟩ Washington, Govt. print. off., 1914.

₁**Logan, Kirk Harold**₁ 1879–
... Underground corrosion. ⟨Issued November 27, 1945⟩ Washington, U. S. Govt. print. off., 1945.

ii, 312 p. incl. illus. (incl. map) tables, diagrs. 23½ cm. (U. S. National bureau of standards. Circular ... C 450)

At head of title: U. S. Dept. of commerce ... National bureau of standards ...
"By Kirk H. Logan."—p. 1.
"References": p. 271–278.

1. Corrosion and anti-corrosives.   I. Title.
QC100.U555 no. 450·   620.1122   45–-35970
                TA462.L63
                ₁a56g₂₁

NL 0450200   DLC WaS WaWW MdBJ ViU OC1

MANN
SH   **Logan, L   B**
167   Practical carp culture. ₁Youngstown? Ohio
C3   188–?₁
L83   129 p. illus. 24 cm.

           1. Carp. ₁I. Title₁

NL 0450201   NIC NN OC1

SH 167 **Logan, L   B**
C3 L6   Practical carp culture. The chrystalization of ten years experience in the United States. Gathered from more than ₍sic₎ 10,000 successful carp culturists, in all parts of the country, and combined with the best teachings of the centuries of experience in Europe, by L. B. Logan. Youngstown, Ohio, 1888?
       156 p. (p. 130–136 advertisements) illus. 24 cm.
       1. Carp. 2. Fish-culture – U. S. I. Title.

NL 0450202   OU MH DSI CU

Logan, Laura R.
... The goal of nursing education, by Laura R. Logan. [Rochester, N. Y., 1925]
   6 p.
   Reprinted from The American journal of nursing, July, 1925.

NL 0450203   OU

---

*
RC206   **Logan, Leatha.**
.L6
1943   Who conquered yellow fever? ₁Huntington, Ind., Whitelock Press, 1943₁
    40 p. ports. 23cm.
    "Biographical sketches."

    1. Yellow fever. 2. Reed, Walter, 1851–1902.
I. Title.

NL 0450204   ViU

Logan, Leonard, 1891–   ed.
Logan's Oklahoma history map book, ed. by Leonard Logan, jr. ... rev. by V. E. Danner ... 2d ed. Oklahoma City, Okl., V. E. Danner, ₁1916.

47 p. illus. (maps) 21 x 28ᶜᵐ. $0.35
Bibliography: p. 2.

1. Oklahoma—Hist.   I. Danner, Vernice Earle, 1882–
                               16–25204
Library of Congress   F695.L83
     A 446680

NL 0450205   DLC

Logan, Leonard Aylesworth, 1909–
Liquid-film heat-transfer coefficients in a forced-circulation evaporator, by Leonard A. Logan ... ₁New York, 1934₁

cover-title, p. ₁1044₁–1047. 1 illus., diagrs. 29½ᵐ.
Thesis (PH. D.)—University of Michigan, 1934.
By L. A. Logan, N. Fragen, and W. L. Badger.
"Reprinted from Industrial and engineering chemistry, vol. 26 ... October, 1934."
"Literature cited": p. 1047.

1. Heat—Transmission. 2. Evaporating appliances.   I. Fragen, N., joint author.   II. Badger, Walter Lucius, 1886–   joint author.   III. Title: Evaporator, Forced-circulation.

                                35–7923
Library of Congress   TP363.L6 1934
Univ. of Michigan Libr.   660

NL 0450206   MiU OU OCU DLC

Logan, Leonard Marion, 1891–
Principles of economics: a manual, by Leonard Logan ... Norman, Okl., University litho publishers, 1934.

1 p. l., III l., 204, 204A–204B, 205–431, 431a–431d, 432–466 p. illus., diagrs. 23ᵐ.
"List of texts used in references": leaf III.

1. Economics.   CA 34–421 Unrev'd
Library of Congress   HB171.5.L75
    Copyright A 75158   330.1

NL 0450207   DLC

₁**Logan, Leonard Marion**₁ 1891–
A social and economic survey of six counties in southeastern Oklahoma: Atoka, Bryan, Choctaw, Coal, McCurtain and Pushmataha counties. Norman, Okl., Southeastern Oklahoma development association, Oklahoma state Planning and resources board, the University of Oklahoma, 1946.

xi, 239 p. incl. illus., maps, tables. 23ᵐ.
Foreword signed: Leonard Logan.
"Sources of data": p. ₁237₁–239.

1. Oklahoma—Econ. condit. 2. Oklahoma—Soc. condit.   I. Title.
   HC107.O5L64   330.9766   47–32439

NL 0450208   DLC Or ICU TxU

Logan, Leonard Marion, 1891–
Specimen chapter of Principles of economics; a manual ... New edition, 1934. Norman, Okl., University litho publishers [1934]
Pamphlet
Lithoprinted.

NL 0450209   CtY

Logan, Leonard Marion, 1891–
... The stabilization of the petroleum industry, by Leonard M. Logan. Norman, 1930.

6 p. l., 248 p., 1 l. incl. tables. 24½ cm. (Oklahoma. Geological survey. Bulletin no. 54)
Bibliography: p. ₁235₁–240.

1. Petroleum industry and trade—U. S.   I. Title.
QE153.A2 no. 54   G S 31–24
—— Copy 2.   HD9565.L6 1930a
U. S. Geol. Survey. Libr.
for Library of Congress   ₁a50g₂₁†

DLC
NL 0450210   DI–GS MtBuM WaS OrU CU ViU MoU TNJ OrP

Logan, Leonard Marion, 1891–
Stabilization of the petroleum industry ₁by₁ Leonard M. Logan, jr. Norman, University of Oklahoma press, 1930.
6 p. l., 248 p., 1 l. 24ᵐ.
"First edition."
"One thousand copies of this book were printed for sale."
Bibliography: p. ₁233₁–240.

1. Petroleum industry and trade—U. S.   I. Title.   30–31998
Library of Congress   HD9565.L6
    Copyright A 30780   338.2

TxU OO OC1 Ok
NL 0450211   DLC WaTC MB MiU OU OC1W CU InU NcD TU

Logan, Lloyd.
Boys and girls of Ridgeway, by Lloyd Logan. Rock Island, Ill., Augustana book concern ₁1926₁
180 p. front., plates. 17½ᵐ.

CONTENTS.—The armor of light.—How the New Year came in.—A prisoner of honor.—Young Florida financiers.—Nannette's investment.—Nannette's sea voyage.—Choosing the May queen.—Mammy Eliza 'splains.—A diamond in the rough.—Under the harvest moon.—From an angel's point of view.—Heart of gold—Providing Christmas dinner.

1. Title.   26–17611
Library of Congress   PZ7.L828Bo

NL 0450212   DLC

VOLUME 338

LOGAN, LLOYD.
Boys and girls of Ridgeway, by Lloyd Logan. [2. ed.]
Rock Island, Ill., Augustana book concern [1927, c1926]
180 p. front., plates. 18cm.

CONTENTS. -- The armor of light. -- How the New Year came in. -- A
prisoner of honor. -- Young Florida financiers. -- Nannette's investment. --
Nannette's sea voyage. -- Choosing the May queen. -- Mammy Eliza 'splains.
-- A diamond in the rough. -- Under the harvest moon. -- From an angel's
point of view. -- Heart of gold. -- Providing Christmas dinner.

I. Title.

NL 0450213   NN

Logan, Lloyd.
My life with a pat of butter; from hearthstone to horizon, by
Lloyd Logan. Philadelphia: The Union Press [cop. 1915]. 32 p.
12°.

Title and text within ornamental border.
"This story of country life won...a prize of two hundred dollars, offered by
The Ladies' home journal. The author has enlarged it for publication in this form."

I. Country life, U. S.

August 27, 1919.

NL 0450214   NN

Logan, Lloyd, 1890–
An investigation of the manufacture of water gas with
especial reference to the decomposition of steam ... By Lloyd
Logan ... Baltimore, 1929.
7 p. l., 105 numb. l., 1 l. incl. plates, tab., diagrs. 27½ x 21½ᶜᵐ.

Thesis (ᴘʜ. ᴅ.)—Johns Hopkins university, 1930.
Biographical note.
Imprint date changed in manuscript to 1931.
Mimeographed.
Bibliography: leaves 92-97.

1. Water-gas. 2. Steam.

Library of Congress   TP760.L6 1930   33–30252
Johns Hopkins Univ.   Libr.

665.7

DLC MH
NL 0450215   MdBJ NN MB NIC CU NcU ICJ CtY MiU OCl OU

Logan, Louise.
Doctor Tam and nurse Merton, by Louise Logan ... New
York, Arcadia house, inc., 1941.
256 p. 19½ᶜᵐ.

I. Title.   42–2571

Library of Congress   PZ3.L8293Do

NL 0450216   DLC

Logan, Louise.
Nurse, by Louise Logan ... New York, Arcadia house, inc.,
1940.
256 p. 19½ᶜᵐ.

I. Title.   40–31632

Library of Congress   PZ3.L8293Nu

NL 0450217   DLC

Logan, Louise.
Nurse Merton, army spy, by Louise Logan ... New York,
Arcadia house, inc., 1942.
256 p. 19½ᶜᵐ.

I. Title.   42–14630

Library of Congress   PZ3.L8293Num

NL 0450218   DLC

Logan, Louise.
Nurse Merton comes home, by Louise Logan. New York,
Arcadia house, inc., 1946.
256 p. 19ᶜᵐ.

I. Title.   46–819

Library of Congress   PZ3.L8293Nun

NL 0450219   DLC

Logan, Louise.
Nurse Merton, desert captive, by Louise Logan. New York,
Arcadia house, inc., 1943.
255 p. 19ᶜᵐ.

I. Title.   43–9101

Library of Congress   PZ3.L8293Nuo

NL 0450220   DLC

Logan, Louise.
Nurse Merton in the Caribbean, by Louise Logan. New
York, Arcadia house, inc., 1943.
256 p. 19½ᶜᵐ.

I. Title.   43–2626

Library of Congress   PZ3.L8293Nup

NL 0450221   DLC OU

Logan, Louise.
Nurse Merton in the Pacific, by Louise Logan. New York,
Arcadia house, inc., 1944.
256 p. 19½ᶜᵐ.

I. Title.   44–7516

Library of Congress   PZ3.L8293Nur

NL 0450222   DLC WaSp

Logan, Louise.
Nurse Merton on the Russian front, by Louise Logan. New
York, Arcadia house inc., 1945.
256 p. 19ᶜᵐ.

I. Title.   45–1223

Library of Congress °   PZ3.L8293Nus

NL 0450223   DLC ICRl

Logan, Louise.
Nurse Merton, Washington assignment, by Louise Logan.
New York, Arcadia house, inc., 1943.
256 p. 19½ᶜᵐ.

I. Title.   43–16770

Library of Congress   PZ3.L8293Nut

NL 0450224   DLC

Logan, Louise.
Susan Merton, civilian, by Louise Logan. New York, Arcadia house, inc., 1946.
256 p. 19½ᶜᵐ.

I. Title.   46–19792

Library of Congress   PZ3.L8293Sr

NL 0450225   DLC WaE

Logan, Louise.
Susan Merton, first lieutenant, by Louise Logan ... New
York, Arcadia house, inc., 1942.
256 p. 19½ᶜᵐ.

1. World war, 1939– —Fiction. I. Title.

Library of Congress   PZ3.L8293St   42–20820

NL 0450226   DLC

Logan, Louise.
Susan Merton, nurse, by Louise Logan ... New York,
Arcadia house, inc., 1941.
254 p. 19½ᶜᵐ.

I. Title.   41–15446

Library of Congress   PZ3.L8293Su

NL 0450227   DLC

Logan, Louise.
Susan Merton on the home front, by Louise Logan ... New
York, Arcadia house, inc., 1944.
256 p. 19½ᶜᵐ.

I. Title.   44–4510

Library of Congress   PZ3.L8293Sw

NL 0450228   DLC WaSp

Logan, Louise.
Susan Merton's daughter, by Louise Logan. New York,
Arcadia house, inc., 1947.
255 p. 19½ᶜᵐ.

I. Title.

PZ3.L8293Sx   47–17701

NL 0450229   DLC WaE

Logan, Lyman S., joint author.

Haney, Lewis Henry, 1882–
Brokers' loans; a study in the relation between speculative
credits and the stock market, business, and banking, by Lewis
H. Haney, Lyman S. Logan [and] Henry S. Gavens ... New
York and London, Harper & brothers, 1932.

VOLUME 338

Logan, M.
An address to the naval and commercial maritime interests of the public, on the new establishment of the spire buoy and marine pyramid; briefly explaining the importance and great necessity of an entire change of system, in the ineffectual plans, at present employed for the preservation of seamen's lives; with the immense national interest and property depending on the perfection or complete security of coast-navigation. By M. Logan... London: Printed by W. Marchant, 1815. 17, 3 p. 26½cm.

Manuscript notes.

PROUDFIT COLLECTION.
892099A. 1. Buoys. 2. Shipping— Safety measures.
June 30, 1937

NL 0450231 NN

Logan, M
Observations relative to the invention of the marine pyramid, or spire-buoy; extracted from Logan's theory and practice of current and coast sailing, with the art and practice of complete buoyage; for the safety of seamen, trade, and shipping, in dangerous navigation. London, H. L. Galabin, 1798. iv, 8–21, 23 p. illus. 27cm.

1. Buoys.
March 10, 1948

NL 0450232 NN

Logan, M. Frances.
Stories of New York state, by M. Frances Logan... Rochester, N. Y.: Dept. of Public Instruction [192-?]. 63 p. illus. (incl. map.) 12°.

HANFORD COLLECTION.
469798A. 1. New York (state)— Hist., Juvenile. I. Rochester, N. Y.
Public Instruction Department.
August 19, 1930

NL 0450233 NN

Logan, M Frances
Stories of Rochester, by M. Frances Logan. Rochester, N. Y., Rochester shop school press, 1914. 28 p. illus.

Contents.--The wampum belt.--The first white baby.--The white dog.--The bridge.--Opening the Canal.

NL 0450234 NNC NBU

Logan, M Frances.
Stories of Rochester. Rochester, N.Y. Dept.of public instruction [1921] 63 p. illus.,map. 19 cm.

1.Rochester, N.Y. - Hist.

NL 0450235 NjP NN CtY

Logan, M.H., 1855-
see Logan, Milburn Hill, 1855.

PZ7
.L835D **Logan, M J M**
Di's Jumbo. New York, T. Whittaker [188-?] 64 p. illus. 17cm.

NL 0450237 ViU

Logan, Malcolm.
... The aeroplane simply explained ... by Malcolm Logan ... 2d ed. London, Sir I. Pitman & sons, ltd. [1941]
47 p. illus., diagrs. 18½ᶜᵐ. (Pitman's "Simply explained" series)
"First edition, June, 1939. Second edition, Sept., 1940. Reprinted, March, 1941."

1. Aeroplanes. I. Title.
41-20681
Library of Congress TL670.L63 1941
629.13334

NL 0450238 DLC

Logan, Malcolm.
The Civil air guard book, by Malcolm Logan. With a foreword by Captain Harold Balfour ... London, Nicholson & Watson, limited, 1939.
vii, 151, [1] p. front., pl., diagrs. 19ᶜᵐ.
"First published in 1939."
Illustrated lining-papers in colors.

1. Gt. Brit. Civil air guard. 2. Aeroplanes—Piloting. I. Title.
42-14719
Library of Congress TL560.3.G7L6
629.13071142

NL 0450239 DLC

4036E
.109 **Logan, Malcolm.**
Flying simply explained; a simple explanation of the general procedure of flying a light aeroplane. London, I. Pitman [1939]
45 p. illus. 19 cm. (Pitman's "Simply explained" series)

1. Aeroplanes—Piloting. I. Title.

NL 0450240 MB

TL760
L831gL **Logan, Malcolm**
Gliding and soaring simply explained. Drawings by Francis Rodker. London, I. Pitman [1942]
32p. illus. 19cm. (Pitman's "Simply explained" series)

1.Gliding and soaring I.Title

NL 0450241 CoD

Logan, Malcolm, joint author.

[Sann, Paul]
Must we have slums? [New York] New York city housing authority, 1937.

Logan, Malcolm Roderick, 1901–
The home front digest, by Malcolm Logan. [New York] Howell, Soskin [1942]
3 p. l., 9-231 p. illus. 19½ cm.
Page 231 is mounted on inside of back cover.

1. Civilian defense. 2. World war, 1939-1945—Economic aspects— U. S. I. Title.
UA926.L56 355.23 42-19244 rev

NL 0450243 DLC WaS OrP Or NcU OClh OClW CaBVaU

PZ3
.L82843 **Logan, Malcolm Roderick, 1901-**
On **Logan, Carolynne Chitwood.**
One of these seven, a Justus Drum mystery, by Carolynne and Malcolm Logan. New York, Mystery house, 1946.

Logan, Malcolm Roderick, 1901-

Nixon, Laurence A *ed.*
What will happen and what to do when war comes, edited by Larry Nixon. By Elmer C. Walzer [and others] ... New York, The Greystone press [*1939]

Logan, Margaret, joint author
SF525
.C973 **Cumming, A R**
Beekeeping, craft and hobby [by] A. R. Cumming and Margaret Logan. Edinburgh, Oliver and Boyd [1950]

Logan, Margaret Ann, 1840–1919.
Sweet alyssum; poems by Margaret A. Logan. Buffalo, C. W. Moulton, 1894.
vi p., 1 l. [9]–104 p. 17½ᵐ.

I. Title.
35-36701
Library of Congress PS2249.L616
811.49

NL 0450247 DLC MsU TNJ NBuHi ViU NBuG

Logan, Margaret C
S124me.1 ... Plant succession on the Oreti river sand dunes. By Margaret C.Logan ... and J.E.Holloway ... [n.p.,1934]
"Reprinted from the Transactions of the Royal society of New Zealand, vol.64,1934."
"Literature cited": p.139.

NL 0450248 CtY

Logan, Marguerite.
A guide to the teaching of the new geography, by Marguerite Logan ... Ann Arbor, Mich., Edwards brothers, inc., 1934.
2 p. l., ii–iv, 45, 45a–45k, 46–104 numb. l. incl. illus., plates, diagrs. 27ᵐ.
"Lithoprinted."
Contains bibliographies.

1. Geography—Study and teaching.
36-13027
Library of Congress G73.L67
Copyright AA 161596 910.7

NL 0450249 DLC IU ICU

Logan, Marguerite.
A guide to the teaching of the new geography, by Marguerite Logan ... [Ann Arbor, Mich., Edwards brothers, inc., 1941]
ix, 24, 21-24, 21-224 p. incl. illus. (maps) plates, diagrs. 27 x 21½ᵐ.
Pages 21-24 in triplicate.
Lithoprinted.
"Second edition."
Includes bibliographies.

1. Geography—Study and teaching.
41-6992
Library of Congress G73.L67 1941
910.7

NL 0450250 DLC

VOLUME 338

Logan, Maria, fl.1793.
*EC75   Poems on several occasions. By Maria Logan.
18286   York:Printed for the author,by Wilson,Spence,
793p   and Mawman.Anno 1793.
         4°. 14p.,1l.,[9]-64p. 23.5cm.
         "Subscribers' names": p.[5]-14 (1st count).

NL   0450251   MH NcU

LOGAN,MARIA, fl. 1793
    Poems on several occasions. By Maria
Logan. Second edition. York, Printed for
the author by Wilson, Spence, and Mawman,
1793.
    64 p.   4to

    Bound in modern wrappers; uncut.

NL   0450252   InU CtY MdBP IU

Logan, Marjorie.
    Design in the fine arts in the United States,
1900-1930
        see under Bassett, Agnes.

HX15   Logan, Mark
Y3   The anatomy of McCarthyism, by Mark Logan and
v.40:4   Sam Douglas. [New York, New Century Publishers, 1953]
x   22 p. 19cm. [Yates collection, v. 40, no. 4]

         Cover title.
         "Appeared originally in the June 1953 issue of the monthly
         magazine, Political Affairs."

           1. McCarthy, Joseph Raymond, 1909-1957. 2. Communism -
         - U.S. - 1917- . I. Douglas, Sam, joint author. II. Title.

NL   0450254   CU-B WHi NN KU

Logan, Martha, *pseud.*
    see
McLean, Nemadji Beth (Bailey) 1892–

Logan, Martha, 1702–1779.
    Works by this author printed in America before 1801 are available
    in this library in the Readex Microprint edition of Early American
    Imprints published by the American Antiquarian Society.
    This collection is arranged according to the numbers in Charles
    Evans' American Bibliography.

NL   0450256   DLC

[Logan, Martha, 1702-1779.]
    Directions for managing a kitchen-garden every month in
the year./ Done by a lady. (In: South Carolina almanack.
Germantown, 1755. 12°. l. 8 verso — 10 recto.)

    Believed to be the earliest American treatise on the subject known to be extant.

1. Gardening (Kitchen). 2. Title.   May 11, 1915.

NL   0450257   NN

Logan, Marvel Mills, 1875–
    U. S. *Congress. Senate. Committee on the judiciary.*
    ... Establish uniform requirements affecting government con-
tracts ... Report. ⟨To accompany S. 215⟩ ... [Washington,
U. S. Govt. print. off., 1935]

Logan, Marvel Mills, 1875–
    U. S. *Congress. Senate. Committee on claims.*
    ... French spoliations ... Report. ⟨To accompany S.
2106⟩ ... [Washington, U. S. Govt. print. off., 1937]

Logan, Marvel Mills, 1875–
    U. S. *Congress. Senate. Committee on military affairs.*
    ... Glenn H. Curtiss ... Report. ⟨To accompany H. R.
11980⟩ ... [Washington, U. S. Govt. print. off., 1933]

Logan, Marvel Mills, 1875–
    U. S. *Congress. Senate. Committee on mines and mining.*
    ... Interstate oil compact to conserve oil and gas ... Report.
⟨To accompany S. J. Res. 183⟩ ... [Washington, U. S. Govt.
print. off., 1937]

Logan, Marvel Mills, 1875-1939.
    Proposal to reorganize judicial branch of the
government. Speech in the U. S. Senate, March 2,
1937. Washington, D. C., Government printing
office, 1937.
    Pam.

NL   0450262   KyBgW

JK416   Logan, Marvel Mills, 1875-1939.
.A5   U. S. *Congress. Senate. Committee on the judiciary.*
1939   ... Providing for the more expeditious settlement of disputes
         with the United States, and for other purposes ... Report.
         ⟨To accompany S. 915⟩ [Washington, U. S. Govt. print. off.,
         1939]

Logan, Marvel Mills, 1875–
    Religion and national defense. Speech in
the Senate of the U.S., March 2, 1938.
Washington, U.S. government printing office,
1938.

    Pam.

NL   0450264   KyBgW

Logan, Marvel Mills, 1875–
    ... Reorganization of the federal judiciary; speech of Hon.
M. M. Logan of Kentucky in the Senate of the United States ...
[Washington, U. S. Govt. print. off. 1937]
    16 p. 23½ᵐ.
    Caption title.
    At head of title: (Not printed at government expense)
    "Printed in the Congressional record of July 22, 1937."

    1. U. S. Supreme court.   I. Title.   41-32177

NL   0450265   DLC

Logan, Marvel Mills, 1875–
    U. S. *Congress. Senate. Committee on the judiciary.*
    ... To amend Antitrust act ... Report. ⟨To accompany S.
3154⟩ ... [Washington, U. S. Govt. print. off., 1936]

Logan, Marvel Mills, 1875–
    U. S. *Congress. Senate. Committee on post offices and post
roads.*
    ... To amend the law relating to appointment of postmasters.
Report of the Committee on post offices and post roads on
S. 3022, a bill to amend the law relating to appointment of
postmasters together with the Minority views of Messrs.
O'Mahoney, Logan, La Follette, and Views of Mr. Bridges ...
Washington, U. S. Govt. print. off., 1937.

Logan, Marvel Mills, 1875–
    U. S. *Congress. Senate. Committee on mines and mining.*
    ... War minerals relief statutes ... Report. ⟨To accompany
S. 1432⟩ ... [Washington, U. S. Govt. print. off., 1935]

Logan, Mary, *pseud.*
    see Berenson, Mary (Smith)

Logan, Mary E   *comp.*
    The loganberry, compiled and published by Mary E.
Logan (Mrs. J. H. Logan) Oakland, Calif., [1955.
    20 p. illus. 23 cm.
    Includes bibliography.

    1. Loganberries.

    SB386.L61.8   634.714   KR—91959 †

    DNAL
    TU TxU OU MiU IU ViU WaS MU OrP WaSpG OrSaW IEN
NL   0450270   DLC CaBVa IdU OrCS IEN NcD CU NIC

Logan, Mary Simmerson (Cunningham) "Mrs. J.
A. Logan," 1838-1923, ed.
    ... The American sentinel: a patriotic illustrated monthly.
v. 1, no. 1; Oct. 1898. New York, The American sentinel,
1898.

Logan, Mary Simmerson (Cunningham) 1838-
1923, ed.
    The home manual, everybody's guide in
social, domestic, and business life, a
treasury of useful information for the million... prepared by Mrs. John A. Logan,
assisted by Prof. William Mathews, Catherine Owen, and Will Carleton. Boston,
Thayer [c1889]
    vi, 507p. illus.

NL   0450272   MCR MH

Logan, Mary Simmerson (Cunningham) "*Mrs.* J. A. Logan,"
1838-1923, *ed.*
    The home manual. Everybody's guide in social, domestic,
and business life. A treasury of useful information for the
million ... Prepared by Mrs. John A. Logan, assisted by Prof.
William Mathews, Catherine Owen [pseud.] and Will Carleton ... Chicago, Ill., Philadelphia, Pa. [etc.] H. J. Smith & co.
[1889]
    2 p. l., vi p., 1 l., 507 p. illus., plates, ports. (incl. front.) 24½ᵐ.
    1. Encyclopedias and dictionaries. I. Mathews, William, 1818-1909,
joint ed. II. Nitsch, Mrs. Helen Alice (Mathews) d. 1889, joint ed. III.
Carleton, Will, 1845-1912, joint ed.
                                                            19—3002
    Library of Congress   AG105.L8

NL   0450273   DLC WaS OrCS IdU OrU ViU MiD MH

*
AG105   Logan, Mary Simmerson (Cunningham) 1838-1923,
.L8   ed.
1889
         The home manual. Everybody's guide in
         social, domestic, and business life. A
         treasury of useful information for the
         million. Prepared by Mrs. John A. Logan,
         assisted by Prof. William Mathews, Catherine
         Owen [pseud.] and Will Carleton ... New
         York, A. Peniston, 1889.
             vi p., 2 l., 15-533 p. illus., plates, ports.
         26ᵐ.
             1. Encyclopedias and   dictionaries. I.Mathews,
         William, 1818-1909,   ed. II.Nitsch, Helen
         Alice (Mathews) d.   1889, joint ed. III.Car-
         leton, Will, 1846-   1912, joint ed.

NL   0450274   ViU

VOLUME 338

Logan, Mary Simmerson (Cunningham) 1838-1923.
The home manual. Everybody's guide in social, domestic, and business life. Prepared by Mrs. John A. Logan. Philadelphia, Standard Pub. Co., ₍c1889₎
533p. illus.

NL 0450275   ICRL

MANN
TX
145
L83
Vault

Logan, Mary Simmerson (Cunningham) 1838-1923.
The home manual. Everybody's guide in social, domestic and business life. A treasury of useful information for the million,... Prepared by Mrs. John A. Logan, William Mathews, Catherine Owen and Will Carleton. Washington, Brodix, ₍c1889₎
viii, 512 p. illus. 24 cm.

1. Women's encyclopedias and dictionaries. I. Mathews, William, 1818-1909. II. Nitsch, Helen Alice (Matthews) d. 1889. III. Carleton, Will, 1845-1912. IV. Title.

NL 0450276   NIC MH

LOGAN, *Mary Simmerson (Cunningham) 1838-1923.*
Letters of Mrs. John A. Logan (Oct. 6, 1921) and Gen. John A. Logan (June 5, 1884) to C. B. Watson, and letter of Judge Watson Nov. 11, 1921) to Miss Marvin concerning the Logan letters.
1, 1, 5, p.

NL 0450277   Or

1889

Logan, Mrs. Mary Simmerson (Cunningham) 1838-1923.
The Logan memorial hall. Mrs. Mary S. Logan tells the story of its inception. Washington, the Post, 1889.
1 L 12° [Toner Excerpts]

NL 0450278   DLC

Logan, Mary Simmerson (Cunningham) "Mrs. J.A. Logan," 1838-
Thomas, Katherine Elwes.
Official, diplomatic, and social etiquette of Washington, comp. by Katherine Elwes Thomas, with an introductory note by Mrs. John A. Logan. New York, The Cassell publishing co. ₍1895₎

Logan, Mary Simmerson (Cunningham) "Mrs. J. A. Logan," 1838-1923, ed.
Our national government; or, Life and scenes in our national capital. Portraying the wonderful operations in all the great departments, and describing every important function of our law-making bodies ... With sketches of the presidents and their wives ... from Washington's to Taft's administration. Edited by Mrs. John A. Logan ... Minneapolis, Minn., H. L. Baldwin company ₍1908₎
1 p. l., xxxii, 33-770 p. incl. illus., plates, ports., facsims. front., plates, ports. 23ᶜᵐ.
Title vignette.
Originally published in 1901 (except the last two chapters) with title: Thirty years in Wash-   ington ...
1. Washington, D. C.   2. U. S.—Executive departments.
3. Presidents—U. S.—Biog.   I. Title.
Library of Congress   F194.L83   9-8747 Revised

OC1WHi
NL 0450280   DLC WaS WaTC OrU OkU MB NcD NjP MnU OC1

Logan, *Mary Simmerson (Cunningham) "Mrs. J.A. Logan," 1838-1943.*
Our national government, or life and scenes in our national capital. Minn., 1909.

NL 0450281   DN

Logan, Mary Simmerson (Cunningham) "*Mrs. J. A. Logan,*" 1838-1923.
... The part taken by women in American history, by Mrs. John A. Logan; with special introductions by Mrs. Donald McLean ... Mrs. Matthew T. Scott ... Mrs. Harriet Taylor Upton ₍and others₎   Wilmington, Del., The Perry-Nalle publishing co., 1912.
xii p., 1 l., 927 p. front., plates, ports. 24 cm.
"Partial list of books consulted": p. vi.

1. Women in the U. S.—Biog.   I. Title.

E176.L83   12—2975

OFH NjP NN Vi NBuU CoU OrU
NL 0450282   DLC MtU WaS NcD GU OrU OFH PIm OO OC1

Logan, Mary Simmerson (Cunningham) "*Mrs. J. A. Logan,*" 1838-
Reminiscences of a soldier's wife; an autobiography, by Mrs. John A. Logan ... New York, C. Scribner's sons, 1913.
xvi, 470 p. front., plates, ports., facsims. 21½ᶜᵐ. $2.50

1. U. S.—Pol. & govt.—1865-   2. U. S.—Hist.—Civil war—Personal narratives. 3. Washington, D. C.—Soc. life & cust.   I. Title.

Library of Congress   E661.L83   13—22377

CaBVaU
NjP OO ViU OC1 NN WaSp Or FMU NcGU KU-M WaS CaBVa
NL 0450283   DLC OrCS OrP WaT KEmT NBuU CLU NcD MB

Logan, Mary Simmerson (Cunningham) "Mrs. J.A. Logan," 1838-1923.
Reminiscences of a soldier's wife; an autobiography, by Mrs. John A. Logan ... New York, C. Scribner's sons, 1916.
xvi, 470 p. front., plates, ports., facsims. 21.5 cm.
1. U. S.- Pol. & govt. - 1865 -   2. U. S.- Hist.- Civil war - Personal narratives. 3. Washington, D. C.- Soc. life & cust. I. Title.

NL 0450284   NcD OC1W

Logan, Mary Simmerson (Cunningham) "*Mrs. J. A. Logan,*" 1838-1923.
Thirty years in Washington; or, Life and scenes in our national capital. Portraying the wonderful operations in all the great departments, and describing every important function of our national government ... With sketches of the presidents and their wives ... from Washington's to Roosevelt's administration. Edited by Mrs. John A. Logan ... Hartford, Conn., A. D. Worthington & co. ₍1901₎
1 p. l., xxxii, 33-752 p. incl. illus., plates, facsims. front. (port.) plates. 23ᶜᵐ.

Title vignette.
Republished in 1908, with two additional chapters, under title: Our national government ...

1. Washington, D. C.   2. U. S. — Executive departments.   3. Presidents—U. S.—Biog.   I. Title.

Library of Congress   F194.L82   1-27897 Revised

MeB CaOTP ICRL DSI CoFS
OO NN NcD MB WaE MtHi DI FU TxFTC AAP FTaSU UU
NL 0450286   DLC IdB Or WaSpG CU OOxM OC1 MiU ODW ViU

Logan, Mrs. Mary Taylor, ed.

Taylor, Harrison D   1802-1889.
Ohio County, Kentucky, in the olden days; a series of old newspaper sketches of fragmentary history, by Harrison D. Taylor, prepared for publication in book form by his granddaughter, Mary Taylor Logan, with an introduction by Otto A. Rothert. Louisville, Ky., J. P. Morton & company, incorporated, 1926.

Logan, Maurice S   1859-
Musicology; a text-book for schools and for general use, by Maurice S. Logan. New York, Cochrane publishing company; ₍etc., etc.₎ ₍1909₎
231 p., 2 l. incl. tables, charts. 21ᶜᵐ. $1.50

1. Music—Manuals, text-books, etc.   I. Title.

Library of Congress   MT6.L88   9—28086

NL 0450288   DLC WaS

MT6
L65

Logan, Maurice S   , 1859-
Musicology; a text-book for schools and for general use by Maurice S. Logan. New York, Hinds, Noble & Eldredge ₍c1909₎
228p., 4 l. incl. tables, charts. 21cm.

1. Music - Manuals, text-books, etc.
2. Musicology.

NL 0450289   IaU MtU CU IMunS NN TU MB IU CoU WU

Logan, Maurice S   1859-
Sabbath theology; a reply to those who insist that Saturday is the only true Sabbath day, by Maurice Logan ... New York, Lord's day alliance of the U. S. ₍1913₎
xvii, ₍2₎, 20-451, ₍1₎ p. front., illus. 19¼ᶜᵐ.

I. Title.

16-8264

NL 0450290   DLC

Logan, Maurice S   1859-
Sabbath theology; a reply to those who insist that Saturday is the only true Sabbath day, by Maurice S. Logan ... New York city, Pub. under the auspices of the New York Sabbath committee ₍1913₎
xvii, ₍2₎, 20-451 p. front., illus. 19¼ᶜᵐ. $1.50

* I. Title.

13-25393 Revised

NL 0450291   DLC NcD MB NjNbS

LOGAN, Milan A₍lexander₎.
A method for the determination of calcium in the presence of large quantities of magnesium and phosphate. A method for the determination of magnesium in the presence of large quantities of phosphate. A study of calcium excretion. ₍Thesis, Harvard University, 1928.₎
Manuscript. 4°. 2 plates and table.

NL 0450292   MH

Logan, Milan Alexander.
₍Miscellaneous pamphlets, reprints, etc.₎
v. 23 cm.

NL 0450293   OCU

Logan, M₍ilburn₎ H₍ill₎ 1855-
A system of organic chemistry, by M. H. Logan ... San Francisco, Dempster bros., 1893.
181, ₍clxxxii₎-cci p. tables. 21ᶜᵐ.

1. Chemistry, Organic.

Library of Congress   QD253.L83   4-30371†

NL 0450294   DLC

VOLUME 338

Logan, Milla (Zenovich)
Bring along laughter, by Milla Logan. New York, Random house ₁1947₎
viii, 247 p. 21ᶜᵐ.
"First printing."

ɪ. Title.
PS3523.O35B7						818.5						47-561

NL 0450295			DLC Or OrP WaS WaSp WaT CU-B TU

Logan, Milla (Zenovich)
Cousins and commissars; an intimate visit to Tito's Yugoslavia. New York, C. Scribner's Sons, 1949.
222 p. 22 cm.

1. Yugoslavia—Descr. & trav. 2. Yugoslavia—Soc. condit.
ɪ. Title.
DR309.L6						914.97						49-11123*

								NcC OU MtBC Or OrP OrU WaE WaT OrStbM
NL 0450296			DLC CaBVa IdB WaS MU OkU MoU CoU PP PPFr

Logan, Myrtle Fuller.
The vase of bronze, by Myrtle Fuller Logan. Boston, The Christopher publishing house ₁ʻ1927₎
45 p. 20¼ᵐ.
Poems: p. 27-45.

ɪ. Title.
											27-24014
Library of Congress			PS3523.O353V3 1927

NL 0450297			DLC

Logan, Olive (Logan) 1839-1909.
The American abroad. By Olive Logan. ₁n. p., 1882₎
cover-title, 16 p. 21½ᵐ.

1. American exchange in Europe.
											3-6596 Revised
Library of Congress			D910.L83

NL 0450298			DLC

Logan, Mrs. Olive (Logan) 1839-1909.
The ancestry of Brudder Bones. By Olive Logan. n. p., 1879.
p. [687]-98	illus.	26 cm.
From- Harper's, April 1879.
Cover title.

NL 0450299			RPB

Logan, Olive (Logan) 1839-1909.
Apropos of women and theatres. With a paper or two on Parisian topics. By Olive Logan ... New York, Carleton; London, S. Low, son, & co., 1869.
240 p. 19ᵐ.

ɪ. Title.
											42-46847
Library of Congress			PS2249.L62A8

				WaSpG ICU NN IU MiU MB MWA OCU NBuG MiU TxU
NL 0450300			DLC OrP IaU NIC CU MsU MiDA CaOTP IEN NcU

Logan, Olive (Logan) 1839-1909.
Apropos of women and theatres. With a paper or two on Parisian topics. New York, Carleton; London, S. Low, 1869.
(American culture series, 203:9)
Microfilm copy (positive) made in 1962 by University Microfilms, Ann Arbor, Mich.
Collation of the original: 240 p.

ɪ. Title.
Microfilm 01291 reel 203, no. 9 E						Mic 63-42

NL 0450301			DLC FTaSU KEmT PSt ICRL MoU

LOGAN, Mrs. Olive (Logan), 1839-1909.
Apropos of women and theatres, with a paper or two on Parisian topics. New York, Carleton, etc., etc., 1870.

Binder's title: Women and theatres.

NL 0450302			MH

Logan, Olive (Logan) 1839-1909.
Apropos of women and theatres. With a paper or two on Parisian topics. New York, Carleton, 1872.
240 p.	19 cm.
1. Woman. 2. Actresses. ɪ. Title.

NL 0450303			MdBP

Logan, Olive (Logan) 1839-1909.
Before the footlights and behind the scenes: a book about "the show business" in all its branches: from puppet shows to grand opera; from mountebanks to menageries; from learned pigs to lecturers; from burlesque blondes to actors and actresses: with some observations and reflections (original and reflected) on morality and immorality in amusements: thus exhibiting the "show world" as seen from within, through the eyes of the former actress, as well as from without, through

the eyes of the present lecturer and author. By Olive Logan ... Philadelphia, Pa. ₁etc.₎ Parmelee & co.; San Francisco, Cal., H. H. Bancroft & co., 1870.
xv, ₁17₎-612 p.	illus., plates, ports.	22½ᵐ.

1. Actors—Correspondence, reminiscences, etc.		ɪ. Title.
											44-11056
Library of Congress			PN2287.L6A25

				NB ViU WaU TU PBL ICN PSt
				CtY MiD ODW OCl OU MiU ICarbS PPEB NcU InU KU GU
NL 0450305			DLC WaS MtU OrU CaBVaU NIC MoU OO NcD

₁Logan, Mrs. Olive (Logan)₎ 1839-1909
Chateau Frissac; or, Home scenes in France./ By Chroniqueuse ₁pseud.₎ ... London, Tinsley brothers, 1862.
viii, 827 p.	18½ᵐ.

ɪ. Title.
											8-28120
Library of Congress			PZ3.L8205C

NL 0450306			DLC

PZ3
.L8295		**Logan, Mrs. Olive (Logan), 1839-1909**
Ch				Chateau Frissac; or, Home scenes in France.
				By Olive Logan ... New York, D. Appleton and company, 1865.
				viii, 329 p.	19ᶜᵐ.

				I. Title.	II. Title: Home scenes in France.

NL 0450307			MB CtY NNC NN MH OClW

M-film
810.8		Logan, Mrs. Olive (Logan), 1859-1909.
Am35			Chateau Frissac; or, Home scenes in France.
37-5		By Olive Logan... New York, D. Appleton, 1865.
				viii, 329 p.

				Microfilm (positive) Ann Arbor, Mich., University Microfilms, 1967. 5th title of 7. 35 mm. (American fiction series, reel 37.5)

NL 0450308			KEmT CU

Logan, Mrs. Olive (Logan) Sikes, 1839-1909
Olive Logan's Christmas story, Somebody's stocking ... New York, The American news company ₁ʻ1867₎
16 p.	23½ᵐ.

											8-28116†
Library of Congress			PZ3.L8295S

NL 0450309			DLC

FILM
4274		Logan, Olive (Logan) 1859-1909.
PR
v.2		Olive Logans Christmas Story: Somebody's
reel		stocking, New York, American News Co.
L11		₁cop. 1867₎
				16 p.	(Wright American fiction, v.II, 1851-1875, no. 1576, Research Publications Microfilm, Reel L-11)

				1.	Christmas stories.
				I.	Title.

NL 0450310			CU KEmT

Micro
3			Logan, Olive (Logan) 1839-1909
				Olive Logan's Christmas Story, Somebody's stocking. New York, The American News Company ₁c1867₎
				16p.	24cm.

				Micro-transparency (negative). Louisville, Ky., Lost Cause Press, 1969. 2 cards. 7.5x12.5cm. (L. H. Wright. American fiction, 1851-1875, no.1576)

NL 0450311			PSt

Logan, Mrs. Olive (Logan), 1839-1909
Get thee behind me, Satan! A home-born book of home-truths. By Olive Logan (Mrs. Wirt Sikes) ... New York, Adams, Victor & co., 1872.
296 p.	19½ᵐ.

1. Home.										9—5664
Library of Congress			HQ734.L7

NL 0450312			DLC InU ICRL ViU TU NcA-S MiU MB

Logan, Mrs. Olive (Logan), 1839-1909.
... The good Mr. Bagglethorpe. By Olive Logan ... New-York, The American news company, 1869.
27 p.	23ᵐ.
At head of title: Olive Logan's new story.

											8-28118†
Library of Congress			PZ3.L8295G

NL 0450313			DLC MB

VOLUME 338

M-film
810.8
Am35
69-2

Logan, Mrs. Olive (Logan) 1839-1909
The good Mr. Bagglethorpe. By Olive Logan.
New York, The American news company, 1869.
27 p.

At head of title: Olive Logan's new story.
Microfilm (positive) Ann Arbor, Mich.,
University Microfilms, 1968. 2nd title of 13.
35 mm. (American fiction series, reel 69.2)

NL 0450314   KEmT CU

Micro
3

Logan, Olive (Logan) 1839-1909
The Good Mr. Bagglethorpe. By Olive Logan.
New-York, The American News Company, 1869
[c1868]
27p. 23cm.
At head of title: Olive Logan's new story.
Micro-transparency (negative). Louisville,
Ky., Lost Cause Press, 1969. 2 cards.
7.5x12.5cm. (L. H. Wright. American fiction,
1851-1875, no.1575)

NL 0450315   PSt

Logan, Olive (Logan) 1839-1909.
The mimic world, and public exhibitions; their history,
their morals, and effects. Philadelphia, New-World Pub.
Co., 1871.
500 p. illus., ports. 22 cm.

1. Theater—U. S.   I. Title.

PN2287.L6A3   11-19289 rev*

NL 0450316   WaU NIC NNC FTaSU CU TxU
DLC PSt MH OC OrP MB NN TxU MiU NcD LU

Logan, Mrs. Olive (Logan) 1839-1909.
Olive Logan's new Christmas story. John Morris's
money ... New York, The American news company, 1867.
55 p. 24cm.

8-28117†

Library of Congress   PZ3.L8295J

NL 0450317   DLC MB

FILM
4274
PR
v.2
reel
L11

Logan, Olive (Logan) 1839-1909.
Olive Logan's new Christmas story: Somebody's stocking. John Morris's money.
New York, American News Co., 1867.
55 p. (Wright American fiction, v.II,
1851-1875, no. 1577, Research Publications
Microfilm, Reel L-11)

1. Christmas stories.

NL 0450318   CU KEmT

DC
733
L83
1861

Logan, Olive (Logan) 1839-1909.
Photographs of Paris life; a record of the
politics, art, fashion, and anecdote of Paris
during the past eighteen months, by
Chroniqueuse [pseud.], London, W. Tinsley,
1861.
xv, 344 p. 19cm.

1. Paris—Descr.   I. Title.

NL 0450319   NIC MH

[Logan, Mrs. Olive (Logan)] 1839-1909.
Photographs of Paris life; being a record of the politics, art,
fashion, and anecdote of Paris, during the past eighteen months.
By Chroniqueuse [pseud.], 2d ed. London, Tinsley brothers,
1862.
xv, 344 p. 19cm.

1. Paris—Descr.   I. Title.
4-26540 Revised

Library of Congress   DC733.L83

NL 0450320   DLC

Logan, Olive (Logan) 1839-1909.
A talk about the green-room and its people.
[New York. 186-?] 481-486 pp. 22½ cm.
Relates to the American stage.

K4945 — T.r. — United States. Theatres.

NL 0450321   MB

Logan, Mrs. Olive (Logan) 1839-1909.
They met by chance: a society novel. By Olive Logan,
(Mrs. Wirt Sikes,) ... New York, Adams, Victor & co.
[1873]
1 p. l., [7]-320 p. 19cm.

Library of Congress   PZ3.L8295T   11-7159

NL 0450322   DLC OU InU ViU CLSU

FILM
4274
PR
v.2
reel
L11

Logan, Olive (Logan) 1839-1909.
They met by chance: A society novel.
New York, Adams, Victor [c1873]
320 p. (Wright American fiction, v.II,
1851-1875, no.1578, Research Publications
Microfilm, Reel L-11)

NL 0450323   CU

Micro
3

Logan, Olive (Logan) 1839-1909
They met by chance: a society novel. By
Olive Logan, (Mrs. Wirt Sikes). New York,
Adams, Victor & Co. [c1873]
320p. 19cm.
Micro-transparency (negative). Louisville,
Ky., Lost Cause Press, 1970. 8 cards.
7.5x12.5cm. (L. H. Wright. American fiction,
1851-1875, no.1578)

NL 0450324   PSt

Logan, P. B., 1870-
see   Logan, Preston Breckinridge, 1870-

Logan (P. W.) Catarrhal mucous membrane.
16 pp. 8°. [n. p., 1885.]
Repr. from: South. Pract., Nashville, 1885, vii.

NL 0450326   DNLM

L747
L83

Logan, Patton L.
Service records of the ex-members of company
13, second officers training camp, Ft. Oglethorpe,
Ga., August-November, 1917. [Pref. Pittsburgh,
1919]
30 p. 23 cm.

NL 0450327   PPiHi

Logan, Paul.
Keeping quality of precooked frozen chicken
a la king
see under title

Logan, Preston Breckinridge, 1870-
Interesting facts concerning the Associate, Associate reformed and United Presbyterian churches in America, by
Rev. P. B. Logan. [Oxford, Pa., The Oxford press, 1904]
26 p. plates, facsim. 23½ cm.

1. United Presbyterian church of North America—Hist. 2. Associate synod of North America—Hist. 3. General synod of the Associate Reformed church—Hist. 4. Oxford, Pa. United Presbyterian
church.

BX8982.L7   4—18500

NL 0450329   DLC NN

Logan, R
Report on the financial condition of the Kashmir State,
by R. Logan. Bombay, Printed at the Government Central
Press, 1891.
iii, 78 p. 34 cm.

1. Finance, Public—Kashmir—Accounting.   I. Title.

HJ9927.I 4L63   70-281700
MARC

NL 0450330   DLC

Logan, R. A.

Canada. Dept. of the interior. Northwest Territories
and Yukon branch.
... Canada's Arctic Islands. Log of Canadian expedition, 1922, by J. D. Craig ... With an appendix: Aviation in the Arctic, by Major R. A. Logan, Department of
national defence. Ottawa, F. A. Acland, printer, 1923.

Logan, R. A.

Canada. Dept. of the interior. Northwest territories and
Yukon branch.
... Les îles canadiennes de l'Océan arctique. Journal de
l'expédition canadienne de 1922, par J. D. Craig ... Commission des limites internationales. Avec appendice: L'aviation dans la région arctique, par le Major R. A. Logan, Ministère de la défense nationale. Ottawa, F. A. Acland, imprimeur
du roi, 1924.

Logan, R   F
First Cuban expedition. Diary of M. C. Taylor.
(In Southern magazine. July, 1894. p. 608-655)
pam.

NL 0450333   KyBgW

Logan (R. F.) How to prevent cholera. 25 pp.
8°. Shelbyville, A. C. Ellis, 1873.

NL 0450334   DNLM

VOLUME 338

Logan, R. S.
    see Logan, Robert S., 1864-

Logan, Ralph André
    The sign of the quadrupole interaction energy
in diatomic molecules, by R. A. Logan, R. E.
Coté and P. Kusch. ₍n.p.,₎ 1952₎
    cover-title, ₍280₎-287 p. diagrs., tables.
27 cm.

    R. A. Logan's thesis, Columbia university.
    "Reprinted from the Physical review, vol. 86,
no. 3 ... May 1, 1952."
    Bibliographical footnotes.

NL 0450336   NNC

Logan, Rayford Whittingham, 1897–
    The African mandates in world politics. ₍Washington₎
Public Affairs Press ₍1949, *1948₎
    x, 207 l., 208–220 p. map. 28 cm.
    Includes "References."

    1. Mandates—Africa. 2. Germany—Colonies—Africa. 3. Africa—
Politics. I. Title.
        DT31.L64   960   49–1742*

    OU NNC MH PSt PPT OC1W PPD
NL 0450337   DLC OrU WaS WaT CU CoU ViU MB TxU ICU

Logan, Rayford Whittingham,   ed.
    The attitude of the southern white press toward Negro suf-
frage, 1932–1940; edited by Rayford W. Logan, PH. D., with a
foreword by Charles H. Wesley, PH. D. Washington, D. C.,
The Foundation publishers, 1940.
    cover-title, xii, 115 p. 23ᶜᵐ.

    1. Negroes—Politics and suffrage. 2. Press—Southern states.
I. Title.
    Library of Congress   JK1929.A2L6
                                                    40–30270
    Copyright A 142872   ₍41c2₎   324.15

    ViHaI
NL 0450338   DLC MB NcD PP OC1W OCU ViU OU OC1

Logan, Rayford Whittingnam.
    The diplomatic relations of the United States with Haiti,
1776–1891, by Rayford W. Logan. Chapel Hill, The University of North Carolina press, 1941.
    xi p., 2 l., 516 p. 24ᶜᵐ.
    Bibliography: p. ₍459₎–496. Bibliographical foot-notes.

    1. U. S.—For. rel.—Haiti. 2. Haiti—For. rel.—U. S.   I. Title.
    Library of Congress   E183.8.H2L6
                                                    41–5260
                                                    327.73097294

    ViU OC1 OCU Or MtU KU ICarbS OrCS OrU NB
NL 0450339   DLC WaS MB NIC NcD PPT PSt PU PBm OO

Logan, Rayford Whittingham.
    Education in Haiti, by Rayford W. Logan ... ₍Washing-
ton₎, 1930₎
    cover-title, p. 401–460. 25ᶜᵐ.
    "Reprinted from the Journal of negro history, volume xv, no. 4,
October, 1930."
    Bibliographical foot-notes.

    1. Education—Haiti.

                                                    A 35–597

    Title from Teachers Col-   lege Libr. Printed by L. C.

NL 0450340   NNC-T NN CU NcD PPPL PBm OO

Logan, Rayford Whittingham, 1897–   ed.

    The Journal of Negro history. v. 1–
    Jan. 1916–
    Washington ₍etc.,₎ Association for the Study of Negro Life
and History.

Logan, Rayford Whittingham, 1897–
    The Negro and the post-war world, a primer, by Rayford
Whittingham Logan ... Washington, D. C., The Minorities
publishers, 1945.
    viii p., 1 l., 95 p. 23ᶜᵐ.
    Bibliography: p. 89–95.

    1. Negro race. 2. Negroes.   I. Title.
                                                    46–376
    Library of Congress °   GN645.L5₎
                                                    325.26

    MB ViU-L ViHaI CU IU KU NBuC CSaT PSt AAP CoGrS
NL 0450342   DLC Or WaT CaBVaU KEmT NBuU NcD NcGU TxU

Logan, Rayford Whittingham, 1897–
    The Negro in American life and thought: the nadir, 1877–
1901. New York, Dial Press, 1954.
    x, 380 p. 21 cm.
    Bibliographical references included in "Footnotes" (p. 341–365)

    1. Negroes—Civil rights. 2. Negroes—Hist.   I. Title.
        E185.61.L64   54–6000
                                            *301.451 325.260973

    PPT OO WHi MiU OrP OrPR OrSaW OrU Wa WaS WaWW
    OrLgE OrMonO OFH OU OOxM OC1U OC1 ODW OC1W PPPL
    MB NN ViU NcD PPD NcGU OrAshS OrCS NIC KyU KyBB
NL 0450343   DLC IdPI MtBC MtU Or PP PSt PHC TU TxU

Logan, Rayford Whittingham.
    Operation of the Mandate System in Africa.
    Journal of Negro History, vol. 13, no. 4, Oct.
1928, p. 423–477.

NL 0450344   MH-L

Logan, Rayford Whittingham.
    The operation of the mandate system in Africa, 1919–1927,
with an introduction on the problem of the mandates in the
post-war world, by Rayford W. Logan. Washington, D. C.,
The Foundation publishers, inc., 1942.
    xii, 50 p. 24½ᶜᵐ.

    1. Mandates—Africa.   I. Title.
                                                    42–51430
    Library of Congress   JQ3505.L6
                                                    321.027

NL 0450345   DLC OrU WaS PPD PPT PU OU OC1

Logan, Rayford Whittingham, 1897–
    The Senate and the Versailles mandate system, by Rayford
W. Logan ... Washington, D. C., The Minorities publishers,
1945.
    vi p., 1 l., 112 p. 22½ᶜᵐ.
    Bibliography: p. 105–106.

    1. U. S. Senate. 2. Mandates.   I. Title.
                                                    45–8821
    Library of Congress °   JX4021.L8
                                                    321.027

    MiU NcD ViU-L ViHaI TxU IU WaS CoU GU WaSpG
NL 0450346   DLC CaBVaU OrU GU-L MB OrPS NNUN PPT

Logan, Rayford Whittingham, 1897–   ed.
    What the Negro wants, edited by Rayford W. Logan ...
Chapel Hill, The University of North Carolina press ₍1944₎
    xxiii p., 1 l., 352 p. 23ᶜᵐ.
    "Who's who": p. 345–352.

    1. Negroes.   I. Title.
                                                    44–47086
    Library of Congress   E185.61.L65
                                                    325.260973

    PPPrHi KEmT NcU OCU
    WaS WaT WaTC MtBC PPLas MiU IdPI CoU WaWW MH-AH MBtS
    OO OC1 ODW ViU OU IdU MtU Or OrCS OrP WaSpG OrSaW
NL 0450347   DLC OrU CaBVa CaBVaU NcC NcD NcRS OC1W

Logan, Rhea Dawn, 1898–
    Drama and the machine ... by Dawn Logan ...
Columbus, The Ohio state university, 1934.
    2 p. l., 379, [1] no. l.
    Thesis (PH. D.) - Ohio state university.

NL 0450348   OU

Logan, Richard Fink.
    Abandonment of agricultural land in the up-
lands of Western New England.

    Thesis - Harvard, 1949.

NL 0450349   MH

Logan, Robert.
    Genealogical chart of the royal family of Great Britain in the Scot-
tish, Anglo-Saxon, Norman, Welsh, Guelph, and Wetten lines.
    With collateral branches.
    Edinburgh. Macniven & Wallace. [1891.] (5) ff. Folded chart.
75 cm.

    H7031 — Genealogy. English sovereigns. — English sovereigns.

NL 0450350   MB MH

BW5360 Logan, Robert.
.L83   The United Free Church; an historical
        review of two hundred and twenty-five
        years, 1681–1906.. Edinburgh, Mac-
        Niven & Wallace, 1906.
            xii, 272 p. 20ᶜᵐ.

            Revision of a lecture given to the
        Guild of St. Mary's, Moffat, Dec. 1904.

NL 0450351   MH-AH ScCleA   *

Logan, Robert Briggs.
    The blue book of dogs: sporting dogs, working dogs, non-
sporting dogs, including spaniels, retrievers, setters, pointers,
etc., by Robert Briggs Logan. With 57 full-color illustrations
of the different breeds painted by Ole Larsen. Racine, Wis.,
Whitman publishing company, °1941.
    1 p. l., 5–61, ₍1₎ p. col. illus. 9 x 14ᶜᵐ.
    Cover-title: Dogs.
    Companion volume to the author's The red book of dogs.

    1. Dogs. 2. Dogs—Pictures, illustrations, etc.   I. Title.
    Library of Congress   SF430.L6
                                                    41–10986
                                                    636.72

NL 0450352   DLC WaSp

VOLUME 338

Logan, Robert Briggs.
The red book of dogs: sporting dogs (hounds), terriers, toy dogs, including pack hunters, coursers, toy spaniels, etc., by Robert Briggs Logan. With 57 full-color illustrations of the different breeds painted by Ole Larsen. Racine, Wis., Whitman publishing company, °1941.
1 p. l., 5–61, ₁1₁ p. col. illus. 9 x 14ᶜᵐ.
Companion volume to the author's The blue book of dogs.

1. Dogs. 2. Dogs—Pictures, illustrations, etc. ɪ. Title.

Library of Congress   SF430.L62   41–10087
                                                         636.75

NL 0450353   DLC WaSp

PS
2249
L6Z75
Logan, Robert Restalrig.
Biographical sketch of Algernon Sydney Logan, by his son. Philadelphia, National Pub. Co., 1934.
117 p.   illus., music, ports.   22cm.

1. Logan, Algernon Sydney, 1849–1925.

NL 0450354   CoU

Logan, Robert Restalrig.
Lichens from the temple, by Robert Restalrig Logan. New York and London, G. P. Putnam's sons, 1914.
ix, 116 p. 18ᶜᵐ. $1.00
Poems, reprinted in part from the Forum and the American magazine.

ɪ. Title.

Library of Congress   PS3523.O355L5 1914   14–18365

NL 0450355   DLC NcD MiU

Logan, Robert Restalrig, ed.
The Starry cross. v. 1–
Jan., 1892–
Philadelphia, Pa., 1892–19

Logan, Robert Restalrig, 1274–   ed.

Logan, Algernon Sydney, 1849–1925.
Vistas from the stream, by Algernon Sydney Logan; comments upon men and events and opinions upon life and art jotted down in note books from 1881 to 1925 ... Collected ed. Philadelphia, National publishing company, 1934.

₁Logan, Robert S   ₁ 1864–
The railway problem from the view point of both capital and labor. January, 1908. ₁n. p., 1908₁
cover-title, 11 p. 16¼ᶜᵐ.

1. Railroads and state—U. S. 2. Railroads and state—Canada. ɪ. Title.

                                                         ca 15–914 Unrev'd
Library of Congress   HE2757.1908.L6
                          ₁a35b1₁   385.0162

NL 0450358   DLC

₁Logan, Robert S   ₁ 1864–
The railway problem from the view point of both capital and labor. March, 1908. ₁n. p., 1908₁
15 p. 16¼ᶜᵐ.
A revised and enlarged edition of the author's pamphlet of the same name, published in January, 1908.

1. Railroads and state—U. S. ₁1. Railroads—Government ownership₁ 2. Railroads and state—Canada. ɪ. Title.

Bur. of railway econ. Libr.   A 15–238
  for Library of Congress   [HE2757 1908.L   ]

NL 0450359   DBRE NN

Logan, Robert S   1864–
Synoptical history of the Grand trunk system of railways, by R. S. Logan.   March, nineteen hundred and twelve. ₁London? 1912₁
32 p, fold. map. 23ᶜᵐ.

1. Grand trunk railway.   ɪ. Title.

                                                         A 14–2416
Title from Bureau of   Railway Economics.   Printed by L. C.

NL 0450360   DBRE

HD9567
.T3T4
Logan, Robert V., ed
Texas petroleum directory.   1947–
St. Louis, Petroleum Personnel Research.

[LOGAN, Robert William] 1843–1887.
Aritmatik; kapas an make tu iteitan peirak kana, pual apat, me aimu, me alean feneni, me inet. [n.p.,n.d.].

pp. 46.
Caption title.   2234.137.16

NL 0450362   MH

Logan, Robert William, 1843–1887.
Kapas fel, puk eu.
see under title

Logan, Robert William, 1843–1887.
Last words and work of Rev. Robt. W. Logan, a missionary of the A. B. C. F. M. at Ruk, Micronesia, together with memorial papers. Oakland, Calif., Pacific Press Pub. Co., 1888.
78 p. 16 cm.
Cover title.

BV3678.L6A3   49–34832*

NL 0450364   DLC CtY

Logan, Robert William, 1843–1887.
... Mortlok catechism ...   Honolulu, H. I., 1888.
84 p.   14. 5 cm.
Published by the A. B. C. F. M. for the Ruk mission.
Title also in Mortlock.

NL 0450365   CtY

[LOGAN, Robert William] 1843–1887.
Nor an lamalam kana; kapas an mortlok. [Cincinnati, Advance Pr. co., 1881.]

Unpaged.
Ms.note: Mortlok Island hymns by Rev. R. W. Logan, printed by 7th St. Cong. church, Cincinnati.

NL 0450366   MH RPB OClWHi

Logan, Robert William, 1843–1887.
Puk an ais fel, me ais an lamalam kana lan kapas an re Ruk. Mortlok catechism. Prepared by Rev. Robert W. Logan. Pub. by the A. B. C. F. M. for the Ruk mission. Honolulu, H. I., Press publishing company steam print, 1888.
84 p. 14ᶜᵐ.

ɪ. American board of commissioners for foreign missions. ɪɪ. Title. ɪɪɪ. Title: Mortlok catechism.

                                                         ca 18–390 Unrev'd
Library of Congress   PL6256.M8Z71 1888

NL 0450367   DLC MiU NN

Logan, Robert William, 1843–1887, tr.

Bible. *O. T. Historical books. Truk. 1900.*
Puk an Jenesis, Eksotows, Lifitikows, Rut me Ester; popun Testament an lom, auili sowni kapas an ipru, auili ngani kapas an truk me mortlok. New York, American Bible society, 1900.

Logan, Robert William, 1843–1887.
Puk an kël, me kël an lamalam kana lan kapas an Ruk me Mortlok. Mortlok hymn book, 2d ed. Prepared by Rev. Robert W. Logan. Pub. by the A. B. C. F. M. for the Ruk mission. Honolulu, Press publishing company steam print, 1888.
76 p. 14¼ᶜᵐ.
Titles of hymns in English.

1. Hymns, Mortlok.   ɪ. American board of commissioners for foreign missions. ɪɪ. Title. ɪɪɪ. Title: Mortlock hymn book.

                                                         ca 18–559 Unrev'd
Library of Congress   PL6256.M8Z71 1888 a

NL 0450369   DLC

Logan, Robert William, 1843–1887.

Bible. *N. T. Mortlock.*
Testament Sefa an amam Samol o Rán Amanau Jisos Kraist; auili jonai kapas an re kris uili nanai kapas an mortlok. New York, American Bible society, 1905.

Logan, Robert William, 1843–1887.
The work of God in Micronesia. 1852–1883. An historical sketch. By Rev. Robert W. Logan... Boston: Amer. board of commissioners for foreign missions, 1884.   16 p.   18cm.
Cover-title.
Map on p. ₁3₁ of cover.

1. Missions, Foreign—Micro-   nesia. ɪ. American board of commissioners for foreign missions.
                                                    September 22, 1939

NL 0450371   NN CtY OO

266
L82w
Logan, Robert William, 1843–1887.
The work of God in Micronesia. 1852–1889. An historical sketch by Rev. Robert W. Logan.   Boston, American board of commissioners for foreign missions, 1890.
cover-title, 22p.

1. Missions—Micronesia.   ɪ. Title.

NL 0450372   IU

Logan, Mrs. S. C. Night in India. 8 pp.
₍*Nineteenth Cent.* v. 36, 1894, p. 71.₎—Night travelling in India. 11 pp. ₍*Nineteenth Cent.* v. 37, 1895, p. 101.₎

NL 0450373   MdBP

Logan, S. H.
see Logan, Sydney H   , 1881–

VOLUME 338

Logan, S. R.
  Functional grammar
    see under Baer, Jeanette.

1887 Logan, Samuel, m. d.
  Divulsion in stricture of the urethra. From the
  New Orleans medical and surgical journal. New
  Orleans, J. A. Gresham [1874]
  1 p. l., 49–68 p. 8°.
                        Trace collection

NL 0450376 DLC ICAC

Logan, Samuel Crothers, 1823–1907.
  Affliction, the Christians Servant. A Discourse ...
  With a short memoria of Mrs. A. J. Hand ...
  Scranton, 1872.
  3 p. 8°. [In vol. 40, Funeral Sermons]

NL 0450377 CtY

Logan, Samuel Crothers, 1823–1907.
  A city's danger and defense. Or, Issues and results of
  the strikes of 1877, containing the origin and history of
  the Scranton city guard. By Samuel C. Logan, d. d.
  Scranton, Pa. [Philadelphia, Press of the J. B. Rodgers
  printing co.] 1887.
  viii, 355 p. front., illus. (plans) plates, ports. 22½ᶜᵐ.
  The Scranton city guard formed companies A, B, C and D of the 13th
  Pennsylvania regiment.
  1. Scranton, Pa.—Riot, 1877. 2. Railroad strike, 1877. 3. Scranton city
  guard. 4. Pennsylvania infantry. 13th regiment.
                                          1–15951 Revised
  Library of Congress   F159.S4L8 |

     NcD CU PBa PHi DL OC1 ICJ TxU MB NN
NL 0450378 DLC ScU FTaSU FU NIC NcU NNC LU–NO

Logan, Samuel Crothers, 1823–1907.
  Correspondence Between The Rev. S. C. Logan,
  Pittsburgh, Pa., and The Rev. Dr. J. Leighton
  Wilson, Columbia, S. C. [Columbia, S. C. Printed
  at the Office of the Southern Presbyterian, 1868]
  8 vo. Stitched.
  On religious work among the freedmen.
  Brock Collection, October, 1922.

NL 0450379 CSmH CtY

Logan, Samuel Crothers, 1823–1907.
  The life of Thomas Dickson. A memorial. By Samuel C. Logan, d. d. Scranton, Pa., 1888.
  3 p. l., 155 p. plates, ports. 23½ᶜᵐ.

  1. Dickson, Thomas, 1824–1884.
                                          16–5655
  Library of Congress   CT275.D46L6

NL 0450380 DLC FTaSU OkU CU PP PHi NN

Logan, Sheldon.

  Works by this author printed in America before 1801 are
  available in this library in the Readex Microprint edition of
  Early American Imprints published by the American Anti-
  quarian Society.
  This collection is arranged according to the numbers in
  Charles Evans' American Bibliography.

NL 0450381 DLC

Logan, Sheldon.
  A Masonic funeral discourse delivered at the
  interment of Brother Samuel Works, esq., at
  Westmoreland, July 20th, Anno Lucis 5795, By
  Brother Sheldon Logan, esq. Printed at Walpole,
  N. H. by I. Thomas and D. Carlisle, Jun., 1795.
  12 p. 12 mo.

NL 0450382 RPJCB NHi

Logan, Spencer, 1911–
  A Negro's faith in America, by Spencer Logan. New York,
  The Macmillan company, 1946.
  vi p., 1 l., 88 p. 21ᶜᵐ.
  "First printing."

  1. Negroes.   i. Title.
                                          46–4456
  Library of Congress   E185.61.L66
                                          325.260973

       TU PSt PPPrHi KyLx
       KMK MtBC OrP OrU WaS WaT Or OrCS OrSaW Wa WaSp WaWW
NL   ViHaI ViU MB PPPL PU PP NBuU LU KyU KEmT GU AAP
0450383 DLC CaBViP IdB IdU NcC NcD NcRS ICJ

LOGAN, STANLEY.
  Milestones; a few caricatures. [London, 1913]
  [40] p. (chiefly illus.) 16cm.

  1. Actors and acting--Cartoons, satire, etc. 2. Theatres--Gt. Br.--
  Eng.--London--Royal. 3. Caricatures--Stage. 4. Theatres--England--
  London--Royal.

NL 0450384 NN

Logan, Sydney H   1881–
  Canadian and world economic conditions; addresses by S. H.
  Logan ... and Sir John Aird ... of the Canadian bank of
  commerce, at the annual meeting of shareholders, January
  9th, 1934, Toronto, Canada. [Toronto? 1934]
  cover-title, 27 p. 22ᶜᵐ.

  1. Canada—Econ. condit.—1918–   2. Economic conditions—1918–
  i. Aird, Sir John, 1855–   ii. Canadian bank of commerce. iii. Title.
                                          34–24820
  Library of Congress   HC115.L66
                                          330.971

NL 0450385 DLC DS CtY NN

330.971 Logan, Sydney H   1881–
L828c   Canadian and world economic conditions; ad-
1935   dresses by S. H. Logan and Sir John Aird of the
         Canadian Bank of Commerce at the annual meeting
         of shareholders, January 8th, 1935, Toronto,
         Canada. [Toronto? 1935]
         25p. 22cm.
         Cover title.
         1. Canada - Econ. condit. - 1918–   2. Eco-
         nomic conditions - 1918–   I. Aird, Sir John,
         1855–1938. II. Canadian Bank of Commerce. III.
         Title.

NL 0450386 TxU MH MH-BA

Logan, Sydney H   1881–
  Canadian and world economic conditions (with an outline
  of the functions of money and banking); addresses by S. H.
  Logan ... and Sir John Aird ... of the Canadian bank of commerce at the annual meeting of shareholders, January 14th,
  1936, Toronto, Canada. [Toronto? 1936]
  cover-title, 24 p. 21½ᶜᵐ.

  1. Canada—Economic conditions—1918–   2. Economic conditions—1918–   3. Banks and banking. i. Aird, Sir John, 1855–
  ii. Canadian bank of commerce. iii. Title.
                                          8 D 36–32
  Library, U. S. Dept. of   State HC115.L6 1936

NL 0450387 DS CaOTP MH-BA

Logan, T. G.

Cheadle, John Begg.
  Cases on alienation and descent of Indian lands of the
  Five civilized tribes and the Osage nation, by John Begg
  Cheadle ... and T. G. Logan ... [Norman, Okla., 1923]

Logan, T. M., 1808–1876.
    see Logan, Thomas Muldrup, 1808–1876.

Logan, T. M., 1840–1914
    see Logan, Thomas Muldrup, 1840–1914.

Logan, Thomas.
  Biological physics, physic & metaphysics; studies and
  essays, by Thomas Logan ... Ed. by Quintin McLennan
  ... and P. Henderson Aitken ... London, H. K. Lewis,
  1910.
  3 v. illus., diagrs. 22½ᶜᵐ.
  Half-title: Vetera et nova; or, Extracts from the diary of a medical
  practitioner.
  CONTENTS.—I. Biological physics.—II. Physic.—III. Metaphysics.
  1. Biology. 2. Medicine. 3. Philosophy.   i. McLennan, Quintin,
  joint ed. ii. Aitken, Patrick Henderson, joint ed.
                                          A 10–2398
  Title from Harvard Univ.   Printed by L. C.

NL 0450391 MH MiU ICJ ICRL DNLM PPC

W 4   LOGAN, Thomas, fl. 1799
E23   Dissertatio medica inauguralis, de dyspepsia ... Edinburgi,
1799   C. Stewart, 1799.
L. 2   32 p. 20 cm.
        Diss. - Edinburgh.
        ----- Copy 2.
        Imperfect; half title wanting.

NL 0450392 DNLM PPC

Logan, Thomas Ackley, 1829–1906.
  Breech-loaders. By "Gloan" [pseud.] New York,
  The American news company [°1873]
  vi, [7]–192 p. illus. 20½ᶜᵐ.

  1. Shot-guns.   i. Title.

NL 0450393 ViU

Logan, Thomas Ackley, 1829–1906.
  Breech-loaders. By "Gloan" [pseud.] New York, G. E.
  Woodward [etc.] 1873.
  vi, [7]–192 p. illus. 20½ᶜᵐ.

  1. Shot-guns.   i. Title.
                                          7–34750
  Library of Congress   SK274.L8 |

NL 0450394 DLC OC OKentU MB OC1

Case LOGAN, THOMAS B.
Y   History of Timothy Tugg Mutton. A novellette.
255   St. Louis, Mo., Printed by M. Niedner, 1852.
.L 831   108p. 21cm.

NL 0450395 ICN

VOLUME 338

FILM
4274
PR
v.2
reel
L11
Logan, Thomas B
 History of Timothy Tugg Mutton. *J.* novellette, by Tho's. B. Logan. ... Stereotype ed.
St. Louis, Mo., M. Niedner, 1852.
 108 p. (Wright American fiction, v.II,
1851-1875, no. 1578 A, Research Publications
Microfilm, Reel L-11)

NL 0450396   CU

285.173
P928
no.339
Logan, Thomas D
 The liberality of orthodoxy. Philadelphia, Presbyterian Board of Publication
and Sabbath-School Work ₍C1887₎
 32 p. 19 cm. (₍Presbyterian tracts₎
no. 339)

 "...prepared as a lecture to be delivered
before the students of the Western Theological
Seminary ..."

NL 0450397   NcD DLC

[LOGAN, Thomas Dale], 1851-
 Memoir of John T. Logan. Compiled by his
youngest son. n.p.,1885.
 pp. 62. Port.   US 16982.10

NL 0450398   MH

[LOGAN, Thomas Dale], 1851-
 Memoir of Mrs. Henrietta B. Logan. Compiled
by her youngest son. n.p. [1904].
 pp. 51. Port.   US 16932.10

NL 0450399   MH

Logan, Thomas F., inc., New York.
South Manchuria railway company. FOR OTHER EDITIONS
                                   SEE MAIN ENTRY
 Manchuria, land of opportunities. Illustrated from
photographs, with diagrams and maps. New York,
South Manchuria railway company, 1924.

Logan (Thomas F.) inc., New York.

 see also

Lord and Thomas.

Logan, Thomas Francis, 1881-1928

 see also

Logan (Thomas F.) inc., New York.

Logan, Thomas Muldrup, 1808-1876.
 Abstract of meteorological observations for Sacramento,
California ... for the year ending March 31, 1854, ₍and₎
Meteorological table for Sacramento, California, for the year
ending March 31, 1855. By Thomas M. Logan, M. D.
 (*In* Smithsonian institution. Annual report. 1854. Washington,
1855. 23½ cm. p. 259-262. tables)

 1. Meteorology—Observations.
                                           S 15—15a
Smithsonian Institution.   Library
for Library of Congress   Q11.S66 1854
                             ₍a48b½₎

NL 0450403   DSI OU DAS

Logan, Thomas Muldrup, 1808-1876.
 ... Abstract of observations made during the years 1853,
1854, and 1855, at Sacramento, California. By Thomas M.
Logan, M. D.
 (*In* Smithsonian institution. Annual report, 1855. Washington,
1856. 23½ cm. p. ₍191₎-210)
 At head of title: Meteorology.

 1. Sacramento, Calif.—Climate.   I. Title.

Q11.S66 1855   S 15-30
Smithsonian Institution.   Library
for Library of Congress   ₍a55c½₎†

NL 0450404   DSI OU MiU DLC

Logan, Thomas M₍uldrup₎ 1808-1876.
 Address of Thos. M. Logan, M. D., president of the
American medical association. Delivered in St. Louis
(Mo.), May 6th, 1873. ₍St. Louis, 1873₎
 25 p. 23ᶜᵐ. ₍American medical association. President. Addresses₎
 Reprinted from Transactions of the American medical association, Phila-
delphia, 1873, vol. XXIV, p. 75-97.   *Toner collection.*

                                           5-164†
Library of Congress   R708.L83

NL 0450405   DLC CU DNLM

LOGAN, Thomas Muldrup, *1808-1876.*
 Annual table of the necrology of Sacramento, 1850-64.
 [Sacramento? 1851-65.] Broadsides and newspaper cuttings. 4°.

Sheet D 3920   Sept. 13, 1899

NL 0450406   MB

Logan, Thomas Muldrup, 1808-1876.
 The climate of Sacramento, California. By Thomas M.
Logan, M. D.
 (*In* Smithsonian institution. Annual report. 1857. Washington, 1858.
23½ᵐ. p. ₍283₎-309)

 1. Sacramento, Cal.—Climate.
                                           S 15-52
Library of Congress   Q11.S66 1857
Library, Smithsonian   Institution

NL 0450407   DSI OO MiU OU DLC

RC626
851L
LOGAN, Thomas Muldrup, 1808-1876.
 Land scurvy; its pathology, symptoms,
causes and treatment; poisonous properties of food and water in a state of
fermentation or putrefaction. [New
Orleans,1851]
 468-480p. 19cm.
 From Southern Medical Reports, vol. 2.
1850.
 Reproduced from the original in the
Stanford-Lane   Medical Library.
1.Scurvy 2.
I.Title

NL 0450408   CtY-M

Logan, Thomas Muldrup, 1808-1876.
 Medical history of the year 1868, in California. A
paper read before the "Sacramento society for medical
improvement," February 16th, 1869, and pub. by order
of the Society. By T. M. Logan ... San Francisco, Cal.,
Printed by F. Clarke, 1869.
 iv, ₍5₎-24 p. 22½ᵐ.

 1. Medicine—California. 2. Medicine—Hist.—California.   I. Sacramento society for medical improvement.

                                           7-24207†
Library of Congress   R171.L83

NL 0450409   DLC MB DNLM

R154
.L9L6
Toner
Coll.
Logan, Thomas Muldrup, 1808-1876.
 Memoir of C. A. Luzenberg, M. D., president
of the Louisiana medico-chirurgical society.
By Thomas M. Logan, M. D. Published by the
society. New-Orleans, Printed by J. B. Steel,
1849.
 58 p. front. (port.) 22½cm.

 "Addenda": 1 leaf inserted.

 1. Luzenberg, Charles Aloysius, 1805-1848.
I. Louisiana medico-chirurgical society.

TxU
NL 0450410   DLC LNHT MH MB IU LU LNHT OC PPC ScC

Logan, Thomas Muldrup, *1808-1876.*
 Meteorological Report (for 1872)
(Extr. Trans. State Ag. Soc. 1872
8 Sacramento. 1873.)
 p. 217-221

NL 0450411   DAS

Logan, Thomas Muldrup, 1808-1876.
 Meteorology. Abstract of observations made
during the years 1853, 1854, and 1855, at
Sacramento, California
 see his ... Abstract of observations made
during the years 1853 ...

Logan, Thomas Muldrup, 1808-1876.
 Reception of General Logan...
 see South Carolina Infantry. Washington
light infantry, 1807.

WC
262
L831r
1853
LOGAN, Thomas Muldrup, 1808-1876
 Report of the cholera at Sacramento
in 1852 ... ₍n. p., 1853?₎
 p. 488-500.
 Reprint from the New Orleans
medical and surgical journal, v. 9,
1852-53.   DLC Toner collection

NL 0450414   DNLM DLC

R881
1872
L82
Logan, Thomas Muldrup, 1808-1876.
 Report on the annual museum for the
exhibition of the American medical association,
in Philadelphia, and the contributions from
California, by Thos. M. Logan ... Read before
the Sacramento society for medical improvement,
on the 23rd of July, 1872, and ordered for
publication. Sacramento, T. A. Springer,
state printer, 1872.
 22 p. illus. 22cm.

 1. Medical museums. I. American medical
association.

NL 0450415   CLU MB DNLM

Logan, Thomas Muldrup, 1808-1876.
 Report on the medical topography and epidemics of California ... Philadelphia,Col-
lins,printer,1859.
 1p.₤.,₍5₎-58p. fold.map,4 fold.diagrs.
22½cm.
 "Extracted from the Transactions of the
American medical association."

 1. Epidemics - California. 2. Medical geography - California.

NL 0450416   CtY-M CtY

VOLUME 338

Logan, Thomas Muldrup, 1808–1876.
Report on the medical topography and epidemics of California. By Thomas M. Logan ... Philadelphia, Collins, printer, 1865.
75 p. 2 col. diagr. 23ᶜᵐ.
Extracted from the Transactions of the American medical association.

1. Medical geography—California. 2. California—Epidemics.
8—7237
Library of Congress   RA807.C2L8

NL 0450417   DLC DNLM CtY-M NjP MH

WZ
270
L832v
1874
LOGAN, Thomas Muldrup, 1808–1876
Valedictory address ... at the commencement exercises of the Medical Department of the University of California; held in Pacific Hall, San Francisco, October 29th, 1874. [Sacramento? Cal., 1874]
17 p. 23 cm.
Names of faculty and graduates: p. [2]

NL 0450418   DNLM CLU

Logan, Thomas Muldrup, 1840–1914.
Education and progress, an address delivered before the Educational association of Virginia, July 6, 1876, by Gen'l T. M. Logan. [Richmond, Va., 1876]
16 p. 22 cm.

Caption title.

1. Education – Addresses, essays, lectures. I. Title.

NL 0450419   Vi ViN MH RPB

Logan, Thomas Muldrup, 1840–1914.
The nationalization of America. An address delivered before the Association of Hood's Texas Brigade, at Waco, Texas, June 27th, 1877.
[Richmond. 1877.] 8 pp. 8°.
There is no title-page.

G7359 — United States. Pol. hist. — T.r.

NL 0450420   MB

Logan, Thomas Muldrup, 1840–1914.
The opposition in the South to the free school system. A paper read before the American social science association, at Saratoga, September 6th, 1877, the subject under discussion being: "The question of education in the Southern states." By Gen. T. M. Logan, of Richmond, Va. [Richmond? Va., 1877]
9 p. 21.5 cm.

Caption title.

1. Public schools – Southern states. 2. Education – Addresses, essays, lectures. I. Title.   LC69.L8
11 – 39

NL 0450422   Vi

Logan, Thomas Muldrup, 1840–1914.
Oration delivered by Gen. T. M. Logan, at the reunion of the Hampton legion, in Columbia, S. C., 21st July, 1875. Pub. by his friends in Charleston, S. C. Charleston, S. C., Walker, Evans & Cogswell, printers, 1875.
28 p. 23ᶜᵐ.

1. Southern states—Pol. & govt.—1865–   2. Reconstruction.
12—9014
Library of Congress   E668.L84

NL 0450423   DLC NcD ScU MB ViU

Logan, Thomas Swindall, 1903–
The dissociation pressures of hydrated cupric sulfate at 35 degrees centigrade, by Thomas S. Logan ... [Ithaca, N. Y., 1932]
1 p. l., 10 p., 1 l. 1 illus., diagrs. 26½ᶜᵐ.
Thesis (PH. D.)—Johns Hopkins university, 1931.
Biography.
"Reprinted from the Journal of physical chemistry, 36 ... 1932."

1. Cupric sulphate. 2. Hydrates. 3. Dissociation.
32–21624
Library of Congress   QD181.C9L6 1931
Johns Hopkins Univ.   Libr.
546.56

NL 0450424   MdBJ OU DLC

Logan, V
Grass silage in dairy cattle rations. Ottawa, 1955.
11 p. illus. 25 cm. (Canada. Dept. of Agriculture. Publication 929)

1. Ensilage. 2. Cattle—Feeding and feeding stuffs. I. Title.

NL 0450425   MiU

Logan, Virginia K., 1850–1940.
In a brahmin garden
see under   Logan, Frederic Knight, 1871–1928.

Logan, Virginia K., 1850–1940.
Songs of Cupid ...
see under   Logan, Frederic Knight, 1871–1928.

Logan, Virginia K., 1850–1940.
Wishing that dreams would come true
see under   Logan, Frederic Knight, 1871–1928.

Logan, W. E.
see   Logan, William Edmond, 1798–1875.

Logan, W. H., d. 1883
see   Logan, William Hugh, d. 1883.

3166
.594
Logan, W   McGregor,   ed.
Collection of Spanish proverbs, with a literal translation into English, for the use of those who are learning either language... London, Seguin, 1830.
71 p. 15 ᶜᵐ.

Added t.-p. in Spanish; Spanish and English on opposite pages.

1. Proverbs, Spanish.

NL 0450431   NjP

Logan, W. McGregor, tr.

ML50
.W363
F72
Weber, Karl Maria Friedrich Ernst, *freiherr von*, 1786–1826.
[Der freischütz. Libretto. English]

Der freischutz; or, The seventh bullet. An opera, in three acts, by Carl Maria von Weber. Printed from the acting copy, with remarks, biographical and critical, by D.—G. ... Embellished with a fine engraving, by Mr. White, from a drawing taken in the theatre, by Mr. R. Cruikshank. London, J. Cumberland [18—]

WFA
L832c
1871
LOGAN, Wade Minor
Consumption: its pathology and treatment; to which is appended an essay on the use of alcohol in the treatment of consumption. Philadelphia, Butler, 1871.
90 p.
WFA L832c   60–9375

NL 0450433   DNLM ODW

Logan, Walter.
The double-bedded room.
(In Wilson, J. M., editor. Tales of the Borders and of Scotland. Vol. 5, pp. 205–224.) Edinburgh. 1885.)

F8586 — T.r.

NL 0450434   MB

Logan, Walter.
Ellen Arundel.
(In Wilson, J. M., editor. Tales of the Borders and of Scotland. Vol. 9, pp. 238–242. Edinburgh. 1885.)

NL 0450435   MB

Logan, Walter.
The recluse of the Hebrides.
(In Wilson, J. M., editor. Tales of the Borders and of Scotland. Vol. 9, pp. 230–237. Edinburgh. 1885.)

F8581 — T.r.

NL 0450436   MB

Logan, Walter.
The story of Clara Douglas.
(In Wilson, J. M., editor. Tales of the Borders and of Scotland. Vol. 4, pp. 191–206. Edinburgh. 1885.)

NL 0450437   MB

Logan, Walter Ewart Miller, 1911–
An introduction to the forests of central and southern Ethiopia. [Oxford] Imperial Forestry Institute, Univ. of Oxford, 1946.
58 p. fold. col. map, tables. 25 cm. (Institute paper, no. 24)
Errata slip inserted.
"References": p. 55–56.

1. Forests and forestry—Ethiopia. (Series: Oxford. University. Imperial Forestry Institute. Institute paper no. 24)
A 48–6109*
Rochester. Univ. Libr.   SD105.E8L6
for Library of Congress

NL 0450438   NRU

VOLUME 338

LOGAN, *Walter Ewart Miller, 1911-*
Report of a study of American softwood logging and milling methods with special reference to their potentialities in Kenya. [Nairobi, Govt. printer, 1953]
iv, 125 p. illus., map, diagrs. 25cm.

"Commonwealth fund fellowship, 1950-51."
On cover: "Colony and protectorate of Kenya."
Bibliography, p. 122.

1. Lumbering--U.S.   2. Sawmills--U.S. I. Kenya
Colony and Protectorate.   t. 1953.

NL 0450440   NN NNC IEN

Logan, Walter O., joint author.
TL521
.A33
no.785   Miller, Cearcy D
Preknock vibrations in a spark-ignition engine cylinder as revealed by high-speed photography, by Cearcy D. Miller and Walter O. Logan, Jr. Washington, U. S. Govt. Print. Off., 1944 [i. e. 1947]

Logan, Walter Seth. 1847-1906.
Address at a hearing before the River and Harbor Committee of the House of Representatives . . . Washington, D. C., January 23rd, 1902, on the question of the construction of a deepwater canal through or around Sabine Lake, Texas.
= [New York? 1902?] 7 pp. 8°.
Logan represented the Forward Reduction Company at the hearing.

F4511 — Forward Reduction Co. — Texas. R.Rs.

NL 0450442   MB

Logan, Walter S[eth] 1847-1906.
An argument for an eight-hour law, by Walter S. Logan. New York, The Knickerbocker press, 1894.
24 p. 22ᵐ.
An address before the Manhattan liberal club, Dec. 22, 1893.   3-15085

NL 0450443   DLC NN PU NNC DL WHi

Logan, Walter Seth, 1847-1906.
Arizona and some of her friends; the toasts and responses at a complimentary dinner given by Walter S. Logan, at the Marine and field club, N. Y., Tuesday July 28th, 1891, to Hon. John N. Irwin, governor of Arizona, and Herbert H. Logan of Phœnix, Arizona. [New York? 1891]

HG4521 Logan, Walter S[e]th, 1847-1906.
.L9   The art of investing from the viewpoint and experience of a lawyer. [New York, 1903?]
[8]p.
1 pam.   16°

NL 0450445   DLC IU MH

Logan, Walter Seth, 1847-1906.
Cuautle
see his   The siege of Cuautla, the Bunker Hill of Mexico.

Logan, Walter Seth, 1847-1906.
The despotism of the dollar. Address delivered before the Connecticut society of the Sons of the American revolution at their annual banquet in New Haven, February 22nd, 1902, by Walter S. Logan ... [New York? 1902?]
8 p. 20½ᵐ.
Caption title.

1. Sons of the American revolution, Connecticut society.   I. Title.

Library of Congress   HB805.L83   3—14326

NL 0450447   DLC MB

E
203   Logan, Walter Seth, 1847-1906.
R45   How the war came to an end. An address
v.6   at a meeting of the Sons of the American
no.9   Revolution, November 25, 1895. [n.p., 1895?]
       8 p. 24cm.

1. U. S.--Hist.--Revolution--Addresses, sermons, etc.

NL 0450448   NIC

Beinecke   Logan, Walter Seth, 1847-1906.
Library   Irrigation for profit, by Walter S. Logan,
Zc56   president of the Castle Dome Canal Company of
890to   Arizona. [n.p., 189-?]
       cover-title, 29 p. 24 cm.

1. Castle Dome Canal Company. 2. Irrigation – Arizona. I. Title (1)
NUC

NL 0450449   CtY MH

Logan, Walter Seth, 1847-1906
Irrigation on the Yaqui river.
n.p., [1892?]
80 p.   8°

NL 0450450   MWA NN

Logan, Walter Seth, 1847-1906.
Laissez faire. Address delivered before the Post-graduate class of the Georgetown, D.C., law school, on April 26th, 1902. [n.p., 1902]
20p.

NL 0450451   DLC

Logan, Walter Seth, 1847-1906.
Laissez faire. Address delivered before the post-graduate class of the Georgetown, D. C., Law School . . . 1902.
= [New York. 1902.] 20 pp. 12°.
Favors a compromise between the laissez faire system and state ownership.

F7237 — Trusts. — State interference. — Georgetown University, D. C. Addresses.

NL 0450452   MB

Logan, Walter Seth, 1847-1906.
Laissez faire. Address delivered before the post-graduate class of the Georgetown, D. C., Law school, on Saturday evening, April 26th, 1902, by Walter S. Logan ... [Washington? D. C., 1902?]
20 p. 20ᵐ.
Caption title.

1. Laissez-faire.

Library of Congress   HD3616.U47L7   8-17459†

NL 0450453   DLC MdBP

Logan, Walter Seth, 1847-1906.
The lawyer as an artist. Address before the women lawyers' club of New York city... [n.p., 19-]
12p.

NL 0450454   DLC

Logan, Walter Seth, 1847-1906.
The lawyer as an artist. Address before the Women lawyers' club of New York city at its meeting February 23, 1905 ... by Walter S. Logan. [New York? 1905?]
21 p. 22ᵐ.

1. Lawyers. [1. Attorneys]   6-15759

NL 0450455   WaU-L DLC IU MH NIC CU NcD MiU OU MB NN

Logan, Walter Seth, 1847-1906.
The lawyer's view. An address . . . at the Lake Mohonk International Arbitration Conference, June 1, 1899.
= [New York?] 1899. 4 pp. 8°.
Reprinted from Report of the Fifth Annual Meeting of the Lake Mohonk Conference on International Arbitration, pp. 18-22 [*5574.140.1899].
Opposes international arbitration and advocates a permanent international tribunal which shall have power to decide the great questions that arise between nations.

Jan. 9.   1904
F2650 — Arbitration. International.

NL 0450456   MB

Logan, Walter Seth, 1847-1906, counsel for defendant.
... Leonora A. Arnold and another, appellants against Charles A. Chesebrough, individually, etc., and another, respondents. Respondent's brief. Walter S. Logan, counsel for respondent ... New York, Hamilton steam print, 1892.
1 p.l., v, 352 p.   25.5 cm. (At head of title: U. S. Circuit court of appeals, for the 2d circuit)
On cover: What is marriage. By Walter S. Logan.
1. Marriage. I. Arnold, Leonora Augusta, appellant. II. Chesebrough, Charles A., defendant.

NL 0450457   ViU

Logan, Walter S[eth] 1847-1906.
The limitation of inheritances. Annual address before the New York state bar association, Albany, January 16th, 1900 ... [Brooklyn, N. Y., The Eagle press, 1900]
20 p. 8°.

1-13797

NL 0450458   DLC MiU NN MB

Logan, Walter Seth, 1847-1906.
A Mexican law suit. An address delivered before the Department of jurisprudence of the American social science association, at Saratoga, September 5, 1895, by Walter S. Logan, followed by remarks by Hon. Matias Romero, Mexican minister to the United States. Brooklyn, Eagle book and job printing department, 1895.
56 p. 22½ᵐ.

1. Law—Mexico. 2. Civil procedure—Mexico. 3. Criminal procedure—Mexico. 4. Mexico—Constitutional law. 5. Mexico—Hist. I. Romero, Matias, 1837-1898. II. Title.

28-15845

NL 0450459   DLC CU-B ICN

Logan, Walter Seth, 1847-1906.
A Mexican night; the toasts and responses at a complimentary dinner given by Walter S. Logan, at the Democratic club, New York city, December 16th, 1891, to Señor Don Matis Romero, Mexican minister to the United States. [New York, Printed by A. B. King] 1892.

VOLUME 338

LOGAN, Walter Seth, *1847-1906*.
Mining for profit. n.p., [1891?].

pp. 37.
Chiefly an account of the Santa Juliana
silver mine.

NL 0450461　　MH MB NN

Logan, Walter Seth, 1847-1906.
A more socialistic state; oration before the Phi beta
kappa society of Middlebury college, Vermont, delivered
June 25th, 1901, by Walter S. Logan ... [New York, C. B.
Merwin, printer, 1901?]
28 p. 21½ᵐ.

1. Political science. 2. Socialism.
8-19416

Library of Congress　　JC216.L83

NL 0450462　　DLC OClW MiU NN

Logan, Walter Seth, 1847-1906.
Needed modifications of our patent laws. By Walter S.
Logan. [n. p., n. d.]
p. 35-46. 24½ᵐ.
Caption title.

1. Patent laws and legislation—U. S.　　I. Title.
37-19528

NL 0450463　　DLC

Logan, Walter Seth, 1847-1906.
Santa Juliana. Annual report to the stockholders, April 22d,
1891. By Walter S. Logan. [New York, 1891.] 16 p., 1 pl.
8°.
Cover-title.

1. Silver.—Mines and mining: Com-　　panies: Mexico. 2. Title.
November 24, 1915.

NL 0450464　　NN

Logan, Walter Seth, 1847-1906.
The siege of Cuautla, the Bunker Hill of Mexico. An address before the New York historical society, April 4th, 1893,
by Walter S. Logan ... New York, Knickerbocker press, 1893.
27 p. 22ᵐ.

1. Mexico—Hist.—Wars of independence, 1810-1821. 2. Cuautla, Mexico—Siege, 1812. 3. Morelos y Pavón, José María Teclo, 1765-1815.
I. New York historical society. II. Title.
1—3976

Library of Congress　　F1391.C89L7

OClWHi MWA MB MH NN Nh NNH OFH
NL 0450465　　DLC TxU MH-B OFH PPAmP PU PHi OO MiU

Logan, Walter Seth, 1847-1906.
A soldier of the Revolution. Address delivered at the grave
of Captain Gideon Hollister in the old burying ground in the town
of Washington, Lichfield county, Connecticut, on July 4, 1900, by
Walter S. Logan. n.p., 1900. 51 p. 8°.

1. Hollister, Gideon. 2. U. S.—　　History: Revolution: Speeches.
June 29, 1921.

NL 0450466　　NN

Logan, Walter Seth, 1847-1906.
Thomas Hooker, the first American Democrat; an ad-
dress by Walter Seth Logan, delivered before the New
York society of the Order of the founders and patriots of
America, February 19, 1904. [New York, 1904]
28 p. 23ᵐ. [Order of the Founders and patriots of America. New
York society. Publications. no. 6]

1. Hooker, Thomas, 1586-1647. 2. Connecticut—Hist.—Colonial period.
4-33480
Library of Congress　　E186.6.N39
　　　　　　　　　　F97.H77

NL 0450467　　DLC MWA MB NN OO MiU

LOGAN, WALTER SETH, 1847-1906.
Thomas Hooker, the first American democrat. An
address delivered before the New York society of the
Order of the founders and patriots of America,
Feb. 19, 1904. [New York, New York society of
the Order of the founders and patriots of America.
28 p. 24cm.

Film reproduction. Negative.
1. Hooker, Thomas, 1586-　　1647.

NL 0450468　　NN

Logan [Walter Seth] *1847-1906.*
A working plan for a permanent international tribunal.
Address delivered at the Lake Mohonk Arbitration Con-
ference. June 3, 1896. 10 pp. 8°.
Repr.: Report of the Arbitration Conference.
Gift of Mrs. Henry R. Hoyt.

NL 0450469　　NN

Logan, Walter S[eth], *1847 - 1906*
Yaqui, the land of sunshine and health; what I saw in Mexico.
New York: A. B. King, 1894. 37 p. 8°. *YA 27046*

1. Mexico.—Description, 1893. 2. Irri-　　gation, Mexico. 3. Title.
April 17, 1912.

NL 0450470　　NN ICRL DLC LNHT

Logan, Warren.
Resources and material equipment [of Tuskegee]. Portrait. Plate.
(In Washington, Booker T., editor. Tuskegee, its people. Pp.
35-55. New York. 1905.)

F8608

NL 0450471　　MB

F468　　Logan, Wilfred David, 1923-
M48M4　　Graham Cave, an archaic site in Montgomery County,
no.2　　Missouri, by Wilfred D. Logan; with an appendix:
Anthrop.　Recent excavations in Graham Cave, by Carl H. Chap-
Library　man. [Columbia, Mo., 1952?]
　　　101 p. illus., maps. (Memoir of the Missouri
　　　Archaeological Society, no.2)

Bibliography: p.83-86.

I. Chapman, Carl Haley, 1915-　　II. Title.

NL 0450472　　CU IEdS ICF ICN DI OKentU FTaSU CLU

BS　　Logan, William
598　　History of Freemasonry in the city of
.D8　　Durham, in connection with the Marquis of
L6　　Granby lodge, No. 124, of the Antient Fra-
　　　ternity of Free and Accepted Masons. Introd.
　　　by William James Hughan. London, G. Kenning,
　　　1886.
　　　107 p. 22 cm.

1. Freemasons. Durham, Eng. Marquis of
Granby Lodge.

NL 0450473　　WU

Logan, William.
Materia medica. Ms.notes. Edin., 1749.

NL 0450474　　PPL

Logan, William.
Memoranda in husbandry on my plantation.
1748-58.
[50] p.

NL 0450475　　DNAL

Logan, William, *Judge*
Historical review of the great
Keokuk water-power legislation & con-
struction. Address delivered by Judge
William Logan at dedication exercises,
Tuesday, August 26, 1913. [Keokuk?
Ia.,1913?]
cover-title, 15p. 1 illus.(mounted)
26cm.

NL 0450476　　IHi

Logan, William, librarian.
A list of books, maps and pamphlets, obtained
by the Charleston library society...
see under　Charleston library society,
Charleston, S. C.

[Logan, William] of Logan, supposed author.
A letter to an English member of Parliament,
from a gentleman in Scotland ...
see under　Willison, John, 1680-1750.

Logan, William, of Logan.
A view of the present state of Scotland,
in regard to the tenures and slavish dependen-
cies of the subjects of that part of North
Britain. In a memorial ... Recommended to
all well-wishers to the liberty and freedom
of the subjects of Great Britain. London,
Printed for J.Wilford, 1733.
1 p.l., ii, 24 p. 21 cm.

NL 0450479　　MH-BA CtY

LOGAN, W[illiam], of Madras *Civil Service*
A collection of treaties, engagements and
other papers of importance relating to British
affairs in Malabar. 2d ed. Madras, Govt.
press,1891.

This edition forms a third volume of the
author's Malabar. Preface.

NL 0450480　　MH CtY NN CaBVaU

954.8　　Logan, William, *of Madras Civil Service*
L828c　　A collection of treaties, engagements and
　　　other papers of importance relating to Brit-
　　　ish affairs in Malabar; edited with notes by
　　　W. Logan. 2d ed. Madras, Reprinted by the
　　　Superintendent, Government Press, 1951.
　　　xxvi, 402,xlii p. 25cm.

First published in 1879.
To accompany the editor's Malabar.

1.Malabar, India - Hist. - Sources. I.T.

NL 0450481　　MiDW WaU WU

VOLUME 338

LOGAN, William, of Madras Civil Service.
Malabar. Madras, printed by R.Hill,1887.

2 vol. 1.8°. Plates,plans and maps. (2 in pockets.)

NL 0450482   MH CtY MB

DS485 Logan,William,of the Madras civil service.
.M35L8   Malabar by William Logan... Madras,Reprinted
by the superintendent,government press,1906-
v. front.,plates,fold.maps. 25⁰⁰.

First printed 1887.

1.Malabar.

NL 0450483   ICU

Logan, William, *of Madras Civil Service.*
Malabar. Madras, Printed by the Superintendent, Govt.
Press, 1951.
2 v. illus., fold. maps. 25 cm.

1. Malabar, India.

DS485.M35L6   S A 67-3998

NL 0450484   DLC MiU CU NSyU WaS MiDW

DS485
.M35L6 Logan, William, of Madras Civil Service.
1951
Malabar. Madras, Reprinted by the Superintendent, Government Press, 1951.
3 v. illus., maps. 25cm.
Errata slip inserted, v. 1.
Vol. 3 has title: A collection of treaties,
engagements and other papers of importance relating
to British affairs in Malabar, edited with notes
by W. Logan, Madras Civil Service. 2d ed.
Vols. 1-2 first pub. 1887; (v.3) first pub. 1879.
1. Malabar, India—Hist. 2. East India Company
(English) I. Title: A collection of treaties,
engagements and other   papers of importance relating to British   affairs in Malabar.

NL 0450485   ViU OrU ICU NcD CU-A

DS   Logan, William, *of Madras* Civil Service
485   Malabar. (2. ed.) Madras, Superintendent,
.M35   Govt. Press. 1951.
L6   2 v. illus. 25 cm.

1. Malabar, India.

NL 0450486   WU

Logan, William, fl. 1745.
William Logan's Journal of a Journey to Georgia,
1745. [Philadelphia, 1912]
[1]-16, 162-186 p. 8vo.
Excerpt from: The Pennsylvania Magazine of
History and Biography. Philadelphia, 1912.
Vol. XXXVI, Nos. 141-142, January-April, 1912.

NL 0450487   GU-De

Logan, William, *1747-1772.*
Chemistry; ms. notes [1770]
see under Black, Joseph, 1728-1799.

Logan, William, *1747-1772.*
Course of lectures on rhetoric and belles lettres
see under Blair, Hugh, 1718-1800.

Logan, William, 1747-1772.
Observations on the effects of sea water in the scurvy and
scrophula: in which a new theory of those diseases is attempted;
with some reasons why bathing in fresh water must be much
superior to that of the sea. By William Logan ... 2d ed.
London, E. and C. Dilly, MDCCLXXI.
2 p. l., 45 p. 23⁰⁰.

1. Scurvy. 2. Scrofula. 3. Sea-water—Therapeutic use.   I. Title.
36-31036
Library of Congress   RC663.L6 1771

NL 0450490   DLC DNLM

Logan, William, 1747-1772.
Tentamen medicum inaugurale, de regimine phthisicorum:
quod ... ex auctoritate ... Gulielmi Robertson ... Academiæ
edinburgenæ præfecti ... pro gradu doctoris ... eruditorum
examini subjicit Gulielmus Logan, Philadelphiensis. Ad diem
12 junii (1770) ... Edinburgi, apud Balfour, Auld, et Smellie,
academiæ typographos, M,DCC,LXX.
37 p. 20⁰⁰.

Tuberculosis.
34-40051
Library of Congress   RC311.1.L6

NL 0450491   DLC CtY-M DNLM PPAmP MiU-C

SL22   Logan, William, *1813-1879*
L83   The early heroes of the temperance reformation. By William Logan ... Glasgow,Scottish
temperance league[etc.,etc.]1873.
3p.ℓ.,[v]-xii,[13]-249p. front.(port.)
16.5cm.

NL 0450492   NNUT

Logan, William, 1813–1879.
The early heroes of the temperance reformation. By William Logan... Glasgow: Scottish Temperance League, 1874.
3 p.L., (i)vi-xii, (1)14-249 p., front. (port.)   16°.

BLACK TEMPERANCE COLL.
1. Temperance.—Biography.   2. Temperance.—History.
November 19, 1917.

NL 0450493   NN

HV   Logan, William, 1813-1879
5030   The early heroes of the temperance
L6   reformation. Glasgow, Scottish Temperance
League, 1883.
249p. illus. 17cm.

1. Temperance   I. Title

NL 0450494   WU

176.5   Logan, William, *1813-1879.*
L831e2   An exposure, from personal observation, of
female prostitution in London, Leeds and
Rochdale, and especially in the city of
Glasgow ... 2nd ed. Glasgow, G. Gallie
& R. Fleckfield, 1843.
2 p.ℓ., (7) -48 p. 18cm.

1. Prostitution — Gt. Brit. I. Title.

NL 0450495   LNHT MH IU

Logan, William, *1813-1879.*
An exposure, from personal observation, of female prostitution
in London, Leeds, and Rochdale, and especially in the city of
Glasgow; with remarks on the cause, extent, results, and remedy
of the evil. By William Logan, ... Third edition. Glasgow,
G. Gallie, and R. Fleckfield; [etc., etc.], 1843.
48 p. 17⁰⁰, bound 21⁰⁰.

NL 0450496   ICJ

Logan, William, 1813–1879.
The great social evil: its causes, extent, results, and remedies.
By William Logan ... London, Hodder and Stoughton, 1871.
xii, (13,-240 p. 19⁰⁰.

1. Prostitution—Gt. Brit.   I. Title.
8--29045
Library of Congress   HQ186.L83

NL 0450497   DLC NN ICJ DNLM ViU IEG FMU MfBP

LOGAN,William,*1813-1879.*
The moral statistics of Glasgow by William
Logan,commissioner of the Scottish temperance
league... Glasgow,1849.
pp.76. 17.5cm.

NL 0450498   MH-AH NN

Logan, William, *1813-1879, ed.*
Regeneration...
see under Anderson, William, 1799-1872.

Logan, William, *1813-1879, ed.*
Re-union in the heavenly kingdom...
see under Anderson, William, 1799-1872.

Logan, William, 1813-1879, ed.
Words of comfort for parents bereaved of little
children. Edited by W. Logan. New York, R.
Carter & Bros., [18-?]
337 p. 12°.

NL 0450501   NN

Logan, William, 1813–1879, *ed.*
Words of comfort for parents bereaved of little children.
Edited by William Logan ... with an introductory historical
sketch, by the Rev. William Anderson ... 4th ed., enl., 11th
thousand. London, J. Nisbet & co., 1867.
x, (4), (xi)-xxiii, (15)-492 p. 17½⁰⁰.

1. Children—Death and future state. 2. Consolation.   I. Title.
45-33953
Library of Congress   BV4907.L6 1867

NL 0450502   DLC

LOGAN, William, *1813-1879*
Words of comfort for parents bereaved of little children. With an introductory historical
sketch by William Anderson. 5th ed., enlarged
13th thousand. London,1868. Also engr.t.p.

NL 0450503   MH-AH ViLxW

VOLUME 338

BV
4907
L55
1874
Logan, William, 1813–1879, ed.
Words of comfort for bereaved parents.
Rev. and abridged ed. London, Religious
Tract Society ₍1874₎
270 p. 17 cm.
Date from B.M.

1. Children - Death and future state.
2. Consolation. I. Title.

NL 0450504   NRCR

Logan, William, 1813–1879, ed.
Words of comfort for parents bereaved of little
children. Ed. by William Logan ...   New York,
R. R. Carter and brothers, 1870.
337 p., 18 p.   18 cm.
1. Infant salvation. 2. Consolation.

NL 0450505   CU RPE RPB

Logan, William Ambrose.
A series of abstract commercial rules for teaching practical
commercial calculation ... ₍San Antonio, Tex., The author,
1871₎
₍18₎ p. 21ᶜᵐ.

1. Ready-reckoners.

Library of Congress   QA111.L83   3–32279

NL 0450506   DLC

Logan, William Augustus, 1871–   comp.
Road to heaven; twenty-eight Negro spirituals. Edited
by Allen M. Garrett. University, Ala., University of Alabama Press, 1955.
87 p. 28 cm.
Unacc. melodies.

1. Negro spirituals. I. Title.

M1670.L8R6   M 55–1018

TxU OrP CU OU LU KyLxCB MU NBuC CoU InU GU
NL 0450507   DLC Or FU PPT PP NN MB OC1 MsU NcD NcU

Logan, William Barnett.
Dress of the day; war-and-after reminiscences of the British
navy, by William Barnett Logan. London, Albert E. Marriot
limited ₍1930₎
254 p. 19ᶜᵐ.
On cover: A war-and-after novel of the British navy.

1. European war, 1914–1918—Fiction. 2. Gt. Brit.—Navy—Fiction.
I. Title.

A 36–484

Title from Hoover War   Libr. Stanford Univ. D526.2.L831
₍3₎   Printed by L. C.

NL 0450508   CSt-H CtY NN

Logan, William Boyd, 1910–
Criteria for evaluating a state-wide in-school
distributive education program. 1952.
288 l.
Thesis - Ohio State University.
Doctoral dissertation.

NL 0450509   OU

FILM
658.8
L82c
Logan, William Boyd, 1910–
Criteria for evaluating a State-wide in-
school distribution education program.
Ann Arbor, University Microfilms ₍1952₎
₍University Microfilms, Ann Arbor, Mich.₎
Publication no.24,071₎
(Doctoral dissertation)
Microfilm copy (positive) of typescript.
Collation of the original: ix, 288l. illus.
Thesis--Ohio State University.
Bibliography: leaves 204-216.

NL 0450510   IU MnCS GU

HF5429
.B37
Logan, William Boyd, joint author.

Beckley, Donald K
The retail salesperson at work, by Donald K. Beckley and
William B. Logan. 1st ed. New York, McGraw-Hill Book
Co., 1948.

BX8901
.C9
Logan, William C., ed.

The Cumberland Presbyterian review. v. ₍-20₎;
-Oct. 1884. St. Louis, Mo. ₍etc.₎ 1845/47–84.

Logan, Sir William Edmond, 1798–1875.
American Gold Mining Company, on the Portage River, a tributary
of the Du Loup and Chaudière Rivers, Canada East. Description of its property . . . with surprising statements of the press
respecting the gold fields, quartz, washings, &c., throughout the
region of the Chaudière, Du Loup, Portage, and Gilbert Rivers.
Boston. Mudge. 1864. 16 pp. 23 cm.

L2958 — Quebec, Province. Mines ₍ ₎ mining. — American Gold Mining
Company, Canada East. — Gold. Mining, etc.

NL 0450513   MB

Logan, Sir William Edmond, 1798–1875.
Considerations relating to the Quebec group, and the upper
copper-bearing rocks of Lake Superior. By Sir W. E. Logan ...
₍Montreal? 1861₎ 9 p. incl. diagrs. 21½cm.
Caption-title.
"Read before the Natural History Society, May, 1861." — Slip wanted on p. ₍1₎

100822. 1. Geology, Stratigraphic,   Carboniferous—Canada—Quebec.
October 28, 1936

NL 0450514   NN

Logan, Sir William Edmond, 1798–1875.
Correspondence on the taconic System, etc.
1861
see under Barrande, Joachim, 1799–1883.

Logan, Sir William Edmond, 1798–1875
Description of the oil territory in the vicinity of Gaspe bay, Canada East. Phil.,1865.

NL 0450516   Nh PBL

Logan, Sir William Edmond, 1798–1875.

Canada. Geological survey.
... Descriptive catalogue of a collection of the economic minerals of Canada ₍by Sir W. E. Logan₎ and of its crystalline
rocks ₍by T. Sterry Hunt₎ Sent to the London International
exhibition for 1862. Montreal, Printed by J. Lovell ₍1862₎

Logan, Sir William Edmond. 1798–1877.
Descriptive catalogue of economic minerals of Canada.
(In Canada. Geological Survey. Descriptive catalogue of a collection of the economic minerals of Canada. Pp. 3–59. Montreal.
[1862.])

G3245 — Canada. Miner. — Geology. Economic.

NL 0450518   MB

Logan, Sir William Edmond, 1798–1875.
Esquisse géologique du Canada, pour servir à l'intelligence de la carte géologique et de la collection des miné-
raux économiques envoyées à l'Exposition universelle de
Paris, 1855. Par W. E. Logan ... et T. Sterry-Hunt ...
Paris, H. Bossange et fils, 1855.
100 p. 18½ᵐ.

1. Geology—Canada. I. Hunt, Thomas Sterry, 1826–1892, joint author.
5–3218

Library of Congress   QE185.L83

TxU ICJ Nh NjP PPL CaBViP
NL 0450519   DLC PPAmP DI-GS CaBVaU IU CtY CU CaOTP

Logan, Sir William Edmond, 1798–1875.
Figures and descriptions of Canadian organic
remains
see under Canada. Geological Survey.

Logan, Sir W₍illiam₎ E₍dmond₎ 1798–1875.
₍Gold₎ Extract from Report of progress of Geological
survey of Canada, for 1847–48. By W. E. Logan ...
Montreal, Lovell and Gibson, 1849.
9 p. 21½ᵐ.

1. Gold.

Library, U. S. Geol.   survey   G S 6–120

NL 0450521   DI-GS

Logan, Sir William Edmond, 1798–1875.
Letter addressed to Mr. Joachim Barrande, on
the rocks of the Quebec group at Point Levis.
Montreal, Lovell (pr.) ₍1863₎
14 p.   map.

NL 0450522   CaOTU CtY Nh

Logan, Sir William Edmond, 1798–1875.
Life of Sir William E. Logan ...
see under Harrington, Bernard James, 1848–
1907.

Logan, Sir William Edmond, 1798–1875.
Notes on the gold of eastern Canada
see under Canada. Geological Survey.

3278. LOGAN, SIR WILLIAM EDMOND, 1798–1875.
On the foot-prints occurring in the Potsdam sandstone of Canada. By
W.E. Logan, Esq., F.G.S. (From the Quarterly Journal of the Geological
Society of London for August 1852, Vol.VIII.) [n.p. n.d.]
1 p.l., [199]–225 p. 3 illus. (diagrs.). 7 fold.plates. fold.map. 2 fold.plans (1 col.)
two fold.plans duplicated.   Contains at 214–225: Description of the Impressions
and Foot-prints of the Protichnites from the Potsdam Sandstone of Canada. By Prof.
Owen, F.R.S., F.G.S. &c.   20 x 13 cm.
The Library has also the ms. diaries of Sir Wm. E. Logan, who was the first
director of the Geological Survey of Canada, 1843–1875.

NL 0450525   CaOTU

VOLUME 338

Logan, Sir William Edmond, 1789-1875.
On the history of Eozoön Canadense
see under title

Logan, Sir W[illiam] E[dmond], 1798-1875.
On the occurrence of a track and foot-
prints of an animal in the potsdam sandstone of Lower Canada. [N.p.n.pub.]1851,
1 illus.nar.D.

NL 0450527   CaBViP

Logan, Sir William Edmond, 1798-1875.
Canada. *Geological survey.*
... Rapport sur le rivage septentrional du Lac Huron
Montréal, De imprimerie de Lovell et Gibson, 1849.

Logan, Sir William Edmond, 1789-1875.
Remarks on the fauna of the Quebec group of rocks,
and the primordial zone of Canada, addressed to
Joachim Barrande.   Montreal, Lovell (pr.), 1861.
[5] p.

NL 0450529   CaOTU Nh

Logan, Sir William Edmond, 1798-1875-
Canada. *Geological survey.*
Remarks on the mining region of Lake Superior; addressed to the committee of the Honorable the executive
council, and report on mining locations claimed on the
Canadian shores of the lake, addressed to the Commissioner of crown lands, by W. E. Logan, provincial geologist. Montreal, Printed by Lovell & Gibson, 1847.
31 p. 21ᶜᵐ.

1. Mines and mineral resources—Ontario.   I. Logan, Sir William Edmond, 1798-1875.

GS6-513

Library, U. S. Geol.   survey

NL 0450530   DI-GS CaBViP

Logan, Sir William Edmond, 1798-1875.
Report of progress, 1875-76
see under   Canada. Geological Survey.

Logan, Sir William Edmond, 1798-1875.
Canada. *Geological survey.*
... Report of progress from its commencement to 1863; illus-
trated by 498 wood cuts in the text and accompanied by an
atlas of maps and sections ... Montreal, Dawson brothers;
London, Paris and New York, Ballière, 1863-[65]

Logan, Sir William Edmond, 1798-1875.
Report on the geology of Newfoundland for 1865
see under   Murray, Alexander, 1811-1885.

Logan, Sir William Edmond, 1798-1875.
Canada. *Geological survey.*
... Report on the north shore of Lake Huron. Montreal,
Printed by Lovell & Gibson, 1849.

Logan, Sir William, E[dmond] 1798-1875.
... Reports of Sir W. E. Logan ... and Edward Hartley ... on a part of the Pictou coal field, Nova Scotia, with
an appendix on coal and iron ores and a geological map.
From the reports of the Geological survey of the Do-
minion of Canada for 1867-69.   Montreal, Dawson bros.;
New York, B. Westermann & co.; [etc., etc.] 1870.
2 p. l., [3]-186 p. illus., fold. col. map, fold. tab. 25ᶜᵐ.

1. Coal mines and mining — Nova Scotia — Pictou Co. 2. Iron ores —
Nova Scotia—Pictou Co.   I. Hartley, Edward.

Library, U. S. Geol.   survey   G S 6-129

NL 0450535   DI-GS

Logan, Sir William Edmond, 1798-1875.
Reports on a geological survey of the Province of
Canada.
Montreal, 1845-47.
8vo.

NL 0450536   NN

Logan, Sir William Edmond, 1798-1875.
A sketch of the geology of Canada, serving to explain
the geological map and the collection of economic minerals
sent to the Universal exhibition at Paris, 1855. By W. E.
Logan ... and T. Sterry Hunt ... (Translated from the
French) Paris, H. Bossange & son, 1855.
[44] p. 25ᶜᵐ. (In [Canada. Executive committee for the Paris exhibition, 1855] Canada at the Universal exhibition of 1855. Toronto, 1856.
p. 411-454)
French edition published 1855 with title: Esquisse géologique du Canada.
1. Geology—Canada.   I. Hunt, Thomas Sterry, 1826-1892, joint author.
5—27940
Library of Congress   T800.G1C2

NL 0450537   DLC Nh

Logan, Sir William Edmond, 1798-1875.
Summary report of progress, May 1, 1869.
Ottawa, 1869.

NL 0450538   NN

Logan, William Henry, 1843-1910.
Sermons, numbered 121-142, preached at
various churches in Penna., N.J. and Md.
1881-1895.
16 sermons. mss.
Numbers missing: 131,132,134,137,138,139.

NL 0450539   PPPrHi

Logan, William Henry, 1865-
Sermons, numbered 1-142, preached at
various churches in Pennsylvania, New Jersey,
New York, Delaware, and Maryland 1873-1895.
90 items. mss.
Some sermons missing.

NL 0450540   PPPrHi

[Logan, William Hugh] d. 1883.
Le bas-bleu; or, The fall of the leaf. A farce. In two
acts. Performed at the Theatre-Royal, Edinburgh, for the first
time, March 30, 1836 ... Edinburgh, Printed for private circulation [by the Edinburgh printing company] 1836.
vi p., 1 l., [9]-39, [1] p. 22ᶜᵐ.
"Fifty copies ... have been printed at the private expense of the playwright, and ... not one will be sold."
I. Title.
31-15479
Library of Congress   PR4891.L5B3   822.8

NL 0450541   DLC InU MH

[LOGAN, William Hugh.] d. 1883.
A cap and bells for those whom it may fit.
pp. 14.
(In his Nugae histrionicae, 1834).
A criticism on the Edinburgh Theatre.

NL 0450542   MH

Logan, William Hugh, d. 1883.
A cap and bells for those whom it may fit. [Anon.]
[Leith, 1834.] 14 pp. 17½ cm.
There is no title-page.
Relates to the Edinburgh theatres.
J362 — Anon. ref. — Edinburgh, Scotland. Theatres.

NL 0450543   MB MH

---

*
Z999
.M354
1880
Logan, William Hugh, d. 1883.
Catalogue of the extensive and valuable
library, in dramatic, antiquarian and general
literature, poetry, ballads, &c., of W.H.
Logan; which will be sold by auction by T.
Chapman & Son, on Tuesday, March 20, 1883, and
five following lawful days. Edinburgh, Cols-
ton [1883]
77 p. 26cm. [With Maidment, James. Catalogue.
Edinburgh, 1880]
1. Bibl.—Rare   books. 2. Rare books—
Catalogs.

NL 0450544   ViU

Logan, William Hugh, d. 1883, joint ed.
Crowne, John, 1640?-1712.
The dramatic works of John Crowne, with prefatory
memoir and notes ... Edinburgh, W. Paterson; [etc., etc.]
1873-74.

Logan, William Hugh, d. 1883, joint ed.
Lacy, John, d. 1681.
The dramatic works of John Lacy, comedian, with prefatory
memoir and notes. Edinburgh, W. Paterson; [etc., etc.] 1875.

Logan, William Hugh, d. 1883, joint ed.
Tatham, John, fl. 1632-1664.
The dramatic works of John Tatham. With introductions
and notes. Edinburgh, W. Paterson; [etc., etc.] 1879.

Logan, William Hugh, d. 1883, ed.
Wilson, John, 1626-1696.
The dramatic works of John Wilson. With prefatory memoir, introductions, and notes. Edinburgh, W. Paterson; [etc.,
etc.] 1874.

Logan, William Hugh, d. 1883, joint ed.
Marmion, Shackerley, 1603-1639.
The dramatic works of Shackerley Marmion with prefatory
memoir, introductions and notes. Edinburgh, W. Paterson;
[etc., etc.] 1875.

Logan, William Hugh, d. 1883, ed.
Cokayne, Sir Aston, bart., 1608-1684.
The dramatic works of Sir Aston Cokain. With prefatory
memoir, introductions, and notes. Edinburgh, W. Paterson;
[etc., etc., 1874]

VOLUME 338

[LOGAN, WILLIAM HUGH] d. 1883.
The Edinburgh Rosciad; for the summer season, 1834...
[Edinburgh] Imprinted at Modern Athens, 1834.   8 p.
16cm.

775775A. 1. Poetry, Scottish. I. Title.

NL 0450551   NN MH MB

Logan, William Hugh, d. 1883, comp.
Fragmenta Scoto-dramatica. 1715-1758 ... Edinburgh,
1835.
48 p. 17 cm.
Consists chiefly of advertisements and other extracts from newspapers relating to the drama in Scotland.
"A very few copies have been printed at the private expense of the
editor [W. H. Logan]."
Micro-opaque.

1. Theater—Edinburgh—Hist.   I. Title.

PN2605.E3L8   17—25899

UU
NL 0450552   DLC MB CSmH CtY ICRL FU MsU NcU ICN ICU

Logan, William Hugh, d. 1883.
Letter from a gentleman in town to his friend in the country, re-
garding Keeley, the theatre, and other matters connected with
the drama in Edinburgh. [Anon.]
[Edinburgh. 1834.] 8 pp. 17½ cm.
Signed H. M.

J361—Keeley, Robert. 1793-1869.—Anon. ref.—Edinburgh, Scotland. Theatres.

NL 0450553   MB MH

[LOGAN, William Hugh.] d. 1883.
Letter from a gentleman in town to his friend
in the country, regarding Keeley, the theatre,
and other matters connected with the drama in
Edinburgh.
Signed H.M.
pp. 8.
(In his Nugae histrionicae, 1834.)
This book may be consulted in the rooms of
the Theatre collection.

NL 0450554   MH

Logan, William Hugh. d. 1883, ed.
Digges, West, 1720-1786.
Letters which passed between Mr. West Digges, come-
dian, and Mrs. Sarah Ward, 1752-1759 ... Edinburgh,
T. Stevenson, 1833.

Logan, William Hugh, d. 1883.
Clark, William, advocate.
Marciano; or, The discovery. A tragi-comedy, by William Clark, advocate. Edinburgh, Reprinted for private
circulation, 1871.

PN   [Logan, William Hugh] d. 1883.
2605   Nugae histrionicae. Emanations from
E3   the pen of Peregrine Spitfire, gent.
L83   [pseud.] Edinburgh, Buchanan, 1834.
            4 v. in 1. 20cm.
            The third and fourth parts have
            caption titles only.
            Contents.--Letter from a gentleman in
            town to his friend in the country,
            regarding Keel   ey, the theatre, and
            other matters   connected with the

Continued in next column

Continued from preceding column

drama in Edinburgh.--The Edinburgh
Rosciad: for the summer season, 1834.
3d ed.--Plays and players at the Edinburgh Adelphi Theatre.   4th ed.--A
cap and bells for those whom it may fit.

NL 0450558   NIC

[Logan, William Hugh] d. 1883.
... Nugae histrionicae. Emanations from the pen
or Peregrine Spitfire, gent. [pseud.] .. [Pt. I]
Edinburgh, Buchanan and co., 1834.
2 p.l., [3]-8, 8, 8, 14 p.   17.5 cm.
No more published.
Contents.   Letter from a gentleman in town to his
friend in the country, regarding Keeley, the theatre,
and other matters connected with the drama in
Edinburgh. -Plays and players at the Edinburgh
Adelphi theatre, July, 1834. -The Edinburgh
Rosciad; for the summer season, 1834.

-A cap and bells for those whom it may fit.
The Edinburgh Rosciad has individual t.-p.

NL 0450560   CtY MH

Logan, William Hugh, d. 1883.
A pedlar's pack of ballads and songs. With illustrative
notes, by W. H. Logan. Edinburgh, W. Paterson, 1869.
xv, 479, [1] p. illus. 19cm.
"Most of the ballads are from original broadsides in the possession of
Mr. Maidment."—Pref., p. viii.

1. English ballads and songs. 2. Scottish ballads and songs.   I. Maidment, James, 1795?-1879.   II. Title.

Library of Congress   PR4891.L5P4
                                                19—5472

MB NcU TU ViU OrU CaBVaU
NL 0450561   DLC TxU WU MdBP OU NcD CtY OCl OCU MiU

[LOGAN, William Hugh.] d. 1883?
Plays and players at the Edinburgh Adelphi
theatre. July 1834.
pp. 8.
(In his Nugae histrionicae.)

NL 0450562   MH MB

[LOGAN, William Hugh.] d. 1883
Plays and players at the Edinburgh Adelphi
theatre, July 1834. 4th ed. [Edinburgh, 1834?]
nar. 16°. pp. 8.
Caption title.   Thr 467.69

NL 0450563   MH

4K   Logan, William Hugh, d. 1883
8197   The pocket bill-book: or, A
            practical digest of the law of bills,
            promissory-notes, and bankers' cheques.
            Edinburgh, Edinburgh Print. and Pub.
            Co., 1842.
                    437 p.

NL 0450564   DLC-P4

Logan, William Hugh, d. 1883, supposed author.
Rummio and Judy; or, Oh, this love!!
This love! This love! A serio-comic-parodi-
tragedi-farcical burlesque
            see under   Lloyd, Horace Amelius.

Logan, William Hugh, d. 1883.
The Scotch banker; or, A popular exposition of the practice
of banking in Scotland. By W. H. Logan ... 3d ed. Edinburgh, Oliver & Boyd; [etc., etc.], 1847.
5 p. l., 218 p. fold. tab. 14½cm.

1. Banks and banking—Scotland.
                                          6–18487 Revised
Library of Congress   HG1601.L7

NL 0450566   DLC CaBVaU NjR MH-BA

Kress   Logan, William Hugh, d. 1883.
Room   The Scotish banker; or, A popular exposi-
            tion of the practice of banking in Scotland
            ... Edinburgh, Fraser and Crawford [etc.,
            etc.] 1839.
            4 p. l., 134 p. front. (fold. table) 15 cm.

X 1. Banks and banking - Scotland.   XI. Title.

NL 0450567   MH-BA

H   LOGAN, WILLIAM HUGH, d. 1883.
7743   The Scotish banker; or, A popular exposition
.518   of the practice of banking in Scotland. 2d ed.
            Edinburgh, Gallie and Bayley [etc.] 1844.
            218p. fold. table. 15cm.

NL 0450568   ICN MH-BA NcU

C.6650 Logan, William Hugh, d.1883.
The Scotish banker; or, A popular exposition of the practice of banking in Scotland . . . 2d ed. Edinburgh, J.D.
Lowe [etc., etc.] 1845.
5 p. l., 218 p. fold. table. 15 cm.

NL 0450569   MH-BA

332.1   Logan, William Hugh, d. 1883
L828s   The Scottish banker; or, A popular
1850   exposition of the practice of banking
            in Scotland. A new ed.   London, 1850.
            218p. tables (1 fold.)

NL 0450570   IU

Logan, William Newton, 1869-1941.
U. S. Bureau of mines.
... Analyses of Indiana coals ... Washington, U. S. Govt.
print. off., 1927.

557.62   Logan, William Newton, 1869-1941
M691b   Brick clays and clay industry of northern
            Mississippi. 1907. (Mississippi. State
            geological survey. Bulletin. #2)

NL 0450572   OrU

557.62   Logan, William Newton, 1869-1941
M691b   Brick clays and clay industry of southern
            Mississippi. 1908. (Mississippi. State
            Geological survey. Bulletin. #4)

NL 0450573   OrU

VOLUME 338

Logan, William Newton, 1869–1941.
The ceramic materials of Indiana, by W. N. Logan, Division of geology ... Indianapolis, 1929.
12 p. incl. maps, tables. 22½ᵐ. (Indiana. Department of conservation. Publication no. 91)
"Available geological reports": p. 12.

1. Shale. 2. Clay—Indiana. I. Title.
G S 30—37

U. S. Geol. survey. Library   (252) P no. 91
for Library of Congress   ₍a41k1₎

NL 0450574   DI-GS MtBuM OrCS InU OU

Logan, William Newton, 1869–
... Circular on the underground waters of Mississippi, by W. N. Logan ... Agricultural College, Miss., 1905.
16 p. illus., diagrs. 23ᶜᵐ.
At head of title: Mississippi agricultural experiment station.
"Largely a summary of bulletin no. 89."

1. Water, Underground—Mississippi. I. Mississippi. Agricultural experiment station, Agricultural College. II. Title.
G S 19—45

U. S. Geol. survey. Library   S(236) M7
for Library of Congress   ₍a41b1₎

NL 0450575   DI-GS

Logan, William Newton, 1869–1941.
... Clays of Mississippi ... By William N. Logan. Nashville, Brandon ₍printing company, 1907–₎08.
2 v. illus., plates, 2 fold. maps. 23ᵐ. (Mississippi. State geological survey. Bulletins no. 2, 4)
CONTENTS.—pt. I. Brick clays and clay industry of northern Mississippi.—pt. II. Brick clays and clay industry of southern Mississippi.

1. Clay—Mississippi.
G S 9—15
U. S. Geol. survey. Library   (236) M6b no. 2, 4
for Library of Congress   QE129.A2 no. 2, 4
                                   TN942.L77

OU OO OCl DLC
NL 0450576   DI-GS MtBuM WaS MoU GU CU OCU MiU ICJ

Logan, William Newton, 1869–1941.
... Contributions to the paleontology of the upper cretaceous series, by William Newton Logan ... Chicago, 1899.
3 p. l., p. 207–216. pl. XXII–XXVI. 24ᶜᵐ. (Field Columbian museum. Publication 36. Geological series. Vol I, no. 6)
Each plate accompanied by guard sheet with brief explanation.

1. Paleontology—Cretaceous. 2. Mollusks, Fossil. 3. Paleontology—Kansas.
Library of Congress   QE1.F4
                         tached. QE734.L83
4—10870

OCU MB NN OU
NL 0450577   DLC INS MtBuM WaTC MoU   OO OCl MiU

Logan, William Newton, 1869–1941.
Economic geology of Indiana.
(*In* Indiana. Department of Conservation. Handbook of Indiana geology. Pp. 571–1058. Illus. Plates. Maps. Plans. Tables. Geological sections. Indianapolis. 1922.)
Bibliography, pp. 664, 797, 798, 1057, 1058.

M5728 — Geology, Economic.

NL 0450578   MB

Logan, William Newton, 1869–1941.
The elements of practical conservation, by W. N. Logan. Indianapolis, Ind., C. E. Pauley & co., printer ₍1927₎.
236 p. illus. 23ᵐ.
The conservation of natural resources.
Bibliography: p. 236.

1. Natural resources. 2. U. S.—Econ. condit. I. Title: Conservation.

Library of Congress   HC106.3.L6
29—18378

NL 0450579   DLC Or NcD OClW OO MiU OU

Logan, William Newton, 1869–1941.
The foundry sands of Indiana, by W. N. Logan ... Indianapolis, 1930.
12 p. incl. 2 maps, tab. 22½ cm. (Indiana. Dept. of conservation. Publication no. 92)
Issued by the Division of geology.

1. Sand. ₍1. Molding sand₎ 2. Foundry supplies. I. Indiana. Dept. of conservation. Division of geology. II. Title.
G S 30—186

U. S. Geol. Survey. Libr.   (252) P no. 92
for Library of Congress   ₍a50d1₎

NL 0450580   DI-GS MtBuM OrCS PPAN OU OkU

Logan, William Newton, 1869–
Geological conditions in the oil fields of southwestern Indiana, by W. N. Logan ... Indianapolis, Wm. B. Burford, contractor for state printing and binding, 1924.
125 p. illus., tables, diagrs. 22½ᵐ. (Indiana. Dept. of conservation. Publication no. 42)

1. Geology—Indiana. 2. Petroleum—Indiana. I. Title.
G S 25—21
U. S. Geol. survey. Library   (252) P no. 42
for Library of Congress   TN872.I 6L55

NL 0450581   DI-GS MtBuM CU ViU MsU OU OClW NN DLC

Logan, William Newton, 1869–1941.
... The geology of the deep wells of Indiana, by W. N. Logan ... Division of geology ... Conservation commission ... Indianapolis, The Department of conservation. W. B. Burford, contractor for state printing and binding, 1926.
540 p. maps, tables. 23ᵐ. (Indiana. Dept. of conservation. Publication no. 55)

1. Wells. 2. Water, Underground—Indiana. 3. Geology—Indiana. I. Title.
G S 26—271
U. S. Geol. survey. Library   (252) P no. 55
DLC for Library of Congress   QE109.L6

DLC MB NN
NL 0450582   DI-GS MtBuM OrCS ViU MiU CU OCl OO OU

Logan, William Newton, 1869–1941.
Stephenson, Lloyd William, 1876–
... The ground-water resources of Mississippi, by Lloyd W. Stephenson, William N. Logan, and Gerald A. Waring. With discussions of the chemical character of the waters, by C. S. Howard. Prepared in cooperation with the Mississippi State geological survey. Washington, U. S. Govt. print. off., 1928.

QE109
.A5
1922

Indiana. *Division of Geology.*
Handbook of Indiana geology, by W. N. Logan ₍and others₎ Indianapolis, Wm. B. Burford, contractor for State printing and binding, 1922.

TN942
.L78

Logan, William Newton, 1869–1941.
... Kaolin of Indiana, by W. N. Logan ... Indianapolis, W. B. Burford, contractor for state printing, 1919.
181 p. illus. (incl. maps) fold. map, diagrs. 22½ cm. (*Half-title*: Indiana. Dept. of conservation. Publication no. 6)
At head of title: Division of geology.
Bibliography: p. 13–14.

1. Kaolin. I. Indiana. Dept. of conservation. Division of geology.
G S 20—293
U. S. Geol. Survey. Libr.   (252) P ₎ no. 6₎
for Library of Congress   ₍a50f1₎

ICJ NN ViU UU CU CaBVaU MtBuM
NL 0450585   DI-GS WaS OrCS GU PLF OClW OCl OO MiU

Logan, William Newton, 1869–1941.
... Laboratory studies in geology, by W. N. Logan. Agricultural college, Miss., ₍Jackson, Miss.₎ Mississippi agricultural and mechanical college, 1914.
11 p. 20½ᶜᵐ. ₍Bulletin of the Mississippi agricultural and mechanical college. vol.11,no.4. Oct. 1914₎

1. Geology. I. Ser.

NL 0450586   ViU IU

LOGAN, William Newton, 1869–1941.
Laboratory studies in geology. ₍Starkville, Miss.₎ Mississippi agricultural and mechanical college, ₍1914₎.

pp. 41.
"Bulletin of the Mississippi Agricultural and Mechanical College, Vol. 11, No. 1, January, 1914.
"References", pp. 40–41.

NL 0450587   MH

Logan, William Newton, 1869–1941.
Sauers, Charles G.
... McCormick's creek canyon state park: a history and description. By Chas. G. Sauers ... The Department of conservation, state of Indiana, Division of land and waters. ₍Indianapolis, W. B. Burford, contractor for state printing and binding, 1923₎

Logan, William Newton, 1869–1941.
... A North American epicontinental sea of jurassic age ... Chicago, The University of Chicago press, 1900.
1 p. l., 241–273 p. incl. maps. 24 cm.
Thesis (PH. D.)—University of Chicago.
"Reprinted from the Journal of geology, April–May, 1900."

1. Geology, Stratigraphic—Jurassic. 2. Geology—North America.

QE681.L8?
4—28826

NL 0450589   DLC ICJ MB NN NjP NIC NBuU

Logan, William Newton, 1869–1941.
... Petroleum and natural gas in Indiana; a preliminary report, by W. N. Logan ... state geologist. Fort Wayne, Ind., Fort Wayne printing company, 1920.
279 p. illus., maps (part fold.) diagrs. (part fold.) 22½ᵐ. (Indiana. Department of conservation. Publication no. 8)

1. Petroleum—Indiana. 2. Gas, Natural—Indiana.
G S 20—426
U. S. Geol. survey. Library   (252) P
for Library of Congress   TN872.I 6L6

OClW MB NN MH GU MtBuM Or WaS CaBVaU
NL 0450590   DI-GS OrCS NBuU CU UU ViU ODW MiU OCl

Logan, William Newton, 1869–1941.
... The pottery clays of Mississippi, by William N. Logan. Nashville, Brandon ₍printing company, 1909?₎
228 p. illus., diagrs. 23½ᵐ. (Mississippi. State geological survey. Bulletin no. 6)

1. Clay—Mississippi. 2. Pottery—Mississippi.
G S 10—298
U. S. Geol. survey. Library   (236) M6b no. 6
for Library of Congress   QE129.A2 no. 6
                                   ₍a40e1₎

DLC OU NN
NL 0450591   DI-GS MtBuM WaS OrU CU MiU OCl OO ICJ

VOLUME 338

Logan, William Newton, 1869–1941.
... The pottery clays of Mississippi, by William N. Logan.
1914. [2d ed.] Jackson, Miss., Tucker printing house [1914]
221 p. incl. illus., maps, tables, profiles. 23½ᶜᵐ. (Mississippi. State geological survey. Bulletin no. 6)
Some illustrations numbered as plates.

1. Clay—Mississippi. 2. Pottery—Mississippi.
                                                    36—11633
Library of Congress   QE129.A2 no. 6, 2d ed.

NL 0450592   DLC MoU NN OO OCU

552.52
L828p
Logan, William Newton, 1869–1941.
... A preliminary report on some of the clays of Mississippi, by W.N. Logan, geologist, and W.F. Hand, chemist. Jackson, Miss., Tucker printing house [1905]
88p. illus.(incl. map) 23cm. (On cover: Bulletin of the Mississippi agricultural and mechanical college. vol.2, no.3)
Geological survey of Mississippi. Bulletin no.3.

NL 0450593   TxU

Logan, William Newton, 1869–1941.
... Preliminary report on the marls and limestones of Mississippi, by William N. Logan. Jackson, Tucker printing house, 1916.
3 p. L., [7]–82 p. front., illus. 28½ cm. (Mississippi. State geological survey. Bulletin no. 13)

1. Marl. 2. Limestone. 3. Geology—Mississippi.
U. S. Geol. Survey. Libr.   (236) M6b no. 13   G S 17—79
for Library of Congress   QE129.A2 no. 13
    — Copy 2.   TN948.M3L7
                                                    (557.62)

OCU ICJ DLC
NL 0450594   DI-GS NN MtBuM WaS OrU MoU CU OU OO OCI

Logan, William Newton, 1869–1941.
... The soils of Mississippi, by William N. Logan ...
Agricultural College, Miss., 1913.
49 p. fold. map. 23½ᶜᵐ. (Mississippi. Agricultural experiment station, Agricultural College. Technical bulletin no. 4)

1. Soils—Mississippi.
                                                    G S 14–713
Library, U. S. Geol.   survey S(236) M67

NL 0450595   DI-GS

Logan, William Newton, 1869–1941.
The soils of Mississippi. Jackson: Tucker Prtg. House, 1913. 49 p., 1 map. 8°. (Mississippi. Agricultural Experiment Station. Technical bull. 4.)

1. Soils. U. S.: Miss.
                                        December 30, 1913.

NL 0450596   NN

Logan, William Newton, 1869–1941.
...The soils of Mississippi   Agricultural college, Miss., 1913   84p. illus. charts folded, cc colored map.   Miss. agricultural exp. sta. Technical bulletin #7)

NL 0450597   OrU-M

Logan, W[illiam] N[ewton], 1869–1941.
Some additions to the cretaceous invertebrates of Kansas.
(In: Kansas. University of Kansas. Kansas University quarterly.
Lawrence, 1899. 8°. v.8A, no. 2, p. 87–98, 4 pl.)

1. Palaeontology (Invertebrata),   U.S.: Kan. 2. Mollusca (Fossil),
U.S.: Kan.   U.S.: Kan.
                                      June 24, 1916.

NL 0450598   NN

Logan, W[illiam] N[ewton], 1869–1941.
Some new cirriped crustaceans from the Niobrara cretaceous of Kansas. (In: Kansas. University of Kansas. Kansas University quarterly. Lawrence, 1896. 8°. v. 6A, no. 4, p. 187–189.)

1. Cirripedia (Fossil), U.S.: Kan.
                                      June 14, 1916.

NL 0450599   NN

Logan, William Newton, 1869–1941.
Spencer County, Indiana. Supplement to Publication 108, "Sub-surface strata of Indiana" ...
see under Indiana. Division of Geology.

Logan, W[illiam] N[ewton], 1869–1941.
The stratigraphy and invertebrate faunas of the jurassic formation in the Freeze-Out hills of Wyoming. (In: Kansas. University of Kansas. Kansas University quarterly. Lawrence, 1900. 8°. v. 9A, no. 2, p. 109–134, 6 pl.)

1. Palaeontology (Invertebrata),   U. S.: Wyoming. 2. Geology,
U. S.: Wyoming.   June 23, 1916.

NL 0450601   NN

Logan, William Newton, 1869–1941.
... The structural materials of Mississippi, a preliminary report, by William N. Logan. Nashville, Brandon [1911]
78 p. illus. 23½ᶜᵐ. (Mississippi. State geological survey. Bulletin no. 9)

1. Building materials.   I. Title.
U. S. Geol. survey. Library   (236) M6b no. 9   G S 12—324
for Library of Congress   QE129.A2 no. 9
                               TN951.M7L8

OCU MiU ICJ DLC OU NN
NL 0450602   DI-GS MtBuM WaS OrU MoU TxFTC CU OO OCI

Logan, William Newton, 1869–1941.
The sub-surface strata of Indiana. Fort Wayne, Fort Wayne Print. Co., 1931.
790 p. illus., maps. 23 cm. (Indiana. Dept. of Conservation. Publication no. 108)
Bibliography: p. 15.
————— Supplement. Knox County, Indiana. Logs, complete to April 2, 1940. [n. p., 1940]
97 p. 28 cm.
                               QE109.L65 Suppl.
1. Geology—Indiana.   I. Title. (Series)
QE109.L65   557.72   G S 32–25 rev*
U. S. Geol. Survey. Libr.
for Library of Congress   [r50d1]†

NL 0450603   DI-GS MtBuM IdU PLF MB OU MiU DLC

Logan, William Newton, 1869–1941.
The temperature sense. (In: Kansas. University of Kansas. Kansas University quarterly. Lawrence, 1895. 8°. v. 3, no. 3, p. 201–204.)

1. Temperature.—Sense of.
                                      March 6, 1916.

NL 0450604   NN

Logan, W[illiam] N[ewton], 1869–1941.
... The underground waters of Mississippi; a preliminary report by W. N. Logan and W. R. Perkins ...
Agricultural college, Miss.; Jackson, Miss., Tucker printing house, 1905.
112 p. illus., diagrs. 23ᶜᵐ. (Mississippi. Agricultural experiment station. Bulletin no. 89)

1. Water, Underground—Mississippi.   I. Perkins, W. R., joint author.

Library, U. S. Geol.   survey   G S 6–525

NL 0450605   DI-GS MtBuM NN

Logan, William Philip Dowie.
General practitioners' records; an analysis of the clinical records of eight practices during the period April 1951 to March 1952, with a foreword by John Charles. London, H. M. Stationery Off., 1953.
vii, 131 p. forms, tables. 25 cm. ([Gt. Brit.] General Register Office. Studies on medical and population subjects, no. 7)
Errata slip inserted.

1. Medical records.   I. Title. (Series)
R727.3.L6   58–18872

NL 0450606   DLC MiU NNC IEN WU DNLM MBCo FU

Logan, William Robertson.
Bacteriology and protozoology in medicine and public health ... Edinburgh, E. & S. Livingstone [194–]
2 pts. in 1 v. (155 p.) 18cm. (Catechism series)
5th ed.

1. Bacteriology - 1901-   2. Protozoa, Pathogenic.

NL 0450607   CU ICU DNLM

Logan, William Robertson.

Lees, David, d. 1934.
Practical methods in the diagnosis & treatment of venereal diseases for medical practitioners and students, by David Lees ... Third edition, edited and revised by Robert Lees ... with the following contributors: R. Cranston Low, William R. Logan, R. C. L. Batchelor ... Edinburgh, E. & S. Livingstone, 1937.

Logan, William Russell, joint author.

Logan, John Douglas.
... Dental prosthetics, by J. Douglas Logan ... and W. Russell Logan ... Second edition. Edinburgh, E. & S. Livingstone, 1934.

G3814
.M266
1950
.M3
Logan, William S.

Manasquan, N. J. Borough Engineer.
Plan showing improved and unimproved municipal roads, Boro of Manasquan, Monmouth County, N. J. William S. Logan, Jr., boro engineer. [Manasquan, 1950]

G3814
.M266
1949
.M3
Logan, William S.

Manasquan, N. J. Borough Engineer.
Zoning map of the Borough of Manasquan, Monmouth Co., New Jersey. As amended Oct. 28, 1947. (Streets added) August 1949. [Manasquan, 1949]

VOLUME 338

Logan-Home, George John Ninian, 1855–
History of the Logan family, by Major G. J. N. Logan Home ... Edinburgh, G. Waterston & sons limited, 1934.
xii, 250 p. illus., plates, ports., facsims., col. coats of arms. 25½ᵐ.

1. Logan family.
34–39658
Library of Congress   CS479.L75 1934
929.2

NL 0450612   DLC NN PHi

Logan-Logejus, Jakob Anton Friedrich.
Meine Erlebnisse als Reiteroffizier unter dem Grossen König in den Jahren 1741–1759. Bearb. und hrsg. von einem deutschen Offizier. Gekürzte Ausg., 2. durchgesehene Aufl. Breslau, W. G. Korn, 1934.
315 p. 20 cm.

1. Austrian Succession, War of, 1740–1748. 2. Seven Years' War, 1756–1763. I. Title.
DD402.L6A3 1934!   50–43938

NL 0450613   DLC NN NNC MiD

Logan-Logejus, Jakob Anton Friedrich
Meine Erlebnisse als Reiteroffizier unter dem grossen König in den Jahren 1741–1759. Bearbeitet und herausgegeben von einem deutschen Offizier. Gekürzte Ausg. 3.Aufl. Breslau, W.G.Korn, 1934.

NL 0450614   MH

Logan, Utah. Agricultural College
see
Utah. State University of Agriculture and Applied Science, *Logan.*

Logan, Utah. Agricultural experiment station
see
Utah. Agricultural experiment station, *Logan.*

LOGAN, Utah. Brigham Young college.

See BRIGHAM YOUNG COLLEGE, Logan, Utah.

NL 0450617   MH

Logan, Utah. Charters.

Logan, *Utah.* Ordinances, etc.
Ordinances of Logan city, Utah, to which are added the city charter and amendments; laws applicable to the city; the city, county and territorial officials, and a comprehensive index. Revised, compiled and arranged—pursuant to an ordinance of the City council adopted May 22, 1890—by S. A. Kenner, attorney ... Salt Lake City, Utah, Printed by the Star printing company, 1890.

Logan, *Utah.* Ordinances, etc.
Ordinances of Logan city, Utah, to which are added the city charter and amendments; laws applicable to the city; the city, county and territorial officials, and a comprehensive index. Revised, compiled and arranged—pursuant to an ordinance of the City council adopted May 22, 1890—by S. A. Kenner, attorney ... Salt Lake City, Utah, Printed by the Star printing company, 1890.
246 p. 23ᵐ.

I. Kenner, Scipio A. II. Logan, Utah. Charters. III. Title.
39–8835
Library of Congress   JS999.L4A5 1890

NL 0450619   DLC MH

Logan, Utah. Ordinances, etc.
The revised ordinances of Logan city, containing all the ordinances in force on the 18th day of April, A. D. 1877, and the rules and order of business of the Logan City council, to which is prefixed the city charter with amendments. Rev., comp. and publishe by authority. Ogden city, Utah, Printed at the Junction office, 1877.
100 p. 20 cm.

NL 0450620   NjP

LOGAN, Utah. Ordinances, etc.
Revised Ordinances, in force 1903. n.p.,n.d.

8vo.

NL 0450621   MH

Logan, Utah. State Agricultural College
see
Utah. State University of Agriculture and Applied Science, *Logan.*

Logan, Utah. State University of Agriculture and Applied Science
see
Utah. State University of Agriculture and Applied Science, *Logan.*

Logan, a family history ...
see under   [Neal, John] 1793–1876.

Logan & Shattuck, attorneys
Supreme Court | State of Oregon. | [*Short rule*] | September Term, 1869. | [*Short rule*] | [*Rule*] | James H. Fiske and Clementine | V. Fiske, Plaintiffs and Respondents. vs. | James Kellogg and W. J. Bradbury, | Defendants and Appellants. | [*Brace connects last 5 lines*] | [*Rule*] | [*Short rule*] | Brief for Appellants. | [*Short rule*] | Logan & Shattuck, and Wm. Strong, | Attorneys for Appellants. | [*Short rule*] | Portland, Oregon: | Himes & Daly, Printers, 87 First Street. | 1869.   [526]
34 p. 14 x 20.5 cm. Printed yellow paper wrappers.
Cover title; no separate title page.

NL 0450625   OrHi

G3894
.L6
1953
.P3
Logan Banner.
Park View Engineering Service, *Charleston, W. Va.* Logan, West Virginia. Logan, Logan Banner, ʿ1953.

Logan basic methods.
Spinal distortions, their cause, prevention & correction. Compiled ... by Logan basic methods. St. Louis, Mo., ʿ1945.
[15] p. illus. 98 pl., 2 port. 29 x 22ᵐ.

1. Spinal adjustment. 2. Chiropractic.
S G 46–103
U. S. Surg.-gen. off. Libr.
for Library of Congress   RM730.L65
†   615.82

NL 0450627   DI-GS DNLM DLC

Logan basic technique
see
Logan basic methods.

Logan city and Cache County directory
see under Polk (R. L.) and Company, inc.
R. L. Polk & co.'s Logan city and Cache County directory.

[Logan, Clark and Demond]
Why the Yaqui first mortgage six percent convertible land grant gold bonds are a desirable investment.   New York, [188?]
21 cm.

NL 0450630   DLC

Logan coal operators' association.

Operators' association of the Williamson field.
The issue in the coal fields of southern West Virginia; statements to President Harding by the Operators association of the Williamson field and the Logan coal operators association. [Washington? D. C., 1921]

JS3
C3 L62
Logan co., Ill. Board of supervisors.
Year book, Logan County, Illinois ... Rules, order of business, standing committees and other information. Board of supervisors. Logan county, Illinois. Lincoln, Ill.
v.
Compiled by Claude C. Tull, county clerk.

NL 0450632   DLC

Logan Co., Idaho. County Commissioners.
Notice of special election for adoption or rejection of the constitution... W. B. George, Clerk. Shoshone, October 2, 1889. John Heiley, Chairman of board of county commissioners of Logan county. [Shoshone, 1889.]
Broadside. 33 cm.

NL 0450633   IdHi

[Logan Co., Ill.]
A few reasons for the location of the Industrial university at Lincoln. n.p.,n.d.[ca.1867]
[4] p. folder, one of which is printed. 26cm.
Caption title.

NL 0450634   IHi

379.773 Logan Co., Ill.--School Survey Committee.
L82f   Final report of the School Survey Committee to the People of Logan County, Illinois. [n.p.] 1948.
14p. group port.,maps, tables. 28cm.

1. Educational surveys. 2. Public schools-- Logan Co., Ill.

NL 0450635   IU

VOLUME 338

379.773 Logan Co., Ill.--School Survey Committee.
L82t   Tentative report of the School Survey Committee
to the people of Logan County, Illinois.
[n.p.] 1947.
14p. group port., maps, tables. 28cm.

1. Educational surveys. 2. Public schools--
Logan, Co., Ill.

NL 0450636   IU

Logan co., Ill. Supervisors, Board
of

see

Logan co., Ill. Board of supervisors.

Logan Co., Ky.
Record of wills in Logan county: Russellville... [1933]
see under Burns, Annie (Walker) 1894-
[supplement]

RH
C2155   Logan County (Ill.) Aberdeen-Angus Association.
Aberdeen-Angus sale. Logan County Fair
Grounds, Sat., March 5, 1955, Lincoln, Ill.
Auctioneer: Hamilton James. Sale manager:
Verlon Elmore.   Aurora, Mo., MWM Color Press
c1955.
1v. (unpaged) illus. 22cm

1. Aberdeen-Angus cattle.

NL 0450639   KU-RH

Logan County (Ohio) agricultural society.
Annual fair.
Bellefontaine, O., 18
v. 22cm.
Advertising matter interspersed.

CA 16-163 Unrev'd
Library of Congress   S555.L83

NL 0450640   DLC

Logan County Baptist Association
see Baptists. Kentucky. Logan County
Baptist Association.

[Logan county historical society]
Logan county, Illinois, centennials.
[Lincoln? Ill., 1953]
folder, [6]p. illus. 23cm.

NL 0450642   IHi

---

fF
892513 LOGAN County, Ohio, marriage records, 1818-
.5   1834.   [n.p., n.d.]
16,16p. 29cm.

Xerox copy.

NL 0450643   ICN

Logan Creek, part of Lower Suttor, and of Lower
Mistake Creek. [With vocabulary of the Narboo
Murre tribe.]   (In E.M. Curr's, The Australian race...   Melbourne, 1886-87.
v. 3.   p. 36-39.   8°.

NL 0450644   NN

The **Logan** emancipation cabinet of letters and relics of
John Brown and Abraham Lincoln, being an article pre-
pared specially for the Chicago tribune.   Chicago, 1892.
40 p. ports. 15 cm.
In case.
L. C. copy imperfect : p. 5-6 wanting.

1. Lincoln, Abraham, Pres. U. S.—Museums, relics, etc. 2. Brown,
John, 1800–1859. I. The Chicago tribune.

E457.65.L8   54–48406

NL 0450645   DLC

Logan female college, *Russellville, Ky.*
Annual session ... and announcements.
Russellville, Ky.
v. plates. 25cm.

CA 9-1198 Unrev'd
Library of Congress   LD7251.R7

NL 0450646   DLC

Logan female college, Russellville, Ky.

Register for collegiate year 1875-6 [and]
announcement for collegiate year 1876-7. Russellville, Ky., Herald print, 1876.
56 p.   24cm.

Contains an examination on Hamlet prepared
by Dr. Furness, and the prize-winning answer-
paper of Miss Mary Lou Stark, daughter of the
president of the college.

NL 0450647   PU-F NN

---

qTS40C Logan-Gregg hardware company.
P69   The story of a hundred years. Pittsburgh,
L83   Logan-Gregg hardware company [1931]

14 p. incl. illus., ports. 28 cm.

NL 0450648   PPiHi

Microfilm Logan Historical Society.
01104   FOR OTHER EDITIONS
no. 297   SEE MAIN ENTRY
AP   The **American** pioneer, a monthly periodical devoted to the
objects of the Logan Historical Society; or, to collecting and
publishing sketches relative to the early settlement and successive improvement of the country. v. 1-2; Jan. 1842–Oct.
1843. Chillicothe [etc.] Ohio, J. S. Williams.

Logan journal
see   The Journal, Logan, Utah.

Logan leader
see   The Journal, Logan, Utah.

Logan Monument Commission
see Illinois. Logan Monument
Commission.

Logan Museum of Archaeology, Beloit, Wis.
see   Beloit College, Beloit, Wis. Logan
Museum.

Logan philological library, Singapore
see   Raffles museum and library, Singapore.

Logan publishing co., St. Louis.

Logan's manufacturers' directory and buyers' guide of
St. Louis, 18   St. Louis, Mo., New Orleans, La.
[etc.] Logan publishing co., 18

25.9   Logan publishing co., St. Louis, comp.
5183   Logan's post office, census, express, telegraph
and railroad directory of the west and south,
twenty states and territories. Also a national
hotes record, and mercantile and manufacturing
list.   St. Louis, Logan publishing co. [1874]
1 p.l., 112 p., 4 l.   12°.

NL 0450655   DLC

Logan publishing co., *St. Louis, comp.*
Logan's post-office, census, express, telegraph, railroad and river directory of the entire West & South,
containing the names of all post-offices ... with a supplement complete to June, 1875. St. Louis, Mo., N. Orleans [etc.] Logan publishing co. [1875]
1 p. l., 100, 30 p. 20cm.

1. The West—Descr. & trav.—Gazetteers. 2. Mississippi Valley—Descr.
& trav.—Gazetteers.

Library of Congress   11–13587
F594.L83

NL 0450656   DLC NcD

Utah Pam Logan Temple, 1884-1934; fiftieth anniver-
v.127   sary souvenir. [Logan, Utah, 1934]
no.12   1v. (unpaged) illus.

Cover title.

1. Mormon Church--Temples--Logan.

me-tc

NL 0450657   UU

Logan, the Mingo chief. A family history
see under [Neal, John] 1793-1876.

VOLUME 338

Logan, the Mingo chief, 1710–1780.
(*In* Ohio archæological and historical quarterly. Columbus, 1911. 23ᵐ.
v. 20, p. 137–175)
"From the Draper manuscripts—Border forays, 2b, chapter 12—in the
Library of the Wisconsin historical society. The notes also herewith
published were made by a recent student of the manuscripts."
"References": p. 168–175.

1. Logan, James, Mingo chief, 1720?–1780.
18-8930
Library of Congress   F486.O51 vol. 20

NL 0450659   DLC

Loganatha Mudaliar, P   S
see
Mudaliar, P   S   Loganatha.

Loganberry culture
see under Aspinwall, Britt.

Loganian Library, *Philadelphia.*
Publications of this body printed in America before 1801 are
available in this library in the Readex Microprint edition of Early
American Imprints published by the American Antiquarian Society.
This collection is arranged according to the numbers in Charles
Evans' American Bibliography.

NL 0450662   DLC

Loganian library, *Philadelphia.*
Catalogus Bibliothecæ Loganianæ: being a choice col
lection of books, as well in the oriental, Greek and Latin
as in the English, Italian, Spanish, French and other languages. Given by the late James Logan esq. of Philadelphia for the use of the publick. Numbered as they now
stand in the library; built by him, in Sixth-street, over
against the State-house square. Philadelphia, Printed by
Peter Miller & comp., 1760.
116 p. 19ᵐ.

10-26689
Library of Congress   Z881.P541L 1760

NL 0450663   DLC IU NcU MB PHi PPL

Loganian Library, Philadelphia
Catalogus Bibliothecae Loganianae; being a choice
collection of books as well in the Oriental, Greek
and Latin as in the English, Italian, Spanish, French
and other languages. Given by the late James Logan
esq. of Philadelphia for the use of the publick.
Numbered as they now stand in the library built by
him in Sixth-street over against the State-house
Square. Philadelphia, Printed by Miller, 1760

116 p.
Microfilm, negative,   of copy in Library of
Congress

NL 0450664   MH

Loganian Library, *Philadelphia*
see also
Philadelphia. Library Company. *Loganian Library.*

Loganian society, Haverford college
see
Haverford college. Loganian society.

Loganov, N
О наказуемости за надувание мяса. ⟨С.-Петербургъ
1884⟩
⟨88⟩–72 p. 23 cm.
Caption title.
Detached from Журналъ гражданскаго и уголовнаго права, т. 9,
1884.

1. Meat industry and trade—Law and legislation—Russia.   I.
Title.   *Title transliterated:* O nakazuemosti za naduvanie miâsa.

55–53864

NL 0450667   DLC

F486   **Logan's campaign - 1786.**
O614
v.22,
p.520–
521

(In Ohio archaeological and historical
publications. Columbus, O., 1913. 23½cm.
v. 22, p. 520–521)
"From the Draper mss., Wisconsin historical
society archives."

NL 0450668   NBuG

F   **LOGAN'S** classified business directory, of
9118   St. Paul, Minneapolis, and surrounding
.S17   towns. Containing the names, business
and location of business, of each person,
firm, company or institution -   St.
Paul, Logan & Ramaley, ⟨1874⟩
237p. 21cm.

NL 0450669   ICN

Logan's collection of highland bagpipe
music, containing marches, quicksteps,
strathspeys, reels, hornpipes and
jigs. Inverness, Logan ⟨1899⟩ 5v.

NL 0450670   CaBVa

Logan's collection of Highland bagpipe music, containing marches,
quicksteps, strathspeys, reels, hornpipes and jigs. Book 1–8...
Inverness: Logan & J. M. Wood Ltd.⟨, ca. 1920.⟩ 8 v. in 1.
obl. 16°.

Book 3–4, 6–8 have imprint: Paterson, Sons & Co., Ltd., Glasgow. Book 8 has at
head of title: Special war memorial number, 1914–1918.
Bound with: Logan's complete tutor for the Highland bagpipe.

1. Bagpipe.
January 19, 1926

NL 0450671   NN NBuG

...**Logan's** complete tutor for the Highland bagpipe and a selection of marches, quicksteps, laments, strathspeys, reels & country
dances, followed by piobaireachd exercises & the famous piobaireachd Cha till Mᶜ. Cruimein, (Mac Crimmon will never return).
Glasgow: Paterson, Sons & Co., Ltd.⟨, 1923.⟩ 40 p. rev. ed.
obl. 16°.

With this is bound: Logan's collection of Highland bagpipe music.

1. Bagpipe.
November 27, 1925

NL 0450672   NN

Logan's Indianapolis directory ⟨v. 1–2, 1867⟩–68 ... ⟨Indian-
apolis⟩ Logan & co. ⟨1867⟩–68.
2 v. illus. 23½ᵐ.
1868 edition contains also "History of Indianapolis, from 1818 to 1868,
by Ignatius Brown".

1. Indianapolis—Direct. 2. Indianapolis—Hist.   I. Brown,
Ignatius.
Library of Congress   F534.I3A18 1867–68   8—13339

NL 0450673   DLC

Logan's manufacturers' directory and buyers' guide of
St. Louis, 18   St. Louis, Mo., New Orleans, La.
⟨etc.⟩ Logan publishing co., 18
v. 17½ᵐ.

1. St. Louis—Direct.   I. Logan publishing co., St. Louis.
7–40730
Library of Congress   F474.S2A184 Copyright

NL 0450674   DLC

The Logans of Knockshinnoch ...
see under [Hyslop, James M'Adam]
1822–1897.

Logan's post office, census, express, telegraph
and railroad directory of the west and south,
twenty states and territories
see under Logan publishing co., St. Louis,
comp.

Logan's post-office, census, express, telegraph,
railroad, and river directory of the entire
West & South, containing the names of all
post-offices ...
see under Logan publishing co., St. Louis,
comp.

Logan's railway and river directory between St.
Louis and St. Paul. [1873]
see under Logan, Abram L. & co.

Logan's railway business directory. [1873]
see under Logan, Abram L. and co., comp.
& publ.

Logan's railway business directory from Saint
Louis to Galveston. [1873]
see under Logan, Abram L. & co., comp.
& publ.

Logan's Terre Haute directory... containing also a classified business directory...
1868/69
Indianapolis: Logan & Co., 1868   8°.
v.
1868/69 is 1st issue.

1. Terre Haute, Ind.—Directories.   February 4, 1929

NL 0450679   NN

VOLUME 338

Logan's Valley (Pa.) Baptist church.
Articles of faith, covenant and rules of order...
A.K. Bell, pastor. Philadelphia, King & Baird, 1853.
31 p. 16 cm.

NL 0450680   NRAB

Logan's Valley (Pa.) Baptist church.
Charter, articles of faith, covenant, and rules of order... Geo. W. Young, pastor. Philadelphia, King & Baird, 1858.
v. 31 p. 16 cm.

NL 0450681   NRAB

HV7595
.L6Q3
1922
Logansport, Ind. Board of metropolitan police commissioners.
Rules and regulations governing the Metropolitan police force and laws and by-laws of the police pension fund of the city of Logansport, Indiana... Adopted July 1, 1922. Logansport, Ind., Hendricks brothers co. [1922]
64 p. 15 cm.
"Name and location of streets in the city of Logansport": p. 53-64.

NL 0450682   DLC

Logansport, Ind. Board of trustees.
Report. 19th 248 1879 /80; 91/92
Logansport, Ind., 1881-92.
2 v.

NL 0450683   DHEW

Logansport, Ind. Broadway Presbyterian Church.
The cook's friend. A collection of valuable recipes. Comp. by the ladies of the Broadway Presbyterian Church. Logansport, Journal Co. Book and Job Print., 1878.
115 p. 23 cm.

1. Cookery, American.   I. Title.

TX715.L79   48-38929*

NL 0450684   DLC

Logansport, Ind. Charters.
Charter of the city of Logansport. Incorporated Feb'y 17, 1838. Logansport, J. C. Douglass, printer--Herald Office, 1841.
18.5 cm. 24p.

Walker 309.

NL 0450685   In

Logansport (Ind.). Controller.
Annual report of the city controller...

[Logansport,   8°.
Cover-title: Annual reports of the heads of departments.

I. Municipal government, U. S.: Ind.:   Logansport.
September 29, 1922.

NL 0450686   NN

Logansport, Ind. Hospital for Insane
see
Indiana. State Hospital, *Logansport.*

Logansport, Ind. Northern Indiana Hospital for Insane
see
Indiana. State Hospital, *Logansport.*

Logansport, *Ind. Ordinances, etc.*
Charter and ordinances of the city of Logansport in force April 1, 1879; to which is added a catalogue of the city officers from the year 1838 to 1878 inclusive, with annotations, court decisions and index. Comp. by Samuel Jacobs, mayor, and W. H. Smith, esq., approved by Maurice Winfield, city attorney, pub. by authority of the Common council. Logansport, Pharos company, printers, 1879.
374 p. 23ᶜᵐ.
I. Jacobs, Samuel. II. Smith, W. H.
                                                          11-13195
Library of Congress   JS999.L5A5 ᵉ1879

NL 0450689   DLC

Logansport, Ind. Ordinances, etc.
Laws and ordinances of the city of Logansport.
Logansport, Wilson, Humpheys, 1893.

NL 0450690   InU

LOGANSPORT, Ind. Ordinances, etc.
Laws and Ordinances governing the City; compiled and edited by D.C.Justice. [Logansport, 1903.]

8vo.

NL 0450691   MH-L

Logansport, *Ind. Ordinances, etc.*
Ordinances governing the city of Logansport, Indiana, passed by the Common council on. and prior to, December 1, 1930, compiled and edited by Robert J. Arthur. Published by authority of the city of Logansport passed April 4, 1927, council record 1, page 584. [Logansport, Ind., The Longwell-Cummings company] 1930.
751 p. 23ᵢᶜᵐ.

I. Arthur, Robert Jameson, 1899-   ed.
Library of Congress   JS999.L5A5 1930   31-2820
Copyright A 33303   352.077286

NL 0450692   DLC

027.22
L831ℓ
Logansport, Ind. Public library.
Logansport-Cass county library.   [Logansport, Ind., 1943?]
16p. illus.(incl.plans)

Caption-title.

1. Logansport, Ind. Public library. 2. Cass co., Ind. Library.

NL 0450693   IU

Logansport, Ind. Public library.
Logansport public library, 1942.
cover-title, 16, [2] p. illus., plans.

NL 0450694   NNC

Logansport, Ind. St. Joseph's *Church.*
Geschichte der St. Josephs gemeinde, zu Logansport, Ind.
see under Hartmann, B.

Lilly
LB 2802
.L 83 L 83
LOGANSPORT, INDIANA--School Trustees
City free schools. Logansport, Ind., 1862.
broadside. 31.8 x 22.2 cm.

Typesigned and dated: D.D. Pratt, S.A. Hall, and J.A. Taylor, Dec. 10, 1862.
Concerns Plan of the schools, Rules for teachers, and Rules for scholars.
From the library of J.K. Lilly.

NL 0450696   InU

Logansport, Ind. Second Presbyterian Church
see Logansport, Ind. Broadway Presbyterian Church.

Logansport, Ind. State Hospital
see
Indiana. State Hospital, *Logansport.*

Logansport and Cass County directory
see Logansport city and Cass County directory.

Logansport and northern Indiana railroad company.
Report of the chief engineer, exhibiting the character and prospects of the road, and also a statement of the secretary, showing the condition of the affairs, of the Logansport and northern Indiana railroad company, presented to the board of directors at their meeting at Logansport, May 1, 1854. New York, Railroad journal job printing office, 1854.
36 p. fold. map. 23¼ᶜᵐ.
L. S. Nash, chief engineer.
I. Nash, L. S.
                                                   A 21-1170
Title from Bureau of   Railway Economics. Printed by L. C.

NL 0450700   DBRE

Logansport and Northern Indiana Railroad Company.
Report of the president & directors.
New York.
v. 23 cm. annual.

HE2791.L8162   57-51641 ‡

NL 0450701   DLC

Logansport & Toledo Railway Company.
Annual report. no. 1-   1902-
[Pittsburgh, Pa]
v. 8°.

NL 0450702   NN

Logansport-Cass county library
see under Logansport, Ind. Public library.

VOLUME 338

... **Logansport** city and Cass County directory ... 1887/8,

Indianapolis, Ind., R. L. Polk & co., 1887-19
v. illus. 24ᶜᵐ.
Title varies: 1887/8-
18   F. J. Sutton's Logansport and Cass County
        directory.
18   Longwell & Cumming's and R. L. Polk & co's Logans-
        port directory.
19   R. L. Polk & co's Logansport city and Cass County
        directory.
Publishers: 1887/8   F. J. Sutton-18   R. L. Polk & co.
1. Logansport, Ind.—Direct. 2. Cass Co., Ind.—Direct. 1. Sutton's
Logansport and Cass County directory. 11. Longwell and Cumming's and
R. L. Polk & co's Logansport directory.

Library of Congress   F534.L83A18   99-4422 (rev. '19)

NL 0450704   DLC MWA NN ICJ

HE2791
L82
Logansport, Crawfordsville & South-western Rail-
way Company.
Logansport, Crawfordsville & South-western
Railway of Indiana. Eight per cent. First
mortgage bonds... New York, Jones & Schuyler,
financial agents of the company [c1872]
24 p.   23 cm.
Map in map collection: Railroads, 1872.

NL 0450705   ICHi NN CSmH

Logansport, Crawfordsville and south western railway
company.
Logansport, Crawfordsville & south western railway of
Indiana. Eight per cent. first mortgage bonds, principal
and interest payable in gold. New-York, J. W. Amerman,
printer, 1871.
26 p. fold. map. 23ᶜᵐ.
"Form of mortgage [dated August 1, 1870,]": p. 7-21.

1. [Railroads—Mortgages]

A 19-626

Title from Bureau of   Railway Economics. Printed by L. C.

NL 0450706   DBRE DLC

25.6   Logansport, Crawfordsville and south western
          railway company.
Logansport, Crawfordsville & south western
railway of Indiana. Eight per cent first mortgage
bonds, coupon and registered.   New York, Jones
& Schuyler [1876]
28 p.   2 maps.   8°.

NL 0450707   DLC

LOGANSPORT directory. Terre Haute, Ind., C. E.
Ebel. 1881/82.

NL 0450708   MH

Logansport, Peoria and Burlington railroad company.
... Agreement with Cruger, Secor &
company, and Charles L. Frost, Edward
Weston, [and] Henry G. Marquand, trustees.   New-York: Frank McElroy, book
and job printer, 1861.
24p.   18cm.

NL 0450709   IHi

Logansport State Hospital, *Logansport, Ind.*
see
Indiana. State Hospital, *Logansport.*

WU   LOGAR, Anton
100   Stomatologija; konzervirajoče zobo-
L831s   zdravstvo. Ljubljana [Komus] 1955-
              v. illus.
              Contents.—1. Anatomija zob.
              1. Teeth

NL 0450711   DNLM

Logar, Cene.
Analiza zavesti. [V Ljubljani] 1940.
73, [2] p. 23 cm. (Razprave Znanstvenega društva v Ljubljani,
18. Filozofski odsek. [Razprave, 1)
Summary in German.
Bibliography: p. [75]

1. Phenomenology. 2. Consciousness.   I. Title.   (Series:
Znanstveno društvo v Ljubljani. Razprave, 18. Series: Znanstveno
društvo v Ljubljani. Filozofski odsek. Razprave, 1)

B829.5.Z6 vol. 1   58-51944 ‡

NL 0450712   DLC LU-NO NNC

LOGAR, Cene.
Analiza zavesti. Kamnik, "Tiskarna Slatnar,"
1940. 73, [2] p. 23cm. (Znanstveno društvo za humanistične
vede v Lujubljani, Yugoslavia. Razprave. 18)

Filozofski odsek. 1.
Summary in German.
Bibliography, p. [75]

1. Knowledge. 2. Brentano,   Franz Clemens, 1838-1917.
I. Series.

NL 0450713   NN

Logar, France
Naši zobje, spisala Dr. France Logar in
Dr. Anton Slivnik. Celje, Družba Sv. Mohorja,
1935.
126p. illus.
Slovenian.

NL 0450714   OC1

Logar, Janez, ed.
Levstikov zbornik. Uredila Janez Logar in Anton Ocvirk.
Ljubljana [Slavistični klub na Univerzi] 1933.
417 p. 25 cm.
Includes bibliography.

1. Levstik, Fran, 1831-1887.   I. Ocvirk, Anton, joint ed. II. Title.

PG1918.LAZ7   60-58389 ‡

NL 0450715   DLC NNC MiU OU FTaSU CtY NN CU

LOGAR, MIHOVIL, 1902-
Musique à mon bébé; petite suite pour petites
mains intelligentes. Piáno à 2 ms. [n. p.]
Edition Frajt [c1929] 12p. 34cm.

CONTENTS.--Sérénade.--Musique de jazz.--Le Poisson d'or.--
C'est mon bébé que s'endort.

I. Suites (Piano)   I. Title.

NL 0450716   NN

Logarithm, traverse and altitude tables
see under U. S. Geographical Surveys
West of the 100th Meridian.

Logarithmen, Die, der natürlichen Zahlen von 1 bis 100000.   n. p.
[18—?] 186 p. 8°.
t-p. missing.

1. Logarithms.—Tables.

June 26, 1911.

NL 0450718   NN

Logarithmen-tafeln. [n. p.]
[312] p. 26½ᶜᵐ.
Title from spine.

1. Logarithms.

NL 0450719   ViU

Logarithmen tafels. [Antwerpen, Standaard-Boekhandel,
1953]
112 p. 24 cm.

1. Logarithms.

QA55.L77   56-45754 ‡

NL 0450720   DLC NjP

Logarithmen von vier decimalstellen
see under [Encke, Johann Franz] 1791-
1865, supposed author.

Logarithmetica britannica
see under Thompson, Alexander John.

A logarithmeticall table ...
see under [Wingate, Edmund] 1596-1656.

Logarithmic and trigonometric tables. Fort
Sills, Okla., Printing plant, The Field artillery school, 1939.
cover-title, 53 p. 18ᶜᵐ.

1. Logarithms. 5-place.
2. Trigonometry - Tables, etc.

NL 0450724   NNC

Logarithmic tables. Table I. Logarithms of
numbers from 1 to 10,000. Table II.
Logarithmic sines, tangents, and secants,
calculated for every degree and minute of
the quadrant. Table III. A traverse table,
calculated for every degree of the compass.
With directions for using. Schenectady,
H. Stevens, 1819.
108 p. 22cm. [With Day, Jeremiah. A treatise
of plane trigonometry. New Haven, 1815]
1. Logarithms.

NL 0450725   ViU RPB

Logarithmorum chilias prima
see under [Briggs, Henry] 1561-1630.

VOLUME 338

Logarithms of a system of equivalents.
 [n.p., 1919?]
  see under [Hamshaw, Clarence M.]

Logarithms of haversines
  see under [Evans, George William] 1861–

Logarithms of sines and cosines, with the
 argument in time
  see under U.S. Nautical almanac office.

Logarithms, trigonometry, statistics; first year college mathematics, by Hollis R. Cooley, Palmer H. Graham, Frederick W. John ¡and¿ Arthur Tilley ... 1st ed. New York and London, McGraw-Hill book company, inc., 1942.
 xii, 280 p. incl. illus., tables, diagrs. 23½ᶜᵐ.
 "References" at end of the last two chapters.

 1. Logarithms. 2. Trigonometry. 3. Mathematical statistics. I. Cooley, Hollis Raymond, 1890– II. Graham, Palmer Hampton, 1887– III. John, Frederick Wallace. IV. Tilley, Arthur, 1891–

 Library of Congress QA37.L8   42–15655
                  510

NL 0450730 DLC NcD

G868.81
L8287es Logarzo, Rafael N
  Estrofas para el bien y la esperanza. Buenos Aires, 1952.
  151p. illus. 18cm.

NL 0450731 TxU

G868.81
L8287v Logarzo, Rafael N
  Versos cristianos. Buenos Aires, 1951.
  109p. 18cm.

NL 0450732 TxU

Logasa, Hannah, 1879–
 Biography in collections suitable for junior and senior high schools, by Hannah Logasa ... New York, The H. W. Wilson company, 1933.
 112 p. 25½ᶜᵐ.
 CONTENTS.—Introduction.—Key to collections analyzed, with bibliographical data (p. ¡17¿–33)—Biographical index.—Subject index.

 1. Biography—Bibl. I. Title.
 Library of Congress Z5301.L83 33–27169
 ———— Copy 2
 Copyright A 62958   016.92

 ODW OC1 TU WaSp Wa
NL 0450733 DLC NcGU OU PSt WaS Or PP PPD MB TU OO

Logasa, Hannah, 1879–
 Biography in collections suitable for junior and senior high schools, by Hannah Logasa ... Rev. and enl. ed. New York, The H. W. Wilson company, 1937.
 5 p. l., ¡9¿–182 p. 26ᶜᵐ.
 "Second edition."
 CONTENTS.—Foreword.—Introduction.—Key to collections analyzed, with bibliographical data (p. ¡19¿–39)—Biographical index.—Subject index.

 1. Biography—Bibl. I. Title.
              37–4453
 Library of Congress Z5301.L83 1937

 Copyright A 104382   016.92

 OC1W OU ViU TU WaT Or
NL 0450734 DLC KEmT PSt NcD IaU WaE OrP PSC PU OEac

Logasa, Hannah, 1879–
 Biography in collections suitable for junior and senior high schools, by Hannah Logasa ... 3d ed., rev. and enl. New York, The H. W. Wilson company, 1940.
 152 p. incl. forms. 26½ᶜᵐ.
 CONTENTS.—Foreword to second and third editions.—Introduction.—Key to collections analyzed, with bibliographical data (p. ¡19¿–43)—Biographical index.—Subject index.

 1. Biography—Bibl. I. Title.
 Library of Congress Z5301.L83 1940 40–27333

 Copyright A 139128   016.92

 IdPI CaBVa
 OC1 ViU OU CU NcC IaU 'IN MtU WaT CaBVaU KEmT OrMonO
NL 0450735 DLC PV PCM TxU PSC PPT PPD PV OOxM OCU

Logasa, Hannah, 1879–
 Book selection handbook for elementary and secondary school. Boston, F. W. Faxon Co., 1953.
 200 p. 23 cm. (Useful reference series, no. 83)

 1. Book selection.
 Z1035.A1L6   028.5   53–10467 ‡

 OO KMK KEmT IdPI WaSp WaSpG OrPS Wa WaS NcGU PWcS
 NcD TxU PRosC PV OOxM OU MtBC Or OrAshS OrCS PPLas
 0450736 DLC CaBVaU IdB MtU PPT MB OC1W PU PPD

Z1037
.A1C45 **Logasa, Hannah,** 1879–
1947
 Chicago. University. *University Extension Division. Home-Study Dept.*
 Book selection for junior and senior high schools: Library science 207, by Hannah Logasa. Chicago, Univ. of Chicago, ⁷1947.

Logasa, Hannah.
 The high school library, its function in education, by Hannah Logasa ... New York, D. Appleton and company ¡ᶜ1928¿
 ix, 283 p. diagr. 19½ᶜᵐ.
 Bibliography at end of each chapter.
 Appendices: North Central association score card for school libraries.—Magazines suitable for the high school library.—Selected book lists.—Selected list of books on school-library organization and administration.— Books on vocations and vocational guidance. — Library schools.

 1. School libraries (High school) I. Title.
            Z675.S3L7 28–17151

 CaBVa OrCS
 CaBVaU KEmT ICarbS MoU OC1 OU MiU ODW OCU MB ViU TU
NL 0450738 DLC KEmT MtU WaTC OrP IdU Wa OrPR Or CoU

Logasa, Hannah, *comp.*
 Historical fiction and other reading references for history classes in junior and senior high schools, compiled by Hannah Logasa ... Philadelphia, McKinley publishing co., 1930.
 131 p. 23ᶜᵐ.
 Based on the author's "Historical fiction suitable for junior and senior high schools", enlarged to include interesting non-fiction and some four hundred additional fiction titles. cf. Pref.
 Classified, with author and title index.

 1. Historical fiction—Bibl. 2. History—Bibl.
 Library of Congress Z5917.H6L8 1930 30–14590

 Copyright A 23588   016.823

 OC1 MB IU ViU MiU
NL 0450739 DLC CaBVa Wa WaS Or WaT CU NcD OCX OO

Logasa, Hannah, 1879– *comp.*
 Historical fiction and other reading references for history classes in junior and senior high schools, compiled by Hannah Logasa ... Rev. and enl. ed. Philadelphia, McKinley publishing co., 1934.
 144 p. 23ᶜᵐ.
 Classified, with author and title index.

 1. Historical fiction—Bibl. 2. History—Bibl.
                34–31585
 Library of Congress Z5917.H6L8 1934
    ¡a41v2¿   016.823

NL 0450740 DLC OrP Or OrU PSt CU MiU OC1 ODW OO

Logasa, Hannah, 1879–
 Historical fiction and other reading references for classes in junior and senior high schools, compiled by Hannah Logasa ... 3d rev. and enl. ed. Philadelphia, McKinley publishing co., 1941.
 193 p. 23½ᶜᵐ.
 Classified, with author and title index.

 1. Historical fiction—Bibl. 2. History—Bibl.
 Library of Congress Z5917.H6L8 1941 41–51670

 Copyright   016.823

 OU PU OCU TU
NL 0450741 DLC Wa NN CU NBuU MtU Or WaS TxU OC1W

Logasa, Hannah, 1879–
 Historical fiction and other reading references for classes in junior and senior high schools. 4th rev. and enl. ed. Philadelphia, McKinley Pub. Co., 1949.
 232 p. 24 cm.
 Classified, with author and title index.

 1. Historical fiction—Bibl. 2. History—Bibl.
 Z5917.H6L8 1949 016.823 49–9334*

 OC1 OOxM OrCS OrP Wa WaE WaS WaSp WaT
 NNC PSC PPPL CaBVa IdB OrPS PPD PP OEac IdU Or PPT
NL 0450742 DLC OrPS KEmT CU NN KyLx ICU TxU IaU

Logasa, Hannah, 1879–
 Historical fiction and other reading references for classes in junior and senior high schools. 5th rev. and enl. ed. Philadelphia, McKinley Pub. Co., 1951.
 280 p. 24 cm.
 Classified, with author and title index

 1. Historical fiction—Bibl. 2. History—Bibl.
 Z5917.H6L8 1951 016.823 52–6213

 MiU TxU Wa CaBVa IdB IdPI IdU OrU WaS
NL 0450743 DLC KyLx CU KEmT OC1Ur PSt NBuT Or OrP

Logasa, Hannah, *comp.*
 ... Historical fiction suitable for junior and senior high schools, comp. by Hannah Logasa ... With an introduction by A. F. Barnard ... Philadelphia, McKinley publishing co., 1927.
 85 p. 23ᶜᵐ. (Publications of the National council for the social studies, no. 1)
 Classified, with author and title index.

 1. Historical fiction—Bibl. I. Barnard, Arthur Fairchild.
                27–26603
 Library of Congress Z5917.H6L8

 OO OU OrSaW WaS CaBVaU CaBViP
NL 0450744 DLC MsSM OrP MtU IdB IU ViU Or OC1h OC1

Logasa, Hannah, 1879–
 An index to one-act plays, compiled by Hannah Logasa and Winifred Ver Nooy. Boston, Faxon, 1924.
 327 p. 25 cm. (Useful reference series, no. 30)
 "Plays written in English or translated into English ... published since 1900."
 ———— Supplement. ¡1st¿–   1924–31—
 Boston, Faxon.
  v. 25 cm. (Useful reference series)
          Z5781.L83 Suppl.
  1. Drama—Bibl. I. Ver Nooy, Winifred, 1891– II. Title: One-act plays. (Series)

 Z5781.L83 016.8082 24–21477 rev 3*

 WaE WaS WaSp WaT WaTC WaWW
 OC1W NcD NcRS Wa CaBVa IdU IdPI MtU OrCS OrP OrSaW
 MsSM NcRS NBuC PPSJ MiU MB ViU NIC TU OU OCU OC1
 InAndC-T DAU WU GAT INJ-P NN KyLE NNC OU MsU NNC
NL 0450745 DLC NcWil NN MeB KEmT MU IEN NN MiU TxU

VOLUME 338

Logasa, Hannah, 1879–

Chicago. University. *University extension division. Home-study dept.*
... Library science 207 (book selection for junior and senior high schools) by Hannah Logasa. ₍Chicago₎ The University of Chicago, °1941.

Logasa, Hannah, 1879–
Regional United States, a subject list, compiled by Hannah Logasa. Boston, The F. W. Faxon company, 1942.
2 p. l., iii–xv, 71 p. 22ᶜᵐ. (*Half-title*: Useful reference series, no. 69)
Map on lining-papers.

1. U. S.—Bibl. 2. U. S.—History, Local—Bibl. 3. United States in literature—Bibl. I. Title.

Library of Congress   Z1236.L6   42–36170
                                        016.9173

OrSaW WaE WaSp WaT
OC1W OCU OU OO OC1 PPD PU TU IdB OrU MtU OrCS Wa
NL 0450748   DLC Or OrPR WaS IdU NcRS PPT PP PSC ViU

Logasa, Hannah, 1879–
The study hall in junior and senior high schools ₍by₎ Hannah Logasa ... New York, The Macmillan company, 1938.
xiii, 190 p. incl. diagrs., forms. 21ᶜᵐ.
"Selected bibliography" at end of each chapter.

1. School management and organization. 2. Study, Method of. 3. School discipline. I. Title.

Library of Congress   LB1620.L6   38–18897
                  ₍a41e2₎   371.3

PPPL NN PPD PP TU OrAshS WaWW WaTC CaBVaU
NL 0450749   DLC WaSp MtU Or WaS OrU OrCS NcD TxU

Logasa, Hannah, 1879–
The study hall in junior and senior high schools ₍by₎ Hannah Logasa ... New York, The Macmillan company, 1932.

Logasa, Hannah, 1879–

Z675
.S3C47
Chicago. University. *University Extension Division. Home-Study Dept.*
Use of libraries in junior and senior high schools: Library science 217, by Hannah Logasa. Chicago, °1947.

IID9575
.R82R78
Logashkin, V. A., joint author.

Rubachev, G   N
Комплексно-хозрасчетный участок па нефтяном промысле. Москва, Гос. научно-техн. изд-во нефтяной и горно-топливной лит-ры, 1952.

PL5125
L828
Logat Nippon. 日馬小辭典. Djakarta, Gunseikanbu, Kokumin Toshokyoku, 2605 ₍i.e. 1945₎
305 p. 15 cm.
"B.P. no. 1576."
Japanese title romanised: Nichi-Ma shō jiten.

1. Japanese language – Dict. – Indonesian.
I. Nichi-Ma shō jiten.

NL 0450753   CtY NIC

PG3216
.L6
Lo Gatto, Anjuta Maver, tr.

Lo Gatto, Ettore, 1890–   *ed. and tr.*
Narratori russi ... a cura di Ettore Lo Gatto; dodici monotipi originali fuori testo del pittore Ercole Brini. Roma, De Carlo ₍1944₎

Lo Gatto, Domenico.
.... Opere marittime. Manuale ad uso degli studenti ingegneri, ingegneri e costruttori. Volume I–[II]. ... . Torino, Società editrice succ. A. F. Negro & c°, [1904–1905].
2 vol. in 1. xx fold. diagr. 25ᶜᵐ.
At head of title: Ing. Domenico Lo Gatto.

NL 0450755   ICJ

891.73
P97
DL82
Lo Gatto, Ettore, 1890–   ed.
Alessandro Puškin nel primo centenario della morte. Scritti di V. Ivanov ₍et al.₎ A cura di Ettore Lo Gatto. Roma, Istituto per l'Europa Orientale, 1937.
347p. port. 25cm.

NL 0450756   IU NNC KU CU NIC

Lo Gatto, Ettore, 1890–
... Gli artisti italiani in Russia ... ₍Roma, La Libreria dello stato, 1934₎
v. illus. (incl. facsim.) plates (part fold.) ports., plans. 29½ x 23ᶜᵐ.
(*Added t.-p.:* L'opera del genio italiano all'estero. ₍ser. 1₎)
"50 esemplari su carta giappone numerati in macchina da I a L ... 500 esemplari su carta velina italiana a mano numerati con cifre arabe da 1 a 500. Esemplare numero 340."
Contents.—I. Gli architetti a Mosca e nelle province.—II. Gli architetti del secolo XVIII a Pietroburgo e nelle tenute imperiali.

1. Architecture—Russia. 2. Architecture, Italian. 3. Art—Russia. I. Title.

Library of Congress   NA1181.L6   38–36880
                                       709.47

NL 0450757   DLC NNC MB NjP WU CU NN MH CtY OC1

₍Lo Gatto, Ettore₎ 1890–
Bibliografia essenziale degli scritti di Aurelio Palmieri.
(*In* L'Europa orientale. Roma, 1926. 24ᶜᵐ. anno VI, 1926, p. ₍519₎–532)
Caption title.
Signed: E. L. G.

1. Palmieri, Aurelio, 1870–1926—Bibl. I. Title.
                                      35–24678
Library of Congress   DR1.E5 vol. 6

NL 0450758   DLC

Lo Gatto, Ettore, comp.
Critici letterari russi... Foligno, Campitelli, 1925.
259 p.

NL 0450759   PP

Lo Gatto, Ettore, 1890–
... Dall'epica alla cronaca nella Russia soviettista. Roma, Istituto per l'Europa orientale ₍1929₎
xv, 213 p. 20½ᶜᵐ.
"Dello stesso autore": p. ₍iv₎

1. Russia—Soc. condit. 2. Communism—Russia. I. Istituto per l'Europa orientale, Rome. II. Title.
                                    36–4742
Library of Congress   DK267.L57
                                      947.084

NL 0450760   DLC NN CtY NcD

PG3337
.LAD45
Lo Gatto, Ettore, 1890–   tr.

Lermontov, Mikhail fUr'evich, 1814–1841.
... Il dæmone e Il novizio. Firenze, G. C. Sansoni ₍1943₎

PG
2976
.L6
Lo Gatto, Ettore, 1890–   ed.
L'estetica e la poetica in Russia. Firenze, G. C. Sansoni [1947]
670 p. illus. 21 cm. (Scrittori d'estetica, 2)

Includes bibliography.

1. Russian literature – Hist. & crit. – Addresses, essays, lectures. 2. Literature – Aesthetics. I. Title.

MiU NjP OU NRU
NL 0450762   WU IaU PU ICU NN IU CtY MB MnU CU NcU

Lo Gatto, Ettore, ed.

L'Europa orientale; rivista mensile pub. a cura dell'Istituto per l'Europa orientale. anno 1– giugno 1921–
Roma, Libreria di Cultura, 1921–

DK112
.M53
Lo Gatto, Ettore, 1890–

Merimée, Prosper, 1803–1870.
... I falsi Demetrii, episodio di storia russa. Traduzione di Tommaso Landolfi, con una nota storica-bibliografica a cura di Ettore Lo Gatto. ₍Firenze, Vallecchi₎1944₎

PG3467
.K8 I 85
Lo Gatto, Ettore, 1890–   tr.

Kuprin, Aleksandr Ivanovich, 1870–1938.
... La fossa; romanzo. Milano, Casa editrice Vitagliano ₍°1921₎

LO GATTO, ETTORE, 1890–
Grammatica della lingua russa (con esercizi e letture), Firenze, G.C. Sansoni, 1950. xvii, 404 p. 22cm.

Bibliography, p. [v]-vi.

1. Russian language--Grammar. 2. Russian language--Exercises and readers.

NL 0450766   NN

Lo Gatto, Ettore, 1890–
... Historia del teatro ruso; version espanola de Francisco J. Bolla. Buenos Aires, Editorial La Universidad ₍°1945₎
3 p. l., 9–299 ₍15₎ p., 2 l., illus.

"Bibliografia general": p. ₍301–304₎; "Catalogo de autores y obras": p. ₍305–315₎.
At head of title: Hector Lo Gatto.

NL 0450767   MiD

Lo Gatto, Ettore, 1890–
In Boemia, Moravia e Slovacchia. ₍Roma₎ Società nazionale Dante Alighieri ₍1939₎
126 p. 19 cm. (Civiltà italiana nel mondo, 8)
"Bibliografia essenziale": p. 121–126.

1. Italy—Relations (general) with the Czechoslovak Republic. 2. Czechoslovak Republic—Relations (general) with Italy. I. Title. II. Series.

DB200.5.L6   A F 48–2392*
New York. Public Libr
for Library of Congress   †

NL 0450768   NN DLC

VOLUME 338

Lo Gatto, Ettore, 1890–
... In Russia, di Ettore Lo Gatto. ₍Roma₎ Società nazionale Dante Alighieri ₍1938₎
1 p. l., ₍5₎–128 p., 1 l. 18½ᶜᵐ. (Civiltà italiana nel mondo. ₍4₎)
"Bibliografia essenziale": p. ₍124₎–126.

1. Italy—Relations (general) with Russia. 2. Russia—Relations (general) with Italy. 3. Literature, Comparative—Italian and Russian. 4. Literature, Comparative—Russian and Italian. I. Società nazionale "Dante Alighieri." II. Title.
45–46000
Library of Congress   DG499.R9L6

NL 0450769   DLC MH

891.7   Lo Gatto, Ettore.
L781   ... Letteratura russa.   Roma, 1928.
208p. (Collezione omnia 1, letterature slave, I)

"Bibliografia essenziale": p.[207]–208.

NL 0450770   IU

Lo Gatto, Ettore, 1890–
... La letteratura russa. 3. ed. aumentata e aggiornata.
Roma, Cremonese, 1944.
iv, 286 p. 22ᶜᵐ.

1. Russian literature—Hist. & crit.
46–1718
Library of Congress   PG2954.L63 1944
891.709

NL 0450771   DLC MiU NNC

PG 3025   LO GATTO,ETTORE,1890–
.L 83   Letteratura soviettista.   Roma, Istituto
per l'Europa orientale, 1931.
167 p. (Piccola biblioteca slava, 2)

1. Russian literature--20th cent.--Hist. &
crit. I. Tc.

NL 0450772   InU MH

Lo Gatto, Ettore, 1890–
Momenti e figure della storia russa. ₍Bologna₎ Cappelli,
1953.
331 p. illus. 20 cm. (Storia e vita, 9)

1. Russia—Hist. I. Title.
DK41.L73
58–44960 ‡

NL 0450773   DLC MH IU NIC

914.73   Lo Gatto, Ettore, 1890–
L82a   Mosca, di Ettore Lo Gatto.   Milano, G. Agnel-
li, 1934.
262, ₍1₎p. plates. 18½cm. (Half-title:
"Metropoli")

1. Moscow--Description.

NL 0450774   IU CU-S

Lo Gatto, Ettore, 1890–   *ed. and tr.*
Narratori russi ... a cura di Ettore Lo Gatto; dodici monotipi
originali fuori testo del pittore Ercole Brini.   Roma, De Carlo
₍1944₎
464 p. plates. 23½ᵐ.

"Dei dodici racconti riuniti in questo volume sono stati tradotti da
Anjuta Maver Lo Gatto: V. Korolenko, In cattiva compagnia; L. Andréev,
Il riso rosso. Tutti gli altri racconti sono stati tradotti da Ettore Lo
Gatto."

Contents.—Puškin, A. La donna di picche.—Gogol', N. Il Vij.—
Turghénev, I. Un re Lear della steppa.—Gončiaróv, I. Un felice
errore.—Dostoevskij, F. La mite.—Tolstój, L. La morte di Iván Il'ič.—
Leskòv, N. L'angelo suggellato.—Korolenko, V. In cattiva compagnia.—
Čechov, A. Il racconto di un ignoto.—Gor'kij, M. Karamora.—Andréev,
L. Il riso rosso.—Bunin, I. Una bella vita.

1. Russian literature—Translations into Italian. 2. Italian literature—Translations from Russian. I. Lo Gatto, Anjuta Maver, tr. II.
Title.
PG3216.L6
47–24924

NL 0450776   DLC

PG3289   Lo Gatto, Ettore, 1890–   tr.
.I 7N3
Narratori sovietici ... Traduzioni di Ettore Lo Gatto, Giovanni Bach, Svetlana Caucci Alfieri, Elena Akmentins dall'-
originale russo. Roma, De Carlo, 1944.

NL 0450778   MH

LO GATTO,Ettore.
Note di storia e letteratura russa.   Roma,
Istituto per l'Europa orientale,1931.

pp.99.
"Piccola biblioteca slava,17."

NL 0450778   MH

Lo Gatto, Ettore, 1890–   comp.
Novellieri slavi; panorama della letteratura novellistica
russa, ucraina, polacca, boema, slovacca, serba, croata, slovena
e bulgara. A cura di Ettore Lo Gatto ed Enrico Damiani.
Tavole fuori testo dei pittori Brini, Gramaticopulo e
Ferrari. Roma, De Carlo, 1946.
914 p. plates. 25 cm. (Enciclopedia della novella)
"Le traduzioni ... tutte condotte sui testi originali, sono dovute ad
Ettore Lo Gatto ... o₎ ad Enrico Damiani."

1. Short stories, Slavic—Translations into Italian. 2. Short stories,
Italian—Translations from Slavic literature. I. Damiani, Enrico,
1892–   joint comp. II. Title.
PG551.I 8L6
66–91954

NL 0450779   DLC NIC

Lo Gatto, Ettore, 1890–
...Pagine di storia e di letteratura russa.   Roma: Anonima
romana editoriale, 1928.   215 p.   8°.   (Istituto per l'Europa
orientale, Rome. Pubblicazioni.   ser. 1¹².)

Contents: I. Europa e Russia nella storia e nel pensiero russo. II. Pagine su
Dostojevskij.

562710A. 1. Russia—Civilization.   2. Dostoyevski, Fiodor Mikhaïlovich,
1821–1881. I. Ser.   May 20, 1932

NL 0450780   NN CoU MH CtY

Lo Gatto, Ettore.
...Poesia russa della rivoluzione.   Roma: A. Stock, 1923.
123 p.   12°.
Bibliographical footnotes.

1. Poetry (Russian).—History and   criticism, 20th century.
November 12, 1923

NL 0450781   NN

891.73   Lo Gatto,Ettore
L831p   ...I problemi della letteratura russa.
Napoli, R.Ricciardi, 1971.
4 p.ℓ.,[xi]–xiii p.,1 ℓ.,132 p.,1 ℓ.
19 cm.
Author's name at head of title.
"Bibliografia":p.[127]–132.

NL 0450782   MiU RPB MH

Lo Gatto, Ettore, tr.
Masaryk, Tomáš Garrigue, pres. Czechoslovak Republic,
1850–
... La Russia e l'Europa; studi sulle correnti spirituali
in Russia. Traduzione di Ettore Lo Gatto ...   Napoli, R.
Ricciardi, 1922–

Lo Gatto, Ettore, 1890–   ed.
Russia; letteratura, arte, storia, a cura di Ettore Lo Gatto.
₍Roma₎ De Carlo, 1945.
vii, ₍1₎, 170, ₍2₎ p. illus. plates (part mounted col.) 28 cm.
Contents.—Dostoevskij, F. Cronaca di Pietroburgo (traduzione e
introduzione di E. Lo Gatto)—Lo Gatto, E. La Russia del passato nel
romanzo storico sovietico.—Belyj, A. Sinfonia nordica (traduzione e
introduzione di A. M. Ripellino)—Čechov, A. Un'impresa commerciale
(traduzione di A. M. Lo Gatto)—Gončiarov, I. Cristo nel deserto (traduzione di E. Lo Gatto)—Kaverin, V. Scudi e candele (traduzione e
introduzione di A. M. Ripellino)—Remizov, A. Disegni di scrittori
(traduzione e nota di E. Lo Gatto)—Ripellino, A. M. Mascherate e
pastorali nel simbolismo russo.—Vinogradov, A. Il guanto perduto o
Stendhal a Mosca (traduzione e introduzione di A. M. Lo Gatto)
1. Russia—Civilization.   2. Russian literature (Selections:
Extracts, etc.)
DK32.7.L6   A F 47–6044
Michigan. Univ. Library
for Library of Congress   †

NL 0450784   MiU NcD NNC DLC

Lo Gatto, Ettore.
...Saggi sulla cultura russa...   Napoli: R. Ricciardi, 1923.
174 p. ports. 12°. (Istituto per l'Europa orientale, Rome.
Pubblicazioni. Serie 13.)
Bibliographical footnotes.
Contents: Introduzione. Sul teatro di Čechov. La servitù della gleba nella
letteratura russa. L'"Oblòmov" di Gončiaròv e l'oblomovismo. Alessandro Herzen.
Vladimiro Korolenko. Sulla fortuna di Dante in Russia.

1. Russian literature.—History and criticism. 2. Chekhov, Anton Pavlovich, 1860–
1904. 3. Serfdom, Russia. 4. Gon-   charov, Ivan Aleksandrovich, 1812–
91: Oblomov. 5. Herzen, Aleksandr   Ivanovich, 1812–70. 6. Korolenko,
Vladimir Galaktionovich, 1853–1921.   7. Dante Alighieri. 8. Series.
August 14, 1923.

NL 0450785   NN MiU CoU IEN

Htb26   Lo Gatto, Ettore, 1890–
L82   ... Saggi sulla cultura russa (Con 8 illustrazioni) Roma,Anonima romana editoriale,1925.
5p.ℓ.,3–174p. 9ports. 19½ᶜᵐ (Pubblicazioni
dell'Istituto per l'Europa orientale in Roma.
1.serie: Letteratura,arte,filosofia. III)
Contents. - Introduzione. - Sul teatro di
Čechov. - La servitù della gleba nella
letteratura russa. - L'"Oblomov" di Gončiaròv e
l'oblomovismo. - Alessandro Herzen. - Vladimiro
Korolenko. - Sulla fortuna di Dante in Russia.

NL 0450786   CtY NRU MH

Lo Gatto, Ettore.
...La servitù della gleba e il movimento di liberazione in
Russia.   Bologna: N. Zanichelli, 1925₎   xii, 200 p.   12°.
(Le grandi civiltà. v. 4.)
Includes bibliographies.

1. Serfdom—Russia. 2. Serfdom   in literature, Russian. 3. Ser.
July 29, 1926

NL 0450787   NN ICU MiD

VOLUME 338

Lo Gatto, Ettore, 1890–
 Spirito e forme della poesia bulgara. ¡Conferenza tenuta il 26 maggio 1928 all' "Istituto nazionale fascista di cultura" in Roma per iniziativa dell' "Associazione accademica bulgara San Clemente"¡ Roma, Istituto per l'Europa orientale ¡19–?¡ ˙
 36 p. 20 cm. (Piccola biblioteca slava, 1)

 1. Bulgarian poetry—Hist. & crit. I. Title.
 PG1010.L6   58–36594

NL 0450788   DLC MH

Lo Gatto, Ettore.
 …Stefano Żeromski; studio critico. ¡Roma:¡ Anonima romana editoriale, 1926. 62 p. 8°. (Istituto per l'Europa orientale, Rome. Pubblicazioni. ser. 1. ¡v.¡ 8.)
 Bibliographical footnotes.

 404209A. 1. Żeromski, Stefan, 186◦   1925. 2. Ser.
                                                March 15, 1929

NL 0450789   NN WU MH

Lo Gatto, Ettore, 1890–
 Storia del teatro russo. Firenze, Sansoni, 1952.
 2 v. illus. (part col.) ports. (part col.) facsims. 22 cm. (Contributi alla storia della "Civiltà europea")
 Includes bibliographies.

 1. Theater—Russia—Hist.
 PN2721.L59   53–33980

       NcD CLSU MdBJ ICU NBuU
NL 0450790   DLC CaBVaU OrU NcGU TxU CU MH NN OU PP

Lo Gatto, Ettore, 1890–
 … Storia della letteratura russa … Roma, Anonima romana editoriale, 1928–
 v. 22½ᶜᵐ. (Pubblicazioni dell' "Istituto per l'Europa orientale," Roma. 1. ser.: Letteratura, arte, filosofia. XIV)
 Includes bibliographies.
 CONTENTS.—I. Dalle origini a tutto il secolo XVI.—II. Le origini della letteratura moderna.—III. La letteratura moderna.

 1. Russian literature—Hist. & crit.
                                                44–18963
 Library of Congress   PG2954.L6
                                                891.709

NL 0450791   DLC CoU NcU IU MiU NN MH CtY NNC NIC CU

Lo Gatto, Ettore, 1890–
 Storia della letteratura russa, di Ettore Lo Gatto. Con 109 illustrazioni nel testo e 68 tavole di cui 4 a colori. 2. ed. riveduta e corr. Firenze, G. C. Sansoni, 1943 ¡i. e. 1944¡
 xi, ¡1¡, 569 p., 1 l. illus., LXVIII pl. (part col.; incl. ports., map, facsims.) on 36 l. 21½ᶜᵐ. (Half-title: "La Civiltà europea")
 Colophon dated 1944.
 Includes bibliographies.

 1. Russian literature—Hist. & crit.
                                                45–22273
 Library of Congress   PG2954.L6 1944
                                                891.709

NL 0450792   DLC OU PU CLU

Lo Gatto, Ettore, 1890–
 Storia della letteratura russa, di Ettore Lo Gatto. 3. ed. nuovamente riveduta e aumentata. Firenze, G. C. Sansoni, 1944.
 xiv p., 1 l., 623, ¡1¡ p. 22½ᶜᵐ. (Half-title: "La Civiltà europea")
 Includes bibliographies.

 1. Russian literature—Hist. & crit.
 PG2954.L6 1944a   891.709   A F 47–3931
 Michigan. Univ. Library
 for Library of Congress   †

NL 0450793   MiU CaBVaU RPB ICU DLC NNC

Lo Gatto, Ettore, 1890–
 Storia della letteratura russa. 4. ed. nuovamente riv., corr. ed aggiornata. Firenze, Sansoni, 1950.
 xiv, 591 p. illus. ports. 22 cm. (La Civiltà europea)
 Includes bibliographies.

 1. Russian literature—Hist. & crit.
 PG2954.L6 1950   891.709   52–66817

NL 0450794   DLC NcD KU CU TU OC1W WaU

Lo Gatto, Ettore, 1890–
 Storia della Russia, di Ettore Lo Gatto … Firenze, G. C. Sansoni, 1946–
 v. illus. (incl. plans) plates (part col.; 1 fold.) ports., col. maps (1 fold.) geneal. tables. 22ᶜᵐ. (Half-title: "La Civiltà europea")
 Includes bibliographies.

 1. Russia—Hist. 2. Russia—Civilization. I. Title.
 DK40.L6   A F 47–2200
 Columbia univ. Libraries
 for Library of Congress   †

       00xM
NL 0450795   NNC MiU CtY ICU MB OU MH DLC NcD IaU

947   Lo Gatto, Ettore, 1890–
L828s   Storia della Russia, di Ettore Lo Gatto.
1946   Firenze, G.C. Sansoni, 1946.
          2v.(1003p.) maps,tables. 22cm.

          Includes bibliographies.

          1. Russia. History. 2. Russia. Civilization. I. Title.

NL 0450796   KU

PG2954   LoGatto, Ettore, 1890–
L58   Studi di letterature slave. Roma, Anonima
          romana editoriale, 1925-1931.
          3 v. 23cm.
          1. Russian literature - Hist. & crit.

NL 0450797   CoU MH ICU CU CtY

Lo Gatto, Ettore, 1890–
 … Il teatro russo. Milano, Fratelli Treves ¡1937¡
 3 p. l., ¡3¡–350 p., 1 l. 19ᶜᵐ. (Il Teatro del novecento, collezione critica di "Scenario," diretta da Silvio d'Amico, v)
 "Bibliografia essenziale": p. ¡315¡–321. "Elenco degli autori e delle opere": p. ¡322¡–338.

 1. Theater—Russia. I. Title.
                                                45–47143
 Library of Congress   PN2721.L6

NL 0450798   DLC WaSpG IU NN NNC

891.7208 Lo Gatto, Ettore, 1890–   ed.
L82t   Teatro russo. Raccolta di drammi e commedie.
          ¡Milano¡ Bompiani, 1955.
          xiv, 1458p. 36 plates (incl. ports.) 22cm.
          (Pantheon)

          1. Russian drama—Collections. 2. Russian
          drama—Translations into Italian. 3. Italian
          drama—Translations from Russian.

NL 0450799   IU FU NcD

Lo Gatto, Ettore, 1890–
 …U R S S, 1931; vita quotidiana, piano quinquennale. ¡Roma:¡ Anonima romana editoriale¡ 1932.¡ viii, 358 p. 23cm. (Istituto per l'Europa orientale, Rome. Pubblicazioni. ser. 2, ¡n.¡ 22.)

 630655A. 1. Russia—Social condi-   tions, 1917– . 2. Economic history
 —Russia, 1917– . I. Ser.
                                                April 19, 1933

NL 0450800   NN ICU MnU CtY IaU

DK
27   Lo Gatto, Ettore, 1890–
.L79   Vecchia Russia. Roma, Istituto per l'Europa
          orientale, 1929.
          87 p. illus.

          1.Russia--Descr.& trav. I.Title.

NL 0450801   MiU

Lo Gatto, Hector
 see Lo Gatto, Ettore, 1890–

Law   Lo Gatto, Luigi, ed. and tr.

 France. Laws, statutes, etc.
  Comentario sulle leggi della procedura civile di C. ¡i. e. G.¡ L. T. ¡i. e. J.¡ Carré. 3. ed. francese, accresciuta nel belgio del confronto con le opere di Pigeau ¡et al.¡ 1. ed. italiana. Arricchita della conferenza degli articoli del codice francese con quelli del Codice pel regno delle Due Sicilie, delle disposizioni legislative emanate posteriormente alle leggi di procedura ne' giudizi civili, e della giurisprudenza della Suprema corte di giustizia napoletana, dall'avvocato Luigi Lo Gatto. Napoli, Dallo stab. dell'Antologia legale di Capasso, 1853–56.

Lo Gatto, Mario
 Mazzini e il socialismo; critiche e punti d'incontro. Napoli, Casa Editrice Armanni, 1949.
 30p. 21cm.
 Bibliographical footnotes.

NL 0450804   RPB

Lo Gatto Napolitano, Maria.
 Il Contratto sociale di Gian Giacomo Rousseau. Napoli, L. Loffredo, 1951.
 109 p. 25 cm.
 Bibliography: p. ¡7¡

 1. Rousseau, Jean Jacques. Contrat social.
                                                A 52–7671
 Chicago. Univ. Libr.
 for Library of Congress

NL 0450805   ICU NN

Rare   Logau, Friedrich von, 1604–1655.
PT   Abdanckung, bey letzter Einsenckung der
1744   Seligen Fr. Reydeburgin, abgeredet, durch
A7   Friedrichen von Logau, auff Brokoth, Fürstl.
1650   Brigischen Rath. ¡n. p., 165–?¡
          ¡6¡ l. 22cm.

          1. Funeral sermons. 2. Reydeburg, Eme-
          rentiana (Nimbtsch und Röberssdorff) I.
          Title.

NL 0450806   NIC

VOLUME 338

Film
PT
35

LOGAU, FRIEDRICH VON, 1604-1655.
    Auferweckte Gedichte, Denen und hinzugefüget Unterschiedene bissher ungedruckte poëtische Gedancken, Heroischen Geistern gewiedmet, Nebst einem nöthigen Register ‹von› S. v. G. ‹pseud.› Frankfurt und Leipzig, J. A. Pleners, 1702.
    352 p.

    Microfilm (negative)
    Original in Göttingen Universitätsbibliothek.

NL 0450807   InU

PT1165
.B58
v.6

LOGAU, FRIEDRICH VON, 1604-1655.
    Auserlesene gedichte von Friedrich von Logau und Hans Assmann von Abschatz. Hrsg. von Wilhelm Müller. Leipzig, F. A. Brockhaus, 1824.
    xxxii, 206 p. 17cm. (Added t.-p.: Bibliothek deutscher dichter des siebzehnten jahrhunderts... VI)

PT1744
1824
    ---- ---- Another copy.

NL 0450808   ICU MH PU NN MdBP

Logau, Friedrich von, 1604-1655.
    Auszug des Besten aus Logau ‹etc.›
    see under title

830
L831
tD.7

Logau, Friedrich von, 1604-1655.
    Deutsche Sprüche. Auswahl von Reinhard Piper. München, R. Piper, 1916.
    99p. 17cm.

NL 0450810   CLSU PU

---

x832L82
K1654

[Logau, Friedrich von] 1604-1655.
    Salomons von Golaw [pseud.] Deutscher sinngetichte drey tausend ... Bresslaw, In verlegung Caspar Klossmanns / Gedruckt in der Baumannischer druckerey durch Gottfried Gründern [1654]
    [9], 237, [1], 247, [1], 261, [1]p. 16½cm.

    Title vignette.
    Added t.-p., engr.

NL 0450811   IU InU CU WU CU-W CtY ICU IU RPB

FILM
4333
PT
Reel
61

[Logau, Friedrich von] 1604-1655.
    Salomons von Golaw [pseud.] Deutscher Sinn-Getichte drey tausend...Bresslaw, In verlegung Caspar Klossmanns/gedruckt in der Baumannischen Druckerey durch Gottfried Gründern[1654]
    3v. 17cm.
    Vol.1 has added t.-p., engr., with ornamental border; Vol.2-3 have half-title only.
    (German Baroque Literature, No.276, reel No. 61 Research Publications, Inc.)
    Microfilm.

NL 0450812   CU

Zg17
L82
638

[Logau, Friedrich von] 1604-1655.
    Erstes[-andres] hundert teutscher Reimen-Sprüche Salomons von Golaw [pseud.] Bresslaw, In Verlegung David Müllers Buchhendl: seel: Erben, 1638.
    [113]p. 12cm.

NL 0450813   CtY

FILM
4333
PT
Reel

[Logau, Friedrich von] 1604-1655
    Erstes[-andres]hundert teutscher Reimen-Sprüche Salomons von Golaw[pseud.] Bresslaw, In Verlegung David Müllers Buchhendl: seel: Erben, 1638.
    [113]p. 12cm.
    Signatures: A-D¹²g10(E₁₀ blank)
    (German Baroque Literature, No.275, reel No. 60 Research Publications, Inc.)
    Microfilm.

NL 0450814   CU

PT 1744
.A6
1849

LOGAU, FRIEDRICH VON, 1604-1655.
    Friedrich von Logau und sein Zeitalter, geschildert in einer Auswahl aus dessen Sinngedichten. Frankfurt am Main, C. B. Lizius, 1849.
    122 p.

NL 0450815   InU CtY MWelC

Logau, Friedrich von, 1604-1655.
    ...Die fruchtschale Friedrich von Logau's; eine auslese aus des dichters spruchernte, dargebracht und mit würdigung von Wilhelm Müller-Rüdersdorf. Görlitz, Verlagsanstalt Görlitzer nachrichten und anzeiger, 1921.
    92 p. 19 ᵐ. (Schlesische heimatbücherei)

NL 0450816   NjP

PT1744
A6
1904

Logau, Friedrich von, 1604-1655.
    Logaubüchlein. [Herausgeber: Otto Erich Hartleben] 1. und 2. Aufl. München, A. Langen, 1904.
    xliii, 144 p.

    I. Hartleben, Otto Erich, 1864-1905, ed.

NL 0450817   CU NcD

Logau, Friedrich von, 1604-1655.

Fleming, Paul, 1609-1640.
    Paul Fleming, Friedr. v. Logau und Adam Olearius, hrsg. von prof. dr. Oesterley. Berlin und Stuttgart, W. Spemann [1885]

Logau, Friedrich von, 1604-1655.
    Sämmtliche Sinngedichte; hrsg. von Gustav Eitner. Tübingen, Litterarischer Verein, 1872.
    817 p. 22 cm. (Litterarischer Verein in Stuttgart. Bibliothek, 113)

    I. Eitner, Gustav, 1835-1901, ed.   (Series: Literarischer Verein in Stuttgart. Bibliothek, 113)

    PT1101.L5 vol. 113   2-9408 rev*

    OC1 OCU MiU OU CU MoU

NL 0450819   DLC CLU MH NcD NN NjP MdBP PBm MB OC1W

Logau, Friedrich von, 1604-1655.
    Sinngedichte von Friedrich von Logau. Herausgegeben von Gustav Eitner. Leipzig, F. A. Brockhaus, 1870.
    liv p., 1 l., 278 p., 1 l. 18¼ᶜᵐ. (Added t.-p.: Deutsche dichter des siebzehnten jahrhunderts ... Hrsg. von K. Goedeke und J. Tittmann. 3. bd.)

    "Ausgaben der gedichte": p. xlix-liv.

    I. *Eitner, Gustav, 1835-1901, ed.

                               3-25641
    Library of Congress   PT1126.G6 bd. 3
                           PT1744.A1 1870

NL 0450820   DLC NIC CU MdBP OC1W OC1 MB NjP OU

PT 1744
.A6
1874

LOGAU, FRIEDRICH VON, 1604-1655.
    Sinngedichte, ausgewählt und erneut von Karl Simrock. Stuttgart, Meyer & Zeller, 1874.
    128 p.

NL 0450821   InU

Logau, Friedrich von, 1604-1655.
    [Sinngedichte.] (In: Fleming, P. Paul Fleming, Friedr. v. Logau und Adam Olearius. [Berlin, 188-?] p. 135-218.)

    1. Poetry, German.   December 14, 1925

NL 0450822   NN

Logau, Friedrich von, 1604-1655.
    Friedrichs von Logau Sinngedichte. Zwölf bücher. Mit anmerkungen über die sprache des dichters, hrsg. von C. W. Ramler und G. E. Lessing ... Leipzig, 1759. In der Weidmannischen buchhandlung.

    (In Lessing, Gotthold Ephraim. ... Sämtliche schriften, hrsg. von K. Lachmann. 3. aufl. besorgt durch F. Muncker. Stuttgart, 1886-1924. 23ᶜᵐ. vol. VII (1891) p. [125]-411.)

    "Wörterbuch": p. 352-411.

    I. Ramler, Karl Wilhelm, 1725-1798, ed. II. Lessing, Gotthold Ephraim, 1729-1781, joint ed.

                 PT2396.A1 1886   25-2213

NL 0450823   DLC CtY OC1W OO OU

Logau, Friedrich von, 1604-1655.
    Friedrichs von Logau Sinngedichte. Zwölf Bücher. Mit Anmerkungen über die Sprache des Dichters; herausgegeben von C. W. Ramler und G. E. Lessing. Leipzig: Weidmann, 1759. xiv, 414, [24], 103 p. front. 16cm.

    168554B. 1. No subject. I. Ramler, Karl Wilhelm, 1725-1798, ed. II. Lessing, Gotthold Ephraim, 1729-1781, ed.   August 10, 1943

NL 0450824   NN CoU ICU KU OC1W MH InU MdBP

FILM
4333
PT
Reel
61

Logau, Friedrich von, 1604-1655
    Friedrichs von Logau Sinngedichte. Zwölf Bücher. Mit Anmerkungen über die Sprache des Dichters, hrsg. von C.W. Ramler und G.E. Lessing... In der Weidmannischen Buchhandlung. Leipzig, 1759.
    xiv,414,[24],103,[1]p. front. 16cm.
    "Wörterbuch": 103,[1]p., at end.
    (German Baroque Literature, No.277, reel No. 61 Research Publications, Inc.)
    Microfilm.

NL 0450825   CU

851.5
L851r

Logau, Friedrich von, 1604-1655.
    Sinngedichte, aufs neue überarb., mit drey Büchern vermehrt, und mit Anmerkungen begleitet von Karl Wilhelm Ramler. Leipzig, Weidmann, 1791.
    2 v. in 1 (738 p.) 17ᶜᵐ.

    I. Ramler, Karl Wilhelm, 1725-1798, ed.

NL 0450826   CSt VtMiM CoU InU

851.5
L83.2

Logau, Friedrich von, 1604-1655
    Friedrich von Logau's sinngedichte, neu ausgewählt von dr. L. H. Fischer. Leipzig, P. Reclam jun. [n.d.]
    120p. 15cm. [Universal-bibliothek 706]

    I. Fischer, Leopold Hermann, 1851-ed.

NL 0450827   IEN WaTC

VOLUME 338

Logau, Friedrich von.
    Friedrich von Logau's Sinngedichte, neu ausgewählt von L.
H. Fischer. Leipzig: P. Reclam, jun. ₍1875₎ 120 p. 24°.

1. Aphorisms (German). 2. Fischer, L. H., of Berlin, editor.
                                                    January 27, 1914.

NL 0450828   NN CU IU TU

Logau, Friedrich von, 1604–1655.
    Sinngedichte, neu ausgewählt von L. H.
Fischer. Leipzig, P. Reclam jun. ₍1876₎
120 p. 15ᶜᵐ. ₍Universal-Bibliothek₎
With Gleim, J. W. L. Ausgewählte Werke. Leipzig ₍1886₎

    I. Fischer, L   H   II. Ser.

NL 0450829   ViU

838   Logau, Friedrich von, 1604–1655
L831s.T   Sinngedichte und epigramme,
    zusammengestellt und mit einer
    vorbemerkung versehen von pfarrer
    Todt... Halle a.S., Hendel ₍1905₎
    103p. front.(facsim.) D.

NL 0450830   IaU CtY OrU

Logau, Friedrich von, 1604–1655.
    Die tapfere wahrheit, sinngedichte von Friedrich von Logau.
München, Hyperionverlag ₍1921₎
    110, ₍1₎ p. 9¼ᵐ.
    "Auswahl nach der von Lessing und Ramler veranstalteten ausgabe
von 1759."

    I. Lessing, Gotthold Ephraim, 1729–1781. II. Ramler, Karl Wilhelm,
1725–1798. III. Title.
                                            32–20819
    Library of Congress   PT1744.A6 1921   831.53

NL 0450831   DLC

Typ   Logau, Georg von, 1485–1553, ed.
522   G. Logi ... Ad inclytvm Ferdinandvm,
29.530   Pannoniae et Bohemiae regem invictissimvm
    hendecasyllabi, elegiae, et epigrammata.
    [Vienna,1529]
    4°. [147] p. 19.5cm.
    Signatures: A⁴,B⁶,C–D⁴,E–F⁶,G–H⁴,I–O⁶ (Fiij
    missigned Eiij).
    Colophon: Viennae Pannoniae Hieronymus Vietor
    silesius excudebat mense maio M.D.XXIX.
    Hand-colored woodcuts of the arms of Ferdinand
    & of Logau on   t.-p. & recto of last leaf
    respectively.

NL 0450832   MH

Logau, Georg ₍ᵥₒₙ₎ 1485–1553. Ad Lycinnam.
4 pp. (Latein. litteraturdenkmæler des 15 u. 16 jahrh.
n. 7, p. 4.)

NL 0450833   MdBP

Logau, Georg von, 1485–1553, ed.

Gratius Faliscus.
    Gratii ... De venatione liber I. P. Ouidij Nasonis Halieuti-
cōn liber acephalus. M. Aurelij Olympij Nemesiani Cynegeticōn lib. I. Eiusdem Carmen bucolicum. T. Calphurnij Siculi
Bucolica. Adriani cardinalis Uenatio. Lvgdvni, apud Seb.
Gryphivm, 1537.

PA   ₍Logau, Georg von₎ 1485–1553, ed.
6135   ... poëtae tres egregij
B8   nunc primum in lucem editi, Gratij...De uenatione
L7   lib.I. P.Ouidij Nasonis Halieuticōn liber acepha-
1534   lus. M.Aurelij Olympij Nemesiani Cynegeticōn lib.
Cage   I... Carmen bucolicum. T.Calphurnij Siculi Bucoli-
    ca. Adriani Cardinalis uenatio. Aldus, 1534.
    Colophon: Venetijs, in aedibus haeredum Aldi
    Manutij, & Andreae soceri...

    ₍6₎ 10, 12–47 l. A–F⁸, G⁴. 8vo.
    At head of title   Hoc volumine continentur

CtY NjP
NL 0450835   DFo NcD MdBE NNC MH MiU PBm MShM ICN

Logau, Gotthold.
    Der Thurm des Sisebut. Tragödie in fünf
Acten. Frankfurt a.M., C. Adelmann, 1854.
    5 p.l., 180 p., 5 l. 16°.

NL 0450836   NN

[Logau, Heinrich Wilhelm von]
    Poetischer Zeitvertreib. Bresslau, Rohrlach, 1725

NL 0450837   MH

Zg17   Logau, Heinrich Wilhelm von
L823   Heinrich Wilhelms von Logau ... Poetisches
737   Vergnügen; hält in sich: 1. Schrift, welche
    Gott geweiht. 2.Frucht, gut und böser Zeit.
    3.Schertz, bey Gelegenheit; Nebst einem Thea-
    tralischen Anhange, genannt: Hildegardis.
    Bresslau und Leipzig,Bey Michael Hubert,1737.
    416p.,incl.front. 17cm.

NL 0450838   CtY OClW

FILM   Logau, Heinrich Wilhelm von
4333   Heinrich Wilhelms von Logau...Poetisches Ver-
PT   gnügen; hult in sich: 1. Schrift, welche Gott ge-
Reel   weiht. 2. Frucht, gut und böser Zeit. 3. Schertz,
596   bey Gelgenheit; Nebst einem Theatralischen Anhange,
    genannt: Hildegardis. Bresslau und Leipzig, Bey
    Michael Hubert, 1737.
    416p., incl.front. 17cm.
    (German Baroque Literature No.1671₍,₎
    reel No. 596, Research Publications, Inc.)

    Microfilm.

NL 0450839   CU

Logau, Johann Zacharias.
    Deutsche bücher, bey Johann Zacharias Logau. St. Peters-
burg, 1786.
    1 p. l., 90 p. 20ᵐ.
    A bookseller's classified list of current literature in stock.
    Imperfect: p. 1–2 wanting.
    A label is mounted over Logau's name with the address in manuscript:
Chr. Tornow, bey der blauen brücke, no. 354.

    1. German literature—Bibl.—Catalogs. 2. Catalogs, Booksellers'—
Petrograd.
                                            31–21125
    Library of Congress   Z2249.L83   017.4

NL 0450840   DLC

Logau, Nicolas von, pseud.
    see Niebelschütz, Götz, baron, 1909–

Logboek van de Blauwe Schuit
    see under [Henkels, F   R   A   ]

The log book. Ann Arbor, Mich.
    see under Ann Arbor, Mich.   High School.

The Log book (1826)
    see under Barker, Matthew Henry, 1790–
1846.

Logbook eines Schiffes von der dritten Expedition Franz Drake's,
28. August, 1595–10. mai, 1596. Nach der englischen Urschrift
hrsg. von G. M. Thomas. (In: F. Kunstmann, Die Entdeckung
Amerikas... München, 1859. 4°. p. 97–122.)

1. Ships—Log books. 2. Drake, Sir Francis, 1540?–96. 3. Thomas,
Georg Martin, translator.
                                            May 7, 1914.

NL 0450845   NN

BX6225.37   Logbook for Adventuring with God. Official
.P98n   publication of the Board of Education and
1953   the American Baptist Convention. Phila-
v.1   delphia, Judson Press, 1953.
in: 31p. illus. 26cm. (Judson graded series,
GTS   7, pt. 1)
    1. Sunday schools—Curricula—American
    Baptist Convention. 2. American Baptist Con-
    vention—Education. I. American Baptist Con-
    vention. II. Title: Adventuring with God.

NL 0450846   IEG

Log-book notes through life
    see under [Little, Elizabeth N   ]
comp.

The log book; or, Nautical miscellany. London, J. Robins & sons ₍1830₎
    1 p. l, 498 p. front., illus. 22¼ᵐ.
    Issued in 32 numbers.

    1. Seafaring life. 2. Naval biography.
                                            15–9977
    Library of Congress   V21.L6

NL 0450848   DLC NNC CSmH

ar W   The Log book; or, Nautical miscellany.
10497   London, J. & W. Robins ₍189–?₎
    iv,508 p. illus. 23cm.

    I. Title: Nautical miscellany.

NL 0450849   NIC

... The log book of a rural uplift van
    see under [Nehru, Shri Shridhar] 1888–

VOLUME 338

Log book of the "Old Ironsides" fair.
no. 1–

Boston, 1901.   nos.   illus.   28cm.
"Published daily during the fair by the Massachusetts society, U. S. daughters of 1812."

1. Warships, U.S.—Constitution.   I. National society of United States
daughters of 1812. Massachusetts.
October 11, 1944

NL 0450851   NN

... A log-book of war
see under   Lauritzen, J., firm,
Copenhagen.

"Logchips on the way." History of the 689th field artillery battalion in the European theatre of operations.   ₁n. p., 1948?₁
80 p.   illus.   24cm.

1. World war, 1939–1945—Campaigns, Western Europe, 1944–1945.   2. World war, 1939–1945—Regt. hist.—U.S.—689th field artillery battalion.
April 30, 1951

NL 0450853   NN

Loge, Christian, *pseud.*
... Gibt es jüdische ritual-morde? Eine sichtung und psychologische klärung des geschichtlichen materials. Graz-Leipzig, U. Moser, 1934.
216 p.   plates.   19ᵐ.
"1.–3. tausend."

1. Ritual murder.   I. Title.
35–16944
Library of Congress   BM717.L63   296

NL 0450854   DLC WU NN ICU CtY NNAJHi

Loge, Eckhard.
... Eine messen- und motettenhandschrift des kantors Matthias Krüger aus der Musikbibliothek Albrechts von Preussen. Kassel, Bärenreiter-verlag, 1931.
59 p.   23ᵐ.   ₁Königsberger studien zur musikwissenschaft, hrsg. vom Musikwissenschaftlichen seminar der Universität ... 12. bd.₁
The author's inaugural dissertation, Königsberg.
"Notenbeispiele" ₁7₁ p. in pocket.

1. Krüger, Matthias, b. ca. 1485.   2. Music—Manuscripts.   I. Königsberg. Staats- und universitäts-bibliothek. Mss. (1740)   II. Title.
32–18296
Library of Congress   ML93.L7
781.969

NL 0450855   DLC

BS
610
L28V48
Loge, Ernst Friedrich.
Geschichtliche Uebersicht von der Gründung und der Thätigkeit der St. Joh.-Loge zum innigen Verein am Riesengebirge im Or. von Landshut in Schlesien, seit ihrem fünfundzwanzigjährigen Bestehen bei der Feier desselben am 24. Mai 1845 vorgetragen.   Landeshut, Carl Lips, 1845.
12 p.   23cm.

NL 0450856   NIC

M1619
869
v.296
Logé, Henri.
₁Across the still lagoon; acc.arr.piano₁
Across the still lagoon; arr. by Frank J. Smith ₁words by₁ Clifton Bingham.   ₁Boston₁ O. Ditson, c1909.   Pl.no. 4-51-62029-5.
6 p.   28ᶜᵐ.   (Secular selections. Female voices, no.10. Octavo ed. no.10, 472)
Caption title.
Vol. 296 in a set lettered: Songs.

1. Part-songs, Secular - Quartets.   2. Choral music, Secular -   Women's voices.   I. Smith, Frank ₁   arr.   II. Title.

NL 0450857   CSt

Loge, Leo.
El camino de la muerte; Perón a través de sus palabras. ₁Buenos Aires, 1955₁
104 p.   19 cm.

1. Perón, Juan Domingo, Pres. Argentine Republic, 1895–
₁. Title.
F2849.P48L6   57–35714 ‡

NL 0450858   DLC MH

Logé, Marc, tr.
Steinilber-Oberlin, Émile, 1878–
The Buddhist sects of Japan, their history, philosophical doctrines and sanctuaries, by E. Steinilber-Oberlin, with the collaboration of Kuni Matsuo; translated from the French by Marc Logé. London, G. Allen & Unwin, ltd. ₁1938₁

Logé, Marc, tr.
Hearn, Lafcadio, 1850–1904.
... Chita, un souvenir de l'Ile Dernière, traduit de l'anglais par Marc Logé.   Paris, Mercvre de France, 1911.

•**Logé, Marc,** tr.
Ward, Mary Augusta (Arnold) "Mrs. Humphry Ward," 1851–1920.
... Élizabeth et la guerre (tr. de l'anglais par Marc Logé).   Paris, P. Lafitte ₁1920₁

Logé, Marc, tr.
Hearn, Lafcadio, 1850–1904.
... Esquisses martiniquaises; traduit de l'anglais par Marc Logé. 2. éd.   Paris, Mercvre de France, 1924.

Logé, Marc, tr.
Hearn, Lafcadio, 1850–1904.
... Fantômes japonais, traduction de Marc Logé.   Paris, H. Piazza ₁*1930₁

Loge, Severin.
... Den store og den lille hind og bukken, roman.   Kristiania ₁etc.₁ Gyldendal, 1923.
139 p.   20ᵐᵐ.

ı. Title.
Library of Congress   PT8950.L73S8 1923   24–4731

NL 0450864   DLC

Loge centrale des véritables francs-maçons...
see under   Barbet du Bertrand, V. R.
1770 – ca. 1830.

Loge Cimbria, New York
see   Danish Brotherhood in America. New York (City) Cimbria Lodge.

Loge des bon amis, Rouen
see   Freemasons. Rouen. Loge des bon amis.

Loge française l'Aménité, Philadelphia
see   Freemasons. Philadelphia. Loge française l'Aménité, No. 73.

Loge française La Sagesse (*Freemasons*)
see
Freemasons. *Portsmouth, Va. Wisdom Lodge No. 16.*

Loge Franco-Yougoslave No. 540 Le General Peigne, Paris
see   Freemasons. Paris. Loge Franco-Yougoslave Le general Peigne, No. 540.

RARE BOOK DEPT.
*XG
.3656
.12
no.17
La loge rouge dévoilée a toutes les têtes couronnées ... Nouvelle édition, seule avouée, avec des additions.   ₁Paris₁ Juillet.1790.
18p.   21.5cm.(8vo)
Title vignette.
Title page & p.₁2₁ printed in red.
An attack on Freemasonry.

NL 0450871   MB NIC

W 4
P23
1940
LOGEAIS, Annie Madeleine, 1911–
La galactorrhée.   Paris, Arnette, 1940.
188 p.   (Paris. Université. Faculté de médecine.   Thèse. 1940. no. 662)

NL 0450872   DNLM CtY

Logeais (Lucien).   •Des principaux emplois de l'eau dans les affections aiguës. 39 pp. 4°.
Paris, 1874, No. 279.

NL 0450873   DNLM

UH425.F84
L82
Logeais, Marcel Pierre Louis, 1898–
... Contribution à l'histoire de la pharmacie militaire pendant la Campagne d'Italie (1792–1797) ...   Paris, Peyronnet, 1937.
123 p., 2 l. incl. port., tables, 3 facsims. 24ᶜᵐ.

At head of title: Année 1936–1937. 3ème série n° 7. Thèse ... par M. Marcel-Pierre-Louis Logeais ...
Thesis, Nancy, 1937.

NL 0450874   NNC CtY

VOLUME 338

Logeais, Pierre Désiré Emile, 1886-
... Étiologie et formes cliniques des infections
gangréneuses anaérobies des membres par
plaies de guerre ...   Paris, 1918.
86 p., 1 l.   24 cm.
Thèse - Univ. de Paris.

NL 0450875   CtY DNLM

W
4
P23
1940

Logeais, Pierre Jean, 1910-
Technique et indications de l'évidement
sous-maxillaire. Paris, Arnette, 1940.
132 p. illus. (Paris. ¡Université¿
Faculté de médecine. Thèse. 1940. no.
667)

NL 0450876   DNLM CtY MnU

Logeard, Jacques, 1912-
... Contribution à l'étude du diagnostic entre
les artérites pulmonaires primitives et
certaines artérites pulmonaires secondaires ...
Paris, 1939.
Thèse - Univ. de Paris.

NL 0450877   CtY

BR133
.N8B4

Logeart, F.

Berthier, André.
... Les vestiges du christianisme antique dans la Numidie
centrale, par André Berthier ... avec la collaboration de: F.
Logeart ... ¡et¿ M. Martin ... Alger, Imprimerie polyglotte
africaine, Maison-Carrée ¡1943¿

[LOGEAS, Henry de Maron, sieur de.]
Le romant heroique, ou sont contenus les memol
rables faits d'armes de Dom Rosidor, prince de
Constantinople, & de Clarisel le Fortuné, etc.,
escritte à la façon des anciens romans. Paris,
A.Courbé, 1632.

pp. (10), 916, (2).
Also with engraved title-page.

NL 0450879   MH

Logeas, Henry de Maron, sieur de.
Les travavx dv prince incognv. Par le Sieur
de Logeas.   A Paris, Chez Tovssainct dv Bray
1634.
11 p.l., 691 (i.e. 701) p.   16 cm.

NL 0450880   OU

Logeat, Marcel, 1886-
... La rate, organe réservoie ...   Paris,
1931.
Thèse - Univ. de Paris.
"Bibliographie": p. [42]-43.

NL 0450881   CtY

Logeay (René). *Contribution à l'étude des
gommes syphilitiques précoces. 63 pp. 8°.
Paris, 1908. No. 405.

NL 0450882   DNLM

Logejus, Jakob Anton Friedrich Logan-
see Logan-Logejus, Jakob Anton Friedrich.

Logeman, D   (van der Willigen)
see Logeman-van der Willigen, D

Logeman, Henri, 1862- *1936.*
A commentary, critical and explanatory, on the Norwegian text of Henrik Ibsen's Peer Gynt: its language,
literary associations and folklore; by H. Logeman ...
The Hague, M. Nijhoff, 1917.
xiv p., 1 l., 484 p. 25½ᵐ.
The text of Peer Gynt is quoted from the 1st edition and the translation from that by Messrs. Archer, unless otherwise indicated. cf. "To be
observed."
"Textual criticism of Henrik Ibsen's Peer Gynt": p. ¡365¿-464.
"Abbreviations and bibliography": p. ¡469¿-476.
1. Ibsen, Henrik, 1828-1906. Peer Gynt. 2. Ibsen, Henrik, 1828-1906—
Bibl.
18-13311

PT8876.L6

TxU OrU WaU CU TxDaM
NL 0450885   DLC CSt NIC CtY InU NcD NcU PPT MiU OC1

Logeman, Henri, 1862-   ed.

Elckerlijc.
... Elckerlijk, a fifteenth century Dutch morality (presumably by Petrus Dorlandus) and Everyman, a nearly
contemporary translation. A contribution to the history
of the literary relations of Holland and England, edited
by Dr. Henri Logeman ... Gand, Clemm (H. Engelcke,
successeur) 1892.

Logeman, Henri, 1862-
... Elckerlyc—Everyman. De vraag naar de prioriteit
opnieuw onderzocht, door H. Logeman. Gand, Vuylsteke,
1902.
175 p. 24½ᵐ. (Université de Gand. Recueil de travaux publiés par la
Faculté de philosophie et lettres. 28. fasc.)
Elckerlyc is attributed to Petrus Dorlandus.

1. Elckerlijc. 2. Everyman. 3. Dorlandus, Petrus, 1454-1507.

Library of Congress   PT5555.E52L6   25-2725

NL 0450887   DLC OC1 MH NN MB

PT923
.E5
1900

Logeman, Henri, 1862-1936, ed.

Historia von Doctor Johann Fausten. *English.*
The English Faust-book of 1592, edited with an introd.
and notes by H. Logeman. Gand, Librairie H. Engelcke,
1900.

Logeman, Henri, 1862-
The etymology of "Yankee," ¡by¿ Henri Logeman.   (In:
Studies in English philology; a miscellany.   Minneapolis, 1929.
p. 403-413.)

455234A. 1. Yankee ¡word¿.   March 18, 1930

NL 0450889   NN

Logeman, Henri, 1862-
Faustus notes. A supplement to the commentaries on Marlowe's "Tragical history of
D. Faustus" ... Gand, H. Engelcke, 1898.
vii p., 1 l., 154 p., 1 l.   25 cm. (Université
de Gand. Recueil de travaux publiés par la
Faculté de philosophie et lettres, 21. fasc.)

NL 0450890   PU NcD NjP OC1 NN OC1W

Logeman, Henri, 1862-
... Faustus notes. A supplement to the commentaries on
Marlowe's "Tragicall history of D. Faustus" ... Gand, H. Engelcke, 1898.
viii p., 1 l., 154 p., 1 l. 25ᵐ. (Université de Gand. Recueil de tra
vaux publiés par la Faculté de philosophie et lettres, 21. fasc.)

DLC copy replaced by microfilm.

1. Marlowe, Christopher, 1564-1593. Doctor Faustus.   I. Title.
1-3529

Library of Congress   PR2664.L6

NL 0450891   DLC NN

Logeman, Henri, 1862-   ed.

Bilderdijk, Willem, 1756-1831.
... De¡goudmaker, blijspel; een indirekte navolging van
Ludvig Holberg's Det arabiske pulver, volgens het enig be-
kende handschrift voor het eerst uitgegeven door Dr. H. Loge-
man ... Gand, Van Rysselberghe & Rombaut; Paris, É.
Champion, 1925.

Logeman, Henri, 1862-
L'inscription anglo-saxonne du reliquaire de la vraie croix
au trésor de l'église des Ss.-Michel-et-Gudule à Bruxelles, par
H. Logeman ...
(In Académie royale des sciences, des lettres et des beaux-arts de
Belgique, Bruxelles. Mémoires couronnés et autres mémoires ... Col-
lection in-8°. Bruxelles, 1891. 21½ᵐ. t. XLV ¡Lettres. no. 8¿ 31 p.
II fold. pl.)
"Présenté à la Classe des lettres de l'Académie royale de Belgique
dans la séance du 1ᵉʳ décembre 1890."
Also published separately.
Bibliographical foot-notes.
1. Inscriptions—Brussels. 2. Inscriptions, Anglo-Saxon. 3. Anglo-
Saxon language—Texts. 4. Cross and crosses—Belgium—Brussels. 5.
Relics and reliquaries.   I. Brussels. St. Michel et Ste. Gudule
(Collegiate church)   II. Title: Reliquaire de la vraie croix.
A C 38-716
Illinois. Univ. Library
for Library of Congress   [A8242.B322 vol. 45]   (082.1)

NL 0450893   IU UU DLC

Ic
C88
y89

Logeman, Henri, 1862-
L'inscription anglo-saxonne du reliquaire
de la vraie croix au trésor de l'église des
Ss. Michel-et-Gudule à Bruxelles, par H.
Logeman ... Gand & Leipzig, H.Engelcke
(Ancienne maison Clemm)[etc.,etc.]1891.
2p.l.,[3]-31p. 2 fold.plates. 21½cm.
"Extrait du tome XLV des Mémoires couronnés
et autres mémoires publiés par l'Académie
royale du Belgium. - 1891."

NL 0450894   CtY NcD ICU MB MH NN

Logeman, Henri, 1862-1936.
The name of the Anglo-Saxon rune Þ (In The
Academy. Vol. XXXIX. 1891. p. 284)

NL 0450895   NIC

Logeman, H 1862-
New Aldhelm glosses. 16 pp.
(Anglia, v. 13, 1891, p. 26.)

NL 0450896   MdBP

Logeman, Henri, 1862-
[Proof sheet reading of the index to Peer
Gynt by Henri Ibsen explained by Henri Logeman]
see under Ibsen, Henri, 1828-1906.

Logeman, Henri, 1862-   ed.

Benedictus, *Saint, abbot of Monte Cassino.*
The rule of S. Benet. Latin and Anglo-Saxon interlinear
version. Ed., with an introduction and notes, by Dr. H. Logeman. London, Pub. for the Early English text society by N.
Trübner and co., 1888.

VOLUME 338

Logeman, Henri, 1862–
... Tenuis en media. Over de stemverhouding bij konsonanten in moderne talen, met een aanhangsel over de fonetiese verklaring der wetten van Verner en Grimm, door Dr. H. Logeman ... Gand, E. van Goethem, 1908.

ix, 206 p. 24ᶜᵐ. (Université de Gand. Recueil de travaux publiés par la Faculté de philosophie et lettres. 36. fasc.)

1. Germanic languages—Phonology. 2. Languages, Modern—Phonology. 3. Verner, Karl Adolf, 1846–1896. 4. Grimm, Jakob Ludwig Karl, 1785–1863. 5. Phonetics. i. Title.

25–21643

PD131.L6

NL 0450899   DLC CU ICU NcD NN MH

Logeman, Willem Martinus, 1821–1894, ed.

Album der natuur ... 1852–Sept. 1909. Haarlem, A. C. Kruseman; ₁etc., etc.₁ 1852–₁1909₁

Logeman, Willem Sijbrand.
How to speak Dutch. A simple method of learning to speak, read and understand the language, by Willem S. Logeman ... 3d ed. Carefully rev. and much enl. With translations into Cape Dutch of all sentences and conversations. By J. F. van Oordt ... London, K. Paul, Trench, Trübner & co., ltd. ₁1901?₁

423, ₁3₁ p. 17½ᶜᵐ.

"Printed in Holland."

1. Dutch language—Conversation and phrase books. 2. Dutch language—Dialects—Africa, South. 3. Afrikaans language—Conversation and phrase books. i. Oordt, J. F. van 1856–1918. ii. Title.

34–4265

Library of Congress   PF111.L6 1901   439.318242

NL 0450901   DLC

Logeman, Willem Sijbrand, joint author.

Strong, Herbert Augustus, 1841–1918.
Introduction to the study of the history of language, by Herbert A. Strong ... Willem S. Logeman ... and Benjamin Ide Wheeler ... London, New York, Longmans, Green, & co., 1891.

Logeman-van der Willigen, D., tr.

Bojer, Johan, 1872–
Der laatste viking, door Johan Bojer, geautoriseerde vertaling uit het noorsch door D. Logeman-van der Willigen. Antwerpen, N. v. Het Kompas ₁1943₁

PT8950
.B6S53

Logeman-van der Willigen, D., tr.

Rung, Otto, 1874–1945.
De paradijsvogel, roman door Otto Rung, uit het deensch vertaald door D. Logeman-van der Willigen. Antwerpen, Uitgeverij De Magneet ₁1945?₁

PT8175
.R8P26

Logemann, Frits.
Ein beitrag zu den missbildungen des ureters. Inaug. diss. Giessen,1902.

NL 0450905   ICRL MH

871.09
L829d

Logemann, Jacob Christoph.
De defunctorum virtutibus in carminibus sepulcralibus latinis laudatis. Roterodami, T. de Vries, 1916.

4p.ℓ.,157,₁1₁p. 25cm.
Thesis - Amsterdam.
"Theses": p.₁155₁-157.
Bibliographical footnotes.

1. Laments. 2. Elegiac poetry, Latin - Hist. & crit.

NL 0450906   TxU NjP CtY

Wason
HD894
L83

Logemann, Johann Heinrich Adolf, 1892–
Het beschikkingsrecht der Indonesische rechtsgemeenschappen, door J. H. A. Logemann en B. ter Haar Bzn. Batavia ₁1927?₁
118 p. 24cm.

Cover title.
"Overgedrukt uit het Indisch tijdschrift van het recht, deel 125."

NL 0450907   NIC

Logemann, Johann Heinrich Adolf, 1892–
College-aantekeningen over het staatsrecht van Nederlands-Indië. 's-Gravenhage, W. van Hoeve, 1947.

208 p. 25 cm.
"Errata": leaf inserted.

1. Indonesia—Constitutional law.

57–36075

NL 0450908   DLC NNC CSt-L MH-L MiU-L NIC NN CtY MiU

LOGEMANN,Johann Heinrich Adolf,1892–
Direct gebied met inheemsche rechtspraak. Weltevreden,G.Kolff & Co.,₁1928?₁.

26 cm. pp.₍17₎.
The paper cover serves as title-page.
pp.₍109₎-125 of a larger work.

NL 0450909   MH

Logemann, Johann Heinrich Adolf, 1892–
De functie van de bestuursdienst; rede in tegenwoordigheid van zijne excellentie den gouverneur-generaal van Nederlandsch-Indië uitgesproken op de twaalfde herdenkingsdag van de Stichting der rechtshogeschool te Batavia de 28ste october 1936, door Dr. J. A. H. Logemann. Groningen, Wolters, 1936.
18 p.

1. Netherlands - Official and employees.

NL 0450910   NcU

Wason
HD2753
15L83

Logemann, Johann Heinrich Adolf, 1892–
De grondslagen der vennootschapsbelasting in Nederland en Indië. 's-Gravenhage, S. S. Korthuis ₁1923₁
x,110 p. 25cm.

Diss.--Leyden.

1. Corporations--Netherlands--Taxation. 2. Corporations--Indonesia--Taxation. I. Title.

NL 0450911   NIC CtY PU ICRL NIC

Logemann, Johann Heinrich Adolf, 1892–
De grondslagen der vennootschapsbelasting in Nederland en Indië ... door Johann Heinrich Adolf Logemann ... 's Gravenhage, Boekdrukkerij S. S. Korthuis ₁1923₁
x p. 1 l., 110 p. 24½ᵐ.
"Stellingen": p. ₁109₁–110.

1. Corporations — Netherlands—Taxation. 2. Corporations — Dutch East Indies—Taxation.

37–37433

Library of Congress   HD2753.N2L6
[336.27] 658.17109492

NL 0450912   DLC PU

Wason
DS644
L83

Logemann, Johann Heinrich Adolph, 1892–
Indonesië. Bewerkt door Evert Vermeer. ₁Amsterdam, Partij van den Arbeid, 1947₁
16 p. 24cm.

1. Indonesia--Pol. & govt.--1942–1949.
I. Title.

NL 0450913   NIC

Logemann, Johann Heinrich Adolf, 1892–
Over de theorie van een stellig staatsrecht. Leiden, Universitaire Pers Leiden, 1948.

viii, 126 p. 25 cm.
Bibliographical footnotes.

1. Constitutional law.

JF56.L6   49–18873*

NL 0450914   DLC NNC

Logemann, Johann Heinrich Adolf, 1892–
Over de theorie van een stellig staatsrecht, door dr J.H.A. Logemann ... Djakarta, "Saksama", 1954.

viii, 132 p. 24cm.
Bibliographical footnotes.

NL 0450915   MH-L

Logemann, Johann Heinrich Adolf, 1892–
Over enkele vraagstukken eener indische staatsrechtsbeoefening ... door dr. J. H. A. Logemann. Weltevreden, G. Kolff & co., 1927.

1 p. ℓ., 33 p. 24½ᵐ.

"Rede in tegenwoordigheid van zijne excellentie den gouverneur-generaal van Nederlandsch-Indië uitgesproken op den derden herdenkingsdag van de stichting der Rechtshoogeschool te Batavia, den 28ᵉⁿ october 1927."

1. Political science. 2. Dutch East Indies—Pol. & govt. i. Title: Indische staatsrechtbeoefening.

40–18783

Library of Congress   JQ763.1927.L6
342.91

NL 0450916   DLC NIC ICRL

Logemann, Johann Heinrich Adolf, 1892–
Over Indië's staatsorde voor 1854, door J. H. A. Logemann ... Amsterdam, Noord-Hollandsche uitgevers-maatschappij, 1934.

cover-title, 46 p. 24½ᵐ. (Mededeelingen der Koniklijke akademie van wetenschappen, Afdeeling letterkunde, deel 78, serie a, no. 5)

1. Dutch East Indies—Politics and government. 2. Netherlands—Colonies—East Indies.

A C 35–372

₁Title from Cleveland   Pub. Libr.
Library of Congress   [AS244.A51 vol. 78, ser. a, no. 5]

NL 0450917   OCl PPAmP

VOLUME 338

Logemann, Johann Heinrich Adolf, 1892–
Het staatsrecht van Indonesië, het formele systeem.
's-Gravenhage, W. van Hoeve, 1954.
214 p. 25 cm.

1. Indonesia—Constitutional law.

55–29286

NL 0450918   DLC CU-L IaU NN NNC MH-L NIC

JQ761
.16
1955
Logemann, Johann Heinrich Adolf, 1892–
Het staatsrecht van Indonesië; het formele
systeem. 2d ed. 's-Gravenhage, W. Van Hoeve,
1955.
216 p.

1.Constitutional law - Indonesia. 2. Government-
Indonesia. 3. H04.2 - Constitutional law.
4. H04.2 - Government. I. Title.

NL 0450919   DS

Logemann, Johann Heinrich Adolf, 1892–
Het staatsrecht van Indonesië; het formele systeem. 3.,
herziene druk. 's-Gravenhage, W. van Hoeve, 1955.
216 p. 25 cm.

1. Indonesia—Constitutional law.

57–16154 ‡

NL 0450920   DLC CtY MH-L CU CtY-L

Logemann, Johann Heinrich Adolf, 1892–
Wegen der rechtswetenschap; rede uitgesproken bij de aanvaarding van het ambt van gewoon hoogleraar in het staats- en administra-
tiefrecht van Nederlandsch-Indie, Suriname en
Curaçao aan de Rijksuniversiteit te Leiden
op de 31ste october 1947. 's-Gravenhage, W.
Van Hoeve ₁1947₎
15 p.

1. Jurisprudence.

NL 0450921   NNC MH-L

Logemann, Wilhelm
Die Eisenbahnen im Wesergebiet. Darmstadt, Röhrig
[195–]

23 p. maps (Die Bundesbahn; amtliches Organ der
Hauptverwaltung der Deutschen Bundesbahn. 1.Beiheft)

NL 0450922   MH

Logemann, Willy, 1909–
Untersuchungen über die autoxydation von
merkaptanen. ... Marburg, 1935.
Inaug. Diss. - Marburg, 1935.
Lebenslauf.

NL 0450923   ICRL CtY

*FC6
M*56m
2324b
Les logemens de la covr, a S. Germain en
Laye.
[Paris?] 1649.
6p. 22.5cm.,in case 28cm.
Moreau 2324 (note).
In folder; in case labeled: Mazarinadee.

NL 0450924   MH WU

Logement; revue du Mouvement Paritaire et
des Comités Interprofessionnels du Logement.
Paris, The [Committee]
v., illus., tables, 28cm.
Title varies:
⁰C.I.L.,   – vol.10:102,
May 1958.
³C.I.L. logement, vol.10:103, June 1958 – vol.
12:107, Dec. 1958.

Logement, vol.12:108, Jan. 1959 –

NL 0450925   MH-SD

Logen, Erich, 1896–
Zur frage der habituellen schulterluxa-
tion und ihrer operativen behandlung.
Inaug. diss. Wuerzburg. 1896.
Bibl.

NL 0450926   ICRL CtY

Logen Drott, no. 168 af Vasa orden af Amerika, *Washington, D. C.*
see Vasa Order of the United States of America, Grand
Lodge. *Drott Lodge No. 168, Washington, D. C.*

Logen Malardrottningens vid Vasa ordens av
Amerika Stockholms besok 1934. Stockholm A.B.
Hasse, 1934.
unp.

NL 0450928   PPAmSwM

Logenhagen, Jacobus, d. 1611.

Augustinus, *Aurelius, Saint, bp. of Hippo.*
Commentaria in sacrosanctvm Iesv Christi Evangelivm
secvndvm Lvcam. Ex omnibus d. Augustini operibus collecta
per fratrem Iacobvm a Logenhagen ... Antverpiæ, apud
Antonium Tilenium Brechtanum, cIɔ.Iɔ.Lxxiiii.

Logenheim (Das) in Hamburg. Festschrift
zur Erinnerung an die Einweihung. Sonntag,
den 28. August 1904. ₍Hamburg, 1904₎
71 (1) p.

NL 0450930   OCH

Logenkalender für Monat. Beilage für
Freimaurer-Zeitung.
see Freimaurer-Zeitung.
Beilage: Logenkalender.

Die Logenschwester
see B'nai B'rith. District no. 8.
Schwesternverband.
Die Zeitschrift.

LOGER, Vincent, l'abbé.
Instruction pastorale, ou Avis necessaires
sur le grand jubilé de l'année sainte du 1.
fevrier 1701. Et le Mandement de Monseigneur
l'archevêque du 12. fevrier 1702.

(In BOIDOT,---l'abbé. Traité, 1751, pp.[273]
280.).

NL 0450933   MH

Loger, Vincent, l'abbé.
Les Pseaumes en forme de prières.
Paris, 1706?
see under Bible. O.T.
Psalms. French. Paraphrases. 1706.

Logerais (J.-B.-F.) *Sur l'altération des fonctions du système cellulaire. 30 pp. 8°. Paris,
an XI [1803. v. 3].

NL 0450935   DNLM

Logerais (Jean-Paul-Henri) [1865–]. *Relation d'une épidémie d'oreillons qui s'est dé-
clarée à Brest au 2e régiment d'infanterie de
marine. [Bordeaux.] 46 pp., 1 l. 4°. Brest,
1889. No. 38.

NL 0450936   DNLM

Victor Jean
Logerais, *Du diabète sucré, de son traitement
par l'eau minérale de Pougues (source Saint-
Léger). De l'action thérapeutique du gaz acide
carbonique fourni par cette source. 40 pp. 8°.
Paris, G. Masson, 1873.

NL 0450937   DNLM

Logerais, Victor Jean
——. Du traitement de certaines affections
chroniques par les eaux minérales de Pougues
(Nievre) et des déviations utérines par un ap-
pareil spécial. Année 1869. 71 pp., 1 pl. 8°.
Paris, V. Masson & fils, 1869.

NL 0450938   DNLM

Logerais (Victor-Jean). Observations médi-
cales sur les eaux minérales de Pougues (Niè-
vre). 58 pp. 8°. Paris, V. Masson & fils, 1867.
[P., v. 1757.]

NL 0450938-1   DNLM

WBI
L832p
1895
LOGERAIS, Victor Jean
Pougues et son traitement. Paris,
Masson, 1895.
194 p.

NL 0450939   DNLM

Logerais (Victor-Jean). *Réflexions sur quelques observations de péritonite aiguë. 40 pp.
4°. Paris, 1840, No. 166, v. 362.

NL 0450940   DNLM

Logerais, Victor Jean.
——. Traitement de la gravelle et de la goutte.
22 pp., 1 l. 8°. Paris, l'cc. Ethion-Péron, 1870.

NL 0450941   DNLM

Logerais, Victor Jean.
——. Traitement des affections du foie, congestion, hypertrophie, coliques hépatiques, par les
eaux de Pougues. 24 pp. 8°. Paris, G. Masson,
1883.

NL 0450942   DNLM

VOLUME 338

Logerais, Victor Jean.
——. Traitement du catarrhe de la vessie.
Études et observations. 15 pp. 8°. Paris, G.
Masson, 1882.

NL 0450943   DNLM

Logerais, Victor Jean.
——. Traitement du catarrhe de vessie par les
eaux de Pougues. 16 pp. 8°. Paris, E. Rousset & Cie., 1879.

NL 0450944   DNLM

Logerais, Victor Jean.
——. Traitement spécial des affections gastro-intestinales le plus ordinairement désignées sous
le nom de dyspepsie par les eaux de Pougues.
16 pp. 8°. Paris, Ve. Ethiou-Pérou, 1881.
The same. 10 pp. 8°. Paris, G. Masson,
1882.

NL 0450945   DNLM

Logereau (Louis) [1859–]. *Contribution
à l'étude des abcès du cerveau consécutifs aux
otites. 50 pp. 4°. Paris, 1906, No. 165.

NL 0450946   DNLM

Logères, Marc de Fontaines de
see Fontaines de Logères, Marc de.

Logerman, Calvin Gene.
A survey of the new manufacturing industries in Kansas,
1940–1949. Manhattan, The College, 1950.
53 p. maps, diagrs., tables. 23 cm. (Kansas. State College of
Agriculture and Applied Science, Manhattan. Engineering Experiment Station. Bulletin, no. 64)
Kansas State College bulletin, v. 34, no. 14.
Bibliography : p. 53.

1. Kansas—Manuf.   (Series)
HD9727.K2L6   338   A 51–9415
Ohio State Univ. Libr.
for Library of Congress   †

NL 0450948   OU TxU DLC

Logerot, Auguste, pub.
Album des principaux monumens de Paris
see under Album des principaux monumens
de Paris.

Logerot, Auguste, ed.
Carte de l'Île d'Haïte
see under Vuillemin, Alexandre A.,
b. 1812.

Map   Logerot, Auguste
G   Carte de la Bretagne comprenant
5833   les départements du Finistère, des
B7   Côtes du Nord, d'Ille et Vilaine, du
1857   Morbihan, et de la Loire Inférieure.
L6   Paris, 1857.
       col. map 53 x 72 cm.

       Scale approx. 12 km. to 1 inch.

       1. Brittany—Maps.

NL 0450951   NIC

Map   Logerot, Auguste
G   Carte de la Normandie comprenant les
5833   Départements de la Seine-Inférieure,
N7   de la Manche, du Calvados, de l'Eure
1857   et de l'Orne. Paris, 1857.
L6   col. map 52 x 70 cm.

       Scale approx. 12 km. to the inch.

       1. Normandy—Maps.

NL 0450952   NIC

912.44 Logerot, Auguste.
8401   Carte du chemin de fer de Paris à Rouen et au
        Havre. Paris, Logerot [1840?]
        64x21cm. fold. to 15x9.5cm.

        Title in French and English.

        1. Railroads—France—Maps.

NL 0450953   IU

Logerot, Auguste, publisher.
Carte spéciale des chemins de fer de la France et de l'Allemagne à
l'usage des voyageurs, indiquant toutes les stations qui desservent les villes, bourgs et communes situés sur le parcours des
lignes exploitées.
Paris. [1867?] Size, 23½ × 34 inches. Scale (computed), 47
kilomètres to 1 inch. Folded.
Submap.—Chemins de fer des environs de Paris.

K8280 — T.r. — France. Geog. Maps. — France. R.Rs. — Germany. Geog. Maps.
— Germany. R.Rs.

NL 0450954   MB

Logerot, Auguste, pub.   *Map 1034.30
Nouveau guide, Le, de l'étranger dans les 20 arrondissements de Paris.
[Carte.]
Paris. Logerot. 1863. Size, 20¼ × 27 inches. Scale, none.
Folded.
Accompanied by Table alphabétique des rues . . . 21 pp. 15 cm.

K3840 — Paris. Descr. Maps.

NL 0450955   MB

Logerot, Auguste.
Le nouveau guide de l'étranger dans les 20 arrondissements
[de Paris]. Paris: Logerot [1868]. 1 p.l., 21 p., 1 folded map.
16°.

Title from cover.

1. Paris.—Guidebooks, 1868.   2. Title.   November 20, 1913.

NL 0450956   NN

Logerot, Auguste, pub.   *Map 1034.31
Nouveau guide, Le, de l'étranger dans les 20 arrondissements de Paris.
[Carte.]
Paris. Logerot. 1874. Size, 20¼ × 27 inches. Scale, none.
Folded.

K3840 — Paris. Descr. Maps.

NL 0450957   MB PP

Logerot, Auguste, pub.
Le nouveau guide de l'étranger dans les 20
arrondissements de Paris. Paris, J. Gaultier,
éditeur, 1876.
map. 51x69 fold. to 16½x11.
*Nomenclature des boulevards, quais, rues,
passages, squares & edifices indiqués sur le
plan de Paris. Paris, Maison Logerot, J. Gaultier,
éditeur, 1876 (51, 1 p. booklet) inserted.

Edf
P21
876N

NL 0450958   CtY

Maps   Logerot, Auguste, pub.
G   Nouveau plan de Paris divisé en 20
5834   arrondissements. Paris, A. Logerot,
P219   1867.
1867   col. map 108 x 76 cm. folded to 12 x
       20 cm.

       No scale.

       1. Paris, France—Maps.

NL 0450959   NIC

Logerot, Auguste, pub.
Nouveau plan de Paris devisé en 20
arrondissements. Paris, 1871.
Size: 25 x 40 inches.
Folded in covers.
Cover-title: Paris et ses environs dans un
rayon de dix kilomètres.

NL 0450960   OCl

LOGEROT, Auguste, publisher.
Nouveau plan de Paris divisé en 20 arrondissements. [Avec] Nomenclature des boulevards, quais, rues . . .
Paris. Logerot. 1889. Size, 25¾ × 39⅝ inches. Scale, none.
Text, 36 pp. 16°.

NL 0450961   MB

Logerot, Auguste, publisher.
Nouvelle carte postale de la France, à l'usage des voyageurs, comprenant le nord de l'Italie, la Suisse, la Hollande, la Belgique et
la partie occidentale de l'Allemagne, les chemins de fer en exploitation, en construction et adoptés, donnant les distances d'un
lieu à un autre en kilomètres.
Paris. 1848. Size, 19½ × 26 inches. Scale (computed), 31.9
geographical miles to 1 inch. View. Folded.
Submaps. — Environs de Paris dans un rayon de 63 kilomètres. — Corse.

K8300 — France. Geog. Maps.

NL 0450962   MB

LOGEROT, Auguste.
Nouvelle carte postale de la république française, à l'usage des voyageurs; comprenant le
nord de l'Italie, la Suisse, la H[   ]lande, la
Belgique et la parue occidentale de l'Allemagne
les chemins de fer en exploitation, en construction et adoptés, donnant les distances d'un
lieu à un autre en kilomètres. Publiée par
A[   ]te Logerot. Paris, 1849.

26 1/2 x 20 1/2 in.
(Routes de France.)   Fr 2040.4

NL 0450963   MH

Logerot, Auguste, pub.
Paris actuel en 20 arrondissements dans un rayon de 7 kilomètres. Paris: Maison Logerot, J. Gaultier [1878]. 1 plan,
folded, 32 × 25 in. 16°.

1. Paris.—Maps.   January 15, 1914.

NL 0450964   NN

VOLUME 338

Logerot, Auguste, publisher.
Paris illustré et ses fortifications [Carte].
Paris. 1847. Size, 19½ × 27⅛ inches. Scale, none. Engraved
title-page. Folded.
Submap. — Environs de Paris. Plan d'ensemble des fortifications de
Paris.
The engraved title-page reads: Nouveau guide du promeneur aux forti-
fications de Paris.

K3898 — Paris. Descr. Maps. — Paris. Fortifications. — Nouveau guide du
promeneur aux fortifications de Paris. — T.r.

NL 0450965   MB

LOGEROT, Auguste, publisher.
Plan de Paris actuel. [Avec] Nomenclature des boulevards, quais,
rues ...
= Paris. Logerot. 1888. Size, 22¹/₁₆ x 28³/₄ inches. Scale
1:16000, or 1333⅓ feet to 1 inch. Text, 36 pp. 16°.

NL 0450966   MB

LOGEROT, Auguste, publisher.
Plan de Paris et ses fortifications. Publié
par Augste Logerot. Dessiné par Maillard et A
Soussaint-Grave par Ch.Dyonnet. P. 1847.

38 3/8 x 26 in.   Fr 7540.1

NL 0450967   MH

Logerot, Auguste, pub.
Souvenir du nouveau Paris, ses monuments,
promenades, boulevarts et grandes voies de
communications; plan simplifié pour se guider
seul dans Paris.   Paris, 1852.
map, 44 x 61 cm in folder 17 cm.
1. Paris - Maps. I. Title.

NL 0450968   CU

Logerot, Auguste, pub.   *Map 1034.29
Souvenir du nouveau Paris: ses monuments, promenades, boulevarts
et grandes voies de communications. Plan simplifié pour se
guider seul dans Paris.
Paris. Logerot. [186-?] Size, 14½ × 21 inches. Scale, none.
Views of buildings, etc. Folded.

K3840 — Paris. Descr. Maps.

NL 0450969   MB

Logerot, Gabrielle
see   Réval, Gabrielle, pseud.

Logerot, Jeanne.
... Contribution à l'étude de l'ultra-filtrable
urinaire ...   Paris, 1930.
Thèse - Univ. de Paris.
"Bibliographie": p. [63]-64.

NL 0450971   CtY

Logerot (Louis). *Recherches sur l'anatomie
pathologique du molluscum contagiosum. 38
pp. 8°. Paris, 1849, No. 276.

NL 0450972   DNLM

M10.5   Logerwell, Frans L
L832s   Survey of literature on high-altitude
phenomena that may affect aircraft electrical
systems.   Washington, U.S. National Advisory Committee for Aeronautics, 1944.
15 p. illus., diagrs., table   27cm.
(U.S. National Advisory Committee for
Aeronautics. Confidential bulletin no.E4J04)

At head of title: Confidential-declassified.
"References":p.8-11.
Processed.

NL 0450973   DAS

Loges, August,1878-
Ueber die combination des hermaphroditismus...
Inaug. diss. Wuerzburg,1907.
Bibl.

NL 0450974   ICRL DNLM CtY

949.4   Loges, Chrétien de.
82e   Essais historiques sur le Mont St. Bernard.
‹n.p.› 1789.
229(1.e.219)p. 17cm.

Error in paging: 145-154 omitted in numbering.
Binder's title: Opuscoli diversi.
Bound with Pini, E. Memoria mineralogica.
Milano, 1783.

NL 0450975   IU NjP MH ICN

Loges, G.
Allgemeine oder irreführende bezeichnungen von fut-
termitteln.
Landw. vers. stat. bd. 68, p. 117-121.   Berlin, 1908.

1. Feeding stuffs.

Library, U. S. Dept. of   Agriculture   Agr 8-636

NL 0450976   DNAL

Loges, G.
Bericht des Futtermittelausschusses, betreffend die
Bernburger beschlüsse.
Landw. vers. stat. bd. 58, p. 368-375.   Berlin, 1908.

1. Bran.

Library, U. S. Dept. of   Agriculture   Agr 5-389

NL 0450977   DNAL

Loges, G.
Die beschaffenheitsgarantie im futtermittelhandel.
Landw. vers. stat. bd. 64, p. 18-25.   Berlin, 1906.

1 Feeding stuffs. Inspection.

Library, U. S. Dept. of   Agriculture   Agr 6-766

NL 0450978   DNAL

Loges, G.
Bestimmung von kochsalzbeimengungen zu futtermit-
teln.
Landw. vers. stat. bd. 81, p. 151-155.   Berlin, 1913.

1. Sodium chlorid. Determination.

Library, U. S. Dept. of   Agriculture   Agr 13-450

NL 0450979   DNAL OU

Loges, G.
Betreffend melassefuttermittel (rundschreiben vom 8.
mai und 18. juli 1912)
Landw. vers. stat. bd. 81, p. 140-142.   Berlin, 1913.

1. Molasses as a feeding stuff.

Library, U. S. Dept. of   Agriculture   Agr 13-448

NL 0450980   DNAL OU

Loges, G.
Die beurteilung des vorkommens von milben in futter-
mitteln.
Landw. vers. stat. bd. 66, p. 230-235.   Berlin, 1907.

1. Mites. 2. Feeding stuffs, Mites in.

Agr 7-1648

NL 0450981   DNAL

Loges, G.
Kalium- oder natriumperchlorat im chilisalpeter.
Landw. vers. stat. bd. 68, p. 132-134.   Berlin, 1908.

1. Sodium nitrate, Potassium perchlorate in. 2. Sodium nitrate, Sodium
perchlorate in.
Agr 8-639

Library, U. S. Dept. of   Agriculture

NL 0450982   DNAL

Loges, G.
Obligatorische angabe des sandgehaltes der futtermit-
tel in den untersuchungsberichten.
Landw. vers. stat. bd. 64, p. 37-39.   Berlin, 1906.

1. Feeding stuffs. Inspection.

Library, U. S. Dept. of   Agriculture   Agr 6-767

NL 0450983   DNAL

Loges, G.
Über die berechnung der kaliverbindungen in kali-
mischdüngern.
Landw. vers. stat. bd. 57, p. 30-32.   Berlin, 1902.

1. Potash fertilizers.

Library, U. S. Dept. of   Agriculture   Agr 5-390

NL 0450984   DNAL

Loges, G.
Ueber die bestimmung des humus in ackererden.
Landw. vers. stat. bd. 28, p. 229-245.   Berlin, 188?

1. Humus. Determination. 2. Soils. Humus content.

Library, U. S. Dept. o   Agriculture   Agr 4-2546

NL 0450985   DNAL

VOLUME 338

Loges, G.
Über eine methode der fettbestimmung durch ausschüttelung mit äther.
Landw. vers. stat. bd. 64, p. 28-35; bd. 66, p. 238-239. Berlin, 1906-07.

1. Fat. Determination.
Agr 6-768   Additions
Library, U. S. Dept. of   Agriculture

NL 0450986   DNAL

Loges, G.
Über milchmelasse.
Landw. vers. stat. bd. 58, p. 400-402.   Berlin, 1903.

1. Molasses feeding stuffs.
Library, U. S. Dept. of   Agriculture   Agr 5-391

NL 0450987   DNAL

Loges, G.
Ueber stickstoffhaltige organische verbindungen in der ackererde.
Landw. vers. stat. bd. 32, p. 201-202.   Berlin, 1886.

1. Soils. Nitrogen content.
Library, U. S. Dept. o   Agriculture   Agr 4-2547

NL 0450988   DNAL

Loges, G.
Untersuchung der superphosphate mit citratlöslicher phosphorsäure.
Landw. vers. stat. bd. 49, p. 60-61.   Berlin, 1898.

1. Superphosphates.
U. S. Dept. of agr. Library
for Library of Congress   [S7.L293] bd. 49]   Agr 4-2548

NL 0450989   DNAL

Loges, G.
Wertberechnung des feinmehls und der phosphorsäure im thomasmehl.
Landw. vers. stat. bd. 43, p. 350-352.   Berlin, 1894.

1. Phosphatic slag. Phosphoric acid content.
Library, U. S. Dept. of   Agriculture   Agr 4-2549

NL 0450990   DNAL

Loges, G.
Zur bestimmung der acidität in futtermittelfetten.
Landw. vers. stat. bd. 56, p. 95-96.   Berlin, 1902.

1. Acidity. Determination. 2. Feeding stuffs, Acidity in.
Library, U. S. Dept. of   Agriculture   Agr 4-2550

NL 0450991   DNAL

Loges, G.
Zur bestimmung der freien fettsäuren in futtermitteln.
Landw. vers. stat. bd. 38, p. 314-316.   Berlin, 1891.

1. Feeding stuffs. Fatty acids content.
Library, U. S. Dept. of   Agriculture   Agr 4-2551

NL 0450992   DNAL

Loges, Hector de Launey les
    see   Launey Les Loges, Hector de.

Loges, Henry des, pseud.
    see   Gouriet de Saint-Senoch, Henry.

Loges, J   Desbrochers des
    see   Desbrochers des Loges, J

Loges, Jean des
    see   Des Loges, Jean. [in supplement]

Loges (Joh. Wolfgangus). *De venæ sectione
in febribus acutis. 28 pp. sm. 4°. Halæ Magdeb., typ. C. Henckelii, [1703].
Ser. also, Träbr (Godofr. Theodorus). De mortuis ex affectibus. sm. 4°. Lipsiæ, 1700.

NL 0450998   DNLM PPC

Loges, Walter, 1899-
Ueber kieferverbaende.
Inaug. diss. Breslau, 1927.
Bibl.

NL 0450999   ICRL

Loges, Walter, 1912-
... Uber Spätschädigungen bei Narkosen mit halogenhaltigen Kohlenwasserstoffen in verschiedenen Dosierungsbereichen und bei wechselnder Einwirkungsdauer ... Leipzig, 1935.
Inaug.-Diss. - Leipzig.
Lebenslauf.

NL 0451000   CtY

Loges D'Artistes. Paris, 1899.

NL 0451001   NjP

LOGETTE,
Catalogue raisonné de la rare et précieuse collection d'estampes [et de quelques tableaux, bronzes, porcelaines, et meubles, du cabinet de feu M. Logette, négociant. Par F.L. Régnault-Delalande. Cette vente se fera dans la maison de feu M. Logette, le mardi 6 mai, et jours suivans. Paris, 1817.

pp. x., 64.
With prices.

NL 0451002   MH

Loges (Albert). *Le lymphangiome congénital de la mercuchelle. 114 pp. 8°. Paris, 1902.

NL 0451003   DNLM

LOGEZ, Eugène.
De l'exercice de la tutelle administrative sur l'administration municipale de Paris. Thèse Paris, V. Giard & E. Brière, 1910.

NL 0451004   MH IU

Wing
ⁱZP
645
.L 625
LOGGAN, DAVID, 1635-1700?
Cantabrigia illustrata, sive, Omnium celeberrimæ istius Universitatis collegiorum, aularum, bibliothecæ academicæ, scholarum publicarum, sacelli coll. regalis, nec non totius oppidi ichnographia... Cantabrigia [1688]
4 leaves. plates(part double, part fold.)double plan. 44cm.

Engraved t.-p.
Mounted portraits inserted.

NL 0451005   ICN PPF MH

---

xfC42
Ox2uEo
Loggan, David, 1635-1700?
Cantabrigia illustrata, sive, Omnium celeberrimæ istius universitatis collegiorum, aularum, bibliothecæ academicæ, scholarum, publicarum, sacelli coll: regalis, nec non totius oppidi ichnographia deliniatore & sculptore Dav: Loggan ... quam proprijs sumptibus typis mandavit & impressit. Cantabrigiae [1690?]
4ℓ. plates(part double, part fold.) double plan. 45cm.

Bound dos à dos with the author's Oxonia illustrata. Oxoniæ, 1675.
Engr. t.p.

NL 0451007   IU CLU-C CtY DFo MH

---

xfC42
Ox2uEo
1715
Loggan, David, 1635-1700?
Cantabrigia illustrata, sive, Omnium celeberrimæ istius universitatis collegiorum, aularum, bibliothecæ academicæ, scholarum publicarum, sacelli coll: regalis nec non totius oppidi ichnographia deliniatore & sculptore Dav: Loggan ... quam proprijs sumptibus typis mandavit & impressit Cantabrigiæ. London, Printed and sold by H. Overton [1716?]
[7], 8p. plates(part double, part fold.) double plan. 43cm.

Bound with the author's Oxonia illustrata. London [ca. 1715]
Engr. t.p.
Probably published in 1716. Cf. David Loggan, Cantabrigia illustrata. Edited by J. W. Clark. Cambridge, 1905. Introd. p.[5]
In this copy the descriptive text (14p.) is bound after the plates.

NL 0451009   IU

VOLUME 338

Loggan, David, 1635-1700?
　　Cantabrigia illustrata, by David Loggan (first published in 1690) ; a series of views of the university and colleges and of Eton college, ed., with a life of Loggan, an introduction, and historical and descriptive notes, by J. W. Clark ... Cambridge, Macmillan and Bowes, 1905.

　　43 l. illus., 29 pl., port., plans. 45 cm.

　　Includes reproduction of original engraved t.-p., dedication, preface, and index of plates, in Latin, with English translation on opposite leaves.
　　Each plate accompanied by a leaf with descriptive letterpress.

Plate XXVIII*: Central sheet of plan of Cambridge by John Hamond, 1592.

1. Cambridge. University — Hist. 2. Cambridge. University — Descr. — Views.   I. Clark, John Willis, 1833-1910, ed.   II. Title.

LF128.L7   6-45180 rev
——— Copy 2. Rosenwald Coll. Bookplate of Howard C. Levis.

ICJ
NL 0451011   DLC CaBVaU CtY NjP NcD OO OCU OC1 PPL MH

Loggan, David, 1635-1700?
　　Loggan's Map of Oxford.

Oxford historical society, ed.
　　... Old plans of Oxford. ₍Oxford, 1899₎

Loggan, David, 1635-1700?
　　Oxonia illustrata, sive omnium celeberrimæ istius universitatis collegiorum, aularum, bibliothecæ Bodleianæ, scholarum publicarum, theatri Sheldoniani; nec non urbis totius scenographia. Delineavit & sculpsit Dav: Loggan ... Oxoniæ, e theatro Sheldoniano, 1675.

　　5 l. 38 fold. pl., 3 fold. plans. 43ᵐᵐ.
　　Engr. t.-p.

1. Oxford. University.

Library of Congress   LF528.L7   7-15047†

NL 0451013   DLC CLU-C CtY KU DFo CtY-M ICN MH NN WU

Loggan, David, 1635-1700?
LLmd67   Oxonia illustrata, sive omnium celeberrimæ
675ℓc   istius universitatis collegiorum, aularum,
　　bibliothecæ Bodleianæ, scholarum publicarum,
　　theatri Sheldoniani; nec non urbis totius sceno-
　　graphia. Delineavit & sculpsit Dav:Loggan ...
　　Oxoniæ,e theatro Sheldoniano;London,printed and
　　sold by H.Overton,1714₎
　　2v.ℓ.,14p. XL double pl.,incl.1 fold.plan.
　　44cm.
　　Illus., engr. t.-p.
　　First published 1675 without letterpress, but
　　with references in the index to pages in Wood's

Historia et antiquitates ... where accounts
　　of the buildings could be found. This 1714 ed.
　　contains accounts of the colleges in English by
　　Samuel Parker.

—— —— Another issue?
　　The t.-p. and plates appear to be the same.
　　Following the t.-p. are 3 engr. leaves in Latin
　　(dedication to Charles II; "Spectatori ingenuo,
　　S" "Index tabularum") from the 1st (1675) ed.

Parker's letterpress (14p.) and the English
　　table (1ℓ) are bound at end, and are followed
　　by another table differently set up, and
　　mounted.
　　"Sold by Tho. Bowles ..." or label pasted
　　below title.

NL 0451016   CtY

xfC42   Loggan, David, 1635-1700?
OxzuEℓo   Oxonia illustrata, sive Omnium celeberrimæ
1715   istius universitatis collegiorum, aularum,
　　Bibliothecæ Bodleanæ, scholarum publicarum,
　　Theatri Sheldoniani; nec non urbis totius
　　scenographia. Delineavit & sculpsit Dav:
　　Loggan. Oxoniæ, E. Theatro Sheldoniano;
　　London, Printed & sold by H. Overton ₍ca.
　　1715₎
　　₍5₎, 14p. 40 plates(part double, part
　　fold., incl.plan) 43cm.

　　Engr. t.-p.
　　In this copy the descriptive text (14p.)
　　is bound after the plates.
　　Bound with the author's Cantabrigia
　　illustrata. London ₍1716?₎

NL 0451018   IU

Lmd67   ₍Loggan, David₎ 1635-1700?
675ℓh   Oxonia illustrata, of het verheerlykt Oxford,
　　vervattende de Gezichten zelve Stad, met haare
　　Gebouwen, Luft-huizen, en andere omleggende
　　Plaatzen ... Amsterdam,by Gerrit Tielenburg
　　₍ca.1720?₎
　　3ℓ.,48pl. 21x26cm.
　　Added t.-p.: Oxonia illustrata, contenant:
　　Les vües de la ville d'Oxford, avec ses edifices,
　　& ses maisons de campagne ... A Leide,chez
　　Pierre Vander Aa,dans l'Academie. [n.d.]
　　"These plates are identical with the 1707

edition of Beeverell, not the 1727. The Oxford
　　plates are from Loggan (1675) reduced." ms.
　　note by Madan on fly-leaf.
　　—— —— Another set of 39 Oxford plates, ex-
　　tracted from Beeverell's Les delices de la
　　Grand' Bretagne, and mounted in a blank book.
　　20x27cm.
　　No title or caption.
　　Binder's title: Oxford views. Beeverell ...

NL 0451020   CtY

₍Loggan, David₎ 1635-1700?
Lmd67   Oxonia illustrata; or Views of the Bodleian
75ℓe   library, the theatre, publick schools, colleges,
　　halls and other publick buildings of the Uni-
　　versity of Oxford. With an account of their
　　foundations and endowments and a succinct
　　description of the buildings. London,sold by
　　John Bowles & son,₍a1715?₎
　　37pl. on 4 sheets. 32½x48½cm.
　　Mounted on cloth, 59x97cm, and fold. to
　　32½x48½cm.
　　In portfolio.

NL 0451021   CtY

LF528   Loggan, David, 1635-1700? Oxonia illustrata.
.W5   FOR OTHER EDITIONS
1944   SEE MAIN ENTRY
Withycombe, Elizabeth Gidley, 1902-
　　A new Loggan view of the Oxford colleges; illustrations by
E. H. New, text by F. ₍i. e. E.₎ G. Withycombe. 3d ed. Oxford,
Printed for the Shakespeare Head press under licence from B.
Blackwell, 1944.

Loggans, Winefred B., joint ed.
TX533
.B7   Bradley, Alice, 1875-   ed.
　　Nutrition simplified; scientific meal planning made easy.
Prepared in conformity with the United States government's
official nutrition program, "The basic seven." Edited by Alice
Bradley ... and Winefred B. Loggans ... Boston, B. Hum-
phries, inc. ₍1944₎

Logge del Vaticano
　　see under Rafaelle Sanzio, 1483-1520.

Loggem, Emmanuel van.

See

Loggem, Manuel van, 1916-

Loggem, Manuel van, 1916-
　　Buiten zijn de mensen; roman. Amsterdam,
De Bezige Bij ₍1954₎
　　172 p.

NL 0451026   NNC MH NN PU DLC-P4

Loggem, Manuel van
Hgk2   De chinese fluitspeler; toneelspel in drie
L721   bedrijven. Bussum,F.G.Kroonder,1947.
C44   79p. 21cm. (Bayard reeks, no.21)

NL 0451027   CtY IEN MH OU

LOGGEM, Manuel van, 1916-
　　Gedichten naar Langston Hughes. ₍Maastricht,
Boosten & Stols,1938.₎

　　25 cm. pp.(24).
　　In Helikon,1938,8ᵉ Jaargang,No.4,pp.74-96.
　　　　　　　　　　PNeth 208.2(8)

NL 0451028   MH

PN3151
.L6
Loggem, Manuel van, 1916-   ed.
　　Handboek voor het amateurtoneel; onder redactie van
Manuel van Loggem in samenwerking met de Nederlandse
Amateur Toneel Unie en het Werkverband Katholiek Ama-
teurtoneel. ₍Amsterdam, De Bezige Bij, 19
　　v. illus. 24 cm.
　　CONTENTS.—
2. Regie, door B. Albach, E. Hoomans en Manuel van Loggem.

1. Amateur theatricals.   I. Title.

PN3151.L6   58-33201

NL 0451029   DLC

LOGGEM, MANUEL VAN, ed.
　　Handboek voor het amateurtoneel. In samenwerking
met de Nederlandse amateur toneel unie en het Werkverband Katholiek amateurotoneel. Amsterdam, De
Bezige bij [1955-60] 4 v. illus. 24cm.

　　[Deel] 1-4.
　　Each vol. has special t.-p.
　　Includes bibliographies.

CONTENTS.—1. Spel, door I. van Dullemen [et al.]—2. Regie, door
B. Albach, E. Hoomans, M. van Loggem.—3. Aankleding, door M. van
Loggem, F.W.S. van Thienen, W. Vesseur.—4. Het huis aan de haven;
toneelstuk in drie bedrijven door Manuel van Loggem. Mise-en-scène van
Peter Oosthoek.

1. Amateur theatricals. 2. Drama, Dutch. I. Nederlandse amateurtoneel
unie. II. Werkverband Katholiek amateurtoneel. III. Dullemen, Inez van.
IV. Albach, Ben.

NL 0451031   NN

Loggem, Manuel van, 1916-
　　Inleiding tot het toneel. ₍1. druk₎ Assen, Born ₍1951₎
　　165, ₍2₎ p. illus., plates, ports. 19 cm. (Pallas reeks, 2)
　　Bibliography : p. ₍167₎

1. Theater. 2. Drama.

PN1655.L6   55-39953

NL 0451032   DLC CU NN

VOLUME 338

PT5854   ₜLoggem, Manuel vanₒ 1916–
.L7516   Insecten in plastic.   Amsterdam, Vereeniging
1952   ter Bevordering van de Belangen des Boekhandels
          ₜ1952ₒ
              77 p. illus.
          — "Geschenk 1952, verschenen ter gelegenheid
          van de Nederlandse Boekenweek van 23 Februari
          tot 5 Maart."

NL   0451033   ICU NNC MH CU MiU NN OU

Loggem, Manuel van, 1916–
    Het kleine heelal. Amsterdam, Amsterdamsche Boek- en
    Courant Mij., 1946.
        257 p. 21 cm.

        I. Title.

        PT5854.L8K6   49–18536*

NL   0451034   DLC NN

Hgk2   **Loggem, Manuel van**
L721   Mozes; de wording van een volk. Roman. Amster-
M85   dam, Amsterdamsche boek- en courantmij, 1947.
                758p. 21cm.

            1.Moses – Fiction.

NL   0451035   CtY NN

Loggem, Manuel van, 1916–
    Oorsprong en noodzaak; het werk van Gerrit Achterberg.
    Assen, Born ₜ1950ₒ
        41 p. 20 cm.

        1. Achterberg, Gerrit, 1905–

        Harvard Univ. Library   A 51–7875
        for Library of Congress

NL   0451036   MH NNC PU NN

Logger (H. J.) Historia morbi oener aan car-
    cinoma mamma gestorvene vrouw. 77–115 pp.
    8°. *Amsterdam, R. J. Berntrop, 1821.*
        Cutting.

NL   0451037   DNLM

W 1   **Logger, Johannes,** 1759–1841.
VE482   Verhandeling over de tekenen van den
deel 1   aart en de verscheidenheid der breuken.
stuk 2   ₜAmsterdam, Van Es, 1797ₒ
1797   viii, ₜ139ₒ–400 p. (Verhandelingen
            bekroond met den prijs van het legaat van
            den heere Johannes Monnikhoff, 1. deel,
            2. stuk)
                Caption title.

            Series: Verhandelingen bekroond
            met den prijs van het legaat van
            Johannes Monnikhoff, 1. deel, 2. stuk

NL   0451039   DNLM

Logger, Johannes, 1759–1841.
    Verhandeling over de
    Enedikt-Holtrop, 1800.
    In: K. Prijsverh. Genootsch. t. Bevord. d. Heelk. te
    Amsterdam, J. S. Van

NL   0451040   DNLM

A logger.
    Forest conservation; suggestions by a logger
        see under   [Gaskill, Edwin A.]

TS 800   **The LOGGER.** v.1–20 no.1; Dec. 1951–1970.
05   Toronto, Ontario Forest Information
            Service.
                v. illus. 44 cm. monthly.

                Title varies: v.1–13, no. 8, Bush news.
            –v.13, no.9– v.18., no. 1, Ontario logger.
                Superseded by Forest scene.
            1. Lumbering – Period.   2. Lumbering – On-
            tario.   I. Ontario Forest Information Ser-
            vice. II.   Bush news. III. On-
            tario log-   ger.

NL   0451042   CaBVaU

Loggere (HERMAN PIETER), *jr.*
    *De middelen tot bewaring van recht der vrouw
    toegekend by echtscheiding, scheiding van tafel en
    bed en scheiding van goederen . . . 4 p.l., 104 pp.
    Amsterdam: D. B. Centen, 1891. 8°.

NL   0451043   NN

Loggers, A   W
    Koken in de tropen; warenkennis, voedingsleer, recepten, door
    A. W. Loggers...   Amsterdam ₜetc.ₒ "Kosmos" ₜ1949ₒ 177 p.
    illus. 22cm.

    540653B. 1. Cookery, Tropical.   May 7, 1951

NL   0451044   NN DNAL InLP

Loggers, H. J.
    Voedselbereiding en brandstoffenbesparing in verband met
    oprichting van centrale keukens. Voordracht over de noodzake-
    lijkheid van massale voeding in verband met het brandstoffen-
    vraagstuk voor Nederland in moeilijke tijden, gehouden in de
    jaarvergadering van gasfabrikanten te Zwolle, op 26 Juni 1917,
    door H. J. Loggers...   Wormer: P. Kuijper, 1917.   28 p.
    12°.

        Cover-title.

    1. Fuel.—Conservation. 2. Cookery   (Cooperative).
                                            December 8, 1920.

NL   0451045   NN

Loggers and logging, the bulletin of the
    Pacific logging congress.
        Portland, Ore, The Congress.
        nos.sq.Q.

NL   0451046   CaBViP

Loggers handbook.
    Portland, Or., Pacific logging congress, ₜ19
        v. illus. (incl. maps, diagrs.) 30ᵐ. annual.
    Publication began in 1941.
    "Papers prepared for the Loggers handbook ... distributed at the ...
        session of the Pacific logging congress."

    1. Lumbering—Congresses.   I. Pacific logging congress.
                                              46–17956
    Library of Congress   TS805.L6
                                              634.982

NL   0451047   DLC TU NN NcD OrPS CtY AzU NcRS

F25   **The Loggers;** or six months in the forests of
I63   Maine. Boston, H. B. Fuller ₜ1870ₒ
                75 p. illus. 18 cm. (The Dirigo series)

                1. Maine – Descr. & trav. – 1820–1900.
            2. Saint Croix Valley, Maine. 3. Lumbermen-
            Correspondence, reminiscences, etc.

NL   0451048   MeB

Loggerville literary society
        see Sandys, William, 1792–1874.
    Transactions of the Loggerville literary society.

PQ4827   **Loggi, Giuseppi**
035   Josephi Loggi Epigrammaton libellus.
E67   Asculi, "Cesari", 1949.
                46 p. 21 cm.

                Verses in Latin.

NL   0451050   RPB

Loggi, R.
    Cinquanta sonneti in dialetto romanesco.
    Rome, Cerroni, 1887.
        56 p.

NL   0451051   PU

LOGGIA, Gaetano La

    See LA LOGGIA, Gaetano.

Loggia, Giuseppe la
        see
    La Loggia, Giuseppe.

La loggia del comune di Roma...
        see under
    [Rossi, Giovanni Battista de, 1822–1894.]

La loggia del palazzo Vescovile
        see under Barichella, Vittoria.

VOLUME 338

Loggia di Andrea di Cione detto l'Orcagna e copia
in legno fattane da Rinaldo da Angelo Barbetti
see under   [Berti, Giovanni Felice]

Loggia massonica "Giandomenico Romagnosi".

See

Freemasons. Rome.   Loggia
"Giandomenico Romagnosi."

Loggie, James J
In memoriam: James J. Loggie
see under Redwood Lumber Manufacturer's
Association.

Loggie di Rafaele nel Vaticano
see under [Raphael Sanzio] 1483-1520.

---

40   Loggin, Robert.
The loyal subject, or, a full and true representation of grand frauds, committed in his majesty's
customs.   London, 1719.
4 p.l., 28 p., 2 l.   12°.   [Miscellaneous
pamphlets. v. 766:10]
By Robert Loggin and John Rotherham.

NL 0451060   DLC

Loggin, Robert.
The present management of the customs.
Being a detection of grand frauds in that
branch of His Majesty's royal revenue, to
the value of above five hundred thousand
pounds per annum, by the false entries of
pepper and tobacco for exportation, as it
has been laid before, and approved by the
regency and the lords of the Treasury.
With an impartial account of the proceed-

ings relating thereunto ...   London, Printed
for the author and sold by J. Roberts [etc.]
1720.
1 p.l., iv, 58 p. 18.5 cm.

Dedication signed: Robert Loggin, John
Rotherham.

NL 0451062   MH-BA PU CtY NIC

[D731 Loggin' the times. v. 1-
.5
L6
Hemet, Calif.
v. in   illus. 51cm.

"Ed. and pub. by and for the personnel of
the Fifth army air forces flying training de-
tachment [Ryan school of aeronautics] Hemet,
Calif."

NL 0451063   CU

Logging; a monthly magazine of men, machinery and
methods ... v. 1–
Jan. 1913–
Duluth, Minn., Steam machinery pub. company, 1913–
v. illus. 31cm.
Title varies: Jan. 1913–Dec. 1914, Steam machinery; a magazine of men,
machinery and methods.
Jan. 1915–   Logging; a monthly magazine of men, machinery
and methods.
Editor: Jan. 1913–   C. H. Mackintosh.

1. Lumbering – Period. 2. Machinery – Period.   I. Mackintosh,
Charles H., ed. II. Steam machinery.

17-15714

Library of Congress   SD430.L7

NL 0451064   DLC MiU

Mann
SD   Logging and milling in the Adirondacks [by]
538   George Parsons [and others] [Ithaca, N. Y]
L83   1931
48 l. illus. 28 cm.

Includes bibliography.

1. Lumbering - Adirondack Mountains.
2. Lumbering -   New York (State)
I. Parsons,   George, 1908-

NL 0451065   NIC

Logging in the South with "caterpillar"
Diesel power

see under

[Caterpillar tractor co.]

SD538   Logging Safety Conference, Syracuse Univer-
qL6   sity.
[Extracts from papers] 1953-

[Syracuse, N.Y.]
v. in   28cm.

Under the co-sponsorship of State Univer-
sity of New York College of Forestry at
Syracuse and the Northeastern Loggers
Association.

1. Lumbering - Congresses. 2. Industrial
accidents -   Congresses.
3. Lumbering -   Safety measures.

NL 0451067   OrCS

SD72(Logging Safety Conference, Syracuse University,
.L8L6   1953.
Logging safety. [Syracuse, N. Y.]
State University of New York, College
of Forestry at Syracuse [1953?]
ii, 29 l. 28cm.
Cover title.
"Extracts from papers presented at the
Logging Safety Conference held in Syra-
cuse, N. Y., May 12 and 13, 1953, under
the co-sponsorship of State University
of New York College of Forestry and the

Northeastern Loggers Association."

1. Lumbering—Safety measures.
I. Syracuse University. State University College of Forestry.

NL 0451069   MB DNAL TU

Loggins, Edward.
Autobiography of Elisha, a prophet in Israel and in
Judah; tr. and arranged for publication by Edward Loggins ... Winona, Miss., E. Loggins, 1909.
166 p. 19cm. $1.50

10-2904

NL 0451070   DLC

Loggins, James Elwyn, 1894–
Veterans' pensions and related benefits, outline guides for the
student. Rev. ed. ... Washington, 1946.
78 p. 23cm.
"First printing, September, 1945."

1. Veterans—Laws and legislation—U. S.   I. Title.
UB357.L57 1946   355.115   47-3245
Brief cataloging

NL 0451071   DLC

Loggins, Vernon, 1893–
Chansons du midi, with translations from Frédéric Mis-
tral. New York, 1947.
30 p. 20 cm.
"Chansons du midi, a cantata in ten numbers for music by Arthur
Oglesbee."
An English translation of Vernon Loggins' Chansons du midi,
which was printed in Paris in 1924 without the translations from
Mistral.
I. Mistral, Frédéric, 1830–1914. II. Oglesbee, Arthur. III. Title.
Full name: Vernon Grady Loggins.
PQ3939.L6C5   841.91   48-14227*

NL 0451072   DLC

Loggins, Vernon, 1893–
The Hawthornes; the story of seven generations of an
American family. New York, Columbia University Press,
1951.
365 p. 23 cm.
Bibliography: p. [339]-354.

1. Hathorne family (William Hathorne, 1607?-1681) I. Title.
Full name: Vernon Grady Loggins.
CS71.H4 1951   51-12495

WaS CaBVaU OrSaW WaWW IdPI WaTC
AAP MB CU TxU MH NNC TU ViU DAU IdU OrP Wa CaBViP
NL 0451073   DLC OrPS OrCS MtBC MtU AU MsU KEmT NcD GU

Loggins, Vernon, 1893–
I hear America... literature in the United States since 1900,
by Vernon Loggins. New York, Thomas Y. Crowell company
[°1937]
viii p., 2 l., 3-378 p. 22½cm.
"Recommended for reading": p. [349]-357.

1. American literature—20th cent.—Hist. & crit. 2. Authors, Ameri-
can. I. Title.
[Full name: Vernon Grady Loggins]
Library of Congress   PS221.L6   37-30711

Copyright A 109967   [10-2]   810.904

MtU WaT IdB OrPR Or
ViU PHC PP PBa PU OClW OOxM ODW OCU OU OCl NcD NcRS
NL 0451074   DLC OrU OrCS CaBVa WaSp OrSaW WaSpG OrP

Loggins, Vernon, 1893–
...Musical productions of Shakespeare's plays on the London
stage during the Restoration period... By Vernon Gray Log-
gins. Chicago, 1917. 50 f. 4°.
Typewritten.
Dissertation, Univ. of Chicago, 1917.
Bibliography, f. 47-50.

1. Shakespeare, William, in music.   2. Opera—Gt. Br.—Eng.—Hist.
3. Stage—Gt. Br.—Eng.—Hist., 1660-   1700.
December 7, 1925

NL 0451075   NN ICU

VOLUME 338

Loggins, Vernon, 1893–
The negro author, his development in America, by Vernon Loggins ... New York, Columbia university press, 1931.
ix p., 1 l., 480 p., 1 l. 20⅟₂ᶜᵐ. (*Half-title*: Columbia university studies in English and comparative literature)
Thesis (PH. D.)—Columbia university, 1931.
Vita.
Published also without thesis note.
"Bibliographies": p. ₍408₎–457.

1. Negro literature—Hist. & crit. 2. Negro authors. 3. Negro literature—Bibl. I. Title.
₍Full name: Vernon Grady Loggins₎
31–32221
Library of Congress PS153.N5L65 1931
Columbia Univ. Libr. 810.9

NL 0451076 NNC DLC OrPR Or ViU

Loggins, Vernon, 1893–
The Negro author, his development in America, by Vernon Loggins ... New York, Columbia university press, 1931.
ix p., 1 l., 480 p., 1 l. 21 cm. (*Half-title*: Columbia university studies in English and comparative literature)
Published also as thesis (PH. D.) Columbia university.
"Bibliographies": p. ₍408₎–457.
1. Negro literature (American)—Hist. & crit. 2. Negro authors. 3. Negro literature (American)—Bibl. 4. American literature—Negro authors—Bibl. I. Title.
Full name: Vernon Grady Loggins.
PS153.N5L65 1931a 810.9 31—32222

NcU WaWW OrAshS CaBVa WaS Or
NL 0451077 DLC MB NcD ViU MH OC1 OCU OC1W MiU OU NN

•**Loggins, Vernon,** 1893– joint ed.

Scarborough, Dorothy, 1858?–1935.
A song catcher in southern mountains; American folk songs of British ancestry, by Dorothy Scarborough ... New York, Columbia university press, 1937.

Loggins, Vernon, 1893–
...Syllabus; a survey of English literature
see under Columbia university.

Loggins, Vernon, 1893–
Two romantics and their ideal life; Elisabet Ney, sculptor; Edmund Montgomery, philosopher. By Vernon Loggins. New York, The Odyssey press, 1946.
6 p. l., 385 p. plates, ports. 21ᶜᵐ.
"First edition."
Bibliographical references included in "Acknowledgments and notes" (p. 353–368)
1. Ney, Elisabet, 1834–1907. 2. Montgomery, Edmund, 1835–1911. I. Title.
₍Full name: Vernon Grady Loggins₎
NB588.N4L6 927.3 46–8079

NL 0451080 DLC WU AU OU CaBVa OrP WaE Wa TxU MH IdU

Loggins, Vernon, 1893–
... Visual outline of American literature, by Vernon Loggins ... New York ₍etc.₎ Longmans, Green and co. ₍ᶜ1933₎
3 p. l., 110 p. incl. front., tables. 21½ᶜᵐ. (Students outline series)
Interleaved.

1. American literature—Outlines, syllabi, etc. I. Title.
₍Full name: Vernon Grady Loggins₎
34–240
Library of Congress PS94.L6

Copyright A 67629 810.2

NL 0451081 DLC ViU NcD PU PPD PSC OC1 OC1JC

Loggins, Vernon, 1893–
William Falkner [sic]
(In the author's I hear America. New York, 1937. 23 cm. p. 109–112)
1. Faulkner, William, 1897– I. Title: I hear America.

NL 0451082 ViU

Loggins, Vernon Grady

see

Loggins, Vernon, 1893–

Loggins, Vernon Gray
see Loggins, Vernon, 1893–

LD3907
.E3
1945
.L6
Loggins, William Francis, 1898–
Teacher certification in South Carolina... New York, 1945.
x, 179 typewritten leaves. tables. 29cm.
Final document (Ed.D.) - New York university, School of education, 1945.
Bibliography: p. ₍154₎–158.

NL 0451085 NNU

Loggio (Ramon Hernandez). Medicina y cirujía de los campos de batalla, ó sea tratado de heridas por armas blancas y de fuego, de las afecciones que las complican, del tratamiento que reclaman etc.; precedido de un epitome de las enfermedades mas comunes en las tropas beligerantes. v. 1. 400 pp. 16°. *Madrid, A. G. Fuentenebro,* 1853.

NL 0451086 DNLM

Loghat el-Arab; revue littéraire, scientifique et historique. Bagdad.
année ₍9 (–1931)
"Sous la direction des Peres Carmes de Mesopotamie."
Title also in Arabic, text in Arabic
No more published after 1931

NL 0451087 MH NN CU

Loghe, Sydney de
see Loch, Frederick Sydney.

₍1808–1881₎.

Loghem (Hendrik van) 1808–1881.
Beoordeeling van het ontwerp van wet betrekkelijk de ondersteuning van behoeftigen, dezer dagen aan de tweede kamer der Staten General ingediend, in verband tot de algemeene beginselen van armenwetgeving. *Deventer: J. de Lange,* 1845. 68 pp. 8°.
In: 56. p. v. 4.

NL 0451089 NN

Loghem, Hendrik van, 1808–1881.
...₍De doctrina acquisitionis secundum principia juris naturalis ... submittit Henricus van Loghem ... Daventriae, J. de Lange, 1830.
5 p.l., 88 p. 20½cm.
Diss.- Leiden.
Bibliographical footnotes.

NL 0451090 MH-L

₍Loghem, Herman van₎
Krispyn, testateur en gelegateerde, of De erfgenaam door list; blyspel. Amsterdam, Erven van J. Lescailje en D. Rank, 1725.
5 p. l., 72 p. incl. front. 16ᵐᵒ.
No. 1 in v. 48 ot a collection lettered "Tooneel-stukken 1669–1760."

I. Title. II. Title: De erfgenaam door list.
21–13920
Library of Congress PT5497.T6 vol. 48, no. 1
Provisional

NL 0451091 DLC ICU CtY MH

Loghem, Herman van, tr.

₍Corneille, Pierre₎ 1606–1684.
Surena, veldheer der Parthen; trevrspel. Amsterdam, I. Duim, 1738.

Loghem, J. B. van, & zoon, *printers, Harlem.*
Proeve van letteren, der boekdrukkerij van J. B. van Loghem en zoon. Haarlem, 1843.
44 l. (2 fold.) 22ᶜᵐ.

1. Type and type-founding. 2. Printing—Specimens.
24–23000
Library of Congress Z250.L83

NL 0451093 DLC

Qa9
70
Loghem, J van
Vijftienhonderd gemengde oefeningen, ter toepassing van de beginselen der reken-, stel-, en meetkunst ... 2.verb.druk ... Deventer, A.J.van den Sigtenhorst,1865.
2p.l.,172p. 18cm.

1.Mathematics - Problems, exercises, etc. x.Van Loghem, J

NL 0451094 CtY

Loghem, Johannes Bernardus van, 1881–
Bouwen; bauen; bâtir; building. Holland. Nieuwe zakelijkheid; neues Bauen; vers une architecture réelle; built to live in. Ir. J. B. van Loghem... Amsterdam: "Kosmos"₍, 1932₎.
144 p. illus. (incl. plans.) 25cm.

651916A. 1. Architecture—Netherlands.
July 13, 1933

NL 0451095 NN IU NNC OC1 DAIA WU

WH
425
L832r
1946
LOGHEM, Johannes Jacobus van.
Het rhesusvraagstuk en erythroblastosis foetalis, door J. J. Van Loghem, Jr., en G. J. Kloosterman. Amsterdam, Scheltema & Holkema, 1946.
68 p. illus.
1. Erythroblastosis - Fetal
2. Rh factor I. Kloosterman, Gerrit Jan

NL 0451096 DNLM

VOLUME 338

Loghem, Johannes Jacobus van.
Waarnemingen bij endocarditis lenta. Wormerveer, Meijer's Boek- en Handelsdrukkerij, 1943.

84 p. illus. 24 cm.

Academisch proefschrift—Amsterdam.
"Stellingen": (2) p. inserted.
"Litteratuur": p. (81)–84.

1. Endocarditis.

RC685.E5L6   49–56148*

NL 0451097   DLC CtY

WA
900
GN4
L8a
1941
LOGHEM, Johannes Jacobus van, 1878-
Algemeene gezondheidsleer. 2.,
herziene en verm. druk. Amsterdam,
Kosmos, 1941.
xvi, 407 p. illus.
1. Public health - Netherlands

NL 0451098   DNLM

Loghem, Johannes Jacobus van, 1878-
Algemeene gezondheidsleer, door prof. dr. J. J. van Loghem.
3., herziene druk. Amsterdam, N. v. uitgevers-maatschappij "Kosmos," 1943.

xvi, 440 p. incl. illus., tables, diagrs. 25ᶜᵐ.

"Litteratuur" at end of each chapter.

1. Hygiene, Public.

RA425.L73 1943   Med 47–94

Columbia univ. Libraries
for Library of Congress   †

NL 0451099   NNC ICU NcD ICRL DLC

WA
900
GN4
L8a
1947
LOGHEM, Johannes Jacobus van, 1878-
Algemeene gezondheidsleer. 4.
herziene en verm. druk. Amsterdam,
Uitgevers-mij. Kosmos, 1947.
xvi, 482 p. illus.
1. Public health - Netherlands

NL 0451100   DNLM

WA
900
GN4
L8a
1950
LOGHEM, Johannes Jacobus van, 1878-
Algemene gezondheidsleer. 5.
herziene en verm. druk. Amsterdam,
Uitgevers-mij. Kosmos, 1950.
xvi, 517 p. illus.
1. Public health - Netherlands

NL 0451101   DNLM

WZ
100
M4865L
1904
LOGHEM, Johannes Jacobus van, 1878-
Elias Metchnikoff. Haarlem,
Tjeenk Willink, 1904.
p. (287)–348. port. (Mannen en
vrouwen van beteekenis in onze dagen,
35, levering 7)
Cover title.
1. Mechnikov, Il'ia Il'ich, 1845-1916

NL 0451102   DNLM

WB
130
L832i
1951
LOGHEM, Johannes Jacobus van, 1878
Inleiding tot de geneeskunde. Haarlem, Bohn, 1951.
232 p. (Volksuniversiteits bibliotheek,
2. reeks, no. 34)
1. Medicine - Popular works

NL 0451103   DNLM

QT
150
L832k
1916
LOGHEM, Johannes Jacobus van, 1878-
Klimaat en ziekte. Amsterdam,
Van Looy, 1916.
38 p.
Rede - Amsterdam (Aanvaarding van
het hoogleeraarsambt) 1916.

NL 0451104   DNLM

Loghem, Johannes Jacobus van, 1878-
Mens sana; proeve van een persoonlijke gezondheidsleer.
Amsterdam, Uitgeversmij "Kosmos," 1948.

246 p. 24 cm.

1. Hygiene.   I. Title.

RA776.L835   49–4162*

NL 0451105   DLC DNLM OU

W 1
ME109
no. 3
1909
LOGHEM, Johannes Jacobus van, 1878-
Over eene op cholera gelijkende
ziekte in Deli. Batavia, Javasche
Boekhandel & Drukkerij, 1909.
11 p. (Medan. Sumatra. Pathologisch Laboratorium. Mededeelingen,
1909 (no.) 3)
Series

NL 0451106   DNLM

---

van Loghem (Johannes Jacobus). * Over het
colon en mesocolon der primaten. (Amsterdam.) 3 p. l., 111 pp., 2 l. 8°. Haarlem, erven
F. Bohn, 1908.

NL 0451107   DNLM

---

van Loghem (Johannes Jacobus). Over tegenstoffen bij immuniteit. 45 pp. 8°. Haarlem,
de erven F. Bohn, 1908.
Forms Nos. 1v–v of Geneesk. Bl. u. Klin. v. de
prakt. Haarlem, 1907–8 v08 —

NL 0451108   DNLM

WC
25556
Loghem, Johannes Jacobus van, 1878-
Tropische gezondheidsleer. Amsterdam,
Uitg. Mij. Kosmos (1933)
113 p. illus.

1. Tropics - Diseases and hygiene.

NL 0451109   CtY

Loghem, Johannes Jacobus van, 1878- *ed.*
Wat het leven mij heeft geleerd, onder redactie van J. J.
van Loghem, H. J. Pos (en) K. F. Proost. Arnhem, Van
Loghum Slaterus, 1952.

286 p. 23 cm.

1. Netherlands—Biog.   I. Title.

DJ283. A2L6   920.0492   53–34898 ‡

NL 0451110   DLC

Loghem, Johannes Jacobus van, 1878–
Verslag van een hygienische informatie-reis naar Egypte, Tor,
Jeruzalem, Tunis en Algerije, door Dr. J. J. van Loghem...
Amsterdam: Het Instituut, 1914. viii, 142 p. diagrs., illus.
(incl. maps), plates, tables. 8°. (Koloniaal Instituut, Amsterdam. Mededeeling no. 3.)

At head of title: Afdeeling tropische Hygiene, no. 1.

1. Hygiene (Public). Levant.   2. Series.
December 12, 1922.

NL 0451111   NN DNLM ICJ

Wason
TX145
C35
Loghem, Johannes Jacobus van, 1878–
Vraagstukken der indische hygiene.
Amsterdam, Uitgave van het Instituut, 1920.
viii,159 p. 25cm. (Koloniaal Instituut
te Amsterdam. Mededeeling no. 14. Afdeeling
Tropische Hygiene. (Mededeeling) no.9)

Bound with Catenius-van der Meijden, J.M.
J., Ons huis in Indië. Semarang (1908)

NL 0451112   NIC NN DNLM CtY

LOGHEM, Johannes Jacobus van, 1878-
Ziekte en parasitisme rede, uitgesproken bij
de aanvaar vanhet hoogleeraarsambt aan de
landbouw-hoogeschool te Wageningen den 16 den
Januari,1919. Amsterdam,S.L.van Looy,1919.

38p. 26cm.

NL 0451113   MH-F

Loghem, Martinus Gesinus Lambert van, 1849-
Fokel. [Novelle.] Door M. G. L. van Loghem (Fiore delle neve).
═ Amsterdam. Veen. [18—?] (1), 280 pp. [Guldens-Serie. No.
3.] 16½ cm., in 8s.

N1337 — T.r. — S.r.c. — Dutch language. Works in Dutch.

NL 0451114   MB

LOGHEM, Martinus Gesinus Lambert van, 1849-
Der Helm Pons de Blignys. Von Fiore della Neve [Pseud.].
(In Aus fremden Zungen. Jahrg. 1, Bd. 2. Stuttgart, 1891.)|

NL 0451115   MB

ML50
.V493K64
1890z
Case
Loghem, Martinus Gesinus Lambert van, 1849-
Verhey, Theodor H   H
(König Arpad. Libretto. German)

König Arpad; romantische Oper in 2 Akten. Text von
Fiore Della Neve (M. G. L. van Loghem), naar de vertelling
De Hunnenborg van J. van Lennep. Musik von Th. H. H.
Verheij. (Rotterdam, Nijgh & van Ditmar, 189-?)

(Loghem, Martinus Gesinus Lambert van,) 1849.
Koningin Wilhelmina-album, onder redactie van Fiore della
Neve. Leiden: E. J. Brill (1899). 271 p. front., plates, ports.
8°.

1. Dutch literature.—Collections.   2. Wilhelmina, queen of the Netherlands, 1880–
January 12, 1922.

NL 0451117   NN

VOLUME 338

839.38
L83ki Loghem,Martinus Gesinus Lambert van,1849-
A

    Liana,door Fiore della Neve [pseud.]Mr.
M.G.L.van Loghem. 2e druk. Sneek, H.Pyt-
tersen tz., [n.d.]
    2 p.ℓ.,112 p.   17 cm.
    A poem.

NL 0451118   MiU

839.38
L83k Loghem,Martinus Gesinus Lambert van,1849-
E

    ...Eene liefde in het zuiden. 6.druk.
Amsterdam, H.J.W.Becht, [n.d.]
    2 p.ℓ.,118 p.   16½ cm.
    Author's pseudonym,Fiore della Neve,at
head of title.

NL 0451119   MiU

    Loghem (Martinus Gesinus Lambert van)
    *Spel en weddenschap . . . 2 p.l., 60 pp. Amster-
dam: Ellerman, Harms & Co., 1880. 8°.*

NL 0451120   MH-L NN

839.38
L83v Loghem,Martinus Gesinus Lambert van,1849-

    Van eene sultane,en andere gedichten,
door Fiore della Neve [pseud.] Sneek, H.
Pijttersen tz., 1884.
    115,[2] p.   17½ cm.

NL 0451121   MiU

    Loghem de Josselin de Jong, Hendrik van
      see   Jong, Hendrik van Loghem de
Josselin de.

W 4   LOGHEM-LANGEREIS, P   Erna van
A52   Serologische reacties bij rheumatische
1950   ziekten. Serological reactions in rheu-
    matic diseases. [Amsterdam, 1950]
    148 p. illus.
    Academisch proefschrift - Univ. van
Amsterdam.
    Summary in English.
    1. Arthritis 2. Rheumatism
    3. Serodiagnosis

NL 0451123   DNLM IU

    Loghinides (Démétrius). *De l'aphasie dans
la paralysie générale. 60 pp. 4°. Paris, 1879,
No. 555.*

NL 0451124   DNLM PPC

    Loghinides (Théodore). *De l'allongement hy-
pertrophique et de l'élongation de la portion sus-
vaginale du col de l'utérus. 108 pp. 4°. Paris,
1885, No. 254.*

NL 0451125   DNLM

    Loghin, Constantin.
      Geschichte der rumänischen literatur, von
C. Loghin und S. Drimmer.   Cernauti,
St. Wicentowicz, 1934.
    vii, 202 p. ports.   20 cm.
    "Literatur": p. vii.

NL 0451126   PU

    Loghin, Constantin
      Istoria literaturii romane din
Bucovina, 1775-1918...
1926.
    [280p.]

NL 0451127   OC1

WJ   LOGHMAN-ÁDHAM, Ali Gholi
300   Hypertension artérielle et mal-
L832h   formations pyéliques et rénales
1949   décelées par l'examen radiologique.
    Paris, Foulon, 1949.
    115 p. illus.
    1. Blood pressure - High
    2. Kidney - Diseases

NL 0451128   DNLM

W 4   LOGHMAN-ADHAM, Mohammed
G32   Étude sur les symptômes cliniques
1944   de la lambliase. Genève, Victoria-Hall,
1944.
    57 p.   (Genève. Université.
Faculté de médecine. Thèse. M. D.
no. 1828)

NL 0451129   DNLM

    Loghman ed Dowleh, Mohammed Hussein Khan
      see   Mohammed Hussein Khan Moïn Atebba,
1878-

    Loghum Slaterus, Adrianus Jan Bemolt van
      see   Bemolt van Loghum Slaterus, Adrianus
Jan.

    Logi, Edamo, ed.
    ...Discorsi scelti a cura di mons.
      see under Augustinus, Aurelius, Saint,
bp. of Hippo. Sermones. Italian. 1930.

    Logi, Edamo, ed.
    Enarrationes in Psalmos
      see under Augustinus, Aurelius, Saint, bp.
of Hippo. Enarrationes in Psalmos. 1931-33.

    Logi, Edamo, ed.
    Le lettere [di S. Girolamo]
      see under Hieronymus, Saint.
Epistolae. Italian.

PQ 4419   LOGI,EDAMO
.M2 L83   La mistica rosa delle aiuole dantesche;
    ossia, La Vergine Madre nella Divina commedia.
    Siena, Tipografia S. Caterina, 1922.
    34 p.

    1. Dante--Divina commedia. '2. Dante--Charac-
ters--Mary,Virgin. / I. Title. II. Title: La
Vergine Madre   nella Divina commedia.

NL 0451135   InU

    Logi, Edamo, ed.
    La regola pastorale
      see under   Gregorius I, the Great, Saint,
pope, 540 (ca.)-604.

    Logi, Johann Anton, *Graf von Losinthal*
    see
    Losy von Losinthal, Johann Anton, *Graf,* 1643 *(ca.)*-1721.

HS   La Logia; organo oficial de la Gran
359   Logia Soberana de Puerto-Rico.
L83   Año 1-
    Nov. 1, 1884-
    Mayaguez.
    v. illus. 20cm.

    Subtitle varies.

NL 0451138   NIC

    Logia Agrapha; detti extracanonici di Gesù.
Firenze, 1951
      see under   Bible. N.T. Apocry-
phal books. Logia Iesou. Italian. 1951.
Faggin.

    Logia Chaldaika
    see Oracula Chaldaica.

    Logia Iesou [from Oxyrrhynchos]
      see Bible. N.T. Apocryphal
books. Logia Iesou.

---

x821
L829   The Logiad; a poem; in five cantos. Ac-
    companied by poetical introductions to each
    canto. Cum notis variorum, to which is sub-
joined The knights; a poetical fragment.
Oxford, 1818.
    vi, 67p. 20cm.

    Signed at end: G.5.
    In manuscript on fly-leaf: Only twelve
copies printed for private circulation.

NL 0451142   IU CtY

VOLUME 338

Logic, *pseud.*
    A few remarks on a proposed central railway terminus for Melbourne. By Logic. Melbourne, Printed at the Herald office, 1862.
    20 p. 21½cm.

    1. Railroads—Melbourne.

    7-36340†

    Library of Congress   HE3539.M5L8

NL 0451143   DLC CSt

LOGIC, LAY, [pseud.].
    'Great Gobble Gobble Gobble and Twit Twittle Twit, or Law versus common sense; a new song with original music. London, W.Hone [18--].

    f°. pp. 4. Colored vign. by G.Cruikshank.
    Leaves mounted.
    Another copy of vign.proof before letters.

NL 0451144   MH

... Logic, by Arnold Ruge, Wilhelm Windelband, Josiah Royce, Louis Couturat, Benedetto Croce, Federigo Enriques and Nicolaj Losskij; tr. by B. Ethel Meyer. London, Macmillan and co., limited, 1913.
    x, 269 p. 23cm. (Encyclopaedia of the philosophical sciences. vol. I)
    CONTENTS.—Introduction, by A. Ruge.—The principles of logic, by W. Windelband.—The principles of logic, by J. Royce.—The principles of logic, by L. Couturat.—The task of logic, by B. Croce.—The problems of logic, by F. Enriques.—The transformation of the concept of consciousness in modern epistemology and its bearing on logic, by N. Losskij.
    1. Logic. 2. Knowledge, Theory of.   I. Ruge, Arnold, 1881–   II. Windelband, Wilhelm, 1848–1915.   III. Royce, Josiah, 1855–1916.   IV. Couturat, Louis, 1868–1914.   V. Croce, Benedetto, 1866–   VI. Enriques, Federigo, 1871–   VII. Losskii, Nikolai Onufrievich, 1870–   VIII. Meyer, B. Ethel, tr.
                                         13–22864
    Library of Congress   B51.F5

NL PPT MiU OC1W OC1 OCU OU ICJ ViU NcD OrPR WaS
    0451145   DLC TxU IdU ScU KEmT OC1U NcU PHC PSC

The logic and law of Col. Johnson's report to the Senate ...
        see under   [Evarts, Jeremiah] 1781–1831.

Logic and money
        see under   [Jones, William Hiter]

... Logic and reality. The symposia read at the joint session of the Aristotelian society and the Mind association at Manchester, July 5th–7th, 1946. London, Harrison and sons, ltd., 1946.
    2 p. L., 232 p. 21½ cm. (Aristotelian society. Supplementary vol. xx)
    CONTENTS.—The inaugural address–Belief and action. By R. B. Braithwaite.—Symposium: Why are the calculuses of logic and arithmetic applicable to reality? I. By G. Ryle. II. By C. Lewy. III. By K. R. Popper.—Symposium: Is anthropology relevant to ethics? I. By L. J. Russell. II. By J. D. Mabbott. III. By A. Macbeath.—Symposium: Other minds. I. By J. Wisdom. II. By J. L. Austen. III. By A. J. Ayer.—Symposium: Can philosophical theories transcend experience? I. By D. M. Emmet. II. By C. H. Whiteley. III. By J. Laird.
    1. Logic. 2. Reality.   I. Aristotelian society for the systematic study of philosophy.   II. Mind association.
    B11.A72 vol. 20   108.2   A 47–3706
    Virginia. Univ. Libr.
    for Library of Congress   [a55e½]†

NL 0451148   ViU CaBVaU DLC

Logic and the cosmic order
        see under   [Anderson, Louis Francis]
1859–

Logic applicable to religion
        see under   [Shields, Charles Woodruff]
1825–1904.

Logic for the million
        see under   [Gilbart, James William] 1794–
1863.

LOGIC made familiar and easy to young gentlemen and ladies, being the fifth volume of the Circle of the sciences, &c. To which is added, a compendious system of metaphysics, or ontology. London, printed for J.Newbery, 1748.

    32°.

NL 0451152   MH

Logic made familiar and easy to young gentlemen and ladies. To which is added, a compendious system of metaphysics, or ontology... The 4th ed. Dublin, H.Saunders [etc.] 1770.
    xl,264p. 10cm.   (The circle of sciences, v.5)

    I. Title   x.ser.

NL 0451153   CtY

Logic made familiar and easy: to which is added, a compendious system of metaphysics, or ontology. Being the fifth volume of the Circle of the sciences ... 4th ed. London, Printed for T.Carnan, and F.Newberry, 1777.
    xl,264 p. 10½ cm.

    L.Circle of the sciences.

NL 0451154   MiU MH

Logic made familiar and easy: to which is added, a compendious system of metaphysics or ontology. Being the fifth volume of the Circle of the sciences, &c. ... The fifth edition. London: Printed for F. Power and co., 1789.   xl, 264 p.   10½cm.

    Dedication signed: John Newbery.

    73189B. 1. Logic. 2. Ontology.   I. Newbery, John, 1713–1767.
    II. Title: Circle of sciences.
    N. Y. P. L.   December 20, 1940

NL 0451155   NN

... Logic notes
        see under   [Forbes, William Henry] 1851–

The logic of facts; or, The conduct of Wm. Rawle towards N. G. Dufief
        see under   [Dufief, Nicolas Govin]
1776?–1834.

Logic of life, a medley of confidence, progress, philosophy, humor
        see under   Harris, Rufus Arnold, 1872–

BC101
.L8
    Logic, ontology, and the art of poetry; being the fourth and fifth volumes of the Circle of the sciences. Considerably enlarged, and greatly improved. London, Printed for T.Carnan, and F.Newbery, junior, 1776.
    xii, 473 p. 18cm.

    1. Logic. 2. Ontology. 3. Poetics.

NL 0451159   ICU MH MdBJ

Logic; or, The art of thinking

    See under

    [Arnauld, Antoine] 1612–1694.

Wing
MS
ZW
1
.5 ℓ
    LOGICA. [Treatise on logic in the form of questions and answers. France,16th or 17th cent.]
    241 ℓ. illus. 10x8cm.

    Binder's title.
    Ms. on paper.

NL 0451161   ICN

Logica.
    Logica. [Nineteen tracts on logic]. [Oxford,Theodoric Rood,1483]
    164ff. 18cm. 4°.
    The Yale medical library has one leaf only.
    Duff 277; Madan 13.

    1.Incunabula in Yale library. 2.Oxford, Theodoric Rood,   1483. 3.Logic.

NL 0451162   CtY-M

FILM
FP
1108
    Logica,Latin. [Oxford, Theodoric Rood, 1483?]
    Duff,277; Proctor,9752; Madan,The early Oxford press,Oxford,1895,p.3.
    Collection of 19 Latin treatises which form a work on logic.
    Includes the "Insolubilia" of Richard Swineshead.
    Short-title catalogue no.16693 (carton 1108)
    Microfilm

    1.Logic—Early works to 1800. I.Swineshead, Richard,fl.1350.   Insolubilia.

NL 0451163   MiU NNC

160
L829
1788
Stark
Lib'y
    Logica elementare, cioè primi principj dell' arte di ragionare. Vercelli, Dalla Tipografia Patria, 1788.
    166p. 20cm.

    Title vignette.
    Tailpieces.

NL 0451164   TxU

    Logica et metaphysica quae traditur in Collegio romano S.J. exeunte anno 1836, et proximo 1837 [n.p.n.d.]
    535,7p. 25cm.
    Reproduced from manuscript.

NL 0451165   KAS

VOLUME 338

Logica genevensis continued. Or the first [-second] part of the fifth check to antinomianism ...
see under   [Fletcher, John William] 1729-1785.

Logica genevensis: or, A fourth check to antinomianism
see under   [Fletcher, John William] 1729-1785.

Logica in isum juventutis academicae
see under   Jennings, John, d. 1723, supposed author.

La logica; o, L'arte del pensare, contenente, oltre alle regole comuni, ...

See under

[Arnauld, Antoine] 1612-1694.

Logica Pamph. collecta ... dum is Pauli Veneti opusculum in Bonon. academia profiteretur anno 1512
see under   Monti, Panfilo.

... Logica Sapientis Rabbi Simeonis, per Sebastianum Munsterum Latine iuxta Hebraismum uersa ...
see under   [Moses ben Maimon] 1135-1204.

Logica; sive, Ars cogitandi...
see under   Arnauld, Antoine, 1612-1694.

Logicae compendium. Praefixa est dissertatio de philosophiae origine ejusque inventoribus aut excultoribus praecipuis. Glasguae, in aedibus academicis excudebant R. et A. Foulis, 1756.
pp. (3), 104.

Print. spec.

NL 0451173   MH

... Logical basis for valuations, read at the annual meeting of the Central electric railway association, held at Claypool hotel, Indianapolis, Ind, on January 19, 1911
see under   [Young, Charles Griffith] 1866-

A logical demonstration of the lawfulness of subscribing the new engagement. Or, promise to be true and faithful to the common-weal as it is now established: in four argvments. As a just apology for such as have conscienciously subscribed: and for satisfaction of others, who may be called to subscribe; especially if they had formerly taken the Solemn league & covenant. London: Printed by J. Macock for G. Calvert, 1650.   8 p. 19cm. (4°.)

Astor library: Dixon collection, 392.   Thomason, v. 1, p. 784.   Union theological seminary: McAlpin collection, v. 2, p. 706.

1. Oaths of allegiance—Gt. Br. wealth and protectorate, 1649-1660   2. Great Britain—Hist.—Common—Pamphlets.   July 1, 1938

NL 0451175   NN CSmH MH IU NNUT-Mc CLU-C

The Logical point; an illustrated monthly for the advancement of the Worlds Panama Exposition, New Orleans — 1915.
v. 1, no. 1-5 (Aug. – Dec., 1910)
New Orleans, 1910.   5 nos.   illus. (incl. ports.)   4°.

No more published.

1. Exhibitions—San Francisco, 1915.   July 21, 1930

NL 0451176   NN ViU OrU LNHT PHi NcD LU

Logical positivism and ethics. The symposia read at the joint session of the Aristotelian Society and the Mind Association at Durham, July 9th-11th, 1948. London, Harrison, 1948.
215 p.   22 cm.   (Aristotelian Society. Supplementary volume, 22)

Contents.—Address.—Ethics without propositions, by W. H. F. Barnes.—Symposium: Are all philosophical questions, questions of language? 1. By Stuart Hampshire. 2. By A. D. Jones. 3. By S. Körner.—Symposium: The emotive theory of ethics. 1. By Richard Robinson. 2. By H. J. Paton. 3. By R. C. Cross.—Symposium: What can logic do for philosophy? 1. By K. R. Popper. 2. By William

Kneale. 3. By A. J. Ayer.—Symposium: Things and persons. 1. By D. M. Mackinnon. 2. By H. A. Hodges. 3. By J. Wisdom.

1. Philosophy—Addresses, essays, lectures. 2. Logical positivism. 3. Ethics.   I. Mind Association.   (Series: Aristotelian Society for the Systematic Study of Philosophy, London. Proceedings. Supplementary volume, 22)
B11.A7 Suppl. vol. 22   104   A 49-1657*

Virginia. Univ. Libr. for Library of Congress   [a50c1]†

NL 0451178   ViU DLC OU

Logical proofs of Greeley's bargain. Conversion of the Democratic party—false pretenses of the so-called Liberal Republicans. [Washington? 1872]
4 p.   23cm.

Caption title.

1. Campaign literature, 1872—Republican.
12-9031
Library of Congress   E675.L83

NL 0451179   DLC

The "logical selection" questionnaire; effects of sedatives on psychological results
see under   Dios Chemical Company, St. Louis.

Logick: or, The art of thinking
see under   [Arnauld, Antoine] 1612-1694.

The Logick Primer.
see under   [Eliot, John] 1604-1690.

Logie, Alfred Ernest, 1871-
Canadian wonder tales, by Alfred E. Logie; drawings by Dorothy Hansacre. Chicago, New York, Row, Peterson and company [1925]
v, 228 p. incl. front., illus. 19cm.

1. Indians of North America—Legends.   I. Title.
Library of Congress   E98.F6L75   26—796

NL 0451183   DLC Or OC1h OC1

Logie, Alfred Ernest, 1871-
Exercises and problems in physical and political geography, by Alfred E. Logie. Chicago, A. Flanagan company [1907]
1 p. l., 5-72 p. illus. 17½cm.

1. Physical geography. 2. Geography—Examinations, questions, etc.
Library of Congress   G131.L8   7—26473

NL 0451184   DLC

Logie, Alfred Ernest, 1871-   comp.
From Abraham Lincoln to Franklin D. Roosevelt; a selection of historical accounts written by people who lived at the time of the events, selected by Alfred E. Logie ... [and] Daniel J. Beeby ... Chicago, New York [etc.] Lyons and Carnahan [1942]
vi, 300 p. illus. (incl. ports., maps) pl. 20½cm.

1. U. S.—Hist.—1865-   I. Beeby, Daniel J., joint comp. II. Title.
Library of Congress   E661.L852   42-17019
973

NL 0451185   DLC OC1

Logie, Alfred Ernest, 1871-   comp.
From Columbus to Lincoln, a selection of letters and other historical accounts written by people of note who lived at the time of the events, selected by Alfred E. Logie ... Chicago, New York, Lyons and Carnahan [1924]
ix, 255 p. incl. front., illus. 19½cm.

1. U. S.—Hist.—Sources.   I. Title.
Library of Congress   E173.L84   24—20069

NL 0451186   DLC Or OLak OC1

Logie, Alfred Ernest, 1871-   comp.
From Columbus to Lincoln; a selection of letters and other historical accounts written by people of note who lived at the time of the events, selected by Alfred E. Logie ... [and] Daniel J. Beeby ... Chicago, New York [etc.] Lyons and Carnahan [1942]
vii, [1], 264 p. illus. (incl. ports.) 20½cm.

1. U. S.—Hist.—Sources.   I. Beeby, Daniel J., joint comp. II. Title.
Library of Congress   E173.L84 1942   42-16040
973

NL 0451187   DLC

Logie, Alfred Ernest, 1871-   comp.
From Lincoln to Coolidge; a selection of interesting and original historical accounts written by people of note who lived at the time of the events, selected by Alfred E. Logie ... Chicago, New York, Lyons and Carnahan [1925]
vi, 357, [1] p. illus., plates. 19½cm.

1. U. S.—Hist.—1865-   I. Title.
Library of Congress   E661.L85   26—12328

NL 0451188   DLC OrSaW Or OEac OLak

VOLUME 338

Logie, Alfred Ernest, 1871–
Markers of great events, by Alfred E. Logie ... illustrated by Ernie King. Chicago, Dallas ₍etc.₎ Lyons & Carnahan ₍*1935*₎
ix, 307 p. illus., col. pl. 19½ᶜᵐ.
Illustrated lining-papers.

1. U. S.—History, Juvenile. 2. U. S.—Historic houses, etc.   I. Title.
Library of Congress   E178.3.L84   36–11535
————— Copy 2.
Copyright A 95504   973

NL 0451189   DLC OC1

Logie, Alfred Ernest, 1871–
Markers of great events, by Alfred E. Logie ... illustrated by Ernie King. Chicago, Dallas ₍etc.₎ Lyons & Carnahan ₍*1940*₎
ix, 310 p. illus., col. pl. 19½ᶜᵐ.
Illustrated lining-papers.

1. U. S.—History, Juvenile. 2. U. S.—Historic houses, etc.   I. Title.
Library of Congress   E178.3.L84 1940   40–36028
————— Copy 2.
Copyright   973

NL 0451190   DLC

Logie, Alfred Ernest, 1871–   joint author.
FOR OTHER EDITIONS
SEE MAIN ENTRY
Sullivan, Ella C   1864–
The story of the old Spanish missions of the Southwest, by Ella C. Sullivan ... and Alfred E. Logie ... Chicago, New York, Lyons and Carnahan ₍*1939*₎

Logie, Alfred Ernest, 1871–
The story reader, by Alfred E. Logie and Claire H. Uecke, assisted by Sarah A. Milner ... New York, Cincinnati ₍etc.₎ American book company ₍*1901*₎
128 p. illus. 19ᶜᵐ. (*On cover:* Eclectic school readings)

1. Readers & speakers—1870–   I. Uecke, Claire H., joint author.
II. Milner, Sarah A., joint author. III. Title.
                                        1–12841 Revised
Library of Congress   PE1119.L77

NL 0451192   DLC OrU NN

STC
16694   ₍Logie, Andrew₎
Cum bono deo. Raine from the clouds, vpon a choicke ₍!₎ angel: or, A returned answere, to that common quaeritur of our adversaries, Where was your church before Luther? Digested into severall meditations ... Aberdene, Imprinted by Edward Raban, 1624.
A–K⁴. 4to.
J.F.K. Johnstone and Robertson, Bibl. Aberdonensis, v. 1, pp. 218–219.
David Laing–Britwell Court–Harmsworth copy.

NL 0451193   DFo

FILM   **Logie, Andrew.**
Cv₍m₎ bono deo. Raine from the clovds, vpon a choicke angel: or, A returned answere, to that common quaeritur of our adversaries, VVhere was your church before Luther? Digested into severall meditations, according to the difference of points. Extorted off the author, for stilling the vncessant, and no lesse clamorous coassation of some Patmicke frogges, against the lawfulnesse of our calling. Aberdene, Imprinted by E.Raban, 1624.

Continued in next column

Continued from preceding column

Title–page mutilated with slight loss of text.
Short-title catalogue no.16694 (carton 844)

1.Church of England—Doctrinal and controversial works. I.Title. II.Title: Raine from the clouds.

NL 0451195   MiU

Logie (Cosmo Gordon). On the cattle disease. 24 pp. 12°. *London, J. Churchill & Sons, 1866.*

NL 0451196   DNLM

Logie, David W.
An account of a trip from Stirling to Braemar, (made from 4th to 11th September, 1893), with a historical and descriptive narrative of the places on the route, by David W. Logie... ₍Stirling₎ Privately printed at the Stirling Sentinel off., 1894.   188 p. map. 19cm.

207923B. 1. Scotland—Highlands   —Descr. and trav.
                                          April 29, 1943

NL 0451197   NN

---

812   **Logie, Elma M**
L829o   An old maid's venture, a comedy in one act, by Elma M. Logie.   Boston, W. H. Baker & co. ₍c1916₎
        8p.   (On cover: Baker's edition of plays)

NL 0451198   IU MH RPB NN

Logie, Elsie, & Logie, Jack.
The golden way to health; twenty carrets.   [N.p.n.pub.n.d.].
32p.S.

NL 0451199   CaBViP

Logie, Gordon.
Furniture from machines. With an introd. by John Gloag. London, G. Allen and Unwin ₍1947₎
xii, 150 p. illus. 26 cm.
Bibliography: p. 143–144.

1. Furniture. 2. Woodworking machinery.

TS880.L6   684   48–22827*

OrCS
MB PU NNC TxU MU MiU NcRS CaBVaU CaBVa Or WaS WaT
NL 0451200   DLC KEmT PU-FA PSt PP PPD NcGU NNU-G NNU-W

Logie, Gordon.
Industry in towns. With a pref. by W. G. Holford. London, Allen and Unwin ₍1952₎
376 p. illus. 26 cm.
Includes bibliography.

1. Manufactures. 2. Factories.   I. Title.

TS145.L57   711.454   52–4835 ‡

PSt ViU OrP MtU GU
NL 0451201   DLC OrU CaBVaU OU OC1 NcU MH NN CtY PU-FA

Logie, Gordon.
The urban scene. London, Faber and Faber ₍1954₎
156 p. illus. 26 cm.

1. Cities and towns—Planning.   I. Title.
                            Full name: Gordon Chalmers Logie.
NA9030.L54 1954   54–36470 ‡

WaS
PU-FA PP OOxM PSt OCU ViU MiU TU IdU MtBC OrCS OrU
NL 0451202   DLC CaBVaU CaBVa NN CtY MH MB NNC NcRS

Logie, Henry Burton, 1883–   ed.
FOR OTHER EDITIONS
SEE MAIN ENTRY
National conference on nomenclature of disease.
Standard classified nomenclature of disease, compiled by the National conference on nomenclature of disease; edited by H. B. Logie ... New York, The Commonwealth fund, 1935.

Logie, Iona Margaret Robertson, 1900–
Careers for women in journalism; a personnel study of 881 women experienced as salaried writers in journalism, advertising, publicity, and promotion, by Iona Robertson Logie ... Scranton, Pa., International textbook company, 1938.
vii p., 1 l., 320 p., 1 l. illus., tables (1 fold.) 21ᶜᵐ.
Thesis (PH. D.)—Columbia university, 1938.
Vita.
Published also without thesis note in Modern school series.
Bibliography: p. 295–299.

1. Women as journalists. 2. Journalism.   I. Title.
Library of Congress   PN4784.W7L6 1938   39–4560
Columbia Univ. Libr.
————— Copy 2.
Copyright A 125635   ₍a40c2₎   070.69

NL 0451204   DLC CU PPT PPD PP NNC

Logie, Iona Margaret Robertson, 1900–
Careers for women in journalism; a composite picture of 881 salaried women writers at work in journalism, advertising, publicity, and promotion, by Iona Robertson Logie ... Scranton, Pa., International textbook company, 1938.
ix, ₍1₎ p., 1 l. 308 p. illus. 21½ᶜᵐ. (*Half-title:* Modern school series)
Issued also as thesis (PH. D.) Columbia university.
Bibliography: p. 295–299.

1. Women as journalists. 2. Journalism.   I. Title.
Library of Congress   PN4784.W7L6 1938 a   39–26148

Copyright A 125636   070.69

OLak OU OOxM OC1 OrU MtU
NL 0451205   DLC KEmT TxU Or WaWW OrCS OC1U CU PU

Logie, Iona Margaret Robertson, 1900–   ed.
Careers in the making; readings in recent biography, with studies in vocational guidance, edited by Iona M. R. Logie ... New York and London, Harper & brothers, 1931.
xvii, 393 p. front., ports. 19½ᶜᵐ.
"First edition."
"A collection of biographical extracts relating to early training, both educational and vocational, and the first steps toward progress in the lives of twenty Americans of our century."—Introd.
"Three hundred biographies of marked vocational interest": p. 375–393.
1. U. S.—Biog. 2. Vocational guidance. 3. Vocational education—
U. S. 4. Biography—Bibl.   I. Title.
                                                   31–28532
Library of Congress   CT214.L6
                           ₍a44v2₎   920.073

CU OU OC1 OrMonO
NL 0451206   DLC FTaSU OrP WaT IdB OrU OrCS ICU MH

Logie, Iona Margaret Robertson, 1900–   ed.
Careers in the making; modern Americans when they were young—and on their way, edited by Iona M. R. Logie ... New York and London, Harper & brothers, 1935.
x, 381 p. front., illus., ports. 19½ᶜᵐ.
"Planned especially to present the early training, both educational and vocational, and the first try-outs or first jobs which figured in the youthful ventures of nineteen modern Americans."—Introd.
List of four hundred biographies: p. 357–381.

1. U. S.—Biog. 2. Vocational guidance. 3. Vocational education—
U. S. 4. Biography—Bibl.   I. Title.
                                                   35–7730
Library of Congress   CT214.L6 1935
                           ₍a44q²4₎   920.073

MB OC1 OC1h OEac IdU
NL 0451207   DLC OrSaW WaSp OrP Or WaS IaU NcRS NN

VOLUME 338

Logie, Iona Margaret Robertson, 1900–
Careers in the making. Second series. Readings in modern biography as studies in vocational guidance, edited by Iona Robertson Logie ... New York, London, Harper & brothers ₍1942₎

viii, 243 p. 22½ᵐ.

"First edition."
Includes bibliographies.

1. U. S.—Biog. 2. Profession, Choice of. 3. Vocational education—U. S. 4. Biography—Bibl. I. Title.

Library of Congress   CT214.L612

42–22755

920.073

NL 0451208   DLC Or OrU IdU NcRS OC1 OEac OC1W OOxM

Logie, John E., tr.

Gjellerup, Karl Adolf, 1857–
The pilgrim Kaminita. A legendary romance, by Karl Gjellerup. Tr. by John E. Logie. New York, E. P. Dutton and company, 1912.

Logie, Lizzie, 1886–
Self-expression in a junior school, by L. Logie ... London, H. Milford, Oxford university press, 1928.

86, ₍1₎ p. incl. illus., 34 pl. (part col.) 25½ᵐ.

"This book is a record of lessons followed for many years at Wingrove junior school."—Foreword.

1. Education of children. ₍1. Children—Education—Occupations and busy work₎ 2. Handicraft. I. Title.

E 30–176

Library, U. S. Office of   Education LB1541.L76

NL 0451210   DHEW CU ICU IU CtY

Logié, Paul.
La Fronde en Normandie. Amiens, 1951–52.

3 v. ports., fold. map. 25 cm.

Bibliography: v. 3, p. ₍171₎–202.

1. Fronde. 2. Normandy—Hist.

DC124.4.L6

56–17961

NL 0451211   MH CLSU MiU WaU LU ICU RPB CU OrU
          DLC OU OC1 NN NRU IaU MB TxU CtY CSt

Logié, Paul.
Les institutions du commerce à Amiens au xviiiᵉ siècle; juridiction consulaire et Chambre de commerce sous l'Ancien Régime et pendant la période révolutionnaire. Amiens, 1951.

150 p. 26 cm. (Bibliothèque de la Société d'histoire du droit des pays flamands, picards et wallons, t. 23)

Includes bibliography.

1. Amiens—Guilds. 2. Boards of trade—France—Amiens. 3. Commercial courts—Amiens. I. Title.

65–52893 ‡

NL 0451212   ICU CU CtY CtY-L MiU-L MH-L
          DLC MH-L NNC-L OU NN RPB NcU NcD NIC

Logie, Paul
Jumièges et Saint-Riquier.

(In Congrès scientifique du XIII centenaire de Jumièges. Rouen, 1954. vol. 1, pp. ₍199₎–207).

NL 0451213   PLatS

₍Logie, Sarah E   Chester₎
PZ265
.L77L7   Little teachers. New York, American Tract
1873   Society ₍c1873₎
          48 p. illus. (Swallow stories. No.II)

NL 0451214   ICU

Logie, Sarah E   Chester.
Out of the fold ... By Sarah Chester Logie ... New York, American tract society ₍1882₎
240 p. front., plates. 17 cm.

I. Title.

PZ7.L8285Ou

12—36243

NL 0451215   DLC

Logie, Ted.
Ted tells (Okanagan) tales; true stories from our Okanagan pioneers. ₍n.d.₎
183 p. illus.

1. Frontier and pioneer life - Washington (State) - Okanagan   Co. I. Title.

NL 0451216   Wa

Logie, Thomas, ed.   FOR OTHER EDITIONS
                               SEE MAIN ENTRY
Halévy, Ludovic, 1834–1908.
... L'abbé Constantin, par Ludovic Halévy, with notes and vocabulary by Thomas Logie ... New ed., with direct-method exercises. Boston, New York ₍etc.₎ D. C. Heath & co. ₍c1916₎

Logie, Thomas.
Bevier, Louis, 1857–
A French grammar, by Louis Bevier, jr. ... With exercises by Thomas Logie, ᴘʜ. ᴅ. New York, H. Holt and company, 1896.

Logie, Thomas.
Phonology of the patois of Cachy (Somme) by Thomas Logie ... ₍Baltimore, The Modern language association?₎ 1892₎

1 p. l., 73 p. illus. 23ᵐ.

Thesis (ᴘʜ. ᴅ.)—Johns Hopkins university.
"Reprinted from the Publications of the Modern language association of America, vol. VII, no. 4, 1892."
"Works consulted": p. 71–73.

1. French language—Dialects—Cachy.

Library of Congress   PC3067.C3L7

3–29682

NL 0451219   DLC MB NjP CU NIC

Logie, Thomas, ed.   FOR OTHER EDITIONS
                               SEE MAIN ENTRY
About, Edmond François Valentin, 1828–1885.
... Le roi des montagnes, par Edmond About. With introduction and notes by Thomas Logie ... Boston, D. C. Heath & co., 1898.

Logie (V.) De l'insomnie; causes et traitement
ill. 106 pp., 1 l. 8°. Gand, E. Vanderhaeghen,
1878. ₍F., v. 2059.₎
Regr. Press / Ann. Soc. de méd. de Gand, 1878, ivi.

NL 0451221   DNLM

DG
Sm57
1901   **Logie, William**
X   A layman's reply to Prof. George Adam
L829   Smith's "Modern criticism and the...preaching of the Old Testament." London, Marshall Brothers, 1902.
          178 p. 24 cm.

1. Smith, George Adam, 1856–1942. Modern criticism and the preaching of the Old Testament. 2. Bible. O.T.—Criticism, interpretation, etc. I. Title.

NL 0451222   KyWAT

LOGIE of Buchan; a favorite Scotch song. London, H. Andrews ₍ca.1810₎ ₍2₎ p. 31cm.

Caption title.
For piano, with interlinear words; part for flute printed on p.₍2₎
First line: O, Logie of Buchan.
Mounted on verso of p.₍2₎:I'm saddest when I sing. Ballad composed and arranged by Henry R. Bishop. ₍Philadelphia? n.d.₎
1. Songs, English   (Scottish composers)
I. Title: O, Logie of   Buchan.

NL 0451223   NN

Logie of Buchan A Favorite Scots Song as Sung by Miss Ryder. Dublin Published by Hime at his Musical circulating Library No. 34 College Green.

First line: O Logie of Buchan! O Logie the Laird!

(IN English popular music of the 1790's)

NL 0451224   OrP

---

*
M1.
.8444   **Logie o' Buchan;** beautiful Scotch and Irish
v.12   melodies arranged for piano forte by Wm.
no.23   Vincent Wallace. Figure 4 in 5 pointed star. Cleveland, S. Brainard & Co., 203 Superior St. ₍not after 1875₎
          9 p. 34cm. ₍Sheet music collection,v.12,no.23₎

1. Piano music. I. Wallace, William Vincent, 1812–1865, arr.

NL 0451225   ViU

LE
3
T53   **Logier, Eugene Bernard Shelley,** 1893–
R7215   Check-list of the amphibians and reptiles
no.41   of Canada and Alaska, by E.B.S. Logier and G.C. Toner. Toronto, 1955.
          v, 88 p. maps. (₍Toronto. Royal Ontario Museum. Life Sciences Division₎ Contributions, no. 41)

Bibliography: p. 76–88.

NL 0451226   CaOTU InU DI CSt CaBVa OrU

Logier, Eugene B. Shelley, 1893–

... A faunal investigation of Prince Edward county, Ontario, by L. L. Snyder, E. B. S. Logier, T. B. Kurata, F. A. Urquhart, and J. F. Brimley. Toronto, Can., The University of Toronto press, 1941.

VOLUME 338

Logier, Eugene B   Shelley.
    The frogs, toads, and salamanders of eastern Canada.
Drawings by the author. ₍n. p.₎ Clarke, Irwin ₍1952₎
    127 p. illus. 24 cm.
    Includes bibliography.

1. Batrachia—Canada.   I. Title.

QL654.L6   597.6   54–1238 ‡

NIC N CU CSt NcRS NcD CaBViP MtBC OrCS
NL 0451228   DLC CaBVaU CaBVa PSt PPAN NNC TxU DNAL

Logier, Eugene Bernard Shelley, 1893–
    ... From egg to tadpole to frog ...
[Toronto] 1947.
    15 p. illus. 23 cm. (Royal Ontario
museum of zoology. Handbook no. 5)

NL 0451229   PPAN

Logier, Eugene Bernard Shelley, 1893–
    ... The reptiles of Ontario ...   [Toronto]
1939.
    63, ii p. incl. maps (1 fold.) VIII pl.
23 cm. (Royal Ontario museum of zoology.
Handbook no. 4)

NL 0451230   PPAN

LE   Logier, Eugene Bernard She77ey₎, 1893–=
3   Some account of the amphibians and
T53   reptiles of British Columbia. ₍Toronto₎
R7215   1932.
no.5   311–336 p. tables. (₍Toronto. Royal
        Ontario Museum. Life Sciences Division₎
        Contributions, no. 5)

        Cover title.
        "Reprinted from Transactions of the Royal
        Canadian Institute, Vol. XVIII, Part 2".
        Bibliography: p. 335–336.

NL 0451231   CaOTU CSt

Logier, L. B.
        see
Logier, Johann Bernhard, *d.* 1846.

Logier, Johann Bernhard, *d.* 1846.
Berlioz, Hector, 1803–1869.
    ... An abridged treatise on modern instrumentation and
orchestration ... also the art of conducting explained. From
Hector Berlioz. Boston, J. White. *1888.

---

xfMT220 Logier, Johann Bernhard, ₍.1846.
L7515   Anweisung zum Unterricht im Clavierspiel
        und der musikalischen Composition nach seiner
        Methode; ein Handbuch für Lehrer und Ältern,
        aus dem Englischen übersetzt.   Berlin, bei
        Wilhelm Logier, 1829.
            iv,71p.
        At head of title: J.B.Logier's.
        Includes 26 exercises.
            1. Piano – Instruction and study. 2. Com-
        position (Music)   I. Title.

NL 0451234   IaU

Logier, Johann Bernhard, *d.* 1846.
    An authentic account of the examination of pupils, in-
structed in the new system of musical education; before
certain members of the Philharmonic society, and others.
By J. B. Logier ... London, R. Hunter, 1818.
    1 p. L, 41, ₍1₎ p. 23 cm.
    No. 3 in a vol. lettered: Tracts on Logier's system of music.

1. Chiroplast. 2. Music—Instruction and study.

MT24.L835 no. 3   20–21470

NL 0451235   DLC NN

LOGIER, JOHANN BERNHARD, 1780–1846.
    Belive me, I never can rove.   London, Clementi
[18—?] 4 p.   34cm.
    Caption title.
    For voice and piano.
1. Songs, English.

NL 0451236   NN

W.C.L. Logier, Johann Bernhard, 1777–1846.
M780.88
A512CW   Bugle andante with variations for the
no.20   piano forte. New York, Published by Dubois
        at his Piano forte and Music store, No. 126
        Broadway. Pr. 75 cts. ₍ca. 1820₎
            8 p. 34 cm.
            Caption title.
            ₍No. 20₎ in a collection of early Ameri-
        can music, ca. 1802–1830.
            1. Variations (Piano) I. Title.

NL 0451237   NcD

---

xfMT221 Logier, Johann Bernard, 1777– 1846
L6   A companion to the royal patent chiroplast
        or hand-director, a new invented apparatus for
        facilitating the attainment of a proper execu-
        tion on the piano forte, by the inventor, J.B.
        Logier. London, Clementi & Co. ₍between 1801
        and 1806₎
            43p. music. 35cm.
        ──── ──── Sequel to the chiroplast companion, to
        facilitate the attainment of a proper method of
        playing on the piano forte, being a succession of₎
        progressive lessons grounded upon the harmonies
        of the early easy   lessons in that work,

        so as to be played with them in concert by
        pupils more advanced in their studies. 30p.
        Bound with: Logier's theoretical and practi-
        cal study for the piano forte... No.1-10.

            1. Chiroplast. I. Title.

NL 0451239   IaU

LOGIER, JOHANN BERNHARD, 1780–1846.
    A companion to the royal patent chiroplast, or hand-
director. A new invented apparatus for facilitating
the attainment of a proper execution on the piano
forte, by the inventor, J.B. Logier. [London] Printed
for the author by J. Green [181-] 42 p. illus. 33cm.

1. Piano--Methods, 1800-1900.   2. Logier system.

NL 0451240   NN

        Logier, Johann Bernhard, 1780–1846.
MT50   Logier's comphrensive course in music,
L832   harmony, and practical composition, ed. by
1888   Carl Stein. Enl. and rev. American ed.
        With an abridged treatise from Hector Ber-
        lioz's standard work on instrumentation,
        with hints on conducting. Boston, C.
        Fischer, c1888.
            xi, 316 p. illus.(music) 27⁵.
            1.Composition(Music) 2. Harmony. 3. In-
        strumentation and orchestration. 4. Con-
        ducting(Music)   I. Stein, Carl, ed.
        II. Berlioz,   Hector,1803–1859.

NL 0451241   CSt

Logier, Johann Bernhard, *d.* 1846.
    ... Logier's₍comprehensive course in music, harmony, and
practical composition, ed. by Carl Stein. With an abridged
treatise from Hector Berlioz's standard work on instrumentation, with hints on conducting. ₍Enl. and rev. American ed.₎ Boston, J. White, *1888.
    xi, 316 p., 1 l. illus. (incl. music) diagrs. 25½ x 20½ cm.
    "Bird's eye view of the rudiments of music ₍by J. Green₎": p. v-xi.

1. Composition (Music) 2. Harmony. 3. Instrumentation and
orchestration. 4. Conducting.   I. Stein, Carl, ed. II. Berlioz, Hector, 1803–1869.

MT24.L83 1888   7–4049

NL 0451242   DLC CLU NcD OClW ICN OCl OU WaS

Logier, Johann Bernhard, 1780–1846.
    ...Logier's comprehensive course in music, harmony, and
practical composition; edited by Carl Stein. With an abridged
treatise from Hector Berlioz's standard work on instrumentation,
with hints on conducting. Boston: C. Fischer, 1920. xi,
316 p. illus. (music.) 4°.
    At head of title: Enlarged and revised American edition.

296587A. 1. Composition ₍music₎.   2. Harmony. 3. Instrumentation
and orc₍estration. 4. Conducting   ₍music₎. 5. ₍erlioz, Hector, 1803–
1869. 6. Stein, Carl, 1824–1902,   editor.
                                                June 8, 1927

NL 0451243   NN

LOGIER, JOHANN BERNHARD, 1780–1846.
    Comprehensive course in music, harmany, and
practical composition. Edited by Carl Stein. With
an abridged treatise from Hector Berlioz's standard
work on instrumentation, with hints on conducting.
Boston, C. Fischer, 1920.   xi, 316 p. music.

    Microfilm (master negative)

NL 0451244   NN

Film   Logier, Johann Bernhard, *d.* 1846.
3138   Logier's comprehensive course in music, har-
Item 6 mony, and practical composition. Boston,
Music   C. Fischer, 1920.
Lib'y   316p. illus.
            Microfilm. New York, New York Public
        Library Photographic Service. 1 reel (various
        items) 35mm.
            1. Harmony. 2. Instrumentation and orches-
        tration. 3. Conducting (Music) I. Stein,
        Carl, ed.

NL 0451245   TxU

Logier, Johann Bernhard, *d.* 1846.
    An explanation and description of the royal patent chiro-
plast, or hand-director. A newly invented apparatus for
facilitating the acquirement of a proper execution on the
piano forte, by J. B. Logier. London, Clementi and co.
₍1814₎
    vi, ₍7₎–24 p. illus. (music) 23 cm.
    No. 1 in a vol. lettered: Tracts on Logier's system of music.

1. Chiroplast.

MT24.L835 no. 1   20–21468

NL 0451246   DLC

Logier, Johann Bernhard, *d.* 1846.
    An explanation and description of the royal patent
chiroplast, or hand-director. A newly invented apparatus
for facilitating the acquirement of a proper execution on
the piano forte. By J. B. Logier ... 2d ed., with additions.
Dublin, Printed by J. Carrick, 1816.
    vi, ₍7₎–28 p. 22 cm. (*In his* A syllabus of the second examination
of Mr. Logier's pupils. Dublin, 1816)

1. Chiroplast.
MT24.L8   7–38718
──── Copy 2. ₍Thorndike pamphlets, v. 5, no. 16₎
AC901.T5 vol. 5, no. 16

NL 0451247   DLC

VOLUME 338

Logier, Johann Bernhard, d. 1846.
First and second companion: a series of
progressive lessons for the piano forte: 1st
companion. Sequel to the (First Companion)
Boston, Ditson.
(In 2 vols.: "Overtures 1. "&2. ")

NL 0451248   CtY

LOGIER, J[ohann] B[ernhard] *d.* 1846.
The first companion to the royal patent
chiroplast or hand-director, a new apparatus
for facilitating the attainment of a proper
execution on the piano forte. 5th ed.
[London], I.Green,[18].

f°. pp.(2), 38. Front.   Mus 349.49 F

NL 0451249   MH

---

fMT222
C7
1823
Music
Library

Logier, Johann Bernhard, d. 1846.
The first companion to the royal patent chiroplast, or hand-
director, a new invented apparatus for facilitating the
attainment of a proper execution on the piano forte, by the
inventor.   9th ed.   [London] Printed for the author by I.
Green [184-?]
38 p.   plate, music. 35cm.   [Bound with Cramer, J. B.
Instructions for the piano forte. [1823?]]

Engraved.
"This work contains the rudiments of music, progressively interwoven in lessons of exercises, calculated for the speedy advancement of the youngest capacity; together with a full description of
the use & application   of the apparatus which has been
honored with the appro-   bation & recommendation of the
most distinguished pro-   fessors. "

NL 0451250   CU

Logier, Johann Bernhard, d. 1846.
The first companion to the royal patent chiroplast or hand
directors, a new invented apparatus for facilitating the attainment of a proper execution on the piano forte, by the inventor,
J. B. Logier. The 10th ed. [n. p.,] H. P. Munroe [18—]
30 p. 33½cm.   [With Hünten, Franz. F. Hunten's celebrated instructions for the piano forte ...   New York [183-?]]

1. Chiroplast. 2. Music—Instruction and study.

                                 43-33355

Library of Congress   MT222.H98

NL 0451251   DLC MB NN

---

fV
768
.523

LOGIER, JOHANN BERNHARD, d.1846.
The first companion to the royal patent
Chiroplast, or hand-director, an apparatus for
facilitating the attainment of a proper execution
on the piano forte. Containing the rudiments of
music, progressively interwoven in lessons & exercises calculated for the speedy advancement of the
youngest capacity ... Together with a full description of the use & application of the apparatus ...
Dublin, Published at Mr Logiers[sic] Music Academy
[184-]
[1]l.,10-41p. music. 37cm.

At head of title: The 19th, a considerably
enlarged edition ...
"Improved edition."
Title-page plate altered probably from that
used for the 18th ed., with altered imprint.
Imperfect?

NL 0451253   ICN

Logier, Johann Bernhard, d. 1846.
A manual, chiefly for the use of preceptors,
parents, governesses, &c., exhibiting the peculiar
method of teaching the art and science of music:
comprising performance on the pianoforte, harmony
and musical composition... according to his
system of musical education.   London, J. Green
[etc., etc.] 1828.
52, 10 p.   27.5 x 22 cm.
[Bound with his System of the science of music.
London, 1827]
10 p. of music at end.

NL 0451254   CtY

---

fV
5
.5185

LOGIER, JOHANN BERNHARD, d.1846.
Nouveau système d'enseignement musical, ou
traité de composition.   Paris,M.Schlesinger
[182-]
III,289p. 35cm.

NL 0451255   ICN

LOGIER, JOHANN BERNHARD, 1780-1846.
Oh turn those killing eyes away; a duett.   Dublin.
S. Holden [181?]   score (7 p.) 32cm.

For solo voices (ST) and piano.
First line: Oh! thou whose tender, serious eye.

1. Vocal duos, Secular (Mixed)--Keyboard acc.

NL 0451256   NN

Logier, Johann Bernhard, *d.* 1846.
A refutation of the fallacies and misrepresentations
contained in a pamphlet, entitled "An exposition of the
new system of musical education," published by a committee of professors in London. By J.B. Logier ... London, R. Hunter [etc.] 1818.
2 p. L, [viii-xi, 55 p.; vi p. (music) 23cm.
No. 5 in a volume lettered: Tracts on Logier's system of music.
"Prospectus of the musical academy of Messrs. Logier, Webbe, and
Kalkbrenner, established on Mr. Logier's new system of musical education, at no. 20, Bedford place, Russell square. [London, 1818"]: 4 p., appended.
1. An exposition of the musical system of Mr. Logier. 2. Chiroplast.
3. Music—Instruction and study.

                                 20-21472

Library of Congress   MT50.L835

NL 0451257   DLC NN

---

fV
768
.53

LOGIER, JOHANN BERNHARD, d.1846.
A second companion to the royal patent
chiroplast or hand director, calculated to accompany the progressive advancement of the musical
student.   London,J.Green[181-]
11p. 34cm.   (with his Sequel to the Second
companion to the chiroplast ... London [181-])

Printed on paper with watermarks date: 1815.

NL 0451258   ICN

Logier, Johann Bernhard, 1777-1846.
A second companion to the royal patent chiroplast, or hand director, calculated to accompany the progressive advancement of the musical
student. [4th ed.] Boston, T.Spear [18-]

16 p.   33 cm.
Engraved.

NL 0451259   MH

Logier, Johann Bernhard, 1777-1846.
Sequel to the First companion to the chiroplast, being a succession of progressive lessons
grounded upon the harmonies of the early easy
lessons in that work.   Boston, Published for
T.Spear by J.L.Hewitt & co. [18-]

27 p.   33 cm.
Engraved.

NL 0451260   MH

Logier, Johann Bernhard, 1777-1846.
Sequel to The first companion, to the chiroplast, being a succession
of progressive lessons grounded upon the harmonies of the . . .
lessons in that work . . . 12th edition.
= London. Green. 1827. 31 pp. F°.

G4687 — Pianoforte. Instruction books. — Chiroplast.

NL 0451261   MB

LOGIER, JOHANN BERNHARD, 1780-1846.
Sequel to the First companion to the chiroplast,
being a succession of progressive lessons grounded upon
the harmonies of the early easy lessons in that work, so
as to be played with them in concert by pupils more advanced
in their studies. Composed by J.B. Logier...
Boston, Published for H.P. Munroe, by John Ashton
[ca. 1833]   27 p.   33cm.

1. Piano--Methods, 1800-1900   2. Logier system. 1. Logier,
Johann Bernhard, 1780-1846.   First companion to the royal patent
chiroplast.

NL 0451262   NN

---

fV
768
.53

LOGIER, JOHANN BERNHARD, d.1846.
Sequel to the Second companion to the chiroplast, being a succession of progressive lessons,
so arranged as to be played in concert with the
easy lessons contained in that work.   London,
J.Green[181-]
28p. 34cm.

Printed on paper with watermark date: 1815.
With this are bound: his A second companion
to the royal patent chiroplast ...   London [181-];
Jousse, John. [The piano-forte made easy ...   London, 181-];   Hook,   James.   A new & corrected
edition of Hook's'   Guida di musica ...
Dublin [181-]

NL 0451263   ICN

Logier, Johann Bernhard, *d.* 1846.
[Marches. Selected, arranged]

A sett of quick and slow marches, troops, &c.   Composed ...
by I. B. Logier.   Dublin, Pub. for the author at B. Cooke's
music shop [179-]
1 p. L, 28 p. 32½cm.
Score: violin and piano. Originally for wind instruments.

1. Marches (Violin and piano)—To 1800.

                                 46-42453

Library of Congress   M222.L8M3

NL 0451264   DLC

Logier, Johann Bernhard, *d.* 1846.
A short account of the progress of J. B. Logier's system of
musical education in Berlin, and its subsequent introduction
by order of the Prussian government into the public seminaries, for its general promulgation through the Prussian
states: with a brief sketch of the present state of music in
Berlin. By J. B. Logier. London, R. Hunter, 1824.
40 p. 28 cm.

No. 7 in a vol. lettered: Tracts on Logier's system of music.

1. Music—Instruction & study—Germany. 2. Chiroplast.

MT24.L835 no. 7   20-21474

NL 0451265   DLC

Logier, Johann Bernhard, 1777-1846.
Spear's first companion to the royal patent
chiroplast, or hand-director, a new apparatus
for facilitating the attainment of a proper
execution on the piano forte.   Boston, Published
by the author at his piano forte and music ware-
house [18-]

16 p.   33 cm.
Engraved.

NL 0451266   MH

VOLUME 338

Logier, Johann Bernhard, *d.* 1846.
A syllabus of the second examination of M'. Logier's pupils, on his new system of musical education. To which is prefixed, a prospectus of its course of instruction, general observations on the comparative merits of the old and new systems of musical education. With an appendix, containing an ample description of the royal patent chiroplast, its use, and the advantages resulting from the application of it in teaching the piano forte. Dublin, Printed by J. Carrick, 1816.
16, vi, ₍₁₇–28 p. 22 cm.
1. Music—Instruction and study.
MT24.L8   7–38719

NL 0451267   DLC

Logier, J₍ohann₎ B₍ernhard₎ *d.* 1846.
System der musik-wissenschaft und der praktischen composition, mit inbegriff dessen was gewöhnlich unter dem ausdrucke general-bass verstanden wird. Von J. B. Logier. Berlin, H. A. W. Logier, 1827.
2 p. L, xi, ₍1₎ 346 p. 27 x 22½ᶜᵐ.
—— Nachträgliche sammlung von aufgaben und beispielen zu J. B. Logier's System der musikwissenschaft und der praktischen composition, wie auch zu dessen Lehrbuch der musikalischen composition, von dem verfasser ... componirt ... Berlin, H. A. W. Logier, 1827.
1 p. L, ii, 16 p. 27 x 22½ᶜᵐ. ₍With his₎ System der musikwissenschaft und der praktischen composition. Berlin, 1827₎
1. Composition (Music)   2. Harmony.   I. Marx, Adolf Bernhard, d. 1866.
MT50.L83   5–4914–5

NL 0451268   DLC CoU NcU CtY CU ICN OOxM

Logier, Johann Bernhard, *d.* 1846.
... Logier's system of and self instructor in the science of music, harmony, and practical composition. ₍Carl Fischer's rev. and amended ed.₎ New York, C. Fischer, 1889–
v. illus. (music) fold. tab. 22½ᶜᵐ.
"Rudiments of music. By Arthur A. Clappé": v. 1, p. ₍5₎–22.
1. Composition (Music)   2. Harmony.   I. Clappé, Arthur A.
                                                        CA 9–1303 Unrev'd
Library of Congress   MT24.L836   1889

NL 0451269   DLC OKentU NN IMunS NIC

Logier, Johann Bernhard, *d.* 1846.
A system of the science of music and practical composition; incidentally comprising what is usually understood by the term thorough bass. By J. B. Logier. London, J. Green, 1827.
3 p. L, ₍xi₎–xix, ₍1₎, 323, ₍1₎ p. front. (port.) illus. (music) 27½ x 22ᶜᵐ.
1. Composition (Music)   2. Harmony.
Library of Congress   MT24.L83 1827   5–4913 Revised
——— Copy 2. Pre-   fixed: Music published by J. Green
... Composed by J. B.   Logier ₍and J. Green₎ (8 p
                          ₍²32d2₎   781

NL 0451270   DLC MdBP OO MB CtY MB

MT Logier, Johann Bernhard, d. 1846.
24   Logier's system of the science of music,
L834   harmony and practical composition. New and
       enl. ed. London, Boosey; New York, Wm. A.
       Pond ₍n. d.₎
       265 p. illus. (music)

       COMPOSITION (MUSIC)
       HARMONY
       Title: Logier's system of the science of music

NL 0451271   KMK MWelC

Logier, Johann Bernhard, *d.* 1846.
Logier's system of the science of music, harmony, and practical composition. New ed. London, Boosey ₍18—₎
8, 8, 232 p. music. 29 cm.
Issued with "A bird's eye view of the rudiments of music" (8 p.) and "A concise history of musical notation" (8 p.) by John Green.
1. Composition (Music) 2. Harmony.   I. Green, John, fl. 1822–1844. II. Title.
MT24.L83   68–129278/MN

NL 0451272   DLC NN CLU

MT   Logier, Johann Bernhard, 1780–1846.
24   Logier's system of the science of music,
L83+   harmony, and practical composition. London,
1843   Boosey ₍1843?₎
          232 p. illus., music. 29cm.

NL 0451273   NIC MB

Logier, Johann Bernhard, d. 1846.
...Logier's system of the science of music, harmony, and practical composition; incidentally comprising thorough base, wit considerable additions, ... Lodnon, ᴮBoosey, [1864]
iv p., 4,8,8, 232p., illus. (music)
At head of title: New edition.

NL 0451274   OO

Logier, Johann Bernhard, 1780–1846.
Themes, written expressly by J. B. Logier, for those who are desirous of additional subjects for exercise in harmony, during the study of The science of music and composition, according to his principles... London: J. Green ₍1829?₎. 2 p.l., 15 p. 4°.
1. Harmony.
                                                       January 14, 1920.

NL 0451275   NN

Logier, Johann Bernhard, d. 1846.
Logier's Theoretical and practical study for the piano forte, comprising a series of compositions selected from the most classical works, ancient and modern: arranged with inverted and fundamental basses and fingered throughout: being a continuation of instruction on his system of musical education ... London, J. Green ₍18
v. 32½ᶜᵐ.
CONTENTS.—
no. 5. Haydn, Joseph. Allegro and Andante.
1. Piano music—Teaching pieces.
                                                       44–30371
Library of Congress   MT245.L8

NL 0451276   DLC ICN IaU MB USID

Logier, Johann Bernhard, 1780–1846.
Logier's theoretical and practical study for the piano forte, comprising a series of compositions selected from the most classical works, ancient and modern: arranged with inverted and fundamental basses and figured throughout: being a continuation of instruction on his System of musical education. no. 1–14... London: J. Green ₍ca. 1832₎. 14 parts in 1 v. f°.
Each number has separate t.-p.; no. 13–14, however, have t.-p. for his: Thoroughbass...a second series of...studies for the piano forte...
Contents: no. 1–2. CORELLI. 1st concerto; 8th concerto. no. 3–4. HANDEL. Occasional overture; Overture to Esther. no. 5–6. HAYDN. Symphony in D. no. 7–8. MOZART. Overture to Zauberflöte; Overture to Figaro. no. 9. CLEMENTI. Sonata in D. no. 10. SCARLATTI. Sonata: Cat's fugue. no. 11–12. BEETHOVEN. Trio ₍Op. 1₎ in Eb, with an acc. for a second piano. no. 13–14. KALKBRENNER. Sonata in C.
1. Piano.—Collections.
                                                       May 3, 1920.

NL 0451278   NN

LOGIER, JOHANN BERNHARD, 1780–1846.
"Time, empty form," a ballad with an accompaniment for the piano forte. Dublin, W. Power [180–?]
3 p. 32cm.
Caption title.
1. Songs, English.

NL 0451279   NN

Logigan, Stefan.
Zur Frage des Bohrlochabstandes ("Well spacing"). Hamburg, Industrieverlag von Hernhaussen ₍1955₎
96 p. illus. 24 cm.
Bibliography: p. 95–96.
1. Boring. 2. Petroleum—Well-boring.   I. Title: Well spacing.
                                                       A 56–1568
Illinois. Univ. Library
for Library of Congress

NL 0451280   IU ICJ

... **Logik.** Tübingen, J. C. B. Mohr (P. Siebeck) 1912
viii, 275 p. 27ᶜᵐ. (Encyclopädie der philosophischen wissenschaften ... 1. bd.) M. 7.
"Die im originale abgelieferten beiträge wurden übersetzt von: Edmund Schweitzer (Royce), Violet Plinke (Couturat), Achille Malavisi (Croce), dr. Karl Büchler (Enriques). Der beitrag von Nikolaj Losskij wurde im russischen original und in der deutschen uebersetzung vom verfasser geliefert."—p. 275.
CONTENTS.—Einleitung, von A. Ruge.—Die prinzipien der logik, von W. Windelband.—Prinzipien der logik, von J. Royce.—Die prinzipien der logik, von L. Couturat.—Die aufgabe der logik, von B. Croce.—Die probleme der logik, von F. Enriques.—Die umgestaltung des bewusstseinsbegriffes in der modernen erkenntnistheorie und ihre bedeutung für die logik, von N. Losskij.
1. Logic. 2. Knowledge, Theory of.   I. Windelband, Wilhelm, 1848–   II. Royce, Josiah, 1855–   III. Couturat, Louis, 1868–   IV. Croce, Benedetto, 1866–   v. Enriques, Federigo, 1871–   VI. Losskij, Nikolaj.
                                                       12–21638
Library of Congress   BC6.L6

NL 0451281   DLC AAP OU

Logik eller den videnskab at taenke
see under   ₍Kraft, Jens₎ 1720–1765.

Die logik und psychologie der Araber im zehnter jahrhundert n. Chr., von Friedrich Dieterici
see under   ₍Ikhwān al-safa, Basra₎

Logike Latreia. The Reasonablenesse of Divine Service: or Non-conformity to Commonprayer, proved, Not conformable to Common Reason
see under   Freeman, Ireneus, pseud.

Login, Edith Dalhousie, ed.

Login, Lena (Campbell) *lady,* 1820–1904.
Lady Login's recollections; court life and camp life, 1820–1904, by E. Dalhousie Login ... London, Smith, Elder & co., 1916.

Login, Edith Dalhousie.
The story of the Campbells of Kinloch, by E. Dalhousie Login ... London, J. Murray, 1924.
ix, 86 p. front., illus., pl., ports., facsim., fold. geneal. tables. 21ᶜᵐ.
Coat of arms on cover.
1. Campbell family.
                                                       26–2774
Library of Congress   CS479.C3 1924

NL 0451286   DLC OClWHi OCl NN

VOLUME 338

Login, Lena (Campbell) *lady,* 1820–1904.
Lady Login's recollections; court life and camp life, 1820–1904, by E. Dalhousie Login ... London, Smith, Elder & co., 1916.

4 p. l., 345 p. col. front., ports., facsim. 23ᶜᵐ.

1. India—Soc. life & cust. 2. Gt. Brit.—Court and courtiers. 3. Dhuleep Singh, maharajah, 1838–1893. I. Login, Edith Dalhousie, ed.

17–14979

Library of Congress   DS475.2.L83A3

NL 0451287   DLC NcD MiU CU CtY ViU NSyU NN

Login, ₍Lena Campbell₎, **lady.**
Recollections, court life and camp life, 1820–1904, by E. Dalhousie Login.   New York: E. P. Dutton and Co., 1916.   345 p. fold. fac., pl., port. (1 col'd.)   8°.

I. Login, E. Dalhousie, editor. 2.   Login, Lena Campbell, lady.
March 22, 1917.

NL 0451288   NN MB MoU OWorP

DS
475.2   **Login, Lena (Campbell)** lady, 1820–1904.
L83   Lady Login's recollections; court life and
A3   camp life, 1820–1904, by E. Dalhousie Login ...
London.   J. Murray, 1917.
345 p. col. front., ports., facsim.

1. India – Social life & customs. 2. Great
Britain – Court and courtiers. 3. Dhuleep,
Singh, maharajah,   1838–1893. I. Login,
Edith Dalhousie.

NL 0451289   WaU

Login, Lena (Campbell) *lady,* 1820– *1904*
Sir John Login and Duleep Singh by Lady Login.   With an introduction by Colonel G. B. Malleson, c. s. i.   London, W. H. Allen & co., 1890.

xx, 580 p. illus., port., fold. map. 22½ᶜᵐ.

1. Login, Sir John Spencer, 1809–1863. 2. Dhuleep Singh, maharajah, 1838–1893.

Library of Congress   DS475.L8L8

2—9325

NL 0451290   DLC MiU CU MnU CtY WU NN OCl MH

Login, M   I
Автоматические и централизованные трамвайные стрелки.   Москва, Изд-во Министерства коммунального хозяйства РСФСР, 1953.
Microfilm copy (negative) made in 1956 by the Library of Congress. Collation of the original, as determined from the film: 47, ₍1₎ p. illus.
Bibliography: p. ₍48₎

1. Street-railroads. 2. Electric railroads—Switches. I. Title. I. Title transliterated: Avtomaticheskie i tsentralizovannye tramvainye strelki.

Microfilm Slavic 749 T   Mic 58–6753

NL 0451291   DLC

Login, M   I
Изготовление стопорных пружинных шайб.   Москва, Гос. научно-техн. изд-во машиностроит. и судострот. лит-ры, 1954.
23, ₍1₎ p. diagrs. 20 cm.
Bibliography: p. ₍24₎

1. Fastenings.   I. Title.   Title transliterated: Izgotovlenie stopornykh pruzhinnykh shaib.

TJ1320.L6   55–28501

NL 0451292   DLC

Login, Spencer Henry Metcalfe, 1851–
Gt. Brit. *Admiralty. Committee on canteen and victualling arrangements in H. M. fleet.*
Navy (canteen and victualling arrangements). Report of the Committee appointed to inquire into the question of the canteen and victualling arrangements in H. M. fleet. Presented to both houses of Parliament by command of His Majesty. London, Printed for H. M. Stationery off., by Eyre and Spottiswoode ₍1907₎

NL 0451294   CU

Login. T.
Roads, railways, and canals for India.
Extracted from "Professional papers on Indian engineering" with practical suggestions.
By T. Login ...   London, E. and F.N. Spon, 1869.
1 p.l., iii, 30 p.   fold. map.   24 cm.
[Henry Morse Stephens collection; pamphlets on India. v. 4, no. 5]

NL 0451294   CU

Login Brothers.
Physicians' Anatomical Aid, patented.   Chicago₎ Login Bros., ₍n.d.₎
6 superimp. pls. (full-p), 2 double pls., 4 pls. (full-p₎.
No. t.-p., label on fr. cover.
Notations on each illus., no text.
(Bound in folio black env. with clasp)
1. Anatomy - Atlases.

NL 0451295   KU-M

Loginov, A
Молодые отряды рабочего класса СССР.₎ ₍Москва₎ Гос-политиздат, 1944.
61, ₍8₎ p. 17 cm.

1. World war, 1939–1945—Russia. 2. Youth—Russia. 3. Labor and laboring classes—Russia. I. Title. Title transliterated: Molodye otriady rabochego klassa SSSR.

DK273.L6   48–34518

NL 0451296   DLC

HC335
.E42   **Loginov, Aleksandr Pavlovich,** joint author.
Ëldinova, L   L
Сборник задач по курсу Государственные доходы СССР.   Москва, Госфиниздат, 1948.

Loginov, Aleksej Petrovich.
Как выполняется пятилетний план.   Москва, Гос. изд-во сельскохозяйственной и колхозно-кооперативной лит-ры, 1931.
156 p. illus. 23 cm.

1. Russia—Economic policy—1928–1932. Title transliterated: Kak vypolniaetsia piatiletnii plan.

HC335.L645   48–37979*

NL 0451298   DLC

Loginov, Anatolii.
Das 800jährige ₍i. e. achthundertjährige₎ Moskau.   Berlin, SWA-Verlag, 1947.
81 p. illus. 22 cm.
Tr. by Eduard Rosenberg.

1. Moscow—Descr. 2. Moscow—Soc. condit. I. Title.

DK601.L813   914.7   49–18436*‡

NL 0451299   DLC MB NcD

Loginov, Anatolii.
Москва на стройке. ₍Москва₎ Молодая гвардия, 1955.
414 p. illus. 23 cm.
At head of title: А. Логинов, П. Лопатин.

1. Cities and towns—Planning—Moscow.   I. Lopatin, Pavel Ivanovich, joint author.   Title transliterated: Moskva na stroike.

NA9212.M6L6   56–28197

NL 0451300   DLC

Loginov, Anatolii.
Москва—столица Советской державы. ₍1147–1947. Москва₎ Гос. изд-во полит. лит-ры, 1947.
Microfilm copy. Negative.
Collation of the original as determined from the film: 77 p.
At head of title: 800 лет Москвы.

1. Moscow.   I. Title.   Title transliterated: Moskva—stolitsa Sovetskoi derzhavy.

Microfilm Slavic 268 DK   Mic 55–3060

NL 0451301   DLC

Loginov, Anatolii.
Наша Москва. ₍Москва₎ Московский рабочий, 1947.
265 p. illus. ports. 22 cm.

1. Moscow—Descr. 2. Moscow—Soc. condit.   Title transliterated: Nasha Moskva.

DK601.L8   48–17226*

NL 0451302   DLC

Loginov, B   G
Интенсификация добычи нефти методом кислотной обработки; опыт промыслов объединения Башнефть. Москва, Гос. научно-техн. изд-во нефтяной и горно-топливной лит-ры, 1951.
158 p. illus. 22 cm.
Bibliography: p. ₍157₎

1. Oil wells—Acidization.   I. Title.   Title transliterated: Intensifikatsiia dobychi nefti metodom kislotnoi obrabotki.

TN871.L58   58–37546

NL 0451303   DLC

Loginov, B   I
Эксплуатационные испытания котлоагрегатов.   Москва, Гос. энерг. изд-во, 1952.
101, ₍2₎ p. illus. 23 cm.
Errata slip inserted.
Bibliography: p. ₍102₎

1. Steam-boilers—Incrustations.   I. Title.   Title transliterated: Ekspluatatsionnye ispytaniia kotloagregatov.

TJ390.L6   53–38264

NL 0451304   DLC

LB2923
.V48   **Loginov, D. S.,** joint author.
Veselov, M   O
Организация работы в советской школе; практическое школоведение. С предисл. Ф. Г. Мопочниенкова. Москва, Работник просвещения, 1928.

VOLUME 338

Loginov, F G
Возрождение Днепрогэса. Киев, Гос. изд-во техн. лит-ры Украины, 1951.
150 p. illus., port., map. 21 cm.

1. Dneprovskaſa gidroĕlektricheskaſa stanſſiſa. I. Title.
Title transliterated: Vozrozhdenie Dneprogĕsa.

TK1486.D6L6   52–36641

NL 0451306   DLC

S241
.V83
no. 31

Loginov, F G
Сталинградская гидроэлектростанция на Волге. Москва, Знание, 1952.
15 p. 22 cm. (Всесоюзное общество по распространению политических и научных знаний. Серия 3, № 31)

1. Volgogradskaia gidroelektricheskaia stantsiia. I. Title.
(Series: Vsesoſuznoe obshchestvo po rasprostraneniſa politicheskikh i nauchnykh znaniſ. Seriſa 3, 1952, no. 31)
Title transliterated: Stalingradskaſa gidroĕlektrostanſſiſa na Volge.

S241 V83 no. 31   53–30894

NL 0451307   DLC

T50
.E33

Loginov, L. I., ed.
ЭТИ. Энциклопедия технических измерений. Редакционная коллегия: Л. В. Залуцкий, Л. И. Логинов, ответственный редактор ¡и др.¿ Изд. 2., стереотипное. Ленинград, Глав. ред. энерг. лит-ры, 1934–

Law

Loginov, Mikhail Osipovich, joint comp.

Russia (*1923– U. S. S. R.*) *Laws, statutes, etc.*
...Сборник постановлений о промысловой кооперации и кустарной промышленности; постановления правительств Союза СССР и союзных республик, составили И. А. Селицкий, М. И. Логиновым и Р. Хойским, с введением Всепромсовета, под редакцией и с предисловием проф. Д. М. Генкина. Москва, Государственное юридическое изд-во РСФСР, 1930.

Loginov, Nikolaĭ Grigor'evich.
Памятка по технике безопасности составителю поездов и сцепщику вагонов. 2. изд. Москва, Гос. трансп. желдор. изд-во, 1954.
71 p. illus. 17 cm.

1. Railroads—Russia—Safety measures. 2. Railroads—Making up trains. I. Title.
Title transliterated: Pamſatka po tekhnike bezopasnosti sostaviteſu poezdov.

TF610.L6 1954   55–29875 rev

NL 0451310   DLC

Loginov, Nikolaĭ Petrovich.
Работа редакции газеты с письмами трудящихся. ¡Москва?¿ Гос. изд-во полит. лит-ры, 1953.
50 p. 20 cm. (В помощь работникам печати)

1. Copy-reading. 2. Journalism—Russia. I. Title.
Title transliterated: Rabota redakſſiſ gazety s pis'mami trudſashchikhſa.

PN4784.C75L6   55–21306 rev ‡

NL 0451311   DLC

Loginov, S P
Экономика судостроительной промышленности СССР; очерки. Ленинград, Гос. изд-во обор. промышл., 1939.
220 p. diagrs. 23 cm.

1. Ship-building—Russia.
Title transliterated: Ĕkonomika sudostroitel'noĭ promyshlennosti SSSR.

VM85.L6   50–42516¡

NL 0451312   DLC

Loginov, V I
Нормирование расхода топлива в котельных установках. Москва, Госпланиздат, 1943.
30 p. 22 cm. (Народное хозяйство на службе Отечественной войны)
"Работа подготовлена и составлена ... В. И. Логиновым и Н. А. Бережным."

1. Coal—Russia. 2. Boilers. I. Berezhnyĭ, N. A., joint author. II. Title. (Series: Narodnoe khozſaĭstvo na sluzhbe Otechestvennoĭ voĭny) *Title transliterated:* Normirovanie raskhoda topliva.

TP326.R9L6   51–50752

NL 0451313   DLC

TK6565
.D4B4

Loginov, V N., joint author.

Belſaev, A F
Кристаллические детекторы и усилители. Москва, Гос. энерг. изд-во, 1951.

Loginov, V N
Радиотелеуправление. Москва, Гос. энерг. изд-во, 1950.
71 p. diagrs. 20 cm. (Массовая радиобиблиотека, вып. 82)

1. Remote control. I. Title.
Title transliterated: Radioteleupravlenie.

TK5777.L6   56–29896

NL 0451315   DLC

Loginov, V N
Радиоизмерения. Москва, Гос. энерг. изд-во, 1954.
119 p. illus. 21 cm. (Массовая радиобиблиотека, вып. 208)

1. Radio measurements. I. Title.
Title transliterated: Radioizmereniſa.

TK6553.L6   55–34138¡

NL 0451316   DLC

TK6560
.L6

Loginov, V N
Справочник по радиодеталям. Москва, Гос. энерг. изд-во, 1949.
79 p. diagrs. 20 cm. (Массовая радиобиблиотека, вып. 41)

1. Radio—Apparatus and supplies. I. Title.
Title transliterated: Spravochnik po radiodetalſam.

TK6560.L6   54–17546

NL 0451317   DLC

Loginov, V. V., *firm, booksellers, Moscow.*
Реэстръ россійскимъ книгамъ, продающимся въ Москвѣ, въ книжной лавкѣ подъ no. 1. и 2., что на Никольской улицѣ во флигелѣ Заиконоспаскаго монастыря, Василья Васильева Логинова. Также на разныхъ ярмаркахъ: нижегородской, коренной, Сумахъ, Харьковѣ, Ростовѣ и другихъ. Москва, въ Тип. И. Московскаго театра, у содержателя А. Похорскаго, 1826.
2 p. l., 167 p. 22½ᶜᵐ.

1. Russian literature—Bibl.—Catalogs. 2. Catalogs, Booksellers'—Russia.

Library of Congress   Z2519.L78   16–22208
——— Copy 2.
Imperfect: t.-p. muti-   lated, 2d prelim. leaf wanting.

NL 0451318   DLC

Loginov, Vasiliĭ
Разсказы. Харбин, Бамбуковая роща, 1929.
290 p. 25 cm.

Title romanized: Razskazy.

PG3476.L663R3   78–466631

NL 0451319   DLC

Loginov-Lesnſak, P 1891–1938.
(Dikoe pole)
Дикое поле; роман. Москва, Московский рабочий ¡1928¿
189 p. 20 cm. (Новинки пролетарской литературы)

I. Title.

PG3476.L663D5 1928   78–215655

NL 0451320   DLC

Law

Loginychev, A., joint ed.

Russia (*1923– U. S. S. R.*) *Laws, statutes, etc.*
Важнейшие решения партии и правительства по сельскому хозяйству, 1946–1949 гг. ¡Сборник составили А. Шаров и А. Логинычев. ¡Киров¿ Кировское обл. гос. изд-во, 1949.

Logio, George Clenton.
Bulgaria, past & present, by George Clenton Logio ... With 25 illustrations & maps ... Manchester, Sherratt & Hughes, 1936.
viii, 480 p. front., illus. (facsim.) plates, port. group, maps. 21ᶜᵐ.
Printed in Bulgaria.
Errata slip inserted.

1. Bulgaria. 2. Bulgaria—Econ. condit.—1918–   37–7528

Library of Congress   DR55.L6
                                                   949.7

NL 0451322   DLC NBuU MU NBC NcD CtY DN ICU NN PBm

Logio, George Clenton.
Bulgaria, problems & politics, by George Clenton Logio ... London, W. Heinemann, 1919.
ix, 285 p. incl. front. (map) illus. (map) 19½ᶜᵐ.

1. Bulgaria—Pol. & govt. 2. European war, 1914–1918—Bulgaria. 3. Eastern question (Balkan) I. Title.   20–439

Library of Congress   DR72.L6

MB OC1W PP MH NjP NN
NL 0451323   DLC OC1 IdU NjN MtU CaBVaU CtY PPD ICJ

VOLUME 338

Logio, George Clenton.
   Essay-uri sociale si stiintifice; tr. din englezeste de M.N.I. Bucuresti, Libraria Pavel Suru, 1928.
   [128p.]

NL 0451324   OC1

Logio, George Clenton.
   Rumania; its history, politics and economics, by George Clenton Logio ... Manchester, Sherratt & Hughes, 1932.
   4 p. l., 207, [1] p. 22ᶜᵐ.

   1. Rumania—Hist. 2. Rumania—Pol. & govt. 3. Rumania—Econ. condit.—1918–

   Library of Congress   DR217.L6
                                      33–4936
                                      949.8

NL 0451325   DLC IdU WaU GU MH CtY NN MB

Logios Hermēs; syngramma philologikon periodikon tetrakis tou etous ekdidomenon. En Lougdounō tōn Batabōn.
   tom 1, no.A; tom 5, no.1 (1866–76)
   Edited by Kontos
   No more published. Nothing published between v.1, no.1 and v.5, no.1 Megalē Hellēnikē Enkyklepaīdeia

NL 0451326   MH NjP OCU NN

Logistates (Achilleus). *Die Transfusion bei abnormer Mischung des Blutes. 18 pp. 8°. Würzburg, C. J. Becker. 1870. _c.

NL 0451327   DNLM

Film   **LOGIOU, J**   1920–
2°4   À propos de trois cas de fièvre
no.15   typhoïde avec meningisme. Paris, 1947.
    28 p. (Paris. [Université] Faculté de médecine. Thèse, 1947, no. 652)
    Film copy.
    1. Brain 2. Paratyphoid
    3. Typhoid – Complications

NL 0451328   DNLM

La logique ... Lettre d'une vieille femme adressée en avril 1871, à M. le chef du pouvoir exécutif, à M. le président et MM. les membres de l'Assemblée. [Versailles, Crété, imprimeur de la préfecture, 1871]
   8 p. 22ᶜᵐ.
   Caption title.

   1. France—Pol. & govt.—1789–1900.   I. Une vieille femme.

                                    13–16278
   Library of Congress   JN2593.1871.L6

NL 0451329   DLC

La logique dans l'histoire
     see under   Bauer, Arthur, 1850–

La logique de l'esprit et du coeur, a l'usage des dames
     see under   [Blanchet, Jean] 1724–1778.

Logique de Port-Royal
     see under   [Arnauld, Antoine] 1612–1694.

La logiqve dv prince
     see under   [La Mothe Le Vayer, François de] 1583–1672.

... **Logique et méthodologie, exposés publiés sous la direction de Thomas Greenwood. ...**
     see under   Greenwood, Thomas, 1901–   ed.

La logique; ou, L'art de penser
     see under   [Arnauld, Antoine] 1612–1694.

Logische Studien im Gebiete der Jurisprudenz
     see under   Fuchs, Wilhelm, 1886–

Logistes, *pseud.*
   see
Glasgow, George, 1891–

U168   **Logistics.** v.1–2; Oct.1945–July 1947. Washing-
.L83   ton, D.C., Army Ordnance Association.
    2 v. in 1. illus., ports. quarterly.
    Merged into Ordnance, the official bi-monthly magazine of the Army Ordnance Association.

   1. Logistics—Period.

NL 0451338   ICU IU MB MH-BA

Lo-Giudice, G   Crimi
     see   Crimi Lo-Giudice, G.

---

41   **Logiudice, C**   Natalio.
L822A   La anestesia por gases en los animales domésticos (publicación preliminar) ... por los doctores C. N. Logiudice [y] G. M. Aranges. La Plata, 1946.
    2 pts. in 1.   25.5 cm.
    At head of title: Ministerio de justicia e instrucción pública, Universidad nacional de la Plata, Facultad de medicina veterinaria.
    Paged continuously.
    Only [pt. 1] is "Publicación preliminar."

NL 0451340   DNAL

Logiudice, C. Natalio. ... Contribución al estudio de la pleuresia sero-fibrinosa del caballo ... Bruxelles, Impr. G. Bothy, 1911. 109p. illus. 26cm.
   Tésis—La Plata.

NL 0451341   CU

Logiudice, C. Natalio.
   ... Escuela de veterinaria de Bruselas (por) C. N. Logiudice... La Plata, Taller grafico J. Sese y cª, 1913.
   14 p. fold. pl.   23 cm.
   At head of title: Universidad nacional de La Plata, Facultad de agronomia y veterinaria.
   Extracto del tomo X, de la Revista de la facultad de agronomia y veterinaria.

NL 0451342   DHEW

Logiudice, C. Natalio.
   —— ... Los quistes del ovario en la gallina ... La Plata, J. Sesé, 1914. 8p. 2 pl. 26cm.
   At head of title: Universidad nacional de la Plata. Facultad de agronomia y veterinaria.

NL 0451343   CU

---

41   **Logiudice, C**   Natalio.
.822   ... La uretrostomia perineal en el caballo (retajo) ... Buenos Aires, López, 1938.
    10 p. illus. 27 cm.
    At head of title: Facultad de medicina veterinaria de La Plata.
    Bibliografía: p. 10.
    1. Urethrotomy. 2. Horses. Diseases. I. La Plata. Universidad nacional. Facultad de medicina veterinaria.

NL 0451344   DNAL

Lo Giudice, Carmelo.
   Il vangelo. Roma, Edizioni "La Civiltà Cattolica " [1953]
   336 p. (Manuali del pensiero Cattolico, 16)

NL 0451345   DCU

LO GIUDICE, Emmanuele.
   Ragioni a favor dell' inclito regimento suizzero Tschoudy e suo consiglio militare, da esaminarsi nella suprema giunta di guerra. Napoli, 1749.
   f°. (16) p.

NL 0451346   MH-L

Lo Giudice, Francesco.
   ...L'assicurazione contro le malattie per gli addetti al commercio in Italia. Ancona, Stab. tipografico artistico marchigiano poligrafica Ancona ex combattenti, [1935]
   156 p.incl.tables. 225 ᶜᵐ.
   At head of title: Scuola di perfezionamento in medicina legale ed infortunistica nella R.Università di Padova.
   "Bibliografia": p.[147]-153.

NL 0451347   NjP

QL1   **Lo Giudice, Pietro**
P3   Le condizioni dei laghi di Ganzirri e del
no.12   Faro (Messina); in speciale rapporto alla molluschicoltura. Note ed appunti. Pavia, Mattei & C., 1913.
    14 p. 25 cm. (Pavia. Universita. Istituto Zoologico. Lavori n. 12)
    "Bibliografia consultata": p. 14.

   1. Mollusks – Sicily. (Series)

NL 0451348   DI

VOLUME 338

Lo Giudice, Pietro.
100107 ... . Studi sui *cnidosporidi*, del dott. Pietro lo Giudice. Pavia, Mattei, Speroni & c., 1912.
91 p. 1 fold. pl. 25ᶜᵐ.
At head of title: Istituto zoologico della R. Università di Pavia.
"Bibliografia consultata," p. 84–88.

NL 0451349 ICJ DI

QL1.
P3
no.2
Lo Giudice, Pietro
Sulla struttura delle branchie nei pesci; nota preliminare ... Pavia, Mattei, Speroni & C. [1910]
5 p. illus. 25 cm. (Pavia. Universita. Istituto Zoologico. Lavori n. 2)
"Bibliografia": p. 5.

1. Gills. 2. Fishes - Anatomy. I. Title: Branchie nei pesci, Struttura delle. (Series)

NL 0451350 DI

QL1
P3
no.15
Lo Giudice, Pietro
Sulle condizioni fisico-biologiche del Mar Piccolo di Taranto in rapporto alla mitilicoltura e alla ostricoltura e sullo stato attuale delle zone patrimoniali del predetto mare. Indagini preliminari. Pavia, Mattei & C.,1913.
24 p. fold. map, tables. 25 cm. (Pavia. Universita. Istituto Zoologico. Lavori n.15)

1. Mollusks - Italy. 2. Oyster-culture - Italy. 3. Taranto, Gulf of. (Series)

NL 0451351 DI

QL1
P3
no.5
Lo Giudice, Pietro
Sulle diverse razze locali o "famiglie" (Heincke) di accinghe (Engraulis encrasicholus Cuv.); nota. Pavia, Mattei, Speroni & C., 1911.
6 p. 25 cm. (Pavia. Universita. Istituto Zoologico. Lavori n. 5)

1. Anchovies. (Series)

NL 0451352 DI

QL1
P3
no.6
Lo Giudice, Pietro
Sullo sviluppo del "Myxobolus ellipsoides" Thel. Nota preliminare. Pavia, Mattei, Speroni & C., 1911.
9 p. illus. 25 cm. (Pavia. Universita. Istituto Zoologico. Lavori n. 6)
"Bibliografia": p. 8–9.

1. Parasites - Fishes. 2. Sporozoa. (Series)

NL 0451353 DI

BQV192
.C2
L032
1748

Robbins
Coll.
Logk, Otto, praeses.
Regula cleri tam saecularis, quam regularis, sive Tractatus theologicus canonico-moralis de clero, juxta ordinem XXV. Titulorum lib. iii. Decretal.Gregorii IX... a Tit. I usque XXV. methodice digestus... Pragae in...collegio ad S. Adalbertum praeside Ottone.Logk...solemni disputationi propositus a P. Edmundo Knofflicius Vetero-Pragae, Ignatius Pruscha, 1748.
[1] 539 [3] p.

Head and tail pieces; initials

NL 0451354 CU-L

Lognos, Jean, 1888-
... Le drainage en gynécologie ...
Montpellier, 1913.
25 cm.
Thèse - Univ. de Montpellier.

NL 0451355 CtY DNLM

Logofet, Alexander, tr.

Union of the Siberian creamery and other cooperative associations. *Section of economical statistics.*
"Union of the Siberian creamery and other co-operative associations" and the country served by this organization. Comp. by the Section of economical statistics of the board of the Union of the Siberian creamery associations, May 1919, Omsk, Siberia. Boston, Mass. [Printed by Blanchard printing co.] 1919.

Logofet, D N
На границахъ Средней Азіи; путевые очерки. С.-Петербургъ, В. Березовскій, 1909.
3 v. in 1. illus., fold. maps (1 col.) 24 cm.
On cover: On the frontiers of Central Asia.

1. Asia, Central—Descr. & trav.   I. Title.
Title transliterated: Na granitsakh Srednei Azii.

DS785.L6   60–58165

NL 0451357 DLC

Logofet, Pakhomii
see Pakhomii Logofet, monk, 15th cent.

O logografo; ou, O monitor secreto. Traduzido do Ambigu ... O sonho, ou a visão, ou o dia subsequente ao parto de Maria Luiza. Lisboa,Na Impressão regia,1811.
15p. 23cm. [Binder's title:

NL 0451359 CtY

Le **Logographe,** journal national.
no.

[Paris:] Baudouin, 179   51½cm.
nos.
Daily.
"Les séances...[sont] redigées d'après le travail de la Société logographique."
No. 277–316 (July – Aug., 1792) include semimonthly suppl. no. 1-4.
Ceased publication with no. 316 (Aug. 17, 1792).

1. France—Hist.—Revolution—Per.   and soc. publ. I. Baudouin, François
Jean, 1759–1838, editor. II. Société   logographique, Paris.
                                        January 16, 1934

NL 0451360 NN ICN NjP

Micro-
film
DC
21
Le **Logographe,**journal nationale,rédige par Le Hodey... no.1-158,27 avril-1 oct.1791; [sér. 2,no.1-317,]2 oct.1791-18 âout,1792. [Paris,1791-92.]
475 nos.on 3 reels.
No.317,Aug.18,1792 in manuscript;was never printed.-cf.Hatin,Bibl. ... de la presse périodique française,p.132-33.
Original in the Bibliothèque nationale.
Positive

NL 0451361 ICU OrPS OCU

Logographe, dédié à m. Gratien, évêque de rouen. 2. éd., revue, corrigée et augmentée. [n.p., 1792?]

4 p. 20 cm.

NL 0451362 MH

Λόγοι Ἀπολογητικοί. Foure Apologicall Tracts Exhibited To the Supreme, Self-made Authority, now erected in, under the Commons name of England. Wherein is proved, That their unparallel'd Acts in beheading the most Christian King, nulling the Regall Office, disclaiming the knowne Heir, Charles the II. and declaring it Treason to reself their Errours, Are diametrically opposite to the Scriptures, . . . By T. B. a Conscientious and Orthodox Divine. . . . Printed in the Yeare, 1649.
pp. iv, 32 (1 blank). 182 × 146.

NL 0451363 NNG MnU MH CtY ICN DFo MdBP CSmH

Logoluso, Pietro.
... Su la "Descriptio Italiæ" di Sebastiano Münster (dal II lib. della Cosmographia universalis) con alcune notizie storiche e critiche su l'a. e su la sua Cosmographia. Trani, Tip. A. Laghezza, 1906.
1 p. l., vii, [3]–166 p. 26½ᵐᵐ.
"Indice bibliografico": p. i-iii.

1. Münster, Sebastian, 1489-1552. Cosmographia universalis. 2. Italy—Descr. & trav.
                                        11–34091
Library of Congress   DG423.L7

NL 0451364 DLC

Logoluso, Pietro.
... Su le origini del nome "America." Trani, Tip. A. Laghezza, 1903.
84 p. 26½ᵐᵐ.

1. America—Name. 2. Vespucci, Amerigo, 1451–1512.
                                        11–15751
Library of Congress   E125.V6L8

NL 0451365 DLC

Logomachia: or, The conquest of eloquence
see under Ker, Patrick, fl. 1691.

Logman, H
Sierduiven, verzorging, teelt en rassen, door H. Logman jr. ... Utrecht, W. de Haan [1941]
2 p. l., 79 p. illus., plates. 25½ᵐᵐ. (*Half-title:* De Haan's huisdierenbibliotheek, no. 1)

1. Pigeons.   I. Title.
SF465.L82   A F 47–400
N. Y. st. coll. agr., Cornell   univ. Library
for Library of Congress   [4]†

NL 0451367 DLC IaAS NIC

RC
423
A1
L6
Logopædie en foniatrie. 1-   jaarg.; 1929-   Groningen, J. B. Wolters.

Title varies: 1-   Tijdschrift voor logopaedie en phoniatre.

Tijdschrift voor logopaediie en phoniatre.

NL 0451368 KMK NhD

VOLUME 338

Logophilus, *pseud.*

"" Der Streit über die Zillmer'sche Methode in der Lebensversicherung. Eine Antwort an den Versicherungstechniker von Logophilus. Berlin, Zeitschrift für Versicherungswesen, 1902.
vi, 112 p. 24½^{cm}.

NL 0451369   ICJ

Logophilus (Ptus), *pseud.*

Brief... aan een zyner vrienden wegens de beroeringen te Huisen. *Harlingen: F. van der Plaats,* 1750. 15 pp. sq. 8°.

NL 0451370   NN

Logos, *pseud.*

Variable gears; an explanatory hand-book dealing with variable gears in theory and practice, and including a list arranged alphabetically and year by year of patents relating to variable gears, by "Logos". With illustrations drawn by L. Skelsey. London, W. A. Standring, 1908.

xxiii, 151 p. illus, diagrs. 22^{cm}.

"Patents relating to speed gears": p. xvi-xxiii.
Includes advertising matter.

NL 0451371   ICJ

#LH1
.E516

Logos. v. 1, no. 1-
Oct. 1945-
[Boston] Emmanuel alumnae association, 1945.
v. illus., port. 21 1/2cm.
Includes book reviews.
Editor: Oct. 1945-   Mary E. Martin.

1. Periodicals, English. I. Emmanuel college. Boston, Mass. Alumnae association. II. Martin, Mary E., ed.

NL 0451372   MB

G105
L829

Logos. t.1-   (no.1-   ); jun./agosto 1949

México.
v. 24cm. irregular.

"Revista de la Mesa Redonda de Filosofía de la Facultad de Filosofía y Letras [de la Universidad Nacional Autónoma de México]"

1. Philosophy – Period. I. Mexico (City) Universidad Nacional. Facultad de Filosofía y Letras. Mesa   Redonda de Filosofía.

NL 0451373   TxU CoU DLC

Логосъ; международный ежегодникъ по философіи культуры. Русское изд. ... кн. 1-   Москва, Книгоиздательство "Мусагетъ," 1910-
v. 25¼^{cm}. 2 no. a year.
Editors: 1910-   S. I. Hessen, R. K. Metner, F. A. Stepun.
Includes section "Библіографія."

1. Philosophy—Period. I. Hessen, Sergei Iosifovich, 1887-   ed. II. Metner, Emilii Karlovich, ed. III. Stepun, Fedor Avgustovich, 1884- ed.
Title transliterated: Logos.

43-26896

Library of Congress   B8.R9L6

NL 0451374   DLC InU

[Logos]

AP85
.L55

Λόγος. Χρόνος Α'-   τεῦχος
     Μυτιλήνη.
     v. 25cm.

NL 0451375   OCU

Logos...
   Anno

Napoli [etc.] Libreria edit. F. Perrella, 1937-38.   25cm.
v.

Quarterly.
Anno 20-   also called n. s., anno 1-
July, 1936-1937, "organo della Biblioteca filosofica di Palermo (Accademia di scienze filosofiche)."
Editors: 19   Antonio Aliotta, and others.
Includes section "Recensioni."

1. Philosophy—Per. and soc. publ.   —Italy. I. Aliotta, Antonio, ed.
February 16, 1940

NL 0451376   NN

[Ho logos]

AP85
.16

Ὠ λόγος. Διευθυντὴς: Ἄγγελος Τερζάκης. Ἐκδότης: Ἀριστ. Ν. Μαυρ[ίδη]ς. τ.1-   Ὀκτώβρης 1930-
[Ἀθήνα, τυπ. Ἀριστ. Μ. Μαυρ[ίδη]ς]
v. illus. 24cm.

NL 0451377   OCU

Logos. Ephemeris tes en Christo threskeias, politeias kai philosophias.   Athens. 1-3, 2 Mr 1868 - 13 Mr 1871 //

NL 0451378   OCU

BX4711
.74
.L6

Логосъ; богословскій квартальникъ. т.1- civ./сер. 1950-
Yorkton [etc.] Canada.
v. illus. 26 cm.

Issued by the Ukrainian Redemptorist Fathers, St. Mary, Seminary.
Separately paged supplements accompany some numbers.

1. Catholic Church. Byzantine rite (Ukrainian)—Period. Redemptorists. Eastern Rite Branch. Vice-Province of Yorkton.
Title transliterated: Logos.

BX4711.74.L6   65-48841

NL 0451379   DLC CLU NN

... **Logos;** filosofijos laikraštis ... 1./2.-   metai; 1921/22-
   Kaunas, 1922-
   v.   25^{cm}. 2 no. a year.
At head of title, 1924-   : Ephemeris philosophica Theologicae-philosophicae facultatis in universitate Lituana.
"Leidžia Lietuvos universiteto Teologijos-filosofijos fakulteto filosofijos skyrius."
Editor: 1924-   Pr. Dovydaitis.

1. Philosophy—Period. I. Dovydaitis, Pr., ed. II. Kaunas. Lietuvos universitetas.

Library of Congress   B8.L6L6   29-23475

NL 0451380   DLC MoU

Logos; internationale zeitschrift für philosophie der kultur. bd. 1-22; 1910-33. Tübingen, Mohr, 1910-33.
22 v. 25½^{cm}. 3 nos. a year (irregular)
Editors: 1910-24, Georg Mehlis (with Richard Kroner, 1912-24)—1924-33, Richard Kroner.
Superseded by Zeitschrift für deutsche kulturphilosophie.

1. Philosophy—Period. I. Mehlis, Georg, 1878-   ed. II. Kroner, Richard, 1884-   ed.

Library of Congress   B3.L7   11-11329 Revised

NcD TxU OU MiU OClW OCU NIC PBm PU
NL 0451381   DLC CaBVaU MH ICN GEU TNJ TU FU GU NcU

Logos; introduction aux études philosophiques. (Presses Universitaire de France) Paris, 1, 193-

NL 0451382   PHC

[Ho logos]

PA5201
.16

Ὁ λόγος· μηνιαῖο περιοδικό. Διευθυντές: Ὁ Μπεκὲς καὶ Ι. Χαλκούσης. τ.1-4, Νοέμβριος 1918 - Ἰούλιος 1922. Πόλη [τυπ. Ἑστία]
4 v. 25cm.

NL 0451383   OCU MH

Logos; revista de la Facultad de filosofía y letras ... año 1- (núm. 1-   [Buenos Aires, Universidad de Buenos Aires, 1942 [i. e. 1941]-
v. illus., plates, facsims. 24½^{cm}. 2 nos. a year.

I. Buenos Aires. Universidad nacional. Facultad de filosofía y letras.

AP63.L77   056   47-34061

NL 0451384   DLC CoU GU NIC CtY NN TxU NcD MiU

LOGOS; revista de la sociedad Salón de lectura.

San Cristóbal, Venezuela.   v.   22cm.

Monthly?

1. San Cristóbal, Venezuela (City)—Per. and soc. publ. I. "Salón de lectura, " San Cristóbal, Venezuela.

NL 0451385   NN

Logos; rivista trimestrale di filosofia e di storia della filosofia. Rome.

NL 0451386   OU

Logos, Akademischer Verein
   see   Akademischer Verein "Logos".

Logos autopistos
   see under   [Ford, Thomas] 1598-1674.

The **Logos** of Alpha Kappa Lambda.
v. 1

Berkeley, Cal.[, etc.], 1922-   8°, 4°.
v. illus.

Semi-annual, 1922; 3 times a year, 1924-
Title varies slightly.
Dec., 1922 – June, 1925, cover-title reads: Λόγος.

1. College societies, Greek letter—   Alpha Kappa Lambda.
February 8, 1929

NL 0451389   NN

Λόγος περὶ Φιλαργυρίας. Ἐν Μελίτῃ, Ἀπὸ τὴν ἐξ Ἀμερικῆς Τυπογραφίαν, 1825

36 p.

NL 0451390   MH

VOLUME 338

PA
3949
.A9
F4

Logos peri tes Axias Enos chronou ...
Bienne, Haukoilou, 1835.
31 p. 16cm.

Title transliterated.
With: Demosthenes. Pensées ... Paris, 1818.

NL 0451391   DGU

BT825
.L55

[Logos...kata tou thanatou]
Λόγος προτρεπτικὸς κατκα τοῦ φόβου τοῦ θανάτου... Ἐν Μελίτῃ, 1830.
29 p. 18cm.

1. Death.   I. Title.

NL 0451392   OCU

Logosofía. año 1-   (no. 1-   ),
enero 1941-
Buenos Aires.
v. 27 cm. monthly.

BF1995.L68   48-36109*

NL 0451393   DLC NN

LOGOSOFÍA.
Buenos Aires.   v.   26cm.

Monthly.
Editor: - Dec. 1947, C.B.Gonzalez.
Ceased publication with v. 7, no.84, Dec.1947.

1. Philosophy--Per. and soc.   publ.

NL 0451394   NN

Logosol, pseud.
see
Summerville, Alano Erle, 1881-

Logostos, pseud.
see [Bell, Marcus A   ]

5.893.1 Le LOGOTACHIGRAPHE, journal de la Convention nationale de France. no.1-129; 2 jan.-10 mai 1793. [Paris]
1v. 26cm.

By F.E.Guirat.
Bookplate of Jacques Vieillard.

NL 0451397   ICN

Film
PR 248

Le Logotachigraphe, journal de la Convention nationale de France. 1793.

no.1-129,1793 1 reel

NL 0451398   FTaSU

Rare
DC
178
J86+

Le Logotachigraphe; prospectus. [Paris, Impr. du Patriote françois, 1792?]
4 p. 22cm.
"On souscrit, à Paris, au secrétariat de la société des Amis de la Constitution, aux Jacobins Saint-Honoré, et au bureau de Patriote François."
Inserted in Journal logotachigraphique de la Société des amis de la Constitution. Paris, 1792 (27 cm.)
1. Logography. I. Société des Jacobins, Paris.

NL 0451399   NIC

BL
2450
.I7
L63

Logoteta, Giuseppe de
Il tempio d'Iside e di Serapide di Regio, illustrato da Giuseppe de Logoteta. [Napoli, 1794]
104, [iv] p.

Bibliographical footnotes.

1. Isis. 2. Serapis. 3. Cultus, Egyptian. 4. Cultus, Roman. 5. Reggio Calabria - Antiquities.   I. Title.

NL 0451400   NNC

Logotheta, Simeon
SEE
Symeon, Metaphrastes.

Logotheta, Isidorus Charisius, Philyropolitanus, pseud.
see [Lange, Johann Christian] 1669-1756.

Logothete, Antonio.
... L'influenza del diritto romano sulle codificazioni dell' America latina; conferenza pronunciata nella sede del Centro italiano di studi americani il 14 febbr. 1940-XVIII. Roma, Nuove grafiche s. a., 1940.
22 p. 24ᶜᵐ.

1. Law—Spanish America—Hist. & crit. 2. Roman law.
45-28982

NL 0451403   DLC

Logothetēs, G
... Γραμματικὴ τῆς νέας ἑλληνικῆς γλώσσης, συνταχθεῖσα τῇ συνεργασίᾳ τεσσάρων διδασκάλων τῆς Εὐαγγελικῆς σχολῆς Σμύρνης ... Οἱ πονήσαντες Γ. Λογοθέτης, Σ. Σαμάρας, Μ. Ρόκος, Ε. Ἀντωνιάδης. Ἔκδοσις νεωτάτη, ἐπηυξημένη καὶ ἐπιδιορθωμένη ὑπὸ Γ. Λογοθέτου ... Ἀθῆναι, Ἐκδοτικὸς οἶκος Πέτρου Δημητράκου [1939]
2 v. 20ᶜᵐ.
Title transliterated: Grammatikē

Vol. 2, a comparative grammar of Ancient and Modern Greek, has title: Γραμματικὴ τῆς ἑλληνικῆς-γλώσσης.

At head of title of v. 1. Διὰ τὴν τρίτην καὶ τετάρτην τάξιν.
At head of title of v. 2. Διὰ τὴν πέμπτην, ἕκτην καὶ ἑβδόμην τάξιν.

NL 0451405   NNC

PA5611
.L64A6
1953

[ANTHROPINES HISTORIES]

Logothetes, Georgios
Ἀνθρώπινες ἱστορίες. Διηγήματα [ὑπὸ] Γεωργίου Λογοθέτη. Ἀθῆναι, 1953.
87 p. 22cm.

NL 0451406   OCU

Logothetēs, Iakōbos, compiler.
Σχολικὰ ᾄσματα, ποιήματα καὶ διάλογοι, συνταχθέντα μὲν ὑπὸ Ἰ. Λογοθέτου; ἐκδοθέντα δὲ τὸ πρῶτον ὑπὸ Ἰ. Φασουλαρίδου. [Ἐν Νισύρῳ] Τύποις "Ἀρμονίας," 1909. 88 p. 8°.

1. Poetry (Greek): Modern.   2. Dialogues (Greek): Modern. 3. Phasoularidēs, I., editor.

October 11, 1920.

NL 0451407   NN

B3515
.L6

[Ta aiōnia ideōdē]
Logothetēs, Kōnstantinos Iōannou, 1883-
Τὰ αἰώνια ἰδεώδη. θρησκεία - γλώσσα - πατρίς. Ἐν Ἀθήναις. Ἰωάννης Δ. Κολλάρος & Σια, 1930.
172 p., 2 l. illus. 22cm.

At head of title: Κωνστ. Ι. Λογοθέτου.

NL 0451408   OCU

PA4311 Logothetēs, Kōnstantinos Iōannou, 1883-
.L8   ... Ἡ ἠθικὴ φιλοσοφία τοῦ Πλάτωνος ἐν σχέσει πρὸς τοὺς προδρόμους καὶ τὴν ἐπὶ τὰ μετέπειτα ἠθικὰ φιλοσοφήματα ἐπίδρασιν αὐτῆς· πραγματεία βραβευθεῖσα ἐν τῷ Σωτσείῳ φιλοσοφικῷ διαγωνίσματι ... Ἐν Ἀθήναις, τύποις Π. Δ. Σακελλαρίου, 1913.
372, [4] p. 25ᶜᵐ.
At head of title: Κ. Ι. Λογοθέτου.

1. Plato.

NL 0451409   ICU OCU

B2947 Logothetēs, Kōnstantinos Iōannou, 1883-
.L83   ... Γε. Φρ. Ἔγελος. Λόγος ἐπὶ τῇ συμπληρώσει αἰῶνος ἀπὸ τοῦ θανάτου ἐκείνου ἐν τῇ αἰθούσῃ τῶν τελετῶν τοῦ πανεπιστημίου τῇ 14 Νοεμβρίου 1931 ῥηθείς, ὑπὸ Κ. Ι. Λογοθέτου ... Ἐν Ἀθήναις [Τύποις ἐργαστηρίου γραφικῶν τεχνῶν Σ. Ν. Ταρουσοπούλου] 1931.
25, [1] p. 24ᶜᵐ.
At head of title: Ἐθνικὸν καὶ Καποδιστριακὸν πανεπιστήμιον Ἀθηνῶν.

1. Hegel, George Wilhelm Friedrich, 1770-1831.

NL 0451410   ICU

Logothetēs, Kōnstantinos Iōannou, 1883-
Ἰδανικὰ καὶ παιδεία [ὑπὸ] Κωνσταντίνου Ἰω. Λογοθέτου. Ἐν Ἀθήναις, 1949.
40 p. 26 cm. (Βιβλιοθήκη Ἐθνικοῦ Ἐκπαιδευτικοῦ Συνδέσμου, ἀριθ. 1)
Bibliographical references included in [Σημειώσεις] (p. [31]-40)

1. Civilization, Greek. 2. Greece, Modern—Languages.   I. Title. (Series: Bibliothēkē Ethnikou Ekpaideutikou Syndesmou, arith. 1)
Title transliterated: Idanika kai paideia.

DF79.L6   66-50846

NL 0451411   DLC

VOLUME 338

B398 **Logothetēs, Kōnstantinos** Iōannou, 1883–
I2L8   K. I. Λογοθέτου ... Ἡ περὶ ἰδεῶν Θεωρία τοῦ Πλάτωνος πραγμα-
(C1) τεία βραβευθεῖσα ἐν τῷ Σουτσείῳ φιλοσοφικῷ διαγωνισμῷ ... Ἐν
Ἀθήναις, Τύποις Π. Δ. Σακελλαρίου, 1908.
    [5], 112, [1] p.   24½ᵐ.

    1. Plato.

NL 0451412   ICU

Logothetēs, Kōnstantinos Iōannou, 1883–
    Ἡ φιλοσοφία τῆς Ἀναγεννήσεως καὶ ἡ θεμελίωσις τῆς νεω-
τέρας φυσικῆς. Ἐν Ἀθήναις, Ὀργανισμὸς Ἐκδόσεως Σχολικῶν
Βιβλίων, 1955.
    xxii, 705 p.   28 cm.
    Bibliographical footnotes.

    1. Philosophy, Renaissance.   I. Title.
       Title transliterated: Hē philosophia tēs
                 Anagennēseōs.

B775.L6   64–53676

NL 0451413   DLC OCU

B2949
.L6   **Logothetēs, Kōnstantinos Iōannou,** 1883–
    Η φιλοσοφια του Εγελου, και η επι-
δρασις αυτης επι την νεωτεραν και συγ-
χρονον διανοησιν. Αθηναις, [Τυπ.
Ελληνων επιστημονων] 1939.
    2 v. ([14],822 p.) port. 26cm.

    Contains bibliographies.

NL 0451414   OCU

189
L82p   **Logothetēs, Kōnstantinos Iōannou,** 1883–
    Ἡ φιλοσοφία τῶν πατέρων καὶ τοῦ μέσου
αἰῶνος. Ἐν Ἀθήναις, Ι. Δ. Κόλλαρος,
1930–34.
    2v.   25cm.

    Bibliographical footnotes.

    1. Fathers of the Church.   2. Philosophy,
Medieval.
    Title transliterated: Hē philosophia tōn
paterōn kai tou mesou aiōnos.

NL 0451415   IU OCU DDO

B693 **Logothetēs, Kōnstantinos Iōannou,** 1883–
Z7L8   K. I. Λογοθέτου Ἡ ψυχολογία τοῦ Πλωτίνου ... Ἐν Ἀθήναις,
(C1) 1922.
    [3], 47, 52 p.   23½ᵐ.
    Ἀνατύπωσις ἐκ τοῦ Παλαμᾶ.

    1. Plotinus.

NL 0451416   ICU

Logothetes (Nicolaus). *De hepatitide.* 19
pp. 8°. *Vindobonæ, typ. Congr. Mechitaristica,*
[1833].

NL 0451417   DNLM

LOGOTHETES, PORPHYRIOS, 1859–
    Η Θεολογια του Αθηναγορου.   Εν Λειψια,
Τυπ. Βär & Hermann, 1893.

    39 p.
    Inaug.–Diss. Leipzig.
    Title translit.: Hē Theologia tou Athenagorou.

NL 0451418   DDO NjP OCU

[Logotheti, J.]
    Constantinople. New guide-book by [J.Logotheti]
    Constantinople, 1893.   16°.

NL 0451419   NN NjP

WG
25207   **Logothetis, Andreas P**   , 1881–
    Zur Kenntnis der Azo- und Amidoazokörper.
    Halle a. S., 1904.
    87 p.

    Inaug.–Diss. – Halle.

NL 0451420   CtY PU MH

MAIN
Thesis
QL   **Logothetis, Clearhos,** 1914–
498   The biology of some Tabanidae of New York State.
1947   [Ithaca, N. Y.] 1947.
L832   90 l. illus. 28 cm.

    Thesis (Ph. D.) – Cornell Univ., Sept. 1947.
    --- ----- Archival copy.
    1. Horseflies. 2. Diptera – New York (State)
I. Title.

NL 0451421   NIC

423
L822   **Logothetis , Klearchos,** 1914–
    To DDT kai ta syggenē aytou entomoktona.
    Kēphisia, 1946.
    32 p.

    1. DDT (Insecticide) 2. Entomology,
Economic. Greece. I. Athens, Greece.
Institut phytopathologique Benaki.

NL 0451422   DNAL

Logothetis, H
    Ein beitrag zur kenntnis der urinfisteln des
weibes ... Tübingen, H. Laupp, 1889.
    2 p.l., 20 p. incl. illus.   24 cm.   [Heidel-
berg. Universität. Dissertationen. v. 2, no. 19]
    Inaug.–diss. – Heidelberg.
    "Sonderabzug aus Beiträge zur klinischen
chirurgie. V. Band. I. Heft."

NL 0451423   CU DNLM

Logothetis, Konstantinos I.
    see Logothetēs, Kōnstantinos Iōannou, 1883–

Logothetis, Minas, 1902–
    Beitraege zur kenntnis diarylsubstituierter
alkohole und ketone der acetylen und aethylenreihe.
Inaug. diss. Leipzig, 1929. (Halle.)

NL 0451425   ICRL CtY MH DNLM

Logothétis, Photius, 1897–
    ... La cure hélio-marine et la péritonite
tuberculeuse chez les enfants ...   Paris,
1927.
    23 cm.
    Thèse – Univ. de Paris.
    "Bibliographie": p. [97]–107.

NL 0451426   CtY

Logothetopoulos, Kōnstantinos Iōannou, 1878–
    Gynäkologische chirurgie, von dr. Konstantin Logothetopulos
... mit 145 abbildungen im text. Leipzig, J. A. Barth, 1939.
    vi, 106 p. illus. 27½ᵐ.

    1. Gynecology, Operative.   I. Title.

    Library of Congress   RG104.L6   41–35900
    Copyright A–Foreign   44961
                                    618.1

NL 0451427   DLC PPC

WP
100   **LOGOTHETOPOULOS, Kōnstantinos Iōannou,** 1878–
L832g   Γυναικολογία. Halle, Buchdruckerei
1928   des Waisenhauses, 1928.
    2 v. illus.
    Title transliterated: [Gynaikologia.
    1. Gynecology

NL 0451428   DNLM

Logothetopoulos, Kōnstantinos Iōannou, 1878–
    Ἰδοὺ ἡ ἀλήθεια [ὑπὸ] Κ. Λογοθετοπούλου. Ἀθῆναι, 1948.
    207 p. 22 cm.
    Stamped on verso of p. 207: Ἐκδόσεις Ὁ Αἰώνας Μας.

    1. Greece, Modern—Hist.—Occupation, 1941–1944.   I. Title.
                     Title transliterated: Idou hē alētheia.

    D802.G8L6   66–87987

NL 0451429   DLC

95.3
L82   **Logothetos, Basileios Ch.**
    Meletai kai ereunai diatērēseōs nōpōn
epitrapeziōn staphulōn.   Rhodes, 1949.
    47 p.

    1. Grapes. 2. Greece. Viticulture.
I. Logothetos, Basileios Ch.   Etudes et
recherches sur la conservation des raisins
de table.

NL 0451430   DNAL

95.1
L82   **Logothetos, Basileios Ch.**
    Sumbolē eis tēn hellēnikēn ampelographian.
    Athens, 1947.
    110 p.

    1. Greece. Viticulture.   I.Logothetos,
Basileios Ch.   Contribution a l'
ampelographie hellenique.

NL 0451431   DNAL

Logothetos, P.
    see Logothetes, Porphyrios, 1859–

Logotypy, logography, and stenography
    see under [Needham, Clement R.]

VOLUME 338

ГN281
.L6
Logov, B   S
    Буровой агрегат ЗИВ-150; описание и руководство по эксплоатации. Составили Б. С. Логов, С. П. Штода, Г. А. Чечухин. Москва, Гос. изд-во геол. лит-ры, 1952.
    118 p.   diagrs.   17 x 26 cm.
    At head of title: Техническое управление Министерства геологии. Errata slip inserted.

    1. Boring machinery.   I. Title.
           Title transliterated: Burovoĭ agregat ZIV-150.

    TN281.L6   53-31062

NL 0451434   DLC

Logoz, Paul, 1888-   ed.

    Switzerland. *Laws, statutes, etc.*
    Commentaire du Code pénal suisse. Neuchâtel, Paris, Éditions Delachaux & Niestlé (1941-56)

LOGOZ, Paul, *1888-*
  Essai sur la réhabilitation: droit commercial et droit pénal. Genève, 1911.

  Thèse ---- Genève.

NL 0451436   MH-L

Logoz, Paul, *1888-*
    Juvenile courts in the canton of Geneva, Switzerland
Washington, D. C . 1914.
    1 p.l., 27 l. 27 cm.
    Typewritten
    Translated from article by Dr. Paul Logoz in Schweizerische zeitschrift fur strafrecht (Revue pénale suisse) vol. 27, part 1, p. 61-75, 1914.
    At head of title: Library of Congress,

NL 0451437   DL

Logoz, Paul, *1888-*
    La peine de mort et l'unification du droit pénal en Suisse. Co-rapport présenté par M. Paul Logoz...   Basel: Helbing & Lichtenhahn, 1912.   (1)56-96 p.   8°.   (Schweizerischer Juristenverein. Verhandlungen. Heft 2.)
    Cover-title.

    1. Punishment (Capital), Switzerland.   2. Criminal law, Switzerland.
    3. Series.
                          November 15, 1915.

NL 0451438   NN

Logoz, Paul, *1888-*
    Le projet de Code pénal suisse et les chambres fédérales. Par Paul Logoz ...   (In ₍Festgabe für₎ Carl Stooss. ₍Bern, 1929₎ p. 153-172)

    In Schweizerische zeitschrift für strafrecht. Revue pénale suisse. v. 43.

NL 0451439   NNC

Logoz, Paul, *1888-*
    Le projet de Code pénal suisse; rapport présenté au Conseil national le 6 mars 1928 par **Paul Logoz.** Berne, Pochon-Jent, 1928.
    57 p.

NL 0451440   NNC

Lograr el mayor imperio por un feliz desengaño. En tres actos. [In verse.   Barcelona, J. F. Piferrer, 17-?]
    30 p., 1 l.   8° in fours.
    Headline reads: Comedia nueva.

NL 0451441   NN

PQ
4419
M3L83
Lograsso, Angeline Helen
    Dante e la Madonna.   Roma, Marietti, 1955.
    32 p.   25cm.

    1. Dante--Characters--Mary, Virgin.
    I. Title.

NL 0451442   NIC PBm PHC RPB MH ODaU-M

Lograsso, Angeline Helen
  Piero Maroncelli, poet and patriot-musician and exile.

    Thesis - Radcliffe, 1927

NL 0451443   MH

BT268
G7
Lo Grasso, Giovanni B   1898-
    Ecclesia et status; de mutuis officiis et iuribus fontes selecti. In usum scholarum collegit Ioannes B. Lo Grasso ... Romae, apud aedes Universitatis Gregorianae, 1939.

    xviii, ₍1₎, 345 p. 20cm.

    Bibliographical footnotes.

    1.Church and state-Sources. I.Title.

NL 0451444   MBtS MH NNC

Lo Grasso, Giovanni B   1898-   ed.
    Ecclesia et status; fontes selecti historiae iuris publici ecclesiastici. Ed. 2., recognita et aucta. Romae, Apud Aedes Pontif. Universitatis Gregorianae, 1952.
    xxii, 426 p. 22 cm.
    Includes bibliographical references.

    1. Church and state--Hist.--Sources.   I. Title.
                             A 55-1764
    St. Mary's College,   St. Marys, Kan. Libr.
    for Library of Congress

    WaSpG
NL 0451445   MoSU-D WaU CU CtY DDO CtY-D MoSU DCU

Lo Grasso, Johannes B.
    see Lo Grasso, Giovanni B   1898-

Logre, Benjamin Joseph, 1883-
    L'anxiété de Lucrèce. ₍Paris₎ J. B. Janin ₍1946₎
    356 p. port. 19 cm.
    Bibliographical footnotes.

    1. Lucretius Carus, Titus.   I. Title.
    PA6484.L6   871.1   47-28781*

    OC1W
NL 0451447   DLC OCU NNC PBm ICU NN CLSU CLU CtY

Logre, Benjamin Joseph, 1883-   joint author.

Devaux, Albert, 1874-
    ... Les anxieux; étude clinique, par les docteurs Devaux et Logre; préface du D' Dupré. Paris, Masson & cᵉ, 1917.

ZWZ 100
L82
1923
Logre, Benjamin Joseph, 1883-
    Exposé de titres et travaux scientifiques. Paris, Masson, 1923.
    99p. 27cm.

    Inscribed by the author.

    1.Neurology, Bibl. 2.Psychiatry, Bibl.
    3.Psychopathol-   ogy, Bibl.

NL 0451449   NcD-MC

Logre (Benjamin Joseph) [1883-   ]. *Les oedèmes infectieux du poumon. 1 p. l., 196 pp. 8°. Paris, 1913. No. 228.

NL 0451450   DNLM MH

Logre, Benjamin Joseph, 1883-
    ... Les toxicomanies. Paris, Stock, 1924.
    128 p. 14½ᶜᵐ. (*On cover:* La culture moderne (publiée sous la direction de F. Fels. nᵒ 7))
    "Liste des ouvrages à consulter": p. ₍125₎

    1. Narcotic habit.   I. Title.
    Library of Congress   RC369.L6   24-7498

NL 0451451   DLC DNLM NcD-MC

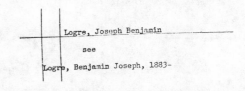

Logre, Joseph Benjamin
    see
Logre, Benjamin Joseph, 1883-

Logreira Moreno, Jorge.
    Mansión interior. 1. ed. ₍Barranquilla, Librería "Loar," 1948₎
    15 l. 22 cm.
    Cover title.

    I. Title.
                            A 52-481
    New York. Public Libr.
    for Library of Congress

NL 0451453   NN MH

Logren, Ernst, *d.* 1944.
    Huvuddragen av Hägerströms filosofi. Uppsala, Wretmans boktr., 1944.
    599, ₍1₎ p. 24 cm.
    Akademisk avhandling--Uppsala.
    "Anförda arbeten av Hägerström": p. ₍600₎

    1. Hägerström, Axel Anders Theodor, 1868-1939.   I. Title.
    B4495.H34L6   52-57356

NL 0451454   DLC NcD PU CtY ICU NNC

VOLUME 338

B4491
.L6
Logren, Ernst, *d.* 1944.
Paradox mot snusförnuft. Essayer utg. av Magnus Selling. Med en inledning av Harald Eklund. ｢Stockholm｣ LTs förlag ｢1952｣
149 p. port. 20 cm.

1. Philosophy, Swedish—Addresses, essays, lectures.   ɪ. Selling, Magnus, ed.   ɪɪ. Title.

A 52-6195

Chicago. Univ. Library
for Library of Congress

NL 0451455   ICU MnU MH NN NcD DLC

Logrhythms.
In: The log, S.S. "Finland."   Boston, 1915.
26 cm.

NL 0451456   RPB

HC
173
.L83
Logrippo, Adelaida.
Las fuerzas económicas Argentinas; antecedentes y desarrollo actual. Rosario, Ediciones Proinco, 1954.
651 p.

1. Argentine Republic—Econ. condit. I. Title.

NL 0451457   MiU InU ICU CSt-H NN

Logrono, Alfredo Beltrán
see   Beltrán Logroño, Alfredo.

Logroño, Arturo, 1892–
Centenario de Luperón, ofrenda del "Listín" a "la primera espada de la restauración," discurso pronunciado en la sesión solemne y pública de la Academia de la historia por el licdo. Arturo Logroño ... septiembre 10 de 1939, Ciudad Trujillo. ｢Santo Domingo, Imp. Listín diario, 1939?｣
14 p. incl. port. 23ᶜᵐ.

ɪ. Luperón, Gregorio, 1839–1897.

｢Full name: Alvaro Arturo Logroño y Cohen｣
42-47423

Library of Congress   F1931.L78

NL 0451459   DLC MH

Logroño, Arturo, 1892–
Compendio didáctico de historia patria, por Arturo Logroño ... Santo Domingo, Imp. La Cuna de América, viuda de Roques & cía., 1912–
v. 19¾ᶜᵐ.

1. Dominican republic—Hist. 2. Haiti—Hist.   ɪ. Title.
｢Full name: Alvaro Arturo Logroño y Cohen｣
42-29776

Library of Congress   F1931.L8

NL 0451460   DLC

Logroño, Arturo, *1892–*

Academia dominicana de la historia.
Homenaje i ofrenda de la Academia dominicana de la historia a los héroes del vuelo domínico-cubano pro faro de Colón. ｢Trujillo, R. D., Imprenta Montalvo, 1938｣

Logroño, Arturo, *1892–*
Dominican republic. *Secretaría de relaciones exteriores.*
... **La primera** administración del generalísimo Trujillo Molina. (Circular informativa dirigida por el lic. Arturo Logroño, secretario de estado de relaciones exteriores, al cuerpo diplomático y consular de la república.) Santo Domingo ｢Imprenta Listín diario｣ 1934.

Logroño, José Cassa
see   Cassa Logroño, José.

Logroño, Juan Alfonso de.
Cõtẽplaciones sobre el rosario d' nr̃a soberana señora virgẽ y madre d' dios sctã Maria: Ordenadas por dõ Gaspar gorricio d' Nouaria mõje de cartuxa: E tornadas ẽ vulgar castellano por el reuerẽdo señor Bachiller Juã alfõso d' Logroño...

At end: F[ue imp]resso enla muy noble ⁊ muy leal cibdad de Se[uilla por] Meynardo vngut aleman/⁊ Lançalao polono compañeros a ocho dias del mes de Julio del año del señor de mill⁊quatrocientos ⁊ nouenta ⁊ cinco.
2 pts. in 1 v.

NL 0451464   NNH

Logroño, Pedro de, *ed.*
Flor de las mejores doce comedias.   Madrid, Diego Diaz de la Carrera 1652
4to.

Huth copy

Edited by Pedro de Logroño

NL 0451465   MWiW-C

Logroño y Cohen, Alvaro Arturo
see   Logroño, Arturo, 1892–

Logroño, Spain (City) Círculo logroñés
see
Círculo logroñés. Logrono｣ Spain.

CD1876
.L6B8
Logroño, Spain (City) Iglesia Colegial de Santa María la Redonda.
Bujanda, Fernando.
Inventario de los documentos del archivo de la insigne Iglesia Colegial de Logroño. Logroño, 1947.

Logroño, Spain (City) Instituto de Estudios Riojanos
see **Spain.** *Consejo Superior de Investigaciones Científicas. Instituto de Estudios Riojanos.*

Logroño, Spain (City) Ordinances, etc.
Ordenanzas hechas por la muy noble y muy leal ciudad de Logroño, con que se rige y govierna el campo de ella; confirmadas por s.m. el año de 1539. Logroño, 1744.

24°.

NL 0451470   MH-L CLL

Logroño Spain (City) Ordinances, etc.
Ordenanzas municipales de la muy noble y muy leal ciudad de Logroño. Año de 1900.   Logroño: Establecimiento tipográfico de "La Rioja," 1901.   255 p.   fold. plans.   4°.

1. Municipal charters and ordi-   nances, Spain: Logroño.
N. Y. P. L.   December 3, 1920.

NL 0451471   NN

Logroño, Spain (City) Ordinances, etc.
Ordenanzas para el gobierno del campo de la m. n. y m. l. ciudad de Logroño, formadas por su muy ilustre ayuntamiento y aprobadas por s. m. (Dios le guarde) y su real y supremo consejo de Castilla en siete de setiembre de mil ochocientos y siete. Logroño, n.d.

24°.

NL 0451472   MH-L

Logroño, *Spain (Province)*
El avance de la provincia de Logroño en un quinquenio, 13 de septiembre 1923 a 13 de septiembre 1928. Logroño, Imprenta y librería moderna ｢1929?｣
46 p. 23½ᶜᵐ.

｢Progreso de España en el periodo 1923–1928. v. 6, no. 2｣

1. Logroño, Spain (Province)—Pol. & govt.   ɪ. Title.

Library of Congress   DP247.P77
33-38373

NL 0451473   DLC

Logroño, *Spain (Province)*
Boletín oficial.
｢Logroño｣
v. 44 cm. 3 no. a week.
Includes legislation.

1. Logroño, Spain (Province)—Pol. & govt.   ɪ. Logroño, Spain (Province) Laws, statutes, etc.

51-21510

NL 0451474   DLC

Logroño, Spain (Province) Camara Oficial de Comercio e Industria.
Memoria descriptiva del desarrollo comercial e industrial de la provincia.
Logroño.
v. in   29 cm. annual.

1. Logroño, Spain (Province)—Econ. condit.

HC387.L6L65
52-32634 ‡

NL 0451475   DLC NN

Law   **Logroño, Spain (Province) Laws, statutes, etc.**

Logroño, *Spain (Province)*
Boletín oficial.
｢Logroño｣

Logrono; a metric drama in two acts
see under ｢Guthrie, Frederick｣

VOLUME 338

Os logros n'uma hospedaria. Farça original em un acto. [Lisbon, 187–?]
1 p.l., 79–128 p. 16°.
In: NQM p.v. 57, no. 2.
n.t.-p.

NL 0451478 NN

WE 253 L832m 1937
LOGRÒSCINO, Domenico
Il morbo di Grocco-Poncet nel quadro delle poliartriti croniche, saggio clinico. Bologna, Cappelli, 1937.
99 p. illus. (Collana di attualità chirurgiche, n. 11)
"Estratto dall'Archivio italiano di chirurgia, vol. 45, fasc. 3., 1937."
1. Joints - Tuberculosis
Series

NL 0451479 DNLM

Logroscino, Nicola, 1698–1765?
[Le chiajese cantarine. Libretto. Italian]

Le chiajese cantarine; pazzia pe mmuseca de Pietro Trinchera, da rappresentarese a lo Teatro nuovo a Monte Cravario nchisto carnevale venturo de chisto corrente anno 1754. [La museca e de Nicola Logroscino, Giacomo Maraucci [e] Domineco Fischetti] Nnapole, Se venneno a la porta de lo teatro [1754]
72 p. 16 cm.
1. Operas — To 1800 — Librettos. I. Maraucci, Giacomo, joint composer. II. Fischietti, Domenico, 1729–1811, joint composer. III. Trinchera, Pietro. Le chiajese cantarine. IV. Title.

ML50.2.C45L6 1754 76–212623

NL 0451480 DLC

M 1500 .L8360 4
Logroscino, Nicola, 1698–1765?
... Il Giunio Bruto in tre atti del Sigre. Nicola Logroscino.
393p. obl. 4°.
Transcript of copy at the Bischöfl. Bibliothek, Münster, 1909.

NL 0451481 DLC

M 1500 .L8360 5
Logroscino, Nicola, 1698–1765?
Il governatore. Musica del Sig. Nicola Logroscino.
3v. in 1. 195, 216, 198p. obl.4°.
Transcript of the copy at the Bischöfl. Bibliothek, Münster, 1909.

NL 0451482 DLC

M 1500 L831
Logroscino, Nicola, 1698–1765?
[L'Olimpiade. Opera in tre atti di Pietro Metastasio. Musica] del Sig. Niccolò Logroscino. [Partitura] [Roma] Argentina 1753.
282 p. Mss. 30 1/2 x 23 cm.
No. t.-p.
Presumably incomplete copy of manuscript.
Unpublished.

NL 0451483 NRU-Mus

The logs of the first voyage, made with the unceasing aid of steam, between England and America
see under Great Western (Steamship)

... Logs, Salt Lake City to Yellowstone park and reverse, roads logged July, 1915; containing logs, park regulations, description of cities [!] and towns and list leading hotel and garages. Supplement log from Pike's Peak, Grand Canyon and Yellowstone log book. [Salt Lake City, R. D. Grow printing co., 1915]
cover-title, 20 p. illus. (incl. map) 21°°. $0.25

1. Automobiles—Road guides. 2. Yellowstone national park—Guidebooks.

Library of Congress GV1024.L55 15–24703

NL 0451485 DLC

Logsdail, Cecil. United States' army. 19 pp.
(*Westm. Rev.* v. 132, 1889, p. 425.)

NL 0451486 MdBP

Logsden, Jimmie
see Logsdon, James L

Logsdon, Carey Liguori
A study of grammars. By ... 1899.
3p.l., 2–27 no.l.

Thesis (PH.D.)-Ohio state univ.

NL 0451488 OU

HF105 .A64 no. 29
Logsdon, Clement Searl.
U.S. *Bureau of foreign and domestic commerce.*
... Business leasehold obligations (wholesale and retail) Washington, U.S. Govt. print. off., 1944.

[Logsdon, Clement Searl]
A guide for local industrial promotion ... [Washington] Dept. of commerce, Bureau of foreign and domestic commerce [1945]
cover-title, 30 p. incl. tables. 27°°. ([U. S.] Bureau of foreign and domestic commerce. Economic (small business) series no. 47)
"Prepared by C. S. Logsdon."—Foreword.
"Some publications of the Bureau of foreign and domestic commerce of interest in community industrial development": p. 30.

1. U. S.—Comm. 2. U. S.—Manuf. I. Title.
Library of Congress ° HF105.A64 no. 47 45–37721
HF3007.L6

(382.06173) 338

NL 0451490 DLC WaTC CaBVaU

[Logsdon, Clement Searl]
A guide for local industrial promotion ... [Washington] U. S. Dept. of commerce, Bureau of foreign and domestic commerce [1946]
1 p. l., 28 p. incl. illus., tables. 23°°. (U. S. Bureau of foreign and domestic commerce. Economic (small business) series no. 47)
"Prepared by C. S. Logsdon."—Foreword.
"Some publications of the Bureau of foreign and domestic commerce of interest in community industrial development": p. 27.

1. U. S.—Comm. 2. U. S.—Manuf. I. Title.
Library of Congress 46–25949
— Copy 2. HF105.A64 no. 47 a
HF3007.L6 1946

(382.06173) 338

NL 0451491 DLC MB

[Logsdon, Clement Searl]
A guide for local industrial promotion. [Washington] U. S. Dept. of commerce, Bureau of foreign and domestic commerce [1946]
1 p. l., 28 p. incl. illus., tables. 23°°.
"Prepared by C. S. Logsdon."—Foreword.
Issued also as Economic (small business) series no. 47 of the U. S. Bureau of foreign and domestic commerce under same title.
"Some publications of the Bureau of foreign and domestic commerce of interest in community industrial development": p. 27.

1. U. S.—Comm. 2. U. S.—Manuf. I. Title.
46–26108
Library of Congress HF3007.L6 1946 a
338

NL 0451492 DLC

Logsdon, Clement Searl
The impact of interstate trade barriers upon the marketing system. [Columbus] The Ohio state uni . 1940.
1p. l., 1v., 156, [1] numb.1.

Thesis (PH.D.) - Ohio state univ.

NL 0451493 OU

[Logsdon, Clement Searl]
... An outline for making surveys. Especially adaptable in evaluating the industrial and commercial status of a community or region and potentialities for improving its position in both the industrial and consumer market. Prepared in Special studies unit, Division of small business. Washington, U. S. Govt. print. off., 1944.
vi, 45, [1] p. illus. 23½°°. (U. S. Bureau of foreign and domestic commerce. Economic series no. 34)

At head of title: United States Dept. of commerce. Jesse H. Jones, secretary. Bureau of foreign and domestic commerce. Amos E. Taylor, director ...
"Prepared by C. S. Logsdon of the Special studies unit."—Foreword. Revision of a publication issued in 1938 as Domestic commerce series no. 105, under title: Suggestions for use in making a city survey (industrial and commercial) by Ada L. Bush. cf. Foreword.
"Sources of related material": p. 44–45.

1. Industrial surveys. I. Title.
Library of Congress ° HF105.A64 no. 34 45–35521
HC28.L6
338.91

NL 0451495 DLC WaTC OCU

Logsdon, Cleo L.
Foundation for industrial development, *Zanesville, O.*
Graphic facts of Zanesville, Ohio ... [Zanesville] Foundation for industrial development, C. L. Logsdon, director, 1942.

Logsdon, Clyde Alvy, 1908–
The American transportation token catalog of United States fare tokens, arranged alphabetically by the stamping on the tokens. Omaha, °1953–
1 v. (loose-leaf) 22 cm.
Kept up to date by numbered supplements.
First ed. published in 1948 under title: Transportation token catalogue.

1. Tokens—U. S. 2. Street-railroads—Fares. 3. Motor bus lines—Fares. I. Title.
CJ4902.L64 737.3 53–37416

NL 0451497 DLC

VOLUME 338

Logsdon, James Desmond, 1905–
The development of public school administration in St. Louis, Missouri. Chicago, 1946.

[1], l, ii–iv, 239 p. 23 cm.

Thesis—Univ. of Chicago.
Bibliography: p. 237–239.

1. St. Louis—Public schools.

LA318.S3L6   379.778   A 47–4429*

Chicago. Univ. Library
for Library of Congress   †

NL 0451498   ICU NcD NcU MH PU DLC OU

LOGSDON, JAMES L.

As long as we're together. Words and music by Jimmie Logsden [sic] and William J. Johnson. New York, Melody trails, inc., c1953.

First line: I love you and you love me.

l. Songs, Popular—1890–   I. Johnson, William J.

NL 0451499   NN

LOGSDON, JAMES L.

I wanna be mama'd. Words and music by Jimmie Logsdon. New York, Melody trails, inc., c1952.

Chorus: For I'm a baby.

1. Songs, Popular—1890–

NL 0451500   NN

LOGSDON, JAMES L.

The love you gave to me. Words and music by Jimmie Logsdon. New York, Melody trails, inc., 1953.

First line: Give me ice, give me snow.

1. Songs, Popular—1890–

NL 0451501   NN

LOGSDON, JAMES L.

That's when I'll love you the best. Words and music by Jimmie Logsdon. New York, Melody trails, inc., c1952.

First line: When the long years, they lay heavy.
Chorus: For I'll remember all the things.

1. Songs, Popular—1890–   2. Old age.

NL 0451502   NN

Ayer
4A
68   Logdson, Katherine S   (Adams)
A biography of John Adams, pioneer and soldier, as told by himself to his daughter, Mrs. Katherine S. Lodgson. San Diego, Calif. [City Print. Co.] 1937.
38p. ports. 22cm.

Signed by the author.

NL 0451503   ICN

Logsdon, Katherine S   (Adams)
Julia of the loyal heart. San Diego [City Printing Co.] 1938.
35 p. 21 cm.

NL 0451504   CU–S

Logsdon, Mayme Irwin, 1887–
Elementary mathematical analysis, with tables, by Mayme Irwin Logsdon ... 1st ed. New York and London, McGraw-Hill book company, inc., 1932–

v. illus., diagrs. 23½ cm.

1. Mathematics. 2. Trigonometry. 3. Geometry, Analytic. I. Title.

QA39.L65   510   32—24657

NL 0451505   DLC MiU OC1ND MiHM IEN NIC

Logsdon, Mayme Irwin, 1887–
... Equivalence and reduction of pairs of hermitian forms ... by Mayme Irwin Logsdon ... [Baltimore, 1922]

1 p. l., p. 247–260. 25½ᶜᵐ.

Thesis (PH. D.)—University of Chicago, 1921.
"Private edition, distributed by the University of Chicago libraries, Chicago, Illinois."
"Reprinted from American journal of mathematics, vol. XLIV, no. 4 October, 1922."

1. Forms (Mathematics)   I. Title.

Library of Congress   QA201.L85   23–10462

NL 0451506   DLC NIC CU OCU OU

Logsdon, Mayme (Irwin) 1887–
A mathematician explains, by Mayme I. Logsdon ... decorative drawings by Chichi Lasley. Chicago, Ill., The University of Chicago press [1935]

xi, [1], 175 p. illus., diagrs. 23½ cm.

Chapter 8, "Mathematical interpretations of geometrical and physical phenomena," by G. A. Bliss.
Bibliography at end of chapter 2 (p. 46)

1. Mathematics. 2. Mathematics—Hist.   I. Bliss, Gilbert Ames, 1876–   II. Title.

QA37.L82   510   36—3954

NL 0451507   DLC NN MB OrSaW CaBVaU OrCS

Logsdon, Mayme (Irwin) 1887–
A mathematician explains, by Mayme I. Logsdon ... decorative drawings by Chichi Lasley. Chicago, Ill., The University of Chicago press [*1936]

xi, [1], 189 p. illus., diagrs. 23½ cm.

"Published October 1935. Second edition March 1936."
Chapter 8, "Mathematical interpretations of geometrical and physical phenomena," by G. A. Bliss.
Bibliography at end of chapters 2 and 9.

1. Mathematics. 2. Mathematics—Hist.   I. Bliss, Gilbert Ames, 1876–   II. Title.

QA37.L82 1936   510   36—8177

CaBVa OrStbM MtBuM PCM WaT NcRS
OrU OrLgE PSC KEmT PU PBa MB OU OC1 NjP NbU OrPS
TU AU KyU KyU–A KMK CU PPT NcD Or OrPR WaTC WaWW
NL 0451508   DLC GAT MiU PV PHC OC1W ODW OCU OO MsU

Logsdon, Mayme (Irwin) 1887–
A mathematician explains. Chicago, University of Chicago Press, 1947.

NL 0451509   KU

Logsdon, Mayne (Irwin)
A mathemetician explains. Chicago, U. Chicago P., 1947.

NL 0451510   KU

Logsdon, Mayme (Irwin) 1887–
... Mathematics 101, 102, 103
see under Chicago. University.

Logsdon, Mayme (Irwin) 1887–
Syllabus for Mathematics 101, 102, 103
see under Chicago. University.

Logsdon, Mayme (Irwin) 1887–
Syllabus for Mathematics 104, 105, 106
see under Chicago. University.

Z10999   Logsdon, Richard Henry, 1912–
The instructional literature of sociology and the administration of college library book collections. 1942.
101 numb. l.

Typewritten.
Thesis (Ph. D.)—University of Chicago.

NL 0451514   ICU

Logsdon, Richard Henry, 1912–
... The instructional literature of sociology and the administration of college library book collections ... by Richard H. Logsdon. Chicago, Ill. [The University of Chicago library, Dept. of photographic reproduction] 1947.

Film copy of type-written manuscript. Positive.
Collation of the original: vi, 101 numb. l. incl. tables.
Thesis (PH. D.)—University of Chicago, 1942.

1. Libraries, University and college. 2. Sociology—Study and teaching. 3. Social sciences—Bibl. 4. Book selection.

Film Z–3   Mic A 47–8

Chicago. Univ. Library
for Library of Congress   †

NBuU FTaSU NNC DLC
NL 0451515   ICU IdU MH OU NN NcU ICU ViU NjP CoU

Logsdon, S   Franklin.
The Lord of the harvest; the manifestation and the ministration of the Holy Spirit. Grand Rapids, Zondervan Pub. House [1954]
153 p. 20 cm.

1. Holy Spirit.   I. Title.

BT121.L57   231.3   54–21459 ‡

NL 0451516   DLC PPEB PPRETS

Logsdon, S   Franklin.
Original sermon outlines, plus hints and helps on how to make sermon outlines. Grand Rapids, Zondervan Pub. House [1954]
128 p. 20 cm.

1. Sermons—Outlines. 2. Preaching.   I. Title.

BV4223.L6   251   54–34229 ‡

NL 0451517   DLC

Logtenburg, Émile, comp.

Jurisprudence commerciale des Flandres et des tribunaux de commerce belges ...
1.–   année; 1886–
Gand, A. Hoste [etc.] 1886–19

VOLUME 338

Logu, Giuseppe de
see Delogu, Giuseppe, 1898–

Logu Ibba, Giovanni de
see
Delogu Ibba, Giovanni, 1664–1738.

Logue, Annie Elizabeth, 1871–   joint author.
Jessup, *Mrs.* Anne Lowden, 1854–
The handicraft book, comprising methods of teaching cord and raffia construction work, weaving, basketry and chair caning in graded schools, by Anne L. Jessup ... and Annie E. Logue ... New York, A. S. Barnes company, 1912.

HD7304   Logue, Charles.
.B7A5
1918   **Boston.** *Committee on housing.*
... Report of committee appointed by Mayor Peters on housing ... ₁Boston, 1919₎

Logue, Charles, 1889–
Forbidden waters; a sparkling comedy of love and intrigue, based on the motion-picture story, by Charles Logue, produced and filmed by Metropolitan pictures corporation and distributed by Producers distributing corporation, starring Priscilla Dean. New York, Jacobsen-Hodgkinson-corp. ₁c1926₎ 135 p. illus. 20cm. (Popular plays and screen library.)

NL 0451523   NN

₁Logue, Charles₎ 1889–
The Hoosier schoolmaster... ₁Culver City, Cal., 1935₎ 109 f. 33cm.

Cover-title.
Reproduced from typewritten copy.
Scenario by Charles Logue, adapted from the novel by Edward Eggleston. Produced by Monogram Productions Inc.

826189A. 1. Moving picture plays—   Texts and outlines. I. Eggleston,
Edward, 1837–1902. The Hoosier   schoolmaster. II. Monogram Pictures
Corporation. III. Title.

August 26, 1936

NL 0451524   NN

[Logue, Charles] 1889–
Make a million ... [shooting script]
see under   Make a million (Motion picture script)

Logue, Charles Hays, 1875–
American machinist gear book; simplified tables and formulas for designing, and practical points in cutting all commercial types of gears, by Charles H. Logue ... New York ₁etc.₎ American machinist, 1910.
4 p. l., 348 p. illus., diagrs. 23½ᶜᵐ.

1. Gearing.   I. Title.
10—16318
Library of Congress   TJ184.L8

NL 0451526   DLC OU ODW MiU ICJ MB NN

Logue, Charles Hays, 1875–
American machinist gear book; simplified tables and formulas for designing, and practical points in cutting all commercial types of gears, by Charles H. Logue ... New York ₁etc.₎ American machinist, 1911.
4 p. l., 348 p. illus., diagrs. 23½ᶜᵐ. $2.50

NL 0451527   ICJ OrP WaS NjP CU

Logue, Charles Hays, 1875–
American machinist gear book; simplified tables and formulas for designing, and practical points in cutting all commercial types of gears, by Charles H. Logue... Revised edition. Reginald Trautschold...editor.   New York: Amer. Machinist, 1915. 344 p. incl. diagrs., illus., tables.   8°.

58628A. 1. Gear cutting. 2. Traut-   schold, Reginald, editor.
September 25, 1922.

NL 0451528   NN WaS OrP IdU ViU OC1

Logue, Charles Hays, 1875–
American machinist gear book; simplified tables and formulas for designing, and practical points in cutting all commercial types of gears, by Charles H. Logue ... Rev. ed. Reginald Trautschold, M. E., editor.   New York, McGraw-Hill book company, inc.; ₁etc., etc.₎ °1918.
5 p. l., 344 p. illus., diagrs. 23½ᶜᵐ. $2.50

1. Gearing.   I. Trautschold Reginald, ed. II. Title.
Library of Congress   TJ134.L8 1918   19–14425

NL 0451529   DLC OrP OCU

Logue, Charles Hays, 1875–
American machinist gear book; simplified tables and formulas for designing, and practical points in cutting all commercial types of gears, by Charles H. Logue ... thoroughly rev. by Reginald Trautschold, M. E. 3d ed. New York ₁etc.₎ McGraw-Hill book company, inc. ₁°1922₎
ix, 353 p. illus., diagrs. 23½ᶜᵐ.   (*Lettered on cover:* Library of machine shop practice) $3.00

1. Gearing.   I. Trautschold, Reginald.   II. Title.
22—24462
Library of Congress   TJ184.L8 1922

MiHM
NL 0451530   DLC ICRL Or WaS TU OC1 MiU ICJ NN MB

Lilly
Library   LOGUE,CHRISTOPHER,1926–
Chen: poem by Christopher Logue.
₁London₎ Vandal Publications, Ltd., n. d.
1 ℓ.   44.5 by 57 cm.

NL 0451531   InU

AC-L
L829fi   Logue, Christopher, 1926–
1955   First testament.   Roma [1955]
16p.   23cm.

"Estratto da Botteghe oscure n.XV."

NL 0451532   TxU

NC
1850   Logue, Christopher, 1926–
L64   New poem to John Neville. ₁n.p., n.d.₎
poster

NL 0451533   KMK

Rare
book   Logue, Christopher, 1926–
coll.   S L. ₁n.p., 19–?₎
Folio   1 sheet. 41cm.
PR6023
.O 38   25 copies of this edition, signed and numbered by author. No.4.
S4

I. Title.

NL 0451534   NcU

LOGUE,CHRISTOPHER,1926–
Sex, war – cars, sex. ₁London₎ n.d.
1 ℓ.   44 by 58 cm.   col. illus.

NL 0451535   InU

NC
1750   Logue, Christopher, 1926–
L6   Sex, war, sex, cars, sex, cleanliness is next to Godliness ₁by₎ Christopher₎ Logue ₁and Derck₎ Boshier ₁n.p., n.d.₎ poster (col.)

NL 0451536   KMK

PR6023   Logue, Christopher, 1926–
f.O3S86   The song of the dead soldier (to the tune of
19—   McCafferty) One killed in the interests of
Modern   certain Tory senators in Cyprus. London,
Poetry   Villiers Publications ₁19—₎
broadside. 51 x 38 cm.
Poem, signed by author.

NL 0451537   ICU InU

821.91   Logue, Christopher, 1926–
L829w   Wand and quadrant. ₁1st ed.₎   Paris,
1953   ₁Olympia Press₎ 1953.
62p.   24cm.   (Collection "Merlin")

"Six hundred copies... three hundred numbered..."

InU NcU ICarbS
ICU NN NNC CtY IaU IU MiU MoSW OU TxU OCU CoU LU
NL 0451538   KU CU CLU PBL PU IEN MH IU NcD MB ICN

PR6023   Logue, Christopher, 1926–
f.O3S84   The weekdream sonnets. Woodcut and seven
1955   emblems by Shinkichi Tajiri. Paris, Jack
Modern   Straw, 1955.
Poetry   ₁12₎ p.   illus.   34cm.
"200 copies numbered 1 to 200 ... +40 copies numbered I to XL ... ₁No.₎15."

IaU NIC KU CoU CLU TxU
NL 0451539   ICU InU MH ICN IEN NN NNC MWelC CtY NcD

Logue, Emily Rose, 1876–
At the foot of the mountain ₁by₎ Emily R. Logue. Philadelphia, H. L. Kilner & co. ₁1898₎
46 p.   21ᶜᵐ.
Poems.

I. Title.
98–257 Revised
Library of Congress   PS3523.O37A8 1898

NL 0451540   DLC

VOLUME 338

Logue, Emily Rose, 1876–
 "The quiet hour," and other verses, by Emily Logue. Philadelphia, D. Reilly; ₎etc., etc.₎ 1907.
  7 p. l., 3–60 p. 18½ᶜᵐ.
  Preface, by Matthew Russell, s. J.

  ɪ. Title.   7–36385
  Library of Congress PS3523.O37Q8 1907

NL 0451541 DLC FU

Logue, Emily Rose, 1876-
 Shadows of an ideal. Philadelphia, P.
Reilly ₍1902₎
 30 l. 24°.

NL 0451542 NN

Logue, Glenn ᴿobert
 An investigation of the distribution of
loads through a reinforced concrete slab ₍by₎
Glenn Robert Logue... and₎ R.H.H.Spidel...
₍Columbus,Ohio state univ. 1913.
 4 p. l., 2-36 no.1.

 Thesis (ᶜ.E.) - Ohio state university.

NL 0451543 OU

TK **Logue, J C**
7872 Transistor switching circuits. Poughkeepsie,
T73L82 N.Y., Engineering Laboratory, International
 Business Machines Corp., 1955.
  105 ℓ. illus. 29cm. (IBM technical
 report)

  1. Junction transistors. 2. Transistors.
3. Switching theory. I. International
Business Machines Corp.

NL 0451544 CLU

JX1977.1
.L6 **Logue, John.**
 The great debate on charter reform; a pro-
posal for a stronger United Nations. New
York, Fordham university press, c1955.
  31 p. (Fordham university. Dept. of
political philosophy and the social sciences.
Publications i the social sciences no. 2)

  1. United Nations. Charter. I. Title.
II. Series.

NL 0451545 DS KEmT NNF NNC-L MsSM LU

Logue, Leona Ann.
 See
Schneiter, Leona (Logue), 1886-

Logue, *Mrs.* **Leona Whitworth.**
 Recent war lyrics; a study of war concepts in modern lyrics,
by Leona Whitworth Logue. With an introduction by Robert
Morss Lovett. New York, The Grafton press ₍1928₎
  65 p. 19½ᶜᵐ.
  "Only five hundred copies of this book have been printed from type
and the type distributed."
  Bibliography: p. 63–65.

  1. War poetry. 2. European war, 1914–1918—Poetry. ɪ. Title.
            29–3201
  Library of Congress PR609.W3L6

NL 0451547 DLC OKentU NIC

Logue, Lester.
 Regional gravity map of Texas

  see under

  Oil and gas journal.

Mann
Microfilm
TX **Logue, Louise Eva.**
745 Some qualities of eggs affecting the gel
L84 strength of custard. ₍Ames, Iowa State
 College, 1940.

  Microfilm copy ₍negative₎ of typescript
filmed by Iowa State College.
  Collation of the original: 51 l. diagrs.,
tables.
  Thesis (M.S.) - Iowa State College of
Agriculture and Mechanic Arts.
Bibliography: leaves 48-49.

NL 0451549 NIC

Logue, Mabel Joanna.
 See
Hopkins, Mabel (Logue), 1893-

Logue, Michael, Cardinal.
 Sermon ₍on Mark ix, 7₎.
 (In Ringrose. The masterpieces of Catholic literature, oratory and
art. Vol. 3, pp. 651–655. Philadelphia, 1901.)

NL 0451551 MB

T917.64
L829t **Logue, Roscoe,** 1885-
 Tumbleweeds and barb wire fences, by Roscoe
Logue ... Amarillo, Tex., Printed by Russell
stationery co., 1936.
  110p. plates, ports. 24cm.
  Illustration on t.-p.
  One of the portraits included in pagination.
  Author's autograph presentation copy to Earl
Vandale.
  1. Frontier and pioneer life - Texas. 2. Texas -
Soc. life & cust. 3. Ranch life. I. Title.

NL 0451552 TxU TxDaM

Logue, Roscoe, 1885-
 Under Texas and border skies, by Roscoe Logue. Amarillo,
Tex., Printed by Russell stationery co., ʿ1935.
  3 p. l., 3–111 p. illus., plates, ports. 24ᶜᵐ.
  Illustration on t.-p.

  1. Texas—Hist.—1846- 2. Frontier and pioneer life—Texas.
ɪ. Title.
             35–6524
  Library of Congress F391.L83

  Copyright A 82930   976.4

NL 0451553 DLC TxU

Txz
976.407 **Logue, Roscoe,** 1885-
L829u Under Texas and border skies. 2d ed. Amarillo,
1935 Tex., Printed by Russell Stationery Co., 1935.
  111p. illus.,ports. 24cm.

  1. Texas - Hist. - 1846- 2. Frontier and pioneer life - Texas. I. Title.

NL 0451554 TxU

LOGUE, THOMAS B.
 Description of the various denominations and kinds of
United States currency...and...directions for using the
"billtector" in detecting counterfeits. Copyright 1936
₍by₎ Thomas B.Logue. ₍n.p., 1936₎ 12 p. 16½cm.

  Diagram of the "billtector" on verso of cover.

  1. Counterfeits and counterfeiting—U.S. 2. Money—U.S.

NL 0451555 NN

Logue, W A.
 The ounce of gold, by W. A. Logue. Rathdrum, Id., The
Silver blade print, 1900.
  2 p. l., ii, 178 p. 19¼ᶜᵐ.

  ɪ. Title.
            0–3904 Revised
  Library of Congress PZ3.L83O

NL 0451556 DLC

Loguen, Jermain Wesley, 1814–1872.
 The Rev. J. W. Loguen, as a slave and as a freeman. A
narrative of real life. Syracuse, N. Y., J. G. K. Truair & co.,
printers, 1859.
  x, ₍11₎–454 p. front. (port.) 18ᶜᵐ.
  Written in the third person, but apparently the work of Loguen.
  Two letters at end of volume are dated 1860.
  "Testimony of Rev. E. P. Rogers," including a poem "Loguen's position": p. 445–450.

  1. Slavery in the U. S.—Fugitive slaves. 2. Slavery in the U. S.—
Anti-slavery movements. 3. Underground railroad. ɪ. Rogers, Ely-
mas Payson, d. 1861.
  Library of Congress E444.L83 14–15518 Revised

 ViU CtY-D FTaSU NIC ICN NN NjP MnHi
L **0451557** **DLC MWA TU CU-A OU NcU OClWHi MiU OO OU**

Loguercio, Leonardo
 ... Teoria generale del consenso
dell'avente diritto. Milano, Casa
editrice Ambrosiana, 1955.
  139, ₍1₎ p. 24½cm.
  Bibliographical footnotes.
  With author's autograph.

NL 0451558 MH-L

BX **Logumenus, pseud.**
1710 Modvs inqvirendi haereticos ad vsvm
L83 Romanae curiae lectu dignissimus; duodecim
 regulis conclusis. Cum earum svm mariis in
 fine. ₍n. p., 1519₎
  ₍15₎ p. 20cm.

  Elaborated from (?) Ars et modvs inqvirendi & damnandi haereticos, which see
also.

NL 0451559 NIC

Logumenus, pseud.
 Modus inqvirendi haereticos... & see also Ars et modus inqvirendi damnandi...

QC721 **Logunov, A A**
.L83 Acceleration of charged particles by a moving
 magnetized medium ₍by₎ A. A. Logunov and IA. P.
 Terletskiĭ. ₍Translated by Columbia Technical
 Translations. White Plains, N. Y., 1954,
  11 l. diagrs.
  Reprinted from Zhurnal eksperimental'noĭ i
teoreticheskoĭ fiziki, v.26, no.2, pp.129–138,
1954.
  Includes bibliography.

  1. Particles.

NL 0451561 ICU

VOLUME 338

Logunov, S. S., joint author.

TL589
.B6
1947

Braslavskiĭ, David Adol'fovich.
Приборы на самолете. ₂2. изд. значительно перер.₎ Допущено в качестве учебного пособия для авиационных техникумов. Москва, Оборонгиз, 1947.

D811.5.L565   48–17209 rev*

NL 0451563   DLC

Logunova, Tat'ĭana Afanas'evna.
В лесах Смоленщины; записки комсомолки-партизанки. ₂Москва₎ Молодая гвардия, 1947.
273 p. illus. 20 cm.

1. World War, 1939–1945—Personal narratives, Russian. 2. World War, 1939–1945—Underground movements—Smolensk, Russia (Province) I. Title.
Title transliterated: V lesakh Smolenshchiny.

D811.5.L565   48–17209 rev*

NL 0451563   DLC

PL866
.G5

Logunova, V. V.

Gluskina, A   E
Очерки истории современной японской демократической литературы. Москва, Изд-во Академии наук СССР, 1955.

Logus, Georgius
see Logau, Georg von, 1485–1553.

Logvin, Grigoriĭ Nikonovich
see
Lohvyn, Hryhoriĭ Nykonovych, 1910–

Logvin, Hrihoriy
see
Lohvyn, Hryhoriĭ Nykonovych, 1910–

Logvine, G
see
Lohvyn, Hryhoriĭ Nykonovych, 1910–

Logvinenko, Nikolaĭ Vasil'evich.
Ископаемые угли Украины. Харьков, Изд-во Харьковского гос. университета, 1953.
120 p. illus. 22 cm.
Bibliography : p. 111–₂119₎

1. Coal—Ukraine.   I. Title.
Title transliterated : Iskopaemye ugli Ukrainy.

TN808.R92U33   55–30586

NL 0451569   DLC

Logvinenko, Nikolaĭ Vasil'evich.
Литология и палеогеография продуктивной толщи донецкого карбона. Харьков, Изд-во Харьковского гос. университета, 1953.
434, ₂2₎ p. illus. 23 cm.
Bibliography : p. 412–₂435₎
——— Microfilm. Microfilm Slavic 551 AC
Made in 1955 by the Library of Congress.
Negative film in the Library of Congress.
1. Petrology—Russia—Donets Basin. 2. Coal—Geology—Russia—Donets Basin.   I. Title.
Title transliterated : Litologiĭa i paleogeografiĭa produktivnoĭ tolshchi donetskogo karbona.

QE451.R8L6   55–36814

NL 0451570   DLC

Logvinenko, T. M., joint author.

Bolkevich, M   I
Дистанция связи отличного качества. Москва, Гос. трансп. жел-дор. изд-во, 1952.

Logvinov, Konstantin Trofimovich.
Динамическая метеорология. Ленинград, Гидрометеорологическое изд-во, 1952.
147, ₂1₎ p. diagrs. 23 cm.
Bibliography : p. 147–₂148₎

1. Dynamic meteorology.   I. Title.
Title transliterated : Dinamicheskaĭa meteorologiĭa.

QC880.L63   53–18333

NL 0451572   DLC

Logvinov, Konstantin Trofimovich.
Dynamische Meteorologie. Berlin, Deutscher Verlag der Wissenschaften, 1955.
154 p. illus. 24 cm.
Translation of Dinamicheskaĭa meteorologiĭa.
Includes bibliography.

1. Dynamic meteorology.   I. Title.

QC880.L6315   56–41290 ;

NL 0451573   DLC MH-GM PPF OrCS WaU FTaSU CU CtY TxU

Logwinow, K   T
see
Logvinov, Konstantin Trofimovich.

Logwinuk, Alexander K.   1922 –
Studies on the fluidization of solid particles.

PhD Chemical Engineering.
1948

NL 0451575   OC1W

RA866
C16
877ℓ

Loh, Alexander
Bad Cannstatt und Dr. Loh's Naturheilstalt. Nebst einem statistischen Berichte über Krankenbehandlung und Curerfolge der Jahre 1869–1877. Wien, W. Braumüller, 1877.
iv, 130, [1]p.   tables.   20cm.

1. Physical medicine - Hydrotherpy - Cannstatt.

NL 0451576   CtY-M

Loh (Alexander). * De pustula maligna. 16 pp. 8°. *Wirceburgi, ex off. C. J. Becker. 1857.*

NL 0451577   DNLM

Loh, Alexander
——— Dr. Alex. Loh's ₎Natur-Heil-Anstalt Wilhelmsbad in Cannstatt (Würtemberg). Methodische Diät- und Wasser-Kuren. Kur-Ort für Brust- und Nerven-Leidende. Elektrische Heil-Anstalt. Prospectus. 2 l. fol. [*Stuttgart, Gebr. Kröner, 1880.*]

NL 0451578   DNLM

WBJ
L833L
1874

LOH, Alexander
Lehrbuch der praktischen Naturheilkunde; nach Steinbacher's kombinirter Naturheilmethode und achtzehnjährigen eigenen Erfahrungen. Berlin, Grieben, 1874.
155 p.

NL 0451579   DNLM

WBJ
L833L
1877

LOH, Alexander
Lehrbuch der praktischen Naturheilkunde; nach Steinbacher's kombinirtem Heilsystem und mehr als zwanzigjährigen Erfahrungen. 2. verm. Aufl. Berlin, Grieben, 1877.
ix, 170 p. (Loh-Steinbacher'sche Naturheilmethode, Bd. 1)
Series

NL 0451580   DNLM

Loh (Alexander). Die Neurasthenie und ihr Behandlung. 10 pp. 8°. *Wiesbaden, C. Schnegelberger, 1890.* *See also*, **Schilling** (J. A.) Bad Cannstatt [etc.] 12°. *Wien, 1871.*

NL 0451581   DNLM

Loh, Arthur Tsung-yuan
see Loh, Tsung-yuan, 1923–

Loh, C   J   von, respondent.
Dissertatio de legione Romana
see under Boecler, Johann Heinrich, 1611–1672, praeses.

Film
300

Loh, Cheng-Shan, 1917–
A descriptive study of selected walled cities in China. ₂Syracuse, N.Y.₎ 1951.
xvi, 148 ℓ.
Thesis—Syracuse University.
Vita.
Bibliography: ℓ.129–142.
For full information, see Dissertation abstract. Microfilm (negative) of typescript. Syracuse, N.Y., Hall & McChesney, ₂1970?₎ 1 reel.

NL 0451584   NSyU

Loh, Chi-yuan
see
Lo, Chih-yüan.

Loh, Dian-yang.
Practical English readers for junior middle schools, by D. Y. Loh. ₂Chungking₎ China Book Co. ₂1944?₎–
v. illus. 19 cm.

1. English language—Text-books for foreigners—Chinese. I. Title.

PE1130.C4L6   56–55379 rev

NL 0451586   MH DLC

VOLUME 338

Loh, Friedrich Wilhelm, 1902-
Die theorie der steuerlehre der deutschen freihande-
lschule.
Inaug. diss. Giessen, 1928. (Gruenberg)
Bibl.

NL 0451587   ICRL MH CtY PU

Loh, Hermann, 1891-
Ueber chorionepitheliom.
Inaug. diss. Marburg, 1919.
Bibl.

NL 0451588   ICRL CtY DNLM

MANN
Film
882
Loh, Homer Chi-Chen.
Americans of Chinese ancestry in Philadelphia.
Philadelphia, 1944.
iv, 216 l. tables.

Thesis - University of Pennsylvania.
Vita.
Bibliography: leaves 202-207.
Microfilm (negative) of typescript. Philadelphia,
University Library, University of Pennsylvania,
1966. 1 reel. 35   mm.

NL 0451589   NIC PU

F
158.9
C5L83
1944a
Loh, Homer Ch'i-Ch'en
Americans of Chinese ancestry in Philadelphia.
Philadelphia, 1944.
iv, 216 l.

Thesis (Ph.D.) - Univ. of Pennsylvania.
Photocopy.
Includes bibliography.

1. Chinese in Philadelphia. I. Title.

NL 0451590   CLU

Loh, Hugo: Histoires tireés de l'Ancien Testament, zum
ersten Male hrsg. nebst Einl., sprachl. Untersuchung u. Anm.
Münster i. W. 1912: Bredt. XXVIII, 178 S., S. XXIX—LXXX. 8°
Münster, Phil. Diss. v. 3. Okt. 1912, Ref. Wiese
[Geb. 10. Mai 89 Karthausen, Kr. Lennep; Wohnort: Münster i. W.; Staats-
angeh.: Preußen; Vorbildung: Realgymn. Barmen Reife O. 08; Studium:
Marburg 4, Münster 4 S.; Rig. 2. Febr. 12.]   [U 12. 6588

NL 0451591   ICRL PU MH

Loh, Hung-yu
see Lu, Hung-yü, 1907-

Film
Z
1081
LOH, JEANNE TAO-TSIN
A storyhour program to introduce to children
representative American composers; a combination
of music and stories, illustrating types of
musical compositions in various historical
periods. [Seattle, Wash.] 1955.
75 l.

Thesis (M. of Librarianship)--Univ. of Washington.
Microfilm. Univ. of Washington Library.

NL 0451593   InU

M1503
L56915
Loh, Johannes
[Im Eva-Paradies, acc. arr. piano]
Im Eva-Paradies; Operette in drei Akten.   Weimar, Wiegand
[c1922]
90 p.

German words.

NL 0451594   CU

LA3999
.L83
Loh, Ling Su.
...The status of primary education in China...
Chicago, 1922.
224 l., 10 numb. l., 3 l. tables. 29ᵐᵐ.

Typewritten.
Thesis (Ph.D.)--University of Chicago, 1922.
Bibliography: 3 l. at end.
"Abstract": 10 l., 2d group of paging.

1. Education of children. 2. Education—China.

NL 0451595   ICU

Loh, Mei-Hung, 1919-
Buckling of rigid frames.   [Ithaca, N.Y.]
1946.
54, vi l. illus. 27cm.

Thesis (Ph.D.)--Cornell University, Feb.
1946.

1. Buckling (Mechanics) 2. Strains and
stresses. I. Title.

NL 0451596   NIC

LOH, Philipp.
Zur reform des reichserbrechts. Edictum unde
respublica! Berlin, 1913.

4° 16 p.

NL 0451597   MH-L

Loh, Pichon Pei Yung, 1928-
The popular upsurge in China: nationalism
and westernization, 1919-1927. Chicago, 1955.
362 l.
Thesis (Ph. D.) - The University of Chicago.
Includes bibliography.
Microfilm of typescript. Chicago, Library Department of Photographic Reproduction,
University of Chicago [n. d.] 1 reel. 35 mm.
1. China - History - Republic, 1912-1949.
2. China - Politics and government - 1912-
1949. I. Title.

NL 0451598   MoSW MoU NNC

Loh, Pichon Pei Yung, 1928-
Sino-Russian diplomatic relations and the effects
upon China, 1919-1929. Chicago, 1951

177 p.
Thesis (M.A.) - University of Chicago
Microfilm, positive, of copy at the University
of Chicago

NL 0451599   MH

Loh, Reinhold, 1901-
Die kongenitale Nierendystopie ...   Giessen,
1935.
Diss. - Giessen.
Lebenslauf.
"Schrifttum": p. 26-27.

NL 0451600   CtY

Loh, S. Y.
see
Lu, Shih-I.

Loh, T. W.

China. *National tariff commission.*
... The revision of the price index numbers. By T. Sheng ...
(With appendices) Shanghai, 1931.

Loh, Tachuen S. K., *tr.*   FOR OTHER EDITIONS
                                SEE MAIN ENTRY
China. *Laws, statutes, etc.*
... The provisional Criminal code of the republic of
China. Tr. by T. T. Yuen & Tachuen S. K. Loh. [Paris,
Impr. de Vaugirard, pref. 1915]

Loh, Tao-ying
see his name in religion
Miao-chi, 1895-1930.

Loh, Theodor Wilhelm Walther

see

Loh, Walther, 1904-

Loh (Theodorus) [1806-   ]. *De fractura colli
ossis femoris.   26 pp., 3 l., 1 pl. 12°. *Berolini,
typog. F. Nietackiana,* [1830]. [P., v. 1547.]

NL 0451606   DNLM PPC

Loh, Tsung-yuan, 1923-
The theory of economic development and planning in an
underdeveloped country, as applicable to China, by Arthur
Tsung-yuan Loh. Urbana, 1952.

8 p. 23 cm.

Abstract of thesis—University of Illinois.
Vita.

1. Industrialization. 2. China—Economic policy.
HC59.L6   A 52-10128
Illinois. Univ. Library
for Library of Congress   †

NL 0451607   IU NIC DNAL DLC

Loh, Walter, 1908-
...Beitrag zum blutbild von gesunden und
kranken hunden unter besonderer berucksichtigung der absoluten zahlenwerte...Butzbach
[1935]
79 p. 22½ cm.

Diss. - Giessen.
Lebenslauf.
"Schrifttumverzeichnis": p. 73-77.

NL 0451608   DNAL CtY

VOLUME 338

Loh, Walther, 1904–
... Zur Bildung und Umbildung des Foramen
epiploicum Winslowii beim Schwein und Wiederkäuer ... Giessen, 1932.
Diss. - Giessen.
Lebenslauf.
"Literaturverzeichnis": p. 29.
Full name: Theodor Wilhelm Walther Loh.

NL 0451609   CtY MiU

Loh, Wellington Hsiao Tung, 1917–
A study of the dynamics of the induction
and exhaust systems of a four stroke engine
by a hydraulic analogy. ₍Cambridge, Mass₎
1946.
Microfilm copy (positive) of typescript
filmed by Massachusetts Institute of Technology Library, 1955.
Collation of the original, as determined
from the film: 101 l. illus.

Thesis--Massachusetts Institute of
Technology.

1. Gas flow. 2. Cylinders. 3. Hydraulics.

NL 0451611   NIC

Loh, Wilhelm, 1904–
Untersuchungen über klimaschwankungen und
über die abhängigkeit der wetterlagen auseinanderfolgender jahreszeiten, durchgeführt anhand
der 100jähr. beobachtungsreihe der meteorologischen
station Darmstadt. ... Giessen, 1936. 36 p.
Inaug. Diss. - Giessen, 1936.
Lebenslauf.
Literaturangabe.

NL 0451612   ICRL CtY

Loh-ka-pang Observatory
see
Lu-chia-pang kuan hsiang t'ai.

Lohagen, Paul, 1887–
Ueber verlagerung der iris und linse nach verletzungen.
Inaug. diss. Giessen, 1919.
Bibl.

NL 0451614   ICRL DNLM

לוחמי החופש בישראל; תולדות השומר, ההגנה, הפלמ"ח, נילי"י, אצ"ל,
לח"י. תל-אביב: ש. פרידמן, תשט"ו.
342 p. 25 cm.

1. Palestine—Defenses.
Title transliterated: Loḥame ha-ḥofesh be-Yisrael.

DS126.L6   56-51313

NL 0451615   DLC

Loḥame ḥerut yisrael.
An outline of foreign policy. Tr. from Hebrew. ₍Jerusalem?₎ 1947.
47 p. 24 cm.

1. Palestine—For. rel.

DS126.4.L615   327.569   48–15904 rev⁴

NL 0451616   DLC OCH

Lohammar, Bengt Gunnar
see
Lohammar, Gunnar, 1902–

Lohammar, Gunnar, 1902–
Wasserchemie und höhere vegetation schwedischer
Seen. Uppsala, Almqvist & Wiksells, 1938.
252p., illus.
Thesis - University at Uppsala.
Reprinted from Symbolae Botanicae Upsaliensis,
v. 3, vo. 1, 1938.

NL 0451618   MH-G

Lohammar, Gunnar, 1902–
... Wasserchemie und höhere vegetation schwedischer seen,
von Gunnar Lohammar. Uppsala, A.-b. Lundequistska bokhandeln ₍1938₎
252 p. illus., maps, tables (part fold.) diagrs. 25¼ᶜᵐ. (Symbolae botanicae upsalienses III:1. Arbeten från Botaniska institutionen i Uppsala)
"Literaturverzeichnis": p. ₍245₎–250.

1. Lakes—Sweden. 2. Fresh-water flora. 3. Water—Composition.
4. Botany—Ecology.
₍Full name: Bengt Gunnar Lohammar₎
Iowa. State coll. Library   A C 39–1632
for Library of Congress

NL 0451619   IaAS NNBG NNC MoU OU MiU CtY PU-B PPAN

Lohan, Eduard, 1861–
De librorum titulis apud classicos scriptores Græcos nobis
occurrentibus. Marpurgi Cattorum, 1890. 4 p.l., (1)6-45(1) p.,
1 l. 8°.
Dissertation, Marburg.

1. Books.—Titles (Greek).
September 23, 1912.

NL 0451620   NN CU ICRL NjP MH

LOHAN, Eduard, 1861–
Poesis malicae generum nominibus quae vis
subjecta sit a classicis scriptoribus Graecis
Pars 1. Progr. Lauban, A. Ludwig, 1898.
4°. pp. (1) 136.   Class 1888.98

NL 0451621   MH

Lohan, François.
Le paradis catholique. 2. éd. Paris,
E. Vaton, 1874.
362 p. 18 cm.

NL 0451622   PLatS

Lohan, Gheorghe V.
... Din limba engleză ... Bucureşti, Tipografia "Lupta",
N. Stroilă, 1927.
174, ₍2₎ p. 23¼ᶜᵐ.

1. English language—Text-books for foreigners—Rumanians. 2. English language—Grammar—1890–   I. Title.
34–37892
Library of Congress   PE1129.R8L6
428.2459

NL 0451623   DLC NN

Lohan, Guillo.
Un contre-rezzou au Hoggar; rapport. Paris, 1903.
pp. 95 +. Map and other illus. (Comité de l'Afrique française. Publ.)

Algeria–Hist. 1872–

NL 0451624   MH

Lohan, L.-F.-D. Guillo
see Guillo Lohan, L.-F.-D.

Lohan, Heinrich Max, 1857–
see Lohan, Max, 1857–

PN6071
.C6L63

Lohan, Maria, joint ed.

Lohan, Robert, ed.
A new Christmas treasury, with more stories for reading
aloud, edited by Robert and Maria Lohan. New York,
Stephen Daye Press ₍1954₎

Lohan, Max, 1857–
Die Gottesidee Lotzes. Marburg, 1888
75 p.
Inaug.-Diss. - Marburg

1. Lotze, Hermann, 1817-1881

NL 0451628   MH NIC ICRL NjP

Lohan, Max, 1857–
...Kann der Sozialismus uns retten? Von Dr. Max Lohan
... Berlin: Verlag der Kulturliga, G.m.b.H. ₍1920?₎ 23 p. 8°.
(Revolutions-Streitfragen. N. F., Heft 8.)
Cover-title.

1. Socialism, Germany, 1920.   2. Series.
April 19, 1922.

NL 0451629   NN

Lohan, Max, 1857–
Die sozialdemokratische Gefahr. Berlin: O. Elsner Verlagsgesellschaft m. b. H., 1910. 92 p. 8°.

1. Social democracy, Germany.
N. Y. P. L.   April 6, 1911.

NL 0451630   NN

Lohan, Max, 1857–
Der vertrag von Versailles, gemeinverständlich dargestellt
und erläutert von dr. Max Lohan ... Berlin, Verlag der Kulturliga g. m. b. h. ₍1920₎
62 p., 1 l. fold. map. 22ᶜᵐ.

1. Versailles, Treaty of, June 28, 1919 (Germany)   I. Title.
33–14737
Library of Congress   D644.L6
940.3141

NL 0451631   DLC NN

VOLUME 338

Lohan, Max, 1857–
Der vertrag von Versailles, gemeinverständlich dargestellt und erläutert von dr. Max Lohan ... Berlin, Verlag der Kulturliga, g. m. b. h. ₁1920₎

63 p. fold. map., diagrs. (part fold.) 22½ᵐᵐ.

On cover: Zweite auflage.

1. Versailles. Treaty of, June 28, 1919 (Germany)   I. Title.

                                             34–6234

Library of Congress   D643.A7L6 1920 a   940.3141

NL   0451632   DLC CSt-H FMU

Lohan, Oswald.
Das deutschtum in den Vereinigten Staaten von Amerika, von Oswald Lohan ... Berlin, C. Heymann; New York, E. Steiger & co., 1913.

2 p. L, 56 p. 23ᵐᵐ.   M. 1

1. Germans in the U. S.

             E184.G3L78   13–15222

NL   0451633   DLC ICJ NN

Lohan, R.
So sieht er aus! Der Schmachfriede von Versailles in seinen Hauptzügen dargestellt, von Dr. R. Lohan.   Berlin: U. Meyer ₁1921?₎.   16 p.   8°.

1. Versailles (Treaty of), 1919.

                                        December 22, 1921.

NL   0451634   NN

Lohan, Ralf, 1902–
Mathematische grundlagen und behandlung des ebenen problems der plastizität. ...
Inaug. Diss. – Berlin, [1935]
Lebenslauf.

NL   0451635   ICRL RPB CtY MiU

Lohan, Ralf, 1902–
... Mathematische grundlagen und behandlung des ebenen problems der plastizität. Leipzig und Berlin, B. G. Teubner, 1935.

1 p. L, p. ₁203₎–236. diagrs. 25ᵐ. (Schriften des Mathematischen seminars und des Instituts für angewandte mathematik der Universität Berlin, hrsg. von L. Bieberbach ... bd. 2, hft. 7)
Issued also as the author's thesis, Berlin, 1935.
Bibliographical foot-notes.

1. Plasticity.

                                     A C 37–507

Iowa. State coll. Library
for Library of Congress

NL   0451636   IaAS MoU OCU

PE2813
.W5
   Lohan, Robert, tr.
     Witham, W   Tasker.
       Americans as they speak and live, by W. Tasker Witham; German version by Robert Lohan; original drawings by Harry Roth. New York, Frederick Ungar publishing co. ₁1945₎

Lohan, Robert.
Amerika du hast es besser. Die Vereinigten Staaten wie sie sind und wie sie geworden sind, von Robert Lohan. New York, F. Ungar ₁1946₎   376 p.   maps.   20cm.

"Benützte Werke," p. ₁369₎–373.

350967B.   1. United States—Civiliza-   tion. 2. United States—Hist.
N.Y.P.L.   June 28, 1948

NL   0451638   NN WaS NNC NRU MiD ICU

Lohan, Robert, *ed.*
Christmas tales for reading aloud, compiled and adapted by Robert Lohan. New York, Stephen Daye press ₁1946₎

5 p. L, 9–395, ₁2₎ p. illus. 23½ᵐ.

1. Christmas stories.   I. Title.

PN6071.C6L6   394.268   46–11955

         Wa NcGU WaSp OrU WaT Or OrCS IdB IdU WaS CaBVa
NL   0451639   DLC ViU CoU PRosC NcC NcD MH MB TxU OU

Lohan, Robert.
A concise German grammar for reference and review. New York, F. Ungar Pub. Co. ₁1955₎

176 p. 22 cm.

1. German language—Grammar—1870–   I. Title.

PF3111.L69   435   55–8444 ‡

NL   0451640   DLC MB WaT WaU NBuC NBuU NcU MiU MB PP

Lohan, Robert.
Es war einmal; sechs schöne deutsche märchen, neu erzählt von Robert Lohan. Mit 18 farbigen originalbildern von Harry Roth. New York, Frederick Ungar publishing co. ₁ᶜ1944₎

80 p. incl. col. plates. 23½ᵐ.

CONTENTS.— Hänsel und Gretel.— Rotkäppchen.— Tischlein, deck dich!—Dornröschen.—Die boshafte ziege.—Der kleine Däumling.

1. Fairy tales.   I. Title.

                                     45–21449

Library of Congress   PZ34.L72

NL   0451641   DLC NN

Lohan, Robert.
German life in literature, described in German for Americans and illustrated by living masterpieces, with a visible vocabulary, by Robert Lohan ... New York, Frederick Ungar publishing company ₁1944₎

165, ₁2₎ p. 23½ᵐ. (His ₁Living German literature₎ vol. I)

1. German literature (Selections : Extracts, etc.)   I. Title.

                               44–6943 Revised

Library of Congress   PT1105.L55

                          ₁r45k2₎   830.82

         OC1ND NcD NcGU NcRS
NL   0451642   DLC NcD OrU OCU OU OC1 OC1JC PPCS PPCCH

Lohan, Robert.
The golden age of German literature, by Robert Lohan ... New York, Frederick Ungar publishing co. ₁1945₎

226 p. 23½ᵐ. (His Living German literature, vol. II)

1. German literature—18th cent. 2. German literature—19th cent. I. Title.

                                   45–8405

Library of Congress °   PT1136.L6

                                   830.82

         OrU WaS
NL   0451643   DLC MtBC OC1 ViU NcU NcD NcRS OC1ND PPCS

Lohan, Robert
The golden age of German literature. ₁2d rev. ed.₎ New York, Frederick Ungar ₁1948₎ 226 p. 24cm. (His Living German literature, vol. II)

1. German literature–18th cent. 2. German literature–19th cent. I. Title.

NL   0451644   MsU Or

Lohan, Robert, *ed.*
Das Herz Europas, ein österreichisches Vortragsbuch, hrsg. von Robert Lohan, Walther Maria Neuwirth ₁und₎ Viktor Trautzl. Wien, Saturn-Verlag ₁194–?₎

271 p. 20 cm.
Verse and prose.
Music: p. ₁240₎–264.

1. Austria in literature.

PT1110.A8L6   50–32458

NL   0451645   DLC

Lohan, Robert.
How to read, write, and speak modern German, by Robert Lohan, PH. D. New York, Frederick Ungar publishing co. ₁1944₎

viii, 263 p. illus. 23½ᵐ.

1. German language—Composition and exercises. 2. German language—Grammar—1870–   I. Title.

Library of Congress   PF3111.L7   44–6712

                                     438.242

NL   0451646   DLC OrU InU PPLas NcD OC1 OU CtY

Lohan, Robert.
How to read, write, and speak modern German. 2d, rev. ed. N.Y., F. Ungar ₁1946ᶜ44₎

263 p. illus. 24cm.

1. German language. Composition and exercises 2. German language. Grammar. 1870–   I. T1.   II. T1. Modern German

NL   0451647   NB NBuU IU FU NNF NcU MiU

Lohan, Robert, ed.
Der letzte Klassiker
      see under   Grillparzer, Franz, 1791–1872.

PT1105
.L5
   Lohan, Robert.
     Living German literature. New York, F. Ungar Pub. Co. ₁1945–
       v. 1, 1954₎

Lohan, Robert, *ed.*
A new Christmas treasury, with more stories for reading aloud, edited by Robert and Maria Lohan. New York, Stephen Daye Press ₁1954₎

406 p. 24 cm.

1. Christmas stories.   I. Lohan, Maria, joint ed.   II. Title.

PN6071.C6L63   808.8   54—12862 ‡

         CaBViP MtU NcGU
         NcD NcRS NN TxU IdPI PPPL PP OC1W NBuU WaTC GU MtBC
NL   0451650   DLC WaS WaSp WaT OrP FTaSU NcU NcC MB

VOLUME 338

Lohan, Robert.
Speaking and speeches. New York, Stephen Daye Press ₍1947₎
279 p. 21ᶜᵐ.

1. Oratory.   ɪ. Title.
PN4121.L63   808.5   47–23264*

NL 0451651   DLC MiU CoU OrU OrCS

Lohan, Robert.
Sprechen und Reden. ₍Wien, Saturn-Verlag, °1936₎
222 p. 19 cm. (Vaterländische Front. Bundeswerbeleitung)
Includes bibliographies.

1. Elocution. 2. Oratory.   ɪ. Title.
PN4124.L6 1936   55–54577 ‡

NL 0451652   DLC

Lohan, Robert.
Sprechen und reden, ein handbuch für alle, die durch das wort wirken wollen oder müssen, von Robert Lohan. Zürich u. Leipzig, Rascher-verlag ₍1938₎
272 p. diagrs. 21ᶜᵐ.
"6.–7. tausend."
"Bücher": p. 221–222.

1. Elocution. 2. Oratory.   ɪ. Title.
                                          42–45503
Library of Congress   PN4124.L6

NL 0451653   DLC NN

Lohan, Robert, comp.
Der Weisheit letzter Schluss. Ein Goethe-Brevier
     see under   Goethe, Johann Wolfgang von, 1749–1832
     Selections.

96.1
L832   **Lohann, G**
             Rose vir my tuin.   Johannesburg, Afrik. Pers-Boekhandel, 1951.
             141 p.

             1. Roses.

NL 0451655   DNAL

Lohaus, Bernard, 1838–1898.

Prussia. *Oberverwaltungsgericht.*
Entscheidungen des Königlichen oberverwaltungsgerichts. Hrsg. von Jebens ... und von Meyeren ... Berlin, C. Heymann, 1877–

W 6
P3   **LOHAUS, H**
             Betriebswirtschaftliche und steuerliche Besonderheiten bei Zahnärzten und Dentisten. Freiburg i. Br., Haufe ₍1955₎
             24 p. (Steuer- und Wirtschafts-Kurzpost. Branchen-Sonderdienst, Heft, Nr. 15)
             1. Dental economics 2. Income tax - Germany

NL 0451657   DNLM

Lohaus, H   W.
Die kolonie Nikolausdorf (Eine in der heide entstandene siedelung.) Beiträge zur geschichte der inneren kolonisation im herzogtum Oldenburg. illus., pl.
Landw. jahrb. bd. 40, p. 83–171.   Berlin, 1911.

1. Colonization, Agricultural. 2. Agriculture. Economic aspects. 3. Nikolausdorf, Germany.
Library, U. S. Dept. of   Agriculture   Agr 11–1092

NL 0451658   DNAL

Lohaus, H   W.
...Die pflege der landwirtschaftlichen Kulturpflanzen, ... Hannover, Jänecke,1908.
72 p. illus.   (Bibliothek der gesamten landwirtschaft. Hrsg. von de. K. Steinbruck, 13. bd.)

NL 0451659   OU

Lohaus, Hermann
Die resultate der hydrocelenbehandlung nach punktion und jodinjection an der Chirurgischen klinik zu Göttingen ...   Herford, Busse, 1886.
42 p. tables.

Inaug.-diss., Göttingen.

1. Hydrocele.

NL 0451660   NNC DNLM

Lohaus, W.
Neukulturen und viehweiden auf heide- und moorboden. Von W. Lohaus ... Mit 5 textabbildungen. Berlin, P. Parey, 1907.
92 p. illus. 23ᶜᵐ.

1. Waste lands—Germany. 2. Agriculture—Germany.
                                          12–29408
Library of Congress   S605.L6

NL 0451661   DLC ICJ

Lohausen, Arno.
Schwäbisch Haller Skizzen. Gezeichnet von Irene Grün.   Schwäbisch Hall, Schwend-Verlag [195–?]
[44] p. illus. 15cm. (Bunte Heimatreihe [Nr.] 1.)

1. Hall, Germany.

NL 0451662   NN

LOHAUSEN, HEINRICH VON, pseud.
Literarische Essays.   Graz, Verlag Stiasny [c1954]
57 p. 19cm. (Dichtung der Gegenwart. Bd. 57)

Steirische Autoren.
CONTENTS.--Prinz Eugen.--Lukas von Hildebrand.--Joseph Haydn.--Friedrich Philipp von Hardenberg.--Lionardo da Vinci.--Wilhelm von Tegetthoff.
Full name: Heinrich Jordis von Lohausen.
1. Biography. I. Series.

NL 0451663   NN MH

4F
Arg
77   **Lohausen, Karl**
             Führer von Buenos Aires und Umgebung, mit statistischen Angaben.
             3. verb. und erweiterte Aufl. Buenos Aires, Kunst und Wissenschaft, c1923 ₍1924₎
             136 p.

NL 0451664   DLC-P4 NN

Lohausen, Wilhelm von Calchum, called, 1584–1640.
     see   Calchum, Wilhelm von, 1584–1640.

Lohauss, Carl Hans
     see Lohauss, Karl, 1880–

Lohauss, Karl, 1880–
Der anatomische bau der laubblätter der festucaceen und dessen bedeutung für die systematik. Von dr. Karl Lohauss. Mit 16 tafeln. Stuttgart, E. Nägele, 1905.
vi, 114 p. xvi pl. 31ᶜᵐ. (*Added t.-p.:* Bibliotheca botanica ... hft. 63)
"Literaturverzeichnis": p. ₍11₎

1. Leaves—Anatomy. 2. Grasses.
                                          6–46040
Library of Congress   QK689.L83

NL 0451667   DLC TxU OU PU–B PPAN MiU MH ICJ

Lohauss, Karl, 1880–
... Beiträge zur anatomie der laubblätter einiger festucaceen-gruppen ... Königsberg, 1905.
2 p. l., 36 p., 1 l., ₍2₎ p. 31ᶜᵐ.
Inaug.-diss.—Königsberg.
"Literaturverzeichnis": leaf at end.
At head of title: Aus dem Botanischen institut zu Königsberg i. Pr.
"Diese dissertation ist ein teil einer grösseren, mit zahlreichen abbildungen versehenen arbeit, die der hohen philosophischen fakultät eingereich wurde und in der Bibliotheca botanica (Verlag E. Nägele, Stuttgart) erscheinen soll."

1. Festuceae. 2. Leaves.
                                          Agr 6–1584
Library, U. S. Dept. of   Agriculture 463L835

NL 0451668   DNAL CtY ICRL NN

Lohbauer, Franz Xaver, 1812–1885, ed.
Rituale ecclesiasticum ad usum Clericorum Ord. FF. Min. S. P. Francisci
     see under   Catholic Church. Liturgy and ritual. Ritual. [Franciscan (Reformata Provincia Antoniano-Bavarica)]

L₍ohbauer₎ J₍ohann₎ C₍aspar₎
Erfahrungen und Läuterungen. Charakterbild in Briefen von dem früh vollendeten J. C. L., gefallen im amerikanischen Kriege 6. Oktober, 1863. Als Manuscript für Freunde gedruckt. Zürich, Gebrüder Lohbauer, 1864.
3 p.l., 164 p. 12°.

NL 0451670   NN OClWHi

Lohbauer, Karl Philipp Johan von, 1777–1809.
Auserlesene Gedichte. Hrsg. von C. Pfeilsticker. Isny, Verlag vom Herausgeber [1909]

NL 0451671   MH

PT 2424
.L68 A17   **Lohbauer, Karl Philipp Johan von,** 1777–1809.
1798   Gedichte. Leipzig, T. Seeger, 1798.
             158 p. music, port.

NL 0451672   InU

VOLUME 338

Lohbauer, Rudolph
Der Feldzug in Russland, 1812, nach den
hundert Bildern Faber du Faur's. Historisch
und ästhetisch erläutert von Rudolph Lohbauer
... Stuttgart, C.F.Autenrieth'sche Kunsthandlung, 1845.
  xivp.,1l.,132p. 2 fold.maps. 26½cm.
  In portfolio with Faber du Faur's "Blätter
aus meinem Portefeuille im Laufe des Feldzugs
1812," [Stuttgart,1845?] which was first
published with text by F.v.Kausler in the
same city, 1831-43.

BB138w
831fb

NL 0451673   CtY

Lohbeck, Don, ed.
Henry Ford and the Jews
see under The Dearborn independent.

Lohbeck, Ernst
Absolute nichtigkeit bei strafbefehl und
strafverfügung. ... Nürnberg, 1934. 84 p.
Inaug. Diss. - Erlangen, 1934.
Bibliography.

NL 0451675   ICRL MH-L

[Lohbeck, Harald]
Hochschulschrifttum, Verzeichnis von Dissertationen und Habilitationsschriften
see under Nationalsozialistische Deutsche
Arbeiter-Partei. Parteiamtliche Prüfungskom-
mission zum Schutze des NS. Schrifttums.

Lohbeck, Heinz Albrecht
Der rechtswidrige vermögensvorteil bei
der erpressung (unter berücksichtigung des
entwurfes zu einem allgemeinen deutschen
strafgesetzbuch von 1927) ... von Heinz
Albrecht Lohbeck ... Springe, J.C.
Erhardt, 1933.
  42 p. 22cm.
  Inaug.-diss.- Erlangen.
  "Literaturverzeichnis": p. [5]-[6]

NL 0451677   MH-L

Lohbeck, Hermann, 1904-
... Karzinoid der Appendix ... Lippstadt, 1932
Inaug.-Diss. - Münster.
Lebenslauf.

NL 0451678   CtY

Lohberg, Hermann.
Kaiser-Anekdoten; heitere Momente, characteristische Skizzen
und leutselige Züge aus dem Leben Kaiser Wilhelm II. Züllichau: H. Liebich [1890]. 62 p. 16°.

1. William II., German emperor. 2.
Anecdotes (German).

MANDEL COLLECTION.
November 8, 1913.

NL 0451679   NN

Lohberg, Paul, 1861-
Anwendung von poisson's theorie der magnetischen
induktion ...
Inaug. diss. Goettingen, 1884

NL 0451680   ICRL

Lohberger, Hans.
Doppelgänger Mensch. Philosophie und Moral
des Zugleich. Graz-Wien-München, Stiasny
[c1954]
  175 p. 19 cm.

NL 0451681   CoU FTaSU NN NIC ICRL

Lohberger, Hans.
Oswald Spenglers Untergang; Einiges über den
Kult der Kultur. Graz, Stiasny Verlag [1955]
  32 p.
  1. Spengler, Oswald, 1880-1936. Der Untergang des Abendlandes.

NL 0451682   NNC NN MH CU NIC DLC-P4

Lohberger, Johannes, 1884-
Über zwei riesige Embryonen von Lamna. Mit 5 Taf.
München 1910: Straub. 45 S., 5 Taf. 4° ¶ (Aus: Abhand-
lungen d. math.-phys. Kl. d. Bayr. Akad. d. Wiss. Suppl.-Bd 4.)
Leipzig, Phil. Diss. v. 18. Nov. 1910, Ref. Chun, Pfeffer
[Geb. 27. Mai 84 Annaberg i. S.; Wohnort: Annaberg: Staatsangeh.: Sachsen;
Vorbildung: Realgymn. Annaberg Reife O. 05; Studium: Leipzig 9 S.;
Rig. 22. Febr. 10.] [U 11.3251]

NL 0451683   ICRL CtY PU CU IU MH

LOHDE, Alice Irmgard, 1906-
Beitrag zum Resorptionsablauf des
Carnofilfadens im Vergleich zum
Katgutfaden. Ochsenfurt a. M., 1938.
  18 p. illus.
  Diss. - Göttingen.
  1. Sutures.

W 4
G59
1938

NL 0451684   DNLM

Lohde, Clarissa, pseud.
see Boetticher, Clarissa (Leyden) 1836-

Lohde, Georg [Ludwig] 1850-
Ueber die entwicklungsgeschichte und den bau einiger
samenschalen ... Naumburg a/S., Druck von G. Paetz,
1874.
  42, [2] p. II fold. pl. 22cm.
  Inaug.-diss.—Leipzig.
  Vita.

1. Seeds—Anatomy.

Library of Congress   QK701.L83   5-24957†

NL 0451686   DLC ICRL

Lohde [Hermannus Ferdinandus Theodorus Al-
bertus] [1814-]. *Sectionis cæsareæ in clinico obstetricio Bonnensi iterum in eadem mu-
liere cum successu institutæ historia. 30 pp., 1 l.
8°. Berolini, typ. Hachtmanniana, [1840].

NL 0451687   DNLM PPC

LOHDE, Johann, 1619-1696.
Historischer Discurs von Erfindung vieler guten Dinge,
zu Hinbringung menschliches Lebens nötig und heilsam,
benebenst ... warhafftigem Berichte von dem schellen-
dorffischen Heyl-Brunnen, zu Gutzschdorff bey Königs-
brück gelegen ... Freybergk, Gedruckt bey Georg
Beuthern, 1647.
  [107] p. illus. 20 cm.

WZ
250
L833h
1647

NL 0451688   DNLM

Lohde, Karl Christian, respondent.
Dissertatio inauguralis juridica de personis
ex mandato praesumto ...
see under Henne, Rudolph Christoph,
praeses.

Lohde, Ludwig, 1806-1875.
Die Abtei-Kirche zu Werden an der Ruhr.
Abdruck aus der Zeitschrift für Bauwesen.
Mitgetheilt von August Stüler. Text von
Ludwig Lohde. Berlin, Ernst & Korn, 1857.
  8 p. 7 plates. 49cm.

NA
5586
W54
L83

1. Werden, Ger. (Benedictine Abbey) 2.
Church archit ecture—Germany. I.
Stüler, Augu st.

NL 0451690   NIC

Lohde, Ludwig, 1806-1875.
Die architektonik der Hellenen nach C.
Bötticher's Tektonik der Hellenen. Nachträge
zur fünften auflage Mauch's Architektonischen
ordnungen der griechen und römer und der
neueren meister. Berlin, Ernst & Korn, 1862.
  43 p. 33 cm.

NL 0451691   PU CtY

Lohde, Ludwig, 1806-1875.

Mauch, Johann Matthäus von, 1792-1856.
Die architektonischen ordnungen der Griechen und
Römer. Hrsg. von J. M. v. Mauch ... 8. durch neue
tafeln verm. aufl. nach dem text, von L. Lohde, neu bearb.
von R. Borrmann ... Mit LXIII tafeln. Berlin, W. Ernst
& sohn, 1896.

Lohde, Ludwig, 1806-1875.
Archiv für ornamentale Kunst
see under Gropius, Martin Karl Philipp,
1824-1880.

Lohde, Ludwig, 1806-1875.
Der dom von Parenzo; ein beitrag zur
kenntniss und geschichte altchristlicher
kunst. Berlin, 1859.
  12p. plates, plans.

f723.1
L83d

NL 0451694   IU NjP

Lohde, Ludwig, 1806-1875, ed.

Gailhabaud, Jules, 1810-1888.
Jules Gailhabaud's Denkmäler des baukunst. Unter mit-
wirkung von Franz Kugler und Jacob Burckhardt hrsg. von
Ludwig Lohde ... Hamburg, J. A. Meissner; [etc., etc.], 1852.

VOLUME 338

Lohde, Ludwig, 1806–1875, ed.
Schinkel's Mobel-Entwürfe, welche bei Einrichtung prinzlicher Wohnungen in den letzten zehn Jahren ausgeführt wurden.   Berlin, Duncker und Humblet, 1835–1837.
4 in 1 v.

NL 0451696   PPF

Lohde, Ludwig, 1806–1875.
Die skene der alten ... von Ludwig Lohde. Mit einer bildtafel. Berlin, Gedruckt auf kosten der Archäologischen gesellschaft, in commission bei W. Hertz (Besssersche buchhandlung), 1860.
24 p. pl. 26ᶜᵐ. (Programm zum Winckelmannsfest der Archäologischen gesellschaft zu Berlin. 20)

1. Theaters, Roman.   I. Title.
Title from Columbia   Univ.   A C 34–523
Library of Congress   [N5325.A8 no. 20]

NL 0451697   NNC CU OCU PU MdBP NN MH

Lohde, Paul Gerhard, 1890–
Statistik sämtlicher Fälle von Hyperemesis gravidarum an der Universitäta-Frauenklinik zu Leipzig von 1887 bis 1914.   Leipzig, 1918.
Inaug.-Diss. - Leipzig.
Lebenslauf.
"Literatur": p. 16.

NL 0451698   CtY ICRL DNLM

Lohde, Richard.
Die anthropologie Pascals; eine strukturstudie zur theorie der menschenkenntnis, von dr. Richard Lohde. Halle/Saale, M. Niemeyer, 1936.
vii, 88 p. 23ᶜᵐ.

1. Pascal, Blaise, 1623–1662. 2. Man.   I. Title.
                                                    39–18377
Library of Congress   B1904.M35L6
                                              194.9

NL 0451699   DLC CU

Lohde, Richard, 1877–
Ueber chronische tabakvergiftung.
Inaug. Diss. Leipzig, 1902.
Bibl.

NL 0451700   ICRL CtY DNLM

Lohe (Adolf). *Ueber den Antheil der weissen Blutkörperchen bei Bildung der normalen und pathologischen Gewebe. 40 pp. 8°. *Tübingen, L. F. Fues. 1869.*

NL 0451701   DNLM

*IF
.2424 Lohe, H   M
.L65   Dichtungen. Jever, C. L. Mettacker, 1850.
           352 p. 14cm.

NL 0451702   MB

Lohe, Hans, 1908–
Ist Corbasil, der ublichen Novokain-Injektionslösung zugesetzt, dem bisher als gefässverengerndes Zusatzmittel gebrauchten Suprarenin uberlegen? ...   Bottrop i.W., 1934.
Inaug. - Diss. - Göttingen.
Lebenslauf.
"Literaturverzeichnis": p. 17–18.

NL 0451703   CtY MiU

Lohe, Hermann: Ueber Neuropathie im Kindesalter m. Berücks. d. sogen. 'Wutkrämpfe'. [Maschinenschrift.] 49 S. 4°. — Auszug: Naumburg a. S. 1923: Hirschfelder. 2 Bl. 8°
Halle, Med. Diss. v. 28. Juli 1923   [U 23. 5026

NL 0451704   ICRL

Lohe, Karl Ferdinand.
Die staatsrechtliche Stellung von Landesregierung und Volksvertretung in Reuss älterer Linie und die Austragung von Gegensätzlichkeiten zwischen beiden (1867–1918), von Dr. phil. Karl-Ferdinand Lohe.   Jena: G. Fischer, 1937.   xvi, 220 p. incl. tables. 24½cm.   (Beiträge zur mittelalterlichen und neueren Geschichte. Bd. 7.)
Author's dissertation, Jena, 1936.
"Literaturverzeichnis", p. [xi]–xiii.

1. Reuss, Germany—Hist.   I. Ser.
                                                  October 15, 1937
        MH CU WU
NL 0451705   NN ICU RPB MiU MH-L CtY NIC CLU NcD

van Lohe (L.) Handleiding tot de kennis der vervalsching van levensmiddelen. 1. Stuk: Onderzoek der melk. viii, 40 pp. 8°. *Amsterdam, H. J. van Kesteren. 1868.*

NL 0451706   DNLM

van Lohe (Ludovicus). *Diss. continens quadam de calculis urinariis. [Leyden.] 1 p. l., 50 pp., 1 l. 8°. *Amstelodami, J. et A. Bakels, 1847.*

NL 0451707   DNLM

950   Lohe, Werner A
L833J   Japan—Sonne Asiens; Wetterleuchten am Pazifik. Berlin, Brunnen-Verlag/W. Bischoff
[1940]
            318 p. maps. 21 cm.

1. Eastern question (Far East) 2. Japan.
For. rel. I. Title.

NL 0451708   NcD CU WaU

Lohe, Werner A
Japan, Sonne Asiens; Wetterleuchten am Pazifik. 3. Aufl. Berlin, Brunnen-Verlag/W. Bischoff [1942]
818 p. maps, diagr. 21 cm.

1. Eastern question (Far East) 2. Japan—For. rel.
DS845.L5 1940   A 50–1974
Columbia Univ.   Libraries
for Library of Congress   †

NL 0451709   NNC NN OrU MH ICU DLC

Lohe, Werner A
... Roosevelt-Amerika. München, F. Eher nachf., 1939.
252 p., 1 l. 22½ᵐ.
Map on lining-paper.

1. U. S.—Pol. & govt.—1933–1945. 2. U. S.—Hist. I. Title.
                                                    46–39051
Library of Congress   E806.L64 1939
                                              973.917

NL 0451710   DLC KMK CoU WU ViU MH UU

Lohe, Werner A
... Roosevelt-Amerika. München, F. Eher nachf., 1939.
Film copy made in 1943 by the Library of Congress. Negative. Collation of the original, as determined from the film: 252, [1] p. fold. map.
Map inserted.

1. U. S.—Pol. & govt.—1933– 2. U. S.—Hist. I. Title.
                                                    43–21208
Library of Congress   Film DD-1 reel 44, no. 12

NL 0451711   DLC CaBVaU

973.917 Lohe, Werner A
L831r   Roosevelt-Amerika. [2. Aufl.] München, F.
1941   Eher, 1941 [c1939]
             248p. map. 23cm.

1. U.S. - Pol. & govt. - 1933–1945. 2. U.S. -
Hist. I. Title.

NL 0451712   TxU CoU

R.D.R. Lohe, Werner A
           Roosevelt-Amerika. [3. Aufl.] München,
F. Eher nachf. [1942, c1939]
           248 p. fold. map. 23 cm.

NL 0451713   NcD PU ViU

Lohe, Werner A
... Roosevelt-Amerika. München, F. Eher nachf. [1943]
248 p., 1 l. double map. 22¾ᵐ.
"4. auflage. 31.–40. tausend."

1. U. S.—Pol. & govt.—1933— 2. U. S.—Hist. I. Title.
                                                    44–45091
Library of Congress   E806.L64 1943
                                              973.917

NL 0451714   DLC OU MU CU CtY CoD IaU NjR NN MB

Ndv43   Lohéac, Jean
F6   ... Le délai-congé en France et la loi du
929:       19 juillet 1923 ... Paris, Rousseau & co., 1929.
             239p. 24cm.
             Thèse - Univ. de Lille.
             "Bibliographie": p.[233]–235.

1. Labor contract. cat^ 2. Labor laws and legislation - France.

NL 0451715   CtY MH

Lohénc (Joseph). *Tuberculose du pancréas 54 pp., 1 l. 8°. *Paris, 1899, No. 468.*

NL 0451716   DNLM

VOLUME 338

WZ   LOHÉAC, Paul
100   Un médecin français en déportation;
L833m   Neuengamme ét Kommandos. ₍Paris₎
1949   Bonne presse ₍1949₎
            302 p. illus., ports.
            1. Concentration camps

NL 0451717   DNLM NN

Loheac, Paul Edouard Marie, 1905–
    ... Les tumeurs des capsules surrénales ...
Lyon, 1928.
    Thèse - Univ. de Lille.
    "Bibliographie": p. [159]–173.

NL 0451718   CtY

655.24 Loheide-Caswell Co.
L83s   Specimen book of monotype faces.   Peoria,
    Ill., Loheide-Caswell co. ₍192–?
    cover-title, ₍38₎p.

    1. Printing--Specimens. 2. Type and type-
founding. I. Title. I. Title: Monotype faces.

NL 0451719   IU

PA3043 Loheit, Fritz, 1905–
.L6   Untersuchungen zur antiken selbstapo-
    logie... vorgelegt von Fritz Loheit...
    Rostock, A.Erben,G.m.b.H., 1928.
    cover-title,58 p.   21 cm.

    Inaug.-diss. - Rostock.
    "Lebenslauf;" p.₍57₎-58.

    1.Autobiography. 2.Classical biogra-
phy. I.Title.

NL 0451720   OCU ICRL PU CtY IU ICU MH

W   Lohel, Roserita, 1914–
4   Über die Persistenz von Teilen des
H46   Duktus thyreoglossus an Hand eines
1939   Fallos: Zyste des Zungengrundes.
    Würzburg, R. Mayr, 1939.
        31 p. illus.

    Inaug.-Diss. - Heidelberg.
    Bibliography: p. 30-31.

NL 0451721   DNLM

Lohen, Christopher a, fl. 1686, respondent.
    ...Disputatio medica de salubri potu calidae...
        see under Beckher, Daniel Christoph,
    1658-1691, praeses.

Lohengrin, pseud.
    see
Sotomayor de Concha, Graciela.

LOHENGRIN,Camilo de.
    Besos y risas;libro de crónicas. Con dibujos
de Arturo Plazaola. Habana,Imp."Avisador
Comercial",1924.

    Illustr.

NL 0451724   MH RPB

Lohengrin (Middle High German poem)
    Lohengrin, ein altteutsches gedicht, nach der abschrift
des vaticanischen manuscriptes von Ferdinand Gloekle.
Hrsg. von J. Görres. Heidelberg, Mohr und Zimmer,
1813.
    2 p. l., cvi, 192 p., 1 l. 19½ᶜᵐ.
    "Ex libris Robert Saitschick".

    I. Gloeckle, Ferdinand. II. Görres, Johann Joseph von, 1776-1848, ed.

CaBVaU
NL 0451725   MiU TxU MH CU NN OC1 ICU PSt CtY PU OC1

Lohengrin (*Middle High German poem*)
    Lohengrin. Zum erstenmale kritisch herausgegeben und mit
anmerkungen versehen von dr. Heinr. Rückert ... Quedlinburg und Leipzig, G. Basse, 1858.
    vi p., 1 l., 292 p. 21¼ᶜᵐ. (*Added t.-p.*: Bibliothek der gesammten
deutschen nationalliteratur ... ₍1. abth.₎, 36. bd.)

    I. *Rückert, Heinrich, 1823-1875, ed.   G-667 Revised

    Library of Congress   PT1371.B6 1. abth., 36. bd.

NL 0451726   DLC CaBVaU WU PSt PU OU OC1W MdBP

Lohengrin (Middle High German poem)
    Lohengrin. Zum Erstenmale kritisch herausgegeben ... von Dr.
Heinr. Rückert.
    Quedlinburg und Leipzig. Basse. 1859. vi, (1), 292 pp. [Biblio-
thek der gesammten deutschen National-Literatur von der ältesten bis auf die neuere Zeit. Abth. I. Band 36.] 21 cm., in 8s.

    E705 — T.r. — S.r.c. — Middle High German. Works in Middle High German.

NL 0451727   MB CU

Lohengrin (Middle High German poem)

    Lohengrin, der Ritter mit dem Schwane. Ein
mittelhochdeutsches Heldengedicht. Erneut
von H. A. Junghans. Leipzig, P. Reclam jun.
₍1879₎
    249 p. 15ᶜᵐ. ₍Universal-Bibliothek₎
    With Laurin. Zwergkönig Laurin. Leipzig ₍1879₎

    I. Junghans, Herman A   II. Ser.

NL 0451728   ViU CU NjP MH NcD CtY

Lohengrin (Middle High German poem)

Fröhlich, Walter, 1880–
    ... Parzival and Lohengrin: the stories told by Professor and
Frau Dr. W. Fröhlich ... With eight illustrations by M. D.
Swales. Cambridge ₍Eng.₎ The University press, 1936.

Lohengrin fifty years after, by one of the folk. London, D. Nutt, 1895.
    25 p. 19ᶜᵐ.   3-12443

NL 0451730   DLC CtY

Lohenner, Adolf, 1892–
    Die lebensdauer der an uteruskarzinom erkrankten
frau.
    Inaug. diss. Giessen, 1920.
    Bibl.

NL 0451731   ICRL DNLM

Lohenschiold, Otto Christian von, 1720-1761.

Giannone, Pietro, 1676-1748.
    Peters Giannone Bürgerliche geschichte des königs-
reichs Neapel ... Ulm, Frankfurth und Leipzig, Auf
kosten der Gaumschen handlung, 1758-1770.

LOHENSCHIOLD, Otto Christian von,*1720-1761.*
    De expugnatione urbis Constantinopoleos per
Muhammetem II. Tubingae,litteris Sigmundianis,
₍1757₎.

    sm.4°. pp. 20.   MG 155.15

NL 0451733   MH

Lohenschiold, Otto Christian von, 1720-1761, *praeses.*
    Dissertatio de modo probabiliori quo primae in Ame-
ricam septentrionalem immigrationes sunt factae ...
Tubingae, litteris Schrammianis ₍1754₎
    24 p. 20ᶜᵐ.

    Cover-title.
    Diss.—Tübingen (F. M. Neuffer, J. D. Klett, respondents)

    1. Indians—Origin. 2. America—Antiq. I. Neuffer, Friedrich Martin, re-
spondent. II. Klett, Justin David, respondent.

NL 0451734   MiU CtY MiU-C

Lohenschiold, Otto Christian von, 1720-1761.
    Dissertatio historico-numismatica...
Tubingae, 1755.

NL 0451735   NjP

Lohenstein, Daniel Casper von, 1635-1683.
    [Werke]. Bresslau, Franckfurt und
Leipzig, 1665-1680.
    11 v. in 1. plates. 17 cm.

NL 0451736   CU

PT1745 Lohenstein,Daniel Casper von, 1635-1683.
.L5A2   ₍Sämmtliche werke₎   Bresslau, Auf
    unkosten Jesaiae Fellgibels buchhändlers
    alldar, 1680.
        6v. in 1. (807p.) plates. 17cm.
        Contents. - Daniel Caspers von Lohen-
    stein Blumen: Rosen. Hyacinthen. -
    Cleopatra, trauerspiel. - Sophonisbe,
    trauerspiel. - Himel-schlüssel, oder
    Geistliche getichte. - Geistliche ge-
    dancken über das LIII capitel des pro-
    pheten Esaias. - Thränen.

NL 0451737   NNU-W

Zg17   Lohenstein, Daniel Casper von, 1635-1683
L83   [Werke] Bresslau,Auf Unkosten Jesaiäe Fell-
689   gibels,1689.
        9pts.in 1v. plates. 17cm.
        Some pts. have added engraved t.ps.
        Each part has separate t.p. and pagination.
        Contents. - Blumen:Rosen. - Geistliche
    Gedancken über das LIII. Capitel des Propheten
    Esaias. - Thränen. - Himel-Schlüssel. -
    Hyacinthen. - Erleuchtete Hoffmann. - Sophonisbe
    - Cleopatra. - Ibrahim Bassa.

NL 0451738   CtY

VOLUME 338

FILM 4333 PT Reel 403
Lohenstein, Daniel Casper von, 1635-1683.
[Werke] Bresslau, Auf Unkosten Jesaiae Fellgibels, Buchhändlers all dar. 1689.
5 pts. in 1v. plates.   17cm.
Some pts. have added engraved t.ps.
Each part has separate t.-p. and pagination.
Contents. - Blumen·Rosen.
- Thränen. - Himmel-Schlüssel. - Hyacinthen. - Erleuchtete Hoffmann. -
(German Baroque Literature, No.1302, reel No. 433, Research Publications, Inc.)
Microfilm.

NL 0451739   CU CaBVaU

PT 1745 L5 A6 1689
Lohenstein, Daniel Casper von, 1635-1683.
[Werke. Bresslau, Auf Unkosten J. Fellgibels, 1689-1701]
5 nos. in 1 v. plates, port. 17 cm.

Binder's title: Lohenstein Gedichte.
Contents. - [no. 1] Sophonisbe. - [no. 2] Cleopatra. - [no. 3] Blumen. - [no. 4] Geistliche Gedancken über das LIII. Capitel des Propheten Esaias. - [no. 5] Ibrahim Sultan, Agrippina, Epicharis ...

NL 0451740   OU

Y 952 .L 75
LOHENSTEIN, DANIEL CASPER VON, 1635-1683.
[Werke]   Bresslau,J.Fellgibels Wittbe und Erben,1701-09.
11v.in 1. plates,ports. 17cm.

Contents.—Sophonisbe, Trauer-Spiel.—Cleopatra, Trauer-Spiel.—Blumen.—Himmel-Schlüssel.—Geistliche Gedancken über das LIII. Capitel des Propheten Esaias.—Hyacinthen.—Agrippina, Trauer-Spiel.—Ibrahim Sultan, Schauspiel.—Ibrahim Bassa, Trauer-Spiel.—Epicharis, Trauer-Spiel.—Der erleuchtete   Hoffmann, aus dem Frantzösischen über-   setzt.

NL 0451741   ICN

Lohenstein, Daniel Casper von, 1635-1683.
Afrikanische Trauerspiele: Cleopatra, Sophonisbe. Hrsg. von Klaus Günther Just. Stuttgart, A. Hiersemann, 1857.
xx, 413 p. map. 24 cm. (Litterariser Verein in Stuttgart. Bibliothek, 294)
I. Just, Klaus Günther, ed. II. Title. III. Title: Cleopatra. IV. Title: Sophonisbe. V. Series.

NL 0451742   MdBP

Lohenstein, Daniel Casper von, 1635-1683.
Daniel Caspers Agrippina, trauerspiel. Bresslau, E. Fellgiebeln, 1665.
6 p. l., 155, [1] p. double front., ports. 16½cm.

Frontispiece is added engr. t.-p.

NL 0451743   CLU CU

PT1745 .L5G8 1708
LOHENSTEIN,DANIEL CASPER VON,1635-1683.
Arminius enucleatus. Das ist:Des unvergleichlichen Daniel Caspari von Lohenstein/herrliche realia, köstliche similia,vortreffliche historien/merckwürdige sententien,und sonderbahre reden. Als köstliche perlen und edelgesteine aus dessen deutschen Taciti oder Arminii ... nebst einem vollkommenem register zusammen getragen von M.Joh.Christoph.Männling ... Stargardt und Leipzig,E.und J.M.Jenisch,1708.
2 v.in 1. front. 17cm.
Title in red and   black.
1.Arminius,B.C.   17-A.D.21.

NL 0451744   ICU MH

Lohenstein, Daniel Casper von.
Daniel Caspers von Lohenstein ... Arminius oder Hermann, nebst seiner durchlauchtigsten Thusnelda in einer sinn-reichen Staats-Liebes und Helden-Geschichte ... in vier Theilen vorgestellet und mit saubern Kupfern ausgezieret. Andere und verb. und verm. Auflage. Leipzig, J. F. Gleditschens sel. Sohn, 1731.
2 v. Portr. 4°.

NL 0451745   MB

Lohenstein, Daniel Casper von, 1635-83.
Auserlesene gedichte. Herausg. von Karl Foerster. 88 pp. (Mueller, W., ..Biblioth. deutsch. dichter des 17 jahrh. v. 14, p. 79.)

NL 0451746   MdBP NN

Z 851 L831b
Lohenstein, Daniel Casper von, 1635-1683.
Blumen. Bresslau, Auf Unkosten Jesaiae Fellgibels, Buchhändlers alldar, 1680.
142p. 17cm.

NL 0451747   TxU OCU NjP

PM 5745 .L5 S6 1689 C
Lohenstein, Daniel Casper von, 1635-1683.
Daniel Caspers von Lohenstein/Blumen. Bresslau, Auf Unkosten Jesaiae Fellgibels, Buchhändlers alldar, 1689.
6 p. l., 152, 47, 94 p. 16¹cm. [With his Sophonisbe, Trauerspiel. Bresslau, 1689]
Added illustrated t.-p., engr., on 2 leaves.
In 3 pts. entitled: Rosen; Himel Schlüssel; Hyacinthen.

Himel-Schlüssel is bound after his Cleopatra in JHU copy.
Imperfect: t.-p. mutilated.

I. Title: Blumen.   II. Title: Rosen. III. Title: Himel-Schlüssel. IV. Title: Hyacinthen.

NL 0451749   MdBJ OU MiU ICU

Lohenstein, Daniel Casper von, 1635-1683.
Blumen. Bresslau, J. Fellgibels sel Wittive und Erben, 1708.
[12],152p. 16cm. [With his Sophonisbe. Bresslau, 1708]

NL 0451750   IEN

Lohenstein, Daniel Casper von, 1635-1683.
Bobertag, Felix, 1841-1907, ed.
C. Hofmann von Hofmannswaldau.—Daniel Caspar von Lohenstein.—Heinrich Anselm von Zigler und Kliphausen.—Heinrich Mühlpfort.—Hans von Assig.—Hans Assmann freiherr von Abschatz.—Christian Gryphius.—August Adolf von Haugwitz.—Johann Christian Hallmann, hrsg. von Felix Bobertag. Berlin und Stuttgart. W. Spemann [1885]

Lohenstein, Daniel Casper von, 1635-1683.
Cleopatra, Trauerspiel.
(In Zweite schlesische Schule I. Hrsg. von Felix Bobertag n.d. p.[109]-333. [Deutsche National-Litteratur, v.36])

Microcard edition.

NL 0451752   ICRL

Zg17 G92 658
[Lohenstein, Daniel Casper von] 1635-1683.
Daniel Caspers [pseud.] Cleopatra, Trauer-Spiel. Bresslau/auf Unkosten Esaiae Fellgibels Buchhändlers daselbst,1661.
[172]p. 15cm. [Bound with Gryphius, A., Freuden und Trauer-Spiele ... Bresslau,1658]
Added engraved t.-p. (double)

NL 0451753   CtY CU PU-F DFo

[Lohenstein, Daniel Casper von] 1635-1683.
Daniel Caspers Cleopatra, Trauer-Spiel. Bresslau, Auf Unkosten Esaiae Fellgibels, 1661.
[160]p. 16cm.
Signatures: A⁸A-J⁸.
(German Baroque Literature, No.1298, reel No. 403, Research Publications, Inc.)
Microfilm.

NL 0451754   CU

Ex 3470 .3 .318
Lohenstein, Daniel Casper von, 1635-
Cleopatra. Bresslau, Auf Unkosten J. Fellgibels, 1680.
200 p. 1 illus. 17 cm.

Imperfect: t.-p. wanting.

NL 0451755   NjP PU-F OCU

PT 1745 L5 A6 1689
Lohenstein, Daniel Casper von, 1635-1683.
Daniel Caspers von Lohenstein Cleopatra, Trauerspiel. Bresslau, Bey J. Fellgibeln Buchh., 1689.
6 p. l., 200 p. plates. 17 cm. (His [Werke, no. 2])

Added title page, engraved.
In verse.

I. Title: Cleopatra.

NL 0451756   OU MiU

FILM 4333 PT Reel 403
Lohenstein, Daniel Casper von, 1635-1683
Daniel Caspers von Lohenstein Cleopatra, Trauerspiel. Bresslau, Bey Jesaiae Fellgibeln Buchh. alldar, 1689.
6p.l.,200p. 17cm.
Engr. t.-p.
(German Baroque Literature, No.1305, reel No. 403, Research Publications, Inc.)
Microfilm.

NL 0451757   CU

832.5 L833e
Lohenstein, Daniel Casper von, 1635-1683.
Cleopatra, Trauer-spiel. Bresslau, J. Fellgibels sel. Wittib und Erben, 1708.
[12],200p. plates. 16cm. [With his Sophonisbe. Bresslau, 1708]

NL 0451758   IEN

Lohenstein, Daniel Casper von, 1635-1683, respondent.
... De voluntate ...
see under Lauterbach, Wolfgang Adam, 1618-1678, praeses.

VOLUME 338

Zg17
L83
679
Lohenstein, Daniel Casper von, 1635-1683
Dem weyland durchlauchtigen Fürsten und
Herrn, Herrn George Wilhelms, Hertzogens in
Schlesien, zu Liegnitz ... gefertigte Lob-
Schrifft. Bresslau und Leipzig, Verlegts
Esaias Fellgibel, 1679.
[164]p. front.(port.) 16½cm.

1. Georg Wilhelm, *duke of Silesia*, 1660-
1675.

NL 0451760   CtY MH

FILM
4333
PT
Reel
403
Lohenstein, Daniel Casper von, 1635-1683
Dem weyland durchlauchtigen Fürsten und Herrn,
Herrn Georg Wilhelm, Hertzogens in Schlesien, zu
Liegnitz...gefertigte Lob-Schrifft. Bresslau und
Leipzig, Verlegts Esaeas Fellgibel, 1679.
[164]p. front.(port.) 17cm.
Signatures:):(8A-Z8x4, (K4 blank)

(German Baroque Literature, No.1301, reel No. 403,
Research Publications, Inc.)
Microfilm.

NL 0451761   CU

Lohenstein, Daniel Casper von, *1635-1683.*

— Daniel Caspers [Epicharis Trauer-Spiel. [1. Aufl.] Breßlau
Fellgiebel 1665. 16 cm.
G. III. §193. 2. 3). An Lohenstein, "Agrippina" angebunden.

NL 0451762   CU CtY

FILM
4333
PT
Reel
403
[Lohenstein, Daniel Casper von] 1635-1683
Daniel Caspers [Epicharis, Trauer-Spiel. Bress-
lau, Bey Esaias Fellgiebeln, 1665.
6p.£.,173,[1]p. double front. ports.   16cm.
(German Baroque Literature, No.1299, reel No. 403,
Research Publications, Inc.)
Microfilm.

NL 0451763   CU

PT1745
.L5E6
1701
LOHENSTEIN,DANIEL CASPER VON,1635-1683.
Daniel Caspars von Lohenstein [Epicharis,trauer-spiel.
Bresslau,Bey E.Fellgiebels wittib und erben,1701.
[16],127,[37]p. 16¼cm.
Added t.-p.engr.(double)

NL 0451764   ICU

832.5
L833e
Lohenstein, Daniel Casper von, 1635-1683.
Erleuchtete Hoffman. [Bresslau? 1708?]
[42]p. 16cm.   [With his Sophonisbe.
Bresslau, 1708]

NL 0451765   IEN

Ex
3470
.3
.336
Lohenstein, Daniel Casper von, 1635-1683.
Geistliche Gedancken über das LIII.
Capitel des Propheten Isaias. Bresslau,
Auf Unkosten J.Fellgibels Buchh.aldar.
[1680]
148 p.

"Thränen": p.[125]-148.
Poems.

NL 0451766   NjP

838
L83
Lohenstein, Daniel Casper von, 1635-1683.
Daniel Caspers von Lohenstein [Geistliche
gedancken uber das LIII.capitel des propheten Esaias. Bresslau, J.Fellgibel,
[1689].
144 p.   17 cm.
Separate half-title for Thranen,p.124-
144.
Bound with his Sophonisbe. 1689.

NL 0451767   Mi OU ICU MdBJ

FILM
4333
PT
Reel
403
Lohenstein, Daniel Casper von, 1635-1683
Daniel Caspers von Lohenstein [Geistliche Ge-
dancken über Das LIII. Capitel des Propheten
Esaias. Bresslau, Auf Unkosten Jesaiae Fellgibels
Buchh. aldar.
144p.   17cm.
(German Baroque Literature, No.1303, reel No. 403,
Research Publications, Inc.)
Microfilm.

NL 0451768   CU CaBVaU

Lohenstein, Daniel Casper von, 1635-1683.
Geistliche Gedancken über das LIII. Capitel des
Propheten Isaias.   Bresslau, J. Fellgibels sel.
Wittib und Erben, 1708.
144 p.   16 cm.   [With his Sophonisbe.
Bresslau, 1708]
"Thränen": p. [123]-144.

NL 0451769   IEN

PT1745
.L5G8
1689
Rare bk
Lohenstein, Daniel Casper von, 1635-1683.
Daniel Caspers von Lohenstein [Grossmüthiger
feldherr Arminius oder Herrmañ, als ein tapfferer
beschirmer der deutschen freyheit/ nebst seiner
durchlauchtigen Thussnelda in einer sinnreichen
staats- liebes- und helden-geschichte dem vaterlande zu liebe ... vorgestellet ... Leipzig, J.
F. Gleditsch, 1689-90.
2 v. in 3. 5 fronts. (incl. port.) plates.
25x20cm.
Ersten th. 6. buch and andern th. 6. buch have
special title-   pages.

Title in red and black; head and tail pieces;
initials.
"Anmerckungen" and "Register" bound separately.
Edited by Benjamin Neukirch.

WU MBAt
NL 0451771   ICU NIC IEN OCU MdBJ ScU OCU PU CaBVaU

FILM
4333
PT
Reel
404
Lohenstein, Daniel Casper von, 1635-1683
Daniel Caspers von Lohenstein [Grossmüthiger
Feldherr Arminius oder Herrmann, als ein tapffrer
Beschirmer der deutschen Freyheit/nebst seiner
durchlauchtigen Thussnelda in einer sinnreichen
Staats- Liebes- und Helden-Geschichte dem Vater-
lande zu Liebe...vorgestellet...Leipzig, J.F.
Gleditsch, 1689-90.
2v. front.(port.)plates.   24x20cm.
Erster Th.6. Buch and anderer Th.6 Buch have
special title-page.
Added engr. t.-p's.

Title in red and black; head and tail pieces;
initials.
Edited by Benjamin Neukirch.
Completed by Christian Wagner.
(German Baroque Literature, No.1309, reel No. 404,(
Research Publications, Inc.)
Microfilm.

NL 0451773   CU NjP

PT1745
.L5G8
1731
LOHENSTEIN,DANIEL CASPER VON,1635-1683.
Daniel Caspers von Lohenstein... Grossmüthiger
feld-herr Arminius oder Herrmann, nebst seiner durchlauchtigsten Thussnelda in einer sinn-reichen staats-
liebes- und helden-geschichte dem vaterlande zu liebe
...vorgestellet... Andere und durch und durch verb.
und verm.aufl.   Leipzig,J.F.Gleditschens sel.sohn,
1731.
4 v.in 2. front.,plates. 25x19½cm.
Part 2-4 have half-title only.

Continued in next column

Continued from preceding column

Title in red and black; head and tail pieces.
Paged continuously.
Edited by Georg Christian Gebauer.

1.Arminius,B.C.17-A.D.21.

NL 0451775   ICU CU MWelC CtY TxU WU CSt CU PBm

FILM
4333
PT
Reel
406
Lohenstein, Daniel Casper von, 1635-1683
...Grossmüthiger Feld-Herr Arminius oder Herr-
mann, nebst seiner durchlauchtigsten Thusnelda in
einer sinn-reichen Staats-Liebes- und Helden-
Geschichte dem Vaterlande zu Liebe, dem deutschen
Adel aber zu Ehren und rühmlicher Nachfolge in vier
Theilen vorgestellet und mit saubern Kupfern ausge-
zieret. Andere und durch und durch verbesserte und
vermehrte Auflage. Leipzig, Bey Johann Friedrich
Gleditschens sel. Sohn, 1731
4v. 2 fronts.(incl.port.)plates.   25cm.
Paged continuously.
Parts 2-4 have half-title only.
Edited by Georg Christian Gebauer.
(German Baroque Literature, No.1310, reel No. 406,(
Research Publications, Inc.)
Microfilm.

NL 0451776   CU

Ex
3470
.3
.386
Lohenstein, Daniel Casper von, 1635-1683.
Himmel-Schlüssel. [Bresslau, Auf
Unkosten J.Fellgibels Buchhändlers aldar,
1680]
47 p.

NL 0451777   NjP

832.5
L833s
Lohenstein, Daniel Casper von, 1635-1683.
Himmel-Schlüssel, oder Geistliche Gedichte.
[Bresslau? 1708?]
[8],48p. 16cm.   [With his Sophonisbe.
Bresslau, 1708]

NL 0451778   IEN

Ex
3470
.3
.386
Lohenstein, Daniel Casper von, 1635-1683.
Hyacinthen. [Bresslau, Auf Unkosten
I.Fellgibels Buchhändlers aldar, 1680]
94 p.

NL 0451779   NjP

832.5
L833s
Lohenstein, Daniel Casper von, 1635-1683.
Hyacinthen. [Bresslau? 1708?]
94p. 16cm.   [With his Sophonisbe.
Bresslau, 1708]

NL 0451780   IEN

PT1745
.L5I2
1689
Rare bk
room
LOHENSTEIN,DANIEL CASPER VON,1635-1683.
Daniel Caspers von Lohenstein [Ibrahim Bassa,trauer-
spiel. Bresslau/I.Fellgiebel/1689.
[20],60 p. 16cm.
Title vignette.

NL 0451781   ICU NIC CU MiU

VOLUME 338

FILM 4333 PT Reel 404
Lohenstein, Daniel Casper von, 1635-1683
Daniel Caspers von Lohenstein. Ibrahim Bassa,
Trauer-Spiel. Bresslau, Verlegts Jesaias Fell-
giebel, Buchhandl. 1689.
10p.l.,60p. 17cm.
Title-vignette.
(German Baroque Literature, No.1307, reel No. 404,
Research Publications, Inc.)
Microfilm.

NL 0451782   CU

Lohenstein, Daniel Casper von, 1638-1683.
Ibrahim Bassa. Trauer-Spiel.
(In Tieck. Deutsches Theater. Vol. 2, pp. 273-344. Berlin.
1817.)

G817 — Ibrahim Bassa. Trauerspiel.

NL 0451783   MB

L832.5 L833i
Lohenstein, Daniel Casper von, 1635-1683.
Ibrahim Sultan, Schauspiel.   Leipzig.
J.C. Kanitzen, 1673.
[12],60,[12]p. 32cm.

NL 0451784   IEN

Zg17 L83 6791
Lohenstein, Daniel Casper von, 1635-1683
Ibrahim Sultan. Schauspiel auf die glück-
seligste Vermählung bey der Röm. Kayser ...
Herrn / Herrn Leopolds und Frauen / Frauen
Claudia Felicitas Ertzhertzogin in Oesterreich
... gewiedmet durch Daniel Caspar von Lohenstein.
Franckfurt und Leipzig / in Verlegung Johann
Adam Kästners. 1679.
41 p. l., 146 p. 16 cm.
Signatures: a⁸b⁸-d⁸e¹A-J⁸
Added engr. t.-p. with imprint Breslau, bey
Joh. Adam Kästner.

Title printed in red and black.
Error in paging: p. 98-99 skipped in numbering;
without loss of text.

NL 0451786   CtY

Zg17 L83 689
Lohenstein, Daniel Casper von, 1635-1683
...Ibrahim Sultan, Schauspiel; Agrippina,
Traurspiel; Epicharis, Traurspiel; und andere
poetische Gedichte, so noch mit Bewilligung des
s. Autoris nebenst desselben Lebens-Lauff und
Epicediis zum Druck verfertiget. Bresslau,Ver-
legts Jesaias Fellgiebel[1685?]
4pts.in 1v. ports. 17cm. [With his [Werke]
Bresslau,1689]
The first three parts have also added engraved
title pages.

NL 0451787   CtY MiU CU

FILM 4333 PT Reel 403
Lohenstein, Daniel Casper von, 1635-1683
Daniel Caspers von Lohenstein Ibrahim Sultan
Schauspiel, Agrippina Traurspiel, Epicharis Traur-
spiel und andere Poetische Gedichte, so noch mit
Bewilligung des S. Autoris Nebenst desselben Lebens-
Lauff und Epicediis, zum Druck verfertiget. In
Bresslau, Verlegts Jesaias Fellgiebel, Buchhandl.
8p.l.,118p.352., 101,[41]p. 1l. blank, 8p.l.,
127,[37]p. 17cm.
(German Baroque Literature, No.1306, reel No. 403,
Research Publications, Inc.)
Microfilm.

NL 0451788   CU

PT1745 .L512 1701
LOHENSTEIN,DANIEL CASPER VON,1635-1683.
...Ibrahim Sultan,schauspiel. Bresslau,Bei E.Fell-
giebels sel.wittib und erben,1701.
[24],118,[58]p. 16½cm.
Added t.-p.,engr.,on 2 l.

NL 0451789   ICU

PT1745 .L5 1701
Lohenstein, Daniel Casper von, 1635-1683.
Daniel Caspars von Lohenstein Ibrahim Sultan, schau-
spiel// Agrippina trauerspiel/ Epicharis trauerspiel/ und
andere poetische gedichte/ so noch mit bewilligung des s.
autoris nebenst desselben lebenslauff und epicediis, zum
druck verfertiget. Bresslau, Bey E. Fellgiebels sel. wittib und
erben, 1701.
6 pt. in 1 v.   ports. 16ᶜᵐ.
Each part has special engr. t.-p. and separate paging.

NL 0451789-1   ICU NIC MdBJ OU InU NjP

FILM 4333 PT Reel 404
Lohenstein, Daniel Casper von, 1635-1683
Kurtz Entworffener Lebens-Lauff, Dess sel. Au-
toris. Bresslau, Verlegts Jesaias Fellgiebel, Buch-
handler.
36p.l.   17cm.
Signatures: A-D⁸-E⁴.
(German Baroque Literature, No.1308, reel No. 404,
Research Publications, Inc.)
Microfilm.

NL 0451790   CU

Zg17 H67 680
Lohenstein, Daniel Casper von, 1635-1683.
... Lob-Rede, bey ... Hn. Christians von
Hofmannswaldau ... Leich-Begängnüsse.
[Breslau?]Auf Unkosten Esaia Fellgiebels sel.
Wittib und Erben[1679?]
[44]p. 16cm. [Bound with Hofmann von
Hofmannswaldau, Christian. C.V.H.Poetische
Geschicht-Reden. Breslau?168-?]

1. Hofmann von Hofmannswaldau, Christian,
1617-1679.

NL 0451791   CtY NIC NjP MB MH OCU CtY

FILM 4333 PT Reel 403
Lohenstein, Daniel Casper von, 1635-1683
D.C. von Lohenstein/Lob-Rede bey...Herrn Christi-
ans von Hofmannswaldau...Leich-Begängnüsse.
[Breslau?] Auf Unkosten Esaia Fellgiebels sel.
Wittib und Erben. [1679.]
28 l.   17cm.
Contains the famous incipit: "Der grosse Pan
ist tot!" With Hofmannswaldau's portrait.
(German Baroque Literature, No.1300,reel No. 403,
Research Publications, Inc.)
Microfilm

NL 0451792   CU CaBVaU

Rare PT 1737 H8 1717
Lohenstein, Daniel Casper von, 1635-1683.
Lob-Rede bey des weyland Hoch Edelgebohr-
nen Gestrengen und Hochbenahmten Herrn Christians von Hofmannswaldau auff Arnolds-Mühle
der Röm.Keys. Maj. Raths, der Stadt Bresslau
Hochverdienten Raths-Praesidis, und dess Königl. Burglehns Nahmslau directoris den 30.
April Anno 1679 in Breslau Hoch Adelich ge-
haltenem Leich-Begängnüsse. Breslau, J.
Fellgiebel [1717?]
[44] p. 17cm.
Bound with Hofmann von Hofmannswaldau,
Ch.: Deutsche Uebersetzungen und Gedichte.
1717.

NL 0451793   NIC MB

Lohenstein, Daniel Casper von, 1635-1683.
Lohensteinius sententiosus; das ist, Des
vortrefflichen Daniel Caspari von Lohenstein
sonderbahre geschichte, curieuse sachen, sinn-
reiche reden ... und andere befindliche merck-
würdigkeiten aus dessen ... schrifften ... colli-
giret und ... ans tage-licht gestellet von Johann Christoph Männling.   Bresslau, 1710.
416 p.   17 cm.
Interleaved with blank pages.

NL 0451794   CU

Lohenstein, Daniel Casper von, 1635-1683.
Römische Trauerspiele; hrsg. von Klaus Günther Just.
Stuttgart, Hiersemann, 1955.
xix, 816 p. 23 cm. (Bibliothek des Literarischen Vereins in Stuttgart, Sitz Tübingen, 293)
CONTENTS.— Lohenstein und die römische Welt.— Agrippina
(1665)—Epicharis (1665)

I. Just, Klaus Günther, ed. II. Title.   (Series: Literarischer
Verein in Stuttgart. Bibliothek, 293)

PT1101.L5 vol. 293   A 56-3468
Rochester. Univ. Libr.
for Library of Congress   [a56d1]†

PSt NcGU NIC OU OO FTaSU MoU AU
NcD ICU TxU NN GASC CaBVaU OrPR DLC CtY CLSU MdBP
NL 0451795   NRU CU-I MU OCU NcD PU NIC ViU MH NcU

Zg17 L83 733
Lohenstein, Daniel Casper von, 1635-1683.
... Sämtliche geist-und weltliche Gedichte
nebst nöthigen Anmerckungen. Leipzig,In
der Zedlerischen Handlung,1733.
[830]p. ports. 17cm.
Various pagings.
Contents. - Sophonisbe. - Cleopatra.-
Blumen.-Hyacinthen.-Himmel-Schlüssel oder
Geistliche Gedichte.-Geistliche Gedancken
über das LIII. Capitel des Propheten Esaias.

NL 0451796   CtY

FILM 4333 PT Reel 407
Lohenstein, Daniel Casper von, 1635-1683
...Sämtliche geist- und weltliche Gedichte nebst
nöthigen Anmerckungen. Leipzig, In der Zedlerischen
Handlung, 1733.
[830]p. ports.   17cm.
Various pagings.
Contents. - Sophonisbe. - Cleopatra. - Blumen. -
Hyacinthen. - Himmel-Schlüssel oder Geistliche
Gedichte. - Geistliche Gedancken über das LIII.
Capitel des Propheten Esaias.
(German Baroque Literature, No.1311, reel No. 407,
Research Publications, Inc.)
Microfilm.

NL 0451797   CU

LOHENSTEIN, Daniel Casper von, 1635-1683.
Sämtliche poetische wercke,welche durchgängig von dem verfasser selbst,mit historisch-
critischen anmerckungen aus alten und neuen
schriftstellern begleitet. Diesen hat man noch
die lebens-geschichte dieses berühmten poeten
beygefüget. Leipzig, J.G.Löwe,1748.

2 vol. Plates.
Bd.ii is without general title-page.

NL 0451798   MH

Lohenstein, Daniel Casper von, 1635-1683.

Flemming, Willi, 1888-   ed.
Das schlesische kunstdrama, hrsg. von univ.-prof. dr. Willi
Flemming. Leipzig, P. Reclam, jun., 1930.

Ex 3470 .3 .386
Lohenstein, Daniel Casper von, 1635-1683.
Sophonisbe; Trauerspiel. Bresslau,
Auf Unkosten J.Fellgiebels Buchhändlers
aldar., 1680.
176 p.

NL 0451800   NjP OCU MH CU

VOLUME 338

838
L83 Lohenstein, Daniel Casper von, 1635-1683.
Daniel Caspers von Lohenstein Sophonisbe
trauerspiel. Bresslau, J. Fellgibel, 1689.
1 p.ℓ., [26], 176 p. fold. front., ports.
17 cm.
Bound with this are his Cleopatra, 1689;
Blumen, 1689; Geistliche gedancken [1689];
Ibrahim Bassa, 1689; and the following works
with a general t.-p. [1689]: Ibrahim Sultan;
Agrippina; Epicharis; Erleuchtete hoffmann;
Kurtz entworffener lebens-lauff desz sel.
autoris.

NL 0451801   MiU ICU OU NNC MdBJ

FILM Lohenstein, Daniel Casper von, 1635-1683
4333   Daniel Caspers von Lohenstein Sophonisbe,
PT   Trauerspiel. Bresslau, Auf Unkosten Jesaiae Fell-
Reel   gibels, Buchhandlers aldar. 1689
403   14p.ℓ.,176p. 17cm.
    Engr. t.-p.
    (German Baroque Literature, No.1304, reel No. 403,
    Research Publications, Inc.)
    Microfilm.

NL 0451802   CU

832.5
L833s Lohenstein, Daniel Casper von, 1635-1683.
Sophonisbe, Trauer-spiel. Bresslau, J.
Fellgibels Sel. Wittbe und Erben, 1708.
[28], 176p. 16cm.

With this are bound the author's Cleopatra.
Bresslau, 1708; Blumen. Bresslau, 1708;
Himmel-Schlüssel. [Bresslau? 1708?] Geist-
liche Gedancken über das III. Capitel des
Propheten Isaias. Bresslau 1708; Erleuchtete
Hoffmann. [Bresslau? 1708? Hyacinthen.
[Bresslau? 1708?]

NL 0451803   IEN

Ex
3470 Lohenstein, Daniel Casper von, 1635-
.3   1683.
.391   [Trauerspiele und gedichte] Breslau, Auf unkosten J. Fellgibels, 1689.
1 v. illus. 16½ cm.

Contents.- Sophonisbe. Cleopatra.
Blumen. Himmel-schlüssel; oder, Geist
liche getichte. Geistliche gedancken.
Thränen. Hyacinthen.

NL 0451804   NjP

Lohenstein, Daniel Casper von, 1635-1683.
Türkische Trauerspiele; hrsg. von Klaus Günther Just.
Stuttgart, Hiersemann, 1953.
xlvii, 285 p. 28 cm. (Bibliothek des Literarischen Vereins in
Stuttgart, Sitz Tübingen, 292)

CONTENTS.—Daniel Casper von Lohenstein, Leben und Werk.—
Lohenstein und die türkische Welt.—Ibrahim Bassa (1653)—Ibrahim
Sultan (1673)

I. Just, Klaus Günther, ed. II. Title. III. Title: Ibrahim Bassa.
IV. Title: Ibrahim Sultan.   (Series: Literarischer Verein in Stuttgart. Bibliothek, 292)

PT1101.L5 vol. 292   A 54-6558

Cincinnati. Univ. Libr.
for Library of Congress   [a56e1]†

GASC ViU CU-S
PSt AU NN DLC ScU GU OU CU-I MU OrPR CaBVaU MoU KMK
NL 0451805   OCU NcGU OO MB LU NIC MdBP TxU NcD PBm

Chi Lohenthal, V
FQ   Bernardo O'Higgins, epopeya lírica. Música
8097   de Remigio Acevedo R. [Santiago de Chile] Es-
.L73B4 cuela Nacional de Artes Gráficas, 1951.
40 p.   20 cm.

NL 0451806   DPU

Loher, Alfons, 1908-
Der Markt des Elektromotors. München, 1952.
148 l. 30 cm.
Typescript (carbon copy)
Inaug.-Diss.—Munich.
Vita.
Bibliography : leaves 147-148.

1. Electric motors.   I. Title.

HD9695.A2L6   56-17779

NL 0451807   DLC

Loher, Arnold.
Die Meistbegünstigungsklausel. Lachen, 1949.
125 p.   22 cm.
Thèse—Neuchâtel.
Bibliography : p. 121-125.

1. Favored nation clause.   I. Title.

HF1721.L6   50-31819

NL 0451808   DLC IU

Loher, August.
Aufzählung der um Simbach am Inn wildwach-
senden Phanerogamen und Gefässkryptogamen.
[Landshut, 1887]
O. Weigel, Cat. 118.

NL 0451809   MH

Loher, C., tr.
Goethe, Johann Wolfgang von, 1749-1832.
... Fausto; traducción de C. Loher y G. Martinez Sierra, ilustraciones de Fontanals. Madrid [Editorial Es-
trella] 1919.

Loher, Rudolf.
*Beitrag zum gröberen und fei-
neren (submikroskopischen) Bau des Zahnschmel-
zes und der Dentinfortsätze von Myotis myotis
[München] 37p. 8°. Berl., 1929.
Also Zschr. Zellforsch., 1929, 10: 1-37.

NL 0451811   DNLM

Loher, Rudolf.
Carl August von Steinheil, der Erfinder und Schöpfer der Klein-
bild-Photographie vor 100 Jahren. Geschichte der Entwicklung
von Kleinbildlinsen in der Steinheilschen Werkstätte. München,
Druck: J. B. Lindl [1938?], 20 p. illus. 21cm.
Cover title.
"Beilage," chart inserted.

1. Steinheil, Karl August von.   2. Photography—Lenses.   I. 1937.

NL 0451812   NN

Loher und Maller.
Loher und Maller, ritterroman erneuert von
Karl Simrock. xviii, 291p. Stuttgart, Cotta,
1868. (Bibliothek der romane, novellen, geschichten u. s. w.)

Originally tr. from Latin into French by
Marguerite de Vaudemont, countess of Lorraine;
and later from French into German by Elisabeth,
countess of Nassau-Saarbrücken.

NL 0451813   OCl IaU MH NIC OCl OClW RPB CU

LOHER und MALLER.
Lother und Maller, eine ritter-geschichte Aus
einer ungedruckten deutschen handschrift. (In
SCHLEGEL, (K.W.) Friedrich VON. Romantische
sagen und dichtungen des mittelalters, 1823.

pp. 189-324.)
The same. (In SCHLEGEL, (K.W.) Friedrich VON
Sämmtliche werke, 1823, VII. 189-324)

NL 0451814   MH

*GC8 Loher und Maller.
Sch362   Lother und Maller, eine Rittergeschichte. Aus
805ℓ   einer ungedruckten Handschrift bearbeitet und
herausgegeben von Friedrich Schlegel.
Frankfurt am Main, bei Friedrich Wilmans. 1805.
274p.   15.5cm.

Attributed by BN to Dorothea von Schlegel.

NL 0451815   MH RPB

Les Loherains
see Geste des Lorrains.
(For the cycle including Garin le Loherain and related chansons)

DH687 Lohest, Cassian.
L833   La défense des Belges devant le Conseil de
guerre allemand [par] Cassian Lohest et Gaston
Kreit. Préfaces du vicomte du Bus de Warnaffe
et me. A. Devigne. Liége, Éditions Pax, 1945.
343 p.   illus.   23½.

1. Belgium - Hist. - German occupation, 1940-
1945. 2. World War, 1939-1945 - Underground movements - Belgium. I. Kreit, Gaston. II. Belgium
(Territory under German occupation, 1940-1944)
Conseil de guerre.   III. Comité de défense
gratuite des Bel   ges devant les tribunaux
de guerre allema   nds. IV. Title.

NL 0451817   CSt-H NN CtY PU IEN NNU-W

Lohest, Jacques.
Conseils d'entreprise et doctrine sociale de l'Église. Louvain, E. Nauwelaerts, 1951.
100 p.   22 cm.

1. Church and social problems—Catholic Church. 2. Belgium—
Soc. condit.   I. Title.   A 52-896

Catholic Univ. of   America. Library
for Library of Congress

NL 0451818   DCU MoSU NcD NN

Lohest, L   comp.
Trois poètes liégeois: Henkart, Reynier et Bassenge, par
L. Lohest. Bruxelles, Éditions "Labor" [1945]
88 p.   18 cm.

1. French literature—Belgian authors—Liége.   I. Henkart,
Pierre Joseph, 1761-1815. II. Reynier, Auguste Benoît, 1759-1792.
III. Bassenge, Jean Nicolas, 1758-1811. IV. Title.

PQ3856.L5L6   68-128064

NL 0451819   DLC MU

Lohest, Marie Joseph Maximin, 1857- 1926.
La géologie & la reconnaissance du terrain houiller du
nord de la Belgique, par Max. Lohest ... Alfred Habets
... et Henri Forir ... Liège, Impr. H. Vaillant-Car-
manne, 1904.
59 p. 24½ᶜᵐ.

1. Coal—Belgium.   I. Habets, Alfred, 1839-   II. Forir, Henri, 1856-

G S 6-894 Revised

Library, U. S. Geol.   survey

NL 0451820   DI-GS OClW

VOLUME 338

ar V Lohest, Marie Joseph Maximin, 1857–*1926.*
19985 Notice sur Julien Fraipont, par
M. Lohest, C. Julin, et A. Rutot.
Bruxelles, M. Hayez, 1925.
69 p. front. (port.) 19cm.

I. Julin, Charles. II. Rutot, Aimé
Louis, 1847–

NL 0451821 NIC CU

Lohest, Marie Joseph Maximin, 1857-1926.
La race humaine de Neanderthal ore de Canstadt
en Belgique. Bruxelles, Hayez, 1886.
46 p.

By Max. Lohest and Julien Fairpont.

NL 0451822 PU

Lohest, Marie Joseph Maximin, 1857-1926.
Recherches sur les poissons des ter-
rains paleozoiques de Belgique. 1885

NL 0451823 DI-GS

Lohest, Marie Joseph Maximin, 1857–*1926.*
Stratigraphie du massif cambrien de Stavelot, par M.
Lohest et H. Forir ... Liége, Impr. H. Vaillant-Car-
manne, 1899–1900.

49 p. illus., 2 pl., diagrs. 33½ᶜᵐ.
Extrait des Annales de la Société géologique de Belgique. tome xxvᵉᵐᵉ.
Bibliography: p. ₍3₎–22.

1. Geology—Belgium. 2. Geology, Stratigraphic—Cambrian. I. Forir,
Henri, 1856– joint author.

G S 14-216

Library, U. S. Geol. survey 332(593) qL83

NL 0451824 DI-GS

Lohest, Max.
See
Lohest, Marie Joseph Maximin, 1857-1926.

Lohf, Paul, 1886–
Türme und tore, von Flandern bis zum Baltikum, mit
185 zeichnungen und 25 kunstdruckbildern; von Paul Lohf.
Wolfshagen-Scharbeutz, F. Westphal ₍1940₎

85, ₍3₎ p. illus., xvi pl. on 8 l. 21½ᶜᵐ.

1. Towers. 2. Spires. 3. Gates. 4. Architecture — Germany.
I. Title.

42-8085
Library of Congress NA2930.L6

729.35

NL 0451826 DLC

Lohf, Paul, 1886–
Türme und Tore, von Flandern bis zum Baltikum, mit 185
Zeichnungen und 43 Kunstdruckbildern. 2., erweiterte Aufl.
Wolfshagen-Scharbeutz, F. Westphal ₍1943₎

103 p. illus., 24 plates. 22 cm.

1. Towers. 2. Spires. 3. Gates. 4. Architecture—Germany.
I. Title.

NA2930.L6 1943 729.36 A F 48-3536*
Columbia Univ. Libraries
for Library of Congress ₍1₎†

NL 0451827 NNC NN DLC

Lohfelder, Edgar, 1907-
Das verfahren mit schiedsurteil in bagatell-
sachen nach dem geltenden reichszivilprozessrecht
und dem reichsdeutschen referentenentwurf einer
ZPO. und das österreichische verfahren in bagatell-
sachen ... Soneberg i. Thür., n.d. 61 p.
Inaug.-Diss.—Jena, [1932]
Lebenslauf.
Bibliography.

NL 0451828 ICRL MiU

Lohfeldt, P(aul) /*875-*
Über primäre Geschwülste der Bursa
omentalis. Hamburg & Leipzig: Voss 1909. 16 S. 8°
¶(Aus: Jahrbücher d. Hamburg. Staatskrankenanst. Bd 14.)
Leipzig, Med. Diss. v. 21. Sept. 1909, Ref. Marchand
[Geb. 22. März 75 Hamburg; Wohnort: Hamburg; Staatsangeh.: Hamburg;
Vorbildung: Wilhelm-Gymn. Hamburg Reife M. 00; Studium: Leipzig 4,
Kiel 1, Freiburg i. B. 1, Berlin 1, Leipzig 3 S.; Coll. 30. Okt. 09; Approb.
28. Jan. 07.]
[U 10. 3022

NL 0451829 ICRL DNLM CtY

LOHFERT, Hans, 1905-
Synthesen von ketonen mehrwertiger phenole.
Inaug.-diss., Kiel. Borna-Leipzig, R.Noske,
1927.

pp.(4),264
"Lebenslauf", at end.

NL 0451830 MH CtY ICRL

Lohff, Alfred, 1879-
George Chapman ... von Alfred Lohff ... Berlin, Druck
von C. Salewski, 1903.

2 p. l., 43, ₍3₎ p. 22ᶜᵐ.
Inaug.-diss.—Berlin.
Lebenslauf.
Chapters I and II of a larger work.

1. Chapman, George, 1559?-1634. 2. Homerus—Translations, English.

₍Full name: Karl Franz Otto Alfred Lohff₎

Library of Congress PA4037.L6 5-790

NL 0451831 DLC CtY PU OU MH NjP

---

881 Lohff, Alfred, 1879-
H81.Ec.Yt George Chapmans Ilias-Übersetzung. Berlin,
Mayer & Müller, 1903.
iv, 113p. 24cm.

1. Homerus. Ilias. 2. Chapman, George,
1559?-1634, tr. 3. Translating and interpreting

NL 0451832 IU MB NIC LU NcD NjR

Lohff, Karl Franz Otto Alfred
see
Lohff, Alfred, 1879-

---

q784.3 Lohfink, E H
Sh37 ... Whispering winds. Polka brillante ... New
v.11 York, J. L. Peters; Chicago, T. G. DeMotte; ₍etc.,
no.10 etc., c1865₎
7p.

Sheet music printed in Chicago prior to 1871.
v.11,no.10₎
Plate no.: 1610. 6.

1. Pianoforte music. I. Title.

NL 0451834 IU

Lohia, Rammanohar, 1910-
Aspects of socialist policy. [Bombay,
Published by M. Limaye for the Socialist
Party, 1952]
91 p. 21 cm.
1. Socialist Party (India) 2. Socialism
in India. I. Title.

NL 0451835 FU CU NN NjP ICU

Lohia, Rammanohar.
... Congress & war ₍by₎ Rammanohar Lohia. ₍Lucknow,
L. Bahadur, secretary, U. P. c. c., 1939?₎
cover-title, 15, ₍1₎ p. 22ᶜᵐ. (U₍nited₎ P₍rovinces₎ c₍ongress₎ c₍ommittee₎
War sub-committee. Bulletin, no. 1)

1. World war, 1939- —India. 2. Indian national congress.
I. Title.
42-48518
Provisional
Library of Congress D754.I 4U5 no. 1

(940.5³54) 940.5354

NL 0451836 DLC

Lohia, Rammanohar.
... Constituent assembly, by Rammanohar Lohia. ₍Luck-
now, L. Bahadur, secretary, U. P. C. C., 1940?₎
cover-title, 16 p. 22ᶜᵐ. (U₍nited₎ P₍rovinces₎ c₍ongress₎ c₍ommittee₎
War sub-committee. Bulletin, no. 2)

1. India—Pol. & govt.—1919- I. Title.
43-26654
Provisional
Library of Congress D754.I 4U5 no. 2

(940.5354) 342.54

NL 0451837 DLC

DS35 Lohia, Rammanohar.
L833 Fragments of a world mind. Calcutta, Maitra
yani ₍1951?₎
262 p. 23cm.

1. Asia - Politics. 2. World politics -
1945- 3. India - Pol. & govt. - 1947-
4. Socialism. 5. Communism. 6. Communism - Anti -communist literature.
I. Title.

NL 0451838 CSt-H CU NN MiU

DS404
.5 Lohia, Rammanohar.
.L6
1953 Fragments of a world mind. Cal₍cutta₎
Maitrāyanī ₍1953?₎
262 p. 22ᶜᵐ.
A collection of articles and statements, some
of which have been published.—cf. Publishers'
note.

1. World politics—Addresses, essays, lectures.
2. India—Addresses, essays, lectures. I. Title.

NL 0451839 ViU

Lohia, Rammanohar.
... India in figures, by Rammanohar Lohia. ₍Lucknow,
L. Bahadur, secretary, U. P. C. C., 1940?₎
cover-title, 21, ₍1₎ p. 22½ᶜᵐ. (United Provinces congress committee.
War sub-committee. Bulletin, no. 3)

1. India—Stat. I. Title.
43-26655
Provisional
Library of Congress D754.I 4U5 no. 3

(940.5354) 315.4

NL 0451840 DLC

VOLUME 338

Lohia, Rammanohar.
... India on China, by Rammanohar Lohia ... foreword by Jawaharlal Nehru ... Allahabad: Published by J. B. Kripalani, general secretary, All India congress committee, 1938. 52 p. illus. (facsims.) 22cm. (Congress political and economic studies. no. 9.)

1. China—Hist.—Invasion of   1937–   2. China—Hist.—Invasion of 1937–   —Public opinion.   I. Title. II. Ser.
          May 2, 1941

NL 0451841   NN NNC CSt-H CtY

BJ49a
A15
v.12
Lohia, Rammanohar
... Indian foreign policy, by Rammanohar Lohia ... Foreword by Jawaharlal Nehru. Allahabad, J. B. Kripalani [pref. 1938] 1p. ℓ., 19p., 1ℓ. 22cm. (Congress political and economic studies, no.12)

1. India - For. rel.   I. Ser.

NL 0451842   CtY NN CSt-H

Lohia, Rammanohar.
Indians in foreign lands, by Rammanohar Lohia ... Foreword by J. B. Kripalani ... Allahabad: Published by the General secretary, All India congress committee, Swaraj Bhawan, 1938. v, 37 p. 22½cm. (Congress political and economic studies. no. 11.)

1. Hindus in foreign countries.   I. Ser.
         June 19, 1942

NL 0451843   NN CSt-H CtY

Lohia, Rammanohar.
... India's stand. [Allahabad, 193–] 16 p. 22cm.
Cover-title.
At head of title: Issued by the All India congress committee.

1. India—Hist., 1919–   I. All-India congress committee.
         April 30, 1941

NL 0451844   NN CtY

Lohia, Rammanohar.
इतिहास चक्र. [लेखक] राममनोहर लोहिया. [अंग्रेजी से धनुवाद: धोमप्रकाश दीपक. इलाहाबाद] लहर प्रकाशन [1955]
96 p. 19 cm.
In Hindi.

1. History—Philosophy.   I. Deepak, Om Prakash, 1927–   tr. II. Title.
Title romanized: Itihāsa cakra.

D16.8.L5515   73-251618

NL 0451845   DLC

Lohia, Rammanohar.
Land utilisation in Champaran ...
     see under   Champaran Farms Enquiry Commission.

HQ799
.I6
Lohia, Rammanohar
Lohia speaks. [Madras, Young world. 1955]
25 p.

1. India - Youth.   2. Youth - India.

NL 0451847   DS

Lohia, Rammanohar.
... The mystery of Sir Stafford Cripps, by Ram Manohar Lohia, PH. D. Bombay, Padma publications ltd. [1942]
2 p. l., iv, 71 p. 18½ᶜᵐ. (Current topics series. General editor: Yusuf Meherally. No. 4)
"First published, September, 1942; second edition, October, 1942."

1. Cripps, Sir Richard Stafford, 1889–1919–   2. India—Pol. & govt.—I. Title.
          43–7533
          Provisional
Library of Congress   DA585.C7L6 1942 a
          954

      CaBVaU HU
NL 0451848   DLC DAU WU MoU MH MiU IU CU VtU NSyU

Lohia, Rammanohar.
Rebels must advance. [Bombay, Published by Inquilab Publishers for the Indian National Congress] 1944.
33 p. 20 cm. (Inquilab Publications, no. 4)
Cover title.

1. India—Hist.—20th cent.   2. Passive resistance to government. I. Title.   (Series)

DS480.45.L6   61–43501

NL 0451849   DLC CU

Lohia, Rammanohar.
The struggle for civil liberties. With a foreword by Jawaharlal Nehru. Allahabad, Foreign Dept., All India Congress Committee [1936]
51 p. 22 cm.
At head of title: Foreign Department publication.

1. Civil rights.   I. Indian National Congress. All India Congress Committee. Foreign Department. II. Title.

JC571.L59   56–50579

NL 0451850   DLC NN CtY CU

Lohia, Rammanohar.
The third camp in world affairs. [2d ed. Bombay, Published by Madhu Limaye for the Socialist Party, 1951]
53 p. 22 cm. (Socialist publications, 3)
Cover title.

1. India—For. rel.   I. Title.   (Series)

DS448.L6 1951   58–25828

NL 0451851   DLC GU CSt-H NN NNC CU

D
16.8
.L83
Lohia, Rammanohar, 1910–
Wheel of history. [Hyderabad] Navahind Publications [1955]
111 p.

1. History—Philosophy.   I. Title.

NL 0451852   MiU ICU PU CU NN

Lohier, F   ed.
Gesta sanctorum patrum fontanellensis coenobii (Gesta abbatum fontanellensium)
     see under   Gesta abbatum fontanellensium.

Lohier et Maillart. German
     see   Loher und Maller.

Lohikoski, Armand.
Dollari on lujassa; vaikutelmia Amerikanmatkalta kevät-kesällä 1946. Helsinki, Kustannustalo [1946]
178 p. illus. 22 cm.

1. U. S.—Descr. & trav.—1940–   I. Title.

E169.L83   60–20241 ‡

NL 0451855   DLC CLU NN

Lohipoika, Eetu, pseud
Kotipuronen; kiehkura runoelmia. Helsinki, Sundvall, 1903
111 p.

NL 0451856   MH

Lohipoika, Eetu, pseud
Vihurissa; kimppunen runoelmia vuodelta 1899. Wiipurissa, Wiipurin sanomain kirjapainossa, 1900
56 p.

NL 0451857   MH

Lohjan historia; julkaistu Lohjan kotiseututkimuksen ystäväin toimeksiannosta. Helsingissä, 1944–
v. illus.
Vol.1 by G.Rein. Vol.2, pt.1.by Väinö Hirsjärvi

NL 0451858   MH NN

Lohkamp, Albert.
... Inhalt und bedeutung des rechts auf arbeit in vergangenheit und gegenwart; das recht auf arbeit als grundprinzip der deutschen volkswirtschaftslehre. Würzburg-Aumühle, K. Triltsch, 1939.
v, 70 p. 21ᶜᵐ. (*Added t.-p.*: Beiträge zum deutschen arbeits- und sozialversicherungsrecht, hrsg. von landgerichtsdirektor dr. Karl Sell ... hft. 8)
Issued also as inaugural dissertation, Bonn.
"Schrifttum": p. 69–70.

1. Right to labor.   42–30848
Library of Congress   HD4903.L6 1939
          331.92

NL 0451859   DLC CU NN

Lohkamp, Gertrud, 1908–
Die geographischen Bedingtheiten in der modernen australischen Literatur... von Gertrud Lohkamp... Düsseldorf: G. H. Nolte, 1936. 47 p. 22cm.
Inaugural-Dissertation — Bonn, 1936.
Lebenslauf.
"Literaturangabe," p. 47.

1. Australian literature—   Hist. and crit.
         August 8, 1939

NL 0451860   NN RPB CtY

Lohkemper, Hans: Der Weltkrieg und der internationale Geldmarkt bis zur Deutschen Revolution. Elberfeld: Bergische Dr- u. Verlagsanst. 1919. IX, 106 S. 8°
Münster, R.- u. staatwiss. Diss. v. 25. April 1919, Ref. Plenge, Schmöle
[Geb. 19. Okt. 94 Elberfeld; Wohnort: Elberfeld; Staatsangeh.: Preußen; Vorbildung: OR. Elberfeld Reife 14; Studium: Bonn 3, Münster 3 S.; Rig. 23. Dez. 18.]
         [U 19.682]

NL 0451861   ICRL

VOLUME 338

Lohl, Erich, 1909–
  Das pädagogische erbe des liberalismus und das völkische weltbild ... von Erich Lohl ... Düsseldorf, Dissertations-verlag G. H. Nolte, 1937.
  vi, 52 p., 1 l. 22^{cm}.

  Inaug.-diss.—Heidelberg.
  Lebenslauf.
  "Schrifttum": p. iv–vi.

  1. Education—Germany. 2. Education—Philosophy. 3. National socialism. I. Title.

  Library of Congress   LA722.L76   41–33884
                                      370.943

NL 0451862   DLC CtY NNC

Lohlen, Christopher Friedrich von, respondent.
    ...Le jure majoratuum...
    see under Gregorovius, Johann Adam, praeses.

Lohlker, Margaret, ed.
AP2
.S1464   **Santa Féan** inter-American. v. 1–2, no. 4; July 1940–Jan./Feb. 1942. Santa Fé, N. M., 1940–42.

Lohlker, Margaret.
  Word-snow ... Lowell, Mass., Alentour house, 1938.
  [12] p. illus. 18 cm.

NL 0451865   RPB

LOHMAN, AIMO R.
  Suomalaisten rykmenttien karoliiniunivormuista ennen vuotta 1756. (In: Sotamuseo, Helsingfors. [Vuosikirja] Helsinki. 21cm. (Osa) 6 (1955) p.24–45. illus.)

  Summary in English.
  Bibliography, p. 43–44.
  1. Military uniforms,   Finnish.

NL 0451866   NN

Lohman, Alexander Frederik de Savornin
    see
Savornin Lohman, Alexander Frederik de, 1837–1924.

Lohman, Anna de Savornin.
  See
Savornin Lohman, Anna Maria de, 1868–1930.

Lohman, Mrs. Anna (Trow) 1812–1878, plaintiff.
  Court of appeals. Ann Lohman, plaintiff in error. Vs. The people of the state of New York, defendants in error. Case furnished by plaintiff in error. James T. Brady, attorney for plaintiff in error. McKeon, district attorney for defendants in error. New York, Gallagher and Morrill, True sun office, 1848.
  51p. 22½cm.
  No.3 in pamphlet volume [Trials] v.4.

NL 0451869   NNU-L

K
.L6
1840   **Lohman, Mrs.** Anna (Trow) 1812–1878, **defendant.**
  Trial of Madame Restell. [Reported in full for the National police gazette.] [New York, 184–?]
  48 p. front., plates. 18½cm.
  Title vignette (portrait).
  Caption title: Court of general sessions. New York, October 25, 1847. Before Recorer [:] Scott, and Aldermen Feeks and Tappan. The trial of Caroline Lohman, alias Madame Restell, for manslaughter in the second degree, by producing abortion upon the body of Maria Bodine, in July, 1846.
    1. Bodine, Maria, b. 1821? I. New York (County) Court of general ses sions. II. National police gazette. III Title.

NL 0451870   ViU

Lohman, Mrs. Anna (Trow) 1812–1878, *defendant.*
  Trial of Madame Restell, alias Ann Lohman, for abortion and causing the death of Mrs. Purdy; being a full account of all the proceedings on the trial, together with the suppressed evidence and editorial remarks ... [New York] For sale at the book stand in Wall st., adjoining the Custom house [etc.] 1841.
  21 p. 21½cm.
  Trial at the Court of general sessions, New York, July, 1841.

  1. Purdy, Mrs. Anna Maria, d. 1841. I. New York (County) Court of general sessions. II. Title.

                                      31–34580

NL 0451871   DLC MB

Lohman, Mrs. Anna (Trow) 1812–1878.
  Trial of Caroline Lohman, Alias Madame Restell, for manslaughter in the second degree, by producing abortion upon the body of Maria Bodine, ... New York, 1846.
  38 p.

NL 0451872   DLC

Lohman, Mrs. Anna (Trow) 1812–1878
  Wonderful trial of Caroline Lohman alias Restell for manslaughter in the second degree, by producing abortion upon the body of Maria Bodine, 1846, Court of General Sessions, New York City. n.p., n.d.
  38 p. Ports.

NL 0451873   MH-L

Lohman, Mrs. Anna (Trow) 1812–1878, *defendant.*
  ... Wonderful trial of Caroline Lohman, alias Restell, [reported in full for the National police gazette.] ... New York city, Burgess, Stringer, & co.; Boston, Redding & co.; [etc., etc., [1847]
  31, [1] p. 1 illus. 22½cm.
  Title vignette (portrait)
  Caption title: Court of general sessions. Trial of Caroline Lohman, alias Madame Restell, [Oct.–Nov. 1847] for manslaughter in the second degree, by producing abortion upon the body of Maria Bodine, in July, 1846 ...
    1. Bodine, Maria, b. 1821? I. New York (County) Court of general sessions. II. National police gazette. III. Title.

                                      31–34371

NL 0451874   DLC DNLM NN NNU–W

Lohman, Arthur H.
  Early days in Two Rivers, Wisconsin, by Arthur H. Lohman, comprising a series of papers read before the Manitowoc County historical society, at Manitowoc, Wisconsin, November, nineteen hundred and seven ... Milwaukee, Wis., Meyer-Rotier printing co. [1909]
  vii, [9]–48 p. front., plates, ports. 23½cm.
  "Published under the auspices of the Congregational church of Two Rivers, Wis., 1909."—p. iv.

  1. Two Rivers, Wis.—Hist.

  Library of Congress   F589.T9L8   28–4559

NL 0451875   DLC WaS NN

Lohman, Bonifacius Christiaan de Savornin
    see   Savornin Lohman, Bonifacius Christiaan jonkheer de, 1883–

Lohman, Carl Avery.
  Bricklaying production, prepared by Carl Avery Lohman. [Ann Arbor, Mich., Edwards brothers, inc., 1942]
  1 p. l., [1], 7 p. incl. tables. 27½ x 21½cm.

  "Lithoprinted."
  "A modified second edition of ... Bricklaying-production and cost 1927, prepared by Carl Avery Lohman."—Foreword.

  1. Bricklaying. 2. Building—Tables, calculations, etc.

  Library of Congress   TH5501.L56   42–50741
                                      693.2

NL 0451877   DLC

Lohman, Carl Avery.
  A practical method for design co-efficients in the rigid frame of building construction, prepared by Carl Avery Lohman ... [Ann Arbor, Mich., Lohman and Lohman, 1942]
  2 v. diagrs. 27½ x 21½cm (v. 2: 21 x 52cm)
  Reproduced from type-written copy.
  Contents.—[v. 1] Specifications.—[v. 2] Charts.

  1. Framing (Building) I. Title.

  Library of Congress   TH2301.L6   42–25873
                                      694.2

NL 0451878   DLC

4DL
Swed   **Lohman, Carl Johan,** 1694–1759.
432   Wördsam åminnelse öfwer Hans högst-sal.
v.2   kongl. May:tz, then stormäcktigste, alles wär i lifstiden högtälskelige och allernådigste konungs och herres, Konung Carl then XII:tes, Swerijes, Göthes och Wendes konungs, Stor-furstes til Finland, Hertigs vti Skåne, Estland, Lifland, Carelen, Brehmen, Verden, Stettin, Pofhern, Cassuben och Wenden, Furstes til Rügen, Herres öfwer Ingermanland och Wismar, så ock

  Pfaltz-grefwes wid Rhein i Beyern, til Jülich, Cleve och Bergen hertigs &c.&c.&c. högst-ängseliga hädanfärd then 30. novembr. anno 1718, yttrad wid dess dyra och konungsliga jordefärd then 26. febr. anno 1719. [3. gången uplagd] Stockholm, P. J. Nyström, 1740.
  [4] p.

  Bound with Nordberg, J. A. Konung Carl den XII:tes historia. Stockholm, 1740. Del 2.

NL 0451881   DLC-P4

Lohman, Caroline.
    see   Lohman, Mrs. Anna (Trow) 1812–1878.

Lohman, Carolus Gabr., respondent.
  Diss. philosophica de obligatione ad rem illicitam
    see under   Ihre, Johan, 1707–1780, praeses.

VOLUME 338

Lohman, Carolus Gabr., respondent.
...Specimen academicum legem naturae
perfectivam...
see under Ihre, Johan, 1707-1780,
praeses.

Lohman, Charles Joseph
The utilisation of naphthenic acids, and
investigation of their metallic salts as
driers... ⌈Cin.,1925.
25 l. tab. diagrs.

Thesis, University of Cincinnati, Chemical
Engineer,1925.
Typewritten.

NL 0451885 OCU

Lohman, Clarence.
The U. S. S. R. in 1931 ⌈by⌉ Clarence Lohman. ⌈Houston,
The author,1945⌉
cover-title, iii, ⌈1⌉ p., 1 l., 40 p., 1 l. 23ᶜᵐ.

1. Russia—Descr. & trav.—1917-   I. Title.
DK27.L6   914.7   47-19689

NL 0451886 DLC TxU MH-L

Lohman, Fred D., illus.

Graham, Mary Nancy, comp.

Christmas carols, selected by Mary Nancy Graham. With
illustrations by F. D. Lohman. Racine, Wis., Whitman publishing company,°1938.

Lohman, Fred D., illus.
FOR OTHER EDITIONS
SEE MAIN ENTRY
Mother Goose.
Mother Goose; a complete compilation of Mother Goose melo-
dies. Illustrators, Fred D. Lohman ⌈and⌉ Ethel Hays. Akron,
O., New York, The Saalfield publishing company ⌈°1941⌉

Lohman, Henrik
... De dominio utili ... submittit
Henricus Lohman ... Groningae, J.
Bolt, 1756.
3 p.l., 16, ⌈2⌉ p. 23½cm.
Diss.- Groningen.

NL 0451889 MH-L

Lohman, Jacob Benjamin
Arboga känning, funnen och upstäld af Jacob
Benj. Lohman. Stockholm, Trykt hos P. J.
Nyström, 1737.
10 p.l., 224, [4] p. illus., 2 double pl.
(incl. front.) 24 x 19¼ cm.

1. Arboga, Sweden.

NL 0451890 CtY

Lohman, Jan Harm
... De diverso mandatorum genere,
quibus legati constituuntur, et obligatione, quae ex iis oritur ... submittit Jan Harm Lohman ... Lugduni
Batavorum, S. Luchtmans ⌈1750⌉
4 p.l., 43, ⌈1⌉ p. 24cm.
Diss. - Leiden.
Engraved title-page.

NL 0451891 MH-L

Lohman, Johannes
... De intercessione mulierum valida
... submittit Johannes Lohman ...
Groningae, J. Dikema, 1796.
2 p.l., 39, ⌈1⌉ p. 23½cm.
Diss. - Groningen.

NL 0451892 MH-L

Lohman, Johannes
... De rebus quae vendi non possunt ...
submittit Johannes Lohman ... Groningae,
J. Dikema, 1796.
2 p.l., 43, ⌈1⌉ p. 23½cm.
Diss.- Groningen.

NL 0451893 MH-L

Lohman, Joseph Dean, 1909-
The police and minority groups; a manual prepared for
use in the Chicago Park District Police Training School
Prepared by Joseph D. Lohman and the supervisory officer.
of the Division of Police, directed by Roger F. Shanahan
chief of police. Chicago, Chicago Park District ⌈1947⌉
xiii, 133 p. maps. 29 cm.
Bibliography: p. 129-133.
Appendices (p. 109-128): A. Illinois statutes affecting race relations.—B. Municipal code of Chicago.
1. Race problems. 2. Chicago—Police. 3. Chicago—Foreign population.   I. Chicago Park District. II. Title.
HV8148.C4L6   323.1   47-5485 rev*

NL 0451894 DLC CoU OrU ViU OU WaU-L

Lohman, Joseph Dean, 1909-
Principles of police work with minority groups, a manual
adapted from The police and minority groups, by Joseph D.
Lohman.   Prepared by Committee on Police Training,
Louisville, Ky. Louisville, Ky., Division of Police, 1950.
xi, 129 p. maps. 29 cm.
Bibliography: p. 125-129.
Appendices (p. 109-123): A. Kentucky laws regarding race rela-
tions.—B. Resolutions of the city of Louisville.
1. Louisville, Ky.—Race question. 2. Louisville, Ky.—Police. 3.
Louisville, Ky.—Foreign population.   I. Louisville, Ky. Committee
on Police Training. II. Title.
HV8148.L62L6 1950   323.1   51-1413

NL 0451895 DLC CU

Lohman, Joseph Deen, ⌈1909-⌉

H83
.C54
1943
Chicago. University. *University extension division. Home-
study dept.*
... Social sciences 2 (introductory general course in the social
sciences) Section A— By Maynard C. Krueger, Joseph D.
Lohman, Gerhard E. O. Meyer ⌈and⌉ Bernard Drell. ⌈Chicago⌉
The University of Chicago, °1943.

QE955
.L8
Lohman, K E
...Pliocene diatoms from the Kettleman hills,
California...
Washington, 1938
p.81-102.   29 cm.
(U.S. Geological survey. Professional paper
189- C [Separate])

NL 0451897 DLC

Lohman, Louis Bothenius, 1738-1807.
... De auctoritate tutorum ... proponit
Lud. Both. Lohman ... Groningae, J. Bolt
⌈1760⌉
3 p.l., 33, ⌈11⌉ p. 23cm.
Diss.- Groningen.
Added engraved title-page.

NL 0451898 MH-L

Lohman, Louis Bothenius, 1803-1856.
... De principiis, quae, tum gallicus,
tum in novissima lege belgicus legislator secutus est in loco, qui est de iure
hypothecae ... offert Ludovicus Bothenius
Lohman ... Groningae, W. Zuidema ⌈1830⌉
4 p.l., 143, ⌈1⌉ p. 18½cm.
Diss.- Groningen.
Bibliographical footnotes.

NL 0451899 MH-L

Lohman, Louis Bothenius, 1803-1856.
Opmerkingen over de wet van 8 november 1815,
Staatsblad no. 51. Groningen, 1886.
(6) + 54 p.
Proefschrift. - Groningen.

NL 0451900 MH-L

Lohman, Marion Lee, 1903-
Hysteriaceae: life histories of certain species ⌈by⌉ Marion Lee
Lohman ... ⌈New York, 1933⌉
cover-title, p. 229-288. illus., pl. xxxiv-xxxv. 24½ᶜᵐ.
Thesis (ph. d.)—University of Michigan, 1931.
"Papers from the Department of botany of the University of Michigan,
no. 367."
"Reprinted from Papers of the Michigan academy of science, arts and
letters, vol. xvii, 1932. Published 1933."
"Literature cited": p. 285-287.

1. Hysteriaceae.
                                           33-15387
Library of Congress QK623.H88L6 1931
Univ. of Michigan Libr.   589.2333

NL 0451901 MiU DLC ViU OCU OU

Lohman, Maurits Adriaan de Savornin, jonkheer, 1865-
De strafwet ten opzichte van de verkiezingen ... door Maurits
Adriaan de Savornin Lohman ... Leiden, S. C. van Does-
burgh, 1890.
3 p. l., 44 p. 22½ᶜᵐ.
Proefschrift—Leyden.
"Stellingen": p. ⌈39⌉-44.

1. Election law—Netherlands. 2. Elections—Netherlands—Corrupt
practices. 3. Criminal law—Netherlands.   I. Title.
                                           36-32502

NL 0451902 DLC

Lohman, Philipp Hans, joint author.

Peterson, James Marvin, 1902-
Money & banking, by J. Marvin Peterson, Delmas R. Caw-
thorne and Philipp H. Lohman ... New York, The Macmillan
company, 1941.

VOLUME 338

Lohman, Philipp Hans, *ed.*
Wall Street explains its operations to a visiting university class; a collection of thirty-one lectures by executives in the investment business. Edited by Philipp H. Lohman and Franc M. Ricciardi. New York, Distributor: New York Institute of Finance ₁1951₁
vi, 274, ₁1₁ p. 21 cm.
Bibliography : p. ₁275₁

1. New York. Stock Exchange.   I. Ricciardi, Franc M., joint ed.
II. Title.

HG4572.L6   332.61   51–1011 rev

NL 0451904   DLC MiU NN CU TxU MtU CaBVa OrPS WaS

Lohman, Reneke
... De jure vectigalium ... submittit Reneke Lohman ... Groningae, J. Dikema, 1796.
2 p.l., 38, ₁2₁ p. 23½cm.
Diss.- Groningen.

NL 0451905   MH-L

Lohman, Scato, 1810-1842.
... De arbitrio judicis generatim, maxime secundum jus nostrum poenale hodiernum, deque art. 12 decreti regii d. d. XI decembris 1813 ... offert Scato Lohman ... Groningae, P. S. Barghoorn ₁1834₁
2 p.l., iv, 143, ₁1₁, iv p. 21cm.
Diss.- Groningen.
Bibliographical footnotes.

NL 0451906   MH-L

Lohman, Stanley William, 1907–
Areas of principal ground-water investigations in the Arkansas, White, and Red River Basins, prepared by S. W. Lohman and V. M. Burtis with the assistance of the district offices of the Ground Water Branch, Water Resources Division, U. S. Geological Survey, 1953. ₁Washington₁ Dept. of the Interior, U. S. Geological Survey ₁1954₁
₁3₁ p. col. map. 69 x 56 cm. (U. S. Geological Survey. Hydrologic investigations. Atlas HA2)
Scale of map 1 : 2,500,000, approximately 1 inch to 40 miles.
"Prepared in cooperation with the States of Arkansas, Colorado, Kansas, Louisiana, Missouri, New Mexico, Oklahoma, and Texas."
Includes bibliography of 161 items keyed to map.
1. Water, Underground   —The West—Bibl.   2. Water, Underground—The West—Maps.   I. Burtis, V. M.
(Series)
G3701s.C3 var.U5   Map 59–874

NL 0451907   DLC

Lohman, Stanley William, 1907–
General availability of ground water and depth to water level in the Arkansas, White, and Red River Basins. Prepared by S. W. Lohman and V. M. Burtis, with the assistance of the district offices of the Ground Water Branch, Water Resources Division, U. S. Geological Survey, 1953. Washington, U. S. Geological Survey ₁1954₁
col. map 41 x 62 cm. (U. S. Geological Survey. Hydrologic investigations. Atlas HA3)
Scale 1. 2,500,000.
"Prepared in cooperation with the States of Arkansas, Colorado, Kansas, Louisiana, Missouri, New Mexico, Oklahoma, and Texas."

1. Water, Underground—Arkansas River watershed—Maps.   2. Water, Underground—Red River watershed (Red River of Louisiana)—Maps.   3. Water, Underground—White River watershed, Ark. & Mo.—Maps.   I. Burtis, V. M.   (Series)
G3701s.C3 var.U5   Map 56–453

NL 0451909   DLC

QE113
.A2
no. 79

Williams, Charles C, 1911–
Geology and ground-water resources of a part of south-central Kansas, with special reference to the Wichita municipal water supply, by Charles C. Williams and Stanley W. Lohman, with analyses by Robert H. Hess and others. Prepared by the State Geological Survey of Kansas and the United States Geological Survey, with the cooperation of the City of Wichita, the Division of Sanitation of the Kansas State Board of Health, and the Division of Water Resources of the Kansas State Board of Agriculture. Topeka, F. Voiland, Jr., State Printer, 1949.

GB1025
.N8L6

Lohman, Stanley William, 1907–
...Geology and ground-water resources of the Elizabeth City area, North Carolina...
Washington, 1936
p.1-57   23 1/2 cm.

NL 0451911   DLC

Lohman, Stanley William, 1907–
... Ground-water conditions in the vicinity of Lawrence, Kansas, by Stanley W. Lohman ... ₁Lawrence, 1941₁
₁17₁–64 p. incl. illus. (incl. maps) tables. 23 cm. (Kansas. State geological survey. Bulletin 38 ₁pt. 2₁)
Caption title.
At head of title: State geological survey of Kansas ... 1941 reports of studies, part 2 ...
"Prepared by the federal Geological survey and the Kansas Geological survey, with the cooperation of the city of Lawrence, the Division of sanitation of the Kansas State board of health, and the Division of water resources of the Kansas State board of agriculture."
"References" : p. 53-54.

1. Water, Underground—Kansas—Lawrence.   2. Lawrence, Kan.—Water-supply.   I. U. S. Geological survey.
QE113.A2   no. 38, pt. 2   (557.81)   G S 42–150 rev 2

U. S. Geol. Survey. Libr.
for Library of Congress   ₁r52j1₁†

NL 0451913   DI-GS MoU DLC MtBuM CU

Lohman, Stanley William, 1907–
... Ground water in northeastern Pennsylvania, by Stanley W. Lohman ... with analyses by Margaret D. Foster, L. A. Shinn and K. T. Williams. (Prepared in cooperation between the United States Geological survey and the Pennsylvania Topographic and geologic survey) Harrisburg, Pa., Dept. of internal affairs, Topographic and geologic survey, 1937.
vi₁, 1 L., 312 p. incl. illus. (maps) plates, tables. fold. map (in pocket) diagrs. (1 fold.) 23½ cm. (Pennsylvania. Topographic and geologic survey. Bulletin W4)
At head of title: Pennsylvania geological survey, fourth series ...
Bibliography : p. 6-11.
1. Water, Underground—Pennsylvania.   2. Geology—Pennsylvania.   I. Foster, Margaret Dorothy, 1895–   II. Shinn, Leo A., 1907–   III. Williams, Kenneth Thurman, 1905–   IV. U. S. Geological survey.   v. Title.
GB1025.P4L6   G S 38—1 ‡

U. S. Geol. Survey. Libr.
for Library of Congress   ₁a65r450₁†

OrU OrCS
NL 0451915   DI-GS MoU OO OCU CU NBuU DLC MsU MtBuM

Lohman, Stanley William, 1907–
... Ground water in south-central Pennsylvania, by Stanley W. Lohman ... with analyses by E. W. Lohr. (Prepared in cooperation between the United States Geological survey and the Pennsylvania Topographic and geologic survey) Harrisburg, Pa., Dept. of internal affairs, Topographic and geologic survey, 1938.
vii, ₁1₁ 315 p. incl. illus., tables. fold. maps (2 in pocket) fold. diagr. 23½ᵐ. (Pennsylvania. Topographic and geologic survey. Bulletin W5)
At head of title: Pennsylvania geological survey, fourth series ...
"Published reports" : p. 5-7.
1. Water, Underground—Pennsylvania.   2. Water—Analysis.   I. Lohr, Edwin Wallace, 1897–   II. U. S. Geological survey.
G S 38–289 Revised
U. S. Geol. survey. Library
for Library of Congress   GB1025.P4L62

MtBuM OrCS CaBVaU
NL 0451916   DI-GS OrU MsU NBuU MoU OO OCU OU DLC CU

Lohman, Stanley William, 1907–   *joint author*

Moore, Raymond Cecil, 1892–
... Ground-water resources of Kansas, by Raymond C. Moore, with chapters by S. W. Lohman, J. C. Frye, H. A. Waite, T. G. McLaughlin and Bruce Latta. Printed by authority of the state of Kansas. ₁Topeka, Kansas state printing plant, W. C. Austin, state printer, 1940₁

Lohman, Stanley William, 1907–
... Ground-water resources of Pennsylvania, by Stanley W. Lohman ... (Prepared in cooperation between the Geological survey, United States Department of the interior, and the Pennsylvania Topographic and geologic survey) Harrisburg, Pa., Dept. of internal affairs, Topographic and geologic survey, 1941.
vi, 32 p. incl. maps, tables. fold. map. 23½ cm. (Pennsylvania. Topographic and geologic survey. Bulletin W 7)
At head of title: Pennsylvania geological survey, fourth series ...
1. Water, Underground—Pennsylvania.   2. Water-supply—Pennsylvania.   I. U. S. Geological survey.   II. Title.
GB1025.P4L624   551.4909748   G S 41—114
U. S. Geol. Survey. Libr.
for Library of Congress   ₁a57r45k₁₁†

MtBuM OrU DLC
NL 0451918   DI-GS OrU MoU OrPS NBuU MsU UU OCU OO

QE113
.A2
no. 73

Lohman, Stanley William, 1907–

Fishel, Vinton Crews, 1907–
Ground-water resources of Republic County and northern Cloud County, Kansas, by V. C. Fishel; with chapters on the Quaternary geology and Cenozoic geologic history, by S. W. Lohman, and analyses by H. A. Stoltenberg. Prepared by the State Geological Survey of Kansas and the U. S. Geological Survey, with the cooperation of the Division of Sanitation of the Kansas State Board of Health and the Division of Water Resources of the Kansas State Board of Agriculture. Lawrence, 1948.

Lohman, Stanley William, 1907–
... Ground-water supplies available for national defense industries in south-central Kansas, by Stanley W. Lohman ... ₁Lawrence, Kan., University of Kansas, 1942₁
19 p. illus. (incl. maps) 23 cm. (Kansas. University. Geological survey. Bulletin 41, pt. 1)
At head of title: State geological survey of Kansas, Bulletin 41. 1942 reports of studies, part 1.
"Prepared by the State geological survey of Kansas and the United States Geological survey, with the cooperation of the Division of sanitation of the Kansas State board of health, and the Division of water resources of the Kansas State board of agriculture."
1. Water, Underground—Kansas.   2. Water-supply—Kansas.   I. Title.
QE113.A2   no. 41,   pt. 1   G S 42–239
U. S. Geol. Survey. Libr.
for Library of Congress   ₁a56r₁₁†

NL 0451920   DI-GS OU OO OCU CU DLC MoU MtBuM

Lohman, Stanley William, 1907–
... Ground-water supplies in Kansas available for national defense industries, by S. W. Lohman, J. C. Frye, H. A. Waite, V. C. Fishel, T. G. McLaughlin, B. F. Latta and G. E. Abernathy. With a chapter on stream flow in Kansas, by George S. Knapp and J. B. Spiegel ... ₁Lawrence, Kan., University of Kansas, 1942₁
₁2₁–68 p. illus. (incl. maps) tables. 23 cm. ₁Kansas. University. Geological survey. Bulletin 41, pt. 2₁
At head of title: State geological survey of Kansas, Bulletin 41. 1942 reports of studies, part 2.

"Prepared by the State geological survey of Kansas and the United States Geological survey, with the cooperation of the Division of sanitation of the Kansas State board of health and the Division of water resources of the Kansas State board of agriculture."
"Reference" : p. 67–68.
1. Water, Underground—Kansas.   2. Water-supply—Kansas.   3. U. S.—Defenses.   4. Stream measurements—Kansas.   I. Knapp, George Selick, 1884–   II. Spiegel, Jacob Birk, 1889–   III. Title.
QE113.A2   no. 41, pt. 2   551.49   G S 42—240

U. S. Geol. Survey. Libr.
for Library of Congress   ₁a56k1₁†

NL 0451922   DI-GS OO OU OCU MoU CU DLC MtBuM

Lohman, Stanley William, 1907–

U. S. *Geological survey. Committee on observation wells.*
... Report of the Committee on observation wells, United States Geological survey; a preliminary manual of methods. R. M. Leggette, chairman, L. K. Wenzel, secretary, R. C. Cady, S. W. Lohman, V. T. Stringfield, R. W. Sundstrom and S. F. Turner. Washington, D. C.,1935.

VOLUME 338

Lohman, Stanley William, 1907–

... Water supplies from wells available for irrigation in the uplands of Ford county, Kansas ₍by₎ S. W. Lohman ... ₍Lawrence, Kans.₎ State geological survey, 1938₎

2 p. l., 10 p. illus. (map) 21ᶜᵐ. (Kansas. University. State geological survey. Mineral resources circular 9)

Bulletin of the University of Kansas, vol. 39, no. 6, March 15, 1938. Prepared in cooperation with the United States Geological survey. Offset-printed.

1. Water, Underground—Kansas—Ford co. 2. Water-supply—Kansas—Ford co. 3. Artesian wells—Kansas—Ford co.

U. S. Geol. survey. Library   (267) K4mc no. 9   G S 38–137

for Library of Congress   ₍GB1025.K2L   ₎

NL 0451924   DI-GS   MsU OU OO OCU ViU MtBuM

LOHMAN, Tina od.
Book of Jewish Recipes. (New York)
The National Jewish Post, (c1942) 112p
21.5cm

1. Cook Books.

NL 0451925   NNJ MB

Lohman, W. H. de Savornin
see   Savornin Lohman, Wilsius Hendrik de.

Lohman, Walter
Bp65   Denkwürdige Tage aus der deutschen Marine-
10   Kolonial- und Seekriegs-geschichte. Ein Tradi-
tionskalender für die Reichsmarine ... Berlin,
Verlag Offene Worte, 1928.
278p. illus.(incl.ports.) 20cm.

NL 0451927   CtY

Lohman, Wigger Onno Gerhard
... De differentia contractuum bonae
fidei ac stricti juris respectu doli ...
subjicit Wigger Onno Gerhard Lohman ...
Lugd. Batav., C. Haak ₍1750₎

2 p.l., 67, ₍1₎ p. 24cm.

Diss. - Leiden.
Engraved title-page.

NL 0451928   MH-L

Lohman, Willem Carel.
Opmerkingen over de leggers der wegen.
Groningen, 1886.
Proefschrift. — Groningen.

NL 0451929   MH-L

Lohman, Wytzius Henricus
... De pactis super futura successione
initis ... submittit Wytzius Henricus
Lohman ... ₍Groningae?₎ 1757₎

3 p.l., 26 p., 1 l. 23cm.

Diss.- Groningen.
Engraved title-page.

NL 0451930   MH-L

Lohmander, C   L.
Om psykologien som vetenskap, ett försök till orientering ... ₍Lund₎ Gleerupska universitets-bokhandeln ₍1903₎

2 p. l., 158 p., 1 l. 21¾ᶜᵐ.

Akademisk afhandling—Lund.
"Litteratur": p. ₍157₎–158.

7-2484

NL 0451931   DLC

Lohmander, Hans.
... Arachnologische fragmente, 1–3, von Hans Lohmander ...
Göteborg, Elanders boktryckeri aktiebolag, 1945.

75 p. illus. 25ᶜᵐ. (Göteborgs kungl. vetenskaps- och vitterhets-samhälles handlingar. 6. följden, ser. B, bd. 3, n:o 9)

Meddelanden från Göteborgs musei Zoologiska avdelning. 111.
"Mitgeteilt am 12. märz 1945."
"Literatur": p. 14, 30, 75.

CONTENTS.—Über eine für die schwedische fauna neue pseudoskorpionart.—Über die schwedischen arten der opilionengattung *Oligolophus* C. L. Koch.—Die salticiden-gattung *Neon* Simon in Südschweden.

1. Arachnida—Sweden.

AS284.G7   föl. 6, ser. B, bd. 3, no. 9   A 47–3366

Illinois.   Univ.   Library
for Library of Congress   ₍3₎†

NL 0451932   IU CtY DLC NcU

Lohmander, Hans.
Landmollusken aus Island gesammelt von Dr. Carl H.
Lindroth (1929) Göteborg, Elanders boktr., 1938.

52 p. illus., maps. 26 cm. (Göteborgs kungl. vetenskaps- och vitterhets-samhälles handlingar, 5. följden, ser. B, bd. 6, no 2)

Meddelanden från Göteborgs musei Zoologiska avdelning. 76.
"Mitgeteilt am 14. März 1938."
"Literatur": p. ₍48₎–50.

1. Mollusks—Iceland. (Series: Göteborgs kungl. vetenskaps- och vitterhets-samhälle. Handlingar, 5. följden, ser. B, bd. 6, no. 2. Series: Gothenburg, Sweden. Museum. Zoologiska avdelningen. Meddelanden, 76)

AS284.G7   föl. 5, ser. B, bd. 6, no. 2   A 48–9252*

Illinois.   Univ.   Library
for Library of Congress   ₍3₎†

NL 0451933   IU NcU CtY NNC DLC

Lohmander, Hans.
Neue Diplopoden aus Persien. Göteborg, Elanders boktr.,
1932.

44 p. illus. 26 cm. (Göteborgs kungl. vetenskaps- och vitterhets-samhälles handlingar, 5. följden, ser. B, bd. 3, n:o 2)

Meddelanden från Göteborgs musei Zoologiska avdelning. 60.
"Vorgelegt am 14. März 1932."
"Literatur": p. ₍43₎–44.

1. Diplopoda. 2. Myriapoda—Persia. (Series: Göteborgs kungl. vetenskaps- och vitterhets-samhälle. 5. följden, ser. B, bd. 3, no. 2. Series: Gothenburg, Sweden. Museum. Zoologiska avdelningen. Meddelanden, 60)

AS284.G7   föl. 5, ser. B, bd. 3, no. 2   A 48–8626*

Illinois.   Univ.   Library
for Library of Congress   †   DLC

NL 0451934   IU DLC ICU NcU

Lohmander, Hans.
On some terrestrial isopods in the United States National museum, by Hans Lohmander ...

(*In* U. S. National museum. Proceedings. Washington, 1928. 23½ᶜᵐ. v. 72, art. 17. 18 p. illus.)

"Literature": p. 18.

1. Isopoda.

Library of Congress   Q11.U55 vol. 72

29-344

NL 0451935   DLC CaBViP WaS OCl MiU OU

Lohmander, Hans.
Südschwedische Spinnen. Göteborg, Elanders boktr.,
1942–

v. illus., maps. 26 cm. (Göteborgs kungl. vetenskaps- och vitterhets-samhälles handlingar, 6. följden, ser. B, bd. 2, n:o 4)

Meddelanden från Goteborgs musei Zoologiska avdelning, 98.
"Literatur": v. 1, p. ₍160₎–168.

CONTENTS.—1. *Gnaphosidae.*

1. Spiders—Sweden.   (Series: Göteborgs kungl. vetenskaps- och vitterhets-samhälle. Handlingar, 6. följden, ser. B, bd. 2, no. 4. Series: Gothenburg, Sweden. Museum. Zoologiska avdelningen. Meddelanden, 98)

AS284.G7   föl. 6, ser. B, bd. 2, no. 4   A 48–4493*
—— Copy 2.   QL457.4.L6

Illinois.   Univ.   Library
for Library of Congress   †

NL 0451936   IU CtY NcU DLC

Lohmander, Hans.
Sveriges Diplopoder.   Göteborg, Elanders boktr., 1925.

115 p. illus., maps. 26 cm. (Göteborgs kungl. vetenskaps- och vitterhets-samhälles handlingar, 4. följden, bd. 30, no. 2)

Meddelanden från Göteborgs musei Zoologiska avdelning, 40.
"Inlämnat den 12 oktober 1925."
"Litteratur": p. ₍112₎–115.

1. Diplopoda. 2. Myriapoda—Sweden.   I. Series: Göteborgs kungl. vetenskaps- och vitterhets-samhälle. Handlingar, 4. följden, bd. 30, no. 2.   II. Series: Gothenburg, Sweden. Museum. Zoologiska avdelningen. Meddelanden, 40.

AS284.G7   föl. 4, bd. 30, no. 2   A 48–1599*

Illinois.   Univ.   Library
for Library of Congress   ₍2₎†

NL 0451937   IU PU CtY ICU DLC NcU

Lohmander, Hans.
Über die Diplopoden des Kaukasusgebietes.   Göteborg,
Elanders boktr., 1936.

196 p. illus. 26 cm. (Göteborgs kungl. vetenskaps- och vitterhets-samhälles handlingar, 5. följden, ser. B, bd. 5 : n:o 1)

Meddelanden från Göteborgs musei Zoologiska avdelning, 71.
"Vorgelegt am 10. Februar 1936."
"Literatur": p. ₍192₎–196.

1. Diplopoda. 2. Myriapoda—Caucasus.   I. Series: Göteborgs kungl. vetenskaps- och vitterhets-samhälle. Handlingar, 5. följden, ser. B, bd. 5, no. 1.   II. Series: Gothenburg, Sweden. Museum. Zoologiska avdelningen. Meddelanden, 71)

AS284.G7   föl. 5, ser. B, bd. 5, no. 1   A 48–8625*

Illinois.   Univ.   Library
for Library of Congress   †

NL 0451938   IU CtY DLC NcU

Lohmander, Hans.
Zwei neue Chernetiden der nordwesteuropäischen Fauna.
Göteborg, Elanders boktr., 1939.

11 p. illus. 26 cm. (Göteborgs kungl. vetenskaps- och vitterhets-samhälles handlingar, 5. följden, ser. B, bd. 6, n:o 11)

Meddelanden från Göteborgs musei Zoologiska avdelning, 82.
"Mitgeteilt am 13. Februar 1939."

1. Chernetidae. 2. Arachnida—Europe.   I. Series: Göteborgs kungl. vetenskaps- och vitterhets-samhälle. Handlingar, 5. följden, ser. B, bd. 6, no. 11.   (Series: Gothenburg, Sweden. Museum. Zoologiska avdelningen, Meddelanden, 82)

AS284.G7   föl. 5, ser. B, bd. 6, no. 11   A 48–9253*

Illinois.   Univ.   Library
for Library of Congress   †

NL 0451939   IU NNC CtY NcU DLC

Lohmann, A. G.
History of the Cleveland Boys' Home, Hudson, Ohio.
₍Cleveland?₎ 1906. 24 p. illus. 8°.

1. Boys.—Homes for, U. S. : Ohio :   Cleveland.

January 31, 1912.

NL 0451940   NN

M2085   **Lohmann, Adolf**
.L6W42   Ein Weihnachtliches Singebuch ₍Zweite Auflage₎
1942   Berlin, Christophorus Verlag Herder KG, 1942.
118 p. 15 x 21 cm.

1. Carols, German. 2. Christmas music.

NL 0451941   MB

M2085   **Lohmann, Adolf, comp.**
.L6W42   Ein Weihnachtliches Singebuch.
₍Gestaltet von Adolf Lohmann und Josef
Diewald₎ Freiburg im Breisgau,
Christophorus-Verlag ₍1955?₎
116 p. illus., 15 x 20cm.
Includes suggested harmonizations.

1. Carols, German. 2. Christmas
music. I. Diewald, Josef, joint author.

NL 0451942   MB

VOLUME 338

Lohmann, Adolph.
Der Wasser-Mahlmühlen-Bau; oder, Anleitung zur richtigen Construction sämmtlicher bei'm Mühlenbau vorkommenden hölzernen und eisernen Räderwerke und Gerinne, mit besonderer Beziehung auf die von Wasserkraft zu betreibenden Mahlmühlen ... Weimar, B. F. Voigt, 1856.

xx, 370 p. 19 cm. and atlas (19 plates) 19 x 23 cm. (Neuer Schauplatz der Künste und Handwerke, 223. Bd.)

1. Mills and mill-work.   I. Title.   (Series)

P O 52–12

U. S. Patent Office.   Library TJ1040.L6
for Library of Congress

NL 0451943   DP NN

Lohmann, Adolph.
Der Wasser-Mahlmühlenbau; oder, Anleitung zur richtigen Konstruktion sämmtlicher beim Mühlenbau vorkommenden Räder und Grinne, mit besonderer Beziehung auf die von Wasserkraft zu betreibenden Mahlmühlen... In zweiter Auflage umgearbeitet und neu hrsg. von Leopold Krüdener... Weimar: B. F. Voigt, 1865.   atlas of plates. obl. 12°.   (Neuer Schauplatz der Künste und Handwerke. Bd. 223(a).)

1. Mills and milling—Machinery.   2. Kruedener, Leopold, editor.   3. Ser.
March 8, 1927

NL 0451944   NN

Lohmann, Adolph.
Wassermahlmühlenbau. Einrichtung kleiner Getreidemühlen, welche durch Wasserräder oder Turbinen betrieben werden ... 3. vollständig neu bearb. Aufl. von Leopold Krüdener. Weimar, B. F. Voigt, 1883.

xi, 158 p. and atlas (21 plates) 23 cm. (Neuer Schauplatz der Künste und Handwerke, 223. Bd.)

1. Mills and mill-work.   I. Krüdener, Leopold, ed.   II. Title. (Series)

P O 52–11

U. S. Patent Office.   Library TJ1040.L6 1883
for Library of Congress

NL 0451945   DP

Lohmann, Albert.
Concentus organi; twenty pieces for the organ of the church composed by Albert Lohmann ... New York, N. Y., J. Fischer & bro. (1937)

52 p. 31cm. (Fischer edition, no. 7310)

1. Organ music (Collected works)   I. Title.
43–43080

Library of Congress   M16.L6

NL 0451946   DLC

Lohmann, Albert.
Missa dominicalis, for three male voices (T. T. B. or T. bar. bass) and organ, composed by Albert Lohmann ... New York, J. Fischer & bro. (1938)

cover-title, 1 p. l., 25 p. 27½cm. (Fischer edition, no. 7455. (Masses, 22d ser.))

Latin words.

1. Masses (Men's voices)—Vocal scores with organ.   I. Title.
44–36208

Library of Congress   M2013.L827D6

NL 0451947   DLC

Lohmann, Albrecht, 1908–
Hypotheken für künftige forderungen... 1930.
45 p.
Inaug. Diss. -Göttingen, 1930.
Lebenslauf.
Bibliography.

NL 0451948   ICRL

Lohmann, Alexander Heinrich, 1904–
Über die inhaltsstoffe der alkannawurzel. ...
Marburg, 1932.   69 p.
Inaug. Diss. - Marburg, 1932.
Lebenslauf.

NL 0451949   ICRL CtY

Lohmann, Alfred
Das gewohnheitsmässige Verbrechen ... von Alfred Lohmann ... Halberstadt, C. Doelle & Sohn, 1898.

35 p. 22½cm.

Inaug.-Diss. - Erlangen.

NL 0451950   MH-L NIC ICRL

Lohmann, Alfred, 1870–
Address to the merchants of Bremen, by the president of the Bremen chamber of commerce, Mr. A. Lohmann. (Bremen, 1914)   5 p. 23cm. bd. 29cm. (Facts about Germany and the war. n: 7.)

Photostatic reproduction on 3 leaves.
Caption-title.

1. European war, 1914–1918—   Germany.   February 29, 1940

NL 0451951   NN

Lohmann, Alfred, 1870–
The economical consequences of the war, by A. Lohmann ... (Bremen? 1914)

cover-title, 23 p. 21½cm.

1. European war, 1914–   —Economic aspects.

Library of Congress   D635.L6   15–1779

NL 0451952   DLC IEN NN NNU-W IU NjP MH

(Lohmann, Alfred) 1870–
The economical consequences of the war. (Bremen? 1914?)

cover-title, 23 p. 21½cm.

1. European war, 1914–   —Economic aspects.   I. Title.
16–14631

Library of Congress   D635.L6 1914 a

NL 0451953   DLC CtY DL IU MH

Lohmann, Alfred, 1870–
L'écroulement de l'Angleterre, par A. Lohmann ... Berlin, G. Stilke (1915?)

27 p. 24cm.

Published also in German under title: Der zusammenbruch Englands. Translations of the "Alien enemies (winding up) ordinance, 1914," enacted by the governor of the Straits Settlements with the advice and consent of the Legislative council, and of extracts from the "Straits budget" of December 10, 1914, and the "Straits times" of December 7, 1914: p. (13)–27.

1. European war, 1914–   —Economic aspects.   2. Aliens—Gt. Brit.   3. Aliens—Straits Settlements.   4. Gt. Brit.—Commercial policy.   I. Straits Settlements. Laws, statutes, etc.   II. Title.
15–12118

Library of Congress   HF3506.2.L83

NL 0451954   DLC

Lohmann, Alfred, 1870–
Great Britain's moral collapse, by A. Lohmann.   Berlin, G. Stilke (1915)

26 p. 23½cm.

Published also in German under title: Der zusammenbruch Englands. The "Alien enemies (winding up) ordinance, 1914," enacted by the governor of the Straits settlements with the advice and consent of the Legislative council, and extracts from the "Straits budget" of December 10, 1914, and the "Straits times" of December 7, 1914: p. 12–26.

1. European war, 1914–1918—Economic aspects.   2. Aliens—Gt. Brit.   3. Aliens—Straits settlements.   4. Gt. Brit.—Commercial policy.   I. Straits settlements. Laws, statutes, etc.   II. Title.
40–19869

Library of Congress   HF3506.2.L82

NL 0451955   DLC CtY OO MH

Lohmann, Alfred, 1870–
Lo sfacelo dell' Inghilterra.   Milano: L. Wiget-Manini (1915). 39 p.   8°.

Author's name at head of title.
Text of the "Alien Enemies (Winding up) Ordinance, 1914," enacted by the governor of the Straits Settlements with the "Straits Budget" of December 10, 1914 and extracts from the Legislative Council, and the "Straits Times" of December 7, 1914; with Italian translations. p. 12–39.

1. European war, 1914–.   —Economic aspects.   2. Commerce, Gt. Br., 1914. 3. Aliens—Jurisprudence, Gt. Br., 1914. 4. Aliens—Straits-Settlements. 5. Title.
October 27, 1915.

NL 0451956   NN IU

[Lohmann, Alfred, 1870–   ]
Die wirtschaftlichen Folgen des Weltkrieges. [Bremen, Druck von C.Schünemann, 1914]

NL 0451957   MH IU CtY

Lohmann, Alfred, 1870–
Der zusammenbruch Englands, von A. Lohmann ... Berlin, G. Stilke, 1915.

47, (1) p. 25cm.

Text of the "Alien enemies (winding up) ordinance, 1914," enacted by the governor of the Legislative council, with the advice and consent of the Legislative council, and extracts from the "Straits budget" of December 10, 1914, and the "Straits times" of December 7, 1914, with German translations: p. (15)–47.

1. European war, 1914–   —Economic aspects.   2. Aliens—Gt. Brit.   3. Aliens—Straits Settlements.   4. Gt. Brit.—Commercial policy.   I. Straits Settlements. Laws, statutes, etc.   II. Title.
15–8567

Library of Congress   HF3506.2.L8

NL 0451958   DLC CaBVaU CtY NN

Lohmann, Alfred (Adalbert Wilhelm) 1878–
Zur automatie der brückenfasern und der ventrikel des herzens ... Leipzig, Veit & comp., 1904.

24 p. illus., diagrs. 23½cm.

Habilitationsschrift—Marburg.
"Litteraturverzeichnis": p. 22–24.
"Diese arbeit erscheint im Archiv für anatomie und physiologie. 1904. Physiologische abtheilung."

1. Heart.

Library of Congress   QP101.L83   7–38694

NL 0451959   DLC CtY DNLM

Lohmann (Aloysius). * Historia præmissa, discrimina, quæ sunt inter anginam membranaceam et diphtheritidem (anginam malignam) exponuntur. 28 pp. 8°. Bonnæ, F. Krüger, 1862. c.

NL 0451960   DNLM

VOLUME 338

780.81
Hl69zL
Lohmann, Anna.
Metrisch-rhythmische Untersuchungen zu
Heinrich von Morungen ... München, 1908.
75p. 22cm.

Inaug.-Diss. - München.

1. Heinrich von Morungen, 13th cent.

NL 0451961   NcU NcD PU

Lohmann, Anne-Marie, 1909-
... Ein Fall von Phantomerscheinungen bei
einer linksseitigen Hemiplegie...   [n.p.] 1935.
Inaug.-Diss. - Halle-Wittenberg.
Lebenslauf.
"Sonderabdruck aus 'Deutsche Zeitschrift für
Nervenheilkunde', Bd. 136, Heft 5/6."
"Literatur": p. 17.

NL 0451962   CtY MiU

Lohmann, Annemarie.
... Zur geistigen entwicklung Thomas Müntzers, von Anne-
marie Lohmann. Leipzig und Berlin, B. G. Teubner, 1931.
3 p. l., 71 p. 24cm. (Beiträge zur kulturgeschichte des mittelalters
und der renaissance ... bd. 47)
"Verzeichnis der angeführten literatur": p. [69]-71.

1. Münzer, Thomas, 1490 (ca.)-1525.

Library of Congress   BX4946.M8L6   32-8572

                                                922.443

NL 0451963   DLC CU MH PU

88H75
DL83
Lohmann, Antonius, 1831-
De Iove Homeri et Sophoclis.   Bero-
lini, G. Schade [1863]

93 p. 20cm.

Inaug. Diss.--Berlin.
Vita.

1. Homerus. Religion and ethics. 2.
Sophocles. I. Title.

NL 0451964   MnU NIC CU

Lohmann, August.
Technik der verbandstoffherstellung, von August Lohmann
... Mit 52 abbildungen. Berlin, J. Springer, 1939.
v, [1], 112 p. illus. 21cm.

1. Bandages and bandaging.   I. Title: Verbandstoffherstellung.
Technik der.
                                                39-33036
Library of Congress   RD113.L8
Copyright A—Foreign   44237
                                                617.98

NL 0451965   DLC

W 4
M22
1953
LOHMANN, Beatrix, 1924-
Ueber Cutis laxa und hyperelastica
bei Anomalien der Hautgefässe und des
Skelettsystems. [Mainz] 1953.
19 l. illus.
Inaug.-Diss. - Mainz.
Typewritten copy.
1. Dermatolysis

NL 0451966   DNLM

Lohmann (Bernard [Ludwig]) [1868-].
*Ein Fall von 6maliger Stieltorsion eines Ova-
rialkystoms. 31 pp. 8°. Greifswald, J. Abel,
1891.

NL 0451967   DNLM MiU

Lohmann, Bernhard.
... Ansätze zur weiterentwicklung des kaufmännischen rechnungswesens, von dr. Bernhard Lohmann. Rostock, C. Hin-
storff [1940]
131 p. 22cm. (Hamburger wirtschafts- und sozialwissenschaftliche
schriften ... hft. 43)
Issued also as inaugural dissertation, Hamburg.
"Schrifttum-verzeichnis": p. 5-8.

1. Retail trade—Accounting. 2. Retail trade—Germany. I. Title.

Library of Congress   HF5645.L58 1940   42-30847

                                                658.87094:

NL 0451968   DLC MH

Lohmann, Bernhard.
Lohmann's musical puzzles of educational value for every
music student & music lover.   New York, N. Y.: The author[,
cop. 1927].   64 p.   diagrs., illus. (port.)   8°.

493717A. 1. Puzzles. 2. Music—   Instruction and study.
                                                September 11, 1930

NL 0451969   NN

Lohmann, Bobo, 1909-
... Die akute Wurmfortsatzentzündung bei
Kranken über 50 Jahre; eine Zusammenstellung
der Krankheitsfälle der Chirurgischen Universi-
tätsklinik zu Göttingen aus den Jahren 1923-
1932...   Bottrop i.W., 1935.
Inaug.-Diss. - Göttingen.
Lebenslauf.
"Schriftenverzeichnis": p. 24-25.

NL 0451970   CtY MiU

Lohmann, Carl Albert, 1887-   ed.

Yale university. Class of 1910.
Thirty years after, class of 1910, Yale college, edited by Carl
A. Lohmann. [New Haven] Printed with the assistance of the
Class secretaries bureau, 1940.

Lohmann, Carl Ernst Julius, 1873-
Beitrag zur chemie und biologie der lebermoose ...
Jena, G. Fischer, 1903.
2 p. l., 42 p., 1 l. 23½cm.
Inaug.-diss.—Jena.
Lebenslauf.

1. Hepaticae.

Library of Congress   QK551.L83   7-1334

NL 0451972   DLC CtY ICRL MH

Lohmann, Carl Ernst Julius, 1873-
Über die giftigkeit der deutschen schachtelhalmarten, insbesondere des duwocks (Equisetum palustre). Von dr. C. E.
Julius Lohmann ...   Berlin, Deutsche landwirtschafts-gesell-
schaft, 1904.
4 p. l., 60 p. II pl. 24cm. (Added t.-p.: Arbeiten der Deutschen land-
wirtschafts-gesellschaft ... hft. 100)
Plates accompanied by guard sheet with descriptive letterpress.

1. [Equisetum] 2. Poisonous plants.

                                                Agr 5-115 Revised
Library, U. S. Dept. of   Agriculture 18D48 no. 100
Library of Congress   S7.D35 hft. 100

NL 0451973   DNAL DLC ICJ NN

Lohmann, Carl Wilhelm.
... Der obere Dünndarm im Röntgenbild. Ein
Beitrag zur Frage der Duodenitis. (Auszug) ...
Berlin [1937]
"Eingereicht zur Erlangung der Würde eines
Dr. med. habil. in der Medizinischen Fakultät
der Friedrich=Wilhelms-Universität zu Berlin."

NL 0451974   CtY

Lohmann (Christ. Wolldemars). *De affectibus paralyticis, eorumque ab aliis impotentia-
rum generibus differentia. 79 pp. 4°. Rostochii, typ. J. J. Adleri, [1736].

NL 0451975   DNLM

Edc
Sa98
804l
Lohmann, Christoph Wilhelm
Fussreise durch Sachsen und dessen romantische Schweizergegenden; einen Theil der
Anhaltschen, Brandenburg und Braunschweig-
schen Lande, nach Hannover, in Sommer
1804 ... Bremen, C. Seyffert, 1805.
xxxviii, 287p. 21cm. (His Vaterländische
Reisen, 1.Teil.)

1. Saxony - Descr. & trav. 2. Germany -
Descr. & trav. -   1800-1850. I. Title.

NL 0451976   CtY

Lohmann, Christoph Wilhelm, tr.
[Prudhomme, Louis Marie] 1752-1830.
Reise nach Guiana und Cayenne, nebst einer übersicht
der ältern dahin gemachten reisen und neuern nachrichten von diesem lande, dessen bewohnern und den dortigen
europäischen colonien, besonders den französischen. Mit
einer karte und einem kupfer. Aus dem französischen ...
Hamburg, B. G. Hoffmann, 1799.

Lohmann, Dietrich,
Ueber die siedepunktsbestimmung chemisch reiner
suostanzen.
Inaug. diss.   Zurich, 1905.

NL 0451978   ICRL OCU

Lohmann, Dietrich Albert Friedrich, 1881-
Lüneburg. Land- und forstwirtschaftlicher provinzialverein.
Festschrift aus anlass des 100 jährigen bestehens des land-
und forstwirtschaftlichen provinzialvereins für das fürstentum
Lüneburg, e. v. 22. märz 1830-1930. Bearb. im auftrage des
vorstandes von generalsekretär Lohmann. Uelzen, Druck von
C. Beckers buchdruckerei [1930]

Lohmann, Elise, 1859-
Nietzsche über Krieg und Frieden in seiner
Wirkung auf das In- und Ausland...   München,
C. Kaiser, 1918.
31 p. 18 cm.
1. Nietzsche, Friedrich Wilhelm, 1844-1900.
2. Peace.

NL 0451980   NcD PHC

Lohmann, Elise, 1859-
Pascal und Nietzsche ... Borna-Leipzig, Druck von R.
Noske, 1917.
vii, 143 p., 1 l. 22½cm.
Inaug.-diss.—Erlangen.
Lebenslauf.
"Literaturverzeichnis": p. [v]-vii.

1. Pascal, Blaise, 1623-1662. 2. Nietzsche, Friedrich Wilhelm, 1844-
1900.

                                                28-14350
Library of Congress   B1903.L6 1917

NL 0451981   DLC NIC CtY PHC PU NN

VOLUME 338

Lohmann, Emilie Friederike Sophie
  see Lohmann, Friederike, 1749-1811.

Lohmann, Erich.
  Arbeitsanweisungen, Arbeitsabläufe, Arbeitsuntersuchungen. Wiesbaden, T. Gabler [1955]
    105 p. diagrs., forms. 21 cm. (Fachbücher für die Wirtschaft)
    Bibliography: p. 103-105.

    1. Office management. I. Title.
    HF5547.L63   A 56-4388
    New York Univ.   Libraries
    for Library of Congress

  NL 0451983   NNU NN DLC

Lohmann, Ernst, 1860-
  Im Kloster zu Sis. Ein Beitrag zu der Geschichte der Beziehungen zwischen dem Deutschen Reiche und Armenien im Mittelalter. Striegau, R. Urban [1904]
    34 p., il. 4°.

  NL 0451984   NN

BV600 Lohmann, Ernst, 1860-
.L85 Die kirche der armen, von Ernst Lohmann ... Berlin, Bund der freunde christlicher bücher, 1927.
    260 p. 19ᶜᵐ.
    Head pieces.
    Contents.—Aus der geschichte der kirche der armen. Der Epheserbrief.

    1. Church. 2. Church history—Primitive and early church. 3. Germany—Church history.

  NL 0451985   ICU

Lohmann, Ernst, 1860-
  Nur ein leben, lebenserinnerungen von Ernst Lohmann. Schwerin i. Mecklb., F. Bahn [1933]
    190, [1] p. illus. (facsim.) plates, ports. 19ᶜᵐ.

    I. Title.
                    [Full name: Ernst Emil Karl Reinhold Lohmann]
    Library of Congress   BX8080.L65A3
    Copyright A—Foreign   24089   34-19475
                                      922.443

  NL 0451986   DLC

LOHMANN, Ernst, 1860-
  Wie der apostel schreibt. Randbemerkungen zu den briefen des apostel Paulus... p. Ernst Lohmann. Frankfurt a M., Verlag Orient, [pref. 1913.]
    70 p. 24 cm.

  NL 0451987   MH-AH

Lohmann, Ernst, 1878-
  Der textkritische wert der syrischen uebersetzung der kirchengeschichte des eusebius ... Halle, 1899.   56 p.
    Inaug. Diss. -Halle-Wittenberg, 1899.
    Vita.
    Full name: Johannes Felix Ernst Lohmann.

  NL 0451988   ICRL CtY NjP MH DDO PU ICU

LOHMANN, Ernst, 1878-
  Tharsis oder Ninive. Ein Beitrag zum Verstaendnis des Buches Jonah. Mit einem Anhang: Das Buch Jona in Berichtigter Übersetzung nebst einigen Erklärenden Anmerkungen. Freienwalde a.O. and Leipzig, Rüger, 1904. 2 p.l. 2-60 p. 18.5 cm.
    1.Bible-German-Jonah. 2.Bible-Commentary-Jonah. 3.Title.

  NL 0451989   NNJ OCH

Lohmann, Ernst, 1904-
  Die erfassung des umsatzes. ... 83 p.
    Inaug. Diss. - Heidelberg, [1936]
    Lebenslauf.
    Literatur und quellenverzeichnis.

  NL 0451990   ICRL CtY NNC

Lohmann, Ernst August, 1904-
  Die bedeutung der umweltseinflüsse für den herkunftswert des saatgutes bei getreide, dargestellt an beseler hafer II. ...Breslau, 1934.   53 p.
    Inaug. Diss. - Breslau, 1934.
    Lebenslauf.
    Bibliography.

  NL 0451991   ICRL MiU CtY

Lohmann, Ernst Walter, 1882-   Das Briefbeförderungsgeschäft der Reichspost. Leipzig 1909: Schmidt. 59 S. 8°
  Leipzig, Jur. Diss. v. 23. Jan. 1909
    [Geb. 12. Okt. 82 Bremen; Wohnort: Oschatz; Staatsangeh.: Sachsen; Vorbildung: Gymn. Wurzen Reife O. 02; Studium: Freiburg i. B. 1, Leipzig 1, Freiburg i. B. 1, Leipzig 5 S.; Rig. 8. Febr. 06.]   [U 09. 2596

  NL 0451992   ICRL

LOHMANN, Ewald, 1901-
  Über aquo-und amnihkomplexe des kupfers und nickels. Inaug.-diss.,Münster i. Westf. [Barmen Graphische kunstanstalt Montanus u. Ehrenstein, 1926?].
    pp. 39.
    "Lebenslauf", p. 39.

  NL 0451993   MH-C CU

Lohmann (Ewald Heinrich) [1868-   ]
  *Ueber acute spontane Osteomyelitis bei Erwachsenen. 44 pp., 1l. 8°. Greifswald, C. Sell, 1892.

  NL 0451994   MiU DNLM

943.2V678
L832 Lohmann, F   W
  Geschichte der Stadt Viersen von den ältesten Zeiten bis zur Gegenwart. Zugleich ein Beitrag zur Geschichte des alten freieidlen Sankt Gereonsstiftes in Köln. Zur Feier der 200 jähr. Zugehörigkeit der Stadt Viersen zum Königreich Preussen. [Viersen] Verlag der Stadt Viersen, 1913.
    xvi, 934 p. facsims., fold. map. 23cm.
    Bibliography: p. vi-ix.
    1. Viersen, Ger. History. 2. Cologne. St. Gereon   (Church)

  NL 0451995   MnU

Tzz
976.411 Lohmann, Ferdinand H
C734ℓ Comfort; ein kurzer Überblick über das Leben und Treiben der Bewohner von der Gründungszeit bis zur Gegenwart. Festschrift zur funfzigjahrigen Jubelfeier der Ansiedelung. Comfort, Tex., W. Pellbaum, 1904.
    50p. 23cm.

    1. Comfort, Tex. - Hist. 2. Germans in Texas.

  NL 0452001   TxU CtY OCU IU NN

Tzz
430.9 Lohmann, Ferdinand H
L832d Die deutsche Sprache; was können wir beitragen zu ihrer Erhaltung in diesem Lande. Chicago, Koelling & Klappenbach, 1904.
    48p. 23cm.

    1. German language - Hist. 2. Germans in the U.S.

  NL 0452002   TxU ICN

Y
952 LOHMANN, FERDINAND H.
.L 76 Texas-blüten. Gedichte. Utica,N.Y., American authors' agency[1906]
    163p. front.(port.) 20cm.

  NL 0452003   ICN NNU-W OCU IU

PT3819
.L75T4 Lohmann, Ferdinand H.
  Texas-blueten.
  Utica, N.Y., Leipzig [1908?].
    1 v.   12°

  NL 0452004   DLC OCU TxU CtY OCU NN

Lohmann, Ferdinand H.
  To my darling, and other poems, by Ferdinand H. Lohmann. N[ew] Y[ork] Broadway publishing co. [1910]
    2 p. l., 3-4, 7-87 p. 20½ᶜᵐ. $0.75

                                      11-685

  NL 0452005   DLC TxU CU NN

Lohmann, Franz.
  Der deutsche Bauer. Emsdetten (Westf.) H. & J. Lechte, 1934.
    122 p. port. table. 19 cm.

    1. Agriculture—Economic aspects—Germany. 2. Peasantry—Germany. 3. Reichsnährstand. I. Title.
    HD1955.L6   50-53981

  NL 0452006   DLC

Lohmann, Franz
  Zur lehre von der grundschuld unter besonderer berücksichtigung der nichtvalutierten grundschuld, ihrer pfändung und ihrer stellung in der zwangsversteigerung. ... Emsdetten, 1933.
    39 p.
    Inaug. Diss. -Erlangen, 1933.
    Bibliography.

  NL 0452007   ICRL MH-L

VOLUME 338

Lohmann, Franz, 1908–
Untersuchungen bei einem energiesparenden Modulationsverfahren... [Berlin, 1936?]
Inaug.-Diss. - Köln.
Lebenslauf.
"Literatur": p. 22.

NL 0452008   CtY

Lohmann, Franziska (Meyer-Estorf) Martienssen–
see Martienssen-Lohmann, Franziska (Meyer-Estorf)
1887–

PT 2424   LOHMANN, FRIEDERIKE;   ) 1749–1811
.L67 J16   Jacobine; eine Geschichte aus der Zeit
1797   des baierschen Successionskrieges. Neue Ausg.
Halberstadt, Gross, 1797.
2 v. in 1.

NL 0452010   InU

PT 2424   LOHMANN, Friederike, 1749–1811.
.L66 A15   Sämmtliche Erzählungen, von Friederike Loh-
1844   mann. Ausgabe letzter Hand, mit einer Vorworte der Verfasserin von Godwie Castle. Leipzig, C. Focke, 1844.
18 v. in 6. port.
Full name: Emilie Friederike Sophie Lohmann.

NL 0452011   InU

Lohmann, Friedrich, 1869–
Die staatliche regelung der englischen wollindustrie
vom xv. bis zum xviii. jahrhundert. Von Dr. Friedrich
Lohmann. Leipzig, Duncker & Humblot, 1900.
x, 100 p. 22ᶜᵐ. (Added t.-p.: Staats- und socialwissenschaftliche forschungen hrsg. von G. Schmoller. 18. bd. 1. hft.)

1. Wool trade and industry—Gt. Brit.—Hist.

Library of Congress   HB41.S7
                                              1-G-1440

NL 0452012   DLC PPAmP MB PU PSC

Lohmann, Friedrich, 1869–
Vauban, seine stellung in der geschichte...
Inaug. diss. Berlin, 1895 (Leipzig)

NL 0452013   ICRL

Lohmann, Friedrich, 1869–
Vauban, seine stellung in der geschichte der nationalökonomie und sein reformplan. Von dr. Friedrich Lohmann. Leipzig, Duncker & Humblot, 1895.
4 p. l., 172 p. 22½ᶜᵐ. (Added t.-p.: Staats- und socialwissenschaftliche
forschungen, hrsg. von Gustav Schmoller. 13. bd. 4. hft.)

1. Vauban, Sébastien Le Prestre de, 1633–1707. 2. Economics—Hist.
                                              G—1742
Library of Congress   HB41.S7

NL 0452014   DLC NcD CU PU MB

LOHMANN, Friedrich, 1889–
Die Grund-oder Freiheitsrechte der Ausländer.
Nach deutschem Reichs-u.preuss. Landesrecht.
Düsseldorf 1913: Blanckertz.

74 S.
Kiel, Jur. Diss. v. 21. Mai 1913.

NL 0452015   MH-L CtY ICRL

Lohmann, Friedrich Wilhelm, 1900–
Der einfluss der typhusschutzimpfung auf morbidi-
taet und mortalitaet des typhus in den vorkriegs-
kriegs- und nachkriegsjahren.
Inaug. diss. Bonn, 1927.
Bibl.

NL 0452016   ICRL CtY

Lohmann, Fritz.
Die Entwicklung der Lokalbahnen in Bayern, von Fritz Lohmann... Leipzig: G. Böhme, 1901. 238 p. incl. table. map.
8°. (Wirtschafts- und Verwaltungsstudien mit besonderer
Berücksichtigung Bayerns. [Bd.] 11.)

1. Railways (Interurban), Germany: Bavaria. 2. Series.
N. Y. P. L.   February 23, 1923.

NL 0452017   NN ICU MH-BA ICJ MB IEN CtY

Lohmann, Georg.
Die entwicklung der flugmaschinen, von Georg Lohmann ...
Berlin, Liebel, 1911.
2 p. l., 41, [3] p. illus. 21¼ᶜᵐ.
"Sonderabdruck aus der Unteroffizier-zeitung."
"Literatur": verso of 2d prelim. leaf.

1. Aeroplanes.

Library of Congress   TL670.L65
                                              33-9471
—— Copy 2.   629.133341

NL 0452018   DLC

Lohmann, Gerhard, 1897–
Das eroeffnungsverfahren im strafprozets.
Inaug. diss. Greifswald, 1921.
Bibl.

NL 0452019   ICRL

Lohmann, Gertrud, 1910–
Friedrich Naumanns deutscher sozialismus ... von Gertrud
Lohmann ... Baruth, Mark-Berlin, Buchdruckerei J. Särchen,
1935.
80 p. 21ᶜᵐ.
Inaug.-diss.—Munich.
Lebenslauf.
"Verzeichnis der literatur und der anmerkungen": p. 65–80.

1. Naumann, Friedrich, 1860–1919. 2. Socialism in Germany.

Library of Congress   HX276.N33L6
                                              41-39294
[2]   335.50948

NL 0452020   DLC PU NjP CtY PBm

W 4   LOHMANN, Günther, 1921–
M96   Zur Frage nach der klinischen Wertig-
1951   keit der kleinen Sella, sowie der Berücken-
bildungen der Sella turcica; statistische
Bearbeitung von 7000 Schädelleeraufnahmen
[München] 1951.
26 ℓ.
Inaug.-Diss. - Munich.
1. Sella turcica

NL 0452021   DNLM

Lohmann, Gustav.
TR680   Haustein, Hans.
.H33   ... Spielende kinder; die zusammenstellung der zitate be-
sorgte Gustav Lohmann. Hamburg, H. Ellermann, 1940.

Lohmann, Gustav Wilhelm Richard
see Lohmann, Richard, 1881–

Lohmann, Hanns, 1907–
... Der chronische Zungenabszess...
Bochum-Langendreer, 1937.
Inaug.-Diss. - Münster.
Lebenslauf.

NL 0452024   CtY

Lohmann, Hans, 1863–1934.
L591.998
.P899   v.I
Die Appendicularien, von Hans Lohmann ... Mit 5 Textfigu-
ren.
(In Römer, F., ed. Fauna arctica. Jena, 1900. 35½ᶜᵐ. 1. Bd., p. 363,–378.
illus.)
"Litteraturverzeichnis": p. 378.

NL 0452025   ICJ

Lohmann, Hans, 1863–
*388oa.79
Die Appendicularien.
[Kiel. 1901.] 11–21 pp. Illus. [Nordisches Plankton. 3.] L 8

G9775 — Appendiculara.

NL 0452026   MB

Lohmann, Hans, 1863–
S22   Die Appendicularien der Deutschen Tiefsee-
0350   Expedition ...
21   (In Wissenschaftliche Ergebnisse der
Deutschen Tiefsee-Expedition. Jena,1932. 34½ᶜᵐ.
v.21, p.[1]–158 incl.illus.,tables,diagrs.
V fold.maps (part.col.).)
Double pagination.
"Schriftennachweis": p.153–154.

NL 0452027   CtY

QL   Lohmann, Hans, 1863–
613   Die Appendicularien im Südatlantischen
L83   Ozean, von H. Lohmann und E. Hentschel.
[Berlin, Walter De Gruyter, 1939,
[153,–243 p. illus., maps, tables.
29 cm. (Wissenschaftliche Ergebnisse der
Deutschen Atlantischen Expedition auf dem
Forschungs- und Vermessungsschiff
"Meteor" 1925–1927, Band 13, Dritter Teil)

NL 0452028   NIC

Lohmann, Hans, 1863–
*388oa.79.3
Die Ascidienlarven des nordischen Planktons.
[Kiel. Lipsius & Tischer. 1911.] 31–47 pp. Illus. [Nordisches
Plankton. 3.] 29 cm, in 8s.

H5609 — Larvae. Ascidian. — S.r.c.

NL 0452029   MB

VOLUME 338

B580.6
D48v LOHMANN, Hans, 1863–
no.4 ... Die besiedelung der hochsee mit
pflanzen, von H. Lohmann... Berlin,
Gebrüder Borntraeger, 1919.

30 p. fold. table, diagrs. (1 fold.)
25cm. (Vorträge aus dem gesamtgebiet
der botanik, hrsg. von der Deutschen
botanischen gesellschaft. hft. 4)
1. Marine flora. I. Title.

NL 0452030 MnU NNBG CtY

Lohmann, Hans, 1863–
Die Bevölkerung des Ozeans mit Plankton; nach den Ergebnissen der Zentrifugenfänge während der Ausreise der "Deutschland" 1911. Zugleich ein Beitrag zur Biologie des Atlantischen
Ozeans, von H. Lohmann... Berlin: R. Friedländer & Sohn,
1920. 617 p. diagrs., illus., maps, plates. f°. (Archiv für
Biontologie. Bd. 4, Heft 3.)
1 map, 15 diagrams in pocket.
Bibliography, p. 448–449.

1. Plankton, Atlantic ocean.
N. Y. P. L.   2. Series.
                                           August 21, 1923.

NL 0452031 NN FMU CaBVaU

Lohmann, Hans, 1863–   *3880a.79.11
Die Cyphonautes der nordischen Meere.
— [Kiel. Lipsius & Tischer. 1911.] 31–40 pp. Illus. Plate.
[Nordisches Plankton. 11.] 29 cm., in 8s.

H5607 — Cyphonautes. — North Sea. Zool. — S.r.c.

NL 0452032 MB

Lohmann, Hans, 1863–   *3880a.79.2
Eier und Cysten des nordischen Planktons.
— [Kiel. Lipsius & Tischer. 1911.] 20 pp. Illus. [Nordisches
Plankton. 2.] 29 cm., in 8s.

H5609 — Eggs. Pelagic. — S.r.c.

NL 0452033 MB PPAN

Lohmann, Hans, 1863–   *3880a.79.2
Eier und sogenannte Cysten der Plankton-Expedition. — Anhang:
Cyphonautes.
— Kiel. Lipsius & Tischer. 1904. 61, (1) pp. Plates. Maps.
[Ergebnisse der Plankton-Expedition der Humboldt-Stiftung.
Band 4. N.] 4°.

F7505 — Eggs. Pelagic. — Cyphonautes.

NL 0452034 MB CtY

Lohmann, Hans, 1863–1934.
Ernst Vanhöffen. Von H. Lohmann.
(In Mitteilungen aus dem Zoologischen museum in Berlin. Berlin,
1918. 28cm. 9. bd., 1. hft., p. [71–90]
"Verzeichnis der von Ernst Vanhöffen veröffentlichten zoologischen
arbeiten": p. 88–90.

1. Vanhöffen, Ernst, 1858–1918.
                                           A C 35–8274
Title from Ohio State   Univ.
Library of Congress   [QL1.B38 bd. 9, hft. 1]

NL 0452035 OU ICJ

549
0125 Lohmann, Hans, 1863–
2.G.a.β ... Die Halacarinen der Plankton-Expedition
von H. Lohmann ...
Kiel[etc.]Lipsius & Tischer,1893. 1p.l.,
[13]–95pp. XIIIpl. 34x28cm.
(Ergebnisse der Plankton-Expedition der
Humboldt-Stiftung, Bd.II.G.a.β)
"Litteraturverzeichniss": pp.[89]–90.

1.Halacarinae. I.Ser.

NL 0452036 CtY MB

Lohmann, Hans, 1863–1934, joint author.

Piersig, Gustav Richard.
... Hydrachnidae und Halacaridae, bearb. von dr. R. Piersig ... und dr. H. Lohmann ... Berlin, R. Friedländer und
sohn, 1901.

Lohmann, Hans, 1863–
Die tierwelt der erde. Rede ... von H. Lohmann. Hamburg, Druck von Lütcke & Wulff, 1929.
22 p. 25½cm.
"Schriftennachweis": p. 22.

1. Zoology—Classification.   I. Title.

Library of Congress   QL351.L6
                                           30–16107

NL 0452038 DLC CtY ICRL DSI NN

Lohmann, Hans, 1863–1934.
Über das Nannoplankton und die Zentrifugierung
kleinster Wasserproben zur Gewinnung desselben
in lebendem Zustande. Leipzig, W. Klinkhardt,
1911.
38p. 5 col. plates. 26cm.
"Sonderabdruck aus 'Internationale Revue der
gesamten Hydrobiologie und Hydrographie', Bd.IV,
Heft 1".

1. Plankton.

NL 0452039 NcU

Lohmann, Hans, 1863–1934.
... Untersuchungen über das pflanzen- und tierleben des hochsee, zugleich ein bericht über die biologischen arbeiten auf der
fahrt der "Deutschland" von Bremerhaven nach Buenos Aires
in der zeit vom 7. mai bis 7. september 1911; von H. Lohmann
... (hierzu 2 tafeln und 14 textfiguren.) Berlin, E. S. Mittler
und sohn [1912]
viii, 92 p. illus., diagrs. (1 fold.) fold. chart. 27cm. (Veröffentlichungen des Instituts für meereskunde an der Universität Berlin ... n. f. A.
Geographisch-naturwissenschaftliche reihe. hft. 1)
Folded diagram and chart in pocket of cover.
1. Marine biology. 2. Scientific expeditions. 3. Deutschland (Ship)

Library of Congress   QH91.L8
                                           13—10020

NL 0452040 DLC PPAN ICJ NN MiU

LOHMANN, Hans, 1863–
Untersuchungen zur feststellung des vollstän
digen gehaltes des meeres an plankton. Kiel,
Schmidt & Klaunig 1908.
4°. 239 pp. 111.

NL 0452041 MH PPAN

Lohmann, Hans, 1863–1934.
Zoologische ergebnisse der von der Gesellschaft für erdkunde
zu Berlin unter leitung dr. von Drygalski's ausgesandten
Grönlandexpedition nach dr. Vanhöffen's sammlungen bearbeitet ... Stuttgart, E. Nägele, 1895–98.

Lohmann, Hans, 1905–
... Zur Kasuistik der akuten gelben Leber-
trophie im Kindesalter... Kiel, 1933.
Inaug.-Diss. - Kiel.
Lebenslauf.
"Literatur": p. [18]

NL 0452043 CtY

Lohmann, Hans Georg, 1908–
Die rechtsnatur der richtlinien des 32 Abs. 1
des gesetzes zur ordnung der nationalen arbeit
vom 20. 1. 1934. ... Würzburg, 1936. 48 p.
Inaug. Diss. - Bonn, 1936.
Lebenslauf.
Literaturverzeichnis.

NL 0452044 ICRL MH-L

LOHMANN, Heinrich, 1880–
Die auferstehung Jesu nach dem neuen testaments und ihre alten und neuen gegner. Essen
Altessen, Heinemann, n.d.
96 p+ 22.4cm. Thesis, Bonn, 1916.

NL 0452045 MH-AH CtY ICRL PU

Lohmann, Heinrich, 1882—
Die rechtmaessige Gewinnung bergfreier und fremder Mine-
ralien. Essen: Ruhr, 1910. 1 p.l., 20 p., 1 l.   4°.
Dissertation, Erlangen.
Repr.: Berg- und Hüttenmännische Zeitschrift. Jahrg. 46.

1. Mines, etc.—Jurisprudence.
N. Y. P. L.   March 7, 1913.

NL 0452046 NN ICRL MH DI-GS

LOHMANN, Heinrich, 1897–
Bestimmung der leichtlöslichen (aufnehmbaren
pflanzennährstoffe des bodens und ihre ausnut-
zung bei verschiedenen bodenarten. Inaug.-
diss. Münster i.W. Borna-Leipzig,Universitäts-
verlag von R.Noske, 1928.
pp.(2), 64. Plate.
"Lebenslauf", at end.

NL 0452047 MH-C

Lohmann, Heinrich Carl, 1892–
Die Ausfuhr Solinger Stahlwaren nach Britisch
Indien, Burma und Ceylon... Würzburg,
1934.
Inaug.-Diss. - Köln.

NL 0452048 CtY

LOHMANN, Heinrich L   , 1880–
Die Ethischen Principien des Helvetius. Inaug.-diss. Würzburg, 1906.

NL 0452049 MH CtY ICRL NjP PU

Lohmann ([Heinrich] W[ilhelm]). Die Gründung von Heilstätten für unbemittelte Lungen-
kranke. Im Auftrage der Aerztekammer der
Provinz Hannover. 15 pp. 8°. Hannover.
Schmorl & von Seefeld Nachf., 1899.

NL 0452050 DNLM

VOLUME 338

Lohmann, Heinz.
SA räumt auf! Aus der kampfzeit der bewegung; aufzeich-nungen, von Heinz Lohmann. Hamburg, Hanseatische ver-lagsanstalt ₍*1933₎
199 p. 20ᶜᵐ.

1. Germany—Pol. & govt.—1918-   2. Nationalsozialistische
deutsche arbeiter-partei.   ɪ. Title.

Library of Congress	DD253.L6	35–3019
Copyright A—Foreign	24533	
	₍2₎	943.085

NL   0452051   DLC ICarbS TNJ MiU NcD

Lohmann, Heinz.
SA räumt auf! Aus der Kampfzeit der Bewegung; auf-zeichnungen. Hamburg, Hanseatische Verlagsanstalt ₍pref. 1935, *1933₎
273 p. 20 cm.

1. Germany—Pol. & govt.—1918-1933.   2. Nationalsozialistische
Deutsche Arbeiter-Partei. Sturmabteilung.   ɪ. Title.

DD253.L6 1935a   55–47990 ‡

NL   0452052   DLC N

Lohmann, Heinz.
SA räumt auf! Aus der Kampfzeit der Bewegung, Auf-zeichnungen. Hamburg, Hanseatische Verlagsanstalt ₍*1935₎
197 p. 19 cm.

1. Germany — Pol. & govt. — 1918-1933.   2. Nationalsozialistische
Deutsche Arbeiter-Partei. Sturmabteilung.

DD253.L6 1935   943.085   52–56850 ‡

NL   0452053   DLC IaU ICRL

DD
253   Lohmann, Heinz.
L62   SA räumt auf! Aus der Kampfzeit der
Bewegung; Aufzeichnungen, von Heinz Lohmann.
Hamburg, Hanseatische Verlagsanstalt [1939]
197 p.   20cm.

NL   0452054   CoU

LOHMANN, Heinz, 1908-
Über aromatische und hydroaromatische Polyke-
tone und Ketonsäuren.   Kiel, R. Eggert, 1935.

23 cm.
Inaugural-Dissertation - Kiel.
"Lebenslauf" at end.

NL   0452055   MH DLC CtY ICRL

Lohmann, Helen.
Character-comedy.   Translated & adapted from Carlo Goldoni's Teatro comico, by Helen Lohmann...   ₍n. p., 19–?₎   8 f.   28cm.

Typescript.

1. Pantomimes, American.   ɪ. Goldoni, Carlo, 1707–1793.
N. Y. P. L.   March 30, 1945

NL   0452056   NN

Lohmann, Helen, tr.

Goldoni, Carlo, 1707–1793.
La locandiera ⟨The mistress of the inn⟩ translated and adapted from the Italian of Carlo Goldoni by Helen Lohmann. New York, Longmans, Green & co., 1927.

Lohmann, Hermann,   Ueber Bauchdeckendesmoide im Anschluss an einen Fall von Bauchdeckendesmoid in einer Appendektomienarbe. [In Maschinenschrift.] 16 S. 4°(2°). — Auszug: Marburg 1921: Kilber. 2 Bl. 8°
Marburg, Med. Diss. v. 23. Juli 1921, Ref. Läwen
[Geb. 11. Nov. 92 Ankum, Hannover; Wohnort: Marburg; Staatsangeh.: Preußen; Vorbildung: G. Carolinum Osnabrück Reife 14; Studium: Münster 1, Straßburg 4, Marburg 4 S.; Coll. 28. Febr. 20; Approb. 1. Jan. 21.]
[U 21. 6012

NL   0452058   ICRL

QA455
.S68
1947

Lohmann, J. A., joint author.

Springer, M
Meetkunde ten dienste van het technisch onderwijs, speciaal voor de opleiding van scheepswerktuigkundigen en aanstaande scheepswerktuigkundigen, door M. Springer en J. A. Lohmann. 3. druk. Amsterdam, V/h C. de Boer Jr., 1947.

QA106
.S6
1947

Lohmann, J. A., joint author.

Springer, M
Rekenkunde, ten dienste van het technisch onderwijs, spe-ciaal voor de opleiding van scheepswerktuigkundigen en aan-staande scheepswerktuigkundigen, door M. Springer en J. A. Lohmann. 5. druk. Amsterdam, C. de Boer Jr., 1947.

Lohmann (Jacob Theodor).   *Beitrag zur Kenntnis der Wirkung des Sabadillins. 30 pp. 8°.   *Marburg*, C. L. Pfeil, 1873.

NL   0452061   DNLM

QD181
.85L8   **Lohmann, Johann,** 1878-
Versuche zur darstellung des nitroxylchlorids, Beitraege zur kenntnis des selens.
Erlangen, 1904.
84p,
Inaug. diss. Erlangen.

NL   0452062   DLC MH PU CtY DNLM

Lohmann, Johann Baptist,   1834-1911.
Betrachtungen auf alle tage des jahres für Priester und Laien von Joh, Bapt. Lohmann, S.J. 3 gänzlich umgearbeitete aufl. des Handbuches der wahren Frömmigkeit von Bruno Vercruysse, S.J. Paderborn, Junfermann buchhandlung, 1884.

2 v. 20 cm.

NL   0452063   PLatS

Lohmann, Johann Baptist, 1834–1911.
Betrachtungen auf alle tage des jahres für priester und laien, von Joh. Bapt. Lohmann s. j. 5., vielfach umgearb., verb. und verm. aufl. Mit einer karte von Palästina ...   Paderborn, Junfermann (A. Pape) 1894.
4 v. in 2. fold. map. 20ᵐ.

1. Church year—Meditations.

41–41653

Library of Congress   BX2184.L65 1894

NL   0452064   DLC WaSpG

Lohmann, Jonann Baptist, 1834–
Betrachtungen über das leben Jesu Christi auf alle tagen des jahres, für priester und gebildete laien, von Joh. Bapt. Lohmann, s. j. 6., vielfach verb. aufl. Mit einer karte von Palästina ... Paderborn, Junfermann sche buchhandlung, 1912.
2 v. fold. map. 23ᵐ.   M. 12

12–21667

NL   0452065   DLC

Lohmann, Johann Baptist, S.J., 1834-1911.
Das Leben unsers Herrn und Heilandes Jesus Christus nach den vier Evangelisten; Eine Evangel-ienharmonie mit erklärenden Anmerkungen von Joh. Bapt. Lohmann, S.J., zweite, verbesserte und vermehrte Auflage ...   Paderborn, Druck under Verlag der Junfermann (Albert Pope), 1889.

319p. map, tables. 21cm.

NL   0452066   PLatS

Lohmann, Johann Baptist, 1834-1911.
Das leben unsers Herrn und Heilanders Jesus Christus nach den vier evangelien ᴱine evangel-ienharmonie mit erklarenden anmerkungen. Dritte ... auflage. ... mit einer karte von Palästrina. Paderborn, Jungermann, 1897.
359p. map.

NL   0452067   OClJC

Lohmann, Johann Baptist, 1834-1911.
Über den Priesterstand; Vorträge. Paderborn Druck und Verlag der Junfermannschen Buchhand-lung (A. Pape) 1896.

256 p. 20.5 cm.

NL   0452068   MH

833
L835h   Lohmann, Johanna Friederike, d. 1830
Herbstblumen meines Geistes, von der Verfas-serinn der Clara Wallburg und Claudine Lahn. Leipzig ₍n.p.₎ 1811.
2v. front. 17cm. (Bibliothek für die gebildete Lesewelt; eine Sammlung gewählter Schriften der vorzüglichsten Schriftsteller Deutschlands zur angenehmen und nützlichen Unterhaltung, Bd.6-7)

NL   0452069   NcU

Lohmann (Johannes).   *Drei Fälle von Sar-kom des Oberschenkels. 26 pp. 8°.   *Erlangen*, E. F. Jacob, 1886.

NL   0452070   DNLM

Lohmann, Johannes.
Reizwirkungen chemischer verbindungen auf die kei-mung der kartoffelknolle.
Landw. jahrb. bd. 61, p. 1-44.   Berlin, 1925.
"Literaturverzeichnis": p. 33-37.

1. Potatoes—Germination₎

Agr 25–795

Library, U. S. Dept. of   Agriculture 18L23 bd. 61

NL   0452071   DNAL

VOLUME 338

Lohmann, Johannes, 1881–
Der Galaterbrief; geist oder fleisch? ₁Von₁ Joh. Lohmann. Bad Blankenburg, Thür. wald, Buchdruckerei und verlag Harfe ₁1931₁
110 p. 20½ᶜᵐ.

1. Bible. N. T. Galatians — Commentaries. 2. Bible—Commentaries—N. T. Galatians.

36–12141

Library of Congress   BS2685.L55   227.4

NL 0452072   DLC NjPT

Lohmann, Johannes, 1881–
Ich kann nicht glauben! ₁Von₁ Joh. Lohmann. Bad Blankenburg, Thür., Buchdruckerei und verlag Harfe ₁1934?₁
71 p. 20½ᶜᵐ.

1. Faith. 2. Germany—Religion—1933.   I. Title.

34–37263

Library of Congress   BV4637.L6   234.2
                           ₂₁

NL 0452073   DLC NNUT

Lohmann, Johannes, 1881–
Das Markusevangelium; das evangelium von der erziehung derer, die Jesus Christus als ihrem führer folgen ₁von₁ Johannes Lohmann. Giessen und Basel, Brunnen-verlag, 1933.
223 p. 24ᶜᵐ.

1. Bible. N. T. Mark—Commentaries. 2. Bible—Commentaries—N. T. Mark.

35–24349

Library of Congress   BS2585.L55   226.3
                           ₂₁

NL 0452074   DLC NjPT CtY

Lohmann, Johannes, 1881–
Der Römerbrief: Christus oder ich? Kleine wegweiser zur einführung in das verständnis des briefes des apostels Paulus an die Römer ₁von₁ Joh. Lohmann. Bad Blankenburg, Thür. wald, Buckdruckerei und verlag "Harfe" g. m. b. h. ₁1929₁
135 p. 21ᶜᵐ.

1. Bible. N. T. Romans—Commentaries.   I. Title.

46–30353

Library of Congress   BS2665.L6

NL 0452075   DLC

Lohmann, Johannes, 1881–
Unsere Zeit im Licht des prophetischen Wortes. 2., erweiterte und neu bearb. Aufl. Bad Blankenburg (Thür. W.) Harfe, 1933.
171 p. 20 cm.
Errata slip inserted.

1. End of the world.   I. Title.

BT875.L79 1933   51–50796

NL 0452076   DLC NN

Lohmann, Johannes, 1895–
Genus und sexus, eine morphologische studie zum ursprung der indogermanischen nominalen genus-unterscheidung, von Johannes Lohmann. Göttingen, Vandenhoeck & Ruprecht, 1932.
94 p., 1 l. 24½ᶜᵐ. (*On cover:* Ergänzungshefte zur Zeitschrift für vergleichende sprachforschung auf dem gebiete der indogermanischen sprachen, nr. 10)
"Die vorliegende arbeit geht auf eine habilitationsschrift zurück, die im jahre 1929 der Philosophischen fakultät der Universität Berlin vorgelegen hat."—Preliminary note.

1. Aryan languages—Gender.   I. Title.

32–13964

Library of Congress   P633.L6
                                      415.15

NL 0452077   DLC PBm PSC PU ViU OU OCU MB MH

Lohmann, Johannes, 1895–
Jacob Wackernagel.

(*In* Jahresbericht über die Fortschritte der klassischen Altertumswissenschaft. Leipzig. 23 cm. Bd. 280 (1943) p. ₁57₁–70)

1. Wackernagel, Jacob, 1853–1938.

[PA3.J3 Bd. 280]   (880.5)   A 50–2116
Northwestern Univ.   Library
for Library of Congress   ₂₁

NL 0452078   IEN

P25
.L49

Lohmann, Johannes, 1895–   ed.

Lexis. Studien zur Sprachphilosophie, Sprachgeschichte und Begriffsforschung. Bd. 1–
Lahr i. B., M. Schauenburg, 1948–

Lohmann, Johannes, 1895–
Wilhelm Schulze. Geboren 15. dezember 1863, gestorben 16. januar 1935. Von J. Lohmann ...

(*In* Jahresbericht über die fortschritte der klassischen altertumswissenschaft ... 1936. Leipzig, 1936. 22ᶜᵐ. 254. bd. (62. jahrg. 4. abt. ₁B₁) p. ₁105₁–122)
"Schriftenverzeichnis": p. 117–122.

1. Schulze, Wilhelm, 1863–1935.   A 42–2547
Rochester. Univ. Library
for Library of Congress   [PA3.J3 bd. 254]
                               ₂₁   (880.5)

NL 0452080   NRU

Lohmann, Joseph.
Deutsche Gegenseitige Versicherungs-Gesellschaft von Cincinnati, und Sonne Gegenseitige Versicherungs-gesellschaft von Cincinnati. Eine Kontroverse
        see under   Rattermann, Heinrich Armin 1832–1923.

Lohmann, Julius

Deutsches persönliches wesen in gegensätzlicher berührung mit dem ausland. Eine studie in vortragsform, von Julius Lohmann...München, C. Kaiser 1916
35 p. 17cm.

1. International law and relations.

NL 0452082   NcD CtY

QD341
.L82

Lohmann, Julius, 1867–
Ueber das γ-phenoxypropylamin. Berlin, 1892.
39p.
Inaug. diss. Berlin.

NL 0452083   DLC CU CtY

Lohmann, Karl.
Die delegation der gesetzgebungsgewalt im verfassungsstaate. (Auszug)
Inaug. diss. Bonn, 1928.

NL 0452084   ICRL

Lohmann, Karl.
... Einführung in die reichskunde, von dr. jur. Karl Lohmann. 4. veränderte und erweiterte auflage. Berlin-Lichterfelde, Langewort, 1941.

55 p.

NL 0452085   NNC CU

Lohmann, Karl.
Hitlers Staatsauffassung, mit einer Einleitung von Joh. v. Leers. Berlin, Junker und Dünnhaupt, 1933.
56 p. 21 cm.

1. National socialism. 2. Hitler, Adolf, 1889–   I. Title.

DD253.L59   51–54595 ‡

NL 0452086   DLC IU NNC CU

Lohmann, Karl.
Kleine Reichsbürgerkunde. 3. erweiterte Aufl. Berlin-Lichterfelde, Langewort, 1938.
42 p. 21 cm.

1. Germany—Pol. & govt.   I. Title.

JN3954.L6 1938   51–46131
Library of Congress

NL 0452087   DLC

BR856
.M5

Lohmann, Karl, joint author.

Michael, Horst.
Der Reichspräsident ist Obrigkeit! Ein Mahnruf an die evangelische Kirche, von Horst Michael ₁und₁ Karl Lohmann. Hamburg, Hanseatische Verlagsanstalt ₁1932₁

QP519
L6
Biochem.
Library

Lohmann, Karl, 1898–
Anleitung zum physiologisch-chemischen Praktikum. Weinheim/Bergstr., Verlag Chemie, 1948.
202 p. illus.

1. Physiological chemistry - Laboratory manuals.

NL 0452089   CU

QP519
.L8

LOHMANN, KARL, 1898–
Anleitung zum physiologisch-chemischen Praktikum. Weinheim Bergstr., Verlag Chemie, 1949.
202 p. illus.

1. Physiological chemistry—Laboratory manuals.

NL 0452090   InU

Lohmann, Karl, 1898–
Die isolierung der aneurin-diphosphorsäure (co-carboxylase) aus bierhefe. Von K. Lohmann ...

(*In* Abderhalden, Emil, ed. Handbuch der biologischen arbeitsmethoden ... Berlin, 1920– 25ᶜᵐ. abt. v. Methoden zum studium der funktionen der einzelnen organe des tierischen organismus. t. 3a, 2. hälfte ₁hft. 9₁ (1938) p. ₁1713₁–1718)

1. ₁Cocarboxylase₁ 2. Yeast.   I. Title: Bierhefe.

A C 30–721
Ohio state univ. Library
for Library of Congress   [QH324.A3 1920 abt. 5, t. 3a]
                               ₁4₁   (574.072)

NL 0452091   OU DLC

VOLUME 338

Lohmann, Karl, 1898–
Über die monojodessigsäurevergiftung des
milchsäure bildenden ferments und der methyl-
glyoxalase.   [Berlin, 1933]
    p. [152]–156.
    Microfilm (negative)
    Extract from Biochemische zeitschrift, bd.
262, 1933.
    On film with Euler, Hans von. Über die
komponenten der dehydrasesysteme. [1935]
    1. Carbohydrates. 2. Enzymes.

NL   0452092   OrU

W 4   Lohmann, Karl, 1910–
F86   Die Bedeutung der Pulsberuhigungskurven
1939   für die Herzleistungsprüfung. «Freiburg
im Breisgau?» 1939.
    27 p. illus.

    Inaug.-Diss. - Freiburg im Breisgau.
    Bibliography: p. 25.

NL   0452093   DNLM

Lohmann, Karl Baptiste, 1887–
    Cities and towns of Illinois; a handbook of community
facts. Urbana, University of Illinois Press, 1951.
    viii, 110 p. illus., maps. 24 cm.
    Bibliography: p. 90–103.

    1. Cities and towns—Planning—Illinois.   I. Title.

        NA9125.I 3L6   711.09773   51–10077

NL   0452094   DLC GU PSt FU DAU WaS MB TxU NN ICU

NA9012   Lohmann, Karl Baptiste, 1887–
.L6   City planning and landscape architecture at the University
of Illinois, an historical record, 1868–1954. Urbana, Dept.
of City Planning and Landscape Architecture, College of
Fine and Applied Arts, 1954.
    14 l. 28 cm.
    Cover title.
    "Teaching staff publications": leaves 11–12.

    1. Illinois. University. College of Fine and Applied Arts. Dept. of
City Planning and Landscape Architecture.   I. Title.
                                                A 54–9365
    Illinois. Univ. Library
    for Library of Congress   [1]

NL   0452095   IU DLC

Lohmann, Karl Baptiste, 1887–
    ... A community-planning primer for Illinois, by Karl B.
Lohmann ... Urbana, Bureau of community planning, College of fine and applied arts, University of Illinois [1935]
    24 p. 23ᶜᵐ. (University of Illinois bulletin. vol. XXXII, no. 50)
    Bibliography: p. 24.

    1. Cities and towns—Planning. 2. Cities and towns—Illinois.
3. Cities and towns—Civic improvement.   I. Title.
                                                A 35–1528
    Title from Illinois Univ.   Printed by L. C.

NL   0452096   IU KMK ICRL OrCS MiU OU OO ViU ICJ OCU

719   Lohmann, Karl Baptiste, 1887–
L83d   The design of park cemeteries _ Rockford,
Ill., 1927.
    11p. illus.

    "Reprint from Parks & recreation _ January-
February, 1927."

    1. Cemeteries. I. Title.

NL   0452097   IU

711   Lohmann, Karl Baptiste, 1887–
L83d   The design of the larger municipal
park.   Rockford, Ill., 1925.
    23p. illus., plate.

    "Reprint from Parks & recreation ...
November-December, 1925."

NL   0452098   IU

Lohmann, Karl Baptiste, 1887–
    Landscape architecture in the modern world, by Karl B.
Lohmann ... Champaign, Ill., The Garrard press, 1941.
    5 p. l., 165 p. front., plates. 23½ᶜᵐ.
    "References" at end of each chapter.

    1. Landscape gardening.   I. Title.
                                                41–8472
    Library of Congress   SB472.L68
                        [2]   710

        MB GU MoU WaS NcRS OC1 OO OCU OU TU
NL   0452099   DLC IdU OrCS OrPR OrU Or CaBVaU NIC NcD

710.2   Lohmann, Karl Baptiste, 1887–
L83p   Planning for things needed in Champaign county.
By Karl B. Lohmann, chairman, Regional planning
commission. United meeting of citizens, committees and Planning board of Champaign county,
Court house, Urbana, September 28, 1936. [Ur-
bana, 1936]
    6 numb.l.
    Mimeographed.
    1. Regional planning. 2. Champaign co., Ill.
--Public works. I. Champaign co., Ill.--Regional
planning commission. II. Title.

NL   0452100   IU

Lohmann, Karl Baptiste, 1887–
    Planning opportunities for towns in Illinois, by Karl B.
Lohmann, M. L. A. Urbana, Ill., The University of Illinois,
1944.
    39, [1] p. illus. (incl. plans, diagrs.) 23ᶜᵐ. (On cover: University of
Illinois bulletin, v. 41, no. 40)

    1. Cities and towns—Planning. 2. Cities and towns—Illinois. 3. Cities
and towns—Civic improvement.   I. Title.
                                                A 44–2279
    Illinois. Univ. Library
    for Library of Congress   [2]

NL   0452101   IU KEmT FU ICRL

q710.1   Lohmann, Karl Baptiste, 1887–
L83pl   Planning to make hometown livable _   New York
city [1930]
    [8]p. illus.

    "Reprinted from the American city."

    1. City planning. I. Title.

NL   0452102   IU

Lohmann, Karl Baptiste, 1887–
    Principles of city planning, by Karl B. Lohmann ... 1st ed.
New York and London, McGraw-Hill book company, inc., 1931.
    x, 395 p. incl. front., illus., ports., plans, diagrs. 23½ᶜᵐ.
    "References" at end of each chapter.

    1. Cities and towns—Planning. 2. Cities and towns—Civic improve-
ment.   I. Title: City planning.
    Library of Congress   NA9080.L55   31–11820
    ——— Copy 2.
    Copyright A 37102   [a40q1]   710

        MiU ICJ OU KEmT CaBVaU OrU WaS IdU OrCS PCM
NL   0452103   DLC NIC OKentU CoU OrP NcD OC1W OC1

Lohmann, Karl Baptiste, 1887–
    A question guide for the study of regional planning, by Karl
B. Lohmann ... Champaign, Ill., Daniels press, 1940.
    6 p. l., 54 numb. l. 27ᶜᵐ.
    Photoprinted.
    "An abbreviated list of reference material": 4th–6th prelim. leaves.

    1. Regional planning.   I. Title.

    Library of Congress   GF51.L58   41–12396
    Copyright AA 335955   [3]   309.1

NL   0452104   DLC NIC CU MtBC DNAL OU

Lohmann, Karl Baptiste, 1887–
    Recreational possibilities [of] southern Illinois [by Karl
B. Lohmann and Norman G. Bittermann. Urbana, 1948]
    25 p. illus., maps. 23 cm. (Joint Committee on Southern Illinois.
Southern Illinois booklet no. 1)

    1. Illinois—Descr. & trav. 2. Regional planning—Illinois.   I. Bit-
termann, Norman George, joint author. II. Title.
                                                A 48–372
    Illinois. Univ. Libr.
    for Library of Congress   [1]

NL   0452105   IU

Lohmann, Karl Baptiste, 1887–
    Regional planning, by Karl B. Lohmann ... Ann Arbor,
Mich., Edwards brothers, inc., 1936.
    2 p. l., iii–v, 143 p. illus. (incl. maps) diagrs. 27 x 21½ᶜᵐ.
    "Lithoprinted."
    "References" at end of each chapter except chapters nineteen and
twenty.

    1. Regional planning.

    Library of Congress   GF51.L6   36–32071
    ——— Copy 2.
    Copyright AA 208141   [3]   711

        NN IU DNAL
NL   0452106   DLC NIC CU Or NcD MiU OU OC1 OCU ICJ MB

309.13   Lohmann, Karl Baptiste, 1887–
L83r   Regional planning ...   Ann Arbor, Mich., Edwards
1937   brothers, inc., 1937.
    143p. illus., maps, diagrs.

    Lithoprinted.
    "References" at end of most chapters.

    1. Regional planning.

NL   0452107   IU NcD

Lohmann, Karl Baptiste, 1887–   comp.
    A regional planning program for Champaign
County, Illinois
        see under Champaign County, Ill. Regional
planning commission.

Lohmann, Karl Baptiste, 1887–
    Urgent county-wide planning needs in Champaign
county
        see under Champaign co., Ill. Regional
planning commission.

Lohmann, Karl Ludwig, 1868–
    Das reichsgesetz vom jahre 1654 über die
steuerpflichtigkeit der landstände. ... Bonn,
C. Georgi, 1893.
    3 p. l., 95, [1] p.   25 cm.   [Bonn.
Universität. Dissertationen. v. 27, no. 8]
    Inaug.-Diss. - Bonn.
    Lebenslauf.
    1. Taxation. Germany-Hist.

NL   0452110   CU

VOLUME 338

Lohmann (Karl Matthias) [1890–]. *Ueber geschwulstartige Hypertrophie des Kiefer-köpfchens und ihre Folgen für den Biss und die Stellung des Unterkiefers. 27 pp. 8°. Tübingen, G. Schnürlen. 1919.

NL 0452111   DNLM

Lohmann, Kurt, 1902–
Die bedeutung der kartoffel brennerei im rahmen der kartoffelverwertung.   Bonn, Land. Hoch, 1929.
Inaug.-Diss. - Bonn.
Bibl.

NL 0452112   ICRL

Lohmann, Martin.
... Die bedeutung der deutschen ansiedlungen in Pennsylvanien, von Martin Lohmann ...   Stuttgart, Ausland und heimat verlags-aktiengesellschaft, 1923.
153, v p. fold. maps. 24½ᵐ. (Schriften des Deutschen ausland-instituts Stuttgart. A. Kulturhistorische reihe ... bd. 12)
"Schrifttum": v p. at end.

1. Germans in Pennsylvania.   I. Title.
Library of Congress   F160.G3L7   26–4813

NL 0452113   DLC CU MU IEN CoU ICU NN OCIC-M

Lohmann, Martin, 1901–
Betriebswirtschaftslehre, Wirtschaftslehre der gewerblichen Unternehmungen. Hamburg, Hanseatische Verlagsanstalt ₁1936₎
176 p. illus. 23 cm. (Grundzüge der Rechts- und Wirtschaftswissenschaft. Reihe B: Wirtschaftswissenschaft)

1. Industrial management. 2. Business.
HD35.L68 1936   658.01   52–54297 ‡

NL 0452114   DLC DGU

Lohmann, Martin, 1901–
Betriebswirtschaftslehre, wirtschaftslehre der gewerblichen unternehmungen, von dr. Martin Lohmann ...   2. erweiterte aufl. Hamburg, Hanseatische verlagsanstalt ₁1943₎
152 p. diagrs. 22½ᵐ. (Added t.-p.: Grundzüge der rechts- und wirtschaftswissenschaft. Reihe s: Wirtschaftswissenschaft, hrsg. von Jens Jessen und E. Wiskemann₎
Includes bibliographies.

1. Industry—Organization, control, etc. 2. Business.   I. Title.
HD35.L68 1943   658.01   A F 47–52
Princeton univ. Library
for Library of Congress   ₍4₎†

ScU NcU
NL 0452115   NjP CU IaU MH GAT WaU InU ICU TxU DLC

Lohmann, Martin, 1901–
Einführung in die Betriebswirtschaftslehre. Tübingen, Mohr, 1949.
202 p. diagrs. 23 cm.
Bibliography: p. 15–20.

1. Industrial management.
HD35.L685   50–34748

NL 0452116   DLC

Lohmann, Martin, 1901–
Einführung in die Betriebswirtschaftslehre.   2., neubearb. und verm. Aufl. Tübingen, Mohr, 1955.
vii, 292 p. diagrs. 24 cm.
Bibliography: p. 9–16.

1. Industrial management.
[HD35.L   ]   A 59–2420
New York Univ.   Libraries
for Library of Congress   ₍8₎

NL 0452117   NNU KU NNU-W

Lohmann, Martin, 1901–
Das rechnungswesen der kartell- und gruppen-wirtschaft, von dr. Martin Lohmann ...   Berlin, J. Springer, 1937.
viii, 143, ₍1₎ p. 24½ᵐ.

1. Corporations—Accounting.   I. Title.   38–39199
Library of Congress   HF5686.C7L63
    ₍2₎   657

NL 0452118   DLC CtY MH

Lohmann, Martin, 1901–
Wandlungen in den betriebs- und finanzierungsformen des deutschen aussenhandels, von professor dr. Martin Lohmann. Jena, G. Fischer, 1938.
iv, 120 p. 23ᵐ.
Bibliographical foot-notes.

1. Germany—Comm.   I. Title.   46–29934
Library of Congress   HF3566.L6
    ₍2₎   382

NL 0452119   DLC NIC IaU NcU NjP NN CtY

Lohmann, Martin, 1901–
Der wirtschaftsplan des betriebes und der unternehmung; die kaufmännische budgetrechnung ... Berlin ₍etc.₎ L.Weiss, 1928.
viii, 152 p. tables, charts.

"Literatur": p. ₍147₎–152.

NL 0452120   MH-BA IU

Lohmann, Martin, 1904–
Erfahrungen ueber die empyembehandlung im kindesalter durch einfache thoracotomie. 1930.

Inaug.- Diss. - Universität zu Berlin.

NL 0452121   OU CtY

Lohmann, Max, 1889–
Die kompensation bei retorsion gegen beleidigungen durch mitglieder deutscher parlamente ... Breslau, Schletter, 1913.
1 p. l., ₍v₎–ix, 60 p., 1 l. 22½ᵐ.
Inaug.-diss.—Bonn.
Lebenslauf.
Issued also as hft. 170 of Strafrechtliche abhandlungen.
"Literaturverzeichnis": p. vii–ix.

1. Libel and slander—Germany. 2. Liberty of speech—Germany. 3. Representative government and representation—Germany.   I. Title.
    ₍Full name: Max Karl Theodor Lohmann₎
        32–12345

NL 0452122   DLC

Lohmann, Max, 1889–
Die kompensation bei retorsion gegen beleidigungen durch mitglieder deutscher parlamente. Von dr. jur. Max Lohmann. Breslau, Schletter, 1913.
ix, 60 p. 23½ᵐ. (Added t.-p.: Strafrechtliche abhandlungen ... hft. 170)
Also issued as inaugural dissertation, Bonn, 1913.
"Literaturverzeichnis": p. ₍vii₎–ix.

1. Libel and slander. ₍1. Libel and slander—Germany; 2. Liberty of speech. ₍2. Freedom of speech—Germany; I. Title.
        29–30737

NL 0452123   DLC MH

Lohmann (Max Ferdinand) [1877–]. *Die Dauererfolge der Laparotomie bei tuberculöser Bauchfellentzündung. [Bonn.] 22 pp., 1 l. 8°. Godesberg, Gebr. Hessler, 1902.

NL 0452124   DNLM MBCo ICRL

Lohmann, Melvin Rudolph, 1914–
A concept of organization and management. ₍Stillwater? Okla.₎ 1954.
vii, 277 l. illus. 28 cm.
Thesis—University of Iowa.

1. Organization. 2. Industrial organization. 3. Management. 4. Industrial management.   I. Title.
HD31.L58   658.01   54–23369

NL 0452125   DLC IU

Lohmann, Melvin Rudolph, 1914–
A concept of organization and management.   Ann Arbor, University Microfilms ₍1954₎
₍University Microfilms, Ann Arbor, Mich.₎ Publication no. 7567)
Microfilm copy (positive) of typescript.
Collation of the original: vii, 277 l.
Thesis—State University of Iowa.
Abstracted in Dissertation abstracts, v. 14 (1954) no. 6, p. 958.

1. Organization. 2. Industrial organization. 3. Management. 4. Industrial management.   I. Title.
        Mic A 54–1403
Iowa. Univ. Library
for Library of Congress   ₍1₎

NL 0452126   IaU IU

Lohmann, O   comp. and arr.
Weihnachtliche Lieder für unsere Zeit.   Bilder von Gerd Jedermann. Berlin, Fehlguth-Verlag ₍19–₎
close score (23 p.)   col. illus.   19 x 20 cm.
For chorus (principally SSA)

1. Carols, German. 2. Choruses, Sacred (Women's voices, 3 pts.), Unaccompanied.   I. Title.
M2085.L6W4   M 53–472
        ₍1₎

NL 0452127   DLC

Lohmann, Otto, 1888– ₍ ₎ Der deutsch-griechische Auslieferungsvertrag vom 12. März 1907. Histor. u. system. Darstellung unter Berücks. d. Gesetzgebung beider Länder. Ein Beitr. z. deutschen Auslieferungsrecht.   Breslau: Schletter 1909.   xv, 65 S. 8°   ¶(Ersch. vollst. als: Strafrechtl. Abhandlungen. H. 108.)
Heidelberg, Jur. Diss. v. 19. Aug. 1909, Ref. v. Lilienthal
₍Geb. 9. März 88 Hanau; Wohnort: Steinau; Staatsangeh.: Preußen; Vorbildung: Gymn. Hanau Reife O. 06; Studium: Straßburg 3, Berlin 1, Marburg 2 S.; Rig. 25. Juni 09.₎   ₍U 10. 1929₎

NL 0452128   ICRL RPB

Lohmann, Otto, 1888–
Der deutsch-griechische auslieferungsvertrag vom 12. märz 1907. Historische und systematische darstellung unter berücksichtigung der gesetzgebung beider länder. Ein beitrag zum deutschen auslieferungsrecht. Von dr. jur. Otto Lohmann ... Breslau, Schletter, 1909.
xv, 194 p. 23½ᵐ. (Added t.-p.: Strafrechtliche abhandlungen ... hft. 108)
Issued in part as inaugural dissertation, Heidelberg, 1909.
"Literatur": p. ₍ix₎–xv.

1. Extradition. 2. Germany—For. rel.—Greece, Modern. 3. Greece, Modern—For. rel.—Germany.   I. Title.
        29–3697

NL 0452129   DLC

VOLUME 338

Lohmann, Otto Wilhelm Ferdinand, 1854–
Die auslassung des relativpronomens im englischen, mit besonderer beruecksichtigung der sprache Shakespeare's ... Von Otto Lohmann ... Halle a/S, Druck von E. Karras, 1879.
2 p. l., [3]–88 p., 1 l. 22½ᶜᵐ.
Inaug.-diss.—Erlangen.
Curriculum vitae.

1. English language—Pronoun. 2. Shakespeare, William—Language—Grammar.
45–50884
Library of Congress   PE1261.L6

NL 0452130   DLC MB MiU NcU

Lohmann, Paul, comp.
Das Lied im Unterricht; 61 Lieder für eine Singstimme mit Klavierbegleitung. Hohe Stimme. Mainz, B. Schott's Söhne [19—] Pl. no. B. S. S 36244.
94 p. 28 cm. (Edition Schott, 2907)

1. Songs (High voice) with piano. I. Title.
M1619.L84L5   M 55–109

NL 0452131   DLC IaU NN MB TxU NRU

784.81
L833t
Lohmann, Paul
Das lied im unterricht; 61 lieder fur eine singstimme mit klavierbegleitung [fur] mittlere oder tiefe stimme. Mainz, B. Schott, n.d.
94p. Q. (Pub. no.2908)
Pl.no. B.S.S 36245.

1.Songs, German. Collections.

NL 0452132   IaU

MT
840
L6
Lohmann, Paul.
Die sängerische Einstellung; vier Stimmbildungs-vorträge der Schule Martiensen-Lohmann. Mit einem Vorwort von Franziska Martienssen. Leipzig, C.F.Kahnt, c1929.
79 p.

1. Singing. I. Title.

NL 0452133   NSyU

Lohmann, Paul.
... Stimmfehler, stimmberatung; erkennen und behandlung der sängerfehler in frage und antwort. Mainz, B. Schott's söhne [1938]
125 p. 21ᶜᵐ.
"Edition Schott 3509."

1. Singing and voice culture. 2. Voice. I. Title.
39–34041
Library of Congress   MT820.L77S7
Copyright A—Foreign   41734
[2]   784.93

NL 0452134   DLC

---

ar W
52379
no.7
Lohmann, Paul, 1880–
Das bürgerliche und das kaufmännische Zurückbehaltungsrecht. Ein Vergleich. Borna-Leipzig, Buchdr. R. Noske, 1908.
viii, 55 p. 22cm.

Inaug.-Diss.—Erlangen.

NL 0452135   NIC NN ICRL

BS1515
.L83
1910
in:
OTS
Lohmann, Paul, 1886–1915.
Die anonymen Prophetien gegen Babel zus der Zeit des Exils. [Berlin, 1910]
91p. 24cm. (Studie zur Entwicklung des prophetischen Spottliedes)
Bibliography: p.[87]–89.
Inaug.-diss.—Rostock i.M.

1. Bible. O.T. Isaiah XIV, 4b–21. 2. Bible. O.T. Isaiah XLVII, 1–15. I. Title.

NL 0452136   IEG MH DCU-H CtY-D ICRL MiU OCH

Lohmann, Paul, 1886–1915, comp.
Palästinajahrbuch des Deutschen evangelischen instituts für altertumswissenschaft des Heiligen Landes zu Jerusalem ...
Berlin, E. S. Mittler & sohn, 19

WAA
L833L
1894
cl.1894,
LOHMANN, Paul, ed.
Lebensmittelpolizei; ein Handbuch für die Prüfung und Beurteilung der menschlichen Nahrungs- und Genussmittel im Sinne des Gesetzes vom 14. Mai 1879, erläutert durch die vorausgegangene Rechtsprechung. Für Chemiker, Ärzte, Juristen, Apotheker und alle Gewerbetreibende der Nahrungsmittelbranche. Leipzig, Günther, 1894.
382 p.

NL 0452138   DNLM ICRL CtY

Lohmann, Peter, 1833–1907.
An dramatische tonsetzer. Von Peter Lohmann. Leipzig, H. Matthes, 1876.
18 p. 18ᵐᵐ.

1. Opera. 2. Composition (Music)
13–33643
Library of Congress   ML2110.L82

NL 0452139   DLC

Lohmann, Peter, 1833–1907.
Appius Claudius. Trauerspiel in 5 Aufzügen. Leipzig, Hermann Luppe, 1858.
64p.

Microcard edition.

NL 0452140   ICRL

Lohmann, Peter, 1833–1907.
Dramatische Werke. Bd. 1–4. Leipzig, J.J. Weber, 1875.
4 v. in 2. 16°.
2. ed.
v.1. Masaniello. Essex. Savonarola. v. 2. v.2. Der Schmied in Ruhla. Die letzten Mauren. Appius Claudius. v.3. Strafford, Karl Stuarts 1. Ende. Wider den Stachel. Gegen den Storm.

NL 0452141   NN OCl OClW

Lohmann, Peter, 1833–1907.
Das Ideal der Oper. Leipzig, von Heinrich Matthes, 1886.

NL 0452142   MA

Lohmann, Peter, 1833–1907.
Ingeborg; oper in 3 Aufzügen...
    see under Geisler, Paul, 1856–1919.

LOHMANN, Peter. 1833–
Offa, König der Angelsachsen. Trauerspiel in 5 Acten. Hannover. Helwing. 1856. 90 pp. [Dramatische Schriften Theil 1.] 8°.

NL 0452144   MB

PT
1155
L83
1876
Lohmann, Peter, 1833–1907, ed.
Pantheon deutscher Dichter. 8. sehr verm. Aufl., 2. Abdruck. Leipzig, H. Matthes, 1876.
400 p. illus. 17cm.

1. German poetry (Collections) I. Title.

NL 0452145   NIC

Lohmann, Peter, 1833–1907.
Der Schmied in Ruhla. Schauspiel in 4 Aufzügen. Leipzig, Hermann Luppe, 1858.
87p.

Microcard edition.

NL 0452146   ICRL

Lohmann, Peter, 1833–1907.
Ueber die dramatische dichtung mit musik. Von Peter Lohmann. Leipzig, H. Luppe, 1861.
39, [1] p. 17½ᶜᵐ.

1. Opera.
13–33642
Library of Congress   ML2110.L8

NL 0452147   DLC

782.09
L833u.2
Lohmann, Peter, 1833–1907.
Ueber die dramatische Dichtung mit Musik. 2. Aufl. Leipzig, H. Mattes, 1864.
60p. 18cm.

1. Opera.

NL 0452148   IEN InU

Lohmann, Peter, 1833–1907.
Ueber Robert Schumann's Faustmusik. Von Peter Lohmann. Leipzig, C. F. Kahnt [1860]
32 p. 19½ᶜᵐ.

1. Schumann, Robert Alexander, 1810–1856. Scenen aus Göthe's Faust.
9–7864
Library of Congress   ML410.S4L63

NL 0452149   DLC ICN MH CtY

J360
.H19
Lohmann, Peter David, ed.

Hamburg. *Rat.*
Hamburgische Rath- und Bürgerschlüsse. 1801/15–1859. Hamburg.

VOLUME 338

Lohmann, Philipp H *ed.*
Wall Street explains its operations to a visiting university class; a collection of thirty-one lectures by executives in the investment business. Edited by Philipp H. Lohman and Franc M. Ricciardi. New York, Distributor: New York Institute of Finance ₁1951₎
vi, 274, ₁1₎ p. 21 cm.
Bibliography : p. ₁275₎

1. New York. Stock Exchange. I. Ricciardi, Franc M., joint ed. II. Title.
HG4572.L6   332.61   51-1011

NL 0452151   DLC CoU MB

Lohmann, R
Lutherische und unierte kirche; ein wort der warnung an die glieder unsrer lutherischen kirche, die ihr beruf in gebiet der pretan schen union fuehrt. ... Berlin, Schultze, 1867.
24p.   O.

Bound with LUehrs, Albrecht. Die union Alt-P Prossen...1868.

NL 0452152   OO

Lohmann, Richard 1881–
...Bootskonstruktion; Bootsbau, Bootstypen; eine Einführung in das Wesen von Segelboot und Segeljacht und eine Anleitung zum Verständnis der Konstruktion, zum Dr. Richard Lohmann... Berlin: R. C. Schmidt & Co., 1925. 111 p. incl. diagrs. illus. 3. ed., rev. 8°. (Segelsport-Bücherei. Bd. 4.)

208320A. 1. Sail-boats. 2. Yacht   building. 3. Ser.
N.Y.P.L.   November 6, 1925

NL 0452153   NN

₁Lohmann, Richard₎ 1881–
... Fliegen und funken. Berlin, J. H. W. Dietz nachfolger ₁1924₎
4 p. l., 11–122, ₁1₎ p., 1 l. incl. illus., plates. 21ᶜᵐ.
Title in blue and yellow.
Author's pseudonym, Ernst Krafft, at head of title.

1. Inventions. 2. Flying-machines. 3. Telegraph, Wireless. 4. Ships.
I. Title.   25-23110
Library of Congress   T19.L6

NL 0452154   DLC

₁Lohmann, Richard₎ 1881–
... 100 jahre eisenbahnunfall. Berlin, J. H. W. Dietz nachfolger, 1925.
61, ₁1₎ p., 1 l. incl. front., illus., diagrs. 21ᶜᵐ.
Author's pseud., Ernst Krafft, at head of title.

1. Railroads—Accidents. I. Title.
Library of Congress   HE1779.L6   26-5488
                                       29171

NL 0452155   DLC

Lohmann, Richard, 1881–
... Hilde Lichtwark; tage einer entwurzelten jugend. Berlin, J. H. W. Dietz nachfolger, 1924.
109 p., 1 l. incl. pl. 19½ x 11½ᶜᵐ.

I. Title.
Library of Congress   PT2623.O45H5 1924   25-16477

NL 0452156   DLC

Lohmann, Richard, 1881–
Ihr aber lebt —; ein spiel aus traum und wirklichkeit in drei akten von Richard Lohmann. Berlin, J. H. W. Dietz, 1924.
112 p. 19½ᶜᵐ.

I. Title.

Library of Congress   PT2623.O45I4 1924   25-605

NL 0452157   DLC

Lohmann, Richard, 1881–
Nova studia Euripidea. n.p. Karras 1904.
32 p.
Halle univ. Ph.D. diss. n.d.
Full name: Gustav Wilhelm Richard Lohmann.

NL 0452158   PU NjP

Lohmann, Richard, 1881–
... Nova studia Euripidea.
(*In* Halle. Universität. Dissertationes philologicae halenses ... Halis Saxonum, 1905. 22½ᶜᵐ. vol. xv. 2 l., p. ₁305₎–466)
At head of title: Richardus Lohmann.
Issued also, in part, as the author's thesis, Halle, 1904.

1. Euripides.
                                       A C 37-1940
Yale univ. Library
for Library of Congress   ₁2₎

NL 0452159   CtY MdBJ NIC PU

Lohmann, Richard, 1881–
...Die Segeljolle; ein Wegweiser und Ratgeber bei der Anschaffung von Schwertbooten, bearbeitet von Dr. Richard Lohmann und Robert Mewes... Berlin: R. C. Schmidt & Co., 1925. viii, 224 p. incl. diagrs., tables. illus. (incl. plans.) 5. ed., rev. 8°. (Segelsport-Bücherei. Bd. 2.)

210024A. 1. Yacht building, 1925.   2. Mewes, Robert, jt. au. 3. Ser.
N.Y.P.L.   November 14, 1925

NL 0452160   NN

Lohmann, Richard
Sozialdemokratie und Schule; eine Kursusdisposition. Berlin, Zentralbildungsausschuss der Sozialdemokratischen Partei Deutschlands, 1921.

12 p. ([Reichsausschuss für sozialistische Bildungsarbeit] Kursusdisposition, 10)

NL 0452161   MH

Lohmann, Richard, 1881–
Vom Kampfrekord zum Massensport, Umrisse einer Geschichte des Sports ₁von₎ Ernst Krafft ₁pseud.₎ Berlin, I. H. W. Dietz Nachfolger, 1925.
63 p. illus. 21 cm.

1. Sports—Hist.   I. Title.

GV571.L6   53-55091 ‡

NL 0452162   DLC

Lohmann, Richard,   · 1881–
...Wie sagt der Segler? Vollständiges Taschenwörterbuch der Sportseglersprache mit sachlichen Erläuterungen und wortgeschichtlichen Gedächtnishilfen, von Dr. Richard Lohmann. ₁Berlin:₎ R. C. Schmidt & Co., 1925. 112 p. incl. diagrs. pl. 16°. (Motorschiff- und Jachtbibliothek. Bd. 13.)
p. 109–112, advertising matter.

207582A. 1. Seamen—Language of   —Germany. 2. Ships, Sailing. 3. Ser.
N.Y.P.L.   October 31, 1925

NL 0452163   NN AU

Lohmann, Robert, 1902–
Die Handelsfrage im Rheinisch-Westfälischen Kohlensyndikat von der Gründung bis zur Gegenwart... von Diplomvolkswirt Robert Lohmann... Bochum: F. W. Fretlöh, 1930. v, 131 p. 8°.

Dissertation, Erlangen, 1930.
Lebenslauf, p. 131.
Bibliography, p. 127–130.

1. Coal—Trade and stat.—Germany.   2. Trusts—Germany.
N.Y.P.L.   July 24, 1931

NL 0452164   NN PU MH MiU

QZ   **LOHMANN, Ruth,** 1904–
150   Biologie der Entzündung. Würzburg,
L833b   Stürtz, 1938.
1938   p. ₁316₎–346. illus.
        Habilitationsschrift - Berlin.
        Reprinted from Zeitschrift für klinische Medizin, 135. Bd., 3. Heft.
        1. Inflammation

NL 0452165   DNLM CtY

Lohmann, Ruth Margaret, 1913–
see
Smith, Mrs. Ruth Margaret (Lohmann) 1913–

338.94 **Lohmann, Th**
L832f   Die fabrik-gesetzgebungen der staaten des europäischen kontinents. Berlin, 1878.
171p.

NL 0452167   IU NN

Pamph.   **LOHMANN, Th   Klemens C**   d.1777.
v.596   Anmerkungen ueber das Bibellesen und die Ursachen warum es versaeumet oder ohne grossen Nutzen angestellet wird. Nebst einer kurzen Anleitung zum rechten Gebrauche derselben, von J.C.C. Lohmann. Wesel, bey Franz. I. Roeder, 1770.
        110p. 15.5cm.

NL 0452168   MH-AH

Lohmann, Theodor,
Der intensitätsverlauf der k-strahlung verschiedener elemente in abhängigkeit von der röhrenspannung... Dresden, 1932.
·Inaug. Diss. Techn. Hochsch. Dresden, 1932.

NL 0452169   ICRL

Lohmann, Volker, 1911–
Der einfluss der hochgespannten hochfrequenzstrome auf die leukocytenverschiebungen im peripher blut ... Hamburg, 1935.

Hamburg
diss.
1935

₁Full name: Volker Oswald Bernhard Lohmann₎

NL 0452170   MiU CtY

Lohmann, W.
Die gründung von Heilstatten... 1880
see Lohmann, Heinrich Wilhelm.

VOLUME 338

Lohmann, Walter, 1889–
    Die besonderen direkten Gemeindesteuern in Preußen. Jena: Fischer 1913. IV, 32 S. 8° ¶ Vollst. als: Abhandlungen d. Staatswiss. Sem. zu Jena. Bd 12, H. 3. Jena, Phil. Diss. v. 3. Juni 1913, Ref. Pierstorff.
    [Geb. 10. Juli 89 Hünze; Wohnort: Hünze; Staatszangeh.: Preußen; Vorbildung: G. Wesel bis 05, Minist.-Dispens v. 5. Dez. 12; Studium: Berlin TeH. 1, U. 1, Jena 5 S.; Rig. 14. Dez. 12.]   [U 13. 3827]

NL 0452172   ICRL PBm PPAmP PU

Lohmann, Walter, 1889–
    Die besonderen direkten gemeindesteuern in Preussen, von dr. Walter Lohmann. Jena, G. Fischer, 1913.
    vi p., 1 l., 185, [1] p. 24ᶜᵐ. (Added t.-p.: Abhandlungen des Staatswissenschaftlichen seminars zu Jena ... 12. bd. 3. hft.)
    Appeared in part as the author's inaugural dissertation, Jena, 1913 (32 p.)
    "Literaturverzeichnis": p. [186]
    1. Taxation—Prussia. 2. Municipal finance—Prussia.
                                   15-7235
Library of Congress   HJ9483.L6

NL 0452173   DLC CU ICJ NN MB MH

Lohmann, Walter, 1890–
    ...Über einen fall von hypophysistumor... Kiel, Schmidt & Klaunig, 1917.
    17 [1] p., 1 l.
    Inaug.-diss. – Kgl. Christian-Albrechts-Universität zu Kiel.
    Lebenslauf.
    "Literatur": at end of thesis.

NL 0452174   MiD-W ICRL CtY DNLM

Lohmann, Walter, 1891–1955.
    Denkwuerdige Tage aus der deutschen Marine-, Kolonial- und Seekriegsgeschichte; ein Traditionskalender für die Reichsmarine, von Kapitänleutnant Walter Lohmann. Berlin: Verlag Offene Worte, 1928. 278 p. incl. tables. illus. (incl. ports.) 12°.
    Bibliography, p. [7–9]
    377320A. 1. Naval history and statistics—Germany. 2. European war, 1914-1918—Naval history and operations. N. Y. P. L.   October 26, 1928.

NL 0452175   NN

VA513   Lohmann, Walter, 1891–1955
.D4
    Die deutschen Kriegsschiffe; Namen und Schicksale, mit einer Einführung von Konteradmiral Walter Lohmann. Potsdam, Rütten & Loening, 1941.

Lohmann, Walter, 1891–1955, ed.
    Grundlagen deutscher seegeltung, im auftrage des Deutschen seegeltungswerkes, herausgegeben von vizeadmiral W. Lohmann, professor dr. F. Dannmeyer [und] dr. G. Lauritzen. Bildwerk: Alfred Ehrhardt. Berlin, Verlag Wehrfront, A. Becker [1942]
    4 p. l., 558 p. illus. (incl. maps) 16 pl. on 8 l., diagrs. 23½ᶜᵐ.
    "Zeitschriftenverzeichnis": p. 553–555.
    1. Merchant marine—Germany. 2. Ship-building—Germany. 3. Ocean. I. Dannmeyer, Ferdinand Diedrich Hermann, 1880–   joint ed. II. Lauritzen, Georg, joint ed.
                       45-32240
Library of Congress   VK73.L6
           [2]   387.5

NL 0452177   DLC MiU ICU OU WaU RPB MH NjP

Lohmann, Walter, 1891-1955, ed.
    Grundlagen deutscher Seegeltung, im Auftrage des Deutschen Seegeltungswerkes, hrsg. von W. Lohmann, F. Dannmeyer [und] G. Lauritzen. Bildwerk: Alfred Ehrhardt. Berlin, A. Becker [1942]
    549 p. illus., plates, maps. 23 cm.
    1. Merchant marine—Germany. 2. Ship-building—Germany. 3. Ocean.
        VK73.L6 1942a   387.5   50-43023

NL 0452178   DLC

Lohmann, Walter, 1891-1955
    ... Kameraden auf see, zwischen minen und torpedos. Berlin, K. Curtius [1943]
    2 p. l., 9–220 p., 1 l. plates. 18½ᶜᵐ.
    1. World war, 1939-1945—Naval operations, German. 2. Mines, Submarine. 3. World war, 1939-1945—Personal narratives, German. I. Title.
    D771.L6   A F 47-4746
    Hoover library, Stanford   univ. for Library of Congress   [2]†

NL 0452179   CSt-H CoU OU MH NN MoU ICU DLC

Lohmann, Walter, 1891-1955.
    Die Offizierslaufbahnen in der Reichsmarine, zugleich ein Ratgeber bei der Berufswahl, von Kapitänleutnant Lohmann. Kiel: W. G. Mühlau, 1922. 23 p. incl. tables. 8°.
    1. Navy (German). 2. Officers   (Military and naval), Germany. N. Y. P. L.   September 4, 1923.

NL 0452180   NN

LOHMANN, WALTER, 1891-1955.
    Die Offizierslaufbahnen in der Reichsmarine; ein Ratgeber bei der Berufswahl. 5 völlig neu bearb. Aufl. Kiel, W. G. Mühlau, 1934. 48 p. 22cm.
    1. Navy, German. 2. Officers, Military and naval—Germany.

NL 0452181   NN

Lohmann, Walter, 1902–
    Ueber substituierte benzoyl-diphenyl-methyl-radikale... Berlin, 1932. 11 p.
    Inaug. Diss. (Auszug)Techn.Hochsch. Berlin, 1932.
    Lebenslauf.

NL 0452182   ICRL

Lohmann, Walter, 1909–
    Der innere vorbehalt gegen wesensbestandteile der ehe nach katholischem kirchenrecht. ... 1935. 66 p.
    Inaug. Diss. – Münster i. W., 1935.
    Lebenslauf.
    Literaturverzeichnis.

NL 0452183   ICRL CtY

LOHMANN, Walter, 1911–
    Neue Versuche zur Verbesserung der Tiefendosistabellen in der Röntgen-Therapie. Würzburg, K.Triltsch, 1938.
    21 cm.
    Inaugural-Dissertation - Bonn.
    "Lebenslauf" at end.

NL 0452184   MH ICRL

Lohmann, W[alter Ferdinand]
    Das arbeitslohn-gesetz. Mit besonderer berücksichtigung der lehren von Ricardo, Marx und H. George. Göttingen, E. A. Huth, 1897.
    2 p. l., 52 p. 8°.
    Inaug.-diss.—Heidelberg.
                                1-G-2800

NL 0452185   DLC

Lohmann, Walter Ferdinand.   331.2 P704
    Das Arbeitslohn-Gesetz. Mit besonderer Berücksichtigung der Lehren von Ricardo, Marx und H. George. Von Dr. W. Lohmann, ... Göttingen, Vandenhoeck und Ruprecht, 1897.
    [2], 93, [1] p. 23½ᶜᵐ.
    "Litteratur," p. 93.

NL 0452186   ICJ CtY CtY-L

Lohmann, Walter Georg.
    Die deutsche kriegsmarine.
    Das deutsche wehrwesen in vergangenheit und gegenwart, von Otto Bleck ... W. Müller-Loebnitz ... Ernst Kabisch ... [u. a.] Stuttgart-Berlin, Konradin-verlag [1936]

Lohmann, Walther
    Harmonische analyse zum selbstunterricht fuer studierende, techniker sowie fuer nichtmatiker. Leicht verstandliche gebrauchsanweisung nach dem hermann'schen ... Berlin, Fischer, ...1921. 32 p.
    "Sonderdruck aus dem Internationalen zentralblatt fur experimentelle phonetik 1921, 31. jahrg. 4. hft."

NL 0452187   OU

Lohmann, Walther, 1911–
    Neue Versuche zur Verbesserung der Tiefendosistabellen in der Röntgen-Therapie... Würzburg, 1938.
    Inaug.-Diss. - Bonn.
    Lebenslauf.
    "Schrifttum": p.25–26.

NL 0452188   CtY

Lohmann, Werner, 1911–   (Dr.med., Berlin)
    ... Die Gelatine als Nahrungs- und Heilmittel ... Berlin [1937]
    Inaug.-Diss. - Berlin.
    Lebenslauf.
    "Literaturangabe": p. 25–28.

NL 0452189   CtY

Lohmann, Werner, 1911–   (Dr.phil., Leipzig)
    Die verteilung des lichtes in den kugelförmigen sternhaufen M 5, M 15 und M 92. ... Berlin, 1936. 39 p.
    Inaug. Diss. - Leipzig, 1936.
    Lebenslauf.

NL 0452190   ICRL CtY

VOLUME 338

Lohmann, Wilhelm, *ed.*
Der aufbau des dritten reiches; taten, reden, gesetze seit dem 30. januar 1933, zusammengestellt von Wilhelm Lohmann. Leipzig, Armanenverlag, 1934.

2 p. l., 84 p. 22½ᶜᵐ.

1. Germany—Politics and government, 1933– 2. Nationalsozialistische deutsche arbeiter-partei. I. Germany. Laws, statutes, etc., 1925–1934 (Hindenburg) II. Title.

A C 36–875

Hoover War Libr.   DD253.L833 Printed by L. C.
                                                          [3]

NL 0452191   CSt-H CU IaU NN CtY MH MiU

Lohmann, Wilhelm, engineer.
    see   Lohmann, Wilhelm, 1900–

PA
6485
.L6
Lohmann, Wilhelm, 1858–
Quaestionum Lucretianarum capita duo. Brunsvigae, typis M. Bruhnii, 1882.
60 p.

Thesis, Berlin.
Includes bibliographical references.

NL 0452193   NNC CtY PBm PU OCU NcD CU-M MH

Lohmann, Wilhelm, 1878–
Disturbances of the visual functions. Translated by Angus MacNab. London, J. Bale, 1913.

185 p. illus. 26 cm.

Includes bibliographies.

1. Eye - Diseases. 2. Visions. I. Title.

NL 0452194   CaBVaU RPB

Lohmann, Wilhelm, *1878–*   L617.75 R200
Disturbances of the visual functions. By Prof. W. Lohmann, ... Translated by Angus Macnab, ... With 39 illustrations in the text, some in colours. Philadelphia, P. Blakiston's Son & Co., 1914.
[8], 185 p. 39 illus. (incl. diagr.) 25½ᶜᵐ.
Bibliographical foot-notes.

NL 0452195   ICJ ICRL ICU DNLM

Lohmann, Wilhelm, *1878–*
Die störungen der sehfunktionen, von dr. med. W. Lohmann ... Mit 39 zum teil mehrfarbigen abbildungen im text. Leipzig, F. C. W. Vogel, 1912.
vii, 206 p. illus. (partly col.) 28ᶜᵐ. M. 10
Bibliographical foot-notes.

1. Eye—Diseases and defects.

Library of Congress   RE925.L7
                                                      12–17639

NL 0452196   DLC DNLM ICJ

Lohmann, Wilhelm, 1884–
Die Reservefonds der Aktiengesellschaften, insbesondere ihre bilanzrechtliche Behandlung ... von Wilhelm Lohmann ... Borna-Leipzig, R. Noske, 1910.

viii, 77 p., 1 l. incl. tables. 22½cm.

Inaug.-Diss. - Heidelberg.
"Lebenslauf": leaf at end.
"Literaturverzeichnis und Abkürzungen": p.[vii]–viii.

NL 0452197   MH-L MH ICRL

Lohmann, Wilhelm, 1886–
Über das Cheirolinglykosid und über Aminodimethylthioäther ... von Wilhelm Lohmann ... Weida i. Th.: Thomas & Hubert, 1912. 54 p. incl. diagr., tables. 8°.

Dissertation, Jena, 1912.

1. Cheirolin glucoside. 2. Amino-   dimethylthioether.
N. Y. P. L.   June 27, 1922.

NL 0452198   NN ICRL CtY PU MH

Lohmann, Wilhelm, 1900–
Beitrag zum schweissen von hochbaustählen unter besonderer berücksichtigung verschiedener elektroden. ... Dortmund, 1933.   32 p.
Inaug. Diss. -Techn. Hochsch. Braunschweig, 1933.
Lebenslauf.

NL 0452199   ICRL

Lohmann, Wilhelm, 1900–   joint author.
Zeyen, Karl Ludwig.
Schweissen der eisenwerkstoffe, von dr.-ing. Karl Ludwig Zeyen und dr.-ing. Wilhelm Lohmann, mit 359 abbildungen und 51 zahlentafeln. Düsseldorf, Verlag Stahleisen m. b. h., 1943.

Lohmann Villena, Guillermo.
Los americanos en las órdenes nobiliarias (1529–1900) Madrid, Consejo Superior de Investigaciones Científicas, Instituto "Gonzalo Fernández de Oviedo," 1947.

2 v. illus. (part col.) 26 cm.

CONTENTS.—1. Santiago.—2. Calatrava. Alcantara. Montesa. Carlos III. Malta.

1. Spanish America—Nobility. 2. Spanish America—Geneal. 3. Orders of knighthood and chivalry—Spain. I. Title.

CS95.L6   929.79998   48–26592*

CaOTP OrU ICU OU RPJCB
NL 0452202   DLC NBuU FU WU OrU CU-S NcD NcU MB PU MH

Lohmann Villena, Guillermo.
... Apuntaciones sobre el arte dramático en Lima durante el virreinato. Lima, Editorial Lumen, s. a., 1941.
32 p. 24½ᶜᵐ.
"Refundición de una conferencia pronunciada en la institución artística 'Insula'."

1. Theater—Lima.   I. Title.

Library of Congress   PN2532.L5L6   42–51043
                                                                          [3]   792

NL 0452203   DLC IU

Lohmann Villena, Guillermo.
... El arte dramático en Lima durante el virreinato. Madrid [Estades, artes gráficas] 1945.
xviii p., 2 l., [3]–647, [1] p. 22ᶜᵐ. (Half-title: Publicaciones de la Escuela de estudios hispanoamericanos de la Universidad de Sevilla. XII [n.° general] serie 2.ª: Monografías, n.° 3)
"Primera edición."
Bibliographical foot-notes.

1. Theater—Lima.   I. Title.

A 45–4890

Iowa. Univ. Library
for Library of Congress   [2]

TxU PBm OU DLC NcU PLF OU DLC AU MU NBuU MB GU
NL 0452204   IaU LU PSt CU-S MoSU NcD OCU ViU ICU

20
73–243
Lohmann Villena, Guillermo
Un cedulario peruano inédito. Madrid, 1946. 28p. 25cm.
"Tirada aparte de la Revista de Indias, núm. 26 (Octbre.-Dicbre, 1946)."
"Indice de los documentos legislativos [en] un abultado códice en la Sección Manuscritos de la Biblioteca Nacional de París." cf. p.[5]

1. Peru - History - Conquest, 1522–1548 - Sources. I. Title.

NL 0452205   PSt

Z
104
L6
Lohmann Villena, Guillermo.
Cifras y claves indianas; capítulos provisionales de un estudio sobre criptografía insiana. Sevilla, 1954.
96 p. facsims. 24 cm.

"Separata del Tomo XI del Anuario de estudios americanos."
Also paged: 285–380.

1. Cryptography. 2. Ciphers. I. Title.

NL 0452206   CU-S

Lohmann Villena, Guillermo.
El conde de Lemos, virrey del Perú. [1. ed.] Madrid, 1946.

xiv, 472 p. plates, ports., fold. map. 22 cm. (Publicaciones de la Escuela de Estudios Hispano-Americanos de la Universidad de Sevilla, 23 (no. general) Ser. 2: Monografías, no. 8)

1. Lemos, Pedro Antonio Fernández de Castro Andrade y Portugal, conde de, 1632–1672. 2. Peru—Hist.—1548–1820. (Series: Sevilla. Universidad. Escuela de Estudios Hispano-Americanos. Publicaciones, 23. Series: Sevilla. Universidad. Escuela de Estudios Hispano-Americanos. Publicaciones. Ser. 2: Monografías, no. 8)

F3444.L5L6   923.285   48–14054 rev*

CtY TxU TNJ CSt FU ICU KU MU DAU CaBVaU
NL 0452207   DLC IaU NcD PU NcU CU OU NNC MnU InU

Lohmann Villena, Guillermo, joint comp.
    ... Los cronistas de convento, selección de...
    see under   Benvenutto Murrieta, Pedro M comp.

F3444
.V55
L6
Lohmann Villena, Guillermo
Don Diego de Villegas y Quevedo, individuo de la Real Academia Española (1696–1751) Madrid, 1944.
50p. 24cm.
"Publicado en Revista de Indias, núm. 15, 1944, págs. 41–88."
P.S.U. copy imperfect: p.1–10 repeated after p.10.

1. Villegas Quevedo y Saavedra, Diego de.

NL 0452209   PSt

F1410
.L572
Lohmann Villena, Guillermo, ed.

León Pinelo, Antonio Rodríguez de, *d. 1660.*
El gran canciller de las Indias. Estudio preliminar, ed. y notas de Guillermo Lohmann Villena. [1. ed.] Sevilla, Consejo Superior de Investigaciones Científicas, 1953.

Lohmann Villena, Guillermo.
... Historia del arte dramático en Lima durante el virreinato ... Lima, Perú, Imprenta americana [1941–
v. 21½ᶜᵐ. (Half-title: Biblioteca histórica peruana, t. III
At head of title: Universidad católica del Perú. Instituto de investigaciones históricas.
"Notas" (chiefly bibliographical) at end of each chapter.
CONTENTS.—I. Siglos XVI y XVII.

1. Theater—Lima. I. Lima. Universidad católica del Perú. Instituto de investigaciones históricas. II. Title.

A 43–1153

Harvard univ. Library
for Library of Congress   [3]

OU TU NcD PU WaU
NL 0452211   MH OrU PSt CaBVaU OrU FU ViU NcU OO

VOLUME 338

Lohmann Villena, Guillermo.
El limeño don Juan de Valencia el del Infante; preceptista taurino y espía mayor de Castilla. Madrid, Instituto Gonzalo Fernández de Oviedo, Consejo Superior de Investigaciones Científicas, 1952.

74 p. 24 cm.

"Trabajo publicado en Miscelánea americanista, t. 3."

1. Valencia el del Infante, Juan de, 1605–1663.

DP185.9.V3L6   59–26877 ‡

NL 0452212   DLC NSyU NcD TxU CLU MiU InU CU NIC NN

Lohmann Villena, Guillermo, ed.

F3444
.P5

Pezuela y Sánchez Muñoz de Velasco, Joaquín de la, *Viceroy of Peru,* 1761–1830.
Memoria de gobierno, ed. y prólogo de Vicente Rodríguez Casado y Guillermo Lohmann Villena. ¡1. ed.¡ Sevilla, 1947.

Lohmann Villena, Guillermo.
Las minas de Huancavelica en los siglos XVI y XVII. ¡1. ed.¡ Sevilla, 1949.

xiv, 465 p. illus., port. 23 cm. (Publicaciones de la Escuela de Estudios Hispano-Americanos de Sevilla, 50 ¡no. general¡ Serie 2, no. 14)

1. Mercury mines and mining—Peru—Huancavelica (City) I. Title. (Series: Seville. Universidad. Escuela de Estudios Hispano-Americanos. Publicaciones, 50. Series: Seville. Universidad. Escuela de Estudios Hispano-Americanos. Publicaciones. Serie 2: Monografías, no. 14)

TN790.L6   50–34769

    ICU PPiU CSt MdBJ IaU NcD FMU CaBVaU
NL 0452214   DLC NBuU NcU ScU MU NNC ICN CtY NjP TxU

F3444
L62

Lohmann Villena, Guillermo
Un opusculo desconocido de Solorzano Pereira sobre la mita.   Sevilla, 1950.
277p. 24cm.

Bibliographical footnotes.
"Separata del tomo VII del Anuario de estudios americanos."

1. Indians, Treatment of - Latin America. 2. Indians of South America - Peru. 3. Spain - Colonies - America. I. Solórzano Pereira, Juan de, 1575–1655. II. Title.

NL 0452215   IaU

LOHMANN VILLENA, GUILLERMO
Pablo de Olavide   (IN: Biblioteca Hombres del Perú. Lima. 20cm. ser. 2, v.15 p.[49]-104 port.)

1. Olavide y Jáuregui, Pablo   Antonio José, 1725–1803.

NL 0452216   NN

LOHMANN VILLENA, GUILLERMO.
Pedro de Peralta.   (IN: Biblioteca Hombres del Perú. Lima. 20cm. ser. 2, v.15   p.[3]-47 port.)

1. Peralta Barnuevo Rocha y   Benavides, Pedro de, 1663–
1743.

NL 0452217   NN

PQ8497
V34Z73

Lohmann Villena, Guillermo
Un poeta virreinal del Peru: Juan del Valle Caviedes.   Madrid, 1948.
28p. 24cm.

Bibliographical footnotes.
"Tirada aparte de la Revista de Indias, no.33-34, Julio-Dicbre., 1948."

1. Valle y Caviedes, Juan del, 1652–1692.

NL 0452218   IaU

PQ 8380
.L 8

LOHMANN VILLENA, GUILLERMO.
Romances, coplas y cantares en la conquista del Perú. n.p., n.pub., n.d.
40 p.
Caption title.
Label mounted on fly leaf: "Separata Revista Mar del Sur. Volumen III, no.9, Lima-Peru, 1950."

1. Peruvian poetry—Hist. & crit. 2. Peru—History—Conquest,1522–1548—Poetry. I. Title.

NL 0452219   InU

Lohmanns, Karl, 1892–
Die Selbsthilfe des Besitzers im Vergleich zur allgemeinen Selbsthilfe ... von Karl Lohmanns ... Crefeld, H. Lambertz, 1914.

55 p. 23cm.

Inaug.-Diss. - Freiburg i. B.
"Literatur-Verzeichnis": p.5-7.

NL 0452220   MH-L ICRL

621.11
L833b

Lohmar, Emil.
Berechnung und Konstruktion der Kolben-Dampfmaschinen. [3.Aufl.] Strelitz in Mecklenburg, M.Hittenkofer [191-?]
123p. illus. 27cm. (Werke für Studium & Bureau)

1.Steam-engines.

NL 0452221   CLSU

Lohmar, Heinz,
Die verhinderung der entgegennahme einer empfangsbedurftigen willenserklärung durch den adressaten... Essen [1926?]
Diss.-Göttingen.

NL 0452222   ICRL

W 4
C69
1939

LOHMAR, Helmut, 1912–
Beeinflussung der Haut durch Diäten geprüft mittels der Lackmusquaddel-methode. Köln, Kubiak, 1939.
13, [2] p.
Inaug.-Diss. - Köln.

NL 0452223   DNLM

41.2
L835

Lohmar, Herbert, 1923–
Verbreitung parasitärer Tierkrankheiten im Rheinisch-Bergischen Kreise. Giessen, 1953.
47 p.

Inaug.-Diss. - Justus Liebig-Hochschule, Giessen.

1. Domestic animals. Parasites.

NL 0452224   DNAL

NL 0452225   ICRL

LOHMAR, Paul.
Schattenseiten der reichs-unfallversicherung. Berlin, C. Heymanns verlag, 1916.

pp. iv, 66.
"Sonderdruck aus 'Die berufsgenossenschaft', zeitschrift für die reichs-unfallversicherung, 1916, nrn 11 und folge."
      Soc 1655.316.10

NL 0452226   MH

Lohmar, Ulrich.
Arbeiterjugend gestern und heute

see under

Schelsky, Helmut, ed.

Lohmar, Walter, 1912–
Der Unfall als Ursache in der Unfallversicherung nach der Reichsversicherungsordnung... Würzburg, 1936.
Inaug.-Diss. - Köln.
Full name: Lohmar, Walter Paul Otto.

NL 0452228   CtY

Lohmar, Walther, 1906–
Quantitative trennung und reindarstellung von kohlenwasserstoffen durch desorption im vakuum. ... Berlin, 1937.
Inaug. Diss. - Freiburg i. Br., 1937.
Lebenslauf.
Literatur.

NL 0452229   ICRL CtY

PT 1799
.Al L8

LOHMAR DER SCHRECKENMAN; ODER, DIE ENTDECKUNG der Geheimnisse des alten Schlosses Tangor. Eine Geister und Zaubergeschichte des itsigen Zeitalters. Strasburg [18—]
292 p. illus.

NL 0452230   InU

Lohmar der Schreckenman, oder die Entdekung der Geheimnisse des alten Schlosses Tangor; eine Geister und Zaubergeschichte des itsigen Zeitalters. Strasburg, 1801.

2 v. illus.

NL 0452231   MH

Lohmei Hagettot
see
Lohame HaGeta'ot, *Israel.*

Lohmeier.
Leitfaden zum selbstunterricht in den anfangsgründen des telegraphen-wesens ... Bearb. und hrsg. von Lohmeier ... und Pohl ... Berlin, V.Moeser, 1870.
viii,158p. illus.,diagrs. 21cm.

1. Telegraph. I. Pohl,   joint author.

NL 0452233   DP

VOLUME 338

Lohmeier, Georg, *d. ca. 1699.*
Der europäischen käyser- und königlichen häuser historische und genealogische erläuterung...mit nöthigen beweissthümern versehen von Johann Ludwig Levin Gebhardi... Luneburg, Gedruckt und verlegt in der Sternischen buchdruckerey, 1730–31.
3 v.in 1.

Title-pages vary.

NL 0452234   NjP MH

Lohmeier, Georg, *d. ca.* 1699.
Der europæischen Reiche historische und genealogische Erläuterung, meistens von mehr als 500 Jahren her, bis auff gegenwärtige Zeit, in XLII Stamm-Taffeln richtig verfasset, und zum Gebrauch der studirenden adelichen Jugend ans Liecht gegeben durch Georg Lohmeier. Lüneburg, J. G. Lipper, 1689.
4 p. l., 42 geneal. tables.   36 cm.

1. Kings and rulers—Genealogy. 2. Royal houses.   I. Title.

D101.7.L7   5–42031

NL 0452235   DLC

929.7
FL833H
₍Lohmeier, Georg₎ *d. ca. 1699.*
Historische Stamm-Tafeln der käyserlichen, königl. und fürstlichen Geschlechte, welche in denen europäischen Ländern, nach dem Verfall der römischen Monarchie biss gegenwärtige Zeit, regieret haben. Nun zum drittenmahl mit vielen durchgehenden Vermehrungen und Verbesserungen herauss gegeben durch den autorem Notitiæ procerum imperii. Franckfurt, J. G. Lippern, 1701.
1 v. (unpag'ed)   37 cm.

1. Royal Houses. 2. Kings and rulers. Genealogy. I. Title.

NL 0452237   NcD

Lohmeier, Gerhard, 1906–
Die besteuerung der deutschen konsumgenossenschaften ... Jena, 1933.   53 p.
Inaug. Diss. –Berlin, 1933.
Lebenslauf.
Bibliography.

NL 0452238   ICRL CtY PU

WBI
L833b
1846
LOHMEIER, Ludwig Heinrich August, 1801–
Die Brom-, Eisen- und Jod-haltigen Soolquellen zu Elmen bei Gross-Salze; ihre wichtigsten Heilbeziehungen und Anweisung zum zweckmässigen Gebrauch derselben.   Halle, Anton, 1846.
iv (i. e. X), 188 p. illus.

NL 0452239   DNLM

Lohmeier, Ludwig Heinrich August, 1801–
Ueber den innern Gebrauch der kochsalzhaltigen Mineralquellen, nebst Nachricht von der Heilkraft und dem Gebrauch einer jodbrom-, eisen- und kochsalzhaltigen Trinkquelle auf dem Soolbade Elmen bei Magdeburg. 53 pp. 8°.
₍s. p., n. d.₎

NL 0452240   DNLM

Lohmeier, Ludwig Heinrich August, 1801–
Ueber warme Sooldunstbäder. Ein Versuch, die Natur, das Wesen und die Heilkraft dieser Bäder zu erklären. 3 p. l., 86 pp., 1 l.
8°. *Magdeburg, W. Heinrichshofen,* 1840.

NL 0452241   DNLM

Lohmeier, Philipp, *d. 1680, praeses.*
... Exercitatio physica de artificio navigandi per aerem ... quam ... præside Philippo Lohmeiero ... publico eruditorum examini subjiciet ad diem 4. martii anno 1676. Franciscus David Frescheur ... Rinthelij, typis Wächterianis ₍1676₎
28 p. 20 x 16⁰.
Diss.–Rinteln.
Copies have been listed with the name of the respondent given as Franciscus David Prescheur (Katalog der historischen abteilung der ersten Internationalen luftschiffahrts-ausstellung zu Frankfurt a. M., 1909, no. 939.)
The author's proposal for an air-ship is like the one described in Lana Terzi's Prodromo ... Brescia, 1670, with no reference to Lana's publication.
1. Air-ships. 2. Lana   Terzi, Francesco, 1631–1687.
I. Frescheur, Franciscus   David, fl. 1676, respondent.
33–12968
Library of Congress   TL654.L3L6 1676   629.13324
₍2₎

NL 0452242   DLC

Lohmeier, Philipp, *d.1680, praeses*
... Exercitatio physica de artificio navigandi per aerem. Qvam ... præside Philippo Lohmeiero ... subjiciet ... Franciscus David Frescheur ... Wittenbergæ, Typis Joh. Borckardi, Acad. typogr. Anno 1679.
₍23₎p. 17cm.
Diss. - Wittenberg.
Signatures: A–C³.
The author's proposal for an air-ship is like the one described in Francesco Lana Terzi's Prodromo, Brescia, 1670.

NL 0452243   CtY CSmH MnU

Lohmeier, Philipp, *d. 1680, praeses.*
... Exercitatio physica de artificio navigandi per aërem, quam ... præside Philippo Lohmeiero ... publico eruditorum examini subjiciet ad diem 4. martii an. 1676. Franciscus David Prescheur... Rinthelii, recusa typis Hermanni Augustini, Enax, 1708.
1 p. l., 30 p. 19½ x 15½ cm.
Diss.–Rinteln.
The respondent's name is given as Franciscus David Frescheur on t-p. of I. C. copy of the original edition, 1676.
The author's proposal for an air-ship is like the one described in Lana Terzi's Prodromo ... Brescia, 1670, with no reference to Lana Terzi's publication.
1. Air-ships. 2. Lana Terzi, Francesco, 1631–1687.   I. Frescheur, Franciscus David,   fl. 1676, respondent.
TL654.L3L6 1708   629.13324   34—34122

NL 0452244   DLC MH

Lohmeier, Philipp, *d. 1680, praeses.*
... Exercitatio physica de artificio navigandi per aërem, qvam ... præside Philippo Lohmeiero ... pvblico ervditorvm examini svbiiciet ad diem 4. martii anno 1676. Franciscvs David Freschevr ... Rinthelii, typis Wächterianis ₍n. d.₎; reprinted 1784₎
2 p. l., ₍3₎–55 p. 20½ x 16 cm.
"Die Lohmeierische dissertation von der kunst in der luft zu schiffen in ihrer urschrift und daneben gesetzten teutschen uebersetzung dem publikum mitzutheilen war sogleich beschlossen als man das original vorfand ... Arolsen, im märzmonat 1784."—Prefatory note, arranged typographically as an added t-p.
Latin and German on opposite pages.

Copies of the original edition (issued as dissertation, Rinteln) have been listed with the name of the respondent given as Franciscus David Prescheur. The German translation is by Kleinschmidt, counsellor of justice in Arolsen. cf. Katalog der historischen abteilung der ersten Internationalen luftschiffahrts-ausstellung zu Frankfurt a. M. 1909, no. 939 and 940.
The author's proposal for an air-ship like the one described in Lana Terzi's Prodromo ... Brescia, 1670, with no reference to Lana's publication.
1. Air-ships. 2. Lana Terzi, Francesco, 1631–1687.   I. Frescheur, Franciscus David, fl. 1676, respondent. II. Kleinschmidt, ..., fl. 1784, tr.
TL654.L3L6 1784   629.13324   33—16359

NL 0452246   DLC MH CSmH

Lohmeier, Philipp, *d. 1680, praeses.*
... Exercitationum physicarum de paradoxis gravitatis & levitatis prima qam præside Philippo Lohmeiero ... publico eruditorum examini submittet Johan. Pestel d. aug. MDCLXXVIII. Rinthelii, ex officina G. C. Wächtern ₍1678₎
1 p. l., 72, ₍4₎ p. 19 x 15½ᵐ.
Inaug.-diss.–Rinteln.

1. Gravitation. I. Pestel, Johann.

Library of Congress   QC178.L33   6–43659†

NL 0452247   DLC

Lohmeier, Philipp, *d. 1680.*
Lana Terzi, Francesco, 1631–1687.
Franz Lana und Philipp Lohmeier von der luftschiffkunst. Ins teutsche übersezt, und mit anmerkungen begleitet ... Tübingen, J. F. Heerbrandt, 1784.

Lohmeier, Philipp, *d. 1680, praeses.*
... Observationes curiosæ miscellaneæ ... Rinthelii, literis G. C. Wächteri ₍1677₎
2 p. l., 32 p. fold. pl. 19 x 15½ᵐ.
Diss.–Rinteln (J. V. Niess, respondent and author)

1. Science—Early works.   I. Niess, Johann Valentin, respondent.

Library of Congress   Q155.L6   15–17657

NL 0452249   DLC

Lohmer, Hubert, 1874–
Operative heilung eines durch graviditaet...
Inaug. Diss. Greifswald, 1898.
Bibl.

NL 0452250   ICRL DNLM MiU

Lohmer, Hubertus, 1840–
De curatione laryngis morborum in locis ipsis adhibita
Inaug. Diss. Greifswald, 1865
Bibl.

NL 0452251   ICRL DNLM

Lohmer, Theodor, 1872–
FOR OTHER EDITIONS
SEE MAIN ENTRY
Bonn. Beethoven-haus.
The Beethoven house at Bonn and its collection, by Th. Lohmer, translated into English by K. Krebs ... 4th ed., based on the guide by F. A. Schmidt and Fr. Knickenberg. Bonn, "Beethoven-haus", 1937.

WO
L834L
1858
LOHMEYER, Carl Ferdinand, 1826–
Lehrbuch der allgemeinen Chirurgie. Lahr, Schauenburg, 1858.
viii, 253 p. illus. (Cyclus organisch verbundener Lehrbücher sämmtlicher medicinischen Wissenschaften, 26. Th., 1. Bd.)

NL 0452253   DNLM ICJ

Lohmeyer, Carl Ferdinand, *b.* 1826.
Die Schusswunden und ihre Behandlung kurz bearbeitet, von C. F. Lohmeyer ... Zweite Ausgabe. Göttingen, G. H. Wigand, 1859.
₍2, vii₎–viii, 207, ₍1₎ p. 22ᵐ.

NL 0452254   ICJ DNLM

VOLUME 338

Lohmeyer, Carl Friedrich Wilhelm, 1868– ed.
Guilelmus, *Blesensis. 12th cent.*
Guilelmi Blesensis Aldae comoedia. edidit Carolus Lohmeyer. Lipsiae, in aedibus B. G. Teubneri, 1892.

Lohmeyer, Carl Friedrich Wilhelm, 1868–
Prolegomena ad Guilelmi Blesensis Aldae comoediam ... scriptor Carolus Lohmeyer ... Lipsiae, typis B. G. Teubneri, 1892.

32 p. 17cm.

Inaug.-diss.—Bonn.
Vita.
Forms part of the introduction ("caput i–ii") to Guilelmi Blesensis Aldae comoedia. ed. Carolus Lohmeyer. Lipsiae, 1892.

1. Guilelmus, Blesensis, 12th cent.

34–6768

Library of Congress   PA8330.G8L6 1892   879.1

NL 0452256   DLC CU CtY ICRL NjP

833G55   Lohmeyer, Dorothea.
Of.1i   Faust und die welt; zur deutung des zweiten teiles der dichtung ... Potsdam, Akademische verlagsgesellschaft Athenaion ₁1930₎
153p.

"Literaturverzeichnis": p. 153.

NL 0452257   IU

Lohmeyer, Dorothea.
Faust und die welt, zur deutung des zweiten teiles der dichtung, von Dorothea Lohmeyer. Potsdam, Akademische verlagsgesellschaft Athenaion ₁1940₎

153 p. 21½cm.

"Literaturverzeichnis": p. 153.

1. Goethe, Johann Wolfgang von. Faust ii.   I. Title.

41–22617

Library of Congress   PT1940.L6

₍2₎   832.62

NL 0452258   DLC InU NjP CoU CtY MH

Micro- Lohmeyer, Dorothea.
film   Faust und die Welt; zur Deutung des zweiten
PT   Teiles der Dichtung. Potsdam, Akademische
33   Verlagsgesellschaft Athenaion ₁1949₎

Negative; original in Library of Congress.

1. Goethe, Johann Wolfgang von. Faust II.

NL 0452259   ICU

DL1   Lohmeyer, Edelgard.
.G8   ... Die schwedische lebensmittelpolitik im kriege, von dr.
v. 4   Edelgard Lohmeyer. Greifswald, L. Bamberg, 1922.

₁1₎, viii, 136 p. incl. tables. 24cm.   (Nordische studien ... iv)

Added t.-p. in Swedish.
"Literaturverzeichnis": p. ₁133₎–136.

1. European war, 1914–1918—Food question—Sweden.

NL 0452260   ICU ICRL PU CSt-H NN

Lohmeyer, Eduard ₁Ludwig Wilhelm₎ 1847–
Die handschriften des Willehalm Ulrichs von Türheim ... Halle, 1882.

2 p. l., ii, 86 p. 21cm.

Inaug.-diss.—Halle.

1. Ulrich von Türheim, 13th cent.

29–7037

Library of Congress   PT1661.U5L6 1882

NL 0452261   DLC TxU CU NIC MH MWelC

Lohmeyer, Eduard Ludwig Wilhelm, 1847–
Die Handschriften des Willehalm Ulrichs von Türheim. Kassel, G. H. Wigand, 1883.
86p. 23cm.

1. Ulrich von Türheim, 13th cent. I. Title.

NL 0452262   NcU

Lohmeyer, Eduard Ludwig Wilhelm, 1847– , compiler.
Unsere Umgangssprache. Verdeutschung der hauptsächlichsten im iäglichen Leben und Verkehr gebrauchten Fremdwörter. Zweite Auflage, neu bearbeitet von Dr. Edward Lohmeyer ... Berlin: Allgemeiner deutscher Sprachverein, 1915. iv, 182 p. 12°. (Allgemeiner deutscher Sprachverein: Verdeutschungsbücher. ₁Bd.₎ 3.)

1. German language.—Dictionaries   (Polyglot). 2. Series.
N.Y.P.L.   November 21, 1916.

NL 0452263   NN OO MiU

Lohmeyer, Eduard Ludwig Wilhelm, 1847–
... Unsere umgangssprache; verdeutschung der hauptsächlichsten im täglichen leben und verkehr gebrauchten fremdwörter. 3, aufl. neubearb... Berlin, 1917.
198 p. 18 cm. (Verdeutschungsbücher des Allgemeinen deutschen sprachvereins, 3)

NL 0452264   RPB

Lohmeyer, Erich, ed.

TA710   Brennecke, Ludwig, 1843–1931.
.B74   Der Grundbau. In 4. Aufl. neubearb. und hrsg. von Erich Lohmeyer. Berlin, W. Ernst, 19

Lohmeyer, Ernst, 1890–1946.
Der Brief an die Philipper übers. und erklärt.. Göttingen, Vandenhoeck & Ruprecht, 1954
see under Bible. N.T. Philippians. German. 1954. Lohmeyer.

Lohmeyer, Ernst, 1890–1946.
Die Briefe an die Philipper, an die Kolosser und an Philemon, ₁übers. und₎ erklärt... Göttingen, Vandenhoeck & Ruprecht, 1930 (Also 1953)
see under Bible. N.T. Epistles of Paul. German. 1930. Lohmeyer. (also with date 1953)

BR129   Lohmeyer, Ernst, 1890–1946.
.A2L8   Christuskult und kaiserkult. Von Ernst Lohmeyer ... Tübingen, J. C. B. Mohr (P. Siebeck) 1919.
₁2₎, 58 p. 22½cm. (On cover: Sammlung gemeinverständlicher vorträge und schriften aus dem gebiet der theologie und religionsgeschichte. 90)

1. Christianity and other religions. 2. Jesus Christ. 3. Cultus, Roman. 4. Roman emperors.

NL 0452268   ICU CtY PBm NNUT MH DDO NcD

Lohmeyer, Ernst, 1890–1946.
Diatheke, ein beitrag zur erklärung. des neutestamentlichen begriffs. Leipzig, Hinrich, 1913.
180p. O. (Untersuchungen zum Neuen Testament, heft 2)

1. Bible. N.T. Criticism, Textual. I. Title

MH
NL 0452269   NcD ViRUT CU NjPT TxFTC CtY DCU OO OCH Cl

Lohmeyer, Ernst, 1890–1946.
Das Evangelium des Markus, übers. und erklärt ... Göttingen, Vandenhoeck & Ruprecht, 1937.
see under Bible. N.T. Mark. German. 1937. Lohmeyer. (also with dates: 1951, 1954.)

Lohmeyer, Ernst, 1890–1946.
Galiläa und Jerusalem, von d. dr. Ernst Lohmeyer ... Göttingen, Vandenhoeck & Ruprecht, 1936.
104 p. 24½ cm. ₁Forschungen zur religion und literatur des Alten und Neuen Testaments, hrsg. von Rud. Bultmann. n. f., 34. hft. Der ganzen reihe 52. hft.₎

Bibliographical foot-notes.

1. Galilee. 2. Jerusalem. 3. Church history — Primitive and early church. 4. Bible. N. T.—Geography.

Full name: Ernst Johannes Lohmeyer

BS2410.L6   270.1   A C 36–4867
California. Univ. Libr.
for Library of Congress   ₁a54d₁₎†

NL 0452271   CU PU OO PPiPT KyWAT DLC

BL1035   Lohmeyer, Ernst, 1890–1946.
.L6   Glaube und geschichte in ver der orientalischen religionen...
Breslau, 1930.
1 pam   8°

NL 0452272   DLC PPDrop

---

003   Lohmeyer, Ernst, 1890–1946.
L832g   Glaube und geschichte in vorderorientalischen religionen. Breslau, F. Hirt, 1931.
27 p. 23 cm. (Breslauer universitätsreden, heft 6)

Rede - Breslau (Einführung in das rektorat) 1930.

NL 0452273   CtY-D PU MH OCH NN

BS   Lohmeyer, Ernst, 1890–
413   Gottesknecht und Davidsohn. ₁Hafniae,
S98   E. Munksgaard, 1945₎
v. 5   155 p. 24cm. (Symbolae biblicae upsalienses. Supplementhäften till Svensk exegetic årsbok, 5)

1. Bible—Hermeneutics. 2. Son of Man. I. Series.

NL 0452274   NIC NN CtY-D NjPT MH ICU NNUT

VOLUME 338

Lohmeyer, Ernst, 1890-1946.
Gottesknecht und Davidsohn. 2. unveränderte Aufl.
Göttingen, Vandenhoeck & Ruprecht, 1953.
155 p. 23 cm. (Forschungen zur Religion und Literatur des Alten und Neuen Testaments, n. F., 43. Heft. Der ganzen Reihe 61. Heft)

1. Jesus Christ—Name. 2. Servant of Jehovah. I. Title.
(Series)
Full name: Ernst Johannes Lohmeyer.
A 53-7633

California. Univ. Libr.
for Library of Congress (2)

NL 0452275   ICU CtY MH-AH KyLxCB CaBVaU TU PSt IaU CLSU
CU PPLT InU NN OCH DDO NcD NNJ NjPT

BS3650 Lohmeyer, Ernst, 1890-
.Z7L83   ... Grundlagen paulinischer theologie, von Ernst Lohmeyer. Tübingen, J. C. B. Mohr (P. Siebeck) 1929.
(3), 235 p. 24ᶜᵐ. (Beiträge zur historischen theologie. 1)

1. Paul, Saint, apostle—Theology.

NL 0452276   InU TxHR
ICU IEG CLU IaU CtY DCU PPWe OO NcD

BS3558 Lohmeyer, Ernst, 1890-
.C9L83   Kultus und Evangelium. Göttingen, Vandenhoeck & Ruprecht, 1942.
128 p.

1. Cultus. 2. Bible. N.T. Gospels—
Criticism, interpretation, etc. I. Title.

NL 0452277   ICU ICMcC CtY-D NjPT DCU NcD PCM

Lohmeyer, Ernst, 1890-
... Kyrios Jesus; eine untersuchung zu Phil. 2, 5-11, von
Ernst Lohmeyer ... Heidelberg, C. Winter, 1928.
89 p. 24ᶜᵐ. (Sitzungsberichte der Heidelberger akademie der wissenschaften. Philosophisch-historische klasse. (Bd. 18; jahrg. 1927/28, 4. abh.)

1. Jesus Christ—Name. 2. Bible. N.T. Philippians II, 5-11—Criticism, interpretation, etc. 3. Bible—Criticism, interpretation, etc.—N.T. Philippians II, 5-11. I. Title.
Full name: Ernst Johannes Lohmeyer.
A C 37-705

Chicago. Univ. Library   AS182.H44 vol. 18
for Library of Congress   [AS182.H44 bd. 18]
(2)   (063)

NL 0452278   ICU MoU CtHC NcD PCC NN OU DDO

Lohmeyer, Ernst, 1890-
Die lehre vom willen bei Anselm von Canterbury ... Lucka
S.-A., R. Berger, 1914.
2 p. l., 74 p., 1 l. 22ᶜᵐ.
Inaug.-diss.—Erlangen.
Lebenslauf.

1. Anselm, Saint, abp. of Canterbury, 1033-1109. 2. Free will and determinism.
Full name: Ernst Johannes Lohmeyer
28-16970

Library of Congress   BJ1463.L65

NL 0452279   DLC PHC PU CtY MH TNJ-R NIC

BS2825 Lohmeyer, Ernst, 1890-1946.   FOR OTHER EDITIONS
L57   SEE MAIN ENTRY
1953   Bible. N.T. Revelation. German. 1953.
Die Offenbarung des Johannes, erklärt von Ernst Lohmeyer. 2., ergänzte Aufl. Tübingen, J. C. B. Mohr, 1953.

Lohmeyer, Ernst, 1890-1946.
Probleme paulinischer Theologie. Stuttgart, W. Kohlhammer (1955)
156 p. 22 cm.

1. Paul, Saint, apostle. 2. Bible. N. T. Epistles of Paul—Theology.
Full name: Ernst Johannes Lohmeyer.

BS2651   A 56—4338
Brown Univ. Library
for Library of Congress   (a62b)†

NL 0452281   MiU CU DDO NcD
RPB DLC NjPT CtY-D ICMcC TNJ-R KyWAT

BR195 Lohmeyer, Ernst, 1890-
.S6LS   ... Soziale fragen im urchristentum, von dr. Ernst Lohmeyer ... Leipzig, Quelle & Meyer, 1921.
136 p. 19ᶜᵐ. (Wissenschaft und bildung ... 172)
"Literatur-verzeichnis": p. (135)-136.

1. Church history—Primitive and early church. 2. Sociology, Christian.

NL 0452282   ICU CtY TxFTC NjP MH

Lohmeyer, Ernst, 1890-
... Das urchristentum ... Göttingen, Vandenhoeck & Ruprecht, 1932-
v. 24ᶜᵐ.

1. Church history—Primitive and early church. I. Title.
Full name: Ernst Johannes Lohmeyer
36-13799

Library of Congress   BR165.L82
(2)   270.1

PCC MH-AH NcD
NL 0452283   DLC TNJ-R DDO PPWe CLSU OCH CtY PPLT

BS2395
.L833u   Lohmeyer, Ernst, 1890-1946.
Urchristliche mystik; neutestamentliche
studien. Darmstadt, Wiessenschaftliche
Buchgesellschaft [1955]
181p.

1. New Testament - Addresses, essays,
lectures. I. Title.

NL 0452284   TNJ-R

Lohmeyer, Ernst, 1890-
Das Vater-unser, erklärt von Ernst Lohmeyer.
Göttingen, Vandenhoeck & Ruprecht [1946]

216 p. 24 cm.

NL 0452285   MH-AH NcD TNJ-R

Lohmeyer, Ernst, 1890-
Das Vater-unser. 2. unveränderte aufl.
Göttingen, Vandenhoeck & Ruprecht (1947)
216 p. 24 cm.

"Literatur": p. (4)

NL 0452286   CtY-D PPWe

BV Lohmeyer, Ernst, 1890-1946.
230   Das Vater-unser. 3. Aufl. Zürich,
L83   Zwingli Verlag (1952)
1952   216 p. 22cm. (Abhandlungen zur Theologie
des Alten und Neuen Testaments, 23)

1. Lord's Prayer. I. Title. II. Series.

NL 0452287   NIC OCH DDO RPB ICU NjPT TxFTC

BR163 Lohmeyer, Ernst, 1890-
.L83   Vom begriff der religiösen gemeinschaft. Eine problem-
geschichtliche untersuchung über die grundlagen des ur-
christentums, von d. dr. Ernst Lohmeyer ... Leipzig und
Berlin, B. G. Teubner, 1925.
(4), 86 p. 23ᶜᵐ. (Added t.-p.: Wissenschaftliche grundfragen. Philosophische abhandlungen ... hrsg. von R. Hönigswald ... III)
Bibliographical foot-notes.

1. Christianity. 2 Church history—Primitive and early church.

NL 0452288   ICU MH TxFTC IaU CU

Lohmeyer, Ernst, 1890-
... Vom göttlichen wohlgeruch, von Ernst Lohmeyer ...
Heidelberg, C. Winter, 1919.
52 p. 24ᶜᵐ. (Sitzungsberichte der Heidelberger akademie der wissenschaften ... Philosophisch-historische klasse. (bd. 10, jahrg. 1919, 9. abh.)
Bibliographical foot-notes.

1. (Odors (in religion, folk-lore, etc.) 2. (Theophanies) 3. Gods.
(Full name: Ernst Johannes Lohmeyer)
A C 36-5205

Title from Univ. of Chi-   cago AS182.H44 vol. 10, pt. 1
Library of Congress   [AS182.H44 bd. 10]

NL 0452289   ICU InU NIC NBuU OCH OU NN DDO

Lohmeyer, Ernst, 1890-1946, ed.
Vom Worte Gottes
see under   Deutscher Theologentag. 3d,
Breslau, 1930.

Lohmeyer, Ernst Johannes
see
Lohmeyer, Ernst, 1890-1946.

Lohmeyer, Friedrich Wilhelm Walther
see Lohmeyer, Walther, 1890-

QT   LOHMEYER, G
260   Was muss der Arzt vom Sport wissen?
L833w   Bearb. von Lohmeyer. Hrsg. von der
1931   Marinemedizinalabteilung des Reichswehr-
ministeriums. Berlin, Mittler (1931)
41 p.
1. Sports I. Germany. Marineleitung.
Marinemedizinalabteilung   Title

NL 0452293   DNLM

Lohmeyer, Georg, 1886-
Über das Verhalten der proteolytischen Fer-
mente der Leukozyten bei Gravidität, puerperalen
Erkrankungen und Tumoren der weiblichen Ge-
schlechtsorgane. Stuttgart, 1914: Union.
14 S. 8°.
Aus: Zeitschrift f. Geburtshülfe u. Gynäkol.
Bd. 76.
Berlin, Med. Diss. v. 15. Jan. 1914, Ref.
Franz.

NL 0452294   CtY DNLM

VOLUME 338

Lohmeyer, Gerhard
C54　　Recht und Zauberei in Nordwest-Amerika.
0569　　[Frankfurt/Main, 1950]
227ℓ. 29cm.
Diss.- Frankfurt/Main.
Bibliography: leaves 9-24. Bibliography at end of each chapter.

1. Indians - North America - Religion and mythology. 2. Indians - North America - Magic.

NL 0452295　　CtY

W 4　　LOHMEYER, Günter, 1919-
G59　　Idiomuskulärer Wulst und Muskelstoff-
1944　　wechsel. [Göttingen, 1944]
19 p.
Inaug. -Diss. - Göttingen.
1. Muscles - Contractions 2. Muscles - Physiology

NL 0452296　　DNLM

Lohmeyer, H.
Evangelisches Choralbuch für Kirche und Haus. 371 Choräle... Nebst einer Zugabe für die Liturgie. Bearbeitet und herausgegeben von H. Lohmeyer. Vierte Auflage.　Bielefeld und Leipzig, Velhagen & Klasing, 1880.
viii, 328 p. incl. front.　24.5 cm.
371, 39 pieces; with music.

NL 0452297　　NNUT

Lohmeyer, H. F.
Missouri, Kansas and Texas railway company of Texas.
Missouri, Kansas and Texas railway of Texas equipment trust. Series A. Lease of railroad equipment, dated July 15, 1914. Girard trust company to the Missouri, Kansas and Texas railway company of Texas. Agreement, dated July 15, 1914. Gilbert Gannon and H. F. Lohmeyer with Girard trust company and the Missouri, Kansas and Texas railway company of Texas. [n. p., 1914?]

Lohmeyer, Hans, 1881-
... Die politik des zweiten reiches, 1870-1918 ...　Berlin, P. Neff, 1939.
2 v. 23ᶜᵐ.
"Anmerkungen" (bibliographical): v. 1, p. 549-[556]; v. 2, p. 557-[568]

1. Germany—For. rel.—1871-1918. 2. Germany—Pol. & govt.—1871-1918. I. Title.
45-27019
Library of Congress　　DD221.L6
[2]　　943.08

NL 0452299　　DLC MU WaU OO NN MnU CtY CSt-H CaBVaU

Lohmeyer, Hans, 1881-
Zentralismus oder selbstverwaltung; ein beitrag zur verfassungs- und verwaltungsreform, von dr. dr. h. c. Lohmeyer ... Berlin, C. Heymann, 1928.
iv, 87 p. incl. tables. 23ᶜᵐ.

1. Germany—Constitutional law. [1. Constitutional law—Germany] 2. Administrative law—Germany. 3. Germany—Pol. & govt.—1918- I. Title.
30-10269

NL 0452300　　DLC

Lohmeyer, Hans, 1892-
Ueber das system tetralin isobutylalkohol-methylalkohol wasser in abhängigkeit von der temperatur. ... 69 p.
Inaug. Diss. -Breslau, [1933]
Lebenslauf.

NL 0452301　　ICRL CtY MiU

Lohmeyer, Hans Albert 1881-
Das wesen der behuenstigung.
Inaug. diss. Breslau, 1904.
Bibl.

NL 0452302　　ICRL

Lohmeyer, Heinrich Karl.
See
Lohmeyer, Karl, 1832- 1909.

Lohmeyer, Hermann, 1898-
Vergil im deutschen geistesleben bis auf Notker III. ...　Berlin, E. Ebering [1926]
31, [1] p. 23ᶜᵐ.
Inaug.-diss.—Halle-Wittenberg.
Lebenslauf.
"Ist hier nur ein teil der eingereichten arbeit als dissertation gedruckt. Die vollständige abhandlung erscheint im verlage von Emil Ebering in Berlin als heft der 'Germanischen studien' ".

1. Vergilius Maro, Publius.

NL 0452304　　PU MiU ICRL MH ICU CtY

Lohmeyer, Hermann, 1898-
... Vergil im deutschen geistesleben bis auf Notker III. Von dr. Hermann Lohmeyer.　Berlin, E. Ebering, 1930.
199, [1] p. 24ᶜᵐ.　(Germanische studien ... hft. 96)
"Das vorliegende buch hat bis auf das letzte, später ausgearbeitete kapitel als dissertation der Philosophischen fakultät der Vereinigten Friedrichs-universität Halle-Wittenberg vorgelegen. Das erste kapitel ist vor kurzem als dissertations-teildruck erschienen."

1. Vergilius Maro, Publius. 2. Literature, Comparative—Latin and German. 3. Literature, Comparative—German and Latin. 4. German literature—Old High German—Hist. & crit. I. Title.
31-4086
Library of Congress　　PA6825.L6
[2]　　873.1

NL 0452305　　NN OU NcU CLSU CU TxU ViU CoU
　　　　　　　DLC MH MU CU CaBVaU OrU PU NcD MH ICU

Lohmeyer, Ingolf, Assistenzarzt im Füs.-Reg. Nr. 37: Aus d. Psychiatr. u. Nervenkl. d. Univ. Kiel. Zur Symptomatologie der Schläfenlappentumoren.　Kiel 1917: Schmidt & Klaunig. 21 S. 8°
Kiel, Med. Diss. v. 2. Aug. 1917, Ref. Siemerling
[Geb. 9. Mai 91 Wehlheiden; Wohnort: Kiel; Staatsangeh.: Preußen; Vorbildung: RG. Kassel Reife 10; Studium: Berlin KW.Ak. 10 S.; Coll. 1. Juni 17; Approb. 13. Dez. 16.]
[U 17. 1031

NL 0452306　　ICRL CtY DNLM

Lohmeyer, Johannes, 1883-
Ueber die bandenspektren des quecksilberchlorid,-bromid und,- jodid.
Inaug. [di]dd. Bonn, 1906 (Leipzig)

NL 0452307　　ICRL CtY MH PU

Lohmeyer, Julius, 1835-1903.
Auf weiter Fahrt
see under title

PT 2424　LOHMEYER, JULIUS, 1835-1903.
.L7 B3　　Die Bescheidenen; Novellen.　Dresden, C. Reissner, 1898.
248 p.

Contents: Tobias Pfefferkorn; Das Pfarrhaus zu Gosbach.

NL 0452309　　InU

Lohmeyer, Julius, 1835-1903.
Julius Lohmeyers Deutsche jugend, mit 6 bunt- und 80 textbildern bewährter künstler. Neue sorgfältige auswahl. 2. aufl. Stuttgart, Loewe [1906]
1v, 128, 128 p. col. front., illus., plates (part col.) 23ᶜᵐ.

I. Title: Deutsche jugend.

42-45705
Library of Congress　　PZ31.L6 1906

NL 0452310　　DLC

Lohmeyer, Julius, 1835-1903, ed.
Deutsche monatsschrift für das gesamte leben der gegenwart ... bd. 1-12; okt. 1901-sept. 1907. Berlin, A. Duncker, 1902-07.

K834 L832　LOHMEYER, Julius, 1835-1903.
qOF　　Die fahrt zum Christkind, ein Weihnachts-märchenbuch... mit bildern von V.P. Mohn und melodien von Th. Krause. Titel, zierleisten u. vorsatzpapier gezeichnet von H. Lichtner.　Berlin [etc.] C. Flemming verlag a.-g. [1889]
48 p.　col. illus.　30cm.

Illus. t.-p. and cover in colors.
In verse.
1. Christmas. Poetry. I. Mohn, Victor Paul, 1842-1911, illus. II. Krause, Theod. 1833-1910. III. Title.

NL 0452312　　MnU

Lohmeyer, Julius, 1835-1903.
Gedichte eines Optimisten.　Leipzig, A.G. Liebeskind, 1885.

NL 0452313　　MH

Lohmeyer, Julius, 1835-1903.
... Der geissbub von Engleberg, von Julius Lohmeyer; with notes, vocabulary, and material for conversational exercises in German, by Dr. Wilhelm Bernhardt.　Boston, D. C. Heath & co., 1905.
vii, 182 p. front. 17ᶜᵐ.　(Heath's modern language series)

I. Bernhardt, Wilhelm, d. 1909, ed. II. Title.
5-29998
Library of Congress　　PT2424.L7G43

NL 0452314　　MH CU IdU OrPR MB TU OCX MiU DLC

Lohmeyer, Julius, 1835-1903.
... Der geissbub von Engleberg, ... Boston, H Heath, 1911.
vii, 182 p. front. 17cm. (Heath's modern language series)

NL 0452315　　OC1

VOLUME 338

Lohmeyer, Julius, 1835-1903.   83
König Nobel; ein heiteres Bilderbuch.   Leipzig: P. E.
Lindner ₁190-?₎.   1 p.l., 46 p.   col'd illus.
sq. f°.

1. Title.   2. Flinzer, Fedor, jt. au.
N.Y.P.L.   July 29, 1911.

NL 0452316   NN

Lohmeyer, Julius, 1835-1903.
Prince Fridolin's courtship. Verses by Jul. Lohmeyer
and Frieda Schanz. Illustrated by Julius Kleinmichel.
Tr. by Sydney Clifton. New York, Sackett & Wilhelms
litho. co. ₁1888₎
₁40₎ p. col. illus. 24½ x 27¼ᶜᵐ.

I. Soyaux, Frau Frida (Schanz) 1859–   joint author. II. Clifton,
Sydney, tr. III. Title.
    Library of Congress   PZ8.3.L832P   CA 17-1696 Unrev'd

NL 0452317   DLC RPB

Lohmeyer, Julius, 1835-1903, ed.
Schalk; blätter für deutschen humor. ₁1.₎–   jahrg.;
13. okt. 1878–
Stuttgart, W. Spemann, 1878-79; Leipzig, F. Thiel,
1879–

Lohmeyer, Julius, 1835-1904.
Der stammhalter; schwank in einem
aufzug, von Julius Lohmeyer. Leipzig,
P.Reclam₁n.d.₎
44p. 14cm.

Bound with this are plays by A.Mahlmann
Marc Michel, Max Möller, E.Raupach, Hans
von Reinfels,F.Philippi,Otto Roquette,
F.Schwab,R.Voss,Oscar Wagner, q.v.

NL 0452319   PSt

Lohmeyer, Julius, 1835-1903.
Der Thierstruwwelpeter; ein lustiges Buch für das kleine Volk,
von Jul. Lohmeyer und Fedor Flinzer. Breslau: C. T. Wiskott₁,
1887₎. 23 l. col'd illus. 26 x 21cm.

On cover : Ein komisches Bilderbuch mit Reimen von Jul. Lohmeyer und Bildern
von Fedor Flinzer.

663984A. 1. Juvenile literature—   Schatzki Coll. of Children's Books.
Fedor, 1832-1911, illustrator.   Picture books, German. I. Flinzer.
N.Y.P.L   II. Title.
                                   August 31, 1933

NL 0452320   NN OCl

Lohmeyer, Julius, 1835-1903.
Was willst du werden? dreiundvierzig Bilder von Oscar
Pletsch. Leipzig: Alphons Dürr ₁1911?₎. illus. 4°.
Unpaged.

1. Pletsch, Oscar, illus. 2. Title.
N.Y.P.L.   March 14, 1912.

NL 0452321   NN

Lohmeyer, Julius, 1835-1903.
Bernhardt, Wilhelm. d. 1909. ed.
... Der weg zum glück, zwei erzählungen für die jugend;
selected and ed. with exercises, notes and vocabulary, by Dr.
Wilhelm Bernhardt. Boston, D. C. Heath & co., 1908.

Lohmeyer, Julius, 1835-1903.
Wir leben noch, und anderes. Neue Novellen, von Julius Lohmeyer. Stuttgart: A. Bonz & Comp., 1901. 250 p. 19½cm.

Contents.—Wir leben noch!—Die Brüder.—Frei und eigen.—Der schwarze Graf.—
Alpenglühen.

969090A. 1. Fiction, German.   I. Title.
N.Y.P.L.   March 14, 1939

NL 0452323   NN

Lohmeyer,_____ Karl, 1832-1909.
De Richardo I Angliae rege cum in Sicilia commorante,
tum in Germania detento ... Regimonti Pr., typis academicis Dalkowskianis ₁1857?₎
cover-title, ₁3₎-62 p. 21ᶜᵐ.
Inaug.-dis.—Königsberg.
Vita.

Subject entries: Richard I, king of England, 1157-1199.   3-29096

    Library of Congress, no.   DA207.L8.

NL 0452324   DLC DDO

Lohmeyer, Karl, 1832-1909.
... .Des herzogs Johann Albrecht zu Meklenburg versuch
auf Livland von dr. Carl Lohmeyer ... Dorpat, Gedruckt bei
E. J. Karow, 1863.
cover-title, ₁3₎-15 p. 22½ᶜᵐ. (Schriften der gelehrten estnischen gesellschaft. n°.3)

1. Livonia—Hist.   2. Johann Albrecht I, duke of Mecklenburg-
Schwerin, 1525-1576.
                         ₁Full name: Heinrich Karl Lohmeyer₎
                                        1—18574
    Library of Congress   DK511.L36L7

NL 0452325   DLC ICU NN

Lohmeyer, Karl i. e. Heinrich Karl, 1832–
Geschichte des buchdrucks und des buchhandels im
herzogthum Preussen (16. und 17. jahrhundert.) Von
Dr. Karl Lohmeyer ... (Abgedruckt aus dem Archiv
für geschichte des deutschen buchhandels. bd. xviii-
xix) Leipzig, 1896-97.
2 v. 22ᶜᵐ.

1. Booksellers and bookselling—Prussia. 2. Publishers and publishing—
Prussia.
    Library of Congress   Z313.L82   6-15501

NL 0452326   DLC

Lohmeyer, Karl, 1832-1909.
Geschichte von Ost- und Westpreussen. Von dr. Karl
Lohmeyer ... 1. abt. 2. aufl. Gotha, F. A. Perthes, 1881.
viii, 290 p. 21ᶜᵐ.
Binder's title: Deutsche landesgeschichten.
First published independently, later included by the publisher in the
series "Deutsche landesgeschichten" which forms the 3. abt. of "Allgemeine staatengeschichte", edited by K. Lamprecht.
No more published.
Contents.—1. abth., 1. buch. Die vorgeschichte. 2. buch. Bildung
und befestigung des Ordensstaates bis 1309. 3. buch. Aufsteigen und
blüthe des Ordensstaates 1309-1407.
1. Teutonic knights—Hist. 2. Prussians (Slavic tribe)
                         ₁Full name: Heinrich Karl Lohmeyer₎
                                        3-33009 Revised
    Library of Congress   DD491.O47L8

NL 0452327   DLC MH

943.1   Lohmeyer, Karl, 1832-1909.
L833g   Geschichte von Ost- und Westpreussen.
         3. Aufl. Gotha, F. A. Perthes, 1908.
         380p. 22cm. (Deutsche landesgeschichten)

            1. Teutonic Knights - Hist. 2. Prussians
         (Slavic tribe)

NL 0452328   NcU CtY NIC MdBP

Lohmeyer, Karl, 1832-1909.
Herzog Albrecht von Preussen. Eine biographische skizze.
Von Karl Lohmeyer. Festschrift zum 17. mai 1890. Danzig,
A. W. Kafemann, 1890.
62 p. 22ᶜᵐ.
"Erweiterter und theilweise umgearbeiteter abdruck aus Allgemeine
deutsche biographie, bd. I, s. 293-310."
"Albrecht-bibliographie": p. ₁55₎-62.
"Der geburtstag des herzogs Albrecht von Preussen", von Karl
Lohmeyer (Separat-abdruck aus der Altpr. monatsschrift, bd. xxvii,
hft. 1 u. 2. 1890)": 3 p. laid in.
1. Albrecht, duke of Prussia, 1490-1568. 2. Teutonic knights—Hist.
                         ₁Full name: Heinrich Karl Lohmeyer₎
                                        29-2090
    Library of Congress   DD491.O57L8

NL 0452329   DLC NIC

---

arW   Lohmeyer, Karl, 1832-1909.
39093   Hilfsbuch für den Unterricht in der
        brandenburgisch- preussischen Geschichte,
        für höhere Lehranstalten und Mittelschulen
        von K. Lohmeyer und A. Thomas. Halle a. S.,
        Buchhandlung des Waisenhauses, 1886.
        v, 108 p. 22cm.

            I. Thomas, A   joint author.

NL 0452330   NIC

---

arW   Lohmeyer,_____ Karl, 1832-1909.
38593   Hilfsbuch für den Unterricht in der deut-
        schen Geschichte bis zum westfälischen Frie-
        den; von K. Lohmeyer und A. Thomas. Halle
        a. S., Verlag der Buchhandlung des Waisen-
        hauses, 1886.
        iv, 98 p. 22cm.

            I. Thomas, A   joint author.

NL 0452331   NIC

Lohmeyer, K₁arl₎, 1832–   Ger 3905.20
Hilfsbuch für den unterricht in der deutschen und brandenbur-
gisch-preussischen geschichte, vom ausgange des mittelalters bis
zur jetztzeit von K. Lohmeyer und A. Thomas. 2ᵃ, nach den
neuen lehrplänen vermehrte und verbesserte aufl. von Emil
Knaake und K. Lohmeyer. Halle a. S., buchhandlung des Waisenhauses, 1892.
pp. vi, (1), 164. Geneal. tables.

Brandenburg||

NL 0452332   MH

Lohmeyer, Karl, 1832–   AH 866.6
Ist Preussen das Bernsteinland der alten gewesen? Königsberg,
A. Rosbach, 1872.
pp. (2), 17.

Bernsteinland|i

NL 0452333   MH

LOHMEYER, KARL, 1832-1909.
St. Adalbert, Bischof von Prag, der erster
christliche Apostel und Märtyrer bei den
Preussen.

"Separat-Abdruck aus der Zeitschrift für
Preussische Geschichte und Landeskunde ₁1872,
vol. 9, p. 1-41₎."

NL 0452334   DDO

VOLUME 338

Lohmeyer, Karl   1832–
  ... Voigt-bibliographie. Verzeichniss aller von Johannes Voigt veröffentlichten schriften, zusammengestellt von Karl Lohmeyer. ₍Königsberg, 1898₎
    ₍295₎-308 p. 22½ᶜᵐ.
  "Separatabdruck aus der Altpreuss. monatsschrift. bd. xxxv. hft. 3 u. 4."

  1. Voigt, Johannes, 1786-1863—Bibl.

Library of Congress   Z8943.5.L7   6-15502

NL 0452335   DLC

Lohmeyer, Karl, 1832-1909.
  Witowd, grossfürst von Litauen (+ 1430) ₍Heidelberg, 1886₎
    27 p.   23 cm.
  "Separat-abdruck aus den Mitt₍eilungen₎d₍.₎ Lit₍auischen₎ ₍litt₎erarischen₎ ges₍ellschaft₎ bd. II."
  Caption title.

NL 0452336   PU

Lohmeyer, Karl, 1832-1909.
  Zur altpreussischen Geschichte; Aufsätze und Vorträge, von Karl Lohmeyer.   Gotha: F. A. Perthes, 1907.   321 p.   8°.

  Bibliographical footnotes.

  1. Prussia—Hist.
N. Y. P. L.   April 14, 1926

NL 0452337   NN MH

Lohmeyer, Karl, 1878–
  Aus dem leben und den briefen des landschaftsmalers und hofrats - Georg Wilhelm Issel, 1785-1870. ₍Heidelberg. In Kommission bei Gustav Köster, 1929₎
    159 p.   30 plates incl. front.(port.) 23½ cm.

  1. Issel, Georg Wilhelm, 1785-1870.

NL 0452338   DNGA

Lohmeyer, Karl, 1878–
  Die barockbauten der abtei Prüm und ihre meister, von Karl Lohmeyer.
  (*In* Bonner jahrbücher. Jahrbücher des Vereins von altertumsfreunden im Rheinlande. Bonn, 1912. 27½ᶜᵐ. hft. 122, p. ₍111₎-136. illus., pl. xiii-xviii (incl. plans))

  1. Prüm, Ger. Sankt Salvator (Benedictine abbey) 2. Architecture, Baroque.   i. Title.
Metropolitan mus. of art,   A C 40-2708
  for Library of Congress   N. Y. Library
                             [DD491.R4B7 hft. 122]
                             ₍2₎   (943.42)

NL 0452339   NNMM OU

Lohmeyer, Karl, 1878–
  Die baumeister des rheinisch-fränkischen barocks, von Karl Lohmeyer.   Wien, Augsburg, Dr. B. Filser, 1931.
    14, ₍161₎-206, ₍107₎-204 p. illus. (incl. ports., plans) 31 x 23½ᶜᵐ.
  Reprinted from the Wiener jahrbuch, 1928-29, with addition of an index: Verzeichnis der baumeister, bauherrn und bauorte.

  1. Architects, German. 2. Architecture, Baroque. 3. Architecture, German. i. Title.
                                                 32-15625
Library of Congress   NA1066.L6   724.1943

NL 0452340   DLC MWiCA OC1 CtY CU NN PP

Lohmeyer, Karl, 1878–
  Die baumeister des rheinisch-fränkischen barocks, von Karl Lohmeyer.   Wien, Augsburg, Dr. B. Filser, 1936.
    14, ₍161₎-206, ₍107₎-204 p. illus. (incl. ports., plans) 31 x 23½ᶜᵐ.
  Reprinted from the Wiener jahrbuch, 1928-29, with addition of an index: Verzeichnis der baumeister, bauherrn und bauorte.
  "Copyright 1931."

NL 0452341   NcD

Lohmeyer, Karl, 1878–
  Festschrift für Karl Lohmeyer
    see under   Schwingel, Karl, ed.

Lohmeyer, Karl, 1878–
  Friedrich Joachim Stengel, fürstäbtlich fuldischer Ingenieur, Hofarchitekt und Bauinspektor ... 1694-1787. Düsseldorf, Schwann, 1911.
    x, 187 p. illus., ports. (Mitteilungen des Historischen Vereins für die Saargegend, 11)

NL 0452343   MH NjP IU MB NNC

Lohmeyer, Karl, 1878–
  Die Fürstlich nassau-saar-brückische Porzellan manufaktur, Ottweiler, NS.   Leipzig, Klinkhardt & Biermann, 1924. 20 p. 10 plates. (14 figs.) 30cm.

  Bibliography, p. 20.

  1. Pottery—Manufacture—Germany—Ottweiler.

NL 0452344   NN

PT   Lohmeyer, Karl, 1878–
2130   Goethe und die niederelbische Küstenlandschaft. ₍Cuxhaven? 1934?₎
E29L83   20 p.

          "Sonderdruck aus dem Jahrbuch der Männer vom Morgenstern; Heimatbund an Elb- und Wesermündung, Jahg.26,Vereinsjahr 1932/33 u. 1933/34."

          1. Goethe, Johann Wolfgang von, 1749-1832 - Homes and haunts - Elbe. I. Title.

NL 0452345   CLU

Lohmeyer, Karl, 1878–
  Heidelberger maler der romantik, von Karl Lohmeyer; mit 15 (davon 13 farbigen) tafeln und 338 textabbildungen. Heidelberg, C. Winter, 1935.
    xii, 446 p., 1 l. illus., xv pl. (part col.; incl. front., port.) 28½ x 22ᶜᵐ.
  "Literarische quellen": p. 437-440.

  1. Painting—Heidelberg. 2. Romanticism in art. i. Title.

Library of Congress   ND586.H4L6   37-12339
                             ₍2₎   759.3

NL 0452346   DLC MWiCA NN

J18   Lohmeyer, Karl, 1878–
Se45   Johannes Seiz, kurtrierischer Hofarchitekt, Ingenieur sowie Obristwachtmeister und Kom-
+914L   mandeur der Artillerie, 1717-1779. Die Bautätigkeit eines rheinischen Kurstaates in der Barockzeit. Heidelberg, C.Winters, 1914.
            xiii,222p. illus. 30cm. (Heidelberger Kunstgeschichtliche Abhandlungen. Bd.1)

          1.Seitz, Johannes, 1717-1779. I.Ser.

NL 0452347   CtY MH MoU MiU NjP InU CU CSt KyU WU

Lohmeyer, Karl, 1878–
  Kultur- und Familiengeschichtliches aus verloren geglaubten Saarbrücker Stadtgerichtsprotokollen zur Zeit des 30jährigen Krieges der lothringischen und französischen Besetzungen und der Reunionsbestrebungen Ludwig XIV., von Karl Lohmeyer. Saarbrücken: Buchgewerbehaus Aktiengesellschaft, 1939. 161 p. 22½cm. (Saarbrücker Abhandlungen zur südwestdeutschen Kunst und Kultur. Bd. 2.)

  Contents.—Die Besetzung der städtischen Ämter von Saarbrücken und St. Johann, 1672-1692.—Kultur- und Familiengeschichtliches aus den Jahren 1642-1649.—Kultur- und Familiengeschichtliches aus den Jahren 1672-1693.

42887B. 1. Court records—Germany   —Saarbrücken. 2. Saarbrücken,
Germany—Geneal. I. Saarbrücken,   Germany. Courts: Stadtgericht.
II. Ser.
N. Y. L.   October 7, 1940

NL 0452349   NN

DD   Lohmeyer, Karl, 1878–
86.7   Max Toeppen. Königsberg in Pr., R. Leupold,
T57L83   1894.
              36 p.

            Separat-Abdruck aus der Altpreuss. Monatsschrift Bd. XXXI, Hft. 1 u. 2.
            "Verzeichniss der Schriften M. Toeppen's": p.28-36.

            1. Toeppen, Max Pollux, 1822-1893.

NL 0452350   CLU

Lohmeyer, Karl, 1878–
  Ottweiler in der Kunst des 18. Jahrhunderts. ₍Ottweiler, 1950₎
    80 p. illus., ports. 21 cm. (Veröffentlichungen der Arbeitsgemeinschaft für Landeskunde, Bd. 1)

  1. Art—Ottweiler. (Series: Arbeitsgemeinschaft für Landeskunde. Veröffentlichungen, Bd. 1)

N6886.O85L6   55-42755

NL 0452351   DLC

NA7595   Lohmeyer, Karl, 1878–
P55L6   Palagonisches Barock; das Haus der Laune
f   des "Prinzen von Palagonia." Frankfurt a.M. Hauserpresse ₍1941-43₎
            66 p. plans,plates. 31cm.
            Includes bibliographical references.

            1.Villa Palagonia. 2.Architecture, Baroque, Sicily. I.Title. MUC SC

NL 0452352   CSt

q728.84   Lohmeyer, Karl, 1878–
L83p   Palagonisches Barock. Das Haus der Laune des "Prinzen von Palagonia."   Berlin, Maximilian-Gesellschaft, 1942.
            66p. mounted illus. 31cm.

            "Es wurden 350 Exemplare gedruckt -- Nr.123."

            1. Palagonia, Sicily. Villa Palagonia.

NL 0452353   IU NjP CtY ICU NNC CU PU MH MiU

Lohmeyer, Karl, 1878–
  Die Sagen der Saar, von ihren Quellen bis zur Mündung. Saarbrücken, Minerva-Verlag, 1952.
603 p. illus., map. 20cm.

  "Quellen und Nachweise," p. 437-560.

  1. Folk tales, German—Sarre valley.

NL 0452354   NN ICarbS InU MH

VOLUME 338

B
8547
.52
Lohmeyer, Karl, 1878-
Die sagen des Saarbrücker und Birkenfelder landes. 2.stark erweit.
aufl. Saarbrücken,1924.

NL 0452355   ICN MH

398.2
L832s
Lohmeyer, Karl, 1878-
Die sagen von der Saar, Blies, Nahe, vom Hunsrück, Soon- und Hochwald, gesammelt von Karl Lohmeyer. Zugleich dritte, weit mehr als verdoppelte
aufl. der Sagen des Saarbrücker und Birkenfelder
landes. Saarbrücken, Gebr. Hofer a.g., 1935.
616p. plates, port.

1. Legends, German. 2. Legends--Rhine river
and valley.

NL 0452356   IU

Lohmeyer, Karl, 1878-   ed.
Schönbornschlösser: die Stichwerke Salomon
Kleiners, Favorita ob Mainz
see under Kleiner, Salomon, 1703-1759.

Lohmeyer, Karl, 1878-
Südwestdeutsche Gärten des Barock und der Romantik,
mit ihren in- und ausländischen Vorbildern, nach dem Ar-
beitsmaterial der saarländischen und pfälzischen Hofgärt-
nerfamilie der Koellner. Saarbrücken, Buchgewerbehaus
Aktiengesellschaft, 1937.
vii, 187 p. illus., ports., plans. 29 cm. (Saarbrücker Abhandlungen zur südwestdeutschen Kunst und Kultur, Bd. 1)

1. Landscape gardening—Germany. 2. Gardens—Germany—Saarbrücken.   I. Title.   (Series)

SB477.G4L6   51-47352

NL 0452358   DLC MiU FMU MWiCA CtY NN NjP NNC

Lohmeyer, Karl, 1878-   ed.
Verzeichnis der im Kurpfälzischen Museum
der Stadt Heidelberg vom 1. Juni bis 1. Oktober
1927 ausgestellten Werke von Ernst Fries
see under Heidelberg. Kurpfälzisches
Museum.

Lohmeyer, Karl, 1878-
Die Wallfahrtskirche zum Heiligen Blut in Walldürn, von
Karl Lohmeyer. Augsburg: B. Filser, cop. 1929. 44 p.
illus., plan, plates. 8°. (Deutsche Kunstfuehrer. Bd. 43.)

Plates printed on both sides.
Bibliography, p. 42.

597706A. 1. Architecture, Ecclesi-   astical—Germany—Walldürn.
I. Ser.
N.Y.P.L.   July 6, 1932

NL 0452360   NN NjP MH

Lohmeyer, Karl, 1878-
Der Windsheimer Zwölfbotenaltar von Tilman
Riemenschneider

see under

Poensgen, Georg, ed.

Lohmeyer, Karl, 1884-   Ger 39.2.3 (11)
Das hofrecht und hofgericht des hofes zu Loen; ein beitrag zur
geschichte der Münsterschen amtsverfassung. Münster, Westfalen, F. Coppenrath, 1906.
pp. iv, (4), 8o. (Münstersche beiträge zur geschichtsforschung; neue folge, 11.)

Feudalism-Germany||Series

NL 0452362   MH PU

Lohmeyer, Kurt, 1904-
... Steinstaublunge und Tuberkulose... Düs-
seldorf, 1935.
Inaug.-Diss. - Tübingen.
Lebenslauf.
"Literatur": p. 13.

NL 0452363   CtY DNLM

LOHMEYER, Robert, 1879-
Untersuchungen über die gradation von bromsil-
ber-gelatine-trockenplatten,etc. Inaug.-diss.
Marburg a.L., 1907.
Phys 2830.5.4

NL 0452364   MH ICRL NNC

PF 3576 LOHMEYER, THEODOR
.L833   Beiträge zur Etymologie deutscher Flussnamen. Göttingen, Vandenhoeck & Ruprecht, 1881.
126 p.

1. German language—Etymology—Names. 2. Names—
Geographical—Germany. I. Tc.

NL 0452365   InU CU PU NIC

LOHMEYER, Theodor.
De Vocabulis in Oppiani Halieuticis aut pecu-
liariten usurpatis aut primum exstantibus.
Dis sertatis inauguralis. Berol [1866.]

"Vita," p. 99.   Go 8.50

NL 0452366   MH ICRL NjP

929.4
L832h
Lohmeyer, Theodor.
Die Hauptgesetze der germanischen Flussnamenge-
bung, hauptsächlich an nord- und mitteldeutschen
Flussnamen erläutert. Ein zum grössten Teile in
der Sitzung des Hessischen Geschichtsvereins zu
Marburg am 27. März 1903 gehaltener Vortrag.
Kiel, Lipsius & Tischer, 1904.
ix, 32p. 25cm.

1. Names, Geographical - Germany. 2. German
language - Etymology - Names.

NL 0452367   TxU MH NIC

Lohmeyer, Walfried.
Aus der sattelperspektive; kriegsskizzen eines husaren-frei-
willigen, von Walfried Lohmeyer ... Dresden und Leipzig,
E. Pierson, 1917.
3 p. l., [3]-116 p. 19½ᵐ.

1. European war, 1914-1918—Personal narratives, German.   I. Title.
20—8421
Library of Congress   D640.L65

NL 0452368   DLC

Lohmeyer, Walter.
Dein Körper: eine Lebens- und Menschenkunde für jedermann im Lichte neuer wissenschaftlicher Forschung.
[Einsiedeln] Benziger [1952]
340 p. illus. 23 cm.

1. Physiology, Human.   I. Title.

Temple Univ. Library
for Library of Congress   QP34L84
[1]
A 53-260

NL 0452369   PPT

Lohmeyer, Walter Gottfried, ed.
Gebühr, Otto, 1877-
Das Otto Gebühr-buch, herausgegeben von dr. Walter Gott-
fried Lohmeyer. Berlin, A. Scherl g. m. b. h. [1927]

Lohmeyer, Walther, ed.
Der Lebenskreis der Frau; ein Ratgeber in allen Fragen
des Frauenlebens, unter Mitwirkung von Forschern, Ärzten,
Erziehern und Lebensberatern. Vollständig neu bearb. und
bebildert mit Farbtafeln nach Gemälden alter und neuer
Meister und mit vielen Fotografien nach dem Leben. Olten,
O. Walter [1953]
495 p. illus. 28 cm.

1. Woman. 2. Family.   I. Title.

Ohio. State Univ. Libr.
for Library of Congress   HQ46.L6 1953
[1]
A 55-407

NL 0452371   OU

Lohmeyer, Walther, 1890-
... Die dramaturgie der massen. Mit 4 bühnenplänen. Berlin und Leipzig, Schuster & Loeffler, 1913.
323 p. incl. 4 plans. 24½ᵐ.
"Quellen": p. [303]-315.

1. Drama—Technique. 2. Drama—Hist. & crit. 3. Theater.
I. Title.
13—13928
Library of Congress   PN1690.L7

MiU NN
NL 0452372   DLC IU OU MB FU FTaSU CU MH CtY NjP

830.92 Lohmeyer,   Walther, 1890-
L83m   Die massenszenen im älteren deutschen
drama. Stuttgart, 1912.
54p.

Inaug.-diss.—Heidelberg.

Full name: Friedrich Wilhelm Walther Lohmeyer.

NL 0452373   IU PU

QK
911
.A5
v. 3
Lohmeyer, Wilhelm.
Die Pflanzengesellschaften der Eilenriede bei
Hannover; Erläuterungen zur Vegetationskarte.
Stolzenau/Weser, Zentralstelle für Vegetations-
kartierung, 1951.
72 p. illus. (col., fold. map) (Angewandte Pflanzensoziologie, 3)

Includes bibliographies.
1. Forests and forestry - Germany - Eilenriede.
I. Title. II. Se-   ries.

NL 0452374   MiEM

Lohmeyer, Wolfgang.
... Erste Gedichte. Baden-Baden, H. Bühler, jr., 1947. 70 p.
20cm.

NL 0452375   NN IEN

VOLUME 338

Lohmüller, Karl
Schwoba-Spässla; heitere Gedichtla für d'Schwobaleutla
en Dorf ond Stadt. [Stuttgart, Verlag Buchversand
Tetzner, 1923?]

NL 0452376 MH

LOHMOELDER, Ruth P.
Social security for social workers; a study of
the extent of coverage for social workers in
existing state and local retirement programs in
the various states. Salt Lake City, Utah, Utah
Congress of Social Workers, 1942.

Manifold copy. 28 cm. ff.(2),33,(1).
Paper cover serves as title-page.

NL 0452377 MH-PA

Lohmüller, Albert.
Sterblichkeitsuntersuchungen auf Grund des Materials der Stuttgarter Lebensversicherungsbank a. G. (alte Stuttgarter) 1854–
1901. Von Dr. Albert Lohmüller, ... Mit 3 Tafeln und 3
Abbildungen im Text. Jena, G. Fischer, 1907.
[6], 170, [2] p. incl. tables. 4 fold. diagr. 24⁴ᵐ.
"Literaturverzeichnis," 1 p. at end.

NL 0452378 ICJ PU MH NN NIC ICRL CtY

LOHMÜLLER, Fritz.
Ueber rectovaginalfisteln. Inaug.-Diss.
Bonn, 1905.

NL 0452379 MBCo ICRL DNLM

Film 353
Lohmüller, Gertrud,
Die Frau im Werk von Virginia Woolf; ein
Beitrag zur psychologischen und stilistischen
Untersuchung des neuesten englischen Frauen-
romans. Tübingen, A. Becht, 1937.

Microfilm copy.
Collation of the original: 103p.
Inaug.-Diss. - Tübingen.
Lebenslauf.
Bibliography: p. 99-102.

NL 0452380 IEN

Lohmüller, Gertrud.
... Die frau im werk von Virginia Woolf; eine beitrag zur
psychologischen und stilistischen untersuchung des neuesten
englischen frauenromans, von Gertrud Lohmüller. Leipzig,
R. Noske, 1937.
2 p. l., 102 p. 22½ᵐ. (Aus schrifttum und sprache der Angelsachsen,
hrsg. von dr. Rudolf Hittmair und dr. Robert Spindler. bd. 8)
Issued also as inaugural dissertation, Tübingen.
"Literaturverzeichnis": p. 99-102.
1. Woolf, Mrs. Virginia (Stephen) 2. Women in literature and art.
I. Title.
Library of Congress PR6045.O72Z8 1937 39-12472
[2] 823.91

NL 0452381 DLC ICN MH

Lohmüller, Helmut, 1904–
Die französische theorie der malerei im 17.
jahrhundert ... von Helmut Lohmüller ... Marburg,
1933.
2 p. l., 112 p., 1 l. 23⁴.

Thesis, Marburg.
"Literatur": p. [111,-112.

1. Painting, French.

NL 0452382 NNC CtY DLC PU ICRL

Lohmüller, Johannes.
Overberg und unsere Zeit; zum 200. Geburtstag. Trier,
Paulinus-Verlag, 1954.
56 p. port. 21 cm.
"Quellenangabe": p. 55-56.
"Die Beiträge dieser Schrift sind auch erschienen im Heft 2/1954
der Zeitschrift 'Pädagogische Nachrichten.'"

1. Overberg, Bernhard, 1754-1826. I. Title.
A 54-7285
Catholic Univ. of America. Library
for Library of Congress [3]

NL 0452383 DCU

Lohmüller, Johannes, ed.
Schule und Berufsberatung. Trier, Paulinus-Verlag
[1954]
60 p. 21 cm.
"Die Beiträge dieser Schrift sind auch erschienen in Heft 1, 1954
der Zeitschrift Pädagogische Nachrichten."

1. Vocational guidance. I. Title.
LC1047.G3L6 55-24816

NL 0452384 DLC

Lohmueller, Karl, 1901–
... Ileus verminosus ... München, 1926.
Inaug.-Diss. - München.
Curriculum vitae.
"Literaturverzeichnis": p. 39-46.

NL 0452385 CtY

Lohmüller, Karl, 1907–
Die entwicklung des metallschlägergewerbes
unter besonderer berücksichtigung der verhältnisse
in der feingoldschlägerei in mittelfranken. ...
Lichtenfels, 1936. 96 p.
Inaug. Diss. - Erlangen, 1936.
Lebenslauf.
Literatur-Verzeichnis.

NL 0452386 ICRL CtY

Lohmüller, Lore, 1904–
... Ueber Entfettungs- und Mast-Kuren...
Bonn, 1930.
Inaug.-Diss. - Bonn.
Lebenslauf.
"Zeitschriften": p. 66-68.

NL 0452387 CtY DNLM

Lohmüller, Max, 1873–
... Ueber Sarcome der Extremitäten...
Bonn [1898]
Inaug.-Diss. - Bonn.

NL 0452388 CtY DNLM ICRL

Lohmüller, Wolfgang.
Attacke in verlorenes Land. Berlin, West-Ost-Verlag
[1940?]
107 p. 20 cm.

1. World War, 1939-1945—Campaigns—Poland.
D765.L6 51-52247

NL 0452389 DLC

Law Lohmüller, Wolfgang, ed.

Germany (Federal Republic, 1949–   ) Laws, statutes, etc.
Gesetz über Verbesserungen der gesetzlichen Unfallversicherung vom 10. August 1949. Gesetz über die Behandlung der Verfolgten des Nationalsozialismus in der Sozialversicherung vom 22. August 1949. Gesetz über die Gewäh-
rung von Unfall- und Hinterbliebenenrenten an die Opfer
der Naziunterdrückung vom 5. März 1947. Alle 3 Gesetze,
das 3. unter Mitarbeit von Marcel Frenkel, ausführlich
erläutert und mit Hinweisen auf Rechtslehre und Rechtsprechung versehen von Wolfgang Lohmüller. Düsseldorf-
Gerresheim, K. H. Pelzer [1950]

NL 0452391 DLC

Lohmüller, Wolfgang.
Sturm über Flandern, ein Kriegsbericht. Berlin, West-
Ost-Verlag [1942]
107 p. 19 cm.

1. World War, 1939-1945—Campaigns—Western. 2. World War,
1939-1945—Personal narratives, German. I. Title.
D756.L6 52-48606

NL 0452391 DLC

Lohmuller, Martin Nicholas, 1919–
... The promulgation of law, by the Rev. Martin Nicholas
Lohmuller ... Washington, D. C., The Catholic university
of America press, 1947.
xi, 130 p. 23 cm. (The Catholic university of America. Canon
law studies, no. 241)
Thesis (J. C. D.)—Catholic university of America, 1947.
"Biographical note": p. [127]
Bibliography: p. 117-122.
1. Canon law. I. Title.
BX1935.L6 348 A 48-1183
© 1Jun47; Catholic university of America press, inc.;
AA54894.
Catholic Univ. of America. Library
——— Copy 2.
for Library of Congress [4]†

NL 0452392 DCU DLC GU-L CLL OU

Lohn, Agnette Midgarden.
The voice of the big firs [by] Agnette Midgarden Lohn.
[St. Paul, Printed by the Pioneer co., ᶜ1918]
428 p., 1 l. front. 19ᶜᵐ.

I. Title.
Library of Congress PZ3.L832V 18-6026

NL 0452393 DLC OrU Or

PT Lohn, Maria
2623 Die Geheimnisvollen auf Schloss Herblingen;
.O46 romantische Erzahlung. [Schaffhausen,
G4 Scherrer, 1952]
244 p. 23 cm.

NL 0452394 WU

Lohn, Władysław, 1889–
Chrystus nauczający; ustanowienie i układ
urzędu nauczycielskiego. Kraków, Wydawn.
Księży Jezuitów, 1927.
204 [1] p.

Bibliography: p. [199]-204.

NL 0452395 MiD

Lohn, Władysław, 1889–
De SS. Trinitate, schema tractatus. St. Marys, Kan., St.
Mary's College, 1949.
351 p. 28 cm.
At head of title: Universitas Sancti Ladovici.
A reissue, with slight changes, of the 2d ed. published by the
Pontificia università gregoriana at Rome in 1931.
Bibliographical footnotes.

1. Trinity. I. Title.
BT111.L58 1949 49-51917

NL 0452396 DLC

VOLUME 338

232
L83v Lohn, Władysław, 1889–
De Verbo incarnato, hominum Redemptore,
schema tractatus. Romae, Apud Aedes Universitatis Gregorianae, 1930.
402 p. 22 cm.
Includes bibliographical references.

1. Incarnation. 2. Redemption.

NL 0452397 MoSU-D

231
L83d Lohn, Władysław, 1889–
Doctrina Graecorum et Russorum de proces-
sione Spiritus Sancti a solo Patre exponitur atque diiudicatur. Romae ₍Apud Aedes
Universitatis Gregorianae₎ 1934.
127 p. 23 cm. (His Compendium quaestionum
selectarum de quibus Orientales schismatici
cum Catholicis disceptarunt. 1)
No more published.
Bibliographical footnotes.
1. Holy Spirit--Procession. 2. Orthodox
Eastern Church   --Doctrinal and controversial   works. I. Title.

NL 0452398 MoSU-D DDO IMunS

Der Lohn der Tat. ₍Hamburg, Friederichsen, De Gruyter,
194–₎
31 p. illus. (part col.) 30 cm.
Cover title.

1. Germany. Heer—Medals, badges, decorations, etc.

UB435.G3L63   70-277372

NL 0452399 DLC MH

Lohndorff, Ernst Friedrich, 1899–
see Löhndorff, Ernst Friedrich, 1899–

Lohne, Alf, 1915–
Det beste i livet; trygg lykke i utrygge tider. Oslo, Norsk
bokforlag ₍1955₎
177, ₍8₎ p. illus. (part col.) 24 cm.
Bibliographical references in "Kildeangivelse" (p. ₍178₎–₍180₎)

1. Seventh-Day Adventists—Doctrinal and controversial works.
I. Title.

BX6154.L57   A 56–6681

Minnesota. Univ. Libr.
for Library of Congress   ₍8₎

NL 0452401 MnU DLC-P4 DLC

Lohneiss, Andrew J.

G3784
.M699
1949 Packard, Ansel A
.P3   Sketch showing outline of the division of Middletown
from colonial times to the present. Data ₍by₎ A. A. Packard,
drawn ₍by₎ A. J. Lohneiss. ₍Middletown, Conn., 1949₎

Lohneiss, G.

See

Loehneyss, Georg Engelhard von, 1552–1622.

Lohner, Adelheid, joint author.

DQ36
.M374 **Mazzucchetti, Lavinia.**
... L'Italia e la Svizzera; relazioni culturali nel settecento e
nell' ottocento. Con 75 ritratti in 19 tavole fuori testo. Milano, U. Hoepli, 1943.

Lohner, Adelheid, joint author.

Mazzucchetti, Lavinia.
Die Schweiz und Italien; kulturbeziehungen aus zwei jahr-
hunderten, von dr. Lavinia Mazzucchetti und dr. Adelheid
Lohner. Einsiedeln ₍etc.₎ Benziger verlag, 1941.

Lohner, Alfons, 1905–
... Über die Wirkung des Thalliums auf
Knochen- und Zahnsystem ... München, 1936.
Inaug.-Diss. - München.
Lebenslauf.

NL 0452406 CtY

Lohner, Bernhardus, respondent.
*De partu difficili
see under Wedel, Georg Wolffgang, 1641–
1721, praeses.

DQ 851
.T5 L6 Lohner, Carl Friedrich Ludwig, 1786–1863.
1942   ... Aufzeichnungen zur eigenen lebens-
geschichte und ein nachruf, mit einer einleitung herausgegeben von Hans Gustav Keller.
Thun, Druck- und verlagsanstalt Adolf Schaer,
1942.
15 p. 23cm.

At head of title: Carl Friedrich Ludwig
Lohner, regierungsrat und landammann der
republik Bern (1786–1863)
r Bibliographical foot-notes.

NL 0452408 MdBJ

Lohner, Carl Friedrich Ludwig, 1786–1863.
Johann Gottlieb Schrämli, Pfarrer in Amsoldingen (1792–1841);
Aufzeichnungen. Mit einer Einleitung hrsg. von Hans Gustav
Keller.   Thun, A. Schaer, 1942. 10 p. 23cm.

Bibliographical footnotes.

Schrämli, Johann Gottlieb,   1792–1841.

NL 0452409 NN NjP MH

Lohner, Carl Friedrich Ludwig, 1786–1863.
Die Münzen der Republik Bern. Zürich, Meyer & Zeller,
1846.
viii, 270 p. 3 plates. 23 cm.

1. Coins. 2. Numismatics—Switzerland.

CJ3268.B4L5   14–20064 rev*

NL 0452410 DLC DSI

Lohner, Carl Friedrich Ludwig, 1786–1863.   Swi 992.4
Die reformirten kirchen und ihre vorsteher im eidgenössischen
freistaate Bern, nebst den vormaligen klöstern. Thun, J. J.
Christen, ₍1864–67₎.
pp. viii, 700.
Published in 2 parts.

NL 0452411 MH

PS3511
.A862Z7367 Lohner, Edgar, 1919–
1950   Thematik, Symbolik und Technik im Werk
William Faulkners. ₍Ann Arbor, University
Microfilms₎ 1950.
150, ₍1₎ l. map. 31cm.
Reproduced from typescript.
Inaug.-Diss.—Bonn.
Literaturverzeichnis: leaves 147–150.
Lebenslauf: leaf ₍151₎

1. Faulkner, William, 1897–   —Criticism
& interpretation.   I. Title.

NL 0452412 ViU MsU

342.494
L833s Lohner, Erich.
Staatsreform; zur Neugestaltung des
Eidgenössischen Volksstaates. Bern, A.
Francke, 1938.
127p. 21cm.

1. Switzerland. Constitution. 2. Switzerland. Pol. & govt. I. Title.

NL 0452413 IEN

Lohner, Ernst
Die aufforderungsdelikte im entwurf eines
schweizerischen strafgesetzbuches und in den
kantonalen gesetzgebungen. ... Bern, 1937.
71 p.
Inaug. Diss. - Bern, 1937.
Literaturverzeichnis.

NL 0452414 ICRL

Lohner, Erwin, 1927–
Irrtümliche Annahme und Nichtannahme privilegierender
und qualifizierender Tatbestandsmerkmale durch den Täter.
München, 1954.
vii, 220 l. 29 cm.
Typescript (carbon copy)
Inaug.-Diss.—Munich.
Vita.
Bibliography: leaves iv–vi.
1. Mistake (Criminal law)—Germany (Federal Republic, 1949–   )
2. Aggravating circumstances—Germany (Federal Republic, 1949–   )
3. Extenuating circumstances—Germany (Federal Republic, 1949–   )
I. Title.
                                    59–19346

NL 0452415 DLC

Lohner, H   , 1906–
... Beobachtungen über die Geburt bei Becken-
endlage... Würzburg, 1933.
Inaug.-Diss. - Köln.
Lebenslauf.
"Literaturverzeichnis": p.24–25.

NL 0452416 CtY

Lohner, Heidi.
Deutschlands anteil an der italienischen romantik, von Heidi
Lohner. Bern-Leipzig, P. Haupt, 1936.
vii, 152 p. 23½ᶜᵐ. (Added t.-p.: Sprache und dichtung; forschungen
zur sprach- und literaturwissenschaft ... hft. 62)

"Bibliographie": p. ₍148₎–152; bibliographical foot-notes.

1. Literature, Comparative—German and Italian. 2. Literature, Comparative—Italian and German. 3. Romanticism—Italy. I. Title.

                                    A C 37–492

Northwestern univ. Libr.
for Library of Congress   ₍2₎

PU MU GU FTaSU IaU OrU CaBVaU
NL 0452417 IEN CU ICRL NIC CU NBC TxU UU NcD PSC

VOLUME 338

PL15
.L83
Lohner, Ludwig.
Vergangenheit, Gegenwart und Zukunft der
Automobile. Vortrag gehalten im Niederöster-
reichischen Gewerbevereine am 15. Jänner 1897.
Wien, Verlag des Niederösterreichischen Gewerbe-
vereins, 1897.
25 p.

1. Automobiles--Hist.

NL 0452418   ICU

Lohner, Otto, 1912-
Die besonderen ehrenstrafen der 30 bis 39
des militärstrafgesetzbuches gegen wehr-
pflichtige des beurlaubtenstandes. ...
Düsseldorf, 1937.   46 p.
Inaug. Diss. - Bonn, 1937.
Lebenslauf.
Literatur-Verzeichnis.

NL 0452419   ICRL

Lohner, Tobias, 1619-1697.
Bibliotheca Manualis Concionatoria, in qua de
Virtutibus, Vitiis, Sacramentis, Novissimis, &c.
Nempe, Definitiones, Divisiones, Sententiae S.
Scripturae et SS. Patrum, &c.   Venice, J.J.
Hertz, 1695.
vol.

NL 0452420   WaSpG

Lohner, Tobias, 1619-1697.
Bibliotheca manualis concionatoria
ordine alphabetico digesta. ed. novissima ... in 7 tomos distributa, cui
nunc primum accedit opusculum, Instructio
practica de munere concionandi, exhortandi,
catechizandi. Bassani, 1787.
7v.

NL 0452421   MoSU-D

Lohner, Tobias, 1619-1697.
Biblotheca manualis consionatoria, ordeine
alphabetico digesta. Editio novissima et a cura-
tissime emendata. Cura et studio DD. Alphonsi
Cordier et Joannis-Baptistae Baud. Parisiorum,
Hippolytum Walser, 1869.
5v.

NL 0452422   OC1JC

BR95
.L83
Seabury
Lohner, Tobias, 1619-1697.
Bibliotheca manualis concionatoria; ordine
alphabetico digesta...Editio novissima et
accuratissime emendata ad commodorem usum in
quinque tomos distributa cui ultimo accedit
opusculum...Parisiis, Apud Ludovicum Vivès,
1880.
5v. 27cm.

1. Roman Catholic Church. Dictionaries. 2.
Theology. Dictiona . Latin. I. Title.

NL 0452423   IEG

G95
L832b
Lohner, Tobias, 1619-1697.
Bibliotheca manualis concionatoria, ordine
alphabetico digesta. Novis titulis adaucta;
sententiis ss. patrum et doctorum illustrata
similitudinibus, motivis, mediis et doctrinis
asceticis locupletata ingeniosis pro formanda
concione in omnia themata conceptibus referta
ac indice concionatorio in evangelia festorum
et dominicarum, necnon indice generali adornata
Editio novissima et accuratissime emendata.

Cui ultimo accedit opusculum instructio
practica de munere concionandi, exhortandi et
catechizandi. Parisiis, H. Walzer, 1887.
5 v.   28 cm.

1. Catholic church - Doctrine.   I. Title.

NL 0452425   CtY-D

LOHNER,TOBIAS,1619-1697
Appendix, uberiorem materiam considera-
tionum viro apostolico perutilium suppeditat
in aureis suis opusculis, qvas instructiones
practicas inscribit R. P. Tobias Lohner ...
Praesertim in memoriali boni sacerdotis ...
Coloniae Agrippinae, Suptibus haeredum
Joannis Weidenfeldt, & Godefredi de Berges,
1682.
120 p.   8vo

Head and tail pieces.
Bound with Archdekin, Richard. Theologia
tripartita.   Coloniae Agrippinae, 1683.

NL 0452427   InU

BV 4224
L73
1691
Lohner, Tobias, 1619-1697.
Auctarium amplissimum bibliothecae manualis
concionatoriae, novis titvlis adavctvm; selectis-
simis SS. Patrum et doctorum sententiis illustratum; rarioribus quoque & fusius enarratis historijs, similitudinibus, motivis, medijs, & doctrinis asceticis locupletatum; nec non ingeniosi-
oribvs pro formanda concione conceptibus, ex fa-
mosissimis quibusvis auctoribus collectis, non
modice refertum; ac indice quadruplici adornatum;
auctorum uno ... in hoc opere contentarum.   Dilingae, Typis, & sumptibus J. C. Bencard, 1691.

976, 79 p.   34 cm.

Added title page, engraved.
Title vignette.

NL 0452429   OU PLatS WaSpG

Y264.025
L832
Lohner, Tobias, 1619-1697.
Compendium ritualis pro administratione Sacramentorum, aliorúmque
mvnervm pactoralivm, quae frequentiùs
à pastoribus animarum obiri consueverunt, ritè suscipienda. In usum et
commodum parochorum, aliorúmque
sacerdotum curam animarum habentium
collectum.   Dilingae, typis &
sumptibus J.C. Bencard, per Joannem
Federle, 1681.
232 p.   17cm.
I.Catholic Church.
Liturgy and ritual. Sacramentary. II. Title.

NL 0452430   MnU

684.6
Jes.5
L833cor
1698
LOHNER, Tobias, 1619-1697.
Compendium ritualis pro administratione
sacramentorum, aliorúmque munerum pastoralium,
quae frequentiûs à pastoribus animarum
obiri consueverunt, ritè suscipienda. In
usum et commodum parochorum, aliorúmque
sacerdotum curam animarum habentium collectum
... Dilingae, typis & sumpt. Joannis Caspari
Bencard ... 1698.
1p.l.,232p.   16.5cm.

Continued in next column

Continued from preceding column

1st issued (1681) as part of his Instructio practica nona de sacerdotii orginine
et praestantia ...

NL 0452432   MH-AH

BX2435
L6
Lohner, Tobias, 1619-1697.
Geistliche Aussfertigung Philotheae; oder, Einer Gottliebenden
und Christo durch die drey Ordens- Gelübt vermählten Seelen.
Das ist: Kurtze und gründliche Unterweisungen wie sich ein
Geistliche Ordens- Person in ihrem Geistlichen Beruff nach dem
Willen Gottes richten und verhalten soll.   Dilingen, J.C.
Bencard, 1678.
3 v. in 1.

Title varies slightly.

1. Vows.   2. Monastic and religious life.   3. Profession (in
religious orders, congregations, etc.   4. Spiritual direction.
I. Title.

NL 0452433   CU

Div.S.
265.62
L833I
Lohner, Tobias, 1619-1697.
Instructio practica de confessionibus
rite, ac fructuose excipiendis. Doctrinas
tam generales, quam speciales ad varios hominum status accommodatas complectens ...
Editio 5. Patavii, Ex typograph. semin. a-
pud Jo: Manfrè, 1717.
347 p.   16 cm.

1. Confession. I. Title.

NL 0452434   NcD

265.6
L833I
1741
Lohner, Tobias, 1619-1697.
Instructio practica de confessionibus rite,
ac fructuose excipiendis, doctrinas tam
generales, quam speciales ad varios hominum
status accommodatas complectens.   Ad junio-
rum sacerdotum potissimam utilitatem, ac in-
structionem ex variis auctoribus collecta.
Editio septima.   Patavii, Ex Typ.Semin.apud
J.Manfre, 1741.
516p.   14cm.

1.Confession. I.Title.

NL 0452435   CLSU

Lohner, Tobias, S.J., 1619-1697.
Instructio practica de munere concionandi,
exhortandi, catechizandi, continens non tantûm
praecepta ad artem concionandi discendam accom-
modata, sed etiam ideas & conceptus practicos
pro concionibus in festis B.V. & ss. dedicati-
onis, patrocinii, novi anni, Paschatis, Paras-
ceves; item in primitiis sacerdotum, peregrin-
ationibus, Confregatione Rosarii, funeribus &
sepulturis, & apud rusticos instituendis.   Ad
neo-parochorum, aliorumque curam animarum ger-
entium usum, & utilitate compsita.   Ingol-
stadii, Joannes Andreas de la Haye, 1722.
760p 17cm

NL 0452437   MnCS

Lohner, Tobias, 1619-1697.
Instructio practica octava institutiones
theologiae mysticae, seu facilem &
practicum modum Exercitia Spiritualia
S.P. Ignatii Loyolae per octiduum faciendi...
Dilingae, Typis & Sumptibus Joann.   Caspari
Bencard, 1680.
677 p.

NL 0452438   MoSU-D

VOLUME 338

Lohner, Tobias, S.J., 1619-1697.
Instructio practica prima ss. missae sacrificio juxta ritum romanae ecclesiae offerendo,
una cum rubricis ejusdem missae brevibus notis
illustratis. Editio decima. Dilingae, Joann.
Caspar Bencard, 1739.
320p 16cm

NL 0452439   MnCS MH-AH

Lohner, Tobias, S.J., 1619-1697.
Instructio practica prima - undecima ...
Dilingae, Typis et sumptibus Joann. Caspari
Bencard, 1670-1718.
11 v. 17 cm.
Library has: Instructio practica 3-11 in 5 v.
Each volume has special title page. Volumes vary
in editions.

NL 0452440   PLatS

242
912   Lohner, Tobias, S.J., 1619-1697.
L83   Instructio practica quarta pastorum continens
1701   doctrinas, & industrias ad pastorale munus pie,
fructuose, ac secure obeundum pertinentes...
Editio quarta.   Dilingae, Joannes Caspar Bencard, 1701.
282p 16cm

Bound in pigskin; boards; blind-pressed;
clasps.

NL 0452441   MnCS

Lohner, Tobias, S.J., 1619-1697.
Instructio practica quinta de confessionibus
rite ac fructuose excipiendis... Editio quarta.
Dilingae, Joannes Caspar Bencard, 1701.
211p 16cm

Bound with his Instructio practica quarta.
1701.

NL 0452442   MnCS

684.6   LOHNER, Tobias, 1619-1697.
Jes.5   Instructio practica secunda de horis
L833ips   canonicis juxta rubricas breviarii Romani
1735   ritè recitandis. In qua etiam ipsa rubricae
notis brevibus illustratae, & martyrologij
Romani nomina suis accentibus signata continentur, ad faciliorem discentium usum ac
praxin ... Editio septima ... Dilingae,
typis & sumptibus Joann. Caspari Bencard ...
1735.
8p.l.,221,[9]p. music. 17.5cm.

1st ed. (1670) has title: Instructio
practica de officio divinio ...

NL 0452444   MH-AH MnCS

Lohner, Tobias, S.J., 1619-1697.
Instructio practica septima de munere concionandi, exhortandi, catechizandi ... Editio
altera correctior. Dilingae, J. C. Bencard,
1682.
551 p. 17 cm.

NL 0452445   PLatS

242
912   Lohner, Tobias, S.J., 1619-1697.
L83   Instructio practica tertia de conversatione
1717   apostolica a curatoribus animarum pie & fructuose
instituenda... Editio quarta.   Dilingae,
Joann. Caspar Bencard, 1721.
352p 16cm

Bound with his Instructio practica prima de
ss. missae sacrificio.   1717.

NL 0452446   MnCS

Lohner, Tobias, S.J., 1619-1697.
Instructissima bibliotheca manualis concionatoria. Dilingae, Joannes Caspar Bencard, 1681.
4v 34cm

Library has vols. 1, 2, & 4 bound in one.
Contents: v.1, De virtutibus; v.2, De vitiis;
v.3, De sacramentis, novissimis...; v.4, De materiis rarius in praxi occurrentibus.

NL 0452447   MnCS

Lohner, Tobias, S.J., 1619-1697.
Instructissima bibliotheca manualis
concionatoria, in qua de virtutibus,
vitiis, sacramentis, novissimis, aliisque similibus materiis in ecclesiastica
cathedra tractari solitis, copiosa, et
selecta pro concionibus, exhort at ioni-
bvs aliisque spiritualibus instructioni-
bus materia. Nempe definitiones, divisiones, sententia, ss. scripturae & ss.
patrum, historiae sacrae & profanae, sim-
ilitudines, motiva, media doctrinae as-

ceticae, conceptus, praedicabiles, miscellanea, axiomata, & proverbia, & tandem loca authorum susiùs de tali materia
tractantium, ex optimis quibusque author-
bus, singulari delectu & industria collecta, facilique, ordinata, & grata methodo digesta proponuntur. Opus omnibus
animarum pastoribus, necnon divini verbi
praeconibus, & vitae asceticae studiosis

inprimis utile, & ad levandos concionum
labores accomodatum; cui praeter alios
indices copiosus index conceptum brevium
pro concionibus in dominicis & festis instituendis adjectus est. Editio tertia.
Pro commodiori usu ex quatuor tomis in
unum per omnes materias ordine alphabetico propositas redacta. Opera ac stvdio
R.P.Tobiae Lohner.   Venetiis, apud Jo:
Jocobum Hertz,   1695-
v.

NL 0452450   WaSpG

Lohner, Tobias, 1619-1697.
Instructissima bibliotheca manualis concionatoria ... Editio
qvarta. Quàm plurimis historijs memorabilibus, novisque
titulis perutilem & curiosam materiam continentibus tertia fere
svi parte adaucta, opera & studio r. p. Tobiæ Lohner ... Augustae Vindelicorum, Sumptibus J. C. Bencard, 1698
4 v. 33ᵐ.

NL 0452451   OU

Lohner, Tobias, 1619-1697.
Instructissima bibliotheca manualis concionatoria ... Editio
qvarta. Quàm plurimis historijs memorabilibus, novisque
titulis perutilem & curiosam materiam continentibus tertia fere
svi parte adaucta, opera & stvdio r. p. Tobiæ Lohner ... Uene-
tiis, sumptibus Jo: Jacobi Hertz, 1700.
4 v. 33ᵐ.
On cover: Biblioteca manualis concionatoria.

1. Homiletical illustrations. I. Title.

Library of Congress   BV4224.L6 1700

4-20821 Revised

NL 0452452   DLC

BV 4224
.L 6   Lohner, Tobias, 1619-1697.
1708 Q   Instructissima bibliotheca manualis
concionatoria ... Editio quinta.
Quamplurimis historiis memorabilibus,
novisque titulis perutilem & curiosam
materiam continentibus tertia fere sui
parte adaucta, opera & studio r.p. Tobiae
Lohner ... Venetiis, sumptibus Michaelis
Hertz, 1708.
4 v. 33cm.

NL 0452453   MdBJ

Lohner, Tobias, S.J., 1619-1697.
Instructissima bibliotheca manualis concionatoria, in qua de virtutibus, vitiis,
sacramentis ... grata methodo digesta proponuntur ... Ed. 5... tertia fere sui parte
adaucta ... Augustae Vindelicorum & Dilingae, sumptibus Joannis Caspari Bencard, 1712.
3 v. 34 cm.

Added engraved title page.

NL 0452454   PLatS MnCS

Lohner, Tobias, S.J., 1619-1697.
Instructissima bibliotheca manualis
concionatoria, in qua de virtutibus, vitiis,
sacramentis, novissimis, aliisq; similibus
materiis in ecclesiastica cathedra tractari
solitis, copiosa, et selecta pro concionibus,
exhortationibus, aliisque spiritualibus
instractionibus materia. Editio Sexta.
Venetiis, Sumptibus Hertzianis, 1722.
4 v.

NL 0452455   MoSU-D

WE
4667   Lohner, Tobias, 1619-1697.
Instructissima bibliotheca manualis concionatoria. Editio sexta. Quam plurimis historijs
memorabilibus, novisque titulis perutilem &
curiosam materiam continentibus adaucta.
Augustae Vindelicorum & Dilingae, Sumptibus
I. C. Bencard, 1732.
3 v. illus.

NL 0452456   CtY

f 48
L833   Lohner, Tobias, 1619-1697.
in   Instructissima bibliotheca manualis concionatoria ... Editio
1728   octava prioribus multo locupletior ...   Venetiis, ex typographia
Law   Hertziana, 1736-38 [v.1, 1738]
Library   6 v. in 4. 37cm.

Vol. 5 has title: Instructiones practicae, in quibus agitur de
sanctissimo sacrificio missae de mystica theologia. 1. editio
veneta. Vol. 6 has title: Instructiones practicae, in quibus
agitur de sacerdotii origine ... 1. editio veneta.

1. Homiletical illustrations. I. Title.

NL 0452457   CU

WB
766   Lohner, Viktor
L833m   Mensch und Heilpflanze. 2. Aufl. Linz,
1948   Pirngruber, 1948.
175 p.

Die Gebräuchlichsten Heilkräuter Österreichs; Beilage zu Mensch und Heilpflanze
(8 p. of col. illus.) pasted on back cover.

1. Botany, Medical

NL 0452458   DNLM DNAL OC1

VOLUME 338

Lohnert, Fritz, 1919–
   Die bankmässige Prüfung der Kreditwürdigkeit von In-
dustriebetrieben seit der Währungsreform. Mannheim,
1950.
   84 p. 21 cm.

   Inaug.-Diss.—Mannheim.
   Vita.
   Bibliography: p. 81–84.

   1. Credit—Germany.   I. Title.

   HG3729.G3L6   52–33688

NL 0452459   DLC MH-BA

――――――――――――――――――――――――

Lohnert, Karl: Untersuchungen über die Auffassung von
Rechtecken. Mit 12 Textfig. Leipzig & Berlin: W. Engel-
mann 1913. 78 S. 8° ¶Aus: Psychol. Studien hrsg. v.
Wundt. Bd 9.
Leipzig, Phil. Diss. v. 9. Dez. 1913, Ref. Wundt, Volkelt
[Geb. 27. Okt. 85 Untröviskwin; Wohnort: Leipzig; Staatsangeh.: Baden;
Vorbildung: OR. Heidelberg Reife 05; Studium: Heidelberg 4, Leipzig 10 S.]
                                              [U 13. 4112]

NL 0452460   ICRL MH RPB IU CtY

――――――――――――――――――――――――

Lohnes, August, 1886–
   Die Einfluss der Bibel auf die Dichtungen des Francis Quarles.
Heidelberg, 1909.   viii, 123 p.   23cm.

   Film reproduction. Negative.
   Inaug.-Diss. — Strassburg i. E.
   Vita.
   Bibliography, p. [vii]–viii.

   1. Quarles, Francis, 1592–1644.

NL 0452461   NN TxU MH CtY PU ICRL

――――――――――――――――――――――――

Lohnes, Friedrich: Das Verhalten der Blutplättchen bei Ulcus ventriculi und den bösartigen Tumoren. Giessen 1922: Christ. 11 S. 8°
Giessen, Med. Diss. v. 18. Juli 1922   [U 22. 2021]

NL 0452462   ICRL DNLM CtY

――――――――――――――――――――――――

Lohnes, Horace L., joint comp.
National petroleum association.
   A digest of state gasoline tax laws in effect December 1,
1927, compiled by Washington office, National petroleum asso-
ciation, Western petroleum refiners association. Fayette B.
Dow. Horace L. Lohnes ... [Washington, D. C.] °1927.

――――――――――――――――――――――――

Lohnes (Jo. Henricus Benjamin.) *De utilitate
hydrargyri in febre typhode inflammatoria, an-
nexis thenibus chirurgicis de tetano. 63 pp. 8°.
Tubingæ, lit. Fuesianis, [1814].
  Also, in: Wümm. Samml. med.-prakt. Diss. [etc.] 8°.
Tübingen, 1829, 8, 341–365.

NL 0452464   DNLM

――――――――――――――――――――――――

Lohneyss, Georg Engelhard von, 1552–1622.
   see Loehneyss, Georg Engelhard von,
1552–1622.

――――――――――――――――――――――――

Lohnhardt, Hellmut, 1908–
   Beitrag zur agglutination beim infektiosen
abortus.. Leipzig, 1935.
   22 p. 22 cm.

   Inaug.-diss. - Leipzig.
   Lebenslauf.
   "Literatur": p. 22.

   [Full name: Otto Hellmut Lohnhardt]

NL 0452466   DNAL

――――――――――――――――――――――――

Lohnis, Felix, 1874–
   see Löhnis, Felix, 1874–

――――――――――――――――――――――――

Lohnstein, Hugo, 1864–1918.
   Beitrag zur aetiologie, diagnose und therapie
der fremdkörper der blase nach kriegsverletzungen, von ... H. Lohnstein ... Tübingen,
Laupp, 1918.
   cover-title, p. 280–288. illus., col. plates.

   "Sonderabdruck aus Bruns' Beiträge zur klinischen chirurgie ... band 109, heft 2 (51.
kriegschirurgisches heft; kriegschirurgischer
band XI, heft 2)"
   "Literatur": p. 288.

NL 0452468   NNC

――――――――――――――――――――――――

WCA   LOHNSTEIN, Hugo, 1864–1918
L834b   Beiträge zur pathologischen Anatomie
1906   der chronischen Gonorrhöe.   Berlin,
        Coblentz, 1906.
            80 p. illus.

NL 0452469   DNLM ICRL

――――――――――――――――――――――――

Lohnstein (Hugo) [1864–1918]. *Untersuchungen über den Einfluss der Nahrung auf die
Zusammensetzung des Harns. 51 pp. 8°. Berlin, G. Bernstein, 1886.

NL 0452470   DNLM ICRL MiU

――――――――――――――――――――――――

Lohnstein, Rudolf, 1866–
   Ueber lineare homogene differentialgleichungen
zweiter ordnung, welche integrale besitzen, durch
deren umkehrung sich eindeutige funktionen zweier
variablen ergeben...   Berlin, P. Stankiewicz,
1890.
   2 p.l., 68 p., 2 l.   28 cm.   (German mathematical dissertations. Berlin, v. 8)
   Inaug.-Diss. - Berlin.
   Vita.

NL 0452471   RPB NjP

――――――――――――――――――――――――

Lohnstein (Theodor) [1866–   ]. Ein neues
Urometer. 10 pp. 8°. Berlin, 1894.
  Repr. from: Allg. med. Centr.-Ztg., Berl., 1894, lxiii.

NL 0452472   DNLM

――――――――――――――――――――――――

Lohnstein, Theodor, 1866–
   Ueber den einfluss der capillaritaet auf die gleichge-
wichts-verhaeltnisse schwimmender koerper.
Inaug. Diss.   Berlin, 1891.

NL 0452473   ICRL CtY RPB

――――――――――――――――――――――――

Lohnstein, Walter.
   Der schulz der glaeubiger von gesellschaften
mit beschraenkter haftung. 1920.
   Dissertation.

NL 0452474   PU

――――――――――――――――――――――――

Lohnstein (Zacharias) [1804–   ]. *De morbis hereditariis. 30 pp., 1 l. 8°. Berolini, lit.
Polschii, 1825.

NL 0452475   DNLM

――――――――――――――――――――――――

Der Lohnsteuer-Jahresausgleich, mit der Jahreslohnsteuer-
tabelle. 1950–
   Neuwied a. Rhein, H. Luchterhand.
      v. 30 cm.
   Issued by Bundesminister der Finanzen.

   1. Withholding tax — Germany (Federal Republic, 1949–   )
   I. Germany (Federal Republic, 1949–   ) Bundesministerium der
Finanzen.

                                              55–31979

NL 0452476   DLC

――――――――――――――――――――――――

Lohnsteuer-Tabelle für die Republik Österreich. Grosse
Ausg.
   Wien, C. Piel.
      v. 30 cm.

   1. Income tax—Austria—Law.

                                              53–19622 †

NL 0452477   DLC

――――――――――――――――――――――――

Loho-Sobolewski, Jan.
   ... Prawo opiekuńcze w dawnej Litwie, napisał Jan Loho-
Sobolewski. We Lwowie, Nakł. Towarzystwa naukowego,
1937.
   2 p. l., [3]–198, [1] p. 23½cm.   (Studja nad historją prawa polskiego im.
Oswalda Balzera. t. xv.-zesz. 2)

   "Z zasiłkiem Ministerstwa wyzn. rel. i ośw. publ."
   "Das vormundschaftsrecht im ehemaligen Litauen" (summary):
p. [173]–198.
   "Bibliografia": p. [172]–177.

   1. Guardian and ward—Lithuania.   I. Title.

                                              39–17283

NL 0452478   DLC

――――――――――――――――――――――――

Lohoff (Bernhard). *Ueber Tracheotomie bei
Larynxtuberculose. 37 pp. 8°. Würzburg, P.
Scheiner, 1891.

NL 0452479   DNLM

――――――――――――――――――――――――

Lohoff, Carl.
   ... Odontogenes neoplasma in den kieferhöhlen eines
pferdes ... Stuttgart, Druck der Union deutsche verlagsgesellschaft, 1903.
   2 p. l., 35 p. illus. 22 cm.

   Inaug.-diss.—Bern.
   At head of title: Aus dem Hygienischen institut der Tierärztlichen
hochschule zu Berlin.
   "Literatur": p. 34–35.

   1. Maxillary sinus—Tumors. 2. Horses—Diseases.

   SF867.L83   Agr 7—1725
   U. S. Nat'l Agr. Libr.   41L83
   for Library of Congress   [a64b-h†]

NL 0452480   DNAL DNLM DLC

――――――――――――――――――――――――

Lohoff (Georgius Henricus) [1805–   ]. *De
castratione. 22 pp., 1 l. 8°. Berolini, typ. fratrum Unger, 1830.

NL 0452481   DNLM

――――――――――――――――――――――――

Lohoff, Gerhard, 1903–
   Die entschädigungsansprüche der arbeitnehmer
aus stillegungen in der kaliindustrie. Ein
beitrag zur gesetzesauslegung. ... 1934.   47 p.
   Inaug. Diss. - Halle-Wittenberg, 1934.
   Lebenslauf.
   Bibliography.

NL 0452482   ICRL

VOLUME 338

Lohoff, Günther, 1908–
Das befristete rechtsgeschäft und verwandte
erscheinungen ... Göttingen, 1931.   39 p.
Inaug. Diss. –Göttingen, 1931.
Lebenslauf.
Bibliography.

NL 0452483   ICRL

JN3954
.S28
Lohoff, Günther, joint author.

Schulze, Hans, *municipal employee of Mühlhausen.*
Verwaltungsfachkunde, lehrstoffe und arbeitsaufgaben für
die verwaltungsfachklassen der berufs- und berufsfachschulen,
von Hans Schulze ... und dr. Günther Lohoff ... Grafen-
hainichen, R. Herrosé, 1943.

Lohoff, Heinrich.
... Ursprung und entwicklung der religiösen volkskunde.
Griefswald, L. Bamberg, 1934.
158 p. 23ᶜᵐ. (Deutsches werden; Greifswalder forschungen zur deutschen geistesgeschichte, hrsg. von Leopold Magon und Wolfgang Stamm-
ler. hft. 6)
"Die arbeit hat zugleich als dissertation der Philosophischen fakultät
der Ernst-Moritz-Arndt-universität Greifswald vorgelegen."—p. ₍2₎
"Literaturverzeichnis": p. 155–158.
CONTENTS.—Das problem: Begründung und begrenzung. Daten aus
der entwicklung der religiösen volkskunde.—Die anfänge der religiösen
volkskunde: Raymund Dapp. F. E. A. Heydenreich.—Schluss.
1. Folk-lore. 2. Religion—Philosophy. 3. Germany—Religion. 4. Dapp,
Raymund, 1744–1819. 5. Heydenreich, Friedrich Erdmann August, 1763–
1847. I. Title.
                                                    38–23440
Library of Congress   BR853.L6
                      ₍3₎   261

NL 0452485   DLC CU CtY NNUT ICU

LOHOFF, Isaac.
Specimen juridicum inaugurale exhibens casus
in quibus possessor invitus possessionem amitt-
it. Lugduni Batai., 1790.

(2) + 19 + (1) p.
Diss. — inaug. — Leyden.

NL 0452486   MH-L

Lohoff, Wilhelm, 1900–
... Die hintere Rachenwand im Röntgenbild...
[Berlin, 1927]
Inaug.-Diss. - Berlin.
Lebenslauf.
"Literatur-Verzeichnis": p.[36]

NL 0452487   CtY

Law   Lohr, ————, ed.

Law   Gentz, Erwin, *ed.*
Das landjahr, die gesetzlichen grundlagen und wichtigsten
bestimmungen für den handgebrauch zusammengestellt und
hrsg. von Erwin Gentz ... Eberswalde, R. Müller ₍1936₎
333 p. 17¼ cm.
———— Ergänzungsband 1937, von dr. Lohr ... Eberswalde, R. Müller, 1937.

Lohr, Aemilliana, Sister, 1896–
see Lohr, Aemiliana.

Lohr, Alfred, 1887–
...Beiträge zur Flugmeteorologie der Azoren, von Dr. Alfred
Lohr... Hamburg: A. Preilipper, 1938. 44 p. illus. (incl.
charts), 3 pl. 30cm. (Germany. Seewarte, Direktion der.
Aus dem Archiv der Deutschen Seewarte und des Marineobserva-
toriums. Bd. 58, Nr. 5.)

"Literatur-Verzeichnis," 1 p. at end of text.

1. Meteorology—Azores. I. Ser.
N.Y.P.L.   March 20, 1940

NL 0452490   NN

Lohr, Alfred, 1887–
...Ergebnisse der Hamburger Flugzeugaufstiege der deut-
schen Seewarte. Oktober 1927 bis Dezember 1929. Bearbeitet
von Dr. Alfred Lohr. Reihe 1– Hamburg: H. W. Köbner
& Co., 1931. no. charts, plates, tables. 4°. (Germany.
Seewarte, Direktion der. Aus dem Archiv der deutschen See-
warte. Bd. 49, Nr. 10.)
Similar observations made in 1921 and 1922 are published in the Annalen der
Hydrographie und maritimen Meteorologie of the Seewarte, Bd. 50, 1922, Heft 4, Bd.
51, 1923, Heft 5.
Contents: Reihe 1. Oktober 1927 bis Juli 1928.

1. Meteorology, Aeronautical—   Germany—Hamburg. I. Ser.
N.Y.P.L.   March 26, 1932

NL 0452491   NN

Lohr, Alfred, 1887–
Ueber Widerstandsänderungen von Amalgamen und einigen
leichtschmelzbaren Legierungen mit der Temperatur und der Zeit
... Von Alfred Lohr... Erlangen: Junge & Sohn, 1914.
72 p. incl. diagrs., tables. 8°.

Cover-title.
Dissertation, Erlangen.

1. Electricity—Resistance of alloys.   2. Amalgams.
N.Y.P.L.   July 9, 1925

NL 0452492   NN NIC CtY MH DNLM DNAL PU

Lohr, Anton, 1878–1920, ed.
Dichtungen; für die deutsche Familie ausgewählt ...
see under Heine, Heinrich, 1797–1856.

Lohr, Anton, 1878–1920
Geschichte der englischen literatur. Kempten, Kösel, 1911.
xii, 342 p.

"Quellen und literaturachweise": p. ₍x₎–xii.

1. English literature - History and criticism.

NL 0452494   NNC

LOHR, Anton, 1878–1920.
Richard Flecknoe. Sein leben und seine werke
Inaug.-diss., München. Naumburg, a.S.,1904.

NL 0452495   MH NNF NcD PU

Lohr, Anton, 1878–1920.
Richard Flecknoe. Eine literarhistorische untersuchung
von dr. Anton Lohr. Leipzig, A. Deichert nachf. (G.
Böhme) 1905.
xii, 114 p. 23½ cm. (Added t.-p.: Münchener beiträge zur romani-
schen und englischen philologie. Hrsg. von H. Breymann und
J. Schick. xxxiii)
"Werke Flecknoe's": p. ₍viii₎–x; "Referenzen": p. xi–xii.

1. Flecknoe, Richard, d. 1678?

PB13.M8 vol. 33   5–7433

      OCl PSt NjP
NL 0452496   DLC NN MB PBm PU PSC OClW MiU ViU OU

Lohr, Anton, 1878–1920, ed.
Die Warte, monatsschrift für literatur und kunst.
München, Allgemeine verlags-gesellschaft m. b. h., 19

NA
5586
091
L83
Lohr, Anton, 1886–
Kirche und Kloster zu Ottobeuren; ein
Führer mit 73 Abbildungen, von A. Hessenbach
₍pseud.₎ Ottobeuren, G. Braun ₍192–?₎
61 p. illus., map, plan. 23cm.

1. Ottobeuren, Ger. (Benedictine abbey)

NL 0452498   NIC MnCS

Lohr, Anton, 1886–
Sind wir machtlos gegen diesen Völkermord?
Eine nationale Frage an die Völker deutscher
Sprache, eine Gewissensfrage an die Brautleute
und Eheleute! ... Den Buchschmuck zeichnete
Josef Hengge... Augsburg, 1915.
29, [2] p. 23.5 cm. [Religious aspects of
the war] By Anton Hessenbach, pseud.
Literatur-Nachweise," p. [30–31]

NL 0452499   CtY

₍Lohr, August, and F. W. Heine.₎
Panorama battles of Chattanooga, fought Nov. 23–25, 1863...
Chicago: W. J. Jefferson ₍1885?₎. 16 p., 2 l., 1 map, 1 plan. 8°.

1. Panoramas. 2. United States.—   History : Civil war : Military, 1863.
Nov. 23–25. 3. Title. 4. Heine, F. W.
N.Y.P.L.   December 26, 1912.

NL 0452500   NN

Lohr, August, 1882–
see Lohr, August, 1882–

Lohr, August, 1892–
Ueber die retroperitonealen epidermoide und dermoide
Inaug. diss. Giessen, 1917.
Bibl.

NL 0452502   ICRL DNLM

Lohr, Burgin E.   Chapel Hill, 1922.
Geology and soils of the Burhenglen Knob
quadrangle.

NL 0452503   NcU

Lohr, Charles William.
Church Establishments expedient and beneficial.
A lecture, delivered in ... Norwich, ... 16th
April, 1847... Norwich, n.d.
33 p. 8°. [In v. 837, College Pamphlets]

NL 0452504   CtY

VOLUME 338

Lohr, Edwin Wallace, 1897–

FOR OTHER EDITIONS
SEE MAIN ENTRY
joint author.

Collins, William Dennis, 1875–
... Chemical character of surface waters of Virginia, by
W. D. Collins, E. W. Lohr, K. T. Williams, H. S. Haller, and
O. C. Kenworthy ... Richmond, Division of purchase and
printing, 1932.

GB1025
.P4L59

Lohr, Edwin Wallace, 1897–

Lohman, Stanley William, 1907–
... Ground water in north-central Pennsylvania, by Stanley
W. Lohman ... with analyses by E. W. Lohr. (Prepared in co-
operation between the United States Geological survey and the
Pennsylvania Topographic and geologic survey) Harrisburg,
Pa., Dept. of internal affairs, Topographic and geologic survey,
1939.

GB1025
.P4L62

Lohr, Edwin Wallace, 1897–

Lohman, Stanley William, 1907–
... Ground water in south-central Pennsylvania, by Stanley
W. Lohman ... with analyses by E. W. Lohr. (Prepared in co-
operation between the United States Geological survey and the
Pennsylvania Topographic and geologic survey) Harrisburg,
Pa., Dept. of internal affairs, Topographic and geologic survey,
1938.

QE173
.A2
no. 45

Lohr, Edwin Wallace, 1897–

Cady, Richard Carlysle, 1907–1943.
... Ground-water resources of the Shenandoah valley, Virginia, by R. C. Cady, with analyses by E. W. Lohr. University, Va., 1936.

Lohr, Edwin Wallace, 1897–
The industrial utility of public water supplies in the east
North-Central States, 1952, by E. W. Lohr, P. N. Brown,
and W. L. Lamar. Washington, 1953.

iv, 125 p. map, tables. 26 cm. (Geological Survey circular, 253)

1. Water-supply—Northwest, Old. 2. Water—Analysis. I. Title.
(Series: U. S. Geological Survey. Circular, 253)

QE75.C5 no. 253   551.48   G S 53–102
U. S. Geol. Survey. Libr.
for Library of Congress   [3]†

NL 0452509   DI-GS DLC WaTC

QE75
.C5
no. 197

Lohr, Edwin Wallace, 1897–
The industrial utility of public water supplies in the East
South Central States, 1952, by E. W. Lohr [and others]
Washington, 1952.

69 p. map, tables. 27 cm. (Geological Survey circular 197)

1. Water-supply—Southern States. 2. Water—Analysis. I. Title.
(Series: U. S. Geological Survey. Circular 197)

[QE75.C5 no. 197]   G S 52–235
U. S. Geol. Survey. Libr.
for Library of Congress   [3]

NL 0452510   DI-GS WaTC DLC

Lohr, Edwin Wallace, 1897–
The industrial utility of public water supplies in the the
[sic] Middle Atlantic States, 1952, by E. W. Lohr, W. F.
White, and N. H. Beamer. Washington, 1953.

iv, 129 p. map, tables. 26 cm. (Geological Survey circular 283)

1. Water-supply — Middle States. 2. Water — Composition.
(Series: U. S. Geological Survey. Circular 283)

QE75.C5 no. 283   551.49   G S 53–22
——— Copy 2.   GB701.L6
U. S. Geol. Survey. Libr.
for Library of Congress   [3]†

NL 0452511   DI-GS PPD DLC

QE75
.C5
no. 203

Lohr, Edwin Wallace, 1897–
The industrial utility of public water supplies in the
Mountain States, 1952, by E. W. Lohr [and others] Wash-
ington, 1952.

79 p. map, tables. 27 cm. (Geological Survey circular 203)
U. S. Geol. Survey. Libr.

"Erratum": slip laid in.

1. Water-supply—The West.   (Series: U. S. Geological Survey.
Circular 203)
[QE75.C5 no. 203]   G S 53–27

NL 0452512   DLC WaTC

Lohr, Edwin Wallace, 1897–
The industrial utility of public water supplies in the New
England States, 1952, by E. W. Lohr and W. F. White.
Washington, 1953.

iv, 80 p. map, tables. 27 cm. (Geological Survey circular 288)

1. Water-supply — New England. 2. Water — Composition. I.
White, Walter Finch, 1911– joint author. II. Title. (Series:
U. S. Geological Survey. Circular 288)

QE75.C5 no. 288   628.1   G S 53–235
——— Copy 2.   GB701.L62
U. S. Geol. Survey. Libr.
for Library of Congress   [3]†

NL 0452513   DI-GS DLC

Lohr, Edwin Wallace, 1897–
The industrial utility of public water supplies in the
Pacific States, 1952, by E. W. Lohr [and others] Washing-
ton, 1952.

iii, 89 p. map, tables. 26 cm. (Geological Survey circular 232)

1. Water-supply—Pacific coast.   (Series: U. S. Geological Survey. Circular 232)
[QE75.C5 no. 232]   G S 53–50
U. S. Geol. Survey. Libr.
for Library of Congress   [3]

NL 0452514   DI-GS WaTC OrP WaS WaWW

Lohr, Edwin Wallace, 1897–
The industrial utility of public water supplies in the South
Atlantic States, 1952, by E. W. Lohr [and others] Washing-
ton, 1953.

iv, 162 p. map, tables. 26 cm. (Geological Survey circular 269)

1. Water-supply — Atlantic States. 2. Water-supply — Southern
States. 3. Water—Composition.   (Series: U. S. Geological Survey. Circular 269)

QE75.C5 no. 269   628.110975   G S 53–201
——— Copy 2.   TD223.5.L63
U. S. Geol. Survey. Libr.
for Library of Congress   [a61d]†

NL 0452515   DI-GS DLC

Lohr, Edwin Wallace, 1897– joint author.

Collins, William Dennis, 1875–
... The industrial utility of public water supplies in the
United States, 1932, by W. D. Collins, W. L. Lamar and E. W.
Lohr. Washington, U. S. Govt. print. off., 1934.

Lohr, Edwin Wallace, 1897–
The industrial utility of public water supplies in the United
States, 1952, by E. W. Lohr and S. K. Love. Washington,
U. S. Govt. Print. Off., 1954.

2 v. fold. maps, diagrs., tables. 23 cm. ([U. S.] Geological Sur-
vey. Water-supply paper 1299–1300)
"Errata sheet" slip inserted in each vol.
Includes bibliographies.
CONTENTS.— pt. 1. States east of the Mississippi River.— pt. 2.
States west of the Mississippi River.
1. Water-supply—U. S. 2. Water—Composition. I. Love, Samuel
Kenneth, 1903– joint author. II. Title. (Series)

TC801.U2 no. 1299–1300   G S 54–311
——— Copy 2.   GB701.L63
U. S. Geol. Survey. Libr.
for Library of Congress   [10]†

NL 0452517   DI-GS OCU PPD OCl MB DLC

Lohr, Edwin Wallace, 1897–
The industrial utility of public water supplies in the West
North-Central States, 1952, by E. W. Lohr [and others]
Washington, 1952.

109 p. map, tables. 26 cm. (Geological Survey circular 206)

1. Water-supply, Industrial—Northwestern States. 2. Water—Composition. I. Title. (Series: U. S. Geological Survey. Circular
206)

QE75.C5 no. 206   TD223.L6   G S 52–234
——— Copy 2.
U. S. Geol. Survey. Libr.
for Library of Congress   [a62d]†

NL 0452518   DI-GS WaTC DLC NNC OCl

Lohr, Edwin Wallace, 1897–
The industrial utility of public water supplies in the West
South-Central States, 1952, by E. W. Lohr [and others]
Washington, 1952.

iv, 123 p. map, tables. 27 cm. (Geological Survey circular 221)

1. Water-supply—Southwest, New.   (Series: U. S. Geological
Survey. Circular 221)
[QE75.C5 no. 221]   G S 52–293
U. S. Geol. Survey. Libr.
for Library of Congress   [3]

NL 0452519   DI-GS WaTC OCl

Lohr, Ernst. Ueber p-Methylmercaptophenylhydrazin. [Maschinen-
schrift.] 43 S. 4° [Lag nicht vor.] — Auszug [Autogr.]: [Giessen
1923.] 2 Bl. 8°
Giessen, Phil. Diss. v. 25. Juni 1923   [U 23. 3705

NL 0452520   ICRL

Lohr, Ernst Emil.   Ger 6209.6
Die schleswig-holsteinische frage, ihre vorgeschichte und entwickelung bis zur erhebung der herzogtümer gegen Dänemark, am
24. april 1848. Der kampf bei Eckernförde und die koburgische
legende, am 5. april 1849. Giessen, J. Ricker, 1895.
pp. iii +. Geneal. table and map. (Giessener studien auf
dem gebiete der geschichte, 7.)

Schleswig–Holstein   uestion|Eckernförde, Battle of, 1848

NL 0452521   MH MnU MB

LOHR, Ernst Emil.
Die vorgeschichte zur schleswigholsteinischen
frage bis zum jahre 1810. Inaug.-diss. [Gies-
sen,1894.]

pp. 32+
"Vita", after p.32.   Ger 2230.58

NL 0452522   MH ICRL CU PU

Lohr, Erwin, 1880–1951.
Atomismus und kontinuitätstheorie in der neuzeitlichen
physik, von dr. phil. Erwin Lohr ... Berlin, B. G. Teubner,
1926.

82 p. 23 cm. (Added t.-p.: Wissenschaftliche grundfragen ... VI)
Bibliographical foot-notes.

1. Atoms. 2. Continuity. 3. Physics—Philosophy. I. Title.

Library of Congress   QC6.L47   30–763

NL 0452523   DLC OO

VOLUME 338

QC173 Lohr, Erwin, 1880–
.L8   Atomismus und kontinuitätstheorie in der neuzeitlichen physik, von dr. phil Erwin Lohr ... Leipzig ʈetc.ʈ B. G. Teubner, 1926.
    82 p. 22ᶜᵐ. (Added t.-p.: Wissenschaftliche grundfragen ... vi)

    1. Atoms. 2. Continuity.

NL 0452524   ICU MH

Lohr, Erwin, 1880–
    Ein einfacher Zusammenhang zwischen Brechungsexponent, Zähigkeit und Dichte bei Gasen.
    (In Kaiserliche Akademie der Wissenschaften, Vienna. Sitzungsberichte. Mathematisch-naturwissenschaftliche Klasse. Band 116, Halbband 2, Abteilung 2A, pp. 1281–1288. Wien. 1907.)

G9650 — Gases.

NL 0452525   MB

13545   Lohr, Erwin, 1880–
Y   Entropieprinzip und geschlossenes
v.93   Gleichungssystem. ʈWien, K.K. Hof- und Staatsdruckerei, 1917ʈ
    ʈ339ʈ–421 p. 29cm. (Akademie der Wissenschaften, Vienna. Mathematisch-naturwissenschaftliche Klasse. Denkschriften, Bd. 93)

    1. Thermodynamics.

NL 0452526   NIC NN

Lohr, Erwin, 1880–1951.
    Mechanik der Festkörper. Berlin, W. de Gruyter, 1952.
    488 p. illus. 25 cm.

    1. Mechanics.   ɪ. Title.

QA805.L6   52–3515 ‡

NL 0452527   DLC InLP NN TxU CSt

Lohr, Erwin, 1880–
    Vektor- und dyadenrechnung für physiker und techniker, von Erwin Lohr ... Mit 34 figuren im text. Berlin, W. de Gruyter & co., 1939.
    xv, 411 p. diagrs. 19½ᶜᵐ. (Half-title: Arbeitsmethoden der modernen naturwissenschaften)
    Published Edwards Bros. under the auspices of the Alien Property Custodian.

    1. Vector analysis.   ɪ. Title: Dyadenrechnung.
    Harvard univ. Library   A C 40–2322
    for Library of Congress
             QA261.L6 1939 a
        ʈa45c1ʈ†   512.89

NL 0452528   MH PSt OrCS NBuU CtY OO OU DLC TU

QA261   Lohr, Erwin, 1880–1951.
L6   Vektor- und Dyadenrechnung für Physiker
1950 und Techniker. 2. Aufl. mit einem Nachtrag. Berlin, De Gruyter, 1950.
    xv, 488 p. 19cm.

NL 0452529   CSt NN IU RPB CU NcU MH NjP TxU

Lohr, Erwin, 1880–
    Wärmestrahlung und kontinuitätstheorie, von Erwin Lohr.
    (*In* Akademie der wissenschaften in Wien. Mathematisch-naturwissenschaftliche klasse. Denkschriften. Wien, 1924. 29½ᶜᵐ. 99. bd. p. ʈ1ʈ–37)
    "Vorgelegt in der sitzung am 9. märz 1922."

    1. Heat—Radiation and absorption. 2. Continuity.   ɪ. Title.
                        A C 37–1571
    Stanford univ. Library
    for Library of Congress   ʈAS142.V314 bd. 99ʈ
        ʈ2ʈ   (506)

NL 0452530   CSt

Lohr, Erwin, 1880–*1951.*
    Zur differentialform des entropieprinzips, von E. Lohr.
    (*In* Akademie der wissenschaften in Wien. Mathematisch-naturwissenschaftliche klasse. Denkschriften. Wien, 1924. 29½ᶜᵐ. 99. bd. p. ʈ39ʈ–41)
    "Vorgelegt in der sitzung am 8. märz 1922."

    1. Thermodynamics.   ɪ. Title: Entropieprinzip.
                        A C 37–1572
    Stanford univ. Library
    for Library of Congress   ʈAS142.V314 bd. 99ʈ
        ʈ2ʈ   (506)

NL 0452531   CSt

LD3907   Lohr, Evelyn, 1918–
.G7   Patristic demonology in Old English
1947 literature... New York, 1946.
.L6   v, 92 typewritten leaves. 29cm.
    Thesis (Ph.D.) - New York university, Graduate school, 1947.
    Bibliography: p.90–92.
      1.Demonology. 2.Anglo-Saxon literature - Hist. & crit. 3.Christian literature, Early - Hist. & crit. I.Title.

NL 0452532   NNU

Lohr, Evelyn.
    Patristic demonology in Old English literature. New York, New York University, 1949.
    17 p. 23 cm.
    Abridgment of thesis—New York University.
    Bibliographical footnotes.

    1. Anglo-Saxon literature—Hist. & crit. 2. Demonology. 3. Devil in literature. ɪ. Title.

    BF1517.G7L6   829.09   51–35223

NL 0452533   DLC NcD MsU OrU TxU NcU NIC

M1562 Lohr, Felix
L635G4
    Die General-Probe im Gesangverein; Gesangs-Humoreske in Potpourri-Form für Männerchor mit Pianoforte. Op.112. Offenbach a/Main, J. André, c1896.
    21 p.

    For chorus (TB) and piano. German words.

NL 0452534   CU

Lohr, Ferenc.
    A filmszalag útja. Budapest, Királyi Magyar Természettudományi Társulat, 1941.
    viii, 344 p. illus. (part col.) 22 cm. (A Királyi Magyar Természettudományi Társulat Könyvkiadóvállalata ʈkiadványaʈ, 130. köt.)

    1. Cinematography.   ɪ. Title.

    TR850.L67   66–94405

NL 0452535   DLC CoU

Lohr, Florian, 1909–
    ... Untersuchungen über den Gehalt des Blutserums an Calcium and Kalium bei Paradentosekranken... Köln, 1932.
    Inaug.-Diss. - Köln.
    Lebenslauf.
    "Literatur- Verzeichnis": p.15.

NL 0452536   CtY

---

folio Lohr, Franz Joseph, 1705–
BX   Evangelische Milch, das ist sowohl
8066 für den Prediger, als Zuhörer, auss-
.L6   und leicht-eingehende ewige
E9   Wahrheiten auf alle Sonntag des
1753 gantzen Jahrs... von A. R. D. Francisco Josepho Lohr. Editio II. Augspurg, M. Rieger, 1735–65.
    6 v. 36 cm.
    1.Lutheran Church--Sermons.
    2.Sermons, German.

NL 0452537   MH-AH

Lohr, Fredrick.
    Anarchism, a philosophy of freedom. Foreword by Mat Kavanagh. By Fredrick Lohr. ʈLondon, F. Lohr, 1942ʈ
    68 p. 26½ᶜᵐ.
    "The substance of a series of four lectures which were delivered in London in December 1941 and January 1942."—Foreword.
    On cover: De luxe ed.

    1. Anarchism and anarchists.
                      43–18370
    Library of Congress   HX833.L6
        ʈ2ʈ   335.83

NL 0452538   DLC IU NN CSt-H

Lohr, Friedrich.
    A day in ancient Rome; being a revision of Lohr's "Aus dem alten Rom," with numerous illustrations, by Edgar S. Shumway ... New York, Chautauqua press, 1885.
    96 p. illus. (incl. plans) 20 cm.

    1. Rome (City)—Descr. 2. Rome (City)—Antiq. ɪ. Title.

    DG63.L82   4–31276 rev

            KyWAT OU OU OO OClW
NL 0452539   DLC NcD NIC MtU OrSaW WaTC MdBP MB

Lohr, Friedrich.
    A day in ancient Rome; being a revision of Lohr's "Aus dem alten Rom," with numerous illustrations, by Edgar S. Shumway ... 40th thousand. Boston, D. C. Heath & company, 1887.
    96 p. illus. (incl. plans) 20 cm.

    1. Rome (City)—Descr. 2. Rome (City)—Antiq. ɪ. Title.

    DG63.L83   4–31277 rev

NL 0452540   DLC CoU

Lohr, Friedrich.
    A day in ancient Rome; being a revision of Lohr's "Aus dem alten Rom", with numerous illustrations by Edgar S.Shumway. Boston, D.C.Heath & co., 1891.

NL 0452541   MH

Lohr, Friedrich.
    A day in ancient Rome. Being a revision of Lohr's "Aus dem alten Rom" with numerous illustrations, by Edgar S.Shumway. Boston, D.C Heath & co., 1893.

NL 0452542   MH NcU

VOLUME 338

213.376
L833
Lohr, Friedrich.
A day in ancient Rome; being a revision of Lohr's "Aus dem alten Rom" _ by Edgar S. Shumway _ Bost., D.C. Heath & co., 1908.
96p. illus., maps. 21cm.

1. Rome (City) Descr. 2. Rome (City) Antiq. I. Shumway, Edgar Solomon, 1856- ed. and tr.

NL 0452543   N

Lohr, Friedrich.
A day in ancient Rome, being a revision of Lohr's "Aus dem alten Rom" with numerous illustrations, by Edgar S. Shumway ... Boston, D. C. Heath & co., 1910.
96 p. illus.. 19 cm.

NL 0452544   ViLxW

87J97
DZ6
v.3
Lohr, Friedrich,
De infinitivi apud P. Pap. Statium et Iuvenalem usu ... defendet Fridericus Lohr ... Marpurgi, typis academicis N. G. Elwerti, 1876.
1 p. l., 74 p., 1 l. 23½cm.

Thesis, Marburg.
Volume of pamphlets.

1. Statius, Publius Papinius. 2. Juvenalis, Decimus Junius.

NL 0452545   NNC NIC CU DLC MH PU PBm

Lohr, Friedrich.
Ein Gang durch die Ruinen Roms (Palatin und Kapitol) Gütersloh, C. Bertelsmann, 1900.
72 p. illus. 22 cm. (Gymnasial-Bibliothek, 7. Heft)

1. Rome (City) Capitol. 2. Rome (City) Palatine Hill. I. Title.

DE3.G8 Heft 7   61-56866 ‡

NL 0452546   DLC CU

DG
63
L83
T7
Lohr, Friedrich.
Trans Tiberim, die Insel, vom forum olitorium bis zum Monte Testaccio; ein Gang durch die Ruinen Roms (Fortsetzung) Gütersloh, C. Bertelsmann, 1915.
148 p. illus., maps. 22cm. (Gymnasial-Bibliothek. 57)

1. Rome (City)--Descr. 2. Tiber River and Valley--   Descr. I. Series.

NL 0452547   NIC

Lohr (Gottfried). * Ein Beitrag zur Casuistik der Osteoporose. 17 pp. 8°. *München, Kastner & Lossen,* 1900.

NL 0452548   DNLM

56.7
L83
Lohr, Hans Gerhard.
Über Futtergrundlagen und Viehhaltung im Ilmenau-Meetze-Gebiet, insbesondere unter dem Einfluss der dortigen Meliorationen. Hannover, 1951.
40 p.

Inaug.-Diss. - Tierärztliche Hochschule, Hannover.

1. Reclamation of land. Germany. 2. Germany. Domestic   animals.

NL 0452549   DNAL

QC310
L6
Lohr, Harold Russell, 1922-
Heats of formation of some aqueous ions of americium. [Berkeley, 1950]
52 l. diagrs., tables.

Thesis (Ph.D.) - Univ. of California, June 1950.
Also issued as UCRL [i.e. University of California Radiation Laboratory] 686
Bibliography: p.35-36.

NL 0452550   CU

WG
330
qL883p
1936
LOHR, Henriette Antoinette.
Paroxysmale tachycardie als homogenetisch rhythme. Amsterdam, Meulenhoff, 1936.
211 p. illus.
Summary in Dutch and English.
1. Heart - Arrhythmia

NL 0452551   DNLM

RC685
.T2L8
LOHR, HENRIETTE ANTOINETTE.
Paroxysmale tachycardie als homogenetisch rhythme... Nijmegen, 1936.
[3], 211 p. diagrs. (part fold.) 26cm.
Proefschrift--Groningen.
Summary in English.
"Geraadpleegde literatuur": p.195-211.

1. Heart--Diseases.

NL 0452552   ICU ICRL

Lohr, Hermann.
Die Entwicklung des Dekorationsmalergewerbes im Grossherzogtum Baden und der heutige Zustand desselben in der Stadt Baden-Baden.
(In Verein fuer Socialpolitik. Schriften. 69. Pp. 271-311. Leipzig, 1897.)

Dec. 27,   1901
E2511 — House painting. — Decorati. — Mural decoration. — Baden, Grand Duchy. Fine arts.

NL 0452553   MB

Lohr, Ina, ed.
Alte niederländische Weihnachtslieder zusammen mit Variationen aus dem 17. Jahrhundert für ein Melodieinstrument (Blockflöte, Geige u. a.); hrsg. von Ina Lohr. Oude Nederlandsche Kerstliederen... Basel, H. Majer [1936] 16 p. 14 x 22cm.

Songs for 1 voice from Florimond van Duyse's Het oude Nederlandsche lied, and one-part instrumental versions from J. J. van Eyck's Der Fluyten Lusthof (1646) and Etienne Roger's Oude en nieuwe Hollantse boeren lieties en contredansen (ca. 1700). Dutch and German, or Dutch and Latin, words.

"Dialektübertragung von Marie Rohner," 2 l. laid in.
CONTENTS.—Ave Maria [2 voices]—Laet ons mit hartzen reyne.—Puer nobis nascitur.—O salich, heylich Bethlehem.—Huc ad regem pastorum.—Een Kindeken is ons geboren.—Met desen nieuwen jare.

1. Carols, Dutch. 2. Instrumental
N. Y. P. L.   music, 1-part—Collections—To 1800.   CARNEGIE CORP. OF NEW YORK. November 24, 1944

NL 0452555   NN

Lohr, Ina.
[Die Geburt unseres Herrn Jesus Christus. German]
Die Geburt unseres Herrn Jesus Christus, wie sie uns der Evangelist Lukas erzählt hat; für Singstimmen, Geigen und Bratsche gesetzt von Ina Lohr. Kassel, Bärenreiter-Verlag [1948]
score (23 p.) 32 cm. (Bärenreiter-Ausgabe, 2168)
Sacred cantata.

1. Cantatas, Sacred (Women's voices)—Scores. 2. Christmas music. I. Title.

M2033.L87G4   M 53-507

NL 0452556   DLC

Lohr, Ina, 1903-
Maria Aegyptiaca

see under

Faber Du Faur, Irmgard von, 1894-

Lohr, Ina.
Solmisation und Kirchentonarten. [2. Aufl., Basel, Hug [Vorwort 1948]
70 p. illus. 21 cm.

1. Solmization. 2. Musical intervals and scales. I. Title.

MT44.L6 1948   57-22256 ‡

NL 0452558   DLC IEG ICU

HQ781
L6
Lohr, Inez Durfee, 1896-
Motion pictures on child life; a list of 16 mm. films. Washington, Federal Security Agency, Social Security Administration, Children's Bureau [1952]
60 p. 27 cm.

1. Child welfare—Film catalogs. [2. Child care—Film catalogs] 3. [Moving pictures—Catalogs] I. U. S. Children's Bureau. II. Title.

362.7084   SS 52—11
U. S. Social Security   Administration. Library for Library of Congress   [52f5]

Or
NL 0452559   DHEW CLSU DCU MH OU PBm DNLM MBU DLC

Lohr, Inez Durfee, 1896-   comp.
Motion pictures on child life. [Washington, G.P.O., 1952]

Supplement, no.1- 1954-
v.

NL 0452560   MBU

Lohr, James Martin, 1879-
The tensile strengths of the copper-zinc alloys ... by James Martin Lohr ... [Ithaca, N. Y., 1913]
1 p. l., 25 p. illus., diagrs. 26½cm.
Thesis (PH. D.)—Cornell university, 1913.
"Reprinted from the Journal of physical chemistry, vol. XVII, no. 1, Jan., 1913."

1. Alloys.

     13-20019
Library of Congress   TA490.L7
Cornell Univ. Libr.

NL 0452561   NIC DLC MiU

Lohr (Joh. Andreas). * De febrilibus metastasibus. 18 pp., 2 l. 4°. *Gottingae, ex off. Schulzians, F. A. Rosenbusch,* [1769].

NL 0452562   DNLM NNNAM

VOLUME 338

LOHR, Joh. Hermann von, 1862–
Ueber die einwirkung von chlor auf resorcin.
Inaug.-diss. Marburg. 1892.

NL 0452563   MH-C CU

Lohr, Josef Albert, 1883–
... Beiträge zur bakteriologie der gehirnrückenmarks-
seuche der pferde ... Dresden, Buchdr. O. Franke, 1910.
58 p., 1 l. 23ᶜᵐ.
Inaug.-diss.—Leipzig.
Lebenslauf.
"Literaturverzeichnis": p. [54]–58.

1. Cerebro-spinal meningitis (Horse)

Agr 12–530

Library, U. S. Dept. of   Agriculture 41L832

NL 0452564   DNAL DNLM ICRL CtY

Lohr, Joseph J
Dictionary of foreign words and phrases on stamps, seals and
posters, tr. into English, by Joseph J. Lohr.   New York, 1940.
21 p.   23cm.

1. Postage stamps—Dictionaries.   2. Posters—Dictionaries.   3. Seals
(Numismatics)—Dictionaries.
N. Y. P. L.   June 30, 1947

NL 0452565   NN

Lohr, Julius.
Missions-album... Bilder aus unsern missions-
stationen in Indien... St. Louis [n. d.]
1 p. l., 20 plates.   16 x 19 cm.

NL 0452566   CtY-D

Lohr, Lawrence Luther.

North Carolina. *Dept. of public instruction.*
... A county-wide plan for the organization of the schools
of Lincoln county, North Carolina. Made by George
Howard, jr., director Division of school organization [and]
Lawrence L. Lohr, assistant supervisor of high schools, 1923.
Approved by the State board for county-wide planning.
Raleigh, N. C., State superintendent public instruction [1923]

Lohr, Lawrence Luther.

Latshaw, Harry Franklin.
... The Lohr-Latshaw Latin form test for high schools,
by Harry Franklin Latshaw, M. A. Chapel Hill, N. C.,
Bureau of educational research, School of education,
University of North Carolina [1923]

TA23
.C4
1952
Lohr, Lenox Riley, 1891–   ed.
Centennial of Engineering, 1952, inc.
[Centennial of engineering, 1852–1952; history and pro-
ceedings of symposia. Edited by Lenox R. Lohr. [Chicago,
1953]

Lohr, Lenox Riley, 1891–
Fair management, the story of A Century of Progress
Exposition; a guide for future fairs. Chicago, Cuneo Press,
1952.
300 p. illus. 24 cm.

1. Chicago. Century of Progress International Exposition, 1933–
1934.   I. Title.

T501.B1L6   606   52–14383

PU-W OCl CaBVa
NL 0452570   DLC ICN GAT WaU Wa OrP MB NN NNC IEN

Lohr, Lenox Riley, 1891–
50 years of motor cars, 1895–1945 [by] Major Lenox R. Lohr
... New York, The Newcomen society of England, American
branch, 1946.
28 p. incl. front. illus.   23ᶜᵐ.
Text on p. [2]–[4] of cover.
"This Newcomen address ... was delivered during the '1945 Springfield
dinner' of the Newcomen society of England, held at Hotel Kimball,
Springfield, Massachusetts, U. S. A., on November 30, 1945, in celebration of the 50th anniversary of America's first automobile race."
"First printing: April 1946."

1. Automobiles.   I. Newcomen society for the study of the history
of engineering and technology, London. American branch.   II. Title.

HE5623.L6   629.209   46–7646

NL 0452571   DLC MB WHi CU ICJ ICU

[Lohr, Lenox Riley] 1891–
Formulae for the solution of geometrical transposition
ciphers ... Geneva, Ill., Riverbank laboratories, 1918.
24 p. illus. 28½ᶜᵐ. ([Riverbank laboratories] Publication no. 19)
"Two hundred copies of this publication were printed of which this
is no. 97."
The author's names are supplied in ms. on the t.-p.

1. Ciphers.   I. Friedman, William Frederick, 1891–   joint author.
II. Title.

Library of Congress   Z104.L83   20–9075

NL 0452572   DLC CLSU

Lohr, Lenox Riley, 1891–
Magazine publishing, by Lenox R. Lohr ... Baltimore, The
Williams & Wilkins company, 1932.
xiv, 328 p. illus., plates, diagrs. 21ᶜᵐ.
Bibliography: p. 303–304.

1. Journalism.   2. Periodicals.   I. Title.
Library of Congress   PN4832.L6   32–19137
— Copy 2.
Copyright A 53242   [5]   070

NN MB OCU ViU
NL 0452573   DLC NcU OrU OrCS MtU PP NcRS OCl OU OO

Lohr, Lenox Riley, 1891–
The partnership of religion and radio, by Lenox R. Lohr ...
[New York] Reprinted by the Federal council of churches of
Christ in America [1938]
1 p. l., 16 p. 21¾ᶜᵐ.
"An address by Lenox R. Lohr, president, National broadcasting
company, to the biennial meeting of the Federal council of churches of
Christ in America, at the hotel Statler, Buffalo, New York, December 7,
1938."

1. Radio broadcasting.   2. Religion.   I. Title.

A 41–1327

Columbia univ.   Libraries
for Library of Congress   [3]

NL 0452574   NNC MH MB

Lohr, Lenox Riley, 1891–
Social phases of advertising, by Lenox R. Lohr. [New York?
1938]   11 p.   21cm.
"An address . . before the third annual National federation of sales executives
convention and the eighth annual Southwestern sales managers conference, at Dallas,
Texas . May 19, 1938."

1. Advertising.   I. Title.
N. Y. P. L.   October 20, 1939

NL 0452575   NN

Lohr, Lenox Riley, 1891–
Some social and political aspects of broadcasting, by Lenox R.
Lohr.   [Washington? D. C., 1938]   18 p.   20½cm.
"Address by Lenox R. Lohr . . delivered at the round table conference on 'New
issues in transportation and communication' held in connection with the twenty-sixth
annual meeting of the Chamber of commerce of the United States at Washington,
D. C., May 4, 1938."

1. Radio—Social and economic   aspects.
N. Y. P. L.   July 9, 1940

NL 0452576   NN NjR

Lohr, Lenox Riley, 1891–
Television broadcasting; production, economics, technique,
by Lenox R. Lohr ... with a foreword by David Sarnoff ...
1st ed.   New York and London, McGraw-Hill book company,
inc., 1940.
xiv, 274 p. illus., diagrs. 23½ cm.
"'The three Garridebs', a typical television script with production
directions": p. 225–265.
"Rules of the Federal communications commission governing television broadcast stations, June 18, 1940": p. 266–269.

1. Television.   I. Doyle, Sir Arthur Conan, 1859–1930.   The adventure of the three Garridebs.   II. Title.

Library of Congress   TK6630.L57   40–14320
[50v1]   621.388

NcD NIC NcRS DAU ViU Or CaBVa
NL 0452577   DLC NIC PPD PPT PSt PP OOxM OCl OU ICJ

627.09761
M973
Lohr, Lenox Riley, 1891–
164464 ... Wilson dam at Muscle Shoals on the Tennessee River near
Sheffield, Florence and Tuscumbia, Alabama, is located 166
miles west of Chattanooga, Tennessee, and 148 miles east of
Memphis, Tennessee, on the Southern Railway System ...
Washington, D. C., [1926].
27 p. illus., maps (1 double). 24½ᶜᵐ.
At head of title: Southern Railway System.
"Information contained herein in regard to Muscle Shoals was prepared by
Captain L. R. Lohr, Corps of Engineers, U. S. Army, ... and is distributed by
the Southern Railway System."

NL 0452578   ICJ RPB NNC

Lohr, Ludwig.
see Löhr, Ludwig.

Lohr, Max, 1864–1931.
see Löhr, Max Richard Hermann, 1864–1931.

325.73   Lohr, Otto, 1872–
L83a   Die anfänge deutscher einwanderung in
Nordamerika. (in Deutsche erde, 12 jahr-
gang, 1913, heft 4, p.99–104)

NL 0452581   IU

VOLUME 338

Lohr, Otto, 1872–
　... A brief historical review of the achievements of German
nationals in the early days of American colonization. The
period from 1564 to 1682 inclusive, by Otto Lohr ... Hoboken
₍N. J.₎ 1923.
　7, ₍1₎ p. 20½ᵐ. (The Concord society. Historical bulletin no. 1)

　1. Germans in the U. S. 2. U. S.—Hist.—Colonial period.
　Library of Congress　　　　E184.G3L83　　　　23–6800

NL 0452582　　DLC MWA NN

E364.6　LOHR, OTTO, 1872–
.G3L8　　Das deutschamerikanertum vor hundert
　　　jahren and der krieg von 1812–1815, von
　　　Otto Lohr, New York ... ₍Chicago₎ German-
　　　American historical society of Illinois,
　　　1915. 59p.

　　　"Separatabdruck aus dem Jahrbuch der
　　　Deutsch-amerikanischen historischen
　　　gesellschaft von Illinois. Jahrgang 1914."
　　　Autographed by author.

NL 0452583　　InU

Lohr, Otto, 1872–
　The first Germans in North America and the German
element of New Netherland, by Otto Lohr. New York
₍etc.₎ G. E. Stechert & co., 1912.
　15, ₍1₎ p. 22½ᵐ. $0.25

　1. Germans in the U. S. 2. Germans in New York (State)　ı. Title.
　Library of Congress　　　E184.G3L84　　　13–1110

NL 0452584　　DLC PU PHi PPLT ODW ICJ NN

DD119　　Lohr, Otto, 1872–　　joint ed.
.3
.B4 •　Beyer, Hans Joachim, 1908–　　ed.
　　　Grosse Deutsche im ausland; eine volksdeutsche geschichte
　　　in lebensbildern, herausgegeben von Hans Joachim Beyer und
　　　Otto Lohr. Stuttgart, Union deutsche verlagsgesellschaft
　　　₍1939₎

E184　　Lohr, Otto, 1872–　　tr.
.A1C715
　　　Creel, George, 1876–
　　　Neueinwanderergruppen in den Vereinigten Staaten im
　　　ersten Weltkrieg, nebst einem statistischen Anhang. Aus
　　　dem Englischen übers. von Otto Lohr und Fritz Kotzel.
　　　₍Stuttgart₎ Publikationsstelle Stuttgart–Hamburg, 1944.

F105　　Lohr, Otto, 1872–　　tr.
.A1K625
　　　Koenig, Samuel.
　　　Das Volksgruppengemisch in den Vereinigten Staaten am
　　　Beispiel von Connecticut; gekürzte Übersetzung der Schrift:
　　　Immigrant settlements in Connecticut; their growth and
　　　characteristics. Hartford, Connecticut, State Depart-
　　　ment ₍1₎ of Education, 1938, von Samuel Koenig. In Ver-
　　　bindung mit dem Artikel: Group frustration in Connecticut,
　　　in: American journal of sociology, Bd. 46, 1940 ₍1. e. Bd. 47,
　　　1941₎ S. 157–166, von David Rodnik ₍1₎ Aus dem Engli-
　　　schen übers. von Otto Lohr und Robert Huber. ₍Stuttgart₎
　　　Publikationsstelle Stuttgart–Hamburg, 1944.

Lohr, Paul.
　Le printemps d'Yver und die quelle zu Fair Em, von
dr. Paul Lohr.' Berlin, E. Felber, 1912.
　2 p. l., 57, ₍2₎ p. 22ᵐᵐ. (Added t.-p.: Literarhistorische forschungen ...
hft. xlix)

　1. Yver, Jacques, 1520–1572. Le printemps d'Yver. 2. Fair Em.
　　　　　　　　　　　　　　　　　　　　　12–15533
　Library of Congress　　　PN35.L6　vol. 49

NL 0452588　　DLC OU MiU NN CU NcU PU NN MH

Lohr, Paul Louis, 1885–
　Untersuchungen über die blattanatomie von alpen- und
ebenenpflanzen. ... Groningen, M. de Waal, 1919.
　2 p. l., 61, ₍1₎ p., 1 l. illus., 12 fold. tables. 23½ᵐ.
　!naug.-diss.—Basel.
　Vita.
　"Corrigenda": 1 leaf laid in.
　"Separatabdruck von dem ₍Recueil des travaux botaniques néerlandais₎
volume xvi. livraison ı. 1919."
　"Literatur-verzeichnis": p. ₍58₎-59.

　1. Botany—Ecology. 2. Leaves—Anatomy. 3. Alpine flora.

NL 0452589　　MiU MH CtY ICRL IaU

Lohr, Vergil Claybourne, joint author.
　　　　　　　　　　　　　FOR OTHER EDITIONS
　　　　　　　　　　　　　SEE MAIN ENTRY
Holley, Clifford.
　　Mastery units in physics (revised) by Clifford Holley ...
₍and₎ Vergil C. Lohr ... edited by W. R. Teeters ... Chicago,
Philadelphia ₍etc.₎ J. B. Lippincott company ₍°1939₎

Lohrberg, Arthur.
　Aenderungen in der Handelspolitik Britisch-Indiens, von Dr.
Arthur Lohrberg ... ₍Hamburg,₎ 1927. 30 p. 8°.
　Cover-title.
　Published in part as the author's inaugural dissertation. Hamburg, 1926.
　Repr.: Übersee-Jahrbuch, 1927.

388042A.　1. Protection—India.　　　1916–1927.
N. Y. P. L.　　　　　　　　　　　　　　　December 21, 1928

NL 0452591　　NN MiU

Lohre, Heinrich, 1876–　　ed.
　Märkische sagen, gesammelt und herausgegeben von professor dr. H. Lohre. Mit titelbild. Leipzig-Gohlis, H. Eich-
blatt, 1921.
　xvi, 199, ₍1₎ p. front., illus. 19½ᵐ. (Half-title: Eichblatts Deutscher
sagenschatz. bd. 2)
　"Quellen": p. 187–196.

　1. Legends—Brandenburg. 2. Folk-lore—Brandenburg.　ı. Title.
　　　　　　　　　　　　　　　　　　　　A C 37–1896
　Chicago. Univ. Library　　　PT915.E34　vol. 2
　for Library of Congress　　　₍2₎

NL 0452592　　ICU MH IU OCl ICN ICarbS

Lohre, Heinrich, 1876–
　... Von Percy zum Wunderhorn. Beiträge zur geschichte
der volksliedforschung in Deutschland. Von Heinrich
Lohre. Berlin, Mayer & Müller, 1902.
　xii, 136 p. 23½ cm. (Added t.-p.: Palaestra ... xxii)
　Series title also at head of t.-p.
　"Fr. D. Gräter und die mitarbeiter der 'Bragur' ": p. 89–112.
　"Die ersten 37 seiten dieser arbeit erschienen schon im sommer
1901 unter dem titel 'Zur geschichte des volksliedes im 18. jahrhun-
dert,' als Berliner dissertation."—Vorbemerkung.
　1. Percy, Thomas, bp. of Dromore, 1729–1811. Reliques of ancient
English poetry. 2. Arnim, Ludwig Achim, freiherr von, 1781–1831. Des
knaben wunderhorn. 3. Folk-songs, German—Hist. & crit. 4. Gräter,
Friedrich David, 1768–1830.　ı. Title.
　PD25.P3　no. 22　　　　　　　　　4–1558
　—— Copy 2.　　　　PT507.L7

　　　OU MB MH ViU NjP
NL 0452593　　DLC MoU CU NcU PU PSC PBm MiU OO OCl OCL

　Zur geschichte des volksliedes im 18 jahrhundert. Inaug.-diss. Berlin,1901.

　1 pam.　　　　　　　　　　25222.36.15

NL 0452594　　MH ICRL CtY OCl MH

Lohren, Arnold.
　Afghanistan; oder, Die englische handelspolitik in Indien, beleuchtet vom standpunkte
deutscher handels-interessen... von A. Lohren.
Potsdam, Gropius'sche buchhandlung (M. Stein)
1878.
　34 p. fold., map. 24 cm. in cover 26 cm.
　"Vortrag gehalten im Verein für deutsche
volkswirthschaft, Berlin, 27. november 1878".
　1. Gt. Brit. – Commercial policy. 2. Eastern
question (Central Asia) 3. Afghanistan.

NL 0452595　　CU

HG297　Lohren, Arnold.
.L85　　Die Durchführung der Goldwährung beleuchtet
　　　vom Standpunkte der Handelsbilans. Berlin,
　　　B. Behr's Buchhandlung (E. Bock) 1881.
　　　134 p.
　　　Stamp over imprint reads: Potsdam, Gropius'sch.
　　　Buch- & Kunsthandlung O. Postorius.

　　　1. Gold standard. 2. Balance of trade.

NL 0452596　　ICU ICJ

Lohren, Arnold.
　Die entwicklung der deutschen Woll-Industrie
vor und nach dem Abschluss des deutschfranzösi-
schen Handelsvertrags. Eine historischstatistische
Kritik der Rede des Staatsministers. Dr. Delbrück
im Reichstag am 22. Februar 1879. Berlin,
B. Behr, 1879.
　46 p. 8°.
　In: TK p. v. 48, no. 19.

NL 0452597　　NN

Lohren, Arnold.
　Entwurf eines Fabrik-und Werkstätten-Gesetzes
zum Schutz der Frauen-und Kinder-Arbeit; herge-
leitet vom Standpunkte der ausländischen Konkurrenz. Potsdam: Gropius, 1877.
　v. 1 l., 121 (1) p. 8°.
　In: TK p. v. 49, no. 13.

NL 0452598　　NN NcD

H
703　Lohren, Arnold.
.51　　Grundzüge zur rationellen bestimmung
　　　der minimal-zölle und untersuchung der
　　　ursachen des verfalles der deutschen in-
　　　dustrie... Potsdam,1876. (with List,
　　　Friedrich. Die lehren der handelspo-
　　　litischen geschichte der civilisirten
　　　staaten Europa's... 1877)

NL 0452599　　ICN NN

Lohren, Arnold
　Die kämm-maschinen für wolle,baumwolle,
flachs und seide geordnet nach ihren
systemen, von A.Lohren ... mit einem
atlas in folio,37 tafeln enthaltend...
Stuttgart,J.G.Cotta, 1875-96.
　3v.in 2. 23cm. and atlas of XXXVII double
pl. 31cm.
　Title of teil 3 reads:"Die kämm-maschinen
nebst hechel- und dressing-maschinen."

　1. Carding-machines.

NL 0452600　　DP

VOLUME 338

Lohren, Arnold.
Kolonialgeld, ein beitrag zur beurteilung der währungsfrage, von A. Lohren ... Köln, M. DuMont-Schauberg, 1886.
46 p. 22ᵐ.

1. Currency question—Germany.   I. Title.
1—20726
Library of Congress   HG999.L84

NL 0452601   DLC ICJ

Lohren, Arnold.
Eine kritik des bimetallismus. Korreferat über die währungsfrage in der Freien wirthschaftlichen vereinigung des Reichstags erstattet von Arnold Lohren ... Hrsg. von dr. Hans Kleser. Köln, M. Du Mont-Schauberg, 1885.
19 p. 25¼ᵐ.

1. Bimetallism.
1—20727
Library of Congress   HG1002.L83

NL 0452602   DLC NcD

Lohren, Arnold.
Minimalzolle für Getreide und Rohstoffe. Referat über die Stellung der Landwirthschaft zum Zollprogramm des Fürsten Bismarck, gehalten auf dem Congress deutscher Landwirthe, Berlin am 24. Februar, 1879. Berlin, B. Behr, 1879.
36 p. 8°.
In: TK p.v. 49 no. 11.

NL 0452603   NN

4HJ   Lohren, Arnold.
440   Das System des Schutzes nationaler Arbeit aufgestellt und vertheidigt. Potsdam, Gropius'sche Buchhandlung, 1880.
312 p.

NL 0452604   DLC-P4 NN

Lohrengel (Robert) [1870-]. *Hysterische Psychose mit schweren Lähmungen; Mutismus, Schlucklähmung, Paraplegie. 26 pp. 8°. Tübingen, F. Pietzcker. 1898.

NL 0452605   DNLM ICRL

PN6461   Lohrengel, W
.L63   Altes Gold; deutsche Sprichwörter und Redensarten, nebst einem Anhange. Clausthal, Grosse, 1860.
83p.

1. Proverbs, German. I. Title.

NL 0452606   NcU ICN CU

Lohrentz, Fritz, 1892-
Die zivilrechtliche Stellung der unehelichen Kinder und ihre Reform. (Auszug) ... von Fritz Lohrentz ... Königsberg i. Pr., O. Kümmel, 1920.
14 p., 1 l. 21½cm.
Inaug.-Diss. - Königsberg i. Pr.
"Lebenslauf": leaf at end.

NL 0452607   MH-L DNLM ICRL

H
289.747
L83s   Lohrenz, Gerhard
Sagradowka; die Geschichte einer mennonitischen Ansiedlung im Süden Russlands. Von Gerhard Lohrenz... Rosthern, Sask., Echo-Verlag; Druck von J. Regehr, North Kildonan, Man., 1947.

112 ₍3₎p. illus., ports., map. 23cm.
(Historische Schriftenreihe, Buch 4)

NL 0452608   ViHarEM MH-AH IEG

NK8   Lohrenz, John H   1893-
L833g   Glaubenshelden in der christlichen Hiedenmission ₍i.e. Heidenmission₎ von J.H. Lohrenz und Maria Lohrenz. H₍i₎llsboro, Kan., Mennonite Brethren Pub. House, 1919.
175 p. 20 cm.

1. Missionaries. I. Lohrenz, Maria joint author. II. Title.

NL 0452609   CtY-D

KB
H   Lohrenz, John H   1893-
L833m   The Mennonite Brethren church. Hillsboro, Kan., Board of Foreign Missions of
1950   the Conference of the Mennonite Brethren Church, 1950.
335p. illus. 25cm.

1. Mennonite Brethren Church. History.
2. Mennonite Church. History. 3. Mennonites. 4. Mennonites in Kansas.

NL 0452610   KU CtY-D ViHarEM MH-AH NN CoFS

Lohrenz, John H   1893-
What hath God wrought! The Mennonite Brethren Mission to the Telugus of India, 1898-1948. Hillsboro, Kansas, Board of Foreign Missions of the Conference of the Mennonite Brethren Church of North America, 1948.

30p. 19 1/2cm. map on back cover.

NL 0452611   ViHarEM

Lohrenz, Kuno.
Nützliche und schädliche insekten im walde, von Kuno Lohrenz ... Halle a. S., H. Gesenius, 1907.
viii, 117 p. 16 col. pl. (incl. front.) 22ᵐ.

1. Trees. Pests.
Agr 8-1145
Library, U. S. Dept. of   Agriculture   423L832

NL 0452612   DNAL ICJ

Lohrenz, Kuno.
Nützliche und schädliche insekten in garten und feld, von Kuno Lohrenz ... Anhang. Gesetz, betreffend die bekämpfung der reblaus vom 6. juli 1904. Halle a. S., H. Gesenius, 1905.
vii, ₍1₎, 99 p. 16 col. pl. 22ᵐ.

1. Entomology, Economic.
Agr 9-915
Library, U. S. Dept. of   Agriculture   423L832G

NL 0452613   DNAL CU NjP ICJ

427   Lohrenz, Kuno.
L833   Praktischer leitfaden für käfersammler. Eine gründliche anleitung zum fangen, züchten, ueberwintern, präparieren und sammeln der käfer, ihrer eier, larven und puppen. Leipzig [19—]
72 p. illus. 19 cm. (On cover: Bibliothek Ernst. bd. 190)
Cover-title: Leitfaden für käfersammler...

NL 0452614   DNAL

Lohrer, Alfons, 1884-   Das Versicherungsvertragsgesetz und die allgemeinen Unfall- und Haftpflichtbedingungen der Versicherungsgesellschaften. München 1912: Wild. 80 S. 8°
Erlangen, Jur. Diss. v. 22. Jan. 1913, Ref. Sehling
[Geb. 9. Mai 84 München; Wohnort: München; Staatsangeh.: Bayern; Vorbildung: Ludwigs-Gymn. München Reife Juli 03; Studium: München 8 S.; Rig. 25. Nov. 12.]   [U 12. 5020]

NL 0452615   ICRL CtY NIC NN

Lohrer, Alice, 1907-
In what respects should we strengthen our library program? ₍Springfield, V. L. Nickell, Superintendent of Public Instruction, State of Illinois, 1951.
32 p. (Illinois Secondary School Curriculum Program. Consensus study no. 6. Inventory B)

1. School libraries.

NL 0452616   NNC LU

Z
675   Lohrer, Alice, 1907-
.I3   Indianapolis school library survey, 1953-1954.
L85   ₍Prepared for the Board of School Commissioners of Indianapolis. n.p., 1954?₎
50 p. illus. 28 cm.
Parts 1-2 only of the 3 pts.issued.
"Part III of this study is published separately and is of value primarily to the Indianapolis schools. It consists of thumb-nail sketches and recommendations for the ... elementary schools."

1.School libraries. I.Indianapolis. Board of School Commissioners. II. Title. Full name: Mary Alice Lohrer.

NL 0452617   MiU CU NNC

027.08
qL833   Lohrer, Alice, 1907-
Indianapolis school library survey, 1953-1954. Urbana, Illinois, University of Illinois, Library School ₍1954₎

2 pts. in 1 v. (50 p.) illus. 28cm.

"Part 3 of this study is published separately and is of value primarily to the Indianapolis schools." - p. 50.

1. School libraries in Indiana. Indianapolis.

NL 0452618   MnU

no. 199   Lohrer, Alice, 1901-
The teacher librarian training program, 1900-1944. Chicago, 1944.

Microfilm (positive) made by the Chicago University Library Dept. of Photographic Reproduction.
Collation of the original: 148 l.
Thesis (M.A.) - Chicago University.
Bibliography: l. 141-148.

1. Librarians.   I. Title.

NL 0452619   NjR

VOLUME 338

Z
675
.S3
I 4
Lohrer, Alice,   comp.
What should we do to strengthen our school
library program? Prepared by Alice Lohrer
[and others] [Springfield] Supt. of Public
Instruction, State of Illinois, 1953.
2 v. in 1. (Illinois Curriculum Program.
Consensus study, no. 6. Inventory 6)

Bound with: Manual for discussion leaders;
why are these principles important in our
school library program? (Consensus study, no.6)

1. School libraries--Illinois. I. Title.
II. Manual for discussion leaders: why are
these principles important in our school
library program? (Series)

NL 0452621   INS LU NNC

Lohrer, Frieda, 1906-
     see   Löhrer, Frieda, 1906-

Lohrer, Joseph.
Rettung durch das kind oder Untergang! München, Graphische Kunstanstalt [193-?]
69 p. 18 cm.

1. Population.   I. Title.

HB881.L65   55-53994 ‡

NL 0452623   DLC NNC

Lohrer (Julius). * Ueber den Uebergang der Am-
moniaksalze in den Harn. 37 pp. 8°. *Dorpat,*
E. J. Karow. 1862.

NL 0452624   DNLM

Lohrer, Liselotte (Bäuerle)
Faust
     see under   Goethe, Johann Wolfgang von,
1749-1832. Faust. Two or more versions.

Lohrer, Liselotte (Bäuerle)
Sebastian Sailers Komödien. Giessen, Von Münchowsche
Universitäts-Druckerei, 1943.
108 p. 25 cm. (Giessener Beiträge zur deutschen Philologie, 81)
"Verzeichnis der benutzten Werke": p. 100-108.

1. Sailer, Sebastian, 1714-1777.   (Series)

Chicago. Univ. Libr.   A 49-337*
for Library of Congress   [1]

NL 0452626   ICU MoU PBm

Lohrer, Nicolas
     see
Lorer, Nikolaĭ Ivanovich, 1795-1873.

Lohrer, Otto
Beitraege zur anatomischen systematik.
Inaug. Diss. Marburg, 1885.

NL 0452628   ICRL MH

Lohrer, Wilhelm
Gibt es eine gerichtsbarkeit des reiches im
deutschen reiche?
Inaug. Diss. Erlange, 1905
Bibl.

NL 0452629   ICRL NIC

Lohri, Anne.
A study of St. Thomas in the mediaeval saint's legend ... April, 1934.

v,[2],2-179 leaves. 29cm.

Research report - University of
Southern California, 1934.
Typewritten.

NL 0452630   CLSU

Lohrisch, Hans.
Methoden zur untersuchung der menschlichen faeces. Von
Hans Lohrisch ... Mit 49 abbildungen im text.
(*In* Abderhalden, Emil, ed. Handbuch der biologischen arbeits-
methoden ... Berlin, 1920-   25cm. abt. IV. Angewandte chemi-
sche und physikalische methoden. t. 6, 1. hälfte (1926) p. [33]-356
incl. illus., tables)
Bibliographical foot-notes.

1. Feces--Analysis.   A C 36-2669

Title from Ohio State   Univ.
Library of Congress   [QH324.A3 1920 abt. 4, t. 6]
       [2]   (574.072)

NL 0452631   OU

Lohrisch (Hans Rudolf) [1877-   ]. *Zur
pathologischen Anatomie der posttraumati-
schen Erkrankungen des Rückenmarks. 40
pp., 1 l. 8°. *Leipzig, B. Georgi,* 1901.

NL 0452632   DNLM CtY

Lohrisch, Hermann, 1882-
De papinii statii silvarum poetae studiis rhetoricis.
. Inaug. Diss. Halle, 1905.

NL 0452633   ICRL NjP PU CtY CU MH

Lohrisch, Hermann, 1882-
Im Siegessturm von Lüttich an die Marne; Erlebnisse eines
Mitkämpfers aus den ersten Wochen des Weltkriegs, von Dr.
Herm. Lohrisch... Mit...einem Briefanhang aus dem Kriege
1870/71.   Leipzig: Quelle und Meyer, 1917.   vii p., 1 l., 186 p.
maps (2 double, 1 fold.)   8°.

1. European war, 1914-   .—Cam-   paigns, West. 2. European war,
1914-   .—Personal narratives (Ger-   man).
N. Y. P. L.   October 28, 1919.

NL 0452634   NN DLC-P4 CSt-H NjP

HF3567
.V6
Lohrisch, Lothar, joint ed.
1909-
Voss, Friedrich Wilhelm, ed.
Ost-Handel; Handbuch für den Handel mit Ländern im
Osten. Schriftleitung: Fr. W. Voss, L. Lohrisch. Redak-
tionelle Bearbeitung: H. Baron v. Fölkersamb. [Köln, Deut-
scher Wirtschaftsdienst [*1955-

Lohrisch, Lothar, ed.
Stahl- und Eisenbau. Hrsg. in Zusammenarbeit mit dem
Wirtschaftsverband Stahl- und Eisenbau. [Köln, K. Stan-
ber, 1955]
149 p. illus. 32 cm. (Westdeutsche Wirtschafts-Monographien,
Folge 4)
Includes bibliography.

1. Building, Iron and steel.   2. Steel industry and trade—Germany
(Federal Republic, 1949-   )   3. Iron industry and trade—Germany
(Federal Republic, 1949-   )   I. Title.

TA684.L56   64-39098 ‡

NL 0452636   DLC

Lohrisch, Lothar, ed.
Steinkohle. [Köln-Lindenthal, K. Stauber, 1953]
164 p. illus., ports., diagrs. 31 cm. (Westdeutsche Wirtschafts-
Monographien, Folge 1)
Bibliography: p. 162-163.

1. Coal—Germany (Federal Republic, 1949-   )   2. Coal trade-
Germany (Federal Republic, 1949-   )   I. Title.   (Series)

TN808.G3L6   59-17882

NL 0452637   DLC

Lohrisch, Lothar, 1909-
Die verwirklichung des führergrund-
satzes bei der erneuerung des rechts
der kapitalgesellschaften ... von Lo-
thar Lohrisch ... Düsseldorf, G.H.
Nolte, 1936.
viii, 26 p., 1 l. 22cm.
Inaug.-Diss. [Köln.
"Lebenslauf": 1 l. at end.
"Literatur-Verzeichnis": p. vi-viii.

NL 0452638   MH-L CtY

Lohrisch (Robert) [1853-   ]. *Ueber die
Wirkungen des Jaborandi. 33 pp. 8°. *Berlin,*
F. Lange. [1875].

NL 0452639   DNLM

Lohrisch, Werner.
Bestimmung von waermeuebergangszahlen durch dif-
fusionsversuche.
Inaug. diss. - Muenchen, (Tech. Hoch.) 1928.

NL 0452640   ICRL

Lohrisch, Wilhelm Hermann, 1882-
     see   Lohrich, Hermann, 1882-

Lohrke, Eugene
     see   Loehrke, Eugene William, 1892-

LOHRMANN, Gabriel.
Dissertatio theologica, qva eviden ter demonstratur, ex ipsorum vul[]sic dictorum reforma-
torum qvi nempe absolutum electionis aeternae
decretum expresse non staturin imo etiam nos-
trates,dur ipsis istud attribuunt,absoluti men-
dacii arguere hand verentusententia ac doctrinis commentitium ac fictum istud absolutu
decretum. Jenae, 1682.

4°. pp.(2), [ ].   Tr. 448.(1)

NL 0452643   MH

VOLUME 338

Lohrman, Herbert Paul, 1900–
A history of early Tuscarawas County, Ohio, for the schools ₁by₁ H. P. Lohrman ... published by the Tuscarawas County historical society. New Philadelphia, O., Acme printing company ₁ᶜ1930₁
54 p. illus. 23½ᶜᵐ.

1. Tuscarawas Co., O.—Hist.
Library of Congress   F497.T9L83
———— Copy 2.
Copyright A 20262   ₁2₁   977.166   30–12285

NL 0452644   DLC OC1WHi OC1C–M

Lohrman, Herbert Paul, 1900–
Field experience in teacher education... 1942.
Thesis (PH.D.) – Ohio state univ. 1942.

NL 0452645   OU

LOHRMANN, F.
Die Gefahr des Haltens von Tieren, Rostock. Inaug.-Diss. Cassel, 1903.

NL 0452646   MH-L ICRL

Lohrmann, Gustav, 1879–
Ueber die sekundaeren skelettveraenderungen... Inaug. diss. Greifswald, 1905.

NL 0452647   ICRL MiU DNLM

Lohrmann, Heinrich Friedrich.
Die altnordische bauernsaga in der deutschen erziehung, von dr. Heinrich Fr. Lohrmann. Erfurt, K. Stenger, 1938.
148, ₁1₁ p. 23ᶜᵐ. (Added t.-p.: Volkhafte schularbeit; beiträge zur deutschen erziehung, hrsg. von dr. Arthur Hoffmann ... Walter Kramer ... ₁und₁ Richard Vogel)
"Eingesehenes schrifttum": p. 147–₁149₁

1. Sagas—Study and teaching.   I. Title.
Library of Congress   PT7181.L6   46–33854
₁2₁   839.6

NL 0452648   DLC WU NN CtY CU

Lohrmann, Heinrich Friedrich, joint author.
Lübbe, Fritz.
Deutsche Dichtung in Vergangenheit und Gegenwart, ein Führer durch die deutsche Literatur, von Fritz Lübbe und Heinrich Fr. Lohrmann. 5. Aufl. Hannover, C. Meyer, 1943.

Lohrmann, Heinrich Friedrich.
Die entwicklung zur realistischen seelenhaltung im zeitdrama von 1840 bis 1850, von Heinrich-Friedrich Lohrmann. Berlin, Junker und Dünnhaupt, 1931.
3 p. l., ₁5₁–112 p. 23ᶜᵐ. (Added t.-p.: Literatur und seele; beiträge zur psychogenetischen literaturwissenschaft ... bd. 1)
"Literaturverzeichnis": p. 111–112.

1. German drama—19th century—History and criticism.

Title from Wisconsin   Univ. Printed by L. C.   AC33–2077

NL 0452650   WU OO NN MH RPB

Lohrmann, Ludwig
Vermischte Gedichte ... 1. Bd. 1816.
iv, [5]–188, [2] p. 17ᶜᵐ.
No more published.

NL 0452651   CtY

Lohrmann, Marta, 1902–
... Prothetische Behandlung erworbener Gaumendefekte...   Kufstein [1926]
Inaug.-Diss. - München.
Lebenslauf.
Literaturverzeichnis: p. 15.

NL 0452652   CtY

Lohrmann, Rudolf Gerhard.
Zur beurteilung von eisenkerner in der schwachstromtechnik. Inaug. diss. Dresden, Tech. hoch., n.d. (Berlin, 1929)

NL 0452653   ICRL

Lohrmann, Wilhelm Gotthelf, 1796–1840.
Karte des Mondes. Mittlere Libration. Nach eigenen Messungen und Beobactungen in den Jahren 1822–1836. Leipzig, Johann Ambrosius Barth [n.d.] Broadside 60x85 cm. (in portfolio)
Title engr. in German, French, and English. Lithographed by Werner.

NL 0452654   ICJ

Lohrmann, Wilhelm Gotthelf, 1796–1840.
Mondcharte in 25 sectionen und 2 erläuterungstafeln, von Wilhelm Gotthelf Lohrmann. Mit erläuterungen und selenographischen ortsbestimmungen unter benutzung des von den herren F.W. Opelt und M.Opelt revidirten und ergänzten materials zugleich als supplement zu Lohrmann's Topographie der sichtbaren mondoberfläche abth. I. Hrsg. von dr.J.F.Julius Schmidt ... Leipzig, J.A.Barth, 1878.
4 p. l., 49, ₁1₁, 4 p. incl. tables. front. (port.) 31½ x 27ᶜᵐ. and portfolio of 27 pl. 32½ x 28ᶜᵐ.
1. Moon—Photographs, maps, etc. I. Schmidt, Johann Friedrich Julius, 1825–   1840, ed. II. Title.
QB595.L83

NL 0452655   MiU ICJ CtY NjP DN-Ob

Lohrmann, Wilhelm Gotthelf, 1796–1840.
Die Sammlungen der mathematisch-physicalischen Instrumente und der Modellkammer in Dresden
see under   Dresden. Mathematisch-physikalischer Salon.

Lohrmann, Wilhelm Gotthelf, 1796–1840.
Topographie der sichtbaren Mondoberflaeche. Erste Abtheilung. Auf Kosten des Verfassers. Dresden, bei demselben; Leipzig, bei J. F. Hartknoch, 1824.
₁12₁, 110, xviii p. plates. 30ᶜᵐ.
No more published.

1. Moon - Surface.

NL 0452657   NNC DN-Ob

Lohrscheid, Ernst Jakob,   . Ueber Kaliumsulfat-Zusatz zur Injektionslösung. [In Maschinenschrift.] 25 S. m. 1 Tab. 4°(2°). — Auszug: Bonn (1921): Kendler. 2 Bl. 8°
Bonn, Med. Diss. v. 25. Okt. 1921, Ref. Kantorowicz
[Geb. 25. Juli 97 Bonn; Wohnort: Bonn; Staatsangeh.: Preußen; Vorbildung: G. Bonn Reife 16; Studium: Bonn 8 S.; Coll. 25. Okt. 21; Zahnärztl. Approb. 25. Mai 21.]
[U 21. 2741]

NL 0452658   ICRL

Lohrum (Carolus Philippus). * De processuum peritonei differentia et metamorphosi. 15 pp. 8°. Wirceburgi, F. E. Nitribitt, 1841.

NL 0452659   DNLM PPC

Lohrum (Joh.) * Beiträge zur Geschichte und Kritik des ausführenden Wendungsverfahrens durch Unterstützung und Benutzung der Selbstwendung. 35 nn. 8°. Giessen, W. Keller, 1861. c.

NL 0452660   DNLM

Lohse (A.) * Ueber den secundären Verschluss von Knochenhöhlen durch die Naht. [Erlangen.] 17 pp. 8°. Nürnberg, G. P. J. Bieling-Dietz, 1882.

NL 0452661   DNLM

Lohse, Bernd.
Australien und Südsee heute, Länder der Sehnsucht. Frankfurt am Main, Umschau Verlag ₁1953₁
212 p. illus. 25 cm.

1. Australia—Descr. & trav. 2. Oceanica—Descr. & trav.
DU22.L52   54–29001 ‡

NL 0452662   DLC CLU NN

Lohse, Bernd, ed.
Europa-Camera. 1951–
Frankfurt am Main, Frankfurter Societäts-Druckerei.

Lohse, Bernd.
Kanada, Land von morgen? Frankfurt am Main, Umschau Verlag ₁1954, ᶜ1955₁
215 p. illus. 25 cm.

1. Canada—Descr. & trav.   I. Title.
F1015.L86   55–17558 ‡

NL 0452664   DLC CaBVa NhD PPG

Lohse, Bernhard, 1928–
Das Passafest der Quartadecimaner. Gütersloh, C. Bertelsmann, 1953.
147 p. 23 cm. (Beiträge zur Förderung christlicher Theologia. 2. Reihe: Sammlung wissenschaftlicher Monographien, 54. Bd.)
Includes bibliography.

1. Quartodecimans.   I. Title.
BV55.L6   54–1882 ‡

NL 0452665   IaU PPiPT IEG TNJ-R NjPT NjNbS MoSU-D
DLC CBBD NcD NNJ CtY-D OCH ICU MH-AH

VOLUME 338

ND588
.H16L8
Lohse, Bruno, 1911-
Jakob Philipp Hackert, leben und anfänge seiner
kunst ... ₍Emsdetten (Westf.) 1936₎
170 p.
Inaug.-diss.--Frankfurt a. M.
"Bibliographie"₁ p.117-142.

1. Hackort, Jacob Philipp, 1737-1807.

NL 0452666   ICU GU OU WaU NN CtY NjP CSt

Lohse, Charlotte.
The mysterious continent; the story of the adventurous sailors who discovered the south Pacific islands, by Charlotte Lohse
and Judith Seaton. Maps and illustrations by W. R. Lohse.
Indianapolis, New York, The Bobbs-Merrill company ₍1944₎
165 p. incl. front., illus. maps (part double) 22ᶜᵐ.
"First edition."

1. Oceanica—Disc. & explor. 2. Explorers.   ɪ. Seaton, Judith, joint
author. ɪɪ. Title.

Library of Congress   DU22.L53   44-8979
                         ₍5₎   999

NL 0452667   DLC NIC Wa WaS Or OrP TxU OO OC1

HD
4815
Z99
no.71
Lohse, Dorothea.
Die Arbeitsbeanspruchung der weiblichen
Arbeitskräfte in bäuerlichen Betrieben mit
Sonderkulturen. ₍Hohenheim, 1955₎
126 p. diagrs. (part fold.) tables (part
fold.) 21 cm.

Diss. - Landwirtschaftliche Hochschule,
Hohenheim.

NL 0452668   NIC

Lohse, Eduard, 1924-
Märtyrer und Gottesknecht; Untersuchungen zur urchrist-
lichen Verkündigung vom Sühntod Jesu Christi. Göttingen,
Vandenhoeck & Ruprecht, 1955.
219 p. 25 cm. (Forschungen zur Religion und Literatur des Alten
und Neuen Testaments, n. F., 46. Heft. Der ganzen Reihe, 64. Heft)
Habilitationsschrift—Mainz.
Bibliography : p. ₍214₎-219.

1. Atonement (Judaism)   2. Atonement.   3. Servant of Jehovah.
4. Bible. N. T.—Theology.   ɪ. Title.   (Series)

BT265.L6   A 56-4861
California. Univ. Libr.
for Library of Congress   ₍a58c1₎†

        ICU NNC NcD NN NIC CtY-D NjPT
NL 0452669 CU WaWW DLC MH-AH IEG NjP NNJ PU DDO OCH

Lohse, Eduard, 1924-
Mark's witness to Jesus Christ. ₍Translated from the German by Stephen Neill₎ New York, Association Press ₍1955₎
98 p. 20 cm. (World Christian books ₍8₎)

1. Bible. N. T. Mark—Criticism, interpretation, etc.   ɪ. Title.

BS2585.L57   226.3   55-7567 rev ‡

        PPEB ICU OrP
NL 0452670 DLC ICU MB NcD PPT PP OO KyU KyLxCB FU

Lohse, Eduard, 1924-
Die Ordination im Spätjudentum und im Neuen Testament. Berlin, Evangelische Verlagsanstalt ₍1951₎
108 p. 24 cm.
Diss.—Göttingen.

1. Semikkah.   ɪ. Title.

BM652.L6   54-592 ‡

        NNUT PPDrop PPEB CtY-D MH-AH NN OCH PPiPT
NL 0452671 DLC NNJ NcD DDO NjPT NNC PPLT MH ICU

Lohse, Erhard, 1907-
Versuch einer typologie der felszeichnungen von
Bohuslän ... von Erhard Lohse ... Dresden, Git-
tel ₍1934₎
36 p., 1 l. 6 plates. 29½ᶜᵐ.

Thesis, Leipzig.
Plates in cover-pocket.
"Literaturverzeichnis": p. 5-7.

1. Sweden - Antiquities. 2. Petroglyphs.
3. Art, Primitive.

NL 0452672   NNC CtY DLC ICRL PU

Lohse, Ernst, 1909-
Histologische untersuchungen über die
streptokokkenmastitis des rindes... 1933.
37 p.

NL 0452673   DNAL

Lohse, Ernst Gustav
      see
Lohse, Gustav, 1901-

LOHSE, Félix.
La prostitution des mineures en France avant
et après la loi du 11 Avril 1908. Thèse.
Paris, 1913.

NL 0452675   MH-L

HB849
.I55
1935a
Lohse, Franz, joint ed.

International congress for studies on population. 2d, Berlin,
1935.
Bevölkerungsfragen; bericht des Internationalen kongresses
für bevölkerungswissenschaft, Berlin, 26. august-1. september
1935, herausgegeben im auftrage des präsidenten und des ar-
beitsausschusses von dr. Hans Harmsen und dr. Franz Lohse.
Mit 64 abbildungen. München, J. F. Lehmann, 1936.

NL 0452676

Lohse, Franz, 1908-
Die entwicklung der trampschiffahrt in der
nachkriegszeit. ... Dresden, 1934. 73 p.
Inaug. Diss. - Kiel, 1934.
Lebenslauf.
Literatur-Verzeichnis.

NL 0452677   ICRL CtY

Lohse, Fred.

Steigendes Jahr; sechs Lieder für Sopran und Klavier.
Gedichte von Gottfried Kölwel. Leipzig, Edition Peters
₍1955₎
14 p. 27 cm. (Collection Litolff, Nr. 5183)

For soprano and piano.

CONTENTS.—Lob der Osterkraft.—Hingebung.—Nach dem grossen
Wind.—Sommerlied.—Letzter Sommer.—Ausblick.

1. Songs (High voice) with piano.   ɪ. Kölwel, Gottfried, 1889-
ɪɪ. Title.

M1621.L   M 59-1061

NL 0452678   DLC

Lohse, Friedrich.
...Ein Jahrhundert Eisenbahn, von Friedrich Lohse... Berlin: Verlag der Verkehrswissenschaftlichen Lehrmittelgesellschaft
m.b.H., 1930. 55 p. incl. diagrs., tables. illus., plates. 2. ed.
8°. (Verkehr und Wissen. Heft l.)

Plates printed on both sides.
"Diese Schrift ist aus einem im Rahmen staatswissenschaftlicher Fortbildungskurse
(Stettin 1929) gehaltenen Vortrag des Verfassers hervorgegangen."

1. Railways—Hist. I. Ser.
N. Y. P. L.   July 17, 1931

NL 0452679   NN IU

W 4
W95
1955
LOHSE, Friedrich, 1925-
Untersuchungen zur tubulären
Rückresorptionskapazität für Glukose
bei langdauernder Zuckerbelastung.
Würzburg, 1955.
13 p. illus.
Inaug.-Diss. - Würzburg.
1. Glucose - Assimilation & excretion
2. Kidneys - Function tests

NL 0452680   DNLM

Lohse, Friedrich Wolfgang
      see Lohse, Wolfgang, 1892-

QD445
.C8L8
Lohse, Fritz.
Die bromcyanpyridinreaktion und ihre
anwendung auf einige arylamin-sulfon- und -
carbonsaeuren.
Leipzig, 1906.
85p.
Inaug. diss. Dresden, tech. hoch.

NL 0452681   DLC

Lohse ₍Fritz₎ ₍1897- ₎. *Ein Fall von
Plaut-Vincent'scher Angina mit nachfolgen-
der Diphtherie. 10 pp. 8°. Leipzig, 1922.

NL 0452682   DNLM CtY ICRL

Lohse, G
Drachenkämpfer und befreier in der älteren
griechischen und deutschen sage; eine mythologische
skizze. ₍Wurzen, 1907₎ 29p.26cm.

Wissenschaftliche beilage zum progr.des Königl.
gymn.zu Wurzen,1907, nr.686.

NL 0452683   CU NjP

Lohse, G., y compañia, sucesores.
Alegato de buena prueba...
      see under Enríquez, Gumesindo.

Lohse, G., y compañia sucesores, plaintiff.

Compañía telefónica mexicana.
Contestación de la Compañía telefónica mexicana al alegato
de buena prueba de los Sres. G. Lohse y cᵃ. sucesores en el juicio
que siguen sobre la validez de los privilegios de 24 y 25 de
mayo de 1886. Pedimento del Sr. promotor fiscal y sentencia
del Juzgado 1°. de distrito de esta capital. México, Impr. de
F. Diaz de Leon, 1888.

VOLUME 338

Lohse, Gerhart.
... Geschichte der Ortsnamen im östlichen Friesland zwischen Weser und Ems; ein Beitrag zur historischen Landeskunde der deutschen Nordseeküste, von Gerhart Lohse. Oldenburg i. O.: G. Stalling, 1939. 223 p. chart. 23cm. (Oldenburger Forschungen. Heft 5.)

"Abkürzungen und Literaturnachweise," p. [201]-209.

1. Geography—Names—Germany—
N. Y. P. L.   Friesland, East. I. Ser.
                                   October 1, 1940

NL 0452686   NN

Lohse, Gerhart.
Grundsätzliches zur Bildung, Bibliographie und Katalogisierung altnordischer Büchertitel. Köln, Greven, 1954.
45 p. 21 cm. (Arbeiten aus dem Bibliothekar-Lehrinstitut des Landes Nordrhein-Westfalen, Heft 5)

1. Icelandic and Old Norse literature—Addresses, essays, lectures.

PT7119.L6   58-48798 ‡

NL 0452687   DLC MU NNC IU MiU NIC

Z720
.J8C6   Lohse, Gerhart, joint author.

Corsten, Hermann, 1889–
Kölner Schule. Festgabe zum 60. Geburtstag von Rudolf Juchhoff. Hrsg. von Hermann Corsten und Gerhart Lohse. Köln, Greven Verlag, 1955.

NL 0452688

Lohse, Gerhart.
Xanten und das Nibelungenlied.
(In Bonner Jahrbücher des Rheinischen Landesmuseums in Bonn und des Vereins von Altertumsfreunden im Rheinlande. Kevelaer, Rhld. 28 cm. Heft 153 (1953) p. [141]-145)

1. Nibelungenlied. 2. Xanten, Ger.

[DD491.R4B7 Heft 153]   A 54-6815

Chicago. Univ. Libr.
for Library of Congress   [3]

NL 0452689   ICU

W 4
M961   LOHSE, Gisela, 1928–
1954   Über Zahnverfärbungen. [München?]
             1954.
             75 ℓ. illus.
             Inaug.-Diss. - Munich.
             Typewritten copy.
             1. Teeth - Enamel

NL 0452690   DNLM

Lohse, Gottfried, 1879–
Ueber einen Fall von Meningealapoplexie...
Leipzig, 1907.
Inaug.-Diss. - Leipzig.
Lebenslauf.
"Literatur": p.[33]

NL 0452691   CtY ICRL DNLM

Lohse, Günter, joint ed.

Heiss, Friedrich, 1897–   ed.
Deutschland und der korridor; in zusammenarbeit mit Günter Lohse und Waldemar Wucher, herausgegeben von Friedrich Heiss. Berlin, Volk und reich verlag, 1939.

DD190
.F8H4   Lohse, Günter, joint ed.

Heiss, Friedrich, 1897–   ed.
Deutschland und der Westraum; in zusammenarbeit mit Günter Lohse und Waldemar Wucher herausgegeben von Friedrich Heiss. Berlin, Volk und reich verlag, 1941.

Lohse, Günter.
Die gebrochene Neutralität, Belgiens und Hollands Entscheidung für England. [Essen] Essener Verlagsanstalt [1943]
268 p. 21 cm.
Bibliography: p. 267-268.

1. Belgium—Neutrality. 2. Netherlands—Neutrality.

D749.L618   55-45164

NL 0452694   DLC WU OKentU NcD MiU IU NcD IaU NN

Lohse, Günter.
De geschonden neutraliteit, de beslissing van Nederland en België voor Engeland. Vertaald door Jacques Melis. Amsterdam, Uitgeverij Westland, 1944.
327 p. 20 cm.

1. Netherlands—Neutrality. 2. Belgium—Neutrality. i. Title.

D749.L62   48-41740*‡

NL 0452695   DLC

D763
.N6H4   Lohse, Günter.

Heiss, Friedrich, 1897–
... Der sieg im norden: ein bericht vom einsatz des deutschen volksheeres in Dänemark und Norwegen, mit einer aussenpolitischen einleitung von legationsrat Günter Lohse und einem militärpolitischen beitrag von oberst Rudolf ritter von Xylander. Berlin, Volk und reich verlag, 1942.

D743
.2
.H37   Lohse, Günter.

Heiss, Friedrich, 1897–
Der Sieg im Westen, ein Bericht vom Kampf des deutschen Volksheeres in Holland, Belgien und Frankreich. Mit einer aussenpolitischen Einleitung von Günter Lohse und einem militärpolitischen Beitrag von Rudolf Ritter von Xylander. Prag, Volk und Reich Verlag, 1943.

Lohse, Gustav, 1901–
... Über subkutane Veletzungen intraabdomineller Organe durch stumpfe Gewalt... Schwerin (Mecklb.) [1927?]
Inaug.-Diss. - Hamburg.
Lebenslauf.
"Literatur": p. 20-21.
x. Lohse, Ernst Gustav, 1901–

NL 0452697   CtY MiU

QD341
.L9L82   Lohse, Gustav Otto, 1870–
             Ueber benzophenonderivate.
             Greifswald, 1895.
             26p.
             Inaug. diss. Greifswald.

NL 0452698   DLC CtY DNLM

Lohse, H
Die Rhein-brücke bei Cöln... Nach amtlichen quellen. Berlin, Ernst, 1863.
24p. plates (part fold., part double) tables, diagrs. F.

NL 0452699   IaU

LOHSE, H. W.
Om kali- og fosforsyre-gødskningens teori. The theory of potash and phosphorus fertilization. n.p., 1930.
Diagrs.
Cover serves as title-page.
"Den kgl. veterinaer- og landbohøjskoles. Adeling fen landbruigets plantedyrkning, meddelelse nr. 8, Februar, 1930", pp. [19]-99.

NL 0452699-1   MH

Lohse, Hans
Schmalkalden; Wanderung durch eine alte Stadt. [Bilder zeichneten H.Siebert und A.Oehring] Hrsg. von der Leitung des Schmalkalder Schlossmuseums. Schmalkalden [1949]

NL 0452700   MH

Lohse, Hans, 1886–
Klinische Erfahrungen über das Auftreten der Grippe des Jahres 1918 im Bereich einer Armee des westlichen Kriegsschauplatzes... Kiel, 1919.
Inaug.-Diss. - Kiel.
Lebenslauf.
"Literatur": p.[25]

NL 0452701   CtY DNLM

Lohse, Heinz, 1899–
Das spontane bauchdeckenhaematom.
Inaug. diss. Leipzig, [1929.]
Bibl.

NL 0452702   ICRL CtY

Lohse, Henry William.
Catalytic chemistry, by Henry William Lohse ... Brooklyn, N. Y., Chemical publishing co., inc., 1945.
xiv, 471 p. illus., diagrs. 22ᵐ.
Includes bibliographical references.

1. Catalysis. i. Title.
                                   45-8719
Library of Congress *   QD501.L8139
                                   [20]

PSC CaBVaU WaT OrU OrCS MtU IdU CaBVa CaBVaU
ICJ DNAL MiHM NcC NcD NcGU NcRS PPSKF PPAtR PPLas
NL 0452703   DLC NIC CU TxU PBm PSt PPD PP ViU MB TU

LOHSE, Herbert.
Vorgänger (sc. im besitz) § 858 II; 2 B.G. Rechtsvorgänger (sc. des gegenwärtigen besitzers) § 861, II B.G.B. Würzburg, 1917.
(5)43 p.
Inaug.-diss. —— Würzburg.

NL 0452704   MH-L ICRL

VOLUME 338

Lohse (Herbert Conrad) [1877-]. *Ein Beitrag zu der Lehre von der Einwirkung des heissen Rades auf den menschlichen Stoffwechsel. 21 pp. 8°. Halle s. S., E. Karras, 1900.

NL 0452705   DNLM MiU

Lohse, Hermann, 1890-
Die Sicherheitsleistung durch Hinterlegung nach dem Rechte des Bürgerlichen Gesetzbuchs ... von Hermann Lohse ... Greifswald, J. Abel, 1913.

51 p. 22½cm.

Inaug.-Diss. - Greifswald.
"Literatur": p.[3]-5.

NL 0452706   MH-L ICRL

Lohse, Herwart, 1880-
Quaestiones chronologicae ad Xenophontis Hellenica pertinentes ... Lipsiae, typis Roberto Noske, 1905.

3 p. l., 106 p. col. table. 23 cm.

Inaug.-diss.—Leipzig.
Vita.

1. Greece—Hist.—Chronology. 2. Xenophon. Hellenica.

PA4494.H5L7   6-38019 rev

NL 0452707   DLC CU CtY

Lohse, J., tr.

Rosenberg, Adolf, 1850-1906.
Leonardo da Vinci, by Adolf Rosenberg; tr. by J. Lohse; with 128 illustrations from pictures and drawings. Bielefeld and Leipzig, Velhagen & Klasing; [etc., etc.] 1903.

Lohse, J.
Vittoria Colonna. Florence, Giulio Giannini & son, n. d.
72 p. illus.

NL 0452709   MiD TU

Lohse, J   , writer on insurance.
Wie ist ein fortbestand der Hamburgischen allgemeinen versorgungs-tontine zu sichern? Beleuchtet von J. Lohse, H. Boutin, Fr. Heinrich Coqui. Hamburg, J.P.Erie, 1832.
14 p. 19.5 cm.

1. Hamburgische versorgungs-tontine.
2. Insurance, Life - Tontine policies. I. Boutin, H   , joint author. II. Coqui, Fr Heinrich, joint author. III. Title.

NL 0452710   MH-BA

Lohse, Johanna. Erdbeben in Neu-Seeland.
6 pp. (Deutsch rundschau, v. 49, 1886, p. 302.)

NL 0452711   MdBP

Lohse, Johanne.
Mistaken views on the education of girls. 16°. Christchurch, N. Z., 1884.

NL 0452712   DNLM

Lohse, Karl.
Die Technik des Kontobuch-Einbandes im Handwerks- und im Fabrikbetrieb, von Karl Lohse.   Halle s. S.: W. Knapp, 1926.
54 p.   8°.

1 mounted, col'd sample.

1. Bookbinding. 2. Account books.
N.Y.P.L.   January 20, 1928

NL 0452713   NN ICJ

Lohse, Karl.
Der Werkstoff Pappe, seine Entstehung und Verarbeitung. Für Buchbinder, Kartonager und andere graphischen Gewerbe auf Grund handwerklicher Erfahrungen zusammengetragen von Karl Lohse.   Stuttgart: "Das Deutsche Buchbinderhandwerk", M. Hettler, 1937.   79 p. incl. diagrs.   illus.   23½cm.

1. Pasteboard. I. Das Deutsche   Buchbinderhandwerk.
N.Y.P.L.   May 17, 1940

NL 0452714   NN

Lohse, Kurt, 1907-
Entwicklung und system des bahnpolizeirechts unter berücksichtigung preussischen landesrechts ... [Altdamm] 1933.

NL 0452715   MiU

Lohse, Oscar, 1878-
Über additionen an verbindungen, die ein system konjugierter kohlenstoff doppelbindungen enthalten. ... 41 p.
Inaug. Diss. - Berlin, [1904].
Lebenslauf.

NL 0452716   ICRL CtY

Lohse, Oswald
    see Lohse, Wilhelm Oswald, 1845-1915.

Lohse, Otto, 1863-
Die Übertragung des Aktienrechts ... von Otto Lohse. Dessau, Anhaltische Buchdruckerei Gutenberg, 1908.

58 p., 1 l. 22cm.

Inaug.-Diss. - Heidelberg.
"Lebenslauf": leaf at end.
"Literaturverzeichnis": p.[3]

NL 0452718   MH-L ICRL NN

Lohse, Otto Joseph.
Kinder- heil- und -erholungsstätten. Bericht von Dr. Lohse ... Leipzig, Duncker & Humblot, 1907.
4 p. l., [3]-99, [1] p. incl. tables. 23cm. (Added t.-p.: Schriften des Deutschen vereins für armenpflege und wohltätigkeit. 80. hft.)

1. Children—Hospitals and asylums. 2. Charities—Germany.

8-3500
Library of Congress   HV274.D4 80. hft.

NL 0452719   DLC CU

Lohse, Otto Joseph.
Zwangsmassregeln gegen arbeitsscheue und gegen säumige nährpflichtige. Hauptbericht erstattet von dr. Lohse ... Mitbericht erstattet von stadtrat Samter ... Leipzig, Duncker & Humblot, 1909.
vi, 80 p. 23cm. (Added t.-p.: Schriften des Deutschen vereins für armenpflege und wohltätigkeit. 88. hft.)

1. Labor laws and legislation—Germany. 2. Unemployed. I. Samter, Hans.

10-773
Library of Congress   HV274.D4

NL 0452720   DLC CU ICJ NN

Lohse, Remie.
The miniature camera in professional hands, by Remie Lohse. New York, The Studio publications, inc.; London, The Studio, ltd. [*1939]
119 p. incl. 48 pl. 23cm.
A collection of the author's photographs.

1. Photographs. I. Title.
Library of Congress   TR690.L6   39-10047
——— Copy 2.
Copyright A 128092   [5]   779

NL 0452721   DLC MH-FA Or OrCS OrU NcRS OU OCl

Lohse, Remie.
... Rhythm and repose. New York, London, A. A. Knopf, 1937.
5 p. l., [80] p. of illus., 1 l. 30¼cm.
"First edition."
Issued in box.

1. Photography, Artistic. 2. Human figure in art. I. Title.
Library of Congress   TR675.L6   37-22794
——— Copy 2.
Copyright A 109734   [3]   779

NL 0452722   DLC CU

Lohse (Richard). *Ueber das Recidiv des Ileotyphus. Nach dem Material der medicinischen Klinik zu Freiburg i. Br. in den Jahren 1885-97. 41 pp. 8°. Freiburg i. Br., U. Hochrather, 1898.

NL 0452723   DNLM ICRL

Lohse, Richard Paul, 1902-
L'architecture internationale de demain
    see under   Bauen+ [i. e. und] Wohnen (Zürich)

Lohse, Richard Paul, 1902-
Neue Ausstellungsgestaltung. Nouvelles conceptions de l'exposition. New design in exhibitions. [Version française par André Rivoire; English translations by the English Institute] Erlenbach-Zürich, Verlag für Architektur [1953]
260 p. illus. 24 x 29 cm.

1. Exhibitions. I. Title.

T396.L6 1953   606   53—22888

CtY NcU KMK MdBWA Or OrU MtBC CaBVaU NTR
NL 0452725   DLC GAT OOxM OC1 NcRS TxU MB NNC MiD CU

Lohse, Richard Paul, 1902-

Bauen+ [i. e. und] Wohnen (Zürich)
Neues Bauen - gutes Wohnen. Individuelle Wohn- und Ferienhäuser aus neun Ländern; ausgewählte Beispiele aus der Zeitschrift "Bauen + Wohnen." [Von] Richard P. Lohse, Jacques Schader [und] Ernst Zietzschmann, hrsg. von Adolf Pfau. Ravensburg, O. Maier [1954]

VOLUME 338

728
L834N
Lohse, Richard Paul, 1902–
New buildings, pleasant homes,
by R. P. Lohse [and others].
Zurich, Baven & Wohnen, c1954.
183 p. (chiefly illus.)

Text in German, French, and
English.

NL 0452727   WaT

Lohse, Richard Paul, 1902–
New design in exhibitions; 75 examples of the new form
of exhibitions. New York, Praeger [1954]
260 p. illus, plans. 24 x 29 cm. (Books that matter)
German, French, and English.
First ed. published in Switzerland, 1953 under title: Neue Ausstellungsgestaltung. Nouvelles conceptions de l'exposition. New design
in exhibitions.

1. Exhibitions.   I. Title.

T396.L6 1954   606   54-9291

OC1SA
NcC PBL TxU OrU CaBVa OrAshS OrCS OrU Wa OOxM PPD
NL 0452728   DLC WaT WaS CU ViU PPMoI MB ICJ OC1W PP

LOHSE, Rudolf:
Über die Lichtabsorption, die Radiolumineszei
dem Farbstoffcharakter und die Ausbleichfähig-
keit der Fulgide. Weida i. Th. 1909: Thomas
& Hubert.
103 S.
Leipzig, Phil.Diss. v.23. Sept. 1909.

NL 0452729   MH-C CtY OCU PU ICRL

Lohse, Rudolf, Arzt: Die Behandlung der Arthritis deformans
des Hüftgelenks. (Aus d. chir. Universitätskl. d. Charité
in Berlin.) [In Maschinenschrift.] 66 S. 4º[2º]. — Auszug:
Berlin (1921): Ebering. 2 Bl. 8º
Berlin, Med. Diss. v. 4. Febr. 1921, Ref. Köhler, Hildebrand
[Geb. 15. Dez. 92 Salzwedel; Wohnort: Berlin; Staatsangeh.: Preußen; Vorbildung: G. Wittenberg Keife 12; Studium: Tubingen 2, Berlin 8 S.; Coll.
1. Febr. 21; Approb. 12. Aug. 20.]   [U 21. 2445

NL 0452730   ICRL

Lohse, Rudolf, 1906–
Handbuch des Druckers für die Verarbeitung von Druck-
farben. Leipzig, Fachbuchverlag, 1952.
102 p. illus. 24 cm.

1. Color-printing.   I. Title.

Z258.L675   53-25126 ‡

NL 0452731   DLC CtY

Lohse, Rudolf, 1906–
Webwaren von A bis Z. Leipzig, Fachbuchverlag, 1954.
116 p. 16 cm.

1. Textile industry and fabrics—Dictionaries—German.   I. Title.

A 55-423
Georgia. Inst. of Tech.   Library
for Library of Congress   [3]

NL 0452732   GAT

Lohse, Udo, 1872–
Amerikas giessereiwesen, von professor U. Lohse ...
Mit 54 abbildungen. Berlin, VDI-verlag, g. m. b. h.,
1926.
2 p. l., 59 p. illus. 21ᶜᵐ.
1. Founding. 2. Metal-work—U. S.   I. Title.
Library of Congress   TS230.L6   26-6973

NL 0452733   DLC

Lohse, Udo, 1872–
Formsandaufbereitung und Gussputzerei. Berlin, J.
Springer, 1938.
62 p. diagrs. 23 cm. (Werkstattbücher für Betriebsbeamte,
Konstrukteure und Facharbeiter, Heft 68)

1. Sand, Foundry.   I. Title.   (Series)

TS243.5.L6   57-55213

NL 0452734   DLC PPF NN

Lohse, Udo, 1872–
Maschinenformerei. Berlin, J. Springer, 1938.
64 p. diagrs. 23 cm. (Werkstattbücher für Betriebsbeamte, Konstrukteure und Facharbeiter, Heft 66)

1. Machine molding (Founding)   (Series)

TS243.L6   57-55210

NL 0452735   DLC NN

47J
129
Lohse, Udo, 1872–
Moldeado y preparación de tierras,
por U. Lohse y Fr. Naumann. Barcelona, Editorial Labor, 1944.
293 p.

(Trabajos de taller; guía práctica
del mecánico moderno, 17)

NL 0452736   DLC-P4

Lohse, Udo, 1872–
VDI-wegweiser durch das schrifttum der eisen- und stahl-
gusstechnik; im auftrage des Vereines deutscher ingenieure im
NSBDT zusammengestellt und bearbeitet von Udo Lohse ...
Berlin, VDI-verlag, gmbh, 1939.
4 p. l., 40 p. 21ᶜᵐ.
"Auszüge aus den wichtigsten veröffentlichungen führender deutscher,
englischer und amerikanischer fachzeitschriften über das gebiet der
eisen-, temper- und stahlgiesserei aus den jahren 1937 und 1938."—Vorwort.
1. Founding—Bibl.   I. Verein deutscher ingenieure, Berlin.   II. Title.
Library of Congress   Z7914.F7L8   40-38020
Copyright A—Foreign   45568
                            [2]   018.62174

NL 0452737   DLC NN

Lohse, Werner, 1900–
Ueber einen fall von osteodystrophia fibrosa des
schaedels. Ein beitrag zur diagnostik und thera-
pie der osteodystrophia fibrosa.
Inaug. diss. Berlin, 1928
Bibl.

NL 0452738   ICRL CtY OU

Lohse, Wilhelm Oswald, 1845–1915.
Abbildungen von Sonnenflecken, nebst Bererkunger
uber astronomische Zeichnungen und deren Verviel-
faltigung.
Potsdam, 1883
3 pl. 9 p. 30cm.
Potsdam, Publ. Astrophysik. Obs., 3, 1882–83,
p. 293–301.

NL 0452739   DN-Ob

Lohse, Wilhelm Oswald, 1845–1915.
Beobachtungen und Untersuchungen über die
physische Beschaffenheit der Planeten Jupiter und
Mars.
Potsdam, 1882.
2 pl. (4) + 76 p.
Potsdam, Publ. Astrophysik Obs., 3, 1882–83, p. 1–76.

NL 0452740   DN-Ob

Lohse, Wilhelm Oswald, 1845–1915.
Beobachtungen und Untersuchungen über die
physische Beschaffenheit des Jupiter, und Beobachtungen des Planeten Mars. Potsdam, 1878.
1 p. l., 95–132 p., 2 pl. sq. f°. (Astrophysikalischen Observatoriums zu Potsdam. Publi-
cationen. Nr. 2. Bd. 1., St. 2.)

NL 0452741   NN

Lohse, Wilhelm Oswald, 1845–1915.
Darstellung empfindlichen Bromsilbers für
Emulsionen. Potsdam, 1881.
1 p. 8°.
n.t.-p.
Repr.: Liesegang's Photograph. Archiv. Bd.
22. Hft. 4. 1881.

NL 0452742   NN DN-Ob

Lohse, Wilhelm Oswald, 1845–1915.
Doppelsterne. Potsdam, 1901.
168 p. 2 tab. 4°. (Publikationen des
Astrophysikalischen Observatoriums zu Potsdam.
Bd. 20)

NL 0452743   NN

Lohse, Wilhelm Oswald, 1845–1915.
Planetographie: eine Beschreibung der
im Bereiche der Sonne zu beobachtenden
Korper... Lpz. J. J. Weber, 1894.

NL 0452744   MA

Lohse, Wilhelm Oswald, 1845–1915.
Präeparation von Emulsionsplatten bei Tages-
licht. [Potsdam? 1877]
2 l. 8°.
n.t.-p.
Repr.: Liesegang's: "Photograph. Archiv,
Hft. 4.

NL 0452745   NN

Lohse, Wilhelm Oswald, 1845–1915.
Star photography.
London, 1881.
(2) p. 22cm.
Astron. Reg., 19, 1881, p. 87–89.

NL 0452746   DN-Ob

VOLUME 338

Lohse, Wilhelm Oswald, 1845-1915.

Tafeln für numerisches Rechnen mit Maschinen.   **E.5121.6
— Leipzig. Engelmann. 1909. vi, 122, (1) pp. 29 cm., in 4s.

H2587 — Calculating machines. — Tables. Mathematical.

    ViU DBS
NL 0452747   MB CU NNU-W RPB ICJ MH IaU MiU DN-Ob WU

Lohse, Wilhelm Oswald, 1845-1915.
    ... Tafeln für numerisches rechnen mit maschinen. 2. aufl.
neubearb. von P. V. Neugebauer. Leipzig, W. Engelmann,
1935.
    3 p. l., 113 p. 29ᶜᵐ.
At head of title: Lohse.
Preface and introduction in German and English.

    1. Mathematics—Tables, etc. 2. Trigonometry—Tables, etc.
I. Neugebauer, Paul Victor, 1878-   II. Title.
                                                    35-36025
    Library of Congress   QA47.L65 1935
        (2)   510.835

NL 0452748   DLC DN-Ob RPB OOxM OU

Lohse, Wilhelm Oswald, 1845-1915.
    Ueber einen rotirenden Spectralapparat.
[Berlin, J. Springer, 1881]
    22-25 p.   4°.
    n.t.-p.
    Repr.: Zeitschrift für Instrumentenkunde.
Author's autograph on t.-p.

NL 0452749   NN

Lohse, Wilhelm Oswald, 1845-1915.
    Ueber Schmidts neuen Stern im Schwan. Ber-
lin, Buchdruckerei d. Kgl. Ak. d. Wiss. 1878.
    20 p.   8°.
    Repr: Kgl. Akad. d. Wiss. Monatsbericht,
Dec. 1877.

NL 0452750   NN

Lohse, Wilhelm Oswald, 1845-1915.
    Untersuchungen über die physische Beschaffenheit des Plane-
ten Jupiter.   Potsdam, 1911.   4 p.l., (1)6-182 p., 1 diagr., 11 pl.
4°.   (Astrophysikalisches Observatorium zu Potsdam. Publikationen. v. 21.)

I. Jupiter (planet)—Observations,   1881-1909.
N.Y.P.L.   November 9, 1911.

NL 0452751   NN

Lohse   (Wolfgang) [1892-   ]. *Lungentuberkulose und Schwangerschaft. 61 pp.
8°. Leipzig [1921].

Full name: Friedrich Wolfgang Lohse.

NL 0452752   DNLM CtY ICRL

Lohsee (Carolus Guilelmus). * De tumoribus in
cavo narium et pharyngis obviis, qui polypi
dicuntur. 45 pp. 8°. Gryphiæ, F. G. Kunike,
1852.
                                                C.

NL 0452753   DNLM

Lohsee, Ernst.
AC831   Tulliana. Berlin, R. Gaertner, 1890.
B432   18 p.
1890   "1890. Programm Nr. 62."
         Programmschrift - Leibniz-Gymnasium, Berlin.

    1. Cicero, Marcus Tullius.

NL 0452754   CSt

Lohsee (Franz). *Beitrag zur Behandlung des
Tetanus. 30 pp., 1 l. sm. 8°. Berlin, G. Schade,
[1883].

NL 0452755   DNLM PPC

Lohsing, Ernst, 1878-
Austria. *Laws, statutes, etc.*
    Kommentar zum österreichischen strafrecht, hrsg. von dr.
Ludwig Altmann ... und dr. Siegfried Jacob ... unter mitwirkung von dr. Erwin Höpler ... dr. Ernst Lohsing ... (und)
dr. Karl Mager ... Wien, Manz, 1927-

LOHSING, Ernst, 1878-
    Militär- und zivilstrafverfahren nach öster-
reichischem recht: beiträge zur ihrer abgrenzung
in krieg und frieden. Graz, Wien, 1915.

NL 0452757   MH-L PU-L

Law   Lohsing, Ernst, 1878-   ed.
                    FOR OTHER EDITIONS
                    SEE MAIN ENTRY
Austria. *Laws, statutes, etc.*
    Österreichisches Anwaltsrecht; ein Kommentar (von)
Ernst Lohsing. 2. Aufl. neu bearb. und ergänzt von Rudolf
Braun. Wien, Springer, 1950.

Lohsing, Ernst, 1878-
    Österreichisches strafprozessrecht in systematischer darstel-
lung, von dr. Ernst Lohsing ... Graz und Wien, U. Moser
(J. Meyerhoff) 1912.
    xxiv, 808 p. 24ᶜᵐ.
    "Abkürzungen": p. xv-xvii.

    1. Criminal procedure—Austria.

                                                17-4007

NL 0452759   DLC PU-L

Lohsing, Ernst, 1878-
    Österreichisches Strafprozessrecht in systematischer Dar-
stellung. 2. Aufl. Graz, U. Mosers Buchhandlung, 1920.
    xviii, 846 p. 24 cm.
    ——— Nachtrag zur zweiten Auflage. Graz, U. Mosers
Buchhandlung, 1920-23.
    5 v. 24 cm.
    Bound with main work.

    1. Criminal procedure—Austria.   I. Title.

                                                76-431802

NL 0452760   DLC WU

4K   Lohsing, Ernst, 1878-
Aus.   Österreichisches Strafprozetz-
157   recht. 3. Aufl. Wien, Druck und
      Verlag der Österreichischen Staats-
      druckerei, 1932.
                600 p.

NL 0452761   DLC-P4 CU ICU

Lohsing, Ernst, 1878-
    Österreichisches strafprozessrecht von
dr. Ernst Lohsing. 4. aufl., neubearb.
und ergänzt von dr. Eugon Serini. Wien,
Österreichische staatsdruckerei, 1952.
    xv, 707 p. 25cm.
    Includes bibliographies.

NL 0452762   MH-L CtY-L

LOHSING, Ernst, 1878-
    Das verbot der reformatio in pejus im straf-
verfahrens. Wien, 1907.
    (4) + 54 p.
    "Sonderabdruck aus der Jurist. vierteljah-
resschrift, n.f.XXIII bd".

NL 0452763   MH-L

Lohsmann, Karl.
    Das programm der unabhängigen arbeiter-
bewegung Österreichs. Von Karl Lohsmann.
Wien, K. Lohsmann, 1928.
    55 p. 23 cm.
    1. Labor and laboring classes - Austria.

NL 0452764   CU

Lohss, Hedwig
    see Staiger, Hedwig (Lohss) 1892-

Lohss, Max, 1888-
    ... Beiträge aus dem landwirtschaftlichen wortschatz Würt-
tembergs nebst sachlichen erläuterungen, von Max Lohss ...
Heidelberg, C. Winter, 1913.
    xiv, 115 p. illus. maps (1 fold.) diagrs. 29ᶜᵐ. (Wörter und sachen;
kulturhistorische zeitschrift für sprach- und sachforschung ... beiheft 2)
    "Verzeichnis der gebrauchten bücher": p. xiii-xiv.

    1. German language—Dialects—Württemberg. 2. German language—
Terms and phrases. 3. Agriculture—Terminology.
                                                    A C 33-3626

    Title from Johns Hopkins   Univ. Printed by L. C.

NL 0452766   MdBJ NcD CtY CU ViU NN MH NjP

Lohss, Max, 1888-
    Der Pflug im landwirtschaftlichen Wortschatz
des Schwäbisch-Württembergischen. Heidelberg: Winter
1913. XVI, 29 S., 2 Kt. 4° ¶Vollst. u. d. T.: Beiträge
aus d. landw. Wortschatz Württembergs, als: Wörter u.
Sachen. Beih. 2.
Straßburg, Phil. Diss. v. 27. Juli 1912, Ref. Henning
[Geb. 20. Mai 88 Welzheim; Wohnort: Welzheim; Staatsangeh.: Württemberg; Vorbildung: OR. Eßlingen Reife 06, Erg. RG.; Studium: Stuttgart
TeH. 1, Tübingen 3, London 1, Tübingen 3, Straßburg 1 S.] [U 13 4549

NL 0452767   ICRL CtY IU MH PU

Lohsse (Arthurus Æmilius) [1829-]. *De
acuta flava atrophia hepatis. 30 pp., 1 l. 8°.
Halis Sax., typ. Gebauerio-Schwetschkianis. [1854].

NL 0452768   DNLM

LOHSSE, Herbert.
    Ein beitrag zu der lehre von der einwirkung
des heissen bades auf den menschlichen stoffwechsel. Halle a.d. 1900.

NL 0452769   MBCo ICRL

VOLUME 338

Lohstoeter, Friedrich, tr.

Benedict, Clare.
Sechs monate, märz-august, 1914 [by] Clare Benedict.
[Cleveland, C. Hauser, printer, *1917]

RC78 Lohstöter, Ilse, joint author.
.H45 FOR OTHER EDITIONS
1946 SEE MAIN ENTRY
Herlyn, Karl Ewald, 1902–
Praktikum der Röntgendiagnostik, von Karl-Ewald Herlyn und Ilse Lohstöter. 3. verm. und verb. Aufl. Berlin
[etc.] Urban & Schwarzenberg, 1946.

Lohstoeter, *Mrs.* Lotte Olga (Beutner)
... Zinzendorf, an evaluation, by Lotte Olga Lohstoeter ...
[Pittsburgh, 1930]
9 p. 23ᶜᵐ.
Caption title.
Abstract of thesis (PH. D.)—University of Pittsburgh, 1930.
Vita.
"Reprinted from University of Pittsburgh bulletin, vol. 27, no. 3,
November, 1930."

1. Zinzendorf, Nicolaus Ludwig, graf von, 1700–1760.

Library of Congress BX8593.Z6L6 1930 33–36386
Univ. of Pittsburgh Libr.
————— Copy 2. [2] 922.443

NL 0452772 PPiU DLC

Lohuis, Delmont, 1914–
Sodium and potassium content of Wisconsin lake waters
and their residues [by] D. Lohuis, V. W. Meloche and C.
Juday ...
(*In* Wisconsin academy of sciences, arts and letters. Transactions. Madison, Wis., 1938. 25 cm. v. 31, p. 285–304 incl. 2 tab.
diagrs.)
From the Department of chemistry, University of Wisconsin, and
the Limnological laboratory of the Wisconsin geological and natural
history survey. Notes and reports, no. 84.
1. Lakes—Wisconsin. 2. Water—Analysis. I. Meloche, Villiers
Willson, 1895– joint author. II. Juday, Chancey, 1871– joint
author.
Full name: Delmont John Lohuis.
[AS36.W7 vol. 31] A 39–703
Wisconsin. Univ. Libr.
for Library of Congress [a56c]]

NL 0452773 WU

Lohuis, Gilbertus, *Father,* 1891–
Christus ons leven; lijdensoverwegingen. [Hilversum, Gooi
& Sticht, 1951.
130 p. 20 cm.

1. Jesus Christ—Passion—Meditations. I. Title.
Secular name: Henricus Lohuis.
A 54–5054

Harvard Univ. Library
for Library of Congress [3]

NL 0452774 MH

Lohuis, Gilbertus, 1891–
De Katholieke Mis. Hilversum, N.V.
Gooi & Sticht, 1952.
125 p.

NL 0452775 DCU

Lohuis, Gilbertus, 1891–
De stem van het kruis. Proza: Gilb. Lohuis; poëzie:
Gabriël Smit; teekeningen: Harrie Sterk. Bussum, Ons
Leekenspel [1941]
38 p. illus. 25 cm.

1. Jesus Christ—Seven last words. 2. Jesus Christ—Poetry.
I. Smit, Gabriël, 1910– II. Title.
Secular name: Henricus Lohuis.
BT455.L73 56–52727 ‡

NL 0452776 DLC

Lohuis, Henricus
see his name in religion
Lohuis, Gilbertus, 1891–

Lohuizen, Ir. Th. K. van.
Zwei Jahre Wohnungsstatistik in Rotterdam; eine neue
Methode der Statistik über Wohnungsbedarf und Wohnungsvor-
rat, von Ir. Th. K. van Lohuizen... Hrsg. vom Nederlandsch
Instituut voor Volkshuisvesting, Amsterdam. Berlin: C. Hey-
mann, 1922. 48 p. incl. tables. diagr. 4°.

1. Habitations.—Statistics, Nether- lands: Rotterdam, 1920–22.
N. Y. P. L. May 3, 1924.

NL 0452778 NN

Lohuizen, Johanna Engelberta (de Leeuw) van
see Lohuizen-de Leeuw, Johanna Engelberta van, 1919–

Lohuizen-de Leeuw, Johanna Engelberta van, 1919–
The Scythian period; an approach to the history, art,
epigraphy and palaeography of north India from the 1st
century B. C. to the 3rd century A. D. Leiden, Brill, 1949.
xii, 435 p. illus. 28 cm.
Proefschrift—Utrecht.
"Stellingen" : [3] p. inserted.
Bibliography : p. [400]–422.

1. Indo-Scythians. I. Title.

DS451.L6 934 50–16669

NL 0452780 DLC TxU HU OU PU OC1 CtY MH

Lohuizen-de Leeuw, Johanna Engelberta van, 1919–
The "Scythian" period; an approach to the history, art,
epigraphy and palaeography of north India from the 1st
century B. C. to the 3rd century A. D. Leiden, E. J. Brill, 1949.
435 p. illus., plates. 28 cm. (Orientalia Rheno-Traiectina, v. 2)
Issued also as thesis, Utrecht.
Bibliography : p. [400]–422.

1. Indo-Scythians. I. Title. (Series)

DS451.L6 1949a 934 51–33346

ICU
NL 0452781 DLC MnU CU NcD NN NNC MB CU NIC OC1

Lohuizen-de Leeuw, Johanna Engelberta van,
1919–
Sir William Jones, 1746–1794, by J. E. van
Lohuizen-de Leeuw. Leiden [1946]
p. 288–297. port. 26 cm.
Caption title.
"Overdruk uit 'Orientalia neerlandica.'"
1. Jones, Sir William, 1746–1794.

NL 0452782 OrU

Lohvyn, Hryhoriĭ Nykonovych, 1910–
Чигирин, Суботів; архітектурно-історичний нарис.
Київ, Вид-во Академії архітектури Укр. РСР, 1954.
69 p. illus. 23 cm.
At head of title: Академія архітектури Української РСР. Інсти-
тут історії і теорії архітектури. Г. Н. Логвин.

1. Architecture—Chigirin—History. 2. Architecture—Subbotov—
History.
Title romanized: Chyhyryn, Subotiv.
NA1197.C53L6 56–39937 ‡

NL 0452783 DLC

Lohwag, Ernst, 1847–1918.
Iphigenie in Delphi. Tragödie in 5 Akten. [In
verse] Wien, A. Hölder, 1880.
2 p.l., 82 p. 12°.
In NGB p. v. 19 no. 5.

NL 0452784 NN

Lohwag, Ernst, 1847–1918, ed.

Wissenschaftlicher klub, *Vienna.*
Monatsblätter des Wissenschaftlichen klub in Wien ...
L– jahrg.
Wien, 1880–

834L833 Lohwag, Ernst, 1847–1918.
On Neue bahnen. Poetische versuche.
Wien, 1879.
131p.

NL 0452786 IU

Lohwag, Ernst, 1847–1918.
Der Planetenkongress; ein Weltspiel in drei Akten. Wien:
W. Braumüller, 1912. 80 p. 8°.

1. Drama (German). 2. Title.
N. Y. P. L. April 26, 1912.

NL 0452787 NN

Lohwag, Heinrich, 1884–
... Anatomie der asco- und basidiomyceten, von dr. Heinrich
Lohwag ... Mit 348 textabbildungen. Berlin, Gebrüder Born-
traeger, 1941.
xi, 572 p. illus. 27ᶜᵐ. (Handbuch der pflanzenanatomie ... hrsg. von
K. Linsbauer ... II. abt.: [Spezieller teil] 3. teilbd.: Pilze und symbio-
sen, bd. vi)
Issued as lfg. 40.
"Literaturverzeichnis" : p. 529–553.

1. Ascomycetes. 2. Basidiomycetes.
Agr 41–580
U. S. Dept. of agr. Library 463.4H194 bd. 6, teilbd. 3
for Library of Congress [QK641.H3 abt. 2, t. 3, bd. 6]
[3] (581.4)

NL 0452788 DNAL CU NNBG MH–F NcD

Lohwag, Heinrich, 1884–
Zur Anatomie der Boletaceae. Von Heinrich Loh-
wag und Maria Peringer. Berlin, R. Friedlaender
& Sohn, 1937.
[295]–331p. illus. 24cm.
Reprinted from Annales Mycologici, v.35, no.5/6
1937.
Contains bibliography.

1. Boletaceae. I. Peringer, Maria, joint auth.

NL 0452789 NcU

Lohwag, Heinrich, 1884–
Zur entwicklungsgeschichte und morphologie
der Gastromyceten: ein beitrag zur systematik der
Basidiomyceten. Dresden, Heinrich, 1926.
177–334 p. illus. O.
Sonderabdruck aus "Beihefte zum botanischen
centralblatt" bd. 42 (1926) abt. 2.
1. Mushrooms.
2. Fungi.

NL 0452790 NcU

VOLUME 338

LOHWAG, Kurt
Erkenne und Bekämpfe den Hausschwamm und
seine Begleiter. Wien, G. Fromme ₍1955₎

61 p. illus. 24cm. (Austria. Forstliche Bundesversuchsanstalt, Mariabrunn.
Schriftenreihe, Bd.3)

Bibliography: p. 59-60.

1. Dry-rot. I. Title. (Series)

NL 0452791   MnU-A CtY LU

Lohwag, Kurt
634.95
B862T   A mild maceration process for lignified
no.3   tissues. Translated by D. Mueller-Dombois.
Vancouver, 1953.
1 l. 28cm. (British Columbia. University.
Faculty of Forestry. Translation no.3)

Title also in German.
Translation of an article from "Z. Wiss.
Mikroskopie 54(1): 95-96 (1937)"

NL 0452792   NcD

Lohwag, Kurt
Moose des waldes; bestimmungsschlüssel für
anfänger. Mit geleitwort von Otto Porsch.
Mit ... 30 originalzeichnungen von Helene
Guggenthall-Schack. Wien, F. Deuticke, 1940.
viii, 64 p. illus.

Bibliography: p. ₍vii₎-viii.

1. Musci.

NL 0452793   NNC DNAL MH IaAS

588.2
L83m   Lohwag, Kurt.
1948   Moose des Waldes, Bestimmungsschlüssel für
Anfänger. 2. erweiterte Aufl. Mit 63 Abbildungen, davon 30 Originalzeichnungen von
Helene Guggenthall-Schack. Wien, F. Deuticke, 1948.
vii, 66p. illus., 8 plates. 18cm.

Bibliography: p. ₍vi₎-vii.

1. Mosses. I. Title.

NL 0452794   IU OrCS

91.7
L83   Lohwag, Kurt.
Neue Methoden der Champignonkultur.
[Wien, 1953]
5 p.

1. Mushrooms. Austria.

NL 0452795   DNAL

589.22
L83t   Lohwag, Kurt.
Taschenbuch der wichtigsten Speise- und
Giftpilze. Wien, G. Fromme, 1948.
vii, 111p. illus. 20cm.

Bibliography: p.104.

1. Mushrooms.

NL 0452796   IU NcU OrCS

Ld14
1   Lohwasser, Heinz, 1900-
Der allgemeine gesundheitliche Zustand der
deutschen Schulkinder, insbesondere der
Rostocker Schuljugend ... Rostock,1928.
Pamphlet
Inaug.-Diss. - Rostock.
Lebenslauf.
"Literatur": p.[1] at end.

NL 0452797   CtY DNLM

Lohwasser, Paul: Das Recht auf Beschäftigung innerhalb des bürger-
lich-rechtlichen Dienstvertrages. [Maschinenschrift.] v. 66 S.
4°. —Auszug: (Königsberg i. Pr. [1924]: Pohlmann) 1928. 1 Bl. 8°
Breslau, R.- u. staatswiss. Diss. v. 10. Dez. 1923 [1924]   [U 24.1426]

NL 0452798   ICRL

Lohweg, Ernst, 1911-
... Über den Einfluss von Eisen auf die alkoho-
lische Gärung... Bottrop i.W., 1935.
Inaug.-Diss. - Münster.
Lebenslauf.

NL 0452799   CtY DNLM

Lohweg, Hans
Die rechtliche natur der aneignung und
eigentumsaufgabe
Inaug. Diss. Erlangen, 1931.
Bibl.

NL 0452800   ICRL MH-L

Loi, Lodovico, joint author.

Sanfelice, Francesco.
... Di alcune infezioni del bestiame studiate in Sardegna
nel quadriennio 1892-96, da Francesco Sanfelice ... e Lodovico Loi ... Cagliari, Tipo-litografia commerciale,
1897.

Loi, Michelle.
Nous qui sommes les plus heureux. Paris, P. Seghers
₍1954₎
39 p. 18 cm. (Collection P. S., no. 405)
On cover: Poésie 54.

I. Title.

A 55-2246

Illinois. Univ. Library
for Library of Congress   (2)

NL 0452802   IU NN CU

Loi, N   I
Обобщенные методы труда трубопрокатчиков Челябин-
ского трубного завода. Москва, Гос. научно-техн. изд-во
лит-ры по черной и цветной металлургии, 1953.

Microfilm copy (negative) made in 1956 by the Library of Congress.
Collation of the original, as determined from the film: 31 p. diagr.
At head of title: Н. И. Лой и В. П. Кречковский.

1. Pipe. I. Krechkovskiĭ, V. P., joint author. II. Title.
Title transliterated: Obobshchennye
metody truda truboprokatchikov.

Microfilm Slavic 747 T   Mic 58-6865

NL 0452803   DLC

Loi, Raimon de, *pseud*.
see   Jameson , Raymond De Loy, 1896-

Loi, Salvatore.
Cagliari medaglia d'oro, a cura dell'Istituto del nastro azzurro,
Federazione provinciale di Cagliari. Cagliari, Tip. Coiana, 1952.
27 p. illus., ports. 22cm. (Collana "Sardegna eroica")

1. World war, 1939-1945—Italy—
Hist., 20th cent. I. Istituto del nastro
al valor militare. Federazione
Cagliari. 2. Cagliari, Italy—
azzurro fra combattenti decorati
provinciale di Cagliari. II. Title.

NL 0452805   NN

Loi, Salvatore.
Jugoslavia 1941 ₍i. e. mille novecento quarantuno. 1. ed.₎
Torino, Edizioni de "Il Nastro azzurro" ₍1953₎
222 p. illus., ports., map. 22 cm. (Collana dei libri azzurri, n. 1)

1. World War, 1939-1945—Yugoslavia.

D766.6.L64   55-25827

NL 0452806   DLC NN MH

La loi de l'homme
see under   [Hervieu, Paul Ernest] 1857-
1915.

... La loi de la presse: Discours de MM. Eugène Pelletan,
Jules Simon, Jules Favre, Ernest Picard, Garnier-
Pagès, Guéroult, Riondel, Berryer, Carnot; avec le text
de la loi votée le 9 mars 1868, par le Corps législatif.
Paris, Degorce-Cadot ₍1868₎
2 p. l., 299 p. 18ᶜᵐ. (Bibliothèque libérale)
At head of caption title : Extraits du Moniteur universel.
1. Liberty of the press. 2. Press—France. I. Moniteur universel,
Paris. II. Pelletan, Eugène i. e. Pierre Clément Eugène, 1813-1884. III. Si-
mon, Jules François Simon Suisse, known as Jules, 1814-1896. IV. Favre,
Jules i. e. Gabriel Claude Jules, 1809-1880. V. Picard, Ernest i. e. Louis
Joseph Ernest, 1821-1877. VI. Garnier-Pagès, Louis Antoine, 1803-1878.
VII. Guéroult, Adolphe, 1810-1872. VIII. Riondel, Louis Fabin, 1824-1889.
IX. Berryer, Pierre Antoine, 1790-1868. X. Carnot, Hippolyte i. e. Lazare
Hippolyte, 1801-1888.

5-10358

Library of Congress   Z657.L83

NL 0452808   DLC

La loi de répartition en profondeur... [Bone.
... 1917.]

see *under*

[Souleyre, A]

Loi de vestrogothie
see under   Västgötalagen.

La loi des circonstances
see under   [La Gervaisais, Nicolas Louis
Marie Magon] marquis de, 1765-1838.

Loi du 10 juin 1937; les allocations familiales pour
les classes moyennes
see under   [Fallon, Valère] 1875-

VOLUME 338

Loi fondamentale de l'Empire russe. Projet d'une constitution russe élaboré par un groupe de la Ligue de l'affranchissement (constitutionnalistes-démocrates russes). Préface de Pierre Struve ... Paris, Société nouvelle de librairie et d'édition, 1905.
xxxv, 189 p., 2 l. 25½ᵐ.

1. Russia. Constitution. I. Soîûz osvobozhdenîîâ. II. Struve, Petr Berngardovich, 1870–

NL 0452813   DLC CtY ICJ NN InU

Loi Gombette
see
Lex Burgundionum.

Loi pour la direction des aérostats; la navigation aérienne théoriquement et pratiquement démontrée, par A.-M. Paris, Imprimerie centrale de N. Chaix et cⁱᵉ, 1859.
2 p. l., ₍3₎–16 p. 22ᵐ.

1. Aeronautics. I. M., A.- II. A.-M. III. Title: La navigation aérienne.
Library of Congress   TL544.L5
                 43–19865

NL 0452815   DLC

Loi salique
see   Salic law.

La loi sans motifs, ou état de la discussion
see under   [La Gervaisais, Nicolas Louis Marie Magon, marquis de] 1765–1838.

Loi sur l'exercice de la médecine et de la pharmacie, discutée à la chambre des pairs. 36 pp. 8°. [Paris, L. Martinet, n. d.] [Also, in: P., v. 467.]
Repr. from: Rev. scient. et industr. du Dr. Quesneville, Par.

NL 0452818   DNLM

Loi sur la médecine. Dentistes. [Mémoire à la chambre des députés.] 12 pp. 4°. [Paris, Pollet & Cie., 1845.] [P., v. 1750.]

NL 0452819   DNLM

La loi sur le repos du dimanche ...
see under   [Lombard, Frank] 1837–

Loi sur les droits de succession et de mutation par décès, du 17 décembre 1851
see under   [Parent, Jean Jacques Florimond] 1806–1859, ed.

La loi sur les tribunaux pour enfants, conditions d'application
see under   Prevost, Eugène.

Loîâ, Ìân Vilfûmovich
see
Loja, Jānis, 1896–

JX3545   **Loiaconi, M.**
.C27L42   Catellani, Enrico Levi-, 1856–
     ... Lezioni di diritto internazionale redatte dagli studenti M. Loiaconi e V. Papalia. Padova, "La litotipo," 1921.

NL 0452824   DLC-P4 CU

4PQ   Loiacono, S   R
Span.-   Las mejores poesias de la lengua española.
299   Prólogo de Felix F. Corso. Madrid, Libreria Perlado [1939]
     387 p.   (Biblioteca clasica universal, 7)

NL 0452824   DLC-P4 CU

Loiacono, Vincenzo
see   Lojacono, Vincenzo, 1885–

Loiano, Seraphinus A
see   Serafino da Lojano, padre, 1870–1933.

HF5645   **Loib, J., ed.**
.D72   FOR OTHER EDITIONS
                 SEE MAIN ENTRY
   Dröll, Karl.
     ... Kaufmännisches rechnen. Neu bearbeitet von dr. J. Loib und O. Tischler ... 29. aufl. Leipzig und Berlin, B. G. Teubner, 1942–43.

Loibas, Jörg.
Europa wird es schaffen. München, W. de Bouché, 1952.
64 p. 21 cm. (Schriftenreihe der Gesellschaft für Wehrkunde München, Heft 8)

1. Europe—Hist.—Addresses, essays, lectures. I. Title.
D213.L6   56–44691 ‡

NL 0452828   DLC MH

LOIBAS, JÖRG.
Europa wird es schaffen. München, W. de Bouché, 1952. 64 p. 21cm. (Gesellschaft für Wehrkunde. Schriftenreihe. Heft 8)

Film reproduction. Negative.

1. Orient and Occident.   2. Europe--Hist.

NL 0452829   NN

Loibl, Franz.
...Pinselzeichnen, ... und L.M.K. Capeller...
[München, Natur & kultur, n.d.] Technische jugend-buecherei, no.6]
27 p. illus. (part col.)

NL 0452830   OCl

FILM   Loibl, Johann.
7482   Gerhart Hauptmanns Insel der grossen Mutter, oder, Das Wunder von Île des Dames. 1938.
     150 l.
     Diss.--Vienna.
     Includes bibliography.
     Microfilm (negative) of typescript. Wien, Oesterr.Nationalbibliothek, 1966. 1 reel.

     1.Hauptmann,Gerhart Johann Robert,1862-1946. Die Insel der   grossen Mutter.

NL 0452831   MiU

Loibl (Josef). *Zur klinischen Brauchbarkeit des Präparates "Neguvon" der Farbenfabriken vorm. Friedr. Bayer & Co., Leverkusen. [München.] 48 pp. 8°. Griesbach [n. d.].

NL 0452832   DNLM

PT2623   Loibl, Maria (Neuhauser) 1906–
.0503   Österreichische Sonette; ein Zwiegesang.
1946   2. Aufl. Wien, Amandus-Edition, 1946 [°1945]
     1 v. (unpaged) 21 cm.

     Poems.

NL 0452833   ViU

W 4   LOIBL, Michaela, 1926–
M96   Ueber Diazomethanvergiftungen; unter
1949   besonderer Berücksichtigung eines in der Medizinischen Poliklinik der Universität München beobachteten Falles. München, 1949.
     ₍17₎ l.
     Inaug.-Diss. - Munich.
     Typewritten copy.
     1. Azo compounds 2. Gas poisoning

NL 0452834   DNLM

Law   Loibl, Richard, ed.

   Vienna. *Laws, statutes, etc.*
     Die Bauordnung für Wien, mit einigen einschlägigen Gesetzen, Verordnungen und Gemeinderatsbeschlüssen in der derzeit gültigen Fassung. [von] R. Loibl [und] F. Schubert. Wien, Globus Verlag, 1950.

Law   Loibl, Richard, ed.

   Vienna. *Laws, statutes, etc.*
     Die Bauordnung für Wien samt Ausführungs- und Nebengesetzen. Mit erläuternden Bemerkungen und Erkenntnissen des Verwaltungsgerichtshofes; nach dem Stande vom Dezember 1949. Hrsg. von Franz Schubert [und] Richard Loibl. Wien, Druck und Verlag der Österreichischen Staatsdruckerei, 1950–

Loichen (Ernst). Die Sarkome an den Gliedmassen. 61 pp. 8°. Berlin, E. Ebering, 1921. Forms Heft 4 (Abt. Chir.), of Beitr. z. Heilk.

NL 0452837   DNLM

VOLUME 338

Loida, Willy, 1875–
Ueber die Ausscheidung von Typhusbazillen und Darmbakterien im Urin Typhuskranker. Koenigsberg, 1901.
Inaug.-diss. - Koenigsberg.
Bibl.

NL 0452838   ICRL CtY DNLM MBCo

Loidis, *pseud.*   624.8 Q300
"...... Swing bridges. By "Loidis". London, The Publishers of the "Railway engineer", [1903].
115 p. 51 diagr., 1 pl. 18¼ᵐ.   (The railway series of text books and manuals by railway men for railway men. — No. 3.)

NL 0452839   ICJ NN

Loidl, Franz, 1905–1945.
Abraham a Sancta Clara und das judentum (Studie über das judentum in Wien und Österreich im barock) von dr. Franz Loidl ...   Wien, J. Lichtner [1941]
31 p.

NL 0452840   NN InU

LOIDL, FRANZ, 1905–
Entweihte Heimat; KZ. Ebensee. Linz, H. Muck [1946?] 67 p. illus. 21cm.

Film reproduction. Negative.

1. Ebensee, Austria (Labor camp).

NL 0452841   NN

Loidl, Franz, 1905–
Erzbischof Friedrich Xaver Katzer, Ebensee-Milwaukee, 1844–1903. Wien, J. Lichtner, 1953.
72 p. port. 21 cm.
Bibliographical references in "Anmerkungen" (p. 64–71)

1. Katzer, Friedrich Xaver, Abp., 1844–1903.
                                              A 53–8499
Catholic Univ. of   America. Library
for Library of Congress   [3]

NL 0452842   DCU NcD

Loidl, Franz, 1905–
... Menschen im barock; Abraham a Sancta Clara über das religiös-sittliche leben in Oesterreich in der zeit von 1670 bis 1710. Wien, L. Krempel, 1938.
4 p. l., xii, 367 p. 23ᵐ.
"Quellen- und literatur-nachweis": p. 356–367.

1. Abraham a Sancta Clara, pater, 1644–1709. 2. Austria—Soc. life & cust.   I. Title.
                                              42–11338
Library of Congress   BX4705.A22L6

NL 0452843   DLC CSt MH

Loidl, Franz.
Weihbischof Dr. Johann Baptist Schneider (1840–1905) Wien, J. Lichtner, 1951.
122 p. 21 cm.
"Quellen- und Literatur-Nachweis": p. 121–122.

1. Schneider, Johann Baptist, Bp., 1840–1905.
                                              A 52–2277
Catholic Univ. of   America. Library
for Library of Congress   [3]

NL 0452844   DCU

Loidl, Franz, 1905–
...Invalidenhauskirche St. Johann von Nepomuk in Wien. Wien, J. Lichtner, 1948. 36 p.   1 illus.   21cm.
"Quellen- und Literatur-Nachweis," p. 36.

1. Vienna—Churches—Invaliden-   hauskirche St. Johann von Nepomuk.
N. Y. P. L.   September 26, 1950

NL 0452845   NN

Loidl, Josef, 1905–1945.
Ruanda-Urundi, zwei Königreiche auf dem Weg zur Kirche, nach Missionsberichten der Weissen Väter. Wien, Missionsdruckerei St. Gabriel, Mödling bei Wien, 1946.
[6], 82 p. plates, port. 20 cm.
Bibliography : 4th prelim. page.

1. Missions—Ruanda, Africa. 2. Missions—Urundi, Africa.

BV3625.R8L6   49–15223*

NL 0452846   DLC

Loidolt, Alfred, 1925–
Die Beziehungen Österreichs zu den Vereinigten Staaten zur Zeit des amerikanischen Bürgerkrieges, 1861–1865. Wien, 1949.
Microfilm copy (negative) Made by Photo Section, Vienna University Library.
Collation of the original, as determined from the film: [13], 117, [10].
Diss.—Vienna.
Vita.
Bibliography: leaves [5]–[10] (1st group)

1. U. S.—For. rel.—Austria. 2. Austria—For. rel.—U.S. 3. U. S.—For. rel.—1861–1865. 4. U. S.—Hist.—Civil War—Foreign public opinion.   I. Title.
Microfilm 5878 E   Mic 59–7753

NL 0452847   DLC

Za   Loïdoros; petit livre de médisances.
L78   Cavete ... Paris, Béthune et Plon, imprimeurs [1841]
          xxxiii, 145p. illus. 4½cm.
          Dedication signed: Alois Bᵒⁿ de Rebfrac [pseud.]

NL 0452848   CtY

W 4   LOIECIUS, Joannes, fl. 1607, respondent.
B29   ... De cardialgia conclusiones ... Basileae, Typis
1607   Excertierianis, 1607.
L.1   [12] p. 20 cm.
          Thesis - Basel.

NL 0452849   DNLM

Loier, Peter de.
    see Le Loyer, Pierre, sieur de la Brosse, 1550–1634.

Loiero, Francesco Antonio, 1911–
La letteratura precettistica di galateo in Francia ed in Italia sino alla fine del trecento (The literature of manners in France and in Italy until the end of the 14th century) Ann Arbor, University Microfilms [1954]
([University Microfilms, Ann Arbor, Mich.] Publication no. 8176)
Microfilm copy of typescript. Positive.
Collation of the original: 305 l.
Thesis—Syracuse University.
Vita.
Bibliography : leaves 290–304.

1. French literature—Old French—Hist. & crit. 2. Italian literature—Early to 1400—Hist. & crit.   I. Title.

Microfilm AC–1   no. 8176   Mic 55–3763

NL 0452851   DLC CU

Loignon (Léonidas). *Étude sur les luxations congénitales de l'épaule. 65 pp. 4°. Paris, 1866. No. 307.

NL 0452852   DNLM

Loignon, S.
Ponts biais; tracé des épures, coupe des pierres et détails sur la construction des différents systèmes d'appareils de voutes biaises, mis à la portée de tous les agents de travaux et appareilleurs ...   Paris, C. Bernard, 1872.
[2], 76, [1] p. and atlas of XIV pl.

NL 0452853   ICU

LOIK, pseud, ed.

ANDERSEN, H[ans Christian], 1805–1875.
Plac hig vihan ar Mor. Gant H. Andersen; troet gant R. Hemon, skeudennaeout gant Loik. Brest, Kenta Mouladur, 1928.

NL 0452854   MH

Loik, Hans Gerhart.
Im Steinkohlenbergwerk. [Halle (Saale)] Mitteldeutscher Verlag [1949]
32 p. illus. 21 cm. (Werner und Peter auf Entdeckungsfahrten, Heft 6)

1. Mines and mineral resources—Juvenile literature.

PZ36.L59   52–22731

NL 0452855   DLC

W 4   LOIKASEK, Wilhelm, 1919–
M96   Unspezifische Reiztherapie unter dem
1953   Gesichtspunkt der Stimulierung des Hypo-
          physen-Nebennierensystems, mit
          besonderer Berücksichtigung der Pyrifer-
          wirkung. [München, 1953?]
          44 l.
          Inaug.-Diss. - Munich.
          1. Endocrine glands 2. Fever therapy

NL 0452856   DNLM

[Loĭko, Lidiià Pavlovna] 1854–
Надо знать не меньше ... Конспекты лекцій. С.-Петербургъ [Тип. Н. П. Собко] 1906.
110 p. 19 cm.
At head of title: Л. Л-о.
Bibliography : p. [95]–102.

1. Socialism. 2. Socialism in Russia.   I. L. L-o. II. L-o, L.
III. Title.   Title romanized: Nado znat' ne men'she.

HX314.L6 1906   74–284529

NL 0452857   DLC

VOLUME 338

HX314
.L6
1917

Loĭko, Lidiia Pavlovna, 1854–
Надо знать не меньше … ; конспекты лекцій. 2., доп. изд. Петроградъ, Революціонная мысль, 1917.
112 p. 19 cm.
Bibliography: p. ₍98₎–104.

1. Socialism. 2. Socialism in Russia. ɪ. Title.
Title transliterated: Nado znat' ne men'she.

HX314.L6 1917 59–57341

NL 0452858 DLC

DK254
.L8A3

Loĭko, Lidiia Pavlovna, 1854–
От "Земли и воли" к ВКП(б), 1877–1928; воспоминания. Москва, Гос. изд-во, 1929.
247 p. 20 cm.

1. Revolutionists, Russian — Correspondence, reminiscences, etc. ɪ. Title. *Title transliterated:* Ot "Zemli i voli" k VKP(b).

54–55913

NL 0452859 DLC

PG3476
.B38M6

Loĭko, N., joint author.

Bek, Aleksandr Al'fredovich, 1903–
Молодые люди; роман. Москва, Трудрезервиздат, 1954.

S663
.L6

Loĭko, P G
Заготовка и применение торфяных удобрений. Москва, Гос. изд-во сельхоз. лит-ры, 1954.
110 p. illus. 20 cm.

1. Peat—White Russia. 2. Fertilizers and manures. ɪ. Title. *Title transliterated:* Zagotovka i primenenie torfianykh udobreniĭ.

S663.L6 55–59815 ‡

NL 0452861 DLC

The "loil" legislature of Alabama
see under [Screws, Benjamin H   ]

Loilier, C.
… Notes Diverses sur le Matériel des Chemins de Fer, par C. Loilier. Saint-Nicolas, P. Trenel, imprimeur de la Société, 1867.
8 p. fold. plates. 8 vo. 3/4 green calf, gilt, red label, gilt top, original brown paper covers bound in, by Rivière.
At head of title: Extrait du Bulletin Mensuel de la Société des anciens Élèves des écoles impériales d'Arts et Métiers. (Mois de juillet 1867) Exposition Universelle.
From Anderson Galleries, 10–11 Mr. 19, no. 283.

NL 0452863 CSmH

Loillier (François-Xavier). * Considérations sur trois cas d'anciennes luxations traumatiques réduites. 30 pp. 4°. *Paris,* 1873, No. 478.

NL 0452864 DNLM

Loimann, Gustav, 1853–1902. Franzensbad in Böhmen und seine Heilmittel. Führer für Curgäste und Aerzte. 2. Aufl. 2 p. l., 51 pp., 1 map. 12°. *Wien, W. Braumüller,* 1887.
——. The same. 3. Aufl. 2 p. l., 65 pp., 1 map. 12°. *Wien & Leipzig, W. Braumüller* 1893.

NL 0452865 DNLM

WBI
L834f
1855

LOIMANN, Gustav.
Franzensbad in chirurgischen Krankheitsfällen. Wien, Ueberreuter, 1855.
60 p.

NL 0452866 DNLM

RM822.M9
L83

Loimann, Gustav, 1853–1902.
Kritische studien über moor und mineralmoor-bäder … Halle a. S., Marhold, 1898.
32 p. tables. (Archiv der balneotherapie und hydrotherapie … II. bd., hft. 1)

1. Baths, Moor and mud. I. Archiv der balneotherapie und hydrotherapie, 2. bd., hft 1.

NL 0452867 NNC DNLM

Div.S.
273.7
L834E

Loimaranta, Sakari.
Erikssonien mystillis-separatistinen liike vuoteen 1745. Lahti ₍Suomen₎ 1940.
xxv, 315 p. fold. map. 23 cm.

Thesis - Helsinki.
Published also as Suomen Kirkkohistoriallisen Seuran toimituksia, 43.
Bibliography: p. xv–xxv.
1. Pietism. Finland. 2. Eriksson, Eerik. 3. Eriksson, Jaakko. 4. Mysticism. Finland. I. Title.

NL 0452868 NcD NNC NjP

Loimaranta, Sakari.
Erikssonien mystillis-separatistinen liike vuoteen 1745. Helsinki, Suomen Kirkkohistoriallinen Seura, 1941.
xxv, 330 p. 23 cm. (Suomen Kirkkohistoriallisen Seuran toimituksia, 43)
Bibliography: p. xv–xxv.

1. Pietism—Finland. 2. Eriksson, Eerik. 3. Eriksson, Jaakko. 4. Mysticism—Finland. I. Title. (Series: Suomen Kirkkohistoriallinen Seura, Helsingfors. Toimituksia, 43)

BX4982.F5L6 50–48242

NL 0452869 DLC CtY-D

Loimaranta, Yrjö.
Viipurin Hiippakunta vuosina 1937–1942; Viipurin Hiippakunnan pappeinkokoukselle lokak. 6–8 p:nä 1942 esittänyt Yrjö Loimaranta. ₍Mikkeli, 1942₎
124 p. illus. 23 cm.

1. Vyborg, Russia (Diocese)—History.

BX8030.V5L6 76–221340

NL 0452870 DLC

Loin (Joseph) ₍1874–   ₎. *Traitement du lupus tuberculeux par les scarifications ignées méthodiques. [Paris.] 93 pp., 1 l., 7 pl. 8°. *Compiègne,* 1901, No. 185.

NL 0452871 DNLM

Loinaz, Ignacio Agramonte y.
See
Agramonte y Loinaz, Ignacio, 1841–1873.

[LOINDER, J.   ]
Vevey et ses environs. / 3e éd. revue et augmentée. Vevey, [1842].

2 plates.

NL 0452873 MH

Loines, Elma, 1882–   ed.
The China trade post-bag of the Seth Low family of Salem and New York, 1829–1873. Manchester, Me., Falmouth Pub. House, 1953.
ix, 324 p. illus., ports., maps, facsims. 27 cm.
"Harriet Low's Journal, 1829–1834 (much abridged by Katharine Hillard, 1900)": p. 100–234.

1. U. S.—Comm.—China. 2. China—Comm.—U. S. 3. China—Descr. & trav. 4. Lowe family. ɪ. Hillard, Harriet (Low) 1809–1877. Journal. ɪɪ. Title.

DS709.L85 387.5 54—22380

NL 0452874 DLC OrP OrU PBm ICU PP CU NNC NN MB TxU

Loines, Jonas P.

New York (*City*) Board of health.
A report to the Metropolitan board of health on vaccination. 1868. New York, D. Appleton & co. ₍1868₎

Loines, Russel Hillard, 1874–1922.
In a copy of the "vita nuova;" [poem] [Cambridge, Mass., 1895]
Clipping from the Harvard monthly, Nov. 1895, vol. XXI, p. 79, in Dante scrap-book. ₍p. 150₎

NL 0452876 NIC

923.873
L834

Loines, Russell Hillard, 1874–1922.
Russell Hillard Loines, 1874–1922; a selection from his letters and poems with biographical sketch and recollections by his friends. New York, Priv. print. ₍by the Scribner Press₎ 1927.
x, 268 p. ports. 24 cm.

1. Loines, Russell Hillard, 1874–1922.

NL 0452877 NcD LU RPB NN CSt KyLoU MH

1874–1922
Loines, Russell Hillard,   ed.

The Shadow … no. 1–4; Feb–June 1896. Cambridge, Mass., Printed at the Vniversity press, 1896.

Loing Valley. Association des naturalistes de la Vallee du Loing
see Association des naturalistes de la Vallee du Loing *et du Massif de Fontainebleau.*

VOLUME 338

Loinger, Henri, 1914–
... Les causes de la mort dans le cancer (à propos de 282 cas) (Clinique médicale A, 1918–1939) ... Paris, Legrand, 1939.
90, ₁1₎ p. illus. 24½ᶜᵐ. (Strasbourg. Université. Faculté de médecine. ₁Thèse. 1939?₎ no. 82)
Thèse—Strasbourg.

1. Cancer₁—Mortality₎ 2. Death—Causes.
Med 47–1579
U. S. Army medical library   [W4889]
for Library of Congress   ₁2₎

NL 0452880   DNLM CtY

Lointier, Fernand.
Par eux; essai sur la Société des nations, par Fernand Lointier; préface de M. Albert Thomas ... Paris, Éditions Publius ₁1919₎
2 p. l., v, 132 p., 1 l. 20½ᶜᵐ.   fr. 4.50

₁Peace.   ɪ. Title   ɪɪ. Title: Société des nations.
Library of Congress   JX1953.L65   19–12559

NL 0452881   DLC CSt-H NN

Loiola, Ignatiĭ, *Saint*
see
Loyola, Ignacio de, *Saint*, 1491–1556.

Loiola, Ignazio di, Saint.
See
Loyola, Ignacio de, Saint, 1491–1556.

Loiola Pereira, O   de
see **Pereira, O   de Loiola.**

Loiola₁drama₎
see under [Hacket, John, bp. of Lichfield and Coventry] 1592–1670.

Loiola; Stoicus vapulans; Cancer ... London, 1648
see under **Hacket, John, Bp. of Lichfield and Coventry,** 1592–1670.

Loir, *Mme*. Adrien.
Charles-Alexandre Lesueur, artiste et savant français en Amérique de 1816 à 1839, par Mᵐᵉ Adrien Loir. Le Havre, Muséum d'histoire naturelle, 1920.
108 p., 1 l. incl. illus., pl. plates. 25ᶜᵐ.
Part of plates printed on both sides.
"Bibliographie des œuvres de Ch.-Alex. Lesueur": p. 99–103.

1. U. S.—Descr. & trav. 2. Lesueur, Charles Alexandre, 1778–1846.
23–2873
Library of Congress   E165.L84

NL 0452887   DLC MH OClMA NN CtY T ICN PPAN

Loir, Adrien, 1862–
... À l'ombre de Pasteur (souvenirs personnels)   Paris, Le Mouvement sanitaire ₁1938₎
171 p. pl., ports., facsims. 25ᶜᵐ.

1. Pasteur, Louis, 1822–1895.   ɪ. Title.   39–30305
Library of Congress   Q143.P2L6
₁2₎   925

NL 0452888   DLC

1861–
Loir, Adrien, joint author.
Vigné, Charles.
Le Bureau d'hygiène, son organisation, son fonctionnement, par les docteurs Ch. Vigné ... ₁et₎ A. Loir ... Préface de M. Jules Siegfried ...   Paris, J. B. Baillière & fils, 1913.

Loir, Adrien, *1862–*
... Canada et Canadiens.   Paris, E. Guilmoto ₁1908₎
2 p. l., 371 p. 21ᶜᵐ.

1. Canada.   8–37650
Library of Congress   F1008.L83
        (Copyright 1908   Res. no. 2253)

NL 0452890   DLC CaBVaU CtY DNW ICJ NN CaBViPA

Loir, Adrien, 1862–
Le chat; son utilité. La destruction des rats, par le dᵣ et mᵐᵉ Adrien Loir. Préface par le dᵣ Foveau de Courmelles ... ₁Deuxième édition₎   Paris, J.-B. Baillière ₁!₎ et fils, 1931.
1 p. l., 5–159, ₁1₎ p. plates, port. 19ᶜᵐ.

1. Cats.   2. Rats—Extermination.
Agr 32–265
Library, U. S. Dept. of   Agriculture 48L83

NL 0452891   DNAL

WZ 100 qL834   **LOIR, Adrien,** 1862–
A collection of miscellaneous bio-bibliographical material on this person, together with abstracts, résumés, etc. of his works, may be found on the shelves under the above call number.

NL 0452892   DNLM

Loir, Adrien, 1862–
... Diseases of stock and sheep.   (1892)
3 p.

NL 0452893   DNAL

Loir, Adrien, 1862–
Les eaux minérales et thermales de la Tunisie.
Par. , 1900.
1. Mineral waters - Tunis.

NL 0452894   NjP

Loir, Adrien, 1862–
...Hygiene et Judaïsme; conférence faite à l'association, le dimanche, 24 décembre 1922, par le Dᵣ Adrien Loir... ₁Paris, 1922.₎   20 p.   8°.
At head of title: Chema Israël, association d'éducation et de propagande religieuses.

1. Hygiene—Jews. 2. Chema Israël,   Paris.
N. Y. P. L.   September 16, 1926

NL 0452895   NN

Loir, Adrien, 1862–
Le lait condensé, par le docteur A. Loir et le pharmacien Legangneux du Bureau d'hygiène du Havre.   Paris, J.-B. Baillière et fils, 1916.
20 p. 24ᶜᵐ.

1. Milk, Condensed.   ɪ. Legangneux, ——, joint author.
Agr 17–290
Library, U. S. Dept. of   Agriculture 44L832

NL 0452896   DNAL

Loir, *Adrien* La lutte pratique contre la malaria.
13 pp. 8°. Paris, A. Challamel, 1903.
Repr. from: Agricult. prat. d. pays chauds.

NL 0452897   DNLM

SF L834m 1892   **LOIR, Adrien,** 1862–
La microbiologie en Australie. Études d'hygiène & de pathologie comparée poursuivies à l'Institut Pasteur de Sydney. Paris, Steinheil, 1892.
95 p. illus.

L 0452898   DNLM

Loir, Adrien, 1862–   **ed.**
Musea; bulletins trimestriels réunis de la Société des amis de l'Institut océanographique du Havre et de l'Association des conservateurs des collections publiques de France. ₁1.₎ année; mai 1918–
Le Havre ₁1918–

Loir, Adrien, *1862– .*
... Les termites dans les pays tropicaux, leur destruction; par le Dᵣ Adrien Loir ...   Paris, A. Challamel, 1903.
15 p. illus. 25ᶜᵐ.
At head of title: Ministère des colonies. École nationale supérieure d'agriculture coloniale. Cours d'hygiène coloniale.
Extrait de: L'agriculture pratique des pays chauds.

1. Termite.   Agr 3–1236
Library, U. S. Dept. of   Agriculture 432L83

NL 0452900   DNAL

Loir, Adrien, *1862–*
Thérapeutique et voyages au long cours. Paris, 1924.
136 p.   23 cm.

NL 0452901   DAS

VOLUME 338

1862-
Loir, Adrien, joint author.

Vigné, Charles.
... Trentenaire du Bureau d'hygiène du Havre, doyen des bureaux d'hygiène en France. Historique de sa fondation par MM. les docteurs Ch. Vigné ... [et] Adrien Loir. Le Havre, Impr. du journal Le Havre, 1910.

NL 0452903   CtY DNLM

Loir, Auguste Louis Albert, 1890-
... À propos de l'urétérite tuberculeuse dite "primitive" ... Lille, 1919.
24 cm.
Thèse - Univ. de Lille.

NL 0452903   CtY DNLM

1912.67 Loir, Erasme.
9181   Carte géologique de l'Afrique équatoriale franç** établie sur l'ordre de Monsieur le Gouverneur Général Merlin ... D'après les cartes géologiques de M. M. Barrat, Hubert et les travaux de M. M. Arnaud, Arsandaux, Alvernhe ... [et a.] Tracé géographique de la carte établi par Emmanuel Barralier ... Asnieres, 1918.

67½x46½cm.

Échelle: 1/5.000.000.
At head of title: Gouvernement général de l'Afrique équatoriale franç**.
"Cette carte, dressée en 1913, devait

paraitre en 1914, en raison des circonstances elle n'a pu être publiée qu'en 1918."

NL 0452906   IU

Loir (Eugène). *I. Des différences générales des sexes. II.* [etc.]. 35 pp. 4°. *Paris,* 1839, *No. 82,* v. 345.

NL 0452907   DNLM

Loir, Hélène.
GN654   Le Tissage du raphia au Congo belge. Ter-
T4   vueren, Belgique, 1935.
f   66 p. illus.,maps. 37ᶜᵐ. (Annales du
ser.3   Musée du Congo belge [D] Ethnographie. Série
v.3   3: Notes analytiques sur les collections du
no.1   Musée du Congo belge, t.3,fasc.1)
        In portfolio.
        Bibliography: p.[63]-66.

        1.Weaving - Congo, Belgian. I.Title.
Africa

NL 0452908   CSt CtY OCU PU CU MBU NNC

DT 644 LOIR,HÉLÈNE.
.A6   Le tissage du raphia au Congo Belge.
ser.3   Tervueren, 1935.1.e.1936.
v.3   66 p. illus.,plates,maps. (Tervueren,
        Belgium—Musée du Congo Belge. Annales. Eth-
        nographie et anthropologie, ser.3, v.1-3,
        pt.1)

        1. Raffia work. 2. Weaving--Congo,Belgian.
        I. Title.

NL 0452909   InU

Loir, J.
Théorie du tissauge des étoffes de soie, par J. Loir ...
Lyon, Desvigne & cie, 192?-

v. illus., plates (part col.) 39ᶜᵐ.

Samples of silk materials pasted in.

1. Silk. 2. Silk manufacture and trade. 3. Weaving.

P O 24-4

Library, U. S. Patent   Office TS1665.L834

NL 0452910   DHEW NN

Loir, J.
Tissage mécanique; cours de garage des métiers mécaniques à tisser les étoffes de soie, par J. Loir...   Paris: H. Desforges, 1919. 168 p. incl. tables. diagrs. 2. ed. 4°.

535114A.   1. Silk—Manufacture.
N. Y. P. L.   September 17. 1931

NL 0452911   NN

Loir, J.
Tissage mécanique. Cours de garage des métiers mécaniques à tisser les étoffes de soie, par J. Loir...   Lyon: J. Desvigne et ses fils, 1929. 188 p. incl. tables. diagrs. 3. ed. 4°.

504679A.   1. Silk—Manufacture.
N. Y. P. L.   December 30, 1930

NL 0452912   NN

Loir (Joseph-Jean-Adrien). *De la chaleur comme agent chimique.* 31 pp. 4°. *Paris, Fain et Thunot,* 1847. [P., v. 1151.]
Concours.

NL 0452913   DNLM

206   Loir, Joseph Napoléon, 1805-1868.
167   Analyse d'un mémoire sur le baptême con-
942   sidéré dans ses rapports avec l'état civil
         et l'hygiène publique depuis les premiers
         temps du Christianisme jusqu'a nos jours.
         [Paris?1849?]
         189-194 p. 21 cm.

         caption title.
         Provenance: Bp. Whittingham, Maryland
         Diocesan Library.
         1. Baptism.   . Title.

NL 0452914   NNC

HV   LOIR, Joseph Napoléon, 1805-1868.
L832d   De l'état civil des nouveau-nés au
1854   point de vue de l'histoire, de l'hygiène
         et de la loi; nécessité de constater
         les naissances à domicile. Paris,
         Cotillon, 1854.
         viii, 462 p.

NL 0452915   DNLM

Loir, Joseph Napoléon, 1805-1868.
De l'état civil des nouveau-nés au point de vue de l'histoire, de l'hygiène et de la loi. Présentation de l'enfant sans déplacement ... Par le Dr. J. N. Loir ... Paris, A. Durand [etc.], 1865.
xv, 462 p. fold. diagr. 22½ᵐ.

"Ouvrage qui a obtenu un encouragement de l'institut impérial Académie des sciences, prix Montyon de 1854."

1. Infants (New-born)   [1. Infants—France; 2. Children—Law—France. I. Title.

29-23684

NL 0452916   DLC MH-L

Loir, Joseph Napoléon.
—. De l'exécution de l'article 55 du code civil, relatif à la constatation des naissances. 24 pp. 8°. *Paris, Joubert,* 1846. [P., v. 460.]

NL 0452917   DNLM

Loir, Joseph Napoléon, 1805-1868.
Des ulcérations du col de l'utérus, et de leur traitement. 32 pp. 4°. *Paris,* 1835, No. 407.
Concours.

NL 0452918   DNLM

Loir (Joseph-Napoléon). *Dissertation et propositions sur quelques points d'anatomie, de physiologie et de pathologie.* 46 pp. 4°. *Paris,* 1834, No. 45, v. 270.
—. The same. 64 pp. 8°. *Paris, Méquignon-Marvis, père & fils,* 1835. [P., v. 908.]

NL 0452919   DNLM

17   Loir, Joseph Napoléon, 1805-1868.
.1834   Du Baptême considéré dans ses rapports avec
         l'état civil et l'hygiène publique. Étude pour servir
         à l'histoire de l'état civil. Mémoire lu à l'Académie
         des sciences morales et politiques, le 18 août 1849.
         Paris, Joubert, 1849.
         19 p. 8°.
         Extrait de la Revue pratique de droit français.
         T. XVI.

NL 0452920   DLC

Loir,Joseph Napoléon,1805-1868.
Du service des actes de naissance en France et à l'étranger. Nécessité d'améliorer ce service ... Paris, Panckoucke, 1845.
23 p. 21½ᶜᵐ.
"Extrait du Compte rendu de l'Académie des sciences morales et politiques."
Author's autograph presentation copy to M.Guizot.
No.4 in [Guizot collection of pamphlets. v.12] (Binder's title: Mélanges politiques. Ministère du 29 octobre 1840)

1.Registers of birth,etc.--France.

NL 0452921   MiU DNLM

Loir (J[oseph]-N[oir]). *De la statistique appliquée à la mortalité dans le premier mois de la vie.* 15 pp. 4°. [*Paris*], *Panckoucke,* [1848]. *Repr. from : Compt. rend. Acad. d. sc. mor. et polit., Par.,* 1848.

NL 0452922   DNLM

Loir, Lilian A   , 1903-
... Notions de droit administratif à l'usage du médecin fonctionnaire d'hygiène ... Lille [1933]
Thèse - Univ. de Paris.
"Bibliographie": 1 l. at end.

NL 0452923   CtY

Loir, Luigi.   No. 7 in *Cab.80.150.5
Le Val de grâce, Panneau décoratif — Hotel de Ville de Paris. Luigi
=   Loir pinxt. G. Rodriguez sculpt.
    [Paris.] Wittmann. [1906?] Size, 21⅛ × 13¾ inches.

G4074 — Paris, France. Hôtel de Ville. — Val de Grace, Abbey. — Rodrigues, Georges, engraver.

NL 0452924   MB

VOLUME 338

Loir, M.
　Commentaire législatif et pratique de la Loi du 5 août 1933 sur la révision temporaire et la résiliation des baux commerciaux, comprenant des formules d'actes auxquels peut donner lieu son application. par m. Loir ... Bruxelles, Mme F. Larcier, Mme O. Renson, successeur, 1933.
　　77 p., 1 l. 24½^cm.

　　1. Landlord and tenant—Belgium. 2. Leases—Belgium. 3. Forms (Law)—Belgium. I. Belgium. Laws, statutes, etc. II. Title.

　　　　　　　　　　　　　　　　　　　　37-18164

　Library of Congress　　　　　[3]　　　　333.509493

NL 0452925　　DLC

Loir, M　　ed.
　Commentaire législatif et pratique de la Loi du 7 mars 1929 portant révision des articles du Code civil relatifs au bail à ferme, et de la Loi du 7 mai 1929 sur la location des biens ruraux des administrations publiques, comprenant toute la législation annotée concernant la matière et des formules d'actes usuels, par M. Loir ... 3. éd., rev. et augm. de nombreuses décisions de jurisprudence. Bruxelles, F. Larcier, 1933.
　　240 p. 20½^cm.
　　1. Landlord and tenant—Belgium. 2. Farms—Belgium. 3. Belgium—Public lands. 4. Forms (Law)—Belgium. I. Belgium. Laws, statutes, etc. II. Title.
　　　　　　　　　　　　　　　　　　　37-13210

NL 0452926　　DLC

Loir, M　　ed.
　Commentaire législatif et pratique de la loi temporaire du 10 août 1933, relative à la réduction de certains fermages, comprenant des formules d'actes auxquels peut donner lieu son application, par M. Loir ... Bruxelles, F. Larcier, 1933.
　　62 p., 1 l. 24½^cm.

　　1. Landlord and tenant—Belgium. 2. Farms—Belgium. I. Belgium. Laws, statutes, etc. II. Title.

　　　　　　　　　　　　　　　　　　　37-24143

NL 0452927　　DLC

F18　Loir, M
B5.9
L834t　Traité et formulaire des sociétés de personnes
1956　à responsabilité limitée; étude théorique, critique et pratique. Préf. de M. le baron Tibbaut. Bruxelles, F. Larcier, 1956.
　　937 p.　24^cm.
　　"Liste des principaux auteurs cités": p. [81]-82.
　　Bibliography: p. [83]-84.

　　1. Corporations - Belgium. 2. Joint-stock companies - Belgium.

NL 0452928　　MiU-L

Loir, Marcel Du
　see Du Loir, Marcel.

Loir, Maurice, 1852-1924, ed.
　...Au drapeau! Récits militaires extrait des mémoires de G. Bussière et E. Legouis [et autres]... Avec une préface par George Duruy... Paris, Hachette, 1897.
　　vi, 313 p. incl. col. illus., col. plates. col. front. 29½^cm.

　　1. Flags of France. 2. France—History, Military.

NL 0452930　　NjP CtY CSmH

Soc
DC
202.1　Loir, Maurice, *1852-1924*
L6　　Au drapeau. Récits militaires extraits des mémoires de G. Bussière [et al.] Avec une
1905　préface par George Duruy et un tableau historique des régiments français. 4. éd. Paris, Hachette, 1905.
　　313p. illus.

　　1. France - History, Military - 1789-1815.
　　I. Title.

NL 0452931　　FTaSU

　　Loir, Maurice, 1852-1924.
959.9　L'escadre de l'amiral Courbet; notes et souvenirs par Mau-
L834Σ　rice Loir ... 2. éd. Paris [etc.] Berger-Levrault et c^ie, 1886.
　　xi, [1], 370 p. 1 l. incl. front. (port.) maps. 18½^cm.

　　1. Courbet, Amédée Anatole Prosper, 1827-1885. 2. Tongking—Hist. 3. Chinese-French war, 1884-1885.

NL 0452932　　NcD

　　Loir, Maurice, 1852-1924.
　　L'escadre de l'amiral Courbet; notes et souvenirs par Maurice Loir ... 4. éd. Paris [etc.] Berger-Levrault et c^ie, 1886.
　　xi, [1], 370 p., 1 l. incl. front. (port.) maps. 18½^cm.

　　1. Courbet, Amédée Anatole Prosper, 1827-1885. 2. Tongking—Hist. 3. Chinese-French war, 1884-1885.
　　　　　　　　　　　　　　　　　　　3-13530

　Library of Congress　　　DS549.L83

NL 0452933　　DLC DN

LOIR, Maurice, 1852-
　L'escadre de l'amiral Courbet. Notes et souvenirs. 6e éd. Paris, etc., Berger-Levrault et cie,, 1892.

　Port. and maps.
　"Composition de l'escadre de l'Extrême-Orient", pp. [359]-368.

NL 0452934　　MH

　　Loir, Maurice, 1852-1924.
　　L'escadre de l'amiral Courbet. Notes et souvenirs. Paris, Berger-Levrault & Cie., 1892.
　　xii, 370 p., 1 l. maps., port. 12°.
　　7. éd.

NL 0452935　　NN

Wason　Loir, Maurice, 1852-
DS549　L'escadre de l'amiral Courbet; notes et
L83　souvenirs. 9. éd. Paris, Berger-Levrault,
1892　1892.
　　xi, 370 p. 19cm.

NL 0452936　　NIC

Wason　Loir, Maurice, 1852-
DS549　L'escadre de l'amiral Courbet. Illus. de
L83+　M. Brossard de Corbigny. Paris, Berger-
1894　Levrault, 1894.
　　viii, 324 p. illus., maps. 28cm.

　　1. Courbet, Amédée Anatole Prosper, 1827-1885. 2. Tongking—Hist. 3. Chinese-French war, 1884-1885. I. Title.

NL 0452937　　NIC CtY NjP

　　Loir, Maurice, 1852-1924.
　　Études d'histoire maritime; révolution—restauration—empire; par Maurice Loir. Paris, Nancy, Berger-Levrault & cie, 1901.
　　2 p. l., 324 p., 1 l. 18½^cm.
　　Contents.—La marine et la proclamation de la première république.—L'adoption du pavillon tricolore dans la marine.—La livraison de Toulon aux Anglais (1793)—Le combat du Ça-Ira (14-15 mars 1795)—Les plans maritimes du Directoire.—Brueys à Aboukir (1er août 1798)—L'Odyssée d'un marin royaliste J. P. Rivoire de Saint-Hippolyte sous le consulat et l'empire.—Napoléon et la marine.—Un ministre d'autrefois (Charles Le Mercher, baron d'Haussez)
　　1. France. Navy—Hist. 2. France—Hist.—1789-1815. 3. Rivoire de Saint-Hippolyte, J. P., 1775-1815. 4. Haussez, Charles Le Mercher de Longpré, baron d', 1778-　　　1854.
　　　　　　　　　　　　　　　　　　2-21025

　Library of Congress　　　DC153.L83

NL 0452938　　DLC NN

　　Loir, Maurice, 1852-1924.
　　Flotte und Fortschritt ... Uebersetzung aus dem Französischen von A. v. L^***. Berlin, H. Costenoble, 1902.
　　4 p. l., 142 p., 1 l. 8°.
　　Joint author: Gaston M. J. de Caqueray.

NL 0452939　　NN

　　Loir, Maurice, 1852-
　　Gloires et souvenirs maritimes, d'après les mémoires ou les récits de Baudin [et al.] Paris, Hachette, 1895.
　　viii, 331 p. illus. (part col.) 29cm.

　　1. France—History, Naval.

NL 0452940　　AU KU DN CtY NWM

　　Loir, Maurice, 1852-
　　...Gloires et souvenirs maritimes d'après les mémoires ou les récits de Baudin... Paris: Hachette, 1922. viii, 312 p. illus., col'd plates. 6. ed. 4°.

　　"Cet ouvrage est illustré...par MM. Rougeron et Vignerot, et Ducourtioux et Huillard, d'après les aquarelles de M. Alfred Paris et de M. G. Dutriac."

110922A. 1. Navy (French).—His-　　　tory. 2. Toudouze, Georges Gustave, 1877-　　, jt. compiler.
N. Y. P. L.　　　　　　　　　　December 10, 1923.

NL 0452941　　NN FTaSU

　　Loir, Maurice, 1852-1924.
　　Jean-Gaspard Vence, corsaire et amiral, 1747-1808. Paris, Baudoin, 1894.
　　79 p. plates (incl. port., facsims 29cm.

　　1. Vence, Jean-Gaspard, 1747-1808.

NL 0452942　　MnU NIC MiU MB

　　Loir, M[aurice] 1852- and Caqueray, G[aston M. J.] de.
　　La marine & le progrès; les luttes de l'avenir par la science, par les millions. Paris, Hachette et cie, 1901.
　　vi, 367, [1] p. 12°.

　Library of Congress　　　　　　1-F-2175

NL 0452943　　DLC DN

VOLUME 338

Loir, Maurice, 1852–1924.
... La marine française. Illustrations de L. Couturier et F. Montenard. Paris, Hachette et cⁱᵉ, 1893.
3 p. l., 620 p. illus., plates. 31½ᶜᵐ.
Each plate accompanied by guard sheet with descriptive letterpress.

1. France—Navy. 2. France—Navy—Hist. I. Couturier, Léon Antoine Lucien, 1842– illus. II. Montenard, Frédéric, 1849–1926, illus. III. Title.
36–24209
Library of Congress   VA503.L6
[2]   359.0944

NL 0452944   DLC IaU MB MH ICJ DNW MiU NjP DN OCU

Loir, Maurice, 1852–[19]14.   Fr 364.16
La marine royale en 1789. Paris, A. Colin et cie, [1892].
pp. xvi, 319 +.

France–Navy–Hist.||AcS 187030

NL 0452945   MH NN NNC NIC DN PPL

Loir, Maurice Eugène.
Cavalerie. Procédés techniques... La cavalerie dans la bataille. Avec une preface de M. le Général Langlois. Paris R. Chapelot et etc.   1912.
401 p.   23 cm

NL 0452946   DNW MH

Loir, Maurice Eugène.
Cavalry. Technical operations. Cavalry in an army. Cavalry in battle. Tr. by the General staff, War office, from the French of Captain Loir, xx army corps staff. With a preface by General Langlois ... Pub. by permission. London, H. M. Stationery off., Harrison and sons, printers, 1916.
xii, 269 p.—maps (part fold.) diagrs. 22ᶜᵐ.
Twelve folded maps in pocket.
The original was published in 1912, with title: Cavalerie. Procédés techniques. La cavalerie dans l'ensemble de l'armée. La cavalerie dans la bataille.
1. Cavalry. 2. Cavalry drill and tactics.   I. Gt. Brit. General staff.   II. Langlois, Hippolyte, 1839–1912.
17–17587
Library of Congress   UE145.L7

NL 0452947   DLC LU ICJ

Loir, Raymond.
Vieux Damas. Avignon, Aubanel père [1947]
60 p. illus., port. 19 cm.

1. Damascus—Descr.   I. Title.
DS99.D3L65   49–18670*

NL 0452948   DLC

Loir, Sim, Tel. Camille.
De la metrorrhagie interne dans les derniers mois de la grossesse. Paris, 1844.

NL 0452949   NN

Loir-et-Cher, *France (Dept.)*
Budget supplémentaire des recettes et des dépenses départementales. Décision modificative.
Blois.
no. 32 cm.

1. Budget—Loir-et-Cher, France (Dept.)
HJ9047.A3L63   56–30961 ‡

NL 0452950   DLC

Loir-et-Cher. *France (Dept.)*
Compte des recettes et des dépenses départementales.
[Blois]
v. 32 cm.

1. Budget—Loire-et-Cher, France (Dept.)
HJ9047.A3L52   49–44189*‡

NL 0452951   DLC

Loir-et-Cher, *France (Dept.)*
Quatrième centenaire de la découverte de l'Amérique. Comité du Loir-&-Cher chargé d'assurer la participation du département aux congrès, expositions, solennités et fêtes de Huelva, Séville, Grenade et Madrid. Rapport à M. le marquis de Croizier, délégué général du quatrième centenaire de la découverte de l'Amérique pour la France ... sur les travaux du Comité de Loir-&-Cher et la participation du délégué de ce comité au centenaire, suivi d'observations sur l'Espagne, par Ludovic Guignard de Butteville ... Blois, Typographie et lithographie C. Migault et cⁱᵉ, 1893.
105 p., 1 l. front. (port.) 25ᶜᵐ.   MiU–C
1. Colombo, Cristoforo—   Centennial celebrations. 2. Spain.
I. Guignard de Butteville,   Ludovic. II. Title.
34–7758
Library of Congress   E119.L63
[2]   973.15

NL 0452952   DLC NN

Loir-et-Cher, *France (Dept.)*   Rapport
fait au citoyen Corbigny, préfet du département de Loir-et-Cher, par la commission nommée par lui, pour constater les expériences sur la vaccine, mises en pratique par le Cⁿ Desparancieu, officier de santé. 8 pp. 8°. [Blois, an IX, 1801.]
[P., v. 1285; 1927.]

NL 0452953   DNLM

Loir-et-Cher, *France (Dept.) Archives.*   4613.71
Archives départementales, communales et hospitalières, et bibliothèques adminstratives.
— [Blois. Dufresne. 1870.] 8 pp. 8°.
The prefect was the Vicomte de Gauville.

Jan. 14.   1904
Æ.2805 — Loir-et-Cher, Department, France. Arch. — Gauville,   Vicomte de

NL 0452954   MB

Z
5315
.072   Loir-et-Cher, France (Dept.) Archives.
Les ducs d'Orléans et le comté d'Asti; catalogue de documents conservés à Asti, Milan et Turin. Blois, Impr. J. de Grandpré, 1933.
98 p.
Includes bibliography.

1. Orléans, House of—Hist.—Bibl. 2. Asti, Italy—Hist.—Bibl. I. Title.

NL 0452955   MiU

CD1215
f.L8   **Loir-et-Cher (Dept) Archives**
Inventaire sommaire des archives départementales... Loir-et-Cher... Blois, Impr. E. Moreau et cie. [etc.] 1887–
v. 31½cm. (Half-title: Collection des inventaires sommaires des archives départementales...publiée sous la direction du Ministre de l'instruction publique et des beaux-arts. Loir-et-Cher)
Set incomplete.
1. Archives—France—Loir-et-Cher (Dept.) 2. Loir-et-Cher, France (Dept.)—Hist.—Sources.

NL 0452956   ICU

CD 1215
.L3 A43   **Loir-et-Cher, France (Dept.) Archives**
1887 Q
Inventaire sommaire des Archives départementales antérieures à 1790, rédigé par MM. de Martonne, Félix Bruce, de Fleury, Bournon et Roussel, archivistes. Loir-et-Cher. Archives civiles. Séries C, D, E et E supplément (première partie) Blois, Imprimerie E. Moreau et cie, 1887.
1 v. (various paging) 33cm.
Half-title: Collection des inventaires sommaires des ar-   chives départementales antérieures à   1790.||

CD 1215
.L3 A43 --- --- Série E supplément (suite) [Blois,
1887 Q n.d.]
Suppl   p. 33cm.
Caption title.

NL 0452958   MdBJ UU

Loir-et-Cher, *France (Dept.) Archives.*
Inventaire-sommaire des Archives départementales antérieures à 1790. Loir-et-Cher. Clergé séculier. Série G. Blois, Impr. C. Migault, 1894–1913.
2 v. 33 cm.
Half title: Collection des inventaires sommaires des Archives départementales antérieures à 1790.
CONTENTS.—t. 1. Articles 1–967, rédigé par F. Bournon, E. Roussel, A. Bourgeois.—t. 2. Articles 968–2641, rédigé par J. Soyer, A Bourgeois et G. Trouillard.
1. Loir-et-Cher, France (Dept.)—Hist.—Sources—Bibl. I. Title.
CD1215.L3A45   68–38770

NL 0452959   DLC UU

Loir-et-Cher, *France (Dept.) Archives.*
Inventaire-sommaire des Archives départementales antérieures à 1790. Loir-et-Cher. Clergé régulier. Série H. Blois, Impr. J. de Grandpré, 1936–
v. 33 cm.
Half title: Collection des inventaires sommaires des Archives départementales antérieures à 1790.
CONTENTS.—t. 1. Articles 1 H 1–41 H 58, rédigé par G. Trouillard.
1. Loir-et-Cher, France (Dept.)—Hist.—Sources—Bibl. I. Title.
CD1215.L3A452   68–38879

NL 0452960   DLC NjP UU

CD1215
.L3A47   **Loir-et-Cher,** *France (Dept.) Archives.*
Inventaire sommaire des Archives départementales antérieures à 1790. Série F (dons et acquisitions) [Blois, n. d.]
78 p. 33 cm.
Caption title.

1. Loir-et-Cher, France (Dept.)—Hist.—Sources—Bibl. I. Title.
CD1215.L3A47   68–38797

NL 0452961   DLC

VOLUME 338

CD 1215
.L3 A57
1945 Q　　Loir-et-Cher, France (Dept.) Archives.
　　　　Répertoire numérique de la série Q (domaines,
　　enregistrement et timbre), par Guy Trouillard,
　　archiviste du département. Préface et supplé-
　　ment par Jean Martin-Demézil, archiviste de L
　　Loir-et-Cher.　Blois, Grande imprimerie, 1945.
　　　12, 120 p.　33cm.
　　　At head of title: Archives départementales
　　de Loir-et-Cher.

　NL　0452962　　MdBJ

4JN
Fr.
74　　　Loir-et-Cher, France (Dept.) Conseil
　　　général
　　　　Procès-verbaux des délibérations:
　　Session extraordinaire de 1870.　Blois,
　　Impr. M. Marchand [　　]
　　　　15 p.

　NL　0452963　　DLC-P4

　　Loir-et-Cher, France (Dept.) *Conseil général.*
　　Rapports et délibérations.

　　₍Blois₎
　　　　v.　24 cm.
　　Title varies:　　－1965, Rapport du préfet et procès-verbaux des
　　délibérations.

　　　1. Loir-et-Cher, France (Dept.)—Pol. & govt.

　　JS7.F7L22　　　　　　　49–28797 rev*‡

　NL　0452964　　DLC NjP NN MiU

　　Loir-et-Cher, France (Dept.) Cour d'assises
　　　　see　　France. Cour d'assises (Loir-et-Cher)
　　[Supplement]

　　Loir-et-Cher, *France (Dept.) Direction des services agri-
　　coles*
　　　　see
　　France. *Direction des services agricoles de Loir-et-Cher.*

France
Loir-et-Cher,₍Dept.₎ Directoire.　　Fr 1328.300.26
　　Extrait du registre des délibérations du Directoire du
　　département de Loir et Cher, séance du 7 avril 1791.
　　[Blois, Impr. de J.P.J.Masson, 1791]

　　3 p.

　NL　0452967　　MH

France
Loir-et-Cher,₍Dept.₎ Laws, statutes, etc.
　　Recueil des usages locaux du département de Loir-et-Cher,
　classés dans un ordre methodique, par L. Leguay … Paris,
　Noizette, 1888.

　　2 p. l., vii, 262 p. 25¼ᶜᵐ.

　　1. Usage and custom (Law)　　ɪ. Leguay, L., comp. ɪɪ. Title.
　　　　　　　　　　　　　　　　　　　27–21113

　NL　0452968　　DLC MH

Loir-et-Cher, *France (Dept.) Préfecture. Bibliothèque
administrative.*
　　Catalogue de la Bibliothèque administrative de la Préfecture de Loir-et-Cher, par Fernand Bournon, archiviste
du département.　Blois, Impr. E. Moreau et cⁱᵉ, 1881.

　　32 p. 25ᶜᵐ.

　　ɪ. Bournon, Fernand Auguste Marie, 1857–1909, comp.

　　　　　　　　　　　　　　　　　11–34867

　　Library of Congress　　　Z927.B67

　NL　0452969　　DLC

NK5349
L83　　　Loire, Gabriel.
　　　　⋯Le vitrail. Aperçus historiques, artistiques
　　et techniques…　Angers, Librairie du Bon roi
　　René, 1924.　iv,132 p.　19 pl.　23 cm.

　　　"Préface" precedes t.-p.

　　　300.　1. Glass painting and staining--France.
　　　2. Cathedrals--Angers, France.

　NL　0452970　　NCorniC NNC NjP CSt OClMA

Loire, Louis,　　1815－　　　　　　4677.60
　　Anecdotes de la vie littéraire. Préface d'Émile de La Bédollière.
　Paris. Dentu. 1876. 240 pp. [Bibliothèque des curieux.] 16°.

　G666 — T.r. — Anecdotes. — S.r. — La Bédollière, Émile Gigault de, prefacer.

　NL　0452971　　MB NN IU

Loire, Louis,　　　1815－　comp.　　　°°T.77.133
　　Anecdotes de théâtre.　Comédiens — comédiennes — bons mots des
　　coulisses et du parterre.
＝　Paris. Dentu. 1875. 240 pp. [Bibliothèque des curieux.] 18
　　cm., in 8s.
　　Relates to French theatres.

　J363 — T.r. — S.r. — Actors. — France. Theatres. — Anecdotes.

　NL　0452972　　MB WU NjP MH TxU

Loire, Pierre.
　　Doléances et supplications au roi … [Paris?
　1789]
　　28 p.
　　No. 1 of a volume of pamphlets

　NL　0452973　　NjP

Loire, *France (Dept.)*
　　Budget des recettes et des dépenses départementales.

　　Saint-Étienne.
　　　　v. 31 cm.
　　At head of title,　　 : République française. Ministère de l'intérieur.
　　(Direction de l'administration départementale et communale) (Bu-
　　reau des affaires et de la comptabilité départementales)

　　　1. Budget—Loire, France (Dept.)　　ɪ. France. Direction de
　　l'administration départementale et communale.

　　HJ9047.A3L62　　　352.1　　　49–27078*‡

　NL　0452974　　DLC

Loire, *France (Dept.) Archives.*
　　Délibérations et arrêtés du Conseil et du Directoire du
　département de la Loire.　Analyses complètes par Joseph
　de Fréminville, archiviste départemental.　Saint-Étienne,
　Société de l'Impr. Théolier, 1907–20.
　　4 v. (336 p.)　33 cm.
　　Vols. 2–4: cover title.
　　Vols. 2–4 have title: Délibérations et arrêtés du Directoire et de
　l'administration du département de la Loire.
　　Vol. 4: Analyses complètes par Joseph de Fréminville, continuées
　par Louis Biernawski, archiviste départemental.
　　"Tirage à part de l'inventaire ₍de la série L₎"
　　No more published?
　　1. Loire, France (Dept.)—Hist.—Sources—Bibl.　ɪ. Fréminville,
　Joseph Delapoix de,　　　1862–1930.　ɪɪ. Biernawski, Louis.

　　CD1215.L56A42　　　　　　　　68–36507

　NL　0452975　　DLC

　　　　　　　Loire, France (Dept.) Archives.
CD1215
.L56A585
France. *Direction des archives.*
　　État sommaire des papiers de la période révolutionnaire
　conservés dans les Archives départementales, série L.　Loire.
　Extrait du tome premier (Ain à Loire-Inférieure)　Paris,
　Impr. nationale, 1907.

fCD1215　Loire, France (Dept.) Archives.
L65A2　　　Inventaire-sommaire des Archives départe-
　　　mentales…　Saint-Étienne, Société de
　　l'Imprimerie théolier, 1870–
　　　v.　31cm.

　　　1. Archives － France － Loire (Dept.)
　　2. Loire, France　　　(Dept.) － Hist. －
　　Sources.

　NL　0452977　　IaU

CD1215　Loire (Dept.) Archives.
f.L82　　　Inventaire sommaire des archives départementales…
　　Loire…　Saint-Étienne, Impr.Ménard₍etc.₎₁888–
　　　v.　31¼cm.　(Half-title:Collection des inven-
　　taires sommaires des archives départementales…publiée
　　sous la direction du Ministre de l'instruction pu-
　　blique.　Loire)
　　　Set incomplete.
　　　1.Archives--France--Loire(Dept.)　2.Loire,France
　　(Dept.)--Hist.--Sources.　3.Hospitals--France--Loire
　　(Dept.)　4.Charities--France--Loire(Dept.)

　NL　0452978　　ICU

Loire, *France (Dept.) Archives.*
　　Inventaire-sommaire des Archives départementales à 1790.
　Série C. ₍Saint-Étienne, 1862₎
　　13 p. 32 cm.
　　Caption title.
　　Signatures 1–2; no more published.
　　Articles 1–51.

　　1. Loire, France (Dept.)—Hist.—Sources—Bibl.　ɪ. Title.

　　CD1215.L56A436　　　　　　68–36567 rev

　NL　0452979　　DLC

Loire, *France (Dept.) Archives.*
　　Inventaire-sommaire des Archives départementales an-
　térieures à 1790.　Série E. ₍Saint-Étienne, 1867₎
　　72 p. 32 cm.
　　Caption title.
　　Signatures 1–9; no more published.
　　Articles 1–265.

　　1. Loire, France (Dept.)—Hist.—Sources—Bibl.　ɪ. Title.

　　CD1215.L56A443　　　　　　68–36565

　NL　0452980　　DLC

VOLUME 338

CD1215
.L56A44 Loire, *France (Dept.) Archives.*
Inventaire sommaire des Archives départementales antérieures à 1790. Loire. Archives civiles: série E, supplément. Saint-Étienne, Société de l'impr. Théolier, 1899-
19

v. 33 cm.
Half title: Collection des inventaires sommaires des Archives
départementales antérieures à 1790.
Vol. 2 has imprint: Saint-Étienne, Société d'édition et d'impression du centre.
CONTENTS.—t. 1. Arrondissement de Montbrison, rédigé par MM.
Chaverondier et De Fréminville, archivistes.—t. 2. Arrondissement
de Roanne (canton de Saint-Just-en-Chevalet) rédigé par J. Canard,
revu et complété par R. Seve et A. Perret, archivistes en chef de
la Loire.
1. Loire, France (Dept.)—Hist.—Sources—Bibl.
I. Title.

CD1215.L56A44   68-36518

NL 0452981   DLC PU CU

Loire, *France (Dept.) Archives.*
Inventaire sommaire des Archives départementales de la
Loire antérieures à 1790. Série H supplement. Saint-
Étienne, Société anonyme de l'impr. Théolier, 1926-

v. 33 cm.
Cover title.
At head of title, v. 1: Joseph de Fréminville, archiviste honoraire
du département de la Loire.
CONTENTS.—t. 1. Hôpitaux de Chandieu, Charlieu, Roanne, Bourg-
Argental, Boën.

1. Loire, France (Dept.)—Hist.—Sources—Bibl.   I. Title.

CD1215.L56A445   68-36564

NL 0452982   DLC

CD
1215 Loire, France (Dept.) Archives.
A2   Rapport ... Saint-Étienne,
L7   v. 24 cm.
         With this are bound Loire, France (Dept.)
       Archives. Rapport; Loire-Inférieure, France
       (Dept.) Archives.
         Inserted (in volume lettered Rapports des
       archivistes departementaux. Loire. Loire-
       Inférieure. Lot) are Notice sur la forma-
       tion et la composition des archives dé-
       partementales de la Loire,...

NL 0452983   MiU

Loire, *France (Dept.) Archives.*
Répertoire numérique de la série M (personnel et administration générale) Par Louis Biernawski, archiviste en chef
du département. Saint-Étienne, Théolier imprimeur, 1943.
96 p. 32 cm.
At head of title: Archives départementales de la Loire.

1. Loire, France (Dept.)—Hist.—Sources—Bibl.

CD1215.L56A53   68-36551

NL 0452984   DLC

Loire, *France (Dept.) Archives.*
Testaments foréziens, 1305-1316. [n. p.] 1951 [i. e. 1952]
377 p. fold. map. 28 cm.
At head of title: Fondation Georges Guichard.

1. Wills—Forez, France.   I. Title.

CS597.F7L6   56-20973

NL 0452985   DLC CU TxU

Loire, France (Dept.)   Commission
chargée de l'examen des questions relatives aux *enfants trouvés.*
Des enfants trouvés. Rapport fait au Conseil-général de la
Loire, le 24 août 1838, au nom de la Commission chargée de
l'examen des questions relatives aux enfants trouvés, par M.
Smith. Clermond-Ferrand, Impr. de Perol, 1839. 96 p. 21cm.

1. Foundlings—France—Loire.   I. Valentin-Smith, Joannes Erhard.
1796-1891.   Card revised
N. Y. P. L   April 17. 1951

NL 0452986   NN

Loire, *France (Dept.) Commission départementale.*
Procès-verbaux des délibérations.

Saint-Étienne.
   v. in   22 cm.

1. Loire, France (Dept.)—Pol. & govt.

JS7.F7L333   51-27153

NL 0452987   DLC

Loire (Dépt.)   Conseil central d'hygiène publique et de salubrité de Saint-Étienne.
Comptes-rendus des travaux des conseils d'hygiène publique et de salubrité du département
de la Loire pendant les années 1887-90; 1893-4;
1899-1900. Par les secrétaires du Conseil central. 8°. Saint-Étienne, 1899-1901.
   Reports for 1887-90, 1893-4, by V. Guinard; 1899-1900,
by J. Depras.

NL 0452988   DNLM

Loire, *France (Dept.)* Conseil Général.
...Procès-verbaux des délibérations du Conseil Général, précédés des Rapports du préfet. 1869 (sess. extra).

Saint-Étienne,   8°.
   Title varies.

NL 0452989   NN

Loire, *France (Dept.)* Conseil Général.
...Rapports présentés par [le] préfet...

Saint-Étienne,   8°.

NL 0452990   NN

Loire, *France (Dept.) Préfecture.*
Recueil des actes administratifs.

Saint-Étienne.
   v. 23 cm. semimonthly (irregular)

1. Administrative law—Loire, France (Dept.) 2. Loire, France
(Dept.)—Pol. & govt.

                                                                55-29017

NL 0452991   DLC

Loire-Atlantique, *France (Dept.)*
... Adresse des citoyens ... à la Convention
nationale ... [Paris, 1793]
7 p.
No. 4 of volume of pamphlets.

NL 0452992   NjP

Loire-Atlantique, *France (Dept.)*
Budget des recettes et des dépenses départementales.

Nantes.
   v. 32 cm. annual.
   Title varies: Compte des recettes et des dépenses départementales.
   Issued   by the department under its earlier name: Loire-
Inférieure.
   1. Finance, Public—Loire-Atlantique, France (Dept.) I. Loire-
Atlantique, France (Dept.) Compte des recettes et des dépenses
départementales. II. Title.

HJ9047.A3L65   51-23785 rev

NL 0452993   DLC

HJ9047
A3L68 Loire-Atlantique, *France (Dept.)*
Budget supplémentaire des recettes et des dépenses dépar-
tementales. Décision modificative.
Nantes.
   v. 32 cm.
   Vols. for 1952-53 issued by the department under its earlier
name: Loire-Inférieur.

1. Budget—Loire-Atlantique, France (Dept.)   I. Title.

HJ9047.A3L68   56-30312 rev

NL 0452994   DLC

HJ9047
.A3L65 Loire-Atlantique, France (Dept.) Compte des
recettes et des dépenses départmentales.

Loire-Atlantique, *France (Dept.)*
Budget des recettes et des dépenses départementales.

Nantes.

Loire-Atlantique, France (Dept.)
Installation des professeurs à l'École centrale ...
Nates [1796]
69 p.
No. 5 of a volume of pamphlets.

NL 0452996   NjP

Loire-Atlantique, France (Dept.)
Quatrième centenaire de la découverte de
l'Amérique (1492-1892) ...
   see under   Granges de Surgères, [Anatole]
Marquis de, 1850-1902.

Loire-Atlantique, *France (Dept.)*
   see also
Brittany.

N6852
.B8   Loire—Atlantique, France (Dept.) Archives.

Brittany. *Chambre des comptes.*
Artistes français des XVII° et XVIII° siècles (1681-1787)
Extraits des Comptes des états de Bretagne, réunis et an-
notés par le marquis de Granges de Surgères. Paris,
Charavay frères, 1893.

Film
1516   Loire-Atlantique, France (Dept.) Archives.
.595   Histoire nobiliaire, 2,500 actes de l'état civil
       ou notariés, concernant les familles de l'ancienne
       France (XVe-XVIIIe siècle) Reproduits ou ana-
       lysés par le marquis de Granges de Surgères.
       Nantes, Chez L'Auteur, 1895.
         474 p. 22 cm.

       Microfilm (negative) of original in Harvard
       University Library. 1 reel.

NL 0453000   NjP

VOLUME 338

Loire-Atlantique, *France (Dept.) Archives.*
Inventaire-sommaire des Archives départementales antérieures à 1790. Loire-Inférieure. Archives civiles. Séries A à C. Tome 1. Rédigé par F. Ramet. Paris, Impr. et librairie administratives de P. Dupont, 1865.

    5, 12, 2, 438 p.   32 cm.

    Half title: Collection des inventaires-sommaires des Archives départementales antérieures à 1790.
    Includes Article A 1-A 4 ; B 1-B 2945.
    No more published in this edition?

    1. Loire-Atlantique, France (Dept.)—Hist.—Sources—Bibl.
    I. Title.

    CD1215.L6A537   68-38772

  NL 0453001   DLC

Loire-Atlantique, France (Dept.) Archives.
Inventaire-sommaire des archives departementales antérieures à 1790. Archives civiles. Série E supplément. Nantes, E. Grimaud, 1892-
    v.
    Editor of v. 1: Léon Maitre, v. 2: Émile Gabory.
Vol. 2. published by C. Mellinet.
    1. Loir-Atlantique, France (Dept.)—Hist.
Sources.—Bibl. (Series: France. Archives départementales. Inventaire-sommaire des archives départementales antérieures à 1790)

  NL 0453002   UU

Loire-Atlantique, France (Dept.) Archives.
Inventaire-sommaire des archives départementales antérieures à 1790) Archives civiles. Séries C et D. Nantes, E. Grimaud et Fils, 1898.
    xviii, 210 p.
    1. Loire-Atlantique, France (Dept.)—Hist.
Sources.—Bibl. (Series: France. Archives départementales. Inventaire-sommaire des archives départementales antérieures à 1790)

  NL 0453003   UU

Loire-Atlantique, *France (Dept.) Archives.*
Inventaire sommaire des Archives départementales antérieures à 1790. Loire-Inférieure. Archives civiles. Nantes, É. Grimaud, imprimeur-éditeur, 1879-19 (v. 1, 1902)
    v. in   33 cm.
    Half title: Collection des inventaires sommaires des Archives départementales antérieures à 1790.
    Vols. 2, 5, pt. 2 have imprint: Nantes, Impr. C. Mellinet; v. 3 has imprint: Nantes, Impr. de l'Ouest; v. 4: Nantes, Impr. V. Forest et E. Grimaud.
    CONTENTS.—t. 1. Série B: Chambre des comptes de Bretagne, art. B 1-B 1952. Rédigé par L. Maitre.—t. 2. Série B: Chambre des comptes de Bretagne, arts. B 1953-B 2447. Rédigé par L. Maitre et

    E. Gabory.—t. 3. Série E, art. E 1-E 1630. Rédigé par L. Maitre.—t. 4. Series ecclésiastiques. Séries G et H, clergé séculier et régulier. Rédigé par L. Maitre.—t. 5. Série E supplément. Vol. 1 rédigé par L. Maitre; v. 2 rédigé par E. Gabory.   v.

    1. Loire-Atlantique, France (Dept.)—Hist.—Sources.—Bibl.
    I. Title.

    CD1215.L6A535   68-38784

  NL 0453005   DLC ICU

Loire-Atlantique, *France (Dept.) Archives.*
Inventaire sommaire des Archives départementales. Loire-Inférieure. Série L (administration du département de 1790 à l'an VIII). Rédigé par Léon Maitre. Nantes, Impr. C. Mellinet, 1909.
    x, 422 p.   32 cm.
    Half title: Collection des inventaires sommaires des Archives départementales.

    1. Loire-Atlantique, France (Dept.)—Hist.—Sources—Bibl.
    I. Title.

    CD1215.L6A533   68-38777

  NL 0453006   DLC UU

1215 Loire-*Atlantique* ,France (Dept.) Archives.
A2   Rapport ... Nantes
L7   v.   24 cm.
    With Loire,France (Dept.) Archives. Rapport.
    Inserted(in volume lettered Rapports des archivistes departementaux. Loire. Loire-Inférieure. Lot) is Projet de construction d'un nouveau dépôt d'archives départementales [de la Loire-Inférieure] 1914. (13 p.)

  NL 0453007   MiU

Loire-Atlantique, *France (Dept.) Archives.*
Répertoire numérique de la série B (cours et juridictions). Nantes, Impr. C. Mellinet, 1945.
    viii, 158 p.   32 cm.
    Cover title.
    At head of title: Archives départementales de la Loire-Inférieure (antérieures à 1790).

    1. Loire-Atlantique, France (Dept.)—Hist.—Sources—Bibl.

    CD1215.L6A552   68-36744

  NL 0453008   DLC IaU

Loire-Atlantique, *France (Dept.) Archives.*
Répertoire numérique de la série C. II C, domaines et droits joints. Par S. Canal, avec la collaboration de E. Brouillard. Nantes, Impr. de Bretagne, 1948.
    67 p.   32 cm.
    Cover title.
    At head of title: Archives départementales de la Loire-Inférieure (antérieures à 1790).

    1. Loire-Atlantique, France (Dept.)—Hist.—Sources—Bibl.

    CD1215.L6A553   68-38851

  NL 0453009   DLC IaU PU

Loire-Atlantique, *France (Dept.) Archives.*
Répertoire numérique. Série K (lois, ordonnances et arrêtés). Dressé par MM. B. Pocquet du Haut-Jussé et Chevrel, sous la direction de Émile Gabory. Nantes, Impr. C. Mellinet, 1920.
    11 p.   32 cm.
    Cover title.
    At head of title: Archives départementales de la Loire-Inférieure.

    1. Loire-Atlantique, France (Dept.)—Hist.—Sources—Bibl.

    CD1215.L6A55   68-36653

  NL 0453010   DLC IaU

Loire-Atlantique, *France (Dept.) Archives.*
Répertoire numérique. Série Q (domaines). Par Léon Maitre. Nantes, Impr. C. Mellinet, 1911.
    32 p.   32 cm.
    Cover title.
    At head of title: Archives départementales de la Loire-Inférieure.

    1. Loire-Atlantique, France (Dept.)—Hist.—Sources—Bibl.

    CD1215.L6A5515   68-38779

  NL 0453011   DLC IaU

Loire-Atlantique, *France (Dept.) Archives.*
Répertoire numérique de la série S, travaux publics (fonds de la Préfecture). Dressé par L. Rouzeau, sous la direction de S. Canal et H. de Berranger. Nantes, Impr. C. Mellinet, 1955.
    xvi, 119 p.   32 cm.
    Cover title.
    At head of title: Archives départementales de la Loire-Inférieure.

    1. Loire-Atlantique, France (Dept.)—Hist.—Sources—Bibl.

    CD1215.L6A57   68-38807

  NL 0453012   DLC IaU UU

Loire-Atlantique, *France (Dept.) Archives.*
Répertoire numérique de la série T (instruction publique, sciences et arts). Dressé par S. Canal. Nantes, Impr. C. Mellinet, 1941.
    19 p.   32 cm.
    Cover title.
    At head of title: Archives départementales de la Loire-Inférieure.

    1. Loire-Atlantique, France (Dept.)—Hist.—Sources—Bibl.

    CD1215.L6A572   68-38795

  NL 0453013   DLC IaU

Loire-Atlantique, *France (Dept.) Archives.*
Répertoire numérique. Série V (cultes). Dressé par L. Chevrel, sous la direction de Émile Gabory. Nantes, Impr. C. Mellinet, 1913.
    13 p.   33 cm.
    Cover title.
    At head of title: Archives départementales de la Loire-Inférieure.

    1. Loire-Atlantique, France (Dept.)—Hist.—Sources—Bibl.

    CD1215.L6A5517   68-38806

  NL 0453014   DLC IaU

Loire-Atlantique. France (Dept.) Archives.
Série L
    see its   Inventaire-sommaire des archives départementales. Série L.

Loire-Atlantique. *France (Dept.) Commission départementale.*
Procès-verbaux des séances

    Nantes,
     v. 24 cm
    Title varies: Rapport sommaire et procès-verbaux des séances.
    Issued   by the commission under the department's earlier name: Loire-Inférieure.
    At head of title: Conseil général de Loire-Inférieure.— Conseil général de Loire-Atlantique.
    1. Loire-Atlantique, France (Dept.)—Pol. & govt. II. Loire-Atlantique, France (Dept.) Commission départementale. Rapport sommaire et procès-verbaux des séances. I. Loire-Atlantique. France (Dept.) Conseil général.

    JS7.F7L54   65-30728

  NL 0453016   DLC NN

JS7   **Loire-Atlantique,** France (Dept.) Commission
.F7L54   departementale. Rapport sommaire et procès-verbaux des séances
Loire-Atlantique. *France (Dept.) Commission départementale.*
Procès-verbaux des séances.

    Nantes.

Loire-Atlantique, *France (Dept.) Conseil central d'hygiène publique et de salubrité*
    see
Loire-Atlantique, *France (Dept.) Conseil départementale d'hygiène publique et de salubrité.*

W 2   **Loire-Atlantique,** France (Dept.) Conseil
QF7.1   départementale d'hygiène publique et de salubrité.
L8C7e

    Étude sur la situation sanitaire de l'arrondissement de Nantes.
    [1.   année; 1892-
    [Nantes]
     v. illus.
    Title varies slightly.
    Editor: 1892-   G. Bertin.
    1. Public health - France 2. Vital Statistics - France I. Bertin, G

    ed.   Title

  NL 0453020   DNLM

VOLUME 338

Loire-Atlantique, France (Dept.) Conseil
départementale d'hygiene publique et de salubrité.
——. Rapport général sur les travaux du conseil central de salubrité de Nantes et du département de la Loire-Inférieure, adressé à M. A. Chaper, préfet du département. 65 pp. 5° Nantes, Vve. C. Mellinet, 1844. [P., v 1739.]

NL 0453021   DNLM

Loire-Atlantique, *France (Dept.) Conseil départementale d'hygiène publique et de salubrité.*
Rapport sur les travaux.
Nantes.
v. in   illus. 22 cm. annual.
Issued 18   by the council under an earlier name: Conseil central d'hygiène publique et de salubrité; 18   by the council under the department's earlier name: Loire-Inférieure.

1. Hygiene, Public—Loire-Atlantique, France (Dept.)

RA262.L5A3   12-27139 rev

NL 0453022   DLC DNLM

Loire-Atlantique, France (Dept.) Conseil
départementale d'hygiène publique et de salubrité.
Résumé des moyens pratiques conseillés dans
les diverses instructions déjà publiées dans ce
département avec l'indication des mesures
particulières que peuvent exiger nos localités, dans
le cas d'invasion du choléra.   Nantes, Mellinet,
[n. d.]
12 p.   8°.   [P., v. 855]

NL 0453023   DNLM

Loire-Atlantique, *France (Dept.) Conseil général.*
Conseil général du département de la Loire-Inférieure
see its
Procès-verbaux des séances.

Loire-Atlantique, *France (Dept.) Conseil général.*
Procès-verbaux des séances.
Nantes.
v. in   23–25 cm.
Vols. for   include the Rapport of the Préfet. Vols. for   and vols. for the 1st sess. of 1924 are issued with the Rapport. Vols. for the 2d sess., 1898–
are bound with the Rapport.
Title varies: –1861, Conseil général du département de la Loire-Inférieure.
Vols. for   issued by the council under the department's earlier name : Loire-Inférieure.
1. Loire-Atlantique, France (Dept.)—Pol. & govt.

JS7.F7L53   55-25409 rev

NL 0453025   DLC NN

LOIRE-ATLANTIQUE, France (Department). Conseil
général.
Procès-verbaux des séances
Nantes.   v.   8°.
Microfilm (master negative).
Positive in *ZAN-T2195.
Title varies.
Includes supplements.

NL 0453026   NN

JS7
.F7L54
Loire-Atlantique, France (Dept.) Conseil
général.
Loire-Atlantique. *France (Dept.) Commission départementale.*
Procès-verbaux des séances.
Nantes.

---

ar W
46327
Loire-Atlantique, France (Dept.) Laboratoire
de chimie agricole.
Compte-rendu des travaux, 1850-1875, par
A. Bobierre.   Paris, G. Masson, 1876.
395 p.   illus.   23cm.

"Publié avec le concours du Ministre de
l'Agriculture."

I. Bobierre, Adolphe, 1823-1881.

NL 0453028   NIC

Loire-Atlantique, *France (Dept.) Préfecture.*
Exposé
see its
Rapport.

Loire-Atlantique, *France (Dept.) Préfecture.*
Rapport.
Nantes.
v. in   25 cm.
Title varies: 1871, 2d sess.—   Exposé.
Published   by the Préfecture under the department's earlier name : Loire-Inférieure.
Reports for   are in the Procès-verbaux des séances of the Conseil général. Reports for   and for the 1st sess. of 18
1924 are issued with, and reports for the 2d sess., 1898– are bound with the Procès-verbaux des séances.
1. Loire-Atlantique, France (Dept.)—Pol. & govt.

JS7.F7L52   55-25400 rev 2

NL 0453030   DLC NN

Loire-Atlantique, France (Dept.) Préfecture.
Rapport.
Nantes.
v.
Microfilm (master negative)
Positive in *ZAN-T 2159.

NL 0453031   NN

Loire-Atlantique, *France (Dept.) Préfecture.*
Statistique du département de la Loire-Inférieure; par
J. B. Huet, secrétaire général de préfecture: rédigée à la
demande du préfet. Publiée par ordre du ministre de l'intérieur.   Paris, Imp. des sourds-muets, an x [1802]
1 p. l., 70 p. fold. tables. 21 cm. [Statistique des préfets. 32]

1. Loire-Atlantique, France (Dept.)—Stat. I. France. Ministère de l'intérieur. II. Huet de Coetlizan, Jean Baptiste Claude Regnault, 1780-1823. III. Title.
HA1213.A55 vol. 32   40-21268 rev 2

NL 0453032   DLC MH-BA

Kress
Room
Loire-Atlantique, France (Dept.) . Propriétaires de vignobles.
Mémoire sur l'état des vignobles dans le
département de la Loire-Inférieure.   Nantes,
V.Mangin, imprimeur, 1829.
29, [5] p. 21.5 cm.

Signed: H.Ducoudray-Bourgault, président
[and others]
"A nos seigneurs les pairs de France et
messieurs les membres de la Chambre des
députés": 5 pages at end.

NL 0453033   MH-BA

Loire-Atlantique, France (Dept.) Service des enfants assistés.   L362.7 10
.... Enfants assistés. Protection du premier âge. Enfants
moralement abandonnés. Rapports présentés à M. le préfet
.... Nantes, 1897-1905.
1896, 1904. 23½cm.
At head of title: Département de la Loire-inférieure.
E. Lelimouzin, inspecteur départemental de l'assistance publique.

NL 0453034   ICJ DNLM

Loire-Atlantique, France (Dept.) Société
archéologique
see   Société archéologique et historique de
Nantes et de Loire-Atlantique.

Loire, Haute-France (Dept.)
Convention nationale. Rapport sur sa mission
dans le département de la Haute-Loire
see under   Pierret, Jean Nicolas.

Folio
D
129
Loire, Haute-, France (Dept.)
État général des biens des émigrés situés
dans l'étendue du Département de la Haute
Loire, dressé en exécution de la loi des 11 &
12 mars 1773 ... Le Puy, B. Clet [179??]
4? p. 42 cm.

1. Loire, Haute- France (Dept.) - Hist.
2. Émigrés.

NL 0453037   CtY

Loire, Haute-France (Dept.)
Rapport de sa mission dans départemens du Gard,
la Haute-Loire (etc.)
see under   Borie, Jean, 1756-1805.

CD1215
f.L83
Loire, Haute-, France (Dept.) *Archives départementales.*
Inventaire-sommaire des archives départementales
...Haute-Loire... Le Puy,R.Marchessou,1903-
v. 31½cm. [Collection des inventaires sommaires des archives départementales...publiée sous la direction du Ministre de l'intérieur]
Set incomplete.

1.Archives--France--Loire,Haute-(Dept.) 2.Loire,
Haute-,France(Dept.)--Hist.--Sources.

NL 0453039   ICU

CD 1215
.L63
A42
1863 Q
Loire, Haute-, France (Dept.) Archives
départementales.
Inventaire-sommaire des Archives départementales antérieures à 1790, publié par ordre
de S. Exc. M. le comte de Persigny, ministre
de l'intérieur. Département de la Haute-
Loire. Archiviste: M. A. Aymard.   Le Puy,
M.-P. Marchessou, 1863-65.
2 v. 33cm.
Contents.-1.Livraison. Série A.-2.Livraison.
Série B.

NL 0453040   MdBJ

Loire, Haute-, *France (Dept.) Archives départementales.*
Inventaire-sommaire des Archives départementales antérieures à 1790. Hante-Loire. Archives ecclésiastiques.
Série G, clergé séculier. Rédigé par Antoine Jacotin. Le
Puy, R. Marchessou, 1903.
iii, 287 p. 31 cm.
——— Série G (supplément) clergé séculier. Par Étienne Delcambre. Yssingeaux, Impr. P. Michel, 1948.
136 p. 32 cm.
Cover title.
Half title: Collection des inventaires sommaires des Archives départementales, communales et hospitalières antérieures à 1790.
CD1215.L63A44 Suppl.
1. Loire, Haute-,   France (Dept.)—Hist.—Sources—
Bibl.   I. Title.
CD1215.L63A44   68-38785

NL 0453041   DLC CtY MdBJ PU

Loire, Haute-, *France (Dept.) Archives départementales.*
Inventaire sommaire des Archives départementales antérieures à 1790. Série H supplément (Archives hospitalières
du Puy) Par René Jouanne, revu, complété et édité par
Pierre Fournier et Étienne Delcambre. Le Puy, Impr. "La
Haute-Loire," 1931-
v. 33 cm.
Half title: Collection des inventaires sommaires des Archives départementales, communales et hospitalières antérieures à 1790.
CONTENTS.—fasc. 1-2. Fonds de l'Hôtel-Dieu du Puy.
1. Loire, Haute-, France (Dept.)—Hist.—Sources—Bibl.
I. Title.
CD1215.L63A457   68-38769

NL 0453042   DLC

VOLUME 338

Loire, Haute-, *France (Dept.) Archives départementales.*
Inventaire sommaire des Archives départementales antérieures à 1790. Séries 1 H, abbaye de La Chaise-Dieu. Par Antoine Jacotin, revu, complété et édité par Étienne Delcambre. Le Puy, Impr. "La Haute-Loire," 1943.
ii, 246 p. 33 cm.
Cover title.
Half title: Collection des inventaires sommaires des Archives départementales, communales et hospitalières antérieures à 1790.
1. Loire, Haute-, France (Dept.)—Hist.—Sources—Bibl. 2. La Chaise-Dieu, France (Benedictine abbey)—Hist.—Sources—Bibl. i. Title.

CD1215.L63A46   68–36551

NL 0453043   DLC

Loire, Haute-, France (Dept.) Commission météorologique.
Bulletin annuel des observations météorologiques.

NL 0453044   DAS

Loire, Haute-France (Dept.) Conseil Général.
...Rapport du préfet. Procès-verbaux des séances de la Commission Départementale. Procès-verbaux des délibérations du Conseil.

Le Puy,   8°.

NL 0453045   NN NcU

DC
175   Loire, Haute- France (Dept) Députés.
R45   Les représentans du peuple, députés par
no.12   le département de la Haute-Loire, à leurs
        concitoyens... [Paris, Baudouin, 1799]
        3 p. 21cm.
        Dated: Paris, le 28 ventôse an 7.
        Signed: Portal [et al]
        No. 12 in vol. lettered: Pièces sur Reynaud.
            [I. Portal,   Jean Francois, b. 1742.
        [II. Title.

NL 0453046   NIC

French
Rev.
DC
195   Loire, Haute-, France (Dept.) Directoire.
L8+   Rapport général de la gestion, année
        1791. Puy, Impr. de la Société Typographique, 1792.
        149 p. 26cm.

            1. Loire, Haute, France (Dept.)--Hist.--Revolution.

NL 0453047   NIC

PQ
1904.5   Loire, Haute-, France (Dept.) École centrale du
L7   département.
1799   ... Procès-verbal de la fête centenaire de la
Cage   mort de Racine, célébrée au Puy, chef-lieu, par
        l'Ecole centrale du département [1799]
        Colophon: Au Puy, de l'imprimerie de J.B. Lacombe.
        26 [2] p. a¹⁴. 8vo.
        Caption title.

NL 0453048   DFo

Loire, Haute-, *France (Dept.) Préfecture.*
Bulletin d'information et recueil des actes administratifs
Le Puy-en-Velay.
v. in   25 cm. irregular.

1. Administrative law—Loire, Haute-, France (Dept.) 2. Loire, Haute-, France (Dept.)—Pol. & govt.

55–29014

NL 0453049   DLC

Loire, Haute-, *France (Dept.) Préfecture.*
Recueil des actes administratifs
see its
Bulletin d'information et recueil des actes administratifs.

Loire, Haute-, France (Dept.) Société agricole et scientifique
see Société agricole et scientifique de la Haute-Loire.

La Loire; aspect géographique, historique, touristique, économique et administratif du département. [Paris, Alépée, 1949]
247 p. illus., ports., maps (part fold.) profiles. 28 cm. (Les Documents de France)

1. Loire, France (Dept.)   (Series)

DC611.L803L6   54–27665

NL 0453052   DLC

DC17
-D6   **Le Loire;** aspect géographique, historique
L65   touristique, économique et administratif
        du département. [Paris, Alépée, 1953]
        196 p. illus., ports., maps (1 fold.)
        facsims. 28 cm. (Les Documents de France)

        "Ouvrage ... réalisé sous la direction de Roger Géraud."

            1. Loiret, France (Dept.) 2. Géraud, Roger, ed.   (Series)

NL 0453053   RPB InU

La Loire; aspect géographique, historique, touristique, économique et administratif du département. [Réalisé sous la direction de Roger Géraud. Paris, Alépée, 1953]
247 p. illus., maps (1 fold.) ports. 28 cm. (Les Documents de France)

1. Loire, France (Dept.)   i. Géraud, Roger, ed.   (Series)

DC611.L803L6 1953   944'.581   68–35057

NL 0453054   DLC InU

Loire-Inférieure, *France (Dept.)*
see
Loire-Atlantique, *France (Dept.)*

DC611
L827L8   **Loire-Inférieure;** nature du sol et population, agriculture,
(Ge)   mines, industrie, transport et commerce, histoire, art,
        archéologie, tourisme ... Paris, Hachette, 1925.
        64 p. illus. (incl. ports.) fold. map. 18cm.
        Statistics on front lining-papers.

        1. Loire-Inférieure, France (Dept.)

NL 0453056   ICU NN

La Loire médicale; organe officiel de la Société médico-chirurgicale des hôpitaux de Saint-Étienne ...
Saint-Étienne, J. Pichon père, 18
v.   plates, charts. 25cm. monthly.

1. Medicine—Period.

Library of Congress   R41.L8   c A 6–50 Unrev'd

NL 0453057   DLC

La LOIRE vengée, ou Recueil historique des crimes de Carrier et du Comité révolutionnaire de Nantes; avec les détails de la procédure, et des moyens employés par ces scélérats et leurs complices pour se soustraire au glaive de la loi. Paris, Meurant, Lenfant, Houel, an 3. de la République [1795]
2 v. illus.   22 cm.

NL 0453058   CaBVaU NN NIC DLC

Lofreau, Joseph, 1897-
... Sur une épidémie hospitalière de zonas ... Paris, 1926.
Thèse - Univ. de Paris.
Bibliographie: p. [43]

NL 0453059   CtY DNLM

589.222   **Loireau, Léon.**
L83c   Le champignon de couche, culture, obtention du blanc, parasites. Préface de
        Roger Heim. Paris, Laboratoire de Cryptogamie du Museum National d'Histoire Naturelle, 1950.
        96 p. illus. 24cm. (Revue de Mycologie. Mémoire hors-série, no. 5)

            1. Mushrooms.   I. Title.

NL 0453060   LU GU CaBVaU CtY

Loirelle,   **Bruté de**
see **Bruté de Loirelle,**   d. 1783.

Loiret,
...La préparation des charbons; rapport de M. Loiret, ingénieur en chef des mines, à la Commission interministérielle d'utilisation des combustibles... Paris, 1923. 28 p. illus., plans. 4°. (Chaleur & industrie. Suppl. au no. 36. Avril, 1923.)
Cover-title.

1. Charcoal. 2. Chaleur & industrie.
N. Y. P. L.   May 1, 1925

NL 0453062   NN

Loiret, Pierre, 1892-
... Contribution à l'étude de l'ostéomyélite chronique d'emblée des os longs ... Paris, 1924. 24 cm.
Thèse - Univ. de Paris.

NL 0453063   CtY DNLM

VOLUME 338

Loiret, S.
L'exercice des raffineries, ses conséquences commerciales et financières, par S. Loiret.   Nantes, V. Forest et E. Grimaud, 1875. 16 p.   21cm.

1. Beets and beet sugar—Trade   and stat.—France.
N. Y. P. L.   January 21, 1946

NL 0453064   NN

─────────────────────

Loiret (Dept.) *France*
L'administration centrale et le commissaire du Directoire exécutif du département du Loiret au Conseil des Anciens. [P, an 7]

2 p.
At head of title: Corps législatif. Conseil des Anciens
Signed: E. Vinson, président [and others]

NL 0453065   MH

─────────────────────

Loire, France (Dept.)
Exposé de l'organisation des institutions de médecine gratuite et de secours à la vieillesse. 15 juillet 1852.   [Orléans, imp. de Pagnerre, 1852] 16 p.   4°.

NL 0453066   DNLM

─────────────────────

Loiret, France (Dept.)
Rapport d'une mission dans le départemens du Cher...
    see under Leftiot, Jean Alban, 1755-1839.

─────────────────────

Loiret, France (Dept.)
Rapports généraux sur les travaux des conseils d'hygiène et de salubrité publiques du département pendant les années 1858-1885. 5. Par les secrétaires. Orléans, 1859-86.
    8°.
Reports for 1858 and 1859, by Rousse; 1860-1880 by J. de la Pommerais and H. Rabourdin; 1881-1885 by H. Dabourdin.

NL 0453068   DNLM

─────────────────────

Loiret (Dept.) Archives départementales.

Inventaire-sommaire des Archives départementales antérieures a 1790, rédigé par MM. F. Maupré et Jules Doinel, archivistes. Loiret. Archives civiles. Série A— Paris, Imprimerie administrative de Paul DuPont, 1878—
    v. 32cm. (Half-title for v.2-3: Collection des inventaires sommaires des Archives départementales antérieurs a 1790 publiée sous la direction du Ministére de l'instruction

publique et des beaux arts)

Imprint varies.

Contents: t.1. Sér.A, nos.1-1799. t.2. Sér. A, nos.1800-2200 et Sér.B, nos.1-1535. t.3. Archives civiles. Sér.B, nos. 1536-3025. t.4. Archives civiles. Sér.C: Administrations

provinciales... t.5. Archives civiles. Sér.D: Instruction publique, sciences et arts.

1. Archives. France. 2. France. History. Sources. I. Title. II. France. Ministère de l'instruction publique et des beaux arts.

NL 0453071   NcD IaU ICU CU

─────────────────────

Loiret, *France (Dept.) Archives départementales.*
Inventaire sommaire des Archives départementales antérieures à 1790. Loiret. Archives civiles. Série C. Administrations provinciales. Orléans, Impr. P. Pigelet, 1927–
    v. 33 cm.
    Half title: Collection des inventaires sommaires des Archives départementales antérieures à 1790.
    CONTENTS.—t. 1. Intendance de la géneralité d'Orléans et Assemblée provinciale de l'Orléans. Rédigé par C. Bloch et J. Soyer.
    1. Loiret, France (Dept.)—Hist.—Sources—Bibl.   I. Title.

CD1215.L7A45   68-38790

NL 0453072   DLC

─────────────────────

Loiret, *France (Dept.) Archives départementales.*
Inventaire sommaire des Archives départementales antérieures à 1790. Loiret. Archives civiles. Série D. Instruction publique, sciences et arts. Orléans, Impr. P. Pigelet, 1917.
    viii, 280 p. 33 cm.
    Half title: Collection des inventaires sommaires des Archives départementales antérieures à 1790.

    1. Loiret, France (Dept.)—Hist.—Sources—Bibl.   I. Title.

CD1215.L7A452   68-38791

NL 0453073   DLC

─────────────────────

CD1217
.O74D6
Doinel, Jules, 1842-1902.
Inventaire sommaire des archives hospitalières antérieures à 1790, Département du Loiret, ville d'Orléans. Rédigé par Jules Doinel. Revu et publié par Jacques Soyer, archiviste du Département. Orléans, Impr. P. Pigelet, 1920.

Loiret, France (Dept.) Archives départementales

─────────────────────

CD
1215 **Loiret, France (Dept.)** Archives *départementales*
A2   Rapport sur le service des archives...
L8   Orléans,
        24 cm.
    "Tableau des archives communales et hospitalières du Loiret. Première-[quatrième] partie...1913-26" inserted (in volume lettered:Rapports des Archivistes departementaux. Loiret)

NL 0453075   MiU

─────────────────────

Loiret, *France (Dept.) Archives départementales.*
Répertoire de la sous-série 1 F (Collection Henri Herluison). Par Jacques Soyer. Orléans, Impr. A. Pigelet, 1933.
    28 p. 31 cm.

    1. Loiret, France (Dept.)—Hist.—Sources—Bibl.   I. Herluison, Henri, 1835-1905.

CD1215.L7A52   68-38789

NL 0453076   DLC

─────────────────────

Loiret, *France (Dept.) Archives départementales.*
Répertoire des cartes et plans conservés dans les Archives départementales du Loiret. Par Jacques Soyer. Orléans, Impr. P. Pigelet, 1925.
    39 p. 32 cm.

    1. Loiret, France (Dept.)—Hist.—Sources—Bibl.

CD1215.L7A525   68-38788

NL 0453077   DLC MH

─────────────────────

Loiret, France (Dept.) Archives *départementales*
...Répertoire numérique de la série I (non-catholiques) par Jacques Soyer... Orléans, Pigelet, 1935.
    13 p.   31 cm.
    At head of title: Archives départementales du Loiret, antérieures à 1790. "Bibliographie des travaux relatifs aux non-catholiques de l'Orléanais": p.2-4.

NL 0453078   NjP

─────────────────────

Loiret, *France (Dept.) Archives départementales.*
Répertoire numérique de la série K (lois, ordonnances et arrêtés). Dressé par Jacques Soyer. [Orléans, 1912.
    14 p. 32 cm.
    At head of title: Archives départementales du Loiret postérieures à 1790.

    1. Loiret, France (Dept.)—Hist.—Sources—Bibl.

CD1215.L7A55   68-38787

NL 0453079   DLC NcD

─────────────────────

Loiret, France (Dept.) Archives départementales.
... Répertoire numérique de la sous-série ... par Jacques Soyer, archiviste du Département. Orléans, Imprimerie A. Pigelet & Cie, 1933–
    v.
    At head of title: Archives Départementales du Loiret antérieures à 1790.

NL 0453080   NcD

─────────────────────

Loiret, *France (Dept.) Commission départementale.*
Procès-verbaux des séances. Orléans, Impr. du Bourdon-Blanc.
    v. 21 cm.

    1. Loiret, France (Dept.)—Pol. & govt.

JS7.F7L65   54-33979

NL 0453081   DLC

─────────────────────

WA
L834a   **Loiret, France.** *(Dept.)* **Conseil général.**
1851   Assistance publique. Services de médecine gratuite et de secours aux vieillards invalides et aux incurables, établis dans le Département du Loiret. Rapports faits au Conseil général sur ces deux services, conformément à sa délibération du 6. septembre 1850, par Dubessey [et] Dumesnil. Orléans, Pagnerre, 1851.
    48 p.

    I. Dubessey, Jean Baptiste Luc Thérèse, 1796-1859.
    II. Du Mesnil, Octave, 1832-1898. III. Title

NL 0453082   DNLM

─────────────────────

Loiret, France (Dept.) Conseil Général.
... Rapport du préfet
    see Loiret, France (Dept.) Préfecture. Rapport.

─────────────────────

Loiret, *France (Dept.) Conseil général.*
Procès-verbaux des délibérations.

Orléans.
    v. 25 cm.
    Title varies slightly.
    Most volumes, 18 -19 are issued with the Rapport of the Préfet, Aug. 1872, Aug. 1875 and Dec. 1877 are bound with the Rapport for Apr. 1872, Aug. 1875 and Dec. 1877 (JS7.F7L62)

JS7.F7L63   55-15927

NL 0453084   DLC NN

VOLUME 338

Loiret, *France (Dept.) Conseil général. Commission départementale*
see
Loiret, *France (Dept.) Commission départementale.*

Loiret, *France (Dept.) Préfecture.*
Rapport.
Orléans.
　　　v. in　　25 cm.
　　Most volumes, 18　–19　　include Procès-verbaux des délibérations (title varies) of the Conseil général; Apr. 1872, Aug. 1875 and Dec. 1877 are bound with the Procès-verbaux for Aug. 1872, Aug. 1875 and Dec. 1877 (J87.F7L83)

　　1. Loiret, France (Dept.)—Pol. & govt.

JS7.F7L62　　　　　　　　　　　55–45470 rev ‡

NL 0453086　　DLC NjP NN

Loiret, *France (Dept.) Préfecture.*
Recueil des actes administratifs.
₁Orléans₁
　　　v. in　　22 cm.　monthly.

　　1. Administrative law—Loiret, France (Dept.) 2. Loiret, France (Dept.)—Pol. & govt.

　　　　　　　　　　　　　　　　55–28997

NL 0453087　　DLC

4SB
10
Loiret, *France (Dept.) Préfecture.*
Recueil des usages locaux a caractère agricole adoptés par la Chambre départementale d'agriculture. Lot du 3 janvier 1924, art. 24.　Orléans, 1935.
67 p.

NL 0453088　　DLC–P4

Loiret; aspect géographique, historique touristique, économique et administratif du département.
₁Paris,Alépée,n.d.₁　227p.illus., maps.　(Les documents de France)

　　Cet ouvrage a été réalisé sous la direction de Georges Alépée.

NL 0453089　　CaBVa

Le Loiret; aspect géographique, historique, touristique, économique et administratif du département. ₁Réalisé sous la direction de Roger Géraud. Paris, Alépée, 1953₁
　　196 p.　illus., maps (1 fold.), ports. 28 cm. (Les Documents de France)

　　1. Loiret, France (Dept.)　ɪ. Géraud, Roger, ed.　(Series)

DC611.L831L6　　　　　　　　68–44807

NL 0453090　　DLC

Loiret. Dictionnaire historique & biographique illustré.　Paris, E. Flammarion, [1901?]
　　2 p. l., (1) iv–v, 1 l., (1) vi–vii, 1 l., lxxx, 1118 p., 1 l., 240 p.　2 facsim., 143 pl., 66 port.　8°.　(Dictionnaires illustrés départementaux)
　　2. ed.

NL 0453091　　NN

Loirette, Gabriel.
　　Arnaud Amanieu, sire d'Albret et l'appel des seigneurs gascons en 1368, par Gabriel Loirette.　(In: Mélanges d'histoire offerts à M. Charles Bémont.　Paris, 1913.　8°.　p. ₁317–₁340.)

465019A.　1. Albret, Arnaud　　Amanieu, sire d', d. 1401.　2. Great
Britain—Hist.—Edward III, 1327–　　1377.　3. France—Hist., 1368.
N. Y. P. L.　　　　　　　　　　　　April 18, 1930

NL 0453092　　NN

CD1215
.S85A444
Loirette, Gabriel.
Archives départementales des Deux-Sèvres.
　　Inventaire sommaire des Archives départementales antérieures à 1790, Deux-Sèvres.　Série E, articles 1219–2119: chartrier de Saint-Loup, notaires de Saint-Maixent. Rédigé par Alfred Dupond, Séverin Canal et Gabriel Loirette. Niort, Impr. P. Nicolas, 1920.

CD1215
.S85A577
Loirette, Gabriel.
Archives départementales des Deux-Sèvres.
　　Répertoire numérique des Archives départementales antérieures à 1790, Deux-Sèvres.　Archives civiles.　Série C, dressé par Gabriel Loirette, archiviste départemental. Niort, Impr. artistique de l'ouest, 1923.

Lois, *pseud.*
　　Advice to a young woman at service ...
　　　　see under　Savage, Sarah, 1785–1837.

Lois, *pseud.*
Harriet and Ellen
see under title

Lois, *Sister*
　　see Eberdt, Mary Lois, *Sister*, 1913–

Lois, Alfredo.
　　Evolución del transporte de autobuses en Montevideo; conferencia de Don Alfredo Lois... ₁Montevideo₁ Rotary club de Montevideo ₁1944₁　8 l.　illus.　19 x 10cm.

　　1. Motor buses—Uruguay—　　　　Montevideo.

NL 0453098　　NN

Chi
R
25
.C6
Lois, Arturo H.
Colegio médico de Chile.　Proyecto de ley presentado por el dr. Arturo H. Lois. Discutido, modificado y aprobado por los directories de la Amech y de la Femechso, y revisado por el asesor jurídico de la Amech, señor Carlos Salinas, y por una comisión médica especial.　Aprobado en la convención de Talca.　[Santiago, Imp. R. Quevedo O., 1939]
　　cover-title, 8 p.　26.5 cm.

NL 0453099　　DPU

Lois, Jaime Concha
　　see Concha Lois, Jaime.

4BC
36
Lois, Juan S
Elementos de filosofía positiva.
2. ed., revisada ɪ corregida.
Copiapó, Impr. de la Tribuna, 1906–
　　v.　1

NL 0453101　　DLC–P4

Lois, Luis Diaz
　　see Diaz Lois, Luis.

Lois, María Antonieta
see
Lois F , María Antonieta.

Lois, Ramón Llama
see
Llama Lois, Ramón.

Lois, Ricardo J
　　... Catálogo de la biblioteca del Laboratorio central de fitopatología e instrucciones para su uso, por Ricardo J. Lois.　Buenos Aires, 1948. 95 p.　23 cm.　(Argentina republic. Instituto sanidad vegetal. ₁Publicaciones₁ Serie B, no.12)

NL 0453105　　PPAN

Lois, Samuel, d. 1707.
　　Cronycke ofte korte waere beschryvinge der stad Rotterdam, beschreeven door S. Lois, en beginnende van den jaere 1270 tot den jaere 1671... en wyders voorsien met authentyke stukken en contracten, specterende tot de oudheyd, rechten en gerechtigheden dier selve stad...　In 's Gravenhage: By O. en P. van Thol, 1746.　iv, 387 p.　new ed.　8°.

250156A.　1. Rotterdam—Hist.—　　　　Chronology.　2. Rotterdam—
Hist.—Sources.　　　　　　　　　　Hist.—Sources.
N. Y. P. L.　　　　　　　　　　　　October 8, 1926

NL 0453106　　NN CtY MH ICN CU ICU

Lois Estévez, José.
　　Contribución al estudio de la narcoexploración judicial. ₁n. p.₁ 1951.
　　14 p.　24 cm.
　　"Separata de Foro gallego, núm. 74, marzo-abril 1951."

　　1. Narcoanalysis.　ɪ. Title.

　　　　　　　　　　　　　　　　54–24722 †

NL 0453107　　DLC

Lois Estévez, José.
　　... Ensayo de valoración filosófica del derecho según una metodología esencialista.　Madrid, "Instituto editorial Reus," centro de enseñanza y publicaciones (s. a.) 1945.
　　148 p.　22ᵐ.

　　1. Law—Philosophy.

　　　　　　　　　　　　　　　　46–22405

NL 0453108　　DLC

VOLUME 338

Lois Estévez, José.
Estudios sobre los fundamentos de una nueva ciencia jurídica. Santiago de Compostela, Secretariado de Publicaciones, Intercambio Científico y Extensión Universitaria, 1954.
299 p. 20 cm.

1. Jurisprudence. I. Title.

57–45972 ‡

NL 0453109   DLC MH-L

Lois Estévez, José.
La exploración de la capacidad informativa del testigo y su tratamiento jurídicoprocesal. ¡Santiago de Compostela¡ Porto ¡1951¡
154 p. 22 cm. (Colección compostelana de escritos jurídicos)

1. Witnesses. 2. Witnesses—Spain. I. Title.

54–24725 ‡

NL 0453110   DLC MH-L

Law

Lois Estévez, José.
Grandes problemas del derecho procesal. Santiago de Compostela, Porto ¡195–¡
231 p. 21 cm. (Colección compostelana de escritos jurídicos)

1. Civil procedure—Spain. I. Title.

58–37034 ‡

NL 0453111   DLC MH-L

Lois Estévez, José.
... Proceso y forma. (Ensayo de una teoría general del proceso) Santiago de Compostela, Editorial-librería Porto, 1947.
143 p., 2 l. 22cm.
Bibliographical footnotes.

NL 0453112   MH-L

Lois Estévez, José.
Sobre un programa de política universitaria. Santiago de Compostela, Porto ¡1953?¡
83 p. 19 cm.

1. Universities and colleges—Spain. I. Title.

LA918.L6   54–36515 ‡

NL 0453113   DLC

Lois Estévez, José,
... Teoría del fraude en el proceso civil. Santiago de Compostela, Porto, 1948.
166 p. 21cm.
Bibliographical footnotes.

NL 0453114   MH-L

Lois F   , María Antonieta.
Un proyecto para medir el gasto de las familias. México, 1954.
76 p. illus. 24 cm.
Tesis (licenciatura en economía)—Universidad Nacional Autónoma de México.

1. Cost and standard of living. I. Title.

HD6978.L6   57–24605 ‡

NL 0453115   DLC

Lois Goicoechea, Guillermo.
... La cuestión social y el derecho; memoria de prueba para optar al título de licenciado en la Facultad de ciencias jurídicas y sociales de la U. de Chile. ¡Santiago de Chile, M. Dupré del C., impresor¡ 1945.
58 p., 1 l. 26ᶜᵐ.
"Bibliografía": leaf at end.

1. Labor laws and legislation.

46–18763

Library of Congress   HD7809.L65

NL 0453116   DLC

W 4
qC53
1943
Lois Perales, Juan S
Supervivencia de los glóbulos rojos después de las transfusiones. Santiago, 1943.
78, ¡2¡ p. illus.

Tesis - Univ. de Chile.
Bibliography: p. ¡79¡

NL 0453117   DNLM

Lois Perales, Voltaire.
Psicoanálisis en derecho penal. Santiago de Chile, 1948.
88 p. 27 cm. (¡Universidad de Chile¡ Seminario de Derecho Penal. ¡Publicaciones¡ sección 5, v. no. 1)
Tesis (licenciatura en ciencias jurídicas y sociales)—Universidad de Chile.
Bibliography: p. 83–86.

1. Criminal psychology. 2. Psychoanalysis. I. Title. (Series: Chile. Universidad, Santiago. Seminario de Derecho Penal y Medicina Legal. Publicaciones, sección 5, v. 1)

50–34676

NL 0453118   DLC

Lois Perales, Voltaire.
Psicoanálisis y actitudes antisociales. Santiago de Chile, 1949.
127 p. 23 cm.

1. Psychoanalysis. 2. Criminal psychology. I. Title.

BF173.L58   51–29678 rev

NL 0453119   DLC TxU

Lois ... Assises de Jérusalem
see in Académie des inscriptions et belles-lettres, Paris.
Recueil des historiens des croisades. vol. 1–2.

Lois chimiques; ou, Règles générales observées dans l'action réciproque des corps, par un chimiste manufacturier. Bruxelles, Tarlier, 1830.
60 p.

NL 0453121   PU

Les¡ lois civiles dans leur ordre naturel.
Seconde edition.   A Paris, Jean Baptiste Coignard, 1695.
5 v. O.

NL 0453122   NcD

Les lois de la guerre; commentées ...
see under Cinglant, Jean.

Les lois de la guerre. Prisonniers allemands et prisonniers français; comment l'Allemagne et la France observent les Conventions de La Haye.   Paris: G. Cadet, 1915.   15 p.   illus.   8°.
"Extraits de la Convention de La Haye, du 18 octobre, 1907...Reglément concernant...les prisonniers de guerre," on inside of cover.

1. European war, 1914-   —Prison-   ers and prisons.
N. Y. P. L.   June 30, 1916.

NL 0453124   NN

Les lois de la guerre continentale (publication de la section historique du Grand état-major allemand, 1902) tr. et annotées par Paul Carpentier ...   Paris, Librairie générale de droit & de jurisprudence, 1904.
2 p. l., v, 198 p. 19ᶜᵐ.
Translated from the anonymous German work: Kriegsbrauch im landkriege (hrsg. vom Grossen generalstabe. Kriegsgeschichtl. abteilg. 1, 31. hft. 1902) cf. Pref., p. iii and Hinrichs' halbjahrs-katalog, 1902, ii, p. 91.

1. Carpentier, Paul, tr. ii. Prussia. Grosser generalstab. Kriegsgeschichtliche abteilung.

Library of Congress   6–28768

NL 0453125   DLC ICJ

Les lois de la guerre sur terre
see under   ¡Henrard, Paul Jean Joseph¡ 1830–1896.

Lois de la nature ...   Ouvrage divisé en deux parties Nantes, Odé fils et Paris, Arnaud ¡etc.¡ an xi ¡1803¡
2 p. l., ii, ¡2¡, 254, 187 p. 20¡ᶜᵐ.
Attributed to J. F. C. de La Poype.

1. Political science. 2. Social sciences. i. La Poype, Jean François Cornu, baron de, 1758–1851, supposed author.

Library of Congress   JC179.P7   10–16610†

NL 0453127   DLC

Les lois de probabilité dans le ensembles abstraits
see under ¡Levy, Paul¡ mathematician.

... Les lois du nombre et de la vitesse dans l'art de la guerre
see under ¡Fontin, Paul Jean¡ 1859–

4BR
535
Les lois ecclésiastiques de l'Italie, réponse à M. l'évêque d'Orléans. Rome, Bocca frères, 1874.
78 p.

NL 0453130   DLC-P4 NNC-L DS

Les lois ecclésiastiques de l'Italie. Réponse a M. l'évêque d'Orléans. Rome, et Bocca, frères; Paris, Charpentier et cie., 1874.
78 p. 23½ cm.

1. Church and state in Italy.

NL 0453131   DS

VOLUME 338

Lois et coutumes suivies dans le pachalik de
Jérusalem
    see under Albengo.

Lois et documents relatifs au drainage
    see under [Dumas, Ernest Charles Jean
Baptiste] 1827-   comp.

Les **lois** et les institutions judiciaires de la **Russie**.
Paris, E. Dentu, 1864.
  50 p. 22½ᶜᵐ. (With Zezas, Spyridion G. Études historiques sur la
législation russe. Paris, 1862)

  1. Law—Russia.

                            11–25540

Library of Congress

NL 0453134   DLC

YA
.S177   Lois Mead; or, The adopted daughter. New York,
1859.
105p.

NL 0453135   DLC

Lois Mead; or, The Adopted Daughter. New York,
Sheldon & Company, 1871.

NL 0453136   DLC

Lois municipales et économiques de **Languedoc**
    see under Albisson, Jean, 1732-1810.

Lois municipales, rurales, administratives et de
police, contenant par ordre chronologique toutes
les lois, arrêtés, ordonnances et avis du
Conseil-d'état
    see under Duquénel,

Les **Lois** nouvelles; revue de législation et de jurisprudence et revue des travaux législatifs; recueil ... divisé
en quatre parties principales 1ᵉ Revue de législation.—
2ᵉ Revue des travaux législatifs.—3ᵉ Lois et décrets.—
4ᵉ Revue de jurisprudence ... année 1–
1882-19
Paris, Marchal, Billard et cⁱᵉ [etc.], 1882-19
  v. 24½ᶜᵐ.
  Monthly, 1882-88; bimonthly, 1889-19
  Subtitle varies.
  Editors: 1882-84, L. C. Simonet.—1885, C. A. Pret.—1886-87, Amédée
Jumin, Gustave Fortier.—1888-19 Émile Schaffhauser.

——— Table générale des Lois nouvelles 1882-1900 ...
Par Émile Schaffhauser ... avec la collaboration de
Henri Chevresson ... Paris, Aux bureaux des Lois
nouvelles, 1901.
  2 p. l., 184 p. 24ᶜᵐ.

  I. Simonet, L. C., ed. II. Pret, Célestin Aimé, 1852- ed. III. Jumin,
Amédée, ed. IV. Fortier, Gustave, ed. V. Schaffhauser, Émile, 1857- ed.
VI. Chevresson, Henri, comp.

                            17–19673–4

NL 0453140   DLC MH-L

Les **Lois** Nouvelles.
    ... Code expliqué de la presse; traité général de
la police de la presse et des délits de publication
      see under Barbier, Georges, 1854-

Les lois organiques des colonies
    see under International Institute of Differing
Civilizations.

Law

  Lois politiques et administratives. Bruxelles, F. Larcier,
19
      v. 25ᶜᵐ. (Les Novelles; corpus juris Belgici)
  Includes bibliographies.
  CONTENTS.—
  t. 3. Droit budgétaire, par H. Matton.—
  t. 4. Le domaine public. Le domaine privé. Les servitudes légales
d'utilité publique, par G. Dore et F. Dembour. Voirie et constructions,
urbanisme, par V. Bure. L'expropriation pour cause d'utilité publique,
par L. Belva avec la collaboration de A. Coenraets.—t. 5. La santé
publique, par L. J. Thibaut.

  1. Public law—Belgium.   (Series)

                        62–31959

NL 0453143   DLC ICU

Lois Weedon husbandry as it is. 3d ed.,—including "A
word in season about growing wheat",—corrected and
condensed. London. J. Ridgway, 1862.
  78 p. diagr. 17ᶜᵐ. (With Fisher, Joseph. Where shall we get meat?
London, 1866)

  1. Wheat. 1. Title.

                      Agr 34-144

Library, U. S. Dept. of   Agriculture 389F53

NL 0453144   DNAL

Loisance, Yves René, 1915-
    ... Radiologie ambulatoire d'urgence du thorax ...
Rennes, 1939.
    Thèse – Univ. de Paris.

NL 0453145   CtY

Loisch, János, 1878-   ed.

DB785
.S6H3   **Haberern, Jonathan,** 1818-1880.
1926   Natur- und Lebensbilder aus der Zips; mit einem Anhang
hrsg. vom Zipser Verein in Budapest. 3., vollständige Ausg.,
besorgt von Johann Loisch. Budapest, L. Kókai, 1926.

NL 0453147   DLC-P4

4PT
Ger   **Loisch, János,** 1878-
522   Rudolf Weber; ein Zipser Volksdichter. Mit
Webers schönsten Gedichten, hrsg. vom Zipser
Verein in Budapest. Budapest, L. Kokai, 1925.
  126 p.
  I. Zipser Verein in Budapest. II. Weber, Rudolf,
1843-1915.

NL 0453147   DLC-P4

DB785
S6S9   Loisch, János, 1878-   ed.

    A **Szepesség**; emlékkönyv a "Szepesi Egyesület Budapesten"
fennállásának 50. évfordulójára. Szerk. Loisch János.
Budapest, Kókai L., 1926.

NL 0453147

Loisch, Johann
    see Loisch, János, 1878-

Loise, Ferdinand, 1825-1904.
    Anthologie d'auteurs Français et d'auteurs
Belges. Bruxelles, Castaigne. 1895.
    536 p.

NL 0453150   PPCCH

Loise, Ferdinand, 1825-1904.
    Anthologie d'auteurs français et d'auteurs
belges à l'usage de l'enseignement et des familles...
deuxième partie; cinquième ed. Bruxelles. Castaigne
c1908.

NL 0453151   PIm

PQ
295   Loise, Ferdinand, 1825-1904.
N2   Une campagne contre le naturalisme. Paris, H
L6   Oudin, 1883.
    117p. 20cm. (in binder, 22cm.)

    1. French literature - 19th cent. - Hist.
& crit. 2. Naturalism in literature
I. Title

NL 0453152   WU

Loise, Ferdinand, 1825-1904.
    De l'influence de la civilisation sur la poésie, par m. Ferd.
Loise ...
    (In Académie royale des sciences, des lettres et des beaux-arts de
Belgique, Brussels. Mémoires couronnés et autres mémoires ... Col-
lection in-8°. Bruxelles, 1859. 21½ᶜᵐ. t. VIII (no. 4) 261 p.)
  "Mémoire couronné par l'Académie royale, en la séance du 5 mai
1858."
  Bibliographical foot-notes.
  CONTENTS.—Introduction.—Livre 1ᵉʳ. Le monde oriental.—Livre 2ᵉ.
Le monde classique.—Épilogue.
  1. Poetry. 2. Poetry—History and criticism. I. Title: L'influence d⁴
la civilisation sur la poésie.
                  A C 35–1892 Revised
  Title from Illinois Univ.
  Library of Congress   [AS242.B322 vol. 8, no. 4]
                 [r36c2]

NL 0453153   IU NN UU MB PPAmP

Loise, Ferdinand, 1825-1904.
    De l'influence de la civilisation sur la poésie; ou, Histoire de
la poésie, mise en rapport avec la civilisation; par Ferdinand
Loise ... L'Italie et la France, précédées d'une étude sur la
poésie en Europe dans les premiers siècles du christianisme et
aux temps barbares ...
    (In Académie royale des sciences, des lettres et des beaux-arts de
Belgique, Brussels. Mémoires couronnés et autres mémoires ... Col-
lection in-8°. Bruxelles, 1840-1904. 21½ᶜᵐ. t. XIV (1862) no. 1) 794 p.)
  "Mémoire présenté le 7 juillet 1862 et faisant suite au Mémoire cou-
ronné le 5 mai 1858, au concours d'éloquence française."
  Also issued separately with slightly different title and also with title:
Histoire de la poésie, mise en rapport avec la civilisation.
  1. Poetry—History and criticism. 2. Christianity in literature. 3.
Italian poetry—History and criticism. 4. French poetry—
History and criticism. I. Title.
  Title from Illinois Univ.   A C 36–1089
  Library of Congress   [AS242.B322 vol. 14]
             [3]   (082.1)

NL 0453154   IU UU NN

809.1
L834d   **Loise, Ferdinand,** 1825-1904.
      De l'influence de la civilisation sur
la poésie: Histoire de la poésie mise en
rapport avec la civilisation. Le monde
chrétien; l'Europe aux premiers siècles
du christianisme. L'Italie et la
France, jusqu'à nos jours. Bruxelles,
A. Lacroix, Verboeckhoven, 1862.
    704p. 22cm.

    "Extrait du tome XIV des Mémoires de l'Académie
royale de Belgique."

    1. Poetry - Hist.   & crit. 2. Christianity in
literature. 3.   Italian poetry - Hist. &
crit. 4. French   poetry - Hist. & crit.
I. Title. I. Tc

NL 0453155   CLSU KU

Loise, Ferdinand.
    Histoire de la poésie; études sur l'Allemagne
moderne. Brussels. Merzbach, 1878.
    404p.

NL 0453156   OCIW

VOLUME 338

PT 521 L6
Loise, Ferdinand.
Histoire de la Poésie.L'Allemagne dans sa littérature nationale. Depuis les jusqu'aux temps modernes. Bruxelles, A. Vromant, 1873.
356p.

1. German literature--Hist. and crit. 2. German poetry--Hist. and crit. I. Title.

NL 0453157 UU MH

Loise, Ferdinand, 1825-1904.
Histoire de la poésie; l'Allemagne dans sa littérature nationale depuis les origines jusqu'aux temps modernes. 2. éd. Bruxelles, A. Vromant, 1875.
356p.

1. German poetry - Hist. & crit. I. Title. o.c.

NL 0453158 ScU

861.09 L835h 1867
Loise, Ferdinand, 1825-1904.
Histoire de la poésie en rapport avec la civilisation chez les grands peuples modernes de race Latine. L'Espagne. Bruxelles, M. Hayez, 1867.
299p. 22cm.

"Extrait du tome XX des Mémoires couronnés et autres mémoires, publiés par l'Académie royale de Belgique. 1867."

1. Spanish poetry   Hist. & crit. I. Title: Histoire   de la poésie en rapport avec la civilisation.

NL 0453159 KU

Loise, Ferdinand, 1825-1904.
Histoire de la poésie en rapport avec la civilisation. La poésie espagnole. Par Ferdinand Loise ...
(*In* Académie royale des sciences, des lettres et des beaux-arts de Belgique, Brussels. Mémoires couronnés et autres mémoires ... Collection in-8°. Bruxelles, 1840-1904. 21½ᶜᵐ. t. xx (1868) (Lettres. no. 1) 299 p.)
"Ouvrage présenté à l'Académie royale de Belgique, le 8 juin 1867." Also issued separately with title: Histoire de la poésie espagnole.

1. Spanish poetry—History and criticism.

A C 36-1062

Title from Illinois Univ.
Library of Congress   [AS242.B322 vol. 20]
(2)   (082.1)

NL 0453160 IU UU MB NN

PN 1105 L83
Loise, Ferdinand, 1825-1904.
Histoire de la poésie en rapport avec la civilisation dans l'antiquité et chez les peuples modernes de race latine. L'antiquité, monde oriental, monde classique, monde chrétien. Bruxelles, Librairie Alfred Castaigne, 1887.
xvi,400 p. 23cm.

NL 0453161 NIC MiU

Loise, Ferdinand.   Lit 1515.9
Histoire de la poésie en rapport avec la civilisation dans l'antiquité, et chez les peuples modernes de race latine. Paris, E. Thorin, [1888].
pp. xvi, 400.

Poetry)

NL 0453162 MH

Loise, Ferdinand, 1825-1904.
Histoire de la poésie espagnole, par Ferdinand Loise ... Bruxelles, M. Hayez, imprimeur de l'Académie royale, 1868.
3 p. l., (8)-299 p. 21½ᶜᵐ.
"Extrait du tome xx des Mémoires couronnés et autres mémoires, publiés par l'Académie royale de Belgique.—1868."

1. Spanish poetry—Hist. & crit.

Library of Congress   PQ6076.L6   31-10298
(2)   861.09

NL 0453163 DLC IU

809.1 L83h
Loise, Ferdinand.
Histoire de la poésie, mise en rapport avec la civilisation ...   Bruxelles,- 1862.
704p.

Mémoire présenté à l'Académie royale de Belgique le 7 juillet 1862.
Extrait du tome XIV des Mémoires de l'Académie royale de Belgique.

NL 0453164 IU

Loise, Ferdinand.
Histoire de la poésie, mise en rapport avec la civilisation ...   Bruxelles, 1862
see also this De l'influence de la civilisation sur la poésie; ou Histoire de la poésie, mise en rapport avec la civilisation ...

Loise, Ferdinand.   37555-32
Histoire de la poésie mise en rapport avec la civilisation en France depuis les origines jusqu'à la fin du dix-huitième siècle. Paris, E. Thorin, [1888].
pp. viii, 544.

French poetry)

NL 0453166 MH ICN

Loise, Ferdinand.   Ital 6230.16
Histoire de la poésie mise en rapport avec la civilisation en Italie depuis les origines jusqu'à nos jours. Bruxelles, A. Castaigne, etc. etc. 1895.
pp. vi, (1), 487.

Italian poetry)

NL 0453167 MH MeB ICN NIC MB NjP

PT 271 L6
Loise, Ferdinand, 1825-1904.
La littérature allemande dans les temps modernes. Paris, Librairie Sandoz et Fischbacher, 1879.
400p. 24cm.
Bibliographical footnotes.
1. German literature - Early modern (to 1700) - Hist. & crit. 2. German literature - 18th cent. - Hist. & crit. I. Title

NL 0453168 WU MB

PQ 2328 L6
Loise, Ferdinand, 1825-1904.
Le poète philosophe; ou, Réflexions sur les idées philosophiques et religieuses de De Lamartine. Suivi d'une ode à De Lamartine. Paris, H. Casterman, 1857.
100p. 20cm.

1. Lamartine, Alphonse Marie Louis de, 1790-1869 I. Title.

NL 0453169 MU

Loise,   Guillon de
see   Guillon de Loise)

)Loiseau,
Discours sur la révolution opérée dans la monarchie françoise par la Pucelle d'Orléans, prononcé dans l'église cathédrale de cette ville, le 8 mai 1764. Orleans, J. Rouzeau-Montaut, imprimeur, M.DCC.LXIV.
47 p. 16½ᶜᵐ.

1. Jeanne d'Arc, Saint, 1412-1431. I. Title.

33-25886

Library of Congress   DC104.L6   923.544

NL 0453171 DLC

Loiseau, A   . fils.   537.51 P500
Notice illustrée sur les expériences curieuses et amusantes que l'on peut répéter avec la bobine Ruhmkorff, par A. Loiseau fils. Complètement refondue par un praticien. 12ᵉ édition enrichie d'un portrait de Ruhmkorff, suivie d'autres expériences d'électricité et de la description de quelques appareils d'application domestique. .... . Paris, A. Grelot, [1895].
104 p., illus., 1 port. 17ᶜᵐ.

NL 0453172 ICJ

Loiseau, Mlle. A.   No. 3 in 4088.112
Notice sur François Joseph Bélanger, architecte.
=   [Paris, 1865.] 95-101 pp. 8°.
Cut from Revue universelle des arts, vol. 22 (*4060.210.22).
This article is a reprint of a pamphlet printed at Paris in 1818, by C. Ballard.

*Bélanger, François Joseph.
Sheet D 5331   March 6, 1900

NL 0453173 MB

Loiseau (A.-C.-E.-Léon). *Du traitement des névralgies par la cantérisation sulfurique. 32 pp. 4°. Paris, 1860, No. 227.

NL 0453174 DNLM

L'OISEAU,Amelie.
Original rhymes and illustrations of the Seventh regiment in camp. 1897. n.p., cop. 1897.

obl.8°. pp. (32). Illustr.

NL 0453175 MH CtY

---

823 L834s
L'Oiseau, Amelie.
The sins of a widow.   London, F. Tennyson Neely (1898)
83p. 19cm. (Neely's booklet library, No.2)

NL 0453176 NcU

L'Oiseau, Amelie.
The sins of a widow. Confessed by Amelie L'Oiseau ... London, New York, F. T. Neely, 1899.
3 p. l., (5)-83 p. 18ᶜᵐ. (Neely's booklet library, no. 2)

I. Title.

99-562 Revised

Library of Congress   PZ3.L8358

NL 0453177 DLC

VOLUME 338

Loiseau, André.
... L'assurance sur la vie instrument de crédit ... par André Loiseau... Paris, Jouve & cⁱᵉ, 1935.
152 p. 25½ᶜᵐ.
Thèse—Univ. de Paris.
"Bibliographie": p. [149]

1. Insurance, Life—France. 2. Insurance, Life—Finance. 3. Loans—France. ɪ. Title.

Library of Congress   HG8934.L6
                                    [2]   41-19229
                                                  368.30044

NL 0453178   DLC CtY MH-BA

Loiseau, André Noël, 1912-
... Contribution à l'étude de la téleroentgenthérapie totale dans la leucémie myéloïde ... Paris, 1938.
Thèse - Univ. de Paris.

NL 0453179   CtY

Loiseau, Antonius
    see   Loisel, Antoine, 1536-1617.

Loiseau, Arthur, 1830-   1266.69
De modo subjunctivo hanc grammaticam, historicam et philosophicam disquisitionem conscripsit. [Thesis.] Paris, E. Thorin, 1866.
pp. 72.

Aryan languages–Verb||

NL 0453181   MH NcD NcU

[Bonaparte
Collection LOISEAU, ARTHUR, 1830-
No.3094   Étude historique et philologique sur Jean Pillot et sur les doctrines grammaticales du XVe siècle... Paris, E.Thorin, 1866.
144p. 23cm.

NL 0453182   ICN OCU CtY PU NcD

Loiseau, Arthur, 1830-   6257.50
Étude historique et philologique sur Jean Pillot et sur les doctrines grammaticales du xviᵉ siècle. Paris, E. Thorin, 1866.
pp. 144.

NL 0453183   MH NjP ICN NIC CU

440.9   Loiseau, Arthur, 1830-
P646ZL   Étude historique et philologique sur Jean Pillot et sur les doctrines grammaticales du XVI siècle, par Arthur Loiseau... Saint-Cloud, Imprimerie de Madame Veuve Belin, 1866.
144p. 23cm.

Bibliographical footnotes.

1. Pillot, Jean. 2. French language--Grammar.

NL 0453184   LU

LOISEAU, A[rthur], 1830-
Histoire de la langue française, ses origines et son developpement jusqu'à la fin du XVIe siècle. Paris, E.Thorin,1881.
pp.(3). iv,534.

- NL 0453185   MH CU OO

Loiseau, Arthur, 1830-
Histoire de la langue française, ses origines et son développement jusqu'à la fin du xviᵉ siècle, par A. Loiseau ... 2. éd. rev. et cor. Paris, E. Thorin, 1882.
2 p. l., xii, 534 p. 19ᶜᵐ.
Ouvrage couronné par la Société des études historiques.

1. French language—Hist.
                                            1-F-3647
Library of Congress   PC2075.L8

NL 0453186   DLC NIC WU NjP MdBP ViU

PQ 9011   Loiseau, Arthur, 1830-
.L83   Histoire de la littérature portugaise depuis ses origines jusqu'à nos jours. par A. Loiseau ... Paris, E. Thorin, 1866.
viii, 404 p.

1. Portuguese literature--Hist. & crit.

NL 0453187   ICU MH NjP

Loiseau, A[rthur] 1830-
Histoire de la littérature portugaise depuis ses origines jusqu'à nos jours, par A. Loiseau ... 2. éd. Paris, E. Thorin, 1887.
2 p. l., viii, 404 p., 1 l. 19ᶜᵐ.
Imprint covered by A. Fontemoing's label.
"Sources": p. [401]-404.   4-11022

NL 0453188   DLC CU MeB NIC DCU-IA CtY PU OCU

Loiseau, Arthur, 1830-
Histoire des progrès de la grammaire en France depuis l'époque de la renaissance jusqu'à nos jours. P. 1873-5. 3 pts. in 1 v. O.
Note.- Autograph; presentation copy. Extr. fr. Mém. Soc. acad. de Maine-et-Loire.

NL 0453189   CU MH

PC   Loiseau, Arthur, 1830-
2101   Histoire des progrès de la grammaire en France depuis l'époque de la Renaissance jusqu'à nos jours. Paris, E. Thorin, 1874-75.
3 parts in 1. 22cm.

1. French language--Grammar, Historical.

NL 0453190   NIC

Loiseau, Arthur, 1830-
Histoire des progrès de la grammaire en France depuis l'époque de la renaissance jusqu'à nos jours. Paris, E. Thorin, 1875.
3 v. in 1. 23 cm.
Bibliographical footnotes.
1. French language - Grammar.

NL 0453191   MdBP

LOISEAU,A[rthur],1830-
Poésie latine. Paris,E.Thorin,1880.
pp.(2),4.
At head of title: Troisième centenaire de Camoens.

NL 0453192   MH

LOISEAU, Arthur, 1830-
Rapports de la langue de Rabelais avec les patois de la Touraine et de l'Anjou. Angers, 1867.
pp.20.
"Extrait des Memoires de la Societe Academique d'Angers, tom. XXI)".

NL 0453193   MH

W 4   LOISEAU, Bernard Charles, 1927-
P23   La terramycine mérite-t-elle une place parmi les antibiotiques utilisés en phtisiologie? Paris, Taib, 1953.
no. 940   45 p. (Paris. [Université] Faculté de médecine. Thèse, 1953, no. 940)
1. Drugs - Antitubercular
2. Oxytetracyline

NL 0453194   DNLM

Loiseau (C.-F.-F.-X.) - Sur le scorbut. vi, 7-24 pp. 4°. Paris. 1828. No. 78, v.215.

NL 0453195   DNLM PPC

4K   Loiseau, Charles,
1954   Des cas où un pupille romain à plusieurs tuteurs et des règles particulières à cette situation; du conflit des lois françaises et étrangères en matière de tutelle des mineurs. Lons-le-Saunier, 1885.
262 p.

NL 0453196   DLC-P4 CtY MH

Loiseau, Charles.
... Régression du nombre des psychoses alcooliques dans le Morbihan, sous l'influence des restrictions en boissons alcoolisées. ... Paris, Imprimerie R. Foulon, 1944.
46 p.
Thèse.

NL 0453197   DNLM MnU

Loiseau, Charles.
Traité de la tutelle des mineurs en droit international, précédé d'une étude sur la pluralité des tuteurs en droit romain, par Charles Loiseau ... Paris, L. Larose et Forcel, 1887.
2 p. l., 258 p. 26ᶜᵐ.
Bibliographical foot-notes.

1. Guardian and ward. 2. International law, Private. ɪ. Title.
[Full name: Bruno Charles Luc Loiseau]
                                            24-18440
Library of Congress   JX6424.L6

NL 0453198   DLC NcD

1825-1897
Loiseau (Charles). ^ * De la folie sympathique 90 pp. 4°. Paris. 1856. No. 240. v.592.

NL 0453199   DNLM

Loiseau (Charles) [1825-97]. Mémoire sur la folie sympathique. 88 pp. 4°. Paris, J.-B. Baillière, 1856.

NL 0453200   DNLM

MISSISSIPPI

MsG	William Alexander Percy Memorial Library, Greenville.
MsSC*	Mississippi State University, State College.
MsSM	Mississippi State University, State College.
MsU	University of Mississippi, University.

MONTANA

MtBC	Montana State University, Bozeman.
MtBozC*	Montana State University at Bozeman.
MtU	University of Montana, Missoula.

NEW YORK

N	New York State Library, Albany.
NAlU	State University of New York at Albany.
NAurW	Wells College, Aurora.
NB	Brooklyn Public Library, Brooklyn.
NBB	Brooklyn Museum Libraries, Brooklyn.
NBC	Brooklyn College, Brooklyn.
NBM	Medical Research Library of Brooklyn.
NBPol	Polytechnic Institute of Brooklyn, Brooklyn.
NBSU-M	State University of New York, Downstate Medical Center Library, Brooklyn.
NBiSU-H	State University of New York, Harpur College, Binghamton.
NBronSL	Sarah Lawrence College, Bronxville.
NBu	Buffalo and Erie County Public Library, Buffalo.
NBuC	State University of New York, College at Buffalo.
NBuG	Grosvenor Reference Division, Buffalo and Erie County Public Library, Buffalo.
NBuU	State University of New York at Buffalo.
NCH	Hamilton College, Clinton.
NCaS	St. Lawrence University, Canton.
NCorniC	Corning Glass Works Library, Corning. (Includes Corning Museum of Glass Library)
NCoxHi	Greene County Historical Society, Inc., Coxsackie.
NFQC	Queens College Library, Flushing.
NGrnUN*	United Nations Library.
NHC	Colgate University, Hamilton.
NHi	New York Historical Society, New York.
NIC	Cornell University, Ithaca.
NJQ	Queens Borough Public Library, Jamaica.
NL*	Newberry Library, Chicago.
NLC	Not a library symbol.
NN	New York Public Library.
NNAB	American Bible Society, New York.
NNAHI	Augustinian Historical Institute, New York.
NNAJHi	American Jewish Historical Society, New York.
NNB	Association of the Bar of the City of New York, New York.
NNBG	New York Botanical Garden, Bronx Park, New York.
NNC	Columbia University, New York.
NNC-T	— Teachers College Library.
NNCFR	Council on Foreign Relations, New York.
NNCoCi	City College of New York, New York.
NNE	Engineering Societies Library, New York.
NNF	Fordham University, New York.
NNFI	French Institute in the United States, New York.
NNG	General Theological Seminary of the Protestant Episcopal Church. New York.
NNGr	Grolier Club Library, New York.
NNH	Hispanic Society of America, New York.
NNHeb	Hebrew Union College, Jewish Institute of Religion Library, New York.
NNHi	New York Historical Society.
NNJ	Jewish Theological Seminary of America, New York.
NNJIR*	Jewish Institute of Religion, New York.
NNJef	Jefferson School of Social Science, New York. (Library no longer in existence)
NNM	American Museum of Natural History, New York.
NNMM	Metropolitan Museum of Art Library, New York.
NNMor*	Pierpont Morgan Library.
NNNAM	New York Academy of Medicine, New York.
NNNM	New York Medical College, Flower & Fifth Avenue Hospitals, New York.
NNNPsan	New York Psychoanalytic Institute, New York.
NNPM	Pierpont Morgan Library, New York.
NNQ*	Queens Borough Public Library, New York.
NNQC*	Queens College Library, Flushing.
NNRI	Rockefeller Institute for Medical Research, New York.
NNSU-M*	State University of New York College of Medicine at New York City.

NEW YORK *continued*

NNU	New York University Libraries, New York.
NNU-W	— Washington Square Library.
NNUN	United Nations Library, New York.
NNUN-W	— Woodrow Wilson Memorial Library.
NNUT	Union Theological Seminary, New York.
NNUT-Mc	— McAlpin Collection.
NNWML	Wagner College Library, Staten Island.
NNYI	Yivo Institute for Jewish Research, New York.
NNZI	Zionist Archives and Library of Palestine Foundation, New York.
NNerC	College of New Rochelle, New Rochelle.
NNiaU	Niagara University, Niagara University.
NPV	Vassar College, Poughkeepsie,
NRAB	Samuel Colgate Baptist Historical Library of the American Baptist Historical Society, Rochester.
NRU	University of Rochester, Rochester.
NSchU	Union College, Schenectady.
NSyU	Syracuse University, Syracuse.
NUt	Utica Public Library.
NWM	U.S. Military Academy, West Point.
NYPL*	New York Public Library.
NYhI	International Business Machines Corporation, Thomas J. Watson Research Center, Yorktown Heights.

NEBRASKA

NbOC	Creighton University, Omaha.
NbU	University of Nebraska, Lincoln.

NORTH CAROLINA

Nc	North Carolina State Library, Raleigh.
Nc-Ar	North Carolina State Department of Archives and History, Raleigh.
NcA	Pack Memorial Public Library, Asheville.
NcA-S	— Sondley Reference Library.
NcAS*	Sondley Reference Library, Asheville.
NcC	Public Library of Charlotte & Mecklenburg County, Charlotte.
NcCC	Charlotte College Library, Charlotte.
NcCJ	Johnson C. Smith University, Charlotte.
NcCU	University of North Carolina at Charlotte.
NcD	Duke University, Durham.
NcDurC	North Carolina College at Durham, Durham.
NcGU*	University of North Carolina at Greensboro.
NcGW	University of North Carolina at Greensboro.
NcGuG	Guilford College, Guilford.
NcR	Olivia Raney Public Library, Raleigh.
NcRR	Richard B. Harrison Public Library, Raleigh.
NcRS	North Carolina State University at Raleigh.
NcU	University of North Carolina, Chapel Hill.
NcWfC*	Wake Forest College, Winston-Salem.
NcWfSB	Southeastern Baptist Theological Seminary Library, Wake Forest.
NcWilA	Atlantic Christian College, Wilson.
NcWilC	Carolina Discipliniana Library, Wilson.
NcWsW	Wake Forest College, Winston-Salem.

NORTH DAKOTA

NdFA	North Dakota State University, Fargo. (Formerly North Dakota Agricultural College)
NdHi	State Historical Society of North Dakota, Bismarck.
NdU	University of North Dakota Library, Grand Forks.

NEW HAMPSHIRE

Nh	New Hampshire State Library, Concord.
NhD	Dartmouth College, Hanover.
NhU	University of New Hampshire, Durham.

NEW JERSEY

NjGbS	Glassboro State College, Glassboro.
NjHi	New Jersey Historical Society, Newark.
NjMD	Drew University, Madison.
NjN	Newark Public Library.
NjNBR*	Rutgers—The State University, New Brunswick.
NjNbS	New Brunswick Theological Seminary, New Brunswick.
NjNbT*	New Brunswick Theological Seminary.
NjP	Princeton University, Princeton.
NjPT	Princeton Theological Seminary, Princeton.
NjR	Rutgers—The State University, New Brunswick.
NjT	Trenton Free Library, Trenton.

NEW MEXICO

NmA	Albuquerque Public Library, New Mexico.
NmU	University of New Mexico, Albuquerque.
NmUpU	New Mexico State University, University Park.

NEVADA

NvU	University of Nevada, Reno.

OHIO

O	Ohio State Library, Columbus.
OAU	Ohio University, Athens.
OAkU	University of Akron, Akron.
OBerB	Baldwin-Wallace College, Berea.
OBlC	Bluffton College, Bluffton.
OC	Public Library of Cincinnati and Hamilton County, Cincinnati.
OCH	Hebrew Union College, Cincinnati.
OCHP	Historical and Philosophical Society of Ohio, Cincinnati.
OCLlloyd	Lloyd Library and Museum, Cincinnati.
OCU	University of Cincinnati, Cincinnati.
OCX	Xavier University, Cincinnati.
OCl	Cleveland Public Library.
OClCS	Case Institute of Technology, Cleveland.
OClFC	Cleveland State University, Cleveland. (Formerly Fenn College)
OClJC	John Carroll University, Cleveland.
OClMA	Cleveland Museum of Art, Cleveland.
OClSA	Cleveland Institute of Art, Cleveland.
OClW	Case Western Reserve University, Cleveland.
OClWHi	Western Reserve Historical Society, Cleveland.
ODW	Ohio Wesleyan University, Delaware.
ODa	Dayton and Montgomery County Library, Dayton.
ODaStL	St. Leonard College Library, Dayton.
ODaU	University of Dayton, Dayton.
OEac	East Cleveland Public Library.
OFH	Rutherford B. Hayes Library, Fremont.
OGK	Kenyon College, Gambier.
OHi	Ohio State Historical Society, Columbus.
OKentC	Kent State University, Kent.
OO	Oberlin College, Oberlin.
OOxM	Miami University, Oxford.
OSW	Wittenberg University, Springfield.
OTU	University of Toledo, Toledo.
OU	Ohio State University, Columbus.
OWibfU	Wilberforce University, Carnegie Library, Wilberforce.
OWicB	Borromeo Seminary, Wickliffe.
OWoC	College of Wooster, Wooster.
OWorP	Pontifical College Josephinum, Worthington.
OYesA	Antioch College, Yellow Springs.

OKLAHOMA

Ok	Oklahoma State Library, Oklahoma City.
OkEG	Graduate Seminary Library, Enid.
OkS	Oklahoma State University, Stillwater.
OkT	Tulsa Public Library.
OkU	University of Oklahoma, Norman.

OREGON

Or	Oregon State Library, Salem.
OrCS	Oregon State University Library, Corvallis.
OrHi	Oregon Historical Society, Portland.
OrP	Library Association of Portland, Portland.
OrPR	Reed College, Portland.
OrPS	Portland State College, Portland.
OrSaW	Willamette University, Salem.
OrStbM	Mount Angel College, Mount Angel Abbey, Saint Benedict.
OrU	University of Oregon, Eugene.

PENNSYLVANIA

PBL	Lehigh University, Bethlehem.
PBa	Academy of the New Church, Bryn Athyn.
PBm	Bryn Mawr College, Bryn Mawr.
PCA*	Samuel Colgate Baptist Historical Library of the American Baptist Historical Society, Rochester, N. Y.
PCC	Crozer Theological Seminary, Chester.
PCamA	Alliance College, Cambridge Springs.
PCarlD	Dickinson College, Carlisle.
PHC	Haverford College, Haverford.
PHi	Historical Society of Pennsylvania, Philadelphia.
PJA	Abington Library Society, Jenkintown.
PJAlG	Alverthorpe Gallery, Rosenwald Collection, Jenkintown.
PJB	Beaver College, Jenkintown.